Small Business Sourcebook

ISSN 0883-3397

Small Business Sourcebook

The Entrepreneur's Resource

FORTY-SECOND EDITION

Volume 6

General Small Business Resources
(Includes State and Federal Sections)

(Entries 44621-47978)

Holly M. Selden
Project Editor

Small Business Sourcebook, 42nd edition

Project Editor: Holly M. Selden

Editorial Support Services: Pranav Kokate

Composition and Electronic Prepress: Carolyn Roney

Manufacturing: Rita Wimberley

© 2025 Gale, a Cengage Company

ALL RIGHTS RESERVED. No part of this work covered by the copyright herein may be reproduced, transmitted, stored, or used in any form or by any means graphic, electronic, or mechanical, including but not limited to photocopying, recording, scanning, digitizing, taping, Web distribution, information networks, or information storage and retrieval systems, except as permitted under Section 107 or 108 of the 1976 United States Copyright Act, without the prior written permission of the publisher.

This publication is a creative work fully protected by all applicable copyright laws, as well as by misappropriation, trade secret, unfair competition, and other applicable laws. The authors and editors of this work have added value to the underlying factual material herein through one or more of the following: unique and original selection, coordination, expression, arrangement, and classification of the information.

For product information and technology assistance, contact us at
Gale Customer Support, 1-800-877-4253.
For permission to use material from this text or product, submit all requests online at www.cengage.com/permissions.
Further permissions questions can be emailed to
permissionrequest@cengage.com.

While every effort has been made to ensure the reliability of the information presented in this publication, Gale, part of Cengage Group, does not guarantee the accuracy of the data contained herein. Gale accepts no payment for listing and inclusion in the publication of any organization, agency, institution, publication, service, or individual does not imply endorsement of the editors or publisher. Errors brought to the attention of the publisher and verified to the satisfaction of the publisher will be corrected in future editions.

Gale, part of Cengage Group
5191 Natorp Blvd.
Mason, OH 45040

978-1-5358-7663-6 (set)
978-1-5358-7664-3 (vol. 1)
978-1-5358-7665-0 (vol. 2)
978-1-5358-7666-7 (vol. 3)
978-1-5358-7667-4 (vol. 4)
978-1-5358-7668-1 (vol. 5)
978-1-5358-7669-8 (vol. 6)

ISSN 0883-3397

This title is also available as an e-book.
978-1-5358-7670-4
Contact your Gale sales representative for ordering information.

Contents

Volume 1
Introduction vii
User's Guide. ix
List of Small Business Profiles xv
Standard Industrial Classification (SIC) Codes for
  Profiled Small Businesses xix
Licensing Assistance Programs xxxiii
Guide to Publishers. xxxvii
Glossary. lxxxix

Small Business Profiles 1

Provides start-up information, associations and other organizations, educational programs, directories of educational programs, reference works, sources of supply, statistical sources, trade periodicals, video/audio media, trade shows and conventions, consultants, franchises and business opportunities, computerized databases, computer systems/software, libraries, and research centers.

Volume 2
Introduction vii
User's Guide ix
List of Small Business Profiles xv
Standard Industrial Classification (SIC) Codes for
  Profiled Small Businesses xix

Small Business Profiles 623

Volume 3
Introduction vii
User's Guide ix
List of General Small Business Topics xv

General Small Business Topics. 1253

Includes associations and other organizations, educational programs, directories of educational programs, reference works, sources of supply, statistical sources, trade periodicals, video/audio media, trade shows and conventions, consultants, computerized databases, computer systems/software, libraries, and research centers.

Volume 4
Introduction vii
User's Guide ix
List of General Small Business Topics xv

General Small Business Topics. 1827

Volume 5
Introduction vii
User's Guide ix

State Listings. 2393

Offers sources of small business assistance by state, territory, and Canadian province, including small business development centers, small business assistance programs, SCORE offices, better business bureaus, chambers of commerce, minority business assistance programs, financing and loan programs, procurement assistance programs, incubators/research and technology parks, educational programs, legislative assistance, small business development consultants, and publications.

Volume 6
Introduction vii
User's Guide ix

State Listings. 2951

Federal Government Assistance 3111

Lists U.S. federal government agencies and offices, including regional, branch, and district offices, which focus on small business issues, programs, assistance, and policy.

Master Index 3167

Introduction

The appeal of small business ownership remains perpetually entrenched in American culture as one of the most viable avenues for achieving the American Dream. To many entrepreneurs, going into business for themselves represents financial independence, an increased sense of identity and self-worth, and the fulfillment of personal goals. Small business owners strive to make their mark in today's competitive marketplace by establishing healthy businesses that can, over time, become legacies handed down from one generation to the next. Entrepreneurs from each generation tackle the obstacles and adversities of the current business and economic climate to test their business savvy and generate opportunities. Today's entrepreneurs face many of the problems of their predecessors, as well as some distinctly new challenges.

With the rightsizing, downsizing, and reorganization of corporate America, many individuals have decided to confront the risks of developing and operating their own businesses. Small business ownership is rapidly becoming a viable alternative to what is perceived as an equally unstable corporate environment. These entrepreneurs, many of whom have firsthand experience with the problems and inefficiencies inherent in today's large corporations, seek to improve upon an archaic business model and to capitalize on their own ingenuity and strengths. Led by their zeal, many would-be entrepreneurs let their desire, drive, and determination overshadow the need for business knowledge and skill. Ironically, aids in obtaining these components of entrepreneurial success are widely available, easily accessible, and often free of charge.

Small Business Sourcebook (*SBS*) is a six-volume annotated guide to nearly 17,000 listings of live and print sources of information designed to facilitate the start-up, development, and growth of specific small businesses, as well as more than 19,500 similar listings on general small business topics. An additional 12,500 state-specific listings and nearly 1,100 U.S. federal government agencies and offices specializing in small business issues, programs, and assistance are also included. *SBS* covers more than 300 specific small business profiles more than 100 general small business topics.

Features of This Edition

This edition of *Small Business Sourcebook* has been revised and updated, incorporating thousands of changes to names, addresses, contacts, and descriptions of listings from the previous edition. We have also added several hundred podcasts that will help users better understand topics on entrepreneurship and small business ownership.

Contents and Arrangement

The geographical scope of *SBS* encompasses the United States and Canada, with expanded coverage for resources pertaining to international trade and for resources that have a U.S. or Canadian distributor or contact. Internet sites that are maintained outside of the U.S. and Canada are also included if they contain relevant information for North American small businesses. Resources that do not relate specifically to small businesses are generally not included.

The information presented in *SBS* is grouped within four sections: Specific Small Business Profiles, General Small Business Topics, State Listings, and Federal Government Assistance. Detailed outlines of these sections may be found in the Users' Guide following this Introduction. Also included is a Master Index to Volumes 1 through 6.

Specific Small Business Profiles This section includes the following types of resources: start-up information, associations and other organizations, educational programs, directories of educational programs, reference works, sources of supply, statistical sources, trade periodicals, videos and podcasts, trade shows and conventions, consultants, franchises, and business opportunities, computerized databases, computer systems/software, Internet databases, libraries, and research centers. All resources are arranged by business type. Entries range from Accounting Service to Word Processing Service, and include such businesses as Cannabis Dispensaries, Computer Consulting, Food Trucks, and Web Site Design.

General Small Business Topics This section offers such resources as associations, books, periodicals, articles, pamphlets, educational programs, directories of educational

INTRODUCTION

programs, trade shows and conventions, consultants, computerized databases, Internet databases, software, libraries, and research centers. All resources in this section are arranged alphabetically by business topic.

State Listings Entries include government, academic, and commercial agencies and organizations, as well as select coverage of relevant state-specific publications. Listings are arranged alphabetically by state, territory, and Canadian province. Some examples include small business development consultants, SCORE offices, financing and loan programs, better business bureaus, and chambers of commerce.

Federal Government Assistance Listings Entries include federal organizations and agencies specializing in small business issues, programs, assistance, and policy. Listings are arranged alphabetically by U.S. government agency or office; regional or branch offices are listed alphabetically by state.

Master Index All entries in Volumes 1 through 6 are arranged in one alphabetic index for convenience.

Entries in *SBS* include (as appropriate and available):

- Organization, institution, or product name
- Contact information, including contact name, address and phone, toll-free, and fax numbers
- Author/editor, date(s), and frequency
- Availability, including price
- Brief description of purpose, services, or content
- Company and/or personal E-mail addresses
- Web site addresses

SBS also features the following:

Guide to Publishers—An alphabetic listing of nearly 1,000 companies, associations, institutions, and individuals that publish the periodicals, directories, guidebooks, and other publications noted in the Small Business Profiles and General Topics sections. Users are provided with full contact information, including address, phone, fax, and e-mail and URL when available. The Guide to Publishers facilitates contact with publishers and provides a one-stop resource for valuable information.

Method of Compilation

SBS was compiled by consulting small business experts and entrepreneurs, as well as a variety of resources, including direct contact with the associations, organizations, and agencies through Internet research or materials provided by those listees; government resources; and data obtained from other relevant Gale directories. *SBS* was reviewed by a team of small business advisors, all of whom have numerous years of expertise in small business counseling and identification of small business information resources. The last and perhaps most important resource we utilize is direct contact with our readers, who provide valuable comments and suggestions to improve our publication. *SBS* relies on these comprehensive market contacts to provide today's entrepreneurs with relevant, current, and accurate information on all aspects of small business.

Available in Electronic Formats

Licensing. *Small Business Sourcebook* is available for licensing. The complete database is provided in a fielded format and is deliverable on various forms of media. For more information, contact Gale's Business Development Group at 1-800-877-GALE, or visit our website at www.gale.com.

Comments and Suggestions Welcome

Associations, agencies, business firms, publishers, and other organizations that provide assistance and information to the small business community are encouraged to submit material about their programs, activities, services, or products. Comments and suggestions from users of this directory are also welcomed and appreciated. Please contact:

Project Editor
Small Business Sourcebook
27555 Executive Dr., Ste. 270
Farmington Hills, MI 48331
Gale, part of Cengage Group
URL: www.gale.com

User's Guide

Small Business Sourcebook (*SBS*) provides information in a variety of forms and presentations for comprehensive coverage and ease of use. The directory contains four parts within six volumes:

- Specific Small Business Profiles
- General Small Business Topics
- State Listings
- Federal Government Assistance

Information on specific businesses is arranged by type of business; the many general topics that are of interest to the owners, operators, or managers of all small businesses are grouped in a separate section for added convenience. Users should consult the various sections to benefit fully from the information *SBS* offers. For example, an entrepreneur with a talent or interest in the culinary arts could peruse a number of specific small business profiles, such as Restaurant, Catering Service, Cooking School, Specialty/Gourmet Food/Wine Shop, Food Truck, Healthy Restaurant, or Candy/Chocolate Shop. Secondly, the General Small Business Topics section could be consulted for any applicable subjects, such as Service Industry, Retailing, Franchising, and other relevant topics. Then, the appropriate state within the State Listings section would offer area programs and offices providing information and support to small businesses, including venture capital firms and small business development consultants. Finally, the Federal Government Assistance section could supply relevant government offices, such as procurement contacts.

Features Included in Volumes 1 and 2

List of Small Business Profiles. This list provides an alphabetic outline of the small businesses profiled. The page number for the beginning of each profile is indicated.

Standard Industrial Classification (SIC) Codes for Profiled Small Businesses. This section lists four-digit SIC codes and corresponding classification descriptions for the small businesses profiled in this edition. The SIC system, which organizes businesses by type, is a product of the Statistical Policy Division of the U.S. Office of Management and Budget. Statistical data produced by government, public, and private organizations is usually categorized according to SIC codes, thereby facilitating the collection, comparison, and analysis of data as well as providing a uniform method for presenting statistical information. Hence, knowing the SIC code for a particular small business increases access and the use of a variety of statistical data from many sources.

Guide to Publishers. This resource lists alphabetically the companies, associations, institutions, and individuals that publish the periodicals, directories, guidebooks, and other publications noted in the "Small Business Profiles" and "General Topics" sections. Users are provided with full contact information, including address, phone, fax, and e-mail and URL when available. The "Guide" facilitates contact with publishers and provides a one-stop resource for valuable information.

Glossary of Small Business Terms. This glossary defines nearly 400 small business terms, including financial, governmental, insurance, procurement, technical, and general business definitions. Cross-references and acronyms are also provided.

Small Business Profiles A-Z. More than 300 small business profiles are represented in volumes 1 and 2. Profiles are listed alphabetically by business type. Each profile may contain up to sixteen subheadings that correlate to a resource type; entries within are listed alphabetically. These resource types are detailed below:

- *Start-up Information*—Includes periodical articles, books, manuals, book excerpts, kits, and other sources of information. Entries offer title; publisher; address; phone, fax, toll-free numbers; company e-mail and URL addresses; and a description. Bibliographic data is provided for cited periodical articles whenever possible.

- *Associations and Other Organizations*—Includes trade and professional associations whose members gather and disseminate information of interest to small business owners. Entries offer the association's

Small Business Sourcebook • 42nd Edition

name; address; phone, toll-free and fax numbers; company e-mail address; contact name; purpose and objective; a description of membership; telecommunication services; and a listing of its publications, including publishing frequency.

- *Educational Programs*—Includes university and college programs, schools, training opportunities, association seminars, correspondence courses, and other educational programs. Entries offer name of program or institution, sponsor name, address, phone, toll-free and fax numbers, e-mail and URL addresses; and description of program.

- *Directories of Educational Programs*—Includes directories and other publications that list educational programs. Entries offer name of publication; publisher name, address, and phone, toll-free and fax numbers; editor; frequency or date of publication; price; and description of contents, including directory arrangement and indexes.

- *Reference Works*—Includes handbooks, manuals, textbooks, guides, directories, dictionaries, encyclopedias, and other published reference materials. Entries offer name of publication; publisher name, address, and phone, toll-free and fax numbers; e-mail and URL addresses; and, when available, name of author or editor, publication year or frequency, and price. A brief description is often featured.

- *Sources of Supply*—Includes buyer's guides, directories, special issues of periodicals, and other publications that list sources of equipment, supplies, and services related to the operation of the profiled small business. Entries offer publication name; publisher name, address, and phone, toll-free and fax numbers; e-mail and URL addresses; and, when available, editor's name, frequency or publication year, and price. A brief description of the publication, including directory arrangement and indexes, is often provided.

- *Statistical Sources*—Includes books, reports, pamphlets, and other sources of statistical data of interest to an owner, operator or manager of the profiled small business, such as wage, salary, and compensation data; financial and operating ratios; prices and costs; demographics; and other statistical information. Entries offer publication/data source name; publisher (if applicable); address; phone, toll-free and fax numbers of data source; publication date or frequency; and price. A brief description of the publication/data source is often provided.

- *Trade Periodicals*—Includes trade journals, newsletters, magazines, and other serials that offer information about the management and operation of the profiled small business. Such periodicals often contain industry news; trends and developments; reviews; articles about new equipment and supplies; and other information related to business operations. Entries offer publication name; publisher name, address, phone, toll-free and fax numbers, and e-mail and URL addresses; editor name; publication frequency; and price. A brief description of the publication's content is also included, when known.

- *Video/Audio Media*—Includes videos, podcasts, and other audiovisual media offering information on the profiled small business. Entries offer program title; creator or distributor name, address, phone, toll-free and fax numbers, and e-mail and URL addresses; description of program; price; and format(s).

- *Trade Shows and Conventions*—Includes tradeshows, exhibitions, expositions, conventions, and other industry meetings that provide prospective and existing business owners with the opportunity to meet and exchange information with their peers, review commercial exhibits, establish business or sales contacts, and attend educational programs. Entries offer event name; sponsor or management company name, address, phone, toll-free and fax numbers, and e-mail and URL addresses; a description of the event, including audience, frequency, principal exhibits, and dates and locations of event for as many years ahead as provided by the event's sponsor.

- *Consultants*—Includes consultants and consulting organizations that provide services specifically related to the profiled small business. Entries offer individual consultant or consulting organization name, address, and phone, toll-free and fax numbers; company and individual e-mail addresses; and a brief description of consulting services. (For e-mail and URL addresses, see the Small Business Development Consultants subheadings in the State Listings section in Volume 2.)

- *Franchises and Business Opportunities*—Includes companies granting franchise licenses for enterprises falling within the scope of the profiled small business, as well as other non-franchised business opportunities that operate within a given network or system. Entries offer franchise name, address, phone, toll-free and fax numbers, and e-mail and URL addresses, as well as a description of the franchise or business opportunity, which has been expanded whenever possible to include the number of existing franchises, the founding date of the franchise, franchise fees, equity capital requirements, royalty fees, any managerial assistance offered, and available training.

- *Computerized Databases*—Includes diskettes, magnetic tapes, CD-ROMs, online systems, and other computer-readable databases. Entries offer database name; producer name, address, phone, toll-free and fax numbers, e-mail and URL addresses; description; and available format(s), including vendor name.

(Many university and public libraries offer online information retrieval services that provide searches of databases, including those listed in this category.)

- *Computer Systems/Software*—Includes software and computerized business systems designed to assist in the operation of the profiled small business. Entries offer name of the software or system; publisher name, address, phone, toll-free and fax numbers; price; and description.

- *Libraries*—Includes libraries and special collections that contain material especially applicable to the profiled small business. Entries offer library or collection name; parent organization (where applicable); address; phone, toll-free and fax numbers; e-mail and URL addresses; contact name and title; scope of collection; and description of holdings, subscriptions, and services.

- *Research Centers*—Includes university-related and independently operated research institutes and information centers that generate, through their research programs, data related to the operation of the profiled small business. Also listed are associations and other business-related organizations that conduct research programs. Entries offer name of organization; address; phone, toll-free and fax numbers; company web site address; contact name and personal e-mail; a description of principal fields of research or services; publications, including title and frequency; and related conferences.

Features Included in Volumes 3 and 4

General Small Business Topics. This section offers chapters on different topics in the operation of any small business, for example, venture capital and other funding, or compensation. Chapters are listed alphabetically by small business topic; entries within each chapter are arranged alphabetically, within up to 14 subheadings, by resource type:

- *Associations and Other Organizations*—Includes trade and professional associations that gather and disseminate information of interest to small business owners. Entries offer the association's name; address; phone, toll-free and fax numbers; organization e-mail and URL addresses; contact name; purpose and objectives; a description of membership; telecommunication services; and a listing of its publications, including publishing frequency.

- *Educational Programs*—Includes university and college programs, schools, training opportunities, association seminars, correspondence courses, and other educational programs. Entries offer name of program or institution, sponsor name, address, phone, toll-free and fax numbers, e-mail and URL addresses, and description of program.

- *Directories of Educational Programs*—Includes directories and other publications that list educational programs. Entries offer name of publication; publisher name, address, phone, toll-free and fax numbers, and e-mail and URL addresses; editor; frequency or date of publication; price; and description of contents, including arrangement and indexes.

- *Reference Works*—Includes articles, handbooks, manuals, textbooks, guides, directories, dictionaries, encyclopedias, and other published reference materials. Entries offer title of article, including bibliographic information; name of publication; publisher name, address, phone, toll-free and fax numbers, and e-mail and URL addresses; and, when available, name of author or editor, publication year or frequency, and price. A brief description is often featured.

- *Sources of Supply*—Includes buyer's guides, directories, special issues of periodicals, and other publications that list sources of equipment, supplies, and services. Entries offer publication name; publisher name, address, phone, toll-free and fax numbers, and e-mail and URL addresses; editor's name, frequency or publication year, price, and a brief description of the publication, when available.

- *Statistical Sources*—Includes books, reports, pamphlets, and other sources of statistical data of interest to an owner, operator, or manager of a small business, such as wage, salary, and compensation data; financial and operating ratios; prices and costs; demographics; and other statistical information. Entries offer publication/data source name; publisher (if applicable); address; phone, toll-free and fax numbers of data source; publication date or frequency; and price. A brief description is often provided.

- *Trade Periodicals*—Includes journals, newsletters, magazines, and other serials. Entries offer name of publication; publisher name, address, phone, toll-free and fax numbers, and e-mail and URL addresses; and name of editor, frequency, and price. A brief description of the periodical's content is included when known.

- *Video/Audio Media*—Includes videos, podcasts, and other audiovisual media. Entries offer program title; distributor name, address, phone, toll-free and fax numbers, and e-mail and URL addresses; price; description of program; and format(s).

- *Trade Shows and Conventions*—Includes tradeshows, exhibitions, expositions, seminars, and conventions. Entries offer event name; sponsor or management company name, address, phone, toll-free and fax numbers, and e-mail and URL addresses; frequency of event; and dates and locations of the event for as many years ahead as known.

USER'S GUIDE

- *Consultants*—Includes consultants and consulting organizations. Entries offer individual consultant or consulting organization name, address, and phone, toll-free and fax numbers; company and individual e-mail addresses; and a brief description of consulting services. (See also Consultants in the State Listings section.)

- *Computerized Databases*—Includes diskettes, CD-ROMs, magnetic tape, online systems and other computer-readable databases. Entries offer database name; producer, address, phone, toll-free and fax numbers, and e-mail and URL addresses; description; and available format(s), including vendor name. (Many university and public libraries offer online information retrieval services that provide searches of databases, including those listed in this category.)

- *Computer Systems/Software*—Includes software and computerized business systems. Entries offer name of the software or system; publisher name, address, phone, toll-free and fax numbers, and e-mail and URL addresses; price; and description.

- *Libraries*—Includes libraries and special collections that contain material applicable to the small business topic. Entries offer library or collection name, parent organization (where applicable), address, phone and fax numbers, e-mail and URL addresses, scope of collection, and description of holdings and services.

- *Research Centers*— Includes university-related and independently operated research institutes and information centers that generate, through their research programs, data related to specific small business topics. Entries offer name of organization, address, phone, toll-free and fax numbers, e-mail and URL addresses, a description of principal fields of research or services, and related conferences.

Features Included in Volumes 5 and 6

State Listings. This section lists various sources of information and assistance available within given states, territories, and Canadian provinces; entries include governmental, academic, and commercial agencies, and are arranged alphabetically within up to 15 subheadings by resource type:

- *Small Business Development Center Lead Office*— Includes the lead small business development center (SBDC) for each state.

- *Small Business Development Centers*—Includes any additional small business development centers (SBDC) in the state, territory, or province. SBDCs provide support services to small businesses, including individual counseling, seminars, conferences, and learning center activities.

- *Small Business Assistance Programs*—Includes state small business development offices and other programs offering assistance to small businesses.

- *SCORE Offices*—Includes SCORE office(s) for each state. The Service Corps of Retired Executives Association (SCORE), a volunteer program sponsored by the Small Business Administration, offers counseling, workshops, and seminars across the U.S. for small business entrepreneurs.

- *Better Business Bureaus*—Includes various better business bureaus within each state. By becoming a member of the local Better Business Bureau, a small business owner can increase the prestige and credibility of his or her business within the community, as well as make valuable business contacts.

- *Chambers of Commerce*—Includes various chambers of commerce within each state. Chambers of Commerce are valuable sources of small business advice and information; often, local chambers sponsor SCORE counseling several times per month for a small fee, seminars, conferences, and other workshops to its members. Also, by becoming a member of the local Chamber of Commerce, a small business owner can increase the prestige and credibility of his or her business within the community, as well as make valuable business contacts.

- *Minority Business Assistance Programs*—Includes minority business development centers and other sources of assistance for minority-owned business.

- *Financing and Loan Programs*—Includes venture capital firms, small business investment companies (SBIC), minority enterprise small business investment companies (MESBIC), and other programs that provide funding to qualified small businesses.

- *Procurement Assistance Programs*—Includes state services such as counseling, set-asides, and sheltered-market bidding, which are designed to aid small businesses in bidding on government contracts.

- *Incubators/Research and Technology Parks*— Includes small business incubators, which provide newly established small business owners with work sites, business services, training, and consultation; also includes research and technology parks, which sponsor research and facilitate commercialization of new technologies.

- *Educational Programs*—Includes university and college programs, as well as those sponsored by other organizations that offer degree, nondegree, certificate, and correspondence programs in entrepreneurship and in small business development.

- *Legislative Assistance*—Includes committees, subcommittees, and joint committees of each state's senate and house of representatives that are concerned with small business issues and regulations.

- **Consultants**—Includes consultants and consulting firms offering expertise in small business development.
- **Publications**—Includes publications related to small business operations within the profiled state.
- **Publishers**—Includes publishers operating in or for the small business arena within the profiled state.
- **Early Stage Financing**—Includes organizations offering early-stage capital needed to launch and grow new businesses.
- **Venture Capital Firm**—Includes organizations offering financial support to small, early-stage and emerging firms.

Federal Government Assistance. This section lists federal government agencies and offices, many with additional listings for specific offices, as well as regional or district branches. Main agencies or offices are listed alphabetically; regional, branch, or district offices are listed after each main office or agency.

Master Index. This index provides an alphabetic listing of all entries contained in Volumes 1 through 6. Citations are referenced by their entry numbers. Publication titles are rendered in italics.

South Dakota

ASSOCIATIONS AND OTHER ORGANIZATIONS

44621 ■ **Business Network International Heartland--Nebraska, Wyoming, South Dakota, Western Iowa**
3430 Toringdon Way
Charlotte, NC 28277
Free: 855-264-2673
Co. E-mail: info@bniheartland.com
URL: http://bniheartland.com/en-US/index
Contact: Nellie Nutting, Managing Director
E-mail: nellienutting@bni.com

Description: Provides a structured environment for the development and exchange of quality business referrals. Offers members the opportunity to share ideas and contacts in Nebraska, Wyoming, South Dakota and Iowa. **Founded:** 1985. **Geographic Preference:** State.

44622 ■ **South Dakota Agri-Business Association (SDABA)**
320 E Capitol Ave.
Pierre, SD 57501
Ph: (605)224-2445
Fax: (605)224-9913
Co. E-mail: info@sdaba.org
URL: http://www.sdaba.org
Contact: Dave Clark, President
Facebook: www.facebook.com/sdagribusiness

Description: Works as a trade association of agricultural chemical and fertilizer dealers, associate members are companies and sales representatives in the agricultural chemical and fertilizer industry. Conducts lobbying activities. **Founded:** 1962. **Publications:** *Legislative Report* (Weekly). **Educational Activities:** SDABA Ag Expo (Annual). **Geographic Preference:** State.

SMALL BUSINESS DEVELOPMENT CENTERS

44623 ■ **Pierre Small Business Development Center**
221 S Central Ave., Ste. 33
Pierre, SD 57501
Ph: (605)773-2783
Fax: (605)773-2035
Co. E-mail: bob.weyrich@usd.edu
URL: http://business.pierre.org/list/member/south-dakota-small-business-development-center-1108
URL(s): sdbusinesshelp.com/small-business-development-center

Description: Represents and promotes the small business sector. Provides management assistance to current and prospective small business owners. Helps to improve management skills and expand the products and services of members. **Geographic Preference:** Local.

44624 ■ **Rapid City Small Business Development Center (SBDC)**
730 E Watertown St.
Rapid City, SD 57701
URL: http://sdbusinesshelp.com
Contact: Mark Retersdorf, Consultant
E-mail: mretersdorf@wrbsc.com

Description: Represents and promotes the small business sector. Provides management assistance to current and prospective small business owners. Helps to improve management skills and expand the products and services of members. **Geographic Preference:** Local.

44625 ■ **Sioux Falls Small Business Development Center**
c/o Daniel Crook, Consultant
2329 N Career Ave., Ste. 106
Sioux Falls, SD 57107
Ph: (605)367-5757
Fax: (605)367-5755
Co. E-mail: daniel.crook@usd.edu
URL: http://sdbusinesshelp.com/small-business-development-center/contact
Contact: Daniel Crook, Consultant
E-mail: daniel.crook@usd.edu

Description: Represents and promotes the small business sector. Provides management assistance to current and prospective small business owners. Helps to improve management skills and expand the products and services of members. **Geographic Preference:** Local.

44626 ■ **Small Business Development Center Aberdeen, South Dakota**
506 S Main St., Ste. 2
Aberdeen, SD 57401
Ph: (605)367-5757
URL: http://sdbusinesshelp.com
Facebook: www.facebook.com/SBDCAberdeenSD

Description: Represents and promotes the small business sector. Provides management assistance to current and prospective small business owners. Helps to improve management skills and expand the products and services of members. **Geographic Preference:** Local.

44627 ■ **South Dakota Small Business Development Center**
414 E Clark St.
Vermillion, SD 57069
Ph: (605)367-5757
Co. E-mail: mark.slade@usd.edu
URL: http://sdbusinesshelp.com
Contact: Mark Slade, Officer
E-mail: mark.slade@usd.edu

Description: Focuses on offering management assistance to current and prospective small business owners in South Dakota. **Geographic Preference:** State.

44628 ■ **Yankton SBDC**
c/o Sue Stoll, Associate Director
Regional Director
1808 Summit Ave.
Yankton, SD 57078
Ph: (605)665-0751
Co. E-mail: sues@districtiii.org
URL: http://americassbdc.org/find-your-sbdc
Contact: Sue Stoll, Regional Director Associate Director
E-mail: sues@districtiii.org

Description: Provides management assistance to current and prospective small business owners in Yankton. **Geographic Preference:** Local.

SMALL BUSINESS ASSISTANCE PROGRAMS

44629 ■ **South Dakota Governor's Office of Economic Development (GOED)**
711 E Wells Ave.
Pierre, SD 57501
Ph: (605)773-4633
Co. E-mail: goedinfo@state.sd.us
URL: http://sdgoed.com
Contact: Joe Fiala, Director
E-mail: joe.fiala@sdgoed.com
Facebook: www.facebook.com/SDGOED
Linkedin: www.linkedin.com/company/12177566
X (Twitter): x.com/SDGOED
YouTube: www.youtube.com/sdgoed

Description: Advocates on behalf of South Dakota's small business community regarding policy determinations and questions concerning other state agencies. **Publications:** *South Dakota Directory of Research and Expertise*; *South Dakota Resource Directory*.

SCORE OFFICES

44630 ■ **SCORE - Aberdeen**
208 S Main
Aberdeen, SD 57401
Ph: (605)280-3642
Co. E-mail: help@score.org
URL: http://siouxfalls.score.org

Description: Provides professional guidance and information to maximize the success of existing and emerging small businesses. Offers business counseling and workshops.

44631 ■ **SCORE - Sioux Falls**
2329 N Career Ave., Ste. 105
Sioux Falls, SD 57107
URL: http://www.score.org/southdakota/about#contact

Description: Provides professional guidance and information to maximize the success of existing and emerging small businesses. Offers business counseling and workshops. **Founded:** 1966. **Geographic Preference:** Local.

44632 ■ SCORE - South Dakota
Sioux Falls, SD 57107
Ph: (605)280-3642
Free: 800-634-0245
Co. E-mail: help@score.org
URL: http://www.score.org/southdakota
Contact: Cari L. Dilley, Contact
Facebook: www.facebook.com/SCORESouthDakota
Description: Provides professional guidance and information to maximize the success of existing and emerging small businesses. Promotes entrepreneur education in Rapid City area, South Dakota. **Geographic Preference:** Local.

44633 ■ SCORE - Yankton
208 S Main
Aberdeen, SD 57401
URL: http://southdakota.score.org
Description: Provides professional guidance and information to maximize the success of existing and emerging small businesses. Offers business counseling and workshops.

CHAMBERS OF COMMERCE

44634 ■ Aberdeen Area Chamber of Commerce (AACC)
516 S Main St.
Aberdeen, SD 57401
Ph: (605)225-2860
Free: 800-874-9038
Fax: (605)225-2437
Co. E-mail: info@aberdeen-chamber.com
URL: http://aberdeen-chamber.com
Contact: Gail Ochs, President
E-mail: gail@aberdeen-chamber.com
Facebook: www.facebook.com/AberdeenAreaChamberofCommerce
X (Twitter): x.com/AberdeenChamber
Instagram: www.instagram.com/aberdeenareachamberofcommerce
YouTube: www.youtube.com/channel/UCmzH93G21gwjw8qj9abh9Tw
Description: Promotes business and community development in the Brown County, SD area. **Founded:** 1884. **Publications:** *Chamber Progress* (Bimonthly). **Awards:** Aberdeen Area Chamber of Commerce The Woman of Spirit Award (Annual); Aberdeen Area Chamber of Commerce George Award (Annual); Aberdeen Area Chamber of Commerce Star Award (Annual). **Geographic Preference:** Local.

44635 ■ Beresford Chamber of Commerce (BCC)
PO Box 167
Beresford, SD 57004-0167
Ph: (605)763-2021
URL: http://www.uschamber.com/co/chambers/south-dakota/beresford
Description: Provides leadership to create a strong business climate while enhancing the quality of life in Beresford, SD area. **Founded:** 1950. **Geographic Preference:** Local.

44636 ■ Brookings Area Chamber of Commerce and Convention Bureau
415 8th St., S
Brookings, SD 57006
Ph: (605)692-6125
Co. E-mail: info@brookingschamber.org
URL: http://www.brookingschamber.org/convention-visitors-bureau
Description: Promotes business and community development in the Brookings, SD area. **Founded:** 1938. **Geographic Preference:** Local.

44637 ■ *Business Directory*
106 W Kansas St.
Spearfish, SD 57783
Ph: (605)642-2626
Free: 800-626-8013
Co. E-mail: info@spearfishchamber.org
URL: http://spearfishchamber.org
Contact: Melissa Barth, Executive Director
E-mail: director@spearfishchamber.org
URL(s): business.spearfishchamber.org/list
Availability: Online.

44638 ■ Canton Chamber of Commerce
600 W 5th St.
Canton, SD 57013
Ph: (605)764-7864
Co. E-mail: cantonopenairmarket@gmail.com
URL: http://www.cantonsouthdakota.com/ChamberOfCommerce
Contact: Jessie Oliver, President
Description: Promotes business and community development in the Canton, SD area. Sponsors Saturday in the Park & Fishing Derby in the summer and the annual Christmas Parade & Holiday Open House in December. **Founded:** 1881. **Publications:** *Community Education/Chamber of Commerce Newsletter* (Quarterly). **Geographic Preference:** Local.

44639 ■ *The Chamber Advantage*
1 E Kemp
Watertown, SD 57201
Ph: (605)886-5814
Co. E-mail: coc@watertownsd.com
URL: http://www.watertownsd.com
Contact: Tim Sheehan, President
E-mail: tim@watertownsd.com
URL(s): www.watertownsd.com/members/benefits
Released: Monthly **Availability:** Print.

44640 ■ *Chamber Dialogue*
Released: Monthly **Price:** included in membership dues. **Description:** Promotes local events. **Availability:** Print.

44641 ■ *Chamber News*
200 N Phillips Ave., Ste. 200
Sioux Falls, SD 57104
Ph: (605)336-1620
Co. E-mail: gsfcc@siouxfalls.com
URL: http://www.siouxfallschamber.com
Contact: Jeff Griffin, President
E-mail: jgriffin@siouxfalls.com
URL(s): siouxfallschamber.com/news-publications/chamber-news
Released: 10/year **Description:** Features articles on Chamber member businesses and issues of interest in the business community. **Availability:** Print; Online.

44642 ■ Chamberlain-Oacoma Area Chamber of Commerce
118 S Main St.
Chamberlain, SD 57325
Ph: (605)234-4416
Co. E-mail: chamber@midstatesd.net
URL: http://www.chamberlainsd.com
Contact: Kyndra Hosek, President
Facebook: www.facebook.com/mychambercoa
X (Twitter): x.com/ChamberOacoma
YouTube: www.youtube.com/channel/UCRivs2AVOv191cy7BB6GSwQ
Description: Promotes business and community development in Chamberlain, SD area. **Geographic Preference:** Local.

44643 ■ *The Chamberview*
601 N Main St.
Mitchell, SD 57301
Ph: (605)996-5567
Co. E-mail: info@mitchellchamber.com
URL: http://www.mitchellchamber.com
Contact: Geri Beck, Chief Executive Officer
E-mail: gbeck@mitchellsd.com
URL(s): www.mitchellchamber.com/chamberview-newsletter
Released: Monthly; every 1st Monday. **Availability:** Online; PDF.

44644 ■ Custer Area Chamber of Commerce and Visitors Bureau
615 Washington St.
Custer, SD 57730
Ph: (605)673-2244
Free: 800-992-9818
Co. E-mail: info@custersd.com
URL: http://visitcuster.com
X (Twitter): x.com/CusterAreaChamb
YouTube: www.youtube.com/channel/UCdBURr1f5pzUGoA_ZszwZng
Description: Promotes the area of Custer County, SD as a tourist destination. Also promotes new and existing business, community development, and retail trade. **Geographic Preference:** Local.

44645 ■ Deadwood Chamber of Commerce and Visitors' Bureau
501 Main St.
Deadwood, SD 57732
Ph: (605)578-1876
Free: 800-999-1876
Co. E-mail: visit@deadwood.org
URL: http://www.deadwood.org
Contact: Louie Lalonde, President
Facebook: www.facebook.com/historicdeadwood
X (Twitter): x.com/deadwoodsd
Instagram: www.instagram.com/historicdeadwood
Description: Promotes business and community development in the Deadwood-Lead, SD area. **Publications:** *Chamber Circuit* (Monthly). **Geographic Preference:** Local.

44646 ■ *Fish Bytes*
106 W Kansas St.
Spearfish, SD 57783
Ph: (605)642-2626
Free: 800-626-8013
Co. E-mail: info@spearfishchamber.org
URL: http://spearfishchamber.org
Contact: Melissa Barth, Executive Director
E-mail: director@spearfishchamber.org
URL(s): spearfishchamber.org/member-services-benefits
Released: Weekly **Description:** Features chamber's weekly happenings. **Availability:** Electronic publishing; Online.

44647 ■ *Fish Wrapper*
106 W Kansas St.
Spearfish, SD 57783
Ph: (605)642-2626
Free: 800-626-8013
Co. E-mail: info@spearfishchamber.org
URL: http://spearfishchamber.org
Contact: Melissa Barth, Executive Director
E-mail: director@spearfishchamber.org
URL(s): spearfishchamber.org/chamber-news
Released: Monthly **Availability:** Print; PDF.

44648 ■ Greater Madison Area Chamber of Commerce
315 S Egan Ave.
Madison, SD 57042
Ph: (605)256-2454
Co. E-mail: office@chamberofmadisonsd.com
URL: http://www.chamberofmadisonsd.com
Contact: Sarah Cronin, President
Facebook: www.facebook.com/MadisonSDChamber
X (Twitter): x.com/MadisonChamber
Instagram: www.instagram.com/madisonsdchamber
YouTube: www.youtube.com/channel/UCmibW3Y609PPqgJgyrafVFg
Description: Promotes business and community development in the Madison, SD area. **Founded:** 1930. **Geographic Preference:** Local.

44649 ■ Hartford Area Chamber of Commerce (HACC)
125 N Main Ave.
Hartford, SD 57033
Ph: (605)528-3338
Co. E-mail: info@hartfordsdchamber.org
URL: http://www.hartfordsdchamber.org
Contact: Amy M. Farr, Director, Development
Facebook: www.facebook.com/HartfordAreaChamberOfCommerce
X (Twitter): x.com/hartfordchamber
Description: Works to support and foster development in Hartford area. **Founded:** 2013. **Geographic Preference:** Local.

44650 ■ Hot Springs Area Chamber of Commerce
801 S 6th St.
Hot Springs, SD 57747

Ph: (605)745-4140
URL: http://www.hotsprings-sd.com
Contact: Kris Hanson, President
Facebook: www.facebook.com/hotspringssouth
dakota
X (Twitter): x.com/hotspringssd
Instagram: www.instagram.com/hotspringssouth
dakota
Pinterest: www.pinterest.com/hotspringssodak
Description: Promotes business, community development, tourism & community events, and tourism in Hot Springs, SD. **Geographic Preference:** Local.

44651 ■ Lead Area Chamber of Commerce (LACC)
160 W Main St.
Lead, SD 57754
Ph: (605)584-1100
URL: http://www.leadmethere.org
Contact: Marsha Nichols, President
Facebook: www.facebook.com/leadsdchamber
Instagram: www.instagram.com/leadsd_chamber
Description: Promotes business, community development, and tourism in Port Washington area. **Founded:** 1876. **Geographic Preference:** Local.

44652 ■ Lemmon Chamber of Commerce
100 3rd St. W
Lemmon, SD 57638
Ph: (605)374-5716
Co. E-mail: chamber@lemmonsd.com
URL: http://www.lemmonsd.com
URL(s): lemmonsdchamber.com
Facebook: www.facebook.com/
lemmonchamberofcommerce
Description: Promotes business and community development in the Lemmon, SD area. Sponsors Boss Cowman Rodeo and Celebration in July and Christmas Craft Fair in November. **Founded:** 1866. **Publications:** *The Chamber Challenge* (Monthly). **Geographic Preference:** Local.

44653 ■ Milbank Area Chamber of Commerce
1001 E 4th Ave., Ste. 301
Milbank, SD 57252
Ph: (605)432-6656
Free: 800-675-6656
Co. E-mail: chamberinfo@milbanksd.com
URL: http://www.milbanksd.com/chamber
Contact: Dwight Samson, President
Facebook: www.facebook.com/MilbankChamber
Description: Promotes business and community development in the Milbank, SD area. **Geographic Preference:** Local.

44654 ■ Mitchell Area Chamber of Commerce
601 N Main St.
Mitchell, SD 57301
Ph: (605)996-5567
Co. E-mail: info@mitchellchamber.com
URL: http://www.mitchellchamber.com
Contact: Geri Beck, Chief Executive Officer
E-mail: gbeck@mitchellsd.com
X (Twitter): x.com/MitchellCOC
Instagram: www.instagram.com/mitchellcoc
YouTube: www.youtube.com/user/CityofMitchell
Description: Provides leadership to unify community action that enhances the business environment and the quality of life in the Mitchell area. **Founded:** 1917. **Publications:** *The Chamberview* (Monthly). **Geographic Preference:** Local.

44655 ■ Mobridge Chamber of Commerce
212 N Main St.
Mobridge, SD 57601
Ph: (605)845-2387
Free: 888-614-3474
Fax: (605)845-3223
Co. E-mail: info@mobridge.org
URL: http://mobridge.org/chamber
Contact: Kelsey Majeske, Publisher
Facebook: www.facebook.com/Mobri
dgeAreaChamber
X (Twitter): x.com/MobridgeChamber
Pinterest: www.pinterest.com/mobridgearea

Description: Promotes business and community development in Mobridge, SD. **Founded:** 1906. **Geographic Preference:** Local.

44656 ■ Pierre Area Chamber of Commerce
800 W Dakota Ave.
Pierre, SD 57501
Ph: (605)224-7361
Co. E-mail: contactchamber@pierre.org
URL: http://pierre.org
Contact: Tia Kafka, President
E-mail: tkafka@pierre.org
Facebook: www.facebook.com/PierreAreaChamber
Description: Promotes the interests of local and regional individuals, businesses, and organizations. Provides quality services and representation in the areas of government, health, agriculture, education, and culture. **Geographic Preference:** Local.

44657 ■ Redfield Area Chamber of Commerce
626 Main St.
Redfield, SD 57469
Ph: (605)472-0965
Fax: (605)472-4553
Co. E-mail: redfieldchamber@redfield-sd.com
URL: http://chamber.redfield-sd.com
Contact: Dawn Schmidt, Secretary
Facebook: www.facebook.com/Redfield-Area-Chamber-of-Commerce-120488294742539
Description: Promotes business and community development in Redfield, SD area. **Founded:** 1930. **Geographic Preference:** Local.

44658 ■ Sioux Falls Area Chamber of Commerce (SFACC)
200 N Phillips Ave., Ste. 200
Sioux Falls, SD 57104
Ph: (605)336-1620
Co. E-mail: gsfcc@siouxfalls.com
URL: http://www.siouxfallschamber.com
Contact: Jeff Griffin, President
E-mail: jgriffin@siouxfalls.com
Facebook: www.facebook.com/siouxfallschamber
Linkedin: www.linkedin.com/company/sioux-falls-area-chamber-of-commerce
X (Twitter): x.com/sfareachamber
Instagram: www.instagram.com/siouxfallschamber
YouTube: www.youtube.com/channel/UCIchu-C7Va
1cOIrzsgnl_mg
Description: Association promotes business and community development in the Sioux Falls and SD area, also supports industry and agriculture, and maintains convention bureaus. **Founded:** 1907. **Publications:** *Chamber News* (10/year); *Closer Look* (Weekly); *Legislative Lookout* (Daily); *QUICKLY* (Weekly (Thurs.)); *Sioux Falls Community Guide* (Annual). **Awards:** Sioux Falls Area Chamber of Commerce Agri-Business Citizen of the Year (Annual); Sioux Falls Area Chamber of Commerce Farm Family of the Year (Annual). **Geographic Preference:** Local.

44659 ■ Spearfish Area Chamber of Commerce [Spearfish Area Chamber of Commerce and Convention and Visitors Bureau]
106 W Kansas St.
Spearfish, SD 57783
Ph: (605)642-2626
Free: 800-626-8013
Co. E-mail: info@spearfishchamber.org
URL: http://spearfishchamber.org
Contact: Melissa Barth, Executive Director
E-mail: director@spearfishchamber.org
Facebook: www.facebook.com/spearfishchamber
X (Twitter): x.com/spfchamber
Description: Seeks to advance a positive business climate and provide leadership to the promotion and managed growth of the Spearfish, SD area community. Markets Spearfish for the economic benefit of the community. **Founded:** 1919. **Publications:** *Business Directory*; *Fish Bytes* (Weekly); *Fish Wrapper* (Monthly); *Spearfish Map* (Annual). **Geographic Preference:** Local.

44660 ■ *Spearfish Map*
106 W Kansas St.
Spearfish, SD 57783
Ph: (605)642-2626
Free: 800-626-8013
Co. E-mail: info@spearfishchamber.org
URL: http://spearfishchamber.org
Contact: Melissa Barth, Executive Director
E-mail: director@spearfishchamber.org
URL(s): spearfishchamber.org/map
Released: Annual **Availability:** Print; PDF.

44661 ■ Sturgis Area Chamber of Commerce & Visitors Bureau
2040 Junction Ave.
Sturgis, SD 57785
Ph: (605)347-2556
URL: http://sturgisareachamber.com
Contact: Veronica Grosek, Executive Director
Instagram: www.instagram.com/s
turgischamberofcommerce
YouTube: www.youtube.com/channel/UCwDaImL
3bhbJRe1OkJz4NIA
Description: Promotes business and community development in Meade County, SD. **Founded:** 1876. **Geographic Preference:** Local.

44662 ■ Sturgis Chamber of Commerce
2040 Junction Ave.
Sturgis, SD 57785
Ph: (605)347-2556
URL: http://sturgisareachamber.com
Contact: Tim Kugler, President
Description: Promotes business and community development in the area. **Founded:** 1946. **Geographic Preference:** Local.

44663 ■ Vermillion Area Chamber of Commerce
2 E Main St.
Vermillion, SD 57069
Ph: (605)624-5571
Co. E-mail: vcdc@vermillionchamber.com
URL: http://livevermillion.com/chamber-of-commerce
Contact: John Prescott, Treasurer
Facebook: www.facebook.com/LiveVermillion
X (Twitter): x.com/VermillionSD
Instagram: www.instagram.com/vermillionsd
YouTube: www.youtube.com/channel/UCvEwAvw9w
3mIdIIQru3h12g
Description: Promotes business and community development in the Vermillion, SD area. Operates with the Vermillion Development Company. Sponsors competitions and festivals. **Geographic Preference:** Local.

44664 ■ Watertown Area Chamber of Commerce (WACC)
1 E Kemp
Watertown, SD 57201
Ph: (605)886-5814
Co. E-mail: coc@watertownsd.com
URL: http://www.watertownsd.com
Contact: Tim Sheehan, President
E-mail: tim@watertownsd.com
Facebook: www.facebook.com/WatertownChamber
Instagram: www.instagram.com/watertownchamber
YouTube: www.youtube.com/channel/UCqIeQja9a
47JP2PIHq1AwzQ
Description: Seeks to promote the economic prosperity and quality of life in the Watertown area. **Founded:** 1916. **Publications:** *The Chamber Advantage* (Monthly). **Geographic Preference:** Local.

44665 ■ Winner Area Chamber of Commerce (WACC)
246 S Main St.
Winner, SD 57580
Ph: (605)842-1533
Free: 800-658-3079
Co. E-mail: thechamber@gwtc.net
URL: http://www.winnersd.org/winner-area-chamber
Contact: Sarah Myers, President
E-mail: jayandsarahmyers@gmail.com
Facebook: www.facebook.com/cityofwinner

Description: Promotes business and community development in Winner, SD. **Founded:** 1946. **Geographic Preference:** Local.

MINORITY BUSINESS ASSISTANCE PROGRAMS

44666 ■ Native American Economic Development Project - Yankton Sioux Tribe (YST)
PO Box 1153
Wagner, SD 57380
Ph: (605)384-3641
Fax: (605)384-5895
Co. E-mail: ystenrollment@yahoo.com
URL: http://www.yanktonsiouxtribe.net
Contact: Robert Flying Hawk, Chairman
E-mail: robertflyinghawk@gmail.com
Description: Provides individual counseling and technical assistance to entrepreneurs from the Yankton Sioux tribe. Also works to increase circulation of monies with the borders of the reservation.

44667 ■ South Dakota Department of Tribal Government Relations
711 E Wells Ave.
Pierre, SD 57501
Ph: (605)773-3415
Fax: (605)773-6592
Co. E-mail: dtrsocialmedia@state.sd.us
URL: http://sdtribalrelations.sd.gov
Contact: Dave Flute, Secretary
Facebook: www.facebook.com/TribalSD
X (Twitter): x.com/TribalSD
Instagram: www.instagram.com/tribalsd
YouTube: www.youtube.com/channel/UCukV2R2i6exmPsOsrioydOg
Description: Focuses on removing barriers to Native American business development in South Dakota.

FINANCING AND LOAN PROGRAMS

44668 ■ Bluestem Captial Company, LLC
101 S Phillips Ave., Ste. 501
Sioux Falls, SD 57104
Ph: (605)331-0091
Co. E-mail: info@bluestemcapital.com
URL: http://www.bluestemcapital.com
Contact: Steve Kirby, Founder Partner
Description: Invests capital in early- to late-stage companies. **Investment Policies:** Management teams with a proven track record; tested products/services with market barriers; strong co-investors. **Industry Preferences:** Business services; natural resources; medical; real estate; manufacturing.

PROCUREMENT ASSISTANCE PROGRAMS

44669 ■ South Dakota Procurement Technical Assistance Center (West River)
Black Hill Business Development Ctr.
730 E Watertown St.
Rapid City, SD 57701
URL: http://www.aptac-us.org/find-a-ptac/?state=SD
Contact: Amy Meyer, Counselor
E-mail: ameyer@wrbsc.com
Description: Promotes early stage technology based companies to grow and prosper.

INCUBATORS/RESEARCH AND TECHNOLOGY PARKS

44670 ■ Ascent Innovation
525 University Loop, Ste. 101
Rapid City, SD 57701
Ph: (605)716-0001
URL: http://ascent-innovation.com
Facebook: www.facebook.com/ascentinnovationrc
Linkedin: www.linkedin.com/company/ascent-innovation-rapid-city
X (Twitter): twitter.com/AscentRapidCity
Description: Provider of management assistance, cost effective space and professional environment to new and existing small businesses. **Founded:** 2006.

44671 ■ South Dakota Enterprise Institute
2301 Research Pk. Way, Ste. 114
Brookings, SD 57006
Co. E-mail: info@sdei.org
URL: http://www.sdei.org
Contact: Tom Eitreim, Executive Director
Description: A small business incubator designed to facilitate University and industry resources to encourage and assist the establishment of entrepreneurial growth enterprises in the region. Its objectives are to assist the development of commercially viable opportunities identified within the University, establish mentoring support and outreach for regional growth enterprises, and support and/or sponsor academic entrepreneurial programs. **Founded:** 2001.

44672 ■ South Dakota State University - Innovation Center
1175 Medary Ave.
Brookings, SD 57006
URL: http://www.sdstate.edu/cpic
Contact: Erin Miller, Director (Acting)
E-mail: erin.miller@sdstate.edu
Description: A startup business incubator for early-stage tech and science research firms. In addition to lab space, the facility provides office space, conference rooms, smart board technology, free internet, break rooms, and collaboration opportunities. **Founded:** 2008.

EDUCATIONAL PROGRAMS

44673 ■ Mitchell Technical Institute (MTI)
1800 E Spruce St.
Mitchell, SD 57301
Ph: (605)995-3025
Free: 800-684-1969
Fax: (605)995-3083
Co. E-mail: questions@mitchelltech.edu
URL: http://www.mitchelltech.edu
Contact: Mark Wilson, President
E-mail: mark.wilson@mitchelltech.edu
Facebook: www.facebook.com/mitchelltech.edu
Linkedin: www.linkedin.com/school/mitchell-technical-college
X (Twitter): x.com/MitchellTech
Instagram: www.instagram.com/mitchell_tech
YouTube: www.youtube.com/user/mti1969
Description: School offers programs in small business management. **Founded:** 1968.

PUBLICATIONS

44674 ■ *Prairie Business Magazine (PB)*
101 5th St. N
Fargo, ND 58102-4826
Ph: (701)235-7311
Co. E-mail: afredrickson@forumcomm.com
URL: http://www.forumcomm.com
URL(s): www.grandforksherald.com/prairie-business
X (Twitter): twitter.com/prairiebiz
Ed: Kris Bevill. **Released:** Monthly **Description:** Magazine featuring business people and companies from North Dakota, Minnesota and South Dakota. **Availability:** Online.

Tennessee

ASSOCIATIONS AND OTHER ORGANIZATIONS

44675 ■ **Association of Fundraising Professionals Nashville Chapter**
639 Lafayette St.
 Nashville, TN 37203-4226
Co. E-mail: afp.nashville@gmail.com
URL: http://www.afpnashville.org
Contact: Destiney Patton, President
E-mail: destiney.patton@secondharvestmidtn.org
URL(s): afpglobal.org/chapters/afp-tn-nashville
 -tennessee-chapter
Facebook: www.facebook.com/AFPNashvilleChapter
X (Twitter): x.com/AFPNashville
Founded: 1981. **Geographic Preference:** Local.

44676 ■ **Business Network International - Mid-South (BNI)**
3430 Toringdon Way
 Charlotte, NC 28277
Free: 855-264-2673
URL: http://bnimidsouth.com/en-US/index
Contact: Jana Cardona, Executive Director
E-mail: jana@bnimidsouth.com
Description: Provides both men and women a structured environment for the development and exchange of quality business referrals. Offers members the opportunity to share ideas and contacts. **Geographic Preference:** Local.

44677 ■ **Business Network International, Middle Tennessee**
PO Box 158529
 Nashville, TN 37215
Ph: (615)297-0076
Co. E-mail: office@bnitennessee.com
URL: http://bnitennessee.com/en-US/index
Contact: Reed Morgan, Executive Director
Facebook: www.facebook.com/BNITNKYIN
Linkedin: www.linkedin.com/company/bni-middle
 -tennessee-kentucky-southern-indiana
X (Twitter): x.com/BNITNKYIN
YouTube: www.youtube.com/user/BNITNKYIN
Description: Provides both men and women a structured environment for the development and exchange of quality business referrals. Offers members the opportunity to share ideas and contacts. **Geographic Preference:** Local.

44678 ■ **Business Network International South East Tennessee**
PO Box 4483
 Chattanooga, TN 37402
Ph: (765)623-7469
URL: http://bnisetn.com/en-US/index
Contact: Elaine Merritt, Executive Director
E-mail: elaine@bnisetn.com
Description: Provides both men and women a structured environment for the development and exchange of quality business referrals. Offers members the opportunity to share ideas and contacts. **Geographic Preference:** Local.

44679 ■ **Entrepreneurs' Organization - Knoxville Chapter**
Knoxville, TN
Co. E-mail: info@eonetwork.org
URL: http://www.eonetwork.org/knoxville
Description: Provides local resources to members which includes networking events, mentorship, live forums, and leadership development. **Founded:** 1996.

44680 ■ **Entrepreneurs' Organization - Nashville Chapter**
PO Box 1652
 Brentwood, TN 37024-1652
URL: http://www.eonetwork.org/nashville
Contact: Sameera Lowe, Contact
Description: Provides local resources to members which includes networking events, mentorship, live forums, and leadership development. **Founded:** 1994.

44681 ■ **International Association of Women Memphis Chapter**
Memphis, TN
Co. E-mail: localchaptersoffice@iawomen.com
URL: http://community.iawomen.com/memphis/home
Contact: Lenore Trammell, President
Facebook: www.facebook.com/IAWomenMemphis
Description: Serves as network of accomplished women united to achieve professional goals. Provides a forum for sharing ideas and experiences of professional women regarding career success. Promotes an active business and networking community from all industries. **Geographic Preference:** Local.

44682 ■ **International Association of Women Nashville Chapter**
Nashville, TN
URL: http://www.iawomen.com/chapters
Description: Serves as network of accomplished women united to achieve professional goals. Provides a forum for sharing ideas and experiences of professional women regarding career success. Promotes an active business and networking community from all industries. **Geographic Preference:** Local.

44683 ■ **Memphis Bioworks Foundation**
17 W Pontotoc Ave., Ste. 100
 Memphis, TN 38103-3826
Contact: Lorie Jernigan, Contact
Description: An organization for bioscience startups and entrepreneurs. Provides funding, state-of-the-art labs and facilities, and training for the next generation of workers. **Founded:** 2001.

44684 ■ **Mid South Area Business Travel Association (MSA-BTA)**
PO Box 11441
 Memphis, TN 38111-0441
Co. E-mail: info@msabta.org
URL: http://www.msabta.org
Contact: Scott Harmon, President
Facebook: www.facebook.com/MidsouthAreaBTA
X (Twitter): x.com/MidsouthAreaBTA

Description: Represents travel managers and providers. Promotes the value of the travel manager in meeting corporate travel needs and financial goals. Cultivates a positive public image of the corporate travel industry. Protects the interests of members and their corporations in legislative and regulatory matters. Promotes safety, security, efficiency and quality travel. Provides a forum for the exchange of information and ideas among members. **Founded:** 2003. **Geographic Preference:** Regional.

44685 ■ **National Federation of Independent Business Tennessee**
53 Century Blvd., Ste. 250
 Nashville, TN 37214
Ph: (615)874-5288
URL: http://www.nfib.com/tennessee
Contact: Jim Brown, Director
E-mail: jim.brown@nfib.org
Description: Represents small and independent businesses. Aims to promote and protect the rights of members to own, operate and grow their businesses. **Geographic Preference:** State.

SMALL BUSINESS DEVELOPMENT CENTERS

44686 ■ **Tennessee Small Business Development Center (TSBDC)**
3050 Medical Center Pky. Ste. 200
 Murfreesboro, TN 37129
Ph: (615)898-2745
Fax: (615)893-7089
Co. E-mail: pgeho@tsbdc.org
URL: http://tsbdc.org
Contact: Patrick R. Geho, Director
E-mail: pgeho@tsbdc.org
Facebook: www.facebook.com/tsbdc
Linkedin: www.linkedin.com/company/tsbdc
X (Twitter): x.com/tsbdc
Description: Provides management assistance to current and prospective small businesses in Tennessee. **Geographic Preference:** State.

44687 ■ **Tennessee Small Business Development Centers Austin Peay State University (TSBDC)**
200 Commerce St., Ste. S&T
 Clarksville, TN 37040
Ph: (931)221-1370
Fax: (931)221-7748
URL: http://www.apsu.edu/tsbdc
Contact: Lorneth Peters, Director
E-mail: lpeters@tsbdc.org
URL(s): tsbdc.org
Facebook: www.facebook.com/tsbdc
X (Twitter): x.com/tsbdc
Description: Represents and promotes the small business sector. Provides management assistance to current and prospective small business owners. Helps to improve management skills and expand the products and services of members. **Geographic Preference:** Local.

Tennessee

44688 ■ Tennessee Small Business Development Centers Chattanooga State Community College
100 Cherokee Blvd., Ste. 202
Chattanooga, TN 37405
Ph: (423)756-8668
Fax: (423)756-6195
URL: http://www.tsbdc.org/chscc
Contact: Lynn Chesnutt, Director
Description: Represents and promotes the small business sector. Provides management assistance to current and prospective small business owners. Helps to improve management skills and expand the products and services of members. **Geographic Preference:** Local.

44689 ■ Tennessee Small Business Development Centers Cleveland State Community College
3535 Adkisson Dr.
Cleveland, TN 37320
Ph: (423)478-6247
URL: http://tsbdc.org/center/cleveland
Contact: Jennie DeCook, Director
E-mail: jdecook@tsbdc.org
Description: Represents and promotes the small business sector. Provides management assistance to current and prospective small business owners. Helps to improve management skills and expand the products and services of members. **Geographic Preference:** Local.

44690 ■ Tennessee Small Business Development Centers Dyersburg State Community College
Ste. 106
401 Country Club Rd.
Dyersburg, TN 38024
Ph: (731)286-3201
Co. E-mail: info@dscc.edu
URL: http://www.tsbdc.org/dscc
Facebook: www.facebook.com/tsbdc.dscc
Description: Represents and promotes the small business sector. Provides management assistance to current and prospective small business owners. Helps to improve management skills and expand the products and services of members. **Geographic Preference:** Local.

44691 ■ Tennessee Small Business Development Centers Jackson State Community College (TN TSBDC JSCC)
197 Auditorium St.
Jackson, TN 38301
Ph: (731)424-5389
URL: http://tsbdc.org/center/jackson
Contact: Dr. George Pimentel, President
Description: Represents and promotes the small business sector. Provides management assistance to current and prospective small business owners. Helps to improve management skills and expand the products and services of members. **Geographic Preference:** Local.

44692 ■ Tennessee Small Business Development Centers Knoxville
17 Market Sq., No. 201
Knoxville, TN 37902
Ph: (865)246-2663
URL: http://tsbdc.org/pscc
Contact: Laura Overstreet, Director
Facebook: www.facebook.com/KnoxvilleSBDC
Description: Represents and promotes the small business sector. Provides management assistance to current and prospective small business owners. Helps to improve management skills and expand the products and services of members. **Geographic Preference:** Local.

44693 ■ Tennessee Small Business Development Centers Memphis
Maxine A. Smith Ctr., Ste. 112
8800 E Shelby Dr.
Memphis, TN 38125
Ph: (901)333-5085
URL: http://www.tsbdc.org/swtcc
Contact: Dr. Tracy Hall, President
Description: Represents and promotes the small business sector. Provides management assistance to current and prospective small business owners. Helps to improve management skills and expand the products and services of members. **Founded:** 1985. **Geographic Preference:** Local.

44694 ■ Tennessee Small Business Development Centers - Middle Tennessee State University (TSBDC)
3050 Medical Center Pky., Ste. 232
Murfreesboro, TN 37129
Ph: (615)898-2745
Co. E-mail: mtsu@tsbdc.org
URL: http://tsbdc.org/center/murfreesboro
Contact: Galen Longo, Director
Facebook: www.facebook.com/mtsutsbdc
Description: Promotes growth and prosperity in the domestic and international markets of the business community and enhances its economic impact on the State of Tennessee. **Geographic Preference:** Local.

44695 ■ Tennessee Small Business Development Centers - Middle Tennessee State University-Columbia
Rutherford County Chamber of Commerce
3050 Medical Center Pky., Ste. 232
Murfreesboro, TN 37129
Ph: (615)898-2745
Co. E-mail: mtsu@tsbdc.org
URL: http://clients.tsbdc.org/center.aspx?center=47050&subloc=1
Description: To be the premier provider of quality solutions to potential and existing small businesses' needs through consultation, education, referral, and support services. **Geographic Preference:** Local.

44696 ■ Tennessee Small Business Development Centers Tennessee State University Brentwood
Reliant Bank
1736 Carothers Pky., Ste. 100
Brentwood, TN 37027
Ph: (615)963-7179
Co. E-mail: lvaughn@tsbdc.org
URL: http://clients.tsbdc.org/center.aspx?center=47060&subloc=1
Description: Represents and promotes the small business sector. Provides management assistance to current and prospective small business owners. Helps to improve management skills and expand the products and services of members. **Geographic Preference:** Local.

44697 ■ Tennessee Small Business Development Centers Tennessee State University Nashville
330 10th Ave. N, Ste. G-400
Nashville, TN 37203
Ph: (615)963-7179
URL: http://tsbdc.org/center/nashville
Contact: Thomas Tate, Specialist
Description: Represents and promotes the small business sector. Provides management assistance to current and prospective small business owners. Helps to improve management skills and expand the products and services of members. **Geographic Preference:** Local.

44698 ■ Tennessee Small Business Development Centers Tennessee Tech University
1104 England Dr.
Cookeville, TN 38501
Ph: (931)520-6081
URL: http://www.tsbdc.org/ttu
Contact: Mark Farley, Contact
X (Twitter): twitter.com/ttutsbdc
Description: Provides management assistance to current and prospective small business owners in Tennessee. **Geographic Preference:** Local.

44699 ■ Tennessee Small Business Development Centers Volunteer State Community College
300 Bldg., Office 103C
Nashville Pke.
Gallatin, TN 37066
Ph: (615)230-4780
URL: http://tsbdc.org/center/gallatin
Contact: Charles Alexander, Director
E-mail: calexander@tsbdc.org
Description: Represents and promotes the small business sector. Provides management assistance to current and prospective small business owners. Helps to improve management skills and expand the products and services of members. **Geographic Preference:** Local.

SMALL BUSINESS ASSISTANCE PROGRAMS

44700 ■ Tennessee Department of Economic and Community Development - Business Enterprise Resource Office (BERO)
312 Rosa L. Parks Ave.
Nashville, TN 37243
Co. E-mail: ecd.bero@tn.gov
URL: http://www.tn.gov/ecd/small-business/bero
Contact: Wisty Pender, Director
Description: Provides services to minority entrepreneurs through offices located in Nashville, Chattanooga, Knoxville, and Memphis. **Founded:** 1977.

SCORE OFFICES

44701 ■ SCORE - Chattanooga
Franklin Bldg.
5726 Marlin Rd., Ste. 515
Chattanooga, TN 37411
Ph: (423)553-1722
Fax: (423)553-1724
Co. E-mail: chattanooga.score@gmail.com
URL: http://chattanooga.score.org
Facebook: www.facebook.com/SCOREChattanooga
Linkedin: www.linkedin.com/company/score-mentors-chattanooga
X (Twitter): x.com/SCOREChatanooga
Description: Serves as volunteer program in which working and retired business management professionals provide free business counseling to men and women who are considering starting a small business, encountering problems with their business, or expanding their business. Offers free one-on-one counseling, online counseling and low cost workshops on a variety of business topics. **Founded:** 1964. **Geographic Preference:** Local.

44702 ■ SCORE - Greater Knoxville - Library
412 N Cedar Bluff Rd., Ste. 450
Knoxville, TN 37923
Ph: (865)692-0716
Co. E-mail: greaterknoxvillescore@gmail.com
URL: http://greaterknoxville.score.org
X (Twitter): x.com/SCOREKnoxville
Description: Serves as volunteer program in which working and retired business management professionals provide free business counseling to men and women who are considering starting a small business, encountering problems with their business, or expanding their business. Offers free one-on-one counseling, online counseling and low cost workshops on a variety of business topics. **Scope:** Business. **Founded:** 1964. **Holdings:** Articles. **Geographic Preference:** Local.

44703 ■ SCORE - Memphis
5100 Poplar Ave., Ste. 1701
Memphis, TN 38137
Ph: (901)544-3588
Fax: (901)544-0557
Co. E-mail: help@score.org
URL: http://memphis.score.org
Contact: Joe McDonald, Contact
Facebook: www.facebook.com/ScoreMemphis
Linkedin: www.linkedin.com/company/score-memphis

STATE LISTINGS

Description: Serves as volunteer program in which working and retired business management professionals provide free business counseling to men and women who are considering starting a small business, encountering problems with their business, or expanding their business. Offers free one-on-one counseling, online counseling and low cost workshops on a variety of business topics. **Founded:** 1964. **Geographic Preference:** Local.

44704 ■ SCORE - Nashville
2 International Plz., Ste. 500
Nashville, TN 37217
Free: 844-726-7322
Co. E-mail: contact@scorenashville.org
URL: http://www.nashville.score.org
Contact: Bridget Weston, Chief Executive Officer
Linkedin: www.linkedin.com/company/score-mentors-nashville
X (Twitter): x.com/SCORE_nashville
Description: Serves as volunteer program in which working and retired business management professionals provide free business counseling to men and women who are considering starting a small business, encountering problems with their business, or expanding their business. Offers free one-on-one counseling, online counseling and low cost workshops on a variety of business topics. **Geographic Preference:** Local.

44705 ■ SCORE - Winchester
44 Chamber Way
Winchester, TN 37398
URL: http://chattanooga.score.org/branch/winchester-office
Description: Provides professional guidance and information to maximize the success of existing and emerging small businesses. Offers business counseling and workshops.

BETTER BUSINESS BUREAUS

44706 ■ Better Business Bureau of Greater East Tennessee
251 N Peters Rd.
Knoxville, TN 37923
Ph: (865)692-1600
Fax: (865)692-1590
URL: http://www.bbb.org/local-bbb/bbb-of-greater-east-tennessee
Linkedin: www.linkedin.com/company/better-business-bureau-of-greater-east-tennessee
X (Twitter): x.com/BBBGreatEastTN
Description: Seeks to promote and foster the highest ethical relationship between businesses and the public through voluntary self-regulation, consumer and business education, and service excellence. Provides information to help consumers and businesses make informed purchasing decisions and avoid costly scams and frauds; settles consumer complaints through arbitration and other means. **Geographic Preference:** Local.

44707 ■ Better Business Bureau of the Mid-South
3693 Tyndale Dr.
Memphis, TN 38125-8537
Ph: (901)759-1300
Free: 800-222-8754
Fax: (901)757-2997
Co. E-mail: info@bbbmidsouth.org
URL: http://www.bbb.org/local-bbb/bbb-of-the-mid-south
Facebook: www.facebook.com/BBBMemphis
X (Twitter): x.com/bbbmidsouth
Description: Seeks to promote and foster ethical relationship between businesses and the public through voluntary self-regulation, consumer and business education, and service excellence. Provides information to help consumers and businesses make informed purchasing decisions and avoids costly scams and frauds; settles consumer complaints through arbitration and other means. **Founded:** 1948. **Geographic Preference:** Regional.

44708 ■ Better Business Bureau of Middle Tennessee
25 Century Blvd., Ste. 101
Nashville, TN 37214
Ph: (615)242-4222
Fax: (615)250-4245
Co. E-mail: info@gobbb.org
URL: http://www.bbb.org/local-bbb/bbb-of-middle-tennessee
Contact: Lisa Frohnapfel, President
Facebook: www.facebook.com/bbbMidtnSouthky
Linkedin: www.linkedin.com/company/better-business-bureau-of-middle-tn-inc-
X (Twitter): x.com/BBBMidTN
Instagram: www.instagram.com/bbbmidtnsouthky
YouTube: www.youtube.com/channel/UCfWmhDOKfiSQ2Zxc1fHyBWA
Description: Promotes ethical business practices through self-regulation, rather than government or legal intervention, by providing factual reports on businesses, mediation and arbitration services, and advertising review. **Founded:** 1961. **Geographic Preference:** Local.

44709 ■ Better Business Bureau of Southeast Tennessee and Northwest Georgia
508 N Market St.
Chattanooga, TN 37405
Ph: (423)266-6144
Fax: (423)267-1924
Co. E-mail: tngabbb@chattanooga.bbb.org
URL: http://www.bbb.org/local-bbb/bbb-serving-southeast-tennessee-and-northwest-georgia
Description: Seeks to promote and foster the highest ethical relationship between businesses and the public through voluntary self-regulation, consumer and business education, and service excellence. Provides information to help consumers and businesses make informed purchasing decisions and avoid costly scams and frauds; settles consumer complaints through arbitration and other means. **Founded:** 1960. **Awards:** BBB of Southeast Tennessee and Northwest Georgia Torch Award for Marketplace Ethics (Annual). **Geographic Preference:** Local.

CHAMBERS OF COMMERCE

44710 ■ 225 Keith
225 Keith St. SW
Cleveland, TN 37320-2275
Ph: (423)472-6587
Fax: (423)472-2019
Co. E-mail: info@clevelandchamber.com
URL: http://clevelandchamber.com
Contact: Mike Griffin, President
E-mail: mgriffin@clevelandchamber.com
URL(s): clevelandchamber.com/cleveland-chamber/newsletter
Released: Monthly **Description:** Contains business news and Chamber activities. Also includes such features as a Small Business Spotlight, member memos (announcements of awards, recognitions, new staff, relocations, etc.), and Economic Indicators. **Availability:** PDF; Online.

44711 ■ Anderson County Chamber of Commerce (ACCC)
245 N Main St., Ste. 200
Clinton, TN 37716
Ph: (865)457-2559
Fax: (865)463-7480
Co. E-mail: accc@andersoncountychamber.org
URL: http://www.andersoncountychamber.org
Contact: Rick Meredith, President
E-mail: rick@andersoncountychamber.org
Facebook: www.facebook.com/andersoncountychamber
Linkedin: www.linkedin.com/company/anderson-county-chamber-of-commerce
X (Twitter): x.com/ACChamberTN
Instagram: www.instagram.com/acchambertn
Description: Promotes business and community development in Anderson County, TN. Sponsors Antiques Festival, Teachers Appreciation Banquet, Scholarship Golf Tournament, Business Expo and Softball Classic. Conducts charitable activities. **Founded:** 1932. **Publications:** *The Chamber News* (Monthly); *Guidebook and Directory* (Biennial). **Geographic Preference:** Local.

44712 ■ Athens Area Chamber of Commerce
13 N Jackson St.
Athens, TN 37303
Ph: (423)745-0334
Co. E-mail: info@athenschamber.org
URL: http://athenschamber.org
Contact: Karen Raby, Chairman
Facebook: www.facebook.com/athenschamber
Description: Promotes business and community development in Athens, TN area. **Founded:** 1982. **Publications:** *Athens Business* (Monthly). **Geographic Preference:** Local.

44713 ■ Bartlett Area Chamber of Commerce (BACC)
2969 Elmore Pk. Rd.
Bartlett, TN 38134-8309
Ph: (901)372-9457
Fax: (901)372-9488
URL: http://bartlettchamber.chambermaster.com
Contact: John Threadgill, President
E-mail: jthreadgill@bartlettchamber.com
Instagram: www.instagram.com/bartlettareachamberofcommerce
Description: Promotes business and community development in Shelby County, TN. Sponsors Leadership Bartlett program and annual Business Expo. Convention/Meeting: none. **Founded:** 1980. **Publications:** *Bartlett Area Chamber of Commerce--Membership Directory* (Annual); *Your Business Connection* (Monthly). **Geographic Preference:** Local.

44714 ■ Bellevue Harpeth Chamber of Commerce (BHCC)
PO Box 210238
Nashville, TN 37221
Ph: (615)662-2737
Co. E-mail: info@bellevueharpethchamber.com
URL: http://bellevueharpethchamber.com
Contact: Cole Crocker, Co-President
Facebook: www.facebook.com/thebellevuechamber
X (Twitter): x.com/bvuetnchamber
YouTube: www.youtube.com/channel/UCvuRj5oDJSimT9L7THaNZ0A
Description: Promotes business and community development in Bellevue, TN. **Geographic Preference:** Local.

44715 ■ Benton County/Camden Chamber of Commerce
266 Hwy. 641 N
Camden, TN 38320
Ph: (731)584-8395
URL: http://www.bentoncountycamden.com
Contact: Kevin Stepp, President
Facebook: www.facebook.com/bentoncountycamdenchamber
Description: Promotes business and community development in Camden, TN area. **Geographic Preference:** Local.

44716 ■ Blount County Chamber of Commerce
201 S Washington St.
Maryville, TN 37804-5728
Ph: (865)983-2241
Free: 855-257-3964
Fax: (865)984-1386
Co. E-mail: infodesk@blountpartnership.com
URL: http://www.blountchamber.com
Contact: Bryan Daniels, President
E-mail: bdaniels@blountpartnership.com
Facebook: www.facebook.com/blountchamber
Linkedin: www.linkedin.com/company/blountpartnership
X (Twitter): x.com/blountchamber
Instagram: www.instagram.com/blountchamber
YouTube: www.youtube.com/blountchamber
Description: Promotes business and community development in Blount County, TN. **Founded:** 1920. **Publications:** *The Daily Times* (Daily); *Knoxville News Sentinel*. **Geographic Preference:** Local.

44717 ■ Bristol Tennessee/Virginia Chamber of Commerce
PO Box 519
Bristol, TN 37620
Ph: (423)989-4850
Co. E-mail: ashuttle@bristolchamber.org
URL: http://www.bristolchamber.org
Contact: Beth Rhinehart, President
E-mail: brhinehart@bristolchamber.org
Facebook: www.facebook.com/BristolChamber
Linkedin: www.linkedin.com/company/bristol-chamber-of-commerce
X (Twitter): x.com/bristolchamber
Instagram: www.instagram.com/bristol.chamber
YouTube: www.youtube.com/channel/UCdynP_nvQaORkJiKjhjNbGg
Pinterest: www.pinterest.com/bristolchamber
Description: Promotes business and community development in Bristol, located in the states of Tennessee and Virginia. **Founded:** 1909. **Publications:** *Bristol Membership Directory-Newcomers Guide and Business Pages* (Annual). **Geographic Preference:** Regional.

44718 ■ Campbell County Chamber of Commerce (CCCC)
1016 Main St.
Jacksboro, TN 37757
Ph: (423)566-0329
Co. E-mail: info@campbellcountychamber.org
URL: http://campbellcountychamber.com
Contact: Ryne Cummins, President
Facebook: www.facebook.com/campbellcountychamberofcommerce
X (Twitter): x.com/ccchambertn
Description: Provides business and community development in the Campbell County, TN area. **Geographic Preference:** Local.

44719 ■ Carroll County Chamber of Commerce
20740 E Main St.
Huntingdon, TN 38344
Ph: (731)986-4664
Co. E-mail: cchamber@earthlink.net
URL: http://carrollcountyecd.com
Contact: Brad Hurley, President
E-mail: cchamber@earthlink.net
Description: Organized for the purpose of advancing the commercial, industrial, civic, and general interests of the County of Carroll and its trade area. **Geographic Preference:** Local.

44720 ■ *The Chamber News*
245 N Main St., Ste. 200
Clinton, TN 37716
Ph: (865)457-2559
Fax: (865)463-7480
Co. E-mail: accc@andersoncountychamber.org
URL: http://www.andersoncountychamber.org
Contact: Rick Meredith, President
E-mail: rick@andersoncountychamber.org
URL(s): andersoncountychamber.org/the-chamber/the-chamber-news
Released: Monthly; latest edition Jan. 2020. **Description:** Announces events and includes stories of members. **Availability:** Online.

44721 ■ *Chamber News*
107 Main St.
Dayton, TN 37321
Ph: (423)775-0361
Co. E-mail: admin@daytontnchamber.org
URL: http://daytontnchamber.org
Contact: April Curtis, President
E-mail: acurtis@firstbankonline.com
URL(s): daytonchamber.org/news
Availability: Print.

44722 ■ *Chamber News*
208 S Elk Ave.
Fayetteville, TN 37334
Ph: (931)433-1234
Free: 888-433-1238
Fax: (931)433-9087
Co. E-mail: flcchamber@fpunet.com
URL: http://fayettevillelincolncountychamber.com
Contact: Josh Richardson, President
URL(s): www.fayettevillelincolncountychamber.com/newsletters
Released: Monthly **Availability:** PDF.

44723 ■ Chattanooga Area Chamber of Commerce
811 Broad St., No. 100
Chattanooga, TN 37402
Ph: (423)756-2121
URL: http://www.chattanoogachamber.com
Contact: Charles Wood, President
Facebook: www.facebook.com/CHAchamber
Linkedin: www.linkedin.com/company/chattanooga-area-chamber-of-commerce
X (Twitter): x.com/CHAchamber
Instagram: www.instagram.com/chachamber
Description: Promotes regional business growth that creates prosperity and enhances quality of life. **Founded:** 1887. **Awards:** Chattanooga Area Chamber of Commerce Early Innovator Award (Annual); Kruesi Award for Innovation (Annual); Chattanooga Area Chamber of Commerce Small Business Award (Annual). **Geographic Preference:** Local.

44724 ■ Cheatham County Chamber of Commerce
328 Frey St.
Ashland City, TN 37015
Ph: (615)792-6722
Co. E-mail: info@cheathamchamber.org
URL: http://www.cheathamchamber.org
Contact: Misty Keenan, Executive Director
Facebook: www.facebook.com/cheathamchamber
Description: Promotes business and community development in Cheatham County and Middle Tennessee. **Founded:** 1989. **Publications:** *The Chamber Spirit* (Monthly). **Geographic Preference:** Local.

44725 ■ Claiborne County Chamber of Commerce
1732 Main St., Ste. 1
Tazewell, TN 37879
Ph: (423)626-4149
Co. E-mail: chamber@claibornepartnership.com
URL: http://www.claibornepartnership.com
Contact: Daniel England, President
E-mail: daniel.england780@gmail.com
Description: Promotes business and community development in Claiborne County, TN. Encourages tourism in the area. **Geographic Preference:** Local.

44726 ■ Clarksville Area Chamber of Commerce
25 Jefferson St., Ste. 300
Clarksville, TN 37040
Ph: (931)647-2331
Free: 800-530-2487
Fax: (931)645-1574
Co. E-mail: cacc@clarksville.tn.us
URL: http://www.clarksvillechamber.com
Contact: Melinda Shepard, Executive Director
E-mail: melinda@clarksville.tn.us
Facebook: www.facebook.com/ClarksvilleTNChamber
X (Twitter): x.com/clkstnchamber
Instagram: www.instagram.com/clarksvilletnchamber
Description: Works to enhance the quality of living for Clarksville residents by promoting business and economic development, improving the community's welfare, and representing the interests of its members. **Founded:** 1905. **Geographic Preference:** Local.

44727 ■ Clay County Partnership Chamber of Commerce - Clay County Public Library
424 Brown St.
Celina, TN 38551
Ph: (931)243-3338
Co. E-mail: claychamber@twlakes.net
URL: http://dalehollowlake.org/chamber
Contact: Kevin Donaldson, Executive Director
Facebook: www.facebook.com/Clay.County.TN.Chamber
Pinterest: www.pinterest.com/ClayChamber
Description: Promotes business and community development in Celina and Clay County, TN. **Scope:** Fictions. **Services:** open to public. **Holdings:** Books; Dvd's. **Geographic Preference:** Local.

44728 ■ Cleveland/Bradley Chamber of Commerce
225 Keith St. SW
Cleveland, TN 37320-2275
Ph: (423)472-6587
Fax: (423)472-2019
Co. E-mail: info@clevelandchamber.com
URL: http://clevelandchamber.com
Contact: Mike Griffin, President
E-mail: mgriffin@clevelandchamber.com
Facebook: www.facebook.com/CLEchamber
Linkedin: www.linkedin.com/company/cleveland-bradley-chamber-of-commerce
X (Twitter): x.com/CLEchamber
Instagram: www.instagram.com/clechamber
YouTube: www.youtube.com/channel/UC60-pOI3Za9b2CWtr25u5iw
Description: Strives to foster the business development of members, the economic growth of the region, and the highest quality of life for the community. **Founded:** 1925. **Publications:** *225 Keith* (Monthly). **Geographic Preference:** Local.

44729 ■ Cocke County Partnership/Chamber of Commerce
115 Mulbery St., Ste. 200
Newport, TN 37821
Ph: (423)623-7201
Fax: (423)625-1846
Co. E-mail: lramsey@cockecountypartnership.com
URL: http://newportcockecountychamber.com
Contact: Lynn Ramsey, Director
E-mail: lramsey@cockecountypartnership.com
Facebook: www.facebook.com/CockeCountyPartnership
X (Twitter): x.com/ccpchamber
Description: Promotes business and community development in Newport - Cocke County, TN. **Geographic Preference:** Local.

44730 ■ Collierville Area Chamber of Commerce
485 Halle Pk. Dr.
Collierville, TN 38017-7088
Ph: (901)853-1949
Co. E-mail: info@colliervillechamber.com
URL: http://colliervillechamber.com
Contact: Mark Heuberger, President
E-mail: mark@colliervillechamber.com
X (Twitter): x.com/ChamberCville
Description: Promotes business and community development in the Collierville, TN area. **Founded:** 1984. **Publications:** *Chamber Works* (Monthly); *Collierville Magazine* (Annual). **Awards:** Collierville Area Chamber of Commerce Person of the Year (Annual). **Geographic Preference:** Local.

44731 ■ *Collierville Magazine*
485 Halle Pk. Dr.
Collierville, TN 38017-7088
Ph: (901)853-1949
Co. E-mail: info@colliervillechamber.com
URL: http://colliervillechamber.com
Contact: Mark Heuberger, President
E-mail: mark@colliervillechamber.com
URL(s): colliervillechamber.com/about-us/news/collierville-magazine
Ed: Anna Cox Thompson. **Released:** Annual **Description:** Magazine describing the Collierville, TN area. **Availability:** Print; Online; Download; PDF.

44732 ■ Cookeville Area-Putnam County Chamber of Commerce
One W 1st St.
Cookeville, TN 38501
Ph: (931)526-2211
Free: 800-264-5541
Co. E-mail: info@cookevillechamber.com
URL: http://cookevillechamber.com
Contact: Amy New, President
E-mail: anew@cookevillechamber.com
X (Twitter): x.com/ckvlchamber

STATE LISTINGS

Description: Promotes business and community development in the Putnam County, TN area and region. **Geographic Preference:** Regional.

44733 ■ Crockett County Chamber of Commerce
25 N Bells St.
Alamo, TN 38001
Ph: (731)696-5120
Fax: (731)696-4855
Co. E-mail: contact@crockettchamber.com
URL: http://www.crockettchamber.com
Contact: John Cole, Contact
Facebook: www.facebook.com/crockettchamber
X (Twitter): x.com/CCChamber2014
Description: Promotes business and community development in Crockett County, TN. **Founded:** 2012. **Geographic Preference:** Local.

44734 ■ Crossville-Cumberland County Chamber of Commerce
34 S Main St.
Crossville, TN 38555
Ph: (931)484-8444
Free: 877-465-3861
Fax: (931)484-7511
Co. E-mail: info@crossville-chamber.com
URL: http://crossvillechamber.com
Contact: Ethan Hadley, President
E-mail: ethan.hadley@crossville-chamber.com
Facebook: www.facebook.com/crossvillechamber
Description: Promotes business and community development in Crossville, TN area. **Geographic Preference:** Local.

44735 ■ *The Daily Times*
201 S Washington St.
Maryville, TN 37804-5728
Ph: (865)983-2241
Free: 855-257-3964
Fax: (865)984-1386
Co. E-mail: infodesk@blountpartnership.com
URL: http://www.blountchamber.com
Contact: Bryan Daniels, President
E-mail: bdaniels@blountpartnership.com
URL(s): www.thedailytimes.com
X (Twitter): x.com/dailytimes
Ed: Corey Roepken, Bob Norris, Melanie Tucker, Todd Foster. **Released:** Daily **Availability:** Print; Online.

44736 ■ Dayton Chamber of Commerce
107 Main St.
Dayton, TN 37321
Ph: (423)775-0361
Co. E-mail: admin@daytontnchamber.org
URL: http://daytontnchamber.org
Contact: April Curtis, President
E-mail: acurtis@firstbankonline.com
Description: Promotes the advancement of civic, commercial, industrial, recreational, and agricultural interest in Dayton and Rhea County. **Founded:** 1980. **Publications:** *Chamber News*. **Geographic Preference:** Local.

44737 ■ Decatur County Chamber of Commerce (DCCC)
c/o Charles P. Taylor, Sr., Executive Director
139 Tennessee Ave. N
Parsons, TN 38363
Ph: (731)847-4202
Co. E-mail: ctaylor@decaturcountytennessee.org
URL: http://decaturcountytennessee.org
Contact: Charles P. Taylor, Sr., Executive Director
E-mail: ctaylor@decaturcountytennessee.org
Facebook: www.facebook.com/decaturcountychamberofcommerce
Description: Works to improve the economy and quality of life in Decatur County, TN. **Geographic Preference:** Local.

44738 ■ Dickson County Chamber of Commerce
205 S Main St.
Dickson, TN 37055
Ph: (615)446-2349
Co. E-mail: contactus@dicksoncountychamber.com
URL: http://www.dicksoncountychamber.com
Contact: Laura Travis, Chairman
Linkedin: www.linkedin.com/company/dickson-county-chamber-of-commerce
X (Twitter): x.com/discoverdickson
YouTube: www.youtube.com/channel/UCfpDDwZ78wvlf875OX8gtwQ
Description: Aims to promote economic development in Dickson County. **Founded:** 1921. **Geographic Preference:** Local.

44739 ■ Dyersburg-Dyer County Chamber of Commerce
2000 Commerce Ave.
Dyersburg, TN 38024
Ph: (731)285-3433
Co. E-mail: chambernews@dyerchamber.com
URL: http://www.dyerchamber.com
Contact: Slater Barr, President
Facebook: www.facebook.com/dyerchamber
X (Twitter): twitter.com/dyerchamber
YouTube: www.youtube.com/user/dyerchamber
Description: Promotes business and community development in Dyer County, TN. Encourages tourism in the area. **Founded:** 1942. **Publications:** *At Work*. **Awards:** Dyersburg-Dyer County Chamber of Commerce Volunteer Diplomat of the Year (Annual). **Geographic Preference:** Local.

44740 ■ Elizabethton - Carter County Chamber of Commerce
615 E Elk Ave.
Elizabethton, TN 37643
Ph: (423)547-3850
Fax: (423)547-3854
Co. E-mail: info@elizabethtonchamber.com
URL: http://elizabethtonchamber.com
Contact: Danny O'Quinn, President
Facebook: www.facebook.com/ElizChamberTN
X (Twitter): x.com/ElizChamberTN
Instagram: www.instagram.com/elizchambertn
Description: Works to promote business and community development in Elizabethton-Carter County, TN area. **Publications:** *Visitors Guide* (Annual); *Naturally Nice News* (Monthly); *Visitors Guide*. **Geographic Preference:** Local.

44741 ■ Etowah Area Chamber of Commerce
727 TN Ave.
Etowah, TN 37331
Ph: (423)920-5659
Co. E-mail: info@etowahcoc.org
URL: http://www.enterpriseetowah.com
Facebook: www.facebook.com/EtowahChamberofCommerce
Instagram: www.instagram.com/etowahcoc
Description: Works to promote business and community development in Etowah, TN area. **Geographic Preference:** Local.

44742 ■ Fairview Area Chamber of Commerce
PO Box 711
Fairview, TN 37062-0711
Ph: (615)544-0061
URL: http://www.uschamber.com/co/chambers/tennessee
Description: Promotes business and community development in Fairview, TN area. **Geographic Preference:** Local.

44743 ■ Fayetteville - Lincoln County Chamber of Commerce
208 S Elk Ave.
Fayetteville, TN 37334
Ph: (931)433-1234
Free: 888-433-1238
Fax: (931)433-9087
Co. E-mail: flcchamber@fpunet.com
URL: http://fayettevillelincolncountychamber.com
Contact: Josh Richardson, President
Facebook: www.facebook.com/FayettevilleLCChamber
Description: Promotes business and community development in Fayetteville and Lincoln County, TN area. **Founded:** 1809. **Publications:** *Chamber News* (Monthly). **Geographic Preference:** Local.

44744 ■ Fentress County Chamber of Commerce
114 Central Ave., W
Jamestown, TN 38556
Ph: (931)879-9948
Fax: (931)879-6767
URL: http://www.jamestowntn.org
Contact: Steve Boutelle, President
Description: Provides business and community development in the Fentress County, TN area. **Founded:** 1975. **Geographic Preference:** Local.

44745 ■ Franklin County Chamber of Commerce (FCCoC)
44 Chamber Way
Winchester, TN 37398
Ph: (931)967-6788
Co. E-mail: info@franklincountychamber.com
URL: http://www.franklincountychamber.com
Contact: Kayla Doney, Executive Director
Facebook: www.facebook.com/FranklinCountyChamber
X (Twitter): x.com/fctnchamber
Description: Promotes business and community development in Franklin County, TN. **Geographic Preference:** Local.

44746 ■ Gallatin Chamber of Commerce
118 W Main St.
Gallatin, TN 37066
Ph: (615)452-4000
Co. E-mail: info@gallatintn.org
URL: http://www.gallatintn.org
Contact: Kim Baker, Chief Executive Officer
E-mail: kim@gallatintn.org
Facebook: www.facebook.com/gallatinchamber
X (Twitter): x.com/gallatinchamber
Instagram: www.instagram.com/gallatinchamber
YouTube: www.youtube.com/channel/UCGRBPPpbm2oo8opcbNvXyTQ
Description: Promotes business and community development in Gallatin, TN area. **Founded:** 1921. **Geographic Preference:** Local.

44747 ■ Gatlinburg Chamber of Commerce
811 E Pky.
Gatlinburg, TN 37738-4913
Ph: (865)436-4178
Co. E-mail: info@gatlinburg.com
URL: http://www.gatlinburg.com/default.asp
Contact: Brian T. A. Mansfield, Contact
Facebook: www.facebook.com/gatlinburgchamber
YouTube: www.youtube.com/user/gatlinburgdotcom
Pinterest: www.pinterest.com/gatlinburgtn
Description: Promotes business and community development in Gatlinburg, TN. **Founded:** 1940. **Geographic Preference:** Local.

44748 ■ Germantown Area Chamber of Commerce (GACC)
2195 S Germantown Rd.
Germantown, TN 38138
Ph: (901)755-1200
Fax: (901)755-9168
Co. E-mail: info@germantownchamber.com
URL: http://www.germantownchamber.com
Contact: Janie Day, President
E-mail: janie@germantownchamber.com
Facebook: www.facebook.com/germantownchamber
X (Twitter): x.com/gtowntnchamber
Instagram: www.instagram.com/germantownchamber
Description: Promotes business and community development in Germantown, TN. **Founded:** 1973. **Publications:** *Germantown Area Chamber News* (Monthly); *Germantown Magazine* (3/year). **Geographic Preference:** Local.

44749 ■ *Germantown Magazine*
2195 S Germantown Rd.
Germantown, TN 38138
Ph: (901)755-1200
Fax: (901)755-9168
Co. E-mail: info@germantownchamber.com
URL: http://www.germantownchamber.com
Contact: Janie Day, President
E-mail: janie@germantownchamber.com

URL(s): www.germantownchamber.com/germantown-magazine.html
Released: 3/year; spring, summer, fall. **Availability:** Online.

44750 ■ Giles County Chamber of Tourism & Commerce
110 N 2nd St.
Pulaski, TN 38478
Ph: (931)363-3789
Co. E-mail: director@gilescountychamber.com
URL: http://www.gilescountychamber.com
Contact: Jessie Parker, Chief Executive Officer
Description: Strives to create a network to promote, educate and advance business by providing the leadership to generate economic growth and opportunities. **Founded:** 1909. **Publications:** *Giles County Chamber Business Directory* (Quarterly); *Giles County Chamber Quality of Life Book* (Biennial); *Chamber News*. **Geographic Preference:** Local.

44751 ■ Goodlettsville Area Chamber of Commerce
100 N Main St., Ste. D
Goodlettsville, TN 37072
Ph: (615)859-7979
Fax: (615)657-0265
Co. E-mail: info@goodlettsvillechamber.com
URL: http://www.goodlettsvillechamber.com
Contact: Marilee Tice, President
Facebook: www.facebook.com/goodlettsvillechamber
Description: Promotes business and community development in the Goodlettsville area. **Founded:** 1961. **Publications:** *Commerce Connection* (Monthly). **Geographic Preference:** Local.

44752 ■ Greater Gibson County Area Chamber of Commerce
111 W Eaton St.
Trenton, TN 38382
Ph: (731)855-0973
Fax: (731)855-0979
Co. E-mail: lwickersham@gibsoncountytn.com
URL: http://www.gibsoncountytn.com
Contact: Clayton White, President
E-mail: wrencefh@gmail.com
Facebook: www.facebook.com/gibsonchamber
Description: Promotes business and community development in Greater Gibson County, TN. **Geographic Preference:** Local.

44753 ■ Greater Memphis Chamber [Memphis Regional Chamber of Commerce]
22 N Front St., Ste. 200
Memphis, TN 38103-2100
Ph: (901)543-3500
Co. E-mail: info@memphischamber.com
URL: http://memphischamber.com
Contact: Beverly Robertson, President (Acting)
E-mail: brobertson@memphischamber.com
Facebook: www.facebook.com/memphischamber
Linkedin: www.linkedin.com/company/greater-memphis-chamber
X (Twitter): x.com/MemphisChamber
Instagram: www.instagram.com/memphischamber
YouTube: www.youtube.com/memphischamber
Description: Works to establish the Memphis region as a dynamic, growing, energetic metropolitan region strongly connected to the global marketplace. **Founded:** 1838. **Publications:** *The Chamber Prosperity* (Monthly). **Geographic Preference:** Local.

44754 ■ Greene County Partnership (GCP)
115 Academy St.
Greeneville, TN 37743
Ph: (423)638-4111
Co. E-mail: gcp@greenecop.com
URL: http://discovergreenevilletn.com
Contact: Jeff Taylor, Officer
E-mail: jeff@greenecountypartnership.net
Facebook: www.facebook.com/GreeneCountyPartnership
Description: Strives to promote, preserve, and enhance the quality of life and economic well being of all Greene Countians by providing collective leadership and serving as a facilitator, catalyst, and unifying force to achieve common community goals. **Founded:** 1993. **Publications:** *Partners*. **Geographic Preference:** Local.

44755 ■ Hardeman County Chamber of Commerce
112 S Main St.
Bolivar, TN 38008
Ph: (731)658-6554
Co. E-mail: info@hardemancountychamber.com
URL: http://www.hardemancountychamber.com
Contact: Christine Korling-Torres, Executive Director
Facebook: www.facebook.com/hardemancochamber
Description: Promotes business and community development in Hardeman County, TN. **Founded:** 1820. **Publications:** *The Chamber Community News* (Bimonthly). **Geographic Preference:** Local.

44756 ■ Hartsville - Trousdale County Chamber of Commerce
328 Broadway, Rm. 7
Hartsville, TN 37074
Ph: (615)374-9243
Co. E-mail: hartsvilletrousdalecoc@gmail.com
URL: http://www.hartsvilletrousdale.com
Contact: Natalie Knudsen, Executive Director
Description: Promotes business and community development in the Hartsville, TN area. **Geographic Preference:** Local.

44757 ■ Henderson Chester County Chamber of Commerce
111 E Main St.
Henderson, TN 38340
Ph: (731)989-5222
URL: http://www.chestercountychamber.com
Contact: Courtney Insell, President
Facebook: www.facebook.com/HendersonChesterChamber
Description: Promotes business and community development in Chester County, TN. **Founded:** 1976. **Geographic Preference:** Local.

44758 ■ Henderson County Chamber of Commerce (HCCC)
149 E Shores Dr.
Lexington, TN 38351
Ph: (731)968-2126
Co. E-mail: info@hctn.org
URL: http://hctn.org
Contact: Kelli Grice, President
Facebook: www.facebook.com/HendersonCountyChamber
Description: Promotes business and community development in Henderson County, TN. **Founded:** 1983. **Geographic Preference:** Local.

44759 ■ Hendersonville Area Chamber of Commerce (HACC)
100 Country Club Dr., Ste. 104
Hendersonville, TN 37075
Ph: (615)824-2818
Co. E-mail: info@hendersonvillechamber.com
URL: http://www.hendersonvillechamber.com
Contact: Kathleen Hawkins, President
Facebook: www.facebook.com/HendersonvilleChamber
X (Twitter): x.com/hvillechamber
Instagram: www.instagram.com/visithendersonvilletn
YouTube: www.youtube.com/user/Hendersonvilletncoc
Description: Promotes business and community development in Hendersonville, TN. **Founded:** 1970. **Publications:** *It's All About Business* (Monthly); *Portrait of Hendersonville*; *Preferred Business Directory* (Annual). **Geographic Preference:** Local.

44760 ■ Hickman County Chamber of Commerce
405 W Public Sq.
Centerville, TN 37033
Ph: (931)729-5300
Co. E-mail: hickmancountychamber@gmail.com
URL: http://www.hickmancountychamber.org
Contact: Jane Herron, President
E-mail: jahgauv@hellsouth.net
Facebook: www.facebook.com/Hickman.TN.Chamber.Of.Commerce
Description: Promotes business and community development in Hickman County, TN. Sponsors annual Duck River Music and Arts Festival, Business Appreciation Day, Semi-Annual Countywide Yard Sales and various seminars. **Geographic Preference:** Local.

44761 ■ Hohenwald-Lewis County Chamber of Commerce
112 E Main St.
Hohenwald, TN 38462
Ph: (931)796-4084
Co. E-mail: info@hohenwaldlewischamber.com
URL: http://www.hohenwaldlewischamber.com
Contact: Tyler Hinson, President
X (Twitter): x.com/HohenwaldC
Description: Assures economic growth and opportunities; creates a network of business, industrial, and professional leaders; and enhances community's quality of life. **Founded:** 1878. **Geographic Preference:** Local.

44762 ■ Humboldt Chamber of Commerce
1200 Main St.
Humboldt, TN 38343
Ph: (731)784-1842
Co. E-mail: director@humboldtchamber.com
URL: http://humboldtchamber.com
Contact: Christy Crawford, President
Facebook: www.facebook.com/HumboldtTNChamber
Linkedin: www.linkedin.com/company/humboldt-tn-chamber-of-commerce
X (Twitter): x.com/ChamberHumboldt
YouTube: www.youtube.com/channel/UCQgFBNw-Yg7IY0pkGGL5-hg
Pinterest: www.pinterest.com/chamberhumboldt
Description: Promotes business and community development in the Humboldt, TN area. **Founded:** 1905. **Geographic Preference:** Local.

44763 ■ Humphreys County Area Chamber of Commerce
101 W Main St.
Waverly, TN 37185
Ph: (931)296-4865
Co. E-mail: info@humphreyscountychamberofcommerce.com
URL: http://www.humphreyscountychamberofcommerce.com
Contact: Dexter Turner, President
X (Twitter): x.com/hcchamberofcomm
Description: Promotes business and community development in Humphreys County, TN. **Geographic Preference:** Local.

44764 ■ Jackson Area Chamber of Commerce
PO Box 1904
Jackson, TN 38302-1904
Ph: (731)423-2200
Fax: (731)424-4860
Co. E-mail: chamber@jacksontn.com
URL: http://jacksontn.com
Contact: Kyle Spurgeon, President
E-mail: kspurgeon@jacksontn.com
Facebook: www.facebook.com/jacksontnchamber
Linkedin: www.linkedin.com/company/jackson-chamber
X (Twitter): x.com/jaxtnchamber
Instagram: www.instagram.com/jaxtnchamber
YouTube: www.youtube.com/user/jacksontnchamber
Description: Aims to develop and maintain an economic climate that creates and retains jobs and enhances the quality of life for all citizens of Jackson-Madison County and West Tennessee. **Founded:** 1905. **Geographic Preference:** Local.

44765 ■ Jefferson County Chamber of Commerce
532 Patriot Dr.
Dandridge, TN 37725
Ph: (865)397-9642
Fax: (865)397-0164
Co. E-mail: info@jeffersoncountytennessee.com
URL: http://jeffersoncountytennessee.com

Contact: Julie Livesay, Treasurer
Facebook: www.facebook.com/JeffCoTNChamber
Linkedin: www.linkedin.com/company/jefferson-county-chamber-of-commerce
Instagram: www.instagram.com/jeffcountychamberofcommerce
Description: Promotes business and community development in the Jefferson County, TN area. **Geographic Preference:** Local.

44766 ■ Johnson County Chamber of Commerce
716 Shady St.
Mountain City, TN 37683
Ph: (423)727-5800
Fax: (423)727-4943
Co. E-mail: info@johnsoncountytnchamber.org
URL: http://johnsoncountytnchamber.org
Contact: Gina Meade, President
Description: Promotes business and community development in Mountain City, TN. Operates Johnson County Welcome Center; sponsors annual Burley Festival. **Geographic Preference:** Local.

44767 ■ Jonesboro - Washington County Chamber of Commerce
603 E Market St.
Johnson City, TN 37601
Ph: (423)461-8000
Co. E-mail: frontdesk@johnsoncitytnchamber.com
URL: http://www.johnsoncitytnchamber.com
Contact: Bob Cantler, President
E-mail: cantler@johnsoncitytnchamber.com
URL(s): www.johnsoncitytn.org
Facebook: www.facebook.com/JohnsonCityChamber
X (Twitter): x.com/jcchamber
Description: Promotes business and community development in Johnson City, Washington County, and northeastern TN. **Founded:** 1915. **Publications:** *Chamber Membership Directory*; *Johnson City Business Magazine* (Bimonthly). **Geographic Preference:** Local.

44768 ■ Kingsport Area Chamber of Commerce
400 Clinchfield St., Ste. 100
Kingsport, TN 37660
Ph: (423)392-8800
Fax: (423)392-8834
Co. E-mail: kchamber@kingsportchamber.org
URL: http://www.kingsportchamber.org
Contact: Miles Burdine, President
E-mail: mburdine@kingsportchamber.org
Facebook: www.facebook.com/Kingsport.Chamber
X (Twitter): x.com/kptchamber
YouTube: www.youtube.com/channel/UC9q0YFE8meCEFEHr6zlECLw
Description: Provides business and community development in the Kingsport, TN area. **Geographic Preference:** Local.

44769 ■ Knoxville Area Chamber Partnership (KACP)
17 Market Sq., No. 201
Knoxville, TN 37902
Ph: (865)637-4550
Fax: (865)523-2071
URL: http://www.knoxvillechamber.com
Contact: Charles F. Lomax, Chief Executive Officer
Facebook: www.facebook.com/knoxvillechamber
Linkedin: www.linkedin.com/company/knoxville-chamber
X (Twitter): x.com/knoxchamber
Instagram: www.instagram.com/knoxchamber
YouTube: www.youtube.com/user/knoxvillechamber
Description: Provides business and community development in the Knoxville, TN area. **Founded:** 1869. **Publications:** *Regional Manufacturers Directory*; *Partners* (Monthly). **Educational Activities:** Food for Thought. **Geographic Preference:** Local.

44770 ■ Lauderdale Chamber/Economic & Community Development
123 S Jefferson St.
Ripley, TN 38063
Ph: (731)635-9541
Fax: (731)635-9064
URL: http://www.lauderdalecountytn.org
Contact: Susan Worlds, Executive Director
Description: Promotes business and community development in Lauderdale County, TN. **Founded:** 1961. **Publications:** *Chamber Connection* (Weekly). **Geographic Preference:** Local.

44771 ■ Lawrence County Chamber of Commerce - Library
25B Public Sq.
Lawrenceburg, TN 38464
Ph: (931)762-4911
Fax: (931)762-3153
Co. E-mail: info@lawcotn.com
URL: http://www.lawcotn.com
Contact: Ryan Egly, President
E-mail: ryan@lawcotn.com
Facebook: www.facebook.com/LawCoTN
Instagram: www.instagram.com/lawcotn
Description: Local industry, businesses and citizens. Promotes business and community development in Lawrence County. **Scope:** E-books; magazine; journal; abstract. **Founded:** 1817. **Holdings:** Figures not available. **Awards:** Lawrence County Chamber of Commerce Citizen of the Year Award (Annual). **Geographic Preference:** Local.

44772 ■ Lebanon/Wilson County Chamber of Commerce
149 Public Sq.
Lebanon, TN 37087-2751
Ph: (615)444-5503
Fax: (615)443-0596
Co. E-mail: marketing@lebanonwilsonchamber.com
URL: http://www.lebanonwilsonchamber.com
Contact: Melanie Minter, President
E-mail: melanie@lebanonwilsonchamber.com
Facebook: www.facebook.com/lebanonwilsonchamber
X (Twitter): x.com/LebChamber
YouTube: www.youtube.com/LebanonWilsonChamber
Description: Promotes business and community development in Lebanon-Wilson County, TN. **Geographic Preference:** Local.

44773 ■ Livingston - Overton County Chamber of Commerce
222 E Main St.
Livingston, TN 38570
Ph: (931)823-6421
Free: 800-876-7393
Co. E-mail: chamber@twlakes.net
URL: http://www.discoverlivingstontn.com/#homePage
Description: Promotes business and community development in Livingston-Overton County, TN. **Founded:** 1967. **Geographic Preference:** Local.

44774 ■ Loudon County Chamber of Commerce (LCCC)
410 Wharf St.
Loudon, TN 37774
Ph: (865)458-2067
Co. E-mail: info@loudoncountychamber.com
URL: http://www.loudoncountychamberofcommerce.com
Contact: Rodney Grugin, President
Facebook: www.facebook.com/loudoncountychamber
Instagram: www.instagram.com/loudoncountychamber
Description: Seeks to develop and maintain a favorable business climate in Loudon County, TN and to provide leadership in the development of economic growth and quality of life. **Founded:** 1988. **Publications:** *Loudon County Living Guide and Membership Directory* (Annual). **Geographic Preference:** Local.

44775 ■ Lynchburg - Moore County Chamber of Commerce
46 Hiles St.
Lynchburg, TN 37352
Ph: (931)759-4111
Co. E-mail: info@lynchburgtn.com
URL: http://www.lynchburgtn.com
Facebook: www.facebook.com/LynchburgChamberofCommerce
Description: Promotes business and community development in Lynchburg-Moore County, TN. **Geographic Preference:** Local.

44776 ■ Macon County Chamber of Commerce
685 Hwy. 52 BYP W
Lafayette, TN 37083
Ph: (615)666-5885
Fax: (615)666-6969
Co. E-mail: mchamber@nctc.com
URL: http://www.maconcountychamber.org
Facebook: www.facebook.com/Macon-County-Chamber-of-Commerce-222017821145380
Description: Promotes business and community development in Macon County Lafayette, TN area. **Founded:** 1963. **Geographic Preference:** Local.

44777 ■ Manchester Area Chamber of Commerce
110 E Main St.
Manchester, TN 37355
Ph: (931)728-7635
Co. E-mail: info@manchestertnchamber.org
URL: http://www.manchestertnchamber.org
Contact: Katy Riddle, Executive Director
E-mail: katy@manchestertnchamber.org
Linkedin: www.linkedin.com/company/manchester-chamber-of-commerce
X (Twitter): x.com/MACCTN
Instagram: www.instagram.com/manchestercoc931
Description: Works to advance the commercial, industrial, and civic interests of Manchester and its trade area. **Founded:** 1962. **Geographic Preference:** Local.

44778 ■ Marion County Chamber of Commerce
302 Betsy Pack Dr.
Jasper, TN 37347
Ph: (423)942-5103
Co. E-mail: info@marioncountychamber.com
URL: http://marioncountychamber.com
Contact: Carmen O'Hagan, President
Facebook: www.facebook.com/marioncountychamberofcommerce
Description: Promotes business and community development in Marion County, TN area. **Founded:** 1981. **Geographic Preference:** Local.

44779 ■ Marshall County Chamber of Commerce
227 2nd Ave., N
Lewisburg, TN 37091
Ph: (931)359-3863
Co. E-mail: director@marshallchamber.org
URL: http://www.marshallchamber.org
Contact: Vicki Cain, President
Facebook: www.facebook.com/mctnchamber1
X (Twitter): x.com/marshallcotn
Pinterest: www.pinterest.com/mctnchamber
Description: Promotes business and community development in Marshall County, TN. **Founded:** 1920. **Geographic Preference:** Local.

44780 ■ Maury County Chamber and Economic Alliance
106 W 6th St.
Columbia, TN 38402
Ph: (931)388-2155
Fax: (931)380-0335
Co. E-mail: nperry@mauryalliance.com
URL: http://mauryalliance.com
Contact: Wil Evans, President
E-mail: wevans@mauryalliance.com
Facebook: www.facebook.com/mauryalliance
Linkedin: www.linkedin.com/company/maury-county-chamber-and-economic-alliance
X (Twitter): x.com/mauryalliance
Instagram: www.instagram.com/mauryalliance
Description: Promotes business and community development in Columbia, TN area. **Publications:** *Alliance Membership Directory*. **Geographic Preference:** Local.

44781 ■ McMinnville - Warren County Chamber of Commerce
110 S Ct., Sq.
McMinnville, TN 37110
Ph: (931)473-6611
Co. E-mail: dvizi@warrentn.com
URL: http://www.warrentn.com
Contact: Don Vizi, Co-President Co-Chief Executive Officer
E-mail: dvizi@warrentn.com
Facebook: www.facebook.com/mwcchamber
Instagram: www.instagram.com/mcminnvillewarrenchamber
Description: Promotes business and community development in McMinnville-Warren County, TN. **Geographic Preference:** Local.

44782 ■ Millington Chamber of Commerce
7965 Veterans Pky.
Millington, TN 38053
Ph: (901)872-1486
Fax: (901)872-0727
Co. E-mail: admin@millingtonchamber.com
URL: http://www.millingtonchamber.com
Contact: Terry Roland, Executive Director
E-mail: terry.roland@millingtonchamber.com
Facebook: www.facebook.com/profile.php
Description: Promotes business and community development in Millington, TN. **Founded:** 1950. **Geographic Preference:** Local.

44783 ■ *Monday Morning Report*
500 11th Ave. N, Ste. 200
Nashville, TN 37203
Ph: (615)743-3000
URL: http://www.nashvillechamber.com
Contact: Ralph Schulz, President
E-mail: rschulz@nashvillechamber.com
URL(s): www.nashvillechamber.com/enews
Released: Weekly **Availability:** Print; Online.

44784 ■ Monroe County Chamber of Commerce
520 Cook St., Ste. A
Madisonville, TN 37354
Ph: (423)442-4588
Co. E-mail: info@monroecountychamber.org
URL: http://www.monroecountychamber.org
Contact: Brandy Gentry, President
Facebook: www.facebook.com/Monroecountychamberofcommerce
X (Twitter): x.com/MonroeChamber
Description: Promotes business and community development in Monroe County, TN. **Founded:** 1977. **Geographic Preference:** Local.

44785 ■ *Morristimes*
825 W 1st N St.
Morristown, TN 37815
Ph: (423)586-6382
Fax: (423)586-6576
Co. E-mail: macc@morristownchamber.com
URL: http://www.morristownchamber.com
Contact: Marshall Ramsey, President
URL(s): morristownchamber.com/category/morristimes
Released: Monthly **Availability:** Online; PDF.

44786 ■ Morristown Area Chamber of Commerce
825 W 1st N St.
Morristown, TN 37815
Ph: (423)586-6382
Fax: (423)586-6576
Co. E-mail: macc@morristownchamber.com
URL: http://www.morristownchamber.com
Contact: Marshall Ramsey, President
Facebook: www.facebook.com/MorristownChamber
X (Twitter): x.com/tnmacc
Description: Promotes business and community development in Hamblen County, TN. **Founded:** 1911. **Publications:** *Morristimes* (Monthly); *Industrial Directory*; *Morristown Magazine* (Periodic). **Awards:** The R. Jack Fishman Community Service Award (Annual); Morristown Area Small Business Awards of Excellence - Horizon Award (Annual). **Geographic Preference:** Local.

44787 ■ Mt. Juliet Chamber of Commerce
2055 N Mt. Juliet Rd., Ste. 200.
Mount Juliet, TN 37122
Ph: (615)758-3478
Fax: (615)754-8595
Co. E-mail: office@mjchamber.org
URL: http://www.mjchamber.org
Contact: Mark Hinesley, President
E-mail: mark@mtjulietchamber.com
Facebook: www.facebook.com/MtJulietChamber
X (Twitter): x.com/mjchamber
Instagram: www.instagram.com/mtjulietchamber
Description: Promotes business and community development in the Mt. Juliet and West Wilson County, TN area. Conducts charitable programs; sponsors festival. **Founded:** 1963. **Publications:** *Mt. Juliet/West Wilson County Chamber of Commerce-- Membership Directory*. **Geographic Preference:** Local.

44788 ■ Nashville Area Chamber of Commerce (NACC)
500 11th Ave. N, Ste. 200
Nashville, TN 37203
Ph: (615)743-3000
URL: http://www.nashvillechamber.com
Contact: Ralph Schulz, President
E-mail: rschulz@nashvillechamber.com
Facebook: www.facebook.com/nashchamber
Linkedin: www.linkedin.com/company/nashchamber
X (Twitter): x.com/nashchamber
Instagram: www.instagram.com/nashchamber
YouTube: www.youtube.com/user/NashvilleChamber
Description: Provides leadership that fosters growth and prosperity by ensuring the Nashville/Music City region is the best place to operate and grow a business, as well as the most desirable place to live, work, play and visit. **Founded:** 1847. **Publications:** *Business and Professional Organizations Directory*; *Civic and Service Organizations Directory*; *Nashville Health Care Guide*; *Nashville Area Chamber of Commerce Business Directory*; *Religious Resource Guide*; *Tennessee Business Services Directory*; *Tennessee State Chambers Directory*; *Monday Morning Report* (Weekly); *Return on Investment* (Quarterly). **Geographic Preference:** Local.

44789 ■ Oak Ridge Chamber of Commerce
1400 Oak Ridge Tpke.
Oak Ridge, TN 37830
Ph: (865)483-1321
Co. E-mail: info@orcc.org
URL: http://www.oakridgechamber.org
Contact: Christine Michaels, President
E-mail: president@orcc.org
Description: Promotes business and community development in Oak Ridge, TN. **Founded:** 1949. **Publications:** *Acorn* (Quarterly); *Ridges* (Periodic). **Geographic Preference:** Local.

44790 ■ Obion County Chamber of Commerce
214 E Church St.
Union City, TN 38261
Ph: (731)885-0211
Co. E-mail: membership@obioncounty.org
URL: http://www.obioncounty.org
Contact: Lindsay Frilling, President
E-mail: lfrilling@obioncounty.org
X (Twitter): x.com/obionchamber
YouTube: www.youtube.com/channel/UCJJZY2Z5ZefXk5a3lb4CZJA
Description: Promotes business and community development in Obion County, TN. **Founded:** 1922. **Geographic Preference:** Local.

44791 ■ Paris/Henry County Chamber of Commerce - W.G. Rhea Public Library
2508 E Wood St.
Paris, TN 38242
Ph: (731)642-3431
Co. E-mail: pariscoc@paristnchamber.com
URL: http://www.paristnchamber.com
Contact: Betsy Allison, Contact
Facebook: www.facebook.com/ParisHenryCountyChamber
Linkedin: www.linkedin.com/company/the-paris-henry-county-chamber-of-commerce-paris-tennessee
Instagram: www.instagram.com/parishenrycountychamber
Description: Works to improve the economy and quality of life in Paris-Henry County, TN. **Scope:** Genealogy. **Services:** Library open to the public. **Founded:** 1818. **Holdings:** 100 books; microfilm; CD's; magazines; DVD's. **Geographic Preference:** Local.

44792 ■ *Partners*
115 Academy St.
Greeneville, TN 37743
Ph: (423)638-4111
Co. E-mail: gcp@greenecop.com
URL: http://discovergreenevilletn.com
Contact: Jeff Taylor, Officer
E-mail: jeff@greenecountypartnership.net
URL(s): www.greenecountypartnership.com/chamber
Description: Contains the latest news on the activities and events of Partnership. **Availability:** Online.

44793 ■ Pigeon Forge Chamber of Commerce
231 Dollywood Ln.
Pigeon Forge, TN 37863
Ph: (865)453-5700
Free: 855-716-6199
Co. E-mail: info@pigeonforgechamber.com
URL: http://www.pigeonforgechamber.com
Facebook: www.facebook.com/pfchamber
X (Twitter): x.com/PigeonForgeCC
Instagram: www.instagram.com/pigeonforgechamber
YouTube: www.youtube.com/channel/UC8lgceTiLzG6qKOSy7f8KuQ
Pinterest: www.pinterest.com/pfchamberofcommerce
Description: Works to improve the economy and quality of life in Pigeon Forge, TN. **Founded:** 1982. **Geographic Preference:** Local.

44794 ■ Pikeville - Bledsoe County Chamber of Commerce
PO Box 205
Pikeville, TN 37367
Ph: (423)447-2791
Co. E-mail: directors@bledsoe.net
URL: http://www.pikeville-bledsoe.com
Contact: Roberta Smith, Secretary
Description: Works to improve the economy and quality of life in Pikeville-Bledsoe County, TN. **Geographic Preference:** Local.

44795 ■ Portland Chamber of Commerce
106 Main St.
Portland, TN 37148
Ph: (615)325-9032
Fax: (615)325-8399
Co. E-mail: sherri@portlandcofc.com
URL: http://www.portlandcofc.com
Contact: Sherri Ferguson, President
E-mail: sherri@portlandcofc.com
X (Twitter): x.com/portlandtncofc
Pinterest: www.pinterest.com/portlandtnchmbr
Description: Promotes business and community development in Portland, TN. **Founded:** 1962. **Publications:** *Chamber Made News* (Monthly). **Geographic Preference:** Local.

44796 ■ Roane County Chamber of Commerce
1209 N Kentucky St.
Kingston, TN 37763
Ph: (865)376-5572
Fax: (865)376-4978
Co. E-mail: info@roanealliance.org
URL: http://www.roanechamber.com
Contact: Pam May, President
E-mail: pmay@roanealliance.org
Facebook: www.facebook.com/RoaneChamber
X (Twitter): x.com/roanecochamber
Description: Promotes business and community development in the area. **Founded:** 1928. **Geographic Preference:** Local.

44797 ■ Robertson County Chamber of Commerce
405 W Ct., Sq.
  Springfield, TN 37172
Ph: (615)384-3800
Co. E-mail: info@robertsonchamber.org
URL: http://www.robertsonchamber.org
Contact: Jordan Osborne, President
E-mail: josborne@robertsonchamber.org
Facebook: www.facebook.com/robertsoncounty tnchamber
Linkedin: www.linkedin.com/company/robertson-coun ty-chamber-of-commerce
X (Twitter): x.com/RobCoChamber
Instagram: www.instagram.com/robcochambertn
YouTube: www.youtube.com/channel/UCjMg 6-pLOLcKJ4x8jaTUC5A
Description: Advances the economic, civic, social, cultural, and general interests of the City of Springfield, and the County of Robertson and the trade area. **Founded:** 1938. **Educational Activities:** Good Morning Robertson County (Monthly). **Geographic Preference:** Local.

44798 ■ Rutherford County Chamber of Commerce
3050 Medical Center Pky.
  Murfreesboro, TN 37129
Ph: (615)893-6565
Co. E-mail: kbeam@rutherfordchamber.org
URL: http://www.rutherfordchamber.org
Contact: Paul Latture, President
E-mail: platture@rutherfordchamber.org
Facebook: www.facebook.com/rucochamber
Linkedin: www.linkedin.com/company/rutherford-coun ty-chamber-of-commerce
X (Twitter): x.com/rucochamber
YouTube: www.youtube.com/channel/UCLB 4KlZBzwSf58ni4MAdLRg
Description: Works to advance the commercial, industrial, and civic interests of Rutherford County. **Founded:** 1928. **Publications:** *Business Pulse* (Monthly); *Report to the Community*. **Awards:** Rutherford County Chamber of Commerce Business Legend of the Year (Annual); Rutherford County Chamber of Commerce Business Person of the Year (Annual). **Geographic Preference:** Local.

44799 ■ Scott County Chamber of Commerce
12025 Scott Hwy.
  Helenwood, TN 37755
Ph: (423)663-6900
Co. E-mail: info@beng102.sg-host.com
URL: http://www.scottcountychamber.com
Contact: Myke Baird, Director
Facebook: www.facebook.com/scott.county.chamber
YouTube: www.youtube.com/channel/UC _vkCyfjWxgYSzEAZrKj3SQ
Description: Promotes business and community development in Scott County, TN. **Founded:** 1954. **Geographic Preference:** Local.

44800 ■ Sevierville Chamber of Commerce
110 Gary Wade Blvd.
  Sevierville, TN 37862
Ph: (865)453-6411
Free: 888-738-4378
Co. E-mail: info@visitsevierville.com
URL: http://www.scoc.org
Contact: Amanda Marr, Director, Marketing
E-mail: amarr@scoc.org
Facebook: www.facebook.com/seviervillechamber
YouTube: www.youtube.com/user/visitsevierville
Description: Dedicated to the promotion of tourism, industry and economic growth while preserving the history and heritage of Sevierville and Sevier County. **Founded:** 1963. **Publications:** *Sevierville's Smoky Mountains*; *Sevierville Chamber Newsletter* (5/year); *Sevierville Group Tour Planner* (Annual); *Sevierville Marketing Plan*; *Smoky Mountain Coupon Book* (Annual); *Smoky Mountain Wedding Planner* (Annual). **Geographic Preference:** Local.

44801 ■ Seymour Chamber of Commerce
PO Box 438
  Seymour, TN 37865
URL: http://www.seymourtn.org
Contact: Drew Kitts, President
E-mail: dkitts19@gmail.com
Facebook: www.facebook.com/seymourareachamber
Description: United to build a healthy economy and to improve the quality of life in the community. Seeks to promote the civic, commercial, industrial and other interests of in the area. **Founded:** 1922. **Geographic Preference:** Local.

44802 ■ Shelbyville-Bedford County Chamber of Commerce
100 N Cannon Blvd.
  Shelbyville, TN 37160
Ph: (931)684-3482
Co. E-mail: bedfordchamber@sbcchamber.com
URL: http://www.shelbyvilletn.com
Contact: Yolanda Flick, Chief Executive Officer
E-mail: yolanda.flick@sbcchamber.com
Facebook: www.facebook.com/SBCChamber
Description: Promotes business and community development in Shelbyville-Bedford County, TN. **Publications:** *Walk With Us* (Quarterly). **Geographic Preference:** Local.

44803 ■ Smith County Chamber of Commerce
939 Upper Ferry Rd.
  Carthage, TN 37030
Ph: (615)735-2093
Fax: (615)735-9904
Co. E-mail: contactus@smithcountychamber.org
URL: http://smithcountychamber.org
Contact: Patrick Geho, President
Facebook: www.facebook.com/smithcountycoc
YouTube: www.youtube.com/channel/ UCVeXuY0qBzVLONgJ50Qhxrg
Description: Works to promote and support economic, civic, commercial, industrial and educational interest and the welfare of the area. **Founded:** 1974. **Geographic Preference:** Local.

44804 ■ Smithville - DeKalb County Chamber of Commerce
722 S Congress Blvd.
  Smithville, TN 37166
Ph: (615)597-4163
Fax: (615)597-4164
Co. E-mail: swilliams@dekalbcountychamber.org
URL: http://www.dekalbtn.org
Contact: Suzanne Williams, Director
Facebook: www.facebook.com/people/Smithville -DeKalb-County-Chamber-of-Commerce/1000700 21824278
Description: Promotes economic development, education, recreation and culture, and safety and respect in Smithville-DeKalb County, TN. **Geographic Preference:** Local.

44805 ■ South Cumberland Chamber of Commerce (SCCC)
c/o John Payne, Executive Director
  PO Box 353
  Monteagle, TN 37356
Ph: (931)924-5353
Fax: (931)924-5354
Co. E-mail: info@southcumberlandchamber.com
URL: http://southcumberlandchamber.com
Contact: John Payne, Executive Director
Facebook: www.facebook.com/SouthCumberlan dChamber
Description: Promotes economic growth and business development and strengthens cooperation and interaction of the various communities of Monteagle Mountain. **Geographic Preference:** Local.

44806 ■ South Tipton County Chamber of Commerce (STC)
1234 Munford Ave.
  Munford, TN 38058
Ph: (901)837-4600
Fax: (901)837-4602
Co. E-mail: chamber@southtipton.com
URL: http://www.southtipton.com
Contact: Danny Goulder, Agent
Facebook: www.facebook.com/southtiptonchamber
Description: Promotes business and community development in South Tipton County, TN. **Founded:** 1988. **Geographic Preference:** Local.

44807 ■ Sparta-White County Chamber of Commerce
16 W Bockman Way
  Sparta, TN 38583
Ph: (931)836-3552
Fax: (931)836-2216
Co. E-mail: info@spartatnchamber.com
URL: http://spartatnchamber.com
Contact: Marvin Bullock, President
Facebook: www.facebook.com/DISCOVERSPARTA
X (Twitter): x.com/SpartaTNchamber
Description: Promotes business and community development in Sparta-White County, TN. **Geographic Preference:** Local.

44808 ■ Spring City Chamber of Commerce
390 Front St.
  Spring City, TN 37381
Ph: (423)682-0007
Co. E-mail: info@springcitychamberofcommerce.com
URL: http://www.springcitychamberofcommerce.com
Contact: Bailey Hufstetler, Agent
Facebook: www.facebook.com/SpringCityChamber
Description: Promotes business and community development. Preserves the competitive enterprise system and represents member businesses in city, county, and state affairs. **Founded:** 1962. **Publications:** *Spring City Chamber of Commerce-- Membership Directory*; *Chamber News*. **Geographic Preference:** Local.

44809 ■ Spring Hill Chamber of Commerce
5326 Main St.
  Spring Hill, TN 37174
Ph: (931)486-0625
Co. E-mail: info@springhillchamber.com
URL: http://www.springhillchamber.com
Contact: Rebecca Melton, Executive Director
Facebook: www.facebook.com/springhillchamberTN
Linkedin: www.linkedin.com/company/spring-hill -chamber-of-commerce/about
X (Twitter): x.com/shchambertn
Instagram: www.instagram.com/explore/locations/ 164847426872254/spring-hill-chamber-of-com merce-tn
Description: Works to provide networking and marketing opportunities while providing access to economic development assistance. Serves as a link between the local businesses, their peers and the community. **Founded:** 2003. **Geographic Preference:** Local.

44810 ■ Stewart County Chamber of Commerce (SCCC)
117 Visitor Center Ln.
  Dover, TN 37058-0147
Ph: (931)232-8290
Co. E-mail: stewartcountychamber@gmail.com
URL: http://stewartcountychamber.com
Contact: Holly Klein, Jr., President
Facebook: www.facebook.com/StewartCoun tyChamber
Linkedin: www.linkedin.com/in/stewart-county-cham ber-of-commerce-771952b2
X (Twitter): x.com/StwrtCoChamber
Instagram: www.instagram.com/StewartCoun tyChamber
Description: Promotes business and community development in Stewart County, TN. Sponsors festival. **Geographic Preference:** Local.

44811 ■ Tennessee Chamber of Commerce and Industry
414 Union St., Ste. 107
  Nashville, TN 37219
Ph: (615)256-5141
Co. E-mail: info@tnchamber.org
URL: http://tnchamber.org
Contact: Bradley Jackson, President
E-mail: bradley.jackson@tnchamber.org
Facebook: www.facebook.com/TennesseeChamber
X (Twitter): x.com/TNchamber

Description: Represents the interests of business. Lobbies on their behalf. Sponsors workshops and seminars. **Founded:** 1912. **Publications:** *Industrial Relations Bulletin* (Monthly); *Industrial Reporter*; *General Assembly Outcomes* (Annual). **Geographic Preference:** State.

44812 ■ Tullahoma Area Chamber of Commerce (TACC)
PO Box 1205
Tullahoma, TN 37388
Ph: (931)455-5497
Co. E-mail: tullahomachamber@tullahoma.org
URL: http://www.tullahoma.org
Contact: Tisha Fritz, Director
E-mail: tisha@tullahoma.org
Facebook: www.facebook.com/tullahomatnchamber
X (Twitter): x.com/TullahomaCoC
Instagram: www.instagram.com/tullahomatnchamber
Description: Promotes business and community development in Tullahoma, TN. **Geographic Preference:** Local.

44813 ■ Unicoi County Chamber of Commerce
100 S Main Ave.
Erwin, TN 37650
Ph: (423)743-3000
URL: http://www.unicoicounty.org
Facebook: www.facebook.com/ucchamber
Instagram: www.instagram.com/explore/locations/512725083/unicoi-county-chamber-of-commerce
YouTube: www.youtube.com/channel/UCbWQnPNirVpxiByTSvK1A0g
Description: Promotes business and community development in Unicoi County, TN area. **Geographic Preference:** Local.

44814 ■ Wayne County Chamber of Commerce
100 Ct., Cir., Rm. 301
Waynesboro, TN 38485
Ph: (931)722-3575
Co. E-mail: chamber@netease.net
URL: http://www.waynecountychamber.org
Facebook: www.facebook.com/waynecountytennessee
X (Twitter): x.com/waynecountytn
Description: Promotes business, tourism and community in Wayne County TN. **Founded:** 1980. **Geographic Preference:** Local.

44815 ■ White House Area Chamber of Commerce (WCC)
412 Hwy. 76
White House, TN 37188
Ph: (615)672-3937
Fax: (615)672-2828
Co. E-mail: whcoc@bellsouth.net
URL: http://www.whitehousechamber.org
Contact: Mandy Christenson, President
E-mail: mandy@whitehousechamber.org
Facebook: www.facebook.com/whitehousechamber
X (Twitter): x.com/WHAreaChamber
YouTube: www.youtube.com/channel/UCA5zZuQcmK5RN8zjFjH-1Eg
Description: Promotes business and community development in White House, TN and surrounding area. Sponsors various community events. **Founded:** 1984. **Geographic Preference:** Local.

44816 ■ Williamson County Chamber of Commerce (WCCC) [Williamson Inc]
5005 Meridian Blvd., Ste. 150
Franklin, TN 37067
Ph: (615)771-1912
URL: http://cmdev.williamsonchamber.com/list/member/williamson-inc-franklin-615-771-1912-46797
Contact: Til Bourland, President
Description: Promotes business and community development in Franklin, TN area. **Publications:** *Williamson County Magazine* (Annual); *Chamber Perspective* (Annual); *Monthly Perspective* (Monthly). **Educational Activities:** Williamson County - Franklin Chamber of Commerce Luncheon. **Geographic Preference:** Local.

44817 ■ *Williamson County Magazine*
5005 Meridian Blvd., Ste. 150
Franklin, TN 37067
Ph: (615)771-1912
URL: http://cmdev.williamsonchamber.com/list/member/williamson-inc-franklin-615-771-1912-46797
Contact: Til Bourland, President
URL(s): williamsonchamber.com/living
Released: Annual **Description:** Magazine containing information regarding business, education, people, events, history, and cultural aspects of the Franklin, TN area community with a lifestyle concept. **Availability:** PDF; Online.

MINORITY BUSINESS ASSISTANCE PROGRAMS

44818 ■ Memphis Minority Business Development Center (MMBC)
200 Jefferson Ave.
Memphis, TN 38103
Ph: (901)525-6512
Fax: (901)525-5204
Co. E-mail: themmbc@gmail.com
URL: http://www.mmbc-memphis.org
Contact: Jozelle Luster Booker, President
Facebook: www.facebook.com/MMBCContinuum
Linkedin: www.linkedin.com/company/mid-south-minority-business-council
Description: Provides business and consulting services to minority businesses and entrepreneurs. **Founded:** 1989.

44819 ■ Tennessee Department of Economic and Community Development - Business Enterprise Resource Office (BERO)
312 Rosa L. Parks Ave.
Nashville, TN 37243
Co. E-mail: ecd.bero@tn.gov
URL: http://www.tn.gov/ecd/small-business/bero
Contact: Wisty Pender, Director
Description: Provides services to minority entrepreneurs through offices located in Nashville, Chattanooga, Knoxville, and Memphis. **Founded:** 1977.

44820 ■ Tennessee Minority Supplier Development Council (TMSDC)
Plaza 1 Bldg.
Metro Ctr
220 Athens Way, Ste. 105
Nashville, TN 37228
Ph: (615)259-4699
Free: 844-793-1289
Co. E-mail: info@tsmsdc.net
URL: http://tsmsdc.net
Contact: Cheri K. Henderson, President
Linkedin: www.linkedin.com/company/tristate-msdc
X (Twitter): x.com/TriStateMSDC
Description: Provides a direct link between corporate America and minority-owned businesses. Increases procurement and business opportunities for minority businesses of all sizes. **Founded:** 1980. **Geographic Preference:** State.

FINANCING AND LOAN PROGRAMS

44821 ■ The Angel Roundtable (ART)
PO Box 8935
Johnson City, TN 37615
URL: http://www.theangelroundtable.com
Contact: Jason Berry, Executive Director
Description: Network of entrepreneurs and investors in the Northeast Tennessee/Southwest Virginia/Western North Carolina region. Offers investment capital, advice, and mentoring to late seed and early-stage companies. **Founded:** 2012.

44822 ■ Capital Across America, L.P.
414 Union St.
Nashville, TN 37219
Industry Preferences: Women/minority-owned businesses.

44823 ■ Claritas Capital
30 Burton Hills Blvd., Ste. 500
Nashville, TN 37215
Ph: (615)660-8419
URL: http://www.claritascapital.com
Contact: Donna Altshuler, Director
E-mail: daltshuler@claritascapital.com
Linkedin: www.linkedin.com/company/claritas-capital
Description: Partners with private companies and real estate developers. Offers debt and equity capital investments. **Founded:** 2002. **Industry Preferences:** Technology; healthcare management.

44824 ■ The JumpFund
201 W Main St.
Chattanooga, TN 37408
URL: http://www.thejumpfund.com
Contact: Kristina Montague, Managing Partner
Linkedin: www.linkedin.com/company/thejumpfund
Instagram: www.instagram.com/thejumpfund
Description: Women-led venture capital investing in female-led businesses throughout the Southeast United States. **Founded:** 2013. **Investment Policies:** High-growth, scalable, women-led ventures in the Southeaster United States; sustainable competitive advantage; ability to scale rapidly with strong returns; strong business model.

44825 ■ Jumpstart Foundry (JSF)
414 Union St., Ste. 1900
Nashville, TN 37219
Co. E-mail: contact@jsf.co
URL: http://jsf.co
Contact: Vic Gatto, Co-Founder
Facebook: www.facebook.com/jumpstartfoundry
Linkedin: www.linkedin.com/company/jumpstart-foundry
X (Twitter): x.com/jsfoundry
Instagram: www.instagram.com/jsfoundry
YouTube: www.youtube.com/channel/UCd_flj0jlTs-0tvyBYdM6gA
Description: Early-stage venture capital firm for healthcare companies. **Founded:** 2009. **Investment Policies:** Strong, product-focused entrepreneurs with innovative solutions. **Industry Preferences:** Healthcare; consumer health products and services; tech-enabled services; diagnostic devices.

44826 ■ SSM Partners
6070 Poplar Ave., Ste. 560
Memphis, TN 38119
Ph: (901)767-1131
URL: http://ssmpartners.com
Contact: Casey West, Managing Partner
Linkedin: www.linkedin.com/company/ssm-partners
X (Twitter): x.com/i/lists/76034142
Description: Venture capital, growth equity, technology and healthcare. **Preferred Investment Size:** $5,000,000 to $20,000,000. **Industry Preferences:** Internet specific, computer software and services, communications and media, computer hardware, other products, medical and health, consumer related, semiconductors and other electronics.

44827 ■ Start Co.
88 Union Ave., Fl. 2nd
Memphis, TN 38103
Co. E-mail: info@neverstop.co
URL: http://www.neverstop.co
Facebook: www.facebook.com/launchmemphis
Linkedin: www.linkedin.com/company/start-co
X (Twitter): x.com/Start_Co
Instagram: www.instagram.com/start_co
Description: Venture development and accelerator hybrid founded by (and for) Memphis entrepeners. Also operates Upstart, an accelerator program for women-led tech companies. **Founded:** 2008. **Industry Preferences:** Supply chain and logistics; medical devices; civic technology.

PROCUREMENT ASSISTANCE PROGRAMS

44828 ■ Center for Industrial Services (CIS)
193 Polk Ave., Ste. C
Nashville, TN 37210

Ph: (615)532-8657
Free: 888-763-7439
Fax: (615)532-4937
Co. E-mail: cis@tennessee.edu
URL: http://cis.tennessee.edu
Contact: Bernadette Fuller, Consultant
E-mail: bernadette.fuller@tennessee.edu
Facebook: www.facebook.com/UTCIS
Linkedin: www.linkedin.com/company/utcis
X (Twitter): x.com/UTCIS
YouTube: www.youtube.com/channel/
UCyvp9IfWkVfwasOBbcq6gBA

Description: Center specializes to consulting, training and connecting services. **Founded:** 1963.

44829 ■ Institute for Public Service (IPS)
1610 University Ave.
Knoxville, TN 37921
Ph: (865)974-6621
Fax: (865)974-1528
URL: http://www.ips.tennessee.edu
Contact: Kristen Davis, Director, Development
Facebook: www.facebook.com/UTIPS
Linkedin: www.linkedin.com/company/university-of
-tennessee-institute-for-public-service
X (Twitter): x.com/UT_IPS
YouTube: www.youtube.com/channel/UCW
dLQrhLDuMQzvOkYBKs5nA

Description: Helps to utilize available resources to leverage continual improvement in Tennessee's industrial sector for the long-term sustainability of business and jobs in our state. **Founded:** 1971.

44830 ■ Memphis Procurement Technical Assistance Center (PTAC) - Center for Industrial Services (CIS)
193 Polk Ave., Ste. C
Nashville, TN 37210
Ph: (615)532-8657
Free: 888-763-7439
Fax: (615)532-4937
Co. E-mail: cis@tennessee.edu
URL: http://cis.tennessee.edu/programs/procuremen
t-technical-assistance-center-ptac
Contact: Paul H. Jennings, Executive Director
E-mail: paul.jennings@tennessee.edu
Facebook: www.facebook.com/UTCIS
Linkedin: www.linkedin.com/company/utcis
X (Twitter): x.com/UTCIS
YouTube: www.youtube.com/channel/
UCyvp9IfWkVfwasOBbcq6gBA

Description: Assists Utah small businesses who are interested in bidding on federal, state and local government procurements and commercial contracting opportunities covering Box Elder, Cache, and Rich Counties. **Founded:** 1986.

44831 ■ Tennessee Procurement Technical Assistance Center - University of Tennessee - Center for Industrial Services of Knoxville (CIS)
1610 University Ave.
Knoxville, TN 37921
URL: http://www.cis.tennessee.edu
Contact: Beth Phillips, Program Manager
E-mail: beth.phillips@tennessee.edu

Description: Tennessee business and industry are assisted daily by CIS engineering and professional staff in improving their economic competitiveness on a national and global level.

44832 ■ University of Tennessee Center for Industrial Services Chattanooga (UT CIS)
540 McCallie Ave., Ste. 468
Chattanooga, TN 37403
Co. E-mail: cis@tennessee.edu
URL: http://www.cis.tennessee.edu
Contact: George Aslinger, Consultant
E-mail: george.aslinger@tennessee.edu

Description: Helps to utilize available resources to leverage continual improvement in Tennessee's industrial sector for the long-term sustainability of business and jobs in our state.

44833 ■ University of Tennessee Center for Industrial Services Jackson (UT)
605 Airways Blvd., Ste. 109
Jackson, TN 38301-7403
URL: http://www.cis.tennessee.edu
Contact: Dr. Andre Temple, Consultant
E-mail: andre.temple@tennessee.edu

Description: Helps to utilize available resources to leverage continual improvement in Tennessee's industrial sector for the long-term sustainability of business and jobs in our state.

44834 ■ University of Tennessee Center for Industrial Services - Procurement Technical Assistance Center (PTAC)
605 Airways Blvd., Ste. 109
Jackson, TN 38301-7403
Co. E-mail: apex@tennessee.edu
URL: http://www.cis.tennessee.edu/programs/
tennessee-apex-accelerator
Contact: Veronica Clark, Counselor
E-mail: veronica.clark@tennessee.edu

Description: Tennessee business and industry are assisted daily by CIS engineering and professional staff in improving their economic competitiveness on a national and global level. **Founded:** 1986.

44835 ■ University of Tennessee Chattanooga Center for Industrial Services (PTAC) - Procurement Technical Assistance Center
193 Polk Ave., Ste. C
Nashville, TN 37210
URL: http://cis.tennessee.edu

Description: Tennessee business and industry are assisted daily by CIS engineering and professional staff in improving their economic competitiveness on a national and global level. **Founded:** 1986.

44836 ■ University of Tennessee (PTAC) - Institute for Public Service - Center for Industrial Services - Procurement Technical Assistance Center
193 Polk Ave., Ste. C
Nashville, TN 37210
Co. E-mail: ptac@tennessee.edu
URL: http://www.cis.tennessee.edu/beyond-training-u
t-procurement-technical-assistance-center-ptac
Contact: Veronica Clark, Contact
E-mail: veronica.clark@tennessee.edu
Founded: 1986.

INCUBATORS/RESEARCH AND TECHNOLOGY PARKS

44837 ■ CHATT Foundation
727 E 11th St.
Chattanooga, TN 37403
Ph: (423)756-4222
Fax: (423)756-3820
Co. E-mail: kitchen@chattfoundation.org
URL: http://chattfoundation.org
Contact: Baron King, Chief Executive Officer
E-mail: baronk@homelesschattanooga.org
Facebook: www.facebook.com/CHATTFoundation
Linkedin: www.linkedin.com/company/chattfoundation
Instagram: www.instagram.com/chattfoundation

Description: Food incubator providing a fully equipped, licensed and permitted commercial kitchen facility available for shared use and dedicated to providing support to local food entrepreneurs in the Chattanooga area. **Founded:** 1982.

44838 ■ Chattanooga State Community College Small Business Development Center
100 Cherokee Blvd., Ste. 202
Chattanooga, TN 37405
Ph: (423)756-8668
Co. E-mail: chatt@tsbdc.org
URL: http://tsbdc.org/center/chattanooga
Contact: Dr. Rebecca Ashford, President
Facebook: www.facebook.com/TSBDCChattanooga
X (Twitter): x.com/chattstatecc

Description: Leasing and rental service offers office and manufacturing space.

44839 ■ Citizen Kitchens [Food Business Incubator]
4611 Alabama Ave.
Nashville, TN 37209
Co. E-mail: citizenkitchens@gmail.com
URL: http://citizenkitchens.com
Facebook: www.facebook.com/citizenkitchens
X (Twitter): x.com/citizenkitchens
Instagram: www.instagram.com/citizenkitchens

Description: A culinary incubator available to entrepreneurs wanting to grow a food business.

44840 ■ Cleveland Bradley Business Incubator (CBBI)
3505 Adkisson Dr., Ste. 102A
Cleveland, TN 37312
Ph: (423)478-6476
Co. E-mail: h@cbbi.net
URL: http://www.cbbi.net
Contact: Hurley Buff, Executive Director
Facebook: www.facebook.com/people/CBBI/1000
63546491320
Instagram: www.instagram.com/CBBIncubator

Description: Business incubator offering businesses some of the latest innovations in business technology, and an affordable space for businesses to grow. **Founded:** 2000.

44841 ■ The Company Lab (CO.LAB)
1100 Market St., Ste. 100
Chattanooga, TN 37402
Co. E-mail: info@colab.co
URL: http://colab.co
Contact: Tasia Malakasis, Chief Executive Officer
E-mail: tasia@colab.is
Linkedin: www.linkedin.com/company/the-company
-lab
X (Twitter): x.com/thecompanylab
Instagram: www.instagram.com/thecompanylab

Description: A nonprofit startup accelerator that supports entrepreneurial growth in southeast Tennessee. **Founded:** 2010.

44842 ■ Cumberland Business Incubator (CBI)
2569 Cook Rd.
Crossville, TN 38571
Ph: (931)456-4910
Fax: (931)210-5149
Co. E-mail: cbi@roanestate.edu
URL: http://www.cbimakerspace.com/cbi
Contact: Holly Hanson, Director
E-mail: hansonha@roanestate.edu
X (Twitter): x.com/cumbincubator

Description: Provides an environment for development of new business ideas and growth of existing businesses. Services include business coaching, mentoring, marketing, and access to capital. Provides business space with co-working areas, office suites, labs, and conference rooms.

44843 ■ East Tennessee State University (ETSU) - Innovation Lab
2109 W Market St.
Johnson City, TN 37604
Ph: (423)439-8535
Fax: (423)979-8014
Co. E-mail: innovation_lab@etsu.edu
URL: http://www.etsu.edu/ilab
Contact: Dr. Audrey Depelteau, Director
E-mail: depelteau@etsu.edu

Description: A full service small business incubator designed to support entrepreneurs and investors to affect the successful establishment of technology-based start-up and spin-off businesses in order to achieve technology transfer, create jobs, and enhance economic development within the region.

44844 ■ Emerge Memphis
Tennessee St.
Memphis, TN 38103
Ph: (901)300-0824
URL: http://www.emergememphis.org
Contact: Bryan M. Eagle, III, Contact
X (Twitter): x.com/EmergeMemphis

Description: Firm provides strategic support to startup companies, innovators and entrepreneurs. **Founded:** 1999.

44845 ■ Fairview Technology Center (FTC)
c/o Tammy Knigh
1020 Commerce Pk. Dr.
Oak Ridge, TN 37830
URL: http://www.knoxvillechamber.com/fairview-technology-center
Description: A small business incubator providing office and laboratory facilities for start-up technology businsses.

44846 ■ Holston Business Development Center (HBDC)
2005 Venture Pk.
Kingsport, TN 37660
Ph: (423)578-6235
Co. E-mail: hbdc@hbdc.org
URL: http://www.hbdc.org
Contact: Liz Bennett, Director
E-mail: director@hbdc.org
Description: A business incubator that helps business startups become a reality. Provides small business counseling as well as business suites with many amenities included. **Founded:** 2003.

44847 ■ INCubator
811 Broad, Ste. No. 100
Chattanooga, TN 37402
Ph: (423)756-2121
URL: http://chattanoogachamber.com/incubator
Description: The largest business incubator in Tennessee. Helps startups achieve success through a three-year, staged development program that capitalizes on the synergy of the BDC's unique entrepreneurial ecosystem. **Founded:** 1988.

44848 ■ LITE Memphis
650 New York St.
Memphis, TN 38104
Ph: (901)209-9119
Co. E-mail: info@litememphis.org
URL: http://litememphis.org
Contact: Adrian Smith, Executive Director (Acting)
Facebook: www.facebook.com/litememphis
Linkedin: www.linkedin.com/company/let's-innovate-through-education
Instagram: www.instagram.com/litememphis
Description: A 6-month entrepreneurial program where students launch ideas into the community. Provides access to seasoned business mentors and coaches, provides seed funding, and aids students as they transition from college to entrepreneurship. **Founded:** 2013.

44849 ■ Memphis Bioworks
17 W Pontotoc Ave., Ste. 100
Memphis, TN 38103-3826
Contact: Lorie Jernigan, Contact
Description: Business incubator offering more than 34,000 square feet of office space, wet labs and support equipment for biotech and clean-tech start-up companies, as well as a conference and training center.

44850 ■ Mesa Komal
Casa Azafran Community Ctr.
2195 Nolensville Pke.
Nashville, TN 37211
Ph: (615)320-5152
Fax: (615)269-6900
Co. E-mail: info@conamericas.com
URL: http://kitchen.conexionamericas.org
Contact: Java Hemmat, Manager, Relations
Facebook: www.facebook.com/ConexionAmericasMesaKomal
X (Twitter): x.com/conexion_tn
YouTube: www.youtube.com/user/conexionamericas
Description: Kitchen incubator supporting entrepreneurs who own, or want to start their own food business. **Founded:** 2013.

44851 ■ The Mid-South Minority Business Council Continuum and/or The MMBC Continuum
200 Jefferson Ave., Ste. 1000
Memphis, TN 38103
Ph: (901)525-6512
Fax: (901)525-5204
Co. E-mail: themmbc@gmail.com
URL: http://www.mmbc-memphis.org
Contact: Jozelle Luster Booker, President
Facebook: www.facebook.com/MMBCContinuum
Linkedin: www.linkedin.com/company/mid-south-minority-business-council
X (Twitter): x.com/search
Description: Small business incubator exclusively for minority and women-owned businesses. Provides fully-furnished office space, shared office resources, conference rooms, consulting services, and networking events. **Founded:** 1973.

44852 ■ Nashville Business Incubation Center (NBIC)
PO Box 280567
Nashville, TN 37228-9998
Ph: (615)497-8434
Co. E-mail: nbic@nbiconline.com
URL: http://nbiconline.com
Contact: Angela Crane-Jones, Chief Executive Officer
Facebook: www.facebook.com/NBIConline
Linkedin: www.linkedin.com/company/nashville-business-incubation-center
X (Twitter): x.com/mynbic
Instagram: www.instagram.com/mynbic
Description: Firm is engaged in the management and technical assistance to small businesses. **Founded:** 1984.

44853 ■ Start Co.
88 Union Ave., Fl. 2nd
Memphis, TN 38103
Co. E-mail: info@neverstop.co
URL: http://www.neverstop.co
Facebook: www.facebook.com/launchmemphis
Linkedin: www.linkedin.com/company/start-co
X (Twitter): x.com/Start_Co
Instagram: www.instagram.com/start_co
Description: Venture development and accelerator hybrid founded by (and for) Memphis entrepeners. Also operates Upstart, an accelerator program for women-led tech companies. **Founded:** 2008. **Industry Preferences:** Supply chain and logistics; medical devices; civic technology.

EDUCATIONAL PROGRAMS

44854 ■ Belmont University Center for Entrepreneurship
1900 Belmont Blvd.
Nashville, TN 37212
URL: http://www.belmont.edu/business/centers/entrepreneurship/index.html
Contact: Jack C. Massey, Chairman
E-mail: jeff.cornwall@belmont.edu
Description: Provides business students with the training they need to begin their own business by offering hands-on programs,.

44855 ■ Chattanooga State Community College (CSCC)
4501 Amnicola Hwy.
Chattanooga, TN 37406
Ph: (423)697-4400
URL: http://www.chattanoogastate.edu
Contact: Dr. Rebecca Ashford, President
Facebook: www.facebook.com/ChattState
X (Twitter): x.com/ChattStateCC
Instagram: www.instagram.com/chattstate
YouTube: www.youtube.com/user/ChattStateMarketing
Description: Offers degree programs in the fields of business, industrial, and technology. **Founded:** 1965.

REFERENCE WORKS

44856 ■ *"1st Black-Owned Beauty Supply Store in Nashville Made $50,000 in it's First 3 Hours of Opening!"* in *Soultanicals (March 4, 2019)*
URL(s): soultanicals.com/blogs/news/1st-black-owned-beauty-supply-store-in-nashville-made-50-000-in-its-first-3-hours-of-opening
Ed: Ayo Ogun. **Released:** March 04, 2019. **Description:** Roots Beauty Supply, the first Black-owned beauty supply store in Nashville had a fantastic opening day by taking in $50,000 within the first three hours of being open. **Availability:** Online.

44857 ■ *"Memphis BBQ: It's Just About the Pork"* in *Women in Business (Vol. 64, Summer 2012, No. 2, pp. 14)*
Ed: Debbie Gold. **Description:** Several barbeque joints located in Memphis, Tennessee are recommended. Tops BBQ is a barbeque institution with 14 locations across Memphis, Payne's Bar-B-Q is known for its pig sandwich and Central BBQ Memphis serves a pork plate with a dark, heavily smoked crust. **Availability:** Print; PDF; Online.

CONSULTANTS

44858 ■ Management Consulting Services (MCS)
414 Wilson Ave., Ste. 102B
Tullahoma, TN 37388
Ph: (931)455-0155
Fax: (931)455-4375
URL: http://www.theknowisgroup.com
Contact: Noah Risner, Consultant
Description: Provides technical and business management consulting nationwide to businesses requiring specific, short-term services enabling them to improve performance, increase efficiency and maximize profits, specializing in small and growing technology-intensive companies.

44859 ■ ZeroTo510
150 Peabody Pl.
Memphis, TN 38103
Co. E-mail: info@zeroto510.com
URL: http://www.zeroto510.com
Contact: Nate Smith, Director
Facebook: www.facebook.com/zeroto510
Linkedin: www.linkedin.com/company/zeroto510
X (Twitter): x.com/zeroto510
Description: A unique program that enables entrepreneurs with ideas for innovative medical devices to take advantage of this fast path to market. Provides experts, training, mentors, and an infusion of capital to help clients succeed. **Founded:** 2012.

PUBLICATIONS

44860 ■ *Doing Business in Memphis: A Directory of Business and Industry (Tennessee)*
1779 Kirby Pky., Ste. 128
Germantown, TN 38138-0631
Ph: (901)590-0050
Fax: (901)590-0100
URL: http://www.memphisbusiness.com
Contact: Deborah L. Camp, President
URL(s): www.memphisbusiness.com
Price: $251.16, Individuals eBook; $251.16, e-book; $251.16, Individuals for eBook. **Description:** Covers over 10,000 Memphis, Tennessee companies, and 25,000 contact names. **Entries include:** Company name, address, phone, fax, toll-free number, Standard Industrial Classification (SIC) code, names and titles of key personnel, number of employees, descriptions of product/service, product/service provided, e-mail addresses, website, square footage. **Arrangement:** Classified by subject (retail/wholesale, services, real estate and construction, professional, technology, medical, financial, and transportation), then alphabeti-

STATE LISTINGS

cal by company name. **Indexes:** Alphabetical by company name; classified by industrial sections (i.e. Logistics, Services, etc). **Availability:** CD-ROM; E-book.

44861 ■ **Memphis Business Journal**
120 W Morehead St.
 Charlotte, NC 28202
Co. E-mail: circhelp@bizjournals.com
URL: http://www.acbj.com
Contact: Mike Olivieri, Executive Vice President
URL(s): www.bizjournals.com/memphis
Linkedin: www.linkedin.com/company/memphis
 -business-journal
X (Twitter): x.com/MBJMemphis
Released: Weekly **Price:** $4, for digital + print; $4, for digital only; $210, for 52 weeks digital only; $220, for 52 weeks digital + print; $380, for 52 weeks national access; $950, for 52 weeks nationwide + bol. **Availability:** Print; Online. **Type:** Full-text.

44862 ■ **Nashville Business Journal**
120 W Morehead St.
 Charlotte, NC 28202
Co. E-mail: circhelp@bizjournals.com
URL: http://www.acbj.com
Contact: Mike Olivieri, Executive Vice President
URL(s): www.bizjournals.com/nashville
Linkedin: www.linkedin.com/company/nashville
 -business-journal
X (Twitter): x.com/nashvillebiz
Released: Weekly **Price:** $950, for premium unlimited nationwide access 52 weeks; $380, for premium elite nationwide access 52 weeks; $220, for premium plus digital & print 52 weeks; $210, for online premium 52 weeks. **Description:** Regional business newspaper. **Availability:** Print; PDF; Download; Online. **Type:** Full-text.

44863 ■ **Nashville Business Journal**
3100 W End Ave., Ste. 1000
 Nashville, TN 37203
Ph: (615)248-2222
Free: 800-486-3289
Fax: (615)248-6246
Co. E-mail: nashville@bizjournals.com
URL: http://www.bizjournals.com/nashville/news
Contact: Carol Smith, Director, Research
E-mail: csmith@bizjournals.com
Description: Covers business news in the Nashville region and publishes business directories. **Publications:** *Nashville Business Journal--Book of Lists* (Annual); *Nashville Business Journal--Book of Lists* (Annual).

PUBLISHERS

44864 ■ **Doing Business in Memphis**
1779 Kirby Pky., Ste. 128
 Germantown, TN 38138-0631
Ph: (901)590-0050
Fax: (901)590-0100
URL: http://www.memphisbusiness.com
Contact: Deborah L. Camp, President

Description: Firm provides information services. **Founded:** 1990. **Publications:** *Doing Business in Memphis*; *Doing Business in Memphis: A Directory of Business and Industry*.

INFORMATION SERVICES

44865 ■ **Launch Tennessee**
1321 6th Ave. N
 Nashville, TN 37208
Ph: (615)991-2809
Co. E-mail: info@launchtn.org
URL: http://launchtn.org
Contact: Ashley Currie, Director, Marketing Director, Communications
Facebook: www.facebook.com/LaunchTN
Linkedin: www.linkedin.com/company/launchtn
X (Twitter): x.com/LaunchTN
Instagram: www.instagram.com/launchtn
YouTube: www.youtube.com/user/LaunchTN
Description: Supports economic development by connecting entrepreneurs to the resources they need to be successful.

EARLY STAGE FINANCING

44866 ■ **Chattanooga Renaissance Fund (CRF)**
201 W Main St., Ste. 205
 Chattanooga, TN 37408
URL: http://chattanoogarenaissancefund.com
Contact: Miller Welborn, Leader
X (Twitter): x.com/noogafund
Description: Angel capital fund for seed and early-stage companies with solid growth potential. Primarily focused on those beyond the "idea on the back of the napkin" stage, but still looking for mentorship.

44867 ■ **Council Capital**
30 Burton Hills Blvd., Ste. 576
 Nashville, TN 37215
Ph: (615)255-3707
Co. E-mail: pfulner@councilcapital.com
URL: http://www.councilcapital.com
Contact: Chris Feeney, Co-Founder
Description: Private equity firm for healthcare companies positioned for rapid growth. **Founded:** 2000.

VENTURE CAPITAL FIRM

44868 ■ **Altitude Ventures (AV)**
104 Woodmont Blvd., Ste. 218
 Nashville, TN 37205
URL: http://www.altvc.com
Contact: Landon Gibbs, Managing Partner
Description: Early-stage venture capital firm for start-ups that improve healthcare. Also maintains an office in Houston.

44869 ■ **FCA Venture Partners (FCA)**
110 Winners Cir., Ste. 100
 Brentwood, TN 37027

Ph: (615)326-4848
URL: http://www.fcavp.com
Contact: Matt King, Managing Partner
Linkedin: www.linkedin.com/company/fcavp
Description: Invests in fast growing healthcare companies. **Founded:** 1996. **Preferred Investment Size:** $3,000,000 to $3,000,000. **Investment Policies:** Capital efficient business with scalable and disruptive business models; strong management teams; $500,000-$2,000,000 in annual revenue; proven product and customer base. . **Industry Preferences:** Software and software-enabled services in the healthcare industry.

44870 ■ **Gathering of Angels (GOA)**
10387 Magnolia Farm Dr.
 Apison, TN 37302-1702
Ph: (404)606-2193
Co. E-mail: tarbycbryant@gmail.com
URL: http://www.gatheringofangels.com
Contact: Tarby Bryant, Chief Executive Officer
E-mail: tarbycbryant@gmail.com
Description: Angel investment network. **Founded:** 1996.

44871 ■ **Innova Memphis**
1498 UNION AVE., Ste. 228
 Memphis, TN 38104-3725
URL: http://www.innovamemphis.com
Contact: Dean Didato, Partner
Linkedin: www.linkedin.com/company/innova
 -memphis
X (Twitter): x.com/innovamemphis
Description: Invests in early-stage, high-growth companies that have the potential to grow into significant economic contributors. Focus is in the following fields: biosciences, technology, and agtech. **Founded:** 2007.

44872 ■ **MB Venture Partners L.L.C. (MBVP)**
17 W Pontotoc Ave., Ste. 101
 Memphis, TN 38103
Ph: (901)322-0330
Fax: (901)322-0339
URL: http://mbventures.com
Contact: Mike Sherman, Partner
Description: Provider of venture capital for life sciences, biotechnology companies. **Founded:** 2001. **Investment Policies:** Seed, early and later stage. **Industry Preferences:** Biotechnology, and medical and health.

44873 ■ **Nashville Capital Network (NCN)**
3810 Bedford Ave., Ste. 110
 Nashville, TN 37215
Ph: (615)454-3950
URL: http://nashvillecapital.com
Contact: Sid Chambless, Executive Director
E-mail: schambless@nashvillecapital.com
Facebook: www.facebook.com/Nashville-Capital-Ne
 twork-160881990630908
X (Twitter): x.com/NashCapNetwork
Description: Accelerates the development of early-stage Tennessee-based companies. **Founded:** 2003. **Preferred Investment Size:** $500,000 to $2,000,000.

Texas

START-UP INFORMATION

44874 ■ Lubbock Angel Network (LAN)
Description: Member-directed investment club focused on early-stage technology startups. **Founded:** 2015.

ASSOCIATIONS AND OTHER ORGANIZATIONS

44875 ■ Association of Fundraising Professionals East Texas Chapter
PO Box 9414
 Tyler, TX 75711
Co. E-mail: admin@afpetx.org
URL: http://afpglobal.org/chapters/afp-tx-east-texas-chapter
Contact: La'Keidra Lincoln, Administrator
Description: Fosters the development and growth of fundraising professionals. Promotes high ethical standards in the fundraising profession. Provides training opportunities for fundraising professionals.
Geographic Preference: Local.

44876 ■ Association of Fundraising Professionals San Antonio Chapter
PO Box 15314
 San Antonio, TX 78212-8514
Co. E-mail: afpsanantonio@gmail.com
URL: http://www.afpsanantonio.org
Contact: Blair Ortmann, President
Facebook: www.facebook.com/AFPSanAntonio
Instagram: www.instagram.com/afpsanantonio
Description: Professional association for individuals and organizations that generate philanthropic support for a wide variety of charitable institutions. **Geographic Preference:** Local.

44877 ■ Austin Business Travel Association (ABTA)
4301 W William Cannon Dr., Ste. B-150
 Austin, TX 78749
Co. E-mail: info@gbta-austinbta.org
URL: http://gbta-austinbta.org
Contact: John Hampton, Chairman
E-mail: john.a.hampton@ehi.com
Facebook: www.facebook.com/gbtatx
X (Twitter): x.com/GBTA_AustinBTA
Description: Represents travel managers and providers. Promotes the value of the travel manager in meeting corporate travel needs and financial goals. Cultivates a positive public image of the corporate travel industry. Protects the interests of members and their corporations in legislative and regulatory matters. Promotes safety, security, efficiency and quality travel. Provides a forum for the exchange of information and ideas among members. **Founded:** 1990.
Geographic Preference: Local.

44878 ■ Business Marketing Association Houston Chapter (BMAHOU)
PO Box 710350
 Houston, TX 77271-0350
Ph: (713)723-1325
Co. E-mail: info@bmahouston.com
URL: http://bmahouston.com
Contact: Kaitlin Dunlap Cuevas, President
E-mail: kaitlind@dunlapmarketing.com
Facebook: www.facebook.com/anabmhouston
Linkedin: www.linkedin.com/company/anabmhouston
X (Twitter): x.com/anabmhouston
Description: Promotes the development of business-to-business marketing and communications professionals through education, training and networking.
Geographic Preference: Local.

44879 ■ Business Network International - Austin, Dallas, Fort Worth, San Antonio (BNI)
3430 Toringdon Way
 Charlotte, NC 28277
Free: 855-264-2673
URL: http://bnidfw.com/en-US/index
Contact: Amber Volkin, Managing Director
E-mail: ambervolkin@bni.com
URL(s): www.bnidfw.com; www.bni.com/Default.aspx?tabid=223
Facebook: www.facebook.com/bnidfw
X (Twitter): x.com/bnidfw
Description: Provides men and women a structured environment for the development and exchange of quality business referrals. **Geographic Preference:** Local.

44880 ■ Business Network International Northeast Texas [BNI Northeast Texas]
18424 Featherwood Dr.
 Dallas, TX 75252
Ph: (214)336-8255
URL: http://bninet.net/en-US/index
Contact: Keith Foisey, President
Description: Provides both men and women a structured environment for the development and exchange of quality business referrals. Offers members the opportunity to share ideas and contacts.
Geographic Preference: Local.

44881 ■ Business Network International - South Central and South Texas
PO Box 5162
 Abilene, TX 79608
Ph: (512)481-8686
Fax: (512)368-8140
Co. E-mail: steve.black@bni.com
URL: http://bniwesttexas.com/en-US/index
Facebook: www.facebook.com/BNIWTX
Description: Provides both men and women a structured environment for the development and exchange of quality business referrals. Offers members the opportunity to share ideas and contacts.
Geographic Preference: Local.

44882 ■ Business Network International - West Texas
PO Box 5162
 Abilene, TX 79608
Ph: (512)481-8686
Fax: (512)368-8140
Co. E-mail: steve.black@bni.com
URL: http://bniwesttexas.com/en-US/amarillo
Contact: Steve Black, Executive Director
E-mail: steve.black@bni.com
Facebook: www.facebook.com/BNIWTX
Description: Provides both men and women a structured environment for the development and exchange of quality business referrals. Offers members the opportunity to share ideas and contacts.
Geographic Preference: Local.

44883 ■ Central Texas Angel Network (CTAN)
PO Box 5435
 Austin, TX 78763-5435
Ph: (512)518-6054
URL: http://www.ctan.com
Contact: Katie Russel, Executive Director
E-mail: katie@ctan.com
Facebook: www.facebook.com/CentralTexasAngelNetwork
Linkedin: www.linkedin.com/company/central-texas-angel-network
X (Twitter): x.com/CTANAngels
Description: Mentors, supports, and invests in early-stage businesses in Texas. **Founded:** 2006.

44884 ■ Dallas Fort Worth Business Travel Association (DFWBTA)
4400 N O'Connor Rd.
 Irving, TX 75062
Co. E-mail: info@dfw-bta.org
URL: http://www.dfw-bta.org
Contact: Gloria Gonzalez, President
X (Twitter): x.com/GBTA_DFW
Instagram: www.instagram.com/gbta_dfw
Description: Represents travel managers and providers. Promotes the value of the travel manager in meeting corporate travel needs and financial goals. Cultivates a positive public image of the corporate travel industry. Protects the interests of members and their corporations in legislative and regulatory matters. Promotes safety, security, efficiency and quality travel. Provides a forum for the exchange of information and ideas among members. **Founded:** 1970.
Geographic Preference: Local.

44885 ■ Dallas/Fort Worth Chapter of the American Marketing Association (AMA DFW)
3044 Old Denton Rd., Ste. 111-229
 Carrollton, TX 75007
Co. E-mail: membership@dfwama.com
URL: http://amadfw.com
Contact: Angela Neal, President
Facebook: www.facebook.com/dfwama
X (Twitter): x.com/amadfw
YouTube: www.youtube.com/user/DFWAmericanMarketing
Description: Represents individuals and organizations involved in marketing. Improves marketing competencies, practice and leadership. Promotes the importance, efficacy and ethics of marketing. Provides marketing information, education and training.
Geographic Preference: Local.

STATE LISTINGS

44886 ■ Entrepreneurs Foundation of Central Texas
701 Brazos, Ste. 500
Austin, TX 78701
Ph: (512)482-8894
Co. E-mail: info@efctx.org
URL: http://www.entrepreneursfoundation.org
Contact: David Lee, Chairman
Facebook: www.facebook.com/entrepreneursfoundationofcentraltexas

Description: Encourages philanthropic work within corporate communities. Provides volunteer day programs, training for nonprofit board service and seminars on corporate social responsibility and philanthropy to boost employee involvement. Offers resources, consulting services, and strategic and practical support to assist companies in establishing a culture of philanthropy and community participation. **Founded:** 1999. **Geographic Preference:** Local.

44887 ■ Entrepreneurs' Organization - Austin Chapter (EO)
PO Box 10973
Austin, TX 78766
URL: http://www.eonetwork.org/austin/about-our-chapter

Description: Provides local resources to members which includes networking events, mentorship, live forums, and leadership development. **Founded:** 1995.

44888 ■ Entrepreneurs' Organization - Bryan-College Station (EO)
Bryan, TX
Ph: (979)324-4796
URL: http://www.eobcs.com
Contact: David Ohendalski, President
URL(s): www.eonetwork.org/bryan-collegestation/about-our-chapter
Facebook: www.facebook.com/eobcs

Description: Provides local resources to members which includes networking events, mentorship, live forums, and leadership development. **Founded:** 2014.

44889 ■ Entrepreneurs' Organization - Dallas Chapter (EO)
Dallas, TX
URL: http://eodallas.org
URL(s): www.eonetwork.org/dallas
Facebook: www.facebook.com/EODallas
Linkedin: www.linkedin.com/company/eo-dallas
X (Twitter): x.com/EODallas
Instagram: www.instagram.com/eodallasofficial

Description: Provides local resources to members which includes networking events, mentorship, live forums, and leadership development. **Founded:** 1993.

44890 ■ Entrepreneurs' Organization - Fort Worth Chapter (EO)
Fort Worth, TX
Co. E-mail: membership@eofortworth.org
URL: http://www.eonetwork.org/fortworth

Description: Provides local resources to members which includes networking events, mentorship, live forums, and leadership development.

44891 ■ Entrepreneurs' Organization - Houston Chapter (EO)
Houston, TX
Co. E-mail: eohubcomms@eonetwork.org
URL: http://www.eonetwork.org/houston
Facebook: www.facebook.com/eohtown

Description: Provides local resources to members which includes networking events, mentorship, live forums, and leadership development. **Founded:** 1993.

44892 ■ Entrepreneurs' Organization - San Antonio Chapter (EO)
San Antonio, TX
URL: http://www.eonetwork.org/sanantonio

Description: Provides local resources to members which includes networking events, mentorship, live forums, and leadership development. **Founded:** 1993.

44893 ■ Family Firm Institute, Inc. - North Texas Study Group
c/o John Kober
Morgan, Lewis & Bockius LLP
1717 Main St., Ste. 3200
Dallas, TX 75201
Ph: (214)466-4105
Co. E-mail: jkober@morganlewis.com
URL: http://www.ffi.org/about/study-groups/north-texas-study-group
Contact: John Kober, Contact
E-mail: jkober@morganlewis.com

Description: Professional membership association for individuals and organizations working the in family enterprise field. **Geographic Preference:** Local.

44894 ■ Houston Private Equity Association (HPEA)
10401 Westoffice Dr.
Houston, TX 77042-5308
Contact: Dale Wilkins, Contact

Description: Members invest in such industries as business and consumer services, manufacturers, distributors, healthcare and life sciences, energy and chemicals, telecommunications and information technology, and specialty retailers. **Founded:** 1983.

44895 ■ The Indus Entrepreneurs Austin
3925 W braker Ln., Ste. 38034
Austin, TX 78759
Ph: (502)500-6633
Co. E-mail: executivedirector@austin.tie.org
URL: http://austin.tie.org
Contact: Harshal Shah, President
Facebook: www.facebook.com/TheIndusEntrepreneurs.Austin
Linkedin: www.linkedin.com/in/tie-austin-0bb616137
X (Twitter): x.com/tieaustin
Instagram: www.instagram.com/tie_austin

Description: Advocates for the advancement of entrepreneurship and exchange of ideas. Works in fostering entrepreneurship and nurturing entrepreneurs, providing a networking platform for members and helping members integrate with the mainstream community. **Founded:** 1999. **Geographic Preference:** Local.

44896 ■ The Indus Entrepreneurs Houston
PO Box 79164
Houston, TX 77024
Ph: (832)278-2527
Co. E-mail: info@houston.tie.org
URL: http://houston.tie.org
Contact: Dr. Ram Shenoy, President
Facebook: www.facebook.com/Houston.TIE
Linkedin: www.linkedin.com/company/tiehouston
X (Twitter): x.com/tiehstn
YouTube: www.youtube.com/channel/UCLGy6-J2BYYNPtZRRLDxk8Q

Description: Advocates for the advancement of entrepreneurship and exchange of ideas. Works in fostering entrepreneurship and nurturing entrepreneurs, providing a networking platform for members and helping members integrate with the mainstream community. **Founded:** 2013. **Geographic Preference:** Local.

44897 ■ International Association of Business Communicators Austin
Austin, TX
Co. E-mail: communications@austin-iabc.com
URL: http://austin-iabc.com
Facebook: www.facebook.com/IABCAustin
X (Twitter): x.com/iabcaustin
YouTube: www.youtube.com/user/AustinIABC

Description: Represents the interests of communication managers, public relations directors, writers, editors and audiovisual specialists. Encourages establishment of college-level programs in organizational communication. Conducts surveys on employee communication effectiveness and media trends. Conducts research in the field of communication. **Awards:** Austin IABC Bronze Quill Awards (Annual). **Geographic Preference:** Local.

44898 ■ International Association of Business Communicators Houston
PO Box 270238
Houston, TX 77277
Co. E-mail: iabchouston@gmail.com
URL: http://www.iabchouston.com
Contact: Deanna Werner, Co-President
Facebook: www.facebook.com/IABCHouston
Linkedin: www.linkedin.com/company/iabchouston
X (Twitter): x.com/IABCHouston
Instagram: www.instagram.com/iabc_houston
YouTube: www.youtube.com/user/IABCHouston

Description: Represents the interests of communication managers, public relations directors, writers, editors and audiovisual specialists. Encourages establishment of college-level programs in organizational communication. Conducts surveys on employee communication effectiveness and media trends. Conducts research in the field of communication. **Founded:** 1970. **Geographic Preference:** Local.

44899 ■ International Association of Women Austin Chapter
Austin, TX
URL: http://community.iawomen.com/home
Contact: Megan Bozzuto, President

Description: Serves as a network for businesswomen to promote their product or service.

44900 ■ International Association of Women Central Houston Chapter
Houston, TX
Free: 888-852-1600
Co. E-mail: memberservices@iawomen.com
URL: http://www.iawomen.com/chapters/central-houston-chapter
Contact: Karla J. Aghedo, President
Facebook: www.facebook.com/IAWomenHouston

Description: Serves as network of accomplished women united to achieve professional goals. Provides a forum for sharing ideas and experiences of professional women regarding career success. Promotes an active business and networking community from all industries. **Geographic Preference:** Local.

44901 ■ International Association of Women Dallas Chapter
Dallas, TX
Co. E-mail: dallas@iawomen.com
URL: http://community.iawomen.com/dallas/home
Contact: Ada Crenshaw, President

Description: Serves as network of accomplished women united to achieve professional goals. Provides a forum for sharing ideas and experiences of professional women regarding career success. Promotes an active business and networking community from all industries. **Geographic Preference:** Local.

44902 ■ North Texas Angel Network (NTAN)
PO Box 181771
Dallas, TX 75237
Co. E-mail: info@northtexasangels.org
URL: http://www.northtexasangels.org
Contact: Jeff Murphy, Executive Director
Linkedin: www.linkedin.com/company/ntan

Description: Investment group for early-stage companies. **Founded:** 2008. **Investment Policies:** Potential for rapid sales growth; unique product or service meeting a market need or solving a problem; industry-specific strategy.

44903 ■ Texas Association of Business Brokers (TABB)
909 Lake Carolyn Pky., Ste. 320
Irving, TX 75039
Ph: (214)445-6395
URL: http://www.tabb.org
Contact: David Sweeten, President

Description: Disseminates industry information; encourages growth of sales; assists in new industry developments. Represents members in legislative matters and lobbies for recognition of the industry. Coordinates activity among business brokerages and

SMALL BUSINESS DEVELOPMENT CENTERS

44904 ■ Abilene Small Business Development Center
749 Gateway St., No. 301, Bldg. C
Abilene, TX 79602
Ph: (325)670-0300
Co. E-mail: americasbdc.abilene@ttu.edu
URL: http://www.abilenesbdc.org
Description: An outreach program that provides counseling, technical assistance, training workshops, and reference resources for small businesses and entrepreneurs. **Geographic Preference:** Local.

44905 ■ Angelina College Small Business Development Center
3500 S 1st St.
Lufkin, TX 75904
Ph: (936)633-5400
URL: http://www.sbdc.uh.edu/sbdc/Angelina_College_SBDC.asp
Contact: Dianne Amerine, Director
E-mail: damerine@angelina.edu
Description: Represents and promotes the small business sector. Provides management assistance to current and prospective small business owners. Helps to improve management skills and expand the products and services of members. **Geographic Preference:** Local.

44906 ■ Angelo State University Small Business Development Center
69 N Chadbourne St.
San Angelo, TX 76903
Ph: (325)942-2098
Co. E-mail: sbdc@angelo.edu
URL: http://www.angelo.edu/community/small-business-development-center
Contact: David Erickson, Director
E-mail: david.erickson@angelo.edu
Description: Represents and promotes the small business sector. Provides management assistance to current and prospective small business owners. Helps to improve management skills and expand the products and services of members. **Geographic Preference:** Local.

44907 ■ Big Bend Region Minority & Small Business Development Center [Big Bend Small Business Development Center]
500 W Ave. H, Ste. 102
Alpine, TX 79830
URL: http://sbdc.sulross.edu/alpine
Description: Provides management assistance to current and prospective small business owners in Big Bend Region. **Geographic Preference:** Local.

44908 ■ Blinn College Small Business Development Center
108 Blinn Blvd.
Brenham, TX 77833
Ph: (979)830-4137
Co. E-mail: sbdc@blinn.edu
URL: http://www.sbdc.uh.edu/sbdc/Blinn_College_SBDC.asp
Contact: Matthew Wehring, Director
E-mail: matthew.wehring@blinn.edu
Facebook: www.facebook.com/SBDCBlinnCollege
Description: Represents and promotes the small business sector. Provides management assistance to current and prospective small business owners. Helps to improve management skills and expand the products and services of members. **Geographic Preference:** Local.

44909 ■ Brazos Valley Small Business Development Center (BVSBDC)
1733 Briarcrest Dr., Ste. 103
Bryan, TX 77802
Ph: (979)260-5222
Co. E-mail: bvsbdc@uh.edu
URL: http://www.sbdc.uh.edu/sbdc/Brazos_Valley_SBDC.asp
Contact: Jim Pillans, Director
E-mail: jimp@bvsbdc.org
Description: Represents and promotes the small business sector. Provides management assistance to current and prospective small business owners. Helps to improve management skills and expand the products and services of members. **Geographic Preference:** Local.

44910 ■ Brazosport College Small Business Development Center
500 College Dr.
Lake Jackson, TX 77566
Ph: (979)230-3380
Co. E-mail: sbdcinfo@brazosport.edu
URL: http://www.sbdc.uh.edu/sbdc/Brazosport_College_SBDC.asp
Contact: Jennifer Finney, Director
Facebook: www.facebook.com/BrazosportCollegeSBDC
X (Twitter): x.com/UHSBDC
Description: Represents and promotes the small business sector. Provides management assistance to current and prospective small business owners. Helps to improve management skills and expand the products and services of members. **Geographic Preference:** Local.

44911 ■ Collin Small Business Development Center
4800 Preston Pk. Blvd., Ste. 114
Plano, TX 75093
Ph: (972)985-3770
Co. E-mail: sbdc@collin.edu
URL: http://collinsbdc.com
Contact: Marta Gómez Frey, Director
E-mail: mfrey@collin.edu
Facebook: www.facebook.com/CollinSBDC
Linkedin: www.linkedin.com/company/collin-sbdc
X (Twitter): x.com/CollinSBDC
YouTube: www.youtube.com/user/CollinSBDCVideos
Description: Represents and promotes the small business sector. Provides management assistance to current and prospective small business owners. Helps to improve management skills and expand the products and services of members. **Geographic Preference:** Local.

44912 ■ Dallas Small Business Development Center
1402 Corinth St.
Dallas, TX 75215
Ph: (214)860-5848
Co. E-mail: bkralik@dcccd.edu
URL: http://www.dallasmetropolitansbdc.com/new-client-assessment
URL(s): www.ntsbdc.org/local-sbdcs/county-search
Description: Represents and promotes the small business sector. Provides management assistance to current and prospective small business owners. Helps to improve management skills and expand the products and services of members. **Geographic Preference:** Local.

44913 ■ Del Mar College Small Business Development Center
3209 S Staples St.
Corpus Christi, TX 78411
Ph: (361)698-1021
Fax: (361)698-1024
Co. E-mail: sbdc@delmar.edu
URL: http://www.delmar.edu/sbdc
Contact: Ann Fierova, Director
E-mail: afierova@delmar.edu
Facebook: www.facebook.com/DelMarCollegeSBDC
Linkedin: www.linkedin.com/company/delmarsbdc
X (Twitter): x.com/DMCSBDC
Instagram: www.instagram.com/delmarcollegesbdc
Description: Represents and promotes the small business sector. Provides management assistance to current and prospective small business owners. Helps to improve management skills and expand the products and services of members. **Geographic Preference:** Local.

44914 ■ Denton County Small Business Development Center
414 W Pky. St.
Denton, TX 76201
URL: http://dentonedp.com/business/small-business-programs
Contact: Erin Carter, President
Description: Represents and promotes the small business sector. Provides management assistance to current and prospective small business owners. Helps to improve management skills and expand the products and services of members. **Geographic Preference:** Local.

44915 ■ El Paso Community College Small Business Development Center
9050 Viscount Blvd., Bldg. B, Ste. B520
El Paso, TX 79925
Ph: (915)831-7743
Fax: (915)831-7734
URL: http://elpasosbdc.net
Contact: Joseph C. Ferguson, Director
E-mail: jfergu11@epcc.edu
Facebook: www.facebook.com/sbdcelpaso
Linkedin: www.linkedin.com/company/elpasosbdc
Description: Represents and promotes the small business sector. Provides management assistance to current and prospective small business owners. Helps to improve management skills and expand the products and services of members. **Geographic Preference:** Local.

44916 ■ Galveston County Small Business Development Center
319 E Galveston St.
League City, TX 77573
Ph: (409)933-1414
URL: http://www.sbdc.uh.edu/sbdc/Galveston_County_SBDC.asp
Contact: Amy Reid, Director
E-mail: areid2@uh.edu
Description: Represents and promotes the small business sector. Provides management assistance to current and prospective small business owners. Helps to improve management skills and expand the products and services of members. **Geographic Preference:** Local.

44917 ■ Grayson Small Business Development Center (Grayson SBDC)
6101 Grayson Dr.
Denison, TX 75020
Ph: (903)463-8787
URL: http://www.graysonsbdc.org
Description: Represents and promotes the small business sector. Provides management assistance to current and prospective small business owners. Helps to improve management skills and expand the products and services of members. **Geographic Preference:** Local.

44918 ■ Kilgore College Small Business Development Center
911 W Loop 281, Ste. 319
Longview, TX 75604
Ph: (903)757-5857
URL: http://www.kilgorechamber.com/accelerate-2
Description: Represents and promotes the small business sector. Provides management assistance to current and prospective small business owners. Helps to improve management skills and expand the products and services of members. **Geographic Preference:** Local.

44919 ■ Lamar State College Small Business Development Center
1401 Procter St.
Port Arthur, TX 77640
Ph: (409)984-6531
Co. E-mail: euliansm@lamarpa.edu
URL: http://www.sbdc.uh.edu/sbdc/Lamar_State_SBDC.asp
Contact: Dana Espinal, Director
Facebook: www.facebook.com/UHSBDC
Linkedin: www.linkedin.com/company/university-of-houston-small-business-development-center
X (Twitter): x.com/uhsbdc

STATE LISTINGS

Instagram: www.instagram.com/uhsbdcnetwork
YouTube: www.youtube.com/channel/UCJsJh1_fV
dCTtgqzK_B54Ag
Description: Represents and promotes the small business sector. Provides management assistance to current and prospective small business owners. Helps to improve management skills and expand the products and services of members. **Geographic Preference:** Local.

44920 ■ **Lamar University Small Business Development Center**
5091 Rolfe Christopher Dr.
Beaumont, TX 77705
Ph: (409)880-2367
Co. E-mail: sbdc@lamar.edu
URL: http://www.sbdc.uh.edu/sbdc/Lamar_University_SBDC.asp
Contact: David Mulcahy, Director
Facebook: www.facebook.com/lamar.sbdc
Description: Provides management assistance to current and prospective small business owners in Lamar. **Geographic Preference:** Local.

44921 ■ **Lee College Small Business Development Center (SBDC)**
909 Decker Dr., Ste. 105
Baytown, TX 77520
Ph: (281)425-6556
Fax: (281)425-6307
URL: http://www.lee.edu/workforce/sbdc
Contact: Linda Jones-Zbranek, Contact
E-mail: ljoneszbranek@lee.edu
Description: Provides businesses with information and one-on-one consulting assistance to foster economic growth in the community. Working with existing companies and start-up firms. **Geographic Preference:** Local.

44922 ■ **Lone Star College System Small Business Development Center**
3380 College Pk., Dr., Ste. 100
The Woodlands, TX 77384
Ph: (936)294-3737
Co. E-mail: sbdc@lonestar.edu
URL: http://www.sbdc.uh.edu
Contact: Miguel Lopez, Executive Director
Description: Represents and promotes the small business sector. Provides management assistance to current and prospective small business owners. Helps to improve management skills and expand the products and services of members. **Founded:** 1985. **Geographic Preference:** Local.

44923 ■ **Lubbock Small Business Development Center**
5001 W Loop 289, 1st Fl.
Lubbock, TX 79414
Ph: (806)745-1637
Co. E-mail: americasbdc.lubbock@ttu.edu
URL: http://www.lubbocksbdc.org
Contact: Ray Laurent, Regional Director
E-mail: ray.laurent@ttu.edu
X (Twitter): x.com/ttusbdc
Description: Represents and promotes the small business sector. Provides management assistance to current and prospective small business owners. Helps to improve management skills and expand the products and services of members. **Geographic Preference:** Local.

44924 ■ **McLennan Small Business Development Center (MCCSBDC)**
4601 N 19th, Bldg. A Rm. 36B
Waco, TX 76708
Ph: (254)299-8141
Free: 800-349-7232
URL: http://www.mccsbdc.com
Contact: Steve Surguy, Director
E-mail: ssurguy@mclennan.edu
Facebook: www.facebook.com/mccsbdc
X (Twitter): x.com/MCCSBDC
Description: Provides management assistance to current and prospective small business owners in McLennan. **Geographic Preference:** Local.

44925 ■ **Midwestern State University Small Business Development Center (MSU SBDC)**
3410 Taft Blvd.
Wichita Falls, TX 76308
Ph: (940)397-4373
Co. E-mail: msusbdc@msutexas.edu
URL: http://www.msusbdc.org
Contact: Vanda Cullar, Director
E-mail: vanda.cullar@msutexas.edu
Facebook: www.facebook.com/MSUSBDC
X (Twitter): x.com/MSUSBDC
Description: Represents and promotes the small business sector. Provides management assistance to current and prospective small business owners. Helps to improve management skills and expand the products and services of members. **Geographic Preference:** Local.

44926 ■ **Montague County Small Business Development Center**
1517 Centre Pl., Dr., Ste. 350
Denton, TX 76205
Ph: (940)498-6470
Co. E-mail: nctcsbdc@nctc.edu
URL: http://ntsbdc.org/local-sbdcs/county-search/#toggle-id-32
Contact: Lori Logan, Director
Description: Provides management assistance to current and prospective small business owners in Montague County. **Geographic Preference:** Local.

44927 ■ **Navarro Small Business Development Center**
c/o Daniel Short, Director
3205 W 2nd Ave.
Corsicana, TX 75110
Ph: (903)872-8104
URL: http://www.navarrocollegesbdc.org
Contact: Daniel Short, Director
Facebook: www.facebook.com/NCSBDC
Linkedin: www.linkedin.com/company/navarro-college-small-business-development-center
X (Twitter): x.com/NavarroSBDC
Description: Represents and promotes the small business sector. Provides management assistance to current and prospective small business owners. Helps to improve management skills and expand the products and services of members. **Geographic Preference:** Local.

44928 ■ **North Central Texas College - Corinth Small Business Development Center (SBDC)**
3971 FM 2181
Corinth, TX 76210
Ph: (940)498-6470
URL: http://www.nctc.edu/sbdc
X (Twitter): x.com/nctsbdc
Instagram: www.instagram.com/nctsbdc
Description: Provides management assistance to current and prospective small business owners in Corinth. **Founded:** 1924. **Geographic Preference:** Local.

44929 ■ **North Central Texas Small Business Development Center (NCTSBDC)**
1525 W California St.
Gainesville, TX 76240
Ph: (940)498-6470
Co. E-mail: nctcsbdc@gmail.com
URL: http://www.nctc.edu/sbdc
X (Twitter): x.com/nctsbdc
YouTube: www.youtube.com/channel/UCD70cly8I7
1J8eO03Dh_H9A/featured
Description: Represents and promotes the small business sector. Provides management assistance to current and prospective small business owners. Helps to improve management skills and expand the products and services of members. **Geographic Preference:** Local.

44930 ■ **North Texas Small Business Development Center (NTSBDC)**
1402 Corinth St., Ste. 2100
Dallas, TX 75215
Ph: (214)860-5832
Fax: (214)860-5813

Texas ■ 44935

Co. E-mail: contact@ntsbdc.org
URL: http://ntsbdc.org
Contact: Mark Langford, Regional Director
E-mail: m.langford@dcccd.edu
Facebook: www.facebook.com/NorthTexasSBDC
X (Twitter): x.com/NorthTexasSBDC
Description: Provides management assistance to current and prospective small business owners in North Texas. **Geographic Preference:** Local.

44931 ■ **Northeast Texas Small Business Development Center**
105 N Riddle Ave.
Mount Pleasant, TX 75455
Ph: (903)434-8237
Co. E-mail: sbdcinfo@ntcc.edu
URL: http://www.ntcc.edu/sbdc
Contact: Lori Hindman, Contact
E-mail: lhindman@ntcc.edu
Facebook: www.facebook.com/ntsbdc
Description: Represents and promotes the small business sector. Provides management assistance to current and prospective small business owners. Helps to improve management skills and expand the products and services of members. **Geographic Preference:** Local.

44932 ■ **Northwest Texas Small Business Administration Development Center (NWTSBDC)**
5001 W Loop 289
Lubbock, TX 79414
Ph: (806)745-3973
Co. E-mail: nwtsbdc@ttu.edu
URL: http://www.depts.ttu.edu/nwtsbdc
Contact: Judy Wilhelm, Executive Director
E-mail: judy.wilhelm@ttu.edu
Description: Provides counseling and guidance in various areas on such issues as employee relations, marketing, contracting, patents, financial management, and goal setting. **Scope:** Growth, expansion, innovation, increased productivity and improved management for small business. **Educational Activities:** NWTSBDC Seminars.

44933 ■ **Northwest Texas Small Business Development Center (NWTSBDC)**
5001 W Loop 289
Lubbock, TX 79414
Ph: (806)745-3973
Co. E-mail: nwtsbdc@ttu.edu
URL: http://nwtsbdc.org
Contact: Carla Holland, Executive Director
E-mail: carla.holland@ttu.edu
Description: Business assistance provider in the Northwest Texas Region. **Founded:** 1986. **Geographic Preference:** Local.

44934 ■ **Paris Small Business Development Center (SBDC)**
2400 Clarksville St.
Paris, TX 75460
Ph: (903)782-0224
Co. E-mail: parissbdc@gmail.com
URL: http://www.parissbdc.org/contact-paris-sbdc/home
Contact: Jennifer Johnston, Director
E-mail: jjohnston@parisjc.edu
Facebook: www.facebook.com/ParisSBDC
Linkedin: www.linkedin.com/company/paris-sbdc
X (Twitter): x.com/ParisSBDC
Instagram: www.instagram.com/parissbdc
YouTube: www.youtube.com/user/ParisSBDC
Description: Represents and promotes the small business sector. Provides management assistance to current and prospective small business owners. Helps to improve management skills and expand the products and services of members. **Founded:** 1986. **Geographic Preference:** Local.

44935 ■ **Prairie View A&M University Small Business Development Center**
39725 Owens Rd., Ste. 106
Prairie View, TX 77445
Ph: (936)261-9243
Co. E-mail: jtespy@pvamu.edu

URL: http://www.sbdc.uh.edu/sbdc/Prairie_View_AM_University_SBDC.asp
Contact: Jasmin Espy, Director
E-mail: jtespy@pvamu.edu
Facebook: www.facebook.com/Prairie-View-AM-University-SBDC-104179701494650
Linkedin: www.linkedin.com/in/prairie-view-small-business-development-center-9073111ba
Instagram: www.instagram.com/pvamu_sbdc
Description: Represents and promotes the small business sector. Provides management assistance to current and prospective small business owners. Helps to improve management skills and expand the products and services of members. **Geographic Preference:** Local.

44936 ■ Sam Houston State University Small Business Development Center (SHSU SBDC)
1 Financial Plz., Ste. 300
Huntsville, TX 77340
Ph: (936)294-3737
Co. E-mail: sbdcinfo@shsu.edu
URL: http://www.sbdc.uh.edu/sbdc/Sam_Houston_State_University_SBDC.asp
Contact: Rhonda Ellisor, Director
Linkedin: www.linkedin.com/company/uhsbdc
X (Twitter): x.com/UHSBDC
Description: Represents and promotes the small business sector. Provides management assistance to current and prospective small business owners. Helps to improve management skills and expand the products and services of members. **Founded:** 1984. **Geographic Preference:** Local.

44937 ■ San Antonio Small Business Development Center (SA SBDC)
Durango Bldg., 2nd Fl., Ste. 2. 312
501 W Cesar E Chavez Blvd.
San Antonio, TX 78207
Ph: (210)458-2460
Co. E-mail: sasbdc@utsa.edu
URL: http://sasbdc.org
Contact: Richard Sifuentes, Director
Facebook: www.facebook.com/UTSASBDC
Linkedin: www.linkedin.com/company/utsa-small-business-development-center
X (Twitter): x.com/UTSASBDC
Pinterest: www.pinterest.com/utsasbdc
Description: Represents and promotes the small business sector. Provides management assistance to current and prospective small business owners. Helps to improve management skills and expand the products and services of members. **Geographic Preference:** Local.

44938 ■ San Jacinto College Small Business Development Center
6117 Broadway St.
Pearland, TX 77581
Ph: (281)485-5214
Co. E-mail: information@sjcd.edu
URL: http://www.sanjac.edu/about-san-jac/community/small-business-development-center
Contact: Tabitha Godinez, Administrative Assistant
E-mail: tabitha.godinez@sjcd.edu
Description: Represents and promotes the small business sector. Provides management assistance to current and prospective small business owners. Helps to improve management skills and expand the products and services of members. **Geographic Preference:** Local.

44939 ■ Small Business Development and International Trade Center
501 W Cesar E Chavez Blvd.
San Antonio, TX 78207
Ph: (210)458-2470
Fax: (210)458-2476
Co. E-mail: contact.us@texastrade.org
URL: http://texastrade.org
Contact: Cliff Paredes, Regional Director
E-mail: cliff.paredes@utsa.edu
Facebook: www.facebook.com/TexasTrade
Linkedin: www.linkedin.com/company/international-trade-center
X (Twitter): x.com/texastrade
Description: Trade assistance organization specializing in aiding small businesses. **Founded:** 1992. **Geographic Preference:** Local.

44940 ■ South-West Texas Small Business Development Center Network
501 W Cesar Chavez Blvd.,Rm. 4. 370
San Antonio, TX 78207
Ph: (210)458-2450
Fax: (210)458-2425
Co. E-mail: albert.salgado@utsa.edu
URL: http://www.txsbdc.org
Contact: Al Salgado, Director
E-mail: albert.salgado@utsa.edu
Description: Represents and promotes the small business sector. Provides management assistance to current and prospective small business owners. Helps to improve management skills and expand the products and services of members. **Geographic Preference:** Local.

44941 ■ SRSU Rio Grande College Small Business Development Center
3107 Bob Rogers Dr.
Eagle Pass, TX 78852
Co. E-mail: sbdc-rgc@sulross.edu
URL: http://sbdc.sulross.edu/rgc
Contact: Elizabeth Pena, Executive Director
E-mail: epena@sulross.edu
Facebook: www.facebook.com/rgc.sbdc
Instagram: www.instagram.com/riograndecollege.sbdc
Description: Represents and promotes the small business sector. Provides management assistance to current and prospective small business owners. Helps to improve management skills and expand the products and services of members. **Geographic Preference:** Local.

44942 ■ Tarleton State University Small Business Development Center
201 St. Felix St., Ste. 124
Stephenville, TX 76401
Ph: (254)968-0558
Co. E-mail: sbdc@tarleton.edu
URL: http://www.tarleton.edu/cob/signature/sbdc.html
Contact: Kim Leaverton, Membership Chairperson
URL(s): www.tsusbdc.org
Facebook: www.facebook.com/SBDCTarleton
X (Twitter): x.com/tsu_sbdc
Instagram: www.instagram.com/tarletonstate
YouTube: www.youtube.com/c/TarletonState
Description: Represents and promotes the small business sector. Provides management assistance to current and prospective small business owners. Helps to improve management skills and expand the products and services of members. **Geographic Preference:** Local.

44943 ■ Tarrant Small Business Development Center
1150 S Fwy., Ste. 229
Fort Worth, TX 76104
Ph: (817)515-2600
URL: http://www.tarrantsbdc.org
Facebook: www.facebook.com/tarrantsbdc
Linkedin: www.linkedin.com/company/tarrantsbdc
X (Twitter): x.com/tarrantsbdc
Description: Represents and promotes the small business sector. Provides management assistance to current and prospective small business owners. Helps to improve management skills and expand the products and services of members. **Founded:** 1987. **Geographic Preference:** Local.

44944 ■ Texas - Houston Small Business Development Center
1455 W Loop S, Ste. 900
Houston, TX 77027
Ph: (713)752-8400
URL: http://www.sbdc.uh.edu/sbdc/default.asp
Facebook: www.facebook.com/UHSBDC
Linkedin: www.linkedin.com/company/uhsbdc
X (Twitter): x.com/uhsbdc
YouTube: www.youtube.com/channel/UCJsJh1_fVdCTtgqzK_B54Ag
Description: Provides small business support, counseling, education, and information. **Geographic Preference:** Local.

44945 ■ Texas State University San Marcos Small Business Development Center
505 E Huntland Dr., Ste. 460
Austin, TX 78752
Ph: (512)420-9379
Co. E-mail: sbdc@txstate.edu
URL: http://sbdc.mccoy.txstate.edu
Contact: Joe Harper, Executive Director
E-mail: fa12@txstate.edu
Facebook: www.facebook.com/TXStateSBDC
X (Twitter): x.com/txstatesbdc
Description: Represents and promotes the small business sector. Provides management assistance to current and prospective small business owners. Helps to improve management skills and expand the products and services of members. **Geographic Preference:** Local.

44946 ■ Trinity Valley Small Business Development Center (TV-SBDC)
201 W Corsicana St., Bldg., Ste. 6
Athens, TX 75751
Ph: (903)675-7403
URL: http://tvccsbdc.org
Facebook: www.facebook.com/tvccsbdc
X (Twitter): x.com/TVCCSBDC
Description: Represents and promotes the small business sector. Provides management assistance to current and prospective small business owners. Helps to improve management skills and expand the products and services of members. **Founded:** 1987. **Geographic Preference:** Local.

44947 ■ Tyler Small Business Development Center
1530 S Southwest Loop 323, Ste. 100
Tyler, TX 75701
Ph: (903)510-2975
Co. E-mail: dpro@tjc.edu
Facebook: www.facebook.com/TylerSBDC
X (Twitter): twitter.com/TylerSBDC
Description: Represents and promotes the small business sector. Provides management assistance to current and prospective small business owners. Helps to improve management skills and expand the products and services of members. **Geographic Preference:** Local.

44948 ■ University of Houston Coastal Plains Small Business Development Center (UH/CP SBDC)
1112 7th St.
Bay City, TX 77414
Ph: (281)499-9787
Co. E-mail: sbdcfortbend@uh.edu
URL: http://www.sbdc.uh.edu/sbdc/Coastal_Plains_SBDC.asp
Contact: Tori Rayne, Director
Description: Provides management assistance to current and prospective small business owners in Coastal Plains. **Geographic Preference:** Local.

44949 ■ University of Houston Fort Bend Small Business Development Center
117 Ln. Dr., Ste. 29
Rosenberg, TX 77471
Ph: (281)499-9787
Co. E-mail: sbdcfortbend@uh.edu
URL: http://www.sbdc.uh.edu/sbdc/Fort_Bend_County_SBDC.asp
Contact: Stacy Jacobs, Director
Facebook: www.facebook.com/FortBendSBDC
X (Twitter): x.com/FortBendSBDC
Instagram: www.instagram.com/fortbendsbdc
Description: Represents and promotes the small business sector. Provides management assistance to current and prospective small business owners. Helps to improve management skills and expand the products and services of members. **Geographic Preference:** Local.

STATE LISTINGS

44950 ■ University of Houston - Small Business Development Center (UHSBDC)
1455 West Loop S
Houston, TX 77027
Ph: (713)752-8444
Co. E-mail: sbdcmetro@uh.edu
URL: http://www.sbdc.uh.edu/sbdc/default.asp
Contact: LeeVera Smith, Advisor
Facebook: www.facebook.com/UHSBDC
Linkedin: www.linkedin.com/company/uhsbdc
X (Twitter): x.com/uhsbdc
Instagram: www.instagram.com/uhsbdcnetwork
YouTube: www.youtube.com/channel/UCJsJh1_fVdCTtgqzK_B54Ag
Description: Provides help for those starting or expanding their business. Services include consulting, workshops, seminars, specialty programs, business library, and training. **Scope:** Small businesses, entrepreneurship, sales and employee increase and customer base development on the Texas Gulf Coast. **Founded:** 1984. **Educational Activities:** SBDC Business seminars; SBDC Business training workshops.

44951 ■ University of Houston Small Business Development Center Network
1455 W Loop S, Ste. 900
Houston, TX 77027
Ph: (713)752-8444
Co. E-mail: sbdcmetro@uh.edu
URL: http://www.sbdc.uh.edu/sbdc/default.asp
Contact: LeeVera Smith, Advisor
Facebook: www.facebook.com/UHSBDC
Linkedin: www.linkedin.com/company/university-of-houston-small-business-development-center
X (Twitter): x.com/uhsbdc
Instagram: www.instagram.com/uhsbdcnetwork
YouTube: www.youtube.com/channel/UCJsJh1_fVdCTtgqzK_B54Ag
Description: Business consulting, financing packages, business planning for technology, government procurement, and international trade and entrepreneurial training. **Founded:** 1984.

44952 ■ University of Houston Victoria Small Business Development Center
1604 E Airline
Victoria, TX 77901
Ph: (361)485-4485
Free: 877-877-7232
Fax: (361)580-5550
Co. E-mail: sbdc@uhv.edu
URL: http://www.uhv.edu/small-business
Contact: Lindsay Young, Director
E-mail: youngle@uhv.edu
Description: Provides management assistance to current and prospective small business owners in Victoria. **Geographic Preference:** Local.

44953 ■ University of Texas of the Permian Basin Small Business Development Center (SBDC)
1310 N FM 1788, CEED Bldg.
Midland, TX 79707
Ph: (432)552-2455
Co. E-mail: sbdc@utpb.edu
URL: http://www.utpbsbdc.org
Contact: Tyler Patton, Director
URL(s): www.texvet.org/resources/utpb-small-business-development-center
Facebook: www.facebook.com/PBSBDC
Description: Represents and promotes the small business sector. Provides management assistance to current and prospective small business owners. Helps to improve management skills and expand the products and services of members. **Publications:** Making it Happen. **Geographic Preference:** Local.

44954 ■ University of Texas Rio Grande Valley Small Business Development Center (UTRGV-SBDC)
CESS Bldg., Ste. 1. 200, 1407 E Freddy Gonzalez Dr.
Edinburg, TX 78539
Ph: (956)665-7535
Co. E-mail: sbdc@utrgv.edu
URL: http://www.utrgv.edu/sbdc/index.htm
Contact: Maria D. Juarez-Serna, Director
Facebook: www.facebook.com/utrgvsbdc
X (Twitter): x.com/utrgvsbdc
Description: Represents and promotes the small business sector. Provides management assistance to current and prospective small business owners. Helps to improve management skills and expand the products and services of members. **Founded:** 2013. **Geographic Preference:** Local.

44955 ■ West Texas A&M University Small Business Development Center
720 S Tyler St.
Amarillo, TX 79101
Ph: (806)651-5151
Co. E-mail: info@wtsbdc.com
URL: http://www.smallbusinessdevelopmentcenter.com
Contact: Gina Woodward, Director
Facebook: www.facebook.com/wtsbdc
X (Twitter): x.com/wtsbdc
Instagram: www.instagram.com/wtsbdc
YouTube: www.youtube.com/wtsbdc
Description: The WTAMU SBDC provides counseling and seminar training for potential and existing businesses located in the top twenty-five counties of the Texas Panhandle. **Geographic Preference:** Local.

SMALL BUSINESS ASSISTANCE PROGRAMS

44956 ■ Dumac Economic Development Corporation (EDC)
900 N Dumas Ave.
Dumas, TX 79029
Ph: (806)934-3322
Fax: (806)934-0180
URL: http://dumasedc.org
Contact: Shawn Frische, President
Description: Works to retain and expand existing business, recruit targeted businesses, and grow the workforce. **Founded:** 1999.

44957 ■ Houston Business Development, Inc. (HBDI)
5330 Griggs Rd.
Houston, TX 77021
Ph: (713)845-2400
Fax: (713)645-2830
Co. E-mail: info@hbdinc.org
URL: http://www.hbdinc.org
Contact: Marlon D. Mitchell, President
E-mail: m.mitchell@hbdinc.org
Facebook: www.facebook.com/HBDi.org
Description: Supports the expansion of small businesses, stimulates economic growth, and fosters employment opportunities for low- to moderate-income citizens in the Houston metropolitan area. **Founded:** 1986.

44958 ■ Office of the Governor - Texas Economic Development
PO Box 12428
Austin, TX 78711
Ph: (512)936-0100
Co. E-mail: business@gov.texas.gov
URL: http://gov.texas.gov/business
Contact: Adriana Cruz, Executive Director
Facebook: www.facebook.com/TexasEconDev
Linkedin: www.linkedin.com/company/28655937
X (Twitter): x.com/TexasEconDev
Instagram: www.instagram.com/texasecondev
YouTube: www.youtube.com/channel/UCk2mldvOd_Ez6ih92rS69gw
Description: Pursues business expansion and relocation to create jobs and opportunities in Texas. Division includes Business Development, Business Assistance, and Economic Development Finance.

44959 ■ Texas Economic Development Corporation (TxEDC)
PO Box 684702
Austin, TX 78768
Ph: (512)981-6736
URL: http://businessintexas.com
Contact: Robert Allen, President
Facebook: www.facebook.com/GoBigInTexas
Linkedin: www.linkedin.com/company/gobigintexas
X (Twitter): x.com/GoBigInTexas
Instagram: www.instagram.com/GoBigInTexas
YouTube: www.youtube.com/channel/UCMVtDtn-nuM_w6XFph1tkjw
Description: Works with the Governor's Office of Economic Development and Tourism to boos the state's economic development and create global awareness of the business-friendly climate of Texas. Offers tax incentives and financing assistance.

SCORE OFFICES

44960 ■ SCORE - Allen
210 W McDermott Dr.
Allen, TX 75013
Ph: (972)727-5585
URL: http://dallas.score.org/dallas-score-mentoring-locations
Description: Provides professional guidance and information to maximize the success of existing and emerging small businesses. Offers business counseling and workshops.

44961 ■ SCORE - Alvin
105 W Willis St.
Alvin, TX 77511
Ph: (281)331-3944
URL: http://ri.score.org/find-location?state=TX
Description: Provides professional guidance and information to maximize the success of existing and emerging small businesses. Offers business counseling and workshops.

44962 ■ SCORE - Arlington, Texas
201 E Abram St.
Arlington, TX 76010
Ph: (817)871-6002
URL: http://fortworth.score.org
Facebook: www.facebook.com/SCOREFortWorth
X (Twitter): x.com/scorefortworth
Description: Provides professional guidance and information to maximize the success of existing and emerging small businesses. Offers business counseling and workshops.

44963 ■ SCORE - Austin, Texas
5524 Bee Cave Rd., Westland Park
Bldg. M
Austin, TX 78746
Ph: (512)928-2425
URL: http://www.score.org/austin
Facebook: www.facebook.com/SCOREAustin
Linkedin: www.linkedin.com/company/score-austin
X (Twitter): x.com/SCOREAustin
Instagram: www.instagram.com/score_austin
YouTube: www.youtube.com/channel/UCCdjUth2NZ5O78d9HcRbZFQ
Description: Seeks to educate entrepreneurs and help small businesses start, grow and succeed nationwide. Organizes volunteers who are working or retired business owners, executives and corporate leaders who wish to share their wisdom and lessons learned in business. **Geographic Preference:** Local.

44964 ■ SCORE - Bay City
1900 5th St.
Bay City, TX 77414
Ph: (713)202-7640
Co. E-mail: mprice433@gmail.com
URL: http://houston.score.org
Description: Provides professional guidance and information to maximize the success of existing and emerging small businesses. Offers business counseling and workshops.

44965 ■ SCORE - Bedford
2109 Martin Dr.
Bedford, TX 76095
URL: http://fortworth.score.org/mentors/mark-lenz
Contact: Mark Lenz, Contact

Description: Provides professional guidance and information to maximize the success of existing and emerging small businesses. Offers business counseling and workshops.

44966 ■ SCORE - Clear Lake Library
16616 Diana Ln.
Houston, TX 77062
Co. E-mail: ibrahim.saleh@scorevolunteer.org
URL: http://www.score.org/houston/about-us/score-houston-mentoring-locations
Contact: Ibrahim Saleh, Contact
E-mail: ibrahim.saleh@scorevolunteer.org
Description: Provides professional guidance and information to maximize the success of existing and emerging small businesses. Offers business counseling and workshops.

44967 ■ SCORE - Colleyville
100 Main St., 3rd Fl.
Colleyville, TX 76034
URL: http://fortworth.score.org/contact-fort-worth-score
Description: Provides professional guidance and information to maximize the success of existing and emerging small businesses. Offers business counseling and workshops.

44968 ■ SCORE - Coppell
708 Main St.
Coppell, TX 75019
Ph: (214)670-0170
URL: http://dallas.score.org/dallas-score-mentoring-locations
Contact: Tom Baumgarten, Contact
Description: Provides professional guidance and information to maximize the success of existing and emerging small businesses. Offers business counseling and workshops.

44969 ■ SCORE - Corpus Christi
2820 S Padre Island, Ste. 108
Corpus Christi, TX 78415
Ph: (361)879-0017
Fax: (361)879-0764
Co. E-mail: corpuschristi@scorevolunteer.org
URL: http://corpuschristi.score.org
Contact: Bridget Weston, Chief Executive Officer
Facebook: www.facebook.com/SCORECorpusChristi
Linkedin: www.linkedin.com/company/scorecorpuschristi
X (Twitter): x.com/SCORECorpus
Description: Provides professional guidance and information to maximize the success of existing and emerging small businesses. Offers business counseling and workshops. **Founded:** 1964. **Geographic Preference:** Local.

44970 ■ SCORE - Dallas
15301 Spectrum Dr., Ste. 110
Addison, TX 75001
Ph: (214)987-9491
Co. E-mail: help@score.org
URL: http://dallas.score.org
Linkedin: www.linkedin.com/company/score-dallas
X (Twitter): x.com/SCOREdallas
Description: Creates business opportunities for small business owners and potential business owners to achieve success. Provides mentoring services to residents in Dallas, individual counseling and on-site business reviews. Develops business plans and evaluates financial projections. **Founded:** 1965. **Geographic Preference:** Local.

44971 ■ SCORE - Dallas Bill J. Priest Center
1402 Corinth St., Ste. 2110
Dallas, TX 75215
Ph: (214)987-9491
Co. E-mail: help@score.org
URL: http://dallas.score.org/dallas-score-mentoring-locations
Linkedin: www.linkedin.com/company/score-dallas
X (Twitter): x.com/SCOREdallas
Description: Provides professional guidance and information to maximize the success of existing and emerging small businesses. Offers business counseling and workshops.

44972 ■ SCORE - Deer Park
Deer Park Economic Alliance Houston Port Region
203 Ivy Ave., Ste. 206
Deer Park, TX 77536
Ph: (281)946-9253
URL: http://www.score.org/find-location
Description: Provides professional guidance and information to maximize the success of existing and emerging small businesses. Offers business counseling and workshops.

44973 ■ SCORE - Denton
3020 N Locust
Denton, TX 76209
Ph: (940)349-8757
URL: http://www.score.org/find-location
Description: Provides professional guidance and information to maximize the success of existing and emerging small businesses. Offers business counseling and workshops.

44974 ■ SCORE - DeSoto
Desoto, TX
URL: http://dallas.score.org/mentors/terry-j-toomey
Contact: Terry J. Toomey, Contact
Description: Provides professional guidance and information to maximize the success of existing and emerging small businesses. Offers business counseling and workshops.

44975 ■ SCORE - East Texas
1530 S SW Loop
323 TJC W Campus, Ste. 101
Tyler, TX 75701
Ph: (903)510-2975
Co. E-mail: help@score.org
URL: http://easttexas.score.org
Contact: Bridget Weston, Chief Executive Officer
Linkedin: www.linkedin.com/company/score-mentors-east-texas
X (Twitter): x.com/SCOREEastTexas
Description: Provides professional guidance and information to maximize the success of existing and emerging small businesses. Offers business counseling and workshops. **Geographic Preference:** Regional.

44976 ■ SCORE - El Paso
211 N Florence, Ste. 201
El Paso, TX 79901
Ph: (915)209-1790
URL: http://www.score.org/elpaso
Description: Provides professional guidance and information to maximize the success of existing and emerging small businesses. Offers business counseling and workshops. **Geographic Preference:** Local.

44977 ■ SCORE - Euless
1100 Westpark Way
Euless, TX 76040
Co. E-mail: help@score.org
URL: http://fortworth.score.org
Description: Provides professional guidance and information to maximize the success of existing and emerging small businesses. Offers business counseling and workshops.

44978 ■ SCORE - Farmers Branch
2815 Valley View Ln., Ste. 118
Farmers Branch, TX 75234
Ph: (972)243-8966
URL: http://dallas.score.org/dallas-score-mentoring-locations
Description: Provides professional guidance and information to maximize the success of existing and emerging small businesses. Offers business counseling and workshops.

44979 ■ SCORE - Flower Mound
700 Parker Sq., Ste. 100
Flower Mound, TX 75028
Ph: (972)539-0500
URL: http://www.score.org/dallas/about-our-chapter/mentoring-locations
Description: Provides professional guidance and information to maximize the success of existing and emerging small businesses. Offers business counseling and workshops.

44980 ■ SCORE - Fort Worth
1150 S Fwy., Ste. 108
Fort Worth, TX 76104
Ph: (817)871-6002
Co. E-mail: help@score.org
URL: http://fortworth.score.org
Facebook: www.facebook.com/SCOREFortWorth
Linkedin: www.linkedin.com/company/scorefortworth
X (Twitter): x.com/scorefortworth
Description: Serves as volunteer program in which working and retired business management professionals provide free business counseling to men and women who are considering starting a small business, encountering problems with their business, or expanding their business. Offers free one-on-one counseling, online counseling and low cost workshops on a variety of business topics. **Founded:** 1985. **Geographic Preference:** Local.

44981 ■ SCORE - Fort Worth SBA District Office
150 Westpark Way
Euless, TX 76040
URL: http://fortworth.score.org/contact-fort-worth-score
Description: Provides professional guidance and information to maximize the success of existing and emerging small businesses. Offers business counseling and workshops.

44982 ■ SCORE - Frisco
6843 Main St.
Frisco, TX 75034
Ph: (972)335-9522
URL: http://dallas.score.org
Description: Provides professional guidance and information to maximize the success of existing and emerging small businesses. Offers business counseling and workshops.

44983 ■ SCORE - Granbury
3408 E Hwy. 377
Granbury, TX 76049
Ph: (817)871-6002
URL: http://ri.score.org/find-location?state=TX
Description: Provides professional guidance and information to maximize the success of existing and emerging small businesses. Offers business counseling and workshops.

44984 ■ SCORE - Grand Prairie
900 Conover Dr.
Grand Prairie, TX 75051
Co. E-mail: help@score.org
URL: http://fortworth.score.org
Description: Provides professional guidance and information to maximize the success of existing and emerging small businesses. Offers business counseling and workshops.

44985 ■ SCORE - Grapevine
200 Vine St.
Grapevine, TX 76051
Ph: (817)481-1522
URL: http://fortworth.score.org/find-location?state=TX
Description: Provides professional guidance and information to maximize the success of existing and emerging small businesses. Offers business counseling and workshops.

44986 ■ SCORE - HCC Alief Hayes Campus
2811 Hayes Rd., Ste. A-318
Houston, TX 77082
Ph: (713)718-6650
URL: http://houston.score.org
Description: Provides professional guidance and information to maximize the success of existing and emerging small businesses. Offers business counseling and workshops.

44987 ■ SCORE - Houston
8701 S Gessner Dr., No. 1200
Houston, TX 77074

Ph: (713)487-6565
Co. E-mail: scorehouston@gmail.com
URL: http://houston.score.org
Facebook: www.facebook.com/SCOREHouston
Linkedin: www.linkedin.com/company/score-houston
X (Twitter): x.com/SCOREHOUSTON
YouTube: www.youtube.com/channel/UCqH9OdIp4oNFOhZWUyBSo7Q
Description: Provides professional guidance and information to maximize the success of existing and emerging small businesses. Offers business counseling and workshops. **Founded:** 1965. **Publications:** *The SCORE Sheet.* **Educational Activities:** Mid America's Lenders Conference. **Geographic Preference:** Local.

44988 ■ SCORE - Houston Business Solutions
611 Walker St.
Houston, TX 77002
Ph: (832)393-0954
URL: http://houston.score.org/content/locations-and-hours
Description: Provides professional guidance and information to maximize the success of existing and emerging small businesses. Offers business counseling and workshops.

44989 ■ SCORE - Humble
Lake Houston Area Chamber of Commerce
110 W Main St.
Humble, TX 77338
Ph: (281)446-2128
URL: http://www.score.org/find-location?state=TX
Description: Provides professional guidance and information to maximize the success of existing and emerging small businesses. Offers business counseling and workshops.

44990 ■ SCORE - Irving
5201 N O'Connor Blvd., Ste. 100
Irving, TX 75039
Ph: (214)217-8484
Co. E-mail: help@score.org
URL: http://dallas.score.org/content/find-location
Description: Provides professional guidance and information to maximize the success of existing and emerging small businesses. Offers business counseling and workshops.

44991 ■ SCORE - Katy
The Hive in Katy
535 E Fernhurst Dr.
Katy, TX 77450
URL: http://houston.score.org/content/locations-and-hours
Description: Provides professional guidance and information to maximize the success of existing and emerging small businesses. Offers business counseling and workshops.

44992 ■ SCORE - Keller
1100 Bear Creek Pky.
Keller, TX 76248
URL: http://fortworth.score.org/contact-fort-worth-score
Description: Provides professional guidance and information to maximize the success of existing and emerging small businesses. Offers business counseling and workshops.

44993 ■ SCORE - La Camara de Empresarios Latinos de Houston
7041 Harrisburg Blvd.
Houston, TX 77011
Ph: (281)310-1392
URL: http://houston.score.org/branch/la-camara-de-empresarios-latinos-de-houston
URL(s): www.score.org/find-location
Description: Provides professional guidance and information to maximize the success of existing and emerging small businesses. Offers business counseling and workshops.

44994 ■ SCORE - Lewisville
551 N Valley Pky.
Lewisville, TX 75067

Ph: (972)436-9571
URL: http://dallas.score.org
Description: Provides professional guidance and information to maximize the success of existing and emerging small businesses. Offers business counseling and workshops.

44995 ■ SCORE - Lubbock
1500 Broadway, Ste. 101
Wells Fargo Building, Ground Fl.
Hale Center, TX 79041
Ph: (806)507-4702
URL: http://dallas.score.org/about-score-lubbock
Description: Provides professional guidance and information to maximize the success of existing and emerging small businesses. Offers business counseling and workshops. **Geographic Preference:** Local.

44996 ■ SCORE - McKinney
15301 Spectrum Dr., Ste. 110
Addison, TX 75001
Ph: (214)987-9491
Co. E-mail: help@score.org
URL: http://dallas.score.org
Facebook: www.facebook.com/ScoreDallas
Linkedin: www.linkedin.com/company/2517718
X (Twitter): x.com/SCOREdallas
YouTube: www.youtube.com/scoresmallbusiness
Description: Provides professional guidance and information to maximize the success of existing and emerging small businesses. Offers business counseling and workshops.

44997 ■ SCORE - North Richland Hills
9015 Grand Ave.
North Richland Hills, TX 76180
URL: http://www.score.org/find-location
Description: Provides professional guidance and information to maximize the success of existing and emerging small businesses. Offers business counseling and workshops.

44998 ■ SCORE - Northwest Chamber of Commerce
3920 Cypress Creek Pkwy., Ste. 120
Houston, TX 77068
Ph: (281)440-4160
Co. E-mail: scorehouston@gmail.com
URL: http://houston.score.org
Facebook: www.facebook.com/SCOREHouston
Linkedin: www.linkedin.com/company/score-houston
X (Twitter): x.com/SCOREHouston
Description: Provides professional guidance and information to maximize the success of existing and emerging small businesses. Offers business counseling and workshops.

44999 ■ SCORE - Palm Center
5330 Griggs Rd.
Houston, TX 77021
Ph: (713)845-2424
URL: http://houston.score.org/score-houston-mentoring-locations
Description: Provides professional guidance and information to maximize the success of existing and emerging small businesses. Offers business counseling and workshops.

45000 ■ SCORE - Pearland
Pearland Chamber of Commerce
6117 W Broadway St.
Pearland, TX 77581
Ph: (281)485-3634
URL: http://www.score.org/find-location?state=TX
Contact: Yusef Muhammad, President
Description: Provides professional guidance and information to maximize the success of existing and emerging small businesses. Offers business counseling and workshops.

45001 ■ SCORE - Plano
5400 Independence Pkwy,Ste., 200
Plano, TX 75023
Ph: (214)987-9491
URL: http://www.score.org/dallas/about-our-chapter/mentoring-locations

Description: Provides professional guidance and information to maximize the success of existing and emerging small businesses. Offers business counseling and workshops. **Founded:** 1946.

45002 ■ SCORE - Rio Grande Valley
2422 E Tyler Ave., Ste. E
Harlingen, TX 78550
Ph: (956)477-4550
Co. E-mail: gorur.ranganath@scorevolunteer.org
URL: http://riograndevalley.score.org
Facebook: www.facebook.com/SCORERioGrandeValley
Linkedin: www.linkedin.com/company/score-rio-grande-valley
Description: Provides professional guidance and information to maximize the success of existing and emerging small businesses. Promotes entrepreneur education in Lower Rio Grande Valley area, TX. **Founded:** 1964. **Geographic Preference:** Local.

45003 ■ SCORE - Rockwall
697 E I-30
Rockwall, TX 75087
Ph: (214)987-9491
URL: http://dallas.score.org
Description: Provides professional guidance and information to maximize the success of existing and emerging small businesses. Offers business counseling and workshops.

45004 ■ SCORE - San Antonio
615 E Houston St., Ste. 293
San Antonio, TX 78205
Ph: (210)403-5931
Co. E-mail: info.0164@scorevolunteer.org
URL: http://sanantonio.score.org
Contact: Bob Mitchell, President
Facebook: www.facebook.com/SCORESanAntonio
X (Twitter): x.com/SCORESanAntonio
Description: Provides professional guidance and information to maximize the success of existing and emerging small businesses. Offers business counseling and workshops. **Founded:** 1974. **Geographic Preference:** Local.

45005 ■ SCORE - Southlake Chamber of Commerce
1501 Corporate Cir., Ste. 100
Southlake, TX 76092
Ph: (817)871-6002
URL: http://fortworth.score.org
Facebook: www.facebook.com/scorefortworth
Linkedin: www.linkedin.com/company/scorementorsfortworth
X (Twitter): x.com/scorefortworth
Description: Provides professional guidance and information to maximize the success of existing and emerging small businesses. Offers business counseling and workshops.

45006 ■ SCORE - Southlake Public Library
1400 Main St., Ste. 130
Southlake, TX 76092
URL: http://fortworth.score.org
Contact: Ronald F. Shuff, Contact
Facebook: www.facebook.com/SCOREMentors
X (Twitter): x.com/SCOREMentors
Instagram: www.instagram.com/score_mentors
Description: Provides professional guidance and information to maximize the success of existing and emerging small businesses. Offers business counseling and workshops.

45007 ■ SCORE - The Woodlands
505 W Davis St. (aka Hwy. 105 E)
Conroe, TX 77301
Ph: (832)510-4141
Co. E-mail: woodlands@scorevolunteer.org
URL: http://www.houston.score.org/score-houston-mentoring-locations
Description: Provides professional guidance and information to maximize the success of existing and emerging small businesses. Offers business counseling and workshops.

45008 ■ SCORE - Tomball
The Greater Tomball Area Chamber of Commerce
29201 Quinn Rd., Ste. B
Tomball, TX 77375
Ph: (281)351-7222
URL: http://houston.score.org
Description: Provides professional guidance and information to maximize the success of existing and emerging small businesses. Offers business counseling and workshops.

45009 ■ SCORE - Waco
605 Austin Ave.
Waco, TX 76701
Ph: (515)928-2425
URL: http://www.score.org/find-location?state=TX
Description: Provides professional guidance and information to maximize the success of existing and emerging small businesses. Offers business counseling and workshops.

BETTER BUSINESS BUREAUS

45010 ■ Better Business Bureau of Abilene
3300 S 14th St., Ste. 307
Abilene, TX 79605-5052
Ph: (325)691-1533
Fax: (325)691-0309
Co. E-mail: info@abilene.bbb.org
URL: http://www.bbb.org/local-bbb/bbb-of-abilene
Facebook: www.facebook.com/AbileneBBB
X (Twitter): x.com/bbbabilene
Description: Provides business reliability reports and complaint handling, including informal mediation, arbitration and alternative dispute resolution, business/consumer education resources and materials, national and local charitable information and the promotion of ethical business standards and voluntary self-regulation. **Publications:** Consumer Resource Digest (Annual). **Geographic Preference:** Local.

45011 ■ Better Business Bureau of Amarillo, Texas
600 S Tyler St., Ste. 1300
Amarillo, TX 79101
Ph: (806)379-6222
Fax: (806)379-8206
Co. E-mail: info@txpanhandle.bbb.org
URL: http://www.bbb.org/local-bbb/bbb-of-amarillo
Facebook: www.facebook.com/bbbamarillo
Description: Seeks to promote and foster ethical relationship between businesses and the public through voluntary self-regulation, consumer and business education, and service excellence. Provides information to help consumers and businesses make informed purchasing decisions and avoid costly scams and frauds; settles consumer complaints through arbitration and other means. **Founded:** 1939. **Geographic Preference:** Local.

45012 ■ Better Business Bureau of Central East Texas (BBB CET)
6115 New Copeland Rd., Ste. 710
Tyler, TX 75703
Ph: (903)581-5704
Fax: (903)534-8644
Co. E-mail: info@easttexas.bbb.org
URL: http://www.bbb.org/local-bbb/bbb-serving-central-east-texas
Facebook: www.facebook.com/BBBCET
X (Twitter): x.com/bbbcet
Instagram: www.instagram.com/bbbcet
YouTube: www.youtube.com/channel/UCCB4iS0VK9cSyFEGBw15QBQ
Description: Seeks to promote and foster the highest ethical relationship between businesses and the public through voluntary self-regulation, consumer and business education, and service excellence. Provides information to help consumers and businesses make informed purchasing decisions and avoid costly scams and frauds; settles consumer complaints through arbitration and other means. **Founded:** 1985. **Geographic Preference:** Local.

45013 ■ Better Business Bureau Corpus Christi
701 S Brownlee Blvd.
Corpus Christi, TX 78401-3127
Ph: (361)882-7531
URL: http://www.bbb.org/us/tx/corpus-christi
Description: Seeks to promote and foster the highest ethical relationship between businesses and the public through voluntary self-regulation, consumer and business education, and service excellence. Provides information to help consumers and businesses make informed purchasing decisions and avoid costly scams and frauds; settles consumer complaints through arbitration and other means. **Founded:** 1951. **Geographic Preference:** Local.

45014 ■ Better Business Bureau of Greater Houston and South Texas
609 S International Blvd., Ste. A
Weslaco, TX 78596
Ph: (956)968-9678
Co. E-mail: info@bbbhou.org
URL: http://www.bbb.org/local-bbb/bbb-of-greater-houston-and-south-texas
X (Twitter): x.com/bbb_houston
Description: Seeks to promote and foster the highest ethical relationship between businesses and the public through voluntary self-regulation, consumer and business education, and service excellence. Provides information to help consumers and businesses make informed purchasing decisions and avoid costly scams and frauds; settles consumer complaints through arbitration and other means. **Geographic Preference:** Local.

45015 ■ Better Business Bureau serving the Heart of Texas
306 W Broadway Ave.
Fort Worth, TX 76104
Free: 844-477-1099
URL: http://www.bbb.org/local-bbb/bbb-serving-the-heart-of-texas
Facebook: www.facebook.com/CentralTexasBBB
Linkedin: www.linkedin.com/company/better-business-bureau-serving-the-heart-of-texas
X (Twitter): x.com/centraltexasbbb
Instagram: www.instagram.com/centraltexasbbb
YouTube: www.youtube.com/user/CentralTexasBBB
Description: Promotes and fosters ethical relationship between businesses and the public through voluntary self-regulation, consumer and business education and service excellence. **Geographic Preference:** Local.

45016 ■ Better Business Bureau of North Central Texas [Better Business Bureau, Wichita Falls]
2107 Kemp Blvd.
Wichita Falls, TX 76309
Ph: (940)691-1172
Fax: (940)691-1175
URL: http://www.bbb.org/local-bbb/bbb-serving-north-central-texas
Facebook: www.facebook.com/BBBNCTX
Linkedin: www.linkedin.com/company/bbb-north-central-texas
Instagram: www.instagram.com/dallasbbb
YouTube: www.youtube.com/channel/UCJhMdM-B_kaLi_ggUjkqZKw
Description: Seeks to promote and foster the highest ethical relationship between businesses and the public through voluntary self-regulation, consumer and business education, and service excellence. Provides information to help consumers and businesses make informed purchasing decisions and avoid costly scams and frauds; settles consumer complaints through arbitration and other means. **Founded:** 1981. **Geographic Preference:** Local.

45017 ■ Better Business Bureau of San Angelo
3149 Executive Dr.
San Angelo, TX 76904
Ph: (325)949-2989
URL: http://www.bbb.org
Contact: Glenna Friedrich, Contact
Description: Seeks to promote and foster the highest ethical relationship between businesses and the public through voluntary self-regulation, consumer and business education, and service excellence. Provides information to help consumers and businesses make informed purchasing decisions and avoid costly scams and frauds; settles consumer complaints through arbitration and other means. **Founded:** 1979. **Geographic Preference:** Local.

45018 ■ Better Business Bureau of San Antonio, TX
13750 San Pedro Ave., Ste. B10
San Antonio, TX 78232-4463
Ph: (210)490-7272
URL: http://www.bbb.org/us/tx/san-antonio
Description: Seeks to provide and foster the highest ethical relationship between businesses and the public through voluntary self-regulation, consumer and business education, and service excellence. Provides information to help consumers and businesses make informed decisions and avoid costly scams and frauds; settles consumer complaints through arbitration and other means. **Geographic Preference:** Local.

45019 ■ Better Business Bureau Serving Central, Coastal, Southwest Texas & Permian Basin - Austin Office
1805 Rutherford Ln., Ste. 100
Austin, TX 78754
Free: 844-477-1099
Fax: (512)559-6469
URL: http://www.bbb.org/central-texas
Contact: Carrie Hurt, President
Description: Seeks to promote and foster the highest ethical relationship between businesses and the public through voluntary self-regulation, consumer and business education, and service excellence. **Geographic Preference:** Local.

45020 ■ Better Business Bureau of Southeast Texas
550 Fannin St., Ste. 100
Beaumont, TX 77701-2011
Ph: (409)835-5348
Fax: (409)838-6858
URL: http://www.bbb.org/local-bbb/better-business-bureau-in-southeast-texas
Contact: Liz Fredrichs, President
E-mail: lizfredrichs@bbbsetexas.org
Facebook: www.facebook.com/BBBSoutheastTexas
Linkedin: www.linkedin.com/company/better-business-bureau-in-southeast-texas
X (Twitter): x.com/BBBSETX
Description: Seeks to promote and foster the highest ethical relationship between businesses and the public through voluntary self-regulation, consumer and business education, and service excellence. Provides information to help consumers and businesses make informed purchasing decisions and avoid costly scams and frauds; settles consumer complaints through arbitration and other means. **Founded:** 1963. **Geographic Preference:** Local.

CHAMBERS OF COMMERCE

45021 ■ Abilene Chamber of Commerce
400 Pine St., Ste. 500
Abilene, TX 79601
Ph: (325)677-7241
URL: http://www.abilenechamber.com
Contact: Doug Peters, President
E-mail: doug@abilenechamber.com
Facebook: www.facebook.com/abilenechamber
X (Twitter): x.com/abilene_chamber
Instagram: www.instagram.com/abilenechamber
YouTube: www.youtube.com/user/abilenechamber
Pinterest: www.pinterest.com/abilenechamber
Description: Promotes business and community development in Abilene, TX. **Founded:** 1908. **Publications:** Chamber Connection (Monthly). **Geographic Preference:** Local.

STATE LISTINGS

45022 ▪ The Advocate
602 E Commerce St.
  San Antonio, TX 78205
Ph: (210)229-2100
Fax: (210)229-1600
URL: http://sachamber.org
Contact: Richard Perez, President
E-mail: rperez@sachamber.org
URL(s): www.sachamber.org/news/connect-with-us
Availability: Print.

45023 ▪ Alamo Chamber of Commerce
715 US Bus 83
  Alamo, TX 78516
Ph: (956)787-2117
Co. E-mail: alamotx.members.chamber@gmail.com
URL: http://www.alamochamber.com
Contact: Kassandra Elejarza, Executive Director
Facebook: www.facebook.com/
  alamochamberofcommerce
Description: Promotes business and community development in Alamo, TX. **Geographic Preference:** Local.

45024 ▪ Alamo City Black Chamber of Commerce (ACBCC)
202 Connelly St., Ste. 209
  San Antonio, TX 78203
Ph: (210)486-2125
Co. E-mail: info@alamocitychamber.org
URL: http://alamocitychamber.org
Contact: Edwin Miles, Chairman
Facebook: www.facebook.com/AlamoCi
  tyBlackChamber
X (Twitter): x.com/ACBlackChamber
YouTube: www.youtube.com/channel/UCOxKtCVIm9
  _sfhCPOL-y6pA
Description: Works to provide programs which contribute to the economic growth and development of African American minority and small businesses throughout the greater San Antonio area. **Founded:** 1938. **Geographic Preference:** Local.

45025 ▪ Albany Texas Chamber of Commerce
2 Railroad St.
  Albany, TX 76430
Ph: (325)762-2525
Co. E-mail: chamber@albanytexas.com
URL: http://www.albanytexas.com
Contact: Diana Nail, Contact
Facebook: www.facebook.com/albanytx
Description: Promotes business and community development in Albany, TX. Encourages tourism and supports educational and cultural activities. Preserves historical buildings. Gathers and disseminates information. Conducts community social and promotional events. **Geographic Preference:** Local.

45026 ▪ Allen-Fairview Chamber of Commerce
210 W McDermott Dr.
  Allen, TX 75013
Ph: (972)727-5585
Co. E-mail: info@allenfairviewchamber.com
URL: http://www.allenfairviewchamber.com
Contact: Sharon Mayer, Chief Executive Officer
Facebook: www.facebook.com/allenfairviewchamber
Linkedin: www.linkedin.com/company/allen-fairview
  -chamber-of-commerce
X (Twitter): x.com/AllenFairview
Instagram: www.instagram.com/allenfairviewchamber
YouTube: www.youtube.com/channel/UCK6T
  1WQRAhO_N09oWQTmQ4g
Description: Promotes business and community development in Allen, TX. **Founded:** 1982. **Geographic Preference:** Local.

45027 ▪ Alpine Chamber of Commerce (ACC)
PO Box 2325
  Alpine, TX 79831
Ph: (432)837-4144
Co. E-mail: info@alpinetexas.com
URL: http://alpinetexas.com
Contact: Johnathan Wimp, Treasurer
Facebook: www.facebook.com/alpinetxcoc
Description: Promotes business, community development, and tourism in Alpine, TX and Big Bend National Park and region. **Founded:** 1907. **Publications:** *Travel Guide - Big Bend* (Periodic). **Geographic Preference:** Local.

45028 ▪ Alvin-Manvel Area Chamber of Commerce
105 W Willis St.
  Alvin, TX 77511
Ph: (281)331-3944
Co. E-mail: chamber@amacc.org
URL: http://www.alvinmanvelchamber.org
Contact: Cary Perrin, President
E-mail: c_perrin@amacc.org
Facebook: www.facebook.com/alvinmanvelchamber
X (Twitter): x.com/AlvinManvelArea
YouTube: www.youtube.com/user/
  alvinmanvelchamber
Description: Promotes business and community development in the Alvin, TX area. **Publications:** *The Chamber Connection* (Monthly); *Alvin-Manvel Area Chamber of Commerce--Membership Directory* (Annual). **Geographic Preference:** Local.

45029 ▪ Amarillo Chamber of Commerce (ACC)
1000 S Polk St.
  Amarillo, TX 79105
Ph: (806)373-7800
Fax: (806)373-3909
Co. E-mail: chamber@amarillo-chamber.org
URL: http://www.amarillo-chamber.org
Contact: Jason Harrison, President
E-mail: jason@amarillo-chamber.org
Facebook: www.facebook.com/AmarilloChamber
X (Twitter): x.com/AmarilloChamber
Instagram: www.instagram.com/amarillochamber
YouTube: www.youtube.com/user/amarillochamber
Description: Promotes business and community development in Amarillo, TX. Sponsors local festival. **Founded:** 1926. **Publications:** *Clubs and Organizations*; *Community Leaders* (Annual); *Membership Directory and Buyers' Guide* (Annual). **Geographic Preference:** Local.

45030 ▪ Anahuac Area Chamber of Commerce (AACC)
603 Miller St.
  Anahuac, TX 77514
Ph: (409)267-4190
Fax: (409)267-3907
URL: http://www.anahuacareachamber.com
Contact: Elizabeth Royer Kemp, Chairman of the Board
Description: Works to promote business and community development in Anahuac, TX area. **Geographic Preference:** Local.

45031 ▪ Aransas Pass Chamber of Commerce
130 W Goodnight Ave.
  Aransas Pass, TX 78336
Ph: (361)758-2750
Co. E-mail: apcoc@aransaspass.org
URL: http://www.aransaspass.org
Contact: Rosemary Vega, Chief Executive Officer
Facebook: www.facebook.com/aransas.pass
X (Twitter): x.com/AransasPassTX
Description: Promotes business and community development in Aransas Pass, TX. **Founded:** 1937. **Geographic Preference:** Local.

45032 ▪ Arlington Chamber of Commerce (ACC)
505 E Border St.
  Arlington, TX 76010
Ph: (817)275-2613
Fax: (817)701-0893
Co. E-mail: membership@arlingtontx.com
URL: http://www.arlingtontx.com
Contact: Michael Jacobson, President
E-mail: mjacobson@arlingtontx.com
Facebook: www.facebook.com/GreaterArlingtonTX
X (Twitter): x.com/arlingtontx
YouTube: www.youtube.com/user/Arling
  tonTXChamber

Texas ▪ 45038

Description: Promotes business and community development in the Arlington, TX area. Seeks to create job opportunities and diversify the city's economic base. Represents business leadership on policy issues affecting city's economic growth. **Founded:** 1945. **Publications:** *Business Update*. **Awards:** Arlington Chamber of Commerce Outstanding Small Business of the Year Award (Annual). **Geographic Preference:** Local.

45033 ▪ Arlington Hispanic Chamber of Commerce (AHCC)
615 Abram St., No. 98
  Arlington, TX 76010-1600
Contact: Casey Gonzales, Director
Description: Develops, promotes and protects Hispanic business in Arlington and surrounding areas. **Geographic Preference:** Local.

45034 ▪ Asian Chamber of Texas (ACT)
1402 Corinth St., Ste. 1070
  Dallas, TX 75215
Ph: (469)620-2499
Co. E-mail: info@gdaacc.com
URL: http://www.gdaacc.com
Contact: Amy Hofland, Chairman
Description: Seeks to develop leaders, promotes community awareness, and develops business opportunities to members. **Founded:** 1986. **Publications:** *Connections*. **Geographic Preference:** State.

45035 ▪ Athens Chamber of Commerce
201 W Corsicana St.
  Athens, TX 75751
Ph: (903)675-5181
Co. E-mail: athenstxchamber@outlook.com
URL: http://athenstxchamber.org
Contact: Mark Rathe, Contact
Facebook: www.facebook.com/athenscofc
Description: Promotes business and community development in Athens, TX. **Publications:** *Athens Magazine* (Annual); *Discovery Line* (Monthly). **Geographic Preference:** Local.

45036 ▪ Atlanta Area Chamber of Commerce (AACC)
101 N E St.
  Atlanta, TX 75551
Ph: (903)796-3296
Co. E-mail: atlareachamber@gmail.com
URL: http://www.atlantatexas.org/chamber/atlanta
  -chamber-of-commerce.aspx
Contact: Miranda Johnson, Director
E-mail: miranda.johnson@atlantatexas.org
Facebook: www.facebook.com/Atlan
  taAreaChamberofCommerce
Description: Businesses, individuals, and professionals in northeastern Cass County, TX seeking to improve the area's economy and growth. Conducts annual Leadership Institute. Sponsors monthly mixer; Farmer's Market, Hoot and Holler BBQ Cookoff; and Christmas parade. **Founded:** 1945. **Geographic Preference:** Local.

45037 ▪ Azle Area Chamber of Commerce (AACC)
404 W Main St., Ste. 102
  Azle, TX 76020
Ph: (817)444-1112
Co. E-mail: info@azlechamber.com
URL: http://azlechamber.com/home
Contact: Kim Ware, Co-President
Description: Promotes business and community development in Azle, TX. **Founded:** 1959. **Publications:** *Membership Directory*. **Awards:** Azle Area Chamber of Commerce Citizen of the Year (Annual). **Geographic Preference:** Local.

45038 ▪ Baird Chamber of Commerce (BCC)
100 Market St.
  Baird, TX 79504
Ph: (325)854-2003
Co. E-mail: info@bairdchamber.com
URL: http://www.bairdchamber.com
Contact: Leslie Palacio, Coordinator
E-mail: leslie.cityofbaird@gmail.com

Facebook: www.facebook.com/Bair dTexasChamberOfCommerce
Description: Promotes business and community development in Baird, TX. Sponsors annual Trade Festival, and annual art show and sale. **Founded:** 1960. **Geographic Preference:** Local.

45039 ■ **Balch Springs Chamber of Commerce**
Civic Ctr.
12400 Elam Rd.
Balch Springs, TX 75180
Ph: (972)557-0988
Fax: (972)590-8867
Co. E-mail: info@balchspringschamber.org
URL: http://www.balchspringschamber.org
Contact: Alvester Gibson, President
E-mail: ceo@balchspringschamber.org
X (Twitter): x.com/BSCoC
Description: Promotes business and community development in Balch Springs, TX. **Geographic Preference:** Local.

45040 ■ **Ballinger Chamber of Commerce**
811 Hutchings Ave.
Ballinger, TX 76821
Ph: (325)365-2333
Co. E-mail: ballingerareachamberofcommerce @gmail.com
Contact: Steve Smith, President
Facebook: www.facebook.com/ ballingerchamberofcommerce
Description: Promotes business and community development in Ballinger, TX. Sponsors annual Texas State Festival of Ethnic Cultures and Arts and Crafts Show. **Geographic Preference:** Local.

45041 ■ **Bandera County Texas Chamber of Commerce**
158 Hwy. 16 S F
Bandera, TX 78003
Ph: (830)796-3280
Co. E-mail: cowboy@banderatex.com
URL: http://www.banderatex.com
Contact: Angela Munoz, President
Description: Promotes business and community development in Bandera County, TX. Sponsors Funtier Day Parade and Hunters' Barbecue. **Publications:** *Directory of Products and Services* (Periodic). **Geographic Preference:** Local.

45042 ■ **Bastrop Chamber of Commerce (BCC)**
927 Main St.
Bastrop, TX 78602
Ph: (512)303-0558
Co. E-mail: info@bastropchamber.com
URL: http://www.bastropchamber.com
Contact: Becki Womble, President
E-mail: bwomble@bastropchamber.com
Facebook: www.facebook.com/BastropChamber
Linkedin: www.linkedin.com/in/bastroptxchamber
X (Twitter): x.com/BastropTXCOC
YouTube: www.youtube.com/channel/UCM7yAyg1W 4hkjjulCMIoXIA
Description: Promotes business and community development in Bastrop, TX. Promotes a stable business environment. Sponsors local festival. **Founded:** 1922. **Geographic Preference:** Local.

45043 ■ **Baytown Chamber of Commerce (BCC)**
825 Rollingbrook Dr.
Baytown, TX 77521
Ph: (281)422-8359
Co. E-mail: info@baytownchamber.com
URL: http://baytownchamber.com
Contact: Tracey S. Wheeler, President
E-mail: tracey@baytownchamber.com
Facebook: www.facebook.com/Bay townChamberOfCommerce
Description: Promotes business and community development in Baytown, TX. **Founded:** 1945. **Publications:** *DISCOVER Baytown* (Annual). **Educational Activities:** Baytown Business EXPO (Annual). **Awards:** Baytown Chamber of Commerce Fire Fighter of the Year (Quarterly); Baytown Chamber of Commerce Public Safety Recognition (Annual); Public Safety Award of Excellence - Police Officer of the Year (Annual); Public Safety Award of Excellence - Paramedic of the Year (Annual); Public Safety Award of Excellence - Constable Deputy of the Year (Annual). **Geographic Preference:** Local.

45044 ■ **Beaumont Chamber of Commerce (BCC)**
1110 Pk. St.
Beaumont, TX 77701
Ph: (409)838-6581
Co. E-mail: chamber@bmtcoc.org
URL: http://www.bmtcoc.org
Contact: Bill Allen, Co-Chief Executive Officer Co-President
Facebook: www.facebook.com/GreaterBeaumon tChamberofCommerce
X (Twitter): x.com/BMTChamber
Instagram: www.instagram.com/greaterbeaumon tchamber
Description: Promotes business and community development in Southeast Texas. Works with government agencies, educational institutions, and other development organizations to preserve existing jobs, promote better understanding of the free enterprise system, and diversify the industrial base of the region. **Founded:** 1903. **Publications:** *Metropolitan Beaumont* (Bimonthly); *Southeast Texas Business* (Monthly). **Geographic Preference:** Local.

45045 ■ **Bee County Chamber of Commerce**
1705 N St. Mary's St.
Beeville, TX 78102
Ph: (361)358-3267
Fax: (361)358-3966
Co. E-mail: info@experiencebeecounty.org
URL: http://experiencebeecounty.org
Contact: Tracy Florence, Chief Executive Officer
Facebook: www.facebook.com/BeevilleChamber
Instagram: www.instagram.com/beevillechamber
Description: Promotes business and community development in Bee County, TX. **Founded:** 1835. **Geographic Preference:** Local.

45046 ■ **Bellville Chamber of Commerce**
742 W Main
Bellville, TX 77418
Ph: (979)865-3407
Co. E-mail: info@bellville.com
URL: http://www.bellville.com
Contact: Tammy Bond, Manager
Facebook: www.facebook.com/bellvillecoc
Description: Promotes business and community development in Bellville, OH area. **Founded:** 1980. **Geographic Preference:** Local.

45047 ■ **Belton Area Chamber of Commerce**
412 E Central Ave.
Belton, TX 76513
Ph: (254)939-3551
Co. E-mail: info@beltonchamber.com
URL: http://www.beltonchamber.com
Contact: Randy Pittenger, President
Facebook: www.facebook.com/beltonchamber
X (Twitter): x.com/beltonchamber
Instagram: www.instagram.com/beltonchamber
Description: Promotes business and community development in the Belton, TX area. Sponsors 4th of July Celebration. **Founded:** 1936. **Publications:** *Return on Investment* (Monthly). **Geographic Preference:** Local.

45048 ■ **Big Lake Chamber of Commerce**
120 N Main
Big Lake, TX 76932
Ph: (325)884-2980
Fax: (325)884-1416
Co. E-mail: blcoc@verizon.net
URL: http://www.biglakecoc.com
Contact: J. L. Mankin, President
Facebook: www.facebook.com/biglakecoc
Description: Promotes business and community development in Big Lake, TX. **Geographic Preference:** Local.

45049 ■ **Big Spring Area Chamber of Commerce (BSACC)**
215 W 3rd St.
Big Spring, TX 79721
Ph: (432)263-7641
Free: 800-734-7641
Fax: (432)264-9111
Co. E-mail: memberinfo@bigspringchamber.com
URL: http://bigspringchamber.com
Contact: Debby Valverde, Executive Director
E-mail: debbyev@bigspringchamber.com
Facebook: www.facebook.com/Big-Spring-Area -Chamber-of-Commerce-128948388352
X (Twitter): x.com/BSChamberTX
Instagram: www.instagram.com/ bigspringareachamberofcommerce
Description: Promotes business and community development in the Big Spring, TX area. Sponsors festival. **Founded:** 1930. **Publications:** *Focus* (Monthly). **Geographic Preference:** Local.

45050 ■ **Bishop, Texas Chamber of Commerce**
213 E Main St.
Bishop, TX 78343
Ph: (361)584-2214
Co. E-mail: info@bishoptx.com
URL: http://www.bishoptx.com
Facebook: www.facebook.com/bishoptxchamber
Description: Promotes business and community development in Bishop, TX. Conducts charitable activities; sponsors Community Christmas Program. **Founded:** 1910. **Awards:** Bishop Chamber of Commerce - Outstanding Farmer; Bishop Chamber of Commerce Junior Citizen of the Year (Annual); Bishop Chamber of Commerce Lifetime Service Award (Annual); Bishop Chamber of Commerce - Outstanding Business; Bishop Chamber of Commerce Outstanding Newcomer; Bishop Chamber of Commerce - Outstanding Professional. **Geographic Preference:** Local.

45051 ■ **Blanco Chamber of Commerce**
Old Blanco County Courthouse
300 Main St.
Blanco, TX 78606
Ph: (830)833-5101
Fax: (830)833-4381
Co. E-mail: info@blancochamber.com
URL: http://www.blancochamber.com
Contact: Tasha Corradini, President
Facebook: www.facebook.com/blancochamber
Description: Promotes business and community development in Blanco, TX. Conducts charitable events. Sponsors car show and festival. **Publications:** *Blanco Chamber of Commerce--Member Directory and Resource Guide* (Annual). **Geographic Preference:** Local.

45052 ■ **Bolivar Peninsula Chamber of Commerce (BPCOC)**
1750 Hwy. 87
Crystal Beach, TX 77650
Ph: (409)684-5940
Co. E-mail: bolivarpeninsulachamber@yahoo.com
URL: http://www.discoverbolivar.com
Contact: Anne Willis, President
Description: Promotes business and community development in the Bolivar Peninsula area of Texas. Addresses environmental and erosion control issues. Organizes Texas Crab Festival and Crystalland Christmas. Sponsors charities, scholarship programs, Volunteer Fire Departments, Emergency Medical Service, and youth athletic league. **Founded:** 1983. **Publications:** *Telephone Listing* (Monthly). **Geographic Preference:** Local.

45053 ■ **Bonham Area Chamber of Commerce and Economic Development (BACC) [Bonham Economic Development Corporation]**
327 N Main St.
Bonham, TX 75418
Ph: (903)583-4811
Fax: (903)583-7972
Co. E-mail: info@bonhamchamber.com

URL: http://www.fannincountytexas.com
Contact: Alan McDonald, President
Facebook: www.facebook.com/BonhamChamber
X (Twitter): x.com/bonhamisd_
YouTube: www.youtube.com/channel/UCEY
 1eU7Mwx8wJz6RwRUxtgg/videos
Description: Promotes economic, cultural, and community development in Bonham and Fannin County, TX. **Founded:** 1929. **Publications:** *Chamber Chatter* (Monthly); *Image* (Annual). **Geographic Preference:** Local.

45054 ■ Borger Chamber of Commerce (BCC)
613 N Main St.
 Borger, TX 79007
Ph: (806)274-2211
Co. E-mail: borgerchamber1@gmail.com
URL: http://www.borgerchamber.com
Contact: Sarah Archer, Chairman of the Board
E-mail: snarcher02@gmail.com
Facebook: www.facebook.com/borgerchamber
Description: Promotes business and community development in Borger, TX. **Founded:** 1926. **Publications:** *Chamber Guide* (Annual); *Chamber Guide* (Annual); *Mid-Month Memo* (Quarterly). **Educational Activities:** World's Largest Fish Fry (Annual). **Geographic Preference:** Local.

45055 ■ Bowie Chamber of Commerce
101 E Pecan St.
 Bowie, TX 76230
Ph: (940)872-1173
Co. E-mail: info@bowietxchamber.org
URL: http://www.bowietxchamber.org
Contact: Debbie Herriage, Director
Facebook: www.facebook.com/BowieTXChamber
Description: Promotes business, tourism and community development in Bowie, TX. **Founded:** 1928. **Publications:** *Chamber of Commerce Newsletter* (Monthly). **Geographic Preference:** Local.

45056 ■ Brady/McCulloch County Chamber of Commerce
405 S Bridge St.
 Brady, TX 76825
Ph: (325)597-3491
Co. E-mail: erin@bradytx.com
URL: http://www.bradytx.com
Contact: Taylor Hoffpauir, President
Facebook: www.facebook.com/Bra
 dyChamberofCommerce
Instagram: www.instagram.com/bradychamber
Description: Promotes business and community development in Brady, TX and McCulloch County. **Founded:** 1906. **Publications:** *The Heartbeat* (Quarterly). **Awards:** Brady - McCulloch County Chamber of Commerce Lifetime Achievement Award (Annual). **Geographic Preference:** Local.

45057 ■ Breckenridge Chamber of Commerce
100 E Elm St.
 Breckenridge, TX 76424
Ph: (254)559-2301
Fax: (254)559-7104
Co. E-mail: chamber@breckenridgetexas.com
URL: http://www.breckenridgetexas.com
Contact: Luke Grider, President
Facebook: www.facebook.com/Breckenri
 dgeChamberofCommerce
Description: Promotes business and community development in Breckenridge, TX area. **Geographic Preference:** Local.

45058 ■ Bridgeport Area Chamber of Commerce (BACC)
812 A Halsell St.
 Bridgeport, TX 76426
Ph: (940)683-2076
Co. E-mail: info@bridgeportchamber.org
URL: http://www.bridgeportchamber.org
Contact: Nathan Byers, Executive Director
Facebook: www.facebook.com/Bridgepor
 tAreaChamber
Description: Promotes business and community development in Wise County, TX. Sponsors Butterfield Stage Days, lighted Christmas Parade, Rodeo Parade, Wise County Youth Fair, and Holiday Spectacular. Assists in maintaining parks board. **Founded:** 1968. **Publications:** *Bridgeport Chamber of Commerce-The Voice of Business in Bridgeport* (10/year). **Geographic Preference:** Local.

45059 ■ Brownsville Chamber of Commerce (BCOC)
1600 University Blvd.
 Brownsville, TX 78520
Ph: (956)542-4341
Fax: (956)504-3348
Co. E-mail: info@brownsvillechamber.com
URL: http://brownsvillechamber.com
Contact: Esmeralda Villarreal, President
Facebook: www.facebook.com/brownsville.chamber.7
Linkedin: www.linkedin.com/company/btxchamber
X (Twitter): x.com/btxchamber
Instagram: www.instagram.com/brownsvillechamber
YouTube: www.youtube.com/channel/UCTmr
 doFAFiqmrD007wT_HLw
Description: Promotes business and community development in Brownsville, TX. **Founded:** 1937. **Publications:** *Chamber Progress* (Bimonthly). **Geographic Preference:** Local.

45060 ■ Brownwood Area Chamber of Commerce (BCC)
600 E Depot St.
 Brownwood, TX 76801
Ph: (325)646-9535
Fax: (325)643-6686
Co. E-mail: membership@brownwoodchamber.org
URL: http://brownwoodchamber.org
Contact: Kandice Harris, Executive Director
Facebook: www.facebook.com/brownwoodtexas
X (Twitter): x.com/brownwoodtx
Description: Promotes business and community development in Brown County, TX. **Founded:** 1906. **Educational Activities:** Brownwood Area Chamber of Commerce Annual Awards Banquet (Annual). **Geographic Preference:** Local.

45061 ■ Buda Area Chamber of Commerce (BACC)
203 Railroad St., Ste. 1-C
 Buda, TX 78610
Ph: (512)295-9999
Fax: (512)295-3569
Co. E-mail: info@budachamber.com
URL: http://budachambertx.com
Contact: John Hatch, Chairman of the Board
Facebook: www.facebook.com/Bu
 daAreaChamberOfCommerce
X (Twitter): x.com/buda_chamber
Description: Seeks to promote business and community development and enhance the relationship between local businesses and professionals with the public. **Geographic Preference:** Local.

45062 ■ Buffalo Chamber of Commerce
910 N Hill St.
 Buffalo, TX 75831
Ph: (903)332-5810
Fax: (903)322-3849
Co. E-mail: buffalochamberofcommerce@winds
 tream.net
URL: http://www.buffalotex.org
Contact: Susan Shelton, President
E-mail: karsan@kona-ice.com
Facebook: www.facebook.com/BuffaloTXChamber
Description: Promotes business, economic and community development in Buffalo, WY. **Geographic Preference:** Local.

45063 ■ Bulverde Spring Branch Area Chamber of Commerce (BSBACOC) - Bulverde/Spring Branch Library
121 Bulverde Crossing, Ste. 115
 Bulverde, TX 78163
Ph: (830)438-4285
Fax: (830)438-8572
Co. E-mail: office@bsbchamber.com
URL: http://bulverdespringbranchchamber.com
Contact: Rhonda Zunker, President
E-mail: rhonda@bsbchamber.com
Facebook: www.facebook.com/BSBChamber
X (Twitter): x.com/BSBChamber
Instagram: www.instagram.com/bsbchamber
YouTube: www.youtube.com/channel/UCcJ_iy
 -ShMfeyLlJHjK0d9w/videos
Description: Seeks to advance the economic vitality of the Texas Hill Country. **Scope:** Education. **Services:** Interlibrary loan; faxing; copying; printing. **Founded:** 1995. **Holdings:** Audio books; newspapers; magazines; periodicals; CDs; DVDs. **Publications:** *Bulverde Spring Branch Area Chamber of Commerce--Business Directory* (Annual). **Geographic Preference:** Local.

45064 ■ Burkburnett Chamber of Commerce
412 Ave. C
 Burkburnett, TX 76354
Ph: (940)569-3304
Co. E-mail: kristina@burkburnettchamber.com
URL: http://burkburnettchamber.com
Contact: Dr. Morgan Moore, President
Facebook: www.facebook.com/burkburnettchamber
Description: Promotes business and community development in Burkburnett, TX. **Founded:** 1919. **Geographic Preference:** Local.

45065 ■ Burleson Area Chamber of Commerce (BACC)
124 S Main St., Ste. 228
 Burleson, TX 76028
Ph: (817)295-6121
Co. E-mail: burlesonchamber@burleson.org
URL: http://www.burlesonchamber.com
Contact: Andy Pickens, President
E-mail: apickens@burleson.org
Facebook: www.facebook.com/BurlesonChamber
Linkedin: www.linkedin.com/company/burleson
 -chamber-of-commerce
X (Twitter): x.com/BurlesonChamber
Instagram: www.instagram.com/burlesonchamber
Pinterest: www.pinterest.com/burlesonchamber
Description: Promotes business and community development in northern Johnson County, TX. Sponsors the Texas Heritage Trail Ride. **Founded:** 1965. **Geographic Preference:** Local.

45066 ■ Burleson County Chamber of Commerce - Caldwell Office
301 N Main St.
 Caldwell, TX 77836
Ph: (979)567-0000
Co. E-mail: contact@burlesoncountytx.com
URL: http://www.burlesoncountytx.com
Description: Promotes business and community development in Burleson County, TX. Sponsors Kolachee Festival and other special events. **Geographic Preference:** Local.

45067 ■ Burnet Chamber of Commerce
101 N Pierce St., Ste. 1
 Burnet, TX 78611
Ph: (512)756-4297
Co. E-mail: info@burnetchamber.org
URL: http://www.burnetchamber.org
Contact: Wade Langley, President
Facebook: www.facebook.com/Burne
 tChamberofCommerce
X (Twitter): x.com/BurnetChamber
Description: Promotes business and community development in Burnet, TX. **Founded:** 1955. **Geographic Preference:** Local.

45068 ■ *Business Directory*
505 W Davis St.
 Conroe, TX 77301
Ph: (936)756-6644
Fax: (936)756-6462
Co. E-mail: info@conroe.org
URL: http://www.conroe.org
Contact: Scott Harper, President
E-mail: scotth@conroe.org
URL(s): www.chamber.conroe.org/list
Availability: Online.

45069 ■ Business Plan
5400 Independence Pky., Ste. 200.
Plano, TX 75023
Ph: (972)424-7547
Fax: (972)422-5182
Co. E-mail: info@planochamber.org
URL: http://www.planochamber.org
Contact: Kelle Marsalis, President
E-mail: kellem@planochamber.org
URL(s): www.planochamber.org/business-resources
Description: Contains a three-year strategic business plan of the Chamber. **Availability:** Print.

45070 ■ Business Referral Guide
1314 W Moore Ave.
Terrell, TX 75160
Ph: (972)563-5703
Free: 877-Ter-rell
Co. E-mail: angie@terrelltexas.com
URL: http://www.terrelltexas.com
Contact: Carlton Tidwell, President
URL(s): www.terrelltexas.com/membership-benefits
Released: Annual **Availability:** Online.

45071 ■ Business Resource Directory
5400 Independence Pky., Ste. 200.
Plano, TX 75023
Ph: (972)424-7547
Fax: (972)422-5182
Co. E-mail: info@planochamber.org
URL: http://www.planochamber.org
Contact: Kelle Marsalis, President
E-mail: kellem@planochamber.org
URL(s): www.planochamber.org/business-resources
Description: Contains directory of all members listed by alpha and category. **Availability:** Print.

45072 ■ Calvert Chamber of Commerce
300 S Main St.
Calvert, TX 77837
Ph: (979)459-3030
Co. E-mail: info@calverttxchamber.com
URL: http://www.calverttxchamber.com
Contact: Layla Wright, Vice President
Facebook: www.facebook.com/calverttxchamber
Instagram: www.instagram.com/calverttxchamberofcommerce
Description: Promotes business and community development in Calvert, TX. **Founded:** 1929. **Geographic Preference:** Local.

45073 ■ Cameron Chamber of Commerce
102 E First St.
Cameron, TX 76520
Ph: (254)697-4979
Co. E-mail: chamber@cameron-tx.com
URL: http://www.cameron-tx.com
Contact: Micah Holcombe, President
Facebook: www.facebook.com/cameronchamber
Description: Promotes business and community development in the Cameron, TX area. Assists local groups with community betterment projects; sponsors local festival and the Center for Tourism. **Founded:** 1846. **Publications:** *Chamber Newsletter* (Weekly). **Awards:** Cameron Chamber of Commerce Banquet Award (Annual). **Geographic Preference:** Local.

45074 ■ Canton Texas Chamber of Commerce (CTCC)
290 E Tyler St.
Canton, TX 75103
Ph: (903)567-2991
Co. E-mail: info@cantontexaschamber.com
URL: http://www.cantontexaschamber.com
Contact: Blake Fowler, Board Member
Facebook: www.facebook.com/CantonTexasChamber
Description: Promotes business and community development in Canton, TX. **Geographic Preference:** Local.

45075 ■ Canyon Chamber of Commerce (CCC)
1518 5th Ave.
Canyon, TX 79015
Ph: (806)655-7815
Free: 800-999-9481
Co. E-mail: info@canyonchamber.org
URL: http://www.canyonchamber.org
Contact: Casey Renner, President
Facebook: www.facebook.com/canyonchamber1
X (Twitter): x.com/CanyonChamber1
Description: Promotes business, community development, and tourism in the Canyon, TX area. Conducts charitable activities. Sponsors Fourth of July parade, fireworks, entertainment, craft/fun fair and "Fair on the Square" event. **Founded:** 1876. **Geographic Preference:** Local.

45076 ■ Castroville Chamber of Commerce
1115 Angelo St.
Castroville, TX 78009
Ph: (830)538-3142
Co. E-mail: chamber@castroville.com
URL: http://www.castroville.com/chamber-of-commerce.html
Contact: Aaron Padilla, President
E-mail: apadilla@txn.bank
Facebook: www.facebook.com/castrovillechamberofcommerce
Description: Promotes business and community development in Castroville, CA. **Founded:** 1945. **Geographic Preference:** Local.

45077 ■ Cedar Creek Lake Area Chamber of Commerce (CCLACC)
101 W Eubank St., Ste. F
Mabank, TX 75147
Ph: (903)887-3152
Co. E-mail: info@cedarcreeklakechamber.com
URL: http://www.cedarcreeklakechamber.com
Contact: Jo Ann Hanstrom, President
E-mail: joann@cedarcreeklakechamber.com
Facebook: www.facebook.com/CCLACC
Description: Promotes business and community development in Mabank, TX. Sponsors Christmas Tour of Homes, Halloween Festival, annual Western Week, and Chili Cookoff. **Founded:** 2001. **Geographic Preference:** Local.

45078 ■ Cedar Hill Chamber of Commerce
300 Houston St.
Cedar Hill, TX 75104-2678
Ph: (972)291-7817
Fax: (972)291-8101
Co. E-mail: admin@cedarhillchamber.org
URL: http://www.cedarhillchamber.org
Contact: Randall Chase, Executive Director
E-mail: randall@cedarhillchamber.org
Facebook: www.facebook.com/CedarHillChamberofCommerce
X (Twitter): x.com/CedarHillCoC
YouTube: www.youtube.com/channel/UC1_KOQ6suHhoDWP-IGi4aUQ
Pinterest: www.pinterest.com/cedarhillcoc
Description: Promotes business and community development in Cedar Hill, TX. **Geographic Preference:** Local.

45079 ■ Cedar Park Chamber of Commerce and Tourism
200 S Bell Blvd., Ste. C-1
Cedar Park, TX 78613
Ph: (512)401-5070
URL: http://business.cedarparkchamber.org/list/member/city-of-cedar-park-travel-tourism-4712
Contact: Tony Moline, President
Description: Promotes business and community development in Cedar Park, TX. **Founded:** 1973. **Publications:** *Friday Facts* (Monthly). **Geographic Preference:** Local.

45080 ■ Cen-Tex Hispanic Chamber of Commerce (CTHCC)
915 La Salle Ave.
Waco, TX 76706
Ph: (254)754-7111
Co. E-mail: info@wacohispanicchamber.com
URL: http://wacohispanicchamber.com
Contact: Andrea Kosar, President
Facebook: www.facebook.com/CentexHispanicChamberofCommerce
YouTube: www.youtube.com/channel/UCaOKpXy87JjKmW8z5sx23XA
Description: Promotes business and development for the Hispanic community in Waco and Central Texas. **Founded:** 1975. **Geographic Preference:** Local.

45081 ■ Centerville Chamber of Commerce
PO Box 422
Centerville, TX 75833-0422
Ph: (903)536-7261
URL: http://centervilletx.org
Contact: Karen Ellis, President
Facebook: www.facebook.com/centerville.chamber.of.commerce
Description: Promotes business and community development in Centerville, TX area. **Founded:** 1979. **Geographic Preference:** Local.

45082 ■ Central Fort Bend Chamber Alliance (CFBC)
4120 Ave. H
Rosenberg, TX 77469
Ph: (281)342-5464
Co. E-mail: cfbca@cfbca.org
URL: http://www.cfbca.org
Contact: Kristin Weiss, President
E-mail: kweiss@cfbca.org
Facebook: www.facebook.com/centralfortbendchamber
Linkedin: www.linkedin.com/company/centralfortbendchamber
Instagram: www.instagram.com/centralfortbendchamber
Description: Promotes business and community development in Rosenberg and Richmond, TX. **Founded:** 1910. **Publications:** *Chamber Magazine* (Annual); *Focus* (Weekly). **Geographic Preference:** Local.

45083 ■ Chamber Dialogue
505 15th St.
Ozona, TX 76943
Ph: (325)392-3737
Fax: (325)392-3485
Co. E-mail: oztxcoc@aol.com
URL: http://www.ozona.com/index.php
Contact: Shanon Biggerstaff, President
URL(s): www.ozona.com/newsletter-chamber-dialogue
Released: Annual **Description:** Contains report of Chamber activities that relate to the membership or benefit the community. **Availability:** Online; PDF.

45084 ■ Chamber at a Glance
2401 E Missouri
El Paso, TX 79903
Ph: (915)566-4066
Fax: (915)566-9714
Co. E-mail: lescobar@ephcc.org
URL: http://ephcc.org
Contact: Cindy Ramos-Davidson, Chief Executive Officer
E-mail: cindyramosdavidson@ephcc.org
URL(s): ephcc.org/membership
Released: Weekly **Price:** $120, Single issue. **Description:** Contains chamber events, happenings, and articles. **Availability:** Print.

45085 ■ The Chamber Report
700 N Pearl St., Ste. 1200
Dallas, TX 75201
Ph: (214)746-6600
Fax: (214)712-1950
Co. E-mail: information@dallaschamber.org
URL: http://www.dallaschamber.org
Contact: Jim Oberwetter, President
Availability: Print; Online.

45086 ■ The Chamber Today
602 E Commerce St.
San Antonio, TX 78205
Ph: (210)229-2100
Fax: (210)229-1600
URL: http://sachamber.org
Contact: Richard Perez, President
E-mail: rperez@sachamber.org
URL(s): www.sachamber.org/news/connect-with-us

Released: Weekly (Wed.) **Description:** Contains information about chamber activities. **Availability:** Print.

45087 ■ *Chamber Works*
187 W Washington St.
Stephenville, TX 76401
Ph: (254)965-5313
Fax: (254)965-3814
Co. E-mail: chamber@stephenvilletexas.org
URL: http://www.stephenvilletexas.org
Contact: July Danley, President
E-mail: julyd@stephenvilletexas.org
URL(s): www.stephenvilletexas.org/member-benefits
Released: Monthly **Description:** Includes chamber and community activities. **Availability:** Print.

45088 ■ **Childress Chamber of Commerce**
237 Commerce St.
Childress, TX 79201-4523
Ph: (940)937-2567
Co. E-mail: childresschamber1@gmail.com
URL: http://childress-chamber.com
Contact: Susan Leary, Executive Director
Facebook: www.facebook.com/childress.chamber
X (Twitter): x.com/Childresschambr
Instagram: www.instagram.com/ChildressChamber
Description: Promotes business and community development in Childress, TX. Conducts charitable events. Sponsors festival. Sponsors charitable services and competitions. **Founded:** 1909. **Geographic Preference:** Local.

45089 ■ **Cisco Chamber of Commerce (CCC)**
309 Conrad Hilton Blvd.
Cisco, TX 76437
Ph: (254)442-2537
Co. E-mail: ciscochamberofcommerce@gmail.com
URL: http://ciscochamberofcommerce.com
Contact: Darwin Archer, President
Facebook: www.facebook.com/ciscochamberofcommerce
Description: Promotes business and community development in Cisco, TX. Conducts charitable activities. Sponsors festival. **Geographic Preference:** Local.

45090 ■ **City of South Houston Chamber of Commerce**
58 Spencer Hwy.
South Houston, TX 77587
Ph: (713)943-0244
Fax: (713)943-3978
Co. E-mail: sohochamber@att.net
URL: http://www.southhoustonchamber.org
Contact: JoAnn Parish, Chief Executive Officer
Description: Promotes business and community development in the South Houston, TX area. Sponsors Strawberry Festival. **Publications:** *Chamber Chat* (Monthly). **Geographic Preference:** Local.

45091 ■ **Cleburne Chamber of Commerce**
1511 W Henderson St.
Cleburne, TX 76033
Ph: (817)645-2455
Fax: (817)641-3069
Co. E-mail: info@cleburnechamber.com
URL: http://www.cleburnechamber.com
Contact: Heather Juarez, Director
E-mail: heatherj@cleburnechamber.com
Facebook: www.facebook.com/CleburneChamber
X (Twitter): x.com/CleburneChamber
Instagram: www.instagram.com/cleburnechamber
Description: Promotes business and community development in Cleburne, TX. **Founded:** 1916. **Publications:** *Demographics About Cleburne.* **Geographic Preference:** Local.

45092 ■ **Cleveland Area Chamber of Commerce**
908 E Houston St., Ste. 110
Cleveland, TX 77327
Ph: (281)592-8786
Fax: (281)592-6949
Co. E-mail: info@clevelandtxchamber.com
URL: http://www.clevelandtxchamber.com
Contact: Camille Landry, President
Facebook: www.facebook.com/clevelandchamberofcommerce
Instagram: www.instagram.com/clevelandtxchamber
Description: Works to advance the general welfare and prosperity of the Cleveland area so that its citizens and all areas of its business community shall prosper. Provides all necessary means of promotion and gives particular attention and emphasis to economic, civic, commercial, cultural, industrial and educational interests of the area. **Geographic Preference:** Local.

45093 ■ **Clifton Chamber of Commerce**
115 N Ave. D
Clifton, TX 76634
Ph: (254)675-3720
Free: 800-344-3720
Co. E-mail: info@cliftontexas.org
URL: http://cliftontexas.org
Contact: Paige A. Key, President
E-mail: paigekey@cliftontexas.org
Facebook: www.facebook.com/Clifton-Chamber-of-Commerce-331353607714
Description: Promotes business and community development in Clifton, TX. **Geographic Preference:** Local.

45094 ■ **Coldspring/San Jacinto County Chamber of Commerce (CCC)**
31 N Butler St.
Coldspring, TX 77331
Ph: (936)653-2184
Co. E-mail: chambercoldspringtexas@gmail.com
URL: http://www.coldspringtexas.org
Contact: Barbara S. Justice, President
Facebook: www.facebook.com/coldspringchamberofcommerce
Description: Promotes business and community development in San Jacinto County, TX. **Founded:** 1983. **Geographic Preference:** Local.

45095 ■ **Coleman County Chamber of Commerce, Agriculture and Tourist Bureau**
218 Commercial Ave.
Coleman, TX 76834
Ph: (325)625-2163
Free: 800-687-6971
Co. E-mail: chamber@colemantexas.org
URL: http://colemancountytexas.com
Facebook: www.facebook.com/colemanchamber
Description: Promotes business and community development in Coleman, TX. **Geographic Preference:** Local.

45096 ■ **Colleyville Area Chamber of Commerce (CACC)**
Colleyville Business Center, 5601 Colleyville Blvd.
Colleyville, TX 76034
Ph: (817)488-7148
Co. E-mail: info@colleyvillechamber.org
URL: http://www.colleyvillechamber.org
Contact: Chelsea Rose, Co-Chief Executive Officer Co-President
E-mail: chelsea@colleyvillechamber.org
Facebook: www.facebook.com/ColleyvilleChamber
Linkedin: www.linkedin.com/company/colleyville-chamber-of-commerce
X (Twitter): x.com/CVchamberTX
Instagram: www.instagram.com/cvchambertx
Description: Promotes business and community development in Colleyville, TX area. **Founded:** 1976. **Publications:** *Community and Business Directory* (Annual). **Geographic Preference:** Local.

45097 ■ **Collin County Black Chamber of Commerce (CCBCC)**
550 N Central Expy.
McKinney, TX 75070-9998
Ph: (469)424-0120
Co. E-mail: info@ccblackchamber.org
URL: http://www.ccblackchamber.org
Contact: Debra Austin, President
Facebook: www.facebook.com/collincountyblackchamberofcommerce
Linkedin: www.linkedin.com/in/ccbcc
X (Twitter): x.com/CCBLKCHAMBER
Instagram: www.instagram.com/ccblackchamber
Description: Provides advocacy, training and education to Black communities. **Geographic Preference:** Local.

45098 ■ **The Colony Chamber of Commerce**
PO Box 560006
The Colony, TX 75056
Ph: (469)404-4088
Co. E-mail: info@thecolonychamber.org
URL: http://www.thecolonychamber.org
Contact: Jennifer Ondreyka, Executive Director
E-mail: jennifer@thecolonychamber.org
X (Twitter): x.com/TheColonyTX
Description: Promotes business and community development in The Colony, TX. **Founded:** 1977. **Publications:** *The Colony Connection* (Quarterly); *The Commerce Communicator* (Monthly); *The Colony Connection* (Quarterly). **Geographic Preference:** Local.

45099 ■ **Colorado City Area Chamber of Commerce**
157 W 2nd St.
Colorado City, TX 79512
Ph: (325)728-3403
Co. E-mail: ccitychamber@gmail.com
URL: http://www.coloradocitychamberofcommerce.com
Description: Promotes business and community development in Mitchell County, TX. **Geographic Preference:** Local.

45100 ■ **Comanche Chamber of Commerce & Agriculture**
304 S Austin St.
Comanche, TX 76442
Ph: (325)356-3233
Co. E-mail: comanchetxchamber@gmail.com
URL: http://comanchechamber.org
Contact: Denise Imiola, Co-President
E-mail: denise.imiola@gmail.com
Facebook: www.facebook.com/ComancheChamber
Instagram: www.instagram.com/explorecomanchechamber
Description: Promotes business and community development in Comanche, TX. Sponsors Comanche County Pow-Wow. **Founded:** 1942. **Publications:** *The Chamber Report* (Quarterly). **Geographic Preference:** Local.

45101 ■ **Comfort Chamber of Commerce**
630 Hwy. 27
Comfort, TX 78013
Ph: (830)995-3131
Co. E-mail: info@comfort-texas.com
URL: http://www.comfortchamber.com
Contact: Jennifer Cernosek, President
Facebook: www.facebook.com/ComfortTX
YouTube: www.youtube.com/user/ComfortChamber
Description: Promotes business and community development in Comfort, TX. Sponsors July 4th festivities, and Christmas in Comfort celebration. **Founded:** 1946. **Geographic Preference:** Local.

45102 ■ **Commerce Chamber of Commerce (CCC)**
1114 Main St.
Commerce, TX 75428
Ph: (903)886-3950
Fax: (903)886-8012
Co. E-mail: info@commerce-chamber.com
URL: http://commerce-chamber.com
Contact: Amy Welch, Co-President
E-mail: a.welch@securingyourfuture.com
Facebook: www.facebook.com/commerce.chamber
Description: Aims to promote the common business interests of merchants and citizens living and working in the city of Commerce, Texas, and in the immediate area; promote the free enterprise system; encourage the commercial, industrial and agricultural development of the city of Commerce and the immediate area; and assume a role of active leadership in community improvement. **Founded:** 1909. **Geographic Preference:** Local.

45103 ■ *The Connecting Source*
520 N Glenbrook Dr.
  Garland, TX 75040
Ph: (972)272-7551
Fax: (972)276-9261
Co. E-mail: info@garlandchamber.com
URL: http://www.garlandchamber.com
Contact: Karina Olivares, President
E-mail: karina.olivares@garlandchamber.com
URL(s): www.garlandchamber.com/highlighting-mark
  -king-micropac
Availability: Print.

45104 ■ *Connections Magazine*
505 W Davis St.
  Conroe, TX 77301
Ph: (936)756-6644
Fax: (936)756-6462
Co. E-mail: info@conroe.org
URL: http://www.conroe.org
Contact: Scott Harper, President
E-mail: scotth@conroe.org
URL(s): www.conroe.org/guide
Released: 3/year **Availability:** PDF; Online.

45105 ■ Conroe/Lake Conroe Chamber of Commerce
505 W Davis St.
  Conroe, TX 77301
Ph: (936)756-6644
Fax: (936)756-6462
Co. E-mail: info@conroe.org
URL: http://www.conroe.org
Contact: Scott Harper, President
E-mail: scotth@conroe.org
Facebook: www.facebook.com/CLCChamber
Linkedin: www.linkedin.com/company/conroe-lake
  -conroe-area-chamber
X (Twitter): x.com/conroechamber
YouTube: www.youtube.com/channel/UC8E7hK967
  1yXvLyNhgHpxtA
Description: Promotes business and community development in Conroe, TX. **Founded:** 1934. **Publications:** *Greater Conroe/Lake Conroe Area Chamber of Commerce--Membership Directory* (Annual); *Business Directory*; *Connections Magazine* (3/year). **Geographic Preference:** Local.

45106 ■ Coppell Chamber of Commerce
708 Main St.
  Coppell, TX 75019
Ph: (972)393-2829
Fax: (972)537-5581
Co. E-mail: chamber@coppellchamber.org
URL: http://www.coppellchamber.org
Contact: Ellie Braxton-Leveen, President
E-mail: ellie@coppellchamber.org
Facebook: www.facebook.com/coppellchamber
Linkedin: www.linkedin.com/company/coppell-chamber-of-commerce/about
X (Twitter): x.com/CoppellChamber
Instagram: www.instagram.com/coppellchamber
YouTube: www.youtube.com/channel/UC0da66h7Dlz
  1bWskuIIbC7Q
Description: Strives to enhance and promote the business environment and quality of life in the Coppell community. **Founded:** 1990. **Publications:** *Chamber Connection* (Monthly). **Geographic Preference:** Local.

45107 ■ Copperas Cove Chamber of Commerce & Visitors Bureau
204 E Robertson Ave.
  Copperas Cove, TX 76522-2928
Ph: (254)547-7571
Fax: (254)547-5015
Co. E-mail: chamber@copperascove.com
URL: http://copperascove.com
Contact: Charlotte Heinze, Secretary
Facebook: www.facebook.com/
  CopperasCoveChamber
X (Twitter): x.com/CopperasCoveCOC
Instagram: www.instagram.com/
  copperascovechamber
Description: Promotes business and community development in Copperas Cove, TX. **Founded:** 1956. **Geographic Preference:** Local.

45108 ■ Corpus Christi Black Chamber of Commerce (CCBCC)
Del Mar College Ctr. for Economic Development
  3209 S Staples St., Ste. 113
  Corpus Christi, TX 78404
Ph: (361)815-8346
Fax: (361)698-2112
Co. E-mail: cctxblackchamberoc@gmail.com
URL: http://www.blackchambercc.org
Contact: Coretta Graham, President
Facebook: www.facebook.com/blackchambercc
Description: Seeks to empower and sustain African American communities through entrepreneurship and capitalistic activity. **Founded:** 1943. **Geographic Preference:** Local.

45109 ■ Corpus Christi Hispanic Chamber of Commerce
615 N Upper Broadway, Ste. 410
  Corpus Christi, TX 78401
Contact: Teresa Rodriguez, Contact
Description: Aims to serve the business community by developing positive changes through active participation in education, leadership, public affairs and creating business opportunities for its members. Works as the official Hispanic business liaison between the business community and the community at large. **Founded:** 1939. **Geographic Preference:** Regional.

45110 ■ Corsicana/Navarro County Chamber of Commerce
120 N 12th St.
  Corsicana, TX 75110
Ph: (903)874-4731
Co. E-mail: chamber@corsicana.org
URL: http://www.corsicana.org
Contact: Colleen Cox, Vice President, Operations
Facebook: www.facebook.com/CorsicanaCOC
Instagram: www.instagram.com/cnc_chamber
Description: Promotes business and community development in Corsicana, TX. **Founded:** 1918. **Geographic Preference:** Local.

45111 ■ Crockett Area Chamber of Commerce
1100 Edminston Dr.
  Crockett, TX 75835
Ph: (936)544-2359
Fax: (936)544-4355
Co. E-mail: info@crockettareachamber.org
URL: http://www.crockettareachamber.org
Contact: Liza Clark, Executive Director
E-mail: lisa@crockettareachamber.org
Description: Promotes business, community development, and tourism in Houston County, TX. **Founded:** 1926. **Geographic Preference:** Local.

45112 ■ Crosby-Huffman Chamber of Commerce (CHCC)
5317 1st St.
  Crosby, TX 77532
Ph: (281)328-6984
Co. E-mail: chamber@crosbyhuffmancc.org
URL: http://www.crosbyhuffmancc.org
Contact: Kim Harris, President
E-mail: kim@crosbyhuffmancc.org
Facebook: www.facebook.com/CrosbyHuffmanCC
Description: Promotes business and community development in Crosby, TX. **Founded:** 1924. **Publications:** *The Communicator* (Quarterly). **Geographic Preference:** Local.

45113 ■ Crowell Chamber of Commerce
PO Box 164
  Crowell, TX 79227
Ph: (940)684-1310
URL: http://www.crowelltex.com/page7.html
Contact: Lee Hammonds, Treasurer
Description: Works to advance the commercial, financial, industrial and civic interests of the area. **Founded:** 1891. **Geographic Preference:** Local.

45114 ■ Cuero Chamber of Commerce, Agriculture, & Visitor's Center
210 E Main St., Ste. A
  Cuero, TX 77954
Ph: (361)275-2112
Co. E-mail: cuerocc@cuero.org
URL: http://www.cuero.org
Contact: Willis Braden, President
Description: Promotes agriculture, business, tourism, and community development in Cuero, TX. **Founded:** 1970. **Publications:** *Chamber Notes* (Quarterly). **Geographic Preference:** Local.

45115 ■ Cy-Fair Houston Chamber of Commerce (CFHCC)
8711 Hwy. 6 N, Ste. 120
  Houston, TX 77095
Ph: (281)373-1390
Fax: (281)373-1394
Co. E-mail: staff@cyfairchamber.com
URL: http://www.cyfairchamber.com
Contact: Leslie Martone, President
E-mail: leslie@cyfairchamber.com
Facebook: www.facebook.com/CyFairChamber
Linkedin: www.linkedin.com/company/cyfairchamber
X (Twitter): x.com/CyFairChamber
Instagram: www.instagram.com/cyfairchamber
Description: Promotes business and community development in Cypress Fairbanks area, TX. **Founded:** 1986. **Publications:** *Cy-Fair Houston Chamber of Commerce Quarterly News Magazine* (Quarterly). **Awards:** Cy-Fair Houston Chamber of Commerce Large Market Business of the Year (Annual); Cy-Fair Houston Chamber of Commerce Medium Market Business of the Year (Annual); Cy-Fair Houston Chamber of Commerce Small Market of the Year (Annual). **Geographic Preference:** Local.

45116 ■ Daingerfield Chamber of Commerce (DCC)
102 Coffey St.
  Daingerfield, TX 75638-1704
Ph: (903)645-2646
Co. E-mail: daingerfieldcofc@gmail.com
Contact: Charles R. Thomasson, Contact
Facebook: www.facebook.com/Daingerfiel
  dTXChamber
Description: Promotes business, community development, and tourism in Daingerfield, Texas. Sponsors Daingerfield Days Festival, Christmas parade, Awards Banquet and annual Easter Egg Hunt before Easter. **Founded:** 1841. **Geographic Preference:** Local.

45117 ■ Dalhart Area Chamber of Commerce (DACC)
102 E 7th St.
  Dalhart, TX 79022
Ph: (806)244-5646
Co. E-mail: chamber@dalhart.org
URL: http://dalhart.org
Contact: Ashley Posthumus, Co-President
Facebook: www.facebook.com/dalhartchamber
X (Twitter): x.com/DalhartChamber
Instagram: www.instagram.com/dalhartchamber
Description: Promotes business and community development in Dallam and Hartley counties, TX. **Founded:** 1924. **Publications:** *Directory of Businesses*. **Awards:** Dalhart Area Chamber of Commerce Citizen of the Year (Annual). **Geographic Preference:** Local.

45118 ■ Dallas Black Chamber of Commerce (DBCC)
2922 Martin Luther King, Jr., Blvd. Building A, Ste. 104
  Dallas, TX 75215
Ph: (214)421-5200
Fax: (214)421-5510
Co. E-mail: info@dbcc.org
URL: http://dallasblackchamber.org
Contact: Harrison L. Blair, President
Facebook: www.facebook.com/
  DallasBlackChamberOfCommerce
Linkedin: www.linkedin.com/company/
  dallasblackchamber

Instagram: www.instagram.com/dallasblackchamber
Description: Promotes development of minority-owned businesses. **Founded:** 1926. **Publications:** *DBCC Update* (Bimonthly). **Awards:** Dallas Black Chamber of Commerce Quest for Success Award (Annual). **Geographic Preference:** Local.

45119 ■ De Leon Chamber of Commerce and Agriculture
125 S Texas St.
De Leon, TX 76444-1862
Ph: (254)893-2083
URL: http://www.uschamber.com/co/chambers/texas/de-leon
Description: Promotes business and community development in DeLeon, TX. **Founded:** 1881. **Geographic Preference:** Local.

45120 ■ Deaf Smith County Chamber of Commerce (DSCC)
701 Main St.
Hereford, TX 79045
Ph: (806)364-3333
Fax: (806)364-3342
Co. E-mail: deafs@wtrt.net
URL: http://www.herefordtx.org
Contact: Sid C. Shaw, Contact
Facebook: www.facebook.com/Deaf-Smith-County-Chamber-of-Commerce-343024722457132
Description: Promotes business and community development in Deaf Smith County, TX. **Geographic Preference:** Local.

45121 ■ Decatur Chamber of Commerce (DCC)
106 S Trinity St.
Decatur, TX 76234
Ph: (940)627-3107
Co. E-mail: info@decaturtx.com
URL: http://www.decaturtx.com
Contact: Misty Hudson, Executive Director
Facebook: www.facebook.com/DecaturChamber
X (Twitter): x.com/decaturchamber
Description: Promotes business and community development in Decatur, TX. Conducts Christmas fair for underprivileged youth, annual Fun Run, and Chisholm Trail Days. **Founded:** 1950. **Publications:** *Chamber Chatter* (Monthly). **Geographic Preference:** Local.

45122 ■ Deer Park Chamber of Commerce
120 E 8th St.
Deer Park, TX 77536
Ph: (281)479-1559
Co. E-mail: info@deerparkchamber.org
URL: http://www.deerparkchamber.org
Contact: Paula Moorhaj, President
E-mail: paula@deerparkchamber.org
Facebook: www.facebook.com/DeerParkChamberofCommerce
Linkedin: www.linkedin.com/company/deer-park-chamber-of-commerce
Instagram: www.instagram.com/deerparkchamberofcommerce
Description: Promotes business and community development in Deer Park, TX. Conducts charitable, fundraising, and social activities and educational forums. Monitors legislation. Sponsors annual Fall Festival. **Founded:** 1957. **Publications:** *Business Spotlight* (Monthly). **Geographic Preference:** Local.

45123 ■ Del Rio Chamber of Commerce (DRCC)
1915 Veterans Blvd.
Del Rio, TX 78840
Ph: (830)775-3551
Fax: (830)774-1813
Co. E-mail: frontdesk@drchamber.com
URL: http://www.drchamber.com
Contact: Nanca Rodriguez, President
Facebook: www.facebook.com/delriochamber
X (Twitter): x.com/DelRioChamber
YouTube: www.youtube.com/channel/UCfS4XP4y34ihvL6Y68xFZmQ
Description: Promotes business and community development in Val Verde County, TX. **Founded:** 1936. **Geographic Preference:** Local.

45124 ■ Denison Area Chamber of Commerce (DACC)
313 W Woodard St.
Denison, TX 75020
Ph: (903)465-1551
Co. E-mail: information@denisontexas.us
URL: http://www.denisontexas.us
Contact: Diana Theall, President
E-mail: dtheall@denisontexas.us
Facebook: www.facebook.com/denison.chamber
Linkedin: www.linkedin.com/company/denison-area-chamber-of-commerce/about
X (Twitter): x.com/denisonchamber
Instagram: www.instagram.com/denisonchamber
Description: Promotes business and community development in the Denison, TX area. Sponsors National Aerobatic Competition, Lake Fest, and Western Week. **Founded:** 1912. **Publications:** *Windows of Wayne* (Annual); *ChamberWorks*. **Geographic Preference:** Local.

45125 ■ Denton Chamber of Commerce (DCC)
414 W Pky. St.
Denton, TX 76201
Ph: (940)382-9693
Fax: (940)312-6161
URL: http://denton-chamber.org
Contact: Erin Carter, President
E-mail: erin.carter@denton-chamber.org
Facebook: www.facebook.com/DentonChamber
Linkedin: www.linkedin.com/company/denton-chamber-of-commerce-tx-
X (Twitter): x.com/DentonChamber
Instagram: www.instagram.com/dentonchamber
Pinterest: www.pinterest.com/DentonChamber
Description: Promotes business and community development in Denton, TX. Conducts new industry, convention, and visitor recruitment. Provides for leadership development and government relations. **Founded:** 1909. **Publications:** *Community Profile* (Periodic); *Clubs and Organizations*; *Community Profile* (Periodic); *Distinctly Denton* (Annual). **Geographic Preference:** Local.

45126 ■ DeSoto Chamber of Commerce (DCC)
2021 N Hampton Rd., Ste. 145
Desoto, TX 75115
Ph: (972)224-3565
URL: http://www.desotochamber.org
Contact: Vanessa Sterling, President
X (Twitter): twitter.com/DeSoto_Chamber
Description: Promotes business and community development in southwestern Dallas County and northern Ellis County, TX. **Founded:** 1962. **Publications:** *Business News* (Monthly). **Geographic Preference:** Local.

45127 ■ Dimmit County Chamber of Commerce
103 N 6th St.
Carrizo Springs, TX 78834
Ph: (830)876-5205
Co. E-mail: dcchamber@att.net
URL: http://www.dimmitcountychamber.org
Contact: Jimmie Lopez, President
E-mail: sono.1012@yahoo.com
Facebook: www.facebook.com/dimmitcountychamber
Description: Promotes business and community development in Dimmit County, TX. Sponsors Brush Country Days festival. **Founded:** 1930. **Geographic Preference:** Local.

45128 ■ Dumas/Moore County Chamber of Commerce and Visitors Center
1901 S Dumas Ave.
Dumas, TX 79029
Ph: (806)935-2123
Free: 888-840-8911
Fax: (806)935-2124
URL: http://www.dumaschamber.com
Contact: Carl Watson, Executive Director
E-mail: carl@dumaschamber.com
Description: Promotes business, community development, and tourism in Moore County, TX. **Geographic Preference:** Local.

45129 ■ Duncanville Chamber of Commerce (DCC)
300 E Wheatland Rd.
Duncanville, TX 75137
Ph: (972)780-4990
Co. E-mail: pres@duncanvillechamber.org
URL: http://www.duncanvillechamber.org
Contact: Dr. Ginger Hertenstein-Conley, Chairperson
Description: Promotes business and community development in Duncanville, TX. **Founded:** 1954. **Publications:** *How To Go Into Business in Duncanville*; *Duncanville Chamber of Commerce--Membership Directory* (Annual); *Healthy Living Guide* (Periodic). **Educational Activities:** Executive Board Meeting. **Geographic Preference:** Local.

45130 ■ Eagle Pass Chamber of Commerce (EPCC)
400 Garrison St.
Eagle Pass, TX 78853
Ph: (830)773-3224
Free: 888-355-3224
Fax: (830)773-8844
Co. E-mail: chamber@eaglepasstexas.com
URL: http://eaglepasstexas.com
Contact: Jorge Barrera, Vice President
Facebook: www.facebook.com/OfficialEaglePassChamberofCommerce
Description: Promotes business and community development in Eagle Pass, TX. Sponsors International Friendship Fest. **Founded:** 1926. **Publications:** *Maquiladona Directory* (Quarterly). **Geographic Preference:** Local.

45131 ■ Eastland Chamber of Commerce
209 W Main St.
Eastland, TX 76448
Ph: (254)629-2332
Co. E-mail: chamber@eastland.net
URL: http://www.eastlandchamber.com
Contact: Leisha Elrod, Chief Compliance Officer
YouTube: www.youtube.com/channel/UCWk9_af2zn9qidjyGjBdRmg
Description: Promotes business and community development in Eastland, TX. **Founded:** 1921. **Awards:** Eastland Chamber of Commerce Golden Deeds Award (Annual); Eastland Chamber of Commerce Business of the Year (Annual). **Geographic Preference:** Local.

45132 ■ Edinburg Chamber of Commerce (ECC)
Edinburg Depot
602 W University Dr.
Edinburg, TX 78539
Ph: (956)383-4974
Fax: (956)383-6942
Co. E-mail: information@edinburg.com
URL: http://edinburg.com
Contact: Michael J. Williamson, President
Facebook: www.facebook.com/edinburg.chamber
Linkedin: www.linkedin.com/company/edinburgchamber
X (Twitter): x.com/edinburgchamber
YouTube: www.youtube.com/channel/UC6qHpEf3BBZzDtYL4HzS2ww
Description: Strives to improve and enhance the commerce and the quality of life in Edinburg and the region. Fosters service, development, and growth by forging positive relationships, advocating volunteerism, and leadership development. **Founded:** 1932. **Geographic Preference:** Local.

45133 ■ Edwards County Chamber of Commerce (ECCC)
109 S Sweeten St.
Rocksprings, TX 78880-0267
Ph: (830)683-6466
Co. E-mail: edwardscountychamber@gmail.com
Facebook: www.facebook.com/EdwardsCountyChamberOfCommerce
Description: Promotes business in Edwards County. **Geographic Preference:** Local.

45134 ■ El Campo Chamber of Commerce and Agriculture
01 N Mechanic
El Campo, TX 77437
Ph: (979)543-2713
Fax: (979)543-1043
Co. E-mail: ecc@elcampochamber.com
URL: http://www.elcampochamber.com
Contact: Rebecca Munos, President
Facebook: www.facebook.com/ElCampoChamber
X (Twitter): x.com/elcampochamber
Instagram: www.instagram.com/elcampochamber
Pinterest: www.pinterest.com/elcampochamber
Description: Promotes the development of business, commerce, tourism, and agriculture in El Campo, TX. **Founded:** 1928. **Geographic Preference:** Local.

45135 ■ El Paso Chamber of Commerce
303 N Oregon St., Ste. 610
El Paso, TX 79901
Ph: (915)534-0500
Co. E-mail: info@elpaso.org
URL: http://elpaso.org
Contact: David Jerome, President
E-mail: david@elpaso.org
Facebook: www.facebook.com/ElPasoChamber
Linkedin: www.linkedin.com/company/greater-el-paso-chamber-of-commerce
X (Twitter): x.com/EPC915
Instagram: www.instagram.com/elpasochamber
YouTube: www.youtube.com/channel/UC3U1WjPrpeluQLqoYbWULUA
Description: Promotes business and community development in El Paso, IL. **Founded:** 1899. **Publications:** *Directory of Major Employers*. **Geographic Preference:** Local.

45136 ■ El Paso Hispanic Chamber of Commerce (EPHCC)
2401 E Missouri
El Paso, TX 79903
Ph: (915)566-4066
Fax: (915)566-9714
Co. E-mail: lescobar@ephcc.org
URL: http://ephcc.org
Contact: Cindy Ramos-Davidson, Chief Executive Officer
E-mail: cindyramosdavidson@ephcc.org
Facebook: www.facebook.com/ephc
X (Twitter): x.com/ephcc
YouTube: www.youtube.com/channel/UCXIuDI0f6KIKVvkpKuGOLKA
Pinterest: www.pinterest.com/elpasohispanicc
Description: Provides resources, information and education while promoting the awareness and preservation of the Hispanic culture. **Founded:** 2003. **Publications:** *Chamber at a Glance* (Weekly). **Awards:** El Paso Hispanic Chamber of Commerce Education Foundation Scholarship (Annual). **Geographic Preference:** Local.

45137 ■ Electra Chamber of Commerce
112 W Cleveland Ave.
Electra, TX 76360
Ph: (940)495-3577
URL: http://www.electratexas.org
Contact: Sherry Strange, Contact
Description: Promotes business and community development in Electra, TX. **Founded:** 1907. **Geographic Preference:** Local.

45138 ■ Ennis Chamber of Commerce
207 NW Main St.
Ennis, TX 75120
Ph: (972)878-2625
Fax: (972)875-1473
URL: http://www.ennis-chamber.com
Facebook: www.facebook.com/EnnisTxChamberofCommerce
X (Twitter): x.com/EnnisTxChamber
Instagram: www.instagram.com/ennistxchamber
Description: Promotes business and community development in the Ennis, TX area. Holds Ennis Polka Festival, annual Bluebonnet Trails, Ennis Heritage Antique Show and Sale, and Festival of the Train. Maintains Railroad and Cultural Heritage Museum. **Founded:** 1918. **Publications:** *TrendSetter News* (Quarterly). **Geographic Preference:** Local.

45139 ■ Fairfield Chamber of Commerce (FCC)
900 W Commerce St.
Fairfield, TX 75840
Ph: (903)389-5792
Fax: (903)389-8382
Co. E-mail: chamber@fairfieldtx.com
URL: http://fairfieldtexaschamber.com
Contact: Brenda Pate, Executive Director
E-mail: brenda75840@yahoo.com
X (Twitter): x.com/fairfieldcofc
Description: Promotes business and community development in Fairfield, TX. **Founded:** 1993. **Geographic Preference:** Local.

45140 ■ Farmers Branch Chamber of Commerce
13612 Midway Rd., Ste. 603
Farmers Branch, TX 75244
Ph: (972)243-8966
Co. E-mail: info@fbchamber.com
URL: http://farmersbranchchamber.org
Contact: Grace Speese, President
Facebook: www.facebook.com/farmersbranchchamber
Linkedin: www.linkedin.com/company/farmers-branch-chamber-of-commerce
Instagram: www.instagram.com/farmers_branch_chamber
Description: Promotes business and community development in Farmers Branch area. **Founded:** 1967. **Geographic Preference:** Local.

45141 ■ Farmersville Chamber of Commerce (FCC)
201 S Main St.
Farmersville, TX 75442
Ph: (972)782-6533
Fax: (972)782-6603
URL: http://www.farmersvillechamber.com
Contact: Jake Buchanan, President
Facebook: www.facebook.com/Farmersville-Chamber-of-Commerce-113562398845508
X (Twitter): x.com/FarmersChamber1
Description: Promotes business and community development in the Farmersville, TX area. **Geographic Preference:** Local.

45142 ■ Flatonia Chamber of Commerce (FCC)
208 E N Main St.
Flatonia, TX 78941
Ph: (361)865-3920
Co. E-mail: flatoniacofc@sbcglobal.net
URL: http://flatoniachamber.com
Contact: Beverly Z. Ponder, Executive Director
Facebook: www.facebook.com/flatoniachamberofcommerce
X (Twitter): x.com/flatoniachamber
YouTube: www.youtube.com/user/flatoniachamber
Description: Promotes business and community development in Flatonia, TX. **Founded:** 1873. **Geographic Preference:** Local.

45143 ■ Floresville Chamber of Commerce
1805 Railroad St.
Floresville, TX 78114
Ph: (830)251-0944
Co. E-mail: floresvillechamberofcommerce@yahoo.com
URL: http://www.floresvillechamberofcommerce.com
Contact: Mark Burris, President
E-mail: mniburris@hotmail.com
Description: Promotes business and community development in Floresville, TX; Wilson County. **Founded:** 1832. **Geographic Preference:** Local.

45144 ■ Flower Mound Chamber of Commerce
700 Parker Sq., Ste. No. 100
Flower Mound, TX 75028
Ph: (972)539-0500
Fax: (972)539-4307
URL: http://flowermoundchamber.com
Contact: Lori Walker, President
E-mail: l.walker@flowermoundchamber.com
Facebook: www.facebook.com/FlowerMoundChamber
Linkedin: www.linkedin.com/company/flower-mound-chamber
Description: Promotes business and community development in Flower Mound, TX. **Founded:** 1982. **Publications:** *Chamber Connection* (Monthly); *Online Member Directory*. **Geographic Preference:** Local.

45145 ■ Forney Area Chamber of Commerce
PO Box 570
Forney, TX 75126
Ph: (972)564-2233
Co. E-mail: president@forneychamber.com
URL: http://www.forneychamber.com
Contact: Phyllis Lyons, Treasurer
Facebook: www.facebook.com/ForneyChamberOfCommerce
Description: Promotes business and community development in Forney, TX and surrounding areas. Conducts fundraising activities. **Publications:** *Forney: The Antique Capital of Texas*. **Educational Activities:** Forney Area Chamber of Commerce Monthly Business Luncheon (Monthly). **Awards:** Forney Area Chamber of Commerce Citizen of the Year (Annual); Forney Area Chamber of Commerce Helping Hand Award (Annual). **Geographic Preference:** Local.

45146 ■ Fort Bend Chamber of Commerce (FBCC)
445 Commerce Green Blvd.
Sugar Land, TX 77478
Ph: (281)491-0800
Co. E-mail: info@fortbendcc.org
URL: http://fortbendchamber.com
Contact: Keri Schmidt, President
E-mail: keri@fortbendcc.org
Facebook: www.facebook.com/FortBendChamber
Linkedin: www.linkedin.com/company/fort-bend-chamber-of-commerce
X (Twitter): x.com/FortBendChamber
Instagram: www.instagram.com/explore/locations/5389773/fort-bend-chamber-of-commerce
YouTube: www.youtube.com/channel/UCRm_hSeHSpsW6YIcSuXuohg
Description: Promotes business and community development in Sugar Land, Meadows, Missouri City, Stafford, Richmond, Rosenberg, and a portion of Katy, TX. **Founded:** 1972. **Publications:** *Fort Bend Business Resource Book* (Biennial); *Fort Bend Forward* (Weekly). **Educational Activities:** Fort Bend Business Health & Wellness Expo (Annual). **Geographic Preference:** Local.

45147 ■ *Fort Bend Forward*
445 Commerce Green Blvd.
Sugar Land, TX 77478
Ph: (281)491-0800
Co. E-mail: info@fortbendcc.org
URL: http://fortbendchamber.com
Contact: Keri Schmidt, President
E-mail: keri@fortbendcc.org
URL(s): fortbendchamber.com/community-resources-division
Released: Weekly **Availability:** Print; Online.

45148 ■ Fort Davis Chamber of Commerce
100 Memorial Sq. No. 4
Fort Davis, TX 79734
Ph: (432)426-3015
Free: 800-524-3015
Co. E-mail: info@fortdavis.com
URL: http://fortdavis.com
Contact: Adele Coffey, President
Facebook: www.facebook.com/fortdavischamberofcommerce
Description: Promotes business, community development, and Tourism in Ft. Davis, TX. **Founded:** 1979. **Publications:** *Fort Davis Brochure* (Annual); *Fort Davis Visitors' Guide* (Annual). **Geographic Preference:** Local.

45149 ■ Fort Stockton Chamber of Commerce
1000 Railroad Ave.
Fort Stockton, TX 79735
Ph: (432)336-2264
URL: http://www.fortstockton.org
Contact: Arna McCorkle, Executive Director
E-mail: director@fortstockton.org
Facebook: www.facebook.com/fschamber
X (Twitter): x.com/FtStocktonChamb
Description: Promotes business and community development in Fort Stockton, TX. **Founded:** 1920. **Publications:** *Chamber Connection* (Weekly). **Geographic Preference:** Local.

45150 ■ Fort Worth Chamber of Commerce
777 Taylor St., Ste. 900
Fort Worth, TX 76102
Ph: (817)336-2491
Co. E-mail: info@fortworthchamber.com
URL: http://www.fortworthchamber.com
Contact: Brandom Gengelbach, Chief Executive Officer
E-mail: bgengelbach@fortworthchamber.com
Facebook: www.facebook.com/FTWChamber
Linkedin: www.linkedin.com/company/ftwchamber
X (Twitter): x.com/FTWChamber
Instagram: www.instagram.com/FTWChamber
YouTube: www.youtube.com/c/Fortworthchamber
Description: Promotes business and community development in Ft. Worth, TX. **Geographic Preference:** Local.

45151 ■ Fort Worth Metropolitan Black Chamber of Commerce (FWMBCC)
1150 S Fwy., Ste. 211
Fort Worth, TX 76104
Ph: (817)871-6538
Co. E-mail: info@fwmbcc.org
URL: http://www.fwmbcc.org
Contact: Michelle Green-Ford, President
E-mail: mgford@fwmbcc.org
Facebook: www.facebook.com/FWBlackChamber
X (Twitter): x.com/fwblackchamber
Instagram: www.instagram.com/FWBlackChamber
Description: Represents Black owned businesses. Seeks to empower and sustain African American communities through entrepreneurship and capitalistic activity. Provides advocacy, training and education to Black communities. **Founded:** 1979. **Geographic Preference:** Local.

45152 ■ Fredericksburg Chamber of Commerce
306 E Austin St.
Fredericksburg, TX 78624
Ph: (830)997-5000
URL: http://www.fredericksburg-texas.com/home
Contact: Penny C. McBride, President
E-mail: penny@fbgtxchamber.org
Facebook: www.facebook.com/Fredericksburgchamberofcommercetexas
Description: Promotes business and community development in Fredericksburg, TX. Sponsors Night in Old Fredericksburg festival. **Founded:** 1922. **Geographic Preference:** Local.

45153 ■ French-American Chamber of Commerce Dallas/Fort Worth (FACC DFW) [FACC Dallas/Fort Worth Chapter]
10830 N Central Expy., Ste. 152
Dallas, TX 75231
Ph: (972)241-0111
Co. E-mail: info@faccdallas.com
URL: http://www.eacctx.com/other-eacc-chapters
Contact: Erin McKelvey, Executive Director
E-mail: emckelvey@eacctx.com
Facebook: www.facebook.com/pg/faccdallas
Linkedin: www.linkedin.com/company/french-american-chamber-of-commerce-north-texas
X (Twitter): x.com/faccdfw
Instagram: www.instagram.com/faccofdallas
Founded: 1979. **Geographic Preference:** Local.

45154 ■ French-American Chamber of Commerce Houston Chapter
1301 Fannin St., Ste. 2440
Houston, TX 77006
Co. E-mail: contact@facchouston.org
URL: http://nationalfacc.org/organizer/facc-houston
Contact: Franck Avice, President
URL(s): facctexas.com
Linkedin: www.linkedin.com/company/facc-houston
Description: Chamber of commerce of Houston. **Founded:** 1986. **Geographic Preference:** Local.

45155 ■ Friendswood Chamber of Commerce
1100 S Friendswood Dr.
Friendswood, TX 77546
Ph: (281)482-3329
Co. E-mail: info@friendswoodchamber.com
URL: http://www.friendswoodchamber.com
Contact: Carol Ives Marcantel, Co-President
Co-Chief Executive Officer
X (Twitter): x.com/fwdchamber
Description: Promotes business and community development in Friendswood, TX. **Founded:** 1981. **Geographic Preference:** Local.

45156 ■ Frio Canyon Chamber of Commerce
PO Box 743
Leakey, TX 78873
Ph: (830)410-2016
Co. E-mail: contact@friocanyonchamber.com
URL: http://www.friocanyonchamber.com
Contact: Glen Ivey, Co-President
Facebook: www.facebook.com/friocanyonchamber
Instagram: www.instagram.com/friocanyonchamber
Description: Promotes business and community development in Frio Canyon, TX area. **Geographic Preference:** Local.

45157 ■ Friona Chamber of Commerce and Agriculture
621 Main St.
Friona, TX 79035
Ph: (806)250-3491
Co. E-mail: frionachamber@wtrt.net
URL: http://www.friona-chamber.com
Contact: Chris Alexander, Contact
Facebook: www.facebook.com/friona.chamber
Description: Promotes business and community development in Friona, TX. **Founded:** 1906. **Geographic Preference:** Local.

45158 ■ Frisco Chamber of Commerce (FCC)
6843 Main St.
Frisco, TX 75034
Ph: (972)335-9522
Co. E-mail: info@friscochamber.com
URL: http://www.friscochamber.com
Contact: Tony Felker, President
E-mail: tfelker@friscochamber.com
Facebook: www.facebook.com/friscochamber
X (Twitter): x.com/friscochamber
YouTube: www.youtube.com/channel/UCA5WbfJcpWwh8n2WLuFsa8g
Description: Promotes business and community development in Frisco, TX. **Founded:** 1967. **Publications:** *Frisco Flyer* (Monthly). **Geographic Preference:** Local.

45159 ■ Galveston Chamber of Commerce
2228 Mechanic, St., No. 101
Galveston, TX 77550
Ph: (409)763-5326
Fax: (409)763-8271
Co. E-mail: info@galvestonchamber.com
URL: http://galvestonchamber.com
Contact: Gina M. Spagnola, President
E-mail: gspagnola@galvestonchamber.com
Facebook: www.facebook.com/GalvestonChamber
X (Twitter): x.com/GalvChamber
Instagram: www.instagram.com/GalvestonChamber
Description: Promotes business and community development in Galveston Island, TX. **Founded:** 1845. **Publications:** *The Chamber Voice* (Bimonthly). **Geographic Preference:** Local.

45160 ■ Garland Chamber of Commerce
520 N Glenbrook Dr.
Garland, TX 75040
Ph: (972)272-7551
Fax: (972)276-9261
Co. E-mail: info@garlandchamber.com
URL: http://www.garlandchamber.com
Contact: Karina Olivares, President
E-mail: karina.olivares@garlandchamber.com
Facebook: www.facebook.com/garland.chamber
Linkedin: www.linkedin.com/company/garland-chamber-of-commerce
X (Twitter): x.com/GarlandChamber
Description: Promotes business and community development in Garland, TX. **Founded:** 1896. **Publications:** *Garland Chamber of Commerce--Membership Directory/Resource Guide*; *The Connecting Source*; *Membership Directory*. **Geographic Preference:** Local.

45161 ■ Gatesville Area Chamber of Commerce (GCC)
2307 S Hwy. 36
Gatesville, TX 76528
Ph: (254)865-2617
Co. E-mail: chamber@gatesvilletx.info
URL: http://www.gatesvilletx.info
Contact: Lute Sullins, Contact
Facebook: www.facebook.com/gatesvillecoc
X (Twitter): x.com/GatesvilleChamb
Description: Promotes tourism, business, and community development in the Gatesville, TX area. Sponsors Gatesville Shivaree and other festivals. **Founded:** 1939. **Publications:** *Gatesville Chamber of Commerce--Community Guide and Membership Directory* (Annual). **Geographic Preference:** Local.

45162 ■ George West Chamber of Commerce
301 Bowie
George West, TX 78022
Ph: (361)449-2033
URL: http://georgewest.org
Contact: Dr. Roland Quesada, President
Facebook: www.facebook.com/GWCofC
Description: Promotes business and community development in George West, TX. **Geographic Preference:** Local.

45163 ■ Georgetown Chamber of Commerce
1 Chamber Way
Georgetown, TX 78626
Ph: (512)930-3535
Co. E-mail: info@georgetownchamber.org
URL: http://georgetownchamber.org
Contact: Karin Sladek, Chairman of the Board
Facebook: www.facebook.com/georgetownchamber
X (Twitter): x.com/G_Tchamber
Instagram: www.instagram.com/georgetownchamber
YouTube: www.youtube.com/channel/UC9F73kk-xulxbGHngy7IS9g
Pinterest: www.pinterest.com/gtownchamber
Description: Promotes business and community development in Georgetown, TX. **Founded:** 1947. **Publications:** *Business*; *Chamber Link* (Weekly). **Geographic Preference:** Local.

45164 ■ Giddings Area Chamber of Commerce (GACC)
183 E Hempstead
Giddings, TX 78942
Ph: (979)542-3455
Co. E-mail: chambergiddings@gmail.com
URL: http://www.giddingstx.com
Contact: Denice Harlan, Executive Director
Facebook: www.facebook.com/GiddingsChamberofCommerce
Linkedin: www.linkedin.com/company/giddings-area-chamber-commerce
Description: Promotes business and community development in Giddings, TX. Sponsors Giddings Gerburtstag. Operates Economic Development Council. **Founded:** 1921. **Geographic Preference:** Local.

45165 ■ Gladewater Chamber of Commerce (GCC)
215 N Main St.
Gladewater, TX 75647
Ph: (903)845-5501
Co. E-mail: info@gladewaterchamber.org
URL: http://www.gladewaterchamber.org
Contact: Lois Reed, President
Facebook: www.facebook.com/gladewatercoc
X (Twitter): x.com/cocgladewater
Description: Promotes business and community development in Gladewater, TX. Sponsors promotional and fundraising events. **Founded:** 1931. **Publications:** *The Green Light is Go* (Monthly). **Geographic Preference:** Local.

45166 ■ Glen Rose/Somervell County Chamber of Commerce
503 Cottonwood St.
Glen Rose, TX 76043
Ph: (254)897-2286
Co. E-mail: info@glenrosechamber.org
URL: http://www.glenrosechamber.org
Contact: Rhonda Cagle, Contact
Facebook: www.facebook.com/glenrose.chamber
Description: Promotes business and community development in Somervell County, TX. **Founded:** 1961. **Geographic Preference:** Local.

45167 ■ Goliad Chamber of Commerce
138 S Market St.
Goliad, TX 77963
Ph: (361)645-3563
Fax: (361)645-3579
Co. E-mail: info@goliadcc.org
URL: http://www.goliadcc.org
Contact: Cristy Billo, Executive Director
Description: Promotes business and community development in Goliad County, TX. **Geographic Preference:** Local.

45168 ■ Gonzales Chamber of Commerce
304 Saint Louis St.
Gonzales, TX 78629
Free: 888-672-1095
Co. E-mail: admin@gonzalestexas.com
URL: http://gonzalestexas.com
Contact: Megan Zella, President
Facebook: www.facebook.com/GonzalesTXChamberOfCommerce
X (Twitter): x.com/GonzalesChamber
Instagram: www.instagram.com/gonzaleschamber
YouTube: www.youtube.com/user/GonzalesTXChamber
Pinterest: www.pinterest.com/gonzaleschamber
Description: Promotes business development in the area. **Founded:** 1923. **Geographic Preference:** Local.

45169 ■ Grand Prairie Chamber of Commerce
900 Conover Dr.
Grand Prairie, TX 75051
Ph: (972)264-1558
Co. E-mail: info@grandprairiechamber.org
URL: http://www.grandprairiechamber.org
Contact: Michelle Madden, President
E-mail: michelle@grandprairiechamber.org
Linkedin: www.linkedin.com/company/grand-prairie-chamber-of-commerce
X (Twitter): x.com/gptxchamber
Instagram: www.instagram.com/gptxchamber
YouTube: www.youtube.com/channel/UCTwQQ0MNpm2yZqpGi1nkzQg
Description: Promotes business and community development in Grand Prairie, TX. Sponsors Grand Prairie Grand Prix Bike Ride. **Publications:** *Focus* (Weekly). **Geographic Preference:** Local.

45170 ■ Grapevine Chamber of Commerce
200 Vine St.
Grapevine, TX 76051
Ph: (817)481-1522
Co. E-mail: info@grapevinechamber.org
URL: http://www.grapevinechamber.org
Contact: RaDonna Hessel, Chief Executive Officer
E-mail: radonna@grapevinechamber.org
Linkedin: www.linkedin.com/company/grapevine-chamber-of-commerce
X (Twitter): x.com/GrapevineCoC
Description: Promotes business and community development in Grapevine, TX. **Founded:** 1952. **Geographic Preference:** Local.

45171 ■ Greater Angleton Chamber of Commerce
222 N Velasco
Angleton, TX 77515
Ph: (979)849-6443
Fax: (979)849-4520
Co. E-mail: info@angletonchamber.org
URL: http://www.angletonchamber.org
Contact: Anne Allstott, Vice Chairman of the Board
Facebook: www.facebook.com/angletonchamber
Linkedin: www.linkedin.com/company/angleton-chamber-of-commerce
X (Twitter): x.com/angletonchamber
Instagram: www.instagram.com/angletonchamber
YouTube: www.youtube.com/channel/UC9spZVzn2HCcXpCgP5MMSTQ
Pinterest: www.pinterest.com/angletonchamber
Description: Promotes business and community development in Angleton, TX. **Founded:** 1957. **Geographic Preference:** Local.

45172 ■ Greater Austin Chamber of Commerce (GACC)
535 E 5th St.
Austin, TX 78701
Ph: (775)478-9383
Co. E-mail: customers@austinchamber.com
URL: http://austinchamber.com
Contact: Kerry Hall, Co-President Co-Chief Executive Officer
Facebook: www.facebook.com/AustinChamber
Linkedin: www.linkedin.com/company/austinchamber
X (Twitter): x.com/AustinChamber
Description: Promotes business and community development in the area. Also promotes tourism. **Founded:** 1877. **Publications:** *Greater Austin Chamber of Commerce--Membership Directory*; *Major Employers Directory*; *Business Desk Reference* (Periodic); *Chamber Ink* (10/year); *Skyliner* (Periodic); *Directory of Austin-Area Major Employers* (Annual). **Geographic Preference:** Local.

45173 ■ Greater Austin Hispanic Chamber of Commerce (GAHCC)
3601 Far W Blvd., Ste. 204
Austin, TX 78731
Ph: (512)476-7502
Fax: (512)476-6417
Co. E-mail: membership@gahcc.org
URL: http://www.gahcc.org/home
Contact: Emmy Alcocer, Chairman
Facebook: www.facebook.com/gahcc.org
Linkedin: www.linkedin.com/company/greater-austin-hispanic-chamber-of-commerce
X (Twitter): x.com/gahcc
Instagram: www.instagram.com/gahccaustin
Description: Promotes business and community development in the Hispanic communities of Austin, TX. **Founded:** 1973. **Geographic Preference:** Local.

45174 ■ Greater Boerne Chamber of Commerce
121 S Main
Boerne, TX 78006
Ph: (830)249-8000
Co. E-mail: boerne@gvtc.com
URL: http://boerne.org
Contact: Kimberley Blohm, Contact
Facebook: www.facebook.com/boernechamber
Linkedin: www.linkedin.com/company/greater-boerne-chamber-of-commerce
X (Twitter): x.com/boernetxchamber
Instagram: www.instagram.com/boernechamber
YouTube: www.youtube.com/channel/UC1cHf-CAoQ6nuqKCNCCy5sQ
Description: Promotes business and community development in the Kendall County, TX area. Sponsors Weihnachts Fest parade. **Founded:** 1928. **Publications:** *Network News* (Monthly). **Awards:** Aubrey E. "Sandy" Sanderson Memorial Scholarship (Annual). **Geographic Preference:** Local.

45175 ■ Greater Cleveland Chamber of Commerce (GCCC)
908 E Houston St., Ste. 110
Cleveland, TX 77327
Ph: (281)592-8786
Co. E-mail: info@clevelandtxchamber.com
URL: http://clevelandtxchamber.com
Contact: Camille Landry, Co-President
Facebook: www.facebook.com/clevelandchamberofcommerce
Description: Promotes business and community development in the Cleveland, TX area. **Founded:** 1935. **Geographic Preference:** Local.

45176 ■ Greater El Paso Chamber of Commerce (GEPCC)
303 N Oregon St., Ste. 610
El Paso, TX 79901
Ph: (915)534-0500
Co. E-mail: info@elpaso.org
URL: http://elpaso.org
Contact: Stephen Ian Voglewede, Chief Executive Officer
Facebook: www.facebook.com/ElPasoChamber
Linkedin: www.linkedin.com/company/greater-el-paso-chamber-of-commerce
X (Twitter): x.com/EPC915
Instagram: www.instagram.com/elpasochamber
YouTube: www.youtube.com/channel/UC3U1WjPrpeluQLqoYbWULUA
Description: Promotes business and community development in El Paso, TX. **Founded:** 1899. **Publications:** *Manufacturers/Suppliers & Services Directory*; *Directory of Manufacturers and Industrial Suppliers* (Annual); *Spotlight* (Monthly). **Geographic Preference:** Local.

45177 ■ Greater Elgin Chamber of Commerce (ECC)
114 Central Ave.
Elgin, TX 78621
Ph: (512)285-4515
Co. E-mail: info@elgintxchamber.com
URL: http://www.elgintxchamber.com
Contact: Barbara Hollingsworth, Officer
Facebook: www.facebook.com/ElginTXChamber
Linkedin: www.linkedin.com/company/elgin-chamber-of-commerce-elgin-tx
X (Twitter): x.com/ElginChamber
Instagram: www.instagram.com/elgintxchamber
YouTube: www.youtube.com/channel/UCzg1Y-B55rzS3XgGeR17wbA
Description: Promotes business and community development in Elgin, TX. Conducts charitable activities and competitions. Sponsors festival. **Founded:** 1934. **Geographic Preference:** Local.

45178 ■ Greater Heights Area Chamber of Commerce (GHACC)
2050 N Loop W, Ste. 215
Houston, TX 77018
Ph: (713)861-6735
Fax: (713)861-9310
Co. E-mail: info@heightschamber.org
URL: http://heightschamber.org
Contact: Dee Farino, Co-President
Facebook: www.facebook.com/GreaterHeightsAreaChamberofCommerce
Linkedin: www.linkedin.com/company/greater-heights-area-chamber-of-commerce
Description: Promotes business and community development in Greater Heights Area, Houston, TX. **Founded:** 1988. **Geographic Preference:** Local.

45179 ■ Greater Hewitt Chamber of Commerce (GHCC)
101 3rd St.
Hewitt, TX 76643
Ph: (254)666-1200
Fax: (254)666-3181
Co. E-mail: alissa@hewittchamber.com
URL: http://www.hewittchamber.com

Facebook: www.facebook.com/GreaterHewittChamber
X (Twitter): x.com/HewittChamber
Description: Promotes business and community development in the Greater Hewitt, TX area. **Founded:** 1978. **Publications:** *Hewitt Why Not!* (Biweekly). **Geographic Preference:** Local.

45180 ■ Greater Houston Partnership (GHP)
701 Avenida de las Americas, Ste. 900
Houston, TX 77010
Ph: (713)844-3600
Co. E-mail: contact@houston.org
URL: http://www.houston.org
Contact: Bob Harvey, President
E-mail: lacquisto@houston.org
Facebook: www.facebook.com/GreaterHoustonPartnership
X (Twitter): x.com/GHPartnership
Instagram: www.instagram.com/ghpartnership
YouTube: www.youtube.com/user/houvid
Description: Works to promote the business community in Houston. Seeks to establish economic prosperity in the region. **Founded:** 1989. **Publications:** *Here is Houston*; *Houston Chamber of Commerce--Membership Directory & Buyers' Guide* (Annual); *Houston International Business Directory* (Annual); *Houston Area Media Directory*; *Partnership Houston* (Annual); *Partnership Houston: Membership Directory and Resource Guide* (Annual). **Geographic Preference:** Local.

45181 ■ Greater Irving - Las Colinas Chamber of Commerce
5201 N O'Connor Blvd., Ste. 100
Irving, TX 75039
Ph: (214)217-8484
Fax: (214)389-2513
Co. E-mail: chamber@irvingchamber.com
URL: http://www.irvingchamber.com
Contact: Beth Bowman, President
E-mail: bbowman@irvingchamber.com
Facebook: www.facebook.com/irvingchamber
Linkedin: www.linkedin.com/company/greater-irving-las-colinas-chamber-of-commerce
X (Twitter): x.com/IrvingChamber
Instagram: www.instagram.com/irvingchamber
Description: Promotes business and community development in Irving, TX. **Founded:** 1932. **Geographic Preference:** Local.

45182 ■ Greater Keller Chamber of Commerce
420 Johnson Rd., Ste. No. 301
Keller, TX 76248
Ph: (817)431-2169
Co. E-mail: info@kellerchamber.com
URL: http://kellerchamber.com
Contact: JoAnn Malone, Chief Executive Officer
E-mail: jmalone@kellerchamber.com
Facebook: www.facebook.com/KellerChamber
Linkedin: www.linkedin.com/company/greater-keller-chamber-of-commerce/about
YouTube: www.youtube.com/channel/UCPHaMUXD7KCd2BeRwHisHhQ
Description: Promotes business and community development in Keller, TX. **Founded:** 1979. **Publications:** *Community Book/Buyer's Guide* (Annual); *Journal Sponsorship* (Monthly). **Geographic Preference:** Local.

45183 ■ Greater Killeen Chamber of Commerce (GKCC)
1 Santa Fe Plz., Dr.
Killeen, TX 76541
Ph: (254)526-9551
Co. E-mail: info@killeenchamber.com
URL: http://killeenchamber.com
Contact: Phyllis Gogue, Vice President, Development
E-mail: phyllis@killeenchamber.com
Facebook: www.facebook.com/killeenchamber
Linkedin: www.linkedin.com/organization-guest/company/greater-killeen-chamber-of-commerce
X (Twitter): x.com/killeenchamber
YouTube: www.youtube.com/user/KilleenChamber
Pinterest: www.pinterest.com/greater_k

Description: Promotes business and community development in Killeen, Fort Hood, and Harker Heights, TX. Encourages new settlement in the area. Sponsors Festival of Flags. Operates convention and visitors' bureau. **Founded:** 1882. **Publications:** *Newsline* (Monthly). **Geographic Preference:** Local.

45184 ■ Greater Mission Chamber of Commerce (GMCC)
202 W Tom Landry Rd.
Mission, TX 78572
Ph: (956)585-2727
Co. E-mail: gmcc@missionchamber.com
URL: http://www.missionchamber.com
Contact: Brenda Enriquez, President
E-mail: president@missionchamber.com
Facebook: www.facebook.com/MissionChamber
X (Twitter): x.com/MissionCOC
Instagram: www.instagram.com/missionchamber
Description: Promotes business and community development in Mission, TX. Encourages tourism; sponsors winter Texan activities. **Publications:** *The Monitor* (Monthly); *Progress Times* (Monthly). **Geographic Preference:** Local.

45185 ■ Greater New Braunfels Chamber of Commerce
390 S Seguin Ave.
New Braunfels, TX 78130
Ph: (830)625-2385
Free: 800-572-2626
Fax: (830)625-7918
Co. E-mail: info@innewbraunfels.com
URL: http://www.chamberinnewbraunfels.com
Contact: Jonathan Packer, II, President
E-mail: jonathan@innewbraunfels.com
Facebook: www.facebook.com/NBTXChamber
Linkedin: www.linkedin.com/company/nbtxchamber
X (Twitter): x.com/NBTXChamber
Instagram: www.instagram.com/nbtxchamber
YouTube: www.youtube.com/user/nbchamber
Description: Promotes business, economic, and community development in the Greater New Braunfels, TX area. **Founded:** 1919. **Publications:** *Greater New Braunfels Chamber of Commerce--Membership Directory*; *Handelskammer* (Monthly). **Geographic Preference:** Local.

45186 ■ Greater Pampa Area Chamber of Commerce
200 N Ballard St.
Pampa, TX 79065
Ph: (806)669-3241
Co. E-mail: exec@pampachamber.com
URL: http://www.pampachamber.com
Facebook: www.facebook.com/pampachamber
X (Twitter): x.com/PampaChamber
Description: Promotes business and community development in Pampa, TX. **Geographic Preference:** Local.

45187 ■ Greater Pflugerville Chamber of Commerce (GPCC)
PO Box 483
Pflugerville, TX 78691
Ph: (512)251-7799
Fax: (512)251-7802
Co. E-mail: info@pfchamber.com
URL: http://www.pfchamber.com
Contact: Kristen Cepak, Co-President Co-Chief Executive Officer
E-mail: kcepak@pfchamber.com
Facebook: www.facebook.com/PflugervilleChamberofCommerce
Linkedin: www.linkedin.com/company/pflugerville-chamber-of-commerce
X (Twitter): x.com/pflchamber
Instagram: www.instagram.com/pflugervillechamber
Description: Promotes business and community development in Pflugerville, TX area. **Founded:** 1985. **Geographic Preference:** Local.

45188 ■ Greater Quitman Area Chamber of Commerce
100 Governor Hogg Pky.
Quitman, TX 75783
Ph: (903)763-4411

Co. E-mail: quitmanchamber@quitmancoc.com
URL: http://www.quitmancoc.com
Contact: Clay Smith, Chairperson
Description: Provides quality service and leadership to its members and community, builds a healthier local economy and improves the quality of life through working together in a structured voluntary partnership of industrial, business, professional and concerned citizens. **Founded:** 1974. **Publications:** *Chamber Chatter* (Monthly). **Geographic Preference:** Local.

45189 ■ Greater San Antonio Chamber of Commerce
602 E Commerce St.
San Antonio, TX 78205
Ph: (210)229-2100
Fax: (210)229-1600
URL: http://sachamber.org
Contact: Richard Perez, President
E-mail: rperez@sachamber.org
Facebook: www.facebook.com/sachamber
Linkedin: www.linkedin.com/company/the-greater-san-antonio-chamber-of-commerce
X (Twitter): x.com/sachamber
Instagram: www.instagram.com/sachamber
Description: Promotes business and community development in the San Antonio, TX area. Represents the business community in legislative affairs and provides service programs. **Founded:** 1894. **Publications:** *The Greater San Antonio Chamber of Commerce--Clubs and OrganizatiDirectory* (Annual); *The Advocate*; *Area Business Councils/Small Business Update* (Weekly); *The Chamber Today* (Weekly (Wed.))*; *Greater San Antonio Chamber of Commerce--Guide to Shopping Centers*; *Largest Employers Directory* (Annual). **Geographic Preference:** Local.

45190 ■ Greater Schulenburg Chamber of Commerce
618 N Main St.
Schulenburg, TX 78956
Ph: (979)743-4514
Free: 866-504-5294
Co. E-mail: schulenburgchamber@cvctx.com
URL: http://www.schulenburgchamber.org
Contact: Paul Zapalac, President
Facebook: www.facebook.com/schulenburg.chamber
X (Twitter): x.com/SchulenburgCofC
Description: Promotes agricultural, business, and community development in Schulenburg, TX. Operates Travel Information Center. **Founded:** 1925. **Publications:** *Chamber Monthly Newsletter* (Monthly). **Geographic Preference:** Local.

45191 ■ Greater Taylor Chamber of Commerce & Visitors Center
1519 N Main St.
Taylor, TX 76574
Ph: (512)352-6364
Co. E-mail: info@taylorchamber.org
URL: http://www.taylorchamber.org
Contact: Diana Phillips, Contact
Description: Promotes business and community development in Taylor, TX. **Publications:** *Taylor Business* (Monthly). **Geographic Preference:** Local.

45192 ■ Greater Tomball Area Chamber of Commerce
29201 Quinn Rd., Ste. B
Tomball, TX 77377-0516
Ph: (281)351-7222
Free: 866-670-7222
Fax: (281)351-7223
URL: http://www.tomballchamber.org
Contact: Bruce Hillegeist, President
E-mail: bhillegeist@tomballchamber.org
Facebook: www.facebook.com/GreaterTomballChamber
X (Twitter): x.com/tomballchamber
Instagram: www.instagram.com/tomballchamber
Description: Seeks to further business growth and quality of life through business education, community development and partnership between business and government in Tomball, TX. **Founded:** 1965. **Publica-

tions: *Monthly Networking* (Bimonthly); *Progress; The Spirit of Tomball Texas* (Annual). **Geographic Preference:** Local.

45193 ■ Greater Waco Chamber of Commerce (GWCC)
101 S 3rd St.
Waco, TX 76701
Ph: (254)757-5600
Fax: (254)752-6618
Co. E-mail: info@wacochamber.com
URL: http://wacochamber.com
Contact: Matthew Meadors, President
E-mail: mmeadors@wacochamber.com
Facebook: www.facebook.com/GreaterWacoChamber
Linkedin: www.linkedin.com/company/greater-waco-chamber
X (Twitter): x.com/WacoChamber
Instagram: www.instagram.com/wacochamber
YouTube: www.youtube.com/user/GreaterWacoChamber
Description: Promotes business and community development in the Waco, TX area. **Founded:** 1899. **Publications:** *Communicator* (Bimonthly); *ED Update* (Quarterly); *Waco Chamber and Business Quarterly* (Quarterly). **Awards:** Greater Waco Chamber of Commerce Business Innovator Award (Annual). **Geographic Preference:** Local.

45194 ■ Greenville Chamber of Commerce
2713 Stonewall St.
Greenville, TX 75403
Ph: (903)455-1510
Fax: (903)455-1736
Co. E-mail: chamber@greenvillechamber.com
URL: http://greenvillechamber.com
Contact: Shelley Corrales, President
E-mail: shelley@greenvillechamber.com
Facebook: www.facebook.com/
 GreenvilleTXChamber
X (Twitter): x.com/greenvchamber
YouTube: www.youtube.com/channel/UCWEW 31XMwEAujT5zN7zkLYw
Description: Promotes business and community development in the Hunt County, TX area. Sponsors Cotton Jubilee and Fourth of July arts and crafts event. **Founded:** 1913. **Publications:** *Greenville Chamber of Commerce--Membership Directory.* **Awards:** Greenville Chamber of Commerce Athena Leadership Award (Annual); Buck Mickel Award for Business and Community Leadership (Annual); Max Heller Neighborhood Improvement Award (Annual); Greenville Chamber of Commerce Minority Business of the Year (Annual); Greenville Chamber of Commerce Small Business of the Year (Annual). **Geographic Preference:** Local.

45195 ■ Gruver Chamber of Commerce
PO Box 947
Gruver, TX 79040
Ph: (806)733-2424
Fax: (806)733-5038
URL: http://web.amarillo-chamber.org/Chambers-of -Commerce/Gruver-Chamber-of-Commerce-1234
Contact: Linda Weller, Contact
Description: Promotes business, community development, and tourism in the Gruver, TX area. **Geographic Preference:** Local.

45196 ■ *Guide to the Rio Grande Valley*
322 S Missouri Ave.
Weslaco, TX 78596
Ph: (956)968-3141
Co. E-mail: info@rgvpartnership.com
URL: http://business.rgvpartnership.com
Contact: Arlene Garza, President
URL(s): rgvpartnership.com/official-guide-to-the-rio -grande-valley
Released: Annual **Availability:** Print; Online.

45197 ■ Hallettsville Chamber of Commerce
1614 N Texana St.
Hallettsville, TX 77964
Ph: (361)798-2662
Co. E-mail: visit@hallettsville.com
URL: http://www.hallettsville.com

Contact: JoAnn Shimek, Contact
Facebook: www.facebook.com/halle ttsvillechambercommerce
X (Twitter): x.com/hallettchamber
Description: Promotes business, community development, and agriculture in Hallettsville, TX. Conducts membership drives and fundraisers. **Geographic Preference:** Local.

45198 ■ Hamilton Chamber of Commerce (HCC)
204 E Main St.
Hamilton, TX 76531-1920
Ph: (254)386-3216
Co. E-mail: hamiltonchambertx@gmail.com
Contact: Steve Almquist, Contact
Facebook: www.facebook.com/hamiltontexas
Description: Promotes business and community development in Hamilton County, TX. Sponsors annual Hamilton County Dove Festival. **Geographic Preference:** Local.

45199 ■ Harker Heights Chamber of Commerce
552 E FM 2410
Harker Heights, TX 76548
Ph: (254)699-4999
Co. E-mail: gina@hhchamber.com
URL: http://www.hhchamber.com
Contact: Gina Pence, President
E-mail: gina@hhchamber.com
Facebook: www.facebook.com/HarkerHeigh tsChamber
Description: Promotes business and community development in Harker Heights, TX area. **Geographic Preference:** Local.

45200 ■ Harlingen Area Chamber of Commerce (HACC)
311 E Tyler Ave.
Harlingen, TX 78550
Ph: (956)423-5440
Fax: (956)425-3870
Co. E-mail: thechamber@harlingen.com
URL: http://www.harlingen.com
Contact: Jacob Boggus, Secretary
Facebook: www.facebook.com/harlingencoc
Linkedin: www.linkedin.com/in/harlingen-area-chamber-of-commerce-636a7b91
Description: Promotes business and community development in the Harlingen, TX area. **Publications:** *Harlingen Area Business* (Monthly); *Interplex Report and Memberandum* (Bimonthly). **Geographic Preference:** Local.

45201 ■ Haskell Chamber of Commerce
301 S 1st St.
Haskell, TX 79521
Ph: (930)864-2333
Co. E-mail: haskellcc@srcaccess.net
URL: http://haskelltexasusa.com
Contact: Mary Jane Buerkle, President
Facebook: www.facebook.com/HaskellTexasUSA
X (Twitter): x.com/hashtag/haskelltexasusa
Instagram: www.instagram.com/haskelltexasusa
Description: Promotes business and community development in Haskell, OK. **Founded:** 1907. **Geographic Preference:** Local.

45202 ■ Hawkins Area Chamber of Commerce
300 S Beaulah St.
Hawkins, TX 75765
Ph: (903)769-4482
Co. E-mail: hawkinsareachamber@gmail.com
URL: http://www.hawkinschamber.org
Contact: Greg Branson, President
Facebook: www.facebook.com/hawkinschamber
Description: Promotes business and community development in Hawkins, TX. Sponsors annual Hawkins Oil Festival. **Founded:** 1975. **Geographic Preference:** Local.

45203 ■ Hearne Chamber of Commerce
304 S Market St.
Hearne, TX 77859
Ph: (979)595-8150

Co. E-mail: hearnechamberofcommerce@gmail.com
URL: http://www.hearnetxchamber.com
Contact: Fondell Adams, President
Facebook: www.facebook.com/hearnechamber
Description: Promotes business and community development in Robertson County, TX. Sponsors Booger Co. Glory Days the Dogwood Trails, and a Farmers' Market. **Founded:** 1892. **Geographic Preference:** Local.

45204 ■ *The Heartbeat*
405 S Bridge St.
Brady, TX 76825
Ph: (325)597-3491
Co. E-mail: erin@bradytx.com
URL: http://www.bradytx.com
Contact: Taylor Hoffpauir, President
URL(s): www.bradytx.com/member-benefits
Released: Quarterly **Description:** Contains chamber articles and Brady & McCulloch County information. **Availability:** Print.

45205 ■ Henderson Area Chamber of Commerce
201 N Main St.
Henderson, TX 75652
Ph: (903)657-5528
Fax: (903)657-9454
Co. E-mail: info@hendersontx.com
URL: http://www.hendersontx.com
Contact: Courtney Smith, President
Description: Promotes business and community development in Henderson, Tatum, Mt. Enterprise, Overton and New London in Rusk County, TX. **Founded:** 1926. **Geographic Preference:** Local.

45206 ■ Henrietta and Clay County Chamber of Commerce (HCCC)
202 W Omega St.
Henrietta, TX 76365
Ph: (940)538-5261
Co. E-mail: claycountychamber@sbcglobal.net
URL: http://hccchamber.com
Contact: Billy Carlton, President
Facebook: www.facebook.com/Henriettaclaycoun tychamber
Instagram: www.instagram.com/claycounty _turkeyfest
Description: Promotes business and community development in Clay County, TX. **Founded:** 1927. **Geographic Preference:** Local.

45207 ■ *Here is Houston*
701 Avenida de las Americas, Ste. 900
Houston, TX 77010
Ph: (713)844-3600
Co. E-mail: contact@houston.org
URL: http://www.houston.org
Contact: Bob Harvey, President
E-mail: lacquisto@houston.org
URL(s): www.houston.org/relocation-guide-request
Availability: Print; PDF; Online.

45208 ■ Hillsboro Chamber of Commerce (HCC)
115 N Covington St.
Hillsboro, TX 76645
Ph: (254)582-2481
Co. E-mail: memberservices@hillsborochamber.org
URL: http://hillsborochamber.org
Contact: Shannon Epling, Executive Director
E-mail: director@hillsborochamber.org
Facebook: www.facebook.com/Hillsboro-Chamber-of -Commerce-473250002771262
Instagram: www.instagram.com/hillsborotxchamber
YouTube: www.youtube.com/channel/UCoJYxu_JPS 2yOSzTQjhKmrw
Description: Promotes business and community development in the area. **Founded:** 1853. **Publications:** *Chamber Notes* (Monthly); *The Depot Connection* (6/year). **Geographic Preference:** Local.

45209 ■ *Hispanic Chamber News*
3006 General Hudnell Dr.
San Antonio, TX 78226
Ph: (210)225-0462
Co. E-mail: communications@sahcc.org

STATE LISTINGS   Texas ■ 45225

URL: http://www.sahcc.org
Contact: Marina J. Gonzales, President
URL(s): www.sahcc.org/member-requests
Availability: Online.

45210 ■ Hondo Area Chamber of Commerce (HACC)
1113 17th St.
 Hondo, TX 78861
Ph: (830)426-3037
Co. E-mail: info@hondochamber.org
URL: http://www.hondochamber.org
Contact: Jonathan Perterson, President
Facebook: www.facebook.com/HondoChamber
Linkedin: www.linkedin.com/company/hondo-area
 -chamber-of-commerce
Instagram: www.instagram.com/homesweethondo
Description: Promotes business and community development in Hondo, TX. **Geographic Preference:** Local.

45211 ■ Honey Grove Chamber of Commerce (HGCC)
PO Box 92
 Honey Grove, TX 75446
URL: http://www.honeygrovechamber.info
Contact: Kristie Covic, Co-President
Description: Promotes business and community development in Honey Grove, TX. Sponsors Davy Crockett Day and Christmas Parade. **Geographic Preference:** Local.

45212 ■ Hopkins County Chamber of Commerce (HCCC)
110 Main St.
 Sulphur Springs, TX 75482
Ph: (903)885-6515
Co. E-mail: info@hopkinschamber.org
URL: http://www.hopkinschamber.org
Contact: Lezley Brown, President
E-mail: lezley@hopkinschamber.org
Facebook: www.facebook.com/hopkinscochamber
Instagram: www.instagram.com/hopkinscochamber
Description: Promotes business and community development in Hopkins County, TX. Sponsors annual stew contest and annual dairy festival. **Founded:** 1926. **Publications:** *Chamber News*. **Educational Activities:** Dairy Festival (Irregular). **Geographic Preference:** Local.

45213 ■ Houston Intercontinental Chamber of Commerce (HICC)
PO Box 670252
 Houston, TX 77267
Ph: (281)408-0866
Co. E-mail: info@houstonicc.org
URL: http://www.houstonicc.org
Contact: Reggie Gray, President
E-mail: rgray@houstonicc.org
Facebook: www.facebook.com/HoustonICC
Linkedin: www.linkedin.com/company/houston-in
 tercontinental-chamber-of-commerce
X (Twitter): x.com/houstonicc
Description: Promotes business and community development in Northeastern Houston, TX. **Founded:** 1986. **Publications:** *North Houston Greenspoint Business* (Annual); *Pacesetter* (Monthly). **Geographic Preference:** Local.

45214 ■ Houston Metropolitan Chamber of Commerce
12 Greenway Plz., Ste. 1100
 Houston, TX 77046
Contact: Toni J. Franklin, Contact
Description: Promotes business and community development in Bellaire and Greater SW Houston, TX. Sponsors annual festival. **Founded:** 1949. **Publications:** *Chamber Progress* (Monthly). **Geographic Preference:** Local.

45215 ■ Houston Northwest Chamber of Commerce (HNWCC)
4201 Cypress Creek Pky., (FM 1960 W), Ste. 195
 Houston, TX 77068
Ph: (281)440-4160
Co. E-mail: chamberinfo@houstonnwchamber.org
URL: http://www.houstonnwchamber.org
Contact: Bobby Lieb, President
E-mail: bobbyl@houstonnwchamber.org
Facebook: www.facebook.com/HoustonNWChamber
X (Twitter): x.com/HNWCC
YouTube: www.youtube.com/channel/UCJ_wIHCvys
 dG2MbBdhVaBBw
Description: Promotes business and community development in the Northwest Houston, TX area. **Founded:** 1974. **Publications:** *Houston's Great Northwest* (Monthly). **Geographic Preference:** Local.

45216 ■ Houston West Chamber of Commerce (HWCC)
10370 Richmond Ave., Ste. 265
 Houston, TX 77042
Ph: (713)785-4922
Fax: (713)785-4944
Co. E-mail: info@hwcoc.org
URL: http://www.hwcoc.org
Contact: Kari Werner, President
E-mail: kari@hwcoc.org
Facebook: www.facebook.com/HWCOC
X (Twitter): x.com/HoustonWestCOC
Description: Promotes business and community development in West Houston, TX. **Founded:** 1985. **Publications:** *Metro West Magazine* (Periodic). **Awards:** Houston West Chamber of Commerce Star Awards (Annual). **Geographic Preference:** Local.

45217 ■ Howe Area Chamber of Commerce
101 E Haning St.
 Howe, TX 75459
Ph: (903)532-6080
Co. E-mail: info@howechamber.com
URL: http://howechamber.com
Contact: Monte Walker, President
Facebook: www.facebook.com/howechamber
X (Twitter): x.com/HoweChamber
Description: Promotes business and community development in Howe, TX. Sponsors festival and Christmas decoration contest. **Founded:** 1964. **Geographic Preference:** Local.

45218 ■ Hurst - Euless - Bedford Chamber of Commerce (HEBCC)
2109 Martin Dr.
 Bedford, TX 76021
Ph: (817)283-1521
Fax: (817)267-5111
Co. E-mail: chamber@heb.org
URL: http://heb.org
Contact: Mary Martin Frazior, President
E-mail: maryfrazior@heb.org
Facebook: www.facebook.com/HEBChamber
Linkedin: www.linkedin.com/company/the-chamber
 ---hurst-euless-bedford
X (Twitter): x.com/HEBChamber
YouTube: www.youtube.com/user/ChamberHEB
Description: Promotes business and community development in Bedford, Euless, and Hurst, TX. **Founded:** 1955. **Publications:** *Member Update* (Bimonthly). **Awards:** HEB Chamber Community Service Award (Annual). **Geographic Preference:** Local.

45219 ■ Hutto Chamber of Commerce
122 E St.
 Hutto, TX 78634
Ph: (512)759-4400
Co. E-mail: admin@huttochamber.com
URL: http://huttochamber.com
Contact: Tim Jordan, President
Facebook: www.facebook.com/HuttoChamber
Instagram: www.instagram.com/huttochamber
Description: Promotes business and community development in Hutto, TX. **Founded:** 1986. **Geographic Preference:** Local.

45220 ■ Ingleside Chamber of Commerce
2491 State Hwy. 361
 Ingleside, TX 78362
Ph: (361)776-2906
Co. E-mail: inglesidetxchamber@gmail.com
URL: http://www.inglesidetxchamber.com
Contact: Barbara Gregg, President
E-mail: ingchamber2@gmail.com
Facebook: www.facebook.com/ICOCTX
Linkedin: www.linkedin.com/in/ingleside-chamber-of
 -commerce-330597ab
Description: Promotes business and community development in Ingleside, TX. **Founded:** 1984. **Publications:** *Ingleside Chamber of Commerce Newsletter* (Weekly). **Geographic Preference:** Local.

45221 ■ *Ingleside Chamber of Commerce Newsletter*
2491 State Hwy. 361
 Ingleside, TX 78362
Ph: (361)776-2906
Co. E-mail: inglesidetxchamber@gmail.com
URL: http://www.inglesidetxchamber.com
Contact: Barbara Gregg, President
E-mail: ingchamber2@gmail.com
URL(s): www.inglesidetxchamber.com/membership
Released: Weekly **Description:** Contains business and community news. **Availability:** Online.

45222 ■ Jacksboro Chamber of Commerce
302 S Main St.
 Jacksboro, TX 76458
Ph: (940)567-2602
Fax: (940)567-3161
Co. E-mail: office@jacksborochamber.com
URL: http://www.jacksborochamber.com
Contact: Brenda Tarpley, Contact
YouTube: www.youtube.com/channel/UCyF
 1y0olkykkUZCoYdqw3pQ
Description: Promotes business, tourism, and community development in Jacksboro, TX. Sponsors Weekend in Old Mesquiteville festival; conducts Halloween costume contest; promotes jamborees and community holiday festivities. **Founded:** 1947. **Geographic Preference:** Local.

45223 ■ Jacksonville Chamber of Commerce
1714 E Rusk St.
 Jacksonville, TX 75766
Ph: (903)586-2217
Co. E-mail: info@jacksonvilletexas.com
URL: http://www.jacksonvilletexas.com
Contact: Peggy Renfro, President
E-mail: peggy@jacksonvilletexas.com
Facebook: www.facebook.com/JacksonvilleChamber
X (Twitter): x.com/JvilleChamber
YouTube: www.youtube.com/channel/UCkAAuR
 tmIjNC00nrUMtPknw
Description: Promotes business, community, and tourism development in Jacksonville, and Cherokee County, TX. **Founded:** 1928. **Geographic Preference:** Local.

45224 ■ Jasper-Lake Sam Rayburn Area Chamber of Commerce
500 S Wheeler St.
 Jasper, TX 75951
Ph: (409)384-2762
Fax: (409)384-4733
Co. E-mail: jaspercc@jaspercoc.org
URL: http://jaspercoc.org
Contact: Carol A. Clark, President
Facebook: www.facebook.com/jaspertxcoc
X (Twitter): x.com/CoJlsra
Instagram: www.instagram.com/jasperchamber
Description: Promotes business and community development in Jasper, TX. **Founded:** 1926. **Publications:** *Jasper, TX* (Annual). **Awards:** Jasper Lake Sam Rayburn Area Chamber of Commerce Citizen of the Year (Annual); Jasper Lake Sam Rayburn Area Chamber of Commerce Newcomer of the Year (Annual); Jasper Lake Sam Rayburn Area Chamber of Commerce Small Business of the Year (Annual); Jasper Lake Sam Rayburn Area Chamber of Commerce Young Person of the Year (Annual). **Geographic Preference:** Local.

45225 ■ *Jasper, TX*
500 S Wheeler St.
 Jasper, TX 75951
Ph: (409)384-2762
Fax: (409)384-4733
Co. E-mail: jaspercc@jaspercoc.org
URL: http://jaspercoc.org
Contact: Carol A. Clark, President
URL(s): jaspercoc.org/about-us/contact-us

Small Business Sourcebook • 42nd Edition

Released: Annual **Description:** Serves as tourism publication. **Availability:** Print.

45226 ■ Johnson City Chamber of Commerce
100 E Main St. No. 485
Johnson City, TX 78636
Ph: (830)868-7684
Co. E-mail: info@johnsoncitytexaschamber.com
URL: http://www.johnsoncitytexas.info
Contact: Frances Ann Giron, Executive Director
X (Twitter): x.com/jccvc
Description: Promotes business and community development in Johnson City, TX. **Geographic Preference:** Local.

45227 ■ Joshua Area Chamber of Commerce (JACC)
100 N Main St., Ste. A
Joshua, TX 76058
Ph: (817)994-4927
Co. E-mail: admin@joshuachamber.com
URL: http://www.joshuachamber.com
Contact: Kim Henderson, President
Facebook: www.facebook.com/joshuaareachamberofcommerce
Instagram: www.instagram.com/joshuachamber
Description: Promotes business and community development in the Joshua, TX area. **Founded:** 1986. **Geographic Preference:** Local.

45228 ■ Katy Area Chamber of Commerce (KACC)
814 E Ave., Ste. G
Katy, TX 77493
Ph: (281)391-5289
Co. E-mail: info@katychamber.com
URL: http://www.katychamber.com
Contact: Matthew Ferraro, President
E-mail: matthew@katychamber.com
Facebook: www.facebook.com/katychamber
Linkedin: www.linkedin.com/company/katy-area-chamber
X (Twitter): x.com/KatyChamber
Instagram: www.instagram.com/katyareachamber
Description: Promotes business and community development in Katy, TX area. **Founded:** 1962. **Geographic Preference:** Local.

45229 ■ Kerens Chamber of Commerce (KCC)
101 S Colket Ave.
Kerens, TX 75144
Ph: (903)396-2391
Co. E-mail: kerenschamber@txun.net
URL: http://ci.kerens.tx.us/community/chamber-of-commerce
Facebook: www.facebook.com/Kerens-Area-Chamber-of-Commerce-143234105724719
Description: Promotes business and community development in Kerens, TX. **Founded:** 1881. **Geographic Preference:** Local.

45230 ■ *Kerrville*
1700 Sidney Baker St., Ste. 100
Kerrville, TX 78028
Ph: (830)896-1155
Co. E-mail: info@kerrvillechamber.biz
URL: http://www.kerrvilletx.com
Contact: Brad Barnett, President
E-mail: brad@kerrvillechamber.biz
URL(s): www.kerrvillechamber.biz/about-kerrville
Availability: Print.

45231 ■ Kerrville Area Chamber of Commerce
1700 Sidney Baker St., Ste. 100
Kerrville, TX 78028
Ph: (830)896-1155
Co. E-mail: info@kerrvillechamber.biz
URL: http://www.kerrvilletx.com
Contact: Brad Barnett, President
E-mail: brad@kerrvillechamber.biz
Facebook: www.facebook.com/KerrvilleAreaChamberOfCommerce
X (Twitter): x.com/KerrAreaChamber
YouTube: www.youtube.com/channel/UCY-MpR73jzLH96POCikWltw
Description: Promotes business and community development in the Kerrville, TX area. **Founded:** 1922. **Publications:** *Kerrville*; *City Map*. **Geographic Preference:** Local.

45232 ■ Kilgore Chamber of Commerce
1108 N Kilgore St.
Kilgore, TX 75662
Ph: (903)984-5022
Co. E-mail: info@kilgorechamber.com
URL: http://www.kilgorechamber.com
Contact: Jill McCartney, President
E-mail: jmccartney@kilgorechamber.com
Facebook: www.facebook.com/KilgoreChamber
Linkedin: www.linkedin.com/company/kilgorechamber
X (Twitter): x.com/KilgoreChamber
Instagram: www.instagram.com/kilgorechamber
Description: Promotes business and community development in Kilgore, TX. Convention/Meeting: none. **Founded:** 1931. **Publications:** *Chamber Notes* (Monthly). **Awards:** Kilgore Chamber of Commerce Citizen of the Year (Annual). **Geographic Preference:** Local.

45233 ■ Kimble County Chamber of Commerce (KCCC)
c/o CLisa Herring, Executive Director
402 Main Junction
Junction, TX 76849
Ph: (325)446-3190
Co. E-mail: junctiontx@cebridge.net
URL: http://www.junctiontexas.com/chamber-of-commerce
Contact: Steve Brown, Co-President
Facebook: www.facebook.com/Kimble-County-Chamber-of-Commerce-Junction-Visitor-Information-248846105141693
Description: Promotes business, tourism, and community development in Kimble County, TX. Sponsors community activities and encourages hunting in the area. **Founded:** 1914. **Publications:** *Hunting Lease Lists* (Annual). **Geographic Preference:** Local.

45234 ■ Kingsland/Lake LBJ Chamber of Commerce
1309 RR 1431
Kingsland, TX 78639
Ph: (325)388-6211
Co. E-mail: kingslandchamber@gmail.com
URL: http://www.kingslandchamber.org
Contact: Darlene Zubkus, Office Manager
Description: Promotes business and community development in the Texas hill country. Conducts annual Bluebonnet Festival, Aquaboom, and Airfest. **Founded:** 1965. **Geographic Preference:** Local.

45235 ■ Kingsville Chamber of Commerce (KCOC)
635 E King Ave.
Kingsville, TX 78363
Ph: (361)592-6438
URL: http://www.kingsville.org
Contact: Manny Salazar, President
Description: Promotes business and community development in Kleberg County, TX. Provides individual and group assistance. Issues publications. **Founded:** 1908. **Geographic Preference:** Local.

45236 ■ Kountze Chamber of Commerce (KCC)
237 S Pine St.
Kountze, TX 77625
Ph: (409)246-3413
Co. E-mail: info@kountzechamber.com
URL: http://kountzechamber.com
Contact: Donya McLaurin, President
Facebook: www.facebook.com/kountze.chamber
Description: Promotes business and community development in Kountze, TX. **Geographic Preference:** Local.

45237 ■ *Kyle Area Chamber of Commerce Business Directory*
401 Center St.
Kyle, TX 78640
Ph: (512)268-4220
Co. E-mail: info@kylechamber.org
URL: http://www.kylechamber.org
Contact: Julie Snyder, Chief Executive Officer
URL(s): www.kylechamber.org/list
Description: Covers businesses in the city of Kyle. **Availability:** Online.

45238 ■ Kyle Area Chamber of Commerce and Visitor's Bureau
401 Center St.
Kyle, TX 78640
Ph: (512)268-4220
Co. E-mail: info@kylechamber.org
URL: http://www.kylechamber.org
Contact: Julie Snyder, Chief Executive Officer
Facebook: www.facebook.com/Kyle.Texas
X (Twitter): x.com/kyletexas
Pinterest: www.pinterest.com/kyletx
Description: Strives to promote interaction among businesses, tourism, and commerce within the city of Kyle. **Founded:** 1998. **Publications:** *Kyle Area Chamber of Commerce Business Directory*. **Geographic Preference:** Local.

45239 ■ La Grange Area Chamber of Commerce
220 W Colorado St.
La Grange, TX 78945
Ph: (979)968-5756
Co. E-mail: chamber@lagrangetx.org
URL: http://lagrangetx.org
Facebook: www.facebook.com/lagrangeareachamberofcommerce
Description: Promotes business and community development in Fayette County, TX. **Founded:** 1950. **Geographic Preference:** Local.

45240 ■ La Porte-Bayshore Chamber of Commerce
100 W Main St.
La Porte, TX 77572
Ph: (281)471-1123
Co. E-mail: info-lpcc@laportechamber.org
URL: http://www.laportechamber.org
Contact: Brenda Thompson, Vice President
Facebook: www.facebook.com/laportebayshorechamber
Instagram: www.instagram.com/laportebayshorechamber
YouTube: www.youtube.com/channel/UC8VCiKtM_-w8Gl6zc6CxkOw
Description: Promotes business and community development in La Porte, TX. **Geographic Preference:** Local.

45241 ■ Lago Vista and Jonestown Area Chamber of Commerce
20624 FM 1431, Ste. No. 8
Lago Vista, TX 78645
Ph: (512)267-7952
Co. E-mail: info@northlaketravischamber.org
URL: http://northlaketravischamber.org
Contact: Imelda Faught, Co-President
Description: Provides services to members and community through marketing and management of economic development and tourism in the Lago Vista area. **Founded:** 1980. **Awards:** Lago Vista and Jonestown Area Chamber of Commerce Citizen of the Year (Annual). **Geographic Preference:** Local.

45242 ■ Lake Buchanan Inks Lake Chamber of Commerce
19611 E State Hwy. 29
Buchanan Dam, TX 78609
Ph: (512)793-2803
Co. E-mail: buchinksoffice@gmail.com
URL: http://www.buchanan-inks.com
Contact: Chris Taylor, Co-President
Facebook: www.facebook.com/Lake-BuchananInks-Lake-Chamber-of-Commerce-105273731453693
Description: Promotes business and community development in Buchanan Dam, TX. **Founded:** 1963. **Geographic Preference:** Local.

STATE LISTINGS

45243 ■ Lake Cities Chamber of Commerce (LCCC)
3101 Garrison St.
Corinth, TX 76210
Ph: (940)497-3097
Co. E-mail: lccc@lakecitieschamber.com
URL: http://lakecitieschamber.com
Contact: Tina Henderson, President
E-mail: director@lakecitieschamber.com
Facebook: www.facebook.com/lakecitieschamber
Description: Strives to promote business and community development in Lake Cities Communities which include the City of Lake Dallas, the City of Corinth, the Town of Shady Shores, and the Town of Hickory Creek, TX. **Founded:** 1972. **Geographic Preference:** Local.

45244 ■ Lake Granbury Area Chamber of Commerce
3408 E Hwy. 377
Granbury, TX 76049
Ph: (817)573-1622
Fax: (817)573-0805
Co. E-mail: info@granburychamber.com
URL: http://www.granburychamber.com
Contact: Roy Kelley, President
Facebook: www.facebook.com/GranburyChamberofCommerce
X (Twitter): x.com/GranburyChamber
Instagram: www.instagram.com/granburychamber
YouTube: www.youtube.com/channel/UCJWZxkjJqrSAnJ8R24jPAKg
Description: Promotes business and community development in the Granbury, TX area. **Founded:** 1952. **Geographic Preference:** Local.

45245 ■ Lake Houston Area Chamber of Commerce
110 W Main St.
Humble, TX 77338
Ph: (281)446-2128
Fax: (281)446-7483
Co. E-mail: chamber@lakehouston.org
URL: http://www.lakehouston.org
Contact: Austin Bird, Vice Chairman of the Board
E-mail: austin.bird@berkeleyeye.com
URL(s): members.houstonnwchamber.org/list/member/lake-houston-area-chamber-of-commerce-9449
Description: Promotes business and community development in Humble, Kingwood, and Atascosita areas, TX. Sponsors Good Oil Days festival. Holds Chamber Classic Golf Tournament and Health Fair Business-Fest. **Founded:** 1923. **Publications:** *Member Business Link* (Quarterly). **Educational Activities:** Aviation. **Geographic Preference:** Local.

45246 ■ Lake Whitney Chamber of Commerce
106 N Colorado St.
Whitney, TX 76692
Ph: (254)694-2540
Co. E-mail: info@lakewhitneychamber.com
URL: http://lakewhitneychamber.com
Contact: Janice Sanders, Executive Director
Facebook: www.facebook.com/LakeWhitneyChamber
Instagram: www.instagram.com/LakeWhitneyChamber
Description: Promotes business, tourism, and community development in the Whitney, TX area. **Geographic Preference:** Local.

45247 ■ Lamar County Chamber of Commerce
8 W Plz.
Paris, TX 75460
Ph: (903)784-2501
Free: 800-727-4789
Fax: (903)784-2158
Co. E-mail: chamber@paristexas.com
URL: http://www.paristexas.com
Contact: Paul Allen, President
E-mail: paul@paristexas.com
Facebook: www.facebook.com/lamarcountychamberofcommerce
Description: Promotes economic growth and quality of life in Paris and the Lamar County, TX area. **Founded:** 1904. **Publications:** *The Chamber Business Report* (Monthly). **Geographic Preference:** Local.

45248 ■ Lampasas County Chamber of Commerce (LCCC)
205 S US Hwy. 281
Lampasas, TX 76550
Ph: (512)556-5172
Fax: (512)556-2195
Co. E-mail: info@lampasaschamber.org
URL: http://www.lampasaschamber.org
Contact: Alexis Thompson, President
Description: Promotes business and community development in Lampasas County, TX. **Founded:** 1918. **Geographic Preference:** Local.

45249 ■ Laredo Chamber of Commerce
2310 San Bernardo
Laredo, TX 78040
Ph: (956)722-9895
Free: 800-292-2122
Fax: (956)791-4503
URL: http://laredochamber.com
Contact: Edward Glassford, President
Facebook: www.facebook.com/laredochamber
X (Twitter): x.com/laredochamber
Instagram: www.instagram.com/laredochamber
YouTube: www.youtube.com/user/laredochamber
Description: Promotes business and community development in Laredo, TX. Provides membership services and international trade information. **Founded:** 1915. **Publications:** *Laredo Economic Activity Index* (Annual); *Inlandport*; *Chamber Notes* (Monthly); *Inlandport* (Monthly). **Educational Activities:** Economic Outlook. **Awards:** Laredo Chamber of Commerce Business Persons of the Year (Annual); Laredo Chamber of Commerce Customer Service Award (Annual). **Geographic Preference:** Local.

45250 ■ Levelland Area Chamber of Commerce (LACC)
1101 Ave., H
Levelland, TX 79336
Ph: (806)894-3157
URL: http://www.levelland.com
Contact: Mary Siders, President
E-mail: msiders@levelland.com
Facebook: www.facebook.com/levellandchamber
X (Twitter): x.com/levellandcofc
Description: Promotes business and community development in the Levelland, TX area. Sponsors Easter egg hunt, Early Settlers Reunion, Marigolds Arts and Crafts Festival, and teachers' breakfast, Leadership Levelland Program, and Small Business Development Center. **Founded:** 1951. **Geographic Preference:** Local.

45251 ■ Lewisville Area Chamber of Commerce (LACC)
551 N Valley Pky.
Lewisville, TX 75067
Ph: (972)436-9571
Fax: (972)436-5949
Co. E-mail: info@lewisvillechamber.org
URL: http://www.lewisvillechamber.org
Contact: Lori Fickling, President
E-mail: lori@lewisvillechamber.org
URL(s): www.uschamber.com/co/chambers/texas/lewisville
Facebook: www.facebook.com/LewisvilleChamber
Instagram: www.instagram.com/lewisvillecc
Description: Promotes business and community development in Lewisville, TX. **Founded:** 1962. **Publications:** *Chamber Guide* (Annual); *Insider* (Monthly). **Geographic Preference:** Local.

45252 ■ Liberty-Dayton Area Chamber of Commerce (LDACC)
1801 Trinity St.
Liberty, TX 77575
Ph: (936)336-5736
Fax: (936)336-1159
Co. E-mail: chamber@imsday.com
URL: http://www.libertydaytonchamber.com
Contact: Mary Anne Campbell, President
Facebook: www.facebook.com/Liberty-Dayton-Area-Chamber-of-Commerce-332605530098718
Description: Promotes business and community development in Dayton and Liberty, TX. Conducts lobbying activities; encourages proper maintenance of local highways. **Founded:** 1909. **Geographic Preference:** Local.

45253 ■ Lindale Area Chamber of Commerce (LACC)
205 S Main St.
Lindale, TX 75771
Ph: (903)882-7181
Fax: (903)882-1790
URL: http://lindalechamber.org
Contact: Shelbie Glover, President
E-mail: shelbie.glover@lindalechamber.org
Facebook: www.facebook.com/lindalechamber
X (Twitter): x.com/LindaleChamber
Instagram: www.instagram.com/lindalechamber
YouTube: www.youtube.com/user/LindaleChamber
Description: Promotes business and community development in Lindale, TX area. **Geographic Preference:** Local.

45254 ■ *Living Magazine*
URL(s): www.livingmagazine.netwww.mckinneychamber.com/list/member/living-magazine-mckinney-allen-edition-rockwall-4698
Released: Bimonthly **Price:** Free. **Description:** Magazine featuring McKinney, TX community lifestyle topics. **Availability:** Print; Online.

45255 ■ Livingston-Polk County Chamber of Commerce
1001 US Hwy. 59, Loop N
Livingston, TX 77351
Ph: (936)327-4929
Fax: (936)327-2660
Co. E-mail: info@polkchamber.com
URL: http://www.polkchamber.com
Contact: David Burns, President
Description: Promotes business and community development in Livingston, TX and Polk County, TX. **Founded:** 1936. **Publications:** *Chamber Connection* (Monthly). **Geographic Preference:** Local.

45256 ■ Llano County Chamber of Commerce (LCCC)
The Railyard Depot
100 Train Station Dr.
Llano, TX 78643
Ph: (325)247-5354
Fax: (325)248-6917
Co. E-mail: llanochamberinfo@llanochamber.org
URL: http://www.llanochamber.org
Contact: Tony Guidroz, Director
Facebook: www.facebook.com/llanotexaschamber
Linkedin: www.linkedin.com/company/llano-chamber-of-commerce
X (Twitter): x.com/llanotxchamber
Description: Promotes business and community development in Llano County, TX. Sponsors local festivals. **Founded:** 1919. **Publications:** *A Walking Tour of Historic Llano*; *Business Directory*; *Historic Llano*. **Geographic Preference:** Local.

45257 ■ Lockhart Chamber of Commerce (LCC)
702 S Commerce St.
Lockhart, TX 78644
Ph: (512)398-2818
Co. E-mail: staff@lockhartchamber.com
URL: http://www.lockhartchamber.com
Contact: Missie Hagan, Chairman of the Board
Facebook: www.facebook.com/LockhartChamberofCommerce
Description: Promotes business and community development in Lockhart, TX. **Founded:** 1935. **Publications:** *Lockhart Enterprise* (Monthly). **Geographic Preference:** Local.

45258 ■ Longview Chamber of Commerce
410 N Center St.
Longview, TX 75601
Ph: (903)237-4000

Co. E-mail: chamber@longviewtx.com
URL: http://longviewchamber.com
Contact: Kelly Hall, President
E-mail: khall@longviewtx.com
Facebook: www.facebook.com/longviewchamber
X (Twitter): x.com/LongviewChamber
Instagram: www.instagram.com/longviewchamber
YouTube: www.youtube.com/channel/UCSpiz98F0c0SGnfG_zh3ixg
Description: Business incubator for new small businesses. **Publications:** *Impact* (Bimonthly); *Uniquely Longview*. **Geographic Preference:** Local.

45259 ■ Los Fresnos Chamber of Commerce
520 E Ocean Blvd.
Los Fresnos, TX 78566
Ph: (956)233-4488
Co. E-mail: office@losfresnoschamber.com
URL: http://cityoflosfresnos.com/chamber
Contact: Val Champion, Executive Director
Facebook: www.facebook.com/losfresnoschamber
X (Twitter): x.com/LosFresnosCC
Description: Promotes, extends and assists all commerce growth in the Los Fresnos area. **Geographic Preference:** Local.

45260 ■ Louise-Hillje Chamber of Commerce
PO Box 156
Louise, TX 77455-0156
Ph: (979)541-7056
URL: http://www.uschamber.com/co/chambers/texas/louise
Contact: Margaret Holik, Treasurer
Description: Promotes business and community development in Louise, TX. **Founded:** 1959. **Geographic Preference:** Local.

45261 ■ Lubbock Chamber of Commerce (LCC)
1500 Broadway, Ste. 101
Lubbock, TX 79401
Ph: (806)761-7000
Fax: (806)761-7013
Co. E-mail: info@lubbockbiz.org
URL: http://www.lubbockchamber.com
Contact: Kay McDowell, President
E-mail: eddie.mcbride@lubbockbiz.org
Facebook: www.facebook.com/lubbockchamberofcommerce
Linkedin: www.linkedin.com/company/lubbock-chamber-of-commerce
X (Twitter): x.com/LubbockChamber
Instagram: www.instagram.com/lubbockchamber
YouTube: www.youtube.com/user/LubbockChamber
Description: Promotes business and community development in Lubbock, TX area. **Founded:** 1913. **Publications:** *Greater Lubbock* (Monthly). **Geographic Preference:** Local.

45262 ■ Lufkin/Angelina County Chamber of Commerce (LACCC)
1615 S Chestnut St.
Lufkin, TX 75901
Ph: (936)634-6644
Fax: (936)634-8726
URL: http://lufkintexas.org
Contact: Tara Watson-Watkins, President
E-mail: twatkins@lufkintexas.org
Facebook: www.facebook.com/LufkinChamber
Linkedin: www.linkedin.com/company/lufkinchamber
X (Twitter): x.com/lufkinchamber
Instagram: www.instagram.com/lufkinchamber
YouTube: www.youtube.com/channel/UCDExGZ1BME8GhJ7c2hw23MA
Description: Promotes business and community development in Angelina County, TX. Sponsors annual Texas Forest Festival and Angelina County Youth Fair. **Founded:** 1919. **Geographic Preference:** Local.

45263 ■ Madison County Chamber of Commerce
113 W Trinity
Madisonville, TX 77864
Ph: (936)348-3591
Co. E-mail: info@madisonchamber.net
URL: http://madisonchamber.net

Contact: Camilla Viator, Co-President
Facebook: www.facebook.com/madisoncounty.chamberofcommerce.9
Description: Promotes business and community development in Madison County, TX. **Founded:** 1962. **Geographic Preference:** Local.

45264 ■ Mansfield Area Chamber of Commerce (MCC)
114 N Main St.
Mansfield, TX 76063
Ph: (817)473-0507
Co. E-mail: info@mansfieldchamber.org
URL: http://www.mansfieldchamber.org
Contact: Lori Williams, President
E-mail: lori@mansfieldchamber.org
Facebook: www.facebook.com/mansfieldCOC
Linkedin: www.linkedin.com/company/the-mansfield-area-chamber-of-commerce
Instagram: www.instagram.com/themansfieldchamber
YouTube: www.youtube.com/themansfieldareachamberofcommerce
Pinterest: www.pinterest.com/MansfieldCOC
Description: Promotes business and community development in Mansfield, TX. Sponsors annual Hometown Celebration, Golf Tournament, Allie Day, Circus (every two years), Spring and Fall Beautification days, Christmas Parade, Tour of Homes. **Founded:** 1951. **Publications:** *Welcome to Mansfield* (Annual); *Mansfield Chamber Communique* (Monthly). **Geographic Preference:** Local.

45265 ■ Marble Falls - Lake LBJ Chamber of Commerce
916 Second St.
Marble Falls, TX 78654-5721
Ph: (830)693-2815
Co. E-mail: information@marblefalls.org
URL: http://www.marblefalls.org
Contact: Steve Hurst, Chairman of the Board
E-mail: steve@hurstlawllc.com
Facebook: www.facebook.com/MarbleFallsCoC
Instagram: www.instagram.com/VisitMarbleFalls
Pinterest: www.pinterest.com/traveltex/featured-marble-falls-texas
Description: Promotes business and community development in Marble Falls, TX. **Founded:** 1959. **Geographic Preference:** Local.

45266 ■ Marfa Chamber of Commerce
PO Box 635
Marfa, TX 79843
Ph: (432)295-0509
Co. E-mail: marfachamberofcommerce@gmail.com
URL: http://marfachamberofcommerce.org
Contact: Abby Boyd, President
Facebook: www.facebook.com/marfachamber
Instagram: www.instagram.com/marfatxchamber
Description: Promotes business and community development in Marfa, TX. **Geographic Preference:** Local.

45267 ■ Marion County Chamber of Commerce (MCCC)
111 E Austin St.
Jefferson, TX 75657
Ph: (903)665-2672
Co. E-mail: info@marioncountychamber.org
URL: http://marioncountychamber.org
Contact: Paul Moore, President
E-mail: director@marioncountychamber.org
Facebook: www.facebook.com/jeffersontexaschamber
Description: Promotes business community and economic development in Marion County, TX. Encourages tourism. **Founded:** 1950. **Geographic Preference:** Local.

45268 ■ Marlin Chamber of Commerce (MCC)
245 Coleman St.
Marlin, TX 76661
Ph: (254)803-3301
Fax: (254)883-2171
Co. E-mail: marlintxchamber@aol.com
URL: http://marlintexas.com
Contact: Byrleen Terry, Treasurer

Facebook: www.facebook.com/Marlin-Chamber-of-Commerce-1587843868209885/home
Description: Promotes business and community development in Marlin, TX. **Geographic Preference:** Local.

45269 ■ Marshall Texas Chamber of Commerce
110 S Bolivar St., Ste. 101
Marshall, TX 75670
Ph: (903)935-7868
Co. E-mail: info@marshalltexas.com
URL: http://marshalltexas.com
Contact: Stacia Runnels, Executive Director
E-mail: srunnels@marshalltexas.com
Description: Promotes business and community development in the Marshall, TX area. **Publications:** *Focus* (Monthly). **Geographic Preference:** Local.

45270 ■ Mason County Chamber of Commerce
108 Fort McKavitt St.
Mason, TX 76856
Ph: (325)347-5758
Fax: (325)347-5259
Co. E-mail: masontexas@hctc.net
URL: http://masontxcoc.com
Contact: Will Lehmberg, President
X (Twitter): x.com/momizat
YouTube: www.youtube.com/user/momizat
Description: Promotes business and community development in Mason County, TX. **Publications:** *Mason Chamber News* (Bimonthly). **Geographic Preference:** Local.

45271 ■ McAllen Chamber of Commerce [McAllen Convention and Visitors Bureau]
1200 Ash Ave.
McAllen, TX 78501
Ph: (956)682-2871
Co. E-mail: membership@mcallenchamber.com
URL: http://mcallen.org
Contact: Gerry Garcia, Chief Executive Officer
E-mail: ggarcia@mcallenchamber.com
Facebook: www.facebook.com/mcallenchamber
X (Twitter): x.com/McAllenCofC
Description: Promotes business and community development in McAllen, TX. **Founded:** 1926. **Geographic Preference:** Local.

45272 ■ McCamey Chamber of Commerce
201 E 6th St.
McCamey, TX 79752
Ph: (432)652-9300
Co. E-mail: mccameycofc@gmail.com
Contact: Gary Elliott, President
Facebook: www.facebook.com/mccameycofc
Description: Promotes business and community development in McCamey, TX. Conducts charitable activities, July 4th Activities, Teacher's Tea, Wind Energy Bluegrass Festival, Community Calendar, Lighted Christmas Parade, Santa at the Bank, and Merchant Auction. **Founded:** 1958. **Geographic Preference:** Local.

45273 ■ McGregor Chamber of Commerce and Agriculture
303 S Main St.
McGregor, TX 76657
Ph: (254)840-2292
Co. E-mail: office@mcgregorchamber.com
URL: http://mcgregorchamber.com
Contact: Terry Sloan, President
Facebook: www.facebook.com/303main
Linkedin: www.linkedin.com/company/mcgregor-chamber-of-commerce
X (Twitter): x.com/mcgregorchamber
Instagram: www.instagram.com/mcgregorchamber
YouTube: www.youtube.com/channel/UCxbakBCXoTAlvvt6aKAy5zg
Description: Promotes business and community development in McGregor, TX. Conducts seasonal promotions with special events. **Founded:** 1882. **Geographic Preference:** Local.

STATE LISTINGS

45274 ■ McKinney Chamber of Commerce (MCC)
1700 N Redbud Blvd.
McKinney, TX 75069
Ph: (972)542-0163
Fax: (972)548-0876
Co. E-mail: info@mckinneychamber.com
URL: http://www.mckinneychamber.com
Contact: Lisa Hermes, II, President
E-mail: lhermes@mckinneychamber.com
Facebook: www.facebook.com/mckinneychamber
Linkedin: www.linkedin.com/company/mckinney-chamber-of-commerce
X (Twitter): x.com/mckinneychamber
Instagram: www.instagram.com/mckinneychamber
YouTube: www.youtube.com/channel/UCRu8YNMBNQOX35Nc4iLn6Ow
Description: Promotes business and community development in McKinney, TX. Monitors legislation. **Founded:** 1906. **Educational Activities:** State of the City; Business after Hours; McKinney Community Awards Celebration (Annual). **Awards:** McKinney Chamber of Commerce Citizen of the Year (Annual); McKinney Chamber of Commerce Outstanding Business of the Year (Annual). **Geographic Preference:** Local.

45275 ■ *McKinney Focus*
Released: Monthly **Availability:** Print; Online.

45276 ■ *Membership Directory*
404 W Main St., Ste. 102
Azle, TX 76020
Ph: (817)444-1112
Co. E-mail: info@azlechamber.com
URL: http://www.azlechamber.com/home
Contact: Kim Ware, Co-President
URL(s): www.azlechamber.com/members/member-benefits
Availability: Print.

45277 ■ *Membership Directory*
520 N Glenbrook Dr.
Garland, TX 75040
Ph: (972)272-7551
Fax: (972)276-9261
Co. E-mail: info@garlandchamber.com
URL: http://www.garlandchamber.com
Contact: Karina Olivares, President
E-mail: karina.olivares@garlandchamber.com
URL(s): garlandchamber.chambermaster.com/list
Description: Contains information on the association and the City of Garland. **Availability:** Print.

45278 ■ Mercedes Chamber of Commerce (MCC)
320 S Ohio
Mercedes, TX 78570
Ph: (956)565-2221
URL: http://mercedeschamber.com
Contact: Fred Gonzalez, President
Facebook: www.facebook.com/Mercedes-Chamber-of-Commerce-199488804449
X (Twitter): x.com/MercedesEDC
Description: Promotes business and community development in Mercedes, TX. **Founded:** 1930. **Geographic Preference:** Local.

45279 ■ Merkel Chamber of Commerce
100 Kent St.
Merkel, TX 79536
Ph: (325)928-4911
Fax: (325)928-3171
URL: http://merkeltexas.com/our-history
Facebook: www.facebook.com/cityofmerkel
Description: Promotes business and community development in Merkel, TX. **Founded:** 1955. **Geographic Preference:** Local.

45280 ■ Metrocrest Chamber of Commerce
14681 Midway Rd., Ste. 200
Addison, TX 75001
Ph: (972)746-5768
Co. E-mail: info@metrocrestchamber.com
URL: http://metrocrestchamber.com
Contact: Hayden Austin, President
Facebook: www.facebook.com/MetrocrestChamber
X (Twitter): x.com/MetrocrestCofC
Instagram: www.instagram.com/metrocrestchamber
Description: Promotes business and community development in the area. **Publications:** *Metrocrest Membergram*. **Geographic Preference:** Local.

45281 ■ Mexia Area Chamber of Commerce
214 N Sherman
Mexia, TX 76667
Ph: (254)562-5569
URL: http://mexiachamber.com
Contact: Keath Huff, President
Facebook: www.facebook.com/MexiaChamber
Linkedin: www.linkedin.com/company/mexia-area-chamber-of-commerce
Description: Promotes business and community development in Mexia, TX. **Founded:** 1872. **Geographic Preference:** Local.

45282 ■ Midland Chamber of Commerce
303 W Wall St., Ste. 200
Midland, TX 79701
Ph: (432)683-3381
Fax: (432)686-3556
Co. E-mail: info@midland.biz
URL: http://www.midlandtxchamber.com
Contact: Bobby Burns, President
Facebook: www.facebook.com/midlandtxchamber
Linkedin: www.linkedin.com/company/midlandtxchamber
X (Twitter): x.com/MidlandChamber
Instagram: www.instagram.com/midlandtxchamber
Description: Promotes business and community development in the Midland, TX area. **Founded:** 1924. **Publications:** *Citylife* (Semiannual); *Duncanville Chamber of Commerce--Membership Directory* (Annual); *Midland Business Journal* (Monthly); *Midland Chamber of Commerce--Surveys* (Annual). **Geographic Preference:** Local.

45283 ■ Midland Hispanic Chamber of Commerce (MHCC)
208 S Marienfeld St., Ste. 100
Midland, TX 79701
Ph: (432)704-5533
Co. E-mail: info@midlandhcc.com
URL: http://midlandhcc.com
Contact: Luis Sanchez, Executive Director
Facebook: www.facebook.com/midlandhcc
X (Twitter): x.com/midlandhcc
Instagram: www.instagram.com/midlandhcc_
Description: Offers support and office space for early-stage or home-based businesses.

45284 ■ Midlothian Chamber of Commerce (MCC)
513 S 9th St.
Midlothian, TX 76065
Ph: (972)723-8600
Co. E-mail: info@midlothianchamber.org
URL: http://midlothianchamber.org
Contact: Laura Terhune, Co-President Co-Chief Executive Officer
E-mail: laura@midlothianchamber.org
Facebook: www.facebook.com/MidlothianChamber
X (Twitter): x.com/midlochamber
Instagram: www.instagram.com/midlothianchamber
YouTube: www.youtube.com/midlothianchamber
Description: Promotes business and community development in Midlothian, TX. Conducts sporting competitions. Sponsors Mad Hatters Easter Parade, Christmas Light-Up Celebration, and a fall festival and craft sale. Conducts quarterly business seminar. **Founded:** 1936. **Publications:** *FYI - Weekly Bulletin* (Weekly (Mon.)). **Educational Activities:** Multi-Chamber Business Expo. **Awards:** Gene Page Award (Annual); Midlothian Chamber of Commerce Chamber Achievement Award (Annual); Gene Rodgers Community Service Award (Annual). **Geographic Preference:** Local.

45285 ■ Mills County Chamber of Commerce (MCCOC)
1219 Fisher St.
Goldthwaite, TX 76844
Ph: (325)648-3619
Co. E-mail: gcc@centex.net
URL: http://www.goldthwaiteareachamber.com
Contact: Lori Garner, Executive Director
Description: Promotes business and community development in Mills County, TX. **Publications:** none. **Founded:** 1979. **Geographic Preference:** Local.

45286 ■ Mineral Wells Area Chamber of Commerce
511 E Hubbard St.
Mineral Wells, TX 76067
Ph: (940)325-2557
Fax: (940)328-0850
Co. E-mail: info@mineralwellstx.com
URL: http://www.mineralwellstx.com
Contact: David May, President
E-mail: ceo@mineralwellstx.com
Facebook: www.facebook.com/mineralwellstx
X (Twitter): x.com/chambermw
Description: Promotes business and community development in Mineral Wells, TX. Sponsors festivals as well as athletic and community activities. **Founded:** 1925. **Publications:** *Destination Guide* (Semiannual); *Plan of Action* (Annual); *Visitors Guide* (Annual). **Geographic Preference:** Local.

45287 ■ Monahans Chamber of Commerce
1525 E Monahans Pky.
Monahans, TX 79756-4609
Ph: (432)943-2187
Co. E-mail: chamber@monahans.org
URL: http://www.monahans.org
Contact: Randy Crabtree, President
Facebook: www.facebook.com/monahanschamber
X (Twitter): x.com/monahanschamber
YouTube: www.youtube.com/channel/UCf5O3h1paQVxlCnDs2eli9A
Description: Promotes business and community development in Monahans, TX. **Founded:** 2004. **Geographic Preference:** Local.

45288 ■ *Monthly Networking*
29201 Quinn Rd., Ste. B
Tomball, TX 77377-0516
Ph: (281)351-7222
Free: 866-670-7222
Fax: (281)351-7223
URL: http://www.tomballchamber.org
Contact: Bruce Hillegeist, President
E-mail: bhillegeist@tomballchamber.org
URL(s): business.tomballchamber.org/events/details/gtacc-networking-breakfast-37964
Released: Bimonthly **Availability:** Print.

45289 ■ Moulton Chamber of Commerce and Agriculture
405 S Lavaca
Moulton, TX 77975
Ph: (361)401-9886
Co. E-mail: chamber@moultontexas.com
URL: http://www.moultontexas.com
Contact: Danielle Buehring, Contact
Facebook: www.facebook.com/MoultonChamberofCommerce
Description: Promotes business and community development in Moulton, TX. **Geographic Preference:** Local.

45290 ■ Mount Pleasant/Titus County Chamber of Commerce
1604 N Jefferson Ave.
Mount Pleasant, TX 75455
Ph: (903)572-8567
Fax: (903)572-0613
Co. E-mail: info@mtpleasanttx.com
URL: http://www.mtpleasanttx.com
Contact: Richard Bonney, President
Facebook: www.facebook.com/mountpleasanttx
Instagram: www.instagram.com/mountpleasanttx
Description: Promotes business and community development in Titus County, TX. **Publications:** *Chamber Matters* (Quarterly). **Geographic Preference:** Local.

45291 ■ Muleshoe Chamber of Commerce and Agriculture
110 Heritage Dr.
Muleshoe, TX 79347

Ph: (806)272-5873
Co. E-mail: muleshoetxchamber@gmail.com
Facebook: www.facebook.com/muleshoecofc
Description: Promotes business and community development in Muleshoe, TX. **Founded:** 1951. **Publications:** *Muleshoe Journal.* **Geographic Preference:** Local.

45292 ■ *Muleshoe Journal*
110 Heritage Dr.
Muleshoe, TX 79347
Ph: (806)272-5873
Co. E-mail: muleshoetxchamber@gmail.com
URL(s): www.muleshoejournal.com
Price: $27, for online Muleshoe per year; $29, for bailey county per year; $40, for outside bailey county per year; $22, for edition per year. **Description:** Community newspaper. **Availability:** Print; PDF.

45293 ■ **Nacogdoches County Chamber of Commerce (NCCC)**
2516 N St.
Nacogdoches, TX 75965
Ph: (936)560-5533
Fax: (936)560-3920
Co. E-mail: chamber@nactx.com
URL: http://www.nacogdoches.org/index.php
Contact: C. Wayne Mitchell, President
Facebook: www.facebook.com/NacogdochesCountyChamberofCommerce
Linkedin: www.linkedin.com/company/nacogdoches-county-chamber-of-commerce
X (Twitter): x.com/nacchamber
Instagram: www.instagram.com/nacogdocheschamber
YouTube: www.youtube.com/channel/UCWaUhnHlSaLit9-ksqQQdlg
Description: Promotes business and community development in Nacogdoches County, TX. **Founded:** 1920. **Geographic Preference:** Local.

45294 ■ **Navasota Grimes County Chamber of Commerce**
117 S LaSalle St.
Navasota, TX 77868
Ph: (936)825-6600
URL: http://www.navasotagrimeschamber.com
Contact: YoLanda Fultz, President
Facebook: www.facebook.com/NavasotaGrimesChamber
Description: Promotes business and community development in Grimes County, TX. **Founded:** 1916. **Geographic Preference:** Local.

45295 ■ *NETwork*
5001 Denton Hwy.
Haltom City, TX 76117
Ph: (817)281-9376
Co. E-mail: info@netarrant.org
URL: http://www.netarrant.org
Contact: Chris Brooks, Contact
URL(s): www.netarrant.org/networking.html
Released: Monthly **Availability:** Online.

45296 ■ **New Boston Chamber of Commerce**
1 Trail Head Pk. Plz.
New Boston, TX 75570
Ph: (903)628-2581
Co. E-mail: chamber@newbostontx.org
URL: http://www.newbostontx.org
Contact: Tim Graham, President
E-mail: tdgraham89@gmail.com
Description: Promotes business and community development in New Boston, TX. **Publications:** *Chamber Notes* (Quarterly). **Geographic Preference:** Local.

45297 ■ **Nocona Area Chamber of Commerce (NCC)**
304 Clay St., Ste. 3
Nocona, TX 76255
Ph: (940)825-3526
Co. E-mail: noconachamber@nocona.org
URL: http://www.nocona.org/commerce
Contact: Mitzi Fenoglio, President

Description: Promotes business and community development in the Nocona, TX area. Sponsors bicycle and 5K races, Day in the Park, and Red River Romp. Conducts charitable activities. **Geographic Preference:** Local.

45298 ■ **North Channel Area Chamber of Commerce (NCACC)**
13301 E Fwy., Ste. 100
Houston, TX 77015
Ph: (713)450-3600
Co. E-mail: info@ncachamber.com
URL: http://northchannelarea.com
Contact: Margie Buentello, President
E-mail: margie@ncachamber.com
Facebook: www.facebook.com/ncachamber
Linkedin: www.linkedin.com/company/north-channel-area-chamber-of-commerce
X (Twitter): x.com/NCACC_
Instagram: www.instagram.com/ncacc_
YouTube: www.youtube.com/channel/UCfOSC2vL0bWqMrfjBMLgJDA
Description: Promotes business and community development in Northeast Harris County, TX. Sponsors community festival. Conducts charitable activities. **Founded:** 1977. **Geographic Preference:** Local.

45299 ■ **North Dallas Chamber of Commerce (NDCC)**
5710 Lyndon B Johnson Fwy., Ste. 100
Dallas, TX 75240
Ph: (469)923-2100
URL: http://ndcc.org
Contact: Ken S. Malcolmson, President
E-mail: kmalcolmson@ndcc.org
Facebook: www.facebook.com/northdallaschamber
Linkedin: www.linkedin.com/company/north-dallas-chamber-of-commerce
X (Twitter): x.com/ndcc
Instagram: www.instagram.com/northdallaschamber
YouTube: www.youtube.com/user/NorthDallasChamber
Description: Promotes business and community development in Northern Dallas, TX. **Founded:** 1954. **Publications:** *More than News.* **Geographic Preference:** Local.

45300 ■ **North Galveston County Chamber of Commerce**
218 FM 517 W
Dickinson, TX 77539
Ph: (281)534-4380
Fax: (281)534-4389
URL: http://www.northgalvestoncountychamber.com
Contact: Alicen Newman, President
Facebook: www.facebook.com/NorthGalvestonCountyChamber
Description: Promotes business and community development in northern Galveston County, TX. **Founded:** 1948. **Publications:** *Wave* (Monthly). **Geographic Preference:** Local.

45301 ■ **North San Antonio Chamber of Commerce (NSACC)**
12930 Country Pky.
San Antonio, TX 78216
Ph: (210)344-4848
Co. E-mail: info@northsachamber.com
URL: http://www.northsachamber.com
Contact: Cristina Aldrete, President
E-mail: hbarrett@northsachamber.com
Facebook: www.facebook.com/northsachamber
Linkedin: www.linkedin.com/company/north-san-antonio-chamber-of-commerce
X (Twitter): x.com/NorthSAChamber
Instagram: www.instagram.com/northsachamber
YouTube: www.youtube.com/user/NorthSAChamber
Description: Promotes business and community development in San Antonio, TX. **Founded:** 1974. **Publications:** *North Chamber News* (Monthly). **Educational Activities:** Enterprising Women's Conference. **Awards:** North San Antonio Chamber of Commerce Athena Leadership Award (Annual). **Geographic Preference:** Local.

45302 ■ **Northeast Tarrant Chamber of Commerce**
5001 Denton Hwy.
Haltom City, TX 76117
Ph: (817)281-9376
Co. E-mail: info@netarrant.org
URL: http://www.netarrant.org
Contact: Chris Brooks, Contact
Facebook: www.facebook.com/northeasttarrantchamber
Linkedin: www.linkedin.com/company/northeasttarrantchamber
X (Twitter): x.com/netarrant
Description: Promotes business and community development in Northeast Tarrant County, TX. **Founded:** 1957. **Publications:** *NETwork* (Monthly). **Geographic Preference:** Local.

45303 ■ **Nueces Canyon Chamber of Commerce**
103 S Nueces St.
Camp Wood, TX 78833
Ph: (830)597-6241
Co. E-mail: nuecescanyonchamber@gmail.com
URL: http://www.chamber-commerce.net/dir/9320/Nueces-Canyon-Chamber-of-Commerce-in-Camp-Wood
URL(s): www.nuecescanyonchamber.org
Facebook: www.facebook.com/Nueces-Canyon-Chamber-of-Commerce-744470479033826
Description: Promotes business and community development in Camp Wood, TX. **Geographic Preference:** Local.

45304 ■ **Oak Cliff Chamber of Commerce (OCCC)**
400 S Zang Blvd.
Dallas, TX 75208
Ph: (214)943-4567
Co. E-mail: occ@oakcliffchamber.org
URL: http://www.oakcliffchamber.org
Contact: Jim Lake, Chairman of the Board
Facebook: www.facebook.com/Oak-Cliff-Chamber-of-Commerce-105530486724
Description: Promotes business and community development in Oak Cliff area. **Founded:** 1920. **Publications:** *Reporter.* **Geographic Preference:** Local.

45305 ■ **Odessa Black Chamber of Commerce**
700 N Grant Ave., Ste. 200
Odessa, TX 79761
Ph: (432)332-5812
Co. E-mail: info@odessablackchamber.com
URL: http://www.odessablackchamber.com
Contact: Chris E. Walker, President
Description: Represents Black owned businesses. **Geographic Preference:** Regional.

45306 ■ **Odessa Chamber of Commerce**
700 N Grant Ave., Ste. 200
Odessa, TX 79761
Ph: (432)332-9111
Fax: (432)333-7858
URL: http://odessachamber.com
Contact: Valarie Leonard, Controller
E-mail: valariel@odessachamber.com
Facebook: www.facebook.com/ChamberOdessa
Linkedin: www.linkedin.com/company/odessa-chamber-of-commerce
X (Twitter): x.com/OdessaChamber
YouTube: www.youtube.com/user/OdessaChamber
Description: Strives to provide leadership necessary to promote a favorable economic environment, while improving the quality of life in Odessa, Missouri and the surrounding areas. **Founded:** 1934. **Publications:** *Odessa Chamber of Commerce--Membership Directory.* **Geographic Preference:** Local.

45307 ■ **Olney Chamber of Commerce**
108 E Main St.
Olney, TX 76374
Ph: (940)564-5445
Fax: (940)564-3610
Co. E-mail: chamber@brazosnet.com
URL: http://olneytexas.com/board-of-directors

STATE LISTINGS

Contact: Anna Rogers, President
Facebook: www.facebook.com/olneychamber
Description: Promotes business and community development in the Olney, Texas area. **Geographic Preference:** Local.

45308 ■ *Online Member Directory*
700 Parker Sq., Ste. No. 100
Flower Mound, TX 75028
Ph: (972)539-0500
Fax: (972)539-4307
URL: http://flowermoundchamber.com
Contact: Lori Walker, President
E-mail: l.walker@flowermoundchamber.com
URL(s): www.chamberdata.net/businesssearch.aspx?dbid2=txfm
Availability: Online.

45309 ■ Ozona Chamber of Commerce
505 15th St.
Ozona, TX 76943
Ph: (325)392-3737
Fax: (325)392-3485
Co. E-mail: oztxcoc@aol.com
URL: http://www.ozona.com/index.php
Contact: Shanon Biggerstaff, President
Facebook: www.facebook.com/OzonaChamber
X (Twitter): x.com/OzonaChamber
YouTube: www.youtube.com/channel/UC4CA03lwHxPsGwCSojODNrg
Pinterest: www.pinterest.com/OzonaChamber
Description: Promotes business and community development in Ozona, TX. **Founded:** 1962. **Publications:** *Chamber Dialogue* (Annual). **Geographic Preference:** Local.

45310 ■ Palacios Chamber of Commerce
420 Main St.
Palacios, TX 77465
Ph: (361)972-2615
Co. E-mail: palcoc@tisd.net
URL: http://palacioschamber.com
Contact: Sally Kurtz, President
E-mail: skurtz@cftexas.org
YouTube: www.youtube.com/channel/UC5Jngln7dqCapMx4hUkcfyQ
Description: Promotes business, tourism, and community development along the Central Texas coast. Conducts annual fishing tournament and annual awards banquet. **Founded:** 1910. **Geographic Preference:** Local.

45311 ■ Palestine Area Chamber of Commerce (PCC)
401 W Main St.
Palestine, TX 75801
Ph: (903)729-6066
Co. E-mail: info@palestinechamber.org
URL: http://www.palestinechamber.org
Contact: Heather Chancellor, President
E-mail: president@palestinechamber.org
Facebook: www.facebook.com/palestinechamber
X (Twitter): x.com/palestinetxcofc
Instagram: www.instagram.com/palestinechamber
YouTube: www.youtube.com/channel/UC_qrckS-AAtEBxr3zRW-EBA
Description: Promotes business and community development in the area. Sponsors events and festivals. **Founded:** 1846. **Publications:** *Connection* (Weekly). **Geographic Preference:** Local.

45312 ■ Panola County Chamber of Commerce (PCCC)
300 W Panola St.
Carthage, TX 75633
Ph: (903)693-6634
Fax: (903)693-8578
Co. E-mail: cvb@carthagetexas.com
URL: http://www.carthagetexas.us/community/chamber_of_commerce/index.php
Contact: Tommie Ritter Smith, Contact
Facebook: www.facebook.com/Panola-County-Chamber-of-Commerce-152587786101
Description: Promotes business and community development in Panola County, TX. **Founded:** 1946. **Geographic Preference:** Local.

45313 ■ Pasadena Chamber of Commerce
4334 Fairmont Pky.
Pasadena, TX 77504
Ph: (281)487-7871
Fax: (281)487-5530
Co. E-mail: info@pasadenachamber.org
URL: http://www.pasadenachamber.org
Contact: Cristina Womack, President
E-mail: cristina@pasadenachamber.org
Linkedin: www.linkedin.com/company/pasadena-chamber-of-commerce
X (Twitter): x.com/PasadenaTX_CoC
Instagram: www.instagram.com/pasadenachamber_tx
YouTube: www.youtube.com/channel/UC_WdCGMTLc4dCnzVmk61Vmw
Description: Promotes business and community development in Pasadena, TX. Sponsors annual festival. Holds monthly After Hours business mixer and monthly business, industry, and professional luncheons with speakers per year. **Founded:** 1927. **Publications:** *Chambergram* (Monthly); *Pasadena Chamber of Commerce Membership Directory*. **Awards:** Pasadena Chamber of Commerce Small Business of the Year (Annual). **Geographic Preference:** Local.

45314 ■ *Pasadena Chamber of Commerce Membership Directory*
4334 Fairmont Pky.
Pasadena, TX 77504
Ph: (281)487-7871
Fax: (281)487-5530
Co. E-mail: info@pasadenachamber.org
URL: http://www.pasadenachamber.org
Contact: Cristina Womack, President
E-mail: cristina@pasadenachamber.org
URL(s): www.pasadena-chamber.org/directory
Availability: Print.

45315 ■ Pearland Chamber of Commerce
6117 Broadway St.
Pearland, TX 77581
Ph: (281)485-3634
Co. E-mail: cheryl.kepp@pearlandtexaschamber.us
URL: http://www.pearlandchamber.com
Contact: Cheryl Kepp, Senior Vice President
E-mail: cheryl.kepp@pearlandtexaschamber.us
Facebook: www.facebook.com/PearlandChamber
Linkedin: www.linkedin.com/pearlandchamber
X (Twitter): x.com/PearlandChamber
Instagram: www.instagram.com/pearland_chamber
YouTube: www.youtube.com/c/PearlandChamberofCommerce
Description: Promotes business and community development in the Pearland, TX area. **Publications:** *Chamber Connection* (Monthly); *Chambergram* (Weekly). **Awards:** Pearland Area Chamber of Commerce Citizen of the Year Award (Irregular). **Geographic Preference:** Local.

45316 ■ Pecos Area Chamber of Commerce
100 E Dot Stafford St.
Pecos, TX 79772
Ph: (432)445-2406
Fax: (432)445-2407
Co. E-mail: infopecostx@gmail.com
URL: http://visitpecos.com/pecos-chamber
Description: Promotes business and community development in Pecos, TX. **Founded:** 1957. **Publications:** *Pecos Billboard* (Quarterly). **Geographic Preference:** Local.

45317 ■ Perryton-Ochiltree Chamber of Commerce
2000 S Main St.
Perryton, TX 79070
Ph: (806)435-6575
Co. E-mail: ptnchamber@gmail.com
URL: http://www.perryton.org
Contact: Lea Thomas, Co-President
Facebook: www.facebook.com/PerrytonOchiltreeChamberOfCommerce
X (Twitter): x.com/PtnChamber
Instagram: www.instagram.com/perrytonchamber

Description: Promotes business and community development in Perryton, TX. **Founded:** 1958. **Geographic Preference:** Local.

45318 ■ Pilot Point Chamber of Commerce (PPCC)
201 S Jefferson St.
Pilot Point, TX 76258
Ph: (940)686-5385
Co. E-mail: chamber@pilotpoint.org
URL: http://www.pilotpoint.org
Contact: Ric Sadler, President
Facebook: www.facebook.com/PilotPointChamberofCommerce
Description: Promotes business and community development in Pilot Point, TX. **Founded:** 2012. **Geographic Preference:** Local.

45319 ■ Plainview Chamber of Commerce (PCC)
1906 W 5th St.
Plainview, TX 79072
Ph: (806)296-7431
Fax: (806)296-0819
Co. E-mail: info@plainviewtexaschamber.com
URL: http://www.plainviewtexaschamber.com
Contact: Kerry McCormack, President
Facebook: www.facebook.com/PlainviewChamberOfCommerce
Description: Promotes business and community development in the area. **Geographic Preference:** Local.

45320 ■ Plano Chamber of Commerce
5400 Independence Pky., Ste. 200.
Plano, TX 75023
Ph: (972)424-7547
Fax: (972)422-5182
Co. E-mail: info@planochamber.org
URL: http://www.planochamber.org
Contact: Kelle Marsalis, President
E-mail: kellem@planochamber.org
Facebook: www.facebook.com/PlanoChamberofCommerce
X (Twitter): x.com/PlanoTXChamber
Description: Provides resources to maximize business performance through advocacy, education and networking. Over 1,500 business members from Plano and the surrounding area. **Founded:** 1946. **Publications:** *Business Plan*; *Business Resource Directory*. **Awards:** Plano Chamber of Commerce Athena Award (Annual); Plano Chamber of Commerce Citizen of the Year (Annual); Plano Chamber of Commerce Small Business Person of the Year (Annual). **Geographic Preference:** Local.

45321 ■ Port Aransas Chamber of Commerce
403 W Cotter Ave.
Port Aransas, TX 78373
Ph: (361)749-5919
Co. E-mail: info@portaransas.org
URL: http://portaransas.org
Contact: Brett Stawar, Chief Executive Officer
Facebook: www.facebook.com/VisitPortAransas
X (Twitter): x.com/portatexas
Instagram: www.instagram.com/portatexas
YouTube: www.youtube.com/user/PortAransasTexas
Description: Promotes business and community development in Port Aransas, TX area. **Founded:** 1974. **Geographic Preference:** Local.

45322 ■ Port Arthur Chamber of Commerce (PACC)
501 Procter St., Ste. 300
Port Arthur, TX 77640
Ph: (409)963-1107
Fax: (409)962-1997
URL: http://www.portarthurtexas.com
Contact: Pat Avery, President
E-mail: president@portarthurtexas.com
X (Twitter): x.com/GPACC1
Description: Promotes business and community development in Mid-southern Jefferson County, TX. **Founded:** 1899. **Publications:** *Clubs and Organizations Directory* (Periodic); *Manufacturing Directory* (Periodic). **Educational Activities:** Business Expo; Shrimp Fest. **Geographic Preference:** Local.

45323 ■ Port Isabel Chamber of Commerce
c/o Betty Wells, President
421 Queen Isabella Blvd.
Port Isabel, TX 78578
Ph: (956)943-2262
Fax: (956)943-4001
Co. E-mail: portisabelchamber@gmail.com
URL: http://www.portisabelchamber.com
Contact: Betty Wells, Co-President
E-mail: director@portisabel.org
Facebook: www.facebook.com/portisabelchamber
X (Twitter): x.com/pi_chamber
Description: Promotes business and community development in the Port Isabel, TX area. **Publications:** *Historic Port Isabel.* **Geographic Preference:** Local.

45324 ■ Port Mansfield Chamber of Commerce
101 E Port St.
Port Mansfield, TX 78598
Ph: (956)944-2354
Co. E-mail: contact@pmchamber.com
URL: http://www.portmansfieldchamber.com
Contact: Bill Gregson, President
Facebook: www.facebook.com/portmansfieldchamber
Description: Promotes business and community development in Port Mansfield, TX. **Geographic Preference:** Local.

45325 ■ Port Neches Chamber of Commerce (PNCC)
1110 Port Neches Ave.
Port Neches, TX 77651
Ph: (409)722-9155
Fax: (409)722-7380
URL: http://portnecheschamber.org
Contact: Lance Bradley, President
Description: Promotes business and community development in Port Neches, TX. **Founded:** 1941. **Publications:** *Neches News* (Monthly). **Geographic Preference:** Local.

45326 ■ Portland Chamber of Commerce
1211 US Hwy. 181
Portland, TX 78374
Ph: (361)777-4650
Co. E-mail: director@portlandtx.org
URL: http://www.portlandtx.org
Contact: Shelly Stuart, Co-Chief Executive Officer Co-President
E-mail: director@portlandtx.org
Facebook: www.facebook.com/portlandtx.org
Linkedin: www.linkedin.com/in/portlandtxchamberofcommerce
X (Twitter): x.com/visitportlandtx
Instagram: www.instagram.com/visitportlandtx
YouTube: www.youtube.com/channel/UCpvBwWeFtLLCs4aKWN9Yg0g
Pinterest: www.pinterest.com/visitportlandtx
Description: Promotes business and community development in Portland, TX. Sponsors Portland WindFest, Taste of Portland, and Auction. **Founded:** 1963. **Publications:** *Official Guide to Portland* (Periodic). **Geographic Preference:** Local.

45327 ■ Princeton - Lowery Crossing Chamber of Commerce
123 W Princeton Dr., Ste. 200
Princeton, TX 75407
Ph: (815)875-2616
Co. E-mail: info@princetonlowrycrossing.com
URL: http://princetonlowrycrossing.com
Contact: Dave Shouse, President
Description: Promotes business and community development in the area. **Publications:** *Chamber Matters.* **Geographic Preference:** Local.

45328 ■ *Progress Times*
202 W Tom Landry Rd.
Mission, TX 78572
Ph: (956)585-2727
Co. E-mail: gmcc@missionchamber.com
URL: http://www.missionchamber.com
Contact: Brenda Enriquez, President
E-mail: president@missionchamber.com
URL(s): members.missionchamber.com/map
Released: Monthly **Availability:** Print.

45329 ■ Prosper Area Chamber of Commerce
900 N Preston Rd., Ste. E
Prosper, TX 75078
Ph: (972)508-4200
URL: http://www.prosperchamber.com
Facebook: www.facebook.com/ProsperTXChamber
X (Twitter): x.com/ProsperChamber
Description: Promotes business and community development in Prosper, TX area. **Founded:** 1987. **Geographic Preference:** Local.

45330 ■ Ralls Chamber of Commerce
808 Ave. I
Ralls, TX 79357
Contact: Giselle Brock, Contact
Description: Promotes business and community development in Ralls, TX. **Founded:** 1920. **Geographic Preference:** Local.

45331 ■ Red River County Chamber of Commerce
101 N Locust St.
Clarksville, TX 75426
Ph: (903)427-2645
Fax: (903)427-5454
Co. E-mail: redrivercc@windstream.net
URL: http://redrivercoc.org
Contact: Chrissy Witmer, President
Facebook: www.facebook.com/rrccoc
X (Twitter): x.com/rrccoc
Instagram: www.instagram.com/rrccoc
Description: Promotes business and community development in Clarksville, TX. **Founded:** 1921. **Geographic Preference:** Local.

45332 ■ Richardson Chamber of Commerce (RCC)
411 Belle Grove Dr.
Richardson, TX 75080
Ph: (972)792-2800
Co. E-mail: admin@richardsonchamber.com
URL: http://www.richardsonchamber.com
Contact: Kim Quirk, Executive Director
E-mail: kim@richardsonchamber.com
Facebook: www.facebook.com/RichardsonChamber
X (Twitter): x.com/RichardsonCoC
Instagram: www.instagram.com/richardsonchamber
YouTube: www.youtube.com/user/richardsontxchamber
Description: Promotes business and community development in Richardson, TX. **Founded:** 1946. **Publications:** *Richardson Chamber of Commerce Directory.* **Geographic Preference:** Local.

45333 ■ Rio Grande Valley Partnership - Chamber of Commerce
322 S Missouri Ave.
Weslaco, TX 78596
Ph: (956)968-3141
Co. E-mail: info@rgvpartnership.com
URL: http://business.rgvpartnership.com
Contact: Arlene Garza, President
Facebook: www.facebook.com/theRGVPartnership
X (Twitter): x.com/RGVPartnership
Instagram: www.instagram.com/thergvpartnership
Description: Promotes business and community development in the Rio Grande Valley of Texas. **Founded:** 1943. **Publications:** *Agriculture in Rio Grande Valley*; *Business Barometer* (Monthly); *Guide to the Rio Grande Valley* (Annual). **Geographic Preference:** Local.

45334 ■ Rockdale Chamber of Commerce
1203 W Cameron Ave.
Rockdale, TX 76567
Ph: (512)446-2030
Co. E-mail: info@rockdalechamber.com
URL: http://rockdalechamber.com/index.html
Contact: Denise Brock, Executive Director
Facebook: www.facebook.com/RockdaleCoC
X (Twitter): x.com/info2030
Description: Promotes business and community development in Rockdale, TX. **Founded:** 1952. **Publications:** *Chamber E-Newsletter* (Monthly). **Educational Activities:** Planning Conference. **Geographic Preference:** Local.

45335 ■ Rockport-Fulton Chamber of Commerce (RFCC)
319 Broadway St.
Rockport, TX 78382
Ph: (361)729-6445
Free: 800-242-0071
Co. E-mail: membership@1rockport.org
URL: http://www.rockport-fulton.org
Contact: Diane Probst, Co-Chief Executive Officer Co-President
E-mail: president@1rockport.org
Facebook: www.facebook.com/Rockport.Fulton.Chamber
X (Twitter): x.com/CharmofTxCoast
YouTube: www.youtube.com/channel/UCzpNnSiFyrwl4sktSDeuT2Q
Description: Promotes business and community development in Aransas County, TX. Conducts charitable activities. **Founded:** 1912. **Geographic Preference:** Local.

45336 ■ Rockwall Area Chamber of Commerce
697 E I-30
Rockwall, TX 75087
Ph: (972)771-5733
Fax: (972)772-3642
Co. E-mail: communications@rockwallchamber.org
URL: http://www.rockwallchamber.org
Contact: Darby Burkey, President
E-mail: darby@rockwallchamber.org
Facebook: www.facebook.com/rockwallchamber
Linkedin: www.linkedin.com/company/rockwall-area-chamber-of-commerce
X (Twitter): x.com/RockwallChamber
YouTube: www.youtube.com/channel/UCK4CdU2gmEuhPiMCGFRaT4A
Description: Represents the business' interests and promotes a positive growth environment in the Rockwall, Texas area. **Founded:** 1929. **Geographic Preference:** Local.

45337 ■ Round Rock Chamber of Commerce (RRCC)
212 E Main St.
Round Rock, TX 78664
Ph: (512)255-5805
Co. E-mail: info@roundrockchamber.org
URL: http://roundrockchamber.org
Contact: Jason Ball, President
Facebook: www.facebook.com/roundrockchamber
Linkedin: www.linkedin.com/company/round-rock-chamber-of-commerce
X (Twitter): x.com/RRCoC
YouTube: www.youtube.com/channel/UCU6s_6A-TIJ3U8Dkdn8QUMw
Description: Promotes business and community development in Round Rock, TX. Sponsors Frontier Days festival. **Founded:** 1959. **Publications:** *Round Rock Reporter* (Monthly); *Round Rock Welcome Packet* (Semiannual). **Geographic Preference:** Local.

45338 ■ Rowlett Chamber of Commerce
4418 Main St.
Rowlett, TX 75088
Ph: (972)475-3200
Co. E-mail: info@rowlettchamber.com
URL: http://www.rowlettchamber.com
Contact: Michael Gallops, President
E-mail: michael@rowlettchamber.com
Facebook: www.facebook.com/RowlettChamber
X (Twitter): x.com/RowlettChamber
YouTube: www.youtube.com/channel/UCxnPLVTta-rw4wlID6ZHEWQ
Description: Promotes business and community development in Rowlett, TX. **Founded:** 1974. **Publications:** *The Correspondent* (Monthly). **Geographic Preference:** Local.

STATE LISTINGS

45339 ■ Royse City Chamber of Commerce
102 W Old Greenville Rd.
Royse City, TX 75189
Ph: (972)636-5000
Co. E-mail: info@roysecitychamber.com
URL: http://roysecitychamber.com
Contact: Johnny Crenshaw, Chairman
Facebook: www.facebook.com/RoyseChamber
X (Twitter): x.com/roysechamber
Instagram: www.instagram.com/roysecitychamber
Description: Promotes business and community development in Royse City, TX. **Founded:** 1973. **Educational Activities:** FunFest (Annual). **Geographic Preference:** Local.

45340 ■ Rusk Chamber of Commerce
184 N Main St.
Rusk, TX 75785
Ph: (903)683-4242
Co. E-mail: info@ruskchamber.com
URL: http://www.ruskchamber.com
Contact: Tara Hoot, President
E-mail: thoot@austinbank.com
Description: Promotes business and community development in Rusk, TX. Sponsors Indian Summer Arts and Crafts Fair. **Founded:** 1939. **Geographic Preference:** Local.

45341 ■ Sabinal Chamber of Commerce
PO Box 55
Sabinal, TX 78881
URL: http://www.sabinalchamber.org
Contact: Richard H. Nunley, Contact
Facebook: www.facebook.com/SabinalChamber
Description: Promotes business and community development in Sabinal, TX. **Geographic Preference:** Local.

45342 ■ Saginaw Area Chamber of Commerce (SACC)
301 S Saginaw Blvd.
Saginaw, TX 76179-1640
Contact: Tracy Sutton, Contact
Description: Promotes the economic, civic, and cultural welfare of the Saginaw area community. **Founded:** 1972. **Publications:** *Facts by the Tracks* (Monthly). **Geographic Preference:** Local.

45343 ■ Salado Chamber of Commerce
423 S Main St.
Salado, TX 76571
Ph: (254)947-5040
Co. E-mail: chamber@salado.com
URL: http://www.salado.com
Contact: Deanna Whitson, Chairman of the Board
E-mail: deanna.whitson@bxs.com
Facebook: www.facebook.com/SaladoTX
Linkedin: www.linkedin.com/in/salado-chamber-of
-commerce-79a62a170
YouTube: www.youtube.com/channel/
UCleyWiyBWOQyX0ORSDMHelA
Description: Promotes business and community development in Salado. Provide donations to civic organizations; sponsor an annual art show and art fair. **Geographic Preference:** Local.

45344 ■ San Angelo Chamber of Commerce (SACC)
418 W Ave. B
San Angelo, TX 76903
Ph: (325)655-4136
Co. E-mail: chamber@sanangelo.org
URL: http://www.sanangelo.com
Contact: Walt Koenig, President
E-mail: walt@sanangelo.org
X (Twitter): x.com/AngeloChamber
Instagram: www.instagram.com/angelochamber
Description: Promotes business and community development in San Angelo, TX. **Founded:** 1916. **Publications:** *Action Report* (Monthly). **Geographic Preference:** Local.

45345 ■ San Antonio Hispanic Chamber of Commerce (SAHCC)
3006 General Hudnell Dr.
San Antonio, TX 78226
Ph: (210)225-0462
Co. E-mail: communications@sahcc.org
URL: http://www.sahcc.org
Contact: Marina J. Gonzales, President
Facebook: www.facebook.com/sanantonio
.hispanicchamber
X (Twitter): x.com/SAHispanicCC
Instagram: www.instagram.com/sahispaniccc
YouTube: www.youtube.com/user/
SAHispanicChamber
Description: Promotes Hispanic business in San Antonio, TX. **Founded:** 1929. **Publications:** *Hispanic Chamber News*. **Geographic Preference:** Local.

45346 ■ San Antonio Women's Chamber of Commerce (SAWCC)
5150 Broadway St., Ste. No. 404
San Antonio, TX 78209
Ph: (210)299-2636
URL: http://sawomenschamber.org
Contact: Dr. Yvonne Katz, Executive Director
Facebook: www.facebook.com/TheSAWCC
Linkedin: www.linkedin.com/company/san-antonio
-women%27s-chamber-of-commerce
X (Twitter): x.com/TheSAWCC
Instagram: www.instagram.com/thesawcc
Description: Promotes activities for growth and development of women into leadership roles in business, politics, and community. **Founded:** 1988. **Geographic Preference:** Local.

45347 ■ San Augustine County Chamber of Commerce
611 W Columbia St.
San Augustine, TX 75972-1708
Ph: (936)275-3610
Co. E-mail: info@sanaugustinetx.com
URL: http://www.uschamber.com/co/chambers/texas/
san-augustine
Contact: Dan H. Fussell, Contact
URL(s): sanaugustinetx.com
Description: Promotes business and community development in San Augustine County, TX. **Geographic Preference:** Local.

45348 ■ San Benito Chamber of Commerce
258 A Sam Houston Blvd.
San Benito, TX 78586
Ph: (956)361-9111
Co. E-mail: info@chamberofsanbenito.com
URL: http://www.chamberofsanbenito.com
Contact: Toni Crane, Chairman
E-mail: crane1023@gmail.com
Facebook: www.facebook.com/sanbenitochamber
X (Twitter): x.com/Chamber_SB
Instagram: www.instagram.com/chamberofsanbenito
YouTube: www.youtube.com/channel/UCam0w7k
5JE8qFoOitwu43tA
Description: Promotes business and community development in the San Benito, TX area. **Geographic Preference:** Local.

45349 ■ San Marcos Area Chamber of Commerce
202 N CM Allen Pky.
San Marcos, TX 78666
Ph: (512)393-5900
Fax: (512)393-5912
Co. E-mail: admin@sanmarcostexas.com
URL: http://sanmarcostexas.com
Contact: Matthew Worthington, Chairman
Facebook: www.facebook.com/
SanMarcosChamberOfCommerce
Linkedin: www.linkedin.com/company-beta/701651
X (Twitter): x.com/smchamber
Instagram: www.instagram.com/smtx_chamber
Description: Promotes business and community development in San Marcos, TX. **Founded:** 1903. **Geographic Preference:** Local.

45350 ■ San Saba County Chamber of Commerce
113 S High St.
San Saba, TX 76877
Ph: (325)372-5141
URL: http://sansabachamber.org
Contact: Dora Miller, Associate Director
E-mail: dmiller@alamopecan.com
Facebook: www.facebook.com/SanSabaCoun
tyChamber
Description: Works to enhance the quality of life and to promote the economic well-being of San Saba County through leadership, commitment, and participation. **Founded:** 1950. **Publications:** *San Saba County Chamber of Commerce News* (Quarterly). **Geographic Preference:** Local.

45351 ■ Sanger Area Chamber of Commerce (SACC)
300 Bolivar St.
Sanger, TX 76266
Ph: (940)458-7702
Co. E-mail: chamber@sangertexas.com
URL: http://sangertexas.com
Contact: Kelsi Bannahan, President
Facebook: www.facebook.com/
SangerChamberofCommerce
Linkedin: www.linkedin.com/company/sanger
-chamber-of-commerce
X (Twitter): x.com/sangerchamber
Description: Promotes business and community development in the Sanger, TX area. **Founded:** 1976. **Geographic Preference:** Local.

45352 ■ Santa Fe Chamber of Commerce
12425 Hwy. 6, Ste. 1
Santa Fe, TX 77510
Ph: (409)925-8558
Fax: (409)925-8551
Co. E-mail: sfchamber@comcast.net
URL: http://www.santafetexaschamber.com
Contact: Gina Bouvier, President
Facebook: www.facebook.com/santafetexascoc
X (Twitter): x.com/sftxchamber
Description: Promotes business and community development in the Santa Fe, TX area. Sponsors Easter and Christmas festivals. **Geographic Preference:** Local.

45353 ■ Seagoville Chamber of Commerce (SCC)
107 Hall Rd.
Seagoville, TX 75159
Ph: (972)287-5184
Co. E-mail: seagovillechamber@sbcglobal.net
URL: http://www.seagoville.us/92/Community-Links
Contact: James Kimble, Contact
Facebook: www.facebook.com/people/Seagoville
-Chamber-of-Commerce/100064570994333
Description: Promotes business and community development in Seagoville, TX. Sponsors various annual activities. **Founded:** 1975. **Geographic Preference:** Local.

45354 ■ Sealy Chamber of Commerce
309 Main St.
Sealy, TX 77474
Ph: (979)885-3222
Co. E-mail: sealycoc@sbcglobal.net
URL: http://www.sealychamber.com
Contact: Tori Fisher, President
Facebook: www.facebook.com/sealychamber
Linkedin: www.linkedin.com/company/sealy-chamber
-of-commerce
X (Twitter): x.com/SealyChamber
YouTube: www.youtube.com/channel/UChMT3cRJb8
tfvoEsJfX2yFw
Description: Promotes business and community development in the Sealy, TX area. Sponsors annual Sealybration and Fantasy of Lights festivals. **Founded:** 1936. **Publications:** *Sealy Newsletter* (Monthly). **Educational Activities:** General Membership Meeting. **Geographic Preference:** Local.

45355 ■ Seguin Area Chamber of Commerce (SACC)
116 N Camp St.
Seguin, TX 78155
Ph: (830)379-6382
Fax: (830)379-6971
Co. E-mail: cofc@seguinchamber.com
URL: http://www.seguinchamber.com
Contact: Kendy Gravett, President
E-mail: kendy@seguinchamber.com
Facebook: www.facebook.com/seguinchamber

Linkedin: www.linkedin.com/company/seguin-area-chamber-of-commerce
X (Twitter): x.com/seguinchamber
Instagram: www.instagram.com/seguinchamber
YouTube: www.youtube.com/user/SeguinAreaChamber
Description: Promotes business and community development in Guadalupe County, TX. **Founded:** 1937. **Publications:** *Business Line* (Monthly). **Geographic Preference:** Local.

45356 ■ Shamrock Chamber of Commerce
207 N Main St.
Shamrock, TX 79079
Ph: (806)256-2516
Co. E-mail: shamrockedc@gmail.com
URL: http://shamrocktexas.net
Contact: Connie Wilson, Contact
Facebook: www.facebook.com/shamrocktxchamber
Description: Promotes business and community development in Shamrock, TX. Sponsors area festival. **Founded:** 1924. **Geographic Preference:** Local.

45357 ■ Shelby County Chamber of Commerce
100 Courthouse Sq., A-101
Center, TX 75935
Ph: (936)598-3682
Co. E-mail: info@shelbycountychamber.com
URL: http://shelbycountychamber.com
Contact: Deborah Chadwick, President
Facebook: www.facebook.com/ShelbyCountyChamberOfCommerceCenterTX
X (Twitter): x.com/shelbychamber
Description: Promotes business and community development in Shelby County, TX. **Founded:** 1926. **Geographic Preference:** Local.

45358 ■ Shiner Chamber of Commerce
817 N Ave., E
Shiner, TX 77984
Ph: (361)594-4180
Fax: (361)594-4181
Co. E-mail: chamber@shinertx.com
URL: http://www.shinertx.com
Contact: David Patek, Vice President
Instagram: www.instagram.com/shiner_texas
Description: Promotes business and community development in Shiner, TX. **Founded:** 1920. **Geographic Preference:** Local.

45359 ■ Sinton Chamber of Commerce (SCC)
218 W Sinton St.
Sinton, TX 78387
Ph: (361)364-2307
Co. E-mail: info.sintonchamber@gmail.com
URL: http://www.sintonchamber.org
Contact: Estevan Guerra, President
E-mail: sintonchamber@sbcglobal.net
Facebook: www.facebook.com/sintonchamber
Description: Promotes business and community development in Sinton, TX. **Geographic Preference:** Local.

45360 ■ Slaton Chamber of Commerce
PO Box 400
Slaton, TX 79364
Ph: (806)828-6238
Co. E-mail: slatonchamber@gmail.com
URL: http://www.slatonchamberofcommerce.org
Description: Promotes business and community development in Slaton, TX. **Founded:** 1915. **Publications:** *Chamber Chat* (Monthly). **Awards:** Slaton Chamber of Commerce Boss of the Year (Annual); Slaton Chamber of Commerce Man of the Year (Annual); Slaton Chamber of Commerce Woman of the Year (Annual). **Geographic Preference:** Local.

45361 ■ Snyder Chamber of Commerce
2302 Ave., R
Snyder, TX 79549
Ph: (325)573-3558
Co. E-mail: communications@snyderchamber.org
URL: http://www.snyderchamber.org
Contact: Linda Molina, President
Facebook: www.facebook.com/snyderchamberofcommerce
Description: Promotes business, community development and tourism in Snyder, TX. **Geographic Preference:** Local.

45362 ■ Sonora Chamber of Commerce (SCOC)
205 Hwy. 277 N
Sonora, TX 76950
Ph: (325)387-2880
Free: 888-387-2880
Fax: (325)387-5357
Co. E-mail: chamber@sonoratexas.org
URL: http://www.sonoratexas.org
Contact: Donna Garrett, Executive Director
Facebook: www.facebook.com/sonorachamberofcommerce/
Description: Promotes business and community development in Sonora, TX. **Geographic Preference:** Local.

45363 ■ South Belt - Ellington Chamber of Commerce (SBECC)
10500 Scarsdale
Houston, TX 77089
Ph: (281)481-5516
Co. E-mail: info@southbeltchamber.com
URL: http://southbeltchamber.com
Contact: Rebecca Lilley, Chairman
Facebook: www.facebook.com/southbeltcc
X (Twitter): x.com/southbeltcc
Instagram: www.instagram.com/southbeltcc
YouTube: www.youtube.com/channel/UCcLxAUKiSUNTnBx5xmLTWjQ
Description: Promotes business and community development in South Belt-Ellington, TX area. **Founded:** 1984. **Geographic Preference:** Local.

45364 ■ South Padre Island Chamber of Commerce
321 Padre Blvd.
South Padre Island, TX 78597
Ph: (956)761-4412
Co. E-mail: info@spichamber.com
URL: http://www.spichamber.com
Contact: Alita Bagley, President
Facebook: www.facebook.com/spichamber
X (Twitter): x.com/spichamber
Instagram: www.instagram.com/spichamber
Description: Promotes business and community development in South Padre Island, TX. **Founded:** 1989. **Publications:** *Business News* (Monthly). **Educational Activities:** Ladies Kingfish Tournament (Annual). **Geographic Preference:** Local.

45365 ■ South Texas Business Partnership
3315 Sidney Brooks Dr., Ste. 200
San Antonio, TX 78235
Ph: (210)533-1600
Co. E-mail: info@sotxpartnership.org
URL: http://southtexaspartnership.org
Contact: Jessica Furdock, Vice President, Communications
E-mail: jessica@sotxpartnership.org
Facebook: www.facebook.com/sotxpartnership
Linkedin: www.linkedin.com/company/sotxpartnership
X (Twitter): x.com/sotxpartnership
Instagram: www.instagram.com/sotxpartnership
Description: Works to enhance economic growth and planned development of South San Antonio and Southern Bexar County, TX. **Founded:** 1982. **Geographic Preference:** Local.

45366 ■ Southeast Dallas Chamber of Commerce (SEDCC)
802 S Buckner Blvd.
Dallas, TX 75217
Ph: (214)398-9590
Co. E-mail: info@sedcc.org
URL: http://www.sedcc.org
Contact: Mary Bob Wylie, Treasurer
Facebook: www.facebook.com/SoutheastDallasChamber
Description: Promotes business and community development in Southeastern Dallas, TX. **Publications:** *The Business Spotlight* (Monthly). **Awards:** Southeast Dallas Chamber of Commerce Firefighter of the Year (Annual); Southeast Dallas Chamber of Commerce Police Officer of the Year (Annual); SEDCC Awards Scholarship (Annual); Southeast Dallas Chamber of Commerce Principal of the Year (Annual). **Geographic Preference:** Local.

45367 ■ Southlake Chamber of Commerce
1501 Corporate Cir.
Southlake, TX 76092
Ph: (817)481-8200
Co. E-mail: info@southlakechamber.com
URL: http://www.southlakechamber.org
Contact: Mark Guilbert, President
Facebook: www.facebook.com/SouthlakeTexasChamber
X (Twitter): x.com/southlakecofc
Instagram: www.instagram.com/southlakechamber
YouTube: www.youtube.com/channel/UCnifWLsjb47Y3agjXrUj7Wg
Description: Promotes business and community development in Southlake, TX. Sponsors festivals and charitable events. **Publications:** *Community Directory* (Annual); *Southlake Chamber of Commerce News and Views* (Monthly); *Southlake Chamber of Commerce--Community Directory* (Annual). **Awards:** Southlake Chamber of Commerce Citizen of the Year (Annual). **Geographic Preference:** Local.

45368 ■ Spearman Chamber of Commerce (SCC)
211 Main St.
Spearman, TX 79081
Ph: (806)659-5555
URL: http://www.spearmanchamber.org
Contact: Bonnie Thompson, Executive Director
E-mail: bthompson@cityofspearman.com
Facebook: www.facebook.com/spearmantxchamber
Description: Promotes business and community development in Spearman, TX. **Founded:** 1921. **Geographic Preference:** Local.

45369 ■ Springtown Area Chamber of Commerce
112 S Main St.
Springtown, TX 76082
Ph: (817)220-7828
Fax: (817)523-3268
Co. E-mail: info@springtownchamber.org
URL: http://www.springtownchamber.org/home
Contact: Amy Walker, Executive Director
E-mail: director@springtownchamber.org
Description: Promotes business and community development in Springtown, TX. **Founded:** 1979. **Geographic Preference:** Local.

45370 ■ Stephenville Chamber of Commerce
187 W Washington St.
Stephenville, TX 76401
Ph: (254)965-5313
Fax: (254)965-3814
Co. E-mail: chamber@stephenvilletexas.org
URL: http://www.stephenvilletexas.org
Contact: July Danley, President
E-mail: julyd@stephenvilletexas.org
Linkedin: www.linkedin.com/company/stephenville-chamber-of-commerce
X (Twitter): x.com/chambersvilletx
Description: Promotes business and community development in Stephenville, TX. **Founded:** 1911. **Publications:** *Chamber Works* (Monthly). **Geographic Preference:** Local.

45371 ■ Stonewall Chamber of Commerce (SCC)
250 Peach St.
Stonewall, TX 78671
Ph: (830)644-2735
Co. E-mail: stonewallchamber@gmail.com
URL: http://www.stonewalltexas.com
Contact: Melissa Eckert, President
Facebook: www.facebook.com/StonewallChamberOfCommerce
Instagram: www.instagram.com/stonewallchamber

STATE LISTINGS   Texas ■ 45386

Description: Promotes the peach industry, business and tourism, and community development in the Stonewall, TX area. Sponsors local festival. Founded: 1961. Publications: *Stonewall Bulletin* (Monthly). Geographic Preference: Local.

45372 ■ Swedish-American Chamber of Commerce Texas (SACC-TX)
c/o Consulate General of Sweden
3730 Kirby Dr., Ste. 805
Houston, TX 77098
Ph: (713)876-1188
Co. E-mail: texas@sacctx.com
URL: http://sacctx.com
Contact: Jonas Dahlstrom, Chairman
E-mail: jonas.dahlstrom@sacctx.com
Facebook: www.facebook.com/sacctexas
Linkedin: www.linkedin.com/company/sacctexas
X (Twitter): x.com/SACCTEXAS
Description: Business network that promotes trade and investment between Sweden and Texas. Founded: 1983. Geographic Preference: State.

45373 ■ Terrell Chamber of Commerce Convention & Visitors Bureau
1314 W Moore Ave.
Terrell, TX 75160
Ph: (972)563-5703
Free: 877-Ter-rell
Co. E-mail: angie@terrelltexas.com
URL: http://www.terrelltexas.com
Contact: Carlton Tidwell, President
Linkedin: www.linkedin.com/company/terrell-chamber-of-commerce-convention-visitors-bureau
X (Twitter): x.com/terrell_chamber
Instagram: www.instagram.com/_terrell.chamberofcommerce_
YouTube: www.youtube.com/channel/UCR1WSmh2Pvd8KKhyCtwE1jQ
Description: Promotes business and community development in Terrell, TX. Provides community services; sponsors Heritage Jubilee and Civic Auction, Christmas activities, 4th of July fireworks, work in Terrell, and scholarships. Publications: *Business Referral Guide* (Annual). Geographic Preference: Local.

45374 ■ Texarkana Chamber of Commerce
819 N State Line Ave.
Texarkana, TX 75501
Ph: (903)792-7191
Co. E-mail: chamber@texarkana.org
URL: http://www.texarkana.org
Contact: Michael Malone, President
E-mail: mmalone@texarkana.org
Facebook: www.facebook.com/TexarkanaChamberofCommerce
Instagram: www.instagram.com/txk_chamber
Description: Promotes business and community development in Texarkana, TX. Founded: 1912. Publications: *Texarkan* (Quarterly). Educational Activities: Texarkana Chamber of Commerce Roundtable. Geographic Preference: Local.

45375 ■ Texas Association of Business and Chamber of Commerce (TABCC)
316 W 12th St., No. 200
Austin, TX 78701
URL: http://www.txbiz.org/tab-foundation
Contact: Al Arreola, President
Description: Aims to promote business and community development in Texas. Founded: 1922. Publications: *Texas Business Report* (Monthly). Geographic Preference: State.

45376 ■ Texas Association of Mexican-American Chambers of Commerce (TAMACC)
606 Main St.
Buda, TX 78610
Ph: (512)444-5727
URL: http://tamacc.org
Contact: Pauline E. Anton, President
E-mail: president@tamacc.org
Facebook: www.facebook.com/tamacc
Linkedin: www.linkedin.com/company/tamacc
Instagram: www.instagram.com/tamacc1975

Description: Promotes the growth, development, and success of local Hispanic chambers of commerce and serves as the leading advocate of Hispanic business in TX. Founded: 1975. Publications: *TAMACC: The Voice of the Texas Hispanic Business Community* (Quarterly). Educational Activities: Convention and Business Expo (Annual). Geographic Preference: State.

45377 ■ Texas City - La Marque Chamber of Commerce
9702 Emmett F. Lowry Expy.
Texas City, TX 77591
Ph: (409)935-1408
Fax: (409)316-0901
Co. E-mail: info@texascitychamber.com
URL: http://www.tclmchamber.com
Contact: Page Michel, Co-Chief Executive Officer Co-President
E-mail: president@texascitychamber.com
Facebook: www.facebook.com/tclmchamber
Linkedin: www.linkedin.com/company/tclmchamber
Instagram: www.instagram.com/tclmchamber
YouTube: www.youtube.com/channel/UCSX89h-Bj2eEO0talQDqfDg
Description: Promotes business and community development in Galveston County, TX. Conducts annual funfest and shrimp boil. Publications: *Texas City - La Marque Chamber Express*; *Texas City-La Marque Magazine* (Periodic). Geographic Preference: Local.

45378 ■ *Texas City - La Marque Chamber Express*
9702 Emmett F. Lowry Expy.
Texas City, TX 77591
Ph: (409)935-1408
Fax: (409)316-0901
Co. E-mail: info@texascitychamber.com
URL: http://www.tclmchamber.com
Contact: Page Michel, Co-Chief Executive Officer Co-President
E-mail: president@texascitychamber.com
URL(s): www.tclmchamber.com/publications
Ed: Lorrie Koster. Availability: Online.

45379 ■ Texas Tri-County Chamber of Commerce
PO Box 3122
Universal City, TX 78148
Ph: (210)658-8322
URL: http://www.txtricountychamber.org
Contact: Shankar Poncelet, Advisor
Facebook: www.facebook.com/texastricountychamberofcommerce
Linkedin: www.linkedin.com/company/texastricountychamberofcommerce
YouTube: www.youtube.com/channel/UCHylKuX982KozQoZydC4bJQ
Description: Promotes business and community development in Cibolo, Converse, Garden Ridge, Kirby, Live Oak, Marion, Schertz, Selma, Universal City, Windcrest and Randolph Air Force Base, TX. Encourages tourism; operates information center. Publications: *Buyer's Guide* (Periodic); *Metro Brief* (Weekly); *Progress*. Geographic Preference: Local.

45380 ■ Three Rivers Chamber of Commerce
105 N Harborth
Three Rivers, TX 78071
Ph: (361)786-4330
Co. E-mail: trchamber@threeriverstx.org
URL: http://threeriverstx.org
Contact: Rick Sowell, President
Description: Promotes business and community development in Three Rivers, TX area. Founded: 1913. Geographic Preference: Local.

45381 ■ Tri-County Regional Black Chamber of Commerce (TCRBCC)
2626 S Loop W, Ste. 250
Houston, TX 77054
Ph: (832)875-3977
Fax: (281)336-0870
Co. E-mail: info@tricountyregionalblackchamber.org
URL: http://tricountyregionalblackchamber.org
Facebook: www.facebook.com/tcrbcchamber

X (Twitter): x.com/tcrbcchamber
Instagram: www.instagram.com/tcrbcchamber
Description: Represents Black owned businesses. Seeks to empower and sustain African American communities through entrepreneurship and capitalistic activity. Provides advocacy, training and education to Black communities. Geographic Preference: Local.

45382 ■ Trinity Peninsula Chamber of Commerce (TPCC)
PO Box 549
Trinity, TX 75862-0549
Ph: (936)594-3856
Fax: (936)594-0558
Co. E-mail: trpcc@lcc.net
URL: http://www.chamber-commerce.net/dir/10950/Trinity-Peninsula-Chamber-of-Commerce-in-Trinity
URL(s): www.uschamber.com/co/chambers/texas/trinity
Description: Promotes tourism, business, educational, and community development in the Upper Lake Livingston, TX area. Sponsors annual Christmas at the Crossroads Festival, co-sponsors annual Community Fair, and 4th of July Street Dance. Founded: 1949. Geographic Preference: Local.

45383 ■ Troup Chamber of Commerce
106 E Duval
Troup, TX 75789
Ph: (903)842-4113
Co. E-mail: troupchamber@trouptx.com
URL: http://trouptx.com/chamber-of-commerce
Contact: Melanie Brumit, President
Facebook: www.facebook.com/Troup-Chamber-of-Commerce-999720860183748
X (Twitter): x.com/trouptexas
Description: Promotes business and community development in Troup, TX. Geographic Preference: Local.

45384 ■ Tulia Chamber of Commerce
127 SW 2nd St.
Tulia, TX 79088
Contact: Larry A. A. Coe, Contact
Description: Promotes business and community development in Tulia, TX. Geographic Preference: Local.

45385 ■ Tyler Area Chamber of Commerce (TACC)
315 N Broadway Ave., Ste. 100
Tyler, TX 75702
Ph: (903)592-1661
Free: 800-235-5712
Fax: (903)593-2746
Co. E-mail: chamberinfo@tylertexas.com
URL: http://www.tylertexas.com
Contact: Henry Bell, President
E-mail: hbell@tylertexas.com
Facebook: www.facebook.com/TACC1900
Linkedin: www.linkedin.com/company/tyler-area-chamber-of-commerce
X (Twitter): x.com/VisitTyler
YouTube: www.youtube.com/user/TylerTXTourism
Description: Promotes business and community development in Tyler, TX. Founded: 1918. Publications: *Tyler Chamber News* (Weekly). Geographic Preference: Local.

45386 ■ *Tyler Chamber News*
315 N Broadway Ave., Ste. 100
Tyler, TX 75702
Ph: (903)592-1661
Free: 800-235-5712
Fax: (903)593-2746
Co. E-mail: chamberinfo@tylertexas.com
URL: http://www.tylertexas.com
Contact: Henry Bell, President
E-mail: hbell@tylertexas.com
URL(s): www.tylertexas.com/chamber-newsletter
Released: Weekly Description: Includes information concerning the latest activities of the organization. Availability: Online.

45387 ■ Tyler County Chamber of Commerce
717 W Bluff St.
Woodville, TX 75979
Ph: (409)283-2632
Fax: (409)283-6884
Co. E-mail: tylercountycoc@yahoo.com
URL: http://www.tylercountycoc.com
Contact: Cathy Bennett, President
Description: Promotes business and community development in Tyler County, TX. Sponsors Dogwood Festival and promotes tourism. **Founded:** 1984. **Publications:** *Discover Tyler County* (Annual). **Geographic Preference:** Local.

45388 ■ *Uniquely Longview*
410 N Center St.
Longview, TX 75601
Ph: (903)237-4000
Co. E-mail: chamber@longviewtx.com
URL: http://longviewchamber.com
Contact: Kelly Hall, President
E-mail: khall@longviewtx.com
URL(s): longviewchamber.com/join
Availability: Online.

45389 ■ Uvalde Area Chamber of Commerce (UACC)
340 N Getty St.
Uvalde, TX 78801
Ph: (830)278-3361
Fax: (830)278-3363
Co. E-mail: info@uvalde.org
URL: http://www.uvalde.org
Contact: Karla Radicke, President
Facebook: www.facebook.com/UvaldeAreaChamber
Instagram: www.instagram.com/Uvalde_Chamber
Description: Promotes business and community development in Uvalde, TX. **Founded:** 1920. **Publications:** *Uvalde Update* (Bimonthly). **Geographic Preference:** Local.

45390 ■ Van Alstyne Chamber of Commerce
228 E Marshall
Van Alstyne, TX 75495
Ph: (903)482-6066
Co. E-mail: vanalstynechamber@gmail.com
URL: http://www.vanalstynechamber.org
Contact: Donna Kramer-Almon, President
Description: Promotes business and community development in Van Alstyne, TX. **Founded:** 1995. **Geographic Preference:** Local.

45391 ■ Van Area Chamber of Commerce (VACC)
170 W Main St.
Van, TX 75790
Ph: (903)963-5051
Co. E-mail: vanchamber2015@gmail.com
URL: http://www.vanareachamber.com
Contact: Patricia Valentine, President
Facebook: www.facebook.com/vanchamberofcommerce
Description: Promotes business and community development in Van Zandt County, TX. Seeks to attract new industry to the area. Issues publications. **Founded:** 1945. **Geographic Preference:** Local.

45392 ■ Vernon Chamber of Commerce
1614 Main St.
Vernon, TX 76384
Ph: (940)552-2564
Co. E-mail: vernonchamber@sbcglobal.net
URL: http://www.vernontexas.info
Contact: Susie B. Johnston, Contact
Facebook: www.facebook.com/vernontxchamber
Description: Promotes business and community development in Vernon, TX. Encourages diversification in the local economy; acts as official host for visiting individuals and groups; encourages use of Vernon as host of the Tri-State Area Wrestling tournament, Santa Rosa Rodeo, high school playoff games, and Barrel Racing Futurity events. Assists newcomers in locating rental housing; coordinates community events. **Geographic Preference:** Local.

45393 ■ Victoria Chamber of Commerce
7403 Lone Tree Rd., Ste. 211
Victoria, TX 77901
Ph: (361)573-5277
Fax: (361)573-5911
Co. E-mail: info@victoriachamber.org
URL: http://www.victoriachamber.org
Contact: Jeff Lyon, President
Facebook: www.facebook.com/VictoriaChamberOfCommerce
YouTube: www.youtube.com/channel/UCdYfDJd3h08TM1KyX3r1JKg/videos
Description: Promotes business and community development in Victoria, TX. **Founded:** 1922. **Publications:** *Vision* (Periodic). **Geographic Preference:** Local.

45394 ■ Waller Area Chamber of Commerce (WACC)
2313 Main St., Ste. 175
Waller, TX 77484
Ph: (936)372-5300
Co. E-mail: info@wallerchamber.com
URL: http://www.wallerchamber.com
Contact: Anthony Edmonds, President
Facebook: www.facebook.com/people/Waller-Area-Chamber-of-Commerce/100064520476932
X (Twitter): x.com/WallerChamber
Description: Promotes business and community development in Waller, TX area. **Geographic Preference:** Local.

45395 ■ Washington County Chamber of Commerce
314 S Austin St.
Brenham, TX 77833
Ph: (979)836-3695
Co. E-mail: info@brenhamtexas.com
URL: http://www.brenhamtexas.com
Contact: Jamie Rankin, President
E-mail: jamie@brenhamtexas.com
Facebook: www.facebook.com/washingtoncountychamber
X (Twitter): x.com/chamberwashco
Description: Promotes business and community development in Washington County, TX. Sponsors blood drive and Taste of the Country. **Founded:** 1917. **Publications:** *Washington County Magazine* (Annual). **Educational Activities:** Washington County Chamber of Commerce Banquet (Annual). **Awards:** Washington County Chamber of Commerce Man and Woman of the Year Lifetime Achievement Awards (Annual). **Geographic Preference:** Local.

45396 ■ *Washington County Magazine*
314 S Austin St.
Brenham, TX 77833
Ph: (979)836-3695
Co. E-mail: info@brenhamtexas.com
URL: http://www.brenhamtexas.com
Contact: Jamie Rankin, President
E-mail: jamie@brenhamtexas.com
URL(s): www.brenhamtexas.com/about-us
Released: Annual **Availability:** Print; Online.

45397 ■ Waxahachie Chamber of Commerce (WCC)
102 YMCA Dr.
Waxahachie, TX 75165
Ph: (972)935-0539
Co. E-mail: admin@waxahachiechamber.com
URL: http://waxahachiechamber.com
Contact: Kevin Strength, President
Facebook: www.facebook.com/Waxahachie.Chamber
Description: Promotes business and community development in Waxahachie, TX. Conducts Gingerbread Trail Festival. Convention/Meeting: none. **Founded:** 1921. **Publications:** *The Gingerbread Times* (Quarterly). **Geographic Preference:** Local.

45398 ■ Weatherford Chamber of Commerce (WCC)
401 Fort Worth Hwy.
Weatherford, TX 76086
Ph: (817)596-3801
Co. E-mail: info@weatherford-chamber.com
URL: http://www.weatherford-chamber.com
Contact: Judd Duncan, Chairman
X (Twitter): x.com/WfordTXChamber
YouTube: www.youtube.com/channel/UCLKHWPN8KAxe2C3JB4mAXXw/videos
Description: Promotes business and community development in Parker County, TX. **Founded:** 1912. **Publications:** *Chamber News*. **Geographic Preference:** Local.

45399 ■ Weimar Area Chamber of Commerce
100 W Grange
Weimar, TX 78962
Ph: (979)725-9511
Co. E-mail: chamber@weimartexas.org
URL: http://www.weimarchamber.com
Contact: Amy Brandt, President
Facebook: www.facebook.com/WeimarChamber
Description: Promotes business and community development in Weimar, TX. **Founded:** 1987. **Geographic Preference:** Local.

45400 ■ Weslaco Area Chamber of Commerce
275 S Kansas, Ste. B
Weslaco, TX 78596
Ph: (956)968-2102
Fax: (956)968-6451
Co. E-mail: chamber@weslaco.com
URL: http://www.weslaco.com
Facebook: www.facebook.com/Weslaco-Area-Chamber-of-Commerce-74523188033
Linkedin: www.linkedin.com/company/weslacochamber
X (Twitter): x.com/weslacochamber
YouTube: www.youtube.com/channel/UCUA39l0mwzHflQDl2sOka-w
Description: Promotes business and community development in the Weslaco, TX area. **Founded:** 1935. **Geographic Preference:** Local.

45401 ■ West Chambers County Chamber of Commerce (WCCC)
2830 N FM 565, Ste. 200
Mont Belvieu, TX 77523
Ph: (281)576-5440
Co. E-mail: info@thewcccc.com
URL: http://thewcccc.com
Contact: Macie Schubert, President
Facebook: www.facebook.com/TheWCCCC
Description: Promotes business and community development in Mont Belvieu, TX. **Geographic Preference:** Local.

45402 ■ West Columbia Chamber of Commerce (WCCC)
202 E Brazos Ave. W Columbia
West Columbia, TX 77486
Ph: (979)345-3921
Fax: (979)345-6526
Co. E-mail: westcolumbiachamber@gmail.com
URL: http://westcolumbiachamber.com
Contact: Don Bogy, President
Facebook: www.facebook.com/westcolumbiachamber
Description: Promotes business, tourism, and community development in Southeastern Texas. Sponsors San Jacinto Festival. **Founded:** 1957. **Geographic Preference:** Local.

45403 ■ West I-10 Chamber of Commerce
PO Box 100
Pattison, TX 77466
Ph: (281)638-9488
Co. E-mail: chamber@westi10chamber.org
URL: http://www.westi10chamber.org
Contact: Andy Perry, President
E-mail: aperry@houstonexecutiveairport.com
Facebook: www.facebook.com/West-I-10-Chamber-of-Commerce-197396543645075
Description: Promotes business community along I-10 Corridor and surrounding region. **Founded:** 2002. **Geographic Preference:** Local.

45404 ■ Wharton Chamber of Commerce (WCC)
225 N Richmond Rd.
Wharton, TX 77488

Ph: (979)532-1862
Co. E-mail: helpdesk@whartonchamber.com
URL: http://www.whartonchamber.com
Contact: Ron Sanders, Executive Director
E-mail: ron.sanders@whartonchamber.com
Facebook: www.facebook.com/whartonchamber
X (Twitter): x.com/whartonchamber1
Description: Promotes business and community development in Wharton, TX. **Geographic Preference:** Local.

45405 ■ **White Settlement Area Chamber of Commerce (WSACC)**
8211 White Settlement Rd.
White Settlement, TX 76108
Ph: (817)246-1121
Co. E-mail: manager@whitesettlement-tx.com
URL: http://whitesettlement-tx.com
Contact: JoAnna Parker, President
Facebook: www.facebook.com/whitesettlemen tareachamberofcommerce
Description: Promotes business and community development in White Settlement, TX. Sponsors annual White Settlement Days parade. **Founded:** 1950. **Publications:** Chamber Update. **Educational Activities:** WSACC General Membership Meeting (Monthly). **Geographic Preference:** Local.

45406 ■ **Whitehouse Area Chamber of Commerce**
PO Box 1041
Whitehouse, TX 75791
Ph: (903)941-5221
Co. E-mail: info@whitehousetx.com
URL: http://www.whitehousetx.com
Contact: Brent Allen, President
Facebook: www.facebook.com/Whi tehouseAreaChamberOfCommerce
Description: Promotes business and community development in the Whitehouse, TX area. **Founded:** 1953. **Geographic Preference:** Local.

45407 ■ **Whitesboro Area Chamber of Commerce (WCC)**
2535 Hwy. 82 E, Ste. C
Whitesboro, TX 76273
Ph: (903)564-3331
Fax: (903)564-3397
Co. E-mail: chamber@whitesborotx.com
URL: http://www.whitesborotx.com
Contact: LaDonna Milner, Executive Director
Description: Promotes business and community development in the Whitesboro, TX area. **Founded:** 1939. **Awards:** Whitesboro Area Chamber of Commerce Citizen of the Year Award (Annual); Whitesboro Area Chamber of Commerce Humanitarian of the Year Award (Annual). **Geographic Preference:** Local.

45408 ■ **Wichita Falls Board of Commerce and Industry**
900 8th St., Ste. 100
Wichita Falls, TX 76301
Ph: (940)723-2741
Fax: (940)723-8773
Co. E-mail: info@wichitafallschamber.com
URL: http://wichitafallschamber.com
Contact: Henry Florsheim, President
E-mail: henry@wichitafallschamber.com
Facebook: www.facebook.com/WichitaFallsChamber
X (Twitter): x.com/ChamberWF
Instagram: www.instagram.com/wichitafallschamber
Description: Strives to promote the business interests and community development of Wichita Falls, TX. **Founded:** 1968. **Publications:** Directory of Manufactures, Community Profile, Membership Directory; Wichita Falls Board of Commerce and Industry--Membership Directory and Community Guide (Monthly). **Geographic Preference:** Local.

45409 ■ **Wills Point Chamber of Commerce**
307 N 4th St.
Wills Point, TX 75169
Ph: (903)873-3111
Co. E-mail: contact@willspointchamber.com
URL: http://willspointchamber.com
Contact: Janette Blair, Officer
Facebook: www.facebook.com/willspointchamber
X (Twitter): x.com/willspointcoc
Description: Promotes business and community development in Wills Point, TX. **Founded:** 1873. **Geographic Preference:** Local.

45410 ■ **Wimberley Valley Chamber of Commerce**
14100 Ranch Rd. 12
Wimberley, TX 78676
Ph: (512)847-2201
Co. E-mail: info@wimberley.org
URL: http://www.wimberley.org
Contact: Josh Smith, Chairman
Description: Promotes business and community development in Wimberley, TX. **Founded:** 1949. **Publications:** Business News. **Educational Activities:** Wimberley Chamber of Commerce Show (Irregular). **Geographic Preference:** Local.

45411 ■ **Winnsboro Area Chamber of Commerce**
115 W Elm St.
Winnsboro, TX 75494
Ph: (903)342-3666
Co. E-mail: info@winnsboro.com
URL: http://www.winnsboro.com
Contact: Cody Rosier, Co-President
Facebook: www.facebook.com/winnsbororodeo
Description: Promotes business and community development in Winnsboro, TX. **Founded:** 1957. **Geographic Preference:** Local.

45412 ■ **Wise County Chamber of Commerce**
301 E Main, Ste. C
Decatur, TX 76234
Co. E-mail: info@wisecountychamber.com
URL: http://wisecountychamber.com
Contact: Mende Hanley, Chief Executive Officer
Facebook: www.facebook.com/wisecountychamber
X (Twitter): x.com/WiseCountyChamb
Instagram: www.instagram.com/wisecountychamber
Description: Promotes business and community development in the area. **Publications:** The Catalyst (Bimonthly). **Geographic Preference:** Local.

45413 ■ **Wolfforth Area Chamber of Commerce and Agriculture**
PO Box 35
Wolfforth, TX 79382
Ph: (806)855-4159
Fax: (806)855-4159
Co. E-mail: info@wolfforthchamber.org
URL: http://www.wolfforthchamber.org
Description: Promotes business and community development in Wolfforth, TX. **Geographic Preference:** Local.

45414 ■ **Women's Chamber of Commerce of Texas in Austin (WCCT)**
PO Box 26051
Austin, TX 78755
Ph: (512)338-0839
URL: http://www.austinchamber.com/directory/ womens-chamber-of-commerce-of-texas-in-austin
Contact: Bobby Jenkins, President
Description: Promotes business and economic development for women in Texas. **Founded:** 1987. **Publications:** Women's Business (Quarterly). **Educational Activities:** MAPCon (Annual). **Awards:** Texas Business Woman of the Year (Annual). **Geographic Preference:** Local.

45415 ■ **The Woodlands Area Chamber of Commerce**
9320 Lakeside Blvd.
The Woodlands, TX 77381
Ph: (281)367-5777
Co. E-mail: info@woodlandschamber.org
URL: http://www.woodlandschamber.org
Contact: J. J. Hollie, President
E-mail: jjhollie@woodlandschamber.org
Facebook: www.facebook.com/TheWoodlan dsAreaChamber
Linkedin: www.linkedin.com/company/the-woodlands -area-chamber-of-commerce
X (Twitter): x.com/ChamberChatting
Description: Promotes business and community development in the Spring, TX area. **Founded:** 1978. **Geographic Preference:** Local.

45416 ■ **Wylie Chamber of Commerce**
307 N Ballard Ave.
Wylie, TX 75098
Ph: (972)442-2804
Co. E-mail: info@wyliechamber.org
URL: http://www.wyliechamber.org
Contact: Mike Agnew, President
E-mail: magnew@wyliechamber.org
Facebook: www.facebook.com/ WylieChamberofCommerce
Description: Promotes business and community development in Wylie, TX. **Founded:** 1977. **Geographic Preference:** Local.

45417 ■ **Yoakum Area Chamber of Commerce (YACC)**
105 Huck St.
Yoakum, TX 77995
Ph: (361)293-2309
Fax: (361)293-3507
Co. E-mail: info@yoakumareachamber.com
URL: http://www.yoakumareachamber.com
Contact: Mitchell Franz, Chairman
Facebook: www.facebook.com/ YoakumAreaChamberOfCommerce
Description: Promotes business and community development in Yoakum, TX. Conducts tours of saddle and belt factories and operates economic development board. **Founded:** 1966. **Publications:** Visitor's Guide/Chamber Directory (Annual). **Geographic Preference:** Local.

MINORITY BUSINESS ASSISTANCE PROGRAMS

45418 ■ **City of Corpus Christi Development Services Department**
2406 Leopard St.
Corpus Christi, TX 78408
Ph: (361)826-3240
Fax: (361)826-3006
URL: http://www.cctexas.com/ds
Contact: Al Raymond, Director
X (Twitter): x.com/DevelopmentCC

45419 ■ **Dallas/Fort Worth Minority Business Development Council (D/FW MSDC) [Dallas/ Fort Worth Minority Supplier Development Council]**
8828 N Stemmons Fwy., Ste. 550
Dallas, TX 75247
Ph: (214)630-0747
Co. E-mail: info@dfwmsdc.com
URL: http://dfwmsdc.com
Contact: Margo J. Posey, President
E-mail: margo@dfwmsdc.com
Facebook: www.facebook.com/DFWMSDC
Linkedin: www.linkedin.com/company/dfwmsdc
X (Twitter): x.com/dfwmsdc
YouTube: www.youtube.com/channel/UCChRLxi3O djJdcJUyvpF4ew
Description: Aims to grow minority business revenues (access, opportunities, capabilities and utilization) in North Texas, and to foster a business environment that promotes access and opportunity for minority-owned businesses. **Founded:** 1973. **Publications:** Northeast Texas Buyers Guide to Minority Business (Annual). **Geographic Preference:** Local.

45420 ■ **El Paso Minority Business Development Center**
2401 E Missouri Ave.
El Paso, TX 79903
Ph: (915)351-6232
URL: http://www.mbda.gov/business-resources/busi ness-centers
Contact: Terri Reed, Director
Description: Helps small and minority businesses succeed in the free enterprise system.

45421 ■ Houston Minority Supplier Development Council (HMSDC)
3 Riverway, Ste. 555
Houston, TX 77056
Ph: (713)271-7805
Fax: (281)624-4904
Co. E-mail: info@hmsdc.org
URL: http://hmsdc.org
Contact: Ingrid M. Robinson, President
E-mail: ingrid.robinson@hmsdc.org
Facebook: www.facebook.com/HoustonMSDC
X (Twitter): x.com/HoustonMSDC
Instagram: www.instagram.com/houstonmsdc
YouTube: www.youtube.com/user/TheHMSDC
Description: Works to increase and expand business opportunities and business growth for minority business enterprises. **Educational Activities:** HMSDC Business Expo (Annual). **Geographic Preference:** Local.

45422 ■ San Antonio Minority Business Development Enterprise
501 W Cesar E Chavez Blvd., Ste. 3.324, Durango Bldg.
San Antonio, TX 78207-4415
URL: http://sanantoniombdacenter.com
Contact: Orestes Hubbard, Director
E-mail: orestes.hubbard@utsa.edu
Description: Firm provides ongoing consulting, training, technical, research and information services, in tandem with University-based assets and resources and other state, federal and local agencies, to facilitate economic, community and business development throughout South Texas and the Border Region.

45423 ■ State of Texas Office of the Governor - Department of Economic Development and Tourism - Division of Business Development
PO Box 12428
Austin, TX 78711
URL: http://gov.texas.gov/business/page/organization
Contact: Stephanie Mazurkiewicz, Coordinator
Description: Promotes and supports small, minority-owned, and women-owned businesses in the areas of government contracting, capital resource identification, and general business counseling.

45424 ■ Texas Comptroller of Public Accounts (TCPA)
Lyndon B. Johnson State Office Bldg.
111 E 17th St.
Austin, TX 78774
URL: http://comptroller.texas.gov
Contact: Glenn Hegar, Chairman of the Board
Facebook: www.facebook.com/txcomptroller
X (Twitter): x.com/txcomptroller
Instagram: www.instagram.com/txcomptroller
YouTube: www.youtube.com/user/txcomptroller
Description: Provides information and facilitates the use of Texas' in-state procurement process for minority and women-owned businesses.

45425 ■ Women's Business Border Center (WBBC)
2401 E Missouri Ave.
El Paso, TX 79903
Ph: (915)566-4066
Fax: (915)566-9714
Co. E-mail: info@ephcc.org
URL: http://womenbordercenter.com
Contact: Crystal Cholewa, President
Facebook: www.facebook.com/wbbc.ephcc
X (Twitter): x.com/elpasowbbc
Instagram: www.instagram.com/wbbcep
Description: Provides women with financial assistance and training, management, marketing, and procurement services to expand or start a business. **Founded:** 2001.

45426 ■ Women's Business Council Southwest (WBCS)
5605 N MacArthur Blvd., Ste. 220
Irving, TX 75038
Ph: (817)299-0566
Free: 866-451-5997
Co. E-mail: info@wbcsouthwest.org

URL: http://www.wbcsouthwest.org
Contact: Bliss Coulter, President
E-mail: bcoulter@wbcsouthwest.org
Facebook: www.facebook.com/wbcsouthwest
Linkedin: www.linkedin.com/company/wbcsouthwest
X (Twitter): x.com/WBCSouthwest
Pinterest: www.pinterest.com/wbcsouthwest
Description: Works to facilitate business opportunities between women business enterprises and other businesses, corporations, government entities, and institutions. **Founded:** 1995. **Geographic Preference:** Regional.

FINANCING AND LOAN PROGRAMS

45427 ■ Aggie Angel Network (AAN)
1700 Research Pkwy, Ste. 130
College Station, TX 77845
Co. E-mail: mcferrincenter@tamu.edu
URL: http://mcferrinrevventures.com/aggie-angel-network
Contact: Blake Petty, Executive Director
Description: Offers early-stage investment opportunities and advisory services for high-growth technology companies.

45428 ■ Akin Gump Investment Partners 2000 L.P.
2300 N Field St., Ste. 1800
Dallas, TX 75201-2481
Ph: (214)969-2800
Fax: (214)969-4343
Co. E-mail: dallasinfo@akingump.com
URL: http://www.akingump.com
Contact: M. Scott Barnard, Partner
E-mail: sbarnard@akingump.com
Linkedin: www.linkedin.com/company/6923
X (Twitter): x.com/akin_gump
Description: Venture capital firm that engages in investment related activities. **Industry Preferences:** Computer software, Internet specific, and biotechnology.

45429 ■ Alamo Angels
1305 E Houston, Ste. 301
San Antonio, TX 78205
Ph: (726)666-0141
Co. E-mail: info@alamoangels.com
URL: http://alamoangels.com
Contact: Juan Garzon, Executive Director
Facebook: www.facebook.com/alamoangelsofSA
Linkedin: www.linkedin.com/company/alamoangelsofsa
X (Twitter): x.com/AlamoAngelsofSA
Instagram: www.instagram.com/alamoangelsofsa
Description: Identifies, funds, and develops promising startups. Offers financial investment, educational resources, and business services in the Alamo City. **Founded:** 2016.

45430 ■ Ambassadors Impact Network
539 W Commerce St., Ste. 7419
Dallas, TX 75208
Ph: (214)699-5762
URL: http://www.ambassadorsimpact.com
Contact: Eliot Kerlin, Director
Description: Connects faith-driven entrepreneurs with similar investors. **Investment Policies:** Faith-driven team; integrates the Gospel into the operations and activities of the company; working prototype; profitable (or able to break even within 18 months).

45431 ■ Amerimark Capital Corp. (ACC)
320 Decker Dr., Ste. 100
Irving, TX 75062
Ph: (214)638-7878
URL: http://www.amcapital.com
Contact: Charles Martin, President
Description: Investment banking firm provides mergers, acquisitions, corporate finance and management transition planning for privately owned companies. **Founded:** 1988. **Preferred Investment Size:** $500,000 to $2,000,000. **Industry Preferences:** Communications, Internet specific, computer hardware, consumer related, industrial and energy, and business service.

45432 ■ Austin Ventures L.P. (AV)
100 Congress Ave., Ste. 1600
Austin, TX 78701-2746
URL: http://austinventures.com
Contact: Chris Pacitti, Partner
Linkedin: www.linkedin.com/company/austin-ventures
Description: Venture capital firm. **Founded:** 1984. **Preferred Investment Size:** $100,000 to $20,000,000. **Industry Preferences:** Internet specific, communications and media, computer software and services, computer hardware, other products, semiconductors and other electronics, consumer related, medical and health, industrial and energy and biotechnology.

45433 ■ Bankers Capital Corp. (BCC)
8400 Craftsbury Ln.
McKinney, TX 75071
Ph: (214)842-8714
Co. E-mail: info@bankerscapitalcorp.com
URL: http://www.bankerscapitalcorp.com
Description: Provider of real estate financing services. **Founded:** 1990. **Preferred Investment Size:** $100,000 minimum. **Industry Preferences:** Semiconductors and other electronics, consumer related, industrial and energy.

45434 ■ Baylor Angel Network (BAN)
One Bear Pl., No. 98001
Waco, TX 76798
Ph: (254)710-3724
URL: http://hankamer.baylor.edu/angel-network
Contact: Steven Diedrich, Executive Director
E-mail: steven_diedrich@baylor.edu
URL(s): www.baylorangelnetwork.com
Description: Investor network. Provides early stage capital to strong entrepreneurial teams with developed products or services. **Founded:** 2008. **Investment Policies:** Entrepreneurial team with industry; experience; defensible and unique idea and business model; significant market traction; fundable and scalable business model; thoughtful exit strategy; complementary to Baylor University's mission.

45435 ■ BCM Technologies Inc.
1999 Bryan St., Ste. 900
Dallas, TX 75201
Contact: Joseph Petrosino, President
Description: Provider of seed and early stage venture capital investments for technology entrepreneurs, academic institutions, pharmaceutical companies and other sources. **Preferred Investment Size:** $100,000 minimum. **Industry Preferences:** Biotechnology, medical and health.

45436 ■ BlackRiver Busines Capital
14425 Falcon Head Blvd., Bldg. E
Austin, TX 78738-7195
Contact: Robert K. Childers, Member
Description: Finances equipment leasing for less established businesses.

45437 ■ Buena Venture Associates L.P. (BVA)
1612 Summit Ave., Ste. 100
Fort Worth, TX 76102
Ph: (817)800-5221
Co. E-mail: idea@buenaventure.com
URL: http://www.buenaventure.com
Contact: John Pergande, Contact
Description: Firm provides financial services sector with a focus on insurance, loans, stock trading, online banking services, bill payment and bill presentment. **Founded:** 1998. **Preferred Investment Size:** $250,000 to $3,000,000. **Industry Preferences:** Communications, computer software, Internet specific, medical and health.

45438 ■ The Cambria Group
3899 Maple Ave., Ste. 150
Dallas, TX 75219
Ph: (469)513-2200
Fax: (469)513-2201
URL: http://www.cambriagroup.com

STATE LISTINGS

Contact: Natalie D. Cryer, Vice President
E-mail: cryer@cambriagroup.com
Description: Private equity firm. **Founded:** 1996. **Preferred Investment Size:** $5,000,000 to $25,000,000. **Industry Preferences:** Communications and media, semiconductors and other electronics, medical and health, consumer related, industrial and energy, transportation, business service, manufacturing, agriculture, forestry and fishing.

45439 ■ The Capital Network Inc.
3925 W Braker Ln., No. 406
Austin, TX 78759
Contact: Meg Wilson, President
Preferred Investment Size: $100,000 to $500,000. **Industry Preferences:** Communications, computer related, semiconductors and other electronics, biotechnology, medical and health, consumer related, industrial and energy, financial services, business service, manufacturing, agriculture, forestry and fishing.

45440 ■ Capital Southwest Corporation (CSWC)
8333 Douglas Ave., Ste. 1100
Dallas, TX 75225
Ph: (214)238-5700
Fax: (214)238-5701
Co. E-mail: request@capitalsouthwest.com
URL: http://www.capitalsouthwest.com
Contact: Bowen S. Diehl, President
E-mail: bdiehl@capitalsouthwest.com
Linkedin: www.linkedin.com/company/capital-sou
 thwest-corporation
Description: A business development company that, as an internally managed and credit focused BDC, provides capital to middle market companies that have significant growth potential. **Founded:** 1961. **Preferred Investment Size:** $5,000,000 to $15,000,000. **Industry Preferences:** Operates as an investment company.

45441 ■ The Catalyst Group Inc.
1375 Enclave Pky.
Houston, TX 77077
Co. E-mail: inquiries@tcgfunds.com
URL: http://www.tcgfunds.com
Contact: Ron Nixon, Founder Managing Partner
E-mail: rnixon@tcgfunds.com
Linkedin: www.linkedin.com/company/the-catalys
 t-group-inc.-tcg-
Description: Provider of equity and mezzanine capital services. **Founded:** 1990. **Preferred Investment Size:** $1,000,000 to $7,000,000. **Industry Preferences:** Medical and health, business service and manufacturing.

45442 ■ CenterPoint Venture
350 N St., Paul St.
Dallas, TX 75201
Contact: Daniel C. Witte, Manager
Founded: 1996. **Preferred Investment Size:** $60,000 to $10,000,000. **Industry Preferences:** Communications and media, Internet specific, computer software and services, computer hardware, other products, semiconductors and other electronics, medical and health.

45443 ■ Cowtown Angels
1120 S Fwy.
Fort Worth, TX 76104
URL: http://www.cowtownangels.org
Contact: Hayden Blackburn, Executive Director
Linkedin: www.linkedin.com/company/cowtown-an
 gels-investor-network
Description: Members invest individually in early-stage businesses in order to stimulate economic growth in Texas. **Founded:** 2012.

45444 ■ Dallas Angel Network (DAN)
5307 E Mockingbird Ln., Ste. 802
Dallas, TX 75206-5121
Contact: Sammy S. Abdullah, Director
Description: Connects angel investors with high-growth companies and entrepreneurs in Dallas, Houston, and Austin. **Founded:** 2010.

45445 ■ Denton Angels
Denton, TX
Co. E-mail: info@dentonangels.com
URL: http://dentonangels.com
Description: Accredited investor group. Individual members offer capital to high-growth early-stage startups.

45446 ■ Eagle Venture Fund (EVF)
550 Bailey Ave., Ste. 310
Fort Worth, TX 76107
Ph: (443)203-8014
Co. E-mail: info@eagleventurefund.com
URL: http://www.eagleventurefund.com
Contact: Joe Reed, Director
Description: Venture capital and private equity fund hybrid. Invests in early-stage to lower middle-market companies creating significant returns and significant social and economic impact. **Founded:** 2017.

45447 ■ Equitrend Capital, LLC
801 S Fillmore St., Ste. 420
Amarillo, TX 79101-3520
Contact: Charles Dooley, Manager
Description: Offers equity investments to early-stage Texas companies to accelerate business growth and create new jobs.

45448 ■ Essex Woodlands Health Ventures/ Woodlands Venture
21 Waterway Ave., Ste. 225
The Woodlands, TX 77380
Ph: (281)364-1555
Fax: (281)364-9755
Co. E-mail: houston@ewhealthcare.com
URL: http://www.ewhealthcare.com
Contact: Michael R. Minogue, President
Description: Venture capital investments in early and late stage healthcare sectors. **Founded:** 1985. **Preferred Investment Size:** $20,000,000 to $60,000,000. **Industry Preferences:** Medical and health, biotechnology, computer software and services, Internet specific, consumer related, communications and media, other products, industrial and energy.

45449 ■ First Capital Group (FCG)
750 E Mulberry St., Ste. 305
San Antonio, TX 78212
Contact: Jeffrey P. Blanchard, Director
Description: Provider of investment solutions in middle market companies. **Founded:** 1984. **Preferred Investment Size:** $1,000,000 to $6,000,000. **Industry Preferences:** Communications and media, medical and health, consumer related, and business service.

45450 ■ G-51 Capital L.L.C.
900 S Capital of Texas Hwy., Ste. 151
Austin, TX 78746
Contact: Rudy Garza, President
Description: Firm provides venture capital investment services, venture funds and private equity investment for software, hardware, internet and cleantech sectors. **Founded:** 1996. **Preferred Investment Size:** $250,000 to $2,000,000. **Industry Preferences:** Computer software and services, computer hardware, Internet specific, and consumer related.

45451 ■ G51
3939 Bee Caves Rd., Ste. C100 W
West Lake Hills, TX 78746-6429
Contact: N. Rudy Garza, President
Description: Early stage venture capital firm. **Founded:** 1996. **Industry Preferences:** Software; hardware; internet; clean technology.

45452 ■ Genesis Park LP
520 Post Oak Blvd., Ste. 850
Houston, TX 77027
Ph: (713)489-4650
Co. E-mail: partnerships@genesis-park.com
URL: http://www.genesis-park.com
Contact: Simon Haidamous, Director
Linkedin: www.linkedin.com/company/genesis-park
Description: Provider of private equity investments for leveraged and management buyouts and growth financings. **Founded:** 1999. **Preferred Investment Size:** $500,000 to $2,000,000. **Investment Policies:** Start-up, early, first stage, and buyouts. **Industry Preferences:** Communications and media, computer software, finance, industrial and energy.

45453 ■ HO2 Partners
Two Galleria Twr., Ste. 1670 13455 Noel Rd.
Dallas, TX 75240-6620
Ph: (972)702-1107
Fax: (972)702-8234
Co. E-mail: dan@ho2.com
URL: http://www.ho2.com
Contact: Daniel T. Owen, Partner
E-mail: dan@ho2.com
Description: Firm invests on supply chain management software, wireless infrastructure, telecommunications enterprise management and enterprise digital media delivery. **Preferred Investment Size:** $750,000 to $3,000,000. **Industry Preferences:** Communications and computer software.

45454 ■ Houston Angel Network (HAN)
1801 Main St., Ste.1300
Houston, TX 77002
URL: http://www.houstonangelnetwork.org
Contact: Eric Schneider, President
Linkedin: www.linkedin.com/company/the-houston
 -angel-network
X (Twitter): x.com/Houston_Angels
Description: Angel investor network. **Founded:** 2001.

45455 ■ Innovate Angel Funds, LLC
3097 Arapaho Ridge Dr.
College Station, TX 77845
Contact: James Y. Lancaster, Owner
Description: Makes early-stage angel investments in science and technology ventures near the Texas A&M University System. **Founded:** 2009. **Industry Preferences:** Energy; life sciences; technology.

45456 ■ JatoTech Ventures L.P.
350 N Saint Paul St.
Dallas, TX 75201-4240
Description: Provider of venture capital investment for early-stage companies. **Founded:** 2000. **Preferred Investment Size:** $500,000 to $3,000,000. **Investment Policies:** Seed and early stage. **Industry Preferences:** Communications, and semiconductors and other electronics.

45457 ■ Launchpad Ventures
101 Summit Ave., Ste. 215
Fort Worth, TX 76102
URL: http://www.launchpad.in
Description: Works with entrepreneurs and investors to help them grow their ideas, scale their businesses, and increase their profits.

45458 ■ LiveOak Venture Partners
805 Las Cimas Pkwy., Ste. 125
Austin, TX 78746
Ph: (512)498-4900
Co. E-mail: info@liveoakvp.com
URL: http://liveoakvp.com
Contact: David Stewart, Partner
E-mail: david@liveoakvp.com
Description: Early-stage investors for exceptional entrepreneurial teams (as opposed to specific sectors or business models).

45459 ■ Mercury Fund
3737 Buffalo Speedway, Ste. 1750
Houston, TX 77098
Ph: (713)715-6820
Co. E-mail: info@mercuryfund.com
URL: http://mercuryfund.com
Contact: Aziz Gilani, Managing Director
X (Twitter): x.com/mercuryfund
Description: Provider of investment solutions. **Founded:** 2005. **Preferred Investment Size:** $100,000 to $1,500,000. **Investment Policies:** Seed and early stage. **Industry Preferences:** Industrial and energy.

45460 ■ MicroVentures
11601 Alterra Pkwy., Ste. 100
Austin, TX 78758
Free: 800-283-9903
Co. E-mail: help@microventures.com
URL: http://microventures.com
Contact: Tyler Gray, President
Facebook: www.facebook.com/microventures
Description: Full-service investment bank offers venture capital opportunities to both accredited and non-accredited investors. **Founded:** 2009.

45461 ■ Momentum Capital Partners
5535 Airport Fwy.
Haltom City, TX 76117
Ph: (817)920-7599
URL: http://mocappartners.com
Contact: Derrick L. Varnell, Partner
Description: Offers private equity capital to profitable small-market companies. **Founded:** 2000. **Preferred Investment Size:** $3,000,000 to $8,000,000. **Investment Policies:** Companies making $5,000,000 to $20,000,000 in revenues; up to $2,000,000 in EBITDA. **Industry Preferences:** Media; digital marketing; business services.

45462 ■ Murphree Venture Partners (MVP)
1221 Lamar, Ste. 1136
Houston, TX 77010
Ph: (713)655-8500
Fax: (713)655-8503
URL: http://www.murphreeventures.com
Contact: Dennis Murphree, Managing Partner
E-mail: dmurphree@murphreeventures.com
Description: Provider of venture capital for entrepreneurial enterprises. **Founded:** 1987. **Preferred Investment Size:** $2,000,000 to $10,000,000. **Industry Preferences:** Computer software and services, Internet specific, medical and health, industrial and energy, consumer related, semiconductors and other electronics, computer hardware, communications and media.

45463 ■ Natural Gas Partners (NGP)
2850 N Harwood St., 19th Fl.
Dallas, TX 75201
Ph: (972)432-1440
Co. E-mail: inquiries@ngpenergy.com
URL: http://ngpenergy.com
Contact: Elizabeth Hiltbrunner, Director
Linkedin: www.linkedin.com/company/ngpenergycapital
Description: Direct equity investments in energy companies. **Founded:** 1988. **Preferred Investment Size:** $10,000,000 to $500,000,000. **Industry Preferences:** Industrial and energy.

45464 ■ NGP Energy Capital (NGP)
2850 N Harwood St.,19th Fl.
Dallas, TX 75201
Ph: (972)432-1440
Co. E-mail: inquiries@ngpenergy.com
URL: http://ngpenergy.com
Contact: Carolyn Flinchum, Director
Linkedin: www.linkedin.com/company/ngpenergycapital
Description: Private equity firm. Makes direct equity investments in the energy sector. **Founded:** 1988. **Industry Preferences:** Oil and gas acquisitions and development drilling; oilfield services.

45465 ■ PTV Healthcare Capital (PTVHC)
3600 N Capital of Texas Hwy., Ste. B 180
Austin, TX 78746
Ph: (512)872-4000
URL: http://ptvhc.com
Contact: Rick Anderson, Managing Director
YouTube: www.youtube.com/channel/UCiVRQkgQuc3mVSN_oPYD8gQ
Description: Late-stage venture and expansion capital firm focused on healthcare innovation. **Founded:** 2003. **Investment Policies:** Mitigated risk profile; large market opportunity; improving patient outcomes with lower costs for the healthcare system; compelling exit strategy. **Industry Preferences:** Therapeutic medical devices and healthcare diagnostics; information technology; services platforms.

45466 ■ Rio Grande Valley Angel Network (RGVAN)
307 E Railroad St.
Weslaco, TX 78596
Ph: (956)357-0167
Co. E-mail: laurie.simmons@utrgv.edu
URL: http://www.rgvan.org
Contact: Carlos M. Marin, President
Facebook: www.facebook.com/people/Rio-Grande-Valley-Angel-Network/100076462906423
Linkedin: www.linkedin.com/company/rgvan
X (Twitter): x.com/RGVANGELNETWORK
Description: Offers access to capital for scalable enterprises. Works to develop the economic prosperity of the Rio Grande Valley. **Founded:** 2015.

45467 ■ S3 Ventures
6300 Bridge Point Pkwy., Bldg. 1, Ste. 405
Austin, TX 78730
Ph: (512)258-1759
URL: http://www.s3vc.com
Contact: Charlie Plauche, Partner
Description: Venture capital firm. Invests in technology-centric companies across different stages. **Founded:** 2006. **Industry Preferences:** Business technology; digital experiences; healthcare technology.

45468 ■ Saba Investmetnts, LLC
500 W Overland Ave., No. 310
El Paso, TX 79901
Ph: (915)257-7600
Co. E-mail: finance@sabavc.com
URL: http://sabavc.com
Contact: Miguel Fernandez, President
Description: Offers early-stage capital fund designed to catalyze technology innovation in the Rio Grande Innovation Corridor.

45469 ■ Santé Ventures
201 W 5th St., Ste. 1500
Austin, TX 78701
Ph: (512)721-1200
URL: http://sante.com
Contact: Jason Brandt, Chief Financial Officer Chief Compliance Officer
Linkedin: www.linkedin.com/company/sante-ventures
Description: Early-stage venture capital firm for life science and healthcare. **Founded:** 2006. **Investment Policies:** Innovative products; exceptional entrepreneurs; proprietary advantage; recurring revenue stream; well-defined exit strategy. **Industry Preferences:** Life science; healthcare; information technology.

45470 ■ Seed Capital Partners, LP
3008 Taylor St.
Dallas, TX 75226
Contact: Lawrence Goldstein, Contact
Preferred Investment Size: $500,000 to $1,000,000. **Industry Preferences:** Computer software, and Internet specific.

45471 ■ Sentient Ventures
11412 Bee Caves Rd., Ste. 300
Austin, TX 78738
Ph: (512)402-1717
Fax: (512)402-1616
Co. E-mail: info@senven.com
URL: http://senven.com
Contact: David Lee, Managing Director
Description: Equity firm investing in seed, early, and expansion stage companies. Focuses on middle market private equity and subordinated debt transactions. Invests in low tech and traditional businesses. **Founded:** 2002. **Industry Preferences:** Information technology; enterprise CRM software; semiconductors; nanotechnology; wireless; life sciences; intellectual property.

45472 ■ Sevin Rosen Funds (SRF)
PO Box 192128
Dallas, TX 75219
Ph: (972)702-1100
Fax: (972)702-1103
URL: http://www.srfundstest.com
Contact: John Oxaal, Chief Executive Officer
Description: Finance: Venture capital firm. **Founded:** 1981. **Preferred Investment Size:** $100,000 to $10,000,000. **Industry Preferences:** Communications and media, computer software and services, semiconductors and other electronics, consumer related, medical and health, computer hardware, Internet specific, and other products.

45473 ■ South Coast Angel Network (SCAN)
10201 S Padre Island Dr., Ste. 108
Corpus Christi, TX 78418-4466
Contact: James A. Shiner, Director
Description: Introduces investors to early-stage companies in need of funding.

45474 ■ STARTech Early Ventures
911 E ARAPAHO, Ste. 190
Richardson, TX 75081
Contact: Vinse Davidson, President
Description: Venture capital firm provides investment services such as entrepreneurial ecosystems, investment funding for seed stage businesses and office facilities for small-footprint and technology-based companies. **Founded:** 1997. **Preferred Investment Size:** $500,000 to $900,000. **Industry Preferences:** Computer software, and Internet specific, information technology.

45475 ■ Startup Financial Model (SFM)
950 E State Hwy.
Southlake, TX 76092
Free: 833-467-4824
Co. E-mail: hello@startupfinancialmodel.com
URL: http://www.startupfinancialmodel.com
Contact: Wade Myers, Chief Executive Officer
Facebook: www.facebook.com/StartupFinancialModel
Linkedin: www.linkedin.com/company/startup-financial-model
X (Twitter): twitter.com/StartupFinModel
Instagram: www.instagram.com/startupfinancialmodel
YouTube: www.youtube.com/channel/UCm3SmyDDznLcFUJQDH4IROg
Description: Provides support and resources to entrepreneurs to aid in business launches. **Founded:** 2012.

45476 ■ TA Capital
4141 SW Fwy., Ste. 340
Houston, TX 77027
Ph: (713)341-3526
Co. E-mail: contact@ta.capital
URL: http://www.ta.capital
Contact: Dr. Marcus Englert, Managing Partner
Facebook: www.facebook.com/tacventures
X (Twitter): x.com/TACVenture
Description: Trans-Atlantic venture firm with a presence in both the U.S. and Europe. Invests at all stages. **Preferred Investment Size:** $500,000-$15,000,000. **Investment Policies:** Scalable models and capable teams. **Industry Preferences:** E-commerce; internet; digital; software.

45477 ■ Texas Venture Association (TxVCA)
PO Box 1131
Austin, TX 78767
URL: http://texasventurealliance.org
Description: Represents the venture capital industry in Texas. **Founded:** 2004.

45478 ■ TEXO Ventures
6101 W Courtyard Dr., Ste. 2-225
Austin, TX 78730
URL: http://texoventures.com
Contact: Jerry DeVries, Managing Partner
E-mail: devries@texoventures.com
Linkedin: www.linkedin.com/company/texo-ventures
X (Twitter): x.com/TEXOventures
Description: Venture capital firm for innovative healthcare companies. **Founded:** 2009. **Industry Preferences:** Health IT and technology-enabled health services; managed care and benefit design; medical devices and diagnostics; personalized medicine technology.

STATE LISTINGS

45479 ■ Triton Ventures
4833 Spicewood Springs Rd., Ste. 101
Austin, TX 78759
URL: http://www.tritonventures.com
Contact: Laura Kilcrease, Managing Director
E-mail: laura@tritonventures.com
Description: Venture capital firm investing in spin out and startup technology companies. **Founded:** 1999. **Preferred Investment Size:** $500,000 to $4,000,000. **Industry Preferences:** Communications and media, computer software, Internet specific, semiconductors and other electronics, industrial and energy.

45480 ■ Wilco Funding Portal
Wilco, TX
URL: http://tencapital.group/tos
Description: Invests in Texas startups. **Founded:** 2010.

45481 ■ Wingate Partners L.L.P.
750 N St. Paul St., Ste. 1200
Dallas, TX 75201
Ph: (214)720-1313
URL: http://wingatepartners.com
Contact: Frederick B. Hegi, Jr., Partner
Description: Firm is engaged in equity investments. **Founded:** 1987. **Preferred Investment Size:** $25,000,000 to $100,000,000. **Industry Preferences:** Semiconductors and other electronics, medical and health, consumer related, industrial and energy, business service, and manufacturing.

PROCUREMENT ASSISTANCE PROGRAMS

45482 ■ Abilene Small Business Development Center
749 Gateway St., No. 301, Bldg. C
Abilene, TX 79602
Ph: (325)670-0300
Co. E-mail: americasbdc.abilene@ttu.edu
URL: http://www.abilenesbdc.org
Description: An outreach program that provides counseling, technical assistance, training workshops, and reference resources for small businesses and entrepreneurs. **Geographic Preference:** Local.

45483 ■ Angelina College Procurement Assistance Center (ACPAC)
3500 S 1st St.
Lufkin, TX 75901
Ph: (936)633-5432
URL: http://www.acpactx.org
Facebook: www.facebook.com/TexVet
X (Twitter): twitter.com/texvet
Description: Providing free advice to small businesses and industries of East Texas to sell products and services to federal, state, and local government agencies.

45484 ■ City of San Antonio Finance Department - Purchasing Div.
100 W Houston St.
San Antonio, TX 78205
URL: http://www.sanantonio.gov/Finance/about/divisions
Contact: Angelica Mata, Assistant Director
E-mail: angelica.mata@sanantonio.gov

45485 ■ Cross Timbers Procurement Center (CTPC)
202 E Border St., Ste. 323
Arlington, TX 76010
Ph: (817)272-5978
Fax: (817)272-5977
URL: http://www.uta.edu/crosstimbers
Contact: Gregory James, Director
E-mail: gjames@uta.edu
Description: Association helps companies find contracts for work with local, state and federal governments.

45486 ■ Texas Procurement Technical Assistance Center - El Paso Community College - Contract Opportunities Center
9050 Viscount Blvd. Bldg., B, Rm. 545
El Paso, TX 79925
Ph: (915)831-7747
Co. E-mail: coc@epcc.edu
URL: http://www.epcc.edu/Services/CoC
URL(s): www.elpasococ-events.org
Facebook: www.facebook.com/contractopportunitiescenter
Description: Provides specialized and professional assistance to individuals and businesses seeking to learn about contracting and subcontracting opportunities, who are actively seeking contracting and subcontracting opportunities and/or performing under contracts and subcontracts with the U.S. Department of Defense (DOD), other federal agencies, or state and local governments.

45487 ■ Texas Procurement Technical Assistance Center - Pan Handle Regional Planning Commission
415 SW 8th Ave.
Amarillo, TX 79101
Ph: (806)372-3381
Fax: (806)373-3268
Co. E-mail: rrusk@theprpc.org
URL: http://www.theprpc.org
Contact: Michael Peters, Executive Director
E-mail: mpeters@theprpc.org
Description: Assists local governments in planning, developing, and implementing programs designed to improve the general health, safety, and welfare of the citizens in the Texas Panhandle. **Founded:** 1969.

45488 ■ Texas Procurement Technical Assistance Center (TFC) - Texas Facilities Commission
1711 San Jacinto Blvd.
Austin, TX 78701
URL: http://www.tfc.texas.gov/divisions/commissiondmin/prog/hub/hubresources.html
Description: Lead the State of Texas procurement and contracting communities with enhanced services, innovative systems, and best practices to further encourage competition and operational efficiency for the benefit of state agencies, local government entities, and the vendor community.

45489 ■ Texas Procurement Technical Assistance Center - University of Houston Small Business Development Center
1455 W Loop S, Ste. 900
Houston, TX 77027-9530
Ph: (713)752-8400
Co. E-mail: sbdcptac@uh.edu
URL: http://www.sbdc.uh.edu/sbdc/default.asp
Description: Provides business consulting and training to entrepreneurs of small and emerging companies.

45490 ■ Texas Procurement Technical Assistance Center - University of Texas - Permian Basin Small Business Development Center
1310 N FM 1788., CEED Bldg.
Midland, TX 79707
Ph: (432)552-2455
Co. E-mail: sbdc@utpb.edu
URL: http://www.utpbsbdc.org
Contact: Tyler Patton, Director
Facebook: www.facebook.com/PBSBDC
Instagram: www.instagram.com/utpb_sbdc
Description: The University of Texas Permian Basin Small Business Development Center provides business counseling, technical assistance, training workshops, and business plan development for small businesses in our 16 county area.

45491 ■ Texas Tech University - Procurement Services
TTU Plz., Ste. 408, 1901 University Ave.
Lubbock, TX 79409-1094
Ph: (806)742-3844
Fax: (806)742-3820
Co. E-mail: techbuy.purchasing@ttu.edu
URL: http://www.depts.ttu.edu/procurement
Contact: Jennifer Adling, Chief Procurement Officer
E-mail: jennifer.adling@ttu.edu
Description: Provides training and technical assistance to area businesses interested in contracting with federal, state, and local governments.

45492 ■ West Texas A&M University Small Business Development Center
720 S Tyler St.
Amarillo, TX 79101
Ph: (806)651-5151
Co. E-mail: info@wtsbdc.com
URL: http://www.smallbusinessdevelopmentcenter.com
Contact: Gina Woodward, Director
Facebook: www.facebook.com/wtsbdc
X (Twitter): x.com/wtsbdc
Instagram: www.instagram.com/wtsbdc
YouTube: www.youtube.com/wtsbdc
Description: The WTAMU SBDC provides counseling and seminar training for potential and existing businesses located in the top twenty-five counties of the Texas Panhandle. **Geographic Preference:** Local.

INCUBATORS/RESEARCH AND TECHNOLOGY PARKS

45493 ■ 3 Day Startup (3DS)
701 Brazos St., Ste. 533
Austin, TX 78701
Co. E-mail: team@3daystartup.org
URL: http://www.3daystartup.org
Contact: Joel Hestness, Co-Founder
E-mail: jthestness@gmail.com
Facebook: www.facebook.com/3DayStartup
Linkedin: www.linkedin.com/company/3-day-startup
X (Twitter): x.com/3daystartup
Instagram: www.instagram.com/3DayStartup
Description: Teaches entrepreneurial skills to university students in an extreme hands-on environment to aid entrepreneurs in starting their own business. **Founded:** 2008.

45494 ■ AccelerateNFC
1203 Huntington Dr.
Richardson, TX 75080-2930
Contact: Robert Sabella, Manager
Description: A mentor-driven, mentor-funded idea incubator/success accelerator for high potential companies. **Founded:** 2013.

45495 ■ Austin Technology Incubator (ATI)
2815 San Gabriel St.
Austin, TX 78705
Ph: (512)305-0000
Co. E-mail: info@ati.utexas.edu
URL: http://ati.utexas.edu
Contact: Mitch Jacobson, Executive Director
Facebook: www.facebook.com/ATIncubator
Linkedin: www.linkedin.com/company/austin-technology-incubator
X (Twitter): x.com/ATI_UT
Description: Located at the University of Texas at Austin, this incubator specializes in supporting emerging high-risk technology firms. **Founded:** 1989.

45496 ■ Avinde
4500 Williams Dr., St. 212-126
Georgetown, TX 78633-1332
Contact: Terry Chase Hazell, President
Description: A non-profit community driven startup accelerator catering to women launching scalable businesses. **Founded:** 2013.

45497 ■ BioHouston
2450 Holcombe Blvd., TMCxi
Houston, TX 77021
Ph: (713)874-9300
Co. E-mail: info@biohouston.org
URL: http://biohouston.org
Contact: Ann Tanabe, Chief Executive Officer
E-mail: ann.tanabe@biohouston.org
Facebook: www.facebook.com/BioHoustonTX

X (Twitter): x.com/biohouston
Description: Mission is to create an environment that will stimulate technology transfer and research commercialization and to generate economic wealth for the Houston region and making it a global competitor in life science commercialization. **Founded:** 2000.

45498 ■ Biotechnology Commercialization Center (BCC)
The University of Texas Health Science Center at Houston
7000 Fannin St., Ste. 1400
Houston, TX 77030
URL: http://www.uth.edu/otm/faq
Description: Helps to commercialize and incubate UTHSC-H and Houston-based life science technologies, while increasing the number of Texas-based companies. **Founded:** 2009.

45499 ■ Bootstrap Dallas
7831 Amherst Ave.
Dallas, TX 75225
Contact: Chris Walters, Member
Description: Helps Dallas based entrepreneurs by providing resources, training, and introductions into the Dallas startup community. **Founded:** 2011.

45500 ■ The Business Factory
69 N Chadbourne St.
San Angelo, TX 76903
Ph: (325)942-2098
Co. E-mail: businessfactory@angelo.edu
URL: http://www.angelo.edu/community/small-business-development-center/the-business-factory
Contact: Dezaray Johnson, Contact
Description: An incubation program designed for small businesses and entrepreneurs for San Angelo and the Concho Valley Area. Designed for small business and entrepreneurs who enjoy the networking benefits and atmosphere of a professional environment but still want the flexibility of no long-term lease.

45501 ■ Business Technology Center (BTC)
5330 Griggs Rd.
Houston, TX 77021
Ph: (713)845-2400
Fax: (713)645-2830
URL: http://hbdi.org/business-technology-center
Contact: Marlon D. Mitchell, President
Description: A mixed-use business complex, allowing businesses to get a solid start during the early stages of development by providing essential support and assistance.

45502 ■ Capital Factory
701 Brazos St.
Austin, TX 78701
Ph: (512)548-9675
Co. E-mail: frontdesk@capitalfactory.com
URL: http://www.capitalfactory.com
Contact: Joshua Baer, Chief Executive Officer
Facebook: www.facebook.com/capitalfactory
Linkedin: www.linkedin.com/company/capital-factory
X (Twitter): x.com/CapitalFactory
YouTube: www.youtube.com/user/capitalfactory
Description: Works with startups and entrepreneurs to accelerate their companies with co-working space, meeting rooms, and event space. **Founded:** 2009.

45503 ■ Capital Kitchens
1606 W Stassney Ln., Ste. 1
Austin, TX 78745
Ph: (512)686-4456
Co. E-mail: hello@capital-kitchens.com
URL: http://www.capital-kitchens.com
Contact: Caleb Bales, Contact
E-mail: caleb@capital-kitchens.com
Facebook: www.facebook.com/capitalkitchensatx
Linkedin: www.linkedin.com/company/capital-kitchens-culinary-incubator
X (Twitter): x.com/CapitalKitchens
Instagram: www.instagram.com/capitalkitchensaustin
Description: Culinary incubator supporting local food entrepreneurs by providing fully-equipped, commercially-licensed, shared-use kitchens allowing startups to build their business. **Founded:** 2012.

45504 ■ Center for Innovation at Arlington
505 E Border St.
Arlington, TX 76010-7402
Contact: Wes Jurey, President
Description: Firm brings together technology, capital, and talent to match market needs with research capabilities of industry, academia, and government. **Founded:** 2001.

45505 ■ Clean Energy Incubator (CEI)
2815 San Gabriel St.
Austin, TX 78705
URL: http://ati.utexas.edu/companies/energy
Description: A small business incubator offering an environment dedicated specifically to helping young clean energy companies succeed by providing the resources and facilities necessary for qualified startups to attract funding and aggressively compete in the free market. **Founded:** 2001.

45506 ■ Coastal Bend Business Innovation Center (CBBIC)
10201 S Padre Island Dr.
Corpus Christi, TX 78418
Ph: (361)825-3535
Co. E-mail: info@coastalbendinnovation.com
URL: http://cbbic.tamucc.edu
Contact: Doug Milbauer, Director
E-mail: doug.milbauer@tamucc.edu
Facebook: www.facebook.com/CBBICTAMUCC
X (Twitter): x.com/cbbictamucc
Description: A small business incubator that nurtures the development of innovative companies. Provides strategic guidance, access to investors, business mentors, and a ready-made network of business and professional resources. **Founded:** 2009.

45507 ■ The Collide Village (CV)
14681 Midway Rd., 2nd Fl.
Addison, TX 75001
Ph: (469)415-2338
Co. E-mail: info@collidevillage.com
URL: http://collidevillage.com
Contact: Matt Warmuth, Co-Chief Executive Officer
Facebook: www.facebook.com/thecollidevillage
Instagram: www.instagram.com/collidevillage
Description: Business accelerator that invests in startups, teaches them about evidence-based entrepreneurship, and helps founders brand and commercialize their innovations.

45508 ■ Copperas Cove Economic Development Corp. (CCEDC)
207 S 3rd St., Ste. 200
Copperas Cove, TX 76522
Ph: (254)547-7874
Co. E-mail: info@coveedc.com
URL: http://coveedc.com
Contact: Fred Welch, Executive Director
Facebook: www.facebook.com/CopperasCoveEDC
Description: Offers a professional and fully functional environment for you to operate your business to include furnished office space, a private conference room, the use of office equipment and so much more. Also offers free workshops and seminars, general business assistance, and access to networking events. **Founded:** 1990.

45509 ■ Culinary Kitchen & Beyond L.L.C.
2156 W NW Hwy., Ste. No. 312
Dallas, TX 75220
URL: http://www.culinarykitchenandbeyond.com
Contact: Raquel Mireles, Owner
E-mail: raquel@culinarykitchenandbeyond.com
Description: Firm offers commercial kitchen rental services.

45510 ■ The Dallas Entrepreneur Center (DEC)
3662 W Camp Wisdom Rd., No. 2044
Dallas, TX 75237
Ph: (469)480-4466
Co. E-mail: info@thedec.co
URL: http://thedec.co
Contact: Brian McGrath, President
Facebook: www.facebook.com/thedecnetwork
Linkedin: www.linkedin.com/company/thedecnetwork
YouTube: www.youtube.com/channel/UCXkPu7KR8CgdwqjUdkUUQSA
Description: A co-working space created to help entrepreneurs start, build, and grow companies through education, mentorship, and community. **Founded:** 2013.

45511 ■ DFW Excellerator
5307 E Mockingbird Ln. 5th
Dallas, TX 75206
Contact: Leran Liu, President
Description: Business incubator offering co-working space, including conference and training rooms in an atmosphere that is sophisticated, hip, and trendy. Helps high growth companies expand abroad through technology transfer, joint venture, and investment. **Founded:** 2014.

45512 ■ Economic Development Corporation of Weslaco (EDC-Weslaco)
275 S Kansas Ave., Ste. A
Weslaco, TX 78596
Ph: (956)969-0838
Co. E-mail: weslacoedc@gmail.com
URL: http://www.weslacoedc.com
Contact: Benita R. Valadez, President
Facebook: www.facebook.com/WeslacoEDC
Linkedin: www.linkedin.com/in/weslaco-edc-334333117
X (Twitter): x.com/WeslacoEDC
Instagram: www.instagram.com/weslacoedc
YouTube: www.youtube.com/channel/UCg0-A7_-6scxb-2d6xxL_Cg
Description: A non-profit corporation dedicated to the creation of jobs through recruitment of new industry and helping existing companies relocate and/or expand. **Geographic Preference:** Local.

45513 ■ Economic Growth Business Incubator (EGBI)
1144 Airport Blvd., Ste. 260
Austin, TX 78702
Ph: (512)928-2594
Fax: (512)928-2747
Co. E-mail: monica@egbi.org
URL: http://egbi.org
Contact: Joni Foster, Executive Director (Acting) Program Director
E-mail: joni@egbi.org
Facebook: www.facebook.com/EGBIofAustin
X (Twitter): x.com/egbiofaustin
Instagram: www.instagram.com/egbiofaustin
YouTube: www.youtube.com/channel/UCiRSbiPAyQTbP7QjcOVAREQ
Description: Business incubator that meets clients as they start, grow, and sustain grassroots businesses.

45514 ■ Eden Business Incubator
Eden City Hall, 120 Paint Rock Rd.
Eden, TX 76837
URL: http://www.edentexas.com/business/page/eden-business-incubator
Description: Business incubator that nurtures businesses during the early-growth stages. Services include reduced rent with flexible leases for furnished office space, free parking, and a conference/training room. **Founded:** 2010.

45515 ■ Elixir Enterprises LLC
3789 N Beach St., Ste. 209
Fort Worth, TX 76137
Co. E-mail: info@elixirkitchenspace.com
URL: http://www.elixirkitchenspace.com
Contact: John Milam Rideout, Member
Description: Incubator offers two certified kitchens, professional equipment, and permits.

45516 ■ Emergent Incubator
1105 Castle Ct.
Austin, TX 78703
Ph: (512)263-3232
Co. E-mail: info@etibio.com
URL: http://emergenttechnologies.com
Contact: Kris Looney, President
Linkedin: www.linkedin.com/company/emergent-technologies

STATE LISTINGS

X (Twitter): x.com/emergentaustin
Description: Works with start-ups and investors seeking capital to grow a new business. **Founded:** 1989.

45517 ■ Entrepreneur Center of Central Texas
19 N Main St.
Temple, TX 76501
Ph: (254)598-7400
Description: Serves business owners and budding entrepreneurs in Central Texas. Connects entrepreneurs with investors, mentors, and the resources that are critical to accelerate the launch of a startup business.

45518 ■ Entrepreneurs in Community Lawyering (ECL)
2101 Ross Ave.
Dallas, TX 75201
Ph: (214)220-7400
Co. E-mail: ecl@dallasbar.org
URL: http://www.dallasbar.org/?pg=incubatorprogram
Facebook: www.facebook.com/DBAECL
Description: Incubator that helps new attorneys start successful and profitable solo and small firm practices throughout New Mexico.

45519 ■ The Food Lab (TFL)
Austin, TX
URL: http://foodtracks.net/category/foodlab
Contact: Robyn Metcalfe, Contact
E-mail: robyn.metcalfe@austin.utexas.edu
Description: Provides undergraduate awareness of food issues, encourages and motivates students to engage with innovative food systems research, and provides support to startups that leverage University research.

45520 ■ Fort Worth Business Assistance Center (BAC)
1150 S Fwy., Ste. 106
Fort Worth, TX 76104
Ph: (817)871-6025
Fax: (817)392-6031
Co. E-mail: fwbac@fortworthtexas.gov
URL: http://www.fortworthtexas.gov/Home
Facebook: www.facebook.com/fwbac
X (Twitter): twitter.com/FortWorthBAC
Description: Provides information, counseling, educational workshops, and resources for small business owners and start-ups.

45521 ■ The GroundFloor
8117 Preston Rd., Ste. 300
Dallas, TX 75225
URL: http://groundfloordev.com
Contact: Brandon Bolin, President
Description: Accelerator program that invests seed funding and resources in promising social ventures focused on solutions that address challenges facing education, financial stability, and health. **Founded:** 2013.

45522 ■ Harlingen Economic Development Corp.
2424 Boxwood St., Ste. 125
Harlingen, TX 78550
Ph: (956)216-5081
Fax: (956)216-2580
Co. E-mail: rgarza@harlingenedc.com
URL: http://www.harlingenedc.com
Contact: Eric Ziehe, President
Facebook: www.facebook.com/HarlingenEDC
Linkedin: www.linkedin.com/company/harlingenedc
X (Twitter): x.com/harlingenedc
Instagram: www.instagram.com/harlingenedc
YouTube: www.youtube.com/channel/UCEu4BbvRv81DAFCM88encAg
Description: Supports small businesses and entrepreneurs with tools necessary to help them grow into successful businesses. **Founded:** 1990.

45523 ■ Health Wildcatters (HW)
3000 Pegasus Pk. Dr., Ste. 1330
Dallas, TX 75247
URL: http://www.healthwildcatters.com

Contact: Dr. Hubert Zajicek, Chief Executive Officer
Facebook: www.facebook.com/HealthWildcatters
Linkedin: www.linkedin.com/company/health-wildcatters
Instagram: www.instagram.com/healthwildcatters
YouTube: www.youtube.com/channel/UCk8I-igGU2ETOWDUaPi_Q-g
Description: Healthcare startup accelerator focuses on early-stage healthcare startups that come from a variety of niches. **Founded:** 2013.

45524 ■ Hour Kitchen
209 Main St.
Garland, TX 75040
Ph: (214)227-4687
Fax: (214)260-6052
URL: http://www.hourkitchendallas.com
Description: A licensed shared-use commercial kitchen providing food entrepreneurs a service that is economically superior to building or leasing their own commercial facility.

45525 ■ Houston Exponential (HTC)
410 Pierce St.
Houston, TX 77002
Co. E-mail: info@houstonexponential.org
URL: http://www.houstonexponential.org
Facebook: www.facebook.com/HoustonExponential
Linkedin: www.linkedin.com/company/houstonexponential
X (Twitter): x.com/HouEX
Instagram: www.instagram.com/houstonexponential
YouTube: www.youtube.com/channel/UCEIYjsrHfTILDwaEbigTyyA
Description: Firm engaged to assist in the acceleration and commercialization of emerging technology companies. **Founded:** 1999.

45526 ■ Hub Collaborative
404 Jane St., Ste. 100
College Station, TX 77840
URL: http://www.collaborationhub.online
Contact: Brett Milne, Contact
Facebook: www.facebook.com/collaborationhub
X (Twitter): x.com/HUBCollaborativ
Description: A co-working space that provides a variety of environments to help meet our members' business needs.

45527 ■ Hub of Human Innovation
500 W Overland, Ste. 230
El Paso, TX 79901
Contact: Laura Patricia Butler, Contact
Description: A technology incubator that nurtures the development of small businesses, helping them survive and grow during the start-up period when they are most vulnerable. Also assists technology-based businesses that are expanding, relocating, or simply need direction to move their business forward. **Founded:** 2011.

45528 ■ Huntsville Area Technology and Business Complex (HA/tch) - Business Incubator Program
2405 Avenue I
Huntsville, TX 77340
Ph: (936)294-2485
Fax: (936)294-2399
Co. E-mail: info@hatchbusiness.com
URL: http://ha-tch.com
Description: Provides technology-focused entrepreneurs in the Central East Texas region with a unique environment to enhance their companies' chances for success. **Founded:** 2013.

45529 ■ IBM PartnerWorld
Dallas, TX
Free: 800-426-4968
URL: http://www.ibm.com/partnerworld/public
Description: Helps entrepreneurs build, market, and sell high tech solutions.

45530 ■ The Incubaker LLC
1301 Broadmoor Dr.
Austin, TX 78723-3121
Contact: Cody Fields, Manager
Linkedin: www.linkedin.com/company/incubaker

Description: Culinary incubator providing kitchen space for food startups.

45531 ■ InCube Labs L.L.C.
12500 Network Blvd., Ste. 112
San Antonio, TX 78249
Ph: (210)360-1678
URL: http://www.incubelabs.com
Contact: Mir Imran, Chief Executive Officer
Linkedin: www.linkedin.com/company/incube-labs
Description: Firm collaborates with universities and entrepreneurs in Texas and around the country to help identify promising innovations and bring them to market.

45532 ■ Innovation Underground (IU)
216 W 26th St.
Bryan, TX 77803
Co. E-mail: iu@adventgx.com
URL: http://iu.adventgx.com
Contact: Jose Quintana, President
Description: Privately-owned business incubator lends support for local, community-based economic development and historic preservation while encouraging entrepreneurship and innovation to meet the need for business incubation at the community level by engaging experienced entrepreneurs in the process of supporting new startups. **Founded:** 2011.

45533 ■ International Accelerator (IA)
115 Wild Basin Rd., Ste. 307
Austin, TX 78746
Ph: (512)225-9333
URL: http://www.internationalaccelerator.com
Contact: Angelos Angelou, Chief Executive Officer
Facebook: www.facebook.com/internationalaccelerator
Linkedin: www.linkedin.com/company/international-accelerator
X (Twitter): x.com/intlaccelerator
Instagram: www.instagram.com/intlaccelerator
YouTube: www.youtube.com/channel/UCMhp36dM-vdcTHjmMkW7JdQ
Description: Offers a 12-month accelerator program for non-US founders. Offers access to seed funding and other services. **Founded:** 2014.

45534 ■ iStart Valley
3941 Legacy Dr., Ste. 204, No. B206
Plano, TX 75023
URL: http://www.istartvalley.org
Contact: Veena Kollipara, President
Linkedin: www.linkedin.com/company/istart-valley
Description: Business accelerator geared towards helping the workforce to transition their careers to new and emerging industries. **Founded:** 2011.

45535 ■ Jon Brumley Texas Venture Labs
300 W Martin Luther King Jr. Blvd., RRH 1.354, Stop D9700
Austin, TX 78712
Ph: (512)471-5921
Co. E-mail: infotvl@mccombs.utexas.edu
URL: http://www.mccombs.utexas.edu/centers-and-initiatives/jon-brumley-texas-venture-labs
Contact: Mellie Price, Executive Director
E-mail: mellie.price@mccombs.utexas.edu
Facebook: www.facebook.com/TXVentureLabs
Instagram: www.instagram.com/utxventurelabs
Description: Fosters entrepreneurship and innovation for graduate students at the University of Texas at Austin. Offers programs, competitions, and access to the Austin start-up community. Pairs cross-functional graduate student teams with Austin-area startups for a 10-week consulting project.

45536 ■ The Kingdom Builders' Center (KBC)
6011 W Orem Dr.
Houston, TX 77085
Ph: (713)726-2500
Fax: (713)726-2508
URL: http://www.thekbchouston.com
Contact: R. Lee Hall, Chief Executive Officer
Description: Firm supports business startups and entrepreneurs in central Southwest Houston. **Founded:** 2007.

45537 ■ Kitchen Incubator
907 Franklin St., Ste. 150
  Houston, TX 77002-1713
Contact: Lucrece Borrego, Manager
Description: A full service business incubator for craft food and beverage, dedicated to launching small businesses. **Founded:** 2009.

45538 ■ LAUNCH Innovative Business Accelerator
100 Research Pky.
  Waco, TX 76704
URL: http://www.baylor.edu/mediacommunications/news.php?action=story&story=146730
Contact: Gregory W. Leman, Director
Linkedin: www.linkedin.com/showcase/baylor-university---launch-innovative-business-accelerator
Description: Offers start-ups and established companies access to the systems and resources necessary to achieve sustainable innovation and market growth.

45539 ■ Longview Chamber of Commerce
410 N Center St.
  Longview, TX 75601
Ph: (903)237-4000
Co. E-mail: chamber@longviewtx.com
URL: http://longviewchamber.com
Contact: Kelly Hall, President
E-mail: khall@longviewtx.com
Facebook: www.facebook.com/longviewchamber
X (Twitter): x.com/LongviewChamber
Instagram: www.instagram.com/longviewchamber
YouTube: www.youtube.com/channel/UCSpiz98F0c0SGnfG_zh3ixg
Description: Business incubator for new small businesses. **Publications:** *Impact* (Bimonthly); *Uniquely Longview*. **Geographic Preference:** Local.

45540 ■ Manon's Shared Kitchen
8309 Research Blvd.
  Austin, TX 78758
Ph: (512)587-3080
Co. E-mail: info@manons.com
URL: http://www.manonssharedkitchen.com
Facebook: www.facebook.com/ManonsSharedKitchen
Instagram: www.instagram.com/manonssharedkitchen
Description: Kitchen incubator for budding chefs and entrepreneurs.

45541 ■ McAllen Creative Incubator (McA2)
601 N Main St.
  McAllen, TX 78504
Ph: (956)687-2787
URL: http://mcallenincubator.com
Contact: Laura Robles, Coordinator
E-mail: lrobles@mcallenchamber.com
Facebook: www.facebook.com/Creative.Incubator
Description: Firm is a creative incubator service such as providing low-cost studios for artists and organizations with managerial, legal and technical support and various other services.

45542 ■ Neeley Entrepreneurship Center
2900 Lubbock
  Fort Worth, TX 76109
URL: http://neeley.tcu.edu/Entrepreneurship
Description: Entrepreneurship center providing space for student startups in which they can launch and grow their business. The center also has a venture capital fund. **Founded:** 2000.

45543 ■ North Texas Enterprise Center for Technology (NTEC)
2109 W Side Ave.
  Rochelle Park, NJ 07662
Ph: (201)266-8005
URL: http://www.ntec-inc.org
Contact: Jonathan Lewis, Executive Director
Description: Provides startups and entrepreneurs with the resources they need to succeed in Frisco, TX. Offers promising ventures access to expert guidance, enterprise-class infrastructure and a vast professional network. **Founded:** 2003.

45544 ■ RED Labs
701 Brazos St., Ste. 720
  Austin, TX 78701
Contact: Danny Schoening, Director
Description: The University of Houston's coworking space, startup accelerator, and technology entrepreneurship program. **Founded:** 2013.

45545 ■ RedWind Group Inc.
URL: http://redwindgroup.com
Contact: Kyle Smith, Founder
Description: Firm provides support to startups and entrepreneurs including strategic development, organizational design and project implementation. **Founded:** 1999.

45546 ■ Rice Alliance for Technology and Entrepreneurship
McNair Hall, Ste. 103
  6100 Main St.
  Houston, TX 77005-2932
Ph: (713)348-3443
Fax: (713)348-3110
Co. E-mail: alliance@rice.edu
URL: http://alliance.rice.edu
Contact: Brad Burke, Manager Director
E-mail: bburke@rice.edu
Linkedin: www.linkedin.com/company/rice-alliance-for-technology-and-entrepreneurship
X (Twitter): x.com/ricealliance
YouTube: www.youtube.com/user/ricealliance
Description: A catalyst for building successful ventures through education, guidance and connections. Its mission is to support the creation of technology-based companies and the commercialization of new technologies in the Houston community and Southwest. **Founded:** 2000.

45547 ■ Services Cooperative Association (SCA)
9517 Long Point Rd.
  Houston, TX 77055-4203
Contact: C. Dean Kring, Director
Description: A self-funded, not-for-profit cooperative association of business owners, former business owners, and future business owners. An educational, sales, marketing, business development, mentoring, incubation and support organization for the start-up, early stage and poised-for-growth entrepreneur. **Founded:** 1983.

45548 ■ SKU
Austin, TX
Co. E-mail: hi@sku.is
URL: http://sku.is
Contact: Shari Wynne Ressler, Founder
E-mail: shari@rwrlegal.com
Facebook: www.facebook.com/SKUatx
X (Twitter): x.com/skuatx
Description: A business accelerator program for consumer product startups.

45549 ■ SXSW Pitch
PO Box 685289
  Austin, TX 78768
URL: http://www.sxsw.com
Contact: Roland Swenson, Chief Executive Officer
Description: Accelerator event takes place during the annual SXSW interactive festival, to participate in the pitch competition, the 48 startups selected from the U.S. and around the world must have products or services in specified categories. **Founded:** 2009.

45550 ■ TECH Fort Worth (TECHFW)
1120 S Fwy.
  Fort Worth, TX 76104
Ph: (817)339-8968
URL: http://www.techfortworth.org
Contact: Hayden Blackburn, Executive Director
Facebook: www.facebook.com/TECHFortWorth
Linkedin: www.linkedin.com/company/techfw
X (Twitter): x.com/TECHFortWorth
Instagram: www.instagram.com/techfw
YouTube: www.youtube.com/channel/UCdi2Mm29ZyMWaRnOahTfgzA
Description: A nonprofit business incubator and accelerator working with technology startup companies which have based their businesses on proprietary technology they have developed or acquired. It works closely with these companies to create feasible business plans, to develop effective marketing strategies, to build strong management teams, and to launch them successfully into the Fort Worth economy. **Founded:** 1998.

45551 ■ Tech Ranch Austin
8920 Business Pk. Dr., Ste. 250
  Austin, TX 78759
Co. E-mail: info@techranchaustin.com
URL: http://techranchaustin.com
Contact: Kevin Koym, Chief Executive Officer
Linkedin: www.linkedin.com/company/tech-ranch-austin
X (Twitter): x.com/techranch
Description: A supportive community that helps startups move you forward. Offers co-working/office space and a variety of programs. **Founded:** 2008.

45552 ■ Tech Wildcatters (TW)
5960 Berkshire Ln., 6th Fl.
  Dallas, TX 75225
Co. E-mail: info@techwildcatters.com
URL: http://www.techwildcatters.com
Contact: Ricky Tejapaibul, Managing Partner Member
Facebook: www.facebook.com/TechWildcatters
Linkedin: www.linkedin.com/company/tech-wildcatters
X (Twitter): x.com/techwildcatters
Instagram: www.instagram.com/techwildcatters
Description: Experienced business accelerator operating on a 5-tier system, investing time and resources to promising startups. **Founded:** 2009.

45553 ■ Technology Incubator of West Houston (TIWH)
6301 S Stadium Ln., Ste. 111
  Katy, TX 77494
Ph: (281)396-2201
Co. E-mail: flombard@katyedc.org
URL: http://katydock.wordpress.com
Contact: Zachariah R. Bell, President
X (Twitter): x.com/TIWesthouston
Description: Works to advance entrepreneurial success via education, networking, and funding provided by engaged citizens. Supports practical and sustainable opportunities that can be implemented within the community and partners with others to leverage resources and capabilities.

45554 ■ Technology Incubator West Houston (TIWH)
c/o Frank Lombard, Client Administrator
  6301 S Stadium Ln., Ste. 111
  Katy, TX 77494
Ph: (281)396-2201
Co. E-mail: flombard@katyedc.org
URL: http://katydock.wordpress.com
Contact: Zachariah R. Bell, President
X (Twitter): x.com/TIWesthouston
Description: Helps entrepreneurial talent on the west side of Houston. Brings resources and talent together to help successfully launch new businesses and facilitate growth. **Founded:** 2010.

45555 ■ TechStudios L.L.C. (TS)
1701 Brun St., Ste. 100
  Houston, TX 77019
Ph: (713)874-0100
Fax: (888)590-6890
URL: http://techstudios.net/home
Contact: F. Gabriel Garcia, Manager
Description: Incubator offering startup services including business plans, incubation, and management. **Founded:** 2003.

45556 ■ Temple Health & Bioscience District (THBD)
1802 S 1st St.
  Temple, TX 76504
Ph: (254)935-3969
URL: http://templebioscience.org

STATE LISTINGS

Contact: Thomas Baird, Chairman of the Board
Instagram: www.instagram.com/templehbd
Description: Offers lab and office space for early-stage biotech companies.

45557 ■ Texas A&M University - McFerrin Center for Entrepreneurship
4123 TAMU 1700 Research Pky., Ste. 120
College Station, TX 77843-4123
Ph: (979)458-8631
Co. E-mail: mcferrincenter@tamu.edu
URL: http://mcferrin.tamu.edu
Contact: Blake Petty, Executive Director
E-mail: blakepetty@tamu.edu
Facebook: www.facebook.com/TAMUMcFerrin
Linkedin: www.linkedin.com/company/the-mcferrin-center-for-entrepreneurship
X (Twitter): x.com/TAMUMcFerrin
Instagram: www.instagram.com/tamumcferrin
YouTube: www.youtube.com/channel/UCpD_aBEJ5RZkocDIoicKtRA
Description: Provides encouragement, education, networking and assistance to entrepreneurially-minded students, faculty and alumni. Provides business start up acceleration, competitive opportunities, work experiences, and financial support to aspiring entrepreneurs. **Founded:** 1999.

45558 ■ Texas A&M University - Startup Aggieland
Wehner Bldg.
Texas A&M University, 4113 TAMU
College Station, TX 77843-4113
URL: http://mays.tamu.edu/mcferrin-center-for-entrepreneurship/startup-aggieland
Contact: Blake Petty, Partner
Description: Student-designed campus business accelerators for student startups. Offers programs that encourage students to see themselves as founders, innovators and leaders. **Founded:** 1999.

45559 ■ Texas Life-Science Collaboration Center (TLCC)
808 Martin Luther King Jr. St.
Georgetown, TX 78626
Co. E-mail: cs@georgetown.org
URL: http://invest.georgetown.org/business-spotlight
Contact: Dr. Karla Johanning, Chief Executive Officer
Description: Seeks post-incubation medical and biotech companies making the transition from R&D to commercialization. **Founded:** 2007.

45560 ■ Texas Opportunity & Justice Incubator (TOJI)
State Bar of Texas
1414 Colorado St.
Austin, TX 78701
Co. E-mail: txoji@texasbar.com
URL: http://txoji.com
Facebook: www.facebook.com/txoji
Linkedin: www.linkedin.com/company/txoji
X (Twitter): x.com/txoji
Instagram: www.instagram.com/txoji
YouTube: www.youtube.com/channel/UCjNOxYXnccOy_4S6HdzbMVQ
Description: Incubator that works to match new lawyers with an entrepreneurial focus with mentors who can assist them in building sustainable practices aimed at meeting the needs of low- and moderate-income Texans. Provides office space and training for a select group of new attorneys who want to build their own practices. **Founded:** 2017.

45561 ■ Texas Research Alliance (TRA)
500 N Akard St.
Dallas, TX 75201
Ph: (214)746-6606
Co. E-mail: info@texasresearchalliance.org
URL: http://tradfw.org
Contact: Dr. Victor Fishman, Executive Director
Facebook: www.facebook.com/TexasResearchAlliance
Linkedin: www.linkedin.com/company/texas-research-alliance

Description: Serves the entrepreneurial community through creating opportunities to raise capital for technology based start-up ventures in Texas. **Founded:** 2014. **Geographic Preference:** National.

45562 ■ Texas Research & Technology Foundation (TRTF)
URL: http://texasresearchfoundation.com
Contact: Randy Harig, President
Description: Supports the growth of the bioscience and tech-based industry sectors by providing essential infrastructure for scientific advancement, technology innovation, and product development. **Founded:** 1984.

45563 ■ Texas State University - STAR Park
3055 Hunter Rd.
San Marcos, TX 78666
Ph: (512)245-7827
Co. E-mail: starpark@txstate.edu
URL: http://www.txst.edu/ocir/STAR-Park.html
Contact: Harold Strong, Executive Director
E-mail: hes11@txstate.edu
Facebook: www.facebook.com/txstSTARPark
X (Twitter): x.com/txstSTARPark
Instagram: www.instagram.com/txststarpark
Description: Science, Technology and Advanced Research (STAR) Park provides startups and entrepreneurs with flexible wet lab and office spaces. The labs support the needs of a broad range of users requiring chemistry, materials and life sciences lab space to advance a business, product or concept. A conference room, large multipurpose room, leasable offices and an open collaborative space are also included.

45564 ■ Thinktiv
1011 San Jacinto Blvd., Ste. 202
Austin, TX 78701
URL: http://www.thinktiv.com
Contact: Andrew Persoff, Director
Linkedin: www.linkedin.com/company/thinktiv
Description: A business builder focused on helping clients and partners achieve success. **Founded:** 2005.

45565 ■ Tigua Business Center (TBC)
9180 Socorro Rd.
El Paso, TX 79907
Ph: (915)859-8151
Fax: (915)242-0077
URL: http://www.ysletadelsurpueblo.org/tribal-services/department-of-economic-development
Description: Provides support services and a physical location for qualifying small businesses and startups.

45566 ■ Trinity University - Center for Innovation and Entrepreneurship
URL: http://new.trinity.edu/academics/majors-minors/entrepreneurship
Contact: Danny J. Anderson, President
Description: Supports education and training for entrepreneurship and cultivates teams to transform creative ideas into realities. **Founded:** 1869.

45567 ■ Tyler Area Business Incubator (TABI)
1530 S SW Loop 323, Ste. 119
Tyler, TX 75701
Ph: (903)510-2982
Co. E-mail: ttad@tjc.edu
URL: http://www.tjc.edu/info/20188/continuing_studies/163/tyler_area_business_incubator
Description: Business incubator that encourages the development of technology-based products and services which broaden the economic base of the area served by the college. Thirteen to sixteen client businesses operate here throughout the year. **Founded:** 2016.

45568 ■ University of Texas at Austin - College of Pharmacy's Drug Dynamics Institute (DDI) - Drug Dynamics Institute
Austin, TX
Co. E-mail: utechdr@austin.utexas.edu
URL: http://www.drugdynamicsinstitute.com
Contact: Dr. Janet Walkow, Executive Director

Description: Encourages technology start-ups and companies to locate in Austin, where the lack of wet lab space is limiting these efforts. Provides space for startups.

45569 ■ University of Texas at Austin - Office of Technology Commercialization (OTC)
West Pickle Research Building (WPR), Ste. 1. 9A
3925 W Braker Ln.
Austin, TX 78759
URL: http://research.utexas.edu/resources/commercializing-technology
Description: Assists in the formation of startups and promotes collaboration with industry investors and others within the tech commercialization ecosystem.

45570 ■ University of Texas at Brownsville (UTB) - Entrepreneurship and Commercialization Center (ECC)
1304 E Adams St.
Brownsville, TX 78520
Ph: (956)882-4120
Co. E-mail: ecc@utrgv.edu
URL: http://www.utrgv.edu/ecc
Contact: Linda Ufland, Director
E-mail: linda.ufland@utrgv.edu
Facebook: www.facebook.com/UTRGVEntrepreneurship
Linkedin: www.linkedin.com/in/utrgv-ecc
X (Twitter): x.com/UTRGV_ECC
YouTube: www.youtube.com/channel/UCjmjXOj9vHtW9Odx3gpt2vA
Description: Assists entrepreneurs in developing and expanding their business through education. Offers virtual office space, one-on-one consulting, and priority access to professional development programs.

45571 ■ University of Texas Health Science Center - Biotechnology Commercializatinon Center (BCC)
7000 Fannin St.
Houston, TX 77030
URL: http://www.uth.edu/otm
Contact: Christine F. Weaver, Director
E-mail: christine.weaver@uth.tmc.edu
Description: Incubator for start-ups. Helps commercialize Houston-based technologies. Offers laboratory space, capital equipment, collaboration, and expertise.

45572 ■ The University of Texas at San Antonio College of Business - Center for Innovation, Technology and Entrepreneurship (CITE)
1 UTSA Cir.
San Antonio, TX 78249
URL: http://business.utsa.edu/programs/graduate-certificate-technology-management
Contact: Daisy Saucedo, Advisor
E-mail: daisy.saucedo@utsa.edu
Description: Fosters the growth of new technology ventures. Offers the Roadrunner Incubator, an incubator for early-stage student enterprises. **Founded:** 2006.

45573 ■ WT Enterprise Center (WTEC)
2300 N W St.
Amarillo, TX 79124
Ph: (806)374-9777
Fax: (806)374-9778
Co. E-mail: info@wtenterprisecenter.com
URL: http://wtenterprisecenter.com
Contact: Tanikka Bell, Office Manager
Facebook: www.facebook.com/WTEnterpriseCenter
Linkedin: www.linkedin.com/company/wt-enterprise-center
X (Twitter): x.com/wtenterprisectr
Instagram: www.instagram.com/wtenterprisecenter
YouTube: www.youtube.com/channel/UCKhxhLrjmNzYt8xXv2YyBDQ
Description: Applies the principles of business incubation as a catalyst for innovation and entrepreneurial development in order to foster economic growth. Provides facilities, coaching, training programs, education, and leadership to startups. **Founded:** 2001.

45574 ■ Z's Cafe Kitchen Incubator and Commissary
1316 Pennsylvania Ave.
Fort Worth, TX 76104
Ph: (817)348-9000
Fax: (817)423-7521
URL: http://www.zscafe.com

Description: Culinary incubator supporting local entrepreneurs to grow their ideas and skills into sustainable, successful business ventures.

EDUCATIONAL PROGRAMS

45575 ■ Baylor University John F. Baugh Center for Entrepreneurship & Free Enterprise
One Bear Pl., Ste. 98011
Waco, TX 76798-8011
Ph: (254)710-2265
Co. E-mail: entrepreneurship@baylor.edu
URL: http://hankamer.baylor.edu/baugh-center
Contact: Deana Steele, Office Manager
E-mail: deana_steele@baylor.edu

Description: Extends support to the local, national and global business community to facilitate new business and further the goals of established businesses. **Founded:** 1977.

45576 ■ El Paso Community College (EPCC)
9050 Viscount Blvd.
El Paso, TX 79925
Ph: (915)831-3722
Co. E-mail: aayub@epcc.edu
URL: http://www.epcc.edu
Contact: Dr. William Serrata, President
Facebook: www.facebook.com/epccnews
X (Twitter): x.com/EPCCNews
Instagram: www.instagram.com/epccnews
YouTube: www.youtube.com/goepcc

Description: Two-year college offering small business management courses. **Founded:** 1969.

45577 ■ Kilgore College
1100 Broadway Blvd.
Kilgore, TX 75662
Ph: (903)984-8531
Co. E-mail: helpdesk@kilgore.edu
URL: http://www.kilgore.edu
Contact: Dr. Brenda S. Kays, President
E-mail: bkays@kilgore.edu
Facebook: www.facebook.com/kilgore.college
Linkedin: www.linkedin.com/company/kilgore-college
X (Twitter): x.com/kilgorecollege
Instagram: www.instagram.com/kilgorecollege1935
YouTube: www.youtube.com/user/kilgorecollege1935

Description: Academic institution provides undergraduate and post graduate courses and many more. **Founded:** 1935.

LEGISLATIVE ASSISTANCE

45578 ■ State of Texas Office of the Governor Economic Development & Tourism Div.
PO Box 12428
Austin, TX 78711
Ph: (512)463-2000
Co. E-mail: business@gov.texas.gov
URL: http://gov.texas.gov/business
Contact: Adriana Cruz, Executive Director
Facebook: www.facebook.com/TexasEconDev
Linkedin: www.linkedin.com/company/28655937
X (Twitter): x.com/TexasEconDev
Instagram: www.instagram.com/texasecondev
YouTube: www.youtube.com/channel/UCk2mldvOd_Ez6ih92rS69gw

Description: Brings together government efforts to support economic growth through world trade development, domestic business development, and small business assistance.

CONSULTANTS

45579 ■ Idea Labs Consulting
5900 Balcones Dr., Ste. ., 100
Austin, TX 78731
Ph: (512)775-6097
Co. E-mail: info@idealabsconsulting.com
URL: http://www.idealabsconsulting.com
Contact: Malcolm Peace, President
Facebook: www.facebook.com/idealabsconsulting

Description: Assists start-ups by filling needs at crucial stages of their business. Offers sales, marketing, finance, and business strategy planning services. **Founded:** 2011.

45580 ■ McDaniel Consulting
1910 Pacific Ave.
Dallas, TX 75201
Ph: (214)349-6564
URL: http://mcdanielconsulting-gbsfe.com
Contact: Syreeta V. McDaniel, President
E-mail: syreeta@mcdanielconsulting-gbsfe.com

Description: Writes business plans. Offers consulting services to DBEs through the Texas Department of Transportation. **Founded:** 2001.

45581 ■ R Moon Consulting
3636 N Hall St., Ste. 610
Dallas, TX 75219
Ph: (214)382-2964
Free: 888-342-6167
URL: http://rmoonconsulting.com
Contact: Randy Moon, Consultant
Facebook: www.facebook.com/AmeraRMoonConsulting
X (Twitter): x.com/rmoonconsulting

Description: Offers consulting on diversity, employee management, business structures, analytics, and finances, .

45582 ■ RedHouse Associates LLC
802 Lovett Blvd.
Houston, TX 77006
Ph: (713)338-2151
Fax: (713)493-2831
Co. E-mail: info@redhouseassociates.com
URL: http://www.redhouseassociates.com/Home.html
Contact: Douglas J. Erwin, Principal Chairman
E-mail: doug.erwin@redhouseassociates.com
Facebook: www.facebook.com/RedhouseAssociates
Linkedin: www.linkedin.com/company/redhouse-associates-llc
X (Twitter): x.com/The_RedHouse

Description: Offers strategic advice to technology startups to accelerate growth. Offers business strategy, product roadmaps, coaching management, and financial advice. **Founded:** 2011.

PUBLICATIONS

45583 ■ *Austin Business Journal*
120 W Morehead St.
Charlotte, NC 28202
Co. E-mail: circhelp@bizjournals.com
URL: http://www.acbj.com
Contact: Mike Olivieri, Executive Vice President
URL(s): www.bizjournals.com/austin
Linkedin: www.linkedin.com/company/austin-business-journal
X (Twitter): x.com/MyABJ
Instagram: www.instagram.com/austin_business_journal

Ed: Colin Pope. **Released:** Weekly **Price:** $4, for online or print + online 4 weeks; $380, for Nationwide Access 52 weeks; $9, for Nationwide Access 4 weeks; $950, for Nationwide + BOL 52 weeks; $70, Members for premium print and online; $220, for print + online 52 weeks; $245, for Nationwide Access; $210, for online 52 weeks; $70, Members for premium online. **Description:** Newspaper (tabloid) serving business and industry in Central Texas. **Availability:** Print; PDF; Download; Online. **Type:** Full-text.

45584 ■ *Business Update*
505 E Border St.
Arlington, TX 76010
Ph: (817)275-2613
Fax: (817)701-0893
Co. E-mail: membership@arlingtontx.com
URL: http://www.arlingtontx.com
Contact: Michael Jacobson, President
E-mail: mjacobson@arlingtontx.com
URL(s): www.arlingtontx.com/covid-19
Availability: Print.

45585 ■ *Dallas Business Journal*
120 W Morehead St.
Charlotte, NC 28202
Co. E-mail: circhelp@bizjournals.com
URL: http://www.acbj.com
Contact: Mike Olivieri, Executive Vice President
URL(s): www.bizjournals.com/dallas
Facebook: www.facebook.com/dallasbizjournal
Linkedin: www.linkedin.com/company/dallas-business-journal
X (Twitter): x.com/DallasBizNews
Instagram: www.instagram.com/dallasbizjournal

Ed: Rob Schneider. **Released:** Weekly **Price:** $350, for nationwide access; $950, for nationwide + bol; $190, for digital + print; $180, for digital only. **Description:** Metro business journal. **Availability:** Print; Online. **Type:** Full-text.

45586 ■ *Katy Business Association--Directory (Member listings)*
5304 E 5TH St., Ste. 104
Katy, TX 77493-2532
Ph: (832)656-3993
URL: http://thekba.org
Contact: Jennifer Pierce, President
URL(s): thekba.org/members/#!directory/map

Description: Covers list of businesses in Katy, Texas. **Entries include:** Company name, address, contact information, e-mail, and contact person. **Indexes:** Classified by by business category. **Availability:** Print.

45587 ■ *Texas Real Estate Business*
3535 Piedmont Rd. NE, Bldg. 14, Ste. 950
Atlanta, GA 30305
Ph: (404)832-8262
Fax: (404)832-8260
URL: http://francemediainc.com
Contact: Scott France, Publisher
URL(s): rebusinessonline.com/commercial-real-estate-magazines/texas-real-estate-business

Released: Semiweekly **Description:** Magazine that covers the latest news, developments and trends in commercial real estate in Texas. **Availability:** Print; Online.

PUBLISHERS

45588 ■ ABS Consulting Training Services
1701 City Plz. Dr.
Spring, TX 77373
Ph: (281)673-2800
URL: http://www.abs-group.com/Training

Description: Firm publishes law, regulatory and technical books on subjects that include federal safety and code regulations. **Founded:** 1973.

45589 ■ Dockery House Publishing Inc.
1223 Chateau Ln. Hideway
Lindale, TX 75771
Contact: Rodney Dockery, President

Description: Publisher of magazines and fiction books. **Founded:** 1980.

45590 ■ MLM Consultants [Americas MLM Consultants]
2400 Waters Edge Dr.
Granbury, TX 76048-2659
Contact: M. L. Mckean, President

Description: Publishes books, software and resources on business topics.

45591 ■ Mullaney Publishing Group LLP
2306 Lawnmeadow Dr.
Richardson, TX 75080-2339

Description: Publishes on retail business and ecommerce.

EXPANSION AND GROWTH FINANCING

45592 ■ Haddington Ventures, L.L.C. (HV)
1800 Bering Dr.,Ste. 900
Houston, TX 77057
Ph: (713)532-7992
Fax: (713)532-9922
URL: http://www.hvllc.com
Contact: J. Chris Jones, Managing Director
Description: Private equity firm specializing in energy gathering, separation, processing, treatment, compression, and storage. **Founded:** 1998. **Industry Preferences:** Energy.

VENTURE CAPITAL FIRM

45593 ■ Colt Ventures (CV)
2101 Cedar Springs Rd., Ste.1230
Dallas, TX 75201
Ph: (214)397-0176
URL: http://www.coltventures.com
Contact: Darren Blanton, Founder Managing Partner
Description: Venture capital firm focused on precision oncology, gene therapy, and rare diseases. Also manages biotech securities. **Founded:** 2003. **Preferred Investment Size:** $5,000,000 to $15,000,000. **Industry Preferences:** Biotechnology; technology; real estate; oil and gas.

45594 ■ Corsa Ventures
103 E 5th St., Ste. 208
Austin, TX 78701
Co. E-mail: info@corsaventures.com
URL: http://www.corsaventures.com
Contact: Brian Grigsby, Managing Partner
Description: Early-stage venture capital firm for technology companies.

45595 ■ Houston Ventures (HV)
600 Travis, Ste. 3550
Houston, TX 77002
Ph: (832)529-2829
Co. E-mail: info@houven.com
URL: http://www.houven.com
Contact: Chip Davis, Managing Partner
Description: Venture capital firm for early- to growth-stage technology companies in the energy industry.

45596 ■ Mobility Ventures
PO Box 1597
Addison, TX 75001
Ph: (972)991-9942
URL: http://mobilityventures.com
Contact: Arlan Harris, Partner
X (Twitter): x.com/mobilityVC
YouTube: www.youtube.com/user/mobilityventures
Description: Early-stage companies enabling mobility (i.e., solutions leveraging the convergence of wireless infrastructures, the internet, software technologies, applications and services for anytime/anywhere connectivity). . **Industry Preferences:** AI date sciences; mobile marketing; mobile health; mobile commerce; location-based services; energy/power management.

45597 ■ Monument Ventures
Austin, TX
Ph: (512)636-4068
URL: http://www.monumentventures.com
Contact: Bill Vale, Managing Director Co-Founder
Description: Offers business planning, management advisor, and financial advisory services to innovative start-ups.

45598 ■ Pipeline Angels
1321 Upland Dr., Ste. 5167
Houston, TX 77043
Co. E-mail: info@pipelineangels.com
URL: http://pipelineangels.com
Contact: Natalia Oberti Noguera, Chief Executive Officer
Facebook: www.facebook.com/PipelineAngels
Linkedin: www.linkedin.com/company/pipeline-angels
X (Twitter): x.com/PipelineAngels
Instagram: www.instagram.com/pipelineangels
YouTube: www.youtube.com/c/Pipelineangels
Pinterest: www.pinterest.com/pipelineangels
Description: Angel investment funding for women and non-binary femme social entrepreneurs. Offer angel investment bootcamp, networking, and educational opportunities. **Founded:** 2011.

45599 ■ Quantum Capital Group (QEP)
Bank of America Tower
800 Capitol St., Ste. 3600
Houston, TX 77002
Ph: (713)452-2000
Co. E-mail: intro@quantumcap.com
URL: http://www.quantumcap.com
Contact: Gabriel Alonso, President
Description: Private equity capital firm for the energy industry. **Founded:** 1998. **Industry Preferences:** Oil and gas; oilfield services.

45600 ■ Silverton Partners
600 W 7th St.
Austin, TX 78701
Ph: (512)476-6700
Fax: (512)477-0025
Co. E-mail: businessplans@silvertonpartners.com
URL: http://www.silvertonpartners.com
Contact: Roger Chen, Partner
Linkedin: www.linkedin.com/company/silverton-partners
Instagram: www.instagram.com/silvertonvc
Description: Venture capital firm for early-stage companies. **Founded:** 2006.

45601 ■ Trellis Partners
138 Trinity St.
Cedar Creek, TX 78612
Ph: (512)330-9200
URL: http://www.trellis.com
Contact: Alexander C. Broeker, Partner
E-mail: abroeker@trellis.com
Description: Venture capital firm. **Founded:** 1997. **Industry Preferences:** Information technolog.

45602 ■ Yellowstone Capital Partners LLC (YCP)
777 Post Oak Blvd., Ste. 250
Houston, TX 77056
Ph: (713)650-0065
Co. E-mail: info@yellowstonecapital.com
URL: http://www.yellowstonecapital.com
Contact: Omar A. Sawaf, Chief Executive Officer
Description: Private equity venture capital firm. Invests in and acquires small- to mid-sized companies. Also maintains a New York office. **Founded:** 1993. **Industry Preferences:** Energy technology; life science; food and beverages.

Utah

ASSOCIATIONS AND OTHER ORGANIZATIONS

45603 ■ National Association of Women Business Owners Salt Lake City (NAWBO/SLC)
PO Box 526095
Salt Lake City, UT 84152
Ph: (801)487-4600
Co. E-mail: nawboslc@gmail.com
URL: http://www.nawbo.org/salt-lake-city
Contact: Jodi Vawdrey, Advisor
URL(s): www.nawbo.org/about/find-chapter
Facebook: www.facebook.com/nawboslc
X (Twitter): x.com/nawboslc
YouTube: www.youtube.com/channel/UCjUdD39NOFxs5t86_xVcwRw
Founded: 1992. **Geographic Preference:** Local.

SMALL BUSINESS DEVELOPMENT CENTERS

45604 ■ Blanding Small Business Development Center
238 N 100 E
Blanding, UT 84511
URL: http://utahsbdc.org/locations/blanding
Contact: Meghan McFall, Director
E-mail: meghan.mcfall@usu.edu
URL(s): clients.utahsbdc.org/center.aspx?center=59008&subloc=0&mode=e
Description: Represents and promotes the small business sector. Provides management assistance to current and prospective small business owners. Helps to improve management skills and expand the products and services of members. **Geographic Preference:** Local.

45605 ■ Cedar City Small Business Development Center
510 W 800 S
Cedar City, UT 84720
Ph: (435)865-7707
URL: http://utahsbdc.org/locations/cedar-city
Contact: Joni Anderson, Director
Description: Represents and promotes the small business sector. Provides management assistance to current and prospective small business owners. Helps to improve management skills and expand the products and services of members. **Geographic Preference:** Local.

45606 ■ Ephraim Small Business Development Center (SBDC)
151 S Main St.
Ephraim, UT 84627
Ph: (435)283-7376
URL: http://utahsbdc.org/locations/ephraim
Contact: Tim Chamberlain, Director
Description: Represents and promotes the small business sector. Provides management assistance to current and prospective small business owners. Helps to improve management skills and expand the products and services of members. **Founded:** 1982. **Geographic Preference:** Local.

45607 ■ Kaysville Small Business Development Center (SBDC)
450 Simmons Way
Kaysville, UT 84037
Ph: (801)643-0424
URL: http://utahsbdc.org/locations/kaysville
Contact: Andrew Willis, Director
Description: Represents and promotes the small business sector. Provides management assistance to current and prospective small business owners. Helps to improve management skills and expand the products and services of members. **Founded:** 1982. **Geographic Preference:** Local.

45608 ■ Logan Small Business Development Center
1770 Research Pky., No. 140
North Logan, UT 84341-9680
Ph: (435)797-2277
Co. E-mail: sbdc@usu.edu
URL: http://extension.usu.edu/sbdc
Contact: Mike Young, Contact
E-mail: smike.young@usu.edu
Description: Represents and promotes the small business sector. Provides management assistance to current and prospective small business owners. Helps to improve management skills and expand the products and services of members. **Geographic Preference:** Local.

45609 ■ Ogden Small Business Development Center
2605 Monroe Blvd., Rm. 211
Ogden, UT 84401
Ph: (801)626-7232
URL: http://utahsbdc.org/locations/ogden
Contact: Shawn J. Beus, Director
Description: Represents and promotes the small business sector. Provides management assistance to current and prospective small business owners. Helps to improve management skills and expand the products and services of members. **Geographic Preference:** Local.

45610 ■ Orem/Provo Small Business Development Center
815 W 1250 S
Orem, UT 84058
Ph: (801)863-8230
Fax: (801)863-7071
Co. E-mail: sbdc@uvu.edu
URL: http://www.uvu.edu/sbdc
Contact: Camille Pendleton, Regional Director
X (Twitter): x.com/UVU_SBDC
YouTube: www.youtube.com/channel/UCdRQ8whJLNXUH5YVcn4yikA
Description: Represents and promotes the small business sector. Provides management assistance to current and prospective small business owners. Helps to improve management skills and expand the products and services of members. **Geographic Preference:** Local.

45611 ■ Price Small Business Development Center [Price SBDC]
420 N 300 E
Price, UT 84501
Ph: (435)613-5460
URL: http://utahsbdc.org/locations/price
Contact: Austin Preston, Director
Description: Represents and promotes the small business sector. Provides management assistance to current and prospective small business owners. Helps to improve management skills and expand the products and services of members. **Geographic Preference:** Local.

45612 ■ Richfield Small Business Development Center
800 W 200 S, Rm. 155W
Richfield, UT 84701
Ph: (435)283-7376
URL: http://clients.utahsbdc.org/workshop.aspx?ekey=7420001
Contact: Christine Hanks, Director
E-mail: christine.hanks@snow.edu
Description: Provides management assistance to current and prospective small business owners in Richfield. **Geographic Preference:** Local.

45613 ■ Utah Small Business Development Center (USBDC)
195 West 1100 S
Brigham City, UT 84302
URL: http://utahsbdc.org
Contact: Michael Finnerty, Director
E-mail: mike.finnerty@usu.edu
Description: Statewide source of assistance for small businesses in every stage of development. The network has 14 locations across Utah, including 10 regional centers and 5 service locations staffed by more than 30 team members. **Founded:** 1979. **Geographic Preference:** State.

45614 ■ Vernal Small Business Development Center
Utah State University
320 N Aggie Blvd.
Vernal, UT 84078
Ph: (435)722-1779
URL: http://utahsbdc.org/locations/vernal
Contact: Mark Holmes, Director
E-mail: mark.holmes@usu.edu
Description: Represents and promotes the small business sector. Provides management assistance to current and prospective small business owners. Helps to improve management skills and expand the products and services of members. **Geographic Preference:** Local.

STATE LISTINGS   Utah ■ 45633

SCORE OFFICES

45615 ■ Central Utah SCORE
c/o Business Resource, 815 West 1250 S
 Orem, UT 84058
Ph: (801)957-5453
URL: http://utah.score.org
Description: Unites active and retired business management professionals with men and women who are considering starting a small business, encountering problems with their business, or expanding their business. Serves the Utah counties of Tooele, Utah, Wasatch, Duchesne, Summit, Daggett, Uinta, and Carbon.

45616 ■ Ogden SCORE
2314 Washington Blvd.
 Ogden, UT 84401
URL: http://utah.score.org

45617 ■ SCORE - Brigham City
Brigham City Education Ctr.
 Brigham City, UT 84302
Ph: (801)957-5453
URL: http://utah.score.org/find-location-1
Contact: Louay Chebib, Contact
Description: Provides professional guidance and information to maximize the success of existing and emerging small businesses. Offers business counseling and workshops.

45618 ■ SCORE - Kaysville
450 Simmons Way
 Kaysville, UT 84037
Ph: (801)957-5453
URL: http://utah.score.org/find-location-1
Description: Provides professional guidance and information to maximize the success of existing and emerging small businesses. Offers business counseling and workshops.

45619 ■ SCORE - Ogden
2036 Lincoln Ave., Ste. 105
 Ogden, UT 84401
Ph: (801)784-0870
Co. E-mail: scoresaltlake@gmail.com
URL: http://saltlake.score.org
Description: Provides professional guidance and information to maximize the success of existing and emerging small businesses. Offers business counseling and workshops.

45620 ■ SCORE - Salt Lake City
Downtown Salt Lake City Branch
 125 S State Room 2227
 Salt Lake City, UT 84138
Ph: (801)957-5453
Co. E-mail: scoresaltlake@gmail.com
URL: http://utah.score.org
Facebook: www.facebook.com/SCOREUtah
Linkedin: www.linkedin.com/company/score-mentors-utah
X (Twitter): twitter.com/SaltLakeSCORE
Description: Provides professional guidance and information to maximize the success of existing and emerging small businesses. Offers business counseling and workshops.

45621 ■ SCORE - Sandy
SLCC Miller Corp. Partnership Center
 9690 S, 300 W, Rm. 201D
 Sandy, UT 84070
URL: http://utah.score.org
Description: Provides professional guidance, mentoring services and financial assistance to maximize the success of existing and emerging small businesses. Promotes entrepreneur education in Salt Lake City, Utah. **Founded:** 1964. **Geographic Preference:** Local.

45622 ■ SCORE - SLCC Microbusiness Connection Branch
250 West 3900 S
 Salt Lake City, UT 84107
Ph: (801)957-5453
URL: http://utah.score.org/find-location-1
Facebook: www.facebook.com/SCOREUtah

Linkedin: www.linkedin.com/company/score-mentors-utah
X (Twitter): twitter.com/SaltLakeSCORE
Instagram: www.instagram.com/scoreutah_mentors
Description: Provides professional guidance and information to maximize the success of existing and emerging small businesses. Offers business counseling and workshops.

45623 ■ SCORE - Tooele
88 S Tooele Blvd.
 Tooele, UT 84074
Ph: (435)248-1892
URL: http://utah.score.org/find-location-1
Description: Provides professional guidance and information to maximize the success of existing and emerging small businesses. Offers business counseling and workshops.

BETTER BUSINESS BUREAUS

45624 ■ Better Business Bureau Serving Utah
3703 W 6200 S
 Salt Lake City, UT 84129
Ph: (801)892-6009
Fax: (801)892-6002
URL: http://www.bbb.org/local-bbb/bbb-serving-northern-nevada-and-utah
Facebook: www.facebook.com/BBBUtahNevada
Linkedin: www.linkedin.com/company/bbb-serving-utah-nevada
X (Twitter): x.com/BBBUtahNevada
YouTube: www.youtube.com/channel/UCqBgq3o0rSDBmKXldMFnqLg
Description: Seeks to promote and foster the highest ethical relationship between businesses and the public through voluntary self-regulation, consumer and business education, and service excellence. Provides information to help consumers and businesses make informed purchasing decisions and avoid costly scams and frauds; settles consumer complaints through arbitration and other means. **Founded:** 1912. **Geographic Preference:** State.

CHAMBERS OF COMMERCE

45625 ■ Bear Lake Rendezvous Chamber of Commerce (BLRCC)
PO Box 55
 Garden City, UT 84028
Free: 800-448-2327
Co. E-mail: info@bearlakechamber.com
URL: http://www.bearlakechamber.com
Contact: Mark Smoot, President
Description: Promotes business and community development in Bear Lake, UT area. **Geographic Preference:** Local.

45626 ■ Blanding Visitor Center
12 N Grayson Pky.
 Blanding, UT 84511
Ph: (435)678-3662
URL: http://www.utahscanyoncountry.com/blanding-visitor-center
Description: Promotes business and community development in Blanding, UT. **Geographic Preference:** Local.

45627 ■ Brigham City Area Chamber of Commerce
6 N Main
 Brigham City, UT 84302
Ph: (435)723-3931
Fax: (435)723-5761
URL: http://www.boxelderchamber.com
Contact: Monica Holdaway, Chief Executive Officer
E-mail: monica@boxelderchamber.com
Description: Promotes business and community development in Brigham City, UT area. **Founded:** 1965. **Geographic Preference:** Local.

45628 ■ Cache Chamber of Commerce (CCC)
160 N Main
 Logan, UT 84321
Ph: (435)752-2161

Co. E-mail: info@cachechamber.com
URL: http://cachechamber.com
Contact: Jamie Andrus, President
X (Twitter): x.com/CacheChamber
YouTube: www.youtube.com/channel/UCQrzpzo6HETw4wYlendvsyQ
Description: Promotes business and community development in Cache and Rich counties, UT. **Founded:** 1911. **Publications:** *The Insider* (Biweekly). **Geographic Preference:** Local.

45629 ■ Carbon County Chamber of Commerce (CCCC)
751 E 100 N
 Price, UT 84501
Ph: (435)637-2788
Co. E-mail: cccc@carboncountychamber.net
URL: http://www.carboncountychamber.net
Contact: Barbie Haeck, Contact
Description: Promotes business and community development in Carbon County, UT. **Geographic Preference:** Local.

45630 ■ Cedar City Area Chamber of Commerce
510 W 800 S
 Cedar City, UT 84720
Ph: (435)586-4484
Co. E-mail: office@cedarcitychamber.org
URL: http://www.cedarcitychamber.org
Contact: Chris McCormick, President
YouTube: www.youtube.com/channel/UCjGGrWKeNRyhzLMnnNY9xpw
Description: Promotes business and community development in Cedar City, UT. **Publications:** *Chamber Times* (Monthly). **Geographic Preference:** Local.

45631 ■ ChamberWest
3540 S 4000 W, Ste. 240
 West Valley City, UT 84120
Ph: (801)977-8755
Fax: (801)977-8329
Co. E-mail: chamber@chamberwest.org
URL: http://chamberwest.com
Contact: Barbara S. Riddle, President
E-mail: barbara@chamberwest.org
Linkedin: www.linkedin.com/company/chamberwestutah
Instagram: www.instagram.com/chamberwestutah
Description: Promotes business and community development in West Valley City, Taylorsville, and Kearns, Utah. **Founded:** 1963. **Publications:** *ChamberWorks* (Bimonthly). **Geographic Preference:** Local.

45632 ■ Davis Chamber of Commerce
450 S Simmons Way, Ste. 220
 Kaysville, UT 84037
Ph: (801)593-2200
Co. E-mail: info@davischamberofcommerce.com
URL: http://www.davischamberofcommerce.com
Contact: Angie Osguthorpe, President
E-mail: angie@davischamberofcommerce.com
Facebook: www.facebook.com/DavisChamberOfCommerce
X (Twitter): x.com/DavisChamberUT
YouTube: www.youtube.com/user/DavisChamberCommerce
Description: Promotes business and community development in Kaysville, UT. **Founded:** 2001. **Publications:** *The Inside Track* (Weekly); *Wasatch Business Connection* (Monthly). **Geographic Preference:** Local.

45633 ■ Delta Area Chamber of Commerce (DACC)
75 W Main
 Delta, UT 84624
Ph: (435)864-4316
Co. E-mail: deltautahchamber@gmail.com
URL: http://www.deltautahchamber.com
Contact: Justin Taylor, President

45634 ■ Duchesne County Chamber of Commerce (DCACC)
50 E 200 S
Roosevelt, UT 84066
Ph: (435)722-4598
Fax: (435)722-4579
Co. E-mail: info@uintabasin.org
URL: http://www.uintabasin.org
Contact: Irene Hansen, Contact
E-mail: irene@uintabasin.org
Description: Promotes business and community development in the Duchesne County, UT area. Sponsors festival and conducts competitions. **Geographic Preference:** Local.

Description (prior entry): Promotes business and community development in the Delta, UT area. Facilitates business-education partnerships. Provides secretarial services for the Western Utah Mining Association. **Founded:** 1982. **Geographic Preference:** Regional.

45635 ■ Heber Valley Chamber of Commerce Member Directory
475 N Main St.
Heber City, UT 84032
Ph: (435)654-3666
Free: 866-994-3237
Co. E-mail: info@gohebervalley.com
URL: http://www.gohebervalley.com
Contact: Ryan Starks, Executive Director
E-mail: ryanstarks@gohebervalley.com
URL(s): www.gohebervalley.com/member-directory
Description: Contains directory of all members listed alphabetically and categorically. **Availability:** Print.

45636 ■ Heber Valley Chamber of Commerce and Visitor Center (HVCC)
475 N Main St.
Heber City, UT 84032
Ph: (435)654-3666
Free: 866-994-3237
Co. E-mail: info@gohebervalley.com
URL: http://www.gohebervalley.com
Contact: Ryan Starks, Executive Director
E-mail: ryanstarks@gohebervalley.com
X (Twitter): x.com/HeberValley
YouTube: www.youtube.com/user/gohebervalley
Pinterest: www.pinterest.com/hebervalley
Description: Promotes business, tourism, and community development in Wasatch County, UT. Contributes to local charities. Sponsors competitions and festival. **Founded:** 1952. **Publications:** Heber Valley Chamber of Commerce Member Directory; Insider (Annual). **Geographic Preference:** Local.

45637 ■ Hurricane Valley Chamber of Commerce (HVCC)
63 S 100 W
Hurricane, UT 84737
Ph: (435)635-3402
Co. E-mail: office@hvchamber.com
URL: http://www.hvchamber.com
Contact: Ike S. Turner, President
Facebook: www.facebook.com/hurricanevalleychamber
YouTube: www.youtube.com/channel/UCm1LXfrEb6_soEpdh69HsFQ
Description: Works to serve the interests of businesses throughout the Hurricane Valley. **Founded:** 1957. **Geographic Preference:** Local.

45638 ■ Kanab Chamber of Commerce (KCOC)
78 S 100 E
Kanab, UT 84741
Co. E-mail: info@kanabchamber.com
URL: http://www.kanabchamber.org
Contact: Colette Cox, Contact
Facebook: www.facebook.com/KanabAreaChamberofCommerce
Description: Promotes business and community development in the Kanab, UT area. **Geographic Preference:** Local.

45639 ■ Midvale Area Chamber of Commerce
103 E 7060 S
Midvale, UT 84047
Contact: Marie Marshall, Contact
Description: Promotes business and community development in Midvale, UT. **Founded:** 1946. **Publications:** Business and Professional Directory (Annual); Issues (Monthly). **Geographic Preference:** Local.

45640 ■ Moab Area Chamber of Commerce (MACC)
375 S Main St., Ste. 513
Moab, UT 84532
Ph: (435)259-7814
Co. E-mail: info@moabchamber.com
URL: http://www.moabchamber.com
Contact: Lonnie Campbell, President
Facebook: www.facebook.com/MoabChamber
YouTube: www.youtube.com/channel/UC6dR0IaXTP5XgkIxYrP6poQ
Description: Promotes business and community development in Grand County, UT. Sponsors races and other special events. **Founded:** 1958. **Publications:** Community Guide (Biennial). **Educational Activities:** Art Walks. **Awards:** Moab Area Chamber of Commerce Citizen of the Year (Annual). **Geographic Preference:** Local.

45641 ■ Murray Area Chamber of Commerce (MACC)
5411 S Vine St., Ste. 3A
Murray, UT 84107
Ph: (801)263-2632
Co. E-mail: support@murrayareachamber.com
URL: http://murrayareachamber.com/#cid=1808&wid=801
Contact: Matt Gibbons, President
E-mail: president@murraychamber.net
Facebook: www.facebook.com/MurrayChamberOfCommerce
Description: Promotes business and community development in Murray, UT area. **Publications:** Focus (Weekly). **Geographic Preference:** Local.

45642 ■ Ogden/Weber Chamber of Commerce (OWCC)
2380 Washington Blvd., Ste. 290
Ogden, UT 84401
Ph: (801)621-8300
Co. E-mail: chamber@ogdenweberchamber.com
URL: http://www.ogdenweberchamber.com
Contact: Chuck Leonhardt, President
E-mail: chuck@ogdenweberchamber.com
Facebook: www.facebook.com/OWChamber
Linkedin: www.linkedin.com/company/owchamber
X (Twitter): x.com/owchamber
Instagram: www.instagram.com/owchamber
YouTube: www.youtube.com/user/ogdenweberchamber
Description: Seeks to advance prosperity in Weber County. Strives to strengthen relations with key community organizations and companies. Works with the state government to give support and resources for Weber County. **Founded:** 1887. **Publications:** Business Directory; Women in Business (Weekly (Mon.)). **Educational Activities:** Business After Hours (Monthly). **Awards:** Ogden Weber Chamber of Commerce Wall of Fame Award (Annual). **Geographic Preference:** Local.

45643 ■ Park City Chamber of Commerce (PCCC)
1850 Sidewinder Dr., No. 320
Park City, UT 84060
Ph: (435)649-6100
Free: 800-453-1360
Co. E-mail: info@visitparkcity.com
URL: http://www.visitparkcity.com
Contact: Jennifer Wesselhoff, President
Facebook: www.facebook.com/VisitParkCity
X (Twitter): x.com/VisitParkCity
Instagram: www.instagram.com/visitparkcity
YouTube: www.youtube.com/user/VisitParkCity
Description: Promotes business and community development in Park City, UT. **Publications:** Summit Outlook (Quarterly). **Geographic Preference:** Local.

45644 ■ Payson & Santaquin Area Chamber of Commerce
22 S Main St.
Payson, UT 84651-2223
Ph: (801)465-2634
Co. E-mail: paysonsantaquinarea@gmail.com
URL: http://www.paysonsantaquinarea.com
Contact: Stephanie Taylor, President
Facebook: www.facebook.com/PaysonSantaquinChamber
Description: Promotes business and community development in Payson, UT area. **Geographic Preference:** Local.

45645 ■ St. George Area Chamber of Commerce (SGACC)
136 N 100 E
Saint George, UT 84770
Ph: (435)628-1650
URL: http://stgeorgechamber.com
Contact: Don Willie, President
Facebook: www.facebook.com/stgeorgechamber
Linkedin: www.linkedin.com/company/st-george-chamber-of-commerce
YouTube: www.youtube.com/channel/UCOsnBDwkgIBzsEqyxIbrw_w
Description: Promotes business and community development in the Washington County, UT area. **Founded:** 1926. **Publications:** St. George Area Chamber of Commerce Business Directory; Business Directory. **Educational Activities:** Membership Luncheon. **Awards:** St. George Area Chamber of Commerce Entrepreneur of the Year (Annual). **Geographic Preference:** Local.

45646 ■ Salt Lake Chamber (SLACC)
201 S Main St., No. 2300
Salt Lake City, UT 84111
Ph: (801)364-3631
Fax: (801)328-5098
Co. E-mail: info@slchamber.com
URL: http://slchamber.com
Contact: Derek Miller, President
Facebook: www.facebook.com/saltlakechamber
X (Twitter): x.com/saltlakechamber
YouTube: www.youtube.com/user/SaltLakeChamber
Description: Promotes business and community development in the Salt Lake City, UT area. **Founded:** 1902. **Publications:** Business Focus (Monthly); Directory of Members & Buyers Guide; Life in the Valley (Annual). **Educational Activities:** Member Welcome. **Geographic Preference:** Local.

45647 ■ South Salt Lake Chamber of Commerce (SSL)
220 E Morris Ave., Ste. 150
Salt Lake City, UT 84115
Ph: (801)466-3377
Co. E-mail: info@sslchamber.com
URL: http://www.sslchamber.com
Contact: Gary Birdsall, President
E-mail: gary@sslchamber.com
URL(s): sslc.gov
Facebook: www.facebook.com/SSL.Chamber
Description: Promotes business and community development in South Salt Lake, UT area. **Geographic Preference:** Local.

45648 ■ Southwest Valley Chamber of Commerce
2222 W 14400 S, 2nd Fl.
Bluffdale, UT 84065
Ph: (801)280-0595
URL: http://www.swvchamber.org
Contact: Susan Schilling, President
E-mail: susan@swvchamber.org
Facebook: www.facebook.com/SWValleyChamber
Linkedin: www.linkedin.com/company/southwest-valley-chamber-of-commerce-ut
Instagram: www.instagram.com/swvchamber
Description: Promotes business and community development in Southwest Valley Area, UT. **Founded:** 1997. **Geographic Preference:** Local.

STATE LISTINGS

45649 ■ Tooele County Chamber of Commerce
154 S Main St.
Tooele, UT 84074
Ph: (435)882-0690
Co. E-mail: chamber@tooelechamber.com
URL: http://www.tooelechamber.com
Contact: Jared Hamner, Executive Director
Facebook: www.facebook.com/tooelechamber
Linkedin: www.linkedin.com/organization-guest/company/tooele-county-chamber-of-commerce
X (Twitter): x.com/tooelechamber
Instagram: www.instagram.com/tooelechamber
YouTube: www.youtube.com/channel/UCzTcqyA5VrnyF0o9YrtCqKA
Description: Promotes business and community development in Tooele County, UT. **Founded:** 1948. **Publications:** *Visitors Guide and Business Directory* (Annual). **Educational Activities:** Membership Network Luncheon (Monthly). **Awards:** Tooele Citizen of the Year (Annual). **Geographic Preference:** Local.

45650 ■ Utah Valley Chamber of Commerce
2696 N University Ave.
Provo, UT 84604
Ph: (385)482-2555
Co. E-mail: info@thechamber.org
URL: http://www.thechamber.org
Contact: Jeremy Hafen, President
Facebook: www.facebook.com/uvchamber
Linkedin: www.linkedin.com/in/utah-valley-chamber-of-commerce-40311b14
X (Twitter): x.com/uvchamber
YouTube: www.youtube.com/user/utahvalleychamber
Description: Promotes business and community development in Provo and Orem, UT. Conducts networking activities. **Founded:** 1985. **Publications:** *Chamber Insider.* **Educational Activities:** Friday Forum (Annual). **Geographic Preference:** Local.

45651 ■ Vernal Area Chamber of Commerce (VACC)
134 W Main St.
Vernal, UT 84078
Ph: (435)789-1352
Fax: (435)789-1355
Co. E-mail: vchambered@easilink.com
URL: http://www.vernalchamber.com
Contact: Jared Jackson, President
Facebook: www.facebook.com/Vernal-Area-Chamber-of-Commerce-251700434841196
Description: Promotes business and community development in the Vernal, UT area. **Founded:** 1949. **Publications:** *Dinah Says* (Quarterly); *Dinosaur Land* (Annual); *Vernal Directory.* **Awards:** Vernal Area Chamber of Commerce Business of the Month (Monthly); Vernal Area Chamber of Commerce Quarterly Outstanding Public Service Award (Quarterly). **Geographic Preference:** Local.

45652 ■ *Vernal Directory*
134 W Main St.
Vernal, UT 84078
Ph: (435)789-1352
Fax: (435)789-1355
Co. E-mail: vchambered@easilink.com
URL: http://www.vernalchamber.com
Contact: Jared Jackson, President
URL(s): www.vernalchamber.com/about-the-chamber
Availability: Print; Online.

45653 ■ West Jordan Chamber of Commerce (WJCC)
8543 S Redwood Rd., Ste. C
West Jordan, UT 84088
Ph: (801)205-1600
URL: http://wjc-ut.com/#!event-list
Contact: Laurie Gale, President
E-mail: wjccpresident@gmail.com
Facebook: www.facebook.com/WestJordanChamberOfCommerce
Description: Promotes business and community development in West Jordan, UT. **Founded:** 1985. **Publications:** *Business Pulse* (Monthly); *West Jordan Chamber of Commerce--Business Directory.* **Geographic Preference:** Local.

45654 ■ *West Jordan Chamber of Commerce--Business Directory*
8543 S Redwood Rd., Ste. C
West Jordan, UT 84088
Ph: (801)205-1600
URL: http://wjc-ut.com/#!event-list
Contact: Laurie Gale, President
E-mail: wjccpresident@gmail.com
URL(s): wjc-ut.com/member-benefits
Availability: Online.

45655 ■ *Women in Business*
2380 Washington Blvd., Ste. 290
Ogden, UT 84401
Ph: (801)621-8300
Co. E-mail: chamber@ogdenweberchamber.com
URL: http://www.ogdenweberchamber.com
Contact: Chuck Leonhardt, President
E-mail: chuck@ogdenweberchamber.com
URL(s): www.ogdenweberchamber.com/wib
Released: Weekly (Mon.) **Availability:** Print; Online.

MINORITY BUSINESS ASSISTANCE PROGRAMS

45656 ■ Utah Department of Heritage and Arts - Division of Indian Affairs
250 N 1950 W
Salt Lake City, UT 84116
Ph: (801)715-6702
URL: http://indian.utah.gov
Contact: Dustin Jansen, Director
E-mail: djansen@utah.gov
Facebook: www.facebook.com/UtahDivisionOfIndianAffairs
X (Twitter): x.com/UT_Indian
Description: Works to improve the educational, employment, and economic status of minorities in the state. **Founded:** 1999.

FINANCING AND LOAN PROGRAMS

45657 ■ Album VC
3451 N, Triumph Blvd., Ste. 200
Lehi, UT 84043
URL: http://www.album.vc
Contact: John Mayfield, Partner
Linkedin: www.linkedin.com/company/albumvc
X (Twitter): x.com/albumvc
Instagram: www.instagram.com/album.vc
Description: Firm is a real estate developer. **Founded:** 2013.

45658 ■ Banyan Ventures
6550 Millrock Dr., Ste. 175
Holladay, UT 84121
Contact: Darin Gilson, Contact
Description: Offers venture and growth equity for early-stage sustainable businesses in the Intermountain West.

45659 ■ Cougar Capital (CC)
Marriott School of Business
470 Tanner Bldg.
Provo, UT 84602
Ph: (801)422-7437
Co. E-mail: rollinscenter@byu.edu
URL: http://byucougarcapital.org
Contact: Adam Navar, Director
Linkedin: www.linkedin.com/company/cougar-capital
Description: Student-run venture capital and private equity fund at the Marriott School at Brigham Young University. **Founded:** 2005.

45660 ■ Crocker Ventures (CV)
2825 E Cottonwood Pkwy., Ste. 330
Salt Lake City, UT 84121
Ph: (801)702-8580
Fax: (801)702-8585
Co. E-mail: businessplans@crockerventures.com
URL: http://crockerventures.com
Contact: Gary L. Crocker, President
Description: Fund seed- and early-stage companies in life sciences, healthcare, and technology. **Investment Policies:** Strong intellectual property; significant growth potential; meets significant unmet market needs. **Industry Preferences:** Biotechnology/pharmaceuticals; medical devices; drug delivery; diagnostics; information technology.

45661 ■ GSD Capital, LLC
1150 E Riverside Dr., No. 911598
Saint George, UT 84791
Contact: Christopher Lee Russell, Contact
Description: Funds early-stage SaaS companies in the Mountain West. **Founded:** 2010. **Investment Policies:** Limited amount of existing debt; minimum of $50,000 in MRR.

45662 ■ InnoVentures Capital Partners
150 S State, Ste. 100
Salt Lake City, UT 84111
Ph: (801)243-6674
URL: http://innoventurescapitalpartners.com
Contact: Steve Grizzell, Contact
E-mail: steve@innoventures.com
Facebook: www.facebook.com/pages/InnoVentures-Capital-Partners
Linkedin: www.linkedin.com/company/innoventures-capital
Description: Alternative business lender. Works with angel investors, banks, and venture capital firms. **Industry Preferences:** Manufacturing; services; technology.

45663 ■ Kickstart Seed Fund
2750 E Cottonwood Pkwy., Ste. 160
Cottonwood Heights, UT 84121
Description: Seed fund that focuses on the Mountain West area. Aligns technology creators, industry, entrepreneurs, and capital sources behind the funding and mentoring of seed investments. **Founded:** 2008.

45664 ■ Mercato Partners [Savory Mercato Partners]
2750 E Cottonwood Pkwy., Ste. 500
Cottonwood Heights, UT 84121
URL: http://mercatopartners.com
Contact: Zane Busteed, Director
Linkedin: www.linkedin.com/company/mercato-partners
X (Twitter): x.com/mercatopartners
Founded: 2007. **Preferred Investment Size:** $5,000,000-$50,000,000. **Industry Preferences:** Technology and branded consumer markets.

45665 ■ Pelion Venture Partners
2750 E Cottonwood Pkwy., Ste. 600
Salt Lake City, UT 84121
URL: http://pelionvp.com
Contact: Steve Glover, Chief Financial Officer
Linkedin: www.linkedin.com/company/pelion-venture-partners
X (Twitter): x.com/pelion_vp
Instagram: www.instagram.com/pelionvp
Description: Early-stage venture capital firm. **Founded:** 1986.

45666 ■ Peterson Ventures
Peterson Partners L.P.
2755 E Cottonwood Pkwy., Ste. 400
Salt Lake City, UT 84121
Ph: (801)417-0748
Fax: (844)270-1746
Co. E-mail: contact@petersonpartners.com
URL: http://www.petersonpartners.com
Contact: Clint Peterson, Managing Partner
Description: Offers seed-round investing. **Investment Policies:** Large and growing market; capital-efficient business model. **Industry Preferences:** SaaS; digital commerce.

45667 ■ University Venture Fund (UVF)
David Eccles School of Business
1655 Campus Ctr., Dr.
Salt Lake City, UT 84112
Co. E-mail: info@sorensonimpact.com
URL: http://www.uventurefund.com

Contact: Paul Brown, Contact
Description: Venture capital funds; consists of students, mentors, alumni, and investors. **Investment Policies:** Innovative, scalable, and profitable solutions.

45668 ■ Wasatch Venture Corp. / EPIC Ventures
1338 Foothill Dr., Ste. 282
Salt Lake City, UT 84101
Co. E-mail: info@epicvc.com
URL: http://www.epicvc.com
Contact: Jack Boren, Managing Director
Linkedin: www.linkedin.com/company/epicventures
X (Twitter): x.com/epic_ventures
Description: Investment firm provides of software and internet infrastructure venture, capital venture, seed and series investment services. **Founded:** 1994. **Preferred Investment Size:** $500,000 to $3,000,000. **Industry Preferences:** Internet specific, computer software and services, computer hardware, communications and media, semiconductors and other electronics, consumer related, biotechnology, medical and health, and other products.

45669 ■ Wayne Brown Institute
350 E 400 S
Salt Lake City, UT 84111
Ph: (801)595-1141
Co. E-mail: james@kinectcapital.org
URL: http://kinectcapital.org
Contact: James Kemp, Executive Director
Facebook: www.facebook.com/waynebrowninstitute
Linkedin: www.linkedin.com/company/kinectcapital
Instagram: www.instagram.com/venture.capital_org
Description: Venture accelerator. **Founded:** 1983.

PROCUREMENT ASSISTANCE PROGRAMS

45670 ■ Miller Campus Salt Lake Community College Procurement Technical Assistance Center
9750 S 300 W Milller Campus
Sandy, UT 84070
Ph: (801)957-5357
URL: http://www.aptac-us.org/find-a-ptac/?state=UT
Contact: Alex Quayson-Sackey, Regional Manager
E-mail: aquayson@utah.gov
Description: Assists Utah small businesses who are interested in bidding on federal, state and local government procurements and commercial contracting opportunities covering South Salt Lake, Utah, and Tooele Counties.

45671 ■ Southern Utah University - Utah Procurement Technical Assistance Center (UPTAC)
351 W University Blvd.
Cedar City, UT 84720
Co. E-mail: info@suu.edu
URL: http://www.suu.edu/regional/sbdc/ptac.html
Contact: Joni Anderson, Regional Manager
E-mail: andersonjoni@suu.edu
Description: Assists Utah small businesses who are interested in bidding on federal, state and local government procurements and commercial contracting opportunities covering Iron, Garfield, and Beaver Counties.

45672 ■ Utah Governor's Office of Economic Development (PTAC) - Procurement Technical Assistance Center
60 E S Temple, Ste. 300
Salt Lake City, UT 84111-1041
Ph: (801)538-8680
Co. E-mail: business@utah.gov
URL: http://business.utah.gov
Contact: Ryan Starks, Executive Director
E-mail: ryanstarks@utah.gov
Facebook: www.facebook.com/businessutah
Linkedin: www.linkedin.com/company/businessutah
X (Twitter): x.com/businessutah
Instagram: www.instagram.com/businessutah
YouTube: www.youtube.com/channel/UC8Ombh9mGzeKq_KzKyA1oeA
Description: Assists businesses in competing for government and commercial contracts. **Founded:** 2006.

45673 ■ Utah Procurement Technical Assistance Center (UPTAC) - Bear River Association of Governments
170 N Main
Logan, UT 84321
Ph: (435)752-7242
Free: 877-772-7242
Fax: (435)752-6962
URL: http://brag.utah.gov
Contact: Roger C. Jones, Executive Director
E-mail: rogerj@brag.utah.gov
Description: Assists Utah small businesses who are interested in bidding on federal, state and local government procurements and commercial contracting opportunities covering Box Elder, Cache, and Rich Counties. **Founded:** 1971.

45674 ■ Utah Procurement Technical Assistance Center - Dixie Business Alliance
1071 East 100 South
Saint George, UT 84770
Ph: (435)652-7754
URL: http://www.aptac-us.org/find-a-ptac/?state=UT
Contact: Cameron Findlay, Regional Manager
E-mail: findlay@utah.gov
URL(s): business.utah.gov/programs/ptac/contact-ptac
Description: Assists Utah small businesses who are interested in bidding on federal, state and local government procurements and commercial contracting opportunities covering Washington and Kane Counties.

45675 ■ Utah's APEX Accelerator (PTAC)
60 E S Temple, Ste. 300
Salt Lake City, UT 84111-1041
Ph: (801)538-8655
Co. E-mail: apex@utah.gov
URL: http://business.utah.gov/apex
Contact: Chuck Spence, Director
E-mail: cspence@utah.gov
Description: Assists Utah small businesses who are interested in bidding on federal, state and local government procurements and commercial contracting opportunities covering Juab, Millard, Sanpete, Sevier, Piute, and Wayne Counties.

INCUBATORS/RESEARCH AND TECHNOLOGY PARKS

45676 ■ Access Salt Lake
175 W 200 S No. 100
Salt Lake City, UT 84101
Contact: Thor Roundy, Contact
Description: The meeting point for a business ecosystem built to nurture growing companies. Provides coworking space, access to mentors, networking, and lunch-and-learns.

45677 ■ BioInnovations Gateway (BIG)
2500 S State St.
Salt Lake City, UT 84115
Contact: Douglas R. Larson, Contact
Description: An incubator for early-stage life science companies and the training of the next generation of life science professionals. Provides access to laboratories, machines, office space, and resources for entrepreneurs.

45678 ■ CBRC Incubator Kitchen (CBRC)
1300 N 600 W
Logan, UT 84321
Ph: (435)750-3261
URL: http://btech.edu/cbrc-kitchen
Description: Incubator provides help for those culinary entrepreneurs who need a certified kitchen in which to produce their food products. Helps regional businesses launch and grow in a state-of-the-art kitchen.

45679 ■ Grow Utah Ventures
450 S Simmons Way, Ste. 500
Kaysville, UT 84037
Ph: (801)593-2269
Co. E-mail: info@growutah.com
URL: http://www.growutah.com
Contact: T. Craig Bott, President
Facebook: www.facebook.com/growutah
Linkedin: www.linkedin.com/company/grow-utah
X (Twitter): x.com/growutah
Description: A small business incubator dedicated to providing education, financial, and management support to entrepreneurs and businesses along the Wasatch Front. **Founded:** 2005.

45680 ■ Impact Hub Salt Lake
2155 S 2100 E
Salt Lake City, UT 84152
Contact: Soren D. Simonsen, Contact
Description: Offers coworking, shared workspace, and private offices to startups and entrepreneurs so that they can work to grow their business.

45681 ■ Miller Business Innovation Center (MBIC)
9750 S 300 W
Sandy, UT 84070
Contact: Daniel Bingham, Contact
Description: Small business incubator dedicated to the housing and the acceleration of some of Utah's most promising new ventures. **Founded:** 1993.

45682 ■ Miller Business Resource Center (MBRC)
9690 S 300 W Bldg., No. 5 Rm. 101
Sandy, UT 84070
URL: http://themillatslcc.com/event/social-media-bootcamp
Contact: Beth Colosimo, Executive Director
E-mail: beth.colosimo@slcc.edu
Description: Home to the Miller Business Innovation Center, which is a mixed-use incubator providing a combination of physical space as well as training and mentorship to startups. **Founded:** 2007.

45683 ■ Open Legal Services (OLS)
Ph: (801)433-9915
URL: http://openlegalservices.org
Description: Legal incubator helping to create jobs and provide internship and fellowship placements for new attorneys in under-served legal markets throughout Utah.

45684 ■ USU Incubator Kitchen
179 N Main St., Ste. 111
Logan, UT 84321
Co. E-mail: karin.allen@usu.edu
URL: http://extension.usu.edu/foodbiz/incubator-kitchen
Contact: Karin Allen, Contact
E-mail: karin.allen@usu.edu
Description: Incubator kitchen houses 5 complete kitchen units, and can be used by up to 2 groups at a time depending on the types of products being made. The purpose of this facility is to provide food entrepreneurs with access to production space during their start-up phase.

45685 ■ Utah Valley University (UVU) - Business Resource Center
815 W 1250 S
Orem, UT 84058
Ph: (801)863-2720
Co. E-mail: utahvalleybrc@uvu.edu
URL: http://www.uvu.edu/uvbrc
Contact: Peter Jay, Director, Economics
Facebook: www.facebook.com/utahvalleyuniversitybrc
Linkedin: www.linkedin.com/company/uvu-business-resource-center
Instagram: www.instagram.com/uvubusinessresourcecenter
Description: Assists entrepreneurs by providing classes, mentoring, networking, and access to capital to help achieve success. **Founded:** 1941.

EDUCATIONAL PROGRAMS

45686 ■ Salt Lake Community College-Redwood Road Campus (SLCC)
4600 S Redwood Rd.
Salt Lake City, UT 84123
Ph: (801)957-4073
Co. E-mail: help.desk@slcc.edu
URL: http://www.slcc.edu
Contact: Tyson Gregory, Director
E-mail: tyson.gregory@slcc.edu
Description: Provides courses and workshops on topics relevant to entrepreneurs and small business owners.

REFERENCE WORKS

45687 ■ "CrowdFunding Made Simple Conference at University of Utah Ignites Ecosystem of Entrepreneurs and Investors" in Economics Week (June 29, 2012)
Description: The first national conference on crowdfunding was held at the University of Utah Guest House and Conference Center May 31 through June 1, 2012. The event, CrowdFunding Made Simple, gathered entrepreneurs, business owners, professional service providers, investors, government officials and students to provide understanding and potential of crowdfunding, including information on the Jumpstart Our Business Startups (JOBS) Act. **Availability:** Print; Online.

TRADE PERIODICALS

45688 ■ *Utah Valley Business Quarterly*
Pub: Bennett Communications Inc.
URL(s): businessqmag.com
Facebook: www.facebook.com/UVBizQ
Linkedin: www.linkedin.com/company/utah-valley-businessq
Instagram: www.instagram.com/uvbizq
Released: Quarterly; six times a year. **Price:** $32, Individuals for 2 years; $42, Individuals for 3 years; $20, Individuals for per year. **Description:** Contains business news and information for residents and companies in the Utah Valley. **Availability:** Print; Online.

PUBLISHERS

45689 ■ Janco Associates Inc.
843 River Birch Ct.
Park City, UT 84060
Ph: (435)940-9300
Co. E-mail: support@e-janco.com
URL: http://e-janco.com
Contact: M. Victor Janulaitis, Chief Executive Officer
Facebook: www.facebook.com/JancoInc
Description: Management consulting firm is engaged in the creation, sale and strategic application of digital management information systems including information technology infrastructure, salary surveys, job descriptions, templates for disaster recovery and security, policies and procedures that primarily serves c-level executives. **Founded:** 1998. **Publications:** "Disaster Recovery/Business Continuity Template"; "Security Manual Template Bundle"; "Information Systems Position Description Hand guide"; "Personal Computer Policies and Procedures Hand guide"; "Information Systems Metrics Hand guide"; "Client Server Hand guide"; "Metrics Hand guide for the Internet and Information Technology and Practical Guide for it Outsourcing". **Training:** Paperless Books; In sourcing; Performance Metrics: Managing for Excellence; Gaining the Competitive Advantage; User Vision of Performance and Managing the Transition to Client Server. **Special Services:** Zinnote®.

45690 ■ Leadership Excellence L.L.C.
112 E 3800 N
Provo, UT 84604
Description: Publishes business books and newsletters, accepts unsolicited manuscripts and reaches the market through commission representatives, direct mail, reviews and listings, telephone sales, and distributors. **Founded:** 1984. **Publications:** *Executive Excellence: The Newsletter of Personal Development, Managerial Effectiveness, and Organizational Productivity.*

VENTURE CAPITAL FIRM

45691 ■ Alta Ventures (AV)
2600 Executive Pkwy., Ste. 380
Lehi, UT 84043
Ph: (801)653-3926
Co. E-mail: info@altaventures.com
URL: http://altaventures.com
Contact: Paul Ahlstrom, Co-Founder Managing Director
Facebook: www.facebook.com/AltaVentures
Linkedin: www.linkedin.com/company/alta-ventures-mexico/about
X (Twitter): x.com/AltaVentures
YouTube: www.youtube.com/user/ALTAVENTURES
Description: Venture capital firm for early-stage companies in Mexico, where it maintains an office in Monterrey. **Preferred Investment Size:** $2,000,000 to $3,000,000. **Industry Preferences:** Internet; SaaS; mobile computing; consumer; security; communications; healthcare.

45692 ■ Epic Ventures
355 E WELBY Ave.
Salt Lake City, UT 84115
Co. E-mail: info@epicvc.com
URL: http://www.epicvc.com
Contact: Jack Boren, Managing Director
Linkedin: www.linkedin.com/company/epicventures
X (Twitter): x.com/epic_ventures
Description: Partners with technology entrepreneurs at the earliest stages and brings capital outside the Bay Area with a focus primarily on Series A financings. **Founded:** 1994.

45693 ■ Hackers/Founders Utah
Salt Lake City, UT
Ph: (303)893-0507
Description: Technology accelerator providing seed funding, coaching, infrastructure, and support for local entrepreneurs. **Founded:** 2016.

45694 ■ RenewableTech Ventures
370 E S Temple, Ste. 260
Salt Lake City, UT 84111
Co. E-mail: info@renewablevc.com
URL: http://www.renewablevc.com
Contact: Todd Stevens, Founder Managing Director
Description: Invests in early stage innovations in energy, clean technology, green materials, and other clean technologies in Canada and the United States, with a specific focus on underserved regions. .

45695 ■ Signal Peak (SPV)
95 S State St., Ste. 1400
Salt Lake City, UT 84111
Co. E-mail: info@spv.com
URL: http://www.spv.com
Contact: Travis Heath, Chief Financial Officer
Linkedin: www.linkedin.com/company/signal-peak-ventures
Description: A venture capital firm with a focus on making investments in early-stage technology companies in underserved technology hubs across the United States. **Founded:** 2000.

Vermont

ASSOCIATIONS AND OTHER ORGANIZATIONS

45696 ■ Association of Fundraising Professionals Northern New England Chapter (AFP NNE)
PO Box 1794
 Brattleboro, VT 05301
Ph: (802)217-8700
Co. E-mail: admin@afp-nne.org
URL: http://afp-nne.org
Contact: Erika Lee, President
Facebook: www.facebook.com/afpnne
X (Twitter): x.com/afpnne
Description: Supports fundraising professionals from Maine, New Hampshire, and Vermont who are dedicated to upholding the highest standards of ethics and professionalism. **Founded:** 1960. **Geographic Preference:** Regional.

45697 ■ Business Network International Vermont [BNI Vermont]
PO Box 64737
 Burlington, VT 05406
Ph: (802)557-0111
URL: http://bnivermont.com/en-US/index
Contact: Vickie Wacek, Director
E-mail: vickie@bnivermont.com
Facebook: www.facebook.com/BNIVermont
Linkedin: www.linkedin.com/company/bnivermont
X (Twitter): x.com/BNIVermont
Description: Provides both men and women a structured environment for the development and exchange of quality business referrals. Offers members the opportunity to share ideas and contacts. **Founded:** 2001. **Geographic Preference:** State.

45698 ■ Vermont Business Roundtable (VBR)
30 Kimball Ave., Ste. 300
 South Burlington, VT 05403
Ph: (802)865-0410
Fax: (802)865-0662
Co. E-mail: info@vtroundtable.org
URL: http://vtroundtable.org
Contact: Judith W. O'Connell, Chairman
Facebook: www.facebook.com/VTRoundtable
Linkedin: www.linkedin.com/company/vermont-business-roundtable
X (Twitter): x.com/vtroundtable
Description: Represents chief executive officers organized to enable the state of Vermont to formulate and achieve public policy objectives and economic prosperity. **Founded:** 1987. **Publications:** *Roundtable Update.* **Geographic Preference:** State.

SMALL BUSINESS DEVELOPMENT CENTERS

45699 ■ Vermont Small Business Development Center Addison County Economic Development Corporation
1590 US Rte. 7 S, Ste. 8
 Middlebury, VT 05753
URL: http://addisoncountyedc.org/membership-directory/corporate/278906
Description: Provides management assistance to current and prospective small business owners in Center Addison. **Founded:** 2020. **Geographic Preference:** Local.

45700 ■ Vermont Small Business Development Center Bennington County
VT
URL: http://www.vtsbdc.org/region/bennington-county
Contact: Nancy Shuttleworth, Advisor
E-mail: nshuttleworth@vtsbdc.org
Description: Provides management assistance to current and prospective small business owners in Center Bennington County. **Geographic Preference:** Local.

45701 ■ Vermont Small Business Development Center Caledonia/Essex/Orleans Counties
36 E Ave.
 Saint Johnsbury, VT 05819
URL: http://www.vtsbdc.org/region/orleans-county
Contact: Ross Hart, Advisor
E-mail: rhart@vtsbdc.org
Description: Represents and promotes the small business sector. Provides management assistance to current and prospective small business owners. Helps to improve management skills and expand the products and services of members. **Founded:** 1992. **Geographic Preference:** Local.

45702 ■ Vermont Small Business Development Center Grand Isle County
URL: http://www.vtsbdc.org/region/grand-isle-county
Contact: Steve Densham, Advisor
E-mail: sdensham@vtsbdc.org
Description: Provides management assistance to current and prospective small business owners in Center Grand Isle County. **Geographic Preference:** Local.

45703 ■ Vermont Small Business Development Center Lamoille County (VTSBDC)
One Main St.
 Randolph Center, VT 05061
URL: http://www.vtsbdc.org/region/lamoille-county
Contact: Charley Ininger, Advisor
E-mail: cininger@vtsbdc.org
Description: Provides management assistance to current and prospective small business owners in Center Lamoille County. **Geographic Preference:** Local.

45704 ■ Vermont Small Business Development Center Lead Office (VtSBDC)
1 Main St.
 Randolph Center, VT 05061
Ph: (802)349-5546
Free: 800-464-SBDC
Fax: (802)728-3026
URL: http://www.vtsbdc.org
Contact: Linda Rossi, Director
E-mail: lrossi@vtsbdc.org
Facebook: www.facebook.com/vtsbdc
Linkedin: www.linkedin.com/company/vtsbdc
X (Twitter): x.com/vtsbdc
Description: Directly assists small businesses, and offers referrals when necessary. **Founded:** 1992. **Geographic Preference:** State.

45705 ■ Vermont Small Business Development Center Orange/Windsor Counties
Room 30635 Railroad Row
 White River Junction, VT 05001
Co. E-mail: sih06070@vtc.vsc.edu
URL: http://www.vtsbdc.org/about-vt-sbdc/staff-directory
Contact: Scott Holson, Advisor
E-mail: sih06070@vtc.vsc.edu
Description: Represents and promotes the small business sector. Provides management assistance to current and prospective small business owners. Helps to improve management skills and expand the products and services of members. **Geographic Preference:** Local.

45706 ■ Vermont Small Business Development Center Southern Windsor County
URL: http://www.vtsbdc.org/region/windsor-county
Contact: Debra Boudrieau, Advisor
E-mail: dboudrieau@vtsbdc.org
Description: Provides management assistance to current and prospective small business owners in Center Southern Windsor County. **Geographic Preference:** Local.

45707 ■ Vermont Small Business Development Center Washington County
WA
URL: http://www.vtsbdc.org/region/washington-county
Contact: Charley Ininger, Advisor
E-mail: cininger@vtsbdc.org
Description: Provides management assistance to current and prospective small business owners in Center Washington County. **Geographic Preference:** Local.

45708 ■ Vermont Small Business Development Center Windham/Southern Windsor Counties
1 Main St.
 Randolph Center, VT 05061
URL: http://www.vtsbdc.org/vermont-small-business-development-center-announces-state-star-2020
Contact: Linda Rossi, Director
Description: Provides management assistance to current and prospective small business owners in Center Windham/Southern Windsor Counties. **Geographic Preference:** Local.

STATE LISTINGS

Vermont ■ 45726

SMALL BUSINESS ASSISTANCE PROGRAMS

45709 ■ Agency of Commerce and Community Development - Department of Economic Development
1 National Life DriveDeane C. Davis Buldg., 6th Fl.
 Montpelier, VT 05620-0501
URL: http://accd.vermont.gov/economic-development
Description: A full-service business consulting and referral network, coordinating the efforts of the state's regional development corporations, the Vermont Industrial Development Authority, and federal employment training and financing agencies.

45710 ■ Vermont Small Business Development Center Lead Office (VtSBDC)
1 Main St.
 Randolph Center, VT 05061
Ph: (802)349-5546
Free: 800-464-SBDC
Fax: (802)728-3026
URL: http://www.vtsbdc.org
Contact: Linda Rossi, Director
E-mail: lrossi@vtsbdc.org
Facebook: www.facebook.com/vtsbdc
Linkedin: www.linkedin.com/company/vtsbdc
X (Twitter): x.com/vtsbdc
Description: Directly assists small businesses, and offers referrals when necessary. **Founded:** 1992. **Geographic Preference:** State.

SCORE OFFICES

45711 ■ SCORE - Brattleboro
SCORE SE Vermont
75 Cotton Mill Hill
Brattleboro, VT 05301
URL: http://www.score.org/graniteregion/profile/john-couleur
Description: Provides professional guidance and information to maximize the success of existing and emerging small businesses. Offers business counseling and workshops.

45712 ■ SCORE - Burlington, Vermont
60 Main St., Ste. 4
 Burlington, VT 05401
Ph: (802)764-5899
Co. E-mail: scorevermont@scorevolunteer.org
URL: http://www.score.org/vermont/about/our-locations
Description: An all-volunteer organization, providing free mentoring to help start or grow local businesses in Vermont.

45713 ■ SCORE - Montpelier
87 State St.
 Montpelier, VT 05602
Ph: (802)764-5899
Co. E-mail: scorevermont@scorevolunteer.org
URL: http://www.score.org/vermont/about/our-locations
Description: An all-volunteer organization, providing free mentoring to help start or grow businesses in Vermont. **Founded:** 1965. **Geographic Preference:** Local.

CHAMBERS OF COMMERCE

45714 ■ *60 Main Street News*
60 Main St., Ste. 100
 Burlington, VT 05401
Ph: (802)863-3489
Fax: (802)863-1538
Co. E-mail: vermont@vermont.org
URL: http://lccvermont.org
Contact: Catherine Z. Davis, President
E-mail: cathy@vermont.org
URL(s): lccvermont.org/uncategorized/main-street-news
Released: Bimonthly **Availability:** Print; PDF.

45715 ■ Addison County Chamber of Commerce (ACCOC)
93 Ct., St.
 Middlebury, VT 05753
Ph: (802)388-7951
Co. E-mail: info@addisoncounty.com
URL: http://www.addisoncounty.com
Contact: Rob Carter, President
E-mail: rob@addisoncounty.com
X (Twitter): x.com/accocvt
Description: Promotes business and community development in Addison County, VT. **Founded:** 1969. **Publications:** *Addison County Business Directory & Community Profile* (Annual); *Tourism Guide* (Annual); *The Chamber News* (Monthly). **Geographic Preference:** Local.

45716 ■ *Area Guide to Manchester and the Mountains*
Released: Semiannual **Availability:** Print.

45717 ■ Barton Area Chamber of Commerce
PO Box 776
 Barton, VT 05822
Co. E-mail: info@centerofthekingdom.com
URL: http://www.centerofthekingdom.com
Contact: Jethro Hayman, President
Facebook: www.facebook.com/Barton-Area-Chamber-of-Commerce-126691626483
Description: Serves members and the community with networking opportunities, business seminars, and referrals. **Founded:** 1974. **Geographic Preference:** Local.

45718 ■ Bennington Area Chamber of Commerce (BACC)
100 Veterans Memorial Dr.
 Bennington, VT 05201
Ph: (802)447-3311
Co. E-mail: info@bennington.com
URL: http://www.bennington.com
Contact: Brian Maggiotto, President
Description: Serves members and the community with networking opportunities, business seminars, and referrals. **Founded:** 1911. **Publications:** *Bennington Area Guide* (Annual). **Geographic Preference:** Local.

45719 ■ Brandon Area Chamber of Commerce (BACC)
PO Box 267
 Brandon, VT 05733
Ph: (802)247-6401
Co. E-mail: info@brandon.org
URL: http://brandon.org
Contact: Pat Wood, President
Linkedin: www.linkedin.com/company/brandon-chamber-of-commerce
Description: Promotes business and community development in Brandon, VT. **Founded:** 1980. **Publications:** *Chamber News*. **Educational Activities:** Brandon HarvestFest. **Geographic Preference:** Local.

45720 ■ Brattleboro Area Chamber of Commerce (BACC)
180 Main St.
 Brattleboro, VT 05301
Ph: (802)254-4565
Co. E-mail: info@brattleborochamber.org
URL: http://www.brattleborochamber.org
Contact: Gina Pattison, President
Facebook: www.facebook.com/Brattleboro.The.One.and.Only
X (Twitter): x.com/BrattleboroONE
Description: Promotes business and community development in the Brattleboro, VT area. Sponsors festivals and social activities. **Founded:** 1753. **Publications:** *The Chamber Window* (Quarterly). **Geographic Preference:** Local.

45721 ■ *Calendar of Events*
4403 Main St.
 Waitsfield, VT 05673
Ph: (802)496-3409
Co. E-mail: info@madrivervalley.com
URL: http://www.madrivervalley.com/about/chamber
Contact: Eric Friedman, Executive Director
URL(s): www.madrivervalley.com/events
Availability: Print.

45722 ■ Central Vermont Chamber of Commerce
33 Stewart Rd.
 Berlin, VT 05641
Ph: (802)229-5711
Co. E-mail: info@centralvt.com
URL: http://www.centralvt.com
Contact: Kevin Eschelbach, President
Facebook: www.facebook.com/CentralVermontChamber
Linkedin: www.linkedin.com/company/central-vermont-chamber-of-commerce
X (Twitter): x.com/central_vermont
Description: Works to improve the climate for doing business, promotes community, and provides travel marketing in Central Vermont. **Founded:** 1972. **Publications:** *Area Map*; *Community Profile*; *Regional Tourist Brochures*. **Geographic Preference:** Local.

45723 ■ Franklin County Regional Chamber of Commerce (FCRCC)
2 N Main St., Ste. 101
 Saint Albans, VT 05478
Ph: (802)524-2444
Co. E-mail: info@fcrccvt.com
URL: http://www.fcrccvt.com
Contact: Alisha Sawyer, Co-President
Facebook: www.facebook.com/franklincountychambervt
Description: Promotes business and community development in the St. Albans, VT area. **Founded:** 1947. **Publications:** *Chamber Outlook*; *Just To Let You Know...* (Bimonthly); *St. Albans Brochure* (Biennial). **Geographic Preference:** Local.

45724 ■ Great Falls Regional Chamber of Commerce (GFRC)
17 Depot St.
 Bellows Falls, VT 05101
Ph: (802)463-4280
Co. E-mail: info@gfrcc.org
URL: http://www.gfrcc.org
Contact: Kathleen Govotski, President
Facebook: www.facebook.com/gfrcc
X (Twitter): x.com/GFRCC
Description: Promotes business and community development in Windham County, VT and Cheshire County, NH. Sponsors Rockingham Old Home Days Festival and various other events to promote the areas. **Founded:** 1957. **Geographic Preference:** Regional.

45725 ■ Hartford Area Chamber of Commerce (HACC)
5966 Woodstock Rd.
 Quechee, VT 05059-0823
Ph: (802)295-7900
Fax: (802)296-8280
Co. E-mail: info@hartfordvtchamber.com
URL: http://www.hartfordvtchamber.com
Contact: P. J. Skehan, Executive Director
Facebook: www.facebook.com/HartfordAreaChamber.QucheeBalloonFestival
Description: Promotes business and community development in Quechee, VT. Sponsors annual Balloon Festival and crafts fair. **Geographic Preference:** Local.

45726 ■ Heart of Vermont Chamber of Commerce (HVCC)
PO Box 111
 Hardwick, VT 05843
Ph: (802)624-3930
Co. E-mail: chamber@heartofvt.com
URL: http://www.heartofvt.com
Contact: Rachel Kane, President
E-mail: chamber@heartofvt.com
Description: Promotes business and community development in the Hardwick, VT area. **Geographic Preference:** Local.

45727 ■ Island Pond Chamber of Commerce
PO Box 255
Island Pond, VT 05846
Ph: (802)673-1854
Co. E-mail: info@islandpondchamber.org
URL: http://visitislandpond.com
Contact: Jeanne Gervais, President
Facebook: www.facebook.com/IslandPondChamber
Description: Aims to improve the business climate in the Island Pond Area. Participates on the Board of the Brighton Community Forum. Plans activities to draw business and tourists into the area. **Geographic Preference:** Local.

45728 ■ Killington Pico Area Association (KPAA)
2319 US Rte. 4
Killington, VT 05751
Ph: (802)422-5722
Co. E-mail: admin@killingtonpico.org
URL: http://killingtonpico.org
Facebook: www.facebook.com/killingtonpicoareaassociation
X (Twitter): x.com/killingtonarea
Instagram: www.instagram.com/killingtonarea
Description: Serves members and the community with networking opportunities and business seminars. **Founded:** 1974. **Geographic Preference:** Local.

45729 ■ Lake Champlain Islands Economic Development Corporation (LCIEDC)
3501 US Rte. 2
North Hero, VT 05474
Ph: (802)372-8400
Co. E-mail: info@champlainislands.com
URL: http://www.champlainislands.com/region-index
Contact: Karen McCloud, President
Facebook: www.facebook.com/LCIEDC
Linkedin: www.linkedin.com/company/lake-champlain-islands-economic-development-corporation
Instagram: www.instagram.com/champlainislands
Description: Promotes business and community development in Grand Isle County. **Founded:** 2012. **Publications:** *The Vessel* (Quarterly). **Educational Activities:** Business Fair. **Geographic Preference:** Local.

45730 ■ Lake Champlain Regional Chamber of Commerce (LCRCC)
60 Main St., Ste. 100
Burlington, VT 05401
Ph: (802)863-3489
Fax: (802)863-1538
Co. E-mail: vermont@vermont.org
URL: http://lccvermont.org
Contact: Catherine Z. Davis, President
E-mail: cathy@vermont.org
Facebook: www.facebook.com/lcrcc
X (Twitter): x.com/LCChamber
Description: Promotes business and community development in Chittenden County, VT. Advocates for issues favorable to business and the community. **Publications:** *Experience Burlington* (Annual); *60 Main Street News* (Bimonthly). **Geographic Preference:** Regional.

45731 ■ Lyndon Area Chamber of Commerce
PO Box 886
Lyndonville, VT 05851
Ph: (802)626-9696
Co. E-mail: info@lyndonvermont.com
URL: http://www.lyndonvermont.com
Contact: Sarah Lafferty, President
Facebook: www.facebook.com/Lyndon-Area-Chamber-of-Commerce-295519307228848
Description: Provides information on vacationing, business and residential relocation, activities, and world famous bridges. Offers excellent education system. **Geographic Preference:** Local.

45732 ■ Mad River Valley Chamber of Commerce
4403 Main St.
Waitsfield, VT 05673
Ph: (802)496-3409
Co. E-mail: info@madrivervalley.com
URL: http://www.madrivervalley.com/about/chamber
Contact: Eric Friedman, Executive Director
Facebook: www.facebook.com/madrivervalley
X (Twitter): x.com/madrivervalley
Instagram: www.instagram.com/madrivervalley
YouTube: www.youtube.com/channel/UCHTOxTgGdTOyeswUmTftcRQ
Description: Inns, lodges, ski resorts, retailers, restaurants, and sports centers. Promotes business and community development in central Vermont. **Founded:** 1782. **Publications:** *Calendar of Events*. **Geographic Preference:** Local.

45733 ■ Mount Snow Valley Chamber of Commerce
21 W Main St.
Wilmington, VT 05363
Ph: (802)464-8092
Co. E-mail: info@visitvermont.com
URL: http://www.visitvermont.com
Facebook: www.facebook.com/mountsnowvalleychamberofcommerce
X (Twitter): x.com/visit_vermont
YouTube: www.youtube.com/user/MountSnowvermont
Pinterest: www.pinterest.com/mountsnowchambr
Description: Promotes business and community development in the Deerfield Valley, VT area. **Publications:** *Mount Snow/Haystack Chamber - Guide to Southern Vermont* (Annual). **Geographic Preference:** Local.

45734 ■ Northeast Kingdom Chamber of Commerce (NEKCC)
2000 Memorial Dr., Ste. 11
Saint Johnsbury, VT 05819
Ph: (802)748-3678
Free: 800-639-6379
Co. E-mail: nekinfo@nekchamber.com
URL: http://www.nekchamber.com
Contact: Darcie McCann, Executive Director
E-mail: director@nekchamber.com
Facebook: www.facebook.com/NEKChamber
Description: Promotes business, economic and community development in Vermont's St. Johnsbury and Northeast Kingdom area. Handles travel promotion, community/economic development, legislative/governmental relations, business training and promotion of regional projects. **Founded:** 1957. **Geographic Preference:** Local.

45735 ■ *Smugglers Notch Area Vacation Guide*
Released: Annual **Price:** free. **Description:** Contains brief descriptions of area and local businesses. **Availability:** Print.

45736 ■ Springfield Regional Chamber of Commerce
56 Main St., Ste. No. 2
Springfield, VT 05156
Ph: (802)885-2779
Co. E-mail: springfieldrcoc@vermontel.net
URL: http://www.springfieldvt.com
Contact: Jerry Farnum, President
Facebook: www.facebook.com/SpringfieldRegionalChamberofCommerce
Linkedin: www.linkedin.com/company/springfield-regional-chamber-of-commerce
Description: Businesses, organizations, and interested individuals. Promotes business and community development in Springfield, VT. Sponsors Business After Hours Program, Citizens' Forum, radio program, Springfield Home Show, annual Vermont Apple Festival, workshops, and social activities. **Founded:** 1761. **Publications:** *Springfield Community Guide*. **Geographic Preference:** Local.

45737 ■ Stowe Area Association
51 Main St.
Stowe, VT 05672
Ph: (802)253-7321
Free: 800-467-8693
Fax: (802)253-2159
Co. E-mail: askus@gostowe.com
URL: http://www.gostowe.com/about/stowe-area-association
Contact: Dan Snyder, President
Facebook: www.facebook.com/gostowe
X (Twitter): x.com/gostowe
Instagram: www.instagram.com/gostowe
Description: Promotes business and community development in Stowe, VT area. **Founded:** 1947. **Geographic Preference:** Local.

45738 ■ Swanton Chamber of Commerce
PO Box 237
Swanton, VT 05488
Ph: (802)868-7200
Co. E-mail: info@swantonchamber.com
URL: http://swantonchamber.com
Contact: Mark Rocheleau, Secretary
E-mail: mrocheleau@vermontprecisiontools.com
Facebook: www.facebook.com/swantonchamber
Description: Promotes business and community development in Swanton, VT. **Geographic Preference:** Local.

45739 ■ Upper Valley Bi-State Regional Chamber of Commerce (UVB-SRCC)
PO Box 697
White River Junction, VT 05001
Ph: (802)295-6200
Fax: (802)295-3779
URL: http://www.uppervalleychamber.com
Contact: Geoffrey Ross, President
Description: Promotes business and community development in White River Junction, VT. **Publications:** *Business to Business Buyers Guide*. **Geographic Preference:** Regional.

45740 ■ Vermont Chamber of Commerce
751 Granger Rd.
Barre, VT 05641
Ph: (802)223-3443
Co. E-mail: info@vtchamber.com
URL: http://www.vtchamber.com
Contact: Betsy Bishop, President
E-mail: bbishop@vtchamber.com
Facebook: www.facebook.com/vtchamber
Linkedin: www.linkedin.com/company/vermont-chamber-of-commerce
X (Twitter): x.com/VTchamber
Description: Promotes business and community development in the state of Vermont. Conducts educational programs. Lobbies state government. Promotes travel and tourism in the state. **Founded:** 1912. **Publications:** *Vermont Traveler's Guidebook* (Annual); *Vermont Country Inns and B & B's* (Annual); *Vermont--Winter Guide* (Annual); *Legislative Updates* (Weekly); *Vermont Business* (Annual); *Vermont Connections* (3/year). **Awards:** Vermont Chamber of Commerce Citizen of the Year (Annual); Outstanding Business of the Year Award (Annual). **Geographic Preference:** Local.

45741 ■ White River Valley Chamber of Commerce
31 VT Rte. 66., Ste. 1
Randolph, VT 05060
Ph: (802)728-9027
URL: http://www.whiterivervalleychamber.com
Contact: Andrea Easton, President
Description: Commercial and industrial organizations and interested individuals. Promotes business and community development, and tourism in Randolph Center, Braintree, and Brookfield, VT. Sponsors educational programs, 4th of July celebration, Christmas promotion, fall golf classic and operates information booth from June until October. **Publications:** *Chamber E-News* (Monthly); *Randolph Map Brochure* (Semiannual). **Educational Activities:** Business After Hours; White River Valley Chamber of Commerce Dinner. **Geographic Preference:** Local.

45742 ■ Woodstock Area Chamber of Commerce
3 Mechanic St.
Woodstock, VT 05091
Ph: (802)457-3555
Fax: (802)457-1601
Co. E-mail: info@woodstockvt.com
URL: http://www.woodstockvt.com/businesses/woodstock-area-chamber-of-commerce
Contact: Beth Finlayson, Executive Director

E-mail: bfinlayson@woodstockvt.com
Facebook: www.facebook.com/WoodstockvtChamber
X (Twitter): x.com/WoodstockVTCham
Description: Promotes business and community development in the Woodstock, VT area. Sponsors Wassail Festival. **Publications:** *Window on Woodstock*. **Educational Activities:** Woodstock Wassail Celebration. **Geographic Preference:** Local.

MINORITY BUSINESS ASSISTANCE PROGRAMS

45743 ■ Capstone Community Action
20 Gable Pl.
Barre, VT 05641
Ph: (802)479-1053
Free: 800-639-1053
Co. E-mail: info@capstonevt.org
URL: http://www.capstonevt.org
Contact: Sue Minter, Executive Director
Facebook: www.facebook.com/VTCommunityAction
X (Twitter): x.com/VTAction
Description: Provides assistance, support, and training for women to start or grow a business in Vermont. **Founded:** 1965. **Geographic Preference:** Local.

FINANCING AND LOAN PROGRAMS

45744 ■ Aggregate Capital Partners L.L.C.
2463 Stowe Hollow Rd.
Stowe, VT 05672
Contact: David E. Bradbury, Jr., Manager
Description: Firm provides entrepreneurs, senior executives and boards with management consulting, strategic planning, economic development, public relations and new venture development services. **Founded:** 1998. **Preferred Investment Size:** $25,000 to $500,000. **Investment Policies:** Start-up, seed, early and first stage, and expansion. **Industry Preferences:** Internet specific.

45745 ■ North Country Angels (NCA)
60 Lake St., 2nd Fl.
Burlington, VT 05401
Contact: Kenneth H. Merritt, Jr., President
Description: Offers early-stage and seed investments for companies in and around Vermont. Meets once a month to discuss entrepreneurial news, share due diligence activities, build strategic relationships, and review business plans.

INCUBATORS/RESEARCH AND TECHNOLOGY PARKS

45746 ■ Bennington County Industrial Corp. (BCIC)
210 S St., Ste. 6
Bennington, VT 05201
Contact: Richard Zens, President
Description: Provider of free business assistance services.

45747 ■ River Valley Technology Center
307 S St.
Springfield, VT 05156
Ph: (802)885-8300
Fax: (802)885-8454
URL: http://www.rvtc.org
Contact: Scott Farr, Director
Facebook: www.facebook.com/
RiverValleyTechCenter
X (Twitter): x.com/rvtc2
Description: A public/private partnership dedicated to nurturing small technology and precision manufacturing businesses during the start-up stage. It provides a variety of business development assistance including low cost space, shared office services, onsite training and managerial and technical assistance in an environment conducive to new small businesses.

45748 ■ Vermont Center for Emerging Technologies (VCET)
266 Main St.
Burlington, VT 05401
Free: 866-232-9423
URL: http://vcet.co
Contact: David Bradbury, President
E-mail: david@vcet.co
Facebook: www.facebook.com/vcet.co
Linkedin: www.linkedin.com/company/vcetco
X (Twitter): x.com/VCET
Instagram: www.instagram.com/vcet.co
Description: Business incubator with the ability to link client companies to specialty laboratories and equipment, technology licensing, private investment capital resources, and an extensive network of faculty, staff, and student interns and well-positioned alumni from the University of Vermont and the state's leading academic institutions. **Founded:** 2005.

45749 ■ Vermont Food Venture Center (VFVC)
140 Junction Rd.
Hardwick, VT 05843
URL: http://www.hardwickagriculture.org
Contact: Jon Ramsay, Executive Director
E-mail: jon@hardwickagriculture.org
Description: A multi-use food processing facility designed to help startups and entrepreneurs get their food cooking. Provides consultation and business advising and offers 3 kitchens, each with specialty industrial equipment, to food entrepreneurs and farmers.

45750 ■ Vermont Small Business Development Center Lead Office (VtSBDC)
1 Main St.
Randolph Center, VT 05061
Ph: (802)349-5546
Free: 800-464-SBDC
Fax: (802)728-3026
URL: http://www.vtsbdc.org
Contact: Linda Rossi, Director
E-mail: lrossi@vtsbdc.org
Facebook: www.facebook.com/vtsbdc
Linkedin: www.linkedin.com/company/vtsbdc
X (Twitter): x.com/vtsbdc
Description: Directly assists small businesses, and offers referrals when necessary. **Founded:** 1992. **Geographic Preference:** State.

EDUCATIONAL PROGRAMS

45751 ■ Champlain College Center for Innovation & Entrepreneurship (CIE)
375 Maple St.
Burlington, VT 05401
Ph: (802)860-2700
Free: 800-570-5858
Co. E-mail: cie@champlain.edu
URL: http://www.champlain.edu/office/center-for
-innovation-entrepreneurship
Contact: Alex Hernandez, President
Facebook: www.facebook.com/ChamplainCIE
Description: Provides a unique opportunities for student entrepreneurs to gain assistance in building their own business.

45752 ■ Lyndon State College Continuing Education Department
1001 College Rd.
Lyndonville, VT 05851
Ph: (802)626-6413
Free: 800-225-1998
URL: http://www.northernvermont.edu/academics/
non-traditional-students/continuing-education
Contact: John W. Mills, President
E-mail: john.mills@northernvermont.edu
Description: Offers courses for professional, personal, and academic enrichment. Conducts business and management courses on a credit or noncredit basis. Presents institutes, seminars, and workshops. Offers degree programs in small business management, management training, and personnel management. **Founded:** 1911.

PUBLICATIONS

45753 ■ *Vermont Business Magazine*
365 Dorset St.
South Burlington, VT 05403
Ph: (802)863-8038
Fax: (802)863-8069
Co. E-mail: info@vermontbiz.com
URL: http://vermontbiz.com
Contact: Ellen Sheehey, Manager
URL(s): vermontbiz.com/magazine
Facebook: www.facebook.com/vermontbiz
X (Twitter): x.com/vermontbiz
Ed: Timothy McQuiston. **Released:** Monthly **Price:** $45, for 1 year print; $75, for 2 year print; $99, for 3 years print; $4.95, Single issue for 1 copy; $9.90, Single issue for 2 copies; $14.85, Single issue for 3 copies; $19.80, Single issue for 4 copies; $24.75, Single issue for 5 copies; $5, for 1 month online; $30, for 1 year online. **Description:** Regional business magazine. **Availability:** Print; Online.

45754 ■ Vermont Business Magazine (VBM)
365 Dorset St.
South Burlington, VT 05403
Ph: (802)863-8038
Fax: (802)863-8069
Co. E-mail: info@vermontbiz.com
URL: http://vermontbiz.com
Contact: Ellen Sheehey, Manager
Facebook: www.facebook.com/vermontbiz
Linkedin: www.linkedin.com/in/vermont-business
-magazine-96983042
X (Twitter): x.com/vermontbiz
Description: Publisher of business magazines. **Founded:** 1972. **Publications:** *Vermont Business Magazine* (Monthly); *Vermont Business and Manufacturers Directory* (Annual).

VENTURE CAPITAL FIRM

45755 ■ FreshTracks Capital
29 Harbor Rd., Ste. 200
Shelburne, VT 05482
Ph: (802)923-1500
URL: http://www.freshtrackscap.com
Contact: Cairn G. Cross, Managing Director
Co-Founder
Linkedin: www.linkedin.com/company/freshtracks
-capital
X (Twitter): x.com/FreshTracksCap
Description: Seed and early stage venture capital firm focused on businesses in Vermont and surrounding regions. **Founded:** 2000. **Investment Policies:** Depth and experience of the management team; size and applicability of the market; defensiveness of the product/service offered; scalability of the business model. Looks for companies that can scale revenues and achieve profitability in 5-7 years.

Virginia

FEDERAL GOVERNMENT FINANCING PROGRAM

45756 ■ U.S. Trade and Development Agency (USTDA)
1101 Wilson Blvd., Ste. 1100
Arlington, VA 22209
Ph: (703)875-4357
URL: http://ustda.gov
Contact: Thomas R. Hardy, Director, Programs
Facebook: www.facebook.com/USTDA
Linkedin: www.linkedin.com/company/ustda
X (Twitter): x.com/ustda
Instagram: www.instagram.com/ustda_
YouTube: www.youtube.com/ustda
Description: Helps businesses create U.S. jobs through the export of U.S. goods and services for priority development projects in emerging economies. Connects the private sector to early-stage infrastructure projects. Funds feasibility studies, technical assistance and pilot projects. Also connects international buyers with U.S. sellers through reverse trade mission, industry conferences, and workshops.

ASSOCIATIONS AND OTHER ORGANIZATIONS

45757 ■ Association of Fundraising Professionals Central Virginia Chapter
PO Box 25866
Richmond, VA 23260
Ph: (804)585-3150
Co. E-mail: admin@afpcentralva.org
URL: http://community.afpnet.org/afpcentralvachapter
Contact: Abbi Haggerty, President
Facebook: www.facebook.com/CentralVirginiaAFP
Linkedin: www.linkedin.com/company/afp-central-virginia-chapter
Description: Seeks to advance philanthropy by enabling people to practice effective and ethical fundraising. Covers the area from Fredericksburg south to the North Carolina line and from Charlottesville to Williamsburg. **Founded:** 1996. **Geographic Preference:** Local.

45758 ■ Business Network International Shenandoah Valley
3430 Toringdon Way
Charlotte, NC 28277
Free: 855-264-2673
URL: http://bnisv.com
Contact: Steve Garcia, Managing Director
E-mail: stevegarcia@bni.com
Description: Provides both men and women a structured environment for the development and exchange of quality business referrals. Offers members the opportunity to share ideas and contacts. **Geographic Preference:** Local.

45759 ■ Entrepreneurs' Organization - Richmond Chapter (EO)
Richmond, VA
URL: http://www.eonetwork.org/richmond
Description: Provides local resources to members which includes networking events, mentorship, live forums, and leadership development. **Founded:** 2019.

45760 ■ Entrepreneurs' Organization - Southeast Virginia Chapter (EO)
2901 S Lynnhaven Rd., Ste. 120
Virginia Beach, VA 23452-0000
URL: http://www.eonetwork.org/southeastvirginia
Contact: Todd J. Preti, President
Description: Provides local resources to members which includes networking events, mentorship, live forums, and leadership development.

45761 ■ Greater DC Metro Chapter of GBTA (NVBTA)
1101 King St., Ste. 500
Alexandria, VA 22314
URL: http://gbta-greaterdcmetro.org
Contact: Carmen Smith, Co-President
Description: Represents travel managers and providers. Promotes the value of the travel manager in meeting corporate travel needs and financial goals. Cultivates a positive public image of the corporate travel industry. Protects the interests of members and their corporations in legislative and regulatory matters. Promotes safety, security, efficiency and quality travel. Provides a forum for the exchange of information and ideas among members. **Founded:** 1988. **Geographic Preference:** Local.

45762 ■ International Association of Business Communicators - DC Metro (IABC)
200 Little Falls St., Ste. 205
Falls Church, VA 22046
Co. E-mail: info@iabcdcmetro.org
URL: http://iabcdc.org
Contact: Giuseppe Laviano, President
Facebook: www.facebook.com/iabcdc
Linkedin: www.linkedin.com/company/iabcdc
X (Twitter): x.com/IABCDC
Instagram: www.instagram.com/iabcdc
Description: International association for business communication. **Founded:** 2010. **Geographic Preference:** State.

45763 ■ International Association of Women Chesapeake Chapter
Chesapeake, VA
URL: http://www.iawomen.com/chapters/chesapeake-chapter
Description: Serves as network of accomplished women united to achieve professional goals. Provides a forum for sharing ideas and experiences of professional women regarding career success. Promotes an active business and networking community from all industries. **Geographic Preference:** Local.

45764 ■ National Federation of Independent Business Virginia
919 E Main St., Ste. 1160
Richmond, VA 23219
Ph: (804)377-3661
URL: http://www.nfib.com/virginia
Contact: Julia Hammond, Director
Description: Represents small and independent businesses. Aims to promote and protect the rights of members to own, operate and grow their businesses. **Geographic Preference:** State.

45765 ■ Virginia Business Innovation Association (VBIA)
1125 Jefferson Davis Hwy., Ste. 400
Fredericksburg, VA 22401
Ph: (540)654-1096
Fax: (540)654-1400
Co. E-mail: info@vbia.org
URL: http://www.vbia.org
Contact: Lisa Hull, President
E-mail: lhull@nnpdc17.state.va.us
Description: Promotes entrepreneurship and small business development in Virginia. **Founded:** 2000.

45766 ■ Virginia Business Travel Association (VBTA)
PO Box 3540
Glen Allen, VA 23058
Co. E-mail: info@vbta.org
URL: http://vbta.org
Contact: Samantha Bean, President
E-mail: sbean@ltdhospitality.com
Facebook: www.facebook.com/VABTA
Description: Represents travel managers and providers. Promotes the value of the travel manager in meeting corporate travel needs and financial goals. Cultivates a positive public image of the corporate travel industry. Protects the interests of members and their corporations in legislative and regulatory matters. Promotes safety, security, efficiency and quality travel. Provides a forum for the exchange of information and ideas among members. **Founded:** 1993. **Geographic Preference:** State.

SMALL BUSINESS DEVELOPMENT CENTERS

45767 ■ Alexandria Small Business Development Center (ASBDC)
10306 Eaton Pl., Ste. 180
Fairfax, VA 22030
Ph: (703)261-4105
Co. E-mail: help@masonsbdc.org
URL: http://masonsbdc.org
Contact: Timm Johnson, Director
Facebook: www.facebook.com/masonsbdc
X (Twitter): x.com/masonsbdc
Description: Represents and promotes the small business sector. Provides management assistance to current and prospective small business owners. Helps to improve management skills and expand the products and services of members. **Founded:** 1996. **Geographic Preference:** Local.

STATE LISTINGS Virginia ■ 45784

45768 ■ Central Virginia Small Business Development Center (CV SBDC)
300 Preston Ave. Ste. 206
Charlottesville, VA 22902
Ph: (434)295-8198
Co. E-mail: contact@cvsbdc.org
URL: http://www.cvsbdc.org
Contact: Rebecca Haydock, Director
E-mail: rhaydock@cvsbdc.org
Facebook: www.facebook.com/CentralVASBDC
X (Twitter): x.com/CentralVaSBDC
Instagram: www.instagram.com/centralvasbdc
YouTube: www.youtube.com/channel/UC7UGHkGxMwp9hlKSU9TbPFg/videos
Description: Represents and promotes the small business sector. Provides management assistance to current and prospective small business owners. Helps to improve management skills and expand the products and services of members. **Geographic Preference:** Local.

45769 ■ Crater Small Business Development Center of Longwood University
1964 Wakefield St.
Petersburg, VA 23805
Ph: (804)518-2003
URL: http://www.connectva.org/groups/crater-small-business-development-center
Contact: Pat Hood, Director
URL(s): sbdc-longwood.com
Description: Represents and promotes the small business sector. Provides management assistance to current and prospective small business owners. Helps to improve management skills and expand the products and services of members. **Geographic Preference:** Local.

45770 ■ Greater Richmond Small Business Development Center (GRSBDC)
919 E Main St., Ste. 1700
Richmond, VA 23219
URL: http://grsbdc.com/?page_id=129
Contact: Chrystal Neal, Executive Director
E-mail: chrystal.neal@chamberrva.com
Facebook: www.facebook.com/GRSBDC
Description: Represents and promotes the small business sector. Provides management assistance to current and prospective small business owners. Helps to improve management skills and expand the products and services of members. **Founded:** 1998. **Geographic Preference:** Local.

45771 ■ Hampton Roads Small Business Development Center (SBDC)
101 W Main St., Ste. 800.
Norfolk, VA 23510
Ph: (757)664-2592
URL: http://hrchamber.com/programs/small-business-development-center
Description: Represents and promotes the small business sector. Provides management assistance to current and prospective small business owners. Helps to improve management skills and expand the products and services of members. **Founded:** 1990. **Geographic Preference:** Local.

45772 ■ Hampton Roads Small Business Development Center Eastern Shore
c/o E Shore Chamber of Commerce
10956 Pky.
Melfa, VA 23410
Ph: (757)789-3418
URL: http://www.virginiasbdc.org/office-locations
Description: Represents and promotes the small business sector. Provides management assistance to current and prospective small business owners. Helps to improve management skills and expand the products and services of members. **Geographic Preference:** Local.

45773 ■ Hampton Roads Small Business Development Center Franklin
c/o Franklin Business Ctr.
601 N Mechanic St.
Franklin, VA 23851
Ph: (757)562-1958
URL: http://www.hrsbdc.org/en/about-hrsbdc/contact-us/franklin
Description: Represents and promotes the small business sector. Provides management assistance to current and prospective small business owners. Helps to improve management skills and expand the products and services of members. **Geographic Preference:** Local.

45774 ■ Hampton Roads Small Business Development Center Smithfield
c/o Isle of Wight-Smithfield-Windsor Chamber of Commerce
100 Main St.
Smithfield, VA 23431
URL: http://www.hrsbdc.org/en/doing-business-in-hampton-roads/smithfield
Description: Represents and promotes the small business sector. Provides management assistance to current and prospective small business owners. Helps to improve management skills and expand the products and services of members. **Founded:** 1752. **Geographic Preference:** Local.

45775 ■ Hampton Roads Small Business Development Center Suffolk
425 W Washington St.
Suffolk, VA 23434
Ph: (757)514-4000
URL: http://www.suffolkva.us
Contact: Albert S. Moor, II, Manager
URL(s): www.hrsbdc.org/en/doing-business-in-hampton-roads/suffolk
Facebook: www.facebook.com/suffolkva
X (Twitter): x.com/CityofSuffolk
YouTube: www.youtube.com/user/CityofSuffolkVA
Description: Represents and promotes the small business sector. Provides management assistance to current and prospective small business owners. Helps to improve management skills and expand the products and services of members. **Founded:** 1990. **Geographic Preference:** Local.

45776 ■ Hampton Roads Small Business Development Center Williamsburg
4601 Opportunity Way.
Williamsburg, VA 23188
URL: http://www.tncc.edu
Contact: Debra Hamilton-Farley, Associate Director
E-mail: farleyd@tncc.edu
Description: Represents and promotes the small business sector. Provides management assistance to current and prospective small business owners. Helps to improve management skills and expand the products and services of members. **Geographic Preference:** Local.

45777 ■ Longwood University Small Business Development Center Danville
1008 S Main St., Taylor Bldg., Ste. 105
Danville, VA 24541
Ph: (434)797-8482
Fax: (434)797-8447
URL: http://sbdc-longwood.com/danville
Description: Represents and promotes the small business sector. Provides management assistance to current and prospective small business owners. Helps to improve management skills and expand the products and services of members. **Geographic Preference:** Local.

45778 ■ Longwood University Small Business Development Center Farmville
315 W 3rd St.
Farmville, VA 23901
Ph: (434)395-2086
URL: http://sbdc-longwood.com/central-region
Description: Represents and promotes the small business sector. Provides management assistance to current and prospective small business owners. Helps to improve management skills and expand the products and services of members. **Geographic Preference:** Local.

45779 ■ Longwood University Small Business Development Center Martinsville (LSBDC)
Martinsville, VA
Ph: (276)656-5475
URL: http://sbdc-longwood.com/martinsville
Contact: Michael Scales, Business Analyst
E-mail: scalesmc@longwood.edu
Description: Provides management assistance to current and prospective small business owners in Martinsville. **Geographic Preference:** Local.

45780 ■ Longwood University Small Business Development Center South Boston
820 Bruce St.
South Boston, VA 24592
Ph: (434)572-5444
URL: http://sbdc-longwood.com/south-boston-suits-sweet-cees-to-a-tee
Contact: Lin Hite, Director
Description: Represents and promotes the small business sector. Provides management assistance to current and prospective small business owners. Helps to improve management skills and expand the products and services of members. **Geographic Preference:** Local.

45781 ■ Lord Fairfax Small Business Development Center
173 Skirmisher Ln.
Middletown, VA 22645
Ph: (540)868-7093
Fax: (540)868-7095
Co. E-mail: ckriz@lfcc.edu
URL: http://lfsbdc.org
Contact: Christine Kriz, Director
E-mail: ckriz@lfcc.edu
Description: Represents and promotes the small business sector. Provides management assistance to current and prospective small business owners. Helps to improve management skills and expand the products and services of members. **Geographic Preference:** Local.

45782 ■ Lord Fairfax Small Business Development Center at Culpeper (LFSBDC)
Culpeper Economic Development Center
803 S Main St.
Culpeper, VA 22701
Ph: (540)727-0638
URL: http://lfsbdc.org/tag/culpeper
Contact: Christine Kriz, Director
E-mail: ckriz@lfcc.edu
Description: Provides management assistance to current and prospective small business owners in Lord Fairfax. **Geographic Preference:** Local.

45783 ■ Lord Fairfax Small Business Development Center at Fauquier
70 Main St.
Warrenton, VA 20187
Ph: (540)216-7100
URL: http://lfsbdc.org
Contact: Christine Kriz, Director
E-mail: ckriz@lfcc.edu
Description: Represents and promotes the small business sector. Provides management assistance to current and prospective small business owners. Helps to improve management skills and expand the products and services of members. **Founded:** 1993. **Geographic Preference:** Local.

45784 ■ Lynchburg Business Development Center (LBDC)
Business Development Ctr. Inc.
147 Mill Ridge Rd.
Lynchburg, VA 24502
Ph: (434)582-6100
Co. E-mail: bdcdir@lbdc.com
URL: http://lbdc.com
Contact: Byron Steward, Director
Description: Represents and promotes the small business sector. Provides management assistance to current and prospective small business owners.

45785 ■ Virginia   STATE LISTINGS

Helps to improve management skills and expand the products and services of members. **Founded:** 1989. **Geographic Preference:** Local.

45785 ■ Mason Small Business Development Center (SBDC)
4031 University Dr.
Fairfax, VA 22030
Ph: (703)261-4105
Co. E-mail: help@masonsbdc.org
URL: http://masonsbdc.org
Contact: Timm Johnson, Director
Facebook: www.facebook.com/masonsbdc
Linkedin: www.linkedin.com/company/mason-sbdc
X (Twitter): x.com/masonsbdc
Description: Provides counseling services in the areas of business planning, marketing, and finance. **Founded:** 1987. **Geographic Preference:** Local.

45786 ■ Mountain Empire Community College Small Business Development Center (SBDC)
3441 Mountain Empire Rd.
Big Stone Gap, VA 24219
Ph: (276)523-2400
Fax: (276)523-9699
URL: http://www.mecc.edu/sbdc
Contact: Kristen Westover, President
E-mail: kwestover@mecc.edu
Description: Represents and promotes the small business sector. Provides management assistance to current and prospective small business owners. Helps to improve management skills and expand the products and services of members. **Geographic Preference:** Local.

45787 ■ Roanoke Regional Small Business Development Center (RRSBDC)
210 S Jefferson St.
Roanoke, VA 24018
Ph: (540)632-1174
Co. E-mail: hello@roanokesmallbusiness.org
URL: http://roanokesmallbusiness.org
YouTube: www.youtube.com/channel/UCLxYF2OP3NhDgWZquYB1OfA
Description: Provides management assistance to current and prospective small business owners in Roanoke. **Geographic Preference:** Local.

45788 ■ Shenandoah Valley Small Business Development Center (SVSBDC)
220 University Blvd.
Harrisonburg, VA 22807
Ph: (540)568-3227
Co. E-mail: duganaj@jmu.edu
URL: http://www.valleysbdc.org
Contact: Joyce Krech, Director
E-mail: krechjh@jmu.edu
Facebook: www.facebook.com/ValleySBDC
Linkedin: www.linkedin.com/company/shenvalleysbdc
X (Twitter): x.com/valleysbdc
Description: Provides management assistance to current and prospective small business owners in Shenandoah Valley. **Founded:** 1989. **Geographic Preference:** Local.

45789 ■ South Fairfax Small Business Development Center
7001 Loisdale Rd., Ste. C
Springfield, VA 22150
Ph: (703)768-1440
Co. E-mail: info@cbponline.org
URL: http://community-business-partnership-springfield-va.org/CBP-Programs/South-Fairfax-Small-Business-Development-Center-SBDC.aspx
Contact: Gisele Stolz, Director
E-mail: gisele@cbponline.org
Description: Represents and promotes the small business sector. Provides management assistance to current and prospective small business owners. Helps to improve management skills and expand the products and services of members. **Geographic Preference:** Local.

45790 ■ University of Mary Washington Small Business Development Center Fredericksburg Office
Ctr. for Economic Development
1125 Jefferson Davis Hwy., Ste. 400
Fredericksburg, VA 22401
Fax: (540)654-1383
URL: http://economicdevelopment.umw.edu/home/programs/umw-eagleworks-business-incubation-center/locations
URL(s): economicdevelopment.umw.edu/home/programs/sbdc10
Description: Provides management assistance to current and prospective small business owners in Fredericksburg. **Founded:** 1992. **Geographic Preference:** Local.

45791 ■ University of Mary Washington Small Business Development Center Warsaw Office
487 Main St.
Warsaw, VA 22572
Ph: (804)333-0286
Fax: (804)333-0187
Co. E-mail: kwhitman@umw.edu
URL: http://www.umw.edu/directory/department/provost/engagement/center-for-economic-development/small-business-development-center-warsaw
Contact: Joy Corprew, Director
E-mail: jcorprew@umw.edu
Description: Represents and promotes the small business sector. Provides management assistance to current and prospective small business owners. Helps to improve management skills and expand the products and services of members. **Geographic Preference:** Local.

45792 ■ Virginia Highlands Small Business Development Center [Virginia Highlands SBDC]
100 VHCC Dr.
Abingdon, VA 24210
Ph: (276)739-2474
Fax: (276)739-2577
Co. E-mail: cfields2@vhcc.edu
URL: http://vhcc2.vhcc.edu/sbdc
Contact: Cindy Fields, Contact
E-mail: cfields2@vhcc.edu
Description: Provides management assistance to current and prospective small business owners in Virginia Highlands. **Geographic Preference:** Local.

45793 ■ Virginia Small Business Development Center Southwest Virginia Community College
724 Community College Rd. Tazewell Hall, Rm. 125
Cedar Bluff, VA 24609
Ph: (276)964-7345
Co. E-mail: margie.douglass@sw.edu
URL: http://sw.edu/sbdc
Contact: Margie Douglass, Director
E-mail: margie.douglass@sw.edu
Facebook: www.facebook.com/SBDCatSWCC
Linkedin: www.linkedin.com/company/small-business-development-center-at-southwest-virginia-community-college
X (Twitter): x.com/small_swcc
Description: Represents and promotes the small business sector. Provides management assistance to current and prospective small business owners. Helps to improve management skills and expand the products and services of members. **Geographic Preference:** Local.

SMALL BUSINESS ASSISTANCE PROGRAMS

45794 ■ Virginia Department of Agriculture and Consumer Services - Office of International Marketing
102 Governor St.
Richmond, VA 23219
URL: http://www.vdacs.virginia.gov/marketing-international-marketing.shtml

Description: Works to maximize the export of Virginia's agricultural products; provides market, exporter, and sales development assistance.

45795 ■ Virginia Department of Small Business and Supplier Diversity (SBSD)
101 N 14th St., 11th Fl.
Richmond, VA 23219
Ph: (804)786-6585
Fax: (804)786-9736
Co. E-mail: sbsd@sbsd.virginia.gov
URL: http://www.sbsd.virginia.gov
Contact: Matthew James, Director
E-mail: matthew.james@sbsd.virginia.gov
Description: Small business persons appointed by the governor to advise the Department of Economic Development on small business programs and concerns.

45796 ■ Virginia Department of Small Business and Supplier Diversity - Virginia Small Business Financing Authority (VSBFA)
101 N 14th St., 11th Fl.
Richmond, VA 23219
Ph: (804)786-1049
URL: http://sbsd.virginia.gov/virginia-small-business-financing-authority
Description: Assists small businesses by providing information on sources of technical, management, and financial assistance programs. Serves as an ombudsman, helping small businesses to resolve state regulatory problems.

45797 ■ Virginia Economic Development Partnership (VEDP)
901 E Cary St.
Richmond, VA 23219
Ph: (804)545-5600
Co. E-mail: info@vedp.org
URL: http://www.vedp.org
Contact: Jason El Koubi, President
E-mail: jelkoubi@vedp.org
Facebook: www.facebook.com/vaeconomicdevelopmentpartnership
Linkedin: www.linkedin.com/company/virginia-economic-development-partnership
X (Twitter): x.com/vedpvirginia
Description: Consulting program designed to assist Virginia firms in identifying and developing foreign markets for their goods and services. **Founded:** 1995. **Educational Activities:** Farnborough International AirShow (FIA) (Biennial). **Geographic Preference:** State.

SCORE OFFICES

45798 ■ SCORE - Alexandria, Virginia
Alexandria Barrett Library
717 Queen St.
Alexandria, VA 22314
Ph: (202)619-1000
Co. E-mail: michael.shattow@scorevolunteer.org
URL: http://washingtondc.score.org/score-washington-dc-mentoring-locations
Description: Provides professional guidance and information to maximize the success of existing and emerging small businesses. Offers business counseling and workshops.

45799 ■ SCORE - Annadale
Fairfax SkillSource Center
7611 Little River Turnpike, Ste. 300W
Annandale, VA 22003
URL: http://washingtondc.score.org
Description: Provides professional guidance and information to maximize the success of existing and emerging small businesses. Offers business counseling and workshops.

45800 ■ SCORE - Arlington, Virginia
1100 N Glebe Rd., Ste. 1500
Arlington, VA 22201
Ph: (703)228-0808
URL: http://www.score.org/find-location
Facebook: www.facebook.com/SCOREMentors

STATE LISTINGS   Virginia ■ 45819

Description: Provides professional guidance and information to maximize the success of existing and emerging small businesses. Offers business counseling and workshops.

45801 ■ SCORE - Ashburn
43777 Central Station Dr., Ste. 300
Ashburn, VA 20147
Ph: (202)619-1000
URL: http://www.washingtondc.score.org/score-washington-dc-mentoring-locations

Description: Provides professional guidance and information to maximize the success of existing and emerging small businesses. Offers business counseling and workshops.

45802 ■ SCORE - Central Virginia
209 5th St. NE
Charlottesville, VA 22902
Ph: (434)295-6712
URL: http://centralvirginia.score.org
Contact: Kelly Dye, Vice President
E-mail: kelly.dye@firstcitizens.com
Facebook: www.facebook.com/SCORECentralVirginia
Linkedin: www.linkedin.com/company/score-mentors-central-virginia
X (Twitter): x.com/SCORECentralVA

Description: Strives for the formation, growth and success of small businesses. Provides consulting services to existing and emerging small businesses in Central Virginia. Counselors include men and women who have many years of business experience in various fields. Develops business plans and evaluates financial projections. **Geographic Preference:** Local.

45803 ■ SCORE - Culpeper
271 Southgate Shopping Ctr.
Culpeper, VA 22701
URL: http://centralvirginia.score.org

Description: Provides professional guidance and information to maximize the success of existing and emerging small businesses. Offers business counseling and workshops.

45804 ■ SCORE - Fairfax
4031 University Dr., Ste. 100
Fairfax, VA 22030
Ph: (703)277-7700
Co. E-mail: help@score.org
URL: http://washingtondc.score.org
Facebook: www.facebook.com/SCOREWashingtonDC
Linkedin: www.linkedin.com/company/score-mentors-washington-dc
X (Twitter): twitter.com/DCSCORE
YouTube: www.youtube.com/channel/UCK7FwEMkmhEwqCgCU-npf_w

Description: Provides professional guidance and information to maximize the success of existing and emerging small businesses. Offers business counseling and workshops.

45805 ■ SCORE - Front Royal
524 North Royal Ave.
Box No. 53
Front Royal, VA 22630
Ph: (540)622-4266
Co. E-mail: score427@hotmail.com
URL: http://shenandoahvly.score.org/find-location?state=VA
Contact: James K. Martin, Contact

Description: Provides professional guidance and information to maximize the success of existing and emerging small businesses. Offers business counseling and workshops.

45806 ■ SCORE - Gordonsville
Gordonsville Library
319 N Main St.
Gordonsville, VA 22942
URL: http://centralvirginia.score.org/branch/gordonsville-library

Description: Provides professional guidance and information to maximize the success of existing and emerging small businesses. Offers business counseling and workshops.

45807 ■ SCORE - Greater Lynchburg
147 Mill Ridge Rd., Ste. 122
Lynchburg, VA 24502
Ph: (434)582-4560
Co. E-mail: lynchburg@scorevolunteer.org
URL: http://www.opportunitylynchburg.com/start-your-business
URL(s): www.score.org/find-location

Description: Provides professional guidance and information to maximize the success of existing and emerging small businesses. Offers business counseling and workshops. **Geographic Preference:** Local.

45808 ■ SCORE - Hampton Roads
Retail Alliance Bldg.
838 Granby St.
Norfolk, VA 23510
Ph: (757)384-0838
Fax: (757)466-9472
Co. E-mail: help@score.org
URL: http://hamptonroads.score.org
Facebook: www.facebook.com/SCOREHamptonRoads
Linkedin: www.linkedin.com/company/score-hampton-roads
X (Twitter): x.com/ScoreHamptonRds
YouTube: www.youtube.com/channel/UCGj5mwqZmTU_BZ8BVPnxEYQ

Description: Provides professional guidance, mentoring services and financial assistance to maximize the success of existing and emerging small businesses. Promotes entrepreneur education in Norfolk, VA. **Founded:** 1964. **Geographic Preference:** Local.

45809 ■ SCORE - Locust Grove
Wilderness Branch Orange County Library
6421 Flat Run
Locust Grove, VA 22508
Ph: (540)222-7992
URL: http://www.score.org/find-location

Description: Provides professional guidance and information to maximize the success of existing and emerging small businesses. Offers business counseling and workshops.

45810 ■ SCORE - Manassas
9720 Capital Ct., Ste. 203
Manassas, VA 20110
Ph: (703)368-6600
URL: http://washingtondc.score.org/northern-virginia-mentor-locations

Description: Provides professional guidance and information to maximize the success of existing and emerging small businesses. Offers business counseling and workshops.

45811 ■ SCORE - Martinsville
115 Broad St.
Martinsville, VA 24112
Ph: (276)632-6401
Fax: (276)632-5059
URL: http://www.score.org/content/contact-martinsville-score

Description: Provides free and confidential counseling to individuals and groups wishing to start or improve a small business. Membership consists of both retired and active businessmen and women with a wide variety of experiences and backgrounds. Hold monthly meetings for counselor training and development and offer counseling appointments on a weekly basis. **Geographic Preference:** Local.

45812 ■ SCORE - Mineral
Louisa County Library
881 Davis Hwy.
Mineral, VA 23117
Ph: (540)222-7992
URL: http://www.centralvirginia.score.org

Description: Provides professional guidance and information to maximize the success of existing and emerging small businesses. Offers business counseling and workshops.

45813 ■ SCORE - Newport News
11820 Fountain Way, Ste. 30
Newport News, VA 23606
URL: http://www.score.org/williamsburg/content/about-us

Description: Provides professional guidance and information to maximize the success of existing and emerging small businesses. Offers business counseling and workshops.

45814 ■ SCORE - Orange
146A Madison Rd.
Orange, VA 22960
URL: http://www.score.org/orangecounty
Contact: Donald Jennings, Contact

Description: Provides professional guidance and information to maximize the success of existing and emerging small businesses. Offers business counseling and workshops.

45815 ■ SCORE - Reston
1886 Metro Center Dr., Ste. 230
Reston, VA 20190
Ph: (703)707-9045
URL: http://washingtondc.score.org/northern-virginia-mentor-locations

Description: Provides professional guidance and information to maximize the success of existing and emerging small businesses. Offers business counseling and workshops.

45816 ■ SCORE - Richmond, Virginia
PO Box 2515
Midlothian, VA 23113
Ph: (804)350-3569
URL: http://www.score.org/richmond
Facebook: www.facebook.com/SCORERichmond
Linkedin: www.linkedin.com/company/score-mentors-richmond
X (Twitter): x.com/score_richmond
Instagram: www.instagram.com/scorerichmond
YouTube: www.youtube.com/user/RichmondSCORE

Description: Serves as volunteer program in which working and retired business management professionals provide free business counseling to men and women who are considering starting a small business, encountering problems with their business, or expanding their business. Offers free one-on-one counseling, online counseling and low cost workshops on a variety of business topics. **Founded:** 1965. **Geographic Preference:** Local.

45817 ■ SCORE - Roanoke
105 Franklin Rd. SW, Ste. 150
Roanoke, VA 24011
URL: http://www.score.org/blueridge/success-story/feeding-southwest-virginia

Description: Provides professional guidance, mentoring services and financial assistance to maximize the success of existing and emerging small businesses. Promotes entrepreneur education in Roanoke area, VA. **Geographic Preference:** Local.

45818 ■ SCORE - Shenandoah Valley
301 W Main St.
Waynesboro, VA 22980
Ph: (540)942-6755
Fax: (540)942-6755
Co. E-mail: score427@ci.waynesboro.va.us
URL: http://shenandoahvly.score.org
Contact: Joe Noto, Chairman

Description: Provides professional guidance, mentoring services and financial assistance to maximize the success of existing and emerging small businesses. Promotes entrepreneur education in Waynesboro, VA. **Founded:** 1992. **Geographic Preference:** Local.

45819 ■ SCORE - Vienna
8300 Boone Blvd., Ste. 450
Vienna, VA 22182
Ph: (703)790-0600
URL: http://washingtondc.score.org/northern-virginia-mentor-locations
Contact: Len Johnson, Contact

Description: Provides professional guidance and information to maximize the success of existing and emerging small businesses. Offers business counseling and workshops.

45820 ■ SCORE - Virginia Beach
4525 Main St., Ste. 700
Virginia Beach, VA 23462
Ph: (757)455-9338
URL: http://hamptonroads.score.org
Contact: Allen Goldstein, Contact
Facebook: www.facebook.com/SCOREHamptonRoads
Linkedin: www.linkedin.com/company/score-hampton-roads
X (Twitter): x.com/ScoreHamptonRds
Description: Provides professional guidance and information to maximize the success of existing and emerging small businesses. Offers business counseling and workshops.

45821 ■ SCORE - Williamsburg
Chamber of Commerce
421 N Boundary St.
Williamsburg, VA 23185
Ph: (757)229-6511
Fax: (757)229-2047
Co. E-mail: info.williamsburg@scorevolunteer.org
URL: http://www.score.org/williamsburg
Description: Provides professional guidance and information to maximize the success of existing and emerging small businesses. Offers business counseling and workshops. **Founded:** 1985. **Geographic Preference:** Local.

BETTER BUSINESS BUREAUS

45822 ■ Better Business Bureau of Central Virginia
100 Eastshore Dr. Ste. 100
Glen Allen, VA 23059
Ph: (804)648-0016
Fax: (888)244-2312
Co. E-mail: info@richmond.bbb.org
URL: http://www.bbb.org/local-bbb/bbb-serving-central-virginia
Contact: Clark W. J. Evans, Treasurer
Facebook: www.facebook.com/bbbcentralva
Linkedin: www.linkedin.com/company/better-business-bureau-serving-central-virginia
X (Twitter): x.com/BBBCentralVA
Instagram: www.instagram.com/bbbcentralva
Description: Seeks to promote and foster the highest ethical relationship between businesses and the public through voluntary self-regulation, consumer and business education, and service excellence. Provides information to help consumers and businesses make informed purchasing decisions and avoid costly scams and frauds; settles consumer complaints through arbitration and other means. **Geographic Preference:** Local.

45823 ■ Better Business Bureau of Greater Hampton Roads
586 Virginian Dr.
Norfolk, VA 23505
Ph: (757)531-1300
Fax: (757)531-1388
Co. E-mail: info@hamptonroadsbbb.org
URL: http://www.bbb.org/local-bbb/bbb-of-greater-hampton-roads
X (Twitter): x.com/BBBofNorfolk
Instagram: www.instagram.com/bbbofnorfolk
YouTube: www.youtube.com/user/HamptonRoadsBBB
Description: Seeks to promote and foster ethical relationship between businesses and the public through voluntary self-regulation, consumer and business education, and service excellence. Provides information to help consumers and businesses make informed purchasing decisions and avoid costly scams and frauds; settles consumer complaints through arbitration and other means. **Geographic Preference:** Local.

45824 ■ Better Business Bureau of Western Virginia
5115 Bernard Dr., Ste. 202
Roanoke, VA 24018
Ph: (540)342-3455
Fax: (540)345-2289
Co. E-mail: info@roanoke.bbb.org
URL: http://www.bbb.org/local-bbb/bbb-of-western-virginia
Facebook: www.facebook.com/BBBWesternVA
Linkedin: www.linkedin.com/company/bbbwesternva
X (Twitter): x.com/BBBWesternVA
Instagram: www.instagram.com/BBBWesternVA
YouTube: www.youtube.com/channel/UCyb-0ArTdW0VvNGBpkhD5Lg
Description: Seeks to promote and foster the highest ethical relationship between businesses and the public through voluntary self-regulation, consumer and business education, and service excellence. Provides information to help consumers and businesses make informed purchasing decisions and avoid costly scams and frauds; settles consumer complaints through arbitration and other means. **Founded:** 1940. **Geographic Preference:** Local.

45825 ■ International Association of Better Business Bureaus [Better Business Bureau (BBB)]
4250 N Fairfax Dr., Ste. 600
Arlington, VA 22203
Ph: (703)247-9406
Co. E-mail: marketing@iabbb.org
URL: http://www.bbb.org
Facebook: www.facebook.com/BetterBusinessBureau
Linkedin: www.linkedin.com/company/better-business-bureau
X (Twitter): x.com/bbb_us
YouTube: www.youtube.com/channel/UC4pBnbGxCYs8R-NHXWbGWZw
Description: Nonprofit organization that strives to promote and foster ethical relationship between businesses and the public through voluntary self-regulation, consumer and business education, and service excellence. Provides information to help consumers and businesses make informed purchasing decisions and avoid costly scams and frauds; settles consumer complaints through arbitration and other means. **Founded:** 1912. **Geographic Preference:** Local.

CHAMBERS OF COMMERCE

45826 ■ Alexandria Chamber of Commerce (ACC)
333 N Fairfax St., Ste. 302
Alexandria, VA 22314
Ph: (703)549-1000
Co. E-mail: info@thechamberalx.com
URL: http://thechamberalx.com
Contact: Joseph Haggerty, President
Facebook: www.facebook.com/thechamberalx
Linkedin: www.linkedin.com/company/alexandria-chamber-of-commerce
X (Twitter): x.com/thechamberalx
Instagram: www.instagram.com/thechamberalx
Description: Promotes business and community development in Alexandria, VA. **Founded:** 1906. **Publications:** Who's Who in Alexandria Business (Annual); Alexandria Business Guide (Annual); Chamber Currents (Bimonthly). **Geographic Preference:** Local.

45827 ■ Alleghany Highlands Chamber of Commerce & Tourism
110 Mall Rd.
Covington, VA 24426
Ph: (540)962-2178
Free: 888-430-5786
Fax: (540)962-2179
Co. E-mail: info@ahchamber.com
URL: http://ahchamber.com
Contact: Dr. John Rainone, President
E-mail: jrainone@dslcc.edu
Facebook: www.facebook.com/alleghanyhighlandschamber
YouTube: www.youtube.com/user/AlleghanyHighlandsVA
Description: Promotes business and community development in the Alleghany Highlands, VA area. **Founded:** 1906. **Geographic Preference:** Local.

45828 ■ Altavista Area Chamber of Commerce (AACC)
414 Washington St.
Altavista, VA 24517
Ph: (434)369-6665
Fax: (434)369-0068
Co. E-mail: goaltavista@altavistachamber.com
URL: http://altavistachamber.com
Contact: Lauren Odessa, President
E-mail: laurenodessa@altavistachamber.com
Facebook: www.facebook.com/AltavistaAreaChamberofCommerce
Instagram: www.instagram.com/altavistachamber
Description: Promotes business and community development in the Altavista, VA area. **Publications:** Vistas (Monthly). **Geographic Preference:** Local.

45829 ■ Amherst County Chamber of Commerce (ACCC)
328 Richmond Hwy., Ste. A
Amherst, VA 24521
Ph: (434)946-0990
Fax: (434)946-0879
Co. E-mail: information@amherstvachamber.com
URL: http://www.amherstvachamber.com
Contact: Sabrina Kennon, President
Facebook: www.facebook.com/AmherstVAChamber
X (Twitter): x.com/AmherstCoChmbr
Instagram: www.instagram.com/amherstvachamber
Description: Aims to advance the commercial, industrial, professional, domestic and global interests of Amherst County and its trade area. **Publications:** Amherst County Guidebook (Annual); Chamber Business (Monthly). **Geographic Preference:** Local.

45830 ■ Annandale Chamber of Commerce (ACC)
4127 Meadow Ct.
Annandale, VA 22003
Ph: (703)256-7232
Co. E-mail: info@annandalechamber.com
URL: http://www.annandalechamber.com
Contact: Fred Coulter, Secretary
Description: Promotes business and community development in Annandale, VA. Sponsors parade, Health fair and other community activities. **Founded:** 1970. **Publications:** Annandale Chamber of Commerce Newsletter (Monthly); Annandale Community Directory (Annual). **Geographic Preference:** Local.

45831 ■ *Annandale Community Directory*
4127 Meadow Ct.
Annandale, VA 22003
Ph: (703)256-7232
Co. E-mail: info@annandalechamber.com
URL: http://www.annandalechamber.com
Contact: Fred Coulter, Secretary
URL(s): annandalechamber.org/directory
Released: Annual **Availability:** Online.

45832 ■ Arlington Chamber of Commerce
2009 14 St. N, Ste. 100
Arlington, VA 22201
Ph: (703)525-2400
Fax: (703)522-5273
Co. E-mail: chamber@arlingtonchamber.org
URL: http://www.arlingtonchamber.org
Contact: Kate Bates, President
E-mail: president@arlingtonchamber.org
Facebook: www.facebook.com/ArlingtonChamberVA
Linkedin: www.linkedin.com/company/arlington-chamber-of-commerce_297496
X (Twitter): x.com/ArlVAChamber
Instagram: www.instagram.com/arlvachamber
Description: Promotes business and community development in Arlington, VA. **Founded:** 1924. **Publications:** The Arlingtonian (Monthly); Member Directory. **Awards:** Arlington Chamber of Commerce Valor Awards (Annual). **Geographic Preference:** Local.

STATE LISTINGS

45833 ■ *The Arlingtonian*
2009 14 St. N, Ste. 100
Arlington, VA 22201
Ph: (703)525-2400
Fax: (703)522-5273
Co. E-mail: chamber@arlingtonchamber.org
URL: http://www.arlingtonchamber.org
Contact: Kate Bates, President
E-mail: president@arlingtonchamber.org
URL(s): www.arlingtonchamber.org/publications.html
Released: Monthly **Availability:** Print; PDF; Online.

45834 ■ Bath County Chamber of Commerce (BCCC)
2814 Main St., 2Fl. Hot Springs
Hot Springs, VA 24445
Ph: (540)839-5409
Co. E-mail: office@countyofbathchamber.org
URL: http://countyofbathchamber.org
Contact: John Hess, Treasurer
Facebook: www.facebook.com/bathcountychamber
Description: Promotes business and community development in the Bath County, VA area. **Geographic Preference:** Local.

45835 ■ Bedford Chamber of Commerce (BACC)
305 E Main St.
Bedford, VA 24523
Ph: (540)586-9401
Co. E-mail: bacc@baccva.org
URL: http://www.bedfordareachamber.com
Contact: Kayla Waller, Co-President Co-Chief Executive Officer
Facebook: www.facebook.com/BedfordAreaChamberVA
X (Twitter): x.com/BedfrdAreaChmbr
Instagram: www.instagram.com/bedfordareachamber
YouTube: www.youtube.com/channel/UCPLvXXJscrROBAnbc345UiA
Description: Promotes business and community development in Bedford, OH. Sponsors annual town picnic. **Founded:** 1939. **Geographic Preference:** Local.

45836 ■ Blackstone Chamber of Commerce
Deborah Rose
Deborah Rose Executive Director
105 W Broad St.
Blackstone, VA 23824
Ph: (434)294-0280
Co. E-mail: blackstonevachamber@gmail.com
URL: http://www.blackstonechambercommerce.com
Contact: Deborah Rose, Executive Director
Facebook: www.facebook.com/people/Blackstone-Chamber-of-Commerce/100064002014136
Description: Promotes business and community development in Blackstone, VA. Committed in supporting, promoting, and creating economic opportunities that benefit the community. **Founded:** 1960. **Publications:** *FYI* (Monthly). **Geographic Preference:** Local.

45837 ■ Botetourt Chamber of Commerce
23 S Roanoke St.
Fincastle, VA 24090
Ph: (540)473-8280
Co. E-mail: info@botetourtchamber.com
URL: http://botetourtchamber.com
Contact: Kaleigh Duffy, President
Facebook: www.facebook.com/BotetourtChamber
Linkedin: www.linkedin.com/company/botetourt-county-chamber-of-commerce
X (Twitter): x.com/botetourtchambr
YouTube: www.youtube.com/channel/UCoBMUXW3ehVdF6ZMmZH5UrQ
Description: Promotes business and community development in the Botetourt County, VA area. **Founded:** 1945. **Publications:** *Chamber Monitor* (Quarterly). **Geographic Preference:** Local.

45838 ■ Broadway-Timberville Chamber of Commerce
800 Country Club Rd.
Harrisonburg, VA 22802-5033
Contact: Robert Teague, Director
Description: Promotes business and community development in the Broadway-Timberville, VA area. Participates in annual Fall Festival and Arts and Crafts Show. Plans periodic special events. **Founded:** 1959. **Geographic Preference:** Local.

45839 ■ Buckingham Chamber of Commerce [Buckingham County Chamber of Commerce]
PO Box 951
Dillwyn, VA 23936
URL: http://buckinghamchamberofcommerce.com
Contact: Jordan Miles, President
Description: Promotes business and community development in Buckingham County, VA area. **Geographic Preference:** Local.

45840 ■ *Business Directory*
2300 Fall Hill Ave., Ste. 240
Fredericksburg, VA 22401
Ph: (540)373-9400
Fax: (540)373-9570
Co. E-mail: info@fredericksburgchamber.org
URL: http://fredericksburgchamber.org
Contact: Susan Spears, President
E-mail: susan@fxbgchamber.org
URL(s): members.fredericksburgchamber.org/list
Released: Annual **Description:** Contains member listing (alphabetically and categorically). **Availability:** Print.

45841 ■ Central Fairfax Chamber of Commerce (CFCC)
10304 Eaton Pl., Ste. 100
Fairfax, VA 22030
Ph: (703)268-5870
Co. E-mail: info@cfcc.org
URL: http://www.cfcc.org
Contact: Jennifer Rose, Executive Director
E-mail: executivedirector@cfcc.org
Facebook: www.facebook.com/CentralFairfaxChamber
Linkedin: www.linkedin.com/company/central-fairfax-chamber
Description: Promotes business and community development in Central Fairfax, VA area. **Founded:** 1958. **Publications:** *Central Fairfax Directory* (Annual); *Central Fairfax Chamber of Commerce--Membership Directory*. **Geographic Preference:** Local.

45842 ■ *The Chamber Comments*
Ph: (804)733-8131
Co. E-mail: info@petersburgvachamber.com
URL: http://www.petersburgvachamber.com
Contact: Danielle Mw Fitz-Hugh, President
URL(s): www.petersburgvachamber.com/member-benefits
Released: Quarterly; February, May, July, November. **Price:** Included in membership. **Availability:** Print.

45843 ■ The Chamber of Commerce Serving Lexington, Rockbridge County, and Buena Vista
18 E Nelson St., Ste. 101
Lexington, VA 24450
Ph: (540)463-5375
Co. E-mail: info@lexrockchamber.com
URL: http://www.lexrockchamber.com
Contact: Jim Jones, President
X (Twitter): x.com/lexrockchamber
Instagram: www.instagram.com/lexrockchamber
Description: Promotes business and community development in the Lexington-Rockbridge County, VA area. Sponsors small business seminars. **Founded:** 1937. **Publications:** *Doorways* (10/year); *Rockbridge Almanac* (Annual). **Awards:** Lexington-Rockbridge County Chamber of Commerce Business Individual of the Year (Annual). **Geographic Preference:** Local.

45844 ■ ChamberRVA
919 E Main St., Ste. 1700
Richmond, VA 23219
Ph: (804)648-1234
URL: http://www.chamberrva.com
Contact: Brian D. Anderson, President
E-mail: brian.anderson@chamberrva.com
Facebook: www.facebook.com/ChamberRVA
Linkedin: www.linkedin.com/company/chamberrva
X (Twitter): x.com/ChamberRVA
Instagram: www.instagram.com/chamberrva
YouTube: www.youtube.com/user/GRCCRICHMOND
Description: Seeks to improve the economy and quality of life of Greater Richmond region through its programs and initiatives. **Founded:** 1867. **Publications:** *Chamber Currents* (Monthly). **Awards:** Chamber IMPACT Award (Annual). **Geographic Preference:** Local.

45845 ■ Charlottesville Regional Chamber of Commerce (CRCC)
209 5th St. NE
Charlottesville, VA 22902
Ph: (434)295-3141
Fax: (434)295-3144
Co. E-mail: connect@cvillechamber.com
URL: http://www.cvillechamber.com
Contact: Elizabeth Cromwell, President
E-mail: elizabeth.cromwell@cvillechamber.com
Facebook: www.facebook.com/cvillevachamber
Linkedin: www.linkedin.com/company/cvillevachamber
X (Twitter): x.com/cvillevachamber
YouTube: www.youtube.com/channel/UCFcgLYpqJSBnYfqy__IYasw
Description: Promotes business and community development in Albemarle County, VA area. **Founded:** 1913. **Publications:** *ChamberBits* (Weekly); *Chamber Comments* (Bimonthly). **Geographic Preference:** Local.

45846 ■ Chesterfield County Chamber of Commerce
301 Southlake Blvd., Ste. 102
Richmond, VA 23236
Ph: (804)748-6364
Co. E-mail: info@chesterfieldchamber.com
URL: http://chesterfieldchamber.com
Contact: Danielle Fitz, Co-President Co-Chief Executive Officer
Facebook: www.facebook.com/ChesterfieldChamberVa
Linkedin: www.linkedin.com/company/chesterfieldchamberva
X (Twitter): x.com/chesterfieldcc
Description: Works to build an involved and informed Chesterfield business community. Educates and informs both county elected officials and county professional staff as to the consequences and alternatives regarding proposed regulations and processes. Educates the community at large as to the problems and challenges of the business community and the advantage to residents of a healthy and vibrant business community. Provides valuable resources to the members that help their businesses succeed. **Founded:** 1999. **Geographic Preference:** Local.

45847 ■ Chincoteague Chamber of Commerce
6733 Maddox Blvd.
Chincoteague Island, VA 23336
Ph: (757)336-6161
Fax: (757)336-1242
Co. E-mail: info@chincoteaguechamber.com
URL: http://www.chincoteaguechamber.com
Contact: Chris Bott, President
Facebook: www.facebook.com/chincoteaguechamber
X (Twitter): x.com/chincochamber
Instagram: www.instagram.com/chincoteaguechamber
YouTube: www.youtube.com/channel/UClxVR3JTY3LAeMA15S1aqPw
Description: Promotes business and community development in Chincoteague, VA. **Founded:** 1954. **Publications:** *Island Adventure*. **Geographic Preference:** Local.

45848 ■ Clarkesville Lake Country Chamber of Commerce
105 2nd St.
Clarksville, VA 23927
Ph: (434)374-2436
Fax: (434)374-8174
Co. E-mail: clarksvillelakecountry@outlook.com

URL: http://clarksvilleva.com
Contact: Patricia Charles, President
Facebook: www.facebook.com/CLCCOC
Description: Promotes business and community development in Clarkesville, VA and the surrounding area. Sponsors and hosts downtown events such as Big Lake Flea Market, The Virginia Lake Festival and Harvest Days Festival. Supports other events and activities such as the Clarksville Hydroplane Challenge/2006 World Inboard Championship. **Founded:** 1818. **Publications:** *Shoreline* (Bimonthly). **Geographic Preference:** Local.

45849 ■ Colonial Beach Chamber of Commerce (CBCC)
106 Hawthorn St.
 Colonial Beach, VA 22443
Ph: (804)224-8145
Co. E-mail: info@colonialbeach.org
URL: http://www.colonialbeach.org
Contact: Carey Geddes, President
Facebook: www.facebook.com/colonialbeachva
X (Twitter): x.com/CBeachCOC
Description: Promotes business and community service in the Colonial Beach, VA area. **Geographic Preference:** Local.

45850 ■ Colonial Heights Chamber of Commerce (CHCC)
PO Box 411
 Colonial Heights, VA 23834
Ph: (804)526-5872
Fax: (804)526-9637
Co. E-mail: john.brandt@colonialheightschamber.com
URL: http://www.colonialheightschamber.com
Contact: Kat Mayes, President
Facebook: www.facebook.com/colonialheightschamberofcommerce
Description: Promotes business and community development in Colonial Heights, VA. **Founded:** 1949. **Publications:** *Chamber Notes* (Monthly). **Geographic Preference:** Local.

45851 ■ Crewe - Burkeville Chamber of Commerce
PO Box 305
 Crewe, VA 23930
Ph: (434)645-8444
Co. E-mail: creweburkevillechamber@gmail.com
URL: http://www.creweburkevillechamber.com
Description: Seeks to have more community involvement, more involvement from chamber members, induce more businesses into the area, and provide employment opportunities for local citizens in the Crewe-Burkeville, VA area. **Founded:** 1981. **Geographic Preference:** Local.

45852 ■ Culpeper County Chamber of Commerce
629 Sperryville Pke., Ste. 100
 Culpeper, VA 22701
Ph: (540)825-8628
Free: 888-285-7373
Co. E-mail: events@culpeperchamber.com
URL: http://culpeperchamber.com
Contact: Amy Frazier, Co-President Co-Chief Executive Officer
Facebook: www.facebook.com/CulpeperChamber
Instagram: www.instagram.com/culpeperchamber
YouTube: www.youtube.com/channel/UCmv9le0XfJ6mn_8xbWX8iiA
Description: Promotes business and community development in Culpeper County, VA. **Founded:** 1749. **Publications:** *The Chamber ADVANTAGE* (Monthly). **Awards:** Culpeper County Chamber of Commerce Most Improved Small Business Location (Annual); L.B. Henretty Memorial Outstanding Citizen of the Year (Annual); Culpeper County Chamber of Commerce Small Business Person of the Year (Annual). **Geographic Preference:** Local.

45853 ■ Danville Pittsylvania County Chamber of Commerce
150 Slayton Ave.
 Danville, VA 24540
Ph: (434)836-6990
Fax: (434)836-6955
URL: http://www.dpchamber.org
Contact: Anne Moore-Sparks, President
E-mail: anne@dpchamber.org
Facebook: www.facebook.com/dpchamber
Linkedin: www.linkedin.com/company/dpchamber
YouTube: www.youtube.com/channel/UChGsObR43PsESxvCA88DVLA
Description: Improves the business environment of Danville/Pittsylvania County, VA by providing leadership, products, programs and services which promote the success of members. **Founded:** 2001. **Publications:** *Chamber Connections* (Monthly); *Community Resource Guide and Membership Directory* (Annual); *Images of Danville and Pittsylvania County* (Annual). **Awards:** Danville Pittsylvania County Chamber of Commerce Pinnacle Award (Annual); Young Professionals PACE Awards (Annual); Danville Pittsylvania County Chamber of Commerce Educator of the Year (Annual). **Geographic Preference:** Local.

45854 ■ Dickenson County Chamber of Commerce
194 Main St.
 Clintwood, VA 24228
Ph: (276)926-6074
Co. E-mail: chamber@dcwin.org
URL: http://www.dickensonchamber.net
Contact: Rita Surratt, President
E-mail: rsurratt@dickensonva.org
Facebook: www.facebook.com/dickenson.chamber
Description: Promotes business and community development in Dickenson County, VA. **Founded:** 1957. **Geographic Preference:** Local.

45855 ■ Dulles Regional Chamber of Commerce (DRCC)
730 Elden St.
 Herndon, VA 20170
Ph: (571)323-5300
Co. E-mail: communications@dulleschamber.org
URL: http://www.dulleschamber.org
Contact: Joe Martin, Vice President, Operations
E-mail: jmartin@dulleschamber.org
Linkedin: www.linkedin.com/company/dulles-regional-chamber
Description: Promotes business and community development in the Greater Dulles area, including Herndon, Reston, Chantilly, Great Falls, Potomac Falls, Sterling, Ashburn and Centreville. **Founded:** 1959. **Geographic Preference:** Local.

45856 ■ Eastern Shore of Virginia Chamber of Commerce (ESVA)
19056 Pky. Rd.
 Melfa, VA 23410
Ph: (757)787-2460
Co. E-mail: info@esvachamber.org
URL: http://www.esvachamber.org
Contact: Robert Sabbatini, Executive Director
E-mail: executivedirector@esvachamber.org
Facebook: www.facebook.com/esvachamber
Instagram: www.instagram.com/esvachamber
Description: Promotes business and community development in the eastern shore of Virginia. **Founded:** 1953. **Geographic Preference:** Local.

45857 ■ Emporia-Greensville Chamber of Commerce
400 Halifax St.
 Emporia, VA 23847
Ph: (434)634-9441
Fax: (434)634-3485
Co. E-mail: ontrack@telpage.net
URL: http://www.emporiagreensvillechamber.com
Contact: William Robinson, President
Description: Promotes businesses, particularly small businesses, in the Emporia-Greensville area. **Founded:** 1887. **Publications:** *On Track* (Monthly). **Geographic Preference:** Local.

45858 ■ Farmville Chamber of Commerce (FCC)
118A N Main St.
 Farmville, VA 23901
Ph: (434)392-3939
Fax: (434)392-3818
Co. E-mail: info@farmvilleareachamber.org
URL: http://www.farmvilleareachamber.org
Contact: Anne Tyler Paulek, Executive Director
Facebook: www.facebook.com/FarmvilleAreaChamberofCommerce
Description: Promotes business and community development in Farmville, VA. Sponsors Heart of Virginia Festival, candidate debates, and annual Farmville Christmas Show. **Founded:** 1948. **Publications:** *Newcomer's Guide* (Periodic). **Geographic Preference:** Local.

45859 ■ Fauquier County Chamber of Commerce
321 Walker Dr.
 Warrenton, VA 20186
Ph: (540)347-4414
Fax: (540)347-7510
Co. E-mail: mailbox@fauquierchamber.org
URL: http://www.fauquierchamber.org
Contact: Michelle Coe, Chairman
Facebook: www.facebook.com/FauquierChamber
Linkedin: www.linkedin.com/company/fauquierchamber
X (Twitter): x.com/FauquierChamber
Instagram: www.instagram.com/fauquierchamber
Description: Promotes business and community development in Fauquier County and its trade area. **Founded:** 1921. **Publications:** *Chamber Chat* (Monthly). **Awards:** Fauquier County Chamber of Commerce Business Person of the Year (Annual). **Geographic Preference:** Local.

45860 ■ Floyd County Chamber of Commerce
108 W Main St.
 Floyd, VA 24091
Ph: (540)745-4407
Co. E-mail: info@floydchamber.org
URL: http://floydchamber.org
Contact: Vickie Spangler, Treasurer
Facebook: www.facebook.com/FloydChamber
Description: Promotes business and community development in Floyd County, VA. **Founded:** 1989. **Publications:** *Chamber Chatter* (Monthly). **Geographic Preference:** Local.

45861 ■ Fluvanna County Chamber of Commerce (FCCC)
177 Main St.
 Palmyra, VA 22963
Ph: (434)589-3262
Co. E-mail: ofc.mgr@fluvannachamber.org
URL: http://www.fluvannachamber.org
Contact: Darryl Gibson, President
Facebook: www.facebook.com/FluvannaChamber
Linkedin: www.linkedin.com/company/fluvannachamber
Description: Promotes business and community development in Fluvanna County, VA. **Founded:** 1957. **Publications:** *Chamber Newsletter* (Weekly); *Guide to Fluvanna County* (Annual); *Fluvanna County Chamber of Commerce--Membership Directory*. **Geographic Preference:** Local.

45862 ■ Franklin-Southampton Area Chamber of Commerce
108 W 3rd Ave.
 Franklin, VA 23851
Ph: (757)562-4900
Fax: (757)562-6138
Co. E-mail: join@fsachamber.com
URL: http://www.fsachamber.com
Contact: Teresa Beale, Executive Director
E-mail: teresa@fsachamber.com
X (Twitter): x.com/fsachamber
Description: Promotes business and community development in the Franklin-Southampton, VA area. **Founded:** 1954. **Publications:** *Speaking of Business* (Monthly). **Geographic Preference:** Local.

45863 ■ Fredericksburg Regional Chamber of Commerce (FRCC)
2300 Fall Hill Ave., Ste. 240
 Fredericksburg, VA 22401
Ph: (540)373-9400
Fax: (540)373-9570

Co. E-mail: info@fredericksburgchamber.org
URL: http://fredericksburgchamber.org
Contact: Susan Spears, President
E-mail: susan@fxbgchamber.org
Facebook: www.facebook.com/fxbgchamber
Linkedin: www.linkedin.com/company/fxbgchamber
X (Twitter): x.com/fxbgchamber
Instagram: www.instagram.com/fxbgchamber
YouTube: www.youtube.com/channel/UC_zver
_DxKG38n-RO2TMwRA
Description: Promotes business and community development in Fredericksburg, and Stafford and Spotsylvania Counties, VA. **Founded:** 1916. **Publications:** *Business Directory* (Annual); *ChamberAlert*; *ChamberLink* (Monthly). **Awards:** Fredericksburg Regional Chamber of Commerce Business of the Year (Annual); Fredericksburg Regional Chamber of Commerce Chamber Goodwill Awards (Annual); Prince B. Woodard Leadership Award (Annual). **Geographic Preference:** Local.

45864 ■ Front Royal - Warren County Chamber of Commerce
201 E 2nd St.
Front Royal, VA 22630
Ph: (540)635-3185
Fax: (540)635-9758
Co. E-mail: info@frontroyalchamber.com
URL: http://www.frontroyalchamber.com
Contact: Justin Bates, Chairman
Facebook: www.facebook.com/FrontRoyalChamber
Description: Promotes business and community development in Front Royal, VA. Sponsors Virginia Mushroom Festival. **Founded:** 1940. **Publications:** *Gazebo Gazette* (Monthly). **Geographic Preference:** Local.

45865 ■ Goochland County Chamber of Commerce
PO Box 123
Goochland, VA 23063
Ph: (804)556-3811
Co. E-mail: director@goochlandchamber.org
URL: http://www.goochlandchamber.org
Contact: Nancy Burton, President
Facebook: www.facebook.com/gvachamber
Linkedin: www.linkedin.com/company/goochlan
d-county-chamber-of-commerce
X (Twitter): x.com/gvachamber
Instagram: www.instagram.com/gvachamber
YouTube: www.youtube.com/channel/UC2n
1IRUanhDfs6k6JdueY8Q
Description: Promotes business and community development in Goochland County, VA. **Founded:** 1977. **Geographic Preference:** Local.

45866 ■ Greater Augusta Regional Chamber of Commerce (GARCC)
19 Briar Knoll Ct., Ste. 2
Fishersville, VA 22939
Ph: (540)324-1133
Co. E-mail: info@augustava.com
URL: http://www.augustava.com
Contact: Courtney Thompson, President
E-mail: courtney@augustava.com
Facebook: www.facebook.com/GARCCVA
Linkedin: www.linkedin.com/company/greater-augus
ta-regional-chamber-of-commerce
X (Twitter): x.com/AugustaCommerce
YouTube: www.youtube.com/channel/UCXo16kjIL
3cguhhnioFeBjA/featured
Description: Promotes business and community development in the Staunton-Augusta County, VA area. Sponsors Annual Christmas Parade. **Founded:** 1999. **Publications:** *Greater Augusta Regional Chamber of Commerce--Industrial Directory* (Periodic); *Chamber Connection* (Weekly); *Membership and Business Services Guide*; *Industrial Directory*. **Geographic Preference:** Local.

45867 ■ Greater scottsville CHamber of commerce (SCCC)
Old Jail Valley St.
Scottsville, VA 24590
URL: http://www.svillechamber.org
Contact: Linda Lafontaine, President
E-mail: scccpresident@gmail.com

Description: Promotes business and community development in Scottsville, VA. **Geographic Preference:** Local.

45868 ■ Greater Reston Chamber of Commerce (GRCC)
1886 Metro Center Dr., Ste. 230
Reston, VA 20190
Ph: (703)707-9045
Co. E-mail: communications@restonchamber.org
URL: http://www.restonchamber.org
Contact: Charles Kapur, President
E-mail: charlesk@restonchamber.org
Facebook: www.facebook.com/RestonChamber
Linkedin: www.linkedin.com/company/greater-reston
-chamber-of-commerce
X (Twitter): x.com/RestonChamber
Instagram: www.instagram.com/restonchamber
YouTube: www.youtube.com/channel/UCzcG7
6IsWZIaiG3kbHU442Q
Description: Promotes business and community development in Reston, VA. **Founded:** 1982. **Geographic Preference:** Local.

45869 ■ Greater Williamsburg Chamber and Tourism Alliance
421 N Boundary St.
Williamsburg, VA 23185
Ph: (757)229-6511
Free: 800-368-6511
Fax: (757)253-1397
Co. E-mail: wacc@williamsburgcc.com
URL: http://www.businesswilliamsburg.com
Contact: Terry Banez, Chief Executive Officer
Facebook: www.facebook.com/WilliamsburgChamber
YouTube: www.youtube.com/channel/UCve3Nib7XA
53DSb8liGgcUg
Description: Business people united to enhance, promote and serve the business community. Provides the leadership to strengthen the community's economic base and quality of life. **Founded:** 1632. **Awards:** Greater Williamsburg Chamber and Tourism Alliance Corporate Citizen of the Year Award (Annual). **Geographic Preference:** Local.

45870 ■ Halifax County Chamber of Commerce
180 Factory St.
South Boston, VA 24592
Ph: (434)572-3085
Co. E-mail: info@halifaxchamber.net
URL: http://www.halifaxchamber.net
Contact: Mitzi T. McCormick, President
E-mail: mitzi@halifaxchamber.net
Facebook: www.facebook.com/halifaxvachamber
Linkedin: www.linkedin.com/company/halifax-county
-chamber-of-commerce
X (Twitter): x.com/halifaxccc
Instagram: www.instagram.com/halifaxccc
Description: Promotes business and community development in the Halifax County, VA area. Sponsors the Virginia Cantaloupe Festival. **Founded:** 1955. **Geographic Preference:** Local.

45871 ■ Hampton Roads Chamber of Commerce
101 W Main St., Ste. 800
Norfolk, VA 23510
Ph: (757)622-2312
Fax: (757)622-5563
URL: http://www.hrchamber.com
Contact: Bryan K. Stephens, President
Facebook: www.facebook.com/chamber757
Instagram: www.instagram.com/chamber757
YouTube: www.youtube.com/user/hamptonroa
dschamber
Description: Promotes business and community development in the Hampton Roads region of Southeast Virginia. **Founded:** 1984. **Geographic Preference:** Local.

45872 ■ Hanover Association of Businesses and Chamber of Commerce
9097 Atlee Station Rd., Ste. 117
Mechanicsville, VA 23116
Ph: (804)442-2093
Co. E-mail: info@hanoverchamberva.com

URL: http://hanoverchamberva.com
Contact: Mark Lea, President
Facebook: www.facebook.com/hanoverchamberva
Instagram: www.instagram.com/hanoverchamberva
Description: Promotes business and community development in the town of Ashland and Hanover County, VA. **Founded:** 1980. **Publications:** *Strictly Business* (Bimonthly). **Geographic Preference:** Local.

45873 ■ Harrisonburg-Rockingham Chamber of Commerce (HRCC)
800 Country Club Rd.
Harrisonburg, VA 22802
Ph: (540)434-3862
Fax: (540)434-4508
Co. E-mail: information@hrchamber.org
URL: http://www.hrchamber.org
Contact: Christopher Quinn, President
E-mail: chris@hrchamber.org
Facebook: www.facebook.com/hrchamber
Linkedin: www.linkedin.com/company/harrisonburg
-rockingham-chamber-of-commerce
X (Twitter): x.com/HR_Chamber
YouTube: www.youtube.com/user/HRChamber
Description: Promotes business and community development in the Harrisonburg-Rockingham, VA area. Sponsors festivals. **Founded:** 1916. **Publications:** *Advocate* (Quarterly); *Industrial Directory*; *Market Data Population Information* (Annual). **Awards:** Harrisonburg-Rockingham Chamber of Commerce Business Person of the Year (Annual); Harrisonburg-Rockingham Chamber of Commerce Entrepreneur of the Year (Annual). **Geographic Preference:** Local.

45874 ■ Hopewell-Prince George Chamber of Commerce (HPGCC)
PO Box 1297
Hopewell, VA 23860
Ph: (804)541-2461
Co. E-mail: info@hpgchamber.org
URL: http://www.hpgchamber.org
Contact: Becky McDonough, Chief Executive Officer
Facebook: www.facebook.com/HPGChamber
YouTube: www.youtube.com/channel/UCI_nOJjxulo
2BjI-DGZHQiQ
Description: Promotes business and community development in the Hopewell, VA area. **Founded:** 1926. **Geographic Preference:** Local.

45875 ■ Isle of Wight - Smithfield - Windsor Chamber of Commerce (IOW)
100 Main St.
Smithfield, VA 23431
Ph: (757)357-3502
Free: 888-284-3475
Fax: (757)357-6884
Co. E-mail: chamber@theisle.org
URL: http://www.theisle.biz
Contact: Marci Levine, President
Facebook: www.facebook.com/IOWChamber
X (Twitter): x.com/IOWCoChamber
Instagram: www.instagram.com/iowchamber
Description: Promotes business and community development in Isle of Wight County. **Founded:** 1984. **Geographic Preference:** Local.

45876 ■ Loudoun County Chamber of Commerce (LCCC)
19301 Winmeade Dri., Ste. 210
Leesburg, VA 20176
Ph: (703)777-2176
Fax: (703)777-1392
Co. E-mail: info@loudounchamber.org
URL: http://www.loudounchamber.org
Contact: Tony Howard, President
Facebook: www.facebook.com/LoudounChamber
X (Twitter): x.com/loudounchamber
Instagram: www.instagram.com/loudounchamber
YouTube: www.youtube.com/user/loudouncoun
tychamber
Description: Promotes business and community development in the Loudoun County, VA area. **Founded:** 1960. **Publications:** *BizConnect* (Bimonthly); *Loudoun Chamber Business Directory and*

Resource Guide (Annual); *Loudounclear* (Bimonthly). **Educational Activities:** Dulles Connection Expo. **Geographic Preference:** Local.

45877 ■ Louisa County Chamber of Commerce (LCCC)
111 W Main St.
Louisa, VA 23093
Ph: (540)967-0944
Co. E-mail: info@louisachamber.org
URL: http://www.louisachamber.org
Contact: Tracy Hale Clark, Executive Director
E-mail: executivedirector@louisachamber.org
YouTube: www.youtube.com/channel/UCrl0dDWeDQ5ZnKh8XeVFbLA

Description: Promotes business and community development in Louisa County, VA. **Founded:** 1927. **Geographic Preference:** Local.

45878 ■ Luray-Page County Chamber of Commerce
18 Campbell St.
Luray, VA 22835
Ph: (540)743-3915
Co. E-mail: info@luraypage.com
URL: http://www.visitluraypage.com
Contact: Gina Hilliard, President
E-mail: gina.hilliard@luraypage.com
X (Twitter): x.com/VisitLurayPage

Description: Promotes business tourism and community development in the Luray-Page County, VA area. **Geographic Preference:** Local.

45879 ■ Lynchburg Regional Business Alliance (LRBA)
300 Lucado Pl.
Lynchburg, VA 24504
Ph: (434)845-5966
Co. E-mail: info@lynchburgregion.org
URL: http://www.lynchburgregion.org
Contact: Megan A. Lucas, Chief Executive Officer
E-mail: meganlucas@lynchburgregion.org
Facebook: www.facebook.com/LynchburgRegion
Linkedin: www.linkedin.com/company/lynchburgregion
X (Twitter): x.com/LynchburgRegion
YouTube: www.youtube.com/user/lrcclynchburg

Description: Promotes business and community development in the Lynchburg, VA area. **Founded:** 1833. **Publications:** *Commerce Report* (Quarterly); *Lynchburg Life/Business Directory* (Annual). **Educational Activities:** Board Retreat. **Awards:** Lynchburg Regional Chamber of Commerce ATHENA Award (Annual); Lynchburg Regional Chamber of Commerce Small Business Award (Annual). **Geographic Preference:** Local.

45880 ■ Madison County Chamber of Commerce
110 N Main St.
Madison, VA 22727
Ph: (540)948-4455
Co. E-mail: tourism@madison-va.com
URL: http://www.madison-va.com
Contact: Tracey W. Gardner, Director
E-mail: tgardner@madisonco.virginia.gov

Description: Promotes business and community development in the Madison County, VA area. **Publications:** *Madison Chamber of Commerce Business News* (Monthly). **Geographic Preference:** Local.

45881 ■ Martinsville - Henry County Chamber of Commerce (MHCCC)
115 Broad St.
Martinsville, VA 24114
Ph: (276)632-6401
Fax: (276)632-5059
Co. E-mail: mhccoc@mhcchamber.com
URL: http://www.martinsville.com
Contact: Brenell Thomas, Co-President
E-mail: brenell@mhcchamber.com

Description: Encourages a strong local economy by creating an environment where businesses thrive and community and commerce work together for the future of Martinsville-Henry County. **Founded:** 1959. **Geographic Preference:** Local.

45882 ■ *Member Directory*
2009 14 St. N, Ste. 100
Arlington, VA 22201
Ph: (703)525-2400
Fax: (703)522-5273
Co. E-mail: chamber@arlingtonchamber.org
URL: http://www.arlingtonchamber.org
Contact: Kate Bates, President
E-mail: president@arlingtonchamber.org
URL(s): www.arlingtonchamber.org/shopchamber.html

Availability: Print.

45883 ■ Montgomery County Chamber of Commerce (MCCC)
210 Laurel St., Ste. B
Christiansburg, VA 24073
Ph: (540)382-3020
Co. E-mail: membership@montgomerycc.org
URL: http://www.montgomerycc.org
Contact: Steve Baffuto, President
E-mail: president@montgomerycc.org
Linkedin: www.linkedin.com/company/montgomery-county-virginia-chamber-of-commerce
X (Twitter): x.com/MontgChamber

Description: Promotes business and community development in Montgomery County, VA. **Founded:** 2003. **Publications:** *Montgomery County Chamber of Commerce--Business Directory* (Annual). **Geographic Preference:** Local.

45884 ■ Mount Vernon-Lee Chamber of Commerce (MVLCC)
7686 Richmond Hwy., Ste. 203 A
Alexandria, VA 22306
Ph: (703)360-6925
Co. E-mail: info@mountvernonleechamber.org
URL: http://www.mountvernonleechamber.org
Contact: Holly Dougherty, President
Facebook: www.facebook.com/MtVLChamber
Linkedin: www.linkedin.com/company/mount-vernon-lee-chamber-of-commerce
Instagram: www.instagram.com/mtvlchamber
YouTube: www.youtube.com/channel/UCwS-8q4TSDtw90w8q-mdRig

Description: Aims to advance the business and community interests within the trade area of the Mount Vernon and Lee Districts in Fairfax County, Virginia. **Founded:** 1954. **Geographic Preference:** Local.

45885 ■ New Kent Chamber of Commerce
7324 Vineyard Pky.
New Kent, VA 23124
Ph: (804)966-8581
Co. E-mail: office@newkentchamber.org
URL: http://www.newkentchamber.org
Contact: Jessica Hoskins, Treasurer
E-mail: secretary@newkentchamber.org
Facebook: www.facebook.com/newkentchamber
X (Twitter): x.com/newkentchamber
Instagram: www.instagram.com/newkentchamber

Description: Promotes business and community development in the New Kent, VA area. **Geographic Preference:** Local.

45886 ■ Northern Virginia Chamber of Commerce (NVCC)
7900 Westpark Dr., Ste. A550
Tysons Corner, VA 22102-3853
Ph: (703)749-0400
Fax: (703)749-9075
URL: http://www.novachamber.org
Contact: Julie Coons, President
E-mail: jcoons@novachamber.org
Facebook: www.facebook.com/NorthernVAChamber
Linkedin: www.linkedin.com/company/northern-virginia-chamber-of-commerce
X (Twitter): x.com/NOVAChamber

Description: Promotes business and community development in Fairfax County. **Founded:** 1925. **Geographic Preference:** Local.

45887 ■ Orange County Chamber of Commerce (OCCC)
111 Spicers Mill Rd., Ste. B
Orange, VA 22960
Ph: (540)672-5216
Co. E-mail: orangevadirector@gmail.com
URL: http://www.orangevachamber.com
Contact: Donna Waugh Robinson, President
E-mail: waughrobinson@yahoo.com
Facebook: www.facebook.com/orangevachamber
YouTube: www.youtube.com/channel/UCXImRlyN_MeKHudOtLQaz-g

Description: Promotes business and community development in Orange County, VA. **Founded:** 1924. **Geographic Preference:** Local.

45888 ■ Patrick County Chamber of Commerce
334 Patrick Ave.
Stuart, VA 24171
Ph: (276)694-6012
Co. E-mail: patcchamber@embarqmail.com
URL: http://www.patrickchamber.com
Contact: Roger Conner, President
E-mail: rconner@primland.com

Description: Promotes business and community development in the Patrick County, VA area. Sponsors the Virginia Peach Festival. **Founded:** 1791. **Geographic Preference:** Local.

45889 ■ Petersburg Chamber of Commerce
Ph: (804)733-8131
Co. E-mail: info@petersburgvachamber.com
URL: http://www.petersburgvachamber.com
Contact: Danielle Mw Fitz-Hugh, President
Facebook: www.facebook.com/PetersburgVaChamber

Description: Promotes business and community development in Petersburg, VA. **Publications:** *The Chamber Comments* (Quarterly). **Geographic Preference:** Local.

45890 ■ Powhatan Chamber of Commerce
3860 Old Buckingham Rd.
Powhatan, VA 23139
Ph: (804)598-2636
Co. E-mail: info@powhatanchamber.org
URL: http://www.powhatanchamber.org
Contact: Keith Smith, President
Facebook: www.facebook.com/PowhatanChamber

Description: Association of business, professional and civic-minded individuals. Promotes free enterprise system, economic growth and prosperity of Powhatan County. **Founded:** 1988. **Geographic Preference:** Local.

45891 ■ Prince William Chamber of Commerce
9720 Capital Ct., Ste. 203
Manassas, VA 20110
Ph: (703)368-6600
Fax: (703)368-4733
Co. E-mail: info@pwchamber.org
URL: http://www.pwchamber.org
Contact: Debbie Jones, President
E-mail: djones@pwchamber.org
Facebook: www.facebook.com/pwchamber
Linkedin: www.linkedin.com/company/prince-william-chamber-of-commerce
X (Twitter): x.com/pwchamber
YouTube: www.youtube.com/user/pwchamber

Description: Promotes business and community development in the Greater Manassas area. **Publications:** *Inprint* (Bimonthly); *Business and Information* (Annual); *Inprint* (Bimonthly). **Awards:** Prince William Chamber of Commerce Scholarship (Annual). **Geographic Preference:** Local.

45892 ■ Pulaski County Chamber of Commerce (PCCC)
6580 Valley Center Dr., Ste. 302
Radford, VA 24141
Ph: (540)674-1991
Fax: (540)674-4163
Co. E-mail: info@pulaskivachamber.org
URL: http://www.pulaskivachamber.org
Contact: Bill Cunningham, President
Facebook: www.facebook.com/Pulaski-County-Chamber-of-Commerce-102867005722
X (Twitter): x.com/pulaski_chamber

STATE LISTINGS   Virginia ■ 45907

Description: Promotes business and community development in Pulaski County, VA. **Founded:** 1952. **Geographic Preference:** Local.

45893 ■ Radford Chamber of Commerce (RCC)
200 3rd Ave.
  Radford, VA 24141
Ph: (540)639-2202
Co. E-mail: info@radfordchamber.com
URL: http://radfordchamber.com
Contact: Dan McKinney, Executive Director
Facebook: www.facebook.com/Radfor dChamberofCommerce
Linkedin: www.linkedin.com/company/radfor d-chamber-of-commerce
X (Twitter): x.com/radfordchamber
Instagram: www.instagram.com/radfordchamber
Description: Promotes business and community development in Radford, VA. **Founded:** 1944. **Geographic Preference:** Local.

45894 ■ Roanoke Regional Chamber of Commerce (RRCC)
210 S Jefferson St.
  Roanoke, VA 24011-1702
Ph: (540)983-0700
Fax: (540)983-0723
Co. E-mail: business@roanokechamber.org
URL: http://roanokechamber.org
Contact: Joyce Waugh, President
E-mail: jwaugh@roanokechamber.org
Facebook: www.facebook.com/RoanokeChamber
Linkedin: www.linkedin.com/company/ roanokechamber
X (Twitter): x.com/RoanokeChamber
YouTube: www.youtube.com/user/RoanokeChamber
Description: Promotes business and community development in the Roanoke Valley, VA area. **Founded:** 1890. **Publications:** *Business Connections* (Quarterly); *Roanoke Area Industrial Directory*. **Geographic Preference:** Local.

45895 ■ Scott County Chamber of Commerce
190 Beech St., Ste. 202
  Gate City, VA 24251
Ph: (276)386-6665
Fax: (276)386-6158
Co. E-mail: chamber@scottcountyva.com
URL: http://www.scottcountyva.org/chamber.html
Contact: Robert Chapman, President
Facebook: www.facebook.com/Scott-County-Cham ber-of-Commerce-948648098550132
Description: Promotes business and community development in Scott County, VA. **Founded:** 1985. **Geographic Preference:** Local.

45896 ■ Shenandoah County Chamber of Commerce
103 S Main St.
  Woodstock, VA 22664
Ph: (540)459-2542
Co. E-mail: director@shenandoahcountychamber .com
URL: http://www.shenandoahcountychamber.com
Contact: Sharon Baroncelli, President
E-mail: director@shenandoahcountychamber.com
Facebook: www.facebook.com/ShenandoahCoun tyChamberOfCommerce
Linkedin: www.linkedin.com/company/shenandoah -county-chamber-of-commerce
X (Twitter): x.com/ShenandoahCoun tyChamberOfCommerce
Description: Promotes business and community development in the Woodstock, VA area. **Geographic Preference:** Local.

45897 ■ *Shoreline*
105 2nd St.
  Clarksville, VA 23927
Ph: (434)374-2436
Fax: (434)374-8174
Co. E-mail: clarksvillelakecountry@outlook.com
URL: http://clarksvilleva.com
Contact: Patricia Charles, President
URL(s): clarksvilleva.com/festivals-celebrations/other -celebrations/#

Released: Bimonthly **Availability:** Print; Online.

45898 ■ *Smith Mountain Lake Newcomer and Visitor Guide*
16430 Booker T. Washington Hwy.
  Moneta, VA 24121
Ph: (540)721-1203
Fax: (540)721-7796
Co. E-mail: info@visitsmithmountainlake.com
URL: http://www.visitsmithmountainlake.com
Contact: Andy Bruns, Executive Director
E-mail: abruns@visitsmithmountainlake.com
URL(s): www.visitsmithmountainlake.com/visitor -guide
Released: Monthly **Description:** Covers year-round events, activities, amenities and businesses in the Smith Mountain Lake area. **Availability:** Print; Online.

45899 ■ Smith Mountain Lake Regional Chamber of Commerce (SMLRCC)
16430 Booker T. Washington Hwy.
  Moneta, VA 24121
Ph: (540)721-1203
Fax: (540)721-7796
Co. E-mail: info@visitsmithmountainlake.com
URL: http://www.visitsmithmountainlake.com
Contact: Andy Bruns, Executive Director
E-mail: abruns@visitsmithmountainlake.com
X (Twitter): x.com/smlchamber
YouTube: www.youtube.com/user/SMLChamber1
Pinterest: www.pinterest.com/smlchamber1
Description: Smith Mountain Lake business and professional people. Promotes tourism, business, and community growth. Develops and promotes programs designed to encourage economic, social, cultural, and recreational interests of Lake area residents. **Publications:** *Smith Mountain Lake Newcomer and Visitor Guide* (Monthly); *Connections* (Weekly). **Educational Activities:** Business After Hours (Monthly). **Geographic Preference:** Local.

45900 ■ Smyth County Chamber of Commerce
408 Whitetop Rd.
  Chilhowie, VA 24319
Ph: (276)783-3161
Co. E-mail: info@smythchamber.org
URL: http://smythchamber.org
Contact: Sarah Gillespie, Executive Director
Facebook: www.facebook.com/smythchamber
Linkedin: www.linkedin.com/company/chamber-of -commerce-of-smyth-county-inc
X (Twitter): x.com/SmythCoChamber
Description: Promotes business and community development in the Smyth County, VA area. **Founded:** 1981. **Geographic Preference:** Local.

45901 ■ South Hill Chamber of Commerce (SHCC)
201 S Mecklenburg Ave.
  South Hill, VA 23970
Ph: (434)447-4547
Co. E-mail: chamberevents@southhillchamber.com
URL: http://www.southhillchamber.com
Contact: Teri Newman Walker, President
Description: Promotes business and community development in South Hill, VA. Sponsors festival. **Founded:** 1942. **Geographic Preference:** Local.

45902 ■ Surry County Chamber of Commerce (SCCC)
PO Box 353
  Surry, VA 23883-0353
Co. E-mail: surrychamberprez@gmail.com
URL: http://www.surryvachamber.org
Contact: Christopher Squires, President
Facebook: www.facebook.com/surrychamber
Instagram: www.instagram.com/surrychamber
Pinterest: www.pinterest.com/surrychamber
Description: Promotes business and community development in Surry County, VA area. **Founded:** 1991. **Geographic Preference:** Local.

45903 ■ Tappahannock-Essex County Chamber of Commerce
202 S Church Ln.
  Tappahannock, VA 22560
Ph: (804)443-4331
Co. E-mail: info@essex-virginia.org
URL: http://www.essex-virginia.org
URL(s): tecoc.com
Facebook: www.facebook.com/EssexCountyVA
X (Twitter): x.com/EssexCountyGov
Description: Promotes business and community development in the Tappahannock-Essex, VA area. Conducts annual Summer Festival and business fair; sponsors 10K race. **Founded:** 1970. **Publications:** *Update* (Monthly). **Geographic Preference:** Local.

45904 ■ Tazewell Area Chamber of Commerce (TACC)
165 Chamber Dr.
  Tazewell, VA 24651
Ph: (276)988-5091
Co. E-mail: info@tazewellchamber.org
URL: http://www.tazewellchamber.com
Contact: Regina Sayers, President
Facebook: www.facebook.com/tazewellcoun tychamber
Description: Promotes business and community development in the Tazewell, VA area. **Founded:** 1972. **Geographic Preference:** Local.

45905 ■ Top of Virginia Regional Chamber (TVRC)
407 S Loudoun St.
  Winchester, VA 22601
Ph: (540)662-4118
Co. E-mail: office@regionalchamber.biz
URL: http://www.regionalchamber.biz
Contact: Adrian Taylor, Treasurer
Facebook: www.facebook.com/tvrcva
Linkedin: www.linkedin.com/company/top-of-virginia -regional-chamber
X (Twitter): x.com/topofvachamber
Description: Promotes business and community development in the Winchester City, Frederick, and Clarke County, VA area. **Founded:** 1917. **Publications:** *Business Agenda* (Monthly). **Geographic Preference:** Local.

45906 ■ Twin County Chamber of Commerce
405 N Main St. Ste. 9
  Galax, VA 24333
Ph: (276)236-2184
Co. E-mail: info@twincountychamber.com
URL: http://twincountychamber.com
Contact: Anthony Edwards, President
E-mail: anthony@alumni.uncg.edu
Facebook: www.facebook.com/twincoun tychamberofcommerce
Description: Promotes business and community development in the City of Galax and counties of Carroll and Grayson, VA. **Founded:** 1950. **Geographic Preference:** Regional.

45907 ■ Tysons Regional Chamber of Commerce (TRCC)
7925 Jones Branch Dr., Ste. LL200
  Tysons, VA 22102
Ph: (703)281-1333
Fax: (703)242-1482
Co. E-mail: info@tysonschamber.org
URL: http://tysonschamber.org
Contact: Tucker R. Gladhill, President
Facebook: www.facebook.com/ TysonsRegionalChamber
Linkedin: www.linkedin.com/in/tysons-regional -chamber-commerce
X (Twitter): x.com/tysonschamber
Instagram: www.instagram.com/tysonschamber
YouTube: www.youtube.com/channel/UCc9QwLBYb 2Ti-i8KfBOfZiw
Description: Promotes business and community development in the Vienna, VA area. Sponsors Halloween Parade and annual Chili Cook-Off. **Publications:** *Enterprise* (Biweekly); *Greater Vienna Handbook* (Annual). **Educational Activities:** Business Expo. **Geographic Preference:** Local.

45908 ■ Virginia

45908 ■ Vinton Area Chamber of Commerce (VACC)
820 E Washington Ave.
Vinton, VA 24179
Ph: (540)343-1364
Co. E-mail: info@vintonchamber.com
URL: http://www.vintonchamber.com
Contact: Jason Boothe, President
Facebook: www.facebook.com/vintonchamber
X (Twitter): x.com/vintonchamber
YouTube: www.youtube.com/vintonchamber
Description: Promotes business and community development in the Vinton Area, VA. **Founded:** 1950. **Geographic Preference:** Local.

45909 ■ Virginia Association of Chamber of Commerce Executives (VACCE)
1622 Tarklin Valley Rd.
Knoxville, TN 37920
Ph: (404)312-0524
Co. E-mail: info@vachamber.com
URL: http://www.vacceva.org/home
Contact: Danielle Fitz-Hugh, Chairman
Facebook: www.facebook.com/Virginia-Association-of-Chamber-of-Commerce-Executives-452196338538599
X (Twitter): x.com/VACCE4
YouTube: www.youtube.com/user/vachamber
Description: Represents large and small chambers of commerce from localities throughout the state. Strives to develop the professional skills of chamber executives, staff and volunteer leaders. Conducts a forum for integrating the work of the local chambers of commerce to contribute to the growth and development of local communities. **Founded:** 1962. **Geographic Preference:** State.

45910 ■ Virginia Chamber of Commerce (VCC)
919 E Main St., Ste. 900
Richmond, VA 23219
Ph: (804)644-1607
Fax: (804)783-6112
Co. E-mail: info@vachamber.com
URL: http://www.vachamber.com
Contact: Barry DuVal, President
E-mail: b.duval@vachamber.com
Facebook: www.facebook.com/VAChamber
Linkedin: www.linkedin.com/company/virginia-chamber-of-commerce
X (Twitter): x.com/VAChamber
YouTube: www.youtube.com/user/vachamber
Description: Promotes business and community development in Virginia. **Founded:** 1924. **Publications:** *Virginia All-Business Directory* (Annual); *The Advocate* (Monthly); *Government Textbook* (Periodic); *Virginia Industrial Directory* (Annual); *Associations in Virginia* (Annual). **Geographic Preference:** State.

45911 ■ Virginia Peninsula Chamber of Commerce (VPCC)
21 Enterprise Pky., Ste. 100
Hampton, VA 23666
Ph: (757)262-2000
Co. E-mail: info@vpcc.org
URL: http://www.virginiapeninsulachamber.com
Contact: Robert S. McKenna, President
E-mail: bob.mckenna@vpcc.org
Facebook: www.facebook.com/VAPeninsulaChamber
Linkedin: www.linkedin.com/company/virginia-peninsula-chamber-of-commerce
Instagram: www.instagram.com/vapeninsulachamber
Description: Promotes the economic and business interests of the Virginia Peninsula. **Founded:** 1898. **Publications:** *Virginia Peninsula Regional Business Directory* (Annual); *Enterprise* (Monthly); *Glance at the Virginia Peninsula*; *Resource Guide* (Annual). **Educational Activities:** SeaFest. **Awards:** Virginia Peninsula Chamber of Commerce Distinguished Citizens of the Year (Annual). **Geographic Preference:** Local.

45912 ■ Warsaw-Richmond County Chamber of Commerce (WRC) [WRC Chamber of Commerce]
PO Box 1141
Warsaw, VA 22572
Ph: (804)313-2252
Co. E-mail: warsawrcchamber@gmail.com
URL: http://www.wrccoc.com
Contact: Sara Carroll, President
Facebook: www.facebook.com/wrcchamber
Description: Promotes business and community development in the Warsaw, VA area. **Founded:** 1987. **Geographic Preference:** Local.

45913 ■ Washington County Chamber of Commerce
1 Government Center Pl., Ste. D
Abingdon, VA 24210
Ph: (276)628-8141
Fax: (276)628-3984
Co. E-mail: chamber@bvu.net
URL: http://www.washingtonvachamber.org/chamber
Contact: Kristie Helms, President
Facebook: www.facebook.com/washingtoncountyvachamber
X (Twitter): x.com/washcomochamber
Pinterest: www.pinterest.com/washmochamber
Description: Promotes business and community development in Washington County, VA. Organizes Business Night Out mixers, industrial appreciation dinner, Salute to Education banquet, and other events. **Founded:** 1927. **Publications:** *Industrial Directory*. **Geographic Preference:** Local.

45914 ■ Wytheville-Wythe-Bland Chamber of Commerce (WWBCC)
150 E Monroe St.
Wytheville, VA 24382
Ph: (276)223-3365
Fax: (276)223-3412
Co. E-mail: chamber@wytheville.org
URL: http://www.wwbchamber.org
Contact: Jennifer W. Atwell, Executive Director
Facebook: www.facebook.com/Wytheville-Wythe-Bland-Chamber-of-Commerce-156800087718222
Description: Promotes business and community development in the Wytheville-Wythe-Bland, VA area. **Founded:** 1946. **Publications:** *Business Connection*; *Wytheville Chamber of Commerce Business Directory*; *Wytheville/Wythe/Bland Chamber of Commerce Business Directory* (Annual). **Geographic Preference:** Local.

MINORITY BUSINESS ASSISTANCE PROGRAMS

45915 ■ Carolinas-Virginia Minority Supplier Development Council
707 E Main St., Ste. 1375
Richmond, VA 23219
Ph: (804)663-7782
Co. E-mail: info@cvmsdc.org
URL: http://cvmsdc.org
Contact: Dominique Milton, President
E-mail: dominique.milton@cvmsdc.org
Facebook: www.facebook.com/cvmsdc.carolinasvirginia.3
YouTube: www.youtube.com/channel/UC8zuSOeOQLP6F3ZqcZhjGug
Description: Provides a direct link between corporate America and minority-owned businesses. Increases procurement and business opportunities for minority businesses of all sizes. **Geographic Preference:** State.

45916 ■ Metropolitan Business League (MBL)
707 E Main St., Ste. 1615
, Ste. 1615
Richmond, VA 23219
Ph: (804)649-7473
Fax: (804)649-7474
Co. E-mail: info@thembl.com
URL: http://thembl.org
Contact: Scottessa Hurte, President
Facebook: www.facebook.com/theMBL
Linkedin: www.linkedin.com/company/the-metropolitan-business-league
X (Twitter): x.com/thembl
Instagram: www.instagram.com/mblrva
YouTube: www.youtube.com/channel/UCGty70DwUo87xb7ZwzSg0pQ
Description: Seeks to develop, assist and promote minority business in Central Virginia through its programs and services. **Founded:** 1968. **Geographic Preference:** National.

FINANCING AND LOAN PROGRAMS

45917 ■ Blu Venture Investors
1577 Spring Hill Rd.
Vienna, VA 22182
Ph: (703)775-2114
URL: http://www.bluventureinvestors.com
Contact: Benjamin Ebenezer, Principal
Linkedin: www.linkedin.com/company/bluventures
Description: Offers growth-stage funding and active mentorship to early-stage companies with strong returns and SaaS and/or enterprise software models. Promotes job creation and professional development in the Mid-Atlantic community. **Founded:** 2010. **Preferred Investment Size:** $250,000-$1,000,000. **Investment Policies:** Solutions for the U.S. Department of Defense, Homeland Security and Intelligence Community sectors. **Industry Preferences:** Cybersecurity; IoT; digital media; non-invasive biological sciences.

45918 ■ Calvert Social Venture Partners L.P.
VA
Ph: (703)255-4930
Co. E-mail: steve@calvertventures.com
URL: http://www.calvertventures.com
Contact: D. Wayne Silby, Chairman
Description: Firm that seeks to invest in health and human resources, education, environment and energy sectors. **Founded:** 1989. **Preferred Investment Size:** $250,000 to $1,000,000. **Industry Preferences:** Environment.

45919 ■ CAV Angels
PO Box 4292
Charlottesville, VA 22905
Ph: (434)218-5783
Co. E-mail: info@cavangels.com
URL: http://cavangels.com
Contact: Paul Nolde, President
Facebook: www.facebook.com/cavangels

45920 ■ Charlottesville Angel Network (CAN)
250 W Main St., Ste. 201
Charlottesville, VA 22902
URL: http://cvilleangelnetwork.net
Contact: Craig Redinger, Contact
Description: Invests in promising startups in technology, software, consumer products, and advanced materials primarily in Virginia; may partner with co-investors on Series A and B rounds. **Preferred Investment Size:** $100,000-$300,000. **Investment Policies:** Innovations and solutions solving market problems. . **Industry Preferences:** SaaS; digital healthcare; biotech; consumer products; clean energy; educational technology.

45921 ■ Envest Private Equity [Envest Capital Partners]
1206 Laskin Rd., Ste. 101
Virginia Beach, VA 23451
Ph: (757)437-3000
Co. E-mail: info@envestcap.com
URL: http://envestcap.com
Contact: Patrick Keefe, Managing Director
Description: Venture capital firm. Specializes in long-term value creation. **Founded:** 1999. **Industry Preferences:** Manufacturing; assembly; distribution; franchising; business services; healthcare services.

45922 ■ Harbert Venture Partners L.L.C.
5702 Grove Ave., Ste. 200
Richmond, VA 23226
Ph: (804)782-3800

URL: http://www.harbert.net

Description: Provider of venture capital investments for seed, start-up, early stage companies. **Founded:** 2000. **Preferred Investment Size:** $1,000,000 to $4,000,000. **Investment Policies:** Start-up, seed, and early stage. **Industry Preferences:** Communications and media, computer related, software and services, biotechnology and life sciences, medical and health, and industrial and energy.

45923 ■ Meda Angels, LLC (MA)
3033 Wilson Blvd., Ste. 700
Arlington, VA 22201
Ph: (703)340-9878
Co. E-mail: info@medaangels.com
URL: http://www.medaangels.com
Contact: Amir Rafii, MD, Co-Founder

Description: Angel investor group focused on early-stage healthcare companies. **Founded:** 2019. **Industry Preferences:** Digital health; medical devices; robotics; diagnostics; imaging; AI-driven technologies; wellness (food, sports).

45924 ■ NeuroVentures Capital L.L.C.
427 Pk. St.
Charlottesville, VA 22902
Co. E-mail: info@neuroventures.com
URL: http://www.neuroventures.com

Description: Provider of venture capital for seed, start up, early stage investments and much more. **Founded:** 2000. **Preferred Investment Size:** $200,000 to $2,000,000. **Investment Policies:** Start-up, early and first stage, and expansion. **Industry Preferences:** Biotechnology, and medical and health.

45925 ■ New Dominion Angels LLC (NDA)
1775 Tysons Blvd.
McLean, VA 22102
URL: http://www.newdominionangels.com
Contact: Natalie Stephenson, Director

Description: Invests in early-stage mid-Atlantic startups. **Founded:** 2008.

45926 ■ QED Investors
405 Cameron St.
Alexandria, VA 22314
URL: http://www.qedinvestors.com
Contact: Fernando Gonzalez, Chief Executive Officer
Linkedin: www.linkedin.com/company/qed-investors
X (Twitter): x.com/qedinvestors

Description: Boutique venture capital firm for early-stage disruptive financial services companies in the U.S, U.K, and Latin America. **Founded:** 2008.

45927 ■ Third Security, LLC
1881 Grove Ave.
Radford, VA 24141
Ph: (540)633-7900
Fax: (540)633-7939
URL: http://thirdsecurity.com
Contact: Julian P. Kirk, Chief Executive Officer

Description: Venture capital firm primarily focused on emerging to late-stage investments in life sciences. Also operates out of San Francisco and Palm Beach. **Founded:** 1999. **Investment Policies:** Unique value; execution-oriented entrepreneurs; market leadership.

45928 ■ Virginia Capital Partners L.L.C.
1801 Libbie Ave., Ste. 201
Richmond, VA 23226-0000
Co. E-mail: info@vacapital.com
URL: http://vacapital.com
Contact: Frederick L. Russell, Jr., Contact

Description: Investment firm provider of venture capital, growth capital and private equity funds. **Founded:** 1997. **Preferred Investment Size:** $1,000,000 to $5,000,000. **Industry Preferences:** Communications and media, medical and health, consumer related, and transportation, financial services, and business service.

PROCUREMENT ASSISTANCE PROGRAMS

45929 ■ Central Virginia Procurement Technical Assistance Center
1125 Jefferson Davis Hwy., Ste. 400
Fredericksburg, VA 22401
Ph: (703)277-7750
URL: http://www.aptac-us.org/find-a-ptac/?state=VA

Description: Provides assistance to businesses interested in doing business with federal, state, and local governments. Covers cities and counties from Danville to Highland and Shenandoah counties on the Northwestern border across to the eastern shore.

45930 ■ Hampton Roads Virginia Procurement Technical Assistance Center
140 Independence Blvd., Ste. 100
Virginia Beach, VA 23462
Ph: (703)277-7750
URL: http://virginiaapex.org
Contact: Daryl Corley, Counselor

Description: Serves Tidewater, Hampton Roads area in helping business with government at federal, state, and local levels.

45931 ■ The National Center American Indian Procurement Technical Assistance Center - Virginia
Mason Enterprise Ctr., 10306 Eaton Pl.
Fairfax, VA 22030
Ph: (703)277-7750
URL: http://www.aptac-us.org/find-a-ptac/?state=VA
Contact: Lisa Wood, Director
E-mail: lwood22@gmu.edu

Description: Helps to develop and expand an American Indian private sector which employs Indian labor, increases the number of viable tribal and individual Indian businesses, and positively impacts and involves reservation communities, by establishing business relationships between Indian enterprises and private industry.

45932 ■ Procurement Technical Assistance Center of Northern Virginia - Mason Enterprise Center (PTAC)
10306 Eaton PlSte. 180
Fairfax, VA 22030
Ph: (703)277-7750
URL: http://www.aptac-us.org/find-a-ptac/?state=VA
Contact: Elizabeth Torrens, Manager, Operations
E-mail: etorren2@gmu.edu

Description: The center services nine counties in Northern Virginia and the cities they contain. Goal is to increase contracting activity between small businesses, prime government contractors, and the government.

45933 ■ Virginia Department of General Services - Division of Purchases and Supply - Procurement Assistance
1111 E Broad St.
Richmond, VA 23218-1922
Ph: (804)786-3846
Free: 866-289-7367
Fax: (804)371-7877
URL: http://dgs.virginia.gov/ContactUs/tabid/63/Default.aspx

Description: Provides services that make it easier and more convenient to do business with the Commonwealth and make it more simple and cost efficient for the government to do its business.

45934 ■ Virginia Procurement Technical Assistance Center (CPDC) - Crater Planning District Commission
1964 Wakefield St.
Petersburg, VA 23805
Ph: (804)861-1666
Fax: (804)732-8972
Co. E-mail: info@craterpdc.org
URL: http://www.craterpdc.org
Contact: Alec Brebner, Executive Director
E-mail: abrebner@craterpdc.org

Description: The major focus of the Commission's Work program is economic, industrial and small business development.

45935 ■ Virginia Procurement Technical Assistance Center of George Mason University (PTAC)
Mason Enterprise Center., 10306 Eaton Pl., Ste. 180
Fairfax, VA 22030
Ph: (703)277-7750
Fax: (703)352-8195
Co. E-mail: ptac@gmu.edu
URL: http://virginiaptap.org
Contact: Lisa Wood, Director
Facebook: www.facebook.com/VirginiaPTAC
Linkedin: www.linkedin.com/in/virginia-ptap
X (Twitter): x.com/VirginiaPTAC

Description: Exists to increase contracting activity between small businesses, prime government contractors and the government. **Founded:** 1985.

45936 ■ Virginia Procurement Technical Assistance Center - Southwest Virginia Community College
Tazewell Hall Rm. 111FedEx/UPS Deliveries 724 Community College Rd.
Richlands, VA 24641
Ph: (276)964-7334
Fax: (276)964-7361
Co. E-mail: apex.info@sw.edu
URL: http://sw.edu/apex
Facebook: www.facebook.com/ptac.at.southwest.virginia.community.college
Linkedin: www.linkedin.com/showcase/apex-at-southwest-virginia-community-college
X (Twitter): x.com/swcc_tweets
Instagram: www.instagram.com/southwestcommunitycollege

Description: Provide businesses with the marketing know how and technical tools they need to obtain and perform successfully under federal, state and local government contracts - with the mission of creating and retaining jobs, fostering competition and lower costs for the government, and helping to sustain our armed forces' readiness. **Founded:** 1968.

INCUBATORS/RESEARCH AND TECHNOLOGY PARKS

45937 ■ 80Amps
211-B W 7th St.
Richmond, VA 23224
Ph: (804)512-7654
Co. E-mail: info@80amps.com
URL: http://www.80amps.com
URL(s): 80ampsenterprise.com
Facebook: www.facebook.com/80amps
Linkedin: www.linkedin.com/company/2991338
X (Twitter): twitter.com/80amps

Description: A team of entrepreneurs, venture capitalists, creatives, and subject matter experts dedicated to growing brands, products, and the technologies that support them. A micro-venture capital firm providing seed investments to startups. **Founded:** 2012.

45938 ■ 757 Makerspace
237 W 24th St.
Norfolk, VA 23517
Ph: (757)301-1118
Co. E-mail: contact@757makerspace.com
URL: http://www.757makerspace.com
Facebook: www.facebook.com/757Makerspace
X (Twitter): x.com/757makerspace
Instagram: www.instagram.com/757makerspace
YouTube: www.youtube.com/channel/UC7uv931Lo7s1qdCxVtdyt4w

Description: A community workspace for education, creation, entrepreneurial, and prototyping endeavors. **Founded:** 2013.

45939 ■ Alleghany Highlands Economic Development Corp. - Business Assistance Program
1000 Dabney Dr., Ste. 658
Clifton Forge, VA 24422

Ph: (540)862-0936
URL: http://www.ahedc.com/business-incubator
Contact: Terri McClung, Office Manager
E-mail: terri@ahedc.com
Facebook: www.facebook.com/AlleghanyHighlandsEconomicDevelopmentCorp
Linkedin: www.linkedin.com/company/alleghany-highlands-economic-development-corporation
X (Twitter): twitter.com/ahedcva
Description: Available to anyone starting, expanding or sustaining a business in the Alleghany Highlands. Has an entrepreneurial specialist on staff who will help startups with any and all activities associated with a business launch. **Founded:** 2002.

45940 ■ BizWorks
2545 Bellwood Rd.
North Chesterfield, VA 23237
Ph: (804)275-5190
Co. E-mail: info@bizworkscenter.org
URL: http://www.bizworkscenter.org
Contact: Phil Cunningham, President
Linkedin: www.linkedin.com/company/bizworks-enterprise-center
Instagram: www.instagram.com/bizworkscenter
Description: A non-profit small business incubator offering office and warehouse space to new businesses and those transitioning from a non-traditional environment, such as their garage or dining room. Their goal is to bring businesses in and provide the support services they need in order to grow and continue to be a success outside the incubator. **Founded:** 2001.

45941 ■ BizWorks Enterprise Center
2545 Bellwood Rd.
North Chesterfield, VA 23237
Ph: (804)275-5190
Co. E-mail: info@bizworkscenter.org
URL: http://www.bizworkscenter.org
Contact: Doug Carleton, Officer
Facebook: www.facebook.com/BizWorksCenter
Linkedin: www.linkedin.com/company/bizworks-enterprise-center
X (Twitter): x.com/BizWorksCenter
Instagram: www.instagram.com/bizworkscenter
Description: A nonprofit small business incubator offering office and warehouse space to new businesses transitioning from a non-traditional environment. **Founded:** 2001.

45942 ■ Business Development Centre (BDC)
147 Mill Ridge Rd.
Lynchburg, VA 24502
Ph: (434)582-6100
Co. E-mail: bdcdir@lbdc.com
URL: http://lbdc.com
Contact: Brian Runk, President
Description: A small business incubator offering services to business owners and prospective business owners in the cities of Lynchburg and Bedford, the towns of Altavista and Amherst and the counties of Amherst, Appomattox, Bedford and Campbell in Central Virginia. **Founded:** 1989.

45943 ■ Chefscape
1602 Village Market Blvd.
Leesburg, VA 20175
Ph: (703)480-5100
Co. E-mail: cook@chefscapekitchen.com
URL: http://www.chefscapekitchen.com
Facebook: www.facebook.com/chefscapekitchen
Instagram: www.instagram.com/chefscape
Description: Culinary incubator with shared kitchen and event space providing food entrepreneurs with the space to carve out their own business landscape and the services and support for those businesses to blossom and grow.

45944 ■ Community Business Partnership (CBP)
6564 Loisdale Ct., Ste. 600
Springfield, VA 22150
Ph: (703)768-1440
Co. E-mail: info@cbponline.org
URL: http://www.cbponline.org
Contact: Debbie Allen, President
Facebook: www.facebook.com/communitybusinesspartnership
Linkedin: www.linkedin.com/company/community-business-partnership
X (Twitter): x.com/cbponline
Description: Provides entrepreneurial development services such as training, counseling and access to capital for eligible Veterans owning or considering starting a small business. **Founded:** 1995.

45945 ■ The CrossRoads Institute
1117 E Stuart Dr.
Galax, VA 24333
Ph: (276)236-0391
Fax: (276)236-0485
Co. E-mail: info@crossroadsva.org
URL: http://www.crossroadsva.org
Contact: Brenda R. Sutherland, Executive Director
E-mail: bsutherland@crossroadsva.org
Facebook: www.facebook.com/CrossroadsInstitute
X (Twitter): x.com/crossroadsvaorg
Description: Business incubator facility where you can rent an office, manufacturing space, or a commercial kitchen to get your business started, with the advantage of low rent and availability of an on-site business analyst. **Founded:** 2005.

45946 ■ Dan River Business Development Center (DRBDC)
300 Ringgold Industrial Pky.
Danville, VA 24540
Ph: (434)793-9100
Co. E-mail: reception@drbdc.com
URL: http://drbdc.com
Contact: Ralph Hogg, Executive Director
E-mail: wrhogg@drbdc.com
Facebook: www.facebook.com/people/Dan-River-Business-Development-Center/100070229962489
Description: Business incubator that provides to new and existing small businesses: affordable rents, shared support services, shared equipment, and access to a wide range of professional, technical, and financial programs.

45947 ■ Dominion Energy Innovation Center (DEIC)
201 S Duncan St.
Ashland, VA 23005
Ph: (804)368-8610
Co. E-mail: info@dominnovation.com
URL: http://www.dominnovation.com
Contact: Chandra Briggman, President
Facebook: www.facebook.com/DominionEnergyInnovationCenter
Linkedin: www.linkedin.com/company/dominion-energy-innovation-center
X (Twitter): x.com/DEIC_VA
Description: Start-p incubator and co-working space. **Founded:** 2009.

45948 ■ Dominion Resources Innovation Center
201 S Duncan St.
Ashland, VA 23005
Ph: (804)368-8610
Co. E-mail: info@dominnovation.com
URL: http://www.dominnovation.com
Contact: Chandra Briggman, President
Facebook: www.facebook.com/DominionEnergyInnovationCenter
Linkedin: www.linkedin.com/company/dominion-energy-innovation-center
X (Twitter): x.com/DEIC_VA
Description: Incubator providing early stage startups with affordable workspace as well as access to a team of people and the resources needed to move a business forward. **Founded:** 2009.

45949 ■ Entrepreneurs Organization (EO)
500 Montgomery St., Ste. 700
Alexandria, VA 22314
Ph: (703)519-6700
Fax: (703)519-1864
Co. E-mail: info@eonetwork.org
URL: http://www.eonetwork.org
Contact: Carrie Santos, PhD, Chief Executive Officer
Facebook: www.facebook.com/EntrepreneursOrganization
Linkedin: www.linkedin.com/company/entrepreneurs%27-organization
X (Twitter): x.com/EntrepreneurOrg
Instagram: www.instagram.com/entrepreneursorg
YouTube: www.youtube.com/user/EOnetwork
Description: Engages leading entrepreneurs to learn and grow. Serves as a focal point for networking and development of members through small group learning sessions, regular local chapter social and learning events, and global conference-based education programs. **Founded:** 1987. **Publications:** *Overdrive* (Monthly); *Octane* (Quarterly). **Geographic Preference:** Multinational.

45950 ■ Forge
9 Elliewood Ave.
Charlottesville, VA 22903
Co. E-mail: hello@joinforge.co
URL: http://joinforge.co
Contact: Clare Carr, Leader
Facebook: www.facebook.com/joinforge.co
Linkedin: www.linkedin.com/company/forgecville
Instagram: www.instagram.com/meetforge
Description: A platform for experiential education and career development. Trains students in high-demand skills, accelerate their ideas, and connect them to jobs, opportunities, and a tight-knit community. Provides talent to Charlottesville's tech and startup scene. **Founded:** 2012.

45951 ■ Franklin Business Incubator
601 N Mechanic St., Ste. 300
Franklin, VA 23851
URL: http://franklinsouthamptonva.com/franklin-business-center
Description: Business incubator that provides hands-on management assistance, access to financing, and exposure to critical business and technical support services to entrepreneurs. **Founded:** 1907.

45952 ■ Franklin Southampton Economic Development (FSEDI)
601 N Mechanic St., Ste. 300
Franklin, VA 23851
Ph: (757)562-1958
Co. E-mail: info@franklinsouthamptonva.com
URL: http://franklinsouthamptonva.com
Contact: Karl T. Heck, President
E-mail: kheck@franklinsouthamptonva.com
Facebook: www.facebook.com/franklinsouthamptoneconomicdevelopmentinc
Linkedin: www.linkedin.com/company/franklin-southampton-economic-development-inc
X (Twitter): x.com/FSEDIStaff
Description: Mixed use incubator housing office space, support staff, and programs that nurture young firms and expanding businesses. **Founded:** 2005.

45953 ■ George Mason University (GMU) - Mason Enterprise Center (MEC)
202 Church St. SE Ste. 100
Leesburg, VA 20175
Co. E-mail: masonent@gmu.edu
URL: http://enterprise.gmu.edu
Contact: Eddie Hill, Director
Description: Small business incubator that helps grow businesses to the next level. **Scope:** Regional economic development, enterprise development, entrepreneurship, and innovation. **Founded:** 1995.

45954 ■ Hampton University Business Incubator
6 W County St.
Hampton, VA 23663
Ph: (757)722-9283
Fax: (757)224-4285
URL: http://hubi.hamptonu.edu
Description: Business incubator that provides space and nurturing services to new and small businesses during their critical early existence. In addition to office space, the business incubator provides advice, technical assistance, counseling and other services on-site that are often unavailable to new or small businesses due to their cost and/or the location of their offering.

STATE LISTINGS

Virginia ■ 45970

45955 ■ Hatch
Norfolk, VA
Ph: (757)295-8635
Co. E-mail: team@startwithhatch.com
URL: http://www.startwithhatch.com
Contact: George Arbogust, Director
E-mail: george@startwithhatch.com
Facebook: www.facebook.com/startwithhatch
X (Twitter): x.com/startwithhatch
Instagram: www.instagram.com/startwithhatch
YouTube: www.youtube.com/startwithhatch
Description: Dedicated to empowering entrepreneurs from every background, in every industry, and in every business stage. **Awards:** Hatch Innovation Award (Periodic).

45956 ■ The Highland Center
61 Highland Center Dr.
Monterey, VA 24465
Ph: (540)468-1922
Co. E-mail: director@thehighlandcenter.org
URL: http://thehighlandcenter.org
Contact: Rick Moyers, Treasurer
Facebook: www.facebook.com/thehighlandcenter
Description: Accelerates the successful development of small businesses and non-profits through support services, resources, affordable space and networking opportunities. **Founded:** 1998.

45957 ■ INC.spire Education Foundation
1886 Metro Center Dr., Ste. 150
Reston, VA 20190-5235
Contact: Charles Kapur, President
Description: Offers virtual incubation, meaning that we offer physical meeting space (available by reservation only), and for businesses looking for dedicated space to grow your team, we make introductions to various partners who have large office spaces available. **Founded:** 2002.

45958 ■ The Launch Place (TLP)
527 Bridge St., Ste. 200
Danville, VA 24541
Ph: (434)799-5491
Fax: (434)799-5493
Co. E-mail: info@thelaunchplace.org
URL: http://www.thelaunchplace.org
Contact: Eva Doss, President
E-mail: edoss@thelaunchplace.org
Facebook: www.facebook.com/thelaunchplace
Linkedin: www.linkedin.com/company/the-launch-place
X (Twitter): x.com/TheLaunchPlace
Description: An entrepreneurship development organization with the purpose to plan, fund, launch and grow companies in the IT, software, advanced manufacturing and medical device industries. Helps companies to get started or to expand their operations by providing business consulting services, office space, residential and office rent subsidies, and by potentially investing in them through two investment funds. **Founded:** 2005.

45959 ■ Lighthouse Labs
1717 E Cary St.
Richmond, VA 23223
Co. E-mail: info@lighthouselabsrva.com
URL: http://www.lighthouselabsrva.com
Contact: Joe Kunkel, Chairman of the Board
Facebook: www.facebook.com/LighthouseLabsRVA
Linkedin: www.linkedin.com/company/lighthouse-labs-rva
X (Twitter): x.com/rvalighthouse
Instagram: www.instagram.com/lighthouselabsrva
Description: A non-profit, mentor-driven startup acceleration program connecting promising founders with proven mentors, investors, support services, working space and lean startup education to move from idea to viable high growth venture in three months. **Founded:** 2012.

45960 ■ MACH37
1775 Tysons Blvd.
Tysons, VA 22102
URL: http://www.mach37.com
Contact: Jason Chen, Chief Executive Officer
Linkedin: www.linkedin.com/company/mach37-cyber-accelerator
X (Twitter): twitter.com/MACH37cyber
Description: Accelerator program for newly launched technology companies. Named after Mach 37, or "escape velocity," the minimum amount of velocity needed to escape earth's gravitational field, because these companies must push past forces preventing growth. **Founded:** 2013.

45961 ■ Mason Enterprise Center - Leesburg/Loudoun (MEC)
202 Church St. SE, Ste. 100
Leesburg, VA 20175
Ph: (703)466-0466
Co. E-mail: info@masonenterprisecenter.org
URL: http://www.masonenterprisecenter.org
Contact: Susan Henson, Regional Director
E-mail: shenson2@gmu.edu
Facebook: www.facebook.com/MasonEnterpriseCenterLeesburgLoudoun
X (Twitter): twitter.com/MECLeesburg
Description: A small business incubator and development center in downtown Leesburg, VA that is fostering the growth of companies through affordable, professional office and meeting space, shared services, expert training & mentoring, and connections to other entrepreneurs & the community.

45962 ■ Regent University Center for Entrepreneurship (RCE)
1000 Regent University Dr., Classroom Bldg., Ste. 105
Virginia Beach, VA 23464
Ph: (757)352-0452
Co. E-mail: rce@regent.edu
URL: http://regententrepreneur.org
Contact: Dr. John E. Mulford, Director
E-mail: johnmul@regent.edu
Facebook: www.facebook.com/RegentCenterForEntrepreneurship
Linkedin: www.linkedin.com/in/regentcenterforentrep
X (Twitter): x.com/RgntCtr4Entrep
YouTube: www.youtube.com/channel/UCys_854DNNQlvw4sQfFwNYQ
Description: Nurtures businesses, including those in developing nations. **Founded:** 2005.

45963 ■ Richlands Business Incubator (RBI)
1928 Front St.
Richlands, VA 24641
Ph: (276)963-2660
Fax: (276)963-2670
Co. E-mail: amwhitt@tazewellcounty.org
URL: http://rbi.tazewellcounty.org/BRI/RBI_main.html
Description: A business resource center committed to the growth and development of beginning or expanding businesses. Provides new and existing small businesses with management assistance, cost effective space, and a nurturing, professional environment.

45964 ■ Southern Virginia Product Advancement Center (SVPAC)
1100 Confroy Dr., Ste. 1
South Boston, VA 24592
URL: http://www.halifaxvirginia.com/videos/28-about-the-southern-virginia-product-advancement-center
Description: A business incubator and product advancement center that focuses on initiating, supporting, and growing high-tech ventures and technologies.

45965 ■ Startup Virginia (SVA)
1717 E Cary St.
Richmond, VA 23223
Ph: (804)404-5443
Co. E-mail: contact@startupvirginia.org
URL: http://www.startupvirginia.org
Contact: Paige Wilson, Founder
Facebook: www.facebook.com/StartupVirginia
Linkedin: www.linkedin.com/company/startup-virgina
X (Twitter): x.com/theStartupVA
Instagram: www.instagram.com/startupvirginia
Description: Connects entrepreneurs with mentors and assistance programs. Seeks to establish Virginia as a destination for high-growth startups. Offers education and sponsors events. **Founded:** 2016.

45966 ■ Staunton Makerspace
20 S Jefferson St.
Staunton, VA 24401
Ph: (540)324-9427
Co. E-mail: support@stauntonmakerspace.com
URL: http://stauntonmakerspace.org
Facebook: www.facebook.com/stauntonmakerspace
X (Twitter): x.com/stauntonmakers
Instagram: www.instagram.com/stauntonmakers
Description: A community run space where startups and entrepreneurs gather to create, collaborate, and learn.

45967 ■ UMW EagleWorks Business Incubation Center
1301 College Ave.
Fredericksburg, VA 22401
Ph: (540)654-1038
Fax: (540)654-1582
Co. E-mail: eagleworks@umw.edu
URL: http://economicdevelopment.umw.edu/home/programs/umw-eagleworks-business-incubation-center
Contact: Kelsey Whitman, Manager
E-mail: kwhitman@umw.edu
Description: Incubation program that extends business development services to local startup and early-stage companies looking to grow their enterprises. Ssupports entrepreneurs through our access to professional networks, office facilities, consulting services, peer engagement opportunities, and other business resources.

45968 ■ University of Virginia (UVA) - Darden School of Business - i.Lab Incubator [W.L. Lyons Brown III Innovation Laboratory]
100 Darden Blvd.
Charlottesville, VA 22903
URL: http://www.darden.virginia.edu/batten-institute/ventures/ilab
Description: Provides support for Darden MBA student entrepreneurs who are interested in developing early-stage business ventures by providing them with $10,000 in funding, faculty and student support, office space, access to technological expertise and free legal services. **Founded:** 1955.

45969 ■ VentureLab Incubator
100 Darden Blvd.
Charlottesville, VA 22903
Ph: (434)924-3900
Co. E-mail: nobleg@darden.virginia.edu
URL: http://vlab.virginia.edu/?Redirected=true
Contact: Omar Garriott, Executive Director
E-mail: garriotto@darden.virginia.edu
URL(s): www.darden.virginia.edu/batten-institute/ventures/ilab
Description: Summer incubator program of the Batten Institute for Entrepreneurship at the University of Virginia Darden School of Business. Supports the growth and development of early-stage ventures through grants, workspace, workshops, legal advice, and mentorship. **Founded:** 2000. **Investment Policies:** At least one founder should be a current student, faculty, or staff at University of Virginia.

45970 ■ VentureScope, LLC
1775 Tysons Blvd.
Tysons, VA 22102
Co. E-mail: hello@venturescope.com
URL: http://www.venturescope.com
Contact: Jason Chen, Chief Executive Officer
Linkedin: www.linkedin.com/company/venturescope-llc
X (Twitter): x.com/VentureScope
Description: Works with entrepreneurs and startups to help launch, grow, and raise capital. Also assists with writing business plans, establishing brand identity, conducting due diligence, evaluating industry trends, and assessing markets and audiences. **Founded:** 2008.

45971 ■ Virginia Commonwealth University - Virginia Biotechnology Research Park
800 E Leigh St.
Richmond, VA 23219
URL: http://egr.vcu.edu/about/locations-facilities/biotech1
Description: An incubator for early and mid-stage life science, research, and state/federal lab enterprises. Offers tenants a variety of services including a biotechnology library, talent bank, fiber optic telecommunications, conference and office space, and more. **Scope:** Biotechnology and bioscience. **Publications:** *Virginia Biotechnology Research Park News* (Monthly). **Educational Activities:** Virginia Biotechnology Research Park Luncheon programs, Offer exemplary teaching programs.

45972 ■ Virginia Highlands Small Business Incubator (VHSBI)
851 French Moore Jr. Blvd.
Abingdon, VA 24210
Ph: (276)492-2062
Fax: (276)698-3070
Co. E-mail: info@vhsbi.com
URL: http://vhsbi.com
Contact: Jack C. Phelps, Jr., President
Facebook: www.facebook.com/vhsbi
Description: Business incubator established to help start-up and existing business expand and grow in Southwest Virginia. Provides support, guidance, reasonable rent, and necessary services to foster a successful business community.

45973 ■ VT KnowledgeWorks
902 Prices Fork Rd., Ste. 4500
Blacksburg, VA 24061
Ph: (540)231-2861
URL: http://www.vtf.org/sitemap
Contact: Anne B. Keeler, Chief Financial Officer Treasurer
Description: Encourages and enables creative entrepreneurship worldwide, through innovative curriculum, local business resource centers, and a global network of cooperating regions, all focused on three essential contributors to success: clear understanding of fundamental business principles; access to timely, relevant information; and meaningful personal and corporate relationships.

45974 ■ West Piedmont Business Development Center
22 E Church St.
Martinsville, VA 24112
Ph: (276)638-2523
URL: http://www.wpbdc.org
Contact: Lisa Fultz, President
E-mail: lisa@mhcchamber.com
Description: Incubator that attracts, assists, educates and encourages emerging entrepreneurs by providing a favorable environment for their growth and development. Tenants in the Center are provided an advisory team of financial, managerial and business planning professionals to support their businesses as they endeavor to develop, grow and succeed.

EDUCATIONAL PROGRAMS

45975 ■ Brightpoint Community College (JTCC)
13101 Rte. 1
Chester, VA 23831-5316
Ph: (804)796-4000
Free: 800-552-3490
Co. E-mail: mytylerhelpdesk@jtcc.edu
URL: http://brightpoint.edu
Contact: Dr. Edward Raspiller, President
Facebook: www.facebook.com/johntylercc
Linkedin: www.linkedin.com/school/john-tyler-community-college
X (Twitter): x.com/johntylercc
Instagram: www.instagram.com/johntylercc
YouTube: www.youtube.com/user/JohnTylerCommCollege
Description: Two-year college offering a small business management program. **Founded:** 1967.

45976 ■ Mountain Empire Community College (MECC)
3441 Mountain Empire Rd.
Big Stone Gap, VA 24219
Ph: (276)523-2400
Fax: (276)523-9699
Co. E-mail: helpdesk@mecc.edu
URL: http://www.mecc.edu
Contact: Dr. Kristen Westover, President
E-mail: kwestover@mecc.edu
Facebook: www.facebook.com/mountainempirecollege
X (Twitter): x.com/meccva
Instagram: www.instagram.com/meccedu
YouTube: www.youtube.com/channel/UCODiB3XKFFX_wzMiNZCc5Yg
Description: Two-year college offering programs in business management. **Founded:** 1972.

45977 ■ Northern Virginia Community College - Annandale Campus
8333 Little River Tpke.
Annandale, VA 22003
Ph: (703)323-3000
Co. E-mail: anparking@nvcc.edu
URL: http://www.nvcc.edu/annandale/index.html
Contact: Rizwan Rahman, Director, Operations
E-mail: rrahman@nvcc.edu
Facebook: www.facebook.com/NOVACommunityCollege
X (Twitter): x.com/novacommcollege
Description: Two-year college offering a small business management course. **Founded:** 1965. **Publications:** *The Peashooter* (Biweekly).

LEGISLATIVE ASSISTANCE

45978 ■ Virginia Senate Committee on Commerce and Labor
900 E Main St.
Richmond, VA 23219
Ph: (804)698-1076
URL: http://lis.virginia.gov/cgi-bin/legp604.exe?201+com+S02
Description: Handles small business legislation.

CONSULTANTS

45979 ■ Amplifier Advisors
McLean, VA
URL: http://www.amplifieradvisors.com
Contact: Jonathan Aberman, Contact
Description: Consulting firm. Combines technology entrepreneurship and legal, finance, and business-growth expertise to offer solutions to innovation challenges. **Founded:** 2009.

45980 ■ Axcel Innovation
3445 Seminole Tr., No., 289
Charlottesville, VA 22911
URL: http://axcelinnovation.com/axcel_core/index
Description: Provides consulting and program management services for economic development.

PUBLICATIONS

45981 ■ Hanover Association of Business and Chamber of Commerce--Business Directory
11211 Air Pk. Rd., Ste. 2
Ashland, VA 23005
Ph: (804)442-2093
Co. E-mail: info@hanoverchamberva.com
URL: http://hanoverchamberva.com
Contact: Sam Stone, President
URL(s): hanoverchamberva.com/Member-Directory
Released: Annual **Description:** Covers list of businesses in Hanover. Also provides information for companies and families moving to Hanover county and the town of Ashland. **Availability:** Print; Online; Download.

45982 ■ *Virginia Business*
1207 E Main St., Ste. 100
Richmond, VA 23219
Ph: (804)225-9262
URL: http://www.virginiabusiness.com
Contact: Bernie Niemeier, President
E-mail: bniemeier@va-business.com
Facebook: www.facebook.com/VirginiaBiz
Linkedin: www.linkedin.com/company/virginia-business
Instagram: www.instagram.com/virginia_business
Released: Monthly **Price:** $65.95, for print + digital + email newsletters or print subscription only (2 year); $99.95, for print + digital + email newsletters or print subscription only (3 year); $24.95, for digital only + email newsletters (1 year); $34.95, for print only; $34.95, for print + digital + email newsletters subscription only (1 year). **Description:** Contains information about the people and industries most significantly affecting Virginia's economy. **Availability:** Print; Online.

45983 ■ Virginia Business (VB)
1207 E Main St., Ste. 100
Richmond, VA 23219
Ph: (804)225-9262
URL: http://www.virginiabusiness.com
Contact: Bernie Niemeier, President
E-mail: bniemeier@va-business.com
Facebook: www.facebook.com/VirginiaBiz
Linkedin: www.linkedin.com/company/virginia-business
X (Twitter): x.com/virginiabiz
Instagram: www.instagram.com/virginia_business
Description: Publisher: Business-oriented monthly magazine. **Founded:** 1986. **Publications:** *Virginia Business* (Monthly).

PUBLISHERS

45984 ■ Information International
PO Box 79
Great Falls, VA 22066
Co. E-mail: w0yva@yahoo.com
URL: http://www.isquare.com
Contact: K. B. Warner, Manager
Description: Publishes business publications and software, especially startup and entrepreneurial-related, does not accept unsolicited manuscripts and reaches the market through direct mail, and the internet. **Founded:** 1986.

45985 ■ Ivy Software Inc.
1146 Richmond Tappahannock Hwy.
Manquin, VA 23106
URL: http://ivysoftware.com
Contact: Robert N. Holt, President
Description: Publisher of books on business management, accounting and finance, it offers seminars, microcomputer training and stand-up instruction, does not accept unsolicited manuscripts and reaches the market through telephone sales, trade sales and in-office contact. **Founded:** 1986.

45986 ■ Management Concepts Inc. (MC)
8230 Leesburg Pke.
Vienna, VA 22182
Ph: (703)790-9595
Free: 888-545-8571
Fax: (703)790-1371
Co. E-mail: info@managementconcepts.com
URL: http://www.managementconcepts.com
Contact: Stephen L. Maier, President
Facebook: www.facebook.com/managementconcepts
Linkedin: www.linkedin.com/company/management-concepts
X (Twitter): x.com/mgmt_concepts
YouTube: www.youtube.com/user/MgmtConcepts
Description: Firm provides training and consulting services such as professional development, performance improvement, and talent management solutions and a publisher of books and newsletters about federal government contracting and various training courses for federal, state, local, and Indian tribal governments, colleges and universities, non-profit and commercial organizations, and private individuals. **Founded:** 1973. **Publications:** "Brain Break: Understanding the Influence of Brain Functions on Organizational Effectiveness," T+D Magazine, Jun,

2010; "5 Steps to a Robust Work Life Program," Work span, Mar, 2010; "At the Speed of Trust," Feb, 2010; "Workforce Assessments: Fears and Facts," Jan, 2010; "Competing on Analytics: It Takes More Than Technology to Become Better," US Business Review, Jan, 2010; "Overcoming Culture Fatigue in Government," 2009; "Know What's Needed Before Choosing Assessment Tool," 2008; "Understanding Government Contract Law," Mar, 2007; "Governmental and Nonprofit Financial Management," Jan, 2007; "U.S. Military Program Management: Lessons Learned and Best Practices," Dec, 2006; "The Federal Acquisition Action Pack Series," Dec, 2006; "Project Management for Small Projects," Nov, 2006; "Introduction to IT Project Management," Oct, 2006; "Fast Forms for Managing Development Projects," Oct, 2006; "The Earned Value Management Maturity Model," Sep, 2006; "Activity Based Cost Management in Government, 2nd Edition," Aug, 2006; "Essentials for Government Contract negotiators," Jul, 2006; "A-76: Defense Acquisition Guidebook," Jun, 2006; "The Complete Desk Guide," May, 2006; "The COR/COTR Answer Book," 2006; "Quick Reference to Federal Appropriations Law," Mar, 2006; "Integrated Cost and Schedule Control for Project Management," Mar, 2006; "Project Requirements: A Guide to Best Practices," Mar, 2006; "Essentials of Software Project Management"; "Practical Ethics in Public Administration"; "Federal PM Focus". **Training:** Organizational Project Management Maturity Assessment Road map for Improvement; Appropriations Law; The Business Analyst: The Pivotal IT Role of the Future; Harnessing the Power of the Project Manager and Business Analyst Partnership; The Art and Power of Facilitation; Earned Value Made Easy Integrated Project Control; Top Five Challenges for the Senior Business Analyst; Enterprise Portfolio Management Road map From Strategy to Results; Business Analysis; Federal Financial Management; Federal Managers Practicum; Leadership; Don't Make an Ass Out of You and Me: Using Assumptions Effectively.

RESEARCH CENTERS

45987 ■ Virginia Innovation Partnership Corporation (VIPC)
2214 Rock Hill Rd., Ste. 600
Herndon, VA 20170
Ph: (703)689-3000
Fax: (703)689-3041
Co. E-mail: info@virginiaipc.org
URL: http://www.virginiaipc.org
Contact: Bob Stolle, President
E-mail: robert.stolle@virginiaipc.org
Linkedin: www.linkedin.com/company/virginia-innovation-partnership-corporation
X (Twitter): x.com/VirginiaIPC
YouTube: www.youtube.com/user/CenterforInnovativeT
Description: Business accelerator, MACH37, is run out of the Center for Innovation Technology. The accelerator is designed to facilitate the creation of the next generation of cybersecurity product companies. **Scope:** Fiber optics, composite materials, biotechnology, and wireless communications. **Founded:** 1985.

VENTURE CAPITAL FIRM

45988 ■ Blue Heron Capital
1519 Summit Ave., Ste. 200
Richmond, VA 23230
Ph: (804)212-3400
Fax: (804)212-3401
Co. E-mail: info@blueheroncap.com
URL: http://www.blueheroncap.com
Contact: Katharine Mooney, Manager
Linkedin: www.linkedin.com/company/blue-heron-capital
Description: Capital investment firm for early-stage companies, family-owned businesses, and non-core assets of corporations. **Industry Preferences:** Healthcare; tech-enabled businesses.

45989 ■ In-Q-Tel, Inc. (IQT)
2107 Wilson Blvd., Ste. 1100
Arlington, VA 22201
Co. E-mail: info@iqt.org
URL: http://www.iqt.org
Contact: Steve Bowsher, Chief Executive Officer
Linkedin: www.linkedin.com/company/in-q-tel
YouTube: www.youtube.com/c/IQT-INC
Description: Strategic venture capital firm. Accelerates the development and delivery of technologies for national security agencies. Bridges the gap between technology needs of government partner, fluid innovations of start-ups, and the venture community. **Founded:** 1999.

45990 ■ Locus (VCC)
110 Peppers Ferry Rd. NW
Christiansburg, VA 24073
Free: 877-214-3564
URL: http://locusimpact.org
Contact: Clyde Cornett, Chief Executive Officer (Acting) Executive Vice President Chief Financial Officer
Linkedin: www.linkedin.com/company/locusimpact
Description: Partners with organizations and individuals to provide financial resources and advisory services for projects designed to have a positive impact in their community. Works with small business owners around the Commonwealth to find creative ways to support growth and help them meet their goals. **Founded:** 2006.

45991 ■ Newbridge Partners LLC
2804 Baxley Hollow Ct.
Herndon, VA 20171
URL: http://www.yournbpartners.com
Contact: Cathy Daughenbaugh, President
Linkedin: www.linkedin.com/company/newbridge-partners-inc
Description: Founder-focused venture capital firm for technology start-ups. **Founded:** 2015. **Investment Policies:** Talented team; defensible, disruptive technologies; sizable global market. **Industry Preferences:** Computational sciences; life sciences.

45992 ■ Select Venture Partners LLC
159 Lichfield Blvd., Ste. 101
Fredericksburg, VA 22406
Ph: (646)709-3254
Co. E-mail: info@selectvp.com
URL: http://www.selectventurepartners.com
Contact: Adam Slovik, Managing Partner
E-mail: adam.slovik@selectvp.com
Description: Early stage investment management firm for start-ups in the Washington DC, Boston, Philadelphia, New York, and Salt Lake City areas. **Investment Policies:** Seed stage with early revenue and a demonstrated potential to generate approximately $1,000,000 annual revenue. **Industry Preferences:** Cloud services; SaaS; mobile; data analytics; ecommerce.

Washington

ASSOCIATIONS AND OTHER ORGANIZATIONS

45993 ■ Association of Fundraising Professionals Advancement Northwest
1800 James St., Ste. 103
Bellingham, WA 98225
Ph: (360)734-3166
Co. E-mail: office@afpadvancementnw.org
URL: http://afpadvancementnw.org
Contact: Shannon Wong, President
Facebook: www.facebook.com/AFPAdvNW
X (Twitter): x.com/AFPAdvNW
Founded: 2015. **Geographic Preference:** Regional.

45994 ■ International Association of Women Bellevue Chapter
Bellevue, WA
Co. E-mail: localchaptersoffice@iawomen.com
URL: http://www.iawomen.com/chapters/bellevue-chapter
Contact: Marie Bartolotti, Program Manager
E-mail: mbartolotti@iawomen.com
Description: Serves as network of accomplished women united to achieve professional goals. Provides a forum for sharing ideas and experiences of professional women regarding career success. Promotes an active business and networking community from all industries. **Geographic Preference:** Local.

45995 ■ International Association of Women Seattle Chapter
Seattle, WA
Co. E-mail: memberservices@iawomen.com
Facebook: www.facebook.com/IAWomenSeattle
Description: Serves as network of accomplished women united to achieve professional goals. Provides a forum for sharing ideas and experiences of professional women regarding career success. Promotes an active business and networking community from all industries. **Geographic Preference:** Local.

45996 ■ Northwest Mountain Minority Supplier Development Council
545 Andover Pk. W, Bldg. 1., Ste. 109
Tukwila, WA 98188
Ph: (253)243-6959
Fax: (253)243-6961
Co. E-mail: info@nwmmsdc.org
URL: http://nwmmsdc.org
Contact: Fernando Martinez, President
Facebook: www.facebook.com/nwmtnmsdc
Linkedin: www.linkedin.com/company/nwmmsdc
X (Twitter): x.com/NWMTNMSDC
YouTube: www.youtube.com/channel/UCQcOXkONfBFBFWpPJd72DCw
Geographic Preference: Regional.

45997 ■ Puget Sound Business Travel Association (PSBTA)
PO Box 55365
Shoreline, WA 98155
Ph: (425)890-1516
Co. E-mail: administrator@psbta.org
URL: http://psbta.org
Contact: Michelle Amos, President
E-mail: chapterpresident@psbta.org
Facebook: www.facebook.com/PSBTA
Description: Represents travel managers and providers. Promotes the value of the travel manager in meeting corporate travel needs and financial goals. Cultivates a positive public image of the corporate travel industry. Protects the interests of members and their corporations in legislative and regulatory matters. Promotes safety, security, efficiency and quality travel. Provides a forum for the exchange of information and ideas among members. **Geographic Preference:** Local.

45998 ■ Vashon Island Marijuana Entrepreneurs Alliance (VIMEA)
PO Box 2327
Vashon Island, WA 98070
URL: http://www.shangolos.com
Contact: Shango Los, Founder
Description: Advocacy and trade organization for legal marijuana produced on Vashon Island in Washington State.

SMALL BUSINESS DEVELOPMENT CENTERS

45999 ■ America's SBDC Washington Aberdeen (WSBDC)
c/o Mia Johnstone
1620 Edward P. Smith Dr., Bldg. 800, Rm. 858
Aberdeen, WA 98520
URL: http://wsbdc.org/advisor-location/aberdeen
Description: Represents and promotes the small business sector. Provides management assistance to current and prospective small business owners. Helps to improve management skills and expand the products and services of members. **Geographic Preference:** Local.

46000 ■ Edmonds Small Business Development Center (SBDC)
WA
Ph: (425)640-1435
Co. E-mail: snohomishcountysbdc@wsbdc.org
URL: http://www.edmonds.edu/programs-and-degrees/workforce-development-resources/entrepreneurship/sbdc.html
Contact: Amit B. Singh, President
Description: Represents and promotes the small business sector. Provides management assistance to current and prospective small business owners. Helps to improve management skills and expand the products and services of members. **Geographic Preference:** Local.

46001 ■ Ferry County Business Resource Center
147 N Clark Ave., Ste. 6
Republic, WA 99166
Ph: (509)207-8250
Co. E-mail: info@ferrycountysunrise.com
URL: http://ferrycountysunrise.com
Facebook: www.facebook.com/sunriseferrycounty
YouTube: www.youtube.com/channel/UC4NPWhLmcewpO7n54ebw2Hg
Description: Small business resource center available to small business owners and entrepreneurs, for the use of free, high-speed internet in a quiet work environment, to help startups succeed.

46002 ■ Highline Community College Small Business Development Center
2400 S 240th St.
Des Moines, WA 98198
Ph: (206)878-3710
URL: http://sbdc.highline.edu
Contact: John R. Mosby, President
Facebook: www.facebook.com/highlinecollege
Linkedin: www.linkedin.com/school/highline-college
X (Twitter): x.com/highlinetbirds
Instagram: www.instagram.com/highlinecollege
YouTube: www.youtube.com/c/HighlineCollege
Description: Provides management assistance to current and prospective small business owners in Highline. **Founded:** 1961. **Geographic Preference:** Local.

46003 ■ Renton Small Business Development Center
1055 S Grady Way, Renton City Hall
Renton, WA 98057
URL: http://rentonwa.gov/business/default.aspx?id=13018
Description: Represents and promotes the small business sector. Provides management assistance to current and prospective small business owners. Helps to improve management skills and expand the products and services of members. **Geographic Preference:** Local.

46004 ■ Stevens County Business Resource Center
986 S Main, Ste. A
Colville, WA 99114
Ph: (509)684-4571
Free: 800-776-7318
Fax: (509)684-4788
URL: http://tricountyedd.com/business-resources/small-business-center
Contact: Jeff Koffel, Executive Director
E-mail: jkoffel@teddonline.com
Description: Small business resource center available to small business owners and entrepreneurs, for the use of free, high-speed internet in a quiet work environment, to help startups succeed.

46005 ■ Tri-Cities Small Business Development Center (SBDC)
7130 W Grandridge Blvd., Ste. A
Kennewick, WA 99336
Ph: (509)735-1000
Free: 833-492-7232
Co. E-mail: washington@wsbdc.org
URL: http://www.tridec.org/small-business-resources
Contact: Karl Dye, President

STATE LISTINGS   Washington ■ 46020

Description: Represents and promotes the small business sector. Provides management assistance to current and prospective small business owners. Helps to improve management skills and expand the products and services of members. **Geographic Preference:** Local.

**46006 ■ Washington SBDC Lacey
[Washington Small Business Development Center Lacey]**
901 E 2nd Ave., Ste. 210
Spokane, WA 99202
Free: 833-492-7232
Co. E-mail: washington@wsbdc.org
URL: http://wsbdc.org/advisor-location/lacey
Contact: Jennifer Dye, Advisor
E-mail: jdye2@spscc.edu
Linkedin: www.linkedin.com/company/washingtonsbdc
X (Twitter): x.com/wsbdc
YouTube: www.youtube.com/user/WSBDC
Description: Represents and promotes the small business sector. Provides management assistance to current and prospective small business owners. Helps to improve management skills and expand the products and services of members. **Geographic Preference:** Local.

**46007 ■ Washington SBDC Moses Lake
[Washington Small Business Development Center Moses Lake]**
406 W Broadway Ave., Ste. A
Moses Lake, WA 98837
Ph: (509)764-6579
Co. E-mail: allan.peterson@wsbdc.org
URL: http://wsbdc.org/advisor-location/moses-lake
Contact: Allan Peterson, Contact
E-mail: allan.peterson@wsbdc.org
Description: Represents and promotes the small business sector. Provides management assistance to current and prospective small business owners. Helps to improve management skills and expand the products and services of members. **Geographic Preference:** Local.

**46008 ■ Washington SBDC Mount Vernon
[Washington Small Business Development Center Mount Vernon]**
223 S 1st St., Ste. C
Mount Vernon, WA 98273
Free: 833-492-7232
Co. E-mail: washington@wsbdc.org
URL: http://wsbdc.org/advisor-location/mount-vernon
Contact: Kristina Hines, Advisor
Description: Represents and promotes the small business sector. Provides management assistance to current and prospective small business owners. Helps to improve management skills and expand the products and services of members. **Geographic Preference:** Local.

**46009 ■ Washington SBDC Omak
[Washington Small Business Development Center Omak]**
c/o Lew Blakeney
238 E Oak
Omak, WA 98841
Ph: (509)826-5107
Co. E-mail: washington@wsbdc.org
URL: http://wsbdc.org/omak
Contact: Lew Blakeney, Advisor
Description: Represents and promotes the small business sector. Provides management assistance to current and prospective small business owners. Helps to improve management skills and expand the products and services of members. **Geographic Preference:** Local.

**46010 ■ Washington SBDC Port Angeles
[Washington Small Business Development Center Port Angeles]**
c/o Micah Jonet
338 W 1st St., Ste. 105
Port Angeles, WA 98362
Ph: (360)417-3375
Co. E-mail: washington@wsbdc.org
URL: http://wsbdc.org/port-angeles-cie-2

Contact: Micah Jonet, Contact
Description: Represents and promotes the small business sector. Provides management assistance to current and prospective small business owners. Helps to improve management skills and expand the products and services of members. **Geographic Preference:** Local.

**46011 ■ Washington SBDC Pullman
[Washington Small Business Development Center Pullman]**
1615 NE Eastgate Blvd., Section G, Ste. 6W
Pullman, WA 99163
Ph: (509)335-8081
Fax: (509)335-8082
Co. E-mail: aziz.makhani@wsbdc.org
URL: http://wsbdc.org/pullman
Contact: Aziz Makhani, Contact
E-mail: aziz.makhani@wsbdc.org
Description: Represents and promotes the small business sector. Provides management assistance to current and prospective small business owners. Helps to improve management skills and expand the products and services of members. **Geographic Preference:** Local.

**46012 ■ Washington SBDC Seattle
[Washington Small Business Development Center Seattle]**
901 Fifth Ave., Ste. 2900
Seattle, WA 98164
Free: 833-492-7232
Co. E-mail: washington@wsbdc.org
URL: http://wsbdc.org/seattle
Contact: Ellie He, Contact
X (Twitter): twitter.com/wsbdc
Description: Represents and promotes the small business sector. Provides management assistance to current and prospective small business owners. Helps to improve management skills and expand the products and services of members. **Geographic Preference:** Local.

**46013 ■ Washington SBDC Spokane
[Washington Small Business Development Center Spokane]**
901 E 2nd Ave., Ste. 210
Spokane, WA 99202
URL: http://wsbdc.org/about
Description: Represents and promotes the small business sector. Provides management assistance to current and prospective small business owners. Helps to improve management skills and expand the products and services of members. **Geographic Preference:** Local.

**46014 ■ Washington SBDC Tacoma
[Washington Small Business Development Center Tacoma]**
950 Pacific Ave., Ste. No. 425
Tacoma, WA 98402
Free: 833-492-7232
Co. E-mail: washington@wsbdc.org
URL: http://wsbdc.org/locations
Contact: Ann Zimmerman, Advisor
Description: Represents and promotes the small business sector. Provides management assistance to current and prospective small business owners. Helps to improve management skills and expand the products and services of members. **Geographic Preference:** Local.

**46015 ■ Washington SBDC Vancouver
[Washington Small Business Development Center Vancouver]**
915 Broadway
Vancouver, WA 98661
Free: 833-492-7232
Co. E-mail: washington@wsbdc.org
URL: http://wsbdc.org/vancouver-2
Contact: Duane Fladland, Director
E-mail: duane.fladland@wsu.edu
X (Twitter): x.com/wsbdc
Description: Represents and promotes the small business sector. Provides management assistance to current and prospective small business owners.

Helps to improve management skills and expand the products and services of members. **Geographic Preference:** Local.

**46016 ■ Washington SBDC Wenatchee
[Washington Small Business Development Center Wenatchee]**
238 Olds Station, Ste. A100 & A101
Wenatchee, WA 98801
Free: 833-492-7232
Co. E-mail: washington@wsbdc.org
URL: http://wsbdc.org
Contact: Ron Nielsen, Advisor
Description: Represents and promotes the small business sector. Provides management assistance to current and prospective small business owners. Helps to improve management skills and expand the products and services of members. **Geographic Preference:** Local.

**46017 ■ Washington SBDC Yakima
[Washington Small Business Development Center Yakima]**
2520 W Washington Ave., Ste. 1
Yakima, WA 98903
Ph: (509)575-1140
Co. E-mail: washington@wsbdc.org
URL: http://wsbdc.org/advisor-location/yakima
Contact: Mike Darrow, Advisor
Description: Represents and promotes the small business sector. Provides management assistance to current and prospective small business owners. Helps to improve management skills and expand the products and services of members. **Geographic Preference:** Local.

46018 ■ Washington Small Business Development Center (WSBDC)
4420 E 8th Ave.
Spokane, WA 99212
Free: 833-492-7232
Co. E-mail: washington@wsbdc.org
URL: http://wsbdc.org
Contact: Sheryl McGrath, Director
Linkedin: www.linkedin.com/company/washingtonsbdc
X (Twitter): x.com/wsbdc
YouTube: www.youtube.com/user/WSBDC
Description: Enhances economic growth in Washington through a network of facilities statewide that provide the expertise, knowledge and innovation necessary to assist startup and existing businesses succeed. Services include business counseling, professional training, environmental and safety assistance, research, geographic information, technology development assistance, and disadvantaged business outreach. **Geographic Preference:** State.

46019 ■ Western Washington University Small Business Development Center (WWU SBDC)
516 High St.
Bellingham, WA 98225
Ph: (360)650-3000
Co. E-mail: sbdc@wwu.edu
URL: http://sbdc.wwu.edu
Contact: Chris Luxe, Owner
Facebook: www.facebook.com/BellinghamSBDC
X (Twitter): x.com/WWU_SBDC
Description: Represents and promotes the small business sector. Provides management assistance to current and prospective small business owners. Helps to improve management skills and expand the products and services of members. **Founded:** 1983. **Geographic Preference:** Local.

SMALL BUSINESS ASSISTANCE PROGRAMS

46020 ■ Washington Department of Commerce - International Trade & Economic Development Division
1011 Plum St. SE
Olympia, WA 98504-2525
Ph: (360)725-4000
Co. E-mail: communications@commerce.wa.gov

URL: http://www.commerce.wa.gov/Pages/default.aspx
Contact: Lisa Brown, Director
Facebook: www.facebook.com/WAStateCommerce
X (Twitter): twitter.com/wastatecommerce
Description: Assists Washington state businesses in profitably accessing the global markets by providing training and assistance.

46021 ■ **Washington State Department of Commerce - Business Development Div.**
1011 Plum St. SE
Olympia, WA 98504-2525
URL: http://www.commerce.wa.gov/growing-the-economy/business-development
Description: Intercedes with government agencies on behalf of businesses experiencing licensing, taxation, and regulation difficulties.

46022 ■ **Washington State Department of Revenue (DOR)**
PO Box 47450
Olympia, WA 98504-7450
Ph: (360)705-6705
Co. E-mail: revenuenews@dor.wa.gov
URL: http://www.dor.wa.gov
Facebook: www.facebook.com/WARevenue
X (Twitter): x.com/WAStateDOR
YouTube: www.youtube.com/user/WashingtonStateDOR
Description: Provides information about Washington taxes for prospective businesses.

SCORE OFFICES

46023 ■ **Central Washington SCORE**
200 Palouse St., Ste. 101
Wenatchee, WA 98801
Ph: (509)888-2900
Co. E-mail: score663office@gmail.com
URL: http://centralwashington.score.org
Contact: Bridget Weston, Chief Executive Officer
Facebook: www.facebook.com/CentralWashingtonSCORE
Description: Promotes business and community development in the Wenatchee, WA area. **Founded:** 1902. **Geographic Preference:** Local.

46024 ■ **Mid-Columbia Tri-Cities SCORE**
7130 W Grandridge Blvd., Ste. A
Kennewick, WA 99336
Ph: (509)735-1000
Co. E-mail: score590office@gmail.com
URL: http://www.score.org/midcolumbiatricities
Contact: Robert Carroll, Contact
Description: Provides professional guidance and information to America's small business in order to strengthen the local and national economy. **Geographic Preference:** Local.

46025 ■ **SCORE - Auburn**
110 Second St., SW
Auburn, WA 98001
Ph: (253)409-2884
Free: 855-685-0166
Co. E-mail: score.auburnwa@gmail.com
URL: http://tacoma.score.org/auburn
Description: Provides professional guidance and information to maximize the success of existing and emerging small businesses. Offers business counseling and workshops.

46026 ■ **SCORE - Bellevue**
Bellevue, WA
Ph: (206)553-7320
URL: http://seattle.score.org/eastside
Description: Provides professional guidance and information to maximize the success of existing and emerging small businesses. Offers business counseling and workshops.

46027 ■ **SCORE - Bellingham**
1336 Cornwall, Chase Bank, 2nd Fl.
Bellingham, WA 98225
Ph: (360)685-4259
Co. E-mail: admiin.0591@scorevolunteer.org
URL: http://www.score.org/bellingham
Facebook: www.facebook.com/bellinghamscore
Description: Provides professional guidance and information to maximize the success of existing and emerging small businesses. Offers business counseling and workshops. **Geographic Preference:** Local.

46028 ■ **SCORE - Everett**
808 134th St. SW, Ste. 101
Everett, WA 98204
Ph: (206)553-7320
Co. E-mail: snohomish@scorevolunteer.org
URL: http://seattle.score.org/sno-isle-branch
Description: Provides professional guidance and information to maximize the success of existing and emerging small businesses. Offers business counseling and workshops.

46029 ■ **SCORE - Gig Harbor**
Gig Harbor Chamber of Commerce
3125 Judson St.
Gig Harbor, WA 98335
Free: 855-685-0166
Co. E-mail: score.tacoma@gmail.com
URL: http://tacoma.score.org/gig-harbor-score
Description: Provides professional guidance and information to maximize the success of existing and emerging small businesses. Offers business counseling and workshops.

46030 ■ **SCORE - Greater Seattle**
2401 4th Ave., Ste. 450
Seattle, WA 98121
Ph: (206)553-7320
Co. E-mail: greaterseattle@scorevolunteer.org
URL: http://www.score.org/seattle
Facebook: www.facebook.com/SCOREGreaterSeattle
Linkedin: www.linkedin.com/company/score-mentors-greater-seattle
Description: Provides professional guidance and information to maximize the success of existing and emerging small businesses. Offers business counseling and workshops. **Founded:** 1965. **Publications:** SCORE Workshop Brochure. **Geographic Preference:** Local.

46031 ■ **SCORE - Kitsap**
3100 Bucklin Hill Rd., Ste. 100
Silverdale, WA 98383
Ph: (360)328-1380
Co. E-mail: kitsap@scorevolunteer.org
URL: http://seattle.score.org/find-location
URL(s): kitsapscore.org/?_ga=2.111642626.720635290.1626582623-335790367.1626582623
Facebook: www.facebook.com/KitsapSCOREmentors
X (Twitter): x.com/KitsapSCORE
Description: Provides professional guidance and information to maximize the success of existing and emerging small businesses. Offers business counseling and workshops.

46032 ■ **SCORE - Lacey**
4220 6th Ave. SE
Lacey, WA 98503
Free: 855-685-0166
Co. E-mail: score.lacey@gmail.com
URL: http://tacoma.score.org/lacey
Description: Provides professional guidance and information to maximize the success of existing and emerging small businesses. Offers business counseling and workshops.

46033 ■ **SCORE - Longview**
Longview, WA
Ph: (360)545-3210
Co. E-mail: vancouver@scorevolunteer.org
URL: http://vancouver.score.org
Description: Provides professional guidance and information to maximize the success of existing and emerging small businesses. Offers business counseling and workshops.

46034 ■ **SCORE - Mid-Columbia Tri-Cities**
7130 W Grandridge Blvd. Ste. A
Kennewick, WA 99336
Ph: (509)735-1000
Co. E-mail: score590office@gmail.com
URL: http://www.score.org/midcolumbiatricities
Contact: Robert Carroll, Contact
Description: Provides professional guidance and information to maximize the success of existing and emerging small businesses. Offers business counseling and workshops.

46035 ■ **SCORE - Mount Vernon, Washington**
204 W Montgomery
Mount Vernon, WA 98273
URL: http://bellingham.score.org
Contact: Bob W. George, Contact
Description: Provides professional guidance and information to maximize the success of existing and emerging small businesses. Offers business counseling and workshops.

46036 ■ **SCORE - Seattle**
2401 4th Ave., Ste. 450
Seattle, WA 98121
Ph: (206)553-7320
URL: http://seattle.score.org
Description: Provides professional guidance and information to maximize the success of existing and emerging small businesses. Offers business counseling and workshops.

46037 ■ **SCORE - South Sound/Tacoma**
Bates Technical School, Rm. M-123B
1101 S Yakima Ave.
Tacoma, WA 98405
Free: 855-685-0166
Co. E-mail: score.southsound@gmail.com
URL: http://tacoma.score.org
Contact: Nancy Strojny, Secretary
Facebook: www.facebook.com/scoretacomasouthsound
X (Twitter): x.com/scorementors
Description: Provides professional guidance and information to maximize the success of existing and emerging small businesses. Offers business counseling and workshops. **Geographic Preference:** Local.

46038 ■ **SCORE - Spokane**
801 W Riverside Ave., Ste. 444
Spokane, WA 99201
Ph: (509)353-2821
Fax: (509)353-2829
Co. E-mail: info@scorespokane.org
URL: http://www.score.spokane.org
Linkedin: www.linkedin.com/company/score-mentors-spokane
X (Twitter): x.com/SCORESPOKANE
Description: Provides professional guidance and information to maximize the success of existing and emerging small businesses. Offers business counseling and workshops. **Founded:** 1973. **Geographic Preference:** Local.

46039 ■ **SCORE - Vancouver**
4001 Main St., Ste. 121
Box 3
Vancouver, WA 98663
Ph: (360)545-3210
Co. E-mail: vancouver@scorevolunteer.org
URL: http://vancouver.score.org
Contact: Bridget Weston, Chief Executive Officer
Facebook: www.facebook.com/SCOREVancouver
Linkedin: www.linkedin.com/company/score-mentors-vancouver
X (Twitter): x.com/vancouverSCORE
YouTube: www.youtube.com/user/SCORESmallBusiness/featured
Pinterest: www.pinterest.com/scorementors
Description: Provides professional guidance and information to maximize the success of existing and emerging small businesses. Offers business counseling and workshops. **Founded:** 1964. **Geographic Preference:** Local.

46040 ■ **SCORE - Wenatchee**
200 Palouse St., SSte. 1010
Wenatchee, WA 98801
Ph: (509)888-2900
Co. E-mail: ch.admin.0663@scorevolunteer.org

URL: http://centralwashington.score.org
Contact: Bridget Weston, Chief Executive Officer
Description: Provides professional guidance and information to maximize the success of existing and emerging small businesses. Offers business counseling and workshops.

46041 ■ **SCORE - Yakima Valley**
7130 W Grandridge Blvd., Ste. A
Kennewick, WA 99336
Ph: (509)735-1000
Co. E-mail: score590office@gmail.com
URL: http://midcolumbiatricities.score.org
Contact: Bridget Weston, Chief Executive Officer
Description: Provides professional guidance and information to maximize the success of existing and emerging small businesses. Offers business counseling and workshops.

46042 ■ **Yakima Valley SCORE**
1105 S 13th Ave.
Yakima, WA 98907
Co. E-mail: help@score.org
URL: http://midcolumbiatricities.score.org/about-score-yakima-valley
Facebook: www.facebook.com/pg/SCOREMentorsVakimaValley
X (Twitter): twitter.com/SCORE_Yakima
Description: Seeks to educate entrepreneurs and help small businesses start, grow and succeed nationwide. Organizes volunteers who are working or retired business owners, executives and corporate leaders who wish to share their wisdom and lessons learned in business. **Geographic Preference:** Local.

BETTER BUSINESS BUREAUS

46043 ■ **Better Business Bureau Great West + Pacific [BBB Great West + Pacific]**
PO Box 191279
Boise, ID 83719
Ph: (208)342-4649
URL: http://www.bbb.org/local-bbb/bbb-great-west-pacific
Linkedin: www.linkedin.com/company/bbbgwp
Instagram: www.instagram.com/bbbgwp
YouTube: www.youtube.com/bbbgwp
Description: Seeks to promote and foster the highest ethical relationship between businesses and the public through voluntary self-regulation, consumer and business education, and service excellence. Provides information to help consumers and businesses make informed purchasing decisions and avoid costly scams and frauds; settles consumer complaints through arbitration and other means. **Geographic Preference:** State.

46044 ■ **Better Business Bureau of the Inland Northwest**
1206 N Lincoln St., Ste. 200
Spokane, WA 99201-2559
Ph: (509)326-6885
Co. E-mail: info@thebbb.org
URL: http://www.bbb.org/us/wa/spokane/profile/business-associations/associated-industries-of-the-inland-northwest-1296-5000455
Description: Seeks to promote and foster the highest ethical relationship between businesses and the public through voluntary self-regulation, consumer and business education, and service excellence. Provides information to help consumers and businesses make informed purchasing decisions and avoid costly scams and frauds; settles consumer complaints through arbitration and other means. **Geographic Preference:** Regional.

CHAMBERS OF COMMERCE

46045 ■ **Anacortes Chamber of Commerce (ACC)**
819 Commercial Ave.
Anacortes, WA 98221
Ph: (360)293-7911
Co. E-mail: info@anacortes.org
URL: http://anacortes.org
Contact: Christy Lyman, Director
Description: Promotes business and community development in the Anacortes, WA area. Sponsors Anacortes Waterfront Festival. **Founded:** 1904. **Publications:** *The Anacortes Communicator* (Monthly). **Geographic Preference:** Local.

46046 ■ **Asotin Chamber of Commerce**
PO Box 574
Asotin, WA 99402
Ph: (509)243-4242
Co. E-mail: wvaugan@pioneerins.com
URL: http://www.wcce.org/index.php?option=com_civicrm&task=civicrm/profile/view&Itemid=440&reset=1&id=37&gid=9
Contact: Guy Occhiogrosso, Chairman of the Board
Description: Promotes business and community development in the Asotin, WA area. **Geographic Preference:** Local.

46047 ■ **Auburn Area Chamber of Commerce (AACC)**
268 E Main St.
Auburn, WA 98002
Ph: (253)833-0700
Co. E-mail: auburncc@auburnareawa.org
URL: http://www.auburnareawa.org
Contact: Kacie Bray, President
Facebook: www.facebook.com/auburnareawa
Linkedin: www.linkedin.com/company/auburn-area-chamber-of-commerce
X (Twitter): x.com/AuburnAreaCCWA
Instagram: www.instagram.com/auburnareachamberwa
Description: Promotes business and community development in the Auburn, WA area. **Founded:** 1925. **Publications:** *Auburn Works* (Monthly); *Auburn Journal*. **Geographic Preference:** Local.

46048 ■ **Bainbridge Island Chamber of Commerce (BICC)**
395 Winslow Way E
Bainbridge Island, WA 98110
Ph: (206)842-3700
Fax: (206)201-3185
URL: http://bainbridgechamber.com
Contact: Stefan Goldby, President
Facebook: www.facebook.com/BainbridgeChamber
X (Twitter): x.com/BI_Chamber
Instagram: www.instagram.com/bainbridgechamber
Pinterest: www.pinterest.com/bainbridgechamber
Description: Promotes business and community development in Bainbridge Island, Washington. Sponsors Celebrity Auction, and community school activities. **Founded:** 1927. **Publications:** *Business News* (Monthly). **Geographic Preference:** Local.

46049 ■ **Ballard Alliance (BCC)**
5306 Ballard Ave., NW, Ste. 216
Seattle, WA 98107
Ph: (206)784-9705
Co. E-mail: info@ballardalliance.com
URL: http://www.visitballard.com
Contact: Mike Stewart, Executive Director
E-mail: mike@ballardalliance.com
Facebook: www.facebook.com/visitballard
X (Twitter): x.com/visitballard
Instagram: www.instagram.com/visitballard
Pinterest: www.pinterest.com/visitballard
Description: Promotes business and community development in the Ballard neighborhood of Seattle, WA. Sponsors annual SeafoodFest. **Founded:** 1889. **Publications:** *Membership Roster* (Annual). **Geographic Preference:** Local.

46050 ■ *Battle Ground--North Clark County Directory*
Released: Annual **Availability:** Print; Online.

46051 ■ **Bellevue Chamber of Commerce**
330 112th Ave. NE, Ste. 100
Bellevue, WA 98004
Ph: (425)454-2464
Co. E-mail: staff@bellevuechamber.org
URL: http://bellevuechamber.org
Contact: Joe Fain, President
E-mail: joe@bellevuechamber.org
Facebook: www.facebook.com/bellevuechamber
Linkedin: www.linkedin.com/company/bellevuechamber
X (Twitter): x.com/bellevuechamber
Instagram: www.instagram.com/bellevuechamber
YouTube: www.youtube.com/channel/UChPt_YEMdVBIxz2GHhT2BPg
Description: Fosters a healthy business environment by providing strategic leadership, advocacy, tools and resources for business success. **Publications:** *The Edge* (Monthly); *The Membership Directory & Business Resource Guide* (Annual); *The Voice of Business* (Monthly). **Awards:** Eastside Small Business of the Year Award (Annual); Bellevue Chamber of Commerce Eastside Business of the Year Award (Annual); Bellevue Chamber of Commerce Innovative Service of the Year Award (Annual). **Geographic Preference:** Local.

46052 ■ **Bellingham/Whatcom Chamber of Commerce and Industry**
119 N Commercial St., Ste. 110
Bellingham, WA 98225
Ph: (360)734-1330
Fax: (360)734-1332
URL: http://bellingham.com
Contact: Guy Occhiogrosso, President
E-mail: guy@bellingham.com
Facebook: www.facebook.com/bellinghamchamber
Linkedin: www.linkedin.com/company/bellingham-whatcom-chamber-of-commerce-&-industry
X (Twitter): x.com/bham_chamber
YouTube: www.youtube.com/user/bellinghamchamber
Description: County-wide Chamber of Commerce; organizes community festivals and special events. **Founded:** 1914. **Geographic Preference:** Local.

46053 ■ **Benton City Chamber of Commerce**
513 9th St.
Benton City, WA 99320
Ph: (509)588-4984
Fax: (509)588-4778
Co. E-mail: info@bentoncitychamber.org
URL: http://www.bentoncitychamber.org
Contact: Dakota Renz, President
E-mail: president@bentoncitychamber.org
Facebook: www.facebook.com/BentonCityChamber
X (Twitter): x.com/BC_chamber
Instagram: www.instagram.com/bentoncitychamber
Description: Seeks to promote, preserve, and strengthen the prosperity of the businesses and economy of Benton City. **Geographic Preference:** Local.

46054 ■ **Birch Bay Chamber of Commerce**
4819 Alderson Rd. No. 103
Blaine, WA 98230
Ph: (360)371-5004
Co. E-mail: info@birchbaychamber.com
URL: http://birchbaychamber.com
Contact: Dianne Marrs-Smith, President
Facebook: www.facebook.com/BirchBayChamber
Linkedin: www.linkedin.com/in/birch-bay-chamber-of-commerce-19694135
X (Twitter): x.com/VisitBirchBay
YouTube: www.youtube.com/channel/UCgitvosY3roaQYwY1nLEYjQ
Description: Promotes a healthy business climate while recognizing the quality of life at Birch Bay. **Founded:** 1972. **Publications:** *Chamber News*. **Geographic Preference:** Local.

46055 ■ **Blaine Community Chamber of Commerce**
546 Peace Portal Dr.
Blaine, WA 98230
Ph: (360)332-6484
Free: 800-624-3555
Co. E-mail: info@blainechamber.com
URL: http://www.blainechamber.com
Contact: Tim Woodard, President
Facebook: www.facebook.com/blainechamber
Linkedin: www.linkedin.com/company/blaine-chamber-of-commerce
Instagram: www.instagram.com/blainechamber

Description: Promotes business and community development in Blaine, WA. **Founded:** 1950. **Geographic Preference:** Local.

46056 ■ Bonney Lake Chamber of Commerce
20608 State Rte. 410 E
Bonney Lake, WA 98391
Ph: (424)262-3707
Co. E-mail: chamber@thechambercollective.com
URL: http://thechambercollective.com
Contact: Thad Huff, President
E-mail: thadh@openlife.church
Description: Promotes business and community development in Bonney Lake, WA. **Founded:** 1982. **Publications:** *Chamber News.* **Geographic Preference:** Local.

46057 ■ Bremerton Area Chamber of Commerce (BACC)
409 Pacific Ave., Ste. 207
Bremerton, WA 98337
Ph: (360)479-3579
Co. E-mail: chamber@bremertonchamber.org
URL: http://www.bremertonchamber.org
Contact: David Emmons, President
Facebook: www.facebook.com/BremertonChamberofCommerce
Linkedin: www.linkedin.com/company/bremerton-area-chamber-of-commerce
X (Twitter): x.com/bremareachamber
Instagram: www.instagram.com/bremchamber
YouTube: www.youtube.com/channel/UCAFyi8QYWpiBypk3ck-d7dA
Description: Promotes business and community development in the Bremerton, WA area. **Founded:** 1907. **Publications:** *Bremerton Business News* (Monthly). **Educational Activities:** Membership Luncheon (Monthly). **Geographic Preference:** Local.

46058 ■ Buckley Chamber of Commerce
PO Box 295
Buckley, WA 98321
Ph: (360)829-0975
Co. E-mail: buckleychamberofcommerce@gmail.com
URL: http://buckleychamber.org
Contact: Ali Santman, President
Facebook: www.facebook.com/BuckleyChamberofCommerce
Instagram: www.instagram.com/buckleychamberofcommerce
Description: Promotes business and community development in Buckley, WA. Holds monthly board meeting. **Founded:** 1830. **Geographic Preference:** Local.

46059 ■ Burlington Chamber of Commerce (BCC)
520 E Fairhaven Ave.
Burlington, WA 98233
Ph: (360)757-0994
Fax: (360)757-0821
Co. E-mail: info@burlington-chamber.com
URL: http://www.burlington-chamber.com
Contact: Ted Brockmann, Officer
Facebook: www.facebook.com/burlingtonchamber
Linkedin: www.linkedin.com/company/burlington-chamber
X (Twitter): x.com/BurlingtonWa
Instagram: www.instagram.com/burlingtonchamber
Description: Promotes business and community development in Burlington, WA. Sponsors Berry Dairy Days festival, Easter Egg Hunt, and Santa's Farm Parade, and Northwest Coffee Festival. **Founded:** 1961. **Publications:** *In Motion* (Weekly). **Geographic Preference:** Local.

46060 ■ *Business Connections*
500 NW Chamber of Commerce Way
Chehalis, WA 98532
Ph: (360)748-8885
Fax: (360)748-8763
Co. E-mail: thechamber@chamberway.com
URL: http://www.chamberway.com
Contact: Cynthia Mudge, Executive Director
E-mail: director@chamberway.com
URL(s): chamberway.com/relocation-guide/business-connections
Released: Monthly **Availability:** Print; Online.

46061 ■ *Business Directory*
625 S 4th St.
Renton, WA 98057
Ph: (425)226-4560
Co. E-mail: info@gorenton.com
URL: http://www.gorenton.com
Contact: Diane Dobson, President
E-mail: diane@gorenton.com
URL(s): chamber.gorenton.com/list
Availability: Print; Online.

46062 ■ *Business News and Views*
URL(s): www.battlegroundchamber.org/pages/Newsletters
Released: Monthly **Availability:** Print; PDF.

46063 ■ Camas-Washougal Chamber of Commerce
422 NE 4th Ave.
Camas, WA 98607
Ph: (360)834-2472
Fax: (360)834-9171
Co. E-mail: adminassistant@cwchamber.com
URL: http://cwchamber.com
Contact: Lori Reed, President
Facebook: www.facebook.com/camaswashougalchamber
Linkedin: www.linkedin.com/company/camas-washougal-chamber-of-commerce
X (Twitter): x.com/camaswashougal
Instagram: www.instagram.com/camas_washougalchamber
YouTube: www.youtube.com/channel/UCPo9FsDhyQeqdMQUca4WVnQ
Description: Promotes business and community development in Camas and Washougal, WA. Sponsors Camas Days festival. **Publications:** *Camas-Washougal Chamber of Commerce--Business Directory*; *Business Directory*; *Chamber News* (Monthly). **Geographic Preference:** Local.

46064 ■ Cashmere Chamber of Commerce
103 Cottage Ave.
Cashmere, WA 98815
Ph: (509)782-7404
Co. E-mail: info@cashmerechamber.org
URL: http://cashmerechamber.org
Contact: Kris Norman, Co-President
Facebook: www.facebook.com/CashmereChamberofCommerce
Instagram: www.instagram.com/discovercashmere
YouTube: www.youtube.com/channel/UC8NAgl6Elq0Q8qiblqmaRpA
Description: Promotes business and community development in Cashmere, WA area. **Founded:** 1924. **Publications:** *Wenatchee Business Journal* (Quarterly). **Awards:** Cashmere Chamber of Commerce Business of the Year (Annual); Cashmere Chamber of Commerce Citizen of the Year (Annual). **Geographic Preference:** Local.

46065 ■ Central Washington SCORE
200 Palouse St., Ste. 101
Wenatchee, WA 98801
Ph: (509)888-2900
Co. E-mail: score663office@gmail.com
URL: http://centralwashington.score.org
Contact: Bridget Weston, Chief Executive Officer
Facebook: www.facebook.com/CentralWashingtonSCORE
Description: Promotes business and community development in the Wenatchee, WA area. **Founded:** 1902. **Geographic Preference:** Local.

46066 ■ Centralia-Chehalis Chamber of Commerce
500 NW Chamber of Commerce Way
Chehalis, WA 98532
Ph: (360)748-8885
Fax: (360)748-8763
Co. E-mail: thechamber@chamberway.com
URL: http://www.chamberway.com
Contact: Cynthia Mudge, Executive Director
E-mail: director@chamberway.com
Facebook: www.facebook.com/ChamberWay
X (Twitter): x.com/ChamberWay
Instagram: www.instagram.com/chamber.of.commerce
Description: Promotes business and community development in Lewis and Southern Thurston counties, WA. Provides regional tourist information. Sponsors community social and promotional events. Maintains information center. **Founded:** 1845. **Publications:** *Business Connections* (Monthly). **Geographic Preference:** Local.

46067 ■ *CHAMBER NEWS*
URL(s): www.woodlandwachamber.com/newsletter-archive
Released: Quarterly **Availability:** Print; Online; PDF.

46068 ■ Chewelah Chamber of Commerce
401 S Pk. St., Ste. G
Chewelah, WA 99109
Ph: (509)935-8595
Co. E-mail: info@chewelah.org
URL: http://chewelah.org
Contact: Debbie Akers, Vice President
Description: Promotes business and community development in Chewelah, WA. Participates in Miss Chewelah - Auction Beautification. Maintains tourism and visitor's center. **Founded:** 1907. **Publications:** *Around Town - What's Going On* (Bimonthly). **Geographic Preference:** Local.

46069 ■ Clallam Bay - Sekiu Chamber of Commerce
PO Box 355
Clallam Bay, WA 98326
Ph: (360)963-2339
Co. E-mail: chamber@clallambay.com
URL: http://forkswa.com/business-directory/business-listing/services/clallam-bay-sekiu-chamber-of-commerce
Description: Assists in the development of the Clallam Bay-Sekiu and the surrounding areas. **Geographic Preference:** Local.

46070 ■ Cle Elum-Roslyn Chamber of Commerce
401 W 1st St.
Cle Elum, WA 98922
Ph: (509)674-5958
Fax: (509)674-7674
Co. E-mail: cle_elum@cleelum.com
URL: http://www.wcce.org/index.php?option=com_civicrm&task=civicrm/profile/view&Itemid=440&reset=1&id=81&gid=9
Contact: Deloit R. Wolfe, President
Facebook: www.facebook.com/cleelumroslynchamber
Description: Promotes business and community development and tourism in the Cle Elum, WA area. Sponsors festivals and charitable events. **Geographic Preference:** Local.

46071 ■ Colville Chamber of Commerce
986 S Main St., Ste. B
Colville, WA 99114
Ph: (509)684-5973
URL: http://www.colvillechamberofcommerce.com
Description: Promotes business and community development in Colville, WA. Sponsors Rendezvous festival. Serves as a leader in tourism promotions. Sponsors Colville Junior Miss Program and Colville Float. **Founded:** 1910. **Geographic Preference:** Local.

46072 ■ Concrete Chamber of Commerce
East County Resource Ctr.
45770 Main St.
Concrete, WA 98237
Ph: (360)853-8784
Co. E-mail: chamber@concrete-wa.com
URL: http://concrete-wa.com
Contact: Valerie Stafford, President
Facebook: www.facebook.com/ConcreteChamber
Description: Promotes business and community development in Concrete, WA. **Founded:** 1976. **Geographic Preference:** Local.

STATE LISTINGS

46073 ■ Coulee City Chamber of Commerce
PO Box 896
Coulee City, WA 99115
Ph: (509)632-5043
Co. E-mail: tns@accima.com
URL: http://www.wcce.org/index.php?option=com
_civicrm&task=civicrm/profile/view&Itemid=440
&reset=1&id=93&gid=9
Description: Promotes business and community development in Coulee City, WA. **Geographic Preference:** Local.

46074 ■ Coupeville Chamber of Commerce (CCC)
905 NW Alexander
Coupeville, WA 98239
Ph: (360)678-5434
Co. E-mail: info@coupevillechamber.com
URL: http://www.coupevillechamber.com
Contact: Dawn Wilson, Officer
Facebook: www.facebook.com/coupevillechamber
X (Twitter): x.com/visitcoupeville
Instagram: www.instagram.com/coupevillechamber
Description: Serves the business and community interests of Coupeville and Greenbank on Whidbey Island and produces local festivals. Maintains a visitor and Information Center. **Publications:** *The Chamber Notes* (Monthly). **Geographic Preference:** Local.

46075 ■ Davenport Chamber of Commerce (DCC)
PO Box 869
Davenport, WA 99122
URL: http://www.davenportwa.us/index.asp?SEC=F
30EC1F7-6F40-439D-BD21-90FAE51316FB&Type
=B_BASIC
Description: Promotes business and community development in the Davenport, WA area. **Geographic Preference:** Local.

46076 ■ Dayton Chamber of Commerce (DCC)
166 E Main St.
Dayton, WA 99328
Ph: (509)382-4825
Co. E-mail: chamber@historicdayton.com
URL: http://www.historicdayton.com
Contact: Bette Lou Crothers, President
Facebook: www.facebook.com/Day
tonChamberofCommerce
X (Twitter): x.com/visitdaytonwa
Description: Promotes business and community development in Dayton, WA. Conducts area festival. **Founded:** 1946. **Geographic Preference:** Local.

46077 ■ Deer Park Chamber of Commerce
316 E Crawford Ave.
Deer Park, WA 99006
Ph: (509)276-5900
Co. E-mail: info@deerparkchamber.com
URL: http://deerparkchamber.com
Contact: Dr.
Facebook: www.facebook.com/deerparkchamber
Description: Promotes business and community development in Deer Park, WA. **Geographic Preference:** Local.

46078 ■ Economic Alliance Snohomish County (EASC)
808 134th St. SW, Ste. 101
Everett, WA 98204
Ph: (425)743-4567
Co. E-mail: info@economicalliancesc.org
URL: http://www.economicalliancesc.org
Contact: Garry Clark, President
Facebook: www.facebook.com/EconAllianceSC
Linkedin: www.linkedin.com/company/economic-alliance-snohomish-county
X (Twitter): x.com/EconAllianceSC
Instagram: www.instagram.com/econalliancesc
YouTube: www.youtube.com/channel/UCTrCCDyc
5ehtCPB2Ccq-f0g
Description: Helps companies find and successfully achieve contracts for work with the local, state and federal governments. **Founded:** 2011. **Publications:** *Biz2Biz* (Monthly); *Everett Guide* (Annual). **Awards:** John M. Fluke, Sr., Community Service Award (Annual); Henry M. Jackson Citizen of the Year Award (Annual); The Herald Business Journal Executive of the Year (Annual). **Geographic Preference:** Local.

46079 ■ Elma Chamber of Commerce
222 W Main St.
Elma, WA 98541
Ph: (360)482-3055
Co. E-mail: elmachamber@gmail.com
URL: http://elmachamber.org
Contact: Chief Susan Shultz, President
Facebook: www.facebook.com/elmachamber
Description: Promotes business and community development in Elma, WA. **Geographic Preference:** Local.

46080 ■ Enumclaw Chamber of Commerce (EACC)
1421 Cole St.
Enumclaw, WA 98022
Ph: (360)825-7666
URL: http://www.enumclawchamber.com
Contact: Kim Elias, Chairman
Facebook: www.facebook.com/EnumclawChamber
Instagram: www.instagram.com/enumclaw_chamber
Description: Promotes business and community development in the Enumclaw, WA area. Hosts Fourth of July Freedom Celebration and annual Christmas parade. **Founded:** 1902. **Publications:** *View Point* (Monthly). **Geographic Preference:** Local.

46081 ■ Ephrata Chamber of Commerce (ECC)
112 Basin St. SW
Ephrata, WA 98823
Ph: (509)754-4656
Co. E-mail: ephratawachamber@gmail.com
URL: http://www.ephratachamber.org
Contact: Rita Witte, President
Facebook: www.facebook.com/Ephrata-Chamber-of
-Commerce-176164072399863
Description: Promotes business and community development in Ephrata, WA. **Founded:** 1948. **Publications:** *Ephrata Newsletter* (Weekly). **Geographic Preference:** Local.

46082 ■ Ferndale Chamber of Commerce (FCC)
2007 Cherry St.
Ferndale, WA 98248
Ph: (360)384-3042
Fax: (360)384-3009
Co. E-mail: info@ferndale-chamber.com
URL: http://ferndale-chamber.com
Contact: Anya Milton, Executive Director
E-mail: anya@ferndale-chamber.com
Facebook: www.facebook.com/ferndalechamber
X (Twitter): x.com/ferndalechamber
Instagram: www.instagram.com/ferndale_chamber
Description: Promotes business and community development in Ferndale, WA. Conducts hot air balloon festival, international folk dance festival, garage sale, pumpkin contest, and Christmas-tree lighting. Sponsors charitable activities. **Founded:** 1955. **Publications:** *Commerce Communicator* (Quarterly). **Geographic Preference:** Local.

46083 ■ Fife Milton Edgewood Chamber of Commerce (FME)
2018 54th Ave. E
Fife, WA 98424
Ph: (253)922-9320
Co. E-mail: lorab@fmechamber.org
URL: http://fmechamber.org
Contact: Lora Butterfield, President
Facebook: www.facebook.com/fmechamber
X (Twitter): x.com/fmechamber
Description: Promotes commerce, assists in area businesses, and advances the business image of the Fife area. **Founded:** 1986. **Publications:** *Business Matters* (Semimonthly). **Educational Activities:** Fife Area Chamber of Commerce Luncheon (Monthly). **Geographic Preference:** Local.

46084 ■ Forks Chamber of Commerce (FCC)
1411 S Forks Ave.
Forks, WA 98331
Ph: (360)374-2531
Free: 800-443-6757
Fax: (360)374-9253
Co. E-mail: info@forkswa.com
URL: http://forkswa.com
Contact: Lissy Andros, Executive Director
E-mail: director@forkswa.com
Description: Promotes business and community development in Forks, WA. **Founded:** 1926. **Publications:** *Chamber Scoop* (Monthly); *News and Views* (Periodic). **Awards:** Forks Chamber of Commerce Best Business of the Year (Annual); Forks Chamber of Commerce Best Citizen of the Year (Annual); Forks Chamber of Commerce Best Volunteer of the Year (Annual). **Geographic Preference:** Local.

46085 ■ Gig Harbor Peninsula Area Chamber of Commerce [Gig Harbor Chamber of Commerce]
3125 Judson St.
Gig Harbor, WA 98335
Ph: (253)851-6865
Fax: (253)851-6881
Co. E-mail: info@gigharborchamber.com
URL: http://www.gigharborchamber.net
Contact: Miriam Battson, President
E-mail: mbattson@gigharborchamber.com
Facebook: www.facebook.com/
GigHarborChamberofCommerce
X (Twitter): x.com/GHChamber
Instagram: www.instagram.com/gigharborchamber
YouTube: www.youtube.com/channel/UCP447OQB
5xD0GnScLqdIZEA
Description: Promotes business and community development in the Gig Harbor, WA area. Conducts annual parade and picnic; conducts photo competitions. **Founded:** 1980. **Geographic Preference:** Local.

46086 ■ Grand Coulee Dam Area Chamber of Commerce (GCDACC)
17 Midway Ave.
Grand Coulee, WA 99133
Ph: (509)633-3074
Co. E-mail: chamber@grandcouleedam.org
URL: http://grandcouleedam.org
Contact: Ben Hughes, Secretary
Facebook: www.facebook.com/gcdachamber
X (Twitter): x.com/GCDAChamber
Description: Promotes business and community development in the Grand Coulee Dam, WA area. Sponsors Colorama, Laser Light, and 4th of July festivities. **Founded:** 1978. **Geographic Preference:** Local.

46087 ■ Grandview Chamber of Commerce
303 wine country Rd.
Grandview, WA 98930
Ph: (509)882-2100
Co. E-mail: admin@visitgrandview.com
URL: http://www.visitgrandview.com
Contact: Cody Goeppner, Board Member
Facebook: www.facebook.com/visitgrandview
Description: Promotes business and community development in Grandview, WA. **Founded:** 1959. **Publications:** *Chamber News*. **Geographic Preference:** Local.

46088 ■ Granger Chamber of Commerce
121 Sunnyside Ave.
Granger, WA 98932
Ph: (509)854-7304
Co. E-mail: grangerchamber@gmail.com
URL: http://www.grangerchamber.net
Contact: Laurence Guisinger, President
Facebook: www.facebook.com/
grangerchamberofcommerce
Description: Promotes the economic growth and quality of life in Granger, WA. **Founded:** 1909. **Geographic Preference:** Local.

46089 ■ Grays Harbor Chamber of Commerce
506 Duffy St.
Aberdeen, WA 98520
Ph: (360)532-1924
Free: 800-321-1924
Co. E-mail: info@graysharbor.org
URL: http://graysharbor.org
Contact: Lynnette Buffington, Chief Executive Officer
Facebook: www.facebook.com/GreaterGHInc
Linkedin: www.linkedin.com/company/greater-grays-harbor-inc
X (Twitter): x.com/GreaterGHInc
Instagram: www.instagram.com/discovergraysharbor
YouTube: www.youtube.com/channel/UCtkoV4c3z41K28uSgPYY7ug
Description: Promotes business and community development in Grays Harbor County, WA. Holds business forums, retreats, seminars, and workshops. Provides information, advocacy and networking. **Founded:** 1892. **Publications:** *Harbor Insider* (Monthly). **Geographic Preference:** Local.

46090 ■ Greater Eatonville Chamber of Commerce
PO Box 845
Eatonville, WA 98328
Ph: (360)219-5879
URL: http://eatonvillechamber.com
Description: Promotes business and community development in the Eatonville, WA area. **Publications:** *Greater Eatonville Chamber of Commerce Newsletter* (Bimonthly). **Geographic Preference:** Local.

46091 ■ Greater Edmonds Chamber of Commerce (ECC)
121 5th Ave. N
Edmonds, WA 98020
Ph: (425)670-1496
Fax: (425)712-1808
Co. E-mail: business@edmondswa.com
URL: http://edmondschamber.com
Contact: Greg Urban, President
Facebook: www.facebook.com/edmondschamber
X (Twitter): x.com/edmondschamber
Instagram: www.instagram.com/edmondschambercommerce
YouTube: www.youtube.com/user/ATasteOfEdmonds
Description: Promotes business and community development in Edmonds, WA. Sponsors A Taste of Edmonds Festival. **Founded:** 1907. **Publications:** *Preferred Business Directory* (Annual); *Edmonds Chamber of Commerce Preferred Business Directory* (Monthly). **Geographic Preference:** Local.

46092 ■ Greater Federal Way Chamber of Commerce
31919 1st Ave. S, Ste. 202
Federal Way, WA 98003
Ph: (253)838-2605
Fax: (253)661-9050
Co. E-mail: info@fedwaychamber.com
URL: http://www.fedwaychamber.com
Contact: Rebecca Martin, President
Facebook: www.facebook.com/federalwaychamber
X (Twitter): x.com/fedwaychamber
Instagram: www.instagram.com/fedwaychamber
YouTube: www.youtube.com/channel/UC8oC7vu_bk0xgkorSvLW8yQ
Description: Promotes business and community development in the Federal Way, WA area. **Founded:** 1990. **Publications:** *The Chamber* (Annual). **Geographic Preference:** Local.

46093 ■ Greater Goldendale Area Chamber of Commerce
903 E Broadway St.
Goldendale, WA 98620
Co. E-mail: admin@goldendalechamber.org
URL: http://www.goldendalechamber.org
Contact: Jacqueline Eide, President
Facebook: www.facebook.com/goldendale.chamber.7
Linkedin: www.linkedin.com/company/the-greater-goldendale-area-chamber-of-commerce
YouTube: www.youtube.com/channel/UCR8BmwaLbcaUcvUAlz3XU2A
Description: Promotes business and community development in Goldendale, WA. **Founded:** 1986. **Publications:** *Chamber Journal* (Periodic). **Geographic Preference:** Local.

46094 ■ Greater Issaquah Chamber of Commerce (GICC)
155 NW Gilman Blvd.
Issaquah, WA 98027
Ph: (425)392-7024
Co. E-mail: info@issaquahchamber.com
URL: http://www.issaquahchamber.com
Contact: Janet Kelly, Co-Chairman of the Board
Facebook: www.facebook.com/IssaquahChamber
X (Twitter): x.com/Issaquahchamber
Instagram: www.instagram.com/issaquahchamber
YouTube: www.youtube.com/channel/UCF02L88TzRQzKFTBRjE_13Q
Description: Promotes business and community development in Issaquah, WA. Sponsors festival. **Publications:** *Issaquah! Chamber Business News* (Monthly). **Geographic Preference:** Local.

46095 ■ Greater Kingston Community Chamber of Commerce
25864 Washington Blvd. NE No. 100
Kingston, WA 98346
Ph: (360)860-2239
Co. E-mail: director@kingstonchamber.com
URL: http://kingstonchamber.com
Contact: Angela Clark, President
Facebook: www.facebook.com/KingstonChamber
Linkedin: www.linkedin.com/company/greater-kingston-community-chamber-of-commerce
Instagram: www.instagram.com/kingstonchamberwa
Description: Promotes business and community development in Kingston, WA area. **Founded:** 2009. **Geographic Preference:** Local.

46096 ■ Greater Kirkland Chamber of Commerce (GKCC)
400 Urban Pl., Ste. 135
Kirkland, WA 98033
Ph: (425)822-7066
Fax: (425)827-4878
Co. E-mail: info@kirklandchamber.org
URL: http://kirklandchamber.org
Contact: Samantha St. John, Chief Executive Officer
E-mail: samanthas@kirklandchamber.org
Linkedin: www.linkedin.com/company/kirkland-chamber-of-commerce
X (Twitter): x.com/kirklandchamber
YouTube: www.youtube.com/channel/UClc_qOAGwNMovUPeWtphc9g
Description: Promotes business and community development in the Greater Kirkland, WA area. **Founded:** 1957. **Publications:** *Kirkland Works* (Monthly). **Geographic Preference:** Local.

46097 ■ Greater Lake Stevens Chamber of Commerce
10108 Lundeen Pk. Way.
Lake Stevens, WA 98258
Ph: (425)334-0433
Co. E-mail: info@lakestevenschamber.com
URL: http://lakestevenschamber.com
Contact: Matt Tabor, President
Facebook: www.facebook.com/GLSChamber
X (Twitter): x.com/LkStevensChambr
Instagram: www.instagram.com/lkschamber
YouTube: www.youtube.com/channel/UCjqtOBUgDblv1EMyyp6r6yw
Description: Promotes business and community development in the Lake Stevens, WA area. Operates Visitor Information Center. **Founded:** 1981. **Awards:** Greater Lake Stevens Chamber of Commerce Business of the Year (Annual); Greater Lake Stevens Chamber of Commerce Citizen of the Year (Annual); Greater Lake Stevens Chamber of Commerce Junior Citizen of the Year (Annual). **Geographic Preference:** Local.

46098 ■ Greater Maple Valley - Black Diamond Chamber of Commerce
23745 225th Way SE, Ste. 205
Maple Valley, WA 98038
Ph: (425)432-0222
Co. E-mail: info@maplevalleychamber.org
URL: http://www.maplevalleychamber.org
Contact: Erica Dial, Chief Executive Officer
E-mail: ceo@maplevalleychamber.org
Facebook: www.facebook.com/mvbdchamber
X (Twitter): x.com/mvbdchamber
YouTube: www.youtube.com/channel/UCZZnbxrXufgLUXSV1eqe1Mg
Description: Promotes the general welfare and prosperity of the area and its surrounding territory. **Founded:** 1965. **Geographic Preference:** Local.

46099 ■ Greater Marysville - Tulalip Chamber of Commerce
8825 34th Ave. NE, Ste. C
Tulalip, WA 98271
Ph: (360)659-7700
Co. E-mail: membersupport@marysvilletulalipchamber.com
URL: http://www.marysvilletulalipchamber.com
Contact: Ivonne Sepulveda, President
Facebook: www.facebook.com/MarysvilleTulalipChamber
YouTube: www.youtube.com/channel/UCMA8tOtMa-1nxqi6M3QKFCQ
Description: Promotes the community and its total economy and fosters business-government relations to help members operate their business in the best possible environment. Serves as a civic clearinghouse, a public relations counselor, a legislative representative at the local, state, and national levels of government, an information and referral bureau and a research and promotion medium. **Founded:** 1908. **Publications:** *Memberandum* (Monthly). **Geographic Preference:** Local.

46100 ■ Greater Oak Harbor Chamber of Commerce (GOHCC)
32630 State Rte. 20
Oak Harbor, WA 98277
Ph: (360)675-3755
Co. E-mail: info@oakharborchamber.com
URL: http://www.oakharborchamber.com
Contact: Jeff Pleet, President
Facebook: www.facebook.com/oakharborchamber
Description: Promotes business and community development in the Oak Harbor, WA area. Sponsors Holland Happening and Fourth of July festivals. **Founded:** 1957. **Geographic Preference:** Local.

46101 ■ The Greater Othello Chamber of Commerce
705 E Hemlock St.
Othello, WA 99344
Ph: (509)488-2683
Co. E-mail: chamberofcommerceothellowa@gmail.com
URL: http://www.uschamber.com/co/chambers/washington
Contact: Jacklyn Wilhelm, Governor
Facebook: www.facebook.com/othellochamber
Description: Promotes business and community development in Othello, WA. Sponsors 4th of July celebration. **Founded:** 1911. **Geographic Preference:** Local.

46102 ■ Greater Pasco Area Chamber of Commerce
1110 Osprey Pointe Blvd., Ste. 101
Pasco, WA 99301
Ph: (509)547-9755
Co. E-mail: info@pascochamber.org
URL: http://www.pascochamber.org
Contact: Colin Hastings, Executive Director
Facebook: www.facebook.com/PascoChamber
Linkedin: www.linkedin.com/in/pasco-chamber-of-commerce-b4308b68
X (Twitter): x.com/pascochamber
Description: Promotes business and community development in the Pasco, WA area. **Founded:** 1912. **Geographic Preference:** Local.

STATE LISTINGS

46103 ■ Greater Poulsbo Chamber of Commerce (GPCC)
19168 Jensen Way NE
Poulsbo, WA 98370
Free: 888-490-8545
Co. E-mail: membership@poulsbochamber.com
URL: http://poulsbochamber.com/about-us
Contact: Gary Zambor, President
Facebook: www.facebook.com/PoulsboChamber
X (Twitter): x.com/poulsbochamber
Instagram: www.instagram.com/poulsbochamberofcommerce
Description: Promotes business and community development and tourism in the Poulsbo, WA area. Provides visitor and relocation information. **Founded:** 1950. **Publications:** *Poulsbo Exchange* (Monthly); *Visitor Guide* (Annual). **Awards:** Greater Poulsbo Chamber of Commerce Volunteer of the Year (Annual). **Geographic Preference:** Local.

46104 ■ Greater Seattle Chamber of Commerce
1301 5th Ave., Ste. 1500
Seattle, WA 98101
Ph: (206)389-7200
Fax: (888)392-2795
Co. E-mail: info@seattlechamber.com
URL: http://www.seattlechamber.com
Contact: Rachel Smith, President
Linkedin: www.linkedin.com/company/seattle-metropolitan-chamber-of-commerce
X (Twitter): x.com/seattlechamber
Instagram: www.instagram.com/seattlechamber
YouTube: www.youtube.com/user/seattlemetrochamber
Description: Promotes business and community development in Seattle, WA area. **Founded:** 1882. **Publications:** *Directory of Seattle-King County Manufacturers*; *Directory of Major Corporations: Central Puget Sound Region* (Biennial); *Directory of Major Manufacturers: Central Puget Sound Region*; *Events Update*. **Geographic Preference:** Local.

46105 ■ Greater Spokane Incorporated (GSI)
801 W Riverside Ave., Ste. 200
Spokane, WA 99201
Ph: (509)624-1393
Free: 800-776-5263
Fax: (509)747-0077
Co. E-mail: info@greaterspokane.org
URL: http://greaterspokane.org
Contact: Alisha Benson, Chief Executive Officer
E-mail: abenson@greaterspokane.org
Facebook: www.facebook.com/greaterspokane
X (Twitter): x.com/greaterspokane
YouTube: www.youtube.com/user/GSIgreaterspokaneinc
Description: Assists businesses with any aspect of federal, state and local government contracting. Serving 13 counties in Eastern Washington including Spokane, Ferry, Lincoln, Stevens, Pend Oreille, Adams, Franklin, Benton, Whitman, Walla Walla, Columbia, Garfield and Asotin counties. **Founded:** 1974. **Publications:** *Spokane Empire Manufacturing Guide* (Biennial); *Inland-Northwest Manufacturers Directory* (Annual). **Educational Activities:** Spokane Ag Expo (Annual). **Geographic Preference:** Local.

46106 ■ Greater Vancouver Chamber of Commerce (GVCC)
1111 Main St., Ste. 201
Vancouver, WA 98660-2914
Ph: (360)694-2588
Co. E-mail: yourchamber@vancouverusa.com
URL: http://www.vancouverusa.com
Contact: John McDonagh, President
E-mail: jmcdonagh@vancouverusa.com
Facebook: www.facebook.com/greatervancouverchamber
Linkedin: www.linkedin.com/company/greatervancouverchamber
X (Twitter): x.com/vanchamber
Instagram: www.instagram.com/greatervancouverchamber
Description: Promotes business and community development in the Vancouver and Clark County, WA areas. **Founded:** 1890. **Geographic Preference:** Local.

46107 ■ Greater Woodinville Chamber of Commerce
13901 NE 175th St., Ste. N
Woodinville, WA 98072
Ph: (425)481-8300
Fax: (425)481-9743
Co. E-mail: info@woodinvillechamber.org
URL: http://woodinvillechamber.org
Contact: Robin Akkerman, Secretary
E-mail: kimberly@woodinvillechamber.org
Facebook: www.facebook.com/WoodinvilleChamber
X (Twitter): x.com/woodinvillecc
Instagram: www.instagram.com/woodinvillechamber
Description: Aims to promote, strengthen, and represent business community in Woodinville, WA. Serves as a voice to help focus government on the needs of the business community. Provides an environment for business networking and leads economic development efforts within the community. **Founded:** 1962. **Publications:** *Facility Directory* (Periodic); *Off the Vine*. **Geographic Preference:** Local.

46108 ■ Greater Yakima Chamber of Commerce (GYCC)
10 N 9th St.
Yakima, WA 98901
Ph: (509)248-2021
Fax: (509)248-0601
URL: http://www.yakima.org
Contact: Verlynn Best, President
E-mail: verlynn@yakima.org
Facebook: www.facebook.com/greateryakimachamber
Linkedin: www.linkedin.com/company/greater-yakima-chamber-of-commerce
X (Twitter): x.com/YakimaChamber1
Instagram: www.instagram.com/yakimachamber
YouTube: www.youtube.com/user/greateryakimachamber
Description: Strives to improve and preserve the business community of greater Yakima area. **Founded:** 1920. **Publications:** *Meeting, Reception, Banquet Rooms, and Caterers in the Greater Yakima Area* (Annual); *The Chamber Voice* (Bimonthly); *E-Bulletin* (Weekly); *Greater Yakima Chamber of Commerce--Clubs & Organizations Directory* (Annual); *Top Employer's List* (Annual); *Manufacturing Directory for Yakima Valley* (Annual). **Geographic Preference:** Local.

46109 ■ Harbor Insider
506 Duffy St.
Aberdeen, WA 98520
Ph: (360)532-1924
Free: 800-321-1924
Co. E-mail: info@graysharbor.org
URL: http://graysharbor.org
Contact: Lynnette Buffington, Chief Executive Officer
URL(s): graysharbor.org/tag/harbor-insider
Released: Monthly **Availability:** Online.

46110 ■ Jefferson County Chamber of Commerce
2409 Jefferson St.
Port Townsend, WA 98368
Ph: (360)385-7869
Co. E-mail: director@jeffcountychamber.org
URL: http://www.jeffcountychamber.org
Contact: Richard Tucker, President
Facebook: www.facebook.com/jeffcountychamber
Description: Promotes business and community development in the area. **Founded:** 1889. **Publications:** *Chamber/Gram* (Quarterly). **Geographic Preference:** Local.

46111 ■ Kalama Chamber of Commerce
PO Box 824
Kalama, WA 98625
Ph: (360)673-6299
Co. E-mail: kalamachamber@outlook.com
URL: http://www.kalamachamber.com
Contact: Taryn Nelson, Governor
Description: Promotes business and community development in Kalama, WA area. **Publications:** *Chamber News* (Monthly). **Awards:** Kalama Chamber of Commerce Citizen of the Year (Annual); Kalama Chamber of Commerce Totem Award (Annual). **Geographic Preference:** Local.

46112 ■ Kelso Longview Chamber of Commerce
105 N Minor Rd.
Kelso, WA 98626
Ph: (360)423-8400
Fax: (360)423-0432
Co. E-mail: info@kelsolongviewchamber.org
URL: http://kelsolongviewchamber.org
Contact: Bill Marcum, President
E-mail: bmarcum@kelsolongviewchamber.org
Facebook: www.facebook.com/KelsoLongviewChamber
Linkedin: www.linkedin.com/company/kelso-longview-chamber-of-commerce
X (Twitter): x.com/klchamber
Description: Represents business communities and promotes community development of both Kelso and Longview. **Founded:** 1924. **Geographic Preference:** Local.

46113 ■ Kent Chamber of Commerce
524 W Meeker St., Ste. 1
Kent, WA 98032
Ph: (253)854-1770
Fax: (253)854-8567
Co. E-mail: info@kentchamber.com
URL: http://kentchamber.com
Contact: Sarah McNiesh, President
Facebook: www.facebook.com/kentchamberofcommerce
Linkedin: www.linkedin.com/company/kent-chamber-of-commerce
X (Twitter): x.com/KentChamber
Description: Promotes business and community development in Kent, WA. **Founded:** 1948. **Publications:** *Kent Chamber of Commerce Membership Directory & Relocation Guide*; *The Voice of Business* (Biweekly). **Awards:** Kent Chamber of Commerce Best Practices Award (Annual); Kent Chamber of Commerce Company Citizenship Award (Annual); Kent Chamber of Commerce Economic Engine Award (Annual); Kent Chamber of Commerce Education Service Award; Kent Chamber of Commerce Innovators Award; Kent Chamber of Commerce Legislator or Government Employee of the Year Award (Annual); Kent Chamber of Commerce President's Award (Annual); Robert E. Lee Membership Development Award (Annual). **Geographic Preference:** Local.

46114 ■ Kittitas County Chamber of Commerce
609 N Main St.
Ellensburg, WA 98926
Ph: (509)925-2002
Free: 888-925-2204
Co. E-mail: info@kittitascountychamber.com
URL: http://www.kittitascountychamber.com
Contact: Charlie Smith, Vice President
Linkedin: www.linkedin.com/company/kittitas-county-chamber-of-commerce/about
YouTube: www.youtube.com/channel/UCj88Vm103zUgIVWwU_Z6X1A
Description: Promotes agricultural, business, and community development in Ellensburg, WA area. Sponsors triathlon, annual Windfest, and local holiday festivities. **Founded:** 1908. **Publications:** *Chamber Membership Directory* (Annual). **Geographic Preference:** Local.

46115 ■ La Conner Chamber of Commerce
606 Morris St.
La Conner, WA 98257
Ph: (360)466-4778
Free: 888-642-9284
Co. E-mail: info@laconnerchamber.com
URL: http://www.lovelaconner.com
Contact: Chris Jennings, President
Facebook: www.facebook.com/lovelaconner
X (Twitter): x.com/lovelaconner

Instagram: www.instagram.com/lovelaconner
YouTube: www.youtube.com/user/LoveLaConner
Description: Promotes business and commerce in La Conner, WA area. **Publications:** *La Connerite* (Monthly). **Geographic Preference:** Local.

46116 ■ Lacey Thurston County Chamber of Commerce (LTCCC)
809 Legion Way SE
Olympia, WA 98501
Ph: (360)357-3362
Co. E-mail: info@thurstonchamber.com
URL: http://thurstonchamber.com
Contact: David Schaffert, President
Description: Promotes business and community development in the Lacey, WA area. **Founded:** 1961. **Publications:** *Chamber Membership Directory and Profile* (Annual); *Insight*. **Educational Activities:** FORUM Luncheon (Monthly); Lacey Thurston County Chamber of Commerce Executive Committee Meeting. **Geographic Preference:** Local.

46117 ■ Lake Chelan Chamber of Commerce
216 E Woodin Ave.
Chelan, WA 98816
Ph: (509)682-3503
Free: 800-4CH-ELAN
Co. E-mail: info@lakechelan.com
URL: http://www.lakechelan.com
Contact: Mike Steele, Executive Director
E-mail: mike@lakechelan.com
Facebook: www.facebook.com/visitlakechelan
X (Twitter): x.com/visitlakechelan
Instagram: www.instagram.com/lake_chelan
YouTube: www.youtube.com/channel/UCudv0BE 2uDngNJkOP6SBh4g
Pinterest: www.pinterest.com/visitlakechelan
Description: Seeks to support and encourage the economic and business development in the Chelan, WA area. Coordinates the efforts of commerce, industry and the professions in maintaining and strengthening a sound and healthy business climate in the region. Provides networking and learning opportunities for the business community in and around Chelan. **Founded:** 1931. **Educational Activities:** Business After Hours. **Awards:** Lake Chelan Chamber of Commerce President's Award for Beautification (Annual); Lake Chelan Chamber of Commerce Business of the Year (Annual); Lake Chelan Chamber of Commerce Citizen of the Year (Annual). **Geographic Preference:** Local.

46118 ■ Lakewood Chamber of Commerce
6310 Mt. Tacoma Dr. SW
Lakewood, WA 98499
Ph: (253)582-9400
Co. E-mail: chamber@lakewood-wa.com
URL: http://lakewood-chamber.org
Contact: Linda Smith, President
Facebook: www.facebook.com/lakewoodchamber
X (Twitter): x.com/lakewoodcofc
YouTube: www.youtube.com/channel/UC 5-7WmS0qXveu9DPoiEVBIA
Description: Promotes business and community development in Lakewood. Seeks to help enhance business activity and develops partnership for a vital community through political, social, and community leadership. **Founded:** 1972. **Publications:** *Chamber Chat Line* (Monthly). **Educational Activities:** Lakewood Chamber of Commerce Meeting. **Geographic Preference:** Local.

46119 ■ Langley South Whidbey Chamber of Commerce
208 Anthes Ave.
Langley, WA 98260
Ph: (360)221-6765
URL: http://visitlangley.com/about-langley-chamber-of -commerce
Contact: Nancy Rowan, President
E-mail: nrowan04@langleywa.com
Facebook: www.facebook.com/visitlangley
X (Twitter): x.com/VisitLangley
YouTube: www.youtube.com/channel/UCVq 2TmbxRsaFzlKdH8DthPQ
Description: Promotes business and community development in Langley, Washington. **Founded:** 1976. **Geographic Preference:** Local.

46120 ■ Leavenworth Chamber of Commerce
940 Hwy. 2, Ste. B
Leavenworth, WA 98826
Ph: (509)548-5807
Co. E-mail: guestservices@leavenworth.org
URL: http://www.leavenworthchamber.org
Contact: Jesse Boyd, President
X (Twitter): x.com/leavenworth_wa
Instagram: www.instagram.com/leavenworthchamber
YouTube: www.youtube.com/user/WoodyTheNu tcracker
Description: Promotes business and community development in Leavenworth, WA. **Geographic Preference:** Local.

46121 ■ Lewis Clark Valley Chamber of Commerce
502 Bridge St.
Clarkston, WA 99403
Ph: (509)758-7712
Co. E-mail: events@lcvalleychamber.org
URL: http://www.lcvalleychamber.org
Contact: Kristin Kemak, Director
E-mail: lcpresident@lcvalleychamber.org
Facebook: www.facebook.com/lcvalleychamber
Instagram: www.instagram.com/lcvalleychamber
Description: Promotes business and community development in Clarkston, WA. **Publications:** *Lewiston Chamber Business Directory*; *Valley Currents* (Monthly); *Connection* (Monthly); *Local Organizations List* (Annual); *Membership and Buyer's Guide*; *Lewiston Chamber Business Directory*. **Geographic Preference:** Local.

46122 ■ Lopez Island Chamber of Commerce
265 Lopez Rd., Ste. F
Lopez Island, WA 98261
Ph: (360)468-4664
Free: 877-433-2789
Co. E-mail: lopezchamber@lopezisland.com
URL: http://lopezisland.com
Contact: Rhea Miller, President
Description: Promotes business and commerce in Lopez Island, WA. **Founded:** 1792. **Geographic Preference:** Local.

46123 ■ Lynden Chamber of Commerce (LCC)
518 Front St.
Lynden, WA 98264
Ph: (360)354-5995
Fax: (360)354-0401
Co. E-mail: lynden@lynden.org
URL: http://lynden.org
Facebook: www.facebook.com/Lynden-Chamber-of -Commerce-149316018250
X (Twitter): x.com/lyndenchamber
Instagram: www.instagram.com/lyndenchamber
YouTube: www.youtube.com/channel/UCRoUvODbr 1uQkZ-3TQi73fg
Description: Promotes business, tourism, and community development in Lynden, WA. Sponsors local charitable events and festivals. **Founded:** 1928. **Geographic Preference:** Local.

46124 ■ Magnolia Chamber of Commerce
3213 W Wheeler St., No. 42
Seattle, WA 98199
URL: http://discovermagnolia.org
Contact: Daniela Eng, Co-President
Facebook: www.facebook.com/discovermagnolia
Instagram: www.instagram.com/discovermagnolia
YouTube: www.youtube.com/channel/UCGYHa_oTgJ 1yTydL2q7T-Qw/featured
Description: Promotes and develops business and commerce in Magnolia, Seattle, WA. **Geographic Preference:** Local.

46125 ■ McCleary Community Chamber of Commerce
PO Box 53
McCleary, WA 98557-0053
Ph: (360)495-3667
URL: http://www.uschamber.com/co/chambers/wash-ington/mccleary
Contact: Mike Morello, Chief Digital Officer
Description: Promotes the general welfare and prosperity of McCleary and all areas of its business community. **Geographic Preference:** Local.

46126 ■ Mercer Island Chamber of Commerce
7605 SE 27th St., Ste. 206
Mercer Island, WA 98040
Ph: (206)232-3404
Co. E-mail: info@mercerislandchamberofcommerce .org
URL: http://www.mercerislandchamberofcommerce .org
Contact: Suzanne Skone, Manager
Facebook: www.facebook.com/Mercer-Island-Cham-ber-of-Commerce-142864429071108
Instagram: www.instagram.com/mercerislandcham-ber
Description: Supports the growth, development, and advancement of the businesses of Mercer Island. **Founded:** 1946. **Geographic Preference:** Local.

46127 ■ Monroe Chamber of Commerce
125 S Lewis St.
Monroe, WA 98272
Ph: (360)794-5488
URL: http://www.choosemonroe.com/about-us.aspx
Contact: Janelle Drews, Executive Director
E-mail: director@choosemonroe.com
Facebook: www.facebook.com/choosemonroe
Instagram: www.instagram.com/choosemonroe
Description: Comprises of representatives of the business community. Strives to foster business growth and community development. Sponsors Fair Days Parade, annual auction and Community Awards Recognition. Operates Visitor Information Center year round. **Founded:** 1962. **Publications:** *The Chamber Connection* (Biweekly); *Membership and Community Resource Directory* (Annual). **Geographic Preference:** Local.

46128 ■ Moses Lake Area Chamber of Commerce
324 S Pioneer Way
Moses Lake, WA 98837
Ph: (509)765-7888
Free: 800-992-6234
Fax: (866)535-1246
Co. E-mail: information@moseslake.com
URL: http://www.moseslake.com
Contact: Debbie Doran-Martinez, President
E-mail: director@moseslake.com
Facebook: www.facebook.com/MosesLakeChamber
X (Twitter): x.com/mlchamber
Description: Promotes business and community development in the Moses Lake, WA area. **Founded:** 1941. **Awards:** Moses Lake Area Chamber of Commerce President's Award. **Geographic Preference:** Local.

46129 ■ Mount Adams Chamber of Commerce
1 Heritage Plz.
White Salmon, WA 98672
Ph: (509)493-3630
Co. E-mail: mtadamschamber@gmail.com
URL: http://mtadamschamber.com
Contact: Tammara Tippel, Executive Director
E-mail: execdir@mtadamschamber.com
Facebook: www.facebook.com/MtAdamsChamber
Instagram: www.instagram.com/mtadamschamber
Description: Promotes business and community development in the Mid-Columbia area of Washington. Provides relocation and tourism information. Promotes festival, art and wine event. **Geographic Preference:** Local.

46130 ■ *Mount Vernon Chamber Chat*
301 W Kincaid St.
Mount Vernon, WA 98273
Ph: (360)428-8547
Fax: (360)424-6237
Co. E-mail: info@mountvernonchamber.com
URL: http://www.mountvernonchamber.com

STATE LISTINGS

Contact: Andy Mayer, President
E-mail: andy@mountvernonchamber.com
URL(s): www.mountvernonchamber.com/newsletter
Released: Monthly **Availability:** Online; PDF.

46131 ■ Mount Vernon Chamber of Commerce
301 W Kincaid St.
 Mount Vernon, WA 98273
Ph: (360)428-8547
Fax: (360)424-6237
Co. E-mail: info@mountvernonchamber.com
URL: http://www.mountvernonchamber.com
Contact: Andy Mayer, President
E-mail: andy@mountvernonchamber.com
Facebook: www.facebook.com/mountvernonchamber
Linkedin: www.linkedin.com/company/mount-vernon-chamber-of-commerce
X (Twitter): x.com/MountVernonCofC
YouTube: www.youtube.com/channel/UCIzaHEVgdFTvVmhXLz2-0Pg
Description: Promotes business and community development in Mt. Vernon, WA. Sponsors Skagit River Festival. **Founded:** 1917. **Publications:** *Mount Vernon Chamber Chat* (Monthly). **Educational Activities:** Networking Meeting. **Geographic Preference:** Local.

46132 ■ Newport - Oldtown Chamber of Commerce
325 W 4th St.
 Newport, WA 99156
Ph: (509)447-5812
Co. E-mail: info@newportareachamber.com
URL: http://newportareachamber.com
Contact: Jeff Upton, Vice President
Facebook: www.facebook.com/newportareachamber
Description: Works to promote and strengthen the business and economic climate of the area while preserving and enhancing the area's quality of life. **Founded:** 1950. **Publications:** *FOCUS* (Monthly). **Educational Activities:** Newport Chamber Board Meeting (Annual). **Geographic Preference:** Local.

46133 ■ North Mason Chamber of Commerce (NMCC)
30 NE Romance Hill Rd., Ste. 103
 Belfair, WA 98528
Ph: (360)275-4267
Fax: (360)275-0853
URL: http://northmasonchamber.com
Contact: Pam Volz, President
E-mail: pvolz@northmasonchamber.com
Facebook: www.facebook.com/North.Mason.Chamber
Description: Encourages and promotes business, tourism, social, educational, and environmental interests and activities of the North Mason community. Provides a representative voice for the business community on transportation, growth and land use management, health care, education and workforce development issues. **Founded:** 1967. **Geographic Preference:** Local.

46134 ■ Ocean Park Area Chamber of Commerce
1715 Bay Ave., No. 1
 Ocean Park, WA 98640
Ph: (360)665-4448
Co. E-mail: opchamber@opwa.com
URL: http://opwa.com
Contact: Bob Beezley, Treasurer
Instagram: www.instagram.com/oceanparkareachamber
Description: Aims to preserve the competitive enterprise system of business and to promote business and community growth and development. Supports worthwhile civic and/or cultural events for the community. Hosts a Garlic Festival in June, and an Old Fashioned 4th of July including a parade and Art In The Park. **Founded:** 1983. **Geographic Preference:** Local.

46135 ■ Odessa Chamber of Commerce
PO Box 355
 Odessa, WA 99159
Co. E-mail: odessachamber@gmail.com

URL: http://odessachamber.org
Contact: Larissa Zeiler, Treasurer
Facebook: www.facebook.com/odessawachamber
Description: Non-competitive sports enthusiasts. **Geographic Preference:** Local.

46136 ■ Omak Chamber of Commerce (OCC)
PO Box 3100
 Omak, WA 98841
Ph: (509)826-1880
Co. E-mail: omakchamber@gmail.com
URL: http://www.omakchamber.com
Contact: Brian Ellis, President
Facebook: www.facebook.com/omakchamber
Description: Promotes business and community development in Omak, WA. **Geographic Preference:** Local.

46137 ■ OneRedmond
8383 158th Ave. NE, Ste. 225
 Redmond, WA 98052
Ph: (425)885-4014
Co. E-mail: info@oneredmond.org
URL: http://oneredmond.org
Contact: Justine Mulholland, Director
E-mail: justinem@oneredmond.org
Facebook: www.facebook.com/OneRedmondWA
Linkedin: www.linkedin.com/company/oneredmond
X (Twitter): x.com/OneRedmond
Instagram: www.instagram.com/oneredmond
YouTube: www.youtube.com/channel/UCFl1JRs3s7ek2VKLSDRLrIA
Description: Promotes business and community development in the Redmond, WA area. **Founded:** 1945. **Publications:** *Redmond Business* (Monthly). **Geographic Preference:** Local.

46138 ■ Oroville, WA Chamber of Commerce
PO Box 626
 Oroville, WA 98844
Ph: (509)476-2243
Co. E-mail: orovillewa98844@orovillewachamber.com
URL: http://www.orovillewachamber.com
Contact: Rocky DeVon, President
Description: Promotes business and commerce in the area. **Publications:** *Oroville Chamber Update!* (Periodic). **Educational Activities:** Oroville Chamber of Commerce Meeting. **Geographic Preference:** Regional.

46139 ■ Palouse Chamber of Commerce
110 E MAIN ST.
 Palouse, WA 99161
Contact: James Kusznir, Governor
Description: Promotes business and community development in Palouse, WA area. **Geographic Preference:** Local.

46140 ■ Point Roberts Chamber of Commerce
PO Box 128
 Point Roberts, WA 98281
Co. E-mail: info@pointrobertschamberofcommerce.com
URL: http://www.pointrobertschamberofcommerce.com
Contact: Brian Calder, President
Description: Promotes business and community development in Point Roberts, WA. **Geographic Preference:** Local.

46141 ■ Port Orchard Chamber of Commerce (POCOC)
1014 Bay St., Ste. 3
 Port Orchard, WA 98366
Ph: (360)876-3505
URL: http://portorchard.com
Description: Promotes business and community development in the Port Orchard, WA area. Sponsors charitable events. **Founded:** 1943. **Geographic Preference:** Local.

46142 ■ Prosser Chamber of Commerce
1230 Bennett Ave.
 Prosser, WA 99350
Ph: (509)786-3177

Co. E-mail: info@prosserchamber.org
URL: http://www.prosserchamber.org
Contact: John-Paul Estey, Executive Director
E-mail: johnpaul@prosserchamber.org
Description: Promotes business and community development in Prosser, WA area. **Geographic Preference:** Local.

46143 ■ Pullman Chamber of Commerce (PCC)
415 N Grand Ave.
 Pullman, WA 99163
Ph: (509)334-3565
Free: 800-365-6948
Co. E-mail: chamber@pullmanchamber.com
URL: http://pullmanchamber.com
Contact: Marie Dymkoski, Executive Director
E-mail: marie@pullmanchamber.com
Facebook: www.facebook.com/PullmanChamber
X (Twitter): x.com/PullmanChamber
Instagram: www.instagram.com/pullmanchamber
Pinterest: www.pinterest.com/pullmanchamber
Description: Promotes business and community development in Pullman, WA. Sponsors 4th of July Community Celebration and National Lentil Festival. **Founded:** 1956. **Publications:** *Chamber Newsletter* (Weekly). **Geographic Preference:** Local.

46144 ■ Quincy Valley Chamber of Commerce (QVCC)
115 F St. SW
 Quincy, WA 98848
Ph: (509)787-2140
Free: 844-370-6864
Fax: (509)787-4500
Co. E-mail: qvcc@quincyvalley.org
URL: http://www.quincyvalley.org
Contact: Josh Paul, President
Facebook: www.facebook.com/quincyvalleychamberofcommerce
Description: Promotes business and community development and tourism in the Quincy, WA area. Sponsors Farmer-Consumer Awareness day. Conducts fundraising auction. **Founded:** 1947. **Publications:** *Business Phone Directory* (Annual); *The Chamber Chatter* (Weekly). **Geographic Preference:** Local.

46145 ■ Renton Chamber of Commerce
625 S 4th St.
 Renton, WA 98057
Ph: (425)226-4560
Co. E-mail: info@gorenton.com
URL: http://www.gorenton.com
Contact: Diane Dobson, President
E-mail: diane@gorenton.com
YouTube: www.youtube.com/channel/UCBjkzt7nGFpVUhRjv68jxig
Description: Promotes business and community development in the Renton, WA area. **Founded:** 1924. **Publications:** *Business Directory*. **Geographic Preference:** Local.

46146 ■ Ritzville Area Chamber of Commerce
216 E Main Ave.
 Ritzville, WA 99169
Ph: (509)659-1936
Co. E-mail: ritzchamber@gmail.com
URL: http://www.ritzvillechamber.com
Contact: Mary Chamberlain, President
Facebook: www.facebook.com/ritzvillechamber
Description: Promotes business and community development in Ritzville, WA. **Founded:** 1903. **Publications:** *Business Directory*. **Educational Activities:** Business Meeting. **Geographic Preference:** Local.

46147 ■ San Juan Island Chamber of Commerce
165 First St. S
 Friday Harbor, WA 98250
Ph: (360)378-5240
Co. E-mail: chamberinfo@sanjuanisland.org
URL: http://sanjuanisland.org
Contact: Kris Brown, President
Facebook: www.facebook.com/sanjuanislandchamberofcommerce

Description: Promotes business and community development in the Friday Harbor, WA area. **Founded:** 1776. **Publications:** *San Juan Island Chamber of Commerce News* (Weekly). **Geographic Preference:** Local.

46148 ■ Sedro-Woolley Chamber of Commerce
810 Metcalf St.
Sedro Woolley, WA 98284
Ph: (360)855-1841
Fax: (360)855-1582
Co. E-mail: director@sedro-woolley.com
URL: http://sedro-woolley.com
Contact: Linda Tyler, President
Description: Promotes business and community development in Sedro-Woolley, WA. Sponsors Woodfest, Tulip Festival, Blast From the Past, Founders Days, Christmas Parade and tree lighting, and Breakfast with Santa. **Founded:** 1914. **Publications:** *The Exchange* (Monthly). **Educational Activities:** Steelhead Days. **Geographic Preference:** Local.

46149 ■ Sequim-Dungeness Valley Chamber of Commerce
1192 E Washington St.
Sequim, WA 98382
Ph: (360)683-6197
Co. E-mail: membership@sequimchamber.com
URL: http://www.sequimchamber.com
Contact: Leonard Anderson, President
Facebook: www.facebook.com/sequimchamber
Description: Promotes business and community development in the Sequim, WA area. **Founded:** 1936. **Publications:** *Destination Sequim, Travel Planner*. **Geographic Preference:** Local.

46150 ■ Shelton-Mason County Chamber of Commerce (SMCCC)
215 W Railroad Ave.
Shelton, WA 98584
Ph: (360)426-2021
Co. E-mail: info@masonchamber.com
URL: http://masonchamber.com
Contact: Deidre Peterson, Co-President Co-Chief Executive Officer
E-mail: deidre@masonchamber.com
Facebook: www.facebook.com/MasonCountyChamber
YouTube: www.youtube.com/channel/UCgmirCCBAnLPfczVaRt-yNg/videos
Description: Promotes business and community development in Shelton and Mason County, WA. Conducts seminars and workshops; sponsors festivals and parades. Sponsors the Christmas Parade and Annual Auction Bazaar. Conducts community tours. Offers quarterly seminar. **Founded:** 1922. **Publications:** *Chamber News*; *Shelton-Mason County Journal*. **Educational Activities:** Shelton-Mason County Chamber of Commerce Dinner. **Geographic Preference:** Local.

46151 ■ *Shelton-Mason County Journal*
215 W Railroad Ave.
Shelton, WA 98584
Ph: (360)426-2021
Co. E-mail: info@masonchamber.com
URL: http://masonchamber.com
Contact: Deidre Peterson, Co-President Co-Chief Executive Officer
E-mail: deidre@masonchamber.com
URL(s): www.masoncounty.com
Facebook: www.facebook.com/sheltonjournal
X (Twitter): x.com/masonjournal
Released: Last Update 2024. **Price:** $7.50, for in country per month US; $79, for per year in country rate US; $198, for national rate 2 year US; $178, for 2 year national rate US; $99, for per year national rate US; $79, for in country rates per year US; $89, for national rate annual 1 year US; $69, for in country rates annual US; $138, for in country rates 2 year US; $158, for 2 year in county rate US; $9, for per month US; $99, for per year US; $7.50, for online only per month; $79, for online only per month; $69, for 1 year online only; $138, for 2 year online only.
Availability: Print; Online.

46152 ■ Shoreline Chamber of Commerce (SCC)
18560 1st Ave., NE
Shoreline, WA 98155
Ph: (206)361-2260
Co. E-mail: info@shorelinechamber.org
URL: http://shorelinechamberofcommerce.wildapricot.org
Contact: Dale Sutton, Member
Facebook: www.facebook.com/ShorelineChamber
X (Twitter): x.com/shorelinechmbr
Description: Promotes commerce in the Greater Shoreline Area by providing value to its members through business education, networking opportunities and effective representation. **Founded:** 1976. **Publications:** *ShoreLines* (Monthly); *Shoreline Chamber of Commerce--Membership Directory & Buyer's Guide*. **Geographic Preference:** Local.

46153 ■ Silverdale Chamber of Commerce
10315 Silverdale Way NW
Silverdale, WA 98383
Ph: (360)692-6800
Fax: (360)692-1379
Co. E-mail: info@silverdalechamber.com
URL: http://silverdalechamber.com
Contact: David Emmons, President
E-mail: david@silverdalechamber.com
Facebook: www.facebook.com/silverdale.washington
X (Twitter): x.com/SilverChamber
Instagram: www.instagram.com/silverdale_chamber
Description: Promotes business and community development in Silverdale, WA. **Founded:** 1973. **Geographic Preference:** Local.

46154 ■ Skamania County Chamber of Commerce
167 NW 2nd Ave.
Stevenson, WA 98648
Ph: (509)427-8911
Free: 800-989-9178
Co. E-mail: info@skamania.org
URL: http://skamania.org
Contact: Chris Malone, President
Facebook: www.facebook.com/skamania.chamber
Instagram: www.instagram.com/skamaniachamber
Description: Promotes and develops business and commerce in Skamania County, WA. **Founded:** 1854. **Geographic Preference:** Local.

46155 ■ Sky Valley Chamber of Commerce
320 Main St.
Sultan, WA 98294
Ph: (360)793-0983
Fax: (360)793-3241
URL: http://www.skyvalleychamber.com
Contact: Henry Sladek, President
Facebook: www.facebook.com/SkyValleyChamber
Description: Promotes business and community development in Sultan, WA. Conducts Sultan Summer Shindig and other community activities. **Publications:** *Chamber Weekly* (Weekly); *Snohomish County Tourist Bureau* (Periodic). **Geographic Preference:** Local.

46156 ■ Snohomish Chamber of Commerce
21 Ave. A, Ste. 1
Snohomish, WA 98290
Ph: (360)568-2526
Co. E-mail: manager@snohomishchamber.org
URL: http://www.snohomishchamber.org
Contact: Rod Ashley, Secretary
Facebook: www.facebook.com/SnohomishChamberOfCommerce
X (Twitter): x.com/SnohomishCOC
Description: Promotes business and community development in Snohomish, WA. **Geographic Preference:** Local.

46157 ■ SnoValley Chamber of Commerce (SVCC)
128 W 2nd St.
North Bend, WA 98045
Ph: (425)888-6362
Co. E-mail: info@snovalley.org
URL: http://www.snovalley.org
Contact: Michael Hughes, President
Facebook: www.facebook.com/SnoValleyChamber
Instagram: www.instagram.com/snovalleychamber
Description: Promotes business/community growth and development by promoting economic programs designed to strengthen and expand the economic potential of all businesses within the area. **Founded:** 2012. **Publications:** *Chamber Connection* (Monthly). **Geographic Preference:** Local.

46158 ■ Soap Lake Chamber of Commerce
301 Daisy St. N
Soap Lake, WA 98851
Co. E-mail: soaplakecoc@gmail.com
URL: http://www.soaplakecoc.org
Contact: Debbie Noah, President
E-mail: soaplakecoc@gmail.com
Description: Promotes business and commerce in Soap Lake, WA area. **Geographic Preference:** Local.

46159 ■ Southwest King County Chamber of Commerce (SWKCC) [Seattle Southside Chamber of Commerce]
4800 S 188th St., Ste. 250
Seatac, WA 98188
Ph: (206)575-1633
URL: http://www.seattlesouthsidechamber.com
Contact: Annie McGrath, President
E-mail: annie@seattlesouthsidechamber.com
Facebook: www.facebook.com/SeaSouthChamber
Linkedin: www.linkedin.com/company/seattle-southside-chamber-of-commerce
X (Twitter): x.com/SeaSouthChamber
Instagram: www.instagram.com/SeaSouthChamber
Description: Promotes business and community development in Southwest King County, Burien, SeaTac, and Tukwila, WA. **Founded:** 1989. **Publications:** *Business Advocate* (Monthly); *Business Directory & Community Profile* (Annual). **Awards:** Southwest King County Chamber of Commerce Small Business of the Year Award (Annual); Southwest King County Chamber of Commerce Business Advocate Award (Annual). **Geographic Preference:** Local.

46160 ■ Steilacoom Chamber of Commerce
PO Box 88584
Steilacoom, WA 98388
Ph: (253)677-7300
Co. E-mail: info@steilacoomchamber.com
URL: http://www.steilacoomchamber.com
Contact: Larry Whelan, President
Facebook: www.facebook.com/SteilacoomChamber
Description: Supports and promotes local business in the Steilacoom community. **Geographic Preference:** Local.

46161 ■ *Tacoma-Pierce County Business Directory*
950 Pacific Ave., Ste. 300
Tacoma, WA 98402
Ph: (253)627-2175
Fax: (253)597-7305
Co. E-mail: info@tacomachamber.org
URL: http://www.tacomachamber.org
Contact: Tom Pierson, President
E-mail: tomp@tacomachamber.org
URL(s): business.tacomachamber.org/list
Availability: Print.

46162 ■ Tacoma-Pierce County Chamber (TPCC)
950 Pacific Ave., Ste. 300
Tacoma, WA 98402
Ph: (253)627-2175
Fax: (253)597-7305
Co. E-mail: info@tacomachamber.org
URL: http://www.tacomachamber.org
Contact: Tom Pierson, President
E-mail: tomp@tacomachamber.org
Facebook: www.facebook.com/tacomapiercecountychamber
X (Twitter): x.com/Tacoma_Chamber
Instagram: www.instagram.com/tacoma_chamber
Description: Promotes business and community development in Pierce County, WA. **Founded:** 1984. **Publications:** *Chamber Current* (Monthly); *Tacoma-Pierce County Business Directory*; *Tacoma-Pierce*

STATE LISTINGS

County Manufacturing Directory (Annual); *Tacoma-Pierce County Chamber of Commerce--Membership Directory/Buyers Guide* (Annual). **Awards:** Tahoma Environmental Business Award (Annual). **Geographic Preference:** Local.

46163 ■ Thurston County Chamber of Commerce
809 Legion Way SE
Olympia, WA 98501
Ph: (360)357-3362
Co. E-mail: info@thurstonchamber.com
URL: http://members.thurstonchamber.com
Contact: David Schaffert, President
E-mail: dschaffert@thurstonchamber.com
Facebook: www.facebook.com/ThurstonCountyChamber
X (Twitter): x.com/ThurstonChamber
YouTube: www.youtube.com/user/ThurstonCoChamber
Description: Promotes business and community development in Thurston County, WA. **Founded:** 1874. **Publications:** *The Voice-For Free Enterprise* (Monthly). **Educational Activities:** Chamber Forum (Monthly). **Awards:** Thurston County Chamber of Commerce Distinguished Leader Award (Annual). **Geographic Preference:** Local.

46164 ■ Tonasket Chamber of Commerce
246 E 1St. St.
Tonasket, WA 98855
Contact: Marylou Kriner, Governor
Description: Promotes business and community development in Tonasket, WA. **Founded:** 1973. **Geographic Preference:** Local.

46165 ■ Toppenish Chamber of Commerce
504 S Elm St.
Toppenish, WA 98948
Ph: (509)865-3262
Co. E-mail: toppenishchamber@gmail.com
URL: http://www.visittoppenish.com
Contact: Tami Ramirez, President
Description: Promotes business and community development in Toppenish, WA. Sponsors arts, crafts, food fair, 4th of July parade, and ranch party. **Founded:** 1941. **Geographic Preference:** Local.

46166 ■ Town of Conconully Chamber of Commerce
PO Box 127
Conconully, WA 98819
Ph: (509)826-6005
Co. E-mail: clerk@townofconcunully.com
URL: http://www.conconully.com/business-directory
Facebook: www.facebook.com/Conconully
Description: Promotes business and community development in the Conconully, WA area. **Geographic Preference:** Local.

46167 ■ Tri-City Regional Chamber of Commerce (TCRCC)
7130 W Grandridge Blvd., Ste. C
Kennewick, WA 99336
Ph: (509)736-0510
Fax: (509)783-1733
Co. E-mail: info@tricityregionalchamber.com
URL: http://www.tricityregionalchamber.com
Contact: Lori Mattson, President
E-mail: lori.mattson@tricityregionalchamber.com
Facebook: www.facebook.com/TriCityRegionalChamber
Linkedin: www.linkedin.com/company/tri-city-regional-chamber-of-commerce
X (Twitter): x.com/tricitychamber
Instagram: www.instagram.com/tricityregionalchamber
YouTube: www.youtube.com/user/TCRofCommerce
Description: Promotes business and community development in the Kennewick, WA area. **Founded:** 2006. **Publications:** *Commerce Report* (Monthly); *Profile Booklet* (Annual); *Catalyst Magazine*; *Real Estate Magazine*. **Educational Activities:** General Membership Meeting. **Geographic Preference:** Local.

46168 ■ Tumwater Area Chamber of Commerce (TACC)
855 Trosper Rd. SW No. 108-229
Tumwater, WA 98512
Ph: (360)357-5153
Co. E-mail: info@tumwaterchamber.com
URL: http://www.tumwaterchamber.com
Contact: Gabe Toma, President
Facebook: www.facebook.com/tumwater.chamber
Description: Promotes business and community development in Tumwater, WA area. **Publications:** *The New Market* (Monthly); *The Chamber Chat* (Periodic). **Geographic Preference:** Local.

46169 ■ Twisp Chamber of Commerce
201 S Hwy. 20
Twisp, WA 98856
Ph: (509)997-2020
Co. E-mail: twispwashington@gmail.com
URL: http://twispwa.com
Contact: Rich Milsteadt, President
Facebook: www.facebook.com/TwispWA
X (Twitter): x.com/twispwa
Instagram: www.instagram.com/twispwa
YouTube: www.youtube.com/user/TwispWashington
Description: Promotes business and community development in Twisp, WA. **Geographic Preference:** Local.

46170 ■ U District Partnership (UDP)
1415 NE 45TH st., Ste. 401
Seattle, WA 98105
Ph: (206)547-4417
Co. E-mail: social@udistrictpartnership.org
URL: http://udistrictpartnership.org
Contact: Don Blakeney, Executive Director
E-mail: don@udistrictpartnership.org
Facebook: www.facebook.com/udistrictpartnership
X (Twitter): x.com/UDPartnership
Instagram: www.instagram.com/udistrictpartnership
Description: Promotes business and community development in the University District of Seattle, WA. Sponsors University District Streetfair, University Farmers Market, and Junior Grand Seafair Parade. **Founded:** 1915. **Publications:** *University District Business News* (Monthly). **Geographic Preference:** Local.

46171 ■ Walla Walla Valley Chamber of Commerce (WWVCC)
29 E Sumach St.
Walla Walla, WA 99362
Ph: (509)525-0850
Co. E-mail: info@wwvchamber.com
URL: http://www.wwvchamber.com
Contact: Kyle Tarbet, President
E-mail: ktarbet@wwvchamber.com
Facebook: www.facebook.com/wwvchamber
Instagram: www.instagram.com/wwvchamber
Description: Promotes business and community development in the Walla Walla, WA area. Sponsors Walla Walla Balloon Stampede and Walla Walla Sweet Onion Festival. **Founded:** 1875. **Publications:** *Walla Walla Valley Chamber of Commerce--Business Directory*; *Chamber News*. **Awards:** Walla Walla Valley Chamber of Commerce Award of Merit (Annual); Walla Walla Valley Chamber of Commerce Volunteer of the Year (Annual). **Geographic Preference:** Local.

46172 ■ Wenatchee Valley Chamber of Commerce (WVCC)
137 N Wenatchee Ave., Ste. 101
Wenatchee, WA 98801
Ph: (509)662-2116
Fax: (509)663-2022
Co. E-mail: info@wenatchee.org
URL: http://www.wenatchee.org
Contact: Cheri Kuhn, President
Facebook: www.facebook.com/WenatcheeValleyChamber
Linkedin: www.linkedin.com/company/wenatcheevalleychamber
X (Twitter): x.com/VisitWenatchee
Instagram: www.instagram.com/wenatcheevalleychamber
YouTube: www.youtube.com/channel/UC1HzQ_4PfQwIkSJTDgdtUwQ
Description: Promotes business and community development in East Wenatchee, WA. **Founded:** 1903. **Publications:** *Connections* (Monthly); *Wenatchee Valley Chamber of Commerce Business Directory and Relocation Guide*. **Geographic Preference:** Local.

46173 ■ *Wenatchee Valley Chamber of Commerce Business Directory and Relocation Guide*
137 N Wenatchee Ave., Ste. 101
Wenatchee, WA 98801
Ph: (509)662-2116
Fax: (509)663-2022
Co. E-mail: info@wenatchee.org
URL: http://www.wenatchee.org
Contact: Cheri Kuhn, President
URL(s): www.wenatchee.org/relocation-guide
Availability: PDF.

46174 ■ West Plains Chamber of Commerce (WPCC)
PO Box 228
Airway Heights, WA 99001
Ph: (509)747-8480
Co. E-mail: chamber@westplainschamber.org
URL: http://westplainschamber.org
Contact: Mark Losh, Chief Executive Officer
E-mail: mark@westplainschamber.org
Description: Promotes business and community development in Cheney, WA. **Founded:** 1942. **Geographic Preference:** Local.

46175 ■ West Seattle Chamber of Commerce (WSCC)
5639-A California Ave. SW
Seattle, WA 98116
Ph: (206)932-5685
Co. E-mail: info@wschamber.com
URL: http://www.wschamber.com
Contact: Whitney Moore, Executive Director
Facebook: www.facebook.com/west.seattle.chamber
X (Twitter): x.com/WestSeattleCC
Description: Provides a professional forum to discuss and influence policies and programs affecting business and social climate. **Founded:** 1922. **Publications:** *The Bulletin* (Monthly). **Geographic Preference:** Local.

46176 ■ Westport-Grayland Chamber of Commerce
2985 S Montesano St.
Westport, WA 98595-0306
Ph: (360)268-9422
Free: 800-345-6223
Fax: (360)268-1990
Co. E-mail: info@westportgrayland-chamber.org
URL: http://www.westportgrayland-chamber.org
Contact: Dennise Wells, Governor
Facebook: www.facebook.com/ComeToWestport
Description: Promotes business and community development in the Westport, WA area. Sponsors crab races, Seafood festival, Kite Fest, and Surf Festival. **Founded:** 1914. **Geographic Preference:** Local.

46177 ■ White Center Chamber of Commerce (WCCC)
1327 SW 102 St.
Seattle, WA 98146
Ph: (206)763-4196
Fax: (206)763-1042
Co. E-mail: whitentercc@gmail.com
URL: http://www.wcce.org/index.php?option=com_civicrm&task=civicrm/profile/view&Itemid=440&reset=1&id=288&gid=9
Facebook: www.facebook.com/pages/Washington-Chamber-of-Commerce-Executives
Geographic Preference: Local.

46178 ■ Willapa Harbor Chamber of Commerce
PO Box 1249
South Bend, WA 98586
Ph: (360)942-5419

Co. E-mail: info@willapaharbor.org
URL: http://willapaharbor.org
Contact: Dr. Stephen Holland, President
Facebook: www.facebook.com/Willapa-Harbor-Chamber-of-Commerce-604955319583499
Pinterest: www.pinterest.com/WillapaChamber
Description: Promotes business, tourism and community development in North Pacific County. **Geographic Preference:** Local.

46179 ■ Winthrop Chamber of Commerce
202 Riverside Ave.
  Winthrop, WA 98862
Ph: (509)996-2125
Co. E-mail: info@winthropwashington.com
URL: http://winthropwashington.com
Contact: Paul Peterson, Treasurer
Facebook: www.facebook.com/WinthropWashington
X (Twitter): x.com/winthropwa
YouTube: www.youtube.com/user/WinthropWashington
Pinterest: www.pinterest.com/andrelusil/winthrop-washington
Description: Promotes business and community development in Winthrop, WA. **Publications:** *Event Directory* (Annual). **Geographic Preference:** Local.

46180 ■ Yelm Area Chamber of Commerce (YACC)
608 E Yelm Ave.
  Yelm, WA 98597
URL: http://yelmchamber.com/about
Contact: Joe Richardson, President
X (Twitter): x.com/yelm_chamber
Description: Promotes business and community development in Yelm, WA area. **Publications:** *Viewpoint* (Monthly). **Geographic Preference:** Local.

MINORITY BUSINESS ASSISTANCE PROGRAMS

46181 ■ Washington Minority Business Enterprise Center
1437 S Jackson St., Ste. 320
  Seattle, WA 98144
Description: Works to create, grow and sustain minority entrepreneurial opportunities in Washington.

46182 ■ Washington State Office of Minority and Women's Business Enterprises (M/WBE)
1110 Capitol Way S, Ste. 150
  Olympia, WA 98501
Ph: (360)664-9750
Free: 866-208-1064
Fax: (360)586-7079
Co. E-mail: technicalassistance@omwbe.wa.gov
URL: http://www.omwbe.wa.gov
Facebook: www.facebook.com/WSOMWBE
X (Twitter): x.com/OMWBE
Description: Created to increase opportunities for minorities and women wishing to obtain state contracts. **Founded:** 1983.

FINANCING AND LOAN PROGRAMS

46183 ■ Acorn Ventures Inc.
PO Box 6847
  Bellevue, WA 98008
Ph: (425)462-6144
Fax: (425)999-4853
Co. E-mail: info@acornventures.net
URL: http://www.acornventures.net
Contact: Rufus Lumry, President
Description: Firm provides investment management services. **Founded:** 1991. **Preferred Investment Size:** $1,000,000 to $5,000,000. **Industry Preferences:** Communications and media, Internet specific, computer software and services, semiconductors and other electronics, other products, and computer hardware.

46184 ■ Alliance of Angels (AA)
719 2nd Ave., Ste. 1000
  Seattle, WA 98104
Co. E-mail: aoa@allianceofangels.com
URL: http://www.allianceofangels.com
Contact: Dan Menser, Chairman
Facebook: www.facebook.com/profile.php?id=100064472690634
Linkedin: www.linkedin.com/company/alliance-of-angels
X (Twitter): x.com/allianceangels
Description: Angel investor group in the Pacific Northwest. **Founded:** 1997.

46185 ■ Bellingham Angel Investors (BAI)
1501 Eldridge Ave.
  Bellingham, WA 98225-2801
URL: http://www.bellinghamangelinvestors.com
Contact: Jim Thompson, Governor
Description: Invests in early- or middle-stage companies in the Pacific Northwest and British Columbia, with preference to Whatcom, Skagit, and Island counties. **Founded:** 2005.

46186 ■ Benaroya Capital Co.
9675 SE 36th St., Ste. 115
  Mercer Island, WA 98040-3723
Co. E-mail: general@benaroya.com
Contact: Larry Benaroya, Governor
Description: Real estate company engages in the acquisition, development and management of properties. **Founded:** 1956. **Preferred Investment Size:** $500,000 to $3,000,000. **Investment Policies:** Seed, first and second stage. **Industry Preferences:** Communications, and semiconductors and other electronics.

46187 ■ Capria Ventures LLC
1200, Westlake Ave. N, Ste. 510
  Seattle, WA 98104
URL: http://capria.vc
Contact: Will Poole, Managing Partner
Linkedin: www.linkedin.com/company/capria
X (Twitter): x.com/capriavc
Description: Global impact investment firm. **Founded:** 2012.

46188 ■ Craft3
409 Maynard Ave. S, Ste. 200
  Seattle, WA 98104-2959
Free: 888-231-2170
Fax: (360)455-4879
Co. E-mail: info@craft3.org
URL: http://www.craft3.org
Contact: Sonya Lynn, Chief Operating Officer
Facebook: www.facebook.com/Craft3Org
Linkedin: www.linkedin.com/company/craft3
X (Twitter): x.com/Craft3Org
Description: CFDI provides loans to established nonprofits as well as growing and start-up businesses in Oregon and Washington.

46189 ■ E8
PO Box 895
  Bellevue, WA 98009
Co. E-mail: info@e8angels.com
URL: http://www.e8angels.com
Contact: Karin Kidder, Executive Director
Facebook: www.facebook.com/E8Angels
Linkedin: www.linkedin.com/company/element-8-angels
X (Twitter): x.com/E8Angels
Description: Invests in an fosters early-stage cleantech companies whose innovations will increase the sustainability and health of the planet. **Founded:** 2006.

46190 ■ Fluke Venture Partners (FVP)
520 Kirkland Way, Ste. 300
  Kirkland, WA 98033
Ph: (425)896-4322
Fax: (425)827-4683
URL: http://www.flukeventures.com
Contact: Kevin Gabelein, Managing Director
E-mail: gabelein@flukeventures.com
Description: Venture capital firm provides funds and investment services. **Founded:** 1982. **Preferred Investment Size:** $1,000,000 to $3,000,000. **Industry Preferences:** Computer software and services, computer hardware, Internet specific, medical and health, communications and media, consumer related, industrial and energy, biotechnology, semiconductors and other electronics, and other products.

46191 ■ Founders' Co-op
1100 NE Campus Pkwy., Ste. 200
  Seattle, WA 98105
Co. E-mail: info@founderscoop.com
URL: http://www.founderscoop.com
Contact: Chris Devore, Managing Partner
E-mail: chris@founderscoop.com
Linkedin: www.linkedin.com/company/founders-co-op
X (Twitter): x.com/founderscoop
Description: Seed-stage venture fund for software startups in tthe Pacific Northwest. **Founded:** 2008. **Preferred Investment Size:** $250,000 to $750,000 .

46192 ■ Frazier & Company / Frazier Healthcare and Technology Ventures
601 Union, 2 Union Sq., Ste. 3200
  Seattle, WA 98101
Ph: (206)621-7200
URL: http://www.frazierhealthcare.com
Contact: Alan Frazier, Chairman
Founded: 1991. **Preferred Investment Size:** $10,000,000 to $40,000,000. **Industry Preferences:** Computer software and services, Internet specific, medical and health, communications and media, computer hardware, other products, consumer related, industrial and energy, biotechnology, semiconductors and other electronics.

46193 ■ Kirlan Venture Capital Inc.
201 W N River Dr., Ste. 505
  Spokane, WA 99201-2262
Contact: Lisa Hunt, Governor
Preferred Investment Size: $100,000 to $2,000,000. **Industry Preferences:** Communications and media, medical and health, computer software and services, Internet specific, industrial and energy, and computer hardware.

46194 ■ Madrona Venture Group
999 3rd Ave., 34th Fl.
  Seattle, WA 98104
Ph: (206)674-3000
Fax: (206)674-8703
URL: http://www.madrona.com
Contact: Ted Kummert, Partner
Facebook: www.facebook.com/MadronaVentureGroup
X (Twitter): x.com/madronaventures
Instagram: www.instagram.com/Madronaventures
Description: Venture capital firm investing in seed and early-stage companies. . **Founded:** 1995.

46195 ■ Pacific Horizon Ventures (PHV)
500 Union St., Ste. 835
  Seattle, WA 98101
Ph: (206)682-1181
Fax: (206)682-8077
Co. E-mail: phv@pacifichorizon.com
URL: http://pacifichorizon.com
Contact: Donald J. Elmer, Managing Partner
Description: Early-stage venture capital firm for life science technologies addressing healthcare problems in poorly served markets. **Founded:** 1993. **Industry Preferences:** Life science; healthcare.

46196 ■ Paladin Partners
3531 Overlook Dr.
  Langley, WA 98260
Ph: (425)260-5354
URL: http://janismachala.com
Contact: Janis Machala, Chief Executive Officer
Linkedin: www.linkedin.com/in/janismachala
Description: Provider of financial strategies, consulting services, financial advice and financial products. **Industry Preferences:** Communications, computer software, Internet specific, and business service.

46197 ■ SeaPoint Ventures, LLC
405 Thatcher Pass Rd. Decatur Island
  Anacortes, WA 98221
Contact: Thomas Huseby, Governor

Description: Firm provides investment management services. **Founded:** 1997. **Preferred Investment Size:** $300,000 to $4,000,000. **Industry Preferences:** Internet specific, computer software and services, computer hardware, communications and media, and biotechnology.

46198 ■ Second Avenue Partners LLC
1932 1St Ave., Ste. A1
Seattle, WA 98101-1063
Ph: (206)332-1200
Fax: (206)332-1201
Co. E-mail: info@secondave.com
URL: http://www.secondave.com
Contact: Pete Higgins, Co-Founder Partner
Description: Venture capital firm for early-stage investments in the Puget Sound area. **Founded:** 2000. **Industry Preferences:** Internet; consumer; social media; software; clean energy.

46199 ■ Spokane Angel Alliance (SAA)
c/o Tom Simpson
518 W Riverside, Ste. 202
Spokane, WA 99201
Ph: (509)953-2989
Co. E-mail: tom@nwva.com
URL: http://www.spokaneangelalliance.com
Contact: Tom Simpson, President
E-mail: tom@nwva.com
Description: Angel investor group for emerging companies in Eastern Washington, Idaho, and Montana.

46200 ■ Ventures
2100 24th Ave. S, Ste. 380
Seattle, WA 98144
Ph: (206)352-1945
Co. E-mail: info@venturesnonprofit.org
URL: http://www.venturesnonprofit.org
Contact: Octaiviea Renée, President
Facebook: www.facebook.com/venturesnonprofit
Linkedin: www.linkedin.com/company/washington-c-a
X (Twitter): x.com/VenturesNP
Instagram: www.instagram.com/venturesnonprofit
Description: Offers access to business training, capital, coaching, and hands-on learning opportunities to entrepreneurs for whom traditional business development services are out of reach (women, immigrants, people of color, and low-income individuals).

46201 ■ Voyager Capital (VC)
719 2nd Ave., Ste. 1000
Seattle, WA 98104
Ph: (206)438-1800
Co. E-mail: newell@voyagercapital.com
URL: http://www.voyagercapital.com
Contact: Diane Fraiman, Managing Director
Description: Investment firm provides of venture capital and private equity investment services. **Founded:** 1997. **Preferred Investment Size:** $3,000,000 to $12,000,000. **Industry Preferences:** Internet specific, computer software and services, semiconductors and other electronics, communications and media, computer hardware, and other products.

46202 ■ Washington Economic Development Finance Authority (WEDFA)
1000 2nd Ave., Ste. 2700
Seattle, WA 98104
URL: http://wedfa.org
Contact: Rodney Wendt, Executive Director
E-mail: wedfa@wshfc.org
Description: Offers governmental financing to private enterprise and occasionally local governments. **Industry Preferences:** Manufacturing; processing; alternate energy; waste; disposal; recycling; water/sewage treatment.

PROCUREMENT ASSISTANCE PROGRAMS

46203 ■ Economic Alliance Snohomish County (EASC)
808 134th St. SW, Ste. 101
Everett, WA 98204
Ph: (425)743-4567
Co. E-mail: info@economicalliancesc.org
URL: http://www.economicalliancesc.org
Contact: Garry Clark, President
Facebook: www.facebook.com/EconAllianceSC
Linkedin: www.linkedin.com/company/economic-alliance-snohomish-county
X (Twitter): x.com/EconAllianceSC
Instagram: www.instagram.com/econalliancesc
YouTube: www.youtube.com/channel/UCTrCCDyc5ehtCPB2Ccq-f0g
Description: Helps companies find and successfully achieve contracts for work with the local, state and federal governments. **Founded:** 2011. **Publications:** *Biz2Biz* (Monthly); *Everett Guide* (Annual). **Awards:** John M. Fluke, Sr., Community Service Award (Annual); Henry M. Jackson Citizen of the Year Award (Annual); The Herald Business Journal Executive of the Year (Annual). **Geographic Preference:** Local.

46204 ■ Greater Spokane Incorporated (GSI)
801 W Riverside Ave., Ste. 200
Spokane, WA 99201
Ph: (509)624-1393
Free: 800-776-5263
Fax: (509)747-0077
Co. E-mail: info@greaterspokane.org
URL: http://greaterspokane.org
Contact: Alisha Benson, Chief Executive Officer
E-mail: abenson@greaterspokane.org
Facebook: www.facebook.com/greaterspokane
X (Twitter): x.com/greaterspokane
YouTube: www.youtube.com/user/GSIgreaterspokaneinc
Description: Assists businesses with any aspect of federal, state and local government contracting. Serving 13 counties in Eastern Washington including Spokane, Ferry, Lincoln, Stevens, Pend Oreille, Adams, Franklin, Benton, Whitman, Walla Walla, Columbia, Garfield and Asotin counties. **Founded:** 1974. **Publications:** *Spokane Empire Manufacturing Guide* (Biennial); *Inland-Northwest Manufacturers Directory* (Annual). **Educational Activities:** Spokane Ag Expo (Annual). **Geographic Preference:** Local.

46205 ■ Thurston County Economic Development Council (TEDC)
4220 6th Ave. SE
Lacey, WA 98503
Ph: (360)754-6320
Free: 888-821-6652
Co. E-mail: office@thurstonedc.com
URL: http://www.thurstonedc.com
Contact: Michael Cade, Executive Director
E-mail: mcade@thurstonedc.com
Facebook: www.facebook.com/ThurstonEDC
X (Twitter): x.com/thurstoncntyedc
Description: Specializes in identifying opportunity and applying effort that results in creating a vibrant and vital economy. **Founded:** 1982.

46206 ■ Washington Procurement Technical Assistance Center - Columbia River Economic Development Council (CREDC)
805 Broadway, St., Ste. 412
Vancouver, WA 98660
Ph: (306)694-5546
Co. E-mail: info@credc.org
URL: http://www.credc.org
Contact: Jennifer Baker, President
URL(s): washingtonapex.org/columbia-river-economic-development-council
Facebook: www.facebook.com/ColumbiaRiverEDC
Linkedin: www.linkedin.com/company/columbiariveredc
X (Twitter): x.com/ColumbiaRvrEDC
YouTube: www.youtube.com/channel/UC88AP7FNCTVD9uD6M6OBgSw
Description: A proactive, results-oriented public/private partnership working with over 180 associates to assist businesses to relocate or expand in Clark, Cowlitz, and Skamania counties. **Founded:** 1982.

46207 ■ Washington Procurement Technical Assistance Center - Economic Development Alliance of Skagit County (EDASC)
1932 E College Way, Ste. B
Mount Vernon, WA 98273
Ph: (360)336-6114
Fax: (360)336-6116
Co. E-mail: office@skagit.org
URL: http://www.skagit.org
Contact: John Sternlicht, Chief Executive Officer
E-mail: john@skagit.org
Facebook: www.facebook.com/EDASCskagit
Linkedin: www.linkedin.com/company/economic-development-alliance-of-skagit-county
X (Twitter): x.com/EDASC
YouTube: www.youtube.com/channel/UC5kN0N1ucMoL8JQqmyukBwA
Description: Assists companies who are interested in doing business with the government in Island, San Juan, Skagit and Whatcom counties.

46208 ■ Washington Procurement Technical Assistance Center - Grays Harbor Economic Development Council
506 Duffy St.
Aberdeen, WA 98520
Ph: (360)532-7888
Free: 800-321-1924
Fax: (360)532-1924
Co. E-mail: info@graysharbor.org
URL: http://graysharbor.org
Contact: Lynnette Buffington, Chief Executive Officer
Facebook: www.facebook.com/GreaterGHInc
Linkedin: www.linkedin.com/company/greater-grays-harbor-inc
X (Twitter): x.com/GreaterGHInc
YouTube: www.youtube.com/channel/UCtkoV4c3z41K28uSgPYY7ug
Description: Assist local government and businesses to promote the overall economic vitality of the county and its communities, to market and capitalize on the County's assets serving Clallam, Grays Harbor, Jefferson, Kitsap, Mason, Pacific, and Wahkiakum counties.

46209 ■ Washington Procurement Technical Assistance Center - William Factory Small Business Incubator
6501 S 19th St. Bldg., 19 Office Rm., 52 & 54
Tacoma, WA 98466
Ph: (253)722-5800
Co. E-mail: info@williamfactory.com
URL: http://www.williamfactory.com
Contact: Tim Strege, Executive Director
URL(s): washingtonapex.org/about-apex/staff
Facebook: www.facebook.com/William-Factory-Small-Business-Incubator-159143737440207
Instagram: www.instagram.com/williamfactory253
Description: Provides an opportunity to nurture carefully selected, smaller, locally owned entrepreneurs through their formative years serving Pierce County. **Founded:** 1986.

46210 ■ Yakima County Development Associations - Washington Procurement Technical Assistance Center
4220 6th Ave. SE
Lacey, WA 98503
Ph: (360)464-6041
Co. E-mail: info@washingtonapex.org
URL: http://washingtonptac.org
Contact: Tiffany Scroggs, Program Director
E-mail: programmanager@washingtonapex.org
Facebook: www.facebook.com/WashingtonAPEX
Linkedin: www.linkedin.com/company/washington-apex
Description: A public-private non-profit corporation created to enhance the income and employment stability of the local economy serving Asotin, Benton, Columbia, Franklin, Garfield, Kittitas, Walla Walla and Yakima counties.

INCUBATORS/RESEARCH AND TECHNOLOGY PARKS

46211 ■ Applied Process Engineering Laboratory (APEL)
c/o Richard Shaff, Business Manager
350 Hills St.
Richland, WA 99354
Ph: (509)372-5086
URL: http://www.energy-northwest.com/doingbusinesswithus/technicalservices/apel/Pages/default.aspx
Contact: Richard Shaff, Business Manager
E-mail: rashaff@energy-northwest.com
Description: Provides opportunities for efficient and effective business startup and development, validation, and commercialization of new product lines. Entrepreneurs, engineers, scientists, and businessmen developing new product lines all have access to the facility.

46212 ■ The Culinary Cooperative
3223 164th St. SW
Lynnwood, WA 98087
Ph: (206)214-5134
Co. E-mail: theculinarycooperative@gmail.com
Facebook: www.facebook.com/TheCulinaryCooperative
Description: Shared commercial kitchen rents space to new and existing culinary businesses.

46213 ■ ELAP Family Law Fellowship (ELAP)
1239 120th Ave. NE, Ste. J
Bellevue, WA 98005
Ph: (425)747-7274
Fax: (425)747-7504
Co. E-mail: info@elap.org
URL: http://elap.org
Contact: Gerald Shepherd Kröon, Executive Director
Facebook: www.facebook.com/EastsideLegalAssistanceProgram
Linkedin: www.linkedin.com/company/eastside-legal-assistance-program
X (Twitter): x.com/Eastside_Legal
Instagram: www.instagram.com/elap89
Description: Fellowship that allows attorneys without family law experience who are interested in starting their own practice the opportunity to get hands on experience with starting their own legal practice and learning the practice of family law. **Founded:** 1989.

46214 ■ Everett Community College (EvCC) - Small Business Accelerator
909 N Broadway Ave.
Everett, WA 98201
Ph: (425)267-0150
Co. E-mail: learn@everettcc.edu
URL: http://www.everettcc.edu/ccec/small-business-accelerator
Contact: Travis Snider, Leader
Description: Offers expert guidance and tools to established business owners. Programs feature classroom instruction along with one-on-one coaching.

46215 ■ Fledge LLC
6315 Tamoshan Dr. NW
Olympia, WA 98502
URL: http://www.fledge.co
Contact: Erin Kershisnik, Governor
Facebook: www.facebook.com/FledgeLLC
X (Twitter): x.com/fledgellc
YouTube: www.youtube.com/fledgellc
Description: Global network of company accelerators and seed funds. Helps entrepreneurs create impactful companies to scale through short, intense, educational programs, Offers guidance and mentorship.

46216 ■ Ignite Northwest
518 W Riverside
Spokane, WA 99202
Ph: (509)358-2000
Co. E-mail: info@ignitenorthwest.com
URL: http://www.ignitenorthwest.com
Contact: Tom Simpson, Chief Executive Officer
Facebook: www.facebook.com/IgniteINW
Linkedin: www.linkedin.com/company/ignite-northwest
X (Twitter): x.com/ignite_inw
Instagram: www.instagram.com/ignitenorthwest
YouTube: www.youtube.com/channel/UCkH8aCuVqVhmrCRJLUI-k5w
Description: A technology-focused business accelerator that helps companies in the Pacific Northwest grow to create sustained economic impact. **Founded:** 2014.

46217 ■ Innovate Washington Foundation (IWF)
518 W Riverside Ave., Ste. 203
Spokane, WA 99201-0522
Contact: Thomas Simpson, Governor
Description: A nonprofit organization focused on growing the innovation-based economic sectors of the state of Washington. Offers information resource network to entrepreneurs; IPBIZ/NET: through partner institutions, law firms; technical and business assistance to entrepreneurs. **Scope:** Digital, environmental, biotechnological, and renewable energy technologies that lead to commercialization and economic growth in the Inland Northwest. **Publications:** Perspective.

46218 ■ Kenmore Business Incubator (KBI)
7204 NE 175th St.
Kenmore, WA 98028
URL: http://www.kenmorewa.gov/business/kenmore-business-incubator-and-business-resources
Contact: Marilyn Hall, Consultant
E-mail: marilyn@nxlvlup-llc.com
Description: Business incubator that provides low cost office space, mentorship and business development support, and connects business professionals to networking events, workshops and seminars. **Founded:** 2013.

46219 ■ Kindred Kitchen
3315 Broadway
Everett, WA 98201
Ph: (425)512-0343
Co. E-mail: contact@kindredkitchen.com
URL: http://www.kindredkitchen.com
Facebook: www.facebook.com/kindredkitchen.snoco
Instagram: www.instagram.com/kindredkitchen.snoco
Description: Culinary incubator offering classes and training in a commercial kitchen space for food business entrepreneurs.

46220 ■ Kitchen Sisters
501 2nd Ave. W, No. 100
Seattle, WA 98119
Ph: (206)283-0619
Co. E-mail: info@kitchensistersseattle.com
URL: http://www.kitchensistersseattle.com
Contact: Erika Rivas, Contact
Description: A co-working commercial kitchen space designed for food start-ups and small businesses.

46221 ■ Surf Incubator
999 3rd Ave., Ste. 700
Seattle, WA 98104
Ph: (626)594-5518
Co. E-mail: info@surfincubator.com
URL: http://www.surfincubator.com
Contact: Seaton Gras, Chief Executive Officer
Description: Encourages entrepreneurs to focus on executing their business ideas. Brings together mentors, investors, developers, designers and educators. **Founded:** 2009.

46222 ■ Thurston County Small Business Incubator
809 Legion Way SE 3rd Fl.
Olympia, WA 98501
Ph: (360)357-3362
Co. E-mail: info@thurstonchamber.com
URL: http://thurstonchamber.com/Incubator
Facebook: www.facebook.com/ThurstonCountyChamber
X (Twitter): x.com/ThurstonChamber
YouTube: www.youtube.com/user/ThurstonCoChamber
Description: Mission of the incubator is to create jobs by helping entrepreneurs and small businesses access resources they need for growth and long term success. **Founded:** 1874.

46223 ■ Tri-Cities Enterprise Center
415 N Quay, Bldg. B
Kennewick, WA 99336
Ph: (509)735-0408
Fax: (509)783-6004
Co. E-mail: info@owt.com
URL: http://www.owt.com
Description: A non-profit incubator dedicated to ensuring the survival of emerging firms in Benton and Franklin counties of Washington state. **Founded:** 1994.

46224 ■ Tri-County Economic Development District (TEDD)
986 S Main St., Ste. A
Colville, WA 99114
Ph: (509)684-4571
Free: 800-776-7318
Fax: (509)684-4788
Co. E-mail: admin@teddonline.com
URL: http://tricountyedd.com
Contact: Jeff Koffel, Executive Director
E-mail: jkoffel@teddonline.com
Facebook: www.facebook.com/TriCountyEDD
X (Twitter): x.com/tricountyedd
Instagram: www.instagram.com/tricountyedd
YouTube: www.youtube.com/channel/UCc62Z9uRxxQXlQN_4bWfe1Q
Description: Helps to grow local businesses through planning and resource development. **Founded:** 1969.

46225 ■ University of Washington - CoMotion
4545 Roosevelt Way NE, Ste. 400
Seattle, WA 98105
Ph: (206)543-3970
Fax: (206)543-0586
Co. E-mail: uwcomotion@uw.edu
URL: http://www.comotion.uw.edu
Contact: François Baneyx, Director
E-mail: baneyx@uw.edu
Facebook: www.facebook.com/UW.CoMotion
Linkedin: www.linkedin.com/company/uwcomotion
X (Twitter): x.com/UWCoMotion
Instagram: www.instagram.com/uwcomotion
YouTube: www.youtube.com/c/uwcomotion
Description: A collaborative hub delivering the tools and connections that researchers and students need to accelerate the impact of their innovations. **Founded:** 2016.

46226 ■ USI Kitchen Rental
4611 36th Ave. SW
Seattle, WA 98126
Ph: (206)935-0432
URL: http://www.distinguishedfoodskitchenrental.com/product-page/seattle-sorbets-monthly-kitchen-rent
Description: Culinary incubator providing commercial kitchen space for food startups and entrepreneurs. The company has witnessed the birth of countless small businesses.

46227 ■ Washington Procurement Technical Assistance Center - William Factory Small Business Incubator
6501 S 19th St. Bldg., 19 Office Rm., 52 & 54
Tacoma, WA 98466
Ph: (253)722-5800
Co. E-mail: info@williamfactory.com
URL: http://www.williamfactory.com
Contact: Tim Strege, Executive Director
URL(s): washingtonapex.org/about-apex/staff
Facebook: www.facebook.com/William-Factory-Small-Business-Incubator-159143737440207
Instagram: www.instagram.com/williamfactory253
Description: Provides an opportunity to nurture carefully selected, smaller, locally owned entrepreneurs through their formative years serving Pierce County. **Founded:** 1986.

46228 ■ Washington State University Research Technology Park (WSU)
1610 & 1615 NE Eastgate Blvd.
Pullman, WA 99163
Ph: (509)335-7049
URL: http://researchpark.wsu.edu
Facebook: www.facebook.com/WSUPullman
X (Twitter): x.com/wsupullman
YouTube: www.youtube.com/washingtonstateuniv
Description: Offers modern, convenient office space for small, start-up companies.

EDUCATIONAL PROGRAMS

46229 ■ Big Bend Community College (BBCC)
7662 Chanute St. NE
Moses Lake, WA 98837
Ph: (509)793-2222
Free: 877-745-1212
Co. E-mail: outreach@bigbend.edu
URL: http://www.bigbend.edu
Facebook: www.facebook.com/BigBendCC
Linkedin: www.linkedin.com/school/big-bend-community-college
Description: Two-year college offering a small business management program. **Founded:** 1962. **Publications:** *Tumbleweed Times* (Semimonthly; Bimonthly).

46230 ■ Olympic College (OC)
1600 Chester Ave.
Bremerton, WA 98337-1669
Ph: (360)792-6050
Free: 800-259-6718
Co. E-mail: prospect@olympic.edu
URL: http://www.olympic.edu
Contact: Dr. Marty Cavalluzzi, President
E-mail: mcavalluzzi@olympic.edu
Facebook: www.facebook.com/OlympicCollege
X (Twitter): x.com/OlympicCollege
YouTube: www.youtube.com/user/OlympicCollege
Description: Provides a variety of certificate programs and courses specifically designed to assist small businesses. **Founded:** 1948.

46231 ■ South Seattle College (SSC)
6000 16th Ave. SW
Seattle, WA 98106-1499
Ph: (206)934-5300
Co. E-mail: infosouth@seattlecolleges.edu
URL: http://www.southseattle.edu
Contact: Dr. Sayumi Irey, President (Acting)
Facebook: www.facebook.com/southseattlecollege
Linkedin: www.linkedin.com/school/south-seattle-college
X (Twitter): x.com/SouthSeattleCC
Instagram: www.instagram.com/southseattlecollegeutube.com
YouTube: www.youtube.com/user/southseattlecc
Description: Two-year college offering a program in small business management. **Founded:** 1969. **Publications:** *The Sentinel* (Biweekly; Monthly); *The South Seattle Sentinel* (Biweekly).

46232 ■ Spokane Falls Community College (SFCC)
3410 W Whistalks Way
Spokane, WA 99224-5288
Ph: (509)533-3500
Free: 888-509-7944
Co. E-mail: sfccinfo@sfcc.spokane.edu
URL: http://sfcc.spokane.edu
Facebook: www.facebook.com/SpokaneFallsCC
Description: Two-year college offering a small business management program. **Founded:** 1967. **Publications:** *The Communicator*.

46233 ■ Tacoma Community College Business and Industry Resource Center
6501 S 19th St.
Tacoma, WA 98466
Ph: (253)566-5000
URL: http://www.tacomacc.edu
Contact: Adrienne Scarcella, Director
E-mail: ascarcella@tacomacc.edu
Description: Offers day and evening small business courses, for credit or noncredit, at the main campus and at the downtown center. Selected courses also are held on Saturdays to meet the scheduling needs of working students. Classes are co-sponsored by the Tacoma-Pierce County Chamber of Commerce as part of its Small Business Profit Center. Customized training for business and organizations is designed to meet the needs of employees and managers. Training workshops are held on site for the convenience of the participants.

CONSULTANTS

46234 ■ Impact Washington
11812 N Creek Pky. N, Ste. 205
Bothell, WA 98011
Ph: (425)287-6808
Co. E-mail: info@impactwashington.org
URL: http://www.impactwashington.org
Contact: Deloit R. Wolfe, Jr., President
Facebook: www.facebook.com/ImpactWA
X (Twitter): x.com/ImpactWA
YouTube: www.youtube.com/channel/UCIFA1EKQDLPGly-if8jbJdQ
Description: Supports Washington's manufacturing community by consulting on productivity and technology. **Founded:** 1997.

46235 ■ OverAdMedia
2811 E Madison St.
Seattle, WA 98112
Ph: (415)717-3826
Co. E-mail: info@overadmedia.com
URL: http://overadmedia.com
Contact: Michael Warsinske, Contact
E-mail: mike@overadmedia.com
Facebook: www.facebook.com/overadmedia
X (Twitter): x.com/overadmedia
Description: Invests in and offers early-stage advisory services to disruptive digital media and software companies.

46236 ■ Thurston Economic Development Council
4220 6th Ave. SE
Lacey, WA 98503
Ph: (360)754-6320
Co. E-mail: office@thurstonedc.com
URL: http://thurstonedc.com
Contact: Heather Burgess, President
Facebook: www.facebook.com/ThurstonEDC
Linkedin: www.linkedin.com/company/thurston-economic-development-council
X (Twitter): x.com/ThurstonCntyEDC
Instagram: www.instagram.com/thurstonedc
Description: Supports small businesses with business consulting and government contracting assistance. **Founded:** 1982.

PUBLICATIONS

46237 ■ *Herald Business Journal* (HBJ)
11323 Commando Rd. W, Unit Main
Everett, WA 98204-3532
Ph: (360)394-5800
Fax: (360)394-5829
Co. E-mail: contact@soundpublishing.com
URL: http://www.soundpublishing.com
Contact: Josh O'Connor, President
URL(s): www.soundpublishing.com/titles/our-titles
Ed: Mark Carlson. **Released:** Monthly; 1st Wed. **Description:** Community newspaper serving Everett and Snohomish County, Washington. **Availability:** Print.

46238 ■ *Incorporation Forms For Washington*
Released: 1993. **Price:** $12.95 (paper). **Description:** Provides forms for forming your own corporation in the state of Washington.

46239 ■ *Vancouver Business Journal*
1251 Officers Row
Vancouver, WA 98661
URL: http://www.vbjusa.com
Contact: Jessica Swanson, Editor
Facebook: www.facebook.com/vancouverbusinessjournal
X (Twitter): x.com/VBJUSA
Description: Firm is engaged in printing and publishing newspapers. **Publications:** *Vancouver Business Journal* (Weekly (Fri.)).

PUBLISHERS

46240 ■ Cleaning Consultant Services Inc. (CCS)
PO Box 98757
Seattle, WA 98198
URL: http://www.cleaningbusiness.com
Contact: Bill Griffin, Founder
Description: Firm provides engineering and consulting services and deals with claim and dispute resolution, program and material development and cleaning services and also offers business solutions and support services for cleaning professionals, and publishes books on various areas of the cleaning industry. **Scope:** Firm provides engineering and consulting services and deals with claim and dispute resolution, program and material development and cleaning services and also offers business solutions and support services for cleaning professionals, and publishes books on various areas of the cleaning industry. **Founded:** 1973. **Publications:** "Raising the Bar with Science, Training and Upward Mobility," Jan, 2010; "Technology Revolutionizes the Cleaning Process "Cleaning for Health" is the New Mantra," Distribution Sales and Management Magazine, May, 2003; "Bill Griffin's Crystal Balls-Cleaning Trends in the Usa 2001," Floor Care is Hot in 2001," Mar, 2001; "Inclean Magazine (Australia), Feb, 2001; "Maintaining Swimming Pools, Spas, Whirlpool Tubs and Saunas," Executive House keeping, Feb, 2001; "Whats New with Floor Care," 2001. **Training:** Publisher of books and magazines.

46241 ■ Redmond Technology Press
16310 NE 80th St., Ste. 201
Redmond, WA 98052
Ph: (425)881-7350
Fax: (425)786-9244
URL: http://nelson.cpa
Description: Publisher of computer books for business people, including MBAs and effective executives guides. **Founded:** 1986.

46242 ■ Stat Communications Ltd.
250 H St.
Blaine, WA 98230
URL: http://www.statpub.com
Description: Provider of fax and mail services and also provides market information on these commodities for processors, importers and exporters.

EARLY STAGE FINANCING

46243 ■ OverAdMedia
2811 E Madison St.
Seattle, WA 98112
Ph: (415)717-3826
Co. E-mail: info@overadmedia.com
URL: http://overadmedia.com
Contact: Michael Warsinske, Contact
E-mail: mike@overadmedia.com
Facebook: www.facebook.com/overadmedia
X (Twitter): x.com/overadmedia
Description: Invests in and offers early-stage advisory services to disruptive digital media and software companies.

46244 ■ WRF Capital
2815 Eastlake Ave. E, Ste. 300
Seattle, WA 98102
Ph: (206)336-5600
Co. E-mail: info@wrfcapital.com
URL: http://www.wrfseattle.org
Contact: Dr. Tom Daniel, President
Linkedin: www.linkedin.com/company/washington-research-foundation
X (Twitter): x.com/wrfseattle

Description: Specializes in seed, start-up and early stage technology investments. Investment arm of Washington Research Foundation. **Founded:** 1981.

VENTURE CAPITAL FIRM

46245 ■ 9Mile Labs (9ML)
111 S Jackson St.
Seattle, WA 98104
Co. E-mail: info@9milelabs.com
URL: http://www.9milelabs.com
Contact: Kevin Croy, Co-Founder Partner
Facebook: www.facebook.com/9MileLabs
Linkedin: www.linkedin.com/company/9mile-labs
X (Twitter): x.com/9MileLabs

Description: Invests in promising early-stage enterprise business-to-business startups. **Founded:** 2013.

46246 ■ Pioneer Venture Partners LLC (PVP)
1100 Carillon Pt.
Kirkland, WA 98033
Co. E-mail: info@pvpartners.com
URL: http://www.pvpartners.com
Contact: Ben Goux, Chief Financial Officer Partner

Description: Early-stage investment in technology entrepreneurs. **Founded:** 1998.

West Virginia

ASSOCIATIONS AND OTHER ORGANIZATIONS

46247 ■ Business Development Corporation of the Northern Panhandle
324A Penco Rd.
Weirton, WV 26062
Ph: (304)748-5041
Fax: (304)914-4687
Co. E-mail: contact@bhbdc.com
URL: http://www.bhbdc.com
Contact: John Frankovitch, Secretary
Linkedin: www.linkedin.com/company/business
-development-corporation-of-the-northern
-panhandle
YouTube: www.youtube.com/channel/
UCQsELXhKwIz8w93EtHqiqqw
Description: Seeks to promote business through economic and community development. Assists businesses in their expansion and financing needs. Enhances the quality of life and fosters the growth of good jobs within the community. **Geographic Preference:** Local.

46248 ■ Business Network International West Virginia [BNI West Virginia]
456 Sourwood Dr.
Hardy, VA 24101
Ph: (304)410-0960
URL: http://bniwestvirginia.com/en-US/index
Contact: Brian Alcorn, Executive Director
Description: Provides both men and women a structured environment for the development and exchange of quality business referrals. Offers members the opportunity to share ideas and contacts. **Geographic Preference:** State.

46249 ■ West Virginia-Ohio Valley Chapter National Electrical Contractors Association (WV OV NECA) - Library [National Electrical Contractors Association - West Virginia-Ohio Valley Chapter]
50 Dee Dr.
Charleston, WV 25311
Ph: (304)346-1331
Free: 800-873-6176
Fax: (304)345-9005
URL: http://www.wvohneca.org
Contact: Dustin Flinn, President
Scope: Safety; management; marketing. **Founded:** 1901. **Holdings:** Books; video recordings; CD-ROMs. **Geographic Preference:** Local.

SMALL BUSINESS DEVELOPMENT CENTERS

46250 ■ Eastern Panhandle Small Business Development Center
202 Viking Way, Ste. 202
Martinsburg, WV 25401
Ph: (304)380-3279
URL: http://wvsbdc.ecenterdirect.com/network
Contact: Mary Hott, Contact
E-mail: mary.e.hott@wv.gov
X (Twitter): twitter.com/WVSBDC
Description: Represents and promotes the small business sector. Provides management assistance to current and prospective small business owners. Helps to improve management skills and expand the products and services of members. **Geographic Preference:** Local.

46251 ■ Pierpont Community and Technical College of Fairmont State University Small Business Development Center
1201 Locust Ave.
Fairmont, WV 26554
URL: http://www.pierpont.edu/financial-aid/veterans/
veterans-resources
Description: Represents and promotes the small business sector. Provides management assistance to current and prospective small business owners. Helps to improve management skills and expand the products and services of members. **Geographic Preference:** Local.

46252 ■ Pierpont Community and Technical College Small Business Development Center - Fairmont
1201 Locust Ave.
Fairmont, WV 26554
Ph: (304)333-3684
URL: http://www.pierpont.edu/ac/programs/business
-technology
Description: Provides management assistance to current and prospective small business owners in Fairmont. **Geographic Preference:** Local.

46253 ■ Small Business Development Center of West Virginia University at Parkersburg
300 Campus Dr.
Parkersburg, WV 26104
Ph: (304)424-8213
Fax: (304)424-8266
URL: http://www.wvup.edu/faculty-staff/offices
Description: Represents and promotes the small business sector. Provides management assistance to current and prospective small business owners. Helps to improve management skills and expand the products and services of members. **Geographic Preference:** Local.

46254 ■ West Virginia Northern Community College Small Business Development Center (WV SBDC)
State Capitol Complex, 1900 Kanawha Blvd. E,
Bldg. 3, Ste. 600
Charleston, WV 25305
Ph: (304)214-8973
Free: 888-WVA-SBDC
Co. E-mail: askme@wv.gov
URL: http://wvsbdc.com
Contact: Tighe Bullock, President
Facebook: www.facebook.com/WVSBDC
X (Twitter): x.com/wvsbdc
Description: Represents and promotes the small business sector. Provides management assistance to current and prospective small business owners. Helps to improve management skills and expand the products and services of members. **Founded:** 1983. **Geographic Preference:** Local.

46255 ■ West Virginia Small Business Development Center (WV SBDC)
1900 Kanawha Blvd. E
Building 3, Ste. 600
Charleston, WV 25305
Ph: (304)352-3992
Free: 888-WVA-SBDC
Co. E-mail: askme@wv.gov
URL: http://wvsbdc.com
Contact: Steve Johnson, Director
Facebook: www.facebook.com/WVSBDC
Linkedin: www.linkedin.com/company/wvsbdc
X (Twitter): x.com/wvsbdc
YouTube: www.youtube.com/user/WVcommerce
Description: Offers free business counseling on topics such as marketing, financing, and management. **Founded:** 1983. **Publications:** *West Virginia Women and Minority Owned Business Database* (Continuous). **Awards:** Governor's Guaranteed Work Force Training Program (GGWFP). **Geographic Preference:** State.

46256 ■ Workforce Small Business Development Center - Summersville
830 Northside Dr., Ste. 166
Summersville, WV 26651
URL: http://www.wvcommerce.org/travel/
travelplanner/attraction/Region-I-Workforce-Inves
tment-Board-Summersville-Service-Center---SBDC
Description: Represents and promotes the small business sector. Provides management assistance to current and prospective small business owners. Helps to improve management skills and expand the products and services of members. **Geographic Preference:** Local.

SMALL BUSINESS ASSISTANCE PROGRAMS

46257 ■ West Virginia Development Office - Business and Industrial Development Division (BID)
State Capitol Complex, Bldg. 3, Ste. 600
1900 Kanawha Blvd. E
Charleston, WV 25305
Ph: (304)558-2234
Free: 800-982-3386
URL: http://westvirginia.gov/connect-with-us/meet-the
-team
Description: Offers assistance to small business.

SCORE OFFICES

46258 ■ Huntington SCORE
1650 8th Ave.
Huntington, WV 25703

46259 ■ West Virginia

Ph: (304)523-4092
Co. E-mail: score488@unlimitedfuture.org
URL: http://www.score.org/wv/content/locations

46259 ■ SCORE - Clarksburg
1116 Smith St., Ste. 311
Charleston, WV 25301
Ph: (304)347-5463
URL: http://wv.score.org/?_ga=2.125023242.125749
4377.1569863504-436372588.1568312238
Linkedin: www.linkedin.com/company/score-mentors
-west-virginia
Description: Provides professional guidance and information to maximize the success of existing and emerging small businesses. Offers business counseling and workshops.

46260 ■ SCORE - Huntington, West Virginia
1650 8th Ave.
Huntington, WV 25703
Ph: (304)523-4092
Co. E-mail: score488@unlimitedfuture.org
URL: http://www.score.org/wv/content/locations
Description: Provides professional guidance and information to maximize the success of existing and emerging small businesses. Offers business counseling and workshops.

46261 ■ SCORE - West Virginia
1116 Smith St., Ste. 311
Charleston, WV 25301
Ph: (304)347-5463
Co. E-mail: wv.score@scorevolunteer.org
URL: http://wv.score.org
Contact: Bridget Weston, Chief Executive Officer
Facebook: www.facebook.com/SCOREWestVirginia
Linkedin: www.linkedin.com/company/score-mentors
-west-virginia
X (Twitter): twitter.com/scorewvmentors
Description: Provides professional guidance and information to maximize the success of existing and emerging small businesses. Offers business counseling and workshops. **Founded:** 1964. **Geographic Preference:** Local.

CHAMBERS OF COMMERCE

46262 ■ Beckley - Raleigh County Chamber of Commerce (BRCCC)
245 N Kanawha St.
Beckley, WV 25801
Ph: (304)252-7328
Fax: (304)252-7373
Co. E-mail: chamber@brccc.com
URL: http://brccc.com
Contact: Michelle Rotellini, President
Facebook: www.facebook.com/beckleyraleighcoun
tychamberofcommerce
Description: Coordinates the efforts of commerce, industry, and the professions in maintaining and strengthening a sound and healthy business climate in the Beckley-Raleigh County area. Sponsors aggressive programs of work and stimulate activities which will provide for full development and employment of the human and economic resources. **Founded:** 1920. **Geographic Preference:** Local.

46263 ■ Berkeley Springs - Morgan County Chamber of Commerce (BSMCCC)
127 Fairfax St.
Berkeley Springs, WV 25411
Ph: (304)258-3738
Co. E-mail: chamber@berkeleysprings.com
URL: http://www.berkeleyspringschamber.com
Contact: Becky Stotler, President
Facebook: www.facebook.com/
BerkeleySpringsMorganCoChamberofCommerce
25411
Instagram: www.instagram.com/bs_moco_chamber
Description: Promotes business and community development in Berkeley Springs, WV. Sponsors festival. Conducts charitable activities. **Founded:** 1952. **Geographic Preference:** Local.

46264 ■ Chamber of Commerce of the Mid-Ohio Valley (MOV)
501 Avery St., 9th Fl.
Parkersburg, WV 26101
Ph: (304)422-3588
Co. E-mail: info@movchamber.org
URL: http://www.movchamber.org
Contact: Jill Parsons, President
Facebook: www.facebook.com/MOVchamber
X (Twitter): x.com/chambermov
Description: Aims to promote business and industry in the Mid-Ohio Valley, comprised of Washington County in Ohio and the West Virginia counties of Calhoun, Jackson, Pleasants, Ritchie, Roane, Wirt, and Wood. **Founded:** 1909. **Publications:** *Membership Directory/Buyers Guide*.

46265 ■ Charleston Area Alliance
1116 Smith St.
Charleston, WV 25301
Ph: (304)340-4253
Fax: (304)340-4275
Co. E-mail: info@charlestonareaalliance.org
URL: http://charlestonareaalliance.org
Contact: Nicole Christian, President
E-mail: nchristian@charlestonareaalliance.org
Linkedin: www.linkedin.com/company/charleston
-area-alliance
X (Twitter): x.com/azdemparty
Instagram: www.instagram.com/charles
tonareaalliance
Description: Promotes business and community development in Charleston, WV. **Geographic Preference:** Local.

46266 ■ Fayette County Chamber of Commerce (FCCC)
310 Oyler Ave.
Oak Hill, WV 25901
Ph: (304)465-5617
Fax: (304)465-5618
URL: http://www.fayettecounty.com
Contact: Kim Feazell, Vice Chairman of the Board
Facebook: www.facebook.com/fayettecoun
tychamberofcommerce
X (Twitter): x.com/ChamberFayette
Description: Promotes business and community development in Fayette County, WV. **Founded:** 1986. **Geographic Preference:** Local.

46267 ■ Grant County Chamber of Commerce
126 S Main St., Ste. 1
Petersburg, WV 26847
Ph: (304)257-2722
URL: http://grantwvchamber.com
Contact: Kirk Wilson, President
Description: Promotes business, community development, and tourism in Grant County area. **Founded:** 1991. **Geographic Preference:** Local.

46268 ■ Greenbrier County Convention & Visitors Bureau
905 Washington St. W
Lewisburg, WV 24901
Ph: (304)645-1000
Free: 800-833-2068
Co. E-mail: info@greenbrierwv.com
URL: http://greenbrierwv.com
Contact: Kara Dense, President
E-mail: kdense@greenbrierwv.com
Facebook: www.facebook.com/GbrValleyWV
X (Twitter): x.com/gbrvalleywv
Instagram: www.instagram.com/gbrvalleywv
YouTube: www.youtube.com/user/gbcwv
Pinterest: www.pinterest.com/greenbrierwv
Description: Promotes business and community development in Lewisburg, WV and the Greenbrier Valley area. **Founded:** 2001. **Publications:** *Greenbrier Valley Visitors Guide* (Annual); *Travel Wise* (Semiannual). **Geographic Preference:** Local.

46269 ■ *Greenbrier Valley Visitors Guide*
905 Washington St. W
Lewisburg, WV 24901
Ph: (304)645-1000
Free: 800-833-2068

Co. E-mail: info@greenbrierwv.com
URL: http://greenbrierwv.com
Contact: Kara Dense, President
E-mail: kdense@greenbrierwv.com
URL(s): greenbrierwv.com/visitors-guide
Released: Annual **Availability:** Download; Online.

46270 ■ Hampshire County Chamber of Commerce
332 E Main St.
Romney, WV 26757
Ph: (304)822-7221
Fax: (304)822-7221
Co. E-mail: hampshirechamberofcommerce@citlink
.net
URL: http://hampshirereview.com/app/Websites/
HCChamberCommerce/Chamber.html
Contact: Steve Bommarito, President
Description: Promotes business and community development in Hampshire County, WV. **Publications:** *News You Can Use*. **Geographic Preference:** Local.

46271 ■ Harrison County Chamber of Commerce (HCCC)
520 W Main St.
Clarksburg, WV 26301
Ph: (304)624-6331
Fax: (304)624-5190
Co. E-mail: info@harrisoncountychamber.com
URL: http://www.harrisoncountychamber.com
Contact: Katherine D. Wagner, President
E-mail: kathy@harrisoncountychamber.com
Facebook: www.facebook.com/harrisonchamberwv
Linkedin: www.linkedin.com/groups
X (Twitter): x.com/HarCoChamber
Instagram: www.instagram.com/harcochamber
YouTube: www.youtube.com/channel/UCaxO
6UWhqPZ9PKc8h0LohSA
Description: Promotes business and community development in Harrison County, WV. Sponsors symposium. **Founded:** 1994. **Publications:** *The Rising Star* (Quarterly). **Educational Activities:** Harrison County Chamber of Commerce Dinner (Annual). **Geographic Preference:** Local.

46272 ■ *HR Journal*
1624 Kanawha Blvd. E
Charleston, WV 25311
Ph: (304)342-1115
Fax: (304)342-1130
Co. E-mail: forjobs@wvchamber.com
URL: http://www.wvchamber.com
Contact: Steve Roberts, President
E-mail: sroberts@wvchamber.com
URL(s): wvchamber.com/News-Publications/Publica
tions/default.aspx
Availability: Print; PDF.

46273 ■ Huntington Regional Chamber of Commerce (HRCC)
1108 3rd Ave., Ste. 300
Huntington, WV 25701
Ph: (304)525-5131
Co. E-mail: info@huntingtonchamber.org
URL: http://www.huntingtonchamber.org
Contact: Bill Bissett, President
E-mail: bill@huntingtonchamber.org
Facebook: www.facebook.com/huntington.chamber.1
X (Twitter): x.com/ChamberAlerts
Description: Promotes business and community development in Cabell and Wayne Counties. **Publications:** *ChamberLink* (Monthly); *Membership Directory and Lifestyle Guide* (Annual). **Geographic Preference:** Local.

46274 ■ Jefferson County Chamber of Commerce
44 Trifecta Pl., Ste. No. 202
Charles Town, WV 25414
Ph: (304)725-2055
Co. E-mail: chamber@jeffersoncountywvchamber.org
URL: http://www.jeffersoncountywvchamber.org
Contact: Teresa McCabe, President
Facebook: www.facebook.com/JeffCOChamber
Linkedin: www.linkedin.com/company/jefferson-coun
ty-wv-chamber-of-commerce

X (Twitter): x.com/WVJCChamber
Instagram: www.instagram.com/jc_chamber_wv
Description: Promotes business and community development in Jefferson County, WV. **Founded:** 1959. **Geographic Preference:** Local.

46275 ■ Logan County Chamber of Commerce
325 Stratton St.
 Logan, WV 25601
Ph: (304)752-1324
Fax: (304)752-5988
Co. E-mail: logancountychamber@frontier.com
URL: http://www.logancountychamberofcommerce.com
Contact: Debrina Williams, Executive Director
Description: Promotes business and community development in Logan County, WV. **Founded:** 1913. **Geographic Preference:** Local.

46276 ■ Marion County Chamber of Commerce (MCCC)
110 Adams St.
 Fairmont, WV 26554
Ph: (304)363-0442
URL: http://www.marionchamber.com
Contact: Tina Shaw, President
E-mail: mccc@marionchamber.com
Description: Promotes business and community development in Marion County, WV. **Founded:** 1953. **Publications:** *Buyers' Guide* (Periodic); *Economic Profile*; *Momentum* (Monthly). **Educational Activities:** Cavalcade of Trade. **Geographic Preference:** Local.

46277 ■ Marshall County Chamber of Commerce (MCCC)
609 Jefferson Ave.
 Moundsville, WV 26041
Ph: (304)845-2773
Co. E-mail: chamber@marshallcountychamber.com
URL: http://www.marshallcountychamber.com
Contact: Jodi Cunningham, President
Facebook: www.facebook.com/MarshallCountyChamberOfCommerce
Description: Promotes business, community development, and tourism in Marshall County, WV. Sponsors annual Christmas parade and annual Riverfront Festival (featuring a Native American Pow Wow). **Founded:** 1835. **Geographic Preference:** Local.

46278 ■ Martinsburg-Berkeley County Chamber of Commerce
198 Viking Way
 Martinsburg, WV 25401
Ph: (304)267-4841
Co. E-mail: chamber@berkeleycounty.org
URL: http://www.berkeleycounty.org
Contact: Elizabeth Webster, President
E-mail: elizabeth@berkeleycounty.org
Facebook: www.facebook.com/mbcchamber
X (Twitter): x.com/MBCChamber
Description: Promotes business and community development in Martinsburg-Berkeley County, WV. **Founded:** 1926. **Geographic Preference:** Local.

46279 ■ Mason County Area Chamber of Commerce
305 Main St.
 Point Pleasant, WV 25550
Ph: (304)675-1050
Fax: (304)675-1601
URL: http://www.masoncountychamber.org
Contact: Hilda Austin, Executive Director
Description: Promotes business and community development in Mason County, WV. Sponsors Mason County Fair Queen Contest. Holds annual dinner. **Geographic Preference:** Local.

46280 ■ Mineral County Chamber of Commerce
167 S Mineral St., Ste. A
 Keyser, WV 26726
Ph: (304)788-2513
Co. E-mail: lwagoner@mtb.com
URL: http://mineralchamber.com
Contact: Patricia Koontz, President
Facebook: www.facebook.com/mineralcountychamber
Description: Works to stimulate and enhance the business environment and quality of life in Mineral County. **Founded:** 1866. **Geographic Preference:** Local.

46281 ■ Morgantown Area Chamber of Commerce (MACOC)
265 Spruce St., Ste. 100
 Morgantown, WV 26505
Ph: (304)292-3311
Co. E-mail: info@morgantownchamber.org
URL: http://www.morgantownpartnership.com
Contact: Susan Riddle, Treasurer
Facebook: www.facebook.com/morgantownareapartnership
Linkedin: www.linkedin.com/company/morgantown-area-partnership
X (Twitter): x.com/mgtnpartnership
YouTube: www.youtube.com/channel/UCTiaA7nblhdjVw_Ilv652Zw
Description: Promotes business and community development in the Morgantown, WV area. **Founded:** 1920. **Geographic Preference:** Local.

46282 ■ Pendleton County Chamber of Commerce
47 Maple Ave.
 Franklin, WV 26807
Ph: (304)358-3884
URL: http://pendletoncountychamber.com
Contact: Kristen Dingess, Chairman
Facebook: www.facebook.com/penwvco
Description: Promotes business and community development in Pendleton County, KY. Sponsors annual awards banquet. **Founded:** 2002. **Publications:** *Business Ledger* (Quarterly). **Geographic Preference:** Local.

46283 ■ Preston County Chamber of Commerce
157 Plz., Ct., Ste. 8
 Kingwood, WV 26537
Ph: (304)329-0576
Co. E-mail: info@prestonchamber.com
URL: http://www.prestonchamber.com
Contact: Michael McGovern, President
E-mail: mcgovernm@monhealthsys.org
Description: Promotes business and community development in Preston, WV. **Founded:** 1988. **Publications:** *Chamber Chat* (Monthly); *Preston County Chamber of Commerce Business, Services and Information Directory*. **Educational Activities:** Preston County Chamber of Commerce Dinner (Annual). **Geographic Preference:** Local.

46284 ■ Putnam County Chamber of Commerce
971 WV Rte. 34
 Hurricane, WV 25526
Ph: (304)757-6510
Co. E-mail: chamber@putnamcounty.org
URL: http://putnamchamber.org
Contact: Ashley Alford, President
Facebook: www.facebook.com/PutnamCountyChamber
X (Twitter): x.com/PutnamChamber
Instagram: www.instagram.com/putnamchamber
Description: Promotes programs of an economic, industrial, commercial, civic, and cultural nature in Putnam County, WV so that its citizens and business community can prosper. Seeks to enlighten the obstacles which inhibit business expansion and community growth and public awareness regarding local, state, and national issues. **Founded:** 1979. **Awards:** Mayo Lester Community Service Award (Annual). **Geographic Preference:** Local.

46285 ■ Randolph County Convention & Visitors Bureau (RCCVB)
1302 N Randolph Ave.
 Elkins, WV 26241
Ph: (304)636-2780
Free: 800-422-3304
Co. E-mail: bpritt@randolphcountycvb.com
URL: http://www.randolphcountywv.com
Contact: Brenda Pritt, Executive Director
E-mail: bpritt@randolphcountycvb.com
X (Twitter): x.com/RandolphCVB
YouTube: www.youtube.com/watch
Description: Promotes business and community development in Randolph County, WV. Sponsors area festival. Convention/Meeting: none. **Founded:** 1923. **Publications:** *Visitors Guide*. **Geographic Preference:** Local.

46286 ■ Richwood Area Chamber of Commerce (RACC)
c/o Nicole Dudley, Executive Secretary
 38 Edgewood Ave.
 Richwood, WV 26261
Ph: (304)846-6790
Co. E-mail: rwdchamber@frontier.com
URL: http://www.richwoodchamberofcommerce.org
Contact: Eric Blankenship, President
Facebook: www.facebook.com/richwoodchamber
Description: Promotes business and community development in the Richwood, WV area. Sponsors educational and recreational programs. Conducts charitable activities. Sponsors competitions and festival. **Founded:** 1960. **Geographic Preference:** Local.

46287 ■ St. Albans Area Chamber of Commerce
1499 MacCorkle Ave.
 Saint Albans, WV 25177
Ph: (304)727-2971
Co. E-mail: sarecorder@suddenlinkmail.com
URL: http://www.stalbanswv.com
Contact: Scott James, Chairman
E-mail: mayorjames@stalbanswv.com
Facebook: www.facebook.com/cityofstalbanswv
Linkedin: www.linkedin.com/company/stalbanswv
X (Twitter): x.com/stalbanswv
Instagram: www.instagram.com/stalbanswv
YouTube: www.youtube.com/channel/UC81KbUolZFpxZOneqlp0WWQ
Description: Promotes businesses in St. Albans. **Founded:** 1972. **Geographic Preference:** Local.

46288 ■ Summersville Area Chamber of Commerce (SACC)
1 Old Wilderness Rd.
 Summersville, WV 26651
Ph: (304)872-1588
Co. E-mail: info@summersvillechamber.com
URL: http://www.summersvillechamber.com
Contact: Ashleigh Wall, Co-President
Facebook: www.facebook.com/Summersville-Area-Chamber-of-Commerce-232429803856925
Description: Promotes business and community development in the Summersville, WV area. Sponsors festival. **Founded:** 1968. **Geographic Preference:** Local.

46289 ■ *The Town Crier*
3174 Pennsylvania Ave., Ste. 1
 Weirton, WV 26062
Ph: (304)748-7212
Fax: (304)748-0241
Co. E-mail: info@weirtonchamber.com
URL: http://www.weirtonchamber.com
Contact: Brenda L. Mull, President
E-mail: brenda@weirtonchamber.com
URL(s): www.weirtonchamber.com/the-town-crier
Released: Monthly **Price:** $85, for 500 copies.
Description: Publishes events of interest to members. **Availability:** Print; PDF; Online.

46290 ■ *Visitors Guide*
1302 N Randolph Ave.
 Elkins, WV 26241
Ph: (304)636-2780
Free: 800-422-3304
Co. E-mail: bpritt@randolphcountycvb.com
URL: http://www.randolphcountywv.com
Contact: Brenda Pritt, Executive Director
E-mail: bpritt@randolphcountycvb.com
URL(s): randolphcountywv.com/index.php/test-menu-item
Availability: Print; PDF.

46291 ■ Weirton Area Chamber of Commerce (WCC)
3174 Pennsylvania Ave., Ste. 1
Weirton, WV 26062
Ph: (304)748-7212
Fax: (304)748-0241
Co. E-mail: info@weirtonchamber.com
URL: http://www.weirtonchamber.com
Contact: Brenda L. Mull, President
E-mail: brenda@weirtonchamber.com
Facebook: www.facebook.com/WeirtonAreaChamber
Description: Promotes business and community development in Weirton, WV. **Founded:** 1935. **Publications:** *The Town Crier* (Monthly). **Geographic Preference:** Local.

46292 ■ Wellsburg Chamber of Commerce
c/o Jacie Ridgely, Chamber Coordinator
PO Box 487
Wellsburg, WV 26070
Ph: (304)479-2115
Co. E-mail: wellsburgchamber@gmail.com
URL: http://www.wellsburgchamber.com
Contact: Jacie Ridgely, Coordinator
Facebook: www.facebook.com/WellsburgChamber
Description: Promotes business and community development in Wellsburg, WV. **Founded:** 1952. **Publications:** *Community Directory* (Annual). **Geographic Preference:** Local.

46293 ■ West Virginia Chamber of Commerce
1624 Kanawha Blvd. E
Charleston, WV 25311
Ph: (304)342-1115
Fax: (304)342-1130
Co. E-mail: forjobs@wvchamber.com
URL: http://www.wvchamber.com
Contact: Steve Roberts, President
E-mail: sroberts@wvchamber.com
X (Twitter): x.com/WVaChamber
YouTube: www.youtube.com/channel/UCPxdp_2GpNvJqmGVAabWPwQ
Description: Represents all business sectors in every region of the state. Serves as "a proactive leader in the search for solutions to problems, a voice for free competition and streamlined government, a catalyst for progressive thinking and problem solving, and a partner with government as appropriate". **Founded:** 1936. **Publications:** *Chamber Links* (Weekly); *Green Piece* (Semiannual); *HR Journal*; *Directory of Business/Trade/Professional Associations, Chambers of Commerce and Industrial Development Authorities* (Biennial). **Educational Activities:** Human Resources Conference (Annual); Annual Meeting and Business Summit (Annual). **Geographic Preference:** State.

46294 ■ Wheeling Area Chamber of Commerce
1100 Main St.
Wheeling, WV 26003
Ph: (304)233-2575
Co. E-mail: reception@wheelingchamber.com
URL: http://www.wheelingchamber.com
Contact: Kurt Zende, President
E-mail: kzende@wheelingchamber.com
X (Twitter): x.com/WheelingChamber
Instagram: www.instagram.com/wheelingchamber
YouTube: www.youtube.com/channel/UCg8JaWMomR-Joa1vv4yjJFg
Description: Promotes business and community development in Wheeling, WV. **Founded:** 1966. **Geographic Preference:** Local.

FINANCING AND LOAN PROGRAMS

46295 ■ Country Roads Angel Network (CRAN)
3 Quail Cove Rd.
Charleston, WV 25314
Ph: (304)608-2726
Co. E-mail: info@wvcran.com
URL: http://wvcran.com
Contact: Kevin Combs, Chairman Co-Founder
Linkedin: www.linkedin.com/company/country-roads-angel-network
Description: Invests in and mentor startups based in West Virginia. Operates in partnership with the New River Gorge Regional Development Authority and the WV Hive. **Founded:** 2019.

PROCUREMENT ASSISTANCE PROGRAMS

46296 ■ Mid-Ohio Valley Regional Council (MOVRC)
709 Market St.
Parkersburg, WV 26101
Ph: (304)422-4993
Free: 800-924-7047
Fax: (304)422-4998
URL: http://www.movrc.org
Contact: Melissa O'Brien, Executive Director
E-mail: melissa.obrien@movrc.org
Description: Provides advice, assistance, and technical support to businesses and industries interested in becoming involved in the government procurement process.

46297 ■ Regional Contracting Assistance Center Inc. (RCAC)
1116 Smith St., Ste. 401
Charleston, WV 25301
Ph: (304)344-2546
Fax: (304)344-2574
URL: http://www.rcacwv.com
Contact: Kendra Priddy, Director, Marketing
E-mail: krpiddy@rcacwv.com
Linkedin: www.linkedin.com/in/wvrcacptac
Description: Serves as a clearinghouse for information on contracting/subcontracting opportunities, and as a source for technical resources, information, and training. Offers an electronic bid match, access to government and industry regulations and standards, past procurement histories, technical assistance in understanding bid and contract requirements, assistance in bid proposal preparation, training in various aspects of contracting, and assistance in understanding contract pricing, packaging, and administration. **Founded:** 1987.

46298 ■ Regional Contracting Assisting Center, Inc. (RCAC)
1116 Smith St., Ste. 401
Charleston, WV 25301
Ph: (304)344-2546
Fax: (304)344-2574
URL: http://www.rcacwv.com
Contact: Kendra Priddy, Director, Marketing
E-mail: krpiddy@rcacwv.com
Linkedin: www.linkedin.com/in/wvrcacptac
Description: Provides advice and assistance in areas specific to company's government contracting needs such as federal acquisition regulation serving Boone, Lincoln, Logan, McDowell, Mingo, and Wyoming Counties. **Founded:** 1987.

46299 ■ West Virginia Procurement Technical Assistance Center (PTAC)
1116 Smith St., Ste. 401
Charleston, WV 25301
Ph: (304)344-2546
Fax: (304)344-2574
URL: http://www.rcacwv.com
Contact: Kendra Priddy, Director, Marketing
E-mail: krpiddy@rcacwv.com
Linkedin: www.linkedin.com/in/wvrcacptac

INCUBATORS/RESEARCH AND TECHNOLOGY PARKS

46300 ■ Chemical Alliance Zone Inc. (CAZ)
1740 Union Carbide Dr.
South Charleston, WV 25303
Ph: (304)720-1021
URL: http://cazwv.com
Contact: Tom Graff, President
Description: Business incubator supporting startups and entrepreneurs in the chemical industry. **Founded:** 1999.

46301 ■ Eastern Panhandle Technology Innovation Center (EPTIC)
c/o TechConnect W Virginia
W Virginia Regional Technology Pk.,
1740 Union Carbide Dr., Rm. 4203
South Charleston, WV 25303-2732
Ph: (304)502-2004
Co. E-mail: info@techconnectwv.com
URL: http://techconnectwv.org/eastern-panhandle-technology-innovation-center-eptic-now-open-for-business-to-current-and-aspiring-entrepreneurs
Contact: Joe Rice, Director
Description: A nonprofit incubator for regional startup businesses. Offers reduced office rent, mentoring, coaching, networking, education, and access to capital. **Founded:** 2014.

46302 ■ Eastern West Virginia Community & Technical College - Entrepreneurship Incubator
316 Eastern Dr.
Moorefield, WV 26836
Ph: (304)434-8000
Free: 877-982-2322
Fax: (304)434-7000
Co. E-mail: askeastern@easternwv.edu
URL: http://www.easternwv.edu/Workforce/Eastern-s-Entrepreneurship-Incubator.aspx
Contact: Shirley Murphy, Contact
E-mail: smurphy@eastern.wvnet.edu
Description: Business incubator that seeks to foster the development of an entrepreneurial culture. Incubator provides educational resources, computer resources, facilitators and coaches. **Founded:** 2011.

46303 ■ TechConnect
1740 Unioin Carbide Dr., Rm. 4203
South Charleston, WV 25303-2732
Ph: (304)502-2004
Co. E-mail: info@techconnectwv.com
URL: http://techconnectwv.org
Contact: Michele O'Connor, Chairman of the Board
Facebook: www.facebook.com/TechConnectWV
X (Twitter): x.com/#!/techconnectwv
Description: A non-profit coalition committed to the advancement of the innovation economy in West Virginia, focused on four technology sectors: advanced energy, chemicals and advanced materials, biosciences, and biometrics.

46304 ■ Unlimited Future Inc. (UFI)
1650 8th Ave.
Huntington, WV 25703
Ph: (304)697-3007
Co. E-mail: ufi@unlimitedfuture.org
URL: http://www.unlimitedfuture.org
Contact: Ursulette Huntley, Executive Director
E-mail: ursulette@unlimitedfuture.org
Description: This incubator is dedicated to eliminated barriers to the creation of successful businesses. The non-profit center specializes in assisting disadvantaged businesses through the reduction of overhead and other services. **Founded:** 1992.

46305 ■ Upshur County Development Authority - Innovation Center
21 E Main St., Ste. 101
Buckhannon, WV 26201
Ph: (304)472-1757
URL: http://upshurda.com/business-entrepreneurs/innovation-center
Geographic Preference: Local.

46306 ■ West Virginia Wood Technology Center (WWWTC)
10 11th St.
Elkins, WV 26241
Ph: (304)637-7500
Fax: (304)637-4902
Co. E-mail: info@wvwoodtech.com
URL: http://www.wvwoodtech.com
Contact: Robert Morris, Jr., Executive Director
E-mail: robbie@randolphwv.com

STATE LISTINGS

Facebook: www.facebook.com/wvwtc

Description: Offers business support services, work space, and training programs.

EDUCATIONAL PROGRAMS

46307 ■ Southern West Virginia Community and Technical College
2900 Dempsey Branch Rd.
 Mount Gay, WV 25637
Ph: (304)792-9098
Free: 866-798-2821
Co. E-mail: admissions@southernwv.edu
URL: http://www.southernwv.edu
Contact: Pamela Alderman, President
Facebook: www.facebook.com/southernwv
Linkedin: www.linkedin.com/school/southern-wes
 t-virginia-community-and-technical-college
X (Twitter): x.com/SWVCTC
Instagram: www.instagram.com/swvctc
YouTube: www.youtube.com/channel/UCu8
 _mvi00BAZmeVM8TzZifg

Description: Two-year college offering a program in small business management.

46308 ■ West Virginia Northern Community College (WVNCC)
1704 Market St.
 Wheeling, WV 26003
Ph: (304)233-5900
Fax: (304)232-8187
Co. E-mail: info@wvncc.edu
URL: http://www.wvncc.edu
Contact: Dr. Daniel P. Mosser, President
Facebook: www.facebook.com/WVNCC
X (Twitter): x.com/wvncc
Instagram: www.instagram.com/wvncc

Description: Two-year college offering a small business management program. **Founded:** 1972.

Wisconsin

ASSOCIATIONS AND OTHER ORGANIZATIONS

46309 ■ Association of Fundraising Professionals Greater Madison Chapter
PO Box 45046
  Madison, WI 53744
Ph: (608)421-3597
Co. E-mail: admin@afpmadison.org
URL: http://www.afpmadison.org
Contact: Sarah Linn, President
Facebook: www.facebook.com/AFP.GreaterMadisonChapter
Linkedin: www.linkedin.com/company/afp-greater-madison
Description: Provides educational, networking, and professional development opportunities for fundraisers and nonprofit employees in the Madison region as well as throughout southern Wisconsin. **Geographic Preference:** Local.

46310 ■ Business Marketing Association Milwaukee Chapter
12605 W N Ave., Ste. 310
  Brookfield, WI 53005
Co. E-mail: communications@anamke.org
URL: http://anamke.org
Contact: Milt Hwang, President
Linkedin: www.linkedin.com/company/bma-milwaukee
X (Twitter): x.com/bma_milwaukee
Description: Promotes the development of business-to-business marketing and communications professionals through education, training and networking. **Founded:** 1922. **Geographic Preference:** Local.

46311 ■ Business Network International Wisconsin South & Upper Peninsula Michigan
348 Napoleon Rd.
  Michigan Center, MI 49254
Ph: (517)716-1001
URL: http://bniwis.com/en-US/index
Contact: David M. Zemer, Executive Director
Description: Provides both men and women a structured environment for the development and exchange of quality business referrals. Offers members the opportunity to share ideas and contacts. **Founded:** 1985. **Geographic Preference:** Local.

46312 ■ Citizens Utility Board of Wisconsin (CUB)
625 N Segoe Rd., Ste. 101
  Madison, WI 53705
Ph: (608)251-3322
Co. E-mail: staff@cubwi.org
URL: http://cubwi.org
Contact: Eileen Hannigan, President
Facebook: www.facebook.com/cubwi
X (Twitter): x.com/CUBWI
Description: Represents and advocates for residential and small business public utility customers across the state of Wisconsin. Provides public interest legal services to ensure effective representation of residential and small business utility customers before regulatory agencies, the legislature, and the courts. Advocates for reliable, affordable, and sound utility service. Seeks to educate consumers on matters relating to utility regulation and energy policy. **Founded:** 1979. **Publications:** *CUB Reporter* (Annual). **Geographic Preference:** State.

46313 ■ Entrepreneurs' Organization - Wisconsin Chapter (EO)
200 S Washington St. Ste. 401.
  Green Bay, WI 54301
URL: http://www.eonetwork.org/wisconsin
Contact: Scott Bushkie, Contact
Description: Provides local resources to members which includes networking events, mentorship, live forums, and leadership development. **Founded:** 2019.

46314 ■ International Association of Women Milwaukee Chapter
Milwaukee, WI
URL: http://www.iawomen.com/chapters/milwaukee-chapter
Description: Serves as network of accomplished women united to achieve professional goals. Provides a forum for sharing ideas and experiences of professional women regarding career success. Promotes an active business and networking community from all industries. **Geographic Preference:** Local.

46315 ■ Potawatomi Business Development Corporation (PBDC)
Potawatomi Business Development Corporation (PBDC)
3215 W State St., Ste. 300
  Milwaukee, WI 53208
Ph: (414)290-9490
Fax: (414)345-9525
Co. E-mail: info@potawatomibdc.com
URL: http://www.potawatomibdc.com
Contact: Jeffery Johnson, Vice Chairman of the Board
Description: Seeks to promote business through economic and community development. Assists businesses in their expansion and financing needs. Enhances the quality of life and fosters the growth of good jobs within the community. **Scope:** The company is economic development and income diversification business entity of the Forest County Potawatomi Community. **Founded:** 1982. **Geographic Preference:** Local.

46316 ■ Vernon Economic Development Corporation (VEDA)
c/o Susan Noble, Executive Director
1201 N Main St., Ste. 6
  Viroqua, WI 54665
Ph: (608)638-8332
URL: http://www.veda-wi.org
Contact: Mike Breckel, President
Facebook: www.facebook.com/vernoneconomicdevelopmentassociation
Description: Helps entrepreneurs start or expand their businesses. Offers counseling and resources. **Founded:** 2006.

46317 ■ Wisconsin Agri-Business Association (WABA)
2801 International Ln., Ste. 105
  Madison, WI 53704
Ph: (608)223-1111
Fax: (608)223-1147
Co. E-mail: info@wiagribusiness.org
URL: http://wiagribusiness.org
Contact: Howard Hartmann, President
Facebook: www.facebook.com/WIAgBusiness
Description: Provider of programs, services and representation for diverse crop production industry. Leverages legislation and monitors action that directly influences all levels of business. **Founded:** 1971. **Geographic Preference:** State.

46318 ■ Wisconsin Business Innovator's Support Association (WBIA)
1221 Innovation Dr.
  Whitewater, WI 53190
Ph: (414)587-8425
Co. E-mail: secretary@wbisa.org
URL: http://www.wbisa.org
Contact: Mark Johnson, President
E-mail: president@wbisa.org
Linkedin: www.linkedin.com/company/wbisa
X (Twitter): x.com/WisBISA
Description: Seeks to advance business incubation and entrepreneurship. Educates businesses and investors on incubator benefits. Provides information, research and networking resources to help members develop and manage successful business incubation programs. **Founded:** 1998. **Geographic Preference:** State.

SMALL BUSINESS DEVELOPMENT CENTERS

46319 ■ Discovery Center FABLAB
712 S Broadway St.
  Menomonie, WI 54751
URL: http://www.uwstout.edu/outreach-engagement/corporate-relations-economic-engagement/fab-lab
Contact: Michael Cropp, Engineer Specialist
E-mail: croppm@uwstout.edu
Description: A workshop for creative, high-tech innovators and entrepreneurs who have a need to design, prototype, and build things. **Founded:** 2009.

46320 ■ Southwestern Wisconsin Small Business Development Center [Southwestern Wisconsin SBDC]
432 N Lake St., Rm. 423
  Madison, WI 53706
Free: 800-940-7232
Co. E-mail: sbdc@lists.wisconsin.edu
URL: http://wisconsinsbdc.org/centers/southwest-wisconsin-sbdc
Contact: Bon Wikenheiser, Director

E-mail: bon.wikenheiser@business.wisconsin.edu
X (Twitter): x.com/wisconsinsbdc
Description: Represents and promotes the small business sector. Provides management assistance to current and prospective small business owners. Helps to improve management skills and expand the products and services of members. **Geographic Preference:** Local.

46321 ■ University of Wisconsin - Madison Small Business Development Center
975 University Ave., Grainger Hall., No. 1290
Madison, WI 53706
Ph: (608)263-2221
Co. E-mail: sbdc@wsb.wisc.edu
URL: http://sbdc.wisc.edu
Contact: Michelle Somes-Booher, Director
E-mail: michelle.somesbooher@wisc.edu
Facebook: www.facebook.com/UWMADSBDC
Linkedin: www.linkedin.com/showcase/wisconsin-small-business-development-center-sbdc-at-uw-madison
Description: Represents and promotes the small business sector. Provides management assistance to current and prospective small business owners. Helps to improve management skills and expand the products and services of members. **Founded:** 1980. **Geographic Preference:** Local.

46322 ■ University of Wisconsin - Milwaukee Small Business Development Center (SBDC)
161 W Wisconsin Ave., 6th & 7th Fl.
Milwaukee, WI 53203
Ph: (414)227-3240
Co. E-mail: sbdc@uwm.edu
URL: http://uwm.edu/sce/program_area/small-business-development-center
Contact: Athena Agoudemos, Director
E-mail: agoudem4@uwm.edu
Description: Represents and promotes the small business sector. Provides management assistance to current and prospective small business owners. Helps to improve management skills and expand the products and services of members. **Geographic Preference:** Local.

46323 ■ University of Wisconsin - River Falls Small Business Development Center
1091 Sutherland Ave.
River Falls, WI 54022
Ph: (715)425-3472
URL: http://wisconsinsbdc.org/centers/riverfalls
Contact: Katherine Fossler, Director
E-mail: katherine.fossler@uwrf.edu
Facebook: www.facebook.com/sbdcuwrf
Description: Represents and promotes the small business sector. Provides management assistance to current and prospective small business owners. Helps to improve management skills and expand the products and services of members. **Geographic Preference:** Local.

46324 ■ University of Wisconsin - Stevens Point Small Business Development Center
2100 Main St., Rm. 032
Stevens Point, WI 54481
Ph: (715)346-3838
Co. E-mail: uwspce-bus@uwsp.edu
URL: http://wisconsinsbdc.org/centers/stevenspoint
Facebook: www.facebook.com/uwspsbdc
X (Twitter): x.com/wisconsinsbdc
Description: Represents and promotes the small business sector. Provides management assistance to current and prospective small business owners. Helps to improve management skills and expand the products and services of members. **Geographic Preference:** Local.

46325 ■ Wisconsin Small Business Development Center - Lead Office
432 N Lake St., Rm. 425
Madison, WI 53706
Ph: (608)263-7812
Free: 800-940-7232
Fax: (608)263-7830
Co. E-mail: sbdc@lists.wisconsin.edu
URL: http://www.wisconsinsbdc.org

Contact: Bon Wikenheiser, Director
E-mail: bon.wikenheiser@business.wisconsin.edu
Description: Provides educational services, counseling and free business answer line assistance for entrepreneurs and small business owners. **Founded:** 1980. **Geographic Preference:** State.

46326 ■ Wisconsin Small Business Development Center at University of Wisconsin - Eau Claire [SBDC at University of Wisconsin - Eau Claire]
4330 Golf Ter., Ste. 111
Eau Claire, WI 54701
Ph: (715)836-5902
Co. E-mail: sbdc@uwec.edu
URL: http://wisconsinsbdc.org/centers/eauclaire
Contact: Luke Kempen, Director
E-mail: kempenls@uwec.edu
Facebook: www.facebook.com/sbdcuwec
Description: Provides management assistance to current and prospective small business owners in Eau Claire. **Geographic Preference:** Local.

46327 ■ Wisconsin Small Business Development Center at University of Wisconsin - Green Bay [SBDC at University of Wisconsin - Green Bay]
2420 Nicolet Dr.
Green Bay, WI 54311-7001
Ph: (920)366-9065
Co. E-mail: sbdc@uwgb.edu
URL: http://www.uwgb.edu/sbdc/index.asp
Contact: Tara Carr, Officer
E-mail: carrt@uwgb.edu
Facebook: www.facebook.com/uwgbsbdc
X (Twitter): x.com/uwgbSBDC
YouTube: www.youtube.com/user/UWGreenBaySBDC
Description: Represents and promotes the small business sector. Provides management assistance to current and prospective small business owners. Helps to improve management skills and expand the products and services of members. **Geographic Preference:** Local.

46328 ■ Wisconsin Small Business Development Center at University of the Wisconsin - La Crosse
1725 State St.
La Crosse, WI 54601
Ph: (608)785-8783
Co. E-mail: sbdc@uwlax.edu
URL: http://www.uwlax.edu/sbdc
Contact: Anne Hlavacka, Director
E-mail: ahlavacka@uwlax.edu
Facebook: www.facebook.com/UWLaCrosse
X (Twitter): x.com/uwlacrosse
YouTube: www.youtube.com/user/uwlacrossevids
Description: Represents and promotes the small business sector. Provides management assistance to current and prospective small business owners. Helps to improve management skills and expand the products and services of members. **Geographic Preference:** Local.

46329 ■ Wisconsin Small Business Development Center at University of Wisconsin - Oshkosh [SBDC at University of Wisconsin - Oshkosh]
Sage Hall, Rm. 1410
835 High Ave.
Oshkosh, WI 54901
Ph: (920)424-1453
Co. E-mail: sbdc@uwosh.edu
URL: http://wisconsinsbdc.org/centers/oshkosh
Contact: Dan Brosman, Director
E-mail: brosmand@uwosh.edu
Facebook: www.facebook.com/UWOSBDC
X (Twitter): x.com/uwosbdc
Description: Provides management assistance to current and prospective small business owners in Oshkosh. **Founded:** 1980. **Geographic Preference:** Local.

46330 ■ Wisconsin Small Business Development Center at University of Wisconsin - Parkside [SBDC at University of Wisconsin - Parkside]
Molinaro Hall, Rm. D127
900 Wood Rd.
Kenosha, WI 53144
Ph: (262)595-3362
Co. E-mail: sbdc@uwp.edu
URL: http://wisconsinsbdc.org/centers/parkside
Contact: Mary Fischer-Tracy, Director
E-mail: fischert@uwp.edu
Facebook: www.facebook.com/parksidesbdc
Description: Represents and promotes the small business sector. Provides management assistance to current and prospective small business owners. Helps to improve management skills and expand the products and services of members. **Geographic Preference:** Local.

46331 ■ Wisconsin Small Business Development Center at University of Wisconsin - Superior [SBDC at University of Wisconsin - Superior]
108 Erlanson Hall
825 N 18th St.
Superior, WI 54880
Ph: (715)394-8351
Co. E-mail: sbdc@uwsuper.edu
URL: http://www.wisconsinsbdc.org/superior
Contact: Andy Donahue, Director
E-mail: adonahue@uwsuper.edu
URL(s): www.uwsuper.edu/sbdc
Facebook: www.facebook.com/uwsuperiorsbdc
X (Twitter): x.com/uwsuperiorsbdc
Description: Provides management assistance to current and prospective small business owners in Superior. **Geographic Preference:** Local.

46332 ■ Wisconsin Small Business Development Center at University of Wisconsin - Whitewater
800 W Main St., Hyland Hall 1220
Whitewater, WI 53190
Ph: (262)472-7039
Co. E-mail: ask-sbdc@uww.edu
URL: http://wisconsinsbdc.org/centers/whitewater
Contact: Ronald Chisholm, Director
E-mail: chisholr@uww.edu
Facebook: www.facebook.com/UWWSBDC
X (Twitter): x.com/SbdcUww
Description: Represents and promotes the small business sector. Provides management assistance to current and prospective small business owners. Helps to improve management skills and expand the products and services of members. **Geographic Preference:** Local.

SMALL BUSINESS ASSISTANCE PROGRAMS

46333 ■ Common Wealth Development (CWD)
1501 Williamson St.
Madison, WI 53703
Ph: (608)256-3527
Fax: (608)256-4499
URL: http://cwd.org
Contact: Connor Sabatino, President
Facebook: www.facebook.com/commonwealthmadison
X (Twitter): x.com/CommonWealthWI
Description: Offers small business incubation and development, workforce development, and affordable housing programs. **Founded:** 1979.

46334 ■ Council of Small Business Executives (COSBE)
c/o Metropolitan Milwaukee Association of Commerce
275 W Wisconsin Ave., Ste. 220
Milwaukee, WI 53203
URL: http://www.mmac.org/council-of-small-business-executives.html
Contact: Keith Coursin, President

Description: Serves as an advocate for metropolitan businesses to encourage business development, capital investment and job creation. **Geographic Preference:** Local.

46335 ■ Wisconsin Department of Agriculture, Trade and Consumer Protection - Bureau of Consumer Protection
Prairie Oaks State Office Bldg., 2811 Agriculture Dr.
Madison, WI 53718
Free: 800-422-7128
Co. E-mail: datcphotline@wisconsin.gov
URL: http://datcp.wi.gov/Pages/Programs_Services/ConsumerProtection.aspx
Description: Provides marketing services to promote the interests of agriculture and agricultural products domestically and in international markets. **Publications:** Wisconsin Poultry & Egg Directory (Biennial); Something Special from Wisconsin Suppliers Guide (Annual).

46336 ■ Wisconsin Economic Development Corp. (WEDC)
201 W Washington Ave.
Madison, WI 53703
Free: 855-469-4249
URL: http://inwisconsin.com
Contact: Melissa Hughes, Chief Executive Officer
Facebook: www.facebook.com/WEDCcommunity
X (Twitter): x.com/InWisconsin
Instagram: www.instagram.com/wedccommunity
YouTube: www.youtube.com/channel/UCvt7Ja4RujNj1C-zMKPJltQ
Description: Firm provides economic development assistance, community development, entrepreneur services and job creation tax credits. **Founded:** 2004. **Publications:** INsource (Quarterly); INsite (Monthly); INbound (Bimonthly); INvest (Quarterly); INtersections (Monthly); INterconnect (Quarterly).

46337 ■ Wisconsin Economic Devlopment Corporation - Business Development
201 W Washington Ave.
Madison, WI 53703
URL: http://wedc.org/business-development
Description: Provides assistance to existing and potential minority businesses in market assessment, access to credit, capital formation, and coordination of public and private resources. Also certifies minority vendors.

SCORE OFFICES

46338 ■ Central Wisconsin SCORE
700 S Central Ave.
Marshfield, WI 54449
Ph: (715)384-3454
Co. E-mail: karenolson@marshfieldchamber.com
URL: http://centralwisconsin.score.org
Facebook: www.facebook.com/SCORECentralWisconsin
Linkedin: www.linkedin.com/company/score-central-wisconsin-up-michigan
Description: Provides free counseling and low-cost workshops for the Stevens Point, Marshfield and Wisconsin Rapids area. **Geographic Preference:** Local.

46339 ■ Fox Cities SCORE
532 W College Ave.,ste.,104
Appleton, WI 54911
Ph: (920)841-4199
Co. E-mail: marqitsoc@gmail.com
URL: http://www.score.org/foxcities
Contact: Kathleen P. P. Wall, Chairman
Facebook: www.facebook.com/SCOREFoxCities
Linkedin: www.linkedin.com/company/score-fox-cities
X (Twitter): x.com/scorefoxcities
Description: Provides free counseling and low-cost workshops within the Fox Valley. **Founded:** 1964. **Geographic Preference:** Regional.

46340 ■ Green Bay SCORE
2701 Larsen Rd., Rm. 105
Green Bay, WI 54303
Ph: (920)222-2167
Co. E-mail: greenbayscore@gmail.com
URL: http://www.score.org/greenbay
Contact: Tracy Shaw, Chairman
Facebook: www.facebook.com/SCOREGreenBay
Linkedin: www.linkedin.com/company/greenbayscore
Description: Provides free and confidential business counseling tailored to meet the needs of small business owners and personal objectives. **Founded:** 1964. **Geographic Preference:** Local.

46341 ■ Madison SCORE
5262 Anton Dr.
Madison, WI 53719
Ph: (608)535-4978
Co. E-mail: madison.score@scorevolunteer.org
URL: http://www.score.org/madison
Contact: Tracy Shaw, Chairman
Facebook: www.facebook.com/SCOREMadison
Linkedin: www.linkedin.com/company/score-mentors-madison
X (Twitter): x.com/ScoreMadison
Instagram: www.instagram.com/0145_score_madison
YouTube: www.youtube.com/channel/UC0U-FzBQvSh2SyTj6yYwr1w
Description: Provides entrepreneur education for the formation, growth and success of small businesses in the area. **Founded:** 1964. **Geographic Preference:** Local.

46342 ■ SCORE - Central Wisconsin
700 S Central Ave.
Marshfield, WI 54449
Ph: (715)384-3454
Co. E-mail: karenolson@marshfieldchamber.com
URL: http://centralwisconsin.score.org
Contact: Scott Harkins, Chairman of the Board
Linkedin: www.linkedin.com/company/score-mentors-central-wisconsin
Description: Provides professional guidance and information to maximize the success of existing and emerging small businesses. Offers business counseling and workshops.

46343 ■ SCORE - Fox Cities
532 W College Ave., Ste.104
Appleton, WI 54911
Ph: (920)841-4199
Co. E-mail: contactus@score.org
URL: http://www.score.org/foxcities
Contact: Kathleen P. Wall, Chairman
Facebook: www.facebook.com/SCOREFoxCities
Linkedin: www.linkedin.com/company/score-fox-cities
X (Twitter): x.com/scorefoxcities
Description: Provides professional guidance and information to maximize the success of existing and emerging small businesses. Offers business counseling and workshops. **Founded:** 1964.

46344 ■ SCORE - Green Bay
2701 Larsen Rd.
Green Bay, WI 54303-4863
Ph: (920)222-2167
Co. E-mail: help@score.org
URL: http://www.score.org/greenbay
Contact: Paul Carron, Contact
Facebook: www.facebook.com/SCOREGreenBay
Linkedin: www.linkedin.com/company/greenbayscore
X (Twitter): x.com/GreenBaySCORE
Description: Provides professional guidance and information to maximize the success of existing and emerging small businesses. Offers business counseling and workshops. **Founded:** 1964.

46345 ■ SCORE - Iola
E2393 Gjertson Rd.
Iola, WI 54945
Ph: (715)384-3454
URL: http://www.score.org/find-location?state=WI
Description: Provides professional guidance and information to maximize the success of existing and emerging small businesses. Offers business counseling and workshops.

46346 ■ SCORE - Madison, Wisconsin
MG&E Innovation Center, Ste. 37
505 S Rosa Rd.
Madison, WI 53719
Ph: (608)441-2820
Co. E-mail: madison.score@scorevolunteer.org
URL: http://madison.score.org
Contact: Nick Cray, Contact
Facebook: www.facebook.com/SCOREMadison
Linkedin: www.linkedin.com/company/score-mentors-madison
YouTube: www.youtube.com/channel/UC0U-FzBQvSh2SyTj6yYwr1w
Description: Provides professional guidance and information to maximize the success of existing and emerging small businesses. Offers business counseling and workshops. **Founded:** 1964.

46347 ■ SCORE - Manitowoc
202 N 8th St.
Manitowoc, WI 54220
URL: http://www.score.org/greenbay
Description: Provides professional guidance and information to maximize the success of existing and emerging small businesses. Offers business counseling and workshops.

46348 ■ SCORE - Marinette
1320 Main St.
Marinette, WI 54143
URL: http://greenbay.score.org
Contact: Ann M. Hartnell, Contact
Description: Provides professional guidance and information to maximize the success of existing and emerging small businesses. Offers business counseling and workshops.

46349 ■ SCORE - Merrillan
N9393 Buckhorn Dr.
Merrillan, WI 54754
Ph: (715)384-3454
URL: http://centralwisconsin.score.org
Facebook: www.facebook.com/SCORECentralWisconsin
Linkedin: www.linkedin.com/company/score-central-wisconsin-up-michigan
Description: Provides professional guidance and information to maximize the success of existing and emerging small businesses. Offers business counseling and workshops.

46350 ■ SCORE - Oshkosh
120 Jackson St.
Oshkosh, WI 54901
Ph: (920)841-4199
URL: http://foxcities.score.org/find-location?state=WI
Description: Provides professional guidance and information to maximize the success of existing and emerging small businesses. Offers business counseling and workshops.

46351 ■ SCORE - Southeast Wisconsin
310 W Wisconsin Ave., Ste. 585
Milwaukee, WI 53203
Ph: (414)297-3942
Fax: (414)297-1377
Co. E-mail: score.28@scorevolunteer.org
URL: http://sewisconsin.score.org
Facebook: www.facebook.com/SCORESEWisconsin
Linkedin: www.linkedin.com/company/score-se-wisconsin
X (Twitter): x.com/scoresewi
Description: Provides professional guidance and information to maximize the success of existing and emerging small businesses. Offers business counseling and workshops.

46352 ■ SCORE - Stevens Point
55501 Vern Holmes Dr.
Stevens Point, WI 54482
Ph: (715)384-3454
URL: http://www.score.org/find-location?state=WI
Description: Provides professional guidance and information to maximize the success of existing and emerging small businesses. Offers business counseling and workshops.

46353 ■ SCORE - Wausau
700 S CENTRAL Ave.
 Marshfield, WI 54449
Ph: (715)384-3454
URL: http://centralwisconsin.score.org
Linkedin: www.linkedin.com/company/score-central
 -wisconsin-up-michigan
Description: Provides professional guidance and information to maximize the success of existing and emerging small businesses. Offers business counseling and workshops.

46354 ■ SCORE - Wisconsin Rapids
c/o Heart of Wisconsin Chamber
1120 Lincoln St.
 Wisconsin Rapids, WI 54494
Ph: (715)384-3454
URL: http://www.score.org/find-location?state=WI
Description: Provides professional guidance and information to maximize the success of existing and emerging small businesses. Offers business counseling and workshops.

46355 ■ Wausau SCORE
100 N 72nd Ave., Ste. 103 Entrepreneurial & Education Center
 Wausau, WI 54401
Ph: (715)384-3454
URL: http://www.score.org/content/find-location
Description: Provides professional guidance, mentoring services and financial assistance to maximize the success of existing and emerging small businesses. **Geographic Preference:** Local.

BETTER BUSINESS BUREAUS

46356 ■ Better Business Bureau of Wisconsin
10019 W Greenfield Ave.
 Milwaukee, WI 53214
Ph: (414)847-6000
Co. E-mail: info@wisconsin.bbb.org
URL: http://www.bbb.org/local-bbb/wisconsin
Facebook: www.facebook.com/WisconsinBBB
Linkedin: www.linkedin.com/company/better-business
 -bureau-of-wisconsin
X (Twitter): x.com/WisconsinBBB
YouTube: www.youtube.com/channel/UCABiH4MFtf
 tfPtYiN8X1sUg
Description: Seeks to promote and foster the highest ethical relationship between businesses and the public through voluntary self-regulation, consumer and business education, and service excellence. Provides information to help consumers and businesses make informed purchasing decisions and avoid costly scams and frauds; settles consumer complaints through arbitration and other means. **Founded:** 1939. **Geographic Preference:** State.

CHAMBERS OF COMMERCE

46357 ■ *Active Voice*
5501 Vern Holmes Dr.
 Stevens Point, WI 54482
Ph: (715)344-1940
Fax: (715)344-4473
Co. E-mail: info@portagecountybiz.com
URL: http://portagecountybiz.com
Contact: Karen Myers, Director
E-mail: karenm@portagecountybiz.com
URL(s): portagecountybiz.com/digital-magazine
Released: Monthly **Availability:** PDF; Online.

46358 ■ Adams County Chamber of Commerce and Tourism
636 S Main St.
 Adams, WI 53910
Ph: (608)339-6997
Co. E-mail: visitadamscounty@gmail.com
URL: http://www.visitadamscountywi.com
Contact: Jennifer Parr-Murphy, President
Facebook: www.facebook.com/visitadamscountywi
Instagram: www.instagram.com/visitadamscounty

Description: Promotes business and community development in Adams County, WI. Sponsors annual Crazy Days business and retail festival, Castle Rock Triathlon, Waterfest Boat Parade and Holiday Parade & seasonal events. **Founded:** 1945. **Publications:** *Adams County Chamber of Commerce Newsletter*; *Adams County Visitors Guide*. **Geographic Preference:** Local.

46359 ■ Algoma Area Chamber of Commerce
1226 Lake St.
 Algoma, WI 54201
Ph: (920)487-2041
Co. E-mail: info@algomachamber.org
URL: http://visitalgomawi.com/chamber
Contact: Jennifer Highland, President
Facebook: www.facebook.com/AlgomaAreaChamber
Description: Seeks to improve the business climate and promote community development in the Algoma, WI area. Sponsors festivals, promotes tourism and operates visitor center. **Founded:** 1946. **Publications:** *Chamber Beacon* (Quarterly). **Educational Activities:** Wet Whistle Wine Fest (Annual). **Geographic Preference:** Local.

46360 ■ *America's Little Switzerland*
418 Railroad St.
 New Glarus, WI 53574
Ph: (608)527-2095
Free: 800-527-6838
Co. E-mail: info@swisstown.com
URL: http://www.swisstown.com
Contact: Bekah Stauffacher, Executive Director
E-mail: bekah@swisstown.com
URL(s): www.swisstown.com/about-americas-little
 -switzerland
Price: $5, Single issue. **Availability:** Print.

46361 ■ Ashland Area Chamber of Commerce (AACC)
1716 W Lake Shore Dr.
 Ashland, WI 54806
Ph: (715)682-2500
Co. E-mail: info@visitashland.com
URL: http://www.visitashland.com
Description: Represents retailers and businesses. Promotes business and community development in the Ashland, WI area. **Founded:** 1888. **Geographic Preference:** Local.

46362 ■ Baileys Harbor Community Association (BHCA)
8061 Hwy. 57
 Baileys Harbor, WI 54202
Ph: (920)839-2366
Co. E-mail: info@baileysharbor.com
URL: http://www.doorcounty.com/baileys-harbor
Description: Works to advance the commercial, financial, industrial and civic interests of the area. **Founded:** 1979. **Publications:** *Fall is a Favorite Time of Year*. **Geographic Preference:** Local.

46363 ■ Baraboo Area Chamber of Commerce (BCC)
600 W Chestnut St.
 Baraboo, WI 53913
Ph: (608)356-8333
Fax: (608)356-8422
URL: http://www.baraboo.com
Contact: Raegen Trimmer, President
Facebook: www.facebook.com/
 BarabooChamberofCommerce
X (Twitter): x.com/BarabooChamberC
YouTube: www.youtube.com/channel/UCeTER
 5CbUIIuwo6k3OVTGqg
Pinterest: www.pinterest.com/BarabooArea
Description: Represents agribusiness, manufacturing, professional, retail, and tourism businesses. Promotes business and community development in Baraboo, WI. **Founded:** 1951. **Publications:** *Chamber Review* (Monthly). **Geographic Preference:** Local.

46364 ■ Bayfield Chamber of Commerce
42 S Broad St.
 Bayfield, WI 54814
Ph: (715)779-3335

URL: http://bayfield.org
Contact: Lizzie Camstra Hughes, Co-President
Facebook: www.facebook.com/Bayfield.WI
X (Twitter): x.com/bayfield_wi
Description: Promotes business and community development in Bayfield, WI area. **Founded:** 1850. **Awards:** Bayfield Chamber of Commerce Good Neighbor Award (Annual). **Geographic Preference:** Local.

46365 ■ Beaver Dam Area Chamber of Commerce (BDACC) [Beaver Dam Chamber of Commerce]
127 S Spring St.
 Beaver Dam, WI 53916
Ph: (920)887-8879
Co. E-mail: info@beaverdamchamber.com
URL: http://beaverdamchamber.com
Contact: Tracy Propst, Executive Director
Facebook: www.facebook.com/beaverdamchamber
Linkedin: www.linkedin.com/company/beaver-dam
 -area-chamber-of-commerce
X (Twitter): x.com/BDChamber
Instagram: www.instagram.com/visitbeaverdam
YouTube: www.youtube.com/channel/UCXkpmMQ
 4noQv8K4-RK4BAJQ
Description: Promotes business and community development in the Beaver Dam, WI area. Offers a Beaver Dam Health Program to members. **Founded:** 1922. **Publications:** *Chamber Newsletter* (Weekly). **Geographic Preference:** Local.

46366 ■ Bloomer Chamber of Commerce
1731 17th Ave.
 Bloomer, WI 54724
Ph: (715)568-3339
Co. E-mail: bchamber@bloomer.net
URL: http://www.bloomerchamber.com
Contact: Rod Turner, Director
Facebook: www.facebook.com/BloomerChamber
Description: Promotes business and community development in Bloomer, WI area. **Geographic Preference:** Local.

46367 ■ Boscobel Chamber of Commerce
1006 Wisconsin Ave.
 Boscobel, WI 53805
Ph: (608)375-2672
Fax: (608)375-2672
Co. E-mail: chamber@boscobelwi.us
URL: http://boscobelwisconsin.org
Contact: Judy Dayton, Co-President
E-mail: jdayton1000@gmail.com
Facebook: www.facebook.com/visitBoscobel
Description: Promotes business and community development in Boscobel, WI area. **Geographic Preference:** Local.

46368 ■ Boulder Junction Chamber of Commerce
PO Box 286
 Boulder Junction, WI 54512-0286
Ph: (715)385-2400
Free: 800-466-8759
Co. E-mail: boulderjct@boulderjct.org
URL: http://boulderjct.org
Contact: Cherie Sanderson, Co-President
Facebook: www.facebook.com/BoulderJunctionWI
Instagram: www.instagram.com/boulderjunctionwi
YouTube: www.youtube.com/channel/UCTzUF
 _pbnTDelX4KrfC-OGw
Pinterest: www.pinterest.com/boulderjunction
Description: Promotes business and community development in Boulder Junction, WI area. **Geographic Preference:** Local.

46369 ■ Brillion Area Chamber of Commerce
PO Box 123
 Brillion, WI 54110
Co. E-mail: info@brillionchamber.com
URL: http://www.brillionchamber.com
Contact: Tami Gasch, Vice President
Description: Promotes business and community development in Brillion, WI area. **Geographic Preference:** Local.

46370 ■ Brodhead Chamber of Commerce
PO Box 16
Brodhead, WI 53520
Ph: (608)897-8411
Co. E-mail: admin@brodheadchamber.com
URL: http://www.brodheadchamber.com
Contact: Rich Vogel, Contact
Facebook: www.facebook.com/Brodhea
dChamberOfCommerce
Description: Promotes business and community development in Brodhead, WI area. **Founded:** 1987. **Geographic Preference:** Local.

46371 ■ Brooklyn Area Chamber of Commerce (BACOC)
PO Box 33
Brooklyn, WI 53521
Ph: (608)455-1627
Co. E-mail: brooklynareachamber@gmail.com
URL: http://brooklynareachamberofcommerce.org
Contact: Linda Kuhlman, President
Facebook: www.facebook.com/BrooklynACoC
X (Twitter): x.com/brooklynacoc
Description: Promotes and develop Brooklyn area business and at the same time provides education and supports its members businesses. **Founded:** 2000. **Geographic Preference:** Local.

46372 ■ Burlington Area Chamber of Commerce (BACC)
113 E Chestnut St., Ste. B
Burlington, WI 53105
Ph: (262)763-6044
Co. E-mail: info@burlingtonchamber.org
URL: http://www.burlingtonchamber.org
Contact: Stephen Quist, President
Facebook: www.facebook.com/Burling
tonAreaChamber
Description: Promotes business and community development in the Burlington, WI area. Holds festival. **Founded:** 1944. **Publications:** *Burlington, Discover the Treasures* (Monthly); *FOCUS* (Monthly). **Geographic Preference:** Local.

46373 ■ *Business Directory*
1624 Wisconsin Ave.
Grafton, WI 53024
Ph: (262)377-1650
Co. E-mail: chamber@grafton-wi.org
URL: http://grafton-wi.org
Contact: Pam King, Executive Director
E-mail: pam@grafton-wi.org
URL(s): grafton-wi.chambermaster.com/list
Availability: Online.

46374 ■ *Business Directory*
6331 W Mequon Rd.
Mequon, WI 53092
Ph: (262)512-9358
Co. E-mail: info@mtchamber.org
URL: http://www.mtchamber.org
Contact: Dean Rennicke, President
URL(s): www.mtchamber.org/list
Availability: Online.

46375 ■ Cable Area Chamber of Commerce (CACC)
13380 County Hwy. M
Cable, WI 54821
Ph: (715)798-3833
Free: 800-533-7454
Co. E-mail: info@cable4fun.com
URL: http://www.cable4fun.com
Contact: Chad Young, President
Facebook: www.facebook.com/CableAreaChamber
X (Twitter): x.com/Cable4fun
Instagram: www.instagram.com/cable4fun
YouTube: www.youtube.com/user/Cablego
Description: Promotes business and economic development in Cable Area, WI. **Geographic Preference:** Local.

46376 ■ Cadott Community Association
PO Box 40
Cadott, WI 54727-0040
Ph: (715)289-4282
Co. E-mail: cadott-community@googlegroups.com
URL: http://www.cadottcommunity.com
Contact: Brian Dulmas, Co-President
Facebook: www.facebook.com/CadottNaborDays
Description: Supports and promotes business in Caddott Area. **Publications:** *Caddott Chamber* (Monthly). **Geographic Preference:** Local.

46377 ■ Cedarburg Chamber of Commerce (CCC)
N58 W6194 Columbia Rd.
Cedarburg, WI 53012
Ph: (262)377-5856
Co. E-mail: cedarburgchamber@cedarburg.org
URL: http://www.cedarburg.org
Contact: Collin Schaefer, President
E-mail: cfschaefer@ogslaw.org
Facebook: www.facebook.com/Cedarburg
Linkedin: www.linkedin.com/company/cedarburg-chamber-of-commerce
Pinterest: www.pinterest.com/cedarburgchmber
Description: Businesses and individuals. Promotes business and community development in Cedarburg, WI. **Founded:** 1902. **Geographic Preference:** Local.

46378 ■ Chamber of Manitowoc County
1515 Memorial Dr.
Manitowoc, WI 54220
Ph: (920)684-5575
Fax: (920)684-1915
Co. E-mail: info@chambermanitowoccounty.org
URL: http://chambermanitowoccounty.org
Contact: Karen Nichols, Executive Director
E-mail: knichols@chambermanitowoccounty.org
Facebook: www.facebook.com/TheChamberofMani
towocCounty
Linkedin: www.linkedin.com/company/the-chamber-of-manitowoc-county
X (Twitter): x.com/ChamberMtwcCo
Instagram: www.instagram.com/chamberofmani
towoccounty
YouTube: www.youtube.com/user/Mani
towocChamber
Description: Promotes business and community development in Manitowoc County, WI. **Founded:** 1916. **Publications:** *Visitor Guide* (Annual); *Chamber Talk*; *Visitor Guide*. **Awards:** Manitowoc ATHENA Award (Annual); Manitowoc Industry of the Year (Annual); Manitowoc Non-Profit of the Year; Manitowoc Small Business of the Year (Annual). **Geographic Preference:** Local.

46379 ■ *Chamber News*
37 S Main St.
Rice Lake, WI 54868-2299
Free: 877-234-2126
Co. E-mail: chamber@rice-lake.com
URL: http://ricelakechamber.org
Contact: Rick Fleishauer, President
URL(s): ricelakechamber.org/membership/newsle
tters
Released: Monthly **Availability:** Online.

46380 ■ *The Chamber News*
208 N Winsted St.
Spring Green, WI 53588
Ph: (608)588-2054
Co. E-mail: sgacc@springgreen.com
URL: http://www.springgreen.com
Contact: Mike Makarowski, President
URL(s): www.springgreen.com/chamber-news
Released: Monthly **Availability:** Print.

46381 ■ *Chamber Review*
600 W Chestnut St.
Baraboo, WI 53913
Ph: (608)356-8333
Fax: (608)356-8422
URL: http://www.baraboo.com
Contact: Raegen Trimmer, President
URL(s): baraboo.com/baraboo-chamber/newsletter
-archive
Released: Monthly **Description:** Highlights activities of the Chamber and member businesses. Provides other information of use to members. **Availability:** Online.

46382 ■ The Chamber for Superior & Douglas County [Superior Chamber of Commerce]
205 Belknap St.
Superior, WI 54880
Ph: (715)394-7716
Free: 800-942-5313
Fax: (715)394-3810
Co. E-mail: chamber@superiorchamber.org
URL: http://www.superiorchamber.org
Contact: Taylor Pedersen, President
Facebook: www.facebook.com/SuperiorWIChamber
X (Twitter): twitter.com/superiorchamber
Instagram: www.instagram.com/superiordcachamber
YouTube: www.youtube.com/user/Visi
tDouglasCounty
Pinterest: www.pinterest.com/TrvlSuperiorWI
Description: Promotes the success of the economic, civic, and cultural welfare of the community of Superior and Douglas County through various development programs. **Geographic Preference:** Local.

46383 ■ Chetek Area Chamber of Commerce
PO Box 747
Chetek, WI 54728
Ph: (715)924-3200
Free: 800-317-1720
Fax: (715)925-2041
Co. E-mail: info@chetekwi.net
URL: http://www.explorechetek.com
Facebook: www.facebook.com/chetek.chamber
Description: Promotes business and community development in Chetek, WI area. **Geographic Preference:** Local.

46384 ■ Chilton Chamber of Commerce
PO Box 122
Chilton, WI 53014
Ph: (920)418-1650
Co. E-mail: info@chiltonchamber.com
URL: http://chiltonchamber.com
Contact: Glen Calnin, President
Facebook: www.facebook.com/ChiltonChamber
Description: Strives to unite and promote the commercial mercantile and manufacturing interests of the City of Chilton. Improves civic, industrial, and business principles among its members. **Founded:** 1948. **Awards:** Chilton Chamber of Commerce Citizens of the Year (Annual). **Geographic Preference:** Local.

46385 ■ Chippewa Falls Area Chamber of Commerce (CFACC)
1 N Bridge St.
Chippewa Falls, WI 54729
Ph: (715)723-0331
Free: 888-723-0024
Co. E-mail: info@chippewachamber.org
URL: http://www.chippewachamber.org
Contact: Michelle Farrow, Coordinator
Facebook: www.facebook.com/
ChippewaFallsAreaChamberOfCommerce
Description: Works to improve quality of life in the community by providing leadership to promote business interest of members. **Founded:** 1910. **Publications:** *Chamber News*. **Educational Activities:** Chippewa Falls Area Chamber of Commerce Meeting (Annual). **Awards:** Chippewa Falls Area Chamber of Commerce Excellence in Education (Annual). **Geographic Preference:** Local.

46386 ■ Cleveland Chamber of Commerce
PO Box 56
Cleveland, WI 53015
Ph: (920)693-8256
Co. E-mail: chamber@clevelandwi.net
URL: http://clevelandwi.net
Description: Strives to bring new business and industry to Cleveland while helping the existing ones to become more viable. **Geographic Preference:** Local.

46387 ■ Clintonville Area Chamber of Commerce
1 S Main St.
Clintonville, WI 54929
Ph: (715)823-4606

STATE LISTINGS

Co. E-mail: executivedirector@clintonvillewichamber.com
URL: http://clintonvillewichamber.com
Contact: Kelly Trebus, President
E-mail: kelly.trebus.yzu0@statefarm.com
Facebook: www.facebook.com/clintonville.chamber.3
Description: Works to encourage communication and cooperation among business, industry, education, and community by providing leadership to promote the community. **Founded:** 1910. **Geographic Preference:** Local.

46388 ■ *Community Profile*
6331 W Mequon Rd.
Mequon, WI 53092
Ph: (262)512-9358
Co. E-mail: info@mtchamber.org
URL: http://www.mtchamber.org
Contact: Dean Rennicke, President
URL(s): www.mtchamber.org/benefits-programs
Released: Biennial **Availability:** Print.

46389 ■ **Cumberland Chamber of Commerce (CCC)**
1277 2nd Ave.
Cumberland, WI 54829
Ph: (715)822-3378
Co. E-mail: info@cumberlandchamberwi.com
URL: http://www.cumberlandchamberwi.com
Contact: Stacy Rischette, President
Facebook: www.facebook.com/cumberlandchamberofcommerce
Description: Represents businesses and professionals promoting economic and community development in Cumberland, WI. Sponsors annual Rutabaga Festival. **Founded:** 1966. **Geographic Preference:** Local.

46390 ■ **De Forest Area Chamber of Commerce**
151 Commerce St.
DeForest, WI 53532
Ph: (608)846-2922
Co. E-mail: info@deforestarea.com
URL: http://www.deforestarea.com
Contact: Amber Newkirk, President
Facebook: www.facebook.com/deforestwindsorarea
Linkedin: www.linkedin.com/company/dwacoc
Instagram: www.instagram.com/dwa_chamber
Description: Strives to provide leadership to improve business environment and promote economic growth through membership participation and involvement. **Founded:** 1963. **Geographic Preference:** Local.

46391 ■ **Delafield Chamber of Commerce (DCC)**
412 GENESEE St.
Delafield, WI 53018
Ph: (262)370-3861
Free: 888-294-1082
Co. E-mail: council@visitdelafield.org
URL: http://delafieldchamber.com
Contact: Tina Szada, President
Facebook: www.facebook.com/delafieldchamber
Linkedin: www.linkedin.com/company/delafield-chamber-of-commerce
X (Twitter): x.com/DelafieldCham
Description: Promotes business and community development in Delafield, WI. **Founded:** 1940. **Publications:** *Chamber Chronicles* (Quarterly). **Geographic Preference:** Local.

46392 ■ **Delavan - Delavan Lake Area Chamber of Commerce**
52 E Walworth Ave.
Delavan, WI 53115
Ph: (262)728-5095
Co. E-mail: info@delavanwi.org
URL: http://www.delavanwi.org
Contact: Frank Cangelosi, President
Facebook: www.facebook.com/DelavanChamber
Description: Promotes business and community development in Delavan, WI area. **Geographic Preference:** Local.

46393 ■ *Destination Guide*
1125 N Broadway St., Ste. 3
Menomonie, WI 54751
Ph: (715)235-9087
Free: 800-283-1862
Fax: (715)235-2824
Co. E-mail: info@menomoniechamber.org
URL: http://www.menomoniechamber.org
Contact: Ashley DeMuth, Chief Executive Officer
E-mail: ceo@menomoniechamber.org
URL(s): www.menomoniechamber.org/destination-guide
Released: Annual **Description:** Serves as a guide for individuals relocating or planning to visit the Menomonie, WI area. **Availability:** PDF; Online.

46394 ■ **Dodgeville Area Chamber of Commerce**
338 N Iowa St.
Dodgeville, WI 53533
Ph: (608)935-9200
Co. E-mail: projects@dodgeville.com
URL: http://www.dodgeville.com
Contact: Kari Wunderlin, President
Facebook: www.facebook.com/DodgevilleAreaChamberofCommerce
Description: Promotes business and community development in Dodgeville, WI area. **Founded:** 1874. **Geographic Preference:** Local.

46395 ■ **Door County Visitor Bureau (DCVB)**
1015 Green Bay Rd.
Sturgeon Bay, WI 54235-0406
Ph: (920)743-4456
Free: 800-527-3529
Co. E-mail: info@doorcounty.com
URL: http://www.doorcounty.com
Contact: Jack Moneypenny, President
E-mail: jack@doorcounty.com
Description: Promotes the civic and commercial progress of the Door community. **Publications:** *Door County Vacation Planning Guide* (Annual); *Door County Winter Guide*. **Geographic Preference:** Local.

46396 ■ **East Troy Area Chamber of Commerce**
2894 Main St., Ste. 6
East Troy, WI 53120
Ph: (262)642-3770
Fax: (262)642-8769
URL: http://easttroy.org
Contact: Ben Keating, President
Facebook: www.facebook.com/ETChamber
X (Twitter): x.com/ETChamber
Description: Promotes business and community development in East Troy, WI area. **Geographic Preference:** Local.

46397 ■ **Eau Claire Area Chamber of Commerce**
101 N Farewell St., Ste. 101
Eau Claire, WI 54703
Ph: (715)834-1204
Fax: (715)834-1956
Co. E-mail: information@eauclairechamber.org
URL: http://www.eauclairechamber.org
Contact: David Minor, President
E-mail: minor@eauclairechamber.org
Facebook: www.facebook.com/eauclairechamber
Linkedin: www.linkedin.com/company/eau-claire-area-chamber-of-commerce
X (Twitter): x.com/ecareachamber
Instagram: www.instagram.com/eauclairechamber
Description: Promotes business and community development in the Eau Claire, WI area. **Founded:** 1915. **Publications:** *The Update* (Weekly). **Awards:** Eau Claire Area Chamber of Commerce Ambassador of the Year (Annual); Eau Claire Area Chamber of Commerce Athena Award (Annual); Eau Claire Area Chamber of Commerce Outstanding Volunteer; Eau Claire Area Chamber of Commerce Small Business of the Year (Annual). **Geographic Preference:** Local.

46398 ■ **Elkhart Lake Area Chamber of Commerce**
41 E Rhine St.
Elkhart Lake, WI 53020
Ph: (920)876-2922
Free: 877-355-3554
Co. E-mail: chamber@elkhartlake.com
URL: http://www.elkhartlakechamber.com
Contact: Todd Smith, President
Linkedin: www.linkedin.com/company/elkhart-lake-chamber-of-commerce
X (Twitter): x.com/elakechamber
Description: Promotes business and community development in Elkhart Lake, WI area. **Founded:** 1950. **Geographic Preference:** Local.

46399 ■ **Elkhorn Area Chamber of Commerce & Tourism Center, Inc. (EACC)**
203 E Walworth St.
Elkhorn, WI 53121
Ph: (262)723-5788
Fax: (262)723-5784
Co. E-mail: info@elkhornchamber.com
URL: http://www.elkhornchamber.com
Contact: Cathy Billings, Treasurer
Facebook: www.facebook.com/elkhornareachamber
X (Twitter): x.com/elkhorn_chamber
Pinterest: www.pinterest.com/elkhornchamber
Description: Promotes business and community development in the Elkhorn, WI area. Holds annual Christmas Carol town parade. **Publications:** *Commerce Comments* (Monthly). **Geographic Preference:** Local.

46400 ■ **Ellsworth Area Chamber of Commerce (EACC)**
PO Box 927
Ellsworth, WI 54011
Ph: (715)273-6442
Co. E-mail: eteam@ellsworthchamber.com
URL: http://www.ellsworthchamber.com
Contact: Paul Bauer, President
E-mail: paulb@ellsworthcreamery.net
Facebook: www.facebook.com/EllsworthChamber
Description: Works to promote the development of Ellsworth community. **Founded:** 1957. **Geographic Preference:** Local.

46401 ■ **Elroy Area Chamber of Commerce**
PO Box 52
Elroy, WI 53929
Ph: (608)462-2400
Co. E-mail: elroyareachamber@gmail.com
URL: http://elroyareachamber.org
Contact: Kari Preuss, Director
E-mail: elroypl2@wrlsweb.org
Description: Promotes community advancement in the Elroy, WI area by promoting local business and industry. **Geographic Preference:** Local.

46402 ■ **Evansville Area Chamber of Commerce and Tourism**
PO Box 588
Evansville, WI 53536
Ph: (608)882-5131
Co. E-mail: evansvillecoc@litewire.net
URL: http://evansvillechamber.org
Contact: Christina Slaback, Executive Director
E-mail: christina@evansvillechamber.org
Facebook: www.facebook.com/evansvillecoc
Description: Promotes business and community development in Evansville, WI. **Publications:** *Chamber News* (Monthly). **Geographic Preference:** Local.

46403 ■ **Explore Waterford**
123 N River St.
Waterford, WI 53185
Ph: (262)543-5911
Co. E-mail: director@explorewaterford.com
URL: http://explorewaterford.com
Facebook: www.facebook.com/explorewaterfordwi
YouTube: www.youtube.com/channel/UCRo6gBdCkSJjzTeAPMp39EA
Pinterest: www.pinterest.com/explorewaterford

Description: Strives to promote business, tourism and community of the Waterford area through services and representation of the business community. **Publications:** *Business to Business* (Quarterly). **Geographic Preference:** Local.

46404 ■ Falls Chamber of Commerce
PO Box 178
Saint Croix Falls, WI 54024
Ph: (715)483-3580
URL: http://fallschamber.org
Contact: Pam Stratmoen, President
Facebook: www.facebook.com/fallschamber
X (Twitter): x.com/thefallschamber
Description: Promotes business and community development in the city of St. Croix Falls and its trade area. **Founded:** 2009. **Publications:** *Chamber News* (Monthly). **Educational Activities:** Falls Chamber of Commerce Meeting. **Geographic Preference:** Local.

46405 ■ *FDL SHRM*
23 S Main St., Ste. 101
Fond du Lac, WI 54935
Ph: (920)921-9500
Co. E-mail: info@envisiongreaterfdl.com
URL: http://www.envisiongreaterfdl.com
Contact: Sadie Vander Velde, President
E-mail: svandervelde@envisiongreaterfdl.com
URL(s): www.envisiongreaterfdl.com/fdlshrm
Released: Monthly **Price:** $10, Members; $15, Nonmembers. **Availability:** Print; PDF.

46406 ■ Fennimore Area Chamber of Commerce
c/o Jessica Helms, Community Development Manager
850 Lincoln Ave.
Fennimore, WI 53809
Ph: (608)822-3599
Co. E-mail: promo@fennimore.com
URL: http://fennimore.com/chamber-of-commerce
Contact: Jessica Helms, Manager
Description: Promotes business, tourism, and community development in Fennimore, WI. **Founded:** 1970. **Geographic Preference:** Local.

46407 ■ Fond du Lac Area Association of Commerce (FDLAAC)
23 S Main St., Ste. 101
Fond du Lac, WI 54935
Ph: (920)921-9500
Co. E-mail: info@envisiongreaterfdl.com
URL: http://www.envisiongreaterfdl.com
Contact: Sadie Vander Velde, President
E-mail: svandervelde@envisiongreaterfdl.com
Facebook: www.facebook.com/FDLAC
Linkedin: www.linkedin.com/company/chamberofcommerce.com
X (Twitter): x.com/chamberonline
Description: Promotes business and community development in the Fond du Lac, WI area. **Founded:** 2017. **Publications:** *FDL SHRM* (Monthly). **Geographic Preference:** Local.

46408 ■ Forest County Chamber of Commerce
116 S Lake Ave.
Crandon, WI 54520
Ph: (715)478-3450
Co. E-mail: mary.visitforestcounty@gmail.com
URL: http://www.visitforestcounty.com
Contact: Mark Ferris, President
Facebook: www.facebook.com/VisitForestCounty
Description: Seeks to promote the tourism and economic development of Crandon and Forest County. **Founded:** 1978. **Geographic Preference:** Local.

46409 ■ Fort Atkinson Area Chamber of Commerce (FAACC)
244 N Main St.
Fort Atkinson, WI 53538
Ph: (920)563-3210
Co. E-mail: info@fortchamber.com
URL: http://www.fortchamber.com
Contact: Chris Scherer, President
E-mail: chris.scherer@2020evolve.com
Facebook: www.facebook.com/fortchamber
X (Twitter): x.com/Fortchamber1
Instagram: www.instagram.com/fortatkinsonchamber
YouTube: www.youtube.com/user/FtAtkinsonChamber
Description: Represents commercial, industrial, professional, retail, and service businesses. Promotes business and community development in the Fort Atkinson, WI area. **Founded:** 1899. **Publications:** *Focus on Fort*. **Geographic Preference:** Local.

46410 ■ Forward Janesville, Inc. (FJI)
14 S Jackson St., Ste. 200
Janesville, WI 53548
Ph: (608)757-3160
Fax: (608)757-3170
Co. E-mail: forward@forwardjanesville.com
URL: http://www.forwardjanesville.com
Contact: Angela Pakes, President
Facebook: www.facebook.com/Forward-Janesville-Inc-328604918648
Description: Leads private sector economic and community development efforts to ensure the continued health and prosperity of business and industry in Janesville. **Founded:** 1991. **Publications:** *The Report* (Quarterly). **Geographic Preference:** Regional.

46411 ■ Fox Cities Chamber of Commerce and Industry (FCC)
125 N Superior St.
Appleton, WI 54911
Ph: (920)734-7101
Co. E-mail: info@foxcitieschamber.com
URL: http://foxcitieschamber.com
Contact: Becky Bartoszek, President
E-mail: bbartoszek@foxcitieschamber.com
X (Twitter): x.com/FoxCitiesChmbr
Instagram: www.instagram.com/foxcitieschmbr
Description: Business, industry, and individuals in east central Wisconsin. Works to enhance the community's economic well-being, promote balanced development, and assure continued improvement of the quality of life. **Founded:** 1976. **Publications:** *Fox Cities Chamber of Commerce--Membership Directory* (Biennial); *Fox Cities Chamber Business*. **Geographic Preference:** Local.

46412 ■ Fox Lake Chamber of Commerce
PO Box 94
Fox Lake, WI 53933
Ph: (920)928-3777
Co. E-mail: info@foxlakechamber.com
URL: http://www.foxlakechamber.com
Contact: Vicki Matheys, President
Description: Promotes economic, industrial, and community development and tourism in Fox Lake, WI. **Founded:** 1950. **Publications:** *Fox Lake Visitors Guide*. **Geographic Preference:** Local.

46413 ■ Fremont Area Chamber of Commerce (FACC)
PO Box 114
Fremont, WI 54940
Ph: (920)446-3838
Co. E-mail: travelfremontwi@gmail.com
URL: http://travelfremontwi.com
Contact: Allison Gleisner, President
Facebook: www.facebook.com/travelfremont
Description: Promotes business and community development in Fremont, WI area. **Founded:** 1882. **Geographic Preference:** Local.

46414 ■ Galesville Area Chamber of Commerce (GACC)
PO Box 196
Galesville, WI 54630
Ph: (608)582-2868
Co. E-mail: info@galesvillewi.com
URL: http://www.galesvillewi.com
Contact: Sharon Spahr, President
Facebook: www.facebook.com/galesvilleareachamberofcommerce
Description: Promotes business and community development in Galesville, WI. **Founded:** 1995. **Geographic Preference:** Local.

46415 ■ Germantown Area Chamber of Commerce (GACC)
W156 N11251 Pilgrim Rd.
Germantown, WI 53022
Ph: (262)255-1812
Fax: (262)255-9033
Co. E-mail: executivedirector@germantownchamber.org
URL: http://germantownchamber.org
Contact: Lynn Grgich, Executive Director
URL(s): www.germantownchamber.com
Facebook: www.facebook.com/Germantown-Area-Chamber-of-Commerce-WI-638100952886265
Description: Promotes business and community development in the Germantown, WI area. Sponsors seminars, parades, social events, and annual dinner. **Founded:** 1982. **Geographic Preference:** Local.

46416 ■ Grafton Area Chamber of Commerce (GACC)
1624 Wisconsin Ave.
Grafton, WI 53024
Ph: (262)377-1650
Co. E-mail: chamber@grafton-wi.org
URL: http://grafton-wi.org
Contact: Pam King, Executive Director
E-mail: pam@grafton-wi.org
Facebook: www.facebook.com/GraftonChamberofCommerce
X (Twitter): x.com/graftonchamber
Description: Promotes commercial, financial, industrial, and civic development in the Grafton, WI area. Sponsors annual Christmas Party, Holiday Tree Lighting, Farmer's Market, and Grafton Grand Prix. **Founded:** 1975. **Publications:** *Business Directory*. **Geographic Preference:** Local.

46417 ■ Grantsburg Chamber of Commerce
316 S Brad St.
Grantsburg, WI 54840
URL: http://www.grantsburgchamber.org
Contact: Bryan Vilstrup, Contact
Description: Promotes business and community development in Grantsburg, WI area. **Founded:** 1886. **Geographic Preference:** Local.

46418 ■ Greater Beloit Chamber of Commerce (GBCC)
635 3rd St., Ste. 5
Beloit, WI 53511
Ph: (608)365-8835
Co. E-mail: info@greaterbeloitchamber.org
URL: http://greaterbeloitchamber.org
Contact: Aimee Thurner, Director
E-mail: aimeet@greaterbeloitchamber.org
Facebook: www.facebook.com/GreaterBeloitChamber
X (Twitter): x.com/beloitwichamber
Description: Promotes business and community development in the Beloit, WI area. Holds annual festival, seminars, and high school career expo. **Founded:** 1927. **Publications:** *CCGB News* (Monthly); *The Network* (Weekly). **Geographic Preference:** Local.

46419 ■ Greater Brookfield Chamber of Commerce (GBCC)
17100 W Bluemond Rd., Ste. 202
Brookfield, WI 53005
Ph: (262)786-1886
Co. E-mail: bcc@brookfieldchamber.com
URL: http://www.brookfieldchamber.com
Contact: Chad Schultz, Chairman
E-mail: chads@innovative-signs.com
Facebook: www.facebook.com/BfieldChamber
Linkedin: www.linkedin.com/company/greater-brookfield-chamber-of-commerce
Instagram: www.instagram.com/brookfieldchamber
Description: Promotes business and community development in Brookfield, WI. **Founded:** 1957. **Publications:** *Net Works* (Monthly). **Geographic Preference:** Local.

46420 ■ Greater Madison Chamber of Commerce (GMCC) - Library
1 S Pinckney St., Ste. 330
Madison, WI 53701-0071

Ph: (608)256-8348
Co. E-mail: info@madisonbiz.com
URL: http://madisonbiz.com
Contact: Zach Brandon, President
E-mail: zach@madisonbiz.com
Facebook: www.facebook.com/greaterma
disonchamber
Linkedin: www.linkedin.com/company/greater-ma
dison-chamber-of-commerce
X (Twitter): x.com/MadisonBiz

Description: Promotes business and community development in Dane County, WI. **Scope:** Business; economics. **Founded:** 1869. **Holdings:** Figures not available. **Publications:** *Madison/Dane County Manufacturers* (Biennial); *Madison/Dane County Businesses with 50 or More Employees* (Biennial); *Business Beat* (Monthly). **Geographic Preference:** Local.

46421 ■ Greater Mauston Area Chamber of Commerce (GMACC)
1260 N Rd.
Mauston, WI 53948
Ph: (608)847-4142
Co. E-mail: chamber@mauston.com
URL: http://www.mauston.com/chamber
Facebook: www.facebook.com/MaustonChamber

Description: Promotes business and community development in the Mauston, WI area. Sponsors 4th of July Freedomfest. **Founded:** 1945. **Geographic Preference:** Local.

46422 ■ Greater Princeton Area Chamber of Commerce (GPACC)
PO Box 45
Princeton, WI 54968
Ph: (920)295-3877
Co. E-mail: info@princetonwi.com
URL: http://princetonwi.com
Contact: Mark Judas, President
E-mail: mark.judas@usbank.com
Facebook: www.facebook.com/princetonwi
Instagram: www.instagram.com/princetonwichamber

Description: Promotes business and community development in Princeton, WI. Makes charitable contributions; sponsors annual summer flea market. **Geographic Preference:** Local.

46423 ■ Greater Tomah Area Chamber of Commerce
310 N Superior Ave.
Tomah, WI 54660
Ph: (608)372-2166
Free: 833-948-6624
Co. E-mail: info@tomahwisconsin.com
URL: http://www.tomahwisconsin.com
Contact: Tina Thompson, President
Facebook: www.facebook.com/TomahChamberan
dCVB
Linkedin: www.linkedin.com/company/tomah-cham
ber-and-visitor's-center
YouTube: www.youtube.com/user/TomahChamber

Description: Works to foster a cohesive environment where businesses, families, and community can prosper. **Founded:** 1883. **Geographic Preference:** Local.

46424 ■ Greater Union Grove Area Chamber of Commerce (GUGACC)
925-15th Ave.
Union Grove, WI 53182
Ph: (262)878-4606
Fax: (262)878-9125
Co. E-mail: info@uniongrovechamber.org
URL: http://www.uniongrovechamber.org
Contact: Mario Denoto, Co-President
X (Twitter): x.com/UGCHAMBER

Description: Promotes business and community development in the Union Grove, WI area. Conducts Fourth of July Parade, Christmas Cookie Walk, and other community gatherings. Sponsors political candidate forums. **Founded:** 1915. **Geographic Preference:** Local.

46425 ■ Green Bay Area Chamber of Commerce (GBACC)
300 N Broadway, Ste. 3A
Green Bay, WI 54303
Ph: (920)593-3400
URL: http://www.greatergbc.org
Contact: Laurie Radke, President
E-mail: lradke@greatergbc.org
Facebook: www.facebook.com/Grea
terGreenBayChamber
Linkedin: www.linkedin.com/company/grea
tergreenbaychamber
X (Twitter): x.com/ggbchamber
Instagram: www.instagram.com/ggbchamber
YouTube: www.youtube.com/channel/UCOWxu6lsw
3jWoYlRi5_ZugA

Description: Promotes business and community development in the Green Bay, WI area. **Founded:** 1917. **Publications:** *Green Bay Area Chamber of Commerce--Membership Resource Directory* (Annual); *Bay Business Journal* (Bimonthly). **Educational Activities:** Power Networking Breakfast (Monthly). **Geographic Preference:** Local.

46426 ■ Green Lake Area Chamber of Commerce (GLACC)
550 Mill St.
Green Lake, WI 54941
Ph: (920)294-3231
Free: 800-253-7354
Co. E-mail: info@visitgreenlake.com
URL: http://www.visitgreenlake.com
Contact: Paula Bilodeau, President
Facebook: www.facebook.com/greenlakechamber
Instagram: www.instagram.com/greenlakewisconsin
YouTube: www.youtube.com/channel/UCNaChkYu
dDieT5W7yEP2AHQ

Description: Promotes business and community development in the Green Lake, WI area. Sponsors community social and promotional activities. **Founded:** 1965. **Publications:** *Visitors' Guide*. **Educational Activities:** Harvest Days Festival. **Geographic Preference:** Local.

46427 ■ Greendale Chamber of Commerce
PO Box 467
Greendale, WI 53129
Co. E-mail: kjastroch@greendale.org
URL: http://www.greendalechamber.com
Contact: Debra Barth, President
E-mail: barthdebra@harborseniorliving.com

Description: Promotes business and community development in Greendale, WI area. **Founded:** 1980. **Geographic Preference:** Local.

46428 ■ Hartland Area Chamber of Commerce
300 Cottonwood Ave., Ste. 12
Hartland, WI 53029
Ph: (262)367-7059
Co. E-mail: chamberdirector@hartland-wi.org
URL: http://hartland-wi.org
Contact: Lynn Minturn, President
Facebook: www.facebook.com/Hartlan
dChamberofCommerce
X (Twitter): x.com/HartlandWI_Info

Description: Serves the members by providing programs and services, which enhance the business climate and community. **Founded:** 1950. **Publications:** *Chamber Member Directory & Community Guide*; *Hartland Matters* (Monthly). **Geographic Preference:** Local.

46429 ■ Hayward Area Chamber of Commerce (HACC)
15805 US Hwy. 63
Hayward, WI 54843
Ph: (715)634-8662
Co. E-mail: info@haywardareachamber.com
URL: http://www.haywardareachamber.com
Contact: Melissa Jordan, President
Facebook: www.facebook.com/Haywar
dAreaChamberOfCommerce

Description: Promotes business and community development in Hayward, WI. **Publications:** *The Endeavor* (Monthly); *Hayward's Calendar of Events* (Annual). **Educational Activities:** Hayward Fall Festival (Annual). **Geographic Preference:** Local.

46430 ■ Heart of the Valley Chamber of Commerce
101 E Wisconsin Ave.
Kaukauna, WI 54130
Ph: (920)766-1616
Co. E-mail: info@heartofthevalleychamber.com
URL: http://heartofthevalleychamber.com
Contact: Julie van Vonderen, President
Facebook: www.facebook.com/HOVchamber
Linkedin: www.linkedin.com/company/heart-of-the
-valley-chamber-of-commerce
Instagram: www.instagram.com/hovchamber

Description: Aims to assist new and existing Heart of Valley businesses and communities in the endeavors to be successful. Serves its member businesses through educational programs, chamber committees, special events, new hire paperwork and members only benefits. Works year round in diverse ways to strengthen this area's prosperity and livability. **Founded:** 1927. **Geographic Preference:** Local.

46431 ■ Horicon Chamber of Commerce (HCC)
319 E Lake St.
Horicon, WI 53032
Ph: (920)485-3200
Co. E-mail: writeus@horiconchamber.com
URL: http://www.horiconchamber.com
Contact: Vance Mattila, President
Facebook: www.facebook.com/HoriconChamber

Description: Promotes business and community development in Horicon, WI. **Founded:** 1904. **Geographic Preference:** Local.

46432 ■ Hudson Area Chamber of Commerce and Tourism Bureau
502 2nd St.
Hudson, WI 54016
Ph: (715)386-8411
Fax: (715)386-8432
Co. E-mail: info@hudsonwi.org
URL: http://www.hudsonwi.org
Contact: Mary Claire Olson Potter, President
E-mail: maryclaire@hudsonwi.org
Facebook: www.facebook.com/HudsonAreaChamber

Description: Strives to serve its members by promoting the local economy and advocating the interests of the business community while advancing the recreational and cultural opportunities in the Hudson area. **Founded:** 1953. **Geographic Preference:** Local.

46433 ■ Iola - Scandinavia Area Chamber of Commerce
PO Box 167
Iola, WI 54945
URL: http://ischamber.com
Contact: Greg Loescher, President
E-mail: onthelake2@tds.net
Facebook: www.facebook.com/people/Iola-Scan
dinavia-Chamber/100064791156380

Description: Promotes business and community development in Iola and Scandinavia, WI. **Geographic Preference:** Local.

46434 ■ Jefferson Chamber of Commerce
230 S Main St., Ste. 1
Jefferson, WI 53549
Ph: (920)674-4511
Co. E-mail: director@jeffersonchamberwi.com
URL: http://jeffersonchamberwi.com
Contact: Tina Szada, President
Facebook: www.facebook.com/jeffersonchamberwi
Linkedin: www.linkedin.com/in/jefferson-chamber-of
-commerce-92880b181
Instagram: www.instagram.com/jeffersonchamberwi

Description: Promotes business and community development in Jefferson, WI area. **Founded:** 1976. **Publications:** *The Chamber Newsletter* (Monthly). **Geographic Preference:** Local.

46435 ■ Wisconsin

46435 ■ Johnson Creek Area Chamber of Commerce
520 Hartwig Blvd.
Johnson Creek, WI 53038
Ph: (920)699-4949
Co. E-mail: jcacc@johnsoncreekchamber.com
URL: http://www.johnsoncreekchamber.com
Contact: Mitch Weyer, President
Description: Promotes business and community development in Johnson Creek, WI. **Geographic Preference:** Local.

46436 ■ Juneau Chamber of Commerce
PO Box 4
Juneau, WI 53039
Ph: (920)386-0313
Co. E-mail: info@juneaucitychamber.com
URL: http://www.juneaucitychamber.com
Contact: Brett Bolman, President
E-mail: brett.bolman@juneaulanes.com
Description: Promotes business and community development in Juneau, WI area. **Geographic Preference:** Local.

46437 ■ Kenosha Area Chamber of Commerce (KACC)
600 52nd St., Ste. 130
Kenosha, WI 53140
Ph: (262)654-1234
Co. E-mail: info@kenoshaareachamber.com
URL: http://kenoshaareachamber.com
Contact: Laura Thelen, Treasurer
Facebook: www.facebook.com/kenoshachamber
Linkedin: www.linkedin.com/company/kenoshachamber
X (Twitter): x.com/kenoshachamber
Description: Promotes business and community development in Kenosha, WI area. **Founded:** 1916. **Publications:** *Manufacturers Directory of Kenosha: Area Guide* (Annual). **Geographic Preference:** Local.

46438 ■ Kewaunee Area Chamber of Commerce
308 N Main St.
Kewaunee, WI 54216
Ph: (920)388-4822
Free: 800-666-8214
Co. E-mail: admin@kewaunee.org
URL: http://www.kewaunee.org
Contact: Vicki Vollenweider, President
Facebook: www.facebook.com/Kewauneechamberofcommerce
Description: Seeks to provide the leadership necessary to promote Kewaunee's tourism, business and industrial development, while preserving its maritime heritage. Sponsors Trout Festival and Parade. **Geographic Preference:** Local.

46439 ■ La Crosse Area Chamber of Commerce
601 7th St. N
La Crosse, WI 54601
Ph: (608)784-4880
Fax: (608)784-4919
Co. E-mail: info@lacrossechamber.com
URL: http://www.lacrossechamber.com
Contact: Neal Zygarlicke, Chief Executive Officer
E-mail: neal@lacrossechamber.com
Facebook: www.facebook.com/lacrossechamber
Instagram: www.instagram.com/lacrossechamber
YouTube: www.youtube.com/channel/UCUyL8_yM0OB2hviNGrlUdag
Description: Works to improve the business community and regional economy of La Crosse area. **Founded:** 1989. **Publications:** *Chamber Connection* (Monthly). **Geographic Preference:** Local.

46440 ■ Lake Mills Area Chamber of Commerce (LMCC)
200C Water St., Ste.
Lake Mills, WI 53551
Ph: (920)648-3585
Co. E-mail: chamber@lakemills.org
URL: http://lakemills.org
Contact: Terri Benisch, President
Facebook: www.facebook.com/LegendaryLakeMills
Description: Works to enhance, preserve, and protect the quality of life and business in the Lake Mills, WI area. **Founded:** 1836. **Geographic Preference:** Local.

46441 ■ Lakewood Area Chamber of Commerce
PO Box 87
Lakewood, WI 54138
Ph: (715)276-6500
URL: http://www.lakewoodareacoc.org
Contact: Kim Leadbetter, President
Facebook: www.facebook.com/lakewoodareachamber
Description: Promotes business and community development and tourism in the Lakewood, WI area. Sponsors Lakewood Mardi Gras Spring Fling festival. **Founded:** 1975. **Publications:** *Chamber Newsletter* (Weekly). **Geographic Preference:** Local.

46442 ■ Lancaster Area Chamber of Commerce
206 S Madison St.
Lancaster, WI 53813
Ph: (608)723-2820
Fax: (608)723-4789
Co. E-mail: chamber@lancasterwisconsin.com
URL: http://lancasterwichamber.weebly.com
Contact: Ken Stahl, President
Description: Promotes agricultural, business, community, and industrial development in the area. **Geographic Preference:** Local.

46443 ■ Lodi and Lake Wisconsin Chamber of Commerce
114 S Main St.
Lodi, WI 53555
Ph: (608)592-4412
Co. E-mail: info@lodilakewisconsin.org
URL: http://www.lakewisconsin.org
Contact: Mike Clark, Contact
Description: Promotes business and community development in the Lake Wisconsin area. **Publications:** *Lake Wisconsin Chamber of Commerce Brochure* (Annual). **Geographic Preference:** Local.

46444 ■ Lomira Area Chamber of Commerce
Municipal Bldg., 425 Water St.
Lomira, WI 53048
Ph: (920)269-4112
Co. E-mail: lomirachamber@gmail.com
URL: http://www.lomirachamberofcommerce.com
Contact: Kasey Todl, Agent
Facebook: www.facebook.com/LomiraChamber
Description: Promotes business and community development in Lomira, WI. **Founded:** 1972. **Geographic Preference:** Local.

46445 ■ Luxemburg Chamber of Commerce
PO Box 141
Luxemburg, WI 54217
Ph: (920)606-0311
Co. E-mail: jdax@centurytel.net
URL: http://luxemburgchamber.com
Contact: Alex Stodola, President
E-mail: alex@stodolaiga.com
Facebook: www.facebook.com/luxemburgchamber
Description: Promotes business and community development in the Luxemburg, WI area. **Founded:** 1948. **Publications:** *Business Directory*. **Geographic Preference:** Local.

46446 ■ Madeline Island Chamber of Commerce (MICC)
PO Box 274
La Pointe, WI 54850
Ph: (715)747-2801
Co. E-mail: vacation@madelineisland.com
URL: http://www.madelineisland.com
Facebook: www.facebook.com/MadelineIsland
X (Twitter): x.com/madelineisle
Instagram: www.instagram.com/madelineisland
YouTube: www.youtube.com/channel/UCOAdMABS54H2P063rYd14QA
Pinterest: www.pinterest.com/Madeline_Island
Description: Promotes business and community development in Madeline Island, WI. **Geographic Preference:** Local.

46447 ■ Manitowish Waters Chamber of Commerce (MWCC)
5733 Airport Rd. /Hwy. 51
Manitowish Waters, WI 54545
Ph: (715)543-8488
Co. E-mail: chamber@manitowishwaters.org
URL: http://manitowishwaters.org
Contact: Sarah Pischer, Executive Director
Facebook: www.facebook.com/ManitowishWatersChamber
X (Twitter): x.com/travelmw
Pinterest: www.pinterest.com/manitowishwaterschamber
Description: Promotes the organization's members and tourism-based, four-season community. Sponsors several seasonal festivals. **Founded:** 1939. **Publications:** *Manitowish Waters Visitor Guide* (Annual). **Geographic Preference:** Local.

46448 ■ Marinette Menominee Area Chamber of Commerce
601 Marinette Ave.
Marinette, WI 54143
Ph: (715)735-6681
Co. E-mail: info@mandmchamber.com
URL: http://www.mandmchamber.com
Contact: Jan Allman, President
Facebook: www.facebook.com/mandmchamber
X (Twitter): x.com/mmareachamber
Description: Promotes business and community development in both cities and counties of Marinette, WI and Menominee, MI. **Founded:** 1939. **Publications:** *Marinette Chamber Memo* (Monthly). **Geographic Preference:** Regional.

46449 ■ Marshfield Area Chamber of Commerce and Industry (MACCI)
700 S Central Ave.
Marshfield, WI 54449
Ph: (715)384-3454
Co. E-mail: macci@marshfieldchamber.com
URL: http://www.marshfieldchamber.com
Contact: Scott Larson, President
E-mail: larson.scott@marshfieldchamber.com
Facebook: www.facebook.com/MarshfieldChamberWI
Linkedin: www.linkedin.com/company/macciwi
X (Twitter): x.com/MACCIWI
YouTube: www.youtube.com/channel/UC8MFRpxmHIVTHP6vBdf4ztA
Description: Promotes business and community development in the Marshfield, WI area. Sponsors annual Dairy Fest and Arts Weekend. Holds monthly board of directors meeting. **Founded:** 1946. **Publications:** *Perspectives*. **Geographic Preference:** Local.

46450 ■ Mayville Area Chamber of Commerce (MACC)
10 S Main St.
Mayville, WI 53050
Ph: (920)387-5776
Co. E-mail: info@mayvillechamber.com
URL: http://mayvillechamber.com
Contact: Chris Neu, President
Facebook: www.facebook.com/MayvilleAreaChamberofCommerce
Description: Area business personnel striving to promote business and community development in Mayville, WI. Supports community projects, children's holiday programs, and the Audubon Days festival. Provides opportunities to network, "to belong, and to make a difference". **Founded:** 1845. **Publications:** *MACC News*. **Geographic Preference:** Local.

46451 ■ Mazomanie Chamber of Commerce
PO Box 84
Mazomanie, WI 53560
Co. E-mail: mazochamber@gmail.com
URL: http://www.exploremazo.com
Contact: Jennifer Martinez, President
Facebook: www.facebook.com/mazomaniechamber

Description: Promotes business and community development in Mazomanie, WI area. **Geographic Preference:** Local.

46452 ■ McFarland Chamber of Commerce
4869 Larson Beach Rd., Ste. B
McFarland, WI 53558
Ph: (608)838-4011
Fax: (608)838-9463
Co. E-mail: info@mcfarlandchamber.com
URL: http://www.mcfarlandchamber.com
Contact: Becky Rogers, President
Description: Seeks to unite and direct the various businesses in the McFarland area in development and stimulation of the civic, industrial and commercial life. Activities include Family Festival, Citizen of the Year Banquet and Christmas in the Village festivities. **Founded:** 1980. **Awards:** McFarland Citizen of the Year (Annual). **Geographic Preference:** Local.

46453 ■ Medford Area Chamber of Commerce
104 E Perkins St.
Medford, WI 54451-1851
Ph: (541)748-4729
URL: http://www.uschamber.com/co/chambers/wisconsin/medford
Description: Promotes business and community development in Medford, WI area. **Geographic Preference:** Local.

46454 ■ Mellen Area Chamber of Commerce
PO Box 193
Mellen, WI 54546
Ph: (715)274-2330
Co. E-mail: mellen001@centurytel.net
URL: http://www.mellenwi.com
Description: Promotes business and community development in Mellen, WI. **Founded:** 1886. **Geographic Preference:** Local.

46455 ■ *Member Matters*
120 Jackson St.
Oshkosh, WI 54901
Ph: (920)303-2266
Co. E-mail: info@oshkoshchamber.com
URL: http://www.oshkoshchamber.com
Contact: Patti Andresen-Shew, Contact
E-mail: patti@oshkoshchamber.com
URL(s): www.oshkoshchamber.com/member-matters-archive
Released: Monthly **Availability:** Print.

46456 ■ Menomonie Area Chamber and Visitor Center
1125 N Broadway St., Ste. 3
Menomonie, WI 54751
Ph: (715)235-9087
Free: 800-283-1862
Fax: (715)235-2824
Co. E-mail: info@menomoniechamber.org
URL: http://www.menomoniechamber.org
Contact: Ashley DeMuth, Chief Executive Officer
E-mail: ceo@menomoniechamber.org
Facebook: www.facebook.com/menomoniechamber
Instagram: www.instagram.com/menomoniechamber
Description: Promotes business and community development in the Menomonie, WI area. Holds summer and winter festivals. **Founded:** 1938. **Publications:** *Destination Guide* (Annual); *Greater Menomonie Area Chamber of Commerce--Member Directory* (Annual). **Geographic Preference:** Local.

46457 ■ Mequon-Thiensville Chamber of Commerce (MTCC)
6331 W Mequon Rd.
Mequon, WI 53092
Ph: (262)512-9358
Co. E-mail: info@mtchamber.org
URL: http://www.mtchamber.org
Contact: Dean Rennicke, President
Facebook: www.facebook.com/MTchamber.org
Linkedin: www.linkedin.com/in/mequon-thiensville-chamber
X (Twitter): x.com/mtChamberOrg

Description: Promotes business and community development in Mequon and Thiensville, WI and its surrounding area. **Founded:** 1980. **Publications:** *Business Directory*; *Chamber News* (Monthly); *Community Profile* (Biennial). **Educational Activities:** Mequon-Thiensville Chamber of Commerce Luncheon (Monthly). **Geographic Preference:** Regional.

46458 ■ Mercer Area Chamber of Commerce
5150 N Hwy. 51
Mercer, WI 54547
Ph: (715)476-2389
Co. E-mail: info@mercercc.com
URL: http://mercercc.com
Contact: Hank Joustra, Director
Facebook: www.facebook.com/MercerChamber
X (Twitter): x.com/MercerWIChamber
Instagram: www.instagram.com/mercerwichamber
Description: Promotes business and community development in Mercer, WI area. **Geographic Preference:** Local.

46459 ■ Merrill Area Chamber of Commerce (MACC)
705 N Center Ave.
Merrill, WI 54452
Ph: (715)536-9474
Fax: (715)539-2043
Co. E-mail: info@merrillchamber.org
URL: http://www.merrillchamber.org
Contact: Clyde Nelson, Executive Director
E-mail: cnelson@merrillchamber.org
Linkedin: www.linkedin.com/company/merrill-chamber-of-commerce
X (Twitter): x.com/ChamberMerrill
Description: Promotes business and community development in the Merrill, WI area. **Founded:** 1911. **Publications:** *Merrill City Directory* (Periodic); *Merrill, Wisconsin, A City of Progress and Promise*. **Geographic Preference:** Local.

46460 ■ Metropolitan Milwaukee Association of Commerce (MMAC)
275 W Wisconsin Ave., Ste. 220
Milwaukee, WI 53203
Ph: (414)287-4100
Fax: (414)271-7753
Co. E-mail: info@mmac.org
URL: http://www.mmac.org
Contact: Timothy Sheehy, President
E-mail: tsheehy@mmac.org
Facebook: www.facebook.com/MMACMilwaukee
Linkedin: www.linkedin.com/company/mmac
X (Twitter): x.com/MMAC_Chamber
YouTube: www.youtube.com/channel/UC--Ilek8gQjlDJq91VxZjLw
Description: The Metropolitan Milwaukee Association of Commerce (MMAC) and its Council of Small Business Executives (COSBE) serve as advocates for metro Milwaukee companies to encourage business development, capital investment and job creation. **Founded:** 1861. **Publications:** *Selected Office Space in Metro Milwaukee*. **Geographic Preference:** Local.

46461 ■ Middleton Chamber of Commerce (MCC)
7427 Elmwood Ave.
Middleton, WI 53562-3135
Ph: (608)827-5797
Fax: (608)831-7765
Co. E-mail: lisaquam@middletonchamber.com
URL: http://www.middletonchamber.com
Contact: Tyler Emerick, President
Facebook: www.facebook.com/MiddletonWIChamber
Linkedin: www.linkedin.com/company/middleton-chamber-of-commerce---wi
X (Twitter): x.com/MiddletonChambr
YouTube: www.youtube.com/channel/UCdu8XLAnrrMHWAZLeAngUHA
Description: Represents businesses in Middleton, WI united to promote economic development. Acts as a liaison for business people and the community. **Founded:** 1952. **Geographic Preference:** Local.

46462 ■ Mineral Point Chamber of Commerce (MPCCMS)
145 High St.
Mineral Point, WI 53565
Ph: (608)987-3201
Free: 888-764-6894
Co. E-mail: info@mineralpoint.com
URL: http://www.mineralpoint.com
Contact: Lisa Hay, President
E-mail: highstreetsweets@gmail.com
Facebook: www.facebook.com/mineralpoint.wi
X (Twitter): x.com/MPChamber
Instagram: www.instagram.com/mineral.point
Pinterest: www.pinterest.com/joygieseke
Description: Represents business owners. Strives to enrich the economic well being and supports local business and industry in Mineral Point, WI. **Founded:** 1945. **Publications:** *Community Resource Guide*; *Visitor's Guide* (Annual). **Geographic Preference:** Local.

46463 ■ Minocqua Area Chamber of Commerce (MACC)
8216 Hwy. 51
Minocqua, WI 54548
Ph: (715)356-5266
Free: 800-446-6784
Fax: (715)358-2446
Co. E-mail: macc@minocqua.org
URL: http://www.minocqua.org
Contact: Krystal Westfahl, Chief Executive Officer
E-mail: krystal@minocqua.org
Facebook: www.facebook.com/LetsMinocqua
X (Twitter): x.com/NorthToMinocqua
Instagram: www.instagram.com/letsminocqua
YouTube: www.youtube.com/user/MinocquaArea
Description: Promotes businesses in and around the Wisconsin towns of Minocqua, Arbor Vitae, Woodruff, and Lake Tomahawk. **Founded:** 2000. **Publications:** *Northwoods News* (Monthly). **Geographic Preference:** Local.

46464 ■ Mishicot Area Growth and Improvement Committee (MAGIC)
511 E Main St.
Mishicot, WI 54228
Ph: (920)755-3411
Fax: (920)755-3411
Co. E-mail: magic@mishicot.org
URL: http://www.mishicot.org
Contact: Tammy Schmidt, President
Facebook: www.facebook.com/Mishicot-Area-Growth-Improvement-Committee-112540238757413
YouTube: www.youtube.com/user/MishicotMAGIC
Description: Promotes business and community development in Mishicot, WI area. **Founded:** 1847. **Publications:** *Mishicot Newsletter* (3/year). **Awards:** MAGIC Abracadabra Award (Annual); MAGIC Genie Award (Annual); MAGIC Red Carpet Award (Annual). **Geographic Preference:** Local.

46465 ■ *Mishicot Newsletter*
511 E Main St.
Mishicot, WI 54228
Ph: (920)755-3411
Fax: (920)755-3411
Co. E-mail: magic@mishicot.org
URL: http://www.mishicot.org
Contact: Tammy Schmidt, President
URL(s): www.vi.mishicot.wi.gov/magic/pages/newsletters
Released: 3/year; current edition 2023. **Description:** Includes calendar of events, report of activities of organization and community and historical piece. **Availability:** Print; PDF.

46466 ■ Monona East Side Business Alliance (MESBA)
PO Box 6264
Monona, WI 53716
Ph: (608)416-1610
Co. E-mail: connect@mononaeastside.com
URL: http://www.mononaeastside.com
Contact: Leah Hernandez, President
Facebook: www.facebook.com/mononaeastside
X (Twitter): x.com/MononaEastSide
Instagram: www.instagram.com/mononaeastside

YouTube: www.youtube.com/channel/UChG
25fjMVPqdB4jfDXkDbJA
Description: Promotes business and community development in Monona, WI area. **Founded:** 1990. **Geographic Preference:** Local.

46467 ■ Monroe Chamber of Commerce and Industry (MCCI)
1505 9th St.
Monroe, WI 53566
Ph: (608)325-7648
Fax: (608)328-2241
Co. E-mail: contact@monroechamber.org
URL: http://www.monroechamber.org
Contact: Tracy Meier, President
Facebook: www.facebook.com/MonroeWIChamber
Linkedin: www.linkedin.com/company/monroechamberofcommerce
Description: Promotes business, industry, and tourism in the Monroe, WI area. Sponsors Balloon Rally. **Publications:** *Issues* (Monthly); *Visitor Guide*. **Geographic Preference:** Local.

46468 ■ Montello Area Chamber of Commerce (MCC)
PO Box 124
Montello, WI 53949
Ph: (608)297-1318
URL: http://montelloareachamberofcommerce.com
Contact: Debbie Daniels, President
Facebook: www.facebook.com/montellochamberer
Description: Promotes business and community development in the Montello, WI area. **Founded:** 1946. **Geographic Preference:** Local.

46469 ■ Mosinee Area Chamber of Commerce
802 W Ave.
Mosinee, WI 54455
Ph: (715)693-4330
Fax: (715)693-9555
Co. E-mail: macoc@mtc.net
URL: http://www.mosineechamber.org
Contact: Benjamin Krautkramer, President
Facebook: www.facebook.com/mosinee.chamber
Description: Strives to serve as a resource in order to promote the interests of area businesses and the community of Mosinee. **Founded:** 1836. **Publications:** *Chamber News*. **Geographic Preference:** Local.

46470 ■ Mount Horeb Area Chamber of Commerce (MHACC)
300 E Main St.
Mount Horeb, WI 53572
Ph: (608)437-5914
Co. E-mail: info@trollway.com
URL: http://www.mounthorebchamber.com
Contact: Brenda Fritz, Owner
E-mail: littlevikings4k@gmail.com
Facebook: www.facebook.com/MountHorebChamber
Linkedin: www.linkedin.com/company/mounthorebchamber
X (Twitter): x.com/trollswhotweet
YouTube: www.youtube.com/channel/UCVhPJhrpQQDnzTrUiASLdXg
Pinterest: www.pinterest.com/mounthorebwi
Description: Promotes business and community development in Mount Horeb, WI. **Founded:** 1923. **Geographic Preference:** Local.

46471 ■ Mukwonago Area Chamber of Commerce & Tourism Center
100 Atkinson St.
Mukwonago, WI 53149
Ph: (262)363-7758
Co. E-mail: director@mukwonagochamber.org
URL: http://www.mukwonagochamber.org
Contact: Lynn Ewert, President
Facebook: www.facebook.com/MukwonagoChamber
Description: Promotes business and community development in Mukwonago, WI. **Founded:** 1985. **Publications:** *Bear Tracks* (5/year); *Paw Prints* (Bimonthly). **Geographic Preference:** Local.

46472 ■ Muskego Area Chamber of Commerce
S73 W16485 Janesville Rd.
Muskego, WI 53150
Ph: (414)422-1155
Co. E-mail: info@muskego.org
URL: http://www.muskego.org
Contact: Joseph Kreuser, President
Facebook: www.facebook.com/MuskegoChamber
X (Twitter): x.com/MuskegoChamber
Instagram: www.instagram.com/muskegochamber
YouTube: www.youtube.com/channel/UCZY6VqT7UHpZhw0XAW1lK_g
Description: Promotes business and community development in Muskego, WI area. **Founded:** 1957. **Geographic Preference:** Local.

46473 ■ Neillsville Area Chamber of Commerce (NACC)
500 W St.
Neillsville, WI 54456
Ph: (715)743-6444
Co. E-mail: neillsvillechamber@gmail.com
URL: http://neillsville.org
Contact: Dr. Bruce Davis, Contact
E-mail: drbrucedc84@gmail.com
Facebook: www.facebook.com/NeillsvilleChamber
Description: Represents retail and business owners; clubs and organizations. Promotes business and community development in the Neillsville, WI area. Conducts charitable activities. Sponsors annual Harvest Festival. **Publications:** *Teamwork for a Prosperous Community* (Monthly). **Geographic Preference:** Local.

46474 ■ New Berlin Chamber of Commerce and Visitors Bureau (NBCC/VB)
13825 W National Ave.
New Berlin, WI 53151
Ph: (262)786-5280
Co. E-mail: office@newberlinchamber.org
URL: http://www.newberlinchamber.org
Contact: Ed Holpfer, Executive Director
Description: Promotes business and community development in New Berlin, WI. **Founded:** 1959. **Publications:** *Hilites* (Periodic). **Geographic Preference:** Local.

46475 ■ New Glarus Chamber of Commerce
418 Railroad St.
New Glarus, WI 53574
Ph: (608)527-2095
Free: 800-527-6838
Co. E-mail: info@swisstown.com
URL: http://www.swisstown.com
Contact: Bekah Stauffacher, Executive Director
E-mail: bekah@swisstown.com
Facebook: www.facebook.com/newglaruschamber
Instagram: www.instagram.com/new.glarus
Description: Promotes business and community development in New Glarus, WI. **Publications:** *America's Little Switzerland*. **Geographic Preference:** Local.

46476 ■ New Lisbon Area Chamber of Commerce (NLCC)
119 E Bridge St.
New Lisbon, WI 53950
Ph: (608)562-3555
Co. E-mail: nlchambr@mwt.net
URL: http://www.newlisbonchamber.com
Contact: Jenny Kochie, President
Facebook: www.facebook.com/NewLisbonChamber
Description: Strives to promote economy and provide leadership that could influence public policy for the benefit of members. **Geographic Preference:** Local.

46477 ■ New London Area Chamber of Commerce
420 N Shawano St.
New London, WI 54961
Ph: (920)982-5822
URL: http://www.newlondonchamber.com
Contact: Jennifer Leopold, Branch Manager
Facebook: www.facebook.com/NewLondonAreaChamberofCommerce
Linkedin: www.linkedin.com/company/nlchamberofcommerce
X (Twitter): x.com/new_chamber
Instagram: www.instagram.com/nlchamberpride
Description: Represents businesses and individuals organized to promote economic and community development in the New London, WI area. **Founded:** 1932. **Publications:** *Everybody's Business* (Monthly). **Awards:** New London Area Chamber of Commerce Business of the Year Award (Annual); New London Area Chamber of Commerce Chamber Service Award (Annual); New London Area Chamber of Commerce Community Service Award (Annual); New London Area Chamber of Commerce New Business of the Year Award (Annual); New London Area Chamber of Commerce Quality of Life Award (Annual). **Geographic Preference:** Local.

46478 ■ New Richmond Area Chamber of Commerce & Visitors Bureau
245A S Knowles Ave.
New Richmond, WI 54017
Ph: (715)246-2900
Co. E-mail: director@newrichmondchamber.com
URL: http://www.newrichmondchamber.com
Contact: Rob Kreibich, President
E-mail: director@newrichmondchamber.com
Facebook: www.facebook.com/NewRichmondAreaChamberofCommerce
X (Twitter): x.com/nrchamber
Description: Promotes economic and community development in the New Richmond, WI area. Conducts business, industry, community, and education partnership program. Sponsors annual Park Art Fair and Fun Festival. **Publications:** *Chamber Connection* (Monthly). **Geographic Preference:** Local.

46479 ■ *News Break*
104 W Cook St., Ste. A
Portage, WI 53901
Ph: (608)742-6242
Free: 800-474-2525
Co. E-mail: pacc@portagewi
URL: http://portagewi.com
Contact: Marianne Hanson, President
URL(s): portagewi.com/newsbreak-newsletter
Released: Monthly **Description:** Includes business topics and membership updates. **Availability:** PDF; Online.

46480 ■ Oconomowoc Area Chamber of Commerce (OACC)
175 E Wisconsin Ave.
Oconomowoc, WI 53066-3056
Ph: (262)567-2666
Co. E-mail: chamber@oconomowoc.org
URL: http://oconomowoc.org
Contact: Ken Krahe, President
Facebook: www.facebook.com/oconomowocchamber
X (Twitter): x.com/oacc53066
Instagram: www.instagram.com/oconomowocchamberofcommerce
YouTube: www.youtube.com/channel/UCKGErOBouoajYVCfb_x9MoQ
Description: Promotes business and community development in the Oconomowoc, WI area. Offers numerous networking and advertising opportunities. **Founded:** 1969. **Publications:** *Oconomowoc Talk* (Monthly). **Geographic Preference:** Local.

46481 ■ Oconto Falls Area Chamber of Commerce (OFACC)
PO Box 24
Oconto Falls, WI 54154
Ph: (920)846-8306
Co. E-mail: ocontofallschamber@gmail.com
URL: http://ocontofallschamber.com
Contact: Gail Yatso, Vice President
Description: Promotes business and community development in Oconto Falls, WI. **Founded:** 1970. **Geographic Preference:** Local.

46482 ■ Omro Area Chamber of Commerce
130 W Larrabee St.
Omro, WI 54963
Ph: (920)685-6960
URL: http://www.futureomro.org

STATE LISTINGS   Wisconsin ■ 46497

Contact: Stephanie Hawkins, Executive Director
E-mail: shawkins@omro-wi.com
Description: Promotes business and community development in Omro, WI. **Scope:** sales, marketing, customer service, advertisement. **Founded:** 1986. **Subscriptions:** articles books. **Publications:** *The Communicator* (Quarterly). **Educational Activities:** Omro Area Chamber of Commerce Meeting. **Geographic Preference:** Local.

46483 ■ Osceola Area Chamber of Commerce
PO Box 251
Osceola, WI 54020
Ph: (715)755-3300
Co. E-mail: info@myosceolachamber.org
URL: http://www.myosceolachamber.org
Contact: Lisa Erickson, President
URL(s): www.uschamber.com/co/chambers/wisconsin/osceola
Description: Seeks to unite area businesses, industry, and services into a unified voice to promote, preserve, and protect Osceola and the surrounding area for the present and future. **Geographic Preference:** Local.

46484 ■ Oshkosh Chamber of Commerce
120 Jackson St.
Oshkosh, WI 54901
Ph: (920)303-2266
Co. E-mail: info@oshkoshchamber.com
URL: http://www.oshkoshchamber.com
Contact: Patti Andresen-Shew, Contact
E-mail: patti@oshkoshchamber.com
Facebook: www.facebook.com/oshkoshchamber
Linkedin: www.linkedin.com/company/oshkosh-chamber-of-commerce
X (Twitter): x.com/OshkoshChamber
YouTube: www.youtube.com/user/OshkoshChamber
Description: Promotes business and community development in Oshkosh area. **Founded:** 1907. **Publications:** *Member Matters* (Monthly); *NewsWave* (Bimonthly). **Awards:** Oshkosh Chamber of Commerce - Ambassador of the Year (Annual); Alberta S. Kimball Community Service Award (Annual); Oshkosh Chamber of Commerce - Distinguished Service Award (Annual); Oshkosh Chamber of Commerce - Volunteer of the Year. **Geographic Preference:** Local.

46485 ■ Park Falls Area Chamber of Commerce (PFACC)
400 4th Ave., S
Park Falls, WI 54552
Ph: (715)762-2703
Free: 877-762-2703
Co. E-mail: director@parkfalls.com
URL: http://www.parkfalls.com
Contact: Edward Kane, Executive Director
E-mail: director@parkfalls.com
Facebook: www.facebook.com/parkfallschamber
Linkedin: www.linkedin.com/in/park-falls-chamber-director-019565161
X (Twitter): x.com/PrkFallsChamber
YouTube: www.youtube.com/channel/UCNovH3iZUO-nNfJP78H8pyA
Pinterest: www.pinterest.com/parkfallsareachamberofcommerce
Description: Serves resorts, industries, retailers, and service organizations in Ashland, Iron, Price, and Sawyer counties, WI. Promotes community and economic development; provides information; sponsors promotions and events. **Founded:** 1947. **Publications:** *Park Falls - Gateway to the Good Life*. **Educational Activities:** Flambeau Rama Celebration (Annual). **Geographic Preference:** Local.

46486 ■ Pelican Lake Area Chamber of Commerce
PO Box 45
Pelican Lake, WI 54463
Ph: (715)487-5222
Co. E-mail: pelicanlakecc@frontiernet.net
URL: http://pelicanlakewi.org
Facebook: www.facebook.com/pelicanlakewichamber
Description: Businesses. Promotes business and community development in the Pelican Lake, WI area. Sponsors annual Ice Fishing Jamboree. **Founded:** 1962. **Geographic Preference:** Local.

46487 ■ *Perspectives*
700 S Central Ave.
Marshfield, WI 54449
Ph: (715)384-3454
Co. E-mail: macci@marshfieldchamber.com
URL: http://www.marshfieldchamber.com
Contact: Scott Larson, President
E-mail: larson.scott@marshfieldchamber.com
URL(s): www.marshfieldchamber.com/newsletter.html
Released: Latest edition 2024. **Description:** Contains latest information on business and community-related happenings, upcoming programs and networking opportunities, school-to-career information, MACCI's tip of the month and event calendar. **Availability:** PDF.

46488 ■ Phelps Chamber of Commerce
2429 Hwy. 17., Ste. 1
Phelps, WI 54554
Ph: (715)545-3800
Co. E-mail: chamber-office@phelpswi.us
URL: http://www.phelpswi.us
Contact: Quita Sheehan, President
E-mail: quitasheehan@gmail.com
Facebook: www.facebook.com/PhelpsWisconsin
X (Twitter): x.com/PhelpsOnTheLake
YouTube: www.youtube.com/user/PhelpsWisconsin
Pinterest: www.pinterest.com/phelpschamber
Description: Promotes business and community development in Phelps, WI. Sponsors annual Colorama Brunch. **Founded:** 1896. **Geographic Preference:** Local.

46489 ■ Platteville Regional Chamber of Commerce
275 W Business Hwy. 151
Platteville, WI 53818
Ph: (608)348-8888
Co. E-mail: chamber@platteville.com
URL: http://www.platteville.com
Contact: Bryant Schobert, President
Facebook: www.facebook.com/plattevilleregionalchamber
Description: Promotes business and community development in Platteville, WI. **Geographic Preference:** Local.

46490 ■ Plymouth Chamber of Commerce
647 Walton Dr.
Plymouth, WI 53073
Co. E-mail: chamber@plymouthwisconsin.com
URL: http://www.plymouthwisconsin.com
Contact: Mary Hauser, Executive Director
E-mail: maryhauser@plymouthwisconsin.com
Facebook: www.facebook.com/plymouthwicoc
X (Twitter): x.com/plymouthwicoc
Instagram: www.instagram.com/plymouthchamber
Description: Promotes business and community development in Plymouth, WI. **Publications:** *The Chamber Link* (Monthly). **Awards:** Plymouth Chamber Business of the Year Award. **Geographic Preference:** Local.

46491 ■ Port Washington Chamber of Commerce
126 E Grand Ave.
Port Washington, WI 53074-0143
Ph: (262)284-0900
Free: 800-719-4881
Co. E-mail: pwcc@sbcglobal.net
URL: http://www.visitportwashington.com
Facebook: www.facebook.com/PortWashingtonTourism
Description: Promotes business, community development, and tourism in Port Washington area. **Geographic Preference:** Local.

46492 ■ Portage Area Chamber of Commerce (PACC)
104 W Cook St., Ste. A
Portage, WI 53901
Ph: (608)742-6242
Free: 800-474-2525
Co. E-mail: pacc@portagewi.com
URL: http://portagewi.com
Contact: Marianne Hanson, President
Facebook: www.facebook.com/portagechamberwi
Instagram: www.instagram.com/portagechamberwi
YouTube: www.youtube.com/user/PortageChamber
Description: Individuals and businesses working to enhance the quality of life and improve business in the Portage, WI area. Sponsors Taste of Portage. **Founded:** 1973. **Publications:** *News Break!* (Monthly); *Portage Visitor Guides* (Annual). **Geographic Preference:** Local.

46493 ■ Portage County Business Council (PCBC)
5501 Vern Holmes Dr.
Stevens Point, WI 54482
Ph: (715)344-1940
Fax: (715)344-4473
Co. E-mail: info@portagecountybiz.com
URL: http://portagecountybiz.com
Contact: Karen Myers, Director
E-mail: karenm@portagecountybiz.com
Facebook: www.facebook.com/PortageCountyBusinessCouncil
Linkedin: www.linkedin.com/company/826620
X (Twitter): x.com/PoCoBiz
YouTube: www.youtube.com/user/PCBusinessCouncil/videos
Description: Represents over 500 Portage County businesses. Strengthens Portage County's quality of life by promoting a business climate that encourages growth and stability. **Founded:** 1930. **Publications:** *Active Voice* (Monthly). **Geographic Preference:** Local.

46494 ■ *Portage Visitor Guides*
104 W Cook St., Ste. A
Portage, WI 53901
Ph: (608)742-6242
Free: 800-474-2525
Co. E-mail: pacc@portagewi.com
URL: http://portagewi.com
Contact: Marianne Hanson, President
URL(s): portagewi.com/benefits-of-membership
Released: Annual **Availability:** Print; Online.

46495 ■ Potosi - Tennyson Area Chamber of Commerce
105 N Main
Potosi, WI 53820
Ph: (608)763-2261
Fax: (608)763-2537
URL: http://potosiwisconsin.com/chamber-of-commerce/directory/250/village-of-potosi
Contact: Diane Bowe, Manager
Facebook: www.facebook.com/PotosiTennysonAreaChamberOfCommerce/posts/pfbid0c1wVoJZ46hNc4UWRvBxWkaphwFVJ6Jepkw7DZEK1cXN9smW6ApvcT41qDdJ77DW2l
Description: Promotes business and community development in Potosi/Tennyson, WI. **Geographic Preference:** Local.

46496 ■ Poynette Chamber of Commerce
PO Box 625
Poynette, WI 53955
Ph: (608)635-2425
Co. E-mail: poynettechamber@gmail.com
URL: http://poynettechamber.com
Contact: Luke Walz, President
Description: Promotes business and community development in Poynette, WI. **Geographic Preference:** Local.

46497 ■ Prairie Du Chien Area Chamber of Commerce
211 S Main St.
Prairie du Chien, WI 53821-0326
Ph: (608)326-8555
Free: 800-732-1673
Fax: (608)326-7744
Co. E-mail: info@prairieduchien.org
URL: http://www.prairieduchien.org
Contact: Nick Coffield, President

Facebook: www.facebook.com/prairie
duchienchamber

Description: Promotes business and community development in the Prairie du Chien, WI area. **Founded:** 1950. **Publications:** *Prairie du Chien Area.* **Geographic Preference:** Local.

46498 ■ Prescott Area Chamber of Commerce (PACC)
237 Broad St.
Prescott, WI 54021
Ph: (715)629-0047
Co. E-mail: chamberofprescott@gmail.com
URL: http://chamberofprescott.com
Contact: Chad Steger, Board Member
Facebook: www.facebook.com/prescottwichamber
X (Twitter): x.com/PrescottACCWi
Instagram: www.instagram.com/prescottwichamber

Description: Promotes business and community development in the Prescott, WI area. Assists with local festivals. **Founded:** 1979. **Publications:** *Prescott Visitor and New Residents Guide* (Annual). **Geographic Preference:** Local.

46499 ■ Presque Isle Chamber of Commerce
8305 Main St.
Presque Isle, WI 54557
Ph: (715)686-2910
Co. E-mail: info@presqueisle.com
URL: http://www.presqueislewi.org
Contact: Bonnie Byrnes, President
E-mail: bonnie@headwatersrealestate.com
Facebook: www.facebook.com/PresqueIsleChamber
X (Twitter): x.com/PresqueIsleWI

Description: Promotes business and community development in Presque Isle, WI. **Founded:** 1954. **Geographic Preference:** Local.

46500 ■ Pulaski Area Chamber of Commerce
PO Box 401
Pulaski, WI 54162-0401
Ph: (920)822-4400
Co. E-mail: pacc@netnet.net
URL: http://pulaskichamber.org
Contact: Holly Krueger, Co-President
Facebook: www.facebook.com/paccwi

Description: Promotes business and community development in the Pulaski, WI area. **Geographic Preference:** Local.

46501 ■ Racine Area Manufacturers and Commerce (RAMAC)
300 5th St.
Racine, WI 53403
Ph: (262)634-1931
Co. E-mail: ramac@racinechamber.com
URL: http://www.racinechamber.com
Contact: Matt Montemurro, President
E-mail: mjmontemurro@racinechamber.com

Description: Strives to strengthen the economic and business community of Racine area. **Founded:** 1982. **Geographic Preference:** Local.

46502 ■ Randolph Chamber of Commerce
248 W Stroud St.
Randolph, WI 53956
Ph: (920)326-4769
Fax: (920)326-5032
URL: http://www.randolphwis.com
Contact: Ken Ireland, President
Facebook: www.facebook.com/RandolphWIChamber

Description: Promotes business and community development in Randolph, WI. Sponsors annual Maxwell Street Festival. **Publications:** *Business Directory*; *Randolph: A Great Place to Grow.* **Geographic Preference:** Local.

46503 ■ The Report
14 S Jackson St., Ste. 200
Janesville, WI 53548
Ph: (608)757-3160
Fax: (608)757-3170
Co. E-mail: forward@forwardjanesville.com
URL: http://www.forwardjanesville.com
Contact: Angela Pakes, President
URL(s): www.forwardjanesville.com/membership-services/publications

Ed: Laura Barten. **Released:** Quarterly **Availability:** Print; PDF; Online.

46504 ■ Rhinelander Area Chamber of Commerce (RACC)
450 W Kemp St.
Rhinelander, WI 54501
Ph: (715)365-7464
Co. E-mail: info@rhinelanderchamber.com
URL: http://explorerhinelander.com
Facebook: www.facebook.com/RhinelanderWisconsin
YouTube: www.youtube.com/channel/UCjW5uZ1y6Vge9eNsimpyBAQ
Pinterest: www.pinterest.com/rhinelanderwi

Description: Promotes business and community development in the Rhinelander, WI area. **Founded:** 1928. **Geographic Preference:** Local.

46505 ■ Rice Lake Area Chamber of Commerce (RLACC)
37 S Main St.
Rice Lake, WI 54868-2299
Free: 877-234-2126
Co. E-mail: chamber@rice-lake.com
URL: http://ricelakechamber.org
Contact: Rick Fleishauer, President
Facebook: www.facebook.com/ricelake.chamberofcommerce
X (Twitter): x.com/ricelakechamber

Description: Businesses. Promotes business and community development in the Rice Lake, WI area. **Founded:** 1941. **Publications:** *Chamber News* (Monthly). **Geographic Preference:** Local.

46506 ■ Ripon Area Chamber of Commerce (RACC)
114 Scott St.
Ripon, WI 54971
Ph: (920)748-6764
Co. E-mail: info@ripon-wi.com
URL: http://www.ripon-wi.com
Contact: Elizabeth Roy, President
Facebook: www.facebook.com/RiponWisconsin
Instagram: www.instagram.com/riponwisconsin

Description: Promotes business and community development in the Ripon, WI area. Sponsors Dickens of A Christmas festival, Cookie Daze, Maxwell Street Day and Duck-tona $500 Rubber Duck Race. **Founded:** 1940. **Publications:** *Horn Blower* (Bi-monthly); *The Ripon Guide* (Annual). **Geographic Preference:** Local.

46507 ■ River Falls Area Chamber of Commerce and Tourism Bureau
215 W Maple St.
River Falls, WI 54022
Ph: (715)425-2533
Co. E-mail: info@rfchamber.com
URL: http://www.rfchamber.com
Contact: Russ Korpela, Executive Director
E-mail: russ@rfchamber.com
X (Twitter): x.com/RFChamber

Description: Works to improve economic development and quality of life in the community through education, promotion and leadership. Sponsors River Falls Days, Town N' Country Day, Ambassadors Golf Outing, Business Show Case, and many more events. **Founded:** 1955. **Awards:** River Falls Area Chamber of Commerce and Tourism Bureau Ambassador of the Year (Annual); River Falls Area Chamber of Commerce and Tourism Bureau Business of the Year (Annual); River Falls Area Chamber of Commerce and Tourism Bureau Citizen of the Year (Annual); River Falls Area Chamber of Commerce and Tourism Bureau Small Business of the Year (Annual). **Geographic Preference:** Local.

46508 ■ Sauk Prairie Area Chamber of Commerce (SPACC)
109 Phillips Blvd.
Sauk City, WI 53583
Ph: (608)643-4168
Co. E-mail: spacc@saukprairie.com
URL: http://www.saukprairie.com
Contact: Jama Graves, President
Facebook: www.facebook.com/sauk.chamber

Linkedin: www.linkedin.com/company/sauk-prairie-area-chamber-of-commerce
X (Twitter): x.com/SPRiverway
YouTube: www.youtube.com/user/SPChamber
Pinterest: www.pinterest.com/saukprairie

Description: Promotes business and community development in the Sauk City and Prairie du Sac, WI area. **Founded:** 1956. **Publications:** *Sauk Prairie Area Chamber of Commerce Business/Membership Directory.* **Geographic Preference:** Local.

46509 ■ Sauk Prairie Area Chamber of Commerce Business/Membership Directory
109 Phillips Blvd.
Sauk City, WI 53583
Ph: (608)643-4168
Co. E-mail: spacc@saukprairie.com
URL: http://www.saukprairie.com
Contact: Jama Graves, President
URL(s): www.saukprairie.com/list

Availability: Print.

46510 ■ Saukville Chamber of Commerce
639 E Green Bay Ave.
Saukville, WI 53080
Ph: (262)268-1970
Co. E-mail: exec@saukvillechamber.org
URL: http://www.saukvillechamber.org
Contact: Chris King, President
Facebook: www.facebook.com/saukville

Description: Promotes business and community development in the Saukville, WI area. **Founded:** 1915. **Geographic Preference:** Local.

46511 ■ Sayner-Star Lake Chamber of Commerce (SSLCC)
325 Main St.
Sayner, WI 54560
Co. E-mail: learnmore@sayner-starlake.org
URL: http://sayner-starlake.org
Facebook: www.facebook.com/sayner.starlake.chamber
X (Twitter): x.com/SaynerStarLake
YouTube: www.youtube.com/channel/UCGMXAVNxfyHU-uq40SjGIQg
Pinterest: www.pinterest.com/saynerstarchamber

Description: Promotes business and community development in the Sayner, WI area. **Founded:** 1980. **Geographic Preference:** Local.

46512 ■ Shawano Country Chamber of Commerce
1263 S Main St.
Shawano, WI 54166
Ph: (715)524-2139
Co. E-mail: finance@shawanocountry.com
URL: http://www.shawanocountry.com
Contact: Zachary Linsmeyer, President
Facebook: www.facebook.com/shawanocountrychamber
Instagram: www.instagram.com/shawanocountry
YouTube: www.youtube.com/user/VisitShawano
Pinterest: www.pinterest.com/ShawanoCountry

Description: Promotes business and community development in the Shawano, WI area. Acts as civic clearinghouse, public relations counselor, and legislative representative. **Founded:** 1926. **Geographic Preference:** Local.

46513 ■ Sheboygan County Chamber of Commerce
621 S 8th St.
Sheboygan, WI 53081
Ph: (920)457-9491
Co. E-mail: assist@sheboygan.org
URL: http://www.sheboygan.org
Contact: Deidre Martinez, Chief Executive Officer
E-mail: deidre@sheboygan.org
Facebook: www.facebook.com/SheboyganCountyChamber
Linkedin: www.linkedin.com/company/sheboygan-county-chamber-of-commerce

Description: Improves the economic, social and political conditions of Sheboygan County. Advances the status of the county by engaging in forums, addressing the needs of the community and developing beneficial programs for the members. **Founded:** 1914. **Geographic Preference:** Local.

46514 ■ Sheboygan Falls Chamber Main Street
504 Broadway
Sheboygan Falls, WI 53085
Ph: (920)467-6206
Co. E-mail: chambermnst@sheboyganfalls.org
URL: http://sheboyganfalls.org
Contact: Shirl Breunig, Executive Director
E-mail: sbreunig@sheboyganfalls.org
Facebook: www.facebook.com/ChamberMainStreet
Description: Promotes commerce and redevelopment of downtown Sheboygan Falls. **Founded:** 1988. **Publications:** *Word on the Street* (Bimonthly). **Geographic Preference:** Local.

46515 ■ Shell Lake Chamber of Commerce (SLCC)
501 1st St.
Shell Lake, WI 54871
URL: http://www.shelllake.org/chamber-of-commerce
Contact: Shannon Klopp, President
Description: Promotes business and community development in Shell Lake, WI. Sponsors Town and Country Days. Publications: none. **Founded:** 1961. **Geographic Preference:** Local.

46516 ■ Sparta Area Chamber of Commerce
111 Milwaukee St.
Sparta, WI 54656
Ph: (608)269-4123
Co. E-mail: info@bikesparta.com
URL: http://www.bikesparta.com
Contact: Reinhard Mueller, President
Facebook: www.facebook.com/SpartaAreaChamberOfCommerce
X (Twitter): x.com/spartachamber
YouTube: www.youtube.com/channel/UCNJQ6uOexoK47oOwAk63ezw
Pinterest: www.pinterest.com/spartachamber
Description: Fosters community prosperity and improvement of quality of life in the Sparta, WI area through cooperation, education, and active leadership. **Publications:** *The Ambassador* (Monthly). **Educational Activities:** Executive Committee Meeting (Monthly). **Geographic Preference:** Local.

46517 ■ Spooner Area Chamber of Commerce (SACC)
122 N River St.
Spooner, WI 54801
Ph: (715)635-2168
Co. E-mail: info@spoonerchamber.org
URL: http://spoonerchamber.org
Contact: Alex Sutton, Vice President
Facebook: www.facebook.com/spoonerchamber
Instagram: www.instagram.com/spoonerchamber
Description: Promotes business and community development in the Spooner, WI area. **Founded:** 1936. **Geographic Preference:** Local.

46518 ■ Spring Green Area Chamber of Commerce (SGACC)
208 N Winsted St.
Spring Green, WI 53588
Ph: (608)588-2054
Co. E-mail: sgacc@springgreen.com
URL: http://www.springgreen.com
Contact: Mike Makarowski, President
Facebook: www.facebook.com/springgreenareachamberofcommerce
X (Twitter): x.com/sgacc
Instagram: www.instagram.com/explore/tags/springgreenwi
Description: Promotes business and community development in the Spring Green, WI area. Sponsors Arts and Crafts Fair and Country Christmas Festival. Conducts charitable activities. **Founded:** 1968. **Publications:** *The Chamber News* (Monthly). **Geographic Preference:** Local.

46519 ■ Stoughton Chamber of Commerce (SCC)
532 E Main St.
Stoughton, WI 53589
Ph: (608)873-7912
Co. E-mail: stoughton@stoughtonwi.com
URL: http://www.stoughtonwi.com
Contact: Sarah Ebert, President
Facebook: www.facebook.com/StoughtonChamber
Instagram: www.instagram.com/visit_stoughton
YouTube: www.youtube.com/channel/UCXftBhSUmND13gc-JDIIruw
Description: Promotes business and community development in Stoughton, MA. **Founded:** 2012. **Geographic Preference:** Local.

46520 ■ Stratford Area Chamber of Commerce
PO Box 312
Stratford, WI 54484
Co. E-mail: stratfordchamber@gmail.com
URL: http://www.stratfordchamber.org
Contact: Mark Snyder, President
Facebook: www.facebook.com/StratfordAreaChamberOfCommerce
Description: Promotes the commercial, agricultural, industrial, and civic interests of the community. **Founded:** 1900. **Geographic Preference:** Local.

46521 ■ Superior Area Chamber of Commerce
205 Belknap St.
Superior, WI 54880
Ph: (715)394-7716
Free: 800-942-5313
Fax: (715)394-3810
Co. E-mail: chamber@superiorchamber.org
URL: http://www.superiorchamber.org
Contact: John Conley, Treasurer
X (Twitter): x.com/superiorchamber
Instagram: www.instagram.com/superiordcachamber
Description: Promotes business and community development in Superior, NE. **Geographic Preference:** Local.

46522 ■ Tomahawk Chamber of Commerce
208 N 4th St.
Tomahawk, WI 54487
Ph: (715)453-5334
Free: 800-569-2160
Co. E-mail: chambert@gototomahawk.com
URL: http://www.gototomahawk.com
Contact: Andrew Hein, President
Facebook: www.facebook.com/tcocvc
Description: Promotes business and community development in the Tomahawk, WI area. **Founded:** 1949. **Publications:** *Tomatalk* (Monthly); *Visitor Vacation Guide and Membership Directory* (Annual). **Geographic Preference:** Local.

46523 ■ *The Update*
101 N Farewell St., Ste. 101
Eau Claire, WI 54703
Ph: (715)834-1204
Fax: (715)834-1956
Co. E-mail: information@eauclairechamber.org
URL: http://www.eauclairechamber.org
Contact: David Minor, President
E-mail: minor@eauclairechamber.org
URL(s): eauclairechamber.org/communications
Released: Weekly **Availability:** Online.

46524 ■ Verona Area Chamber of Commerce (VACC)
120 W Verona Ave.
Verona, WI 53593
Ph: (608)845-5777
Co. E-mail: info@veronawi.com
URL: http://veronawi.com
Contact: Kassie Gorski, President
Facebook: www.facebook.com/VeronaAreaChamberofCommerce
Linkedin: www.linkedin.com/company/verona-area-chamber-of-commerce
X (Twitter): x.com/VeronaAreaChamb
Instagram: www.instagram.com/veronawichamber
Description: Works to build a healthy Verona economy and improve the quality of life in the communities. Aims to proactively support, promote and enhance economic development and community well-being in Verona. **Founded:** 1966. **Geographic Preference:** Local.

46525 ■ *Visitors' Guide*
550 Mill St.
Green Lake, WI 54941
Ph: (920)294-3231
Free: 800-253-7354
Co. E-mail: info@visitgreenlake.com
URL: http://www.visitgreenlake.com
Contact: Paula Bilodeau, President
URL(s): visitgreenlake.com/online-visitors-guide
Availability: Online.

46526 ■ Washburn Area Chamber of Commerce (WACC)
126 W Bayfield St.
Washburn, WI 54891
Ph: (715)373-5017
Co. E-mail: info@washburnchamber.com
URL: http://washburnchamber.com
Contact: Melissa Martinez, Director
Facebook: www.facebook.com/WashburnAreaChamber
Description: Promotes business and community development in Washburn, WI. **Founded:** 1975. **Publications:** *Chamber News* (Monthly). **Geographic Preference:** Local.

46527 ■ Watertown Area Chamber of Commerce
519 E Main St.
Watertown, WI 53094
Ph: (920)261-6320
Co. E-mail: info@watertownchamber.com
URL: http://www.watertownchamber.com
Contact: Bonnie Hertel, Executive Director
E-mail: bonie@watertownchamber.com
Linkedin: www.linkedin.com/company/watertown-area-chamber-of-commerce
YouTube: www.youtube.com/channel/UCWOc-uLZZd5U8ZlWxJUYFyw
Description: Promotes business and community development in Watertown, WI. **Founded:** 1920. **Geographic Preference:** Local.

46528 ■ Waukesha County Business Alliance
2717 N Grandview Blvd., Ste. 300
Waukesha, WI 53188
Ph: (262)542-4249
Fax: (262)542-8068
Co. E-mail: alliance@waukesha.org
URL: http://www.waukesha.org
Contact: Suzanne Kelley, President
E-mail: skelley@waukesha.org
Facebook: www.facebook.com/WCBizAlliance
Linkedin: www.linkedin.com/company/waukesha-county-chamber-of-commerce
X (Twitter): x.com/wcbizalliance
YouTube: www.youtube.com/user/WCBizAlliance
Description: Strives to enhance the business community of Waukesha County. **Founded:** 1918. **Publications:** *The Link*. **Geographic Preference:** Local.

46529 ■ *Waunakee Area Chamber of Commerce News*
100 E Main St.
Waunakee, WI 53597
Ph: (608)849-5977
Co. E-mail: office@waunakeechamber.com
URL: http://waunakeechamber.com
Contact: Ellen K. Schaaf, Executive Director
E-mail: ellen@waunakeechamber.com
URL(s): www.waunakeechamber.com/events-news.html
Availability: Print.

46530 ■ Waunakee/Westport Chamber of Commerce
100 E Main St.
Waunakee, WI 53597
Ph: (608)849-5977
Co. E-mail: office@waunakeechamber.com

URL: http://waunakeechamber.com
Contact: Ellen K. Schaaf, Executive Director
E-mail: ellen@waunakeechamber.com
Facebook: www.facebook.com/waunakeechamber
X (Twitter): x.com/WaunaChamber
YouTube: www.youtube.com/user/
WaunakeeAreaChamber
Description: Promotes business and community development in the Waunakee, WI area. **Founded:** 1979. **Publications:** *Waunakee Area Chamber of Commerce News*. **Geographic Preference:** Local.

46531 ■ Waupaca Area Chamber of Commerce (WACC)
315 S Main St.
Waupaca, WI 54981
Ph: (715)258-7343
Co. E-mail: info@waupacaareachamber.com
URL: http://www.waupacaareachamber.com
Contact: Terri Schulz, President
E-mail: terri@waupacaareachamber.com
Facebook: www.facebook.com/WaupacaChamber
Instagram: www.instagram.com/risewaupaca
YouTube: www.youtube.com/channel/UCHj5eZ
39HOuNIhU4Ygvf46A
Description: Represents retailers, manufacturers, professionals, and service and community organizations united to promote economic and community development in the Waupaca, WI area. **Founded:** 1931. **Publications:** *Map Brochure* (Semiannual); *Waupaca Area Chamber of Commerce Newsline* (Monthly); *Waupaca Area Chamber of Commerce Progress Report* (Annual). **Geographic Preference:** Local.

46532 ■ Waupun Area Chamber of Commerce (WACC)
321 E Main St.
Waupun, WI 53963
Contact: Craig Much, Contact
Description: Aims to provide business leadership, promote its members' interests and encourage the long-term sustainable development, quality of life and prosperity of the area. **Founded:** 1941. **Geographic Preference:** Local.

46533 ■ Wausau Region Chamber of Commerce (WRCC)
200 Washington St., Ste. 120
Wausau, WI 54403
Ph: (715)845-6231
Co. E-mail: info@wausauchamber.com
URL: http://www.wausauchamber.com
Contact: David Eckmann, President
E-mail: deckmann@wausauchamber.com
Facebook: www.facebook.com/WausauChamber
Linkedin: www.linkedin.com/company/the-wausau
-region-chamber-of-commerce
X (Twitter): x.com/WausauChamber
Instagram: www.instagram.com/wausauchamber
YouTube: www.youtube.com/channel/UCkMMFLvSvb
3tsS2aqNHLVWw
Description: Aims to strengthen businesses in the Wausau region of Wisconsin, and to enhance the community by building business success. **Founded:** 1912. **Publications:** *Businessmatters* (Quarterly); *Businessmatters* (Quarterly); *Membermatters* (Monthly). **Geographic Preference:** Local.

46534 ■ Waushara Area Chamber of Commerce (WACC)
440 W Main St.
Wautoma, WI 54982
Ph: (920)787-3488
Co. E-mail: wausharachamber@gmail.com
URL: http://www.wausharachamber.com
Contact: Helena Waala, Co-President
Facebook: www.facebook.com/people/Waushara
-Area-Chamber-of-Commerce/100066720093888
Description: Promotes business and community development in Waushara County, WI. **Publications:** *WACC News* (Monthly). **Awards:** Waushara Area Chamber of Commerce Business Person of the Year (Annual); Waushara Area Chamber of Commerce Citizen of the Year (Annual). **Geographic Preference:** Local.

46535 ■ Webster Area Chamber of Commerce
PO Box 48
Webster, WI 54893
Ph: (715)349-5999
Co. E-mail: websterwichamber@gmail.com
URL: http://websterwisconsin.com
Contact: Katie Smith, Contact
Description: Promotes business and community development in Webster, WI. **Geographic Preference:** Local.

46536 ■ West Allis/West Milwaukee Chamber of Commerce
6737 W Washington St., Ste. 2141
West Allis, WI 53214
Ph: (414)302-9901
URL: http://www.countyoffice.org/west-allis-west-mil
waukee-chamber-of-commerce-west-allis-wi-414
Description: Promotes business and community development in West Allis and West Milwaukee. **Founded:** 1958. **Publications:** *The Chamber Connection* (Weekly). **Geographic Preference:** Local.

46537 ■ West Bend Area Chamber of Commerce Inc. (WBACC)
304 S Main St.
West Bend, WI 53095
Ph: (262)338-2666
Fax: (262)338-1771
Co. E-mail: info@wbachamber.org
URL: http://www.wbchamber.org
Contact: Toni Gumina, President
E-mail: toni@wbachamber.org
Facebook: www.facebook.com/West-Bend-Area
-Chamber-of-Commerce-397053240504614
Linkedin: www.linkedin.com/company/west-ben
d-area-chamber-of-commerce
YouTube: www.youtube.com/channel/UCczc6J
3RAzvmxYEeg-dXsvw
Pinterest: www.pinterest.com/WestBendWI/the-geo
caching-capital-of-the-midwest
Description: Businesses and individuals organized to promote economic and community development in the West Bend, WI area. **Founded:** 1913. **Publications:** *Comment* (Monthly). **Geographic Preference:** Local.

46538 ■ Westfield Chamber of Commerce (WCC)
PO Box 393
Westfield, WI 53964
Ph: (608)296-4146
Co. E-mail: lb4twin@hotmail.com
URL: http://westfield-wi.com
Description: Promotes business and community development in the area. **Founded:** 1981. **Publications:** *Directory of Community* (Biennial). **Educational Activities:** Community Night. **Geographic Preference:** Local.

46539 ■ Weyauwega Area Chamber of Commerce
PO Box 531
Weyauwega, WI 54983
Ph: (920)209-4405
Co. E-mail: weyauwegachamberinfo@gmail.com
URL: http://weyauwegachamber.org
Contact: Kimberly Rogers, President
Facebook: www.facebook.com/weyauwegachamber
Description: Promotes business and community development in Weyauwega, WI. **Geographic Preference:** Local.

46540 ■ Whitehall Area Chamber of Commerce
PO Box 281
Whitehall, WI 54773
Co. E-mail: info@whitehallwichamber.com
URL: http://www.whitehallwichamber.com
Contact: Dawn Peterson, President
E-mail: dawn.peterson@rcu.org
Facebook: www.facebook.com/whitehallwichamber
Description: Promotes business and community development in Whitehall, WI. **Founded:** 1950. **Geographic Preference:** Local.

46541 ■ Whitewater Area Chamber of Commerce
150 W Main St.
Whitewater, WI 53190
Ph: (608)473-4005
Co. E-mail: info@whitewaterchamber.com
URL: http://www.whitewaterchamber.com
Contact: Lisa Dawsey Smith, Director
Facebook: www.facebook.com/whitewaterchamber
Linkedin: www.linkedin.com/organization-guest/
company/whitewater-area-chamber-of-commerce
X (Twitter): x.com/VisitWhitewater
Description: Promotes business and community development in the Whitewater, WI area. **Publications:** *Solutions* (Monthly). **Geographic Preference:** Local.

46542 ■ Wisconsin Black Chamber of Commerce, Inc.
3020 W Vliet St.
Milwaukee, WI 53233
Ph: (414)306-6460
Fax: (414)933-1656
Co. E-mail: admin@twbcc.com
URL: http://www.twbcc.com
Contact: Ruben W. Hopkins, Chief Executive Officer
E-mail: ruben@twbcc.com
Description: Represents Black owned businesses. Seeks to empower and sustain African American communities through entrepreneurship and capitalistic activity. Provides advocacy, training and education to Black communities. **Geographic Preference:** State.

46543 ■ Wisconsin Manufacturers & Commerce (WMC)
501 E Washington Ave.
Madison, WI 53703
Ph: (608)258-3400
Co. E-mail: mem@wmc.org
URL: http://www.wmc.org
Contact: Kurt Bauer, President
Facebook: www.facebook.com/WisconsinMC
X (Twitter): x.com/WisconsinMC
YouTube: www.youtube.com/c/WMCTV
Description: Wisconsin manufacturers and service companies. Fosters and advances policies which are in the public interest of the state and nation. **Founded:** 1911. **Publications:** *Wisconsin Business Voice* (Quarterly); *Wisconsin Chamber of Commerce Directory*; *Wisconsin Legislative Pocket Directory* (Biennial); *Capitol Watch* (Weekly); *Chamber to Chamber*; *Human Resources Report* (Periodic); *Manufacturing Report* (Periodic); *Member Service Update*; *Sales and Exchange* (Monthly). **Educational Activities:** Wisconsin Safety Congress (Annual). **Awards:** Business Friend of the Environment Awards (Annual); Wisconsin Corporate Safety Award (Annual); Wisconsin Manufacturer of the Year Award (Annual); WMC Working for Wisconsin Award (Annual). **Geographic Preference:** State.

MINORITY BUSINESS ASSISTANCE PROGRAMS

46544 ■ University of Wisconsin-Stevens Point - Small Business Development Center (SBDC)
2100 Main St., Rm. 032 Old Main
Stevens Point, WI 54481-3897
Ph: (715)346-3838
Co. E-mail: uwspce-bus@uwsp.edu
URL: http://www3.uwsp.edu/conted/Pages/SBDC
.aspx
Facebook: www.facebook.com/uwspsbdc
Description: Provides counseling, in-depth studies, workshops, seminars, and communication development to American Indian tribes and individuals in Wisconsin.

46545 ■ Wisconsin Department of Administration - Division of Enterprise Operations - Minority Business Enterprise Program (MBE)
101 E Wilson St., 6th Fl.
Madison, WI 53703

Ph: (608)267-9550
Fax: (608)267-0600
Co. E-mail: doabdmbd@wisconsin.gov
URL: http://www.doa.state.wi.us/Divisions/Enterprise-Operations/Supplier-Diversity-Program/Program-Descriptions#minority

Description: Works to expand and support minority business opportunities in Wisconsin. **Founded:** 1983.

46546 ■ Wisconsin Economic Devlopment Corporation - Business Development
201 W Washington Ave.
Madison, WI 53703
URL: http://wedc.org/business-development

Description: Provides assistance to existing and potential minority businesses in market assessment, access to credit, capital formation, and coordination of public and private resources. Also certifies minority vendors.

FINANCING AND LOAN PROGRAMS

46547 ■ Capital Midwest Fund (CMF)
10556 N Port Washington Rd., Ste. 201
Mequon, WI 53092
Ph: (414)453-4488
URL: http://www.capitalmidwest.com
Contact: Stephen Einhorn, Contact

Description: Invests in revenue-stage technology companies in the Central U.S. **Investment Policies:** Understands technology trends and has used that to solve customer problems and gain market acceptance. **Industry Preferences:** Industrial; manufacturing; healthcare.

46548 ■ Chippewa Valley Angel Investors Network, LLC (CVAIN)
PO Box 3232
Eau Claire, WI 54702
Ph: (715)878-9791
URL: http://cvain.com

Description: Equity investment group for startups in the Greater Chippewa Valley area. **Founded:** 2003. **Investment Policies:** High growth potential; strong market position; sustainable competitive advantage; compelling business plan; proprietary technology; strong management team.

46549 ■ Lubar and Co.
Lubar and Co.
833 E Michigan St., Ste. 1500
Milwaukee, WI 53202
Ph: (414)291-9000
Fax: (414)291-9061
Co. E-mail: info@lubar.com
URL: http://lubar.com
Contact: David J. Lubar, President

Description: Investment firm provides strategic collaboration, guidance, financial security and legacies services. **Founded:** 1960. **Preferred Investment Size:** $10,000,000 minimum. **Industry Preferences:** Communications, computer hardware and software, semiconductors and other electronics, medical and health, consumer related, industrial and energy, transportation, business services, and manufacturing.

46550 ■ Mason Wells Private Equity / M&I Ventures
411 E Wisconsin Ave., Ste. 1280
Milwaukee, WI 53202
Ph: (414)727-6400
Fax: (414)727-6410
URL: http://www.masonwells.com
Contact: Tom Smith, Executive Director
E-mail: tgsmith@masonwells.com

Description: Provider of investment funds, private equity and venture capital investments services for companies. **Founded:** 1998. **Preferred Investment Size:** $500,000 to $8,000,000. **Investment Policies:** Start-up, seed, management buyouts, leveraged buyout, and early stage. **Industry Preferences:** Computer software, biotechnology, financial services, and business service.

46551 ■ N29 Capital Partners, LLC (N)
5256 US Hwy. 51
Manitowish Waters, WI 54545
URL: http://n29capitalpartners.com
Contact: Nicole Justa, Contact
E-mail: nicole@n29capitalpartners.com

Description: Invests in early-stage startup companies with disruptive products or services.

46552 ■ RSA Capital
1222 W Venture Ct.
Mequon, WI 53092
Ph: (262)241-8015
Fax: (262)364-2226
Co. E-mail: info@rsacap.com
URL: http://www.rsacap.com
Contact: Jeffrey A. Bartlett, Principal Managing Director
E-mail: jab@rsacap.com

Description: Provider of direct equity investment, capital, funds and financial advisory consulting services. **Preferred Investment Size:** $2,000,000 to $5,000,000. **Industry Preferences:** Communications, computer software, and Internet specific.

46553 ■ Venture Investors L.L.C.
505 S Rosa Rd., Ste. 201
Madison, WI 53719
Ph: (608)441-2700
URL: http://ventureinvestors.com
Contact: John Neis, Managing Director
E-mail: john@ventureinvestors.com
X (Twitter): x.com/VI_Funds

Description: Financial firm is engaged in venture capital. **Founded:** 1982. **Preferred Investment Size:** $50,000 to $8,000,000. **Industry Preferences:** Biotechnology, medical and health, computer software and services, semiconductors and other electronics, consumer related, Internet specific, industrial and energy, communications and media, and computer hardware.

46554 ■ Wisconsin Investment Partners (WIP)
PO Box 45919
Madison, WI 53744
Co. E-mail: wip.admin@wisinvpartners.com
URL: http://wisinvpartners.com
Contact: Andrea Dlugos, Manager

Description: Angel investment group for seed- and early-stage startups. **Founded:** 2000.

PROCUREMENT ASSISTANCE PROGRAMS

46555 ■ Metropolitan Milwaukee Association of Commerce (MMAC)
275 W Wisconsin Ave., Ste. 220
Milwaukee, WI 53203
Ph: (414)287-4100
Fax: (414)271-7753
Co. E-mail: info@mmac.org
URL: http://www.mmac.org
Contact: Timothy Sheehy, President
E-mail: tsheehy@mmac.org
Facebook: www.facebook.com/MMACMilwaukee
Linkedin: www.linkedin.com/company/mmac
X (Twitter): x.com/MMAC_Chamber
YouTube: www.youtube.com/channel/UC--llek8gQjlDJq91VxZjLw

Description: The Metropolitan Milwaukee Association of Commerce (MMAC) and its Council of Small Business Executives (COSBE) serve as advocates for metro Milwaukee companies to encourage business development, capital investment and job creation. **Founded:** 1861. **Publications:** *Selected Office Space in Metro Milwaukee*. **Geographic Preference:** Local.

46556 ■ Wisconsin Procurement Institute (WPI) - Regional PTAC [Wisconsin Procurement Technical Assistance Centers]
10437 Innovation Dr., Ste. 320
Wauwatosa, WI 53226
URL: http://www.aptac-us.org/find-a-ptac/?state=WI
Contact: Aina Vilumsons, Executive Director

E-mail: ainav@wispro.org

Description: For Wisconsin companies interested in supplying their products and or services to federal, state, local agencies and prime contractors. WPI guides, trains and provides hands-on assistance to firms in developing government business and improving process and technical capabilities to access and compete in the Government marketplace.

INCUBATORS/RESEARCH AND TECHNOLOGY PARKS

46557 ■ ADVOCAP Inc. Business Development Center
19 W First St.
Fond du Lac, WI 54935
Ph: (920)922-7760
Co. E-mail: business@advocap.org
URL: http://www.advocap.org/services/business-development
Contact: Kathy Doyle, Director
E-mail: kathy.doyle@advocap.org

Description: Provider of affordable housing, business development, food and nutrition and many more services. **Founded:** 1966.

46558 ■ Benton Business Incubator
244 Ridge Ave.
Benton, WI 53803-8022
Ph: (608)759-3721
Fax: (608)759-3212
Co. E-mail: bentonincubator@gmail.com
URL: http://bentonwi.us/benton-business-incubator
Contact: Gary McCrea, President
Facebook: www.facebook.com/people/Benton-Business-Incubator/100057725317174

Description: Offers office, manufacturing, and warehouse space to small and medium-sized start-ups. Also offers business-assistance services.

46559 ■ Brown County Culinary Kitchen (BCCK)
2900 Curry Ln.
Green Bay, WI 54311
Ph: (920)421-0995
Co. E-mail: incubator@greatergbc.org
URL: http://bcculinarykitchen.org

Description: Culinary incubator providing a fully equipped, shared-use kitchen that has been inspected and approved for use as a commercial kitchen.

46560 ■ Chippewa Innovation Center (CVIC)
3132 Louis Ave.
Eau Claire, WI 54703
Ph: (715)836-2842
URL: http://www.chippewavalleyinnovationcenter.com
Contact: Deb Nichols, President
Facebook: www.facebook.com/people/Chippewa-Valley-Innovation-Center/100067234954752
YouTube: www.youtube.com/channel/UCopeM7m-F5TCXV0ISaYS2fQ

Description: Encourages new and emerging entrepreneurial businesses in the Chippewa Valley. Offers warehouse/manufacturing space, managerial support, technical assistance, and access to financial programs. **Founded:** 1986.

46561 ■ CVTC Applied Technology Center (CVTC)
2322 Alpine Rd.
Eau Claire, WI 54703
Ph: (715)833-6202
Free: 800-547-CVTC
Fax: (715)874-4672
URL: http://www.cvtc.edu/experience-cvtc/campuses/applied-technology-center

Description: Business incubator designed to accommodate the development of business start-ups for micro fabrication and other advanced manufacturing technologies. Allows projects to move to commercialization faster with access to the latest equipment and technology. **Founded:** 1912.

46562 ■ Delta Properties
612 W Main St.
Madison, WI 53703
Ph: (608)251-3337
Co. E-mail: info@delta-properties.com
URL: http://www.delta-properties.com
Description: Provides low-cost industrial space to encourage economic development.

46563 ■ Entrepreneurial and Education Center
100 N 72nd Ave.
Wausau, WI 54401
Ph: (715)848-2016
Co. E-mail: info@mcdevco.org
URL: http://www.bizstartwausau.com
Facebook: www.facebook.com/EntrepreneurialEducationCenter
Linkedin: www.linkedin.com/company/entrepreneurial-and-education-center
Description: Helps business startups to succeed by providing business advising services as well as a range of resources to grow businesses. **Founded:** 1987.

46564 ■ gener8tor
821 E Washington Ave., Ste. 200-G
Madison, WI 53703
Ph: (414)502-8880
Co. E-mail: info@gener8tor.com
URL: http://www.gener8tor.com
Contact: Maureen Ragalie, Director
E-mail: maureen@gener8tor.com
Facebook: www.facebook.com/gener8tor
Linkedin: www.linkedin.com/company/gener8tor
X (Twitter): x.com/gener8tor
Instagram: www.instagram.com/gener8tor
Description: A nationally ranked accelerator that invests in high-growth startups. Runs programs 3 times per year. Supports the growth of these startups through a network of experienced mentors, technologists, corporate partners, angel investors and venture capitalists. **Founded:** 2012.

46565 ■ Kickapoo Culinary Center (KCC)
16381 Hwy. 131
Gays Mills, WI 54631
Ph: (608)735-4341
URL: http://kickapooculinary.com
Contact: Gays Mills, Contact
Description: Serves as an incubator for serious start-up food businesses.

46566 ■ Madison Enterprise Center (MEC)
1501 Williamson St.
Madison, WI 53703
URL: http://cwd.org
Contact: Brendan Vandenburg-Carroll, Coordinator
E-mail: brendan@cwd.org
Description: A small business incubator for emerging office and light industrial companies.

46567 ■ Milwaukee County Research Park - Technology Innovation Center (TIC)
10437 Innovation Dr., Ste. 123
Wauwatosa, WI 53226-4815
Ph: (414)778-1400
Fax: (414)778-1178
URL: http://technologyinnovationcenter.org
Contact: Mark W. Johnson, Executive Director
E-mail: mwj@mcrpc.org
Facebook: www.facebook.com/TechologyInnovationCenterMKE
Linkedin: www.linkedin.com/company/technology-innovation-center
Instagram: www.instagram.com/technologyinnovationcenter
Description: High technology business incubator that offers wet lab space, conference rooms, office space and facilities, networking opportunities, and business resources. **Founded:** 1993.

46568 ■ Northwest Enterprise Center Network (NWECN)
1400 S River St.
Spooner, WI 54801
Ph: (713)635-2197
Fax: (715)635-7262
URL: http://www.nwrpc.com/882/Northwest-Enterprise-Center-Network
Contact: Richard Roeser, Specialist
E-mail: rroeser@nwrpc.com
Description: Business incubator that provides necessary resources to enhance technology-based business development; resulting in added economic diversification and strength within the region through the creation of high-skill, high wage jobs. Provides a range of business support services and resources that accelerate the success of startups.

46569 ■ Platteville Business Incubator Inc. (PBII)
52 Means Dr., Ste. 114A
Platteville, WI 53818
Ph: (608)888-9588
Co. E-mail: kate@pbii.org
URL: http://www.pbii.org
Contact: Scott Chyko, President
Facebook: www.facebook.com/people/Platteville-Business-Incubator-Inc/100063501253439
Description: A non-profit organization that promotes business startups. Provides access to office space, signage, business planning resources, and financial resources. **Founded:** 2001.

46570 ■ Recipe For Success: HALO Incubator Kitchen
2000 DeKoven Ave. Unit 1
Racine, WI 53403
Ph: (262)633-3235
Fax: (262)633-7374
URL: http://haloinc.org
Contact: Holly Anderle, Executive Director
Facebook: www.facebook.com/HALORacine
YouTube: www.youtube.com/channel/UCqIW86HD8FM3DFIMadG5sCw
Description: An incubator kitchen providing small food businesses with a place to get off the ground and already established businesses extra work space. Also provides guidance for small start up businesses in getting their kitchen license.

46571 ■ St. Croix Valley Business Incubator (SCVBI)
1091 Sutherland Ave.
River Falls, WI 54022
Ph: (715)425-4288
URL: http://www.stcroixinnovation.org
Contact: Sheri Marnell, Director
E-mail: sheri.marnell@uwrf.edu
Facebook: www.facebook.com/stcroixinnovation
Linkedin: www.linkedin.com/company/st-croix-valley-business-innovation-center
Instagram: www.instagram.com/stcroixvalleyinnovation
Description: Business incubator that serves as a one-stop location for the coordinated delivery of business development services. **Founded:** 2010.

46572 ■ SC Johnson iMET
2320 Renaissance Blvd.
Sturtevant, WI 53177
Ph: (262)564-2007
URL: http://www.gtc.edu/campus-life/campus-safety
Description: Provides business development assistance and mentoring and is dedicated to growing small businesses and startups.

46573 ■ Shawano County Economic Progress, Inc. (SCEPI)
1263 S Main St.
Shawano, WI 54166
Ph: (715)526-5839
Fax: (715)524-3127
URL: http://www.shawanoecondev.org
Contact: Paul Kersten, President
Facebook: www.facebook.com/shawanoecondev
Description: Offers technical and financial programs for startups and expansion. **Founded:** 1987.

46574 ■ The Superior Business Center Inc. (SPC)
1423 N 8th St.
Superior, WI 54880
Ph: (715)718-2327
URL: http://www.superiorbusinesscenter.com
Description: Provider of emerging businesses through a variety of resources including affordable office space services. **Founded:** 1989.

46575 ■ University of Wisconsin-Madison - MGE Innovation Center
505 S Rosa Rd., Ste. 201
Madison, WI 53719
Ph: (608)441-8000
Fax: (608)441-8010
URL: http://universityresearchpark.org/property
Description: Enables startups to focus on business development essentials including product development, research, recruitment, and capital investment. Provides office and laboratory space for early stage startups. **Founded:** 1989.

46576 ■ University of Wisconsin--Madison - University Research Park (URP)
505 S Rosa Rd., Ste. 201
Madison, WI 53719
Ph: (608)441-8000
Fax: (608)441-8010
Co. E-mail: info@urp.wisc.edu
URL: http://universityresearchpark.org
Contact: Aaron Olver, Managing Director
Facebook: www.facebook.com/UniversityResearchPark
Linkedin: www.linkedin.com/company/university-research-park
X (Twitter): x.com/UWMadisonURP
Instagram: www.instagram.com/universityresearchpark
YouTube: www.youtube.com/channel/UCP8Ua2LhQV2KqfXgUSbNrCA
Description: A research and technology park that supports early-stage and growth-oriented businesses in a range of sectors including engineering, computational, and life sciences. **Scope:** The 321-acre park facilitates technology transfer between the research produced on the University campus and applied research of industry and provides a long-term endowment income to the University. Leases land to private companies and agencies and offers laboratory and office services to start-up companies. **Founded:** 1984.

46577 ■ Western Dairyland Business Centers (WDBC)
418 Wisconsin St.
Eau Claire, WI 54703
Ph: (715)836-7511
Co. E-mail: info@successfulbusiness.org
URL: http://www.successfulbusiness.org
Contact: Walmsley Johnson-Cole, Specialist
E-mail: walmsley.johnson-cole@wdeoc.org
Facebook: www.facebook.com/westernwiwbc
Linkedin: www.linkedin.com/company/westernwiwbc
X (Twitter): x.com/westernwiwbc
Instagram: www.instagram.com/westernwiwbc
YouTube: www.youtube.com/user/WDEOC
Pinterest: www.pinterest.com/wdwbc
Description: Assists entrepreneurs. Offers training, referrals, financing, technology, business plan development, feasibility studies, and business case management services at various locations. Primarily serves women, minorities, veterans, disable, and low-income individuals.

46578 ■ Whitewater University Technology Park
1221 Innovation Dr.
Whitewater, WI 53190
Ph: (262)472-5290
URL: http://whitewatertechpark.org
Contact: Dr. John Chenoweth, President
Facebook: www.facebook.com/WhitewaterInnovationCenter
Linkedin: www.linkedin.com/company/whitewatertechpark
X (Twitter): x.com/WhitewaterIC
YouTube: www.youtube.com/channel/UCzpn6dEFAnF0KLtaZXFhRSw

STATE LISTINGS Wisconsin ■ 46588

Description: Entrepreneurial community. Provides work space, coaching, and programming.

46579 ■ Wisonsin Innovation Kitchen (WINK)
851 Dodge St.
 Mineral Point, WI 53565
Ph: (608)987-3558
URL: http://wisconsininnovationkitchen.com
Facebook: www.facebook.com/WIInnovationKitchen
Instagram: www.instagram.com/wisconsininnova
 tionkitchen
Description: Community-based commercial food facility owned by Hodan Community Services, an organization supporting people with disabilities. Helps small businesses grow their enterprises. **Founded:** 2010.

46580 ■ Woodland Kitchen and Business Incubator
2740 W Mason St.
 Green Bay, WI 54303
Ph: (920)498-5444
URL: http://www.nwtc.edu/about-nwtc/nwtc-locations/
 aurora/shared-use-kitchens-in-northeast-wisconsin
Contact: H. Jeffrey Rafn, President
E-mail: jeff.rafn@nwtc.edu
Description: A shared-use kitchen incubator. Certified, fully-equipped commercial kitchen for use by growers, food processors, caterers, restaurants, chefs, special event food vendors, bakers, groups, organizations, and more.

LEGISLATIVE ASSISTANCE

46581 ■ Representative Jeff Mursau
PO Box 8953
 Madison, WI 53708
Ph: (608)266-3780
Free: 888-534-0036
Fax: (608)282-3636
Co. E-mail: rep.mursau@legis.wi.gov
URL: http://legis.wisconsin.gov/assembly/mursau/
 Pages/default.aspx
Contact: Jeff Mursau, Representative

CONSULTANTS

46582 ■ BizStarts
1555 N River Center Dr., Ste. 210
 Milwaukee, WI 53212
Ph: (414)973-2334
Co. E-mail: psnyder@bizstarts.com
URL: http://bizstarts.com
Contact: Dan Steininger, President
Facebook: www.facebook.com/bizstarts
X (Twitter): x.com/bizstarts

Description: One-stop resource center. Works with entrepreneurs to launch and grow their businesses. Offers one-on-one coaching and mentoring. **Founded:** 2008.

46583 ■ Lupke & Associates Inc. (L&A)
8709 Blue Heron Way
 Newton, WI 53063
Ph: (920)726-7844
Co. E-mail: info@lupkeassociates.com
URL: http://www.lupkeassociates.com
Contact: Diane Lupke, President
E-mail: rajeev@dyettandbhatia.com
Description: An economic development consultancy supporting startups and entrepreneurs who are innovative, creative, and agile. **Founded:** 1990.

46584 ■ Madison Entrepreneur Resource, Learning and Innovation Network (MERLIN) [MERLIN Mentors]
505 S Rosa Rd., Ste. 10A
 Madison, WI 53719
Ph: (608)441-8053
Co. E-mail: info@merlinmentors.org
URL: http://merlinmentors.org
Contact: Terry Sivesind, Executive Director
Facebook: www.facebook.com/merlinmentors
Linkedin: www.linkedin.com/company/merlin-mentors
Description: Madison-based volunteers who offer early-stage entrepreneurs information and guidance to launch, sustain, and grow their ventures. Established with the cooperation of the Wisconsin School of Business, the Wisconsin Alumni Research Foundation (WARF), and University Research Park at University of Wisconsin-Madison. . **Founded:** 2008.

46585 ■ Potawatomi Business Development Corporation (PBDC)
Potawatomi Business Development Corporation (PBDC)
 3215 W State St., Ste. 300
 Milwaukee, WI 53208
Ph: (414)290-9490
Fax: (414)345-9525
Co. E-mail: info@potawatomibdc.com
URL: http://www.potawatomibdc.com
Contact: Jeffery Johnson, Vice Chairman of the Board
Description: Seeks to promote business through economic and community development. Assists businesses in their expansion and financing needs. Enhances the quality of life and fosters the growth of good jobs within the community. **Scope:** The company is economic development and income diversification business entity of the Forest County Potawatomi Community. **Founded:** 1982. **Geographic Preference:** Local.

PUBLISHERS

46586 ■ Dearborn Real Estate Education
332 Front St., Ste. 500
 La Crosse, WI 54601
Free: 888-562-3129
Co. E-mail: salesops@dearborn.com
URL: http://www.dearborn.com
Contact: Chris Robinson, Director
E-mail: crobinson@dearborn.com
Facebook: www.facebook.com/DearbornRealEstateE
 ducation
X (Twitter): x.com/DearbornRE
YouTube: www.youtube.com/user/DearbornRealEs
 tate
Description: Publishes books for consumers and professionals on finance, business, real estate, and marketing sales. Accepts proposals for new books. Reaches market through commission representatives, direct mail, and telephone sales. Accepts unsolicited manuscripts. **Founded:** 1967. **Publications:** *Mutual Fund Encyclopedia* (Annual); *Hulbert Guide to Financial Newsletters*; *The 100 Best Technology Stocks for the Long Run*; *100 Best Stocks To Own in America*.

46587 ■ Guild Publishing
3118 International Ln.
 Madison, WI 53704
URL: http://www.artfulhome.com
Description: Publisher of artists source books and books on contemporary art for architects and interior designers. **Founded:** 1985.

VENTURE CAPITAL FIRM

46588 ■ Baird Capital
Robert W. Baird and Company Inc.
 777 E Wisconsin Ave.
 Milwaukee, WI 53202
Free: 800-792-2473
URL: http://www.rwbaird.com
Contact: Gordon G. Pan, President
E-mail: gpan@rwbaird.com
Facebook: www.facebook.com/RobertWBairdan
 dCompany
Linkedin: www.linkedin.com/company/robert-w-bair
 d-&-co
X (Twitter): x.com/rwbaird
Instagram: www.instagram.com/rwbaird
YouTube: www.youtube.com/user/RobertWBaird
Description: Offers venture capital, growth equity, and private equity investments in strategically targeted sectors. **Founded:** 1989. **Industry Preferences:** Healthcare; industrial solutions; technology.

Wyoming

ASSOCIATIONS AND OTHER ORGANIZATIONS

46589 ■ Business Network International Heartland--Nebraska, Wyoming, South Dakota, Western Iowa
3430 Toringdon Way
 Charlotte, NC 28277
Free: 855-264-2673
Co. E-mail: info@bniheartland.com
URL: http://bniheartland.com/en-US/index
Contact: Nellie Nutting, Managing Director
E-mail: nellienutting@bni.com
Description: Provides a structured environment for the development and exchange of quality business referrals. Offers members the opportunity to share ideas and contacts in Nebraska, Wyoming, South Dakota and Iowa. **Founded:** 1985. **Geographic Preference:** State.

SMALL BUSINESS DEVELOPMENT CENTERS

46590 ■ Wyoming Small Business Development Center - Lead Office (WSBDC)
1000 E University Ave., Dept. 3922
 Laramie, WY 82071
Ph: (307)766-3405
Fax: (307)766-3406
Co. E-mail: wsbdc@uwyo.edu
URL: http://www.wyomingsbdc.org
Contact: Jill Kline, Director
E-mail: jkline@uwyo.edu
Facebook: www.facebook.com/wyomingsbdc
X (Twitter): x.com/wysbdc
Instagram: www.instagram.com/wyomingsbdc
Description: Provides business support services to businesses in Wyoming. **Geographic Preference:** State.

46591 ■ Wyoming Small Business Development Center - Region 2
111 S Day St.
 Powell, WY 82435
Ph: (570)754-2139
URL: http://www.wyomingsbdc.org
Contact: Devan Costa-Cargill, Regional Director
E-mail: dcostaca@uwyo.edu
Description: Provides management assistance to current and prospective small business owners in Region 2. **Geographic Preference:** Local.

46592 ■ Wyoming Small Business Development Center - Region 4
c/o John Privette, Regional Director
LCCC Pathfinder Bldg., Rm. 406B
1400 E College Dr.
 Cheyenne, WY 82007
Ph: (307)772-7371
Co. E-mail: jprivett@uwyo.edu
URL: http://www.wyomingsbdc.org/contact
Contact: John Privette, Regional Director
E-mail: jprivett@uwyo.edu
Description: Represents and promotes the small business sector. Provides management assistance to current and prospective small business owners. Helps to improve management skills and expand the products and services of members. **Geographic Preference:** Local.

SMALL BUSINESS ASSISTANCE PROGRAMS

46593 ■ Wyoming Business Council (WBC)
214 W 15th St.
 Cheyenne, WY 82002
Ph: (307)777-2800
Co. E-mail: info.wbc@wyo.gov
URL: http://wyomingbusiness.org
Contact: Josh Dorrell, Chief Executive Officer
E-mail: josh.dorrell@wyo.gov
Facebook: www.facebook.com/WyoBizCouncil
X (Twitter): x.com/wyobizcouncil
Instagram: www.instagram.com/wyobizcouncil
YouTube: www.youtube.com/user/wyobizcouncil
Description: Works to attract new businesses; provides technical assistance. **Founded:** 1998.

SCORE OFFICES

46594 ■ Cheyenne SCORE
Cheyenne, WY
URL: http://www.score.org/wyoming
Description: Seeks to educate entrepreneurs and help small businesses start, grow and succeed nationwide. Organizes volunteers who are working or retired business owners, executives and corporate leaders who wish to share their wisdom and lessons learned in business. **Geographic Preference:** Local.

46595 ■ SCORE - Cheyenne
Cheyenne, WY
URL: http://coloradosprings.score.org/about-score -cheyenne
Description: Provides professional guidance and information to maximize the success of existing and emerging small businesses. Offers business counseling and workshops.

BETTER BUSINESS BUREAUS

46596 ■ Better Business Bureau Great West + Pacific [BBB Great West + Pacific]
PO Box 191279
 Boise, ID 83719
Ph: (208)342-4649
URL: http://www.bbb.org/local-bbb/bbb-great-west-pacific
Linkedin: www.linkedin.com/company/bbbgwp
Instagram: www.instagram.com/bbbgwp
YouTube: www.youtube.com/bbbgwp
Description: Seeks to promote and foster the highest ethical relationship between businesses and the public through voluntary self-regulation, consumer and business education, and service excellence. Provides information to help consumers and businesses make informed purchasing decisions and avoid costly scams and frauds; settles consumer complaints through arbitration and other means. **Geographic Preference:** State.

CHAMBERS OF COMMERCE

46597 ■ Buffalo, Wyoming Chamber of Commerce
55 N Main St.
 Buffalo, WY 82834
Ph: (307)684-5544
Free: 800-227-5122
Fax: (307)684-0291
Co. E-mail: info@buffalowyo.com
URL: http://www.buffalowyo.com
Facebook: www.facebook.com/buffalowyochamber
Linkedin: www.linkedin.com/company/buffalo -chamber-of-commerce
X (Twitter): x.com/BuffWyChamber
Description: Promotes business, economic and community development in Buffalo, WY. **Founded:** 1879. **Geographic Preference:** Local.

46598 ■ *Business Directory*
260 W Broadway
 Jackson, WY 83001
Ph: (307)733-3316
Co. E-mail: info@jacksonholechamber.com
URL: http://www.jacksonholechamber.com
Contact: Anna Olson, Co-Chief Executive Officer Co-President
E-mail: anna@jacksonholechamber.com
URL(s): www.jacksonholechamber.com/for-businesses/local-services/financial-services/accountants
Availability: Print.

46599 ■ Campbell County Chamber of Commerce
314 S Gillette Ave.
 Gillette, WY 82716
Ph: (307)682-3673
Co. E-mail: frontoffice@gillettechamber.com
URL: http://gillettechamber.com
Contact: Gail Lofing, Executive Director
E-mail: gaill@gillettechamber.com
Facebook: www.facebook.com/CCCCWyo
X (Twitter): x.com/CCCCWyo
YouTube: www.youtube.com/user/GilletteChamber
Description: Promotes business and community development in Campbell County, WY. **Founded:** 1970. **Publications:** *Business News, Business Agenda, Programs and Services* (Monthly). **Geographic Preference:** Local.

46600 ■ Casper Area Chamber of Commerce (CACC)
500 N Ctr. St.
 Casper, WY 82601
Ph: (307)234-5311
Co. E-mail: information@casperwyoming.org

URL: http://www.casperwyoming.org
Contact: Jason DeWitt, President
E-mail: jdewitt@casperwyoming.org
Facebook: www.facebook.com/casperareachamber
Linkedin: www.linkedin.com/in/casper-chamber-b5a 33484
X (Twitter): x.com/casperchamber
Description: Promotes economic prosperity and quality of life in Casper, WY area. **Founded:** 1903. **Publications:** *Chamber Progress* (Bimonthly). **Geographic Preference:** Local.

46601 ■ *Chamber of Commerce Newsletter*
1155 W Flaming Gorge Way
 Green River, WY 82935
Ph: (307)875-5711
Free: 800-flg-orge
Fax: (307)872-6192
Co. E-mail: office@grchamber.com
URL: http://www.grchamber.com
Contact: Ainhoa Ferrer, President
URL(s): www.grchamber.com/monthly-newsletter
Released: Monthly **Availability:** PDF.

46602 ■ Cody Country Chamber of Commerce
836 Sheridan Ave.
 Cody, WY 82414
Ph: (307)587-2777
Co. E-mail: info@codychamber.org
URL: http://www.codychamber.org
Contact: Greg Pendley, Contact
Facebook: www.facebook.com/CodyWYChamber
X (Twitter): x.com/CodyChamber
Instagram: www.instagram.com/codywychamber
Description: Promotes business and community development in Cody Country, WY. **Founded:** 1900. **Geographic Preference:** Local.

46603 ■ Dubois Chamber of Commerce
708 Meckem St.
 Dubois, WY 82513
Ph: (307)455-2556
Co. E-mail: duboischamber@gmail.com
URL: http://www.duboiswyomingchamber.org
Facebook: www.facebook.com/ DuboisWyChamberOfCommerce
Linkedin: www.linkedin.com/company/dubois -chamber-of-commerce-inc
Description: Promotes business and community development in Dubois, WY. Provides visitor information. Sponsors 4th of July festivities, Hometown Holidays, Cowboy Casino and 10,000 raffles. Assists local charities and organizations promote events. **Founded:** 1963. **Publications:** *Dubois Chamber News* (Weekly). **Geographic Preference:** Local.

46604 ■ Glenrock Chamber of Commerce
204 S 4th St.
 Glenrock, WY 82637
Ph: (307)436-5652
Co. E-mail: info@glenrockchamber.org
URL: http://glenrock.org/?SEC=448DA124-E44D-4A 46-A5DC-C135D9FBEE18
Contact: Kristy Grant, Contact
Description: Aims to promote, represent, and support businesses in the Glenrock area of Wyoming. **Geographic Preference:** Local.

46605 ■ Goshen County Chamber of Commerce
2042 Main St.
 Torrington, WY 82240
Ph: (307)532-3879
Co. E-mail: info@goshencountychamber.com
URL: http://www.goshencountychamber.com
Description: Promotes business and community development in Goshen County, WY. **Publications:** *Goshen Co. Chamber Action Update* (Monthly). **Geographic Preference:** Local.

46606 ■ Greater Cheyenne Chamber of Commerce
121 W 15th St., Ste. 204
 Cheyenne, WY 82001
Ph: (307)638-3388
Fax: (307)778-1407
Co. E-mail: bookkeeper@cheyennechamber.org
URL: http://www.cheyennechamber.org
Contact: Dale G. Steenbergen, President
E-mail: dales@cheyennechamber.org
YouTube: www.youtube.com/channel/UCMZPj 4mmriaUahc9x77LThw
Description: Promotes business and community development in the Cheyenne, WY area. **Founded:** 1907. **Publications:** *Cheyenne Business Weekly* (Monthly). **Geographic Preference:** Local.

46607 ■ Green River Chamber of Commerce
1155 W Flaming Gorge Way
 Green River, WY 82935
Ph: (307)875-5711
Free: 800-flg-orge
Fax: (307)872-6192
Co. E-mail: office@grchamber.com
URL: http://www.grchamber.com
Contact: Ainhoa Ferrer, President
Facebook: www.facebook.com/GreenRiverChamber
Description: Promotes business and community development and tourism in the Green River, WY area. **Founded:** 1921. **Publications:** *Chamber of Commerce Newsletter* (Monthly). **Geographic Preference:** Local.

46608 ■ Greybull Area Chamber of Commerce
521 Greybull Ave.
 Greybull, WY 82426
Ph: (307)765-2100
Co. E-mail: greybullecondev@wyonet.net
URL: http://greybull.com
Description: Promotes business and community development in the Greybull, WY area. **Geographic Preference:** Local.

46609 ■ Jackson Hole Chamber of Commerce
260 W Broadway
 Jackson, WY 83001
Ph: (307)733-3316
Co. E-mail: info@jacksonholechamber.com
URL: http://www.jacksonholechamber.com
Contact: Anna Olson, Co-Chief Executive Officer Co-President
E-mail: anna@jacksonholechamber.com
Facebook: www.facebook.com/JHChamber
X (Twitter): x.com/jhchamber
Instagram: www.instagram.com/jhchamber
Description: Promotes business and community development in Jackson Hole, WY. Bestows scholarships. Sponsors Fall Arts Festival and Old West Days. **Founded:** 1946. **Publications:** *Business Directory*; *Chamber News* (8/year). **Geographic Preference:** Local.

46610 ■ Lander Chamber of Commerce
100 N 1st St.
 Lander, WY 82520
Ph: (307)332-3892
Co. E-mail: info@landerchamber.org
URL: http://landerchamber.org
Contact: Owen Sweeney, Executive Director
Description: Promotes economic development and tourism in the Wind River Country of Wyoming. **Publications:** *Chamber News.* **Educational Activities:** Business After Hours. **Awards:** Lander Area Chamber of Commerce Community Awards (Annual). **Geographic Preference:** Local.

46611 ■ *Member Services Directory*
401 N 10th St.
 Worland, WY 82401
Ph: (307)347-3226
Co. E-mail: wtschamber@rtconnect.net
URL: http://wtschamber.org
Contact: Steve Radabaugh, President
URL(s): www.wtschamber.org/directory
Availability: Print; Online.

46612 ■ Newcastle Area Chamber of Commerce
1323 Washington Blvd.
 Newcastle, WY 82701
Ph: (307)746-2739
URL: http://www.newcastlewyo.com
Facebook: www.facebook.com/Newcas tleAreaChamberofCommerce
Description: Seeks to be a collective voice representing the business interests of Northeastern Wyoming, the Western gateway to the Black Hills. **Founded:** 1889. **Geographic Preference:** Local.

46613 ■ Niobrara Chamber of Commerce
302 S Main, Unit 9
 Lusk, WY 82225
Ph: (307)334-3612
Co. E-mail: luskchamberofcommerce@yahoo.com
URL: http://www.luskwyoming.com/chamber.html
Description: Promotes business and community development in Lusk, WY. **Geographic Preference:** Local.

46614 ■ Platte County Chamber of Commerce (PCCC)
65 16th St.
 Wheatland, WY 82201
Ph: (307)322-2322
Co. E-mail: info@plattechamber.com
URL: http://plattechamber.com
Contact: Shawna L. Reichert, Executive Director
E-mail: director@plattechamber.com
Description: Promotes business and community development in Platte County, WY. Sponsors annual Bike Race, Community Fest, agricultural appreciation banquet, pancake breakfast, and Chugwater Chili Cook-off. **Founded:** 1968. **Geographic Preference:** Local.

46615 ■ Powell Chamber of Commerce (PVCC)
111 S Day St.
 Powell, WY 82435
Ph: (307)754-3494
Co. E-mail: info@powellchamber.org
URL: http://powellchamber.org
Contact: Rebekah Burns, Executive Director
E-mail: rebekah.burns@powellchamber.org
Facebook: www.facebook.com/PowellVisitorCenter
Linkedin: www.linkedin.com/company/powell-visitor -center
X (Twitter): x.com/powellvchamber
Instagram: www.instagram.com/powellvisitorcenter
Description: Promotes the local businesses of Powell, Wyoming. **Founded:** 1909. **Geographic Preference:** Local.

46616 ■ Rawlins-Carbon County Chamber of Commerce
116 4th St., Ste., 2C
 Rawlins, WY 82301
Ph: (307)371-0053
Co. E-mail: rawlinschamber@gmail.com
URL: http://rawlinschamber.org
Contact: Ryane Metevier, Director
Facebook: www.facebook.com/ RawlinsChamberofCommerce
Description: Promotes business and community development in Carbon County, WY. Sponsors annual Carbon County Business Expo and performing arts events. **Founded:** 1949. **Geographic Preference:** Local.

46617 ■ Riverton Chamber of Commerce (RCC)
111 N 1st St.
 Riverton, WY 82501
Ph: (307)856-4801
Fax: (307)857-0873
Co. E-mail: director@rivertonchamber.org
URL: http://www.rivertonchamber.org
Contact: Kimberly Hummel, Vice President
Facebook: www.facebook.com/river tonchamberofcommerce
YouTube: www.youtube.com/channel/ UCRmvaRfPL0lJlwb_A0sU_oQ
Description: Promotes business and community development in the Riverton, WY area. **Founded:** 1906. **Publications:** *The Grand Solution* (Monthly). **Geographic Preference:** Local.

46618 ■ Rock Springs Chamber of Commerce (RSCC)
1897 Dewar Dr.
Rock Springs, WY 82901
Ph: (307)362-3771
Fax: (307)362-3771
URL: http://rockspringschamber.com
Contact: Rick Lee, Chief Executive Officer
E-mail: ceo@rockspringschamber.com
Facebook: www.facebook.com/RockSpringsChamber
Instagram: www.instagram.com/rockspringschamber
Description: Promotes business and community development in Rock Springs, WY. **Founded:** 1938. **Geographic Preference:** Local.

46619 ■ Saratoga/Platte Valley Chamber of Commerce (SPVCC)
210 W Elm St.
Saratoga, WY 82331
Ph: (307)326-8855
Co. E-mail: info@saratogachamber.info
URL: http://www.saratogachamber.info
Contact: Scott McIlvaine, Chairman
Facebook: www.facebook.com/SaratogaPlatteValleyChamber
X (Twitter): x.com/SaratogaWY
YouTube: www.youtube.com/channel/UC7ZulPHFdT6rnF19aR63U9w
Description: Promotes business and community development and tourism in the upper Platte River area of Wyoming. Sponsors ice fishing derby; conducts competitions. **Geographic Preference:** Local.

46620 ■ Sheridan County Chamber of Commerce
54 S Main St.
Sheridan, WY 82801
Ph: (307)672-2485
Fax: (307)672-7321
Co. E-mail: info@sheridanwyomingchamber.org
URL: http://www.sheridanwyomingchamber.org
Contact: Dixie Johnson, Chief Executive Officer
Facebook: www.facebook.com/Sheridan-County-Chamber-of-Commerce-209293219089175
Linkedin: www.linkedin.com/company/sheridan-county-chamber-of-commerce
X (Twitter): x.com/SheridanCoChamb
Instagram: www.instagram.com/sheridanchamber
Description: Promotes business and community development in Sheridan County, WY. **Founded:** 1913. **Geographic Preference:** Local.

46621 ■ Star Valley Chamber of Commerce (SVCCOM)
360 Washington St.
Afton, WY 83110
Ph: (307)885-2759
Co. E-mail: info@starvalleychamber.com
URL: http://starvalleychamber.com
Contact: Sarah Hale, Director
Description: Promotes business and community development in the Star Valley, WY area. **Founded:** 1988. **Geographic Preference:** Local.

46622 ■ Sublette County Chamber of Commerce (SCCC)
19 E Pine St.
Pinedale, WY 82941
Ph: (307)367-2242
Free: 888-285-7282
URL: http://www.sublettechamber.com
Contact: Peter Scherbel, Co-President
Facebook: www.facebook.com/sublettechamber
Instagram: www.instagram.com/sublettechamberwy
Description: Promotes business and community development in the Pinedale, WY area. **Founded:** 1960. **Geographic Preference:** Local.

46623 ■ Sundance Area Chamber of Commerce (SACC)
PO Box 1004
Sundance, WY 82729
Ph: (307)283-1000
Co. E-mail: chamber@sundancewyoming.com
URL: http://www.sundancewyoming.com
Contact: Andy Miller, Treasurer
E-mail: amiller@sundancestate.bank
Facebook: www.facebook.com/SundanceWYChamber
Description: Promotes business and community development in the Sundance, WY area. Conducts annual appreciation barbecue. **Founded:** 1929. **Geographic Preference:** Local.

46624 ■ Thermopolis - Hot Springs Chamber of Commerce
220 Pk. St.
Thermopolis, WY 82443
Ph: (307)864-3192
Free: 877-864-3192
Fax: (307)864-3193
Co. E-mail: info@thermopolischamber.org
URL: http://thermopolischamber.org
Contact: Howie Samelson, President
Facebook: www.facebook.com/thermopolischamber.org
X (Twitter): x.com/ThermopolisCofC
Description: Promotes business and community development in the Thermopolis, WY area. Seeks to attract tourists. Sponsors Fishing Has No Boundaries festival for the handicapped. Conducts the annual Gift of the Water Pageant, commemorating treaty with the Indians. **Founded:** 1919. **Publications:** *Hot Spot* (Bimonthly). **Geographic Preference:** Local.

46625 ■ Worland-Ten Sleep Chamber of Commerce
401 N 10th St.
Worland, WY 82401
Ph: (307)347-3226
Co. E-mail: wtschamber@rtconnect.net
URL: http://wtschamber.org
Contact: Steve Radabaugh, President
Facebook: www.facebook.com/WTSChamber
Description: Promotes business and community development in the Worland, WY area. **Founded:** 1947. **Publications:** *Member Services Directory*; *Worland Business Advocate* (Monthly). **Geographic Preference:** Local.

PROCUREMENT ASSISTANCE PROGRAMS

46626 ■ Wyoming Department of Administration and Information - Procurement Section
200 W 24th St.
Cheyenne, WY 82002
URL: http://ai.wyo.gov

INCUBATORS/RESEARCH AND TECHNOLOGY PARKS

46627 ■ IMPACT 307 (WTBC)
1938 Harney St.
Laramie, WY 82072
Ph: (307)766-6395
Co. E-mail: laramie@uwyo.edu
URL: http://impact307.org
Contact: Fred Schmechel, Director (Acting)
E-mail: fschmech@uwyo.edu
Facebook: www.facebook.com/IMPACT307WY
Linkedin: www.linkedin.com/company/impact307
X (Twitter): x.com/Impact307
Instagram: www.instagram.com/impact.307
Description: Incubator program that is focused on educating and developing business startups throughout Wyoming. Offers a variety of laboratory, office, and shared conference room space for client companies. **Founded:** 2006.

Guam

SMALL BUSINESS DEVELOPMENT CENTERS

46628 ■ Guam Small Business Development Center
NO. 148 Jesus & Eugenia Leon Guerrero Business & Public Administration Bldg.
Mangilao, GU 96923
Ph: (671)735-2590
Fax: (671)734-2002
Co. E-mail: sbdc@pacificsbdc.com
URL: http://www.pacificsbdc.com/locations/guam-sbdc
Contact: Fred Granillo, Director
Description: Offers management assistance to current and prospective small business owners in Guam.
Geographic Preference: State.

46629 ■ Pacific Islands Small Business Development Center Network (PISBDCN)
148 Jesus & Eugenia Leon Guerrero Business & Public Administration Bldg.
Mangilao, GU 96923
Ph: (671)735-2590
Fax: (671)734-2002
Co. E-mail: sbdc@pacificsbdc.com
URL: http://www.pacificsbdc.com
Contact: Fred Granillo, Director
E-mail: fred@pacificsbdc.com
Facebook: www.facebook.com/pacificsbdc
Instagram: www.instagram.com/pisbdcn
YouTube: www.youtube.com/channel/UCFCVvYe-rUoRHEe51cMV7Aw/videos
Description: Works to support the growth and economic development of the U.S.-affiliated Pacific Islands in the Western Pacific region by providing high quality, confidential counseling and training to existing and prospective small businesses. **Founded:** 1995. **Geographic Preference:** Regional.

CHAMBERS OF COMMERCE

46630 ■ Guam Chamber of Commerce (GCC)
372 W Soledad Ave.
Hagatna, GU 96910
Ph: (671)472-6311
Co. E-mail: info@guamchamber.com.gu
URL: http://www.guamchamber.com.gu
Contact: Catherine S. Castro, President
Facebook: www.facebook.com/Guamchamber
Linkedin: www.linkedin.com/company/guam-chamber-of-commerce
X (Twitter): x.com/GUChamber
Description: Promotes increased international trade and tourism. Gathers and disseminates information; conducts promotional activities; represents members' interests. **Founded:** 1924. **Publications:** *Guam Chamber of Commerce--Member Directory*; *The President's Report* (Monthly); *Small Business Focus* (Quarterly). **Educational Activities:** Guam Chamber of Commerce Meeting (Monthly). **Awards:** Dave J. Santos Scholarships (Annual). **Geographic Preference:** National; Local.

Puerto Rico

SMALL BUSINESS DEVELOPMENT CENTERS

46631 ■ **Puerto Rico Small Business and Technology Development Center (PR SBDTC)**
268 Ponce de Leon Ave.
　The Hato Rey Ctr., Ste. 1400
　San Juan, PR 00918
Ph: (787)763-6811
Fax: (787)625-6875
Co. E-mail: lead@prsbtdc.org
URL: http://prsbtdc.org
Contact: Ricardo Martinez, Executive Director
E-mail: rmartinez@prsbdc.org
Facebook: www.facebook.com/prsbtdc
Linkedin: www.linkedin.com/company/prsbtdc
X (Twitter): x.com/prsbtdc
Instagram: www.instagram.com/prsbtdc
Description: Provides advisory services and high quality training entrepreneurs from all sectors. **Founded:** 1997. **Geographic Preference:** State.

46632 ■ **Puerto Rico Small Business and Technology Development Centers Arecibo**
Carr, Ste. 2 Km 80. 4, Bo. San Daniel, Sector Las Canelas
　Arecibo, PR 00614
Ph: (787)878-5269
Co. E-mail: arecibo@prsbtdc.org
URL: http://prsbtdc.org
Contact: Aida Martínez, Regional Director
Description: Represents and promotes the small business sector. Provides management assistance to current and prospective small business owners. Helps to improve management skills and expand the products and services of members. **Geographic Preference:** Local.

46633 ■ **Puerto Rico Small Business and Technology Development Centers Caguas**
Munoz Rivera St., Ruiz Belvis Corner, La Democracia Bldg.
　Caguas, PR 00726
Ph: (787)744-8833
Co. E-mail: caguas@prsbtdc.org
URL: http://prsbtdc.org
Contact: Edwin Torres, Regional Director
Description: Represents and promotes the small business sector. Provides management assistance to current and prospective small business owners. Helps to improve management skills and expand the products and services of members. **Geographic Preference:** Local.

46634 ■ **Puerto Rico Small Business and Technology Development Centers Fajardo**
Batey Central Pk., Union St., No. 195
　Fajardo, PR 00738
Ph: (787)863-2390
Co. E-mail: fajardo@prsbtdc.org
URL: http://prsbtdc.org/index.php/contactos
Contact: Sonia Maldonado, Regional Director
Description: Represents and promotes the small business sector. Provides management assistance to current and prospective small business owners. Helps to improve management skills and expand the products and services of members. **Geographic Preference:** Local.

46635 ■ **Puerto Rico Small Business and Technology Development Centers Ponce**
c/o Inter-American University
　104 Turpeaux Industrial Pk.
　Mercedita, PR 00715
Ph: (787)284-1912
Co. E-mail: ponce@prsbtdc.org
URL: http://prsbtdc.org
Contact: Néstor J. Torres, Regional Director
E-mail: ponce@prsbtdc.org
X (Twitter): x.com/prsbtdc
Description: Represents and promotes the small business sector. Provides management assistance to current and prospective small business owners. Helps to improve management skills and expand the products and services of members. **Geographic Preference:** Local.

SCORE OFFICES

46636 ■ **SCORE - Mayaguez**
127 E DeDeigo St.
　Mayaguez, PR 00680
URL: http://www.score.org/houston/content/angel-curet-en-espanol
Description: Provides professional guidance and information to maximize the success of existing and emerging small businesses. Offers business counseling and workshops.

46637 ■ **SCORE - San Juan Metro**
273 Avenida Juan Ponce de Leon, No. 510
　San Juan, PR 00917
Ph: (787)338-0355
Fax: (787)766-5309
URL: http://sanjuanmetro.score.org
Contact: Rieva Lesonsky, Chief Executive Officer
Facebook: www.facebook.com/SCORESanJuanMetro
Linkedin: www.linkedin.com/company/score-mentors-san-juan-metro
X (Twitter): twitter.com/SCORE_SanJuan
Description: Provides professional guidance and information to maximize the success of existing and emerging small businesses. Offers business counseling and workshops.

CHAMBERS OF COMMERCE

46638 ■ **Cámara De Comercio De Puerto Rico [Puerto Rico Chamber of Commerce (PRCC)]**
954 Ave. Ponce de León, Ste. 406
　San Juan, PR 00907
Ph: (787)721-6060
Fax: (787)723-1891
Co. E-mail: camarapr@camarapr.net
URL: http://camarapr.org
Contact: Luis A. Gierbolini-Rodríguez, Chairman of the Board
Linkedin: www.linkedin.com/in/camaradecomerciopr
X (Twitter): x.com/Camarapr
Description: Promotes business and community development in Puerto Rico. Sponsors trade fairs, exhibitions, seminars, and commercial missions. Conducts lobbying. **Founded:** 1913. **Publications:** *Camara En Accion*; *Comercio y Produccion* (Bi-monthly); *Maritime Register* (Monthly). **Geographic Preference:** Local.

46639 ■ *Camara En Accion*
954 Ave. Ponce de León, Ste. 406
　San Juan, PR 00907
Ph: (787)721-6060
Fax: (787)723-1891
Co. E-mail: camarapr@camarapr.net
URL: http://camarapr.org
Contact: Luis A. Gierbolini-Rodríguez, Chairman of the Board
URL(s): camarapr.org/chamber-in-action
Availability: PDF.

46640 ■ *Maritime Register*
954 Ave. Ponce de León, Ste. 406
　San Juan, PR 00907
Ph: (787)721-6060
Fax: (787)723-1891
Co. E-mail: camarapr@camarapr.net
URL: http://camarapr.org
Contact: Luis A. Gierbolini-Rodríguez, Chairman of the Board
URL(s): camarapr.org/q-a
Released: Monthly **Availability:** Print.

MINORITY BUSINESS ASSISTANCE PROGRAMS

46641 ■ **Puerto Rico Minority Supplier Development Council (PRMSDC)**
VIG Twr., Ste. 150
　1225 Ponce de Leon Ave.
　Santurce, PR 00907-3921
Ph: (787)627-7272
URL: http://prmsdc.org
Contact: Francisco S. Cabrera, President
E-mail: fcabrera@prmsdc.org
Description: Provides a direct link between corporate America and minority-owned businesses. Increases procurement and business opportunities for minority businesses of all sizes. **Founded:** 1982. **Geographic Preference:** State.

FINANCING AND LOAN PROGRAMS

46642 ■ **Advent-Morro Equity Partners**
206 Tetuan St., Ste. 903
　San Juan, PR 00902

Ph: (787)725-5285
URL: http://www.adventmorro.com
Contact: Cyril Meduna, President
E-mail: cmeduna@adventmorro.com

Description: Provider of investment services. **Founded:** 1989. **Preferred Investment Size:** $2,500,000 to $7,500,000. **Industry Preferences:** Communications, computer hardware and software, Internet specific, medical and health, consumer related, financial services, business service, and manufacturing.

PROCUREMENT ASSISTANCE PROGRAMS

46643 ■ Puerto Rico Procurement Technical Assistance Center (FeCC) [Puerto Rico Federal Contracting Center]
PO Box 362350
San Juan, PR 00936-2350
Ph: (787)758-4747
URL: http://www.aptac-us.org/find-a-ptac/?state=PR
Contact: Pedro Acevedo, Program Manager
E-mail: pedro.acevedo@ddec.pr.gov

Founded: 1986.

INCUBATORS/RESEARCH AND TECHNOLOGY PARKS

46644 ■ Parallel 18
1250 Avenida Juan Ponce de Leon
San Juan, PR 00907
Ph: (787)705-9786
Co. E-mail: info@parallel18.com
URL: http://parallel18.com
Contact: Hector Jirau, Executive Director
Facebook: www.facebook.com/p18startups
Linkedin: www.linkedin.com/company/parallel18
X (Twitter): x.com/p18startups
Instagram: www.instagram.com/p18startups

Description: Accelerator who supports startup innovators from around the globe to help them scale from Puerto Rico to global communities beyond the Island. **Founded:** 2015.

Virgin Islands

SMALL BUSINESS DEVELOPMENT CENTERS

46645 ■ **Virgin Islands Small Business Development Center (VI SBDC)**
8666 Lindbergh Bay
 Saint Thomas, VI 00802
Ph: (340)693-1694
Co. E-mail: info@visbdc.org
URL: http://visbdc.org
Contact: Karen Jones, Director
Facebook: www.facebook.com/visbdc
X (Twitter): x.com/visbdc
YouTube: www.youtube.com/channel/UCqhMliF0gD6PAFaakxK00tA
Description: Promotes a more efficient and effective small business sector. Provides assistance to the management of existing and emerging small businesses. **Founded:** 1985. **Geographic Preference:** State.

46646 ■ **The Virgin Islands Small Business Development Center St. Croix**
6300 Estate Peter's Rest, Ste. 4
 Christiansted, VI 00820
Ph: (340)692-4294
Co. E-mail: info@visbdc.org
URL: http://visbdc.org
Contact: Ted J. Gutierrez, Director
E-mail: director@visbdc.org
Facebook: www.facebook.com/visbdc
X (Twitter): x.com/visbdc
YouTube: www.youtube.com/channel/UCqhMliF0gD6PAFaakxK00tA
Description: Provides management assistance to current and prospective small business owners in St. Croix. **Geographic Preference:** Local.

46647 ■ **The Virgin Islands Small Business Development Center St. Thomas/St. John**
8666 Lindberg Bay
 Saint Thomas, VI 00802
Ph: (340)693-1694
Co. E-mail: info@visbdc.org
URL: http://visbdc.org
Facebook: www.facebook.com/visbdc
X (Twitter): x.com/visbdc
YouTube: www.youtube.com/channel/UCqhMliF0gD6PAFaakxK00tA
Description: Provides management assistance to current and prospective small business owners in St. Thomas/St. John. **Geographic Preference:** Local.

SCORE OFFICES

46648 ■ **SCORE - U.S. Virgin Islands**
299 E Broward Blvd., No:123
 Fort Lauderdale, FL 33301
URL: http://www.score.org/broward
Description: Provides professional guidance and information to maximize the success of existing and emerging small businesses. Offers business counseling and workshops.

46649 ■ **U.S. Virgin Islands SCORE**
8666 Lindberg Bay
 Saint Thomas, VI 00802
URL: http://www.score.org/broward/about-score-us-virgin-islands
Description: Unites active and retired business management professionals with men and women who are considering starting a small business, encountering problems with their business, or expanding their business.

CHAMBERS OF COMMERCE

46650 ■ **St. Thomas - St. John Chamber of Commerce (STSJCC)**
6-7 Dronningens Gade
 Saint Thomas, VI 00802
Ph: (340)776-0100
Fax: (340)776-0588
Co. E-mail: chamber.vi@gmail.com
URL: http://www.sttstjchamber.com
Contact: John P. Woods, President
Facebook: www.facebook.com/ChamberVI
Description: Promotes business and community development in the St. Thomas and St. John, VI area. **Geographic Preference:** Local.

LEGISLATIVE ASSISTANCE

46651 ■ **Legislature of the Virgin Islands - Virgin Islands Senate Standing Committee on Economic Development, Agriculture & Planning**
516 Strand St. Complex
 Saint Croix
 Frederiksted, VI 00840
Ph: (340)773-2424
URL: http://legvi.org

REFERENCE WORKS

46652 ■ **"7 Proven Tips for Young Entrepreneurs to Start Off Strong" in business.com (Nov. 15, 2017)**
URL(s): www.business.com/articles/7-tips-for-young-entrepreneurs/
Ed: Nathan Resnick. **Released:** November 15, 2017.
Description: Details seven proven methods that will get young entrepreneurs started on the right path. **Availability:** Online.

Alberta

ASSOCIATIONS AND OTHER ORGANIZATIONS

46653 ■ Association of Fundraising Professionals - Edmonton and Area Chapter
PO Box 4355
Spruce Grove, AB, Canada T7X 3B5
Ph: (780)224-4024
Co. E-mail: info@afpedmonton.ca
URL: http://www.afpedmonton.ca
Contact: Kelly Hoskins, President
E-mail: president@afpedmonton.ca
Facebook: www.facebook.com/AFPEdmonton
X (Twitter): x.com/AFPEdmonton
Instagram: www.instagram.com/afpedmonton
Description: Advances philanthropy through advocacy, research, education and certification programs within the Edmonton area and beyond. Organizes workshops and keynote presentations. Fosters high ethical standards and principles for its members. Represents the interests of the profession locally, provincially and nationally. **Founded:** 1996. **Geographic Preference:** Local.

46654 ■ International Association of Business Communicators Calgary (IABC) [IABC/Calgary]
PO Box 2178, Sta. M
Calgary, AB, Canada T2P 2M4
Linkedin: www.linkedin.com/company/iabcyyc
Description: Represents communication managers, public relations directors, writers, editors, audiovisual specialists, and other individuals in the public relations and organizational communication field in Calgary. **Founded:** 1967. **Publications:** eNetwork (Monthly). **Geographic Preference:** Local.

46655 ■ Venture Capital Association of Alberta (VCAA)
c/o Aviro Capital
400 Crowfoot CR. NW, Ste. 502
Calgary, AB, Canada T3G 5H6
Co. E-mail: hello@vcaa.ca
URL: http://www.vcaa.ca
Contact: Omi Velasco, Executive Director
Linkedin: www.linkedin.com/company/venture-capital-association-of-alberta
Description: Trade association for venture capital, private equity, angel investors and others interested in furthering the industry in Alberta. Seeks to generate opportunities, events, and programs for members.

SMALL BUSINESS DEVELOPMENT CENTERS

46656 ■ Rural Alberta Business Centres (RABC)
4909B-48 St.
Camrose, AB, Canada T4V 1L7
Ph: (780)673-9213
Co. E-mail: camrosenow@camrosebooster.net
URL: http://www.camrosenow.online/2216/feature/rural-alberta-business-centre
Description: Provides small businesses and entrepreneurs with one stop access to information, advice, research services, seminars, and workshops at four walk-in locations across Alberta.

SMALL BUSINESS ASSISTANCE PROGRAMS

46657 ■ Alberta Small Business Resources
Park Plaza ste. 700, 10611 -98th Ave.
Edmonton, AB, Canada T5K 2P7
Ph: (780)422-7722
Free: 800-272-9675
URL: http://www.alberta.ca/small-business-resources
Description: A growing network of business owners, managers and self-employed people connecting together through membership to acquire business products, services and contacts most often afforded only to larger companies. Provides group health benefits, business coaching, professional development, marketing support and peer networking. **Scope:** Firm provides group health benefits, business coaching, professional development, marketing support and peer networking services. **Founded:** 1997.

46658 ■ Community Futures Tawatinaw
10611 - 100 Ave.
Westlock, AB, Canada T7P 2J4
Ph: (780)349-2903
Free: 888-349-2903
URL: http://tawatinaw.albertacf.com
Contact: Blair Kneller, Chairman of the Board
Facebook: www.facebook.com/CommunityFuturesTawatinaw
X (Twitter): x.com/CFTawatinaw
Description: Offers business management tools for entrepreneurs wanting to start, expand, franchise, or sell a business. Also offers other specialized business programs and events. Fosters rural economic growth. **Founded:** 1986.

BETTER BUSINESS BUREAUS

46659 ■ Better Business Bureau Central and Northern Alberta
16102 100 Ave. NW
Edmonton, AB, Canada T5P 0L3
Ph: (780)482-2341
Free: 800-232-7298
Fax: (780)482-1150
Co. E-mail: info@edmonton.bbb.org
URL: http://www.bbb.org/ca/ab/edmonton
Contact: Colin Kuefler, Chairman of the Board
Description: Non profit organization working towards educating people in Southern Alberta and East Kootenay.

46660 ■ Better Business Bureau Serving Southern Alberta & East Kootenay (BBB)
No. 5, 1709 8 Ave. NE.
Calgary, AB, Canada T2E 0S9
Ph: (403)531-8784
Fax: (403)640-2514
URL: http://www.bbb.org/local-bbb/bbb-serving-southern-alberta-and-east-kootenay
Linkedin: www.linkedin.com/company/bbb-serving-southern-alberta-and-east-kootenays
Description: Non profit organization working towards educating people in Southern Alberta and East Kootenay. **Founded:** 1954.

MINORITY BUSINESS ASSISTANCE PROGRAMS

46661 ■ Alberta Womens Entrepreneurs (AWE)
Platform Innovation Ctr.
407 - 9 Ave. SE
Calgary, AB, Canada T2G 2K7
Free: 800-713-3558
Co. E-mail: info@awebusiness.com
URL: http://www.awebusiness.com
Contact: Marcela Mandeville, Chief Executive Officer
Facebook: www.facebook.com/awebusiness
X (Twitter): x.com/awebusiness
Instagram: www.instagram.com/awebusiness
Description: Supports women in business through business advising, business skills development, financing, and networking opportunities. **Founded:** 1995.

FINANCING AND LOAN PROGRAMS

46662 ■ 32 Degrees Capital
Ste., 650, 635 8th Ave SW
Calgary, AB, Canada T2P 3M3
Ph: (403)695-1069
Fax: (403)695-1069
Co. E-mail: info@32degrees.ca
URL: http://www.32degrees.ca
Contact: Larry G. Evans, Managing Partner Co-Founder
Description: Oil- and gas-based private equity firm. **Founded:** 2004. **Investment Policies:** Management teams with a repeatable track record of shareholder value; market-driven business strategies; capital opportunities; scalable resources.

46663 ■ Valhalla Private Capital Inc.
150 9 Ave. SW, Ste. 2030
Calgary, AB, Canada T2P 3H9
Free: 888-406-9005
URL: http://www.valhallaprivatecap.com
Contact: Teruel Carrasco, President
Facebook: www.facebook.com/valhallaprivatecapital
Description: Offers investor and startup programs, angel investing, private equity and debt funds, and M&A advisory services.

INCUBATORS/RESEARCH AND TECHNOLOGY PARKS

46664 ■ Agrivalue Processing Business Incubator (APBI)
4301 65 Ave.
Leduc, AB, Canada T9E 8T2
Ph: (780)980-4244
Fax: (780)980-4250
URL: http://www.alberta.ca/agrivalue-processing-business-incubator
Contact: Ken Gossen, Executive Director
E-mail: ken.gossen@gov.ab.ca
Description: A multi-tenant facility providing the infrastructure and services to support and enhance the establishment and growth of new companies and new business ventures in Alberta. **Founded:** 2007.

46665 ■ The Collective 12 | 12
1212 9th Ave. SE, 2nd Fl.
Calgary, AB, Canada T2G 0T1
Free: 844-344-2174
Co. E-mail: community@thecollective1212.space
URL: http://www.thecollective1212.space
X (Twitter): x.com/Collective12
Instagram: www.instagram.com/thecollective1212
Description: A coworking space that combines the passion and support of a community of entrepreneurs to accelerate their ideas.

46666 ■ Community Futures Wood Buffalo (CFWB)
9912 Franklin Ave., Ste. 105
Fort McMurray, AB, Canada T9H 2K5
Ph: (780)791-0330
Fax: (780)791-0086
Co. E-mail: cfwbadmin@albertacf.com
URL: http://woodbuffalo.albertacf.com
Contact: Bill MacLennan, Treasurer
Description: Helps small startups and entrepreneurs turn business ideas into reality. Specialists help connect you with skills, financing, and resources needed to succeed. **Founded:** 1988.

46667 ■ Creative Destruction Lab (CDL)
Haskayne School of Business, University of Calgary, 2500 University Dr. NW
Calgary, AB, Canada T2N 1N4
Co. E-mail: cdl-rockies@creativedestructionlab.com
URL: http://creativedestructionlab.com
Contact: Natasha Spokes, Director
Linkedin: www.linkedin.com/school/creative-destruction-lab
X (Twitter): x.com/creativedlab
Description: A seed-stage program that focuses on the transition phase from pre-seed to seed-stage funding. Helps innovators transition from science projects to high-growth companies.

46668 ■ Deltatee Enterprises Ltd.
202 - 1439 17th Ave. SE
Calgary, AB, Canada T2G 1J9
Ph: (403)250-3533
Co. E-mail: questions@deltatee.com
URL: http://www.deltatee.com
Contact: Sean Rooke, President
E-mail: seanr@deltatee.com
Description: Provider of business acceleration services. Works closely with our clients to design products most in tune with market demand, ensure timely technical development, devise strategic business plans and, in the end, accelerate revenue generation. **Founded:** 1978.

46669 ■ Economic Development Lethbridge (EDL)
3582 30th St. N
Lethbridge, AB, Canada T1H 6Z4
Ph: (403)331-0022
Free: 800-332-1801
Fax: (403)331-0202
Co. E-mail: info@chooselethbridge.ca
URL: http://www.chooselethbridge.ca
Contact: Trevor Lewington, Chief Executive Officer
E-mail: trevor@chooselethbridge.ca
Description: Supports startups and entrepreneurs by offering a low-cost operating environment with demonstrated savings in areas such as taxation, land, construction and transportation.

46670 ■ Edmonton Unlimited (EU)
10107 Jasper Ave.
Edmonton, AB, Canada T5J 1W8
Co. E-mail: info@edmontonunlimited.com
URL: http://edmontonunlimited.com
Contact: Catherine Warren, Chief Executive Officer
Facebook: www.facebook.com/edmontonunlimited
Linkedin: www.linkedin.com/company/edmonton-unlimited
X (Twitter): x.com/edmontonunltd
Instagram: www.instagram.com/edmontonunlimited
Description: An entrepreneurial community hub that connects entrepreneurs and product builders with skills, community and workspace. **Founded:** 2009.

46671 ■ Explore Edmonton
3rd Fl., World Trade Ctr. 9990 Jasper Ave.
Edmonton, AB, Canada T5J 1P7
Ph: (780)401-7696
Co. E-mail: info@exploreedmonton.com
URL: http://exploreedmonton.com
Contact: Karen Oshry, Chairman of the Board
Facebook: www.facebook.com/ExploreEdmontonCorporation
X (Twitter): x.com/ExploreEdmCo
YouTube: www.youtube.com/user/exploreedmonton
Description: Supports startups and entrepreneurs in the promotion of economic growth in the region. Provides access to investors, other entrepreneurs, and business resources.

46672 ■ Foothills Business Incubator
14 McRae St., 2nd Fl.
Okotoks, AB, Canada T1S 1B5
Co. E-mail: info@cfhighwood.net
Contact: Ursula Sherwood, Executive Director
E-mail: ursulas@cfhighwood.net
Description: Provides short-term business office leasing for business startups wanting to expand or in need of start up assistance.

46673 ■ InnoTech Alberta
250 Karl Clark Rd.
Edmonton, AB, Canada T6N 1E4
Ph: (780)450-5111
Fax: (780)450-5333
Co. E-mail: info@innotechalberta.ca
URL: http://innotechalberta.ca
Contact: Chris Kearney, Executive Director
E-mail: chris.kearney@innotechalberta.ca
Description: Offers a diversified range of scientific, engineering and technological research and testing capabilities, and the facilities to support technology scale-up.

46674 ■ Innovate Calgary
3553 31 St. NW
Calgary, AB, Canada T2L 1Y8
Ph: (403)270-7027
URL: http://innovatecalgary.com
Contact: Dr. John Wilson, President
E-mail: johnw@innovatecalgary.com
Linkedin: www.linkedin.com/company/innovate-calgary
Description: The technology-transfer and business-incubation center for the University of Calgary where startups, entrepreneurs, researchers, investors, industry and partners take innovation and ideas to business. **Founded:** 1986.

46675 ■ International Avenue Technology Centre (IATC)
305, 999 - 8 St. SW
Calgary, AB, Canada T2R 1J5
URL: http://www.rockmountcorp.com/business-incubation.html
Description: Business development facility in Western Canada, offering office, lab, and semi-industrial workshop space as well as facilitating innovation assistance to SMEs and startup companies. assistance to the early growth of semi-industrial firms from commercialization through to pilot production.

46676 ■ Northern Alberta Business Incubator (NABI)
200 Carnegie Dr.
Saint Albert, AB, Canada T8N 5A7
Ph: (780)460-1000
Co. E-mail: info@nabi.ca
URL: http://nabi.ca
Contact: Rajesh Jaiswal, Executive Director
E-mail: rajesh@nabi.ca
Facebook: www.facebook.com/NABI.stalbert
Linkedin: www.linkedin.com/company/nabistalbert
X (Twitter): x.com/NABI_incubator
Instagram: www.instagram.com/nabi.stalbert
Description: Supports startups and entrepreneurs by providing office space, coaching, training, seminar and administrative support services.

46677 ■ Startup Lloydminster
4B, 4010 - 50 Ave.
Lloydminster, AB, Canada T9V 1B2
Ph: (587)789-1361
Co. E-mail: info@startuplloyd.com
URL: http://www.startuplloyd.com
X (Twitter): x.com/startuplloyd
Description: Business incubator that helps nurture growing companies and provides hands-on management assistance, education, and technical and business support services.

46678 ■ Tecterra Inc.
3608 33 St. NW
Calgary, AB, Canada T2L 2A6
Ph: (403)532-4275
URL: http://tecterra.com
Contact: Jonathan Neufeld, Chief Executive Officer
Linkedin: www.linkedin.com/company/tecterra
X (Twitter): x.com/TECTERRA
YouTube: www.youtube.com/user/TECTERRA1
Description: A government-funded non-profit organization that assists start-ups, and small and medium-sized companies (SMEs) to develop and commercialize technology faster than they could on their own Offers a variety of programs including investment, market launch, and geo-placement. **Founded:** 2009.

46679 ■ Verge Economic Development (EDA)
No. 28-419 3rd St., SE
Medicine Hat, AB, Canada T1A 0G9
Ph: (403)952-6014
Linkedin: www.linkedin.com/company/economic-development-alliance-of-southeast-alberta
X (Twitter): x.com/vergeeconomic
Description: Helps startups throughout the entire business cycle and can provide the information and advice you need to be successful. **Founded:** 2002.

PUBLICATIONS

46680 ■ *Nisku Business Directory*
Nisku, AB, Canada
URL: http://www.nisku.org
Description: Covers listings of members, companies located in Nisku Business Park, and Edmonton International Airport. **Arrangement:** Alphabetical by company name. **Availability:** Print.

PUBLISHERS

46681 ■ Visions International Presentations
10020 - 101A Ave. NW, Ste. 100
Edmonton, AB, Canada T5J 3G2
Ph: (780)452-3434
Co. E-mail: hello@visioncreativeinc.com
URL: http://visioncreativeinc.com
Contact: Beverly Lubrin, Project Manager
Instagram: www.instagram.com/visioncreativeyeg
Description: Publishes on personal growth in business. Reaches market through direct mail and Sandhill Book Marketing in Canada and Ten Speed Press in the U.S. **Scope:** Firm provides marketing communications agency services including strategic communication planning and research, brand strategy and execution, campaign development and execution and much more services. **Publications:** "Career Success without a Real Job"; "1001 Best Things Ever

Said about Work"; "101 Really Important Things You Already Know, But Keep Forgetting"; "Real Success Without a Real Job: There Is No Life Like It," Ten Speed Press, 2007; "The Joy of Not Working"; "Retirement Planning Made Easy"; "How to Retire Happy, Wild, and Free". **Training:** Thinking Way Out In Left Field; Leadership for Innovation; The Joy of Not Working.

46682 ■ Word Engines Press Inc.
AB, Canada

Description: Publishes books for managers and professionals. Does not accept unsolicited manuscripts. Reaches market through direct mail and their website. **Founded:** 1998.

EARLY STAGE FINANCING

46683 ■ Alberta Enterprise Fund (AE)
TD Tower, Ste. 1405
  10088 102 Ave.
  Edmonton, AB, Canada T5J 2Z2
Ph: (587)402-6601
Fax: (587)402-6612
Co. E-mail: info@alberta-enterprise.ca
URL: http://www.alberta-enterprise.ca
Contact: Kristina Williams, President
X (Twitter): x.com/ABEnterpriseCor

Description: Invests in venture capital funds with a successful track record, strong global networks, and a commitment to the province of Alberta.

EXPANSION AND GROWTH FINANCING

46684 ■ Avrio Subdebt Inc.
No. 502, 400 Crowfoot Cres. NW
  Calgary, AB, Canada T3G 5H6
Ph: (403)215-5492
URL: http://foragecapitalpartners.com

Description: Offers subordinated debt (subdebt) financing to support growth, acquisitions, management buyouts, and cross-border ventures. **Founded:** 2006. **Industry Preferences:** Food and agriculture.

VENTURE CAPITAL FIRM

46685 ■ Annapolis Capital
Ste., 2530 140 - 4 Ave. SW
  Calgary, AB, Canada T2P 3N3
Ph: (403)231-4430
Co. E-mail: info@anncap.com
URL: http://annapoliscapital.ca
Contact: Peter Williams, Chief Executive Officer

Description: Invests in start-up and early-stage Canadian oil and gas exploration and production companies. **Founded:** 2006. **Preferred Investment Size:** $15,000,000 to $60,000,000 . **Investment Policies:** ROI in 3-7 years. **Industry Preferences:** Oil and gas exploration and production.

46686 ■ AVAC Group
6815 8 St. NE, Ste. 220
  Calgary, AB, Canada T2E 7H7
Ph: (403)274-2774
Co. E-mail: info@avacgrp.com
URL: http://www.avacgrp.com
Contact: Warren Bergen, President

Description: Investment capital for early-stage agricultural technology companies and exit-stage venture-backed technology companies. **Founded:** 1997.

British Columbia

ESTABLISHED STAGE FINANCING

46687 ■ Zynik Capital Corp.
1281 Hornby St., Ste., 632
Vancouver, BC, Canada V6Z 0G8
Ph: (604)654-2555
Co. E-mail: info@zynik.com
URL: http://zynik.com
Contact: Nabil Kassam, President
Description: Specializes in venture capital start-ups, leveraged finances, turnarounds, and buyouts. Identifies under-performing opportunities in a wide range of markets. **Founded:** 1983. **Industry Preferences:** Banking; health and wellness; service industries; technology; resources; manufacturing.

ASSOCIATIONS AND OTHER ORGANIZATIONS

46688 ■ Canadian Federation of Business and Professional Women British Columbia and Yukon [BPW BC and Yukon]
Langley, BC, Canada
URL: http://bpwcanada.com
Contact: Angie Godin, President
Description: Serves as a network for businesswomen in Canada. Seeks to improve the economic, social, and political lives of women.

46689 ■ International Association of Business Communicators British Colombia (IABC BC)
400 - 601 W Broadway
Vancouver, BC, Canada V5Z 4C2
Ph: (604)878-1320
Fax: (604)871-4156
URL: http://iabc.bc.ca
Contact: Carmen Wright, President
E-mail: president@iabc.bc.ca
Facebook: www.facebook.com/iabcbc
X (Twitter): x.com/iabcbc
YouTube: www.youtube.com/user/IABCBC
Description: Represents communication managers, public relations directors, writers, editors, audiovisual specialists, and other individuals in the public relations and organizational communication field. Conducts research in the communication field and encourages establishment of college-level programs in organizational communication. Offers accreditation program and conducts surveys on employee communication effectiveness and media trends. **Founded:** 1980. **Publications:** *Ragged Right - Blog* (Semiweekly). **Awards:** Bronze Quill Awards (Annual); IABC British Columbia Master Communicator Award (Annual). **Geographic Preference:** Local.

SMALL BUSINESS ASSISTANCE PROGRAMS

46690 ■ Community Futures Nicola Valley (CFNV)
2181 Quilchena Ave.
Merritt, BC, Canada V1K 1B8
Ph: (250)378-3923
Free: 888-303-2232
Fax: (250)315-0205
Co. E-mail: admin@cfdcnv.com
URL: http://www.cfdcnv.com
Contact: Jean Perog, Chairman Treasurer Secretary
Facebook: www.facebook.com/CFDCNV
Linkedin: www.linkedin.com/company/community-futures-of-the-nicola-valley
X (Twitter): x.com/CFDCNV
Instagram: www.instagram.com/cfnicolavalley
Description: Offers business counseling and tools for entrepreneurs wanting to start, expand, franchise, or sell a business. **Founded:** 1989.

46691 ■ Small Business Accelerator (UBC)
Room 203, 1961 East Mall Irving K. Barber Learning Centre
Vancouver, BC, Canada V6T 1Z1
URL: http://sba.ubc.ca
Linkedin: www.linkedin.com/company/sba-bc
X (Twitter): x.com/sba_bc
Description: Provides information services to British Columbia entrepreneurs. Offers free online access to business information and tools for market research.

BETTER BUSINESS BUREAUS

46692 ■ Better Business Bureau of Mainland British Columbia (BBB)
500-1190 Melville St.
Vancouver, BC, Canada V6E 3W1
Ph: (604)682-2711
Fax: (604)681-1544
Co. E-mail: contactus@mbc.bbb.org
URL: http://www.bbb.org/local-bbb/bbb-serving-mainland-bc
Facebook: www.facebook.com/BBBmainlandBC
Linkedin: www.linkedin.com/company/bbbmbc
X (Twitter): x.com/bbb_bc
Instagram: www.instagram.com/bbb_mbc
YouTube: www.youtube.com/channel/BBBMainlandBC
Description: Non profit organization working towards educating people in Mainland British Columbia. **Founded:** 1939.

46693 ■ Better Business Bureau of Vancouver Island (BBB)
No. 220-1175 Cook St.
Victoria, BC, Canada V8V 4A1
Ph: (250)386-6348
Fax: (250)386-2367
Co. E-mail: info@vi.bbb.org
URL: http://www.bbb.org/local-bbb/bbb-serving-vancouver-island
Facebook: www.facebook.com/BBBVancouverIsland
Linkedin: www.linkedin.com/company/better-business-bureau-of-vancouver-island
X (Twitter): x.com/VIBBB
YouTube: www.youtube.com/BBBVancouverIsland
Description: Aims to to create and maintain an ethical marketplace in the region of Vancouver Island. **Founded:** 1962. **Publications:** *BBB Accredited Business Directory* (Annual).

FINANCING AND LOAN PROGRAMS

46694 ■ Angel Forum - Vancouver
1095 Mainland St
Vancouver, BC, Canada V6B 6G9
Co. E-mail: hello@angelforum.ca
URL: http://www.angelforum.ca
Contact: Irene Dorsman, Chief Executive Officer
E-mail: irene@angelforum.org
Facebook: www.facebook.com/angelforum
Linkedin: www.linkedin.com/company/angel-forum
X (Twitter): x.com/ANGELforum
Instagram: www.instagram.com/angelforum.ca
YouTube: www.youtube.com/channel/UC8tiaktbofg-MrXLyfzpyxA
Description: Connects promising startups with accredited angel capital. Offers workshops and networking. **Founded:** 1997.

46695 ■ Chrysalix Venture Capital
1111 W Hastings St., Ste. 333
Vancouver, BC, Canada V6E 2J3
Ph: (604)659-5499
Fax: (604)659-5479
Co. E-mail: info@chrysalix.com
URL: http://www.chrysalix.com
Contact: Richard MacKellar, Managing Partner
X (Twitter): x.com/chrysalixvc
Description: Venture capital fund for resource-intensive industries. Invests in intelligent systems, energy technology and resource productivity solutions to deliver environmental sustainability. **Founded:** 2001. **Investment Policies:** Companies that offer innovations in science and technology that drive disruptive impact in resource-intensive industries. **Industry Preferences:** Oil and gas; mining and metals; manufacturing; logistics; construction; transportation; chemical and advanced materials; agriculture; utilities and electric power; asset management; artificial intelligence; data analytics; sensors and components; robotic systems; blockchain.

46696 ■ Discovery Capital
43 - 1238 Eastern Dr.
Port Coquitlam, BC, Canada V3C 6C5
Ph: (604)683-3000
Fax: (604)941-0010
Co. E-mail: info@discoverycapital.com
URL: http://www.discoverycapital.com
Contact: Harry Jaako, President
E-mail: hjaako@discoverycapital.com
Description: Provider of venture capital investments for information technology, communications, health, life sciences, environmental and energy technologies. **Founded:** 1986. **Industry Preferences:** Communications and media, Internet specific, health and life sciences.

STATE LISTINGS

46697 ■ GrowthWorks
1055 W Georgia St., Ste. 2080
Vancouver, BC, Canada V6E 3R5
Ph: (604)633-1418
Co. E-mail: investment@growthworks.ca
URL: http://www.growthworks.ca
Contact: Derek Lew, President
E-mail: derek.lew@growthworks.ca
Description: Firm is a venture capital firm offering regionally based venture capital funds. **Founded:** 1999. **Preferred Investment Size:** $100,000 to $5,000,000. **Industry Preferences:** Communications and media, Internet specific, computer related, semiconductors and other electronics, biotechnology, medical and health, consumer related, industrial and energy, transportation, manufacturing, agriculture, forestry and fishing, and environment.

46698 ■ Nuu-Chah-Nulth Eonomic Developement Corporation (NEDC)
7563 Pacific Rim Hwy.
Port Alberni, BC, Canada V9Y 8Y5
Ph: (250)724-3131
Free: 866-444-6332
Fax: (250)724-9967
Co. E-mail: nedc@nedc.info
URL: http://www.nedc.info
Contact: Jeraldine Marshall, Director, Finance
E-mail: jeraldine@nedc.info
X (Twitter): x.com/nedc1984
Instagram: www.instagram.com/nedc1984
YouTube: www.youtube.com/channel/UCK9uDOj5XXwhYCF6vL_ULCg
Description: Offers financing to Aboriginals on Vancouver Island to start and expand businesses. Services offered free of charge. **Founded:** 1984.

46699 ■ VANTEC Angel Network
c/o SFU VentureLabs,12th Fl., 555 W Hastings St.
Vancouver, BC, Canada V6B 4N6
Co. E-mail: info@vantec.ca
URL: http://www.vantec.ca/cpages/homepage
Contact: Mike Volker, Founder
Linkedin: www.linkedin.com/company/vantecnetwork
X (Twitter): x.com/VANTEC_Networks
YouTube: www.youtube.com/channel/UC8dJcQiNXKXFeD7ltQFLe4Q
Description: Supports early-stage technology ventures in British Columbia. **Founded:** 1999.

46700 ■ Ventures West Capital Ltd.
925 W Georgia St., Ste.1600
Vancouver, BC, Canada V6C 3L2
Contact: David Berkowitz, Director
Description: Provider of venture capital funds, growth capital, mezzanine and early stage investments. **Founded:** 1973. **Preferred Investment Size:** $1,000,000 minimum to $9,999,000. **Industry Preferences:** Communications and media, computer software and services, computer hardware, biotechnology, Internet specific, medical and health, semiconductors and other electronics, industrial and energy related.

46701 ■ Version One Ventures LLC
Vancouver, BC, Canada V6B1C6
URL: http://versionone.vc
Contact: Boris Wertz, Partner
E-mail: boris@versionone.vc
Linkedin: www.linkedin.com/company/version-one-ventures
X (Twitter): x.com/VersionOneVC
Description: Early stage venture capital firm. **Founded:** 2012.

46702 ■ WUTIF Capital Inc. [Western Universities Technology Innovation Fund (WUTIF)]
SFU Venturelabs, 555 W Hastings St., Ste. 1100
Vancouver, BC, Canada V6B 4N6
Co. E-mail: wutif@volker.org
URL: http://wutif.ca
Contact: Michael Volker, President
E-mail: mike@volker.org
Description: Angel fund that co-invests with angel investors in new technology ventures in British Columbia. **Founded:** 2003. **Industry Preferences:** Communications and information technology; health and life sciences technologies; physical sciences; energy; fuel cells.

46703 ■ Yaletown Partners
1122 Mainland St., Ste. 510
Vancouver, BC, Canada V6B 5L1
Ph: (604)688-7807
Co. E-mail: info@yaletown.com
URL: http://yaletown.com
Contact: Salil Munjal, Managing Partner
Linkedin: www.linkedin.com/company/yaletown-partners-inc
Description: Early-stage venture capital investment firm. Targets clean tech and IT companies, particularly in Western Canada and the Pacific Northwest. Also has offices in Toronto, Calgary, and Montreal. **Founded:** 2001. **Industry Preferences:** Sustainability, including smart grid, energy and transportation efficiency and technology for natural resource, agriculture, and power generation industries (cleantech); information and communication technology.

INCUBATORS/RESEARCH AND TECHNOLOGY PARKS

46704 ■ Accelerate Okanagan
201-460 Doyle Ave.
Kelowna, BC, Canada V1Y 0C2
Ph: (250)870-9028
Co. E-mail: contact@accelerateokanagan.com
URL: http://www.accelerateokanagan.com
Contact: Alex Goodhew, Manager
Facebook: www.facebook.com/AccelerateOkanagan
X (Twitter): x.com/accelerateok
YouTube: www.youtube.com/channel/UCBknJ2HAKnB9nY9XuOM25Ug
Description: Business accelerator providing startup basics, venture acceleration, calibration, and capital programs.

46705 ■ Discovery Foundation
400-610 Main St.
Vancouver, BC, Canada V6A 2V3
Ph: (604)734-7275
Co. E-mail: info@discoveryfoundation.ca
URL: http://www.discoveryfoundation.ca
Contact: Dr. David G. Harper, President
E-mail: david@discoveryfoundation.ca
Linkedin: www.linkedin.com/company/the-discovery-foundation
X (Twitter): x.com/tepdiscovery
Instagram: www.instagram.com/thediscoverygroup
Description: Offers a program to teach technology entrepreneurs the business skills and practices essential to grow world-scale BC-based businesses. **Founded:** 2010.

46706 ■ Kamloops Innovation (KIC)
348 Tranquille Rd.
Kamloops, BC, Canada V2B3G6
Ph: (250)434-0200
Co. E-mail: operations@kamloopsinnovation.ca
URL: http://www.kamloopsinnovation.ca
Contact: Michael Andrews, Executive Director
Facebook: www.facebook.com/KamloopsInnovation
Linkedin: www.linkedin.com/company/kamloops-innovation
X (Twitter): x.com/kicpeople
Instagram: www.instagram.com/kamloopsinnovation
Description: Serves the Central Interior region of British Columbia, offering affordable programs that guide, coach and mentor early stage ventures, collaborative and shared office spaces, and host, facilitate, initiate, partner, sponsor, and generally support all sorts of events that help to grow the tech community. **Founded:** 2012.

46707 ■ Launch
400 - 1168 Hamilton St.
Vancouver, BC, Canada V6B 2S2
Co. E-mail: info@launchacademy.ca
URL: http://www.launchacademy.ca
Contact: Ray Walia, Chief Executive Officer
Facebook: www.facebook.com/launchacademyhq
X (Twitter): x.com/launchacademyhq
Instagram: www.instagram.com/launchacademyhq
YouTube: www.youtube.com/user/launchacademy
Pinterest: www.pinterest.com/launchacademy
Description: Incubator offers Launchpad, a three-month program to help startups find their product fit, along with additional resources, mentoring, and networking that tech entrepreneurs need to launch, fund, and grow their startups. **Founded:** 2012.

46708 ■ The Network Hub
422 Richards St., Ste. 170
Vancouver, BC, Canada V6B 2Z4
Ph: (604)767-8778
Co. E-mail: hello@thenetworkhub.ca
URL: http://thenetworkhub.ca
Facebook: www.facebook.com/TheNetworkHub
X (Twitter): x.com/thenetworkhub
Instagram: www.instagram.com/thenetworkhub
YouTube: www.youtube.com/user/TheNetworkHub
Pinterest: www.pinterest.com/thenetworkhub
Description: Specializes in virtual office/mailbox rental, meeting room rental, coworking space & private office space rental in Downtown Vancouver in support of local startups and entrepreneurs. **Founded:** 2006.

46709 ■ Vanouver Island Technology Park (VITP)
2201-4464 Markham St., Victoria
Victoria, BC, Canada V8Z 7X8
Ph: (250)483-3200
Fax: (250)483-3201
Co. E-mail: info@vitp.ca
URL: http://vitp.ca
Contact: Gayle Gorrill, Vice Chairman of the Board
Facebook: www.facebook.com/myVITP
Description: Offers start-up assistance in British Columbia. Funded. **Founded:** 2001.

46710 ■ Venture Acceleration Program (VAP)
1188 West Georgia St., Ste. 900
Vancouver, BC, Canada V6E 4A2
Ph: (604)335-2495
Free: 800-573-0488
URL: http://www.innovatebc.ca/programs/vap
Description: Provides access to a network of resources across British Columbia as it supports the mission to drive economic development in support of entrepreneurs and tech companies.

EDUCATIONAL PROGRAMS

46711 ■ Coast Capital Savings Venture Connection
250 - 13450 102nd Ave.
Surrey, BC, Canada V3T 0A3
Ph: (778)782-8101
Co. E-mail: adm_changinstitute@sfu.ca
URL: http://www.sfu.ca/vc.html
Contact: Dr. Joy Johnson, President
Facebook: www.facebook.com/SFUVC
Linkedin: www.linkedin.com/company/ventureconnection
X (Twitter): x.com/SFUVC
Instagram: www.instagram.com/sfu_vc
Description: Provides support to explore entrepreneurship and business development services for emerging ventures from initial idea through business validation.

PUBLISHERS

46712 ■ Self-Counsel Press Ltd.
1481 Charlotte Rd.
North Vancouver, BC, Canada V7J 1H1
Ph: (604)986-3366
Free: 800-663-3007
Co. E-mail: service@self-counsel.com
URL: http://www.self-counsel.com
Facebook: www.facebook.com/selfcounselpress
Linkedin: www.linkedin.com/company/self-counsel-press
X (Twitter): x.com/SelfCounsel
Pinterest: www.pinterest.com/SCPBooks

Description: Publishes legal, business, and reference books. **Founded:** 1971.

INFORMATION SERVICES

46713 ■ BC Technology Industry Association - Centre4Growth
210-1401 West 8th Ave.
 Vancouver, BC, Canada V6H 1C9
URL: http://wearebctech.com/bctia-centre4growth-expands-to-maple-ridge-and-surrey
Contact: Ernie Daykin, Mayor
Description: Supports startups and entrepreneurs by providing seasoned mentors, access to resources, and help with executing revenue plans. **Founded:** 2010.

RESEARCH CENTERS

46714 ■ Nimbus Synergies
Ste. 300 - 1001 Broadway W
 Vancouver, BC, Canada V6H 4B1
Ph: (604)734-7275
Co. E-mail: info@discoveryparks.com
URL: http://www.nimbusinc.vc
Contact: Paul Geyer, Chief Executive Officer
Linkedin: www.linkedin.com/company/nimbus-synergies
X (Twitter): x.com/nimbussynergies
Instagram: www.instagram.com/thediscoverygroup

Description: Provides capital investment, business mentorship, and value creation for British Columbia's health tech sector. Through The Generator, offers free incubator space for technology startups. **Scope:** Manages a park at University of British Columbia, 75-acre park at Simon Fraser University, and 80-acre park adjacent to British Columbia Institute of Technology that link university research resources with technological and research companies in the parks. **Founded:** 1979.

EXPANSION AND GROWTH FINANCING

46715 ■ Zynik Capital Corp.
1281 Hornby St., Ste., 632
 Vancouver, BC, Canada V6Z 0G8
Ph: (604)654-2555
Co. E-mail: info@zynik.com
URL: http://zynik.com
Contact: Nabil Kassam, President
Description: Specializes in venture capital start-ups, leveraged finances, turnarounds, and buyouts. Identifies under-performing opportunities in a wide range of markets. **Founded:** 1983. **Industry Preferences:** Banking; health and wellness; service industries; technology; resources; manufacturing.

VENTURE CAPITAL FIRM

46716 ■ Global Vision Capital Corp.
750 - 1095 W Pender St.
 Vancouver, BC, Canada V6E 2M6
URL: http://global-vision.ca
Contact: Gregg J. Sedun, President
Description: Private venture capital firm for early-stage opportunities with significant potential. **Industry Preferences:** Resources and mining; technology; ecommerce.

46717 ■ Vanedge Capital Partners Ltd.
1333 W Broadway., Ste. 750
 Vancouver, BC, Canada V6H 4C1
Ph: (604)569-3883
Co. E-mail: info@vanedgecapital.com
URL: http://www.vanedgecapital.com
Contact: Moe Kermani, Managing Partner
X (Twitter): x.com/VanedgeCapital
Description: Early-stage venture capital firm. **Founded:** 2010. **Investment Policies:** Entrepreneurs solving technical and business problems on a global scale. **Industry Preferences:** Applied analytics; analytics tools and platforms; computational biology; hard tech; cyber security; SaaS and digital media.

46718 ■ Zynik Capital Corp.
1281 Hornby St., Ste., 632
 Vancouver, BC, Canada V6Z 0G8
Ph: (604)654-2555
Co. E-mail: info@zynik.com
URL: http://zynik.com
Contact: Nabil Kassam, President
Description: Specializes in venture capital start-ups, leveraged finances, turnarounds, and buyouts. Identifies under-performing opportunities in a wide range of markets. **Founded:** 1983. **Industry Preferences:** Banking; health and wellness; service industries; technology; resources; manufacturing.

Manitoba

ASSOCIATIONS AND OTHER ORGANIZATIONS

46719 ■ BNI Accelerator
200 Rive Ave.
 Winnipeg, MB, Canada R3L 0B2
Ph: (204)955-3548
Co. E-mail: info@bniaccelerator.com
URL: http://bnimanitoba.com/manitoba-bni-accelerators/en-CA/index
Contact: Darcy Berrington, President
Facebook: www.facebook.com/BniAccelerators
Description: Networking organization that offers members the opportunity to share ideas, contacts, and referrals.

SMALL BUSINESS DEVELOPMENT CENTERS

46720 ■ Manitoba Business Gateway
1005 St. Mary's Rd.
 Winnipeg, MB, Canada R2M 3S4
URL: http://www.gov.mb.ca
Description: Resource centres providing information and referrals for a wide range of business and employment information and services. Resources include business startup, business planning, and business expansion and growth.

SMALL BUSINESS ASSISTANCE PROGRAMS

46721 ■ Canada Business Network
407 Provencher Blvd.
 Winnipeg, MB, Canada R2H 0G4
Free: 888-576-4444
URL: http://www.canadabusiness.ca
Facebook: www.facebook.com/CanadaBusiness
X (Twitter): twitter.com/CanadaBusiness
Description: Firm provides information on government services, programs and regulations.

46722 ■ Manitoba Tax Assistance Office
101 - 401 York Ave.
 Winnipeg, MB, Canada R3C 0P8
Ph: (204)948-2115
Free: 800-782-0771
Fax: (204)948-2087
Co. E-mail: tao@gov.mb.ca
URL: http://www.gov.mb.ca/finance/tao
Description: Administers the Small Business Tax Reduction program.

BETTER BUSINESS BUREAUS

46723 ■ Better Business Bureau of Central Canada
1555 St. James St., Unit 207
 Winnipeg, MB, Canada R3H 1B5
Ph: (204)989-9010
Fax: (204)989-9016
URL: http://www.bbb.org/local-bbb/bbb-central-canada
Description: Seeks to promote and foster ethical relationship between businesses and the public through voluntary self-regulation, consumer and business education, and service excellence. Provides information to help consumers and businesses make informed purchasing decisions and avoid costly scams and frauds; settles consumer complaints through arbitration and other means. **Founded:** 1981.

46724 ■ Better Business Bureau of Manitoba and Nortwest Ontario [BBB Serving Manitoba & N.W. Ontario]
1700 Portage Ave.
 Winnipeg, MB, Canada R3J 0E1
Ph: (204)989-9010
Fax: (204)989-9016
URL: http://www.bbb.org/local-bbb/bbb-central-canada
X (Twitter): x.com/BBBManitoba
Description: Non profit organization working towards educating people in Central and Northern Alberta. **Founded:** 1930.

MINORITY BUSINESS ASSISTANCE PROGRAMS

46725 ■ Aboriginal Youth Mean Business!
310-800 Portage Ave.
 510 Selkirk Ave.
 Winnipeg, MB, Canada R3G 0N4
Ph: (204)945-0447
Free: 800-282-8069
Fax: (204)945-5726
URL: http://www.aymb.ca
Description: Provider of business planning, business directory and other business services for organizations, governments and business.

46726 ■ Women's Enterprise Centre of Manitoba (WECM)
207 Donald St., Rm. 100
 Winnipeg, MB, Canada R3C 1M5
Ph: (204)988-1860
Free: 800-203-2343
Fax: (204)988-1871
Co. E-mail: wecinfo@wecm.ca
URL: http://wecm.ca
Contact: Jacqueline Keena, Chairman of the Board
Facebook: www.facebook.com/wecmanitoba
Linkedin: www.linkedin.com/company/wecmanitoba
X (Twitter): x.com/wecmanitoba
Instagram: www.instagram.com/wecmanitoba
Description: Aids women in Manitoba with starting or expanding businesses. **Founded:** 1994.

INCUBATORS/RESEARCH AND TECHNOLOGY PARKS

46727 ■ Manitoba Technology Accelerator (MTA)
800-136 Market St.
 Winnipeg, MB, Canada R3B 0P4
Ph: (204)272-2403
Fax: (204)272-2405
URL: http://mbtechaccelerator.com
Contact: Marshall Ring, Chief Executive Officer
E-mail: mring@mbtechaccelerator.com
Description: Business incubation program committed to the long-term success of science and technology start-up companies. Our program helps you to operate professionally but on a start-up budget, enabling you to reach a higher degree of business success.

46728 ■ North Forge Technology Exchange
441 - 100 Innovation Dr.
 Winnipeg, MB, Canada R3T 6G2
Ph: (204)262-6400
Co. E-mail: info@northforge.ca
URL: http://northforge.ca
Contact: Shane Li, President
Facebook: www.facebook.com/NorthForgeTechnologyExchange
Linkedin: www.linkedin.com/company/northforge-manitoba
X (Twitter): x.com/northforgemb
Instagram: www.instagram.com/northforgemb
YouTube: www.youtube.com/channel/UC2YEbZcW5PVSTMgL-B4HBIw
Description: An innovation-based economic development agency fueling Manitoba's innovation economy through collaboration and access to shared resources. Offers a startup program, rapid prototyping, cloud hosting, a UX lab, investor intelligence, advanced ICT lab, and market intelligence.

CONSULTANTS

46729 ■ Business Networks Inc.
Canada
URL: http://www.businessnetworks.com
Contact: Diane Cunningham, General Manager
E-mail: diane@businessnetworks.com
Description: Provider of business security services.

VENTURE CAPITAL FIRM

46730 ■ CentreStone Ventures
7-1250 Waverly St.
 Winnipeg, MB, Canada R3T 6C6
Ph: (204)453-1230
Fax: (204)453-1293
URL: http://www.centrestoneventures.com
Contact: Dr. Albert D. Friesen, President
Description: Private venture capital for life science companies. **Investment Policies:** Develops products for large markets with unmet clinical needs; technologies based on solid intellectual property; entrepreneurial and technical expertise; potential for market leadership. **Industry Preferences:** Early-stage therapeutics; medical devices; diagnostics; new drug delivery methods.

New Brunswick

SMALL BUSINESS ASSISTANCE PROGRAMS

46731 ■ 3+ Corporation
1273 Main St., Ste. 250
Moncton, NB, Canada E1C 0P4
Ph: (506)858-9550
Free: 888-577-0000
Fax: (506)859-7791
Co. E-mail: info@3plus.ca
URL: http://3plus.ca
Contact: Susy Campos, Chief Executive Officer
E-mail: susy@3plus.ca
Facebook: www.facebook.com/3pluscorporation
Linkedin: www.linkedin.com/company/3pluscorporation
X (Twitter): twitter.com/3PlusCorp
Instagram: www.instagram.com/3pluscorp
Description: Economic development corporation for Dieppe, Moncton, and Riverview. Leverages regional assets to foster new job creation. Promotes the region and works to attract investment.

46732 ■ New Brunswick Department of Economic Development
Sartain MacDonald Bldg., PO Box 6000
Fredericton, NB, Canada E3B 5H1
Ph: (506)453-3115
Free: 888-487-5050
Fax: (506)444-3784
URL: http://www.gnb.ca
Contact: Eric Beaulieu, President

BETTER BUSINESS BUREAUS

46733 ■ Better Business Bureau of Atlantic Provinces
7071 Bayers Rd., Ste. 279
Halifax, NS, Canada B3L 2C2
Ph: (902)422-6581
Free: 877-663-2363
Fax: (902)429-6457
URL: http://www.bbb.org/local-bbb/better-business-bureau-serving-the-atlantic-provinces
Facebook: www.facebook.com/BBBAtlantic

Description: Aims to to create and maintain an ethical marketplace in the region of Newfoundland and Labrador. **Publications:** *Better Business Bureau of Newfoundland and Labrador--Directory and Consumer Guide* (Annual).

FINANCING AND LOAN PROGRAMS

46734 ■ New Brunswick Innovation Foundation (NBIF)
40 Crowther Ln., Ste. 100
Fredericton, NB, Canada E3C 0J1
Ph: (506)452-2884
Free: 877-554-6668
Fax: (506)452-2886
Co. E-mail: info@nbif.ca
URL: http://nbif.ca
Contact: Jeff White, Chief Executive Officer
E-mail: jeff.white@nbif.ca
Facebook: www.facebook.com/NBinnovation
Linkedin: www.linkedin.com/comany/nbif
X (Twitter): x.com/nb_innovation
Instagram: www.instagram.com/nbif_finb
YouTube: www.youtube.com/user/NBIFVideo
Description: Offers venture capital and research investments to organizations in New Brunswick. **Founded:** 2003.

INCUBATORS/RESEARCH AND TECHNOLOGY PARKS

46735 ■ Knowledge Park
40 Crowther Ln., Ste. 100
Fredericton, NB, Canada E3C 0J1
Ph: (506)444-4686
Co. E-mail: info@ignitefredericton.com
URL: http://knowledgepark.ca
Contact: Larry Shaw, Chief Executive Officer
E-mail: larry.shaw@knowledgepark.ca
Facebook: www.facebook.com/KnowledgeParkNB
Linkedin: www.linkedin.com/company/ignite-fredericton
X (Twitter): x.com/knowledgeparknb
Description: Business research and technology park offering office space, a knowledge industry clustering environment, and close proximity to world-renowned research and education partners.

46736 ■ UNB
PO Box 4400
Fredericton, NB, Canada E3B 5A3
Ph: (506)453-4666
Free: 888-895-3344
Co. E-mail: talktous@unb.ca
URL: http://www.unb.ca
X (Twitter): x.com/UNB
YouTube: www.youtube.com/user/unbtube
Description: Jointly sponsored by the University of New Brunswick and the Research and Productivity Council, this incubator supports emerging technology firms. **Founded:** 1785.

CONSULTANTS

46737 ■ OpportunitiesNB (ONB)
250 King St., Pl. 2000
Fredericton, NB, Canada E3B 9M9
Ph: (506)453-5471
Free: 855-746-4662
Fax: (506)444-4277
Co. E-mail: info@onbcanada.ca
URL: http://onbcanada.ca
Contact: Sadie Perron, Chief Executive Officer
Facebook: www.facebook.com/OpportunitiesNB
Linkedin: www.linkedin.com/company/onbcanada
X (Twitter): x.com/ONBCanada
YouTube: www.youtube.com/channel/UCiwU1w28IMFcgVus2PTIS5A
Description: Helps startups and established companies find new markets and resources for growth. **Founded:** 2015.

VENTURE CAPITAL FIRM

46738 ■ Ignite Fredericton
40 Crowther Ln., Ste. 100
Fredericton, NB, Canada E3C 0J1
Ph: (506)444-4686
Free: 800-200-1180
Co. E-mail: info@ignitefredericton.com
URL: http://myignite.ca
Contact: Sarah Corey Hollohan, Chief Executive Officer
E-mail: sarah@myignite.ca
Facebook: www.facebook.com/MyIgniteNB
Linkedin: www.linkedin.com/company/my-ignite
X (Twitter): x.com/MyIgniteNB
Description: Brings together entrepreneurs and stakeholders, providing startup capital to help create a strong and united ecosystem.

Newfoundland and Labrador

ASSOCIATIONS AND OTHER ORGANIZATIONS

46739 ■ International Association of Business Communicators Newfoundland and Labrador (IABC-NL)
PO Box 42, Sta. C
Saint John's, NL, Canada A1C 5H5
Co. E-mail: iabcnl@gmail.com
URL: http://iabcnl.com
Contact: Tanya Alexander, President
Facebook: www.facebook.com/IABCNL
Linkedin: www.linkedin.com/company/iabcnl
X (Twitter): x.com/IABCNL
Instagram: www.instagram.com/iabcnl
YouTube: www.youtube.com/user/IABCNL2012

Description: Represents communication managers, public relations directors, writers, editors, audiovisual specialists, and other individuals in the public relations and organizational communication field in Newfoundland. **Awards:** IABC Newfoundland and Labrador Pinnacle Award of Excellence for a Communications Professional (Annual); IABC Newfoundland and Labrador Pinnacle Award of Excellence for Organization Leaders (Annual). **Geographic Preference:** State.

SMALL BUSINESS ASSISTANCE PROGRAMS

46740 ■ Newfoundland & Labrador Organziation of Women Entrepreneurs (NLOWE)
Regatta Plz., 2nd Fl.
84-86 Elizabeth Ave.
Saint Johns, NL, Canada A1A 1W7
Free: 888-656-9311
Co. E-mail: info@nlowe.org
URL: http://www.nlowe.org
Contact: Jennifer Bessell, Chief Executive Officer
E-mail: jbessell@nlowe.org
Facebook: www.facebook.com/nlowe.org
Linkedin: www.linkedin.com/company/newfoundlan
 d-and-labrador-organization-of-women-en
 trepreneurs-nlowe-
X (Twitter): x.com/nlowe_org
Instagram: www.instagram.com/nlowe_org
YouTube: www.youtube.com/user/NLOWEVideo

Description: Helps women start and grow businesses that take advantage of emerging economic opportunities. **Founded:** 1997.

46741 ■ Nunacor Development Corporation (NDC)
169 Hamilton River Rd.
 Ste. 100
 Happy Valley-Goose Bay, NL, Canada A0P 1C0
Ph: (709)896-5722
Free: 866-446-5035
Fax: (709)896-5739
Co. E-mail: info@nunacor.com
URL: http://nunacor.com
Contact: Andy Turnbull, Chief Executive Officer
Facebook: www.facebook.com/Nunacor
Linkedin: www.linkedin.com/company/nunacor
 -development-corporation
X (Twitter): x.com/nunacor
Instagram: www.instagram.com/royalinnsuites
YouTube: www.youtube.com/channel/
 UCqhZjJnmDyG5IIKfUN9rLXg

Description: Helps start, expand, and support business growth in the region. **Founded:** 2003.

BETTER BUSINESS BUREAUS

46742 ■ Better Business Bureau of Atlantic Provinces
7071 Bayers Rd., Ste. 279
 Halifax, NS, Canada B3L 2C2
Ph: (902)422-6581
Free: 877-663-2363
Fax: (902)429-6457
URL: http://www.bbb.org/local-bbb/better-business
 -bureau-serving-the-atlantic-provinces
Facebook: www.facebook.com/BBBAtlantic

Description: Aims to to create and maintain an ethical marketplace in the region of Newfoundland and Labrador. **Publications:** *Better Business Bureau of Newfoundland and Labrador--Directory and Consumer Guide* (Annual).

INCUBATORS/RESEARCH AND TECHNOLOGY PARKS

46743 ■ Genesis Centre
100 Signal Hill Rd., Ste. 0100
 Saint John's, NL, Canada A1A 1B3
Ph: (709)864-2625
Co. E-mail: genesis@mun.ca
URL: http://www.genesiscentre.ca
Contact: Michelle Simms, President
Facebook: www.facebook.com/genesiscentre
X (Twitter): x.com/Genesis_Centre
Instagram: www.instagram.com/genesis_centre

Description: Business incubator for technology startups. Accelerates startups through all stages of development from pre-incubation and busienss model development to investor readiness. **Founded:** 1997.

Nova Scotia

ASSOCIATIONS AND OTHER ORGANIZATIONS

46744 ■ Association of Fundraising Professionals - Nova Scotia Chapter (AFP)
PO Box 40039, Robie St. RPO
 Halifax, NS, Canada B3K 0E4
Co. E-mail: afpnovascotia@gmail.com
URL: http://community.afpnet.org/afpns/home
Contact: Alison Clements, President
Facebook: www.facebook.com/AFPNovaScotia
Linkedin: www.linkedin.com/company/afp-ns
X (Twitter): x.com/afpns
YouTube: www.youtube.com/channel/UCDU
 1hTURR85Fa6Dl8lXRSzg
Description: Promotes ethical fundraising. Acts in advocacy role on issues that has an impact on the non-profit sector. **Founded:** 1983. **Geographic Preference:** Local.

SMALL BUSINESS ASSISTANCE PROGRAMS

46745 ■ Acadia Entrepreneurshp Centre (AEC)
Acadia University
 21 University Ave
 Rhodes Hall
 Wolfville, NS, Canada B4P 2R6
Description: Offers consulting, training, incubation services .

BETTER BUSINESS BUREAUS

46746 ■ Better Business Bureau of Atlantic Provinces
7071 Bayers Rd., Ste. 279
 Halifax, NS, Canada B3L 2C2
Ph: (902)422-6581
Free: 877-663-2363
Fax: (902)429-6457
URL: http://www.bbb.org/local-bbb/better-business
 -bureau-serving-the-atlantic-provinces
Facebook: www.facebook.com/BBBAtlantic
Description: Aims to to create and maintain an ethical marketplace in the region of Newfoundland and Labrador. **Publications:** *Better Business Bureau of Newfoundland and Labrador--Directory and Consumer Guide* (Annual).

INCUBATORS/RESEARCH AND TECHNOLOGY PARKS

46747 ■ Innovacorp
400-1871 Hollis St.
 Halifax, NS, Canada B3J 0C3
Ph: (902)424-8670
Free: 800-565-7051
Fax: (902)424-4679
Co. E-mail: info@innovacorp.ca
URL: http://innovacorp.ca
Contact: Malcolm Fraser, Chief Executive Officer
Facebook: www.facebook.com/innovacorp
X (Twitter): x.com/innovacorp
YouTube: www.youtube.com/user/InNOVAcorp/fea
 tured
Description: Firm engaged in investment business. **Scope:** Offer business development and commercialization services to firms with new technology-based products and services. **Founded:** 1995.

46748 ■ St. Mary's University (SMUEC) - Entrepreneurship Centre
5907 Gorsebrook Ave.
 Halifax, NS, Canada B3H 1C3
Ph: (902)491-6500
URL: http://arthurlirvingentrepreneurshipcentre.ca
Contact: Michael Sanderson, Director

Description: Works with business startups, providing consulting, training, and coaching services to ensure the company's economic prosperity.

Northwest Territories

BETTER BUSINESS BUREAUS

46749 ■ Better Business Bureau of Central Canada
1555 St. James St., Unit 207
 Winnipeg, MB, Canada R3H 1B5
Ph: (204)989-9010
Fax: (204)989-9016
URL: http://www.bbb.org/local-bbb/bbb-central
 -canada
Description: Seeks to promote and foster ethical relationship between businesses and the public through voluntary self-regulation, consumer and business education, and service excellence. Provides information to help consumers and businesses make informed purchasing decisions and avoid costly scams and frauds; settles consumer complaints through arbitration and other means. **Founded:** 1981.

PUBLISHERS

46750 ■ Nortext Multimedia Inc.
NT, Canada
URL: http://nortext.com
Description: Publishes school books, aboriginal language, business, Nunavut and travel books. **Founded:** 1990.

Ontario

ASSOCIATIONS AND OTHER ORGANIZATIONS

46751 ■ FP Canada
902-375 University Ave.
 Toronto, ON, Canada M5G 2J5
Ph: (416)593-8587
Free: 800-305-9886
Fax: (416)593-7412
Co. E-mail: info@fpcanada.ca
URL: http://www.fpcanada.ca
Contact: Tashia Batstone, President
Facebook: www.facebook.com/OfficialFPCanada
Linkedin: www.linkedin.com/company/fpcanada
X (Twitter): x.com/OfficialFPCan
YouTube: www.youtube.com/c/FPCanadaOfficial
Description: Works in the public interest to champion financial health for all Canadians by certifying professional financial planners. **Scope:** Firm engages in develops and enforces uniform standards of education, experience, examination and ethics for financial planning professionals. **Founded:** 1995.

46752 ■ International Association of Business Communicators Ottawa
PO Box 71034
 Ottawa, ON, Canada K2P 2L9
Ph: (613)627-3027
Co. E-mail: marketing@ottawa.iabc.com
URL: http://ottawa.iabc.com
Contact: Alexandra Sebben, President
Facebook: www.facebook.com/IABCOttawa
X (Twitter): x.com/iabcottawa
Description: Represents communication managers, public relations directors, writers, editors, audiovisual specialists, and other individuals in the public relations and organizational communication field in Ottawa. **Founded:** 1976. **Awards:** Rick Green Award (Annual). **Geographic Preference:** Local.

46753 ■ Maple Leaf Angels (MLA)
95 King St. E, Ste. 300
 Toronto, ON, Canada M5C 1G4
Ph: (416)646-6235
Co. E-mail: info@mapleleafangels.com
URL: http://mapleleafangels.com
Contact: Mohammed Ghalayini, Chairman
Linkedin: www.linkedin.com/company/mapleleafangels
X (Twitter): x.com/mapleleafangels
Description: Organization of accredited investors in the Toronto area who invest in seed and early-stage technology companies. Offers companies support and guidance on business and fundraising strategies, as well as networking opportunities, access to follow-on funding, government incentives, local startup resources, and business services. **Founded:** 2007. **Preferred Investment Size:** $250,000 to $500,000 (seed) or $350,000 to $1,000,000 (early stage). **Industry Preferences:** Fintech; IoT; healthcare.

46754 ■ National Angel Capital Organization (NACO)
MaRS Centre, Heritage Bldg.
 101 College St., Ste. 120G
 Toronto, ON, Canada M5G 1L7
Ph: (416)581-0009
Co. E-mail: contact@nacocanada.com
URL: http://nacocanada.com
Contact: Claudio Rojas, Contact
Facebook: www.facebook.com/NACOCanada
X (Twitter): x.com/NACOCanada
Description: National industry association for regional angel investment groups, accelerators and incubators, and angel investors across Canada. Fosters the emergence of high-growth companies in Canada by filling critical gaps in the national funding ecosystem and working to advance more equitable access to capital for entrepreneurs from all backgrounds and communities. Represents Canada in sharing best practices and connecting on investment opportunities with partners around the world. **Founded:** 2002.

46755 ■ Southwest Ontario Angel Group (SWO Angels)
999 Collip Cir., Ste. 115
 London, ON, Canada N6G 0J3
Ph: (519)858-5043
Co. E-mail: info@swoangel.com
URL: http://www.swoangel.com
Contact: Jon Mycio, Director
Description: Investor group for early-stage businesses.

46756 ■ TechAlliance
333 Dufferin Ave., Unit A
 London, ON, Canada N6B 1Z3
Ph: (226)781-7200
Co. E-mail: hello@techalliance.ca
URL: http://techalliance.ca
Contact: Christina Fox, Chief Executive Officer
E-mail: christina.fox@techalliance.ca
Facebook: www.facebook.com/techalliance
Linkedin: www.linkedin.com/company/techalliance-of-southwestern-ontario
X (Twitter): x.com/techalliance
Instagram: www.instagram.com/techalliancedn
YouTube: www.youtube.com/techalliancelondon
Description: Helps start, grow, and connect companies. Services include seed funding, educational programs and workshops. **Founded:** 2002.

SMALL BUSINESS DEVELOPMENT CENTERS

46757 ■ Lead to Win (LTW)
Carleton University, St. Patrick's Bldg.
 1125 Colonel By Dr.
 Ottawa, ON, Canada K1S 5B6
Ph: (613)520-2600
Co. E-mail: community@leadtowin.ca
URL: http://carleton.ca/innovationhub/lead-to-win-ltw-program
Description: Goal is to make Canada's Capital Region an attractive place to launch and grow businesses. A community comprised of individuals and organizations that come together to support students in post-secondary institutions and community entrepreneurs launch and grow their ventures and deliver community-level outcomes not achievable on their own. **Founded:** 2002.

46758 ■ Sarnia-Lambton Business Development Corp. (SLBDC)
109 Durand St.
 Sarnia, ON, Canada N7T 5A1
Ph: (519)383-1371
Fax: (519)383-8115
Co. E-mail: info@slbdc.com
URL: http://slbdc.com
Contact: Chris Gardner, President
Facebook: www.facebook.com/SLBDCteam
X (Twitter): x.com/SLBDCteam
Description: Provides business counselling and financing to entrepreneurs in Lambton County, as well as assists with various community based economic development projects. Specializes in helping small businesses within the areas of development, finance opportunities, grants/loans, proposals, business plans, starting a business, and consulting. **Founded:** 1988.

46759 ■ The Venture Centre
38 Pine St. N, Ste. 207
 Timmins, ON, Canada P4N 6K6
Ph: (705)360-5800
Free: 800-966-9461
Fax: (705)360-5656
Co. E-mail: info@venturecentre.on.ca
URL: http://venturecentre.on.ca
Contact: Roxanne Daoust, Executive Director
Facebook: www.facebook.com/theventurecentre
X (Twitter): x.com/venture_centre
Instagram: www.instagram.com/venture_centre
Description: A community based, non-profit organization that is dedicated to creating opportunities for entrepreneurship and the pursuit of economic growth in our communities.

SMALL BUSINESS ASSISTANCE PROGRAMS

46760 ■ Bruce Community Futures Development Corporation (CFDC)
233 Broadway St.
 Kincardine, ON, Canada N2Z 2X9
Ph: (519)396-8141
Free: 888-832-2232
Fax: (519)396-8346
URL: http://www.bruce.on.ca
Contact: Barb Fisher, General Manager
E-mail: bfisher@bruce.on.ca
Facebook: www.facebook.com/people/Bruce-Community-Futures-Development-Corporation/100075736010786
X (Twitter): x.com/brucecfdc

STATE LISTINGS

YouTube: www.youtube.com/user/greybrucepartnership
Description: Offers business counseling. Administers loans. Promotes economic development.

46761 ■ FedDev Ontario
101-139 Northfield Dr., W
 Waterloo, ON, Canada N2L 5A6
Free: 866-593-5505
Co. E-mail: info@feddevontario.gc.ca
URL: http://feddev-ontario.canada.ca/en
Contact: Nancy Gardiner, President
Facebook: www.facebook.com/FedDevOntario
Linkedin: www.linkedin.com/company/federal-economic-development-agency-for-southern-ontario
X (Twitter): x.com/FedDevOntario
Instagram: www.instagram.com/FedDevOntario
Description: Advances and diversifies the southern Ontario economy. Offers funding opportunities and business services that support innovation. Also acts as an accelerator through tis Accelerated Growth Service (AGS) program. Maintains additional offices in Toronto, Ottawa, and Peterborough. **Founded:** 2009.

46762 ■ Greenstone Economic Development Corporoation (GEDC)
901 Main St.
 Geraldton, ON, Canada P0T 1M0
Ph: (807)854-2273
Fax: (807)854-2474
Co. E-mail: info@gedc.ca
URL: http://www.gedc.ca
Contact: Calvin Cloutier, President
Facebook: www.facebook.com/GEDCBusinessCenter
Description: Fosters the start-up and operation of enterprise in the region. Offers advisory counseling services, business plan guidance, access to capital, and workshops, seminars and training . **Founded:** 1988.

46763 ■ Kingston Economic Development Corporation
366 King St. E, Ste. 420
 Kingston, ON, Canada K7K 6Y3
Ph: (613)544-2725
Co. E-mail: info@investkingston.ca
URL: http://www.investkingston.ca
Contact: Nour Mazloum, Manager, Communications Manager, Marketing
E-mail: mazloum@investkingston.ca
Description: Assists in community and businesses. Offers programs and services to entrepreneurs; identifies emerging sectors; supports the incubation, acceleration, and transfer of technology to promote future investment opportunities. **Founded:** 1998.

46764 ■ Northern Ontario Heritage Fund Corporation (NOHFC)
Roberta Bondar Pl., 70 Foster Dr., Ste. 200
 Sault Sainte Marie, ON, Canada P6A 6V8
Ph: (705)945-6700
Free: 800-461-8329
Fax: (705)945-6701
Co. E-mail: asknohfc@ontario.ca
URL: http://nohfc.ca/en
Contact: Greg Rickford, Chairman of the Board
Description: Stimulates economic development by providing financial assistance to projects that stabilize, diversify and foster economic growth of the region. Offers small business assistance for startups and expansion. **Founded:** 1988.

46765 ■ Peterborough & the Kawarthas Economic Development (PKED)
270 George St. N, Ste. 102
 Peterborough, ON, Canada K9J 3H1
Ph: (705)743-0777
Co. E-mail: connect@investptbo.ca
URL: http://investptbo.ca
Contact: Rhonda Keenan, President
E-mail: rkeenan@investptbo.ca
Facebook: www.facebook.com/PtboEcDev
Linkedin: www.linkedin.com/company/peterborougheconomicdevelopment
X (Twitter): x.com/PtboEcDev

Instagram: www.instagram.com/ptboecdev
YouTube: www.youtube.com/user/GPAEDCVid
Description: Helps business start up, expand, and relocate in the Peterborough region. **Founded:** 1998.

46766 ■ TheCodeFactory
Ottawa, ON, Canada
URL: http://thecodefactory.ca
Contact: Ian Graham, Contact
Facebook: www.facebook.com/TheCodeFactory
Linkedin: www.linkedin.com/company/thecodefactory
X (Twitter): twitter.com/thecodefactory
YouTube: www.youtube.com/channel/UCXMgC-5qMLcTdenFR1AhBLg
Description: Provides solutions for small businesses and startups, providing shared space, branding, web design, social media management, and content creation.

46767 ■ Thunder Bay Ventures (TBV)
1043 Gorham St., Unit D
 Thunder Bay, ON, Canada P7B 6T6
Ph: (807)768-6650
Co. E-mail: info@thunderbayventures.com
URL: http://www.thunderbayventures.com
Contact: Wayne Fletcher, President
Facebook: www.facebook.com/TBayVentures
Linkedin: www.linkedin.com/company/tbayventures
X (Twitter): x.com/tbayventures
Description: Fosters local economic development in the Thunder Bay Census Metropolitan Area (CMA). Finances start-ups and expansions; offers business services and referrals. **Founded:** 1994.

46768 ■ York Small Business Enterprise Centre (YSBEC)
17250 Yonge St.
 Newmarket, ON, Canada L3Y 6Z1
Free: 877-464-9675
Co. E-mail: ysbec@york.ca
URL: http://www.yorklink.ca/york-small-business-enterprise-centre
Contact: Vivian Ho-Tam, Consultant
E-mail: vivian.ho-tam@york.ca
Description: Offers consulting, business plan development and programs for new startups and small businesses with less than ten employees in the York area.

BETTER BUSINESS BUREAUS

46769 ■ Better Business Bureau of Central Canada
1555 St. James St., Unit 207
 Winnipeg, MB, Canada R3H 1B5
Ph: (204)989-9010
Fax: (204)989-9016
URL: http://www.bbb.org/local-bbb/bbb-central-canada
Description: Seeks to promote and foster ethical relationship between businesses and the public through voluntary self-regulation, consumer and business education, and service excellence. Provides information to help consumers and businesses make informed purchasing decisions and avoid costly scams and frauds; settles consumer complaints through arbitration and other means. **Founded:** 1981.

46770 ■ Better Business Bureau of Greater Toronto Area (BBB)
903 - 30 Duke St., W
 Kitchener, ON, Canada N2H 3W5
Ph: (519)579-3080
Free: 800-459-8875
Fax: (519)570-0072
Co. E-mail: info@mwco.bbb.org
URL: http://www.bbb.org
Facebook: www.facebook.com/BBBCentralON
Linkedin: www.linkedin.com/company/better-business-bureau
Description: Non profit organization working towards educating people in Greater Toronto Area.

46771 ■ Better Business Bureau Serving Eastern, Northern Ontario and the Outaouais [Better Business Bureau of Ottawa]
380 Hunt Club Rd., No. 203
 Ottawa, ON, Canada K1V 1C1
Ph: (519)513-4093
URL: http://www.bbb.org/local-bbb/bbb-of-canada-northern-capital-regions-and-quebec
Contact: Lori Wilson, President

46772 ■ Better Business Bureau of South Central Ontario
110 James St., S
 Hamilton, ON, Canada L8P 2Z2
Ph: (905)667-0321
URL: http://www.bbb.org/ca/on/hamilton/profile/career-counseling/the-career-foundation-0107-1357067
Description: Non profit organization working towards educating people in Central and Northern Alberta.

46773 ■ Better Business Bureau of Western Ontario (BBB)
190 Wortley Rd., Ste. 206
 London, ON, Canada N6C 4Y7
Ph: (519)673-3222
Fax: (519)673-5966
Co. E-mail: info@westernontario.bbb.org
URL: http://www.bbb.org/local-bbb/bbb-serving-western-ontario
Facebook: www.facebook.com/BBBWesternOnt
X (Twitter): x.com/BBBWesternOnt
Instagram: www.instagram.com/bbbwesternont
YouTube: www.youtube.com/channel/UC0xpx-klIwPTsAPDmT9jHrg/feed
Description: Non profit organization working towards educating people in Western Ontario.

CHAMBERS OF COMMERCE

46774 ■ Cambridge Chamber of Commerce (CCC)
750 Hespeler Rd.
 Cambridge, ON, Canada N3H 5L8
Ph: (519)622-2221
Free: 800-749-7560
Fax: (519)622-0177
Co. E-mail: events@cambridgechamber.com
URL: http://www.cambridgechamber.com
Contact: Greg Durocher, President
E-mail: greg@cambridgechamber.com
Facebook: www.facebook.com/cambridgechamberoc
Linkedin: www.linkedin.com/company/cambridge-chamber-of-commerce-canada
X (Twitter): x.com/my_chamber
YouTube: www.youtube.com/thecambridgechamber
Description: Promotes business and community development in Cambridge, NE area. **Founded:** 1973. **Geographic Preference:** Local.

MINORITY BUSINESS ASSISTANCE PROGRAMS

46775 ■ Canadian Aboriginal and Minority Supplier Council (CAMSC)
282 Richmond St. E, Ste. 101
 Toronto, ON, Canada M5A 1P4
Ph: (416)941-0004
Fax: (416)941-9282
Co. E-mail: info@camsc.ca
URL: http://camsc.ca
Contact: Cassandra Dorrington, President
Facebook: www.facebook.com/CAMSCorg
Linkedin: www.linkedin.com/company/camsc1
X (Twitter): x.com/camsc_org
Description: Seeks to facilitate the growth of Aboriginal and minority-owned businesses in Canada by connecting them to procurement opportunities with companies and governments committed to a diverse and inclusive supply chain. **Founded:** 2004.

FINANCING AND LOAN PROGRAMS

46776 ■ Angel One Network
c/o Techlace
801 - 5500 N Service Rd.
Burlington, ON, Canada L7L 6W6
Co. E-mail: admin@angelonenetwork.ca
URL: http://www.angelonenetwork.ca
Contact: Julie Ellis, Chairman of the Board
Linkedin: www.linkedin.com/company/angel-one-investor-network
Description: Member-based nonprofit of investors for early-stage companies in Toronto, Mississauga, Oakville, Burlington, Hamilton, and other communities in Southern Ontario. **Founded:** 2011. **Investment Policies:** Valuations of less than $3,000,000; track record of leadership and performance; solutions addressing major problems for large markets (i.e., more than $100,000,000); demonstrated market share in excess of 20%.

46777 ■ Bedford Capital Ltd.
130 Adelaide St. W, Ste. 2900
Toronto, ON, Canada M5H 3P5
Description: Equity investment firm. **Founded:** 1982. **Investment Policies:** Established business with a positive cash flow; sustainable competitive advantage; proprietary products or services; strong core management team; potential for market leadership; exit strategy within four to seven years.

46778 ■ Birch Hill Equity Partners
4510-81 Bay St.
Toronto, ON, Canada M5J 0E7
Ph: (416)775-3800
Co. E-mail: info@birchhillequity.com
URL: http://www.birchhillequity.com
Contact: Aiden Miller, Director
Description: Mid-market private equity firm. **Founded:** 1994.

46779 ■ Brightspark Financial, Inc. [Brightspark Ventures]
99 Yorkville Ave, Ste. 200
Toronto, ON, Canada M5R 3K5
Co. E-mail: support@brightspark.com
URL: http://brightspark.com/en
Contact: Audrey Ostiguy, Chief Compliance Officer
E-mail: audrey@brightspark.com
X (Twitter): x.com/brightsparkvc
YouTube: www.youtube.com/channel/UCpbNQPF1g4uer8CyADKObww
Description: Venture capital firm for early-stage tech companies. **Founded:** 1999.

46780 ■ Capital Angel Network (CAN)
c/o L-Spark
340 Legget Dr.
Kanata, ON, Canada K2K 1Y6
Co. E-mail: info@capitalangels.ca
URL: http://www.capitalangels.ca
Contact: Dane Bedward, Chief Executive Officer
Linkedin: www.linkedin.com/company/capital-angel-network
X (Twitter): x.com/capitalangels
Description: Invests in startups in the National Capital Region. **Founded:** 2009. **Investment Policies:** Prefers a growing customer base with previous funding. **Industry Preferences:** B2B/Enterprise SaaS; Internet of Things; artificial intelligence; cybersecurity; health and wellness technology.

46781 ■ Celtic House Venture Partners
239 Argyle Ave.
Ottawa, ON, Canada K2P 1B8
Ph: (613)569-7200
URL: http://www.celtic.vc
Contact: David Adderley, Partner
Description: Canadian investment firm offers investment services for early stage and startup companies, technology industry. **Founded:** 1994. **Industry Preferences:** Computer software and services, semiconductors and other electronics, communications and media, Internet specific, medical and health, and computer hardware.

46782 ■ Clairvest Group Inc.
22 St. Clair Ave. E, Ste. 1700
Toronto, ON, Canada M4T 2S3
Ph: (416)925-9270
Fax: (416)925-5753
URL: http://www.clairvest.com
Contact: Michael Wagman, President
E-mail: mwagman@clairvest.com
Description: Private equity management firm provides equity investment, equity partners funds, venture debt and bridge financing for Canadian corporations. **Founded:** 1987. **Preferred Investment Size:** $15,000,000 to $50,000,000.

46783 ■ Crosbie & Company Inc.
150 King St. W, 15th Fl.
Toronto, ON, Canada M5H 1J9
Ph: (416)362-7726
Free: 866-873-7002
Fax: (416)362-3447
Co. E-mail: info@crosbieco.com
URL: http://www.crosbieco.com
Contact: Colin Walker, Managing Director
E-mail: cwalker@crosbieco.com
Description: Provider of financial advisory and investment banking services for private and public companies, business owners, families and shareholder groups. **Founded:** 1989. **Industry Preferences:** Communications and media, computer software, semiconductors and other electronics, medical and health, consumer related, industrial and energy, business service, manufacturing, agriculture, forestry and fishing.

46784 ■ DRI Healthcare
100 King St. W, Ste. 7250
Toronto, ON, Canada M5X 1B1
Ph: (416)863-1865
Co. E-mail: info@drihealthcare.com
URL: http://drihealthcare.com
Contact: Behzad Khosrowshahi, Chief Executive Officer
E-mail: bk@drihealthcare.com
Description: Provider of private equity investments in late venture, buyouts, health-care and life sciences sector. **Founded:** 1992. **Preferred Investment Size:** $3,000,000 to $4,000,000. **Industry Preferences:** Biotechnology, medical and health.

46785 ■ Emerald Technology Ventures Inc.
1320-161 Bay St.
Toronto, ON, Canada M5J 2S1
Ph: (416)900-3453
Co. E-mail: info@emerald.vc
URL: http://emerald.vc
Contact: Frank Balas, Director
Linkedin: www.linkedin.com/company/emeraldvc
Description: Venture capital fund. Also maintains an office in Zurich. **Founded:** 2000. **Industry Preferences:** Emerging industrial technology.

46786 ■ FirePower Capital
47 Front St. E, Ste. 200
Toronto, ON, Canada M5E 1B3
Ph: (647)260-2069
Free: 877-394-9401
Co. E-mail: info@firepowercapital.com
URL: http://www.firepowercapital.com/home
Contact: Ilan Jacobson, Chief Executive Officer
E-mail: ijacobson@firepowercapital.com
Linkedin: www.linkedin.com/company/firepower-capital
X (Twitter): x.com/firepowercap
YouTube: www.youtube.com/channel/UCbioCTy58iQ-6uQ3ZFXjuBA
Description: Offers private capital and M&A advice. Works exclusively for privately-owned Canadian companies. **Founded:** 2012.

46787 ■ First Ascent Ventures (FAV)
10 King St. E, Ste. 900
Toronto, ON, Canada M5C 1C3
Co. E-mail: deals@firstascent.vc
URL: http://firstascentventures.com
Contact: Katharine Tomko, Partner
Linkedin: www.linkedin.com/company/firstascentvc
X (Twitter): x.com/FirstAscent_VC
Description: Venture capital firm for emerging technology companies in Canada. Usually invests at Series A. **Founded:** 2015. **Investment Policies:** Companies building disruptive enterprise B2B software. **Industry Preferences:** Cloud, big data, analytics, mobility, AI, and machine learning.

46788 ■ Genesys Capital
123 Front St. W, Ste. 1503
Toronto, ON, Canada M5J 2M2
Ph: (416)598-4900
Co. E-mail: info@genesyscapital.com
URL: http://www.genesyscapital.com
Contact: Kelly Holman, Co-Founder Managing Director
X (Twitter): x.com/genesyscapital
Description: Venture capital firm. Accelerates the development of commercially viable emerging.life science companies. **Industry Preferences:** Healthcare and biotechnology.

46789 ■ Georgian Angel Network (GAN)
Barrie, ON, Canada
URL: http://www.georgianangelnet.ca
Contact: Michael Badham, President
Linkedin: www.linkedin.com/company/georgian-angel-network
X (Twitter): x.com/GeorgianAngels
Description: Connects investors and entrepreneurs in the Barrie, Collingwood, Simcoe, and Muskoka areas to fund innovation. **Founded:** 2010.

46790 ■ Hedgewood Inc.
99 Yorkville Ave., Ste. 200
Toronto, ON, Canada M5R 3K5
URL: http://hedgewood.com
Contact: Jesse Rasch, Managing Director Founder
Description: Offers venture capital, financing, and asset management services. Focuses on early stage companies in digital media and ecommerce, industries. **Founded:** 2000. **Industry Preferences:** Consumer internet; SaaS; IoT; fintech; DTC food and consumer health products.

46791 ■ iGan Partners
60 Bloor St. W, 9th Fl.
Toronto, ON, Canada M4W 3B8
Ph: (416)925-2433
Co. E-mail: info@iganpartners.com
URL: http://iganpartners.com
Contact: Sam Ifergan, Founder Managing Partner
Linkedin: www.linkedin.com/company/igan-partners
X (Twitter): x.com/iganvc
Description: Venture capital firm. Looks to commercialize and scale disruptive innovations in health technology. **Founded:** 2011. **Investment Policies:** Entrepreneurs with proven healthcare technologies. **Industry Preferences:** Health technology.

46792 ■ Jefferson Partners
250 Yonge St., Ste. 2201
Toronto, ON, Canada M5B 2L7
Co. E-mail: info@jefferson.com
URL: http://www.jeffersonpartners.com
Contact: Jayraj Chheda, Chief Executive Officer
URL(s): www.jefferson.com
Description: Investment firm focusing on web technologies and applications software and services. **Founded:** 1987. **Preferred Investment Size:** $5,000,000 to $15,000,000. **Industry Preferences:** Communications and media, computer software and Internet specific.

46793 ■ Kilmer Capital Partners
Scotia Plz., Ste. 2700
40 King St. W
Toronto, ON, Canada M5H 3Y2
URL: http://www.minkcapital.ca/kilmer-capital-partners
Contact: Lawrence Tanenbaum, Chief Executive Officer
Description: Private equity investment firm focused on small to mid-sized businesses undergoing rapid growth, significant change, or ownership transition. **Founded:** 1954. **Industry Preferences:** Electronics; communication; technology; food; apparel; health care; consumer products; media; entertainment.

46794 ■ McLean Watson Capital Inc.
141 Adelaide St. W, Ste. 1002
Toronto, ON, Canada M5H 3L5
Ph: (416)363-2000
Fax: (416)363-2010
Co. E-mail: information@mcleanwatson.com
URL: http://www.mcleanwatson.com
Contact: John Eckert, Partner
E-mail: john@round13capital.com
Description: Provider of seed, early stage, mid stage and late stage investments for information technology and communications sectors. **Founded:** 1992. **Preferred Investment Size:** $1,000,000 to $5,000,000. **Industry Preferences:** Communications and media, computer software, computer related, semiconductors and other electronics.

46795 ■ Middlefield Capital Corp.
Middlefield Canadian Income PCC
The Well | Spadina Ave., Ste. 3100
Toronto, ON, Canada M5V 0S8
Ph: (416)362-0714
Free: 888-890-1868
Fax: (416)362-7925
URL: http://middlefield.com
Contact: Dean Orrico, President
Facebook: www.facebook.com/middlefieldgrp
Linkedin: www.linkedin.com/company/middlefield-group
X (Twitter): x.com/MiddlefieldGrp
Description: Provider of investment products including mutual funds, closed-end funds, private and public resource funds, real estate funds and venture capital fund for individual and institutional investors. **Founded:** 1979. **Preferred Investment Size:** $3,000,000 minimum. **Industry Preferences:** Communications and media, computer hardware, semiconductors and other electronics, medical and health, consumer related, industrial and energy, transportation, financial services, agriculture, forestry and fishing.

46796 ■ Mosaic Capital Partners
6300 Northam Dr.
Mississauga, ON, Canada L4V 1H7
Ph: (416)367-2888
Co. E-mail: info@mosaicvp.com
URL: http://mosaicvp.com
Contact: Ron Farmer, Managing Director
Description: Provider of mezzanine debt and equity investments for lower middle market companies. **Industry Preferences:** Internet specific.

46797 ■ Northern Ontario Angels
PO Box 2396
Sudbury, ON, Canada P3A 4S8
Free: 888-696-0808
Co. E-mail: info@northernontarioangels.ca
URL: http://northernontarioangels.ca
Contact: Ian Lane, Executive Director
E-mail: ian@northernontarioangels.ca
Facebook: www.facebook.com/NorthernOntarioAngels
Linkedin: www.linkedin.com/company/northern-ontario-angels
X (Twitter): x.com/noa_angels
Instagram: www.instagram.com/northernontarioangels
YouTube: www.youtube.com/channel/UCN3nk_VoORj15SApGZmXbHg
Description: Facilitates business connections between entrepreneurs and accredited angel investors in Northern Ontario.

46798 ■ Onex Corporation
Onex Corporation
161 Bay St.
Toronto, ON, Canada M5J 2S1
Ph: (416)362-7711
URL: http://www.onex.com
Contact: Bobby La Blanc, Chief Executive Officer
Description: Private equity firm manages assets and invests in non-investment grade debt through credit funds and collateralized debt obligations. **Founded:** 1984. **Preferred Investment Size:** $10,000,000 minimum.

46799 ■ Penfund Partners Inc.
Bay Adelaide Ctr., 333 Bay St., Ste. 610
Toronto, ON, Canada M5H 2R2
Ph: (416)865-0707
Fax: (416)364-4149
Co. E-mail: richard@penfund.com
URL: http://penfund.com
Contact: George Elarga, Director
E-mail: gelarga@penfund.com
Linkedin: www.linkedin.com/company/penfund
Description: Provider of debt and equity investments, finance buyouts, acquisitions, recapitalizations, ownership reorganizations and organic growth. **Founded:** 1979. **Preferred Investment Size:** $10,000 to $50,000,000.

46800 ■ Peterborough Region Angel Network (PRAN)
270 George St. N, 3rd Fl.
Peterborough, ON, Canada K9J 3H1
Co. E-mail: pran@innovationcluster.ca
URL: http://www.angelinvestorsontario.ca/angel-investor-groups/the-peterborough-region-angel-network-pran
Description: Angel investor network specializing in challenging business situations. **Investment Policies:** Competitive advantage; high value add; environmentally friendly; strong management skills; potential for international expansion. **Industry Preferences:** Information and communication technology; medical technology; green technology; biotechnology and life sciences.

46801 ■ Priveq Capital Funds
1500 Don Mills Rd., Ste. 711
Toronto, ON, Canada M3B 3K4
Ph: (416)447-3330
Co. E-mail: info@priveq.ca
URL: http://www.priveq.ca
Contact: Bradley W. Ashley, Managing Partner
Description: Provider of mid stage, later stage, expansion capital, management buy-out capital, late venture, industry consolidation and financial restructuring. **Founded:** 1994. **Preferred Investment Size:** $3,000,000 to $7,000,000. **Industry Preferences:** Semiconductors and other electronics, consumer related, industrial and energy, transportation, business services, and manufacturing.

46802 ■ Relay Ventures
446 Spadina Rd., Ste. 303
Toronto, ON, Canada M5P 3M2
Co. E-mail: toronto@relay.vc
URL: http://relay.vc
Contact: Jeannette Wiltse, Partner Chief Financial Officer
E-mail: jeannette@relayventures.com
Linkedin: www.linkedin.com/company/relay-ventures
X (Twitter): x.com/relayventures
Instagram: www.instagram.com/relayventures
Description: Firm operating venture capital firm. **Founded:** 1996. **Preferred Investment Size:** $500,000 to $10,000,000. **Industry Preferences:** Internet specific, other products, computer software and services, and computer hardware.

46803 ■ Round13 Capital
502- 111 Richmond St. W
Toronto, ON, Canada M5H 2G4
Co. E-mail: contact@round13.com
URL: http://round13.com
Contact: Lucie Mabadi, Manager
Linkedin: www.linkedin.com/company/round13capital
Description: Invests in growth-stage companies. **Founded:** 2013.

46804 ■ Roynat Ventures / Roynat Capital Corp.
Scotia Plz., 44 King St. SW
Toronto, ON, Canada M5H 1H1
URL: http://www.roynat.ca/en.html
Contact: Kenneth Pham, Director
E-mail: kenneth.pham@scotiabank.com
Linkedin: www.linkedin.com/company/roynat-capital

Description: Provider of private equity and venture capital investments. **Founded:** 1962. **Preferred Investment Size:** $250,000 to $50,000,000. **Industry Preferences:** Business services, consumer related, industrial and energy, manufacturing, and other products.

46805 ■ Ryerson Angel Network (RAN)
575 Bay St., Rm. TRS 1-007
Toronto, ON, Canada M5G 2C5
URL: http://ryersonentinstitute.org/torontomet-angel-network
Description: Student-led angel network for Canada. Affiliated with Ryerson University.

46806 ■ Skypoint Capital Corp.
1371 E Woodroofe Ave.
Nepean, ON, Canada K2G 1V7
Ph: (613)727-5073
Fax: (613)727-8768
Co. E-mail: info@skypointcorp.com
URL: http://skypointcorp.com
Description: Early-stage venture capital firm. **Industry Preferences:** Telecommunications and information technology.

46807 ■ Tech Capital Partners Inc.
8 Erb St. W
Waterloo, ON, Canada N2L 1S7
Ph: (519)883-8255
Fax: (519)883-1265
Co. E-mail: abouchar@techcapital.com
URL: http://techcapital.com
Contact: Andrew Abouchar, Co-Founder Partner
E-mail: abouchar@techcapital.com
Description: Venture capital firm for early-stage technology development. **Founded:** 2001. **Investment Policies:** Interested in engineers, scientists, or researches who develop technologies that solve difficult industry problems. Also interested in disruptive technologies with the potential to create new markets. **Industry Preferences:** Technology.

46808 ■ Tera Capital Corp.
2678 St. Johns Siderd
Stouffville, ON, Canada L4A 2T4
Ph: (416)368-8372
Free: 888-368-TERA
Fax: (416)368-1427
Co. E-mail: info@teracap.com
URL: http://teracap.com
Contact: Howard Sutton, President
Description: Provider of early stage, mid stage, later stage and growth capital investments. **Founded:** 1996. **Preferred Investment Size:** $250,000 to $1,000,000. **Industry Preferences:** Industrial and energy, biotechnology, financial services, computer hardware, semiconductors and other electronics, biotechnology, and consumer related.

46809 ■ TorQuest Partners
Brookfield Pl., 161 Bay St., Ste. 4240
Toronto, ON, Canada M5J 2S1
Ph: (416)956-7022
Co. E-mail: brock@torquest.com
URL: http://torquest.com
Contact: David Schneuker, Director
E-mail: schneuker@torquest.com
Description: Venture capital firm. **Founded:** 2002.

46810 ■ Trellis Capital Corp.
333 Wilson Ave., Ste. 600
North York, ON, Canada M3H 1T2
URL: http://trelliscapital.com
Contact: Sunil Selby, Founder Managing Partner
Description: Venture capital firm. **Founded:** 2000. **Investment Policies:** Innovative companies with scalable, efficient business models who can disrupt their markets; patented or proprietary innovation; approximately $5 million in revenue. **Industry Preferences:** Industrial technology; advances and specialty materials; clean technology; semiconductors; robotics; information technology.

46811 ■ Venture Niagara Community Futures Development Corporation
20 Pine St. N
Thorold, ON, Canada L2V 0A1
Ph: (905)680-8085
Co. E-mail: inquiries@ventureniagara.com
URL: http://www.ventureniagara.com/niagara-futures-development-corp
Contact: Frank Rupcic, General Manager
Facebook: www.facebook.com/venture.niagara
X (Twitter): x.com/NiagaraVenture
Instagram: www.instagram.com/ventureniagara20
Description: Offers business financing. business advisory services, and community development. **Founded:** 1985.

INCUBATORS/RESEARCH AND TECHNOLOGY PARKS

46812 ■ Accelerator Centre (AC)
295 Hagey Blvd. 1st Fl., W Entrance
Waterloo, ON, Canada N2L 6R5
Ph: (519)342-2400
Co. E-mail: info@acceleratorcentre.com
URL: http://www.acceleratorcentre.com
Contact: Jay Krishnan, Chief Executive Officer
Facebook: www.facebook.com/acceleratorcentre
Linkedin: www.linkedin.com/company/accelerator-centre
X (Twitter): x.com/AC_Waterloo
Instagram: www.instagram.com/accelerator_centre
Description: Helps entrepreneurs move from start-up to scale-up, accelerate their time to market, and help them attract customers, investment and revenue. **Founded:** 2006.

46813 ■ Altitude Accelerator
6 George St., S
Brampton, ON, Canada L6Y 1P1
Ph: (289)373-3050
Co. E-mail: info@altitudeaccelerator.ca
URL: http://altitudeaccelerator.ca
Contact: Pam Banks, Executive Director
Facebook: www.facebook.com/altitudeaccelerator
Linkedin: www.linkedin.com/company/altitudeaccel
X (Twitter): x.com/altitudeaccel
YouTube: www.youtube.com/user/RICCentre
Description: Business incubator working with early stage companies to help define and shape the idea with the hope that it will evolve into a viable business model.

46814 ■ Centennial College Centre of Entrepreneurship
PO Box 631, Station A
Toronto, ON, Canada M1K 5E9
Ph: (416)289-5000
Free: 800-268-4419
URL: http://www.centennialcollege.ca/about-centennial/centres-and-institutes/applied-research-innovation-and-entrepreneurship/our-innovation-areas/innovation-and-entrepreneurship
Description: Coaches and inspires future entrepreneurs. **Founded:** 1987.

46815 ■ Centre for Social Innovation (CSI)
720 Bathurst St.
Toronto, ON, Canada M5S 2R4
Ph: (416)979-3259
Co. E-mail: info@socialinnovation.ca
URL: http://socialinnovation.org
Contact: Tonya Surman, Chief Executive Officer
E-mail: tonya@socialinnovation.ca
Facebook: www.facebook.com/centreforsocialinnovation
Linkedin: www.linkedin.com/company/csitoronto
X (Twitter): x.com/csiTO
Instagram: www.instagram.com/csitoronto
YouTube: www.youtube.com/user/centreforSI
Description: Accelerate business' success and amplies impact through the power of coworking, community and collaboration, providing workspace, tools, resources, and connections to succeed. **Founded:** 2004.

46816 ■ CIMTEC
1151 Richmond St. N
London, ON, Canada N6A 3K7
URL: http://www.cimtecimaging.com
Contact: Aaron Fenster, Chief Executive Officer
E-mail: aaron.fenster@cimtec-canada.ca
X (Twitter): x.com/cimtecimaging
YouTube: www.youtube.com/user/CIMTECCanada
Description: Bridges the innovation gap for Canadian medical inventors by providing them with imaging expertise and business development services that accelerate the development of their innovation, and by investing in the most promising early-stage Canadian companies and licensing unique technologies.

46817 ■ Communitech Hub
151 Charles St. W, Ste. 100
Kitchener, ON, Canada N2G 1H6
Ph: (519)888-9944
Co. E-mail: front.desk@communitech.ca
URL: http://communitech.ca
Contact: Chris Albinson, President
X (Twitter): x.com/communitech
Instagram: www.instagram.com/communitech
Description: A private-public partnership driven by the mission to help tech companies start, grow and succeed. **Founded:** 1997.

46818 ■ Communitech Rev
151 Charles St. W, Ste. 100
Kitchener, ON, Canada N2G 1H6
Ph: (519)888-9944
Fax: (519)804-2224
Co. E-mail: front.desk@communitech.ca
URL: http://communitech.ca
Contact: Chris Albinson, President
Facebook: www.facebook.com/communitechpage
Linkedin: www.linkedin.com/company/communitech
X (Twitter): x.com/communitech
Instagram: www.instagram.com/communitech
Description: A revenue accelerator that drives highly-scalable startups to revenue success as quickly as possible. **Founded:** 1997.

46819 ■ David Johnston Research + Technology Park
200 University Ave. W GSC228
Waterloo, ON, Canada N2L 3G1
Ph: (226)339-8465
URL: http://rtpark.uwaterloo.ca
Contact: Mike Pereria, Manager
E-mail: mike.pereria@uwaterloo.ca
Facebook: www.facebook.com/RTParkUW
X (Twitter): x.com/RTPARKUW
Description: Research and technology park that fosters radical innovation by providing a powerfully supportive base for radical, high impact research.

46820 ■ Downtown Windsor Business Accelerator
1501 Howard Ave.
Windsor, ON, Canada N8X 3T5
Ph: (519)997-2888
Co. E-mail: hello@downtownaccelerator.com
URL: http://www.downtownaccelerator.com
Contact: Christopher Pressey, President
Facebook: www.facebook.com/downtownaccelerator
X (Twitter): x.com/accelerateideas
Description: A co-working space specifically designed to help accelerate the growth of start-up and emerging businesses, featuring on-site training and mentoring programs.

46821 ■ Elgin Business Resource Centre (EBRC)
300 S Edgeware Rd.
Saint Thomas, ON, Canada N5P 4L1
Ph: (519)633-7597
Fax: (877)450-2128
Co. E-mail: kjackson@elgincfdc.ca
URL: http://www.elgincfdc.ca
Contact: Hetty Teuber, President
E-mail: hteuber@elgincfdc.ca
Facebook: www.facebook.com/ElginBusinessResourceCentre
Instagram: www.instagram.com/elginbusinessresourcecentre
Description: Offers business resources, planning, workshops, training, market research, office space, and flexible lending. Encourages job creation through the creation of small businesses enterprises. **Founded:** 1996.

46822 ■ Generator at One
1 St. Paul St., Ste. A301
Sainte Catharines, ON, Canada L2R 7L2
Free: 888-984-3436
Co. E-mail: info@thegeneratoratone.com
URL: http://thegeneratoratone.com
Contact: Jeff Chesebrough, Chief Executive Officer
X (Twitter): twitter.com/search
Description: Acts as a catalyst for interactive digital media and tech growth in Niagara.

46823 ■ Haliburton County Development Corp. (HCDC)
5152 Haliburton County Rd., 21, 2nd Fl.
Haliburton, ON, Canada K0M 1S0
Ph: (705)457-3555
Fax: (705)457-3398
Co. E-mail: info@haliburtoncdc.ca
URL: http://www.haliburtoncdc.ca
Contact: Patti Tallman, Executive Director
E-mail: ptallman@haliburtoncdc.ca
Facebook: www.facebook.com/Haliburtoncdc
Linkedin: www.linkedin.com/company/haliburtoncdc
X (Twitter): x.com/InnovHaliburton
Instagram: www.instagram.com/haliburtoncdc
YouTube: www.youtube.com/channel/UCvuEhYkg9YtC9hfFM-8WyLg
Description: A non-profit organization offering services to promote small business growth and community economic development in Haliburton County. **Founded:** 1985.

46824 ■ Hamilton Technology Centre (HTC)
7 Innovation Dr.
Dundas, ON, Canada L9H 7H9
Ph: (905)667-3909
URL: http://hamiltontechnologycentre.ca
Linkedin: www.linkedin.com/company/hamilton-technology-centre
Description: Private innovation hub fosters technology companies. Offers space and community to new and accelerating companies. **Founded:** 1993.

46825 ■ Innovate Niagara (IN)
386 St. Paul St., Ste., 102
Sainte Catharines, ON, Canada L2R 7E1
Ph: (905)685-3460
Co. E-mail: info@innovateniagara.com
URL: http://www.innovateniagara.com/site/home
Contact: Jeff Chesebrough, Chief Executive Officer
Facebook: www.facebook.com/InnovateNiagara
Linkedin: www.linkedin.com/company/innovateniagara
X (Twitter): x.com/InnovateNiagara
Instagram: www.instagram.com/innovateniagara
Description: Connects innovators to the people and programs required to bring their innovations to market through a suite of in-house programs, resource partners, and network of incubation facilities. **Founded:** 2008.

46826 ■ Invest Ottawa (IO)
7 Bayview Station Rd.
Ottawa, ON, Canada K1Y 2C5
Ph: (613)828-6274
Co. E-mail: clientservices@investottawa.ca
URL: http://www.investottawa.ca
Contact: Michael Tremblay, President
Facebook: www.facebook.com/InvestOttawa
Linkedin: www.linkedin.com/company/invest-ottawa
X (Twitter): x.com/invest_ottawa
Instagram: www.instagram.com/investottawa
YouTube: www.youtube.com/user/InvestOttawa
Pinterest: www.pinterest.com/investottawa
Description: Invest Ottawa's Incite Incubator is the place to be for a startup that is ready to get into high gear. Participants receive regular access to facilities,

meeting space, Invest Ottawa expert staff, peer groups, and other energy-building programming. **Founded:** 1983. **Educational Activities:** BioNorth.

46827 ■ LaunchIt Minto
1 Elora St. Unit 4
Harriston, ON, Canada N0G 1Z0
Ph: (519)510-7400
Co. E-mail: info@launchitminto.com
URL: http://launchitminto.com
Facebook: www.facebook.com/LaunchItMinto
X (Twitter): x.com/launchitminto
Instagram: www.instagram.com/launchitminto
Description: Assists new businesses to start, grow and succeed in a creative environment. Provides training and mentorship program to LaunchIt Tenants, along with local established businesses. Also offers a private meeting room, board room, individual office space, smart television, professional photocopier and access to fibre optic wifi internet to it's tenants. **Founded:** 2014.

46828 ■ MaRS Discovery District
MaRS Centre, South Tower
101 College St., Ste. 100
Toronto, ON, Canada M5G 1L7
Ph: (416)673-8100
Co. E-mail: marsdiscoverydistrict@marsdd.com
URL: http://www.marsdd.com
Contact: Yung Wu, Chief Executive Officer
Facebook: www.facebook.com/MaRSCentre
X (Twitter): x.com/MaRSDD
YouTube: www.youtube.com/c/MaRSDiscoveryDistrict
Description: Works with an extensive network of partners to help entrepreneurs launch and grow innovative companies. **Founded:** 2000.

46829 ■ National Research Council of Canada (NRC)
1200 Montreal Rd. Building M-58
Ottawa, ON, Canada K1A 0R6
Ph: (613)993-9101
Free: 877-672-2672
Fax: (613)991-9096
Co. E-mail: info@nrc-cnrc.gc.ca
URL: http://nrc.canada.ca/en
Linkedin: www.linkedin.com/company/national-research-council
X (Twitter): x.com/nrc_cnrc
Instagram: www.instagram.com/nrc_cnrc
Description: Works with clients and partners to provide innovation support, strategic research, scientific and technical services. **Founded:** 1916.

46830 ■ Northwestern Ontario Innovation Centre (NOIC)
2400 Nipigon Rd.
Thunder Bay, ON, Canada P7C 4W1
Ph: (807)768-6682
Free: 866-768-6682
Fax: (807)768-6683
Co. E-mail: info@nwoinnovation.ca
URL: http://www.nwoinnovation.ca
Contact: Wayne VanderWees, President
Facebook: www.facebook.com/NWOInnovation
X (Twitter): x.com/NWOInnovation
Instagram: www.instagram.com/nwoinnovation
YouTube: www.youtube.com/user/NWOInnovationCentre
Description: Acts as a support system for innovation and strongly believe in collaboration and helping. Helps startups and entrepreneurs with connections, funding, resources, business expertise, and training so that you can achieve success. **Founded:** 1999.

46831 ■ Ontario Centre of Innovation (OCI)
325 Front St. W, Ste. 300
Toronto, ON, Canada M5V 2Y1
Ph: (416)861-1092
Free: 866-759-6014
Fax: (416)861-1092
URL: http://www.oc-innovation.ca
Contact: Dr. Claudia Krywiak, President
E-mail: ckrywiak@oc-innovation.ca
Facebook: www.facebook.com/OCInnovation
Linkedin: www.linkedin.com/company/ontario-centre-of-innovation
X (Twitter): x.com/OCInnovation
Instagram: www.instagram.com/ocinnovation
YouTube: www.youtube.com/user/OceDiscovery
Description: Drives the development of Ontario's economy by helping create new jobs, products, services, technologies and businesses. Co-invests to commercialize innovation originating in the province's publicly funded colleges, universities and research hospitals. We also support and invest in early-stage projects, where the probability of commercial success and potential total return on innovation are substantial. **Founded:** 1987. **Awards:** Martin Walmsley Award for Entrepreneurship (Annual). **Geographic Preference:** National.

46832 ■ Ryerson University - The DMZ
10 Dundas St. E, 6th Fl.
Toronto, ON, Canada M5B 2G9
Ph: (416)979-5000
Co. E-mail: dmz@ryerson.ca
URL: http://dmz.torontomu.ca
Contact: Abdullah Snobar, Executive Director
E-mail: asnobar@ryerson.ca
Facebook: www.facebook.com/TheDMZ
Linkedin: www.linkedin.com/company/thedmz
X (Twitter): x.com/theDMZ
Instagram: www.instagram.com/dmzhq
YouTube: www.youtube.com/user/ryersondmz
Description: Business incubator for emerging tech startups. Helps startups succeed by connecting them with customers, advisors, influencers, and other entrepreneurs.

46833 ■ Sault Ste. Marie Innovation Centre (SSMIC)
99 Foster Dr., Level 6
Sault Sainte Marie, ON, Canada P6A 5X6
Ph: (705)942-7927
Fax: (705)942-6169
Co. E-mail: info@ssmic.com
URL: http://www.ssmic.com
Contact: Dr. Ron Common, President
Facebook: www.facebook.com/ssminnovationcentre
Linkedin: www.linkedin.com/company/sault-ste.-marie-innovation-centre
X (Twitter): x.com/ssmicnews
Instagram: www.instagram.com/ssminnovation
YouTube: www.youtube.com/user/InnovationSSM
Description: Provides a host of services to support the growth of science and technology-focused companies as it works with small/medium sized enterprises (SMEs) to foster innovation, leverage talent through the creation of new jobs and commercialize products and services. **Founded:** 1999.

46834 ■ Spark Centre
2 Simcoe St. S, Ste. 300
Oshawa, ON, Canada L1H 8C1
Ph: (905)432-3999
Co. E-mail: info@sparkcentre.org
URL: http://sparkcentre.org
Contact: Sherry Colbourne, President
Facebook: www.facebook.com/SparkCentre
X (Twitter): x.com/spark_centre
Instagram: www.instagram.com/spark_centre
YouTube: www.youtube.com/channel/UCxLW8ClxEql3rXEJkgmz1Zg
Description: Regional Innovation Centre (RIC) providing resources and services to innovative and technology-based entrepreneurs and businesses less than five years old and making less than $1,000,000 in annual revenue. **Founded:** 2010.

46835 ■ Toronto Business Development Centre (TBDC)
325 Front St. W, Ste. 300
Toronto, ON, Canada M5V 2Y1
Ph: (416)345-9437
Fax: (416)981-3206
Co. E-mail: info@tbdc.com
URL: http://tbdc.com
Contact: Vikram Khurana, Chairman of the Board
Facebook: www.facebook.com/Torontobusinessdevelopmentcentre
Linkedin: www.linkedin.com/company/toronto-business-development-centre
X (Twitter): x.com/thetbdc
Description: Supports the growth of new and emerging businesses by providing access to a range of key resources such as business advisory support and participation in community of successful entrepreneurs. **Founded:** 1990.

46836 ■ Toronto Fashion Incubator (TFI)
285 Manitoba Dr., Exhibition Pl.
Toronto, ON, Canada M6K 3C3
Ph: (416)971-7117
Co. E-mail: tfi@fashionincubator.com
URL: http://fashionincubator.com
Contact: Susan Langdon, Chief Executive Officer
Facebook: www.facebook.com/Torontofashionincubator
X (Twitter): x.com/TorontoFashion
Instagram: www.instagram.com/tfi_fashionincubator
YouTube: www.youtube.com/user/TFIfashionincubator
Description: Incubator dedicated to supporting and nurturing Canadian fashion designers and entrepreneurs. **Founded:** 1987.

46837 ■ University of Windsor (EPIC) - Entrepreneurship Practice and Innovation Centre
401 Sunset Ave.
Windsor, ON, Canada N9B 3P4
Ph: (519)253-3000
Co. E-mail: epicentre@uwindsor.ca
URL: http://www.epicentreuwindsor.ca
Contact: Wen Teoh, Director
E-mail: wteoh@uwindsor.ca
Facebook: www.facebook.com/epicentre.uwindsor
Linkedin: www.linkedin.com/company/epicentre-uwindsor
X (Twitter): x.com/UofW_EPICentre
Instagram: www.instagram.com/epicentre_uwindsor
YouTube: www.youtube.com/user/epicentreuwindsor
Description: A campus-wide initiative created to encourage entrepreneurship on campus, and to support students and graduates interested in launching their own businesses. Hosts more than 60 programs and activities each year, including three incubators on campus. **Founded:** 2014.

46838 ■ Velocity
151 Charles St. W, Ste. 199
Kitchener, ON, Canada N2G 1H6
Ph: (519)804-2240
Co. E-mail: velocity@uwaterloo.ca
URL: http://velocityincubator.com
Contact: Adrien Cote, Executive Director
Facebook: www.facebook.com/velocityincubator
YouTube: www.youtube.com/user/uwvelocity
Description: A leading entrepreneurship program at the University of Waterloo and the largest free startup incubator in the world. Provides the knowledge, tools, space and network that startups and entrepreneurs need for success. The Velocity program includes a student dorm, workspaces in Waterloo region, events, mentor programs and more.

46839 ■ WEtech Alliance
Joyce Entrepreneurship Centre 2455 Wyandotte St. W 2nd Fl.
Windsor, ON, Canada N9B 0C1
Ph: (519)997-2863
Co. E-mail: info@wetech-alliance.com
URL: http://www.wetech-alliance.com
Contact: Yvonne Pilon, President
E-mail: ypilon@wetech-alliance.com
Facebook: www.facebook.com/WeTechAlliance
X (Twitter): x.com/WETECHALLIANCE
YouTube: www.youtube.com/user/WetechAlliance
Description: Champions innovation and aids the growth of tech companies at all stages and champions innovation in Windsor-Essex and Chatham-Kent. **Founded:** 2009.

46840 ■ Wilfrid Laurier University - LaunchPad
Community Innovation Hub, MDC 103, 67 Darling St.
Brantford, ON, Canada N3T 2K6
Ph: (519)802-8709
Co. E-mail: launchpadbrantford@wlu.ca
URL: http://students.wlu.ca/work-leadership-and-volunteering/entrepreneurship/launchpad-brantford/index.html
Facebook: www.facebook.com/LaurierLaunchPadBrantford
X (Twitter): x.com/LaunchPad_Brant
Instagram: www.instagram.com/laurier_launchpad
Description: Business incubator for startups providing mentoring, support, workspace, and networking opportunities. **Founded:** 1911.

EDUCATIONAL PROGRAMS

46841 ■ University of Ottawa - Startup Garage
150 Louis Pasteur Private, Complexe STEM Complex
Ottawa, ON, Canada K1N 6N5
Co. E-mail: ehub@uottawa.ca
URL: http://startupgarage.ca
Description: Offers youth-led ventures the opportunity to accelerate their business by providing four essential tools, including funding, work space, mentorship, and training, through a 3-month program.

CONSULTANTS

46842 ■ Business Advisory Centre of Northumberland (BECN)
600 William St., Ste. 700
Cobourg, ON, Canada K9A 3A5
Ph: (905)372-9279
Free: 800-354-7050
Fax: (905)373-8567
Co. E-mail: bizhelp@northumberlandcounty.ca
URL: http://www.northumberland.ca/en/becn/becn.aspx
Contact: Rob Day, Manager
Facebook: www.facebook.com/BECNorthumberland
Description: Assists small businesses and entrepreneurs with business plan development, marketing plan assistance, and licensing guidance. Offers seminars, workshops, business coaching, and networking opportunities. **Founded:** 1977.

46843 ■ Business Advisory Group (BAG)
5230 S Service Rd.
Burlington, ON, Canada L7L 5P2
Free: 866-278-2480
Co. E-mail: bag@smallbusinessadvisory.com
URL: http://smallbusinessadvisory.com
Contact: Michael Harrison, Officer
Facebook: www.facebook.com/SmallBusinessAdvisory
X (Twitter): x.com/bizadvisorygrp
Description: Offers consulting and mentoring to small and medium-sized businesses. **Founded:** 1984.

46844 ■ Business Enterprise Centre (BEC)
1130 8th St., E
Owen Sound, ON, Canada N4K 1M7
Co. E-mail: bec@grey.ca
URL: http://madeingrey.ca/business-enterprise-centre
Contact: Courtney Miller, Business Manager
E-mail: courtney.miller@grey.ca
Description: Offers Grey County entrepreneurs tools, information, and guidance to start or expand small businesses. .

46845 ■ Canadawide Financial Corporation Ltd. (CFCL)
420 Britannia Rd. E, Ste. 204
Mississauga, ON, Canada L4Z 3L5
Ph: (647)699-9890
Free: 844-699-9890
Co. E-mail: info@canadawidefinancial.ca
URL: http://www.canadawidefinancial.ca
Contact: Pramod Goyal, President
Linkedin: www.linkedin.com/company-beta/995784
Description: Business-based management and consulting firm. Serves small and mid-sized businesses. Specializes in business financing, strategy, financial and legal advice, cash flow, systems and process optimization, operational efficiency, business restructuring, and international growth.

46846 ■ Emerge2 Digital Inc.
554 Parkside Dr.
Waterloo, ON, Canada N2L 5Z4
Ph: (519)886-0100
Free: 888-242-5453
Fax: (519)886-1027
Co. E-mail: sales@emerge2.com
URL: http://emerge2.com
Facebook: www.facebook.com/Emerge2
Linkedin: www.linkedin.com/company/emerge2-digital
X (Twitter): x.com/Emerge2
Instagram: www.instagram.com/emerge2digital
Description: Consultants who develop strategies to grow and enhance small businesses. **Scope:** Consultants who develop strategies to grow and enhance small businesses. **Founded:** 2000.

46847 ■ Ignition Communications
10 Aberdeen Rd. S
Cambridge, ON, Canada N1S 2X4
Ph: (519)574-2196
Co. E-mail: info@ignition.ca
URL: http://www.ignition.ca
Contact: Ellyn Winters, President
Facebook: www.facebook.com/ignitioninc
X (Twitter): x.com/ellynjane
Description: Boutique marketing and PR firm. Specialized in high-growth tech companies. **Founded:** 1994.

46848 ■ MFServices [Marketing Financial Services]
958 Snowbird St.
Oshawa, ON, Canada LIJ 8J8
Ph: (905)579-8064
Fax: (905)579-5688
URL: http://mfservices.ca
Description: Consulting group. Specializes in providing a full range of business services to small and medium-sized companies. Assists in strategic planning, raising capital, liquidation, or launching new products.

46849 ■ Plan2Profit (P2P)
1150 Effingham St.
Ridgeville, ON, Canada L0S 1M0
Free: 844-752-6776
URL: http://plan2profit.ca
Contact: Paul Morgan, Owner
YouTube: www.youtube.com/channel/UCRB4R2vWJCLaYzbxDzaSQUA
Description: Business plan writers. Also consults with business plan clients on pricing, marketing, and strategy. **Founded:** 2002.

46850 ■ Quovis Consulting Corp.
92 Lakeshore Rd. E, Ste. 225
Mississauga, ON, Canada L5G 4S2
Ph: (905)271-7006
Co. E-mail: info@quovisconsulting.com
URL: http://www.quovisconsulting.com
Description: Assists technology-based companies with funding and marketing.

46851 ■ RK Fischer & Associates
ON, Canada
Ph: (289)278-1970
Free: 877-504-2049
Co. E-mail: info@rkfischer.com
URL: http://www.rkfischer.com
Contact: Karen Fischer, Partner
Linkedin: www.linkedin.com/company/rk-fischer-&-associates
X (Twitter): x.com/rkfischer
Instagram: www.instagram.com/rkfischerassoc
YouTube: www.youtube.com/channel/UCdnWK6pHlZay6D5fx8BpGjw
Pinterest: www.pinterest.ca/rkfischerassoc
Description: Small business consultant, coach, and advisory firm. Offers business, marketing, finance, operations, and sales consulting. **Founded:** 2010.

46852 ■ Small Business Centre (SBC)
119 Chatham St. W, Unit 100
Windsor, ON, Canada N9A 5M7
Ph: (519)253-6900
Free: 888-255-9332
Fax: (519)255-9987
Co. E-mail: info@webusinesscentre.com
URL: http://www.webusinesscentre.com
Contact: Sabrina DeMarco, Executive Director
Facebook: www.facebook.com/WEBusinessCentre
Linkedin: www.linkedin.com/company/webusinesscentre
X (Twitter): x.com/wesmallbusiness
Instagram: www.instagram.com/webusinesscentre
Description: Offers consulting, business support, research assistance and networking opportunities to small businesses. Operates as a department of the WindsorEssex Economic Development Corp. **Founded:** 1992.

46853 ■ The Small Business Centre (SBC)
453 Dundas St.
Woodstock, ON, Canada N4S 1C2
Ph: (519)539-2382
Co. E-mail: smallbusiness@cityofwoodstock.ca
URL: http://www.sbcoxford.ca
Contact: Shawn McNamara, Manager
E-mail: smcnamara@cityofwoodstock.ca
Facebook: www.facebook.com/theSmallBusinessCentre
X (Twitter): x.com/woodstocksbec
Instagram: www.instagram.com/thesmallbusinesscentre
YouTube: www.youtube.com/channel/UCV4KfX2OUQeiyf1oD3MNkiw
Description: Offers consulting, business coaching, business plan review, cash flow projection assistance, professional service referrals, workshops, and networking opportunities to small businesses. Operates in partnership with the Province of Ontario, the City of Woodstock, and Oxford County. **Founded:** 2002.

46854 ■ Small Business Centre (SBC)
379 Dundas St., Unit 220
London, ON, Canada N6B 1V5
Ph: (519)659-2882
Co. E-mail: info@sbcentre.ca
URL: http://www.sbcentre.ca
Contact: Frank Snyders, President
Facebook: www.facebook.com/SBCLondon
Linkedin: www.linkedin.com/company/the-london-small-business-centre
X (Twitter): x.com/sbclondon
Instagram: www.instagram.com/sbclondon_
Description: Offers consulting, business coaching, business plan review, professional service referrals, workshops, and networking opportunities to small businesses. Operates in partnership with the Province of Ontario, the City of Woodstock, and Oxford County. **Founded:** 1986.

46855 ■ Venture Accelerator Partners
321 Carlaw Ave, Ste. 202
Toronto, ON, Canada M4M 2S1
Ph: (647)401-7156
Co. E-mail: info@vapartners.ca
URL: http://vapartners.ca
Contact: Mark Elliott, Co-Founder
E-mail: melliott@vapartners.ca
Facebook: www.facebook.com/VentureAcceleratorPartners
Linkedin: www.linkedin.com/company/venture-accelerator-partners-inc
X (Twitter): x.com/vapartners
Instagram: www.instagram.com/vapartners
YouTube: www.youtube.com/user/VAPartners
Description: Offers B2B sales, marketing and lead generation services to startups. **Founded:** 2006.

STATE LISTINGS
Ontario ■ 46873

PUBLISHERS

46856 ■ Bench-Strength Mail Associates
4936 Yonge St., Ste. 250
Toronto, ON, Canada M2N 6S3
Ph: (905)886-4674
Co. E-mail: htse@bsma.ca
URL: http://bsma.ca
Contact: Henry Tse, Contact
E-mail: htse@bsma.ca

Description: Publisher of materials to help people to start their own business. **Founded:** 1982.

46857 ■ Digital Leisure Inc. (DL)
65 W Beaver Creek Rd.
Richmond Hill, ON, Canada L4B 1K4
Ph: (416)802-9818
Co. E-mail: info@digitalleisure.com
URL: http://digitalleisure.com
Facebook: www.facebook.com/DigitalLeisure
Linkedin: www.linkedin.com/company/digital-leisure-inc
X (Twitter): x.com/digitalleisure
YouTube: www.youtube.com/user/Digitalleisure

Description: Publisher of books on video games. **Founded:** 1997.

46858 ■ The Dun & Bradstreet Companies of Canada ULC
Dun & Bradstreet Holdings, Inc. (D&B)
6750 Century Ave., Ste. 305
Mississauga, ON, Canada L5N 0B7
Ph: (904)648-6350
Co. E-mail: info@dnb.com
URL: http://www.dnb.com
Contact: William P. Foley, II, Chairman

Description: Publishes business information reports and directories. Reaches market through sales and service representatives, telephone sales and direct mail. **Founded:** 1841. **Publications:** *Canadian Key Business Directory* (Annual); *Dun & Bradstreet Guide to Canadian Manufacturers (DBGCM)*; *Dun & Bradstreet United States* (Quarterly); *DunsPrint Canada* (Continuous); *Commercial Guide of Venezuela* (Semiannual); *DUNSERVE II* (Bimonthly).

46859 ■ Ivey Publishing
Ivey Business School Foundation, Western University, 1255 Western Rd.
London, ON, Canada N6G 0N1
Free: 800-649-6355
Fax: (519)661-3882
Co. E-mail: cases@ivey.ca
URL: http://www.iveypublishing.ca/s
Contact: Matt Quin, Director
Linkedin: www.linkedin.com/company/ivey-publishing
X (Twitter): x.com/IveyPublishing
YouTube: www.youtube.com/channel/UCd7BGZ_f dQfFlRL_HJ1TsgQ

Description: Publishes business case studies. Publishes CD-ROM's. Reaches market through direct mail and telephone sales. Accepts unsolicited manuscripts.

46860 ■ Laurier Institute
75 University Ave. W
Waterloo, ON, Canada N2L 3C5
Ph: (519)884-0710
Fax: (519)884-0618
Co. E-mail: servicelaurier@wlu.ca
URL: http://www.wlu.ca
Contact: Dr. Deborah MacLatchy, President
E-mail: president@wlu.ca
Facebook: www.facebook.com/WilfridLaurierUniversity
Linkedin: www.linkedin.com/school/wilfrid-laurier-university
X (Twitter): x.com/Laurier
YouTube: www.youtube.com/user/LaurierVideo

Description: Publishes management case studies in all areas of business and economics in English and French. **Scope:** Designs and delivers management training and development programs to organizations throughout the business community. **Founded:** 1983.

46861 ■ maranGraphics Inc.
Mississauga, ON, Canada

Description: Publisher of computer books and manuals. **Founded:** 1975.

46862 ■ Pearson Canada Inc.
Pearson Canada Inc.
26 Prince Andrew Pl.
Don Mills, ON, Canada M3C 2T8
URL: http://www.pearson.com/en-ca.html

Description: Publishes fiction, nonfiction, textbooks, reference books and trade books. **Founded:** 1966.

46863 ■ Productive Publications
380 Brooke Ave.
North York, ON, Canada M5M 2L6
Ph: (416)483-0634
Free: 877-879-2669
Fax: (416)322-7434
Co. E-mail: productivepublications@gmail.com
URL: http://www.productivepublications.ca
Contact: Iain Williamson, Author Publisher

Description: Publisher of fiction and non-fiction books. **Founded:** 1985.

46864 ■ White Mountain Publications
White Mountain Publications
8 Prospect Ave.
Cobalt, ON, Canada P0J 1C0
Ph: (705)679-5555
Free: 800-258-5451
Co. E-mail: wmpub@wmpub.ca
URL: http://www.wmpub.ca
Contact: Deborah Ranchuk, Owner
Facebook: www.facebook.com/wmpub

Description: Publisher of books covering children literature, poetry, nonfiction and how-to books. **Founded:** 1982.

RESEARCH CENTERS

46865 ■ Canadian Innovation Centre Resource Centre (CIC)
Waterloo Research & Technology Park Accelerator Ctr.
295 Hagey Blvd., Ste. 15
Waterloo, ON, Canada N2L 6R5
Ph: (519)885-5870
Fax: (519)513-2421
Co. E-mail: info@innovationcentre.ca
URL: http://innovationcentre.ca
Contact: E. B. Cross, Chairman
E-mail: tcross@innovationcentre.ca
Linkedin: www.linkedin.com/company/canadian-innovation-centre
X (Twitter): x.com/innovationctre

Scope: Technological innovation; invention; entrepreneurship; business start-up; patents; licensing. **Services:** Copying; center open to the public for reference use only. **Founded:** 1975. **Holdings:** Figures not available.

EARLY STAGE FINANCING

46866 ■ JOLT
101 College St., Ste. 230
Toronto, ON, Canada M5G 1L7
Linkedin: www.linkedin.com/company/jolt-accelerator

Description: Invests in great ideas that leverage technology to improve the way people live, learn, work and play. The JOLT Fund LP provides program participants with seed capital while generating a market-rate return for its limited partners. **Founded:** 2012.

46867 ■ York Angel Investors (YAI)
169 Enterprise Dr., 301
Markham, ON, Canada ON L6G
Co. E-mail: info@yorkangels.com
URL: http://yorkangels.com
Contact: Emma Fuller, Officer
Linkedin: www.linkedin.com/company/york-angel-investors
X (Twitter): x.com/YorkAngels

Description: Group of accredited investors investing in early-stage startups. **Founded:** 2008. **Industry Preferences:** Digital media; software; mobile; telecom; web-based services; SaaS; healthcare; biotech; pharmaceuticals; medical equipment; clean technology; retail.

EXPANSION AND GROWTH FINANCING

46868 ■ Eventi Capital Partners (ECP)
250 Yonge St., Ste. 1602
Toronto, ON, Canada M5B 2L7
URL: http://www.eventi.com
Contact: Derek Ruston, Co-Founder

Description: Capital investment firm for tech-driven operating companies in need of growth capital and greater senior management capability to accelerate the transition to scalable ventures. **Founded:** 2002. **Investment Policies:** Seeks domain expertise, recurring revenue, industry leadership, and network leverage. **Industry Preferences:** SaaS; Internet infrastructure; medical devices.

VENTURE CAPITAL FIRM

46869 ■ Beehive Venture Capital
99 Yorkville Ave., Ste. 205
Toronto, ON, Canada M5R 3K5
Co. E-mail: info@hive.vc
URL: http://hive.vc

Description: Venture capital firm. Also maintains offices in New York and Menlo Park. **Founded:** 2018.

46870 ■ Extreme Venture Partners (EVP)
67 Yonge St., Ste. 1600
Toronto, ON, Canada M5E 1J8
Linkedin: www.linkedin.com/company/extreme-venture-partners

Description: An early-stage technology venture capital firm focused on pre-seed & seed startups in the Toronto-Waterloo corridor. **Founded:** 2007.

46871 ■ GCI Capital
4789 Yonge St., Unit 706
North York, ON, Canada M2N 0G3
Ph: (416)218-8838
Co. E-mail: info@gci.vc
URL: http://www.gci.vc
Facebook: www.facebook.com/GCICapital
Linkedin: www.linkedin.com/company/gcicapital

Description: Early-stage venture capital firm. **Founded:** 2013. **Industry Preferences:** Information, communication, technology (ICT); marketplace; digital health; B2B SaaS.

46872 ■ Highline
372 Bay St., 2nd Fl.
Toronto, ON, Canada M5H 2W9
Ph: (647)968-7694
Co. E-mail: hello@highlinebeta.com
URL: http://highlinebeta.com
Linkedin: www.linkedin.com/company/highlinebeta
X (Twitter): x.com/HighlineBeta

Description: A Canadian based pre-seed venture capital firm that supports early stage technology companies that are working hard to bring the future to life.

46873 ■ Lumira Ventures
141 Adelaide St., Ste. 770
Toronto, ON, Canada M5H 3L5
Ph: (416)213-4223
URL: http://www.lumiraventures.com
Contact: Gerry Brunk, Managing Director
Linkedin: www.linkedin.com/company/lumira-ventures

Description: Venture capital firm building transformational health and life science companies. Backs North American companies often bypassed by other investors. Also has offices in Montreal, Vancouver, and Boston. **Industry Preferences:** Biotechnology; medical technologies; digital health; consumer healthcare solutions.

46874 ■ Mantella Venture Partners (MVP)
488 Wellington St. W, Ste. 304
Toronto, ON, Canada M5V 1E3
Ph: (416)479-0779
Co. E-mail: info@mantellavp.com
URL: http://www.mantellavp.com
Contact: Chris Sukornyk, Chief Executive Officer
X (Twitter): x.com/MantellaVP
Description: Invests in exceptional entrepreneurs building market-altering mobile and Internet software businesses.

46875 ■ Pinnacle Capital Inc.
Brookfeild Pl., Bay Wellington Twr.
181 Bay St., Ste. 2830
Toronto, ON, Canada M5J 2T3
Co. E-mail: info@pincap.com
URL: http://www.pincap.com
Description: Invests in small and medium-sized companies at all stages of the company life cycle. Prefers out-of-favor, distressed, and unconventional opportunities. Also has an office in Calgary. **Founded:** 1998.

46876 ■ Sapient Capital Partners Corp.
The Gooderham Flatiron Bldg.
49 Wellington St. E, Ste. 502
Toronto, ON, Canada M5E 1C9
Description: Venture capital firm for small to mid-size technology and tech-enabled service companies. **Founded:** 2005. **Industry Preferences:** Software; web and technology-enabled manufacturing and services.

46877 ■ Whitecap Venture Partners
22 St. Clair Ave. E, Ste. 1010
Toronto, ON, Canada M4T 2S3
Ph: (416)961-5355
Co. E-mail: info@whitecapvp.com
URL: http://www.whitecapvp.com
Contact: Alice Celis, Manager, Accounting
E-mail: alice@whitecastle.ca
Linkedin: www.linkedin.com/company/whitecap-venture-partners
X (Twitter): x.com/Whitecapvp
Description: Early-stage venture capital fund for high-growth companies. **Founded:** 1993. **Industry Preferences:** Information technology; food technology; medical technology.

Prince Edward Island

ASSOCIATIONS AND OTHER ORGANIZATIONS

46878 ■ Innovation PEI
94 Euston St.
　Charlottetown, PE, Canada C1A 7L9
Ph: (902)368-6300
Free: 800-563-3734
Fax: (902)368-6301
Co. E-mail: innovation@gov.pe.ca
URL: http://www.innovationpei.com
Contact: Stefanie Corbett, Chief Executive Officer
Facebook: www.facebook.com/innovationpe
X (Twitter): x.com/Innovation_PEI
YouTube: www.youtube.com/channel/
　UCgovvWxAzGKiMBTsfzSQ12A

Description: Firm engages in providing economic development services in Prince Edward Island. **Founded:** 1991. **Educational Activities:** APEC Annual Business Outlook Conference (Annual).

BETTER BUSINESS BUREAUS

46879 ■ Better Business Bureau of Atlantic Provinces
7071 Bayers Rd., Ste. 279
　Halifax, NS, Canada B3L 2C2
Ph: (902)422-6581
Free: 877-663-2363
Fax: (902)429-6457
URL: http://www.bbb.org/local-bbb/better-business
　-bureau-serving-the-atlantic-provinces
Facebook: www.facebook.com/BBBAtlantic

Description: Aims to to create and maintain an ethical marketplace in the region of Newfoundland and Labrador. **Publications:** *Better Business Bureau of Newfoundland and Labrador--Directory and Consumer Guide* (Annual).

INCUBATORS/RESEARCH AND TECHNOLOGY PARKS

46880 ■ Atlantic Technology Centre (ATC)
176 Great George St.
　Charlottetown, PE, Canada C1A 4K9
Ph: (902)569-7600
Co. E-mail: atcservicedesk@gov.pe.ca
URL: http://atlantictechnologycentre.ca
Contact: Norma Kennific-Bernard, Contact
E-mail: njkennific@gov.pe.ca

Description: Facility provides an ideal setting for growing IT and Media companies to expand their businesses, foster new partnerships, and exist in an atmosphere that promotes and sustains business achievement.

46881 ■ Holman Centre
250 Water St.
　Summerside, PE, Canada C1N 1B6
Ph: (902)436-2246
URL: http://holmancentre.com
Contact: Mike Palmer, Controller
E-mail: mpalmer@srdcpei.com

Description: A coworking space supporting startups and entrepreneurs. Space is configured for each business and aligned in clusters to foster collaborative and creative energy. **Founded:** 1857.

46882 ■ PEI BioAlliance
134 Kent St., Ste. 302
　Charlottetown, PE, Canada C1A 8R8
Ph: (902)367-4400
Fax: (902)367-4404
Co. E-mail: info@peibioalliance.com
URL: http://peibioalliance.com
Contact: Rory Francis, Chief Executive Officer
E-mail: rory@peibioalliance.com
X (Twitter): x.com/BioSciencePEI
YouTube: www.youtube.com/channel/UC-zZwiPWo
　5jHTwo71Rit9vA

Founded: 2005.

Quebec

ASSOCIATIONS AND OTHER ORGANIZATIONS

46883 ■ Canadian Federation of Business and Professional Women Montreal (BPW) [BPW Montreal]
PO Box 32137 Saint-Andre
  Montreal, QC, Canada H2L 4Y5
Co. E-mail: info@bpwmontreal.com
URL: http://www.bpwmontreal.com
Contact: Marie-Chantal Hamel, President
Facebook: www.facebook.com/BPW.montreal
  .canada
Linkedin: www.linkedin.com/company/bpwmontreal
X (Twitter): x.com/BPWMontreal1
Instagram: www.instagram.com/bpw_montreal

Description: Serves as network for businesswomen. Works to improve the economic, political, and social conditions for working women in Canada. **Founded:** 1928.

FINANCING AND LOAN PROGRAMS

46884 ■ Anges Québec
3, Pl. Ville Marie Bureau 12350, Ste. 1-100
  Montreal, QC, Canada H3B 0E7
Ph: (514)642-1001
Co. E-mail: info@angesquebec.com
URL: http://angesquebec.com/en
Contact: Geneviève Harland, Director
Facebook: www.facebook.com/angesquebec
Linkedin: www.linkedin.com/company/anges-qu-bec

Description: Identifies innovative entrepreneurs for angel investors. **Founded:** 2008.

46885 ■ Gestion TechnoCap Inc.
4028 Marlowe
  Montreal, QC, Canada H4A 3M2
Ph: (514)483-6000
Co. E-mail: businessplan@technocap.com
URL: http://www.technocap.com
Contact: Marc Balevi, President

Description: Finance: Venture capital provides investment services. **Founded:** 1993. **Preferred Investment Size:** $1,000,000 to $10,000,000. **Industry Preferences:** Communications and media, computer software, computer related, Internet specific, semiconductors and other electronics, medical and health, industrial and energy.

46886 ■ Inovia Capital
3 Place Ville-Marie, Ste. 12350
  Montreal, QC, Canada H3B 0E7
URL: http://www.inovia.vc
Contact: Natasha Gould, Director
Linkedin: www.linkedin.com/company/inovia-capital
X (Twitter): x.com/inovia

Description: Early stage investment firm focused on high-growth sectors. Also maintains offices in Toronto, London, San Francisco, and London. **Founded:** 2007. **Industry Preferences:** Mobile; internet; digital media.

46887 ■ Investissement Desjardins
5 Complexe Desjardins, C. P. 244
  Montreal, QC, Canada H5B 1B4
Ph: (514)281-7101
Fax: (514)281-6232
URL: http://www.desjardins.com/ca
Contact: Bruno Nadeau, Chairman of the Board
Facebook: www.facebook.com/
  caisseComplexeDesjardins
X (Twitter): x.com/desjardinsgroup
Instagram: www.instagram.com/desjardinscoop
YouTube: www.youtube.com/user/desjardinsgroup

Description: Provider of financial and investment services. **Preferred Investment Size:** $5,000,000 minimum. **Industry Preferences:** Computer software and services, Internet specific, communications and media, biotechnology, other products, medical and health, and industrial and energy.

46888 ■ Teralys Capital (TC)
999 Boul. de Maisonneuve Ouest, Ste. 1700
  Montreal, QC, Canada H3A 3L4
Ph: (514)509-2080
Co. E-mail: info@teralyscapital.com
URL: http://www.teralyscapital.com/en
Contact: Antoaneta Hadjikoleva, Coordinator
E-mail: ahadjikoleva@teralyscapital.com
Linkedin: www.linkedin.com/company/teralys-capital

Description: Private fund manager for venture capital funds from early-stage startups to technology buyouts. **Founded:** 2009. **Industry Preferences:** Information technology; life sciences; clean or industrial innovations.

INCUBATORS/RESEARCH AND TECHNOLOGY PARKS

46889 ■ Ag-Bio Centre
201 rue Monseigneur-Bourget
  Levis, QC, Canada G6V 6Z3
Ph: (418)835-2110
Co. E-mail: info@agbiocentre.com
URL: http://agbiocentre.com
Contact: Julien-Pierre Cote, President
Facebook: www.facebook.com/agbiocentre

Description: Supports the growth of companies in the agri-food, biotechnology, and environmental science industries. Offers guidance and fosters research and development for technology companies.

46890 ■ Bromont Science Park [Parc Scientifique Bromont]
1460 boul. de l'Innovation Office 206
  Bromont, QC, Canada J2L 0J8
Ph: (450)390-0393
Co. E-mail: stephanie.latour@technumquebec.ca
URL: http://technumquebec.ca/parc-scientifique
Contact: Louis Villeneuve, Contact

Description: Incubator, research center, and industrial center for diverse technology fields.

46891 ■ Centre d'Enterprises et d'Innovation de Montreal (CEIM)
33 rue Prince
  Montreal, QC, Canada H3C 2M7
Ph: (514)866-0575
Co. E-mail: info@ceim.org
URL: http://www.ceim.org
Contact: Serge Bourassa, President
Facebook: www.facebook.com/CEIMincubateur
Linkedin: www.linkedin.com/company/ceim
X (Twitter): x.com/CEIM_Qc
YouTube: www.youtube.com/user/CEIM2012/feed

Description: Incubator and accelerator for innovative early- and growth-stage companies with commercial potential. **Founded:** 1996.

46892 ■ CQIB The Life Sciences Incubator
500 Boul. Cartier W
  Laval, QC, Canada H7V 5B7
Ph: (450)688-8377
URL: http://www.cqib.org
Contact: Perry Niro, Executive Director
Linkedin: www.linkedin.com/company/centre-qu-b
  -cois-d'innovation-en-biotechnologie

Description: A business incubator that offers entrepreneurs their own laboratories, a scientific equipment park and business mentoring services to facilitate the launch of innovative biotech firms. **Founded:** 1996.

46893 ■ Drummondville Economic Development Corp. (SDED)
1400 rue Jean-Berchmans-Michaud St.
  Drummondville, QC, Canada J2C 7V3
Ph: (819)477-5511
Fax: (819)477-5512
Co. E-mail: info@sded.ca
URL: http://www.sded.ca
Contact: Julie Biron, Director (Acting) Director General

Description: Runs an incubator that helps start businesses and provides them with organizational, operational and administrative support.

46894 ■ Enablis
1250 blvd. Rene-Levesque W, Ste. 3800
  Montreal, QC, Canada H3B 4W8
Ph: (514)397-8461
Co. E-mail: international@enablis.org
URL: http://enablis.org
Contact: Charles Sirois, Chairman
Facebook: www.facebook.com/enablisglobal
X (Twitter): x.com/enablis
YouTube: www.youtube.com/user/EnablisNetwork

Description: Supports small and medium-sized entrepreneurs creating jobs in developing and emerging countries. **Founded:** 2003.

46895 ■ FounderFuel
Montreal, QC, Canada
Co. E-mail: info@founderfuel.com

URL: http://founderfuel.com
Contact: Katy Yam, General Manager Partner
Facebook: www.facebook.com/FounderFuel
Linkedin: www.linkedin.com/company/founderfuel
X (Twitter): x.com/founderfuel
Instagram: www.instagram.com/founderfuel
Description: Startup accelerator. Helps early-stage companies raise seed capital and go to market. **Founded:** 2011.

46896 ■ Innovation Maritime (IMAR)
53, rue Saint-Germain Ouest
Rimouski, QC, Canada G5L 4B4
Ph: (418)725-3525
Fax: (418)725-3554
Co. E-mail: imar@imar.ca
URL: http://www.innovationmaritime.ca/en/services
Contact: Pierre Parent, President
Description: Promotes excellence and supports marine-sector growth through technological innovation. Develops business solutions through applied research, technical assistance and information distribution. **Founded:** 2001.

46897 ■ Le Camp
125 Charest Est Blvd., 2nd Fl.
Quebec, QC, Canada G1K 3G5
Ph: (418)681-0230
URL: http://lecampquebec.com/en
Contact: Sebastien Tanguay, General Manager
E-mail: sebastien@lecampquebec.com
Facebook: www.facebook.com/lecampquebec
X (Twitter): x.com/lecampquebec
Description: Incubator-accelerator for tech businesses. Offers a range of services adapted to development stage, from pre-startup to internationalization. **Founded:** 2015.

46898 ■ Le Centre d'entreprises et d'innovation de Montreal (CEIM)
33 rue Prince
Montreal, QC, Canada H3C 2M7
Ph: (514)866-0575
Co. E-mail: info@ceim.org
URL: http://www.ceim.org/en
Contact: Christian Perron, President
Facebook: www.facebook.com/CEIMincubateur
X (Twitter): x.com/CEIM_Qc
YouTube: www.youtube.com/user/CEIM2012
Description: Contributes to the start-up and development of innovative businesses in the information technology, multimedia, industrial technology and biotechnology sectors. Services range from coaching start-ups on business plan development, to searching for and negotiating financing and strategic partnerships, to providing sales support for companies having difficulty in building effective sales organizations. **Founded:** 1996.

46899 ■ MONETS Business Accelerators
45 Hansen Ave.
Beaconsfield, QC, Canada H9W 5P4
Ph: (514)697-9894
Fax: (514)697-8475
Co. E-mail: info@monets.ca
URL: http://www.monets.ca
Contact: Dietrich Bodecker, President
Description: Business accelerator offering programs that are designed to strengthen a company's competitive positioning and focus market strategies from conception to implementation.

46900 ■ TandemLaunch
780 Brewster Ave., Ste. RC-016
Montreal, QC, Canada H4C 2K1
Ph: (438)380-5435
Co. E-mail: info@tandemlaunch.com
URL: http://www.tandemlaunch.com/en
Contact: Helge Seetzen, Chief Executive Officer
Facebook: www.facebook.com/TandemLaunchInc
Linkedin: www.linkedin.com/company/tandemlaunch
X (Twitter): x.com/TandemLaunch
Instagram: www.instagram.com/tandemlaunch
YouTube: www.youtube.com/user/tandemlaunch

Description: Startup foundry and seed fund. Works with entrepreneurs to build companies around university technologies. Identifies a problem, finds technologies to solve it, then assembles a team and builds a company. **Founded:** 2010.

46901 ■ Univalor (UV)
3 Place Ville Marie, Ste. 12350, Level L, NO. 1. 180
Montreal, QC, Canada H3B 0E7
Ph: (514)340-3243
Fax: (514)340-3204
URL: http://www.univalor.ca
Contact: Christine Gariépy, President
Facebook: www.facebook.com/UV.Univalor
Linkedin: www.linkedin.com/company/gestion-univalor
X (Twitter): twitter.com/univalor
Description: Helps make businesses more competitive, generate revenue for research and, most importantly, to enrich society. Has a pilot incubation program that offers coaching, mentoring, and hosting services.

CONSULTANTS

46902 ■ Embrase Business Consulting
1361-2 Greene Ave.
Westmount, QC, Canada H3Z 2A5
Co. E-mail: info@embrase.com
URL: http://www.embrase.com
Linkedin: www.linkedin.com/company/embrase
Description: Creates events for start-ups, enterprises, and government to discuss innovation, business, and policy. **Founded:** 2003.

46903 ■ Entrepreneurship Laval (EL)
Pavillon Maurice-Pollack 2305, rue de l'l'Universite, Ste.3122
Laval University, QC, Canada G1V 0A6
Ph: (418)656-5883
Fax: (418)656-3337
Co. E-mail: el@el.ulaval.ca
URL: http://www.eul.ulaval.ca
Contact: Jacques Topping, President
Linkedin: www.linkedin.com/company/entrepreneuriat-laval
X (Twitter): x.com/eul_ulaval
Description: Provides consulting, workshops, and mentoring to startups and entrepreneurs. Supports members of the university community in the development of their entrepreneurial skills in order to encourage business start-ups. **Founded:** 1993.

46904 ■ Flow Ventures
51 Sherbrooke St. W
Montreal, QC, Canada H2X 1X2
Free: 866-322-3569
Co. E-mail: info@flowventures.com
URL: http://flowventures.com
Contact: Elaine Coopersmith, Chief Executive Officer
Linkedin: www.linkedin.com/company/flow-ventures
X (Twitter): twitter.com/flowventures
Description: Provides advisory services to companies throughout the business lifecycle. Services include securing grants and tax credits, raising financing, and planning strategic growth.

46905 ■ TransBIOTech (tbt)
201, Monseigneur-Bourget St.
Levis, QC, Canada G6V 6Z3
Ph: (418)833-8876
Co. E-mail: info@tbt.qc.ca
URL: http://www.tbt.qc.ca/en
Contact: Yvan Boutin, Contact
Facebook: www.facebook.com/transbiotech
Linkedin: www.linkedin.com/company/transbiotech
Description: A center for research and transfer of biotechnology for companies working in life sciences and biotechnology. Provides technical assistance services to small and medium-size enterprises.

PUBLISHERS

46906 ■ White Rock Publishing
60 Rue Voltaire
Gatineau, QC, Canada J9J 2P2

Ph: (613)617-9141
URL: http://www.whiterockpublishing.ca
Contact: Luc Dupont, Contact
E-mail: dupontluc@videotron.ca
Description: Publishes advertising and marketing books. Accepts unsolicited manuscripts. Reaches market through direct mail and wholesalers. **Founded:** 1995.

RESEARCH CENTERS

46907 ■ Chamber of Commerce of Metropolitan Montreal - Info Entrepreneurs - Information Center
393 Saint-Jacques St., Ste. 200
Montreal, QC, Canada H2Y 1N9
Ph: (514)496-4636
Free: 888-576-4444
URL: http://www.infoentrepreneurs.org/en/resource-centre
Scope: International trade; statistics; entrepreneur business start-up; commerce. **Services:** Copying; center open to the public. **Founded:** 1994. **Holdings:** Figures not available.

EXPANSION AND GROWTH FINANCING

46908 ■ Cycle Capital Management (CCM)
1000 Sherbrooke W Ste. 1610
Montreal, QC, Canada H3A 3G4
Ph: (514)495-1022
URL: http://www.cyclecapital.com
Contact: Amit Srivastava, Senior Partner
E-mail: asrivastava@cyclecapital.com
Linkedin: www.linkedin.com/company/cycle-capital
X (Twitter): x.com/CycleCapitalVC
Description: Fosters a sustainable future through impact investment in entrepreneurial cleantech teams. Focused on companies producing more with less, using fewer resources, and transforming those efficiencies into significant returns. **Founded:** 2009. **Industry Preferences:** Agriculture technologies; green chemicals, including biofuels; biomass transformation; smart grid; energy storage technologies; renewable energy; IoT applied to resource management; big data and technologies dedicated to Smart Cities.

VENTURE CAPITAL FIRM

46909 ■ Center of Excellence in Energy Efficiency (C3E)
533, Ave. de la Montagne, Ste. 109
Shawinigan, QC, Canada G9R 1J9
Ph: (819)539-5200
Co. E-mail: info@ceee.ca
URL: http://c3e.ca
Contact: Donald Angers, Chief Executive Officer
E-mail: angers.donald@ceee.ca
Facebook: www.facebook.com/lec3e
Linkedin: www.linkedin.com/company/c3e
X (Twitter): x.com/C3E_energie
Description: A fund specifically dedicated to the commercialization of innovations in energy efficiency of transportation in Canada. Provides a unique funding tool suited to high-risk ventures thus promoting the business maturity and subsequent rounds of financing. **Founded:** 2009.

46910 ■ Desjardins Venture Capital
1020 rue du Marche-Central
Montreal, QC, Canada H4N 1K4
Ph: (514)383-0180
Free: 844-866-9930
Co. E-mail: info@cafedepot.ca
URL: http://www.desjardins.com
Facebook: www.facebook.com/cafedepot.ca
Instagram: www.instagram.com/cafedepot
Description: Offers investment capital and venture capital to innovative start-ups and growing business in Quebec.

46911 ■ Real Ventures
51 rue Sherbrooke O
   Montreal, QC, Canada H2X1X2
URL: http://realventures.com
Contact: Hamzah Nassif, Partner
Facebook: www.facebook.com/realventuresvc
Linkedin: www.linkedin.com/company/real-ventures
X (Twitter): x.com/realventures

Description: Venture capital firm for high-potential start-ups using the latest technologies to leverage data, artificial intelligence, and connectivity to disrupt industries and business models. Also maintains an office in Toronto. **Founded:** 2007.

46912 ■ TVM Capital Life Science Venture Capital
1470 Peel St.Ste. 810
   Montreal, QC, Canada H3A 1T1
Ph: (514)931-4111
Co. E-mail: info@tvm-capital.com
URL: http://tvm-capital.com
Contact: Dr. Hubert Birner, Managing Partner
Linkedin: www.linkedin.com/company/tvm-capital
X (Twitter): x.com/tvmcapital

Description: Transatlantic venture capital for life science companies in Europe, North America, and Asia. Also operates out of Munich. **Founded:** 1984. **Industry Preferences:** Biopharma; diagnostic; medtech; digital health.

Saskatchewan

ASSOCIATIONS AND OTHER ORGANIZATIONS

46913 ■ International Association of Business Communicators Regina (IABC)
Regina, SK, Canada S4P 3B1
Co. E-mail: contact@iabcregina.ca
URL: http://www.iabcregina.ca
Contact: Lisa Adam, President
Facebook: www.facebook.com/IABCRegina
X (Twitter): x.com/iabcregina

Description: Represents communication managers, public relations directors, writers, editors, audiovisual specialists, and other individuals in the public relations and organizational communication field. Conducts research in the communication field and encourages establishment of college-level programs in organizational communication. Offers accreditation program and conducts surveys on employee communication effectiveness and media trends. **Publications:** *Communication World (CW)* (Monthly); *Connections*; *WorldBook* (Annual). **Geographic Preference:** Local.

SMALL BUSINESS ASSISTANCE PROGRAMS

46914 ■ Tourism Saskatchewan
189-1621 Albert St.
Regina, SK, Canada S4P 2S5
Ph: (306)787-9600
Free: 877-237-2273
Co. E-mail: travel.info@tourismsask.com
URL: http://www.tourismsaskatchewan.com
Facebook: www.facebook.com/TourismSaskatchewan
X (Twitter): x.com/saskatchewan
Instagram: www.instagram.com/tourismsask
YouTube: www.youtube.com/user/TourismSaskatchewan
Pinterest: www.pinterest.com/tourismsask

Description: Promotes growth of the tourism industry in Saskatchewan. Subprograms include Tourism Product Development, Tourism Market Development, Industry Organization Support, and Research and Planning Support. **Publications:** *Saskatchewan Fishing & Hunting Guide* (Annual); *Saskatchewan Accommodation Resort and Campground Guide*; *Saskatchewan Vacation Guide* (Annual); *Great Saskatchewan Gift Book* (Semiannual); *Saskatchewan Events Guide* (Annual); *Saskatchewan Winter* (Annual).

BETTER BUSINESS BUREAUS

46915 ■ Better Business Bureau of Central Canada
1555 St. James St., Unit 207
Winnipeg, MB, Canada R3H 1B5
Ph: (204)989-9010
Fax: (204)989-9016
URL: http://www.bbb.org/local-bbb/bbb-central-canada

Description: Seeks to promote and foster ethical relationship between businesses and the public through voluntary self-regulation, consumer and business education, and service excellence. Provides information to help consumers and businesses make informed purchasing decisions and avoid costly scams and frauds; settles consumer complaints through arbitration and other means. **Founded:** 1981.

FINANCING AND LOAN PROGRAMS

46916 ■ SaskMetis Economic Development Corporation (SMEDCO)
237 Robin Cres.
Saskatoon, SK, Canada S7L 6M8
Ph: (306)477-4350
Fax: (306)373-2512
Co. E-mail: smedco@smedco.ca
URL: http://smedco.ca
Contact: Tristan Zachow, Chief Executive Officer
X (Twitter): x.com/saskmetis

Description: Finances startups, acquisitions, and expansions of Metis-controlled small businesses in Saskatchewan.

INCUBATORS/RESEARCH AND TECHNOLOGY PARKS

46917 ■ Community Futures Ventures
c/o Corinne Lubiniecki, General Manager
204 Smith St. E
Yorkton, SK, Canada S3N 3S6
Ph: (306)782-0255
Free: 877-851-9997
Fax: (306)783-2590
Co. E-mail: info@cfventures.net
URL: http://cfsask.ca/ventures
Contact: Corinne Lubiniecki, General Manager
E-mail: corinne.l@cfventures.net
X (Twitter): twitter.com/cfsaskatchewan

Description: Supports small business owners.

46918 ■ Women Entrepreneurs of Saskatchewan Inc. (WESK)
108 - 502 Cope Way
Saskatoon, SK, Canada S7T 0G3
Ph: (306)477-7173
Free: 844-900-9375
Fax: (306)477-7175
Co. E-mail: info@wesk.ca
URL: http://wesk.ca
Contact: Miriam Johnson, Chief Executive Officer
Facebook: www.facebook.com/WESK306
Linkedin: www.linkedin.com/company/women-entrepreneurs-of-saskatchewan-inc-
X (Twitter): x.com/WESK306
Instagram: www.instagram.com/wesk306
YouTube: www.youtube.com/channel/UCzo_UoX7nGbYsc9Tsn3RMiw

Description: Works with women, helping them start, purchase and expand businesses. Provides business advisory and support services, start-up, purchase and expansion lending, mentoring and networking, and many learning opportunities from seminars and webinars to events. **Founded:** 1995.

VENTURE CAPITAL FIRM

46919 ■ PFM Capital Inc.
1925 Victoria Ave., Assinboia Club Bldg., 2nd Fl.
Regina, SK, Canada S4P 0R3
Ph: (306)791-4855
Fax: (306)791-4848
Co. E-mail: pfm@pfm.ca
URL: http://www.pfm.ca
Contact: Randy Beattie, President
E-mail: randybeattie@pfm.ca

Description: Manages private equity and venture capital funds. **Founded:** 1998. **Preferred Investment Size:** $5,000,000 to $20,000,000. **Investment Policies:** Experienced management teams; market segments with growth potential; 5-8 year investment timeframe with clear identifiable exit opportunity.

Yukon Territory

SMALL BUSINESS ASSISTANCE PROGRAMS

46920 ■ Yukon Department of Economic Development
Jim Smith Bldg., 2071 2nd Ave.
 Whitehorse, YT, Canada Y1A 1B2
Free: 800-661-0408
Co. E-mail: inquiry.desk@yukon.ca
URL: http://yukon.ca/en/department-of-economic-development
Contact: Ranj Pillai, Contact
E-mail: ranj.pillai@yukon.ca
Description: Offers a variety of programs and funds for business, industry and communities to help develop and maintain a sustainable and competitive Yukon economy.

Federal Government Assistance

AGENCY FOR INTERNATIONAL DEVELOPMENT

46921 ■ U.S. Agency for International Development - Freedom of Information Act Request - Bureau for Management/ Information and Records Div. (IRD)
1300 Pennsylvania Ave. NW
 USAID Annex, M/MS, Rm. 10.8.OD
 Washington, DC 20523
URL: http://www.usaid.gov/foia-requests

Description: To care for him who shall have borne the battle, and for his widow, and his orphan" by serving and honoring the men and women who are America's veterans. **Founded:** 1961.

46922 ■ U.S. Agency for International Development Library (USAID)
1300 Pennsylvania Ave. NW
 Washington, DC 20004
URL: http://www.usaid.gov/results-and-data/data-resources/usaid-library

Scope: Agriculture; public health; social sciences; scientific disciplines. **Services:** Interlibrary loan; library is open to USAID staff, contractors, and grantees by appointment. **Founded:** 1967. **Holdings:** 20,000 e-journals; 12,000 e-books; books; DVDs. **Subscriptions:** 400 journals and other serials journals and newsletters.

46923 ■ U.S. Agency for International Development - Office of Inspector General (OIG)
1300 Pennsylvania Ave., NW
 Washington, DC 20004
URL: http://oig.usaid.gov
Contact: Adam Kaplan, General Counsel
E-mail: adamkaplan@usaid.gov
Linkedin: www.linkedin.com/company/usaid-oig
X (Twitter): x.com/USAID_OIG

Description: Responsible for providing audit and investigative services to the U.S. Agency for International Development (USAID), the Millennium Challenge Corporation (MCC), the African Development Foundation (ADF), and the Inter-American Foundation (IAF). **Founded:** 1980.

46924 ■ U.S. Agency for International Development (MRC) - Office of Small and Disadvantaged Business Utilization - Minority Resource Center
DC
URL: http://www.usaid.gov/foia/library

Description: A small business advocacy and advisory office with the responsibility for ensuring that these enterprises receive access to USAID programs. The office maintains the USAID Consultant Registry Information System (ACRIS) and publishes The Guide to Doing Business with the Agency for International Development.

46925 ■ U.S. Department of Veterans Affairs (VA) - Office of Small and Disadvantaged Business Utilization - Minorities in Franchising
810 Vermont Ave. NW
 Washington, DC 20420
Free: 866-584-2344
Co. E-mail: vip@va.gov
URL: http://www.va.gov/osdbu
Contact: Robert Wilkie, Secretary
Facebook: www.facebook.com/VAVetBiz
X (Twitter): x.com/vavetbiz
YouTube: www.youtube.com/c/VAOSDBU

Description: A place where minority prospects can explore franchise offerings of companies actively looking to recruit minority franchisees.

BUREAU OF THE CENSUS

46926 ■ Alabama Department of Economic and Community Affairs (ADECA) - Community and Economic Development Programs
401 Adams Ave.
 Montgomery, AL 36104
Ph: (334)242-5370
Fax: (334)242-5099
Co. E-mail: contact@adeca.alabama.gov
URL: http://adeca.alabama.gov/ced
Contact: Kenneth W. Boswell, Director

Description: Provides consultation services to small and developing businesses; provides information on federal grants and projects; and helps businesses to develop export contacts and markets. **Founded:** 1983.

46927 ■ Alaska Department of Labor and Workforce Development - Research and Analysis
1111 W 8th St., Rm. 301
 Juneau, AK 99801
Ph: (907)465-4500
Fax: (907)308-2824
URL: http://live.laborstats.alaska.gov
Contact: Dan Robinson, Contact
E-mail: dan.robinson@alaska.gov

Description: Publishes about economics, labor markets and other special interests for the state of Alaska. Offers two career databases for microcomputers. Distributes for Alaska Census Data Network.

46928 ■ California Department of Finance (SCDC) - State Census Data Center
915 L St.
 Sacramento, CA 95814
Ph: (916)323-4086
Co. E-mail: censusdata4ca@dof.ca.gov
URL: http://dof.ca.gov/forecasting/demographics/california-state-data-center-network

Description: Through a year-long process, the Department of Finance prepares, explains and administers California's annual financial plan, the California Budget. **Founded:** 1979.

46929 ■ Florida Department of Economic Opportunity - Labor Market Information - Florida Census Data Center
107 E Madison St., Caldwell Bldg.
 Tallahassee, FL 32399-4111
URL: http://floridajobs.org/workforce-statistics/data-center/florida-census-data-center

46930 ■ Florida Department of Economic Opportunity - Labor Market Statistics Center - Florida Census Data Center
107 E Madison St., Caldwell Bldg.
 Tallahassee, FL 32399-4120
URL: http://www.floridajobs.org/workforce-statistics/data-center/florida-census-data-center

46931 ■ Illinois State University College of Arts and Sciences - Applied Social Research Unit (ASRU)
PO Box 4950
 Normal, IL 61790-4950
Ph: (309)438-5326
Fax: (309)438-7198
Co. E-mail: asru@ilstu.edu
URL: http://asru.illinoisstate.edu
Contact: Sharon M. Mills, Director

Description: Integral unit of College of Arts and Sciences, Illinois State University. **Founded:** 1987.

46932 ■ Indiana University - Kelley School of Business - Indiana Business Research Center (IBRC)
1309 E 10th St.
 Bloomington, IN 47405
Co. E-mail: ibrc@iu.edu
URL: http://ibrc.kelley.iu.edu
Contact: Carol O. Rogers, Director
E-mail: rogersc@iu.edu
Facebook: www.facebook.com/IUibrc
Linkedin: www.linkedin.com/company/indiana-business-research-center
X (Twitter): x.com/IUibrc

Description: Collects and analyses business and economic data in the state. Information is accessible through the Indiana Information Retrieval System at libraries, universities, and public agencies. Puts out two bimonthly publications. Presents a Business Outlook Panel annually in several cities. **Scope:** Indiana's economic development, population trends, state and local economic indicators, and information technology. **Founded:** 1925. **Publications:** *Indiana Business Review* (Quarterly); *InContext* (Bimonthly); *Indiana Business Review (IBR)* (Quarterly).

46933 ■ Iowa Department of Education - Census Data Center
1112 E Grand Ave.
 Des Moines, IA 50319
Ph: (515)281-6618
Free: 800-248-4483
Co. E-mail: census@iowa.gov
URL: http://www.iowadatacenter.org
Contact: Gary Krob, Coordinator
E-mail: gary.krob@iowa.gov

46934 ■ Maine State Planning Office - Census Information Office
78 State House Sta.
Augusta, ME 04333
URL: http://www.maine.gov/dafs/economist/census-information
Description: A network of organizations (libraries, planning organizations, university departments, and agencies of state government) that makes US Census data products available to the Maine public. The Program also provides assistance in the use of these products.

46935 ■ Maine State Planning Office - Census State Data Center
78 State House Sta.
Augusta, ME 04333
Ph: (207)624-7348
URL: http://www.census.gov/about/partners/sdc/member-network/maine.html
Contact: Angela Hallowell, Contact
E-mail: angela.hallowell@maine.gov
Description: A network of organizations (libraries, planning organizations, university departments, and agencies of state government) that makes US Census data products available to the Maine public. The Program also provides assistance in the use of these products.

46936 ■ Maryland Small Business Development Center Northern Region
401 Thomas Run Rd.
Bel Air, MD 21015
URL: http://www.marylandsbdc.org/locations/northern-region
Contact: Amy Yingling, Regional Director
E-mail: ayingling5@carrollcc.edu
Description: Represents and promotes the small business sector. Provides management assistance to current and prospective small business owners. Helps to improve management skills and expand the products and services of members. **Founded:** 1988. **Geographic Preference:** State; Local.

46937 ■ Montana Department of Commerce - Census and Economic Information Center (CEIC)
301 S Pk. Ave.
Helena, MT 59620-0501
Ph: (406)841-2740
URL: http://ceic.mt.gov
Contact: Mary Craigle, Bureau Chief
E-mail: mcraigle@mt.gov
Description: Provides population and economic information to businesses, government agencies, and the general public for research, planning, and decision-making purposes. **Scope:** Census information. **Founded:** 1970.

46938 ■ Ohio Development Services Agency - Office of Research
77 S High St., 28th Fl.
Columbus, OH 43215-6130
URL: http://development.ohio.gov/about-us/research

46939 ■ Ohio State University Library - Census Data Center
1858 Neil Ave. Mall
Columbus, OH 43210-1286
Ph: (614)292-6785
Co. E-mail: ries.3@osu.edu
URL: http://library.osu.edu/find/subjects/government-documents/statistic-and-census-resources/u-s-census-information/census-of-population-and-housing/2010-census
Contact: Jolie Braun, Contact
Facebook: www.facebook.com/OSULibraries
X (Twitter): twitter.com/OSULibrary
Instagram: www.instagram.com/OSULibraries
Founded: 1870.

46940 ■ Oklahoma Census Data Center - Oklahoma Department of Commerce
900 N Stiles Ave.
Oklahoma City, OK 73104
Ph: (405)815-6552
Free: 800-879-6552
Co. E-mail: info@okcommerce.gov
URL: http://www.okcommerce.gov
Contact: Jon Chiappe, Director, Research Director, Economics
E-mail: jon.chiappe@okcommerce.gov
Facebook: www.facebook.com/okcommerce
Linkedin: www.linkedin.com/company/okcommerce
X (Twitter): x.com/okcommerce
YouTube: www.youtube.com/user/OKcommerce
Description: As the state data center, Commerce receives a constant flow of U.S. Census Bureau statistics and data pertaining specifically to Oklahoma and organized into county and city subcategories. Commerce also regularly received information from the Bureau of Economic Analysis, the Bureau of Labor Statistics, the U.S. Department of Agriculture, and the Oklahoma Employment Security Commission. **Founded:** 1993.

46941 ■ Sacramento State Census Data Center - Department of Finance
915 L St., 8th Fl.
Sacramento, CA 95814-3706
URL: http://www.census.gov/about/partners/sdc/member-network/california.html
Contact: Karen Louie, Contact
E-mail: karen.louie@dof.ca.gov
Description: Through a year-long process, the Department of Finance prepares, explains and administers California's annual financial plan, the California Budget.

46942 ■ U.S. Census Bureau - Atlanta Regional Office
c/o George Grandy Jr., Regional Director
285 Peachtree Center Ave. NE, Ste. 300 Marquis Two Towers
Atlanta, GA 30303-2700
Ph: (404)730-3832
Free: 800-424-6974
Fax: (404)730-3835
Co. E-mail: atlanta.regional.office@census.gov
URL: http://www.census.gov/about/regions/atlanta.html
Contact: George Grandy, Jr., Regional Director

46943 ■ U.S. Census Bureau - Chicago Regional Office
1111 W 22nd St., Ste. 400
Oak Brook, IL 60523-1918
Ph: (630)288-9200
Free: 800-865-6384
Fax: (630)288-9288
Co. E-mail: chicago.regional.office@census.gov
URL: http://www.census.gov/about/regions/chicago.html
Contact: Marilyn A. Sanders, Regional Director

46944 ■ U.S. Census Bureau - Denver Regional Office
6950 W Jefferson Ave., Ste. 250
Lakewood, CO 80235
Ph: (720)962-3700
Free: 800-852-6159
Fax: (303)969-6777
Co. E-mail: denver.regional.office@census.gov
URL: http://www.census.gov/about/regions/denver.html
Contact: Cathy L. Lacy, Regional Director

46945 ■ U.S. Census Bureau - Los Angeles Regional Office
2300 W Empire Ave., Ste. 300
Burbank, CA 91504
Ph: (818)267-1700
Free: 800-992-3530
Fax: (818)267-1714
Co. E-mail: los.angeles.regional.office@census.gov
URL: http://www.census.gov/about/regions/los-angeles.html
Contact: Julie Lam, Regional Director

46946 ■ U.S. Census Bureau - New York City Regional Office
32 Old Slip, 9th Fl.
New York, NY 10005
Ph: (212)584-3400
Free: 800-991-2520
Fax: (212)478-4800
Co. E-mail: new.york.regional.office@census.gov
URL: http://www.census.gov/about/regions/new-york/contact.html
Contact: Leila N. Dickerson, Regional Director

46947 ■ United States Census Bureau New York Regional Office
32 Old Slip, 9th Fl.
New York, NY 10005
Ph: (212)584-3400
Free: 800-991-2520
Fax: (212)584-3402
Co. E-mail: new.york.regional.office@census.gov
URL: http://www.census.gov/about/regions/new-york.html
Contact: Leila N. Dickerson, Regional Director

46948 ■ U.S. Census Bureau - Philadelphia Regional Office
c/o Fernando E Armstrong, Regional Director
100 S Independence Mall W, Ste. 410
Philadelphia, PA 19106-2320
Ph: (215)717-1800
Free: 800-262-4236
Fax: (215)717-0755
Co. E-mail: philadelphia.regional.office@census.gov
URL: http://www.census.gov/about/regions/philadelphia.html
Contact: Fernando E. Armstrong, Regional Director
E-mail: philadelphia.regional.office@census.gov

46949 ■ U.S. Department of Commerce - Commerce Research Library
1401 Constitution Ave. NW
Washington, DC 20230
Ph: (202)482-2825
URL: http://www.commerce.gov
Contact: Ron Jarmin, Director
Facebook: www.facebook.com/Commercegov
Linkedin: www.linkedin.com/company/u-s-department-of-commerce
X (Twitter): x.com/commercegov
YouTube: www.youtube.com/channel/UCDk7XARReoJChTwu1WojgRQ
Description: Provider of job, economic growth, sustainable development, and improved standards of living. **Scope:** Science, technology, engineering, and business. **Founded:** 1903. **Holdings:** Figures not available. **Publications:** *FedWorld*; *Directory of U.S. Private Sector Product Certification Programs*; *U.S. Government Software for Mainframes & Microcomputers* (Annual); *Agriculture & Food*; *United States Census of Agriculture*; *United States Census of Construction Industries* (Quinquennial); *United States Census of Manufactures*; *United States Census of Monthly Retail Trade* (Monthly); *United States Census of Service Industries* (Quinquennial); *Small Business Innovation Research*; *NTIS Alerts: Agriculture & Food* (Biweekly); *NTIS Alerts: Biomedical Technology & Human Factor Engineering* (Biweekly); *NTIS Alerts: Building Industry Technology* (Biweekly); *NTIS Alerts: Communication* (Biweekly); *NTIS Alerts: Energy* (Biweekly); *NTIS Alerts: Environmental Pollution & Control* (Biweekly); *NTIS Alerts: Government Inventions for Licensing* (Biweekly); *NTIS Alerts: Health Care* (Biweekly); *NTIS Alerts: Ocean Sciences and Technology* (Biweekly); *NTIS Alerts: Transportation* (Biweekly); *National Technical Information Service Database*; *Statistical Abstract of the United States*; *Federal Research in Progress (FEDRIP)* (Monthly); *Automated Sources of Information in the Department of Commerce*; *Directory of International and Regional Organizations Conducting Standards-Related Activities*; *Characteristics of Apartments Completed* (Annual); *U.S. Industry and Trade Outlook* (Annual); *Advance Monthly Retail Trade Report*; *1997 NAICS and 1987 SIC Correspondence Tables*; *EPA Information Resources Directory*; *Selected Instruments and Related Products*; *Steel Mill Products* (Annual); *National Audiovisual Center (NAC)*; *Federal Research in Progress Database (FEDRIP)*; *NTIS Database*; *Certified Equipment List Database*; *Defense Library on Disc*; *FDA Surveillance Index for Pesticides Newsletter* (Monthly); *Industrial Patent Activity in the United States*; *Directory of U.S. Government Data-*

FEDERAL GOVERNMENT ASSISTANCE

files for Mainframes & Microcomputers (Annual); Energy Saving Consulting in Hamburg; Davis-Bacon Wage Determination Decisions; Service Contract Wage Determination Database; World News Connection; Export Administration Regulations (EAR); GOV. Research_Center™; Basic Guide to Telecommunications Markets in Latin America and the Caribbean (Irregular); Directory of Japanese Databases (Irregular); NTIS Alerts (Biweekly); NTIS Bibliographic Database; FedWorld: A Program of the United States Department of Commerce.

46950 ■ U.S. Department of Commerce - Bureau of the Census
4600 Silver Hill Rd.
Washington, DC 20230
Ph: (301)763-4636
Free: 800-923-8282
Co. E-mail: pio@census.gov
URL: http://www.census.gov
Contact: Robert Santos, Director
URL(s): www.commerce.gov/bureaus-and-offices/census
Facebook: www.facebook.com/uscensusbureau
Linkedin: www.linkedin.com/company/us-census-bureau
X (Twitter): x.com/uscensusbureau
Instagram: www.instagram.com/uscensusbureau
YouTube: www.youtube.com/user/uscensusbureau
Description: The Census Bureau gathers and disseminates a wide variety of statistics about the people and economy of the United States. It is the principal source in the federal government for business information relating to manufacturers, retail trade, wholesale trade, construction trade, and services. These data are generated both from the regular five-year census programs and from annual, quarterly, and monthly survey programs. Data concerning the number of establishments, production, value added by manufacture, shipments, receipts, employees, payrolls--as well as other general and specific business statistics--are compiled and published periodically. Small business owners interested in learning more about the statistics available from the Census Bureau and how to use them may obtain a set of introductory materials and order forms by contacting Customer Services. Other information may be obtained from Census Bureau regional. In addition, the Census Bureau sponsors a state data center program, which provides (for a fee) local access to the bureau's computer products in all states, the District of Columbia, Puerto Rico, Guam, and the U.S. Virgin Islands.

46951 ■ University of Arkansas at Little Rock - College of Business Administration - Institute for Economic Advancement - Census State Data Center (CSDC)
2801 S University Ave.
Little Rock, AR 72204
Ph: (501)916-5959
Fax: (501)569-8538
URL: http://directory.ualr.edu/search?d=119
Scope: Educational material. **Founded:** 1979.

CORPORATION FOR NATIONAL SERVICE

46952 ■ AmeriCorps (CNCS)
250 E St. SW
Washington, DC 20525
Ph: (202)606-5000
Free: 800-942-2677
Co. E-mail: help@americorps.gov
URL: http://www.americorps.gov
Contact: Michael D. Smith, Chief Executive Officer
Facebook: www.facebook.com/americorps
Linkedin: www.linkedin.com/company/americorps
X (Twitter): x.com/americorps
Instagram: www.instagram.com/americorps
YouTube: www.youtube.com/channel/UC1VuXCdPlovso1vcqi2dMng
Description: Engaged in improving lives, strengthen communities, and foster civic engagement through service and volunteering. **Founded:** 1993.

46953 ■ Corporation for National and Community Service Department of AmeriCorps
Washington, DC
Co. E-mail: help@americorps.gov
URL: http://americorps.gov/serve
Facebook: www.facebook.com/americorps
X (Twitter): x.com/americorps
Instagram: www.instagram.com/americorps
YouTube: www.youtube.com/channel/UC1VuXCdPlovso1vcqi2dMng
Description: Focuses on improving lives, strengthen communities, and foster civic engagement through service and volunteering.

46954 ■ Corporation for National and Community Service Office of Learn and Serve
250 E St. SW, Ste. 300
Washington, DC 20525
Contact: Malcolm Coles, Chief Executive Officer (Acting)
Facebook: www.facebook.com/nationalservice
X (Twitter): twitter.com/nationalservice
Description: Strives to improve lives, strengthen communities, and foster civic engagement through service and volunteering. **Founded:** 1965.

ENVIRONMENTAL PROTECTION AGENCY

46955 ■ Delaware Department of Natural Resources and Environmental Control - Division of Waste and Hazardous Substances (DWHS)
c/o Timothy Ratsep, Director, Richardson & Robbins Buldg., 89 Kings Hwy.
Dover, DE 19901
Ph: (302)739-9400
Free: 800-662-8802
URL: http://dnrec.alpha.delaware.gov/waste-hazardous
Contact: Timothy Ratsep, Director
Founded: 1983.

46956 ■ Environmental Protection Agency - Region 1 (EPA Region 1)
5 Post Office Sq., Ste. 100
Boston, MA 02109-3912
Ph: (617)918-1111
Free: 888-372-7341
URL: http://www.epa.gov/aboutepa/epa-region-1-new-england
Contact: David Bloom, Chief Financial Officer
Facebook: www.facebook.com/EPARegion1
Description: Serves Connecticut, Massachusetts, Maine, New Hampshire, Rhode Island, and Vermont.

46957 ■ Environmental Protection Agency - Region 2 (EPA Region 2)
290 Broadway
New York, NY 10007-1866
Ph: (212)637-3660
Free: 877-251-4575
URL: http://www.epa.gov/aboutepa/epa-region-2
Contact: Lisa F. Garcia, Administrator
Facebook: www.facebook.com/eparegion2
X (Twitter): x.com/EPAregion2
Description: Serves New Jersey, New York, Puerto Rico, and the Virgin Islands.

46958 ■ Environmental Protection Agency - Region 5 (EPA Region 5)
77 W Jackson Blvd.
Chicago, IL 60604
Ph: (312)353-2000
Free: 800-621-8431
Co. E-mail: r5hotline@epa.gov
URL: http://www.epa.gov/aboutepa/epa-region-5
Contact: Juliane Grange, Clerk
E-mail: r5hearingclerk@epa.gov
Description: Serves Illinois, Indiana, Michigan, Minnesota, Ohio, and Wisconsin. **Founded:** 1970.

46959 ■ Environmental Protection Agency - Region 7 (EPA)
11201 Renner Blvd.
Lenexa, KS 66219
Ph: (913)551-7003
Free: 800-223-0425
Co. E-mail: r7actionline@epa.gov
URL: http://www.epa.gov/aboutepa/epa-region-7-midwest
Contact: Mark R. Aaron, Contact
E-mail: aaron.mark@epa.gov
Facebook: www.facebook.com/eparegion7
X (Twitter): x.com/EPAregion7
Description: Serves Iowa, Kansas, Missouri, and Nebraska.

46960 ■ Environmental Protection Agency State Superfund Office - Commission of Environmental Quality - Hazardous and Solid Waste Div. - Superfund and Emergency Response Section
12100 Park 35 Cir.
Austin, TX 78753
URL: http://www.epa.gov/superfund

46961 ■ Environmental Protection Agency State Superfund Office - Department of Ecology - Waste Management Program - Investigations and Cleanup Program
PO Box 47600
Olympia, WA 98504-7600
URL: http://www.ecy.wa.gov/programs/hwtr/index.html

46962 ■ Environmental Protection Agency State Superfund Office - Department of Energy and Environmental Protection - Small Business Assistance
Office of Small & Disadvantaged Business Utilization
1200 Pennsylvania Ave. NW
Washington, DC 20460
URL: http://www.epa.gov/resources-small-businesses/epa-regional-office-small-business-liais
Founded: 1994.

46963 ■ Environmental Protection Agency State Superfund Office (DSWM) - Department of Environment and Conservation - Division of Solid Waste Management
312 Rosa L. Parks Ave.
Nashville, TN 37243
Ph: (615)532-0780
Co. E-mail: solid.waste@tn.gov
URL: http://www.tn.gov/environment/program-areas/sw-solid-waste.html

46964 ■ Environmental Protection Agency State Superfund Office (DENR) - Department of Environment and Natural Resources
610 E Center Ave., No. 301
Mooresville, NC 28115
URL: http://cfpub.epa.gov/ncer_abstracts/index.cfm/fuseaction/display.institutionInfo/location/3748

46965 ■ Environmental Protection Agency State Superfund Office - Department of Environment and Natural Resources - Waste Management Program
1200 Pennsylvania Ave. NW, MC. 5303T
Washington, DC 20460
URL: http://www.epa.gov/tribal-lands/tribal-waste-management-program

46966 ■ Environmental Protection Agency State Superfund Office - Department of the Environment - Recycling in Maryland
1800 Washington Blvd., Ste. 610
Baltimore, MD 21230-1719
URL: http://mde.maryland.gov/programs/land/RecyclingandOperationsprogram/Pages/recylingrates.aspx

46967 ■ Environmental Protection Agency State Superfund Office - Department of Environmental Conservation - Division of Air Quality
4th Fl. One National Life Dr.
Montpelier, VT 05620-3802

URL: http://www.epa.gov/scram/air-modeling-state-modeling-contacts
Contact: Daniel Riley, Contact
E-mail: dan.riley@vermont.gov

46968 ■ Environmental Protection Agency State Superfund Office - Department of Environmental Conservation - Division of Environmental Remediation
625 Broadway
  Albany, NY 12233
Ph: (518)457-7362
Free: 800-457-7362
URL: http://dec.ny.gov/about/contact-us/division-of-environmental-remediation
Contact: Andrew Guglielmi, Division Director

46969 ■ Environmental Protection Agency State Superfund Office - Department of Environmental Management - Waste Management
235 Promenade St.4th Fl.
  Providence, RI 02908
URL: http://dem.ri.gov/environmental-protection-bureau/land-revitalization-and-sustainable-materials-management

46970 ■ Environmental Protection Agency State Superfund Office - Department of Environmental Protection - Bureau of Waste and Recycling
PO Box 4062
  Boston, MA 02211
URL: http://www.mass.gov/topics/recycling-waste-management
Description: Provides environmental protection in Massachusetts.

46971 ■ Environmental Protection Agency State Superfund Office - Department of Environmental Protection - Division of Waste Management
2600 Blair Stone Rd., MS, Ste. 4500
  Tallahassee, FL 32399
Ph: (850)245-8705
URL: http://floridadep.gov/waste
Contact: Timothy Bahr, Director
E-mail: tim.bahr@floridadep.gov
Description: The Florida Department of Environmental Protection is the state's lead agency for environmental management and stewardship, protecting our air, water and land. **Founded:** 1990.

46972 ■ Environmental Protection Agency State Superfund Office - Department of Environmental Protection - Hazardous Waste Management Div.
c/o Janine MacGregor., Director
  401 E State St.
  MC 401-02C
  Trenton, NJ 08625-0420
Ph: (609)633-1418
Fax: (609)777-1951
URL: http://www.nj.gov/dep/dshw
Contact: Janine MacGregor, Director

46973 ■ Environmental Protection Agency State Superfund Office - Department of Environmental Protection - Office of the Commissioner
17 State House Sta.
  32 Blossom Ln.
  Augusta, ME 04333-0017
URL: http://www.maine.gov/dep/commissioners-office/index.html
Contact: David Madore, Director
E-mail: david.madore@maine.gov

46974 ■ Environmental Protection Agency State Superfund Office - Department of Environmental Protection - Small Business Assistance
79 Elm St.
  Hartford, CT 06106
URL: http://www.epa.gov/resources-small-businesses/epa-regional-office-small-business-liaisons

Founded: 1994.

46975 ■ Environmental Protection Agency State Superfund Office - Department of Environmental Quality (DEQ)
1520 E 6th Ave.
  Helena, MT 59601
Ph: (406)444-2544
Fax: (406)444-4386
Co. E-mail: deqcommunicationsteam@mt.gov
URL: http://deq.mt.gov
Contact: Christopher Dorrington, Director
Facebook: www.facebook.com/MTDEQ
X (Twitter): x.com/MTDEQ
Instagram: www.instagram.com/montanadeq
YouTube: www.youtube.com/channel/UCZpuxN606ueNWkZBg7udweA/feed
Description: The Montana Department of Environmental Quality is charged with protecting a clean and healthy environment as guaranteed to our citizens by our State Constitution. **Founded:** 1995.

46976 ■ Environmental Protection Agency State Superfund Office (MDEQ) - Department of Environmental Quality
515 E Amite St.
  Jackson, MS 39201
Ph: (601)961-5758
Free: 888-786-0661
Fax: (601)354-6356
URL: http://www.mdeq.ms.gov
Contact: Chris Wells, Executive Director
Facebook: www.facebook.com/mdeq.ms
X (Twitter): x.com/MDEQ
Instagram: www.instagram.com/mississippideq
YouTube: www.youtube.com/channel/UCbNcaF5M31KXx_cX5Qp32UA

46977 ■ Environmental Protection Agency State Superfund Office - Department of Environmental Quality - Air and Waste Management Div.
1200 North St., Ste. 400
  Lincoln, NE 68509
Co. E-mail: mark.bauer@nebraska.gov
URL: http://www.epa.gov/brownfields/stxcntct.htm#ANCHOR28
Description: Provides grants and technical assistance to communities, states, tribes and others to assess, safely clean up and sustainably reuse contaminated properties.

46978 ■ Environmental Protection Agency State Superfund Office (DAQ) - Department of Environmental Quality - Division of Air Quality
State Office Bldg.
  195 N 1950 W
  Salt Lake City, UT 84116
Ph: (801)536-4000
Fax: (801)536-4099
URL: http://deq.utah.gov/division-air-quality
Contact: Bryce Bird, Director
E-mail: bbird@utah.gov

46979 ■ Environmental Protection Agency State Superfund Office (ECSI) - Department of Environmental Quality - Environmental Cleanup Site Information
700 NE Multnomah St., Ste. 600
  Portland, OR 97232
Ph: (503)229-5696
Free: 800-452-4011
Fax: (503)229-6124
URL: http://www.oregon.gov/deq/hazards-and-cleanup/env-cleanup/pages/ecsi.aspx

46980 ■ Environmental Protection Agency State Superfund Office - Department of Environmental Quality (DEQ) - Land Protection Div. (LPD)
707 N Robinson
  Oklahoma City, OK 73102
Ph: (405)702-5100
Fax: (405)702-5101
URL: http://www.deq.ok.gov/divisions/lpd
Contact: Kelly Dixon, Division Director

Description: Inspects and permits hazardous waste and solid waste treatment, storage and disposal facilities, permits and inspects certain underground injection wells, manages radioactive materials, restores contaminated land to safe and useful conditions (Brownfields, Superfund, Voluntary Cleanup, Land Restoration and Site Cleanup Assistance Program).

46981 ■ Environmental Protection Agency State Superfund Office (EPA) - Department of Environmental Quality - Office of Waste and Water Quality
1110 W Washington St.
  Phoenix, AZ 85007
Ph: (602)771-2379
Free: 800-234-5677
Co. E-mail: communications@azdeq.gov
URL: http://legacy.azdeq.gov/environ/water/index.html
Contact: Trevor Baggiore, Director

46982 ■ Environmental Protection Agency State Superfund Office - Department of Environmental Quality - Waste Programs Div.
1800 Washington Blvd.
  Baltimore, MD 21230
URL: http://www.epa.gov/hwgenerators/links-hazardous-waste-programs-and-us-state-environmental-agencies

46983 ■ Environmental Protection Agency State Superfund Office - Department of Environmental Services - Commissioners Office
29 Hazen Dr.
  Concord, NH 03302-0095
URL: http://www.des.nh.gov/contact/nhdes-jobs
Contact: Ray Wilson, Coordinator
E-mail: raymond.wilson@des.nh.gov
Founded: 1987.

46984 ■ Environmental Protection Agency State Superfund Office - Department of Health and Environment - Bureau of Waste Management - Storage Tank Section
1000 SW Jackson, Ste. 410
  Topeka, KS 66612
URL: http://www.kdhe.ks.gov/990/Storage-Tanks
Contact: Sharon Morgan, Section Chief
E-mail: sharon.morgan@ks.gov
Description: Kansas department of health and safety.

46985 ■ Environmental Protection Agency State Superfund Office (DHEC) - Department of Health and Environmental Control
2600 Bull St.
  Columbia, SC 29201
Ph: (803)898-3301
URL: http://scdhec.gov/environment.htm
Contact: Dr. Edward Simmer, Director
Facebook: www.facebook.com/SCDHEC
Linkedin: www.linkedin.com/company/scdhec
X (Twitter): x.com/scdhec
YouTube: www.youtube.com/user/SCDHEC
Founded: 1973.

46986 ■ Environmental Protection Agency State Superfund Office - Department of Health - Waste Management Div.
1200 Pennsylvania Ave. NW
  Washington, DC 20460
URL: http://www.epa.gov/emergency-response-research/waste-management

46987 ■ Environmental Protection Agency State Superfund Office - Department of Natural Resources - Environmental Protection Div. - Land Protection Branch - Solid Waste Management Program
4244 International Pky.
  Atlanta, GA 30354
Ph: (404)362-2692
URL: http://epd.georgia.gov/about-us/land-protection-branch/solid-waste

46988 ■ Environmental Protection Agency State Superfund Office - Department of Natural Resources - Hazardous Waste Management Program
PO Box 176
Jefferson City, MO 65102
URL: http://www.epa.gov/hw/learn-basics-hazardous-waste

46989 ■ Environmental Protection Agency State Superfund Office - Department of Natural Resources Waste Management - Air Quality Bureau - Water Supply Section
502 E 9th St.
Des Moines, IA 50319-0034
Fax: (515)725-8201
URL: http://www.iowadnr.gov/Environmental-Protection/Water-Quality/Water-Supply-Engineering

46990 ■ Environmental Protection Agency State Superfund Office - Department of Public Health and Environment - Hazardous Materials and Waste Management Div. (HMWMD)
4300 Cherry Creek Dr. S
Denver, CO 80246
Ph: (303)692-3320
Co. E-mail: comments.hmwmd@state.co.us
URL: http://cdphe.colorado.gov/hm

46991 ■ Environmental Protection Agency State Superfund Office - Environmental Protection Agency
17-3304 Mariner Ave.
Barrigada, GU 96913
Ph: (671)300-4751
Co. E-mail: nic.rupley@epa.guam.gov
URL: http://epa.guam.gov
Contact: Steven Philip Carbullido, Chairperson
Facebook: www.facebook.com/GuamEPA
X (Twitter): x.com/guamepa
Instagram: www.instagram.com/guamepa
Founded: 1973.

46992 ■ Environmental Protection Agency State Superfund Office - Environmental Protection Agency - Bureau of Land - Pollution Prevention
c/o Christine Clark, 77 W Jackson Blvd. (LM-8J)
Chicago, IL 60604-3590
Ph: (312)886-9749
Co. E-mail: clark.christine@epa.gov
URL: http://www.epa.gov/p2
Contact: Christine Clark, Contact
E-mail: clark.christine@epa.gov

46993 ■ Environmental Protection Agency State Superfund Office - Pollution Control Agency - Groundwater & Solid Waste Div.
520 Lafayette Rd., N
Saint Paul, MN 55155-4194
URL: http://www.epa.gov

46994 ■ Environmental Protection Agency State Superfund Office - Water Commission - Hazardous and Solid Waste Division - Superfund and Emergency Response Section
12100 Pk. 35 Cir.
Austin, TX 78753
URL: http://www.tceq.texas.gov/response

46995 ■ Hawaii State Department of Health - Environmental Health Administration - Environmental Management Division (EMD)
Hale Ola Bldg., Rm. 222
2827 Waimano Home Rd.
Pearl City, HI 96782-1487
Ph: (808)586-4304
URL: http://health.hawaii.gov/about/links-to-doh-program-information/administration-directory/environmental-health-administration/#EMD

46996 ■ Idaho Department of Environmental Quality - Waste Management and Remediation Division - Hazardous Waste
1410 N Hilton St.
Boise, ID 83706
URL: http://www.deq.idaho.gov/waste-management-and-remediation/hazardous-waste-in-idaho
Contact: Natalie K. Walker, Bureau Chief
E-mail: natalie.walker@deq.idaho.gov

46997 ■ Massachusetts Executive Office of Energy and Environmental Affairs - Massachusetts Department of Environmental Protection - Waste and Recycling
1 Ashburton Pl., 11th Fl.
Boston, MA 02108
URL: http://www.mass.gov/topics/recycling-waste-management

46998 ■ Michigan Department of Environmental Quality - Office of Waste Management and Radiological Protection (OWMRP)
525 W Allegan St., 1 S
Lansing, MI 48909-7742
Ph: (517)284-6651
Free: 800-662-9278
Fax: (517)241-3571
URL: http://www.michigan.gov/egle/about/organization/Materials-Management
Contact: Elizabeth Browne, Director
Holdings: Data covers 1981 to the present; updated twice weekly. **Publications:** *Manifest Tracking Data Base.*

46999 ■ New Hampshire Department of Environmental Services (NHDES) - Office of the Commissioner
29 Hazen Dr.
Concord, NH 03302-0095
URL: http://www.des.nh.gov/about/leadership
Contact: Robert R. Scott, Commissioner
Description: Department offers accounting and budgeting, geological services, human resources management, information technology management, state laboratory services, legal services, strategic planning and priority-setting, pollution prevention coordination and integration and public outreach and information dissemination.

47000 ■ New York State Department of Environmental Conservation (NYSDEC) - Division of Environmental Remediation - Hazardous Waste Management
625 Broadway
Albany, NY 12233
Ph: (518)402-8652
Co. E-mail: info.sqg@dec.ny.gov
URL: http://dec.ny.gov/environmental-protection/waste-management/hazardous-waste
Founded: 1970.

47001 ■ North Dakota Department of Health - Division of Waste Management
4201 Normandy St.
Bismarck, ND 58503-1324
Ph: (710)328-5166
Fax: (701)328-5200
Co. E-mail: waste@nd.gov
URL: http://deq.nd.gov/wm
Contact: Chuck Hyatt, Director

47002 ■ Ohio Environmental Protection Agency - Division of Environmental Response and Revitalization (DERR)
50 W Town St., Ste. 700
Columbus, OH 43215
Ph: (614)644-2924
Fax: (614)644-3146
URL: http://epa.ohio.gov/divisions-and-offices/environmental-response-revitalization
Contact: Lisa Zwissler, Executive Secretary
E-mail: lisa.zwissler@epa.ohio.gov

47003 ■ Oregon Department of Environmental Quality - Land Quality Division - Environmental Cleanup Program
1502 SW Sixth Ave.
Portland, OR 97201
Ph: (503)229-5066
Free: 800-452-4011
URL: http://www.oregon.gov/deq/Hazards-and-Cleanup/env-cleanup/Pages/ecsi.aspx

47004 ■ Pennsylvania Department of Environmental Protection - Bureau of Waste Management
PO Box 69170
Harrisburg, PA 17106-9170
URL: http://www.dep.pa.gov/Business/Land/Waste/Contacts/Pages/default.aspx
Contact: Larry Holley, Director (Acting)
E-mail: ra-epwaste@pa.gov
Description: A state governmental entity in Pennsylvania that's responsible for recycling and solid waste programs. Coordinates the transportation, storage, processing, use, and disposal of hazardous, municipal, and residual wastes.

47005 ■ Rhode Island Department of Environmental Management - Office of Waste Management
c/o Leo Hellested, Administrator
235 Promenade St.
Providence, RI 02908
Ph: (401)222-2797
URL: http://dem.ri.gov/environmental-protection-bureau/land-revitalization-and-sustainable-materials-management
Contact: Leo Hellested, Administrator
E-mail: leo.hellested@dem.ri.gov

47006 ■ State of New Jersey Department of Environmental Protection - Division of Solid and Hazardous Waste
401 E State St.
Trenton, NJ 08625-0420
URL: http://www.nj.gov/dep/dshw
Founded: 1970.

47007 ■ U.S. Environmental Protection Agency - Region 10 (EPA)
1200 6th Ave., Ste. 155
Seattle, WA 98101
Ph: (206)553-1200
Free: 800-424-4372
Co. E-mail: epa-seattle@epa.gov
URL: http://www.epa.gov/aboutepa/epa-region-10-pacific-northwest
Contact: Casey Sixkiller, Administrator
X (Twitter): x.com/EPAnorthwest
Description: Serves Alaska, Idaho, Oregon, and Washington. **Scope:** The environment. **Services:** Interlibrary loan; copying; library open to the public.
Founded: 1970.

47008 ■ U.S. Environmental Protection Agency State Superfund Office - Department of Environmental Management - Land Div.
PO Box 301463
Montgomery, AL 36130-1463
Ph: (334)271-7730
Fax: (334)279-3050
Co. E-mail: landmail@adem.alabama.gov
URL: http://www.adem.alabama.gov/programs/land/default.cnt

47009 ■ U.S. Environmental Protection Agency State Superfund Office - Department for Environmental Protection - Division of Waste Management (DWM)
c/o Tammi Hudson, Director
300 Sower Blvd.
Frankfort, KY 40601
Ph: (502)782-6980
Co. E-mail: waste@ky.gov
URL: http://eec.ky.gov/Environmental-Protection/Waste/Pages/default.aspx
Contact: Tammi Hudson, Director
E-mail: tammi.hudson@ky.gov

47010 ■ U.S. Environmental Protection Agency State Superfund Office - Department of Toxic Substances Control (DTSC)
1001 I St.
Sacramento, CA 95826
Ph: (916)584-3958
URL: http://dtsc.ca.gov

Contact: Meredith Williams, Director
Facebook: www.facebook.com/CaliforniaDTSC
Linkedin: www.linkedin.com/company/californiadtsc
X (Twitter): x.com/CaliforniaDTSC
YouTube: www.youtube.com/user/DTSCgreen
Description: Department for toxic substance control.
Founded: 1970.

47011 ■ U.S. Environmental Protection Agency State Superfund Office - Division of Environmental Protection - Department of Conservation and Natural Resources (DCNR)
901 S Stewart St., Ste. 1003
Carson City, NV 89701
Ph: (775)684-2700
Fax: (775)684-2715
URL: http://dcnr.nv.gov
Contact: James A. Settelmeyer, Director
Facebook: www.facebook.com/NevDCNR
X (Twitter): x.com/NevDCNR
Instagram: www.instagram.com/nevdcnr

47012 ■ U.S. Environmental Protection Agency State Superfund Office - Environmental Improvement Division - Hazardous Waste Bureau (HWB)
c/o Shannon Duran
2905 Rodeo Park Dr. E, Bldg. 1
Santa Fe, NM 87505-6303
Ph: (505)476-6058
Co. E-mail: shannon.duran@state.nm.us
Contact: Shannon Duran, Contact
E-mail: shannon.duran@state.nm.us

47013 ■ U.S. Environmental Protection Agency State Superfund Office (OLQ) - Indiana Department of Environmental Management - Office of Environmental Response - Office of Land Quality
100 N Senate Ave.
Indianapolis, IN 46204
Ph: (317)232-8941
Co. E-mail: info@idem.in.gov
URL: http://www.in.gov/idem/landquality
Founded: 1986.

47014 ■ Vermont Department of Environmental Conservation (DEC)
1 National Life Dr., Davis Bldg. 3rd Fl.
Montpelier, VT 05620-3520
Ph: (802)828-1556
Fax: (802)828-1541
URL: http://dec.vermont.gov
Contact: Kim Greenwood, Division Director Program Manager Administrative Assistant
E-mail: kim.greenwood@vermont.gov
URL(s): www.anr.state.vt.us/dec/dec.htm

47015 ■ Wisconsin Department of Natural Resources - Managing Waste and Materials
101 S Webster St.
Madison, WI 53707-7921
URL: http://dnr.wisconsin.gov/topic/Waste

47016 ■ Wyoming Department of Environmental Quality - Water Quality Div. (WQD)
200 W 17th St.
Cheyenne, WY 82001
Ph: (307)777-7937
Fax: (307)635-1784
URL: http://deq.wyoming.gov/water-quality

EXECUTIVE OFFICE OF THE PRESIDENT

47017 ■ Executive Office of the President - Office of Management and Budget - Administrator of the Small Business Administration
409 3rd St. SW
Washington, DC 20416
URL: http://www.sba.gov/about-sba/organization/contact-sba
Contact: Isabella Casillas Guzman, Administrator
E-mail: sba.administrator@sba.gov

Founded: 1953.

47018 ■ Executive Office of the President - Office of Management and Budget - Office of Federal Procurement Policy
1600 Pennsylvania Ave., NW
Washington, DC 20500
URL: http://www.whitehouse.gov/omb/management/office-federal-procurement-policy
Founded: 1974.

47019 ■ Executive Office of the President (SBA) - Office of Management and Budget - Small Business Administration
1600 Pennsylvania Ave. NW
Washington, DC 20500

EXPORT-IMPORT BANK OF THE UNITED STATES

47020 ■ Export-Import Bank of the United States (EXIM)
811 Vermont Ave. NW
Washington, DC 20571
Ph: (202)565-3946
Co. E-mail: oig.info@exim.gov
URL: http://www.exim.gov
Contact: Reta Jo Lewis, President
Facebook: www.facebook.com/eximbankus
Linkedin: www.linkedin.com/company/eximbankus
X (Twitter): x.com/eximbankus
Instagram: www.instagram.com/eximbankus
YouTube: www.youtube.com/user/EximBankofUS
Description: The Export-Import Bank of the United States assists in financing and in facilitating the export sales of U.S. goods and services. Programs directed at small businesses include pre-export guarantees to assist small and medium-sized businesses in obtaining working capital from financial entities for export-related activities such as inventory purchases or the manufacture of goods; a small business insurance policy, that assists in providing risk protection on export receivables for companies just beginning to export or with limited export volumes; and loan and guarantee programs that enable U.S. banks to offer medium-term, fixed-rate export loans to finance the sales of products and services produced or performed by small businesses. Nonfinancial assistance includes the operation of the Eximbank Hotline (800-565-EXIM). Through this service, Eximbank International Business Development Division is available to assist more business owners in developing competitive export financing plans, answer questions regarding Eximbank financing programs, and explain how to apply for Eximbank assistance, where to locate credit insurance, or how to make maximum use of complementary export programs offered by other U.S. government agencies. In addition, Eximbank offers monthly seminars in Washington, D.C., to help firms new to exporting understand the programs available from the federal government. **Founded:** 1934.

47021 ■ Export-Import Bank of the United States (EXIM) - Global Business Development
811 Vermont Ave. NW
Washington, DC 20571
Ph: (202)565-3946
Free: 800-565-3946
Fax: (202)565-3380
URL: http://www.exim.gov/events/international-rail-opportunities-canada-argentina-mexico-and-turkey
Contact: Kimberly A. Reed, President
Description: Supporting American jobs by facilitating the export of U.S. goods and services. **Founded:** 1934.

47022 ■ Export-Import Bank of the United States - Midwest Regional Office - Chicago Regional Office - U.S. Export Assistance Center (USEAC)
409 3rd St. SW, Fl. 2
Washington, DC 20416
Ph: (202)205-8800
URL: http://www.sba.gov/district/washington-metropolitan-area

Contact: Larry G. Webb, Director
URL(s): www.exim.gov/contact/regional-export-finance-centers/central-region
Description: Through an extensive network of field offices and partnerships with public and private organizations, SBA delivers its services to people throughout the United States, Puerto Rico, the U. S. Virgin Islands and Guam.

47023 ■ Export-Import Bank of the United States - Southwest Regional Office - Houston Regional Office
c/o Mikey Leland Federal Bldg.
1919 Smith St., Ste. 10087
Houston, TX 77002
Ph: (832)810-6448
URL: http://www.exim.gov/contact/regional-export-finance-centers/central-region
Contact: Eric Miller, Regional Director
E-mail: eric.miller@exim.gov
Description: Aims to protect human health and the environment.

FARM CREDIT ADMINISTRATION

47024 ■ Farm Credit Administration (FCA) - Office of Equal Employment Opportunity and Inclusion
1501 Farm Credit Dr.
McLean, VA 22102-5090
URL: http://www.fca.gov/about/offices#eeoi
Contact: Thais Burlew, Director

47025 ■ Farm Credit Administration Office of Equal Employment Opportunity and Inclusion (EEO)
1501 Farm Credit Dr.
McLean, VA 22102-5090
URL: http://www.fca.gov/about/offices
Contact: Thais Burlew, Director
Founded: 1933.

47026 ■ Farm Credit Administration Office of Inspector General (FCA OIG)
1501 Farm Credit Dr.
McLean, VA 22102-5090
Ph: (703)883-4030
Co. E-mail: fca-ig-hotline@rcn.com
URL: http://www.fca.gov/about/inspector-general

47027 ■ Farm Credit Administration Office of Management Services
1501 Farm Credit Dr.
McLean, VA 22102-5090
Ph: (703)883-4056
Fax: (703)883-4056
Co. E-mail: info-line@fca.gov
URL: http://www.fca.gov/about/offices/offices.html
Contact: Stephen G. Smith, Chief Financial Officer
E-mail: smiths@fca.gov
Facebook: www.facebook.com/fcagov
Linkedin: www.linkedin.com/company/farm-credit-administration
X (Twitter): twitter.com/fcagov
YouTube: www.youtube.com/channel/UCMLBjEdJAom6CaT3xRWV6oQ

47028 ■ Farm Credit Administration - Office of Management Services - Office of Procurement
1501 Farm Credit Dr.
McLean, VA 22102-5090
Ph: (703)883-4378
URL: http://www.fca.gov/FCA-Web/fca%20new%20site/about/procurement.html
Contact: Glen R. Smith, Chief Executive Officer
Facebook: www.facebook.com/fcagov
Linkedin: www.linkedin.com/company/farm-credit-administration
X (Twitter): twitter.com/fcagov
YouTube: www.youtube.com/channel/UCMLBjEdJAom6CaT3xRWV6oQ

FEDERAL COMMUNICATIONS COMMISSION

47029 ■ Federal Communications Commission (FCC) - Consumer Inquiries and Complaints Div.
45 L St. NE
　Washington, DC 20554
URL: http://www.fcc.gov/general/consumer-an
　d-governmental-affairs-bureau
Contact: Jessica Rosenworcel, Chairman
E-mail: jessica.rosenworcel@fcc.gov

47030 ■ Federal Communications Commission (FCC-EB) - Enforcement Bureau
45 L St., NE
　Washington, DC 20554
Ph: (202)418-7450
URL: http://www.fcc.gov/reports-research/guides/fcc
　-enforcement-bureau-broadcasters-guide
Contact: Loyaan Egal, Officer
Description: Enforces provisions of the Communications Act, FCC rules, orders, terms and conditions of station authorizations. Major areas of enforcement are consumer protection enforcement, competition enforcement, and public safety/homeland security enforcement.

47031 ■ Federal Communications Commission - Office of Communications Business Opportunities (OCBO)
45 L St., NE
　Washington, DC 20554
Ph: (202)418-0716
Co. E-mail: ocboinfo@fcc.gov
URL: http://www.fcc.gov/communications-business
　-opportunities
Contact: Joy Melody Ragsdale, Director

47032 ■ Federal Communications Commission - Office of General Counsel - Administrative Law Div.
45 L St. NE
　Washington, DC 20554
URL: http://www.fcc.gov/general-counsel/about/
　general/administrative-law-division-office-general
　-counsel

47033 ■ Federal Communications Commission (OMR) - Office of Media Relations
45 L St., NE
　Washington, DC 20554
Ph: (202)418-0500
Free: 888-225-5322
Co. E-mail: mediarelations@fcc.gov
URL: http://www.fcc.gov/media-relations
Contact: Paloma Isabel Perez, Press Secretary

47034 ■ Federal Communications Commission (FCC/OWD) - Office of Workplace Diversity
45 L St. NE
　Washington, DC 20554
Ph: (202)418-1799
URL: http://www.fcc.gov/workplace-diversity
Contact: D'Wana R. Terry, Director

47035 ■ Federal Communications Commission - Wireless Telecommunications Bureau (WTB)
45 L St. NE
　Washington, DC 20554
Ph: (202)418-0600
Fax: (202)418-0787
URL: http://www.fcc.gov/wireless-telecommunications
　?job=home
Contact: Joel Taubenblatt, Bureau Chief
Description: WTB handles virtually all the FCC domestic wireless telecommunications programs, policies and initiatives. Regulates interstate and international communications by radio, television, wire, satellite, and cable; IT industry standard for vendor neutral enterprise Wi-Fi certification and training. **Founded:** 1994. **Publications:** *Annual Statistical Reports of Independent Telephone Companies*; *Minority Employment Report* (Annual); *Directory of Field Contacts for the Coordination of the Use of Radio Frequencies of Commerce* (Annual); *Quarterly Operating Data of 68 Telephone Carriers*.

FEDERAL DEPOSIT INSURANCE CORPORATION

47036 ■ Federal Deposit Insurance Corporation (FDIC) - Boston Area Office
15 Braintree Hill Office Pk.
　Braintree, MA 02184
URL: http://www.fdic.gov/newemployee/resources/
　bos.html
Description: Serves Connecticut, Maine, Massachusetts, New Hampshire, Rhode Island, and Vermont.

47037 ■ Federal Deposit Insurance Corporation (CRO) - Chicago Regional Office
300 S Riverside Plz., Ste. 1700
　Chicago, IL 60606-3447
Ph: (312)382-6000
Free: 800-944-5343
URL: http://www.fdic.gov/contact/regional-offices
Contact: Gregory P. Bottone, Regional Director
Description: Serves Illinois, Indiana, Kentucky, Michigan, Ohio, and Wisconsin. **Founded:** 2007.

47038 ■ Federal Deposit Insurance Corporation - Kansas City Regional Office
1100 Walnut St., Ste. 2100
　Kansas City, MO 64106
Ph: (816)234-8000
Free: 800-209-7459
URL: http://www.fdic.gov/resources/bankers/
　community-reinvestment-act/cra-regional-contacts
　-list.html
Contact: James D. Lapierre, Regional Director
Description: Serves Iowa, Kansas, Minnesota, Missouri, Nebraska, North Dakota, and South Dakota. **Founded:** 1933.

47039 ■ Federal Deposit Insurance Corporation - New York Regional Office
350 5th Ave., Ste. 1200
　New York, NY 10118-0110
Ph: (917)320-2500
Free: 800-334-9593
URL: http://www.fdic.gov/contact/regional-offices
Contact: Frank R. Hughes, Regional Director
Description: Serves Delaware, District of Columbia, Maryland, New Jersey, New York, Pennsylvania, Puerto Rico, and Virgin Islands.

47040 ■ Federal Deposit Insurance Corporation (FDIC) - Office of Diversity and Economic Opportunity - Minority and Women Outreach Program - Northeast Service Center
101 E River Dr.
　East Hartford, CT 06108
Ph: (860)291-4051
Fax: (860)291-4077
URL: http://www.fdic.gov/resources/regulations/fe
　deral-register-publications/97cbia.html

47041 ■ Federal Deposit Insurance Corporation - Office of Diversity and Economic Opportunity - Minority and Women Outreach Program - Southwest Service Center
600 N Pearl St., Ste. 700
　Dallas, TX 75201
Ph: (972)761-8429
Free: 800-568-9161
Fax: (972)455-7094
URL: http://N/A
Description: Serves Colorado, New Mexico, Oklahoma, and Texas.

47042 ■ Federal Deposit Insurance Corporation (FDIC) - San Francisco Regional Office
25 Jessie St. at Ecker Sq., Ste. 2300
　San Francisco, CA 94105-2780
Ph: (415)546-0160
Free: 800-756-3558
URL: http://www.fdic.gov/contact/regional-offices
Contact: Paul P. Worthing, Regional Director
Description: Serves Alaska, Arizona, California, Guam, Hawaii, Idaho, Montana, Nevada, Oregon, Utah, Washington, and Wyoming.

FEDERAL EMERGENCY MANAGEMENT AGENCY

47043 ■ Federal Communications Commission - Homeland Security Policy Council
45 L St. NE
　Washington, DC 20554
Ph: (202)418-7450
Co. E-mail: homeland@fcc.gov
URL: http://www.fcc.gov/about-homeland-security
　-policy-council
Founded: 2001.

47044 ■ U.S. Department of Homeland Security Customs and Border Protection
1300 Pennsylvania Ave. NW
　Washington, DC 20229
Ph: (202)325-8000
URL: http://www.cbp.gov
Contact: Troy A. Miller, Commissioner
Facebook: www.facebook.com/CBPgov
Linkedin: www.linkedin.com/company/customs-an
　d-border-protection
X (Twitter): x.com/cbp
Instagram: www.instagram.com/cbpgov
YouTube: www.youtube.com/user/customsborderpro
　tect
Description: Procures search/detection equipment, data processing services, computer related services, computer programming, uniforms, construction, computer equipment, personal/household goods, repair/maintenance, administrative/general management consulting, investigative services, computer systems design, schools/instruction, security guards, and facilities support services. Provides news releases and fact sheets on border patrol initiatives. **Founded:** 1924. **Publications:** *ACS Interface Development Resource Directory*.

47045 ■ U.S. Department of Homeland Security (FEMA) - Federal Emergency Management Agency
PO Box 10055
　Hyattsville, MD 20782-8055
Ph: (202)646-2500
Free: 800-621-3362
Co. E-mail: fema-congressional-affairs@fema.dhs
　.gov
URL: http://www.fema.gov
Contact: Sherman Gillums, Jr., Director
Facebook: www.facebook.com/FEMA
Linkedin: www.linkedin.com/company/fema
X (Twitter): x.com/fema
Instagram: www.instagram.com/fema
YouTube: www.youtube.com/fema
Founded: 1979.

47046 ■ U.S. Department of Homeland Security - Federal Emergency Management Agency Office of Procurement Operations
245 Murray Dr. SW (Bldg. 410), Rm. 3523-28
　Washington, DC 20528
URL: http://www.dhs.gov/small-business-specialists
Contact: Ana Rangel, Specialist
E-mail: ana.rangel@hq.dhs.gov
Description: Procures information technology services directorate: information systems support, telecommunication equipment and services, computer maintenance and support, computer software and hardware, wide area network support, local area network support INTERNET services, systems development, engineering and integration, and communications security, configuration management, and disaster response support.

47047 ■ **U.S. Department of Homeland Security - Federal Emergency Management Agency, Region 1 - Boston Regional Office**
Boston, MA
URL: http://www.fema.gov/about/organization/region-1
Contact: Lori Ehrlich, Administrator
Description: Serves New Hampshire, Vermont, Rhode Island, Connecticut, and Massachusetts.

47048 ■ **U.S. Department of Homeland Security - Federal Emergency Management Agency Region 2 - New York Regional Office**
26 Federal Plz., Rm. 1337
New York, NY 10278-0002
URL: http://www.cisa.gov/about/regions/region-2
Description: Serves New York, New Jersey, Puerto Rico, and the Virgin Islands.

47049 ■ **U.S. Department of Homeland Security - Federal Emergency Management Agency, Region 3 (FEMA) - Philadelphia Regional Office (R3)**
615 Chestnut St., 6th Fl.
Philadelphia, PA 19106-4404
URL: http://www.fema.gov/about/organization/region-3
Contact: Maryann E. Tierney, Administrator
Description: Serves Delaware, District of Columbia, Maryland, Pennsylvania, Virginia, and West Virginia.

47050 ■ **U.S. Department of Homeland Security - Federal Emergency Management Agency, Region 4 - Atlanta Regional Office**
3003 Chamblee Tucker Rd.
Atlanta, GA 30341-4112
Ph: (770)220-5200
Co. E-mail: fema-r4-newsdesk@fema.dhs.gov
URL: http://www.fema.gov/about/organization/region-4
Contact: Robert Samaan, Administrator
X (Twitter): x.com/FEMARegion4
Description: Serves Georgia, Florida, Kentucky, Mississippi, North Carolina, South Carolina, and Tennessee.

47051 ■ **U.S. Department of Homeland Security - Federal Emergency Management Agency, Region 5 - Chicago Regional Office**
536 S Clark St., 6th Fl.
Chicago, IL 60605
URL: http://www.fema.gov/about/organization/region-5
Contact: Thomas C. Sivak, Administrator
Description: Serves Illinois, Indiana, Michigan, Ohio, Minnesota, and Wisconsin.

47052 ■ **U.S. Department of Homeland Security - Federal Emergency Management Agency, Region 6 - Denton Regional Office**
Washington, DC 20528
Ph: (202)343-1717
URL: http://www.dhs.gov
Contact: Debra Cox, Executive Director
Facebook: www.facebook.com/homelandsecurity
X (Twitter): x.com/dhsgov
Instagram: www.instagram.com/DHSgov
YouTube: www.youtube.com/user/ushomelandsecurity
Description: Serves Arkansas, Louisiana, New Mexico, Oklahoma, and Texas.

47053 ■ **U.S. Department of Homeland Security - Federal Emergency Management Agency, Region 7 - Kansas City Regional Office**
Kansas City, MO
Ph: (816)283-7061
Co. E-mail: femaregion7info@fema.dhs.gov
URL: http://www.fema.gov/about/organization/region-7
Contact: Andrea Spillars, Administrator
X (Twitter): x.com/FEMARegion7
Description: Serves Iowa, Kansas, Missouri, and Nebraska. **Founded:** 2003.

47054 ■ **U.S. Department of Homeland Security - Federal Emergency Management Agency, Region 8 - Denver Regional Office**
Denver, DC
Ph: (303)235-4800
URL: http://www.fema.gov/about/organization/region-8
Contact: Nancy Dragani, Administrator
Description: Serves Colorado, Montana, North Dakota, South Dakota, Utah, and Wyoming.

47055 ■ **U.S. Department of Homeland Security - Federal Emergency Management Agency, Region 9 - Oakland Regional Office**
1111 Broadway, Ste. 1200
Oakland, CA 94607
Ph: (510)627-7100
URL: http://www.fema.gov/about/organization/region-9
Description: Serves Arizona, California, Hawaii, and Nevada.

47056 ■ **U.S. Department of Homeland Security - Federal Emergency Management Agency, Region 10 - Bothell Regional Office**
Bothell, WA
URL: http://www.fema.gov/about/organization/region-10
Contact: Vincent J. Maykovich, Administrator
Description: Serves Alaska, Idaho, Washington, and Oregon. **Founded:** 2003.

47057 ■ **U.S. Department of Homeland Security - Federal Law Enforcement Training Center Artesia**
1300 W Richey Ave.
Artesia, NM 88210
Ph: (575)748-8000
URL: http://www.fletc.gov/artesia-new-mexico

47058 ■ **U.S. Department of Homeland Security - Federal Law Enforcement Training Center Charleston**
2000 Bainbridge Ave.
North Charleston, SC 29405
Ph: (843)566-8551
URL: http://www.fletc.gov/charleston-south-carolina
Founded: 2005.

47059 ■ **U.S. Department of Homeland Security - Federal Law Enforcement Training Center Cheltenham**
9000 Commo Rd.
Camp Springs, MD 20588-4000
Ph: (301)868-5830
URL: http://www.fletc.gov/directory

47060 ■ **U.S. Department of Homeland Security - Federal Law Enforcement Training Center Glynco (FLETC)**
1131 Chapel Crossing Rd.
Brunswick, GA 31525
URL: http://www.fletc.gov
Contact: Benjamine C. Huffman, Director
Facebook: www.facebook.com/fletc
X (Twitter): x.com/FLETC
Instagram: www.instagram.com/fletc
YouTube: www.youtube.com/c/FederalLawEnforcementTrainingCenters
Founded: 1970.

47061 ■ **U.S. Department of Homeland Security - Federal Law Enforcement Training Center - Washington Operations**
1717 H St. NW, 7th Fl., No. 16
Washington, DC 20006
URL: http://www.fletc.gov/site-page/national-capital-region-training-operations
Description: Offers training experiences for law enforcement personnel. **Founded:** 1970.

47062 ■ **U.S. Department of Homeland Security Office of Procurement Operations**
245 Murray Dr. SW
Bldg. 410, Rm. 3523-28
Washington, DC 20528
URL: http://dhs.gov/small-business-specialists

Contact: Ana Rangel, Specialist
E-mail: ana.rangel@hq.dhs.gov

47063 ■ **U.S. Department of Homeland Security - Office of Small and Disadvantaged Business Utilization (OSDBU)**
301 7th St. SW, 4th Fl./ Mail Pickup:, Ste. 5640
Washington, DC 20528
Co. E-mail: dhsosdbu@hq.dhs.gov
URL: http://www.dhs.gov/osdbu
Contact: Darlene E. Bullock, Executive Director

47064 ■ **U.S. Department of Homeland Security - Transportation Security Administration - Small and Disadvantaged Business Office**
3701 W Post Office Rd.
Washington, DC 20528-6032
URL: http://www.tsa.gov/for-industry/small-business
Description: Procures simulators, training development, training courses, installation of checked baggage equipment, health and safety assessments on TSA screening operations, acquisition planning & program management support, safety equipment and supplies, and investigative services.

47065 ■ **U.S. Department of Homeland Security (DHS) - U.S. Coast Guard - Aviation Logistics Center**
1664 Weeksville Rd., Bldg. 35
Elizabeth City, NC 27909-5006
URL: http://www.dcms.uscg.mil/Our-Organization/Assistant-Commandant-for-Engineering-Logistics-CG-4-/Logistic-Centers/Aviation-Logistics-Center
Contact: Zephyr Mays, Officer
E-mail: zephyr.r.mays@uscg.mil
Description: Procures aircraft parts for HH-60, HU-25, HC-130, HH-65; ground service equipment, engines, turbines and components, engine accessories, maintenance and repair, aircraft maintenance/overhaul/repair, electronics, avionics, life support equipment, HAZMAT material, engineering tech support, and ADP services. **Founded:** 2003.

47066 ■ **U.S. Department of Homeland Security - U.S. Coast Guard Office of Contract Operations**
2703 Martin Luther King Jr. Ave., SE
Washington, DC 20593
URL: http://www.dhs.gov/small-business-specialists
Contact: Maria Kersey, Contact
E-mail: maria.l.kersey@uscg.mil
Description: Procures aircraft, vessels, educational services, major electronics equipment, and all equipment and supplies to outfit new vessels and aircraft, with emphasis in oceanography and other marine sciences, including pollution control and abatement.

47067 ■ **U.S. Department of Homeland Security - U.S. Coast Guard Office of Procurement Management**
2100 2nd St. SW
Washington, DC 20593-0001
Ph: (202)372-3671
URL: http://www.dhs.gov/xlibrary/assets/opnbiz/20051001_DHS_OFB_SBS_List.pdf
Contact: Phyllis Miriashtiani, Manager
E-mail: phyllis.c.miriashtiani@uscg.dhs.gov
Facebook: www.facebook.com/homelandsecurity
Linkedin: www.linkedin.com/company/us-department-of-homeland-security
X (Twitter): x.com/dhsgov/media
Instagram: www.instagram.com/dhsgov
YouTube: www.youtube.com/channel/UCpkaznWj_9PIVgO0BRKXu8w

47068 ■ **U.S. Department of Homeland Security - U.S. Coast Guard - Surface Forces Logistics Command - Atlantic (SFLC)**
300 E Main St., Ste. 600
Norfolk, VA 23510
Ph: (757)628-4654
URL: http://www.dhs.gov/osdbu/small-business-specialists
Contact: Mia Mayers, Contact
E-mail: mia.r.mayers@uscg.mil

Description: Procures dry dock and ship repair, engine overhaul, spare parts for vessels, construction, ship repair, and dry-docking of new vessels. **Founded:** 2003.

47069 ■ U.S. Department of Homeland Security - U.S. Coast Guard - Surface Forces Logistics Command - Pacific (SFLC)
Federal Office Bldg., 1301 Clay St.
  Oakland, CA 94612
URL: http://www.dhs.gov/small-business-specialists
Contact: Ramona E. Hatfield, Contact
E-mail: ramona.e.hatfield@uscg.mil
URL(s): www.pacificarea.uscg.mil
Description: Procures dry dock and ship repair, engine overhaul, spare parts for vessels, construction, ship repair, and dry-docking of new vessels. **Founded:** 2002.

47070 ■ U.S. Department of Homeland Security - U.S. Secret Service - Procurement Div.
245 Murray Dr. SW, Bldg. 410, Rm. 3523-28
  Washington, DC 20528
URL: http://www.dhs.gov/small-business-specialists
Description: Procures computer equipment, computer facilities management, passenger car leasing, software, computer systems design, telecommunications, custom computer programming, hardware manufacturing, computer repair, and janitorial services. **Founded:** 2002.

FEDERAL HOME LOAN MORTGAGE CORPORATION

47071 ■ Federal Home Loan Mortgage Corporation (FHLMC) [Freddie Mac]
8200 Jones Branch Dr.
  McLean, VA 22102-3110
Ph: (703)903-2000
Co. E-mail: privacy_mailbox@freddiemac.com
URL: http://www.freddiemac.com
Contact: Mike Hutchins, President
Facebook: www.facebook.com/FreddieMac
Linkedin: www.linkedin.com/company/freddie-mac
X (Twitter): twitter.com/FreddieMac
YouTube: www.youtube.com/user/freddiemac
Description: Government-sponsored entity is principally engaged in providing liquidity, stability, and affordability to the domestic housing market by purchasing residential mortgage loans originated by lenders and packaging the loans into mortgage-related securities, which are then sold in the global capital markets. Additionally, it invests in mortgage loans and mortgage-related securities. **Founded:** 1970. **Publications:** *Secondary Mortgage Markets* (Periodic).

47072 ■ Federal Home Loan Mortgage Corporation - Southeast Region [Freddie Mac]
2300 Windy Ridge Pky. SE, Ste. 200, N Twr.
  Atlanta, GA 30339
Ph: (770)857-8800
Co. E-mail: sbl_se@freddiemac.com
URL: http://www.freddiemac.com/about/contact-us#panelh2
Contact: Steve Taylor, Director
E-mail: steve_taylor@freddiemac.com

47073 ■ Federal Home Loan Mortgage Corporation - Southwest Region
6555 Excellence Way
  Plano, TX 75023
Ph: (972)395-4000
URL: http://www.freddiemac.com

47074 ■ Federal Home Loan Mortgage Corporation - Western Region [Freddie Mac]
444 S Flower Str., 44th Fl.
  Los Angeles, CA 90071
Ph: (213)279-3436
URL: http://www.freddiemac.com

FEDERAL MEDIATION AND CONCILIATION SERVICE

47075 ■ Federal Mediation and Conciliation Service - Eastern Region - Cleveland, Ohio Regional Office
6161 Oak Tree Blvd., Ste. 100
  Independence, OH 44131
Ph: (216)520-4801
Fax: (216)520-4815
URL: http://www.fmcs.gov/aboutus/locations/offices
Contact: Carolyn Brommer, Regional Director
E-mail: cbrommer@fmcs.gov
Founded: 1838.

47076 ■ Federal Mediation and Conciliation Service (FMCS) - Office of Procurement and Operational Support
250 E St. SW
  Washington, DC 20427
URL: http://www.fmcs.gov/aboutus/agency-departments/procurement
Description: Preventing terrorism and enhancing security; managing our borders; administering immigration laws; securing cyberspace; and ensuring disaster resilience.

47077 ■ Federal Mediation and Conciliation Service Office of Public Affairs
250 E St. SW
  Washington, DC 20427
Ph: (202)606-8081
URL: http://www.fmcs.gov/aboutus/agency-departments/office-of-policy-and-strategy/ocpa
Founded: 1838.

47078 ■ Federal Mediation and Conciliation Service - Western Region
250 E St., S W
  Washington, DC 20427
URL: http://www.fmcs.gov/internet
Contact: Pete Donatello, Manager
E-mail: pdonatello@fmcs.gov

47079 ■ Federal Mediation and Conciliation Service - Western Region - Minneapolis, Minnesota Sub-Regional Office
1300 Godward St., Ste. 3950
  Minneapolis, MN 55413
URL: http://www.fmcs.gov/find-a-mediator
Contact: Shane Davis, Manager, Operations
E-mail: sdavis@fmcs.gov
Founded: 1947.

FEDERAL NATIONAL MORTGAGE ASSOCIATION

47080 ■ Government National Mortgage Association, Ginnie Mae Procurement and Contracts (GNMA)
425 3rd St. SW, Ste. 500
  Washington, DC 20024
URL: http://www.ginniemae.gov/about_us/what_we_do/Pages/procurement_contracts.aspx

47081 ■ Government National Mortgage Association - Procurement Management Div.
425 3rd St. SW, Ste. 500
  Washington, DC 20024
URL: http://www.ginniemae.gov/about_us/departments/Pages/management_operations.aspx

FEDERAL TRADE COMMISSION

47082 ■ Federal Trade Commission (FTC) - Bureau of Consumer Protection
600 Pennsylvania Ave., NW
  Washington, DC 20580
URL: http://www.ftc.gov/about-ftc/bureaus-offices/bureau-consumer-protection
Contact: Samuel Levine, Director
Description: Services: Protecting consumers and promoting a fair marketplace. **Founded:** 1914.

47083 ■ Federal Trade Commission (FTC) - Denver Regional Office
1961 Stout St., Ste. 1523
  Denver, CO 80294
Ph: (303)844-3564
URL: http://www.ftc.gov
Contact: Scotte R. Bialecki, Contact
Facebook: www.facebook.com/federaltradecommission
Linkedin: www.linkedin.com/company/federal-trade-commission
X (Twitter): x.com/FTC
YouTube: www.youtube.com/ftcvideos
Description: Serves Colorado, Kansas, Montana, Nebraska, North Dakota, South Dakota, Utah, and Wyoming. **Founded:** 1914.

47084 ■ Federal Trade Commission - East Central Region (ECR)
1111 Superior Ave., Ste. 200
  Cleveland, OH 44114-2507
Free: 877-382-4357
URL: http://www.ftc.gov/about-ftc/bureaus-offices/regional-offices/east-central-region
Contact: Jon Miller Steiger, Director
Description: Serves Delaware, District of Columbia, Maryland, Michigan, Ohio, Pennsylvania, Virginia, and West Virginia.

47085 ■ Federal Trade Commission - Midwest Region
600 Pennsylvania Ave., NW
  Washington, DC 20580
Free: 877-382-4357
URL: http://www.ftc.gov/about-ftc/bureaus-offices/regional-offices/midwest-region
Contact: Todd Kossow, Director
Description: Serves Illinois, Indiana, Iowa, Kansas, Kentucky, Nebraska, North Dakota, Minnesota, Missouri, South Dakota, and Wisconsin.

47086 ■ Federal Trade Commission - Northeast Region
1 Bowling Green
  New York, NY 10004
Free: 877-382-4357
URL: http://www.ftc.gov/about-ftc/bureaus-offices/regional-offices/northeast-region
Contact: William H. Efron, Director
Description: Serves Connecticut, Maine, Massachusetts, New Hampshire, New Jersey New York, Puerto Rico, Rhode Island, Vermont, and U.S. Virgin Islands.

47087 ■ Federal Trade Commission - Northwest Region
600 Pennsylvania Ave., NW
  Washington, DC 20580
Free: 877-382-4357
URL: http://www.ftc.gov/about-ftc/bureaus-offices/regional-offices/northwest-region
Contact: Charles A. Harwood, Director
Description: Works to enforce the federal antitrust laws through merger and anticompetitive conduct investigations and litigation across an array of industries.

47088 ■ Federal Trade Commission (FTC OIG) - Office of Inspector General
Rm. CC-5206 600 Pennsylvania Ave., NW
  Washington, DC 20580
Ph: (202)326-3527
Fax: (202)326-2034
Co. E-mail: oig@ftc.gov
URL: http://www.ftc.gov/office-inspector-general
Contact: Andrew Katsaros, Inspector General
Founded: 1989.

47089 ■ Federal Trade Commission (FTC) - Procurement and General Services Div.
600 Pennsylvania Ave. NW
  Washington, DC 20580
Ph: (202)326-2222
Co. E-mail: opa@ftc.gov
URL: http://www.ftc.gov
Contact: David B. Robbins, Executive Director

47090 ■ Federal Government Assistance

Facebook: www.facebook.com/federaltra
decommission
Linkedin: www.linkedin.com/company/federal-trade
-commission
X (Twitter): x.com/FTC
YouTube: www.youtube.com/user/FTCvideos
Description: The Federal Trade Commission works to preserve a free marketplace by acting as the advocate of consumers and by resisting efforts of any one group to profit at the expense of the general public. The FTC maintains three bureaus and ten regional offices through which to carry out its responsibilities: the Bureau of Competition seeks to prevent business practices that restrain competition by investigating alleged violations, by recommending enforcement action when appropriate, and by participating in an advocacy program; the Bureau of Consumer Protection helps to preserve competition by prohibiting deceptive claims or practices that interfere with the public's ability to make informed purchasing decisions; and the Bureau of Economics offers support to these activities by ensuring that the FTC's actions are based on sound economic principles. FTC regional offices conduct investigations and litigations, offer advice, recommend cases, provide outreach services, sponsor conferences, and coordinate activities with local, state, and regional authorities. **Founded:** 1914.

47090 ■ Federal Trade Commission - Southeast Region
225 Peachtree St. NE, Ste. 1500
Atlanta, GA 30303
Free: 877-382-4357
URL: http://www.ftc.gov/about-ftc/bureaus-offices/
regional-offices/southeast-region
Contact: Anna Burns, Director
Description: Serves Alabama, Florida, Georgia, Mississippi, North Carolina, South Carolina, and Tennessee. **Founded:** 1914.

47091 ■ Federal Trade Commission - Southwest Region
600 Pennsylvania Ave., NW
Washington, DC 20580
Free: 877-382-4357
URL: http://www.ftc.gov/about-ftc/bureaus-offices/
regional-offices/southwest-region
Contact: Matthew Wernz, Regional Director
Description: Serves Arkansas, Louisiana, New Mexico, Oklahoma, and Texas.

47092 ■ Federal Trade Commission - Western Region
10877 Wilshire Blvd., Ste. 700
Los Angeles, CA 90024
Free: 877-382-4357
URL: http://www.ftc.gov/about-ftc/bureaus-offices/
regional-offices/western-region-los-angeles
Contact: Maricela Segura, Director
Description: Serves Arizona, northern California, southern California, Colorado, Hawaii, Nevada, and Utah.

47093 ■ Federal Trade Commission - Western Region
90 7th St.
San Francisco, CA 94103
Free: 877-382-4357
URL: http://www.ftc.gov/about-ftc/bureaus-offices/
regional-offices
Contact: Kerry O'Brien, Regional Director
Description: Serves northern California, southern California, Colorado, Hawaii, Nevada, and Utah. **Founded:** 1918.

GENERAL SERVICES ADMINISTRATION

47094 ■ General Services Administration - Chicago Business Service Center
230 S Dearborn St., Rm. 3190
Chicago, IL 60604
Ph: (312)353-4475
URL: http://www.gsa.gov/node/73201
Contact: Nimisha Agarwal, Chief Financial Officer

Description: Promotes management best practices and efficient government operations through the development of government wide policies. **Founded:** 1949.

47095 ■ General Services Administration - Denver Business Service Center
W 6th Ave., & Kipling St.
Lakewood, CO 80225
Free: 888-999-4777
Co. E-mail: denverfederalcenterr8@gmail.com
URL: http://www.gsa.gov/about-us/regions/welcome
-to-the-rocky-mountain-region-8/buildings-and-facili
ties/colorado/denver-federal-center
Contact: Doug Whiles, Commander
Facebook: www.facebook.com/DenverFederalCenter
Description: Provides acquisition solutions offer private sector professional services, equipment, supplies, and IT to government organizations and the military. **Founded:** 1949.

47096 ■ General Services Administration - Ft. Worth Business Service Center
819 Taylor St.
Fort Worth, TX 76102
Ph: (817)978-2321
URL: http://www.gsa.gov/portal/content/104716
Contact: Nitin Shah, General Counsel
Description: Provides workplaces by constructing, managing, and preserving government buildings and by leasing and managing commercial real estate.

47097 ■ General Services Administration - Kansas City Business Service Center
2300 Main St.
Kansas City, MO 64108
URL: http://www.gsa.gov/portal/category/21472
Description: Serves Iowa, Kansas, Missouri, and Nebraska.

47098 ■ General Services Administration - New York Business Service Center
26 Federal Plz.
New York, NY 10278
Ph: (212)264-9290
URL: http://www.gsa.gov/about-us/regions/welcome
-to-the-northeast-caribbean-region-2/products-an
d-services-region-2/service-centers-division
Description: Serves New Jersey, New York, Puerto Rico, and the Virgin Islands. **Founded:** 1949.

47099 ■ General Services Administration - Northwest Arctic Region
URL: http://www.gsa.gov/about-us/gsa-regions/region
-10-northwestarctic
Description: The Northwest/Arctic Region serves customers primarily located in Alaska, Idaho, Oregon, and Washington, helping them access workspace, telecommunications, information technology, vehicles, and thousands of other goods and services. **Founded:** 1949.

47100 ■ General Services Administration (GSA) - Office of Electronic Government and Technology
1600 Pennsylvania Ave. NW
Washington, DC 20500
URL: http://www.whitehouse.gov/omb/management/
ofcio

47101 ■ General Services Administration - Office of Global Supply - Logistics Operations Ctr.
URL: http://www.gsa.gov/buying-selling/purchasing
-programs/requisition-programs/gsa-global-supply/
oconus-support
Description: GSA provides workplaces by constructing, managing, and preserving government buildings and by leasing and managing commercial real estate.

47102 ■ General Services Administration (GSA) - Office of Small Business Utilization
1800 F St. NW 7th Fl., 3rd Wing (7300)
Washington, DC 20405
Ph: (202)501-1021

URL: http://www.gsa.gov/buy-through-us/new-to-gsa
-acquisitions/how-to-sell-to-the-government/for
-businesses-working-with-gsa
Description: The General Services Administration (GSA), the Federal government's purchasing agent, real estate developer, telecommunications manager, and computer overseer, contracts for over $10 billion worth of commodities and services each year. The GSA's Office of Enterprise Development (OED) develops and oversees GSA procurement preference programs for small, disadvantaged and women-owned businesses. In addition to other pamphlets, the OED publishes four major publications to assist businesses in their marketing efforts: Doing Business with GSA, GSA Small Purchases, GSA Subcontracting Directory (published semiannually), and Forecast of GSA Contracting Opportunities (published annually). Information about upcoming contracting opportunities is placed on GSA's Electronic Bulletin Board. GSA operates Business Service Centers (BSCs) in 11 major metropolitan areas throughout the country. The BSCs implement GSA procurement preference programs by providing assistance, information and counseling to small businesses interested in pursuing Federal Government contracts. Counselors at the BSCs help small businesses understand GSA contracting procedures and locate GSA buyers for their products or services. The BSCs are also involved in monitoring local GSA contracting programs to insure that small, disadvantaged and women-owned businesses are given access to contracts and subcontracts and to find ways to expand their participation. As part of GSA's program, the BSCs sponsor breakfasts and networking seminars to give small businesses an opportunity to meet contracting personnel and each other.

47103 ■ General Services Administration - Washington, DC, Business Services Center
7th & D St. SW
Washington, DC 20407
URL: http://www.gsa.gov/about-us/regions/region
-11-national-capital/buildings-and-facilities/district-of
-columbia
Description: Serves the metropolitan Washington, D.C., area.

47104 ■ U.S. Executive Office of the President - Office of Management and Budget - Office of E-Government and Information Technology
1600 Pennsylvania Ave. NW
Washington, DC 20500
URL: http://www.whitehouse.gov/omb/management/
egov

47105 ■ U.S. General Services Administration - Great Lakes Region - Business Service Center
230 S Dearborn St.
Chicago, IL 60604
URL: http://www.gsa.gov/reference/forms/business
-service-center-activity-report
Description: Serves Illinois, Indiana, Michigan, Minnesota, Ohio, and Wisconsin.

47106 ■ U.S. General Services Administration - Greater Southwest Region - Business Service Center
819 Taylor St.
Fort Worth, TX 76102
Ph: (817)978-2321
URL: http://www.gsa.gov/about-us/regions/welcome
-to-the-greater-southwest-region-7/about-region-7/
key-staff-in-the-greater-southwest-region
Contact: Gerard Badorrek, Chief Financial Officer
Description: Serves Arkansas, Louisiana, New Mexico, Oklahoma, and Texas.

47107 ■ U.S. General Services Administration (GSA) - The Heartland Region - Business Service Center
2300 Main St.
Kansas City, MO 64108
Ph: (816)926-7201
Co. E-mail: ra-heartland-region@gsa.gov
URL: http://www.gsa.gov/portal/category/21472

FEDERAL GOVERNMENT ASSISTANCE

X (Twitter): twitter.com/usgsa
Instagram: www.instagram.com/usgsa
YouTube: www.youtube.com/usgsa
Description: Serves Iowa, Kansas, Missouri, and Nebraska.

47108 ■ U.S. General Services Administration - Mid-Atlantic Region - Office of Business and Public Affairs
100 S Independence Mall W
Philadelphia, PA 19106
URL: http://www.gsa.gov/portal/category/21443
Contact: William Powell, Officer
E-mail: william.powell@gsa.gov
Description: Serves Delaware, Maryland, New Jersey, Pennsylvania, Virginia, and West Virginia.

47109 ■ U.S. General Services Administration - National Capital Region - Business Services Center
7th&D St. SW
Washington, DC 20407
URL: http://www.gsa.gov/forms-library/business-service-center-activity-report
Description: Serves the metropolitan Washington, D.C., area.

47110 ■ U.S. General Services Administration - New England Region - Business Service Center
Thomas P. O'Neill Jr. Federal Bldg.10 Causeway St.
Boston, MA 02222-1076
URL: http://www.gsa.gov/about-us/regions/welcome-to-the-new-england-region-1/about-region-1/key-contacts-in-the-new-england-region
Description: Serves Connecticut, Maine, Massachusetts, New Hampshire, Rhode Island, and Vermont.

47111 ■ U.S. General Services Administration (GSA) - Northwest/Arctic Region - Business Service Center
400 15th St. SW
Auburn, WA 98001
Ph: (253)931-7000
Co. E-mail: press@gsa.gov
URL: http://www.gsa.gov/portal/content/104779
Contact: George Northcroft, Administrator
E-mail: george.northcroft@gsa.gov
Facebook: www.facebook.com/gsa
X (Twitter): twitter.com/usgsa
Instagram: www.instagram.com/usgsa
YouTube: www.youtube.com/usgsa
Description: Serves Alaska, Idaho, Oregon, and Washington.

47112 ■ U.S. General Services Administration-Office of Global Supply-Logistics Operations Center
1800 F St. NW
Washington, DC 20405
URL: http://www.gsa.gov
Contact: Brett Prather, Contact

47113 ■ U.S. General Services Administration - Office of Small Business Utilization (OSBU)
1800 F St., NW
7th fl., 3rd Wing
Washington, DC 20405
URL: http://www.gsa.gov/about-us/regions/region-11-national-capital/small-business-opportunities
Description: The General Services Administration (GSA), the Federal government's purchasing agent, real estate developer, telecommunications manager, and computer overseer, contracts for over $10 billion worth of commodities and services each year. The GSA's Office of Enterprise Development (OED) develops and oversees GSA procurement preference programs for small, disadvantaged and women-owned businesses. In addition to other pamphlets, the OED publishes four major publications to assist businesses in their marketing efforts: Doing Business with GSA, GSA Small Purchases, GSA Subcontracting Directory (published semiannually), and Forecast of GSA Contracting Opportunities (published annually). Information about upcoming contracting opportunities is placed on GSA's Electronic Bulletin Board. GSA operates Business Service Centers (BSCs) in 11 major metropolitan areas throughout the country. The BSCs implement GSA procurement preference programs by providing assistance, information and counseling to small businesses interested in pursuing Federal Government contracts. Counselors at the BSCs help small businesses understand GSA contracting procedures and locate GSA buyers for their products or services. The BSCs are also involved in monitoring local GSA contracting programs to insure that small, disadvantaged and women-owned businesses are given access to contracts and subcontracts and to find ways to expand their participation. As part of GSA's program, the BSCs sponsor breakfasts and networking seminars to give small businesses an opportunity to meet contracting personnel and each other.

47114 ■ U.S. General Services Administration - Rocky Mountain Region - Business Service Center
Free: 888-999-4777
URL: http://www.gsa.gov/about-us/regions/welcome-to-the-rocky-mountain-region-8/buildings-and-facilities/colorado/denver-federal-center
Description: Serves Colorado, Montana, North Dakota, South Dakota, Utah, and Wyoming.

47115 ■ U.S. General Services Administration - Southeast Sunbelt Region - Business Service Center
100 Alabama St., Ste. GR-40
Atlanta, GA 30303-8701
Ph: (404)561-0087
Fax: (404)562-0065
URL: http://www.gsa.gov/portal/content/104712
Contact: Erv Koehler, Administrator Commissioner
Facebook: www.facebook.com/gsa
X (Twitter): twitter.com/usgsa
Instagram: www.instagram.com/usgsa
YouTube: www.youtube.com/usgsa
Description: Serves Alabama, Florida, Georgia, Kentucky, Mississippi, North Carolina, South Carolina, and Tennessee.

INTERNATIONAL TRADE ADMINISTRATION

47116 ■ International Trade Administration - Office of Public Affairs
Mail Stop 3421 U.S. Department of Commerce
Washington, DC 20230
Ph: (202)482-3809
Co. E-mail: publicaffairs@trade.gov
URL: http://www.trade.gov/press
Description: The International Trade Administration's domestic and overseas programs are designed to stimulate the expansion of U.S. exports. Major programs include export counseling and assistance; promotion of U.S. products abroad; coordination and conduct of overseas trade missions; support for the Export Trading Company formation; and management of federal participation in international expositions held in the United States. The ITA gathers, analyzes, and disseminates commercially usable trade and marketing information, including advice on marketing opportunities abroad; information about government assistance available for expanding trade with other nations; location of needed materials and resources; and advice on international trade policy and tariff questions. The ITA operates a network of 48 U.S. and foreign Commercial Service district offices through which to carry out its programs. The ITA's information services, market research, and overseas promotion programs provide opportunities to introduce products abroad at small costs. The ITA, with its variety of low-cost marketing aids, also may assist small firms in locating overseas outlets for their products, namely agents, distributors, licensees, buyers, and suppliers.

47117 ■ International Trade Administration - U.S. Commercial Service - Export Assistance Center
US Department of Commerce
1401 Constitution Ave., NW
Washington, DC 20230
URL: http://www.trade.gov/success-story/bright-future-virginia-woman-owned-solar-energy-firm-shines-first-export-sale

47118 ■ International Trade Administration - U.S. and Foreign Commercial Service - Export Assistance Center
8000 N Blvd., Harry S. Schure Hall, Rm. 104
Old Westbury, NY 11568
URL: http://www.trade.gov/long-island-contact-us
Contact: Nicholas Thomas, Specialist
E-mail: nicholas.thomas@trade.gov
Description: Global network of trade professionals connects U.S. companies with international buyers, providing them with market intelligence, trade counseling, business matchmaking, and advocacy/commercial diplomacy support in New York.

47119 ■ International Trade Administration - U.S. and Foreign Commercial Service - Export Assistance Center
46 E Ohio St., Rm. No. 508
Indianapolis, IN 46204
URL: http://www.trade.gov/indianapolis-contact-us
Contact: Mark Cooper, Director
E-mail: mark.cooper@trade.gov
Description: Global network of trade professionals connects U.S. companies with international buyers, providing them with market intelligence, trade counseling, business matchmaking, and advocacy/commercial diplomacy support in Indiana.

47120 ■ International Trade Administration (EAC) - U.S. and Foreign Commercial Service - Export Assistance Center
1859 Summerville Ave., Ste. 800
North Charleston, SC 29405
URL: http://www.trade.gov/export-solutions

47121 ■ International Trade Administration (ITA) - U.S. and Foreign Commercial Service - Export Assistance Center
13805 58th St. N, Ste. 1-200
Clearwater, FL 33760
URL: http://www.trade.gov/florida-clearwater
Contact: Sandra Campbell, Director
E-mail: sandra.campbell@trade.gov

47122 ■ International Trade Administration (EAC) - U.S. and Foreign Commercial Service - Export Assistance Center
1401 Constitution Ave. NW
Washington, DC 20230
URL: http://www.commerce.gov/bureaus-and-offices/os/legislative-and-intergovernmental-affairs

47123 ■ International Trade Administration - U.S. and Foreign Commercial Service - Export Assistance Center
20 Washington Pl., Ste. 615
Newark, NJ 07102
URL: http://www.trade.gov/new-york-new-york-local-partners
Contact: Susan Widmer, Officer
E-mail: susan.widmer@trade.gov

47124 ■ International Trade Administration - U.S. and Foreign Commercial Service - Export Assistance Center
2302 Martin Ct., Ste. 315
Irvine, CA 92612
URL: http://www.trade.gov/irvine-contact-us
Contact: Jim Mayfield, Director
E-mail: jim.mayfield@trade.gov

47125 ■ International Trade Administration - U.S. and Foreign Commercial Service - Export Assistance Center
Dominican University of California., 50 Acacia Ave.
San Rafael, CA 94901
URL: http://www.trade.gov/california-san-rafael
Contact: Elizabeth Krauth, Director
E-mail: elizabeth.krauth@trade.gov
Description: Global network of trade professionals connects U.S. companies with international buyers, providing them with market intelligence, trade counseling, business matchmaking, and advocacy/commercial diplomacy support in California.

Federal Government Assistance

47126 ■ International Trade Administration - U.S. and Foreign Commercial Service - Export Assistance Center
55 S Market St., Ste. 1040
San Jose, CA 95113
URL: http://www.trade.gov/california-san-jose
Contact: Joanne Vliet, Director
E-mail: joanne.vliet@trade.gov
Description: Global network of trade professionals connects U.S. companies with international buyers, providing them with market intelligence, trade counseling, business matchmaking, and advocacy/commercial diplomacy support in California San Jose.

47127 ■ International Trade Administration - U.S. and Foreign Commercial Service - Export Assistance Center
2001 6th Ave., Ste. 2600
Seattle, WA 98121
URL: http://www.commerce.gov/bureaus-and-offices/os/legislative-and-intergovernmental-affairs
Description: Offers wide range of information about trade to help the U.S exporters. **Founded:** 1978.

47128 ■ International Trade Administration - U.S. and Foreign Commercial Service - Export Assistance Center
200 N Phillips Ave. L101
Sioux Falls, SD 57104
URL: http://www.commerce.gov/bureaus-and-offices/os/legislative-and-intergovernmental-affairs
Contact: Cinnamon King, Director
E-mail: cinnamon.king@trade.gov

47129 ■ International Trade Administration (EAC) - U.S. and Foreign Commercial Service - Export Assistance Center
3 Independent Dr.
Jacksonville, FL 32202
URL: http://www.trade.gov/jacksonville-contact-us
Contact: Jorge Arce, Director
E-mail: jorge.arce@trade.gov

47130 ■ International Trade Administration - U.S. and Foreign Commercial Service - Export Assistance Center
201 Superior Ave. E, Ste. 130
Cleveland, OH 44114
URL: http://www.trade.gov/ohio-cleveland
Contact: Susan Whitney, Regional Director
E-mail: susan.whitney@trade.gov
Description: Global network of trade professionals connects U.S. companies with international buyers, providing them with market intelligence, trade counseling, business matchmaking, and advocacy/commercial diplomacy support in North Ohio.

47131 ■ International Trade Administration - U.S. and Foreign Commercial Service - North Texas U.S. Export Assistance Center (USEAC)
150 Westpark Way., Ste. 235
Euless, TX 76040
URL: http://www.trade.gov/texas-dallas-fort-worth
Contact: Jessica Gordon, Director
E-mail: jessica.gordon@trade.gov

47132 ■ U.S. Department of Commerce - International Trade Administration - U.S. Commercial Service - Central-Southern New Jersey U.S. Export Assistance Center
997 Lenox Dr., Bldg. 3, Ste. 111
Ewing Township, NJ 08628
URL: http://www.commerce.gov/bureaus-and-offices/os/legislative-and-intergovernmental-affairs
Contact: Janice Barlow, Director
E-mail: janice.barlow@trade.gov
Description: Global network of trade professionals connects U.S. companies with international buyers, providing them with market intelligence, trade counseling, business matchmaking, and advocacy/commercial diplomacy support in Pennsylvania. **Founded:** 1903.

47133 ■ U.S. Department of Commerce - International Trade Administration - U.S. Commercial Service - Export Assistance Center
1401 Constitution Ave. NW
Washington, DC 20230
URL: http://www.commerce.gov/work-with-us/services-for-businesses

47134 ■ U.S. Department of Commerce (USEAC) - International Trade Administration - U.S. Commercial Service - Export Assistance Center
1501 Wilson Blvd., Ste. 1225
Arlington, VA 22209
URL: http://2016.export.gov/virginia
Contact: William Fanjoy, Director
E-mail: william.fanjoy@trade.gov

47135 ■ U.S. Department of Commerce - International Trade Administration - U.S. Commercial Service - Export Assistance Center
221 E 11th St., 4th Fl.
Austin, TX 78701
URL: http://www.trade.gov/texas-austin
Contact: Michael Rosales, Director
E-mail: michael.rosales@trade.gov

47136 ■ U.S. Department of Commerce (EAC) - International Trade Administration - U.S. Commercial Service - Export Assistance Center
300 W Pratt St., Ste. 300
Baltimore, MD 21201
URL: http://www.trade.gov/baltimore-contact-us
Contact: Paul Matino, Director (Acting)
E-mail: paul.matino@trade.gov
Description: Serves as both the Baltimore and Washington, D.C., district office.

47137 ■ U.S. Department of Commerce - International Trade Administration - U.S. Commercial Service - Export Assistance Center
1800 5th Ave. N, Ste. 3300
Birmingham, AL 35203
URL: http://www.trade.gov/alabama-birmingham
Contact: Robert Stackpole, Director
E-mail: robert.stackpole@trade.gov

47138 ■ U.S. Department of Commerce (EAC) - International Trade Administration - U.S. Commercial Service - Export Assistance Center
700 W State St., 2nd Fl.
Boise, ID 83720
URL: http://www.trade.gov/us-commercial-service
Contact: Aron Davidson, Director
E-mail: aron.davidson@trade.gov

47139 ■ U.S. Department of Commerce - International Trade Administration - U.S. Commercial Service - Export Assistance Center
55 New Sudbury St., No. 1826A
JFK Federal Bldg.
Boston, MA 02203
URL: http://www.trade.gov/massachusetts-boston
Contact: Jim Paul, Director
E-mail: james.paul@trade.gov
Description: Boston office also services the states of New Hampshire and Vermont.

47140 ■ U.S. Department of Commerce (EAC) - International Trade Administration - U.S. Commercial Service - Export Assistance Center
633 Northland Ave., Door E, Ste. 1109
Buffalo, NY 14211
URL: http://www.trade.gov/san-diego-contact-us
Contact: Rosanna Masucci, Director
E-mail: rosanna.masucci@trade.gov

47141 ■ U.S. Department of Commerce - International Trade Administration - U.S. Commercial Service - Export Assistance Center
46 E Ohio St., Ste. 508
Indianapolis, IN 46204
URL: http://2016.export.gov/indiana
Contact: Mark Cooper, Director
E-mail: mark.cooper@trade.gov

47142 ■ U.S. Department of Commerce - International Trade Administration - U.S. Commercial Service - Export Assistance Center
Charlotte, NC
URL: http://www.trade.gov/charlotte-contact-us
Contact: Greg Sizemore, Director
E-mail: greg.sizemore@trade.gov

47143 ■ U.S. Department of Commerce - International Trade Administration - U.S. Commercial Service - Export Assistance Center
1401 Constitution Ave. NW
Washington, DC 20230
URL: http://www.commerce.gov/bureaus-and-offices/os/legislative-and-intergovernmental-affairs

47144 ■ U.S. Department of Commerce - International Trade Administration - U.S. Commercial Service - Export Assistance Center
36 E 7th St., Ste. 2025
Cincinnati, OH 45202
URL: http://www.trade.gov/ohio-cincinnati
Contact: Marcia Brandstadt, Director
E-mail: marcia.brandstadt@trade.gov

47145 ■ U.S. Department of Commerce (EAC) - International Trade Administration - U.S. Commercial Service - Export Assistance Center
13805 58th St. N, Ste. 1-200
Clearwater, FL 33760
Ph: (727)893-3738
URL: http://www.trade.gov/clearwater-contact-us
Contact: Sandra Campbell, Director
E-mail: sandra.campbell@trade.gov

47146 ■ U.S. Department of Commerce (USEAC) - International Trade Administration - U.S. Commercial Service - Export Assistance Center
201 Superior Ave. E, Ste. 130
Cleveland, OH 44114
URL: http://www.trade.gov/cleveland-contact-us
Contact: Susan Whitney, Regional Director
E-mail: susan.whitney@trade.gov

47147 ■ U.S. Department of Commerce - International Trade Administration - U.S. Commercial Service - Export Assistance Center
1301 Gervais St., Ste. 1100
Columbia, SC 29201
URL: http://www.trade.gov/columbia-contact-us
Contact: Dorette Coetsee, Director
E-mail: dorette.coetsee@trade.gov

47148 ■ U.S. Department of Commerce - International Trade Administration - U.S. Commercial Service - Export Assistance Center
65 E State St., Ste. 1350
Columbus, OH 43215
URL: http://www.trade.gov/ohio-columbus
Contact: Darren Srebnick, Director
E-mail: darren.srebnick@trade.gov
Description: Provides customized international business solutions.

47149 ■ U.S. Department of Commerce - International Trade Administration - U.S. Commercial Service - Export Assistance Center
999 18th St., Ste. 725
N Twr.
Denver, CO 80202

FEDERAL GOVERNMENT ASSISTANCE

URL: http://www.commerce.gov/bureaus-and-offices/os/legislative-and-intergovernmental-affairs
Linkedin: www.linkedin.com/company/u-s--department-of-energy
Description: Denver office also services the states of Montana and Wyoming.

47150 ■ U.S. Department of Commerce - International Trade Administration - U.S. Commercial Service - Export Assistance Center
749 Federal Bldg., 210 Walnut St.
Des Moines, IA 50309
URL: http://www.trade.gov/iowa-des-moines
Contact: Albert Liu, Director
E-mail: albert.liu@trade.gov

47151 ■ U.S. Department of Commerce - International Trade Administration - U.S. Commercial Service - Export Assistance Center
440 Burroughs St., Ste. 390
Detroit, MI 48202
URL: http://www.trade.gov/detroit-contact-us
Contact: Jennifer Moll, Director
E-mail: jennifer.moll@trade.gov

47152 ■ U.S. Department of Commerce (EAC) - International Trade Administration - U.S. Commercial Service - Export Assistance Center
150 Westpark Way, Ste. 235
Euless, TX 76040
URL: http://www.trade.gov/dallas-fort-worth-contact-us
Contact: Jessica Gordon, Director
E-mail: jessica.gordon@trade.gov

47153 ■ U.S. Department of Commerce - International Trade Administration - U.S. Commercial Service - Export Assistance Center
50 Front Ave. SW, Ste. 1038
Grand Rapids, MI 49504
URL: http://www.trade.gov/michigan-grand-rapids
Contact: Kendra Kuo, Director
E-mail: kendra.kuo@trade.gov

47154 ■ U.S. Department of Commerce - International Trade Administration - U.S. Commercial Service - Export Assistance Center
1919 Smith St., Ste. 10079
Houston, TX 77002
URL: http://www.trade.gov
Contact: Jason Wilson, Director
E-mail: jason.wilson@trade.gov
Description: Serves the business needs of Davidson, Forsyth, Guilford, Montgomery, Randolph, Rockingham, and Stokes counties. **Founded:** 1903.

47155 ■ U.S. Department of Commerce - International Trade Administration - U.S. Commercial Service - Export Assistance Center
610 Central Ave., Ste. 150
Highland Park, IL 60035
Ph: (847)681-8010
Fax: (847)681-8012
URL: http://web.ita.doc.gov/ete/eteinfo.nsf/cd2ad821f07f828585256892007bca9a/a318f16d4dcc3780852566d500639c3d?OpenDocument
Contact: Robin F. Mugford, Manager
Founded: 1903.

47156 ■ U.S. Department of Commerce (EAC) - International Trade Administration - U.S. Commercial Service - Export Assistance Center
Hawaii Foreign Trade Zone No. 9
521 Ala Moana Blvd., No. 214
Honolulu, HI 96813
URL: http://www.trade.gov/honolulu-contact-us
Contact: John Holman, Director
E-mail: john.holman@trade.gov

47157 ■ U.S. Department of Commerce - International Trade Administration - U.S. Commercial Service - Export Assistance Center
Mickey Leland Federal Bldg. 1919 Smith St., Ste. 10079
Houston, TX 77002
URL: http://www.trade.gov/texas-houston
Contact: Jason Wilson, Director
E-mail: jason.wilson@trade.gov

47158 ■ U.S. Department of Commerce (EAC) - International Trade Administration - U.S. Commercial Service - Export Assistance Center
1230 Raymond Rd.
Jackson, MS 39204
URL: http://www.trade.gov/mississippi-contact-us
Contact: Carole Moore, Director
E-mail: carol.moore@trade.gov

47159 ■ U.S. Department of Commerce - International Trade Administration - U.S. Commercial Service - Export Assistance Center
1000 Walnut St., Ste. 500
Kansas City, MO 64106
Ph: (816)421-1876
Fax: (816)471-7839
Co. E-mail: office.kansascity@trade.gov
URL: http://2016.export.gov/missouri/eg_us_mo_028279.asp
Contact: Joshua Kaplan, Director
E-mail: joshua.kaplan@trade.gov
Description: Affiliated with the Wichita district office.

47160 ■ U.S. Department of Commerce - International Trade Administration - U.S. Commercial Service - Export Assistance Center
17 Market Sq., No. 201
Knoxville, TN 37902
URL: http://www.trade.gov/knoxville-contact-us
Contact: Jennifer Woods, Director
E-mail: jennifer.woods@trade.gov

47161 ■ U.S. Department of Commerce - International Trade Administration - U.S. Commercial Service - Export Assistance Center
210 Walnut St., 749 Federal Bldg
Des Moines, IA 50309
Ph: (515)284-4590
Co. E-mail: office.desmoines@trade.gov
URL: http://www.trade.gov/des-moines-contact-us
Contact: Ryan Liu, Director
E-mail: albert.liu@trade.gov

47162 ■ U.S. Department of Commerce (EAC) - International Trade Administration - U.S. Commercial Service - Export Assistance Center
1401 Constitution Ave. NW
Washington, DC 20230
URL: http://www.trade.gov
Linkedin: www.linkedin.com/company/u-s--department-of-energy

47163 ■ U.S. Department of Commerce (EAC) - International Trade Administration - U.S. Commercial Service - Export Assistance Center
601 W Broadway, Rm. 634B
Louisville, KY 40202
URL: http://www.trade.gov/louisville-contact-us
Contact: Peggy Pauley, Director
E-mail: peggy.pauley@trade.gov

47164 ■ U.S. Department of Commerce - International Trade Administration - U.S. Commercial Service - Export Assistance Center
22 N Front St., Ste. 200
Memphis, TN 38130
URL: http://www.trade.gov/tennessee-memphis
Contact: Lilliam Baez, Director
E-mail: lilliam.baez@trade.gov

47165 ■ U.S. Department of Commerce (EAC) - International Trade Administration - U.S. Commercial Service - Export Assistance Center
5835 Blue Lagoon Dr., Ste. 203
Miami, FL 33126
URL: http://www.trade.gov/miami-contact-us
Contact: Eduardo Torres, Director
E-mail: eduardo.torres@trade.gov

47166 ■ U.S. Department of Commerce (EAC) - International Trade Administration - U.S. Commercial Service - Export Assistance Center
213 Ct. St., Ste. 903
Middletown, CT 06457
URL: http://www.trade.gov/connecticut-middletown
Contact: Melissa Grosso, Director
E-mail: melissa.grosso@trade.gov
Description: Affiliated with the Providence district office.

47167 ■ U.S. Department of Commerce - International Trade Administration - U.S. Commercial Service - Export Assistance Center
10437 Innovation Dr., Ste. 140
Wauwatosa, WI 53226
URL: http://www.trade.gov/milwaukee-contact-us
Contact: Koreen Grube, Director
E-mail: koreen.grube@trade.gov

47168 ■ U.S. Department of Commerce (EAC) - International Trade Administration - U.S. Commercial Service - Export Assistance Center
330 2nd Ave. South, Ste. 410
Minneapolis, MN 55401
URL: http://www.trade.gov/minneapolis-contact-us
Contact: Mathew Woodlee, Director
E-mail: mathew.woodlee@trade.gov

47169 ■ U.S. Department of Commerce - International Trade Administration - U.S. Commercial Service - Export Assistance Center
55 S Market St., Ste. 1040
San Jose, CA 95113
URL: http://www.commerce.gov/bureaus-and-offices/os/legislative-and-intergovernmental-affairs
Contact: Joanne Vliet, Director
E-mail: joanne.vliet@trade.gov

47170 ■ U.S. Department of Commerce - International Trade Administration - U.S. Commercial Service - Export Assistance Center
801 Broadway., Ste. C372
Nashville, TN 37203
URL: http://www.commerce.gov/bureaus-and-offices/os/legislative-and-intergovernmental-affairs
Contact: Brie Knox, Director
E-mail: brie.knox@trad.gov

47171 ■ U.S. Department of Commerce (EAC) - International Trade Administration - U.S. Commercial Service - Export Assistance Center
1401 Constitution Ave. NW
Washington, DC 20230
URL: http://www.commerce.gov/bureaus-and-offices/os/legislative-and-intergovernmental-affairs

47172 ■ U.S. Department of Commerce (USEAC) - International Trade Administration - U.S. Commercial Service - Export Assistance Center
2302 Martin Ct., Ste. 315
Irvine, CA 92612
URL: http://www.trade.gov/irvine-contact-us
Contact: Jim Mayfield, Director
E-mail: jim.mayfield@trade.gov

47173 ■ U.S. Department of Commerce - International Trade Administration - U.S. Commercial Service - Export Assistance Center
1401 Constitution Ave., NW
Washington, DC 20230
URL: http://www.commerce.gov/bureaus-and-offices/os/legislative-and-intergovernmental-affairs

47174 ■ U.S. Department of Commerce - International Trade Administration - U.S. Commercial Service - Export Assistance Center
1301 Clay St., Ste. 630 N
Oakland, CA 94612
URL: http://www.trade.gov/california-oakland
Contact: Rod Hirsch, Director
E-mail: rod.hirsch@trade.gov

47175 ■ U.S. Department of Commerce - International Trade Administration - U.S. Commercial Service - Export Assistance Center
c/o Ronald Wilson, Director, 301 NW 63rd St., Ste. 420
Oklahoma City, OK 73116
Ph: (405)608-5302
Fax: (405)608-4211
Co. E-mail: office.oklahomacity@trade.gov
URL: http://www.trade.gov/office/oklahoma-city-us-export-assistance-center
Contact: Diane Farrell, Secretary

47176 ■ U.S. Department of Commerce - International Trade Administration - U.S. Commercial Service - Export Assistance Center
1401 Constitution Ave., NW
Washington, DC 20230
URL: http://www.commerce.gov/bureaus-and-offices/os/legislative-and-intergovernmental-affairs
Description: Provides them with market intelligence, trade counseling, business matchmaking, and advocacy/commercial diplomacy support in Long Island.

47177 ■ U.S. Department of Commerce - International Trade Administration - U.S. Commercial Service - Export Assistance Center
1617 JFK Blvd., Ste. 1580
Philadelphia, PA 19103
URL: http://www.trade.gov/pennsylvania-philadelphia
Contact: Antonio Ceballos, Director
E-mail: antonio.ceballos@trade.gov
Description: Philadelphia office also services the state of Delaware.

47178 ■ U.S. Department of Commerce (EAC) - International Trade Administration - U.S. Commercial Service - Export Assistance Center
4041 N Central Ave., Ste. 1010
Phoenix, AZ 85012
Ph: (623)473-6928
URL: http://www.trade.gov/arizona-phoenix
Contact: Leandro Solórzano, Director
E-mail: leandro.solorzano@trade.gov

47179 ■ U.S. Department of Commerce - International Trade Administration - U.S. Commercial Service - Export Assistance Center
William S Moorhead Federal Building, 1000 Liberty Ave., Ste. 807
Pittsburgh, PA 15222
URL: http://www.trade.gov/pittsburgh-contact-us
Contact: Ryan Russell, Director
E-mail: ryan.russell@trade.gov

47180 ■ U.S. Department of Commerce - International Trade Administration - U.S. Commercial Service - Export Assistance Center
1025 Campus Dr. S
Bldg. 47 W
Waterford, MI 48328
Ph: (248)975-9600
Fax: (248)975-9606
Co. E-mail: pontiac.office@trade.gov
URL: http://2016.export.gov/michigan

47181 ■ U.S. Department of Commerce (USEAC) - International Trade Administration - U.S. Commercial Service - Export Assistance Center
1 World Trade Ctr.
121 SW Salmon St., Ste. 242
Portland, OR 97204
Ph: (503)326-3001
Fax: (503)326-6351
URL: http://www.2016.export.gov/eac
Contact: Kellie Holloway-Jarman, Director
E-mail: kellie.holloway@trade.gov
Description: Affiliated with the Boston, Massachusetts, district office.

47182 ■ U.S. Department of Commerce - International Trade Administration - U.S. Commercial Service - Export Assistance Center
1 World Trade Ctr.
121 SW Salmon St.,No. 242
Portland, OR 97204
Ph: (503)326-3001
URL: http://www.trade.gov/portland-oregon-contact-us
Contact: Kellie Holloway Jarman, Director
E-mail: kellie.holloway@trade.gov

47183 ■ U.S. Department of Commerce (EAC) - International Trade Administration - U.S. Commercial Service - Export Assistance Center
315 Iron Horse Way, Ste. 101
Providence, RI 02908
URL: http://www.trade.gov/providence-contact-us
Contact: Keith Yatsuhashi, Director
E-mail: keith.yatsuhashi@trade.gov
Description: Affiliated with the Hartford district office.

47184 ■ U.S. Department of Commerce (USEAC) - International Trade Administration - U.S. Commercial Service - Export Assistance Center
808 W Nye Ln.
Carson City, NV 89703
URL: http://www.trade.gov/reno-contact-us

47185 ■ U.S. Department of Commerce (EAC) - International Trade Administration - U.S. Commercial Service - Export Assistance Center
100 State St., Ste. 410
Rochester, NY 14614
URL: http://www.trade.gov/rochester-contact-us
Contact: Timothy McCall, Director
E-mail: timothy.mccall@trade.gov

47186 ■ U.S. Department of Commerce - International Trade Administration - U.S. Commercial Service - Export Assistance Center
1300 Pennsylvania Ave., NW
Washington, DC 20004
URL: http://legacy.trade.gov/faq.asp
Contact: Aron Davidson, Director
E-mail: aron.davidson@trade.gov
Linkedin: www.linkedin.com/company/u-s--department-of-energy

47187 ■ U.S. Department of Commerce - International Trade Administration - U.S. Commercial Service - Export Assistance Center
1410 Ethan Way, Ste. 131 N
Sacramento, CA 95825
URL: http://www.trade.gov/sacramento-contact-us
Contact: George Tastard, Director
E-mail: george.tastard@trade.gov

47188 ■ U.S. Department of Commerce - International Trade Administration - U.S. Commercial Service - Export Assistance Center
1401 Constitution Ave., NW
Washington, DC 20230
URL: http://www.commerce.gov/bureaus-and-offices/os/legislative-and-intergovernmental-affairs

47189 ■ U.S. Department of Commerce - International Trade Administration - U.S. Commercial Service - Export Assistance Center
350 S Main St., Ste. 464
Salt Lake City, UT 84101
URL: http://www.trade.gov/salt-lake-city-contact-us
Contact: Shelby Daiek, Director
E-mail: shelby.daiek@trade.gov

47190 ■ U.S. Department of Commerce (EAC) - International Trade Administration - U.S. Commercial Service - Export Assistance Center
615 E Houston St., Ste. 207
San Antonio, TX 78205
URL: http://www.commerce.gov/bureaus-and-offices/os/legislative-and-intergovernmental-affairs
Contact: Michael Rosales, Director
E-mail: michael.rosales@trade.gov

47191 ■ U.S. Department of Commerce (EAC) - International Trade Administration - U.S. Commercial Service - Export Assistance Center
9449 Balboa Ave., Ste. 111
San Diego, CA 92123
URL: http://www.trade.gov/san-diego-contact-us
Contact: Aron Davidson, Director
E-mail: aron.davidson@trade.gov

47192 ■ U.S. Department of Commerce - International Trade Administration - U.S. Commercial Service - Export Assistance Center
75 Hawthorne St. 2nd Fl., Ste. 2500
San Francisco, CA 94105
URL: http://www.commerce.gov/bureaus-and-offices/os/legislative-and-intergovernmental-affairs

47193 ■ U.S. Department of Commerce - International Trade Administration - U.S. Commercial Service - Export Assistance Center
55 S Market St., Ste. 1040
San Jose, CA 95113
URL: http://www.trade.gov/california-san-jose
Contact: Joanne Vliet, Director
E-mail: joanne.vliet@trade.gov
Description: Provides them with market intelligence, trade counseling, business matchmaking, and advocacy/commercial diplomacy support.

47194 ■ U.S. Department of Commerce - International Trade Administration - U.S. Commercial Service - Export Assistance Center
1401 Constitution Ave. NW
Washington, DC 20230
URL: http://www.commerce.gov/work-with-us/services-for-businesses

47195 ■ U.S. Department of Commerce - International Trade Administration - U.S. Commercial Service - Export Assistance Center
Dominican University, 50 Acacia Ave.
San Rafael, CA 94901
URL: http://www.trade.gov/california-san-rafael
Contact: Elizabeth Krauth, Director
E-mail: elizabeth.krauth@trade.gov
Description: The U.S. Commercial Service is the trade promotion arm of the U.S. Department of Commerce's International Trade Administration.

FEDERAL GOVERNMENT ASSISTANCE

47196 ■ **U.S. Department of Commerce - International Trade Administration - U.S. Commercial Service - Export Assistance Center**
1309 4th St., SW
Albuquerque, NM 87102
URL: http://www.trade.gov/santa-fe-contact-us
Contact: Indalecio Vallejos, Director
E-mail: indalecio.vallejos@trade.gov

47197 ■ **U.S. Department of Commerce - International Trade Administration - U.S. Commercial Service - Export Assistance Center**
1401 Constitution Ave. NW
Washington, DC 20230
URL: http://www.commerce.gov/bureaus-and-offices/os/legislative-and-intergovernmental-affairs
Description: Provides them with market intelligence, trade counseling, business matchmaking, and advocacy/commercial diplomacy support in Long Island.

47198 ■ **U.S. Department of Commerce (EAC) - International Trade Administration - U.S. Commercial Service - Export Assistance Center**
2001 6th Ave., Ste. 2600
Seattle, WA 98121
URL: http://www.trade.gov/seattle-contact-us
Contact: Diane Mooney, Director
E-mail: diane.mooney@trade.gov
Description: Center market intelligence, trade counseling, business matchmaking and advocacy diplomacy support.

47199 ■ **U.S. Department of Commerce - International Trade Administration - U.S. Commercial Service - Export Assistance Center**
200 N Phillips Ave., L101
Sioux Falls, SD 57104
URL: http://www.trade.gov/south-dakota-sioux-falls
Contact: Cinnamon King, Director
E-mail: cinnamon.king@trade.gov
Description: Provides them with market intelligence, trade counseling, business matchmaking, and advocacy/commercial diplomacy support in South Carolina.

47200 ■ **U.S. Department of Commerce - International Trade Administration - U.S. Commercial Service - Export Assistance Center**
c/o John Autin, dIRECTOR
601 W Broadway, Rm. 634B
Louisville, KY 40202
Ph: (502)582-5066
Fax: (502)582-6573
URL: http://web.ita.doc.gov/ete/eteinfo.nsf/cd2ad8
21f07f828585256892007bca9a/a318f16d4dcc
3780852566d500639c3d?OpenDocument
Contact: John Autin, Director

47201 ■ **U.S. Department of Commerce - International Trade Administration - U.S. Commercial Service - Export Assistance Center**
1401 Constitution Ave. NW
Washington, DC 20230
Co. E-mail: janet.bauermeister@nospam.trade.gov
URL: http://www.commerce.gov
Linkedin: www.linkedin.com/company/u-s--departmen
t-of-energy
Description: Provides them with market intelligence, trade counseling, business matchmaking, and advocacy/commercial diplomacy support in Vermont.

47202 ■ **U.S. Department of Commerce - International Trade Administration - U.S. Commercial Service - Export Assistance Center**
3 Independent Dr.
Jacksonville, FL 32202
URL: http://www.trade.gov/jacksonville-contact-us
Contact: Jorge Arce, Director
E-mail: jorge.arce@trade.gov

47203 ■ **U.S. Department of Commerce - International Trade Administration - U.S. Commercial Service - Export Assistance Center**
36 E 7th St., Ste. 2025
Cincinnati, OH 45202
URL: http://www.trade.gov/cincinnati-contact-us
Contact: Marcia Brandstadt, Director
E-mail: marcia.brandstadt@trade.gov
Description: Provides them with market intelligence, trade counseling, business matchmaking, and advocacy/commercial diplomacy support in North Ohio.

47204 ■ **U.S. Department of Commerce - International Trade Administration - U.S. Commercial Service - Export Assistance Center**
1401 Constitution Ave. NW
Washington, DC 20230
URL: http://www.commerce.gov/bureaus-and-offices/os/legislative-and-intergovernmental-affairs

47205 ■ **U.S. Department of Commerce - International Trade Administration - U.S. Commercial Service - Export Assistance Center (EAC)**
156 E 2nd St.
Tulsa, OK 74103
URL: http://www.trade.gov/oklahoma-tulsa
Contact: Kevin Chambers, Officer
E-mail: kevin.chambers@trade.gov

47206 ■ **U.S. Department of Commerce - International Trade Administration - U.S. Commercial Service - Export Assistance Center**
1401 Constitution Ave. NW
Washington, DC 20230
URL: http://2016.export.gov/westvirginia/index.asp
Contact: Diego Gattesco, Specialist
E-mail: diego.gattesco@trade.gov
Description: Provides them with market intelligence, trade counseling, business matchmaking, and advocacy/commercial diplomacy support in Washington.

47207 ■ **U.S. Department of Commerce (EAC) - International Trade Administration - U.S. Commercial Service - Export Assistance Center**
245 Main St., Ste. 630
White Plains, NY 10601
URL: http://www.trade.gov/westchester-contact-us
Contact: Joan Kanlian, Director
E-mail: joan.kanlian@trade.gov

47208 ■ **U.S. Department of Commerce - International Trade Administration - U.S. Commercial Service - Export Assistance Center**
440 Burroughs St., Ste. 390
Detroit, MI 48202
URL: http://www.trade.gov/detroit-contact-us
Contact: Jennifer Moll, Director
E-mail: jennifer.moll@trade.gov
Description: Provides them with market intelligence, trade counseling, business matchmaking, and advocacy/commercial diplomacy support in Michigan.

47209 ■ **U.S. Department of Commerce - International Trade Administration - U.S. Commercial Service - Orlando U.S. Export Assistance Center**
3452 Lake Lynda Dr., Ste. 185
Orlando, FL 32817
URL: http://www.trade.gov/florida-orlando
Contact: Kenneth Mouradian, Director
E-mail: kenneth.mouradian@trade.gov

47210 ■ **U.S. Department of Commerce - International Trade Administration - U.S. Commercial Service - U.S. Export Assistance Center**
1401 Constitution Ave. NW
Washington, DC 20230
URL(s): www.trade.gov/let-our-experts-help-0
Linkedin: www.linkedin.com/company/u-s-departmen
t-of-commerce

Description: Provides core research infrastructure for the social sciences to support the research, teaching, and service mission of UNC.

47211 ■ **U.S. Department of Commerce - International Trade Administration - U.S. Commercial Service - U.S. Export Assistance Center**
221 E 11th St., 4th Fl.
Austin, TX 78701
URL: http://www.trade.gov/austin-contact-us'
Contact: Michael Rosales, Director
E-mail: michael.rosales@trade.gov
Description: Global network of trade professionals connects U.S. companies with international buyers, providing them with market intelligence, trade counseling, business matchmaking, and advocacy/commercial diplomacy support in Texas.

47212 ■ **U.S. Department of Commerce - International Trade Administration - U.S. Commercial Service - U.S. Export Assistance Center**
300 W Pratt St., Ste. 300
Baltimore, MD 21201
URL: http://www.trade.gov/maryland-baltimore
Contact: Jolanta Coffey, Officer
E-mail: jolanta.coffey@trade.gov
Description: Serves as both the Baltimore and Washington, D.C., district office.

47213 ■ **U.S. Department of Commerce - International Trade Administration - U.S. Commercial Service - U.S. Export Assistance Center**
1800 5th Ave. N, Ste. 3300
Birmingham, AL 35203
URL: http://www.trade.gov/alabama-contact-us
Contact: Robert Stackpole, Director
E-mail: robert.stackpole@trade.gov
Description: Global network of trade professionals connects U.S. companies with international buyers, providing them with market intelligence, trade counseling, business matchmaking, and advocacy/commercial diplomacy support in Alabama.

47214 ■ **U.S. Department of Commerce - International Trade Administration - U.S. Commercial Service - U.S. Export Assistance Center**
700 W State St., 2nd Fl.
Boise, ID 83720
URL: http://www.trade.gov/idaho-boise
Contact: Amy Benson, Director
E-mail: amy.benson@trade.gov
Description: Global network of trade professionals connects U.S. companies with international buyers, providing them with market intelligence, trade counseling, business matchmaking, and advocacy/commercial diplomacy support in Idaho.

47215 ■ **U.S. Department of Commerce - International Trade Administration - U.S. Commercial Service - U.S. Export Assistance Center**
JFK Federal Bldg., 55 New Sudbury St., Ste. 1826A
Boston, MA 02203
URL: http://www.trade.gov/massachusetts-boston
Contact: Jim Paul, Director
E-mail: jpaul@trade.gov
Description: Boston office also services the states of New Hampshire and Vermont.

47216 ■ **U.S. Department of Commerce - International Trade Administration - U.S. Commercial Service - U.S. Export Assistance Center**
633 Northland Ave., Door E, Ste. 1109
Buffalo, NY 14211
URL: http://www.trade.gov/buffalo-contact-us
Contact: Rosanna Masucci, Director
E-mail: rosanna.masucci@trade.gov

47217 ■ U.S. Department of Commerce - International Trade Administration - U.S. Commercial Service - U.S. Export Assistance Center (USEAC)
320 E 9th St.
  Charlotte, NC 28202
URL: http://www.trade.gov/north-carolina-charlotte
Contact: Greg Sizemore, Director
E-mail: greg.sizemore@trade.gov
Founded: 1994.

47218 ■ U.S. Department of Commerce - International Trade Administration - U.S. Commercial Service - U.S. Export Assistance Center
77 W Jackson Blvd., Ste. 707
  Chicago, IL 60604
URL: http://www.trade.gov/chicago-contact-us
Contact: Dan Kim, Director
E-mail: dan.kim@trade.gov

47219 ■ U.S. Department of Commerce - International Trade Administration - U.S. Commercial Service - U.S. Export Assistance Center
36 E 7th St., Ste. 2025
  Cincinnati, OH 45202
URL: http://www.trade.gov/cincinnati-contact-us
Contact: Marcia Brandstadt, Director
E-mail: marcia.brandstadt@trade.gov

47220 ■ U.S. Department of Commerce - International Trade Administration - U.S. Commercial Service - U.S. Export Assistance Center (USEAC)
201 Superior Ave. E, Ste. 130
  Cleveland, OH 44114
URL: http://www.trade.gov/ohio-cleveland
Contact: Susan Whitney, Regional Director
E-mail: susan.whitney@trade.gov

47221 ■ U.S. Department of Commerce - International Trade Administration - U.S. Commercial Service - U.S. Export Assistance Center
65 E State St., Ste. 1350
  Columbus, OH 43215
URL: http://www.trade.gov/ohio-columbus
Contact: Darren Srebnick, Director
E-mail: darren.srebnick@trade.gov
Description: Global network of trade professionals connects U.S. companies with international buyers, providing them with market intelligence, trade counseling, business matchmaking, and advocacy/commercial diplomacy support in Central Ohio.

47222 ■ U.S. Department of Commerce - International Trade Administration - U.S. Commercial Service - U.S. Export Assistance Center
999 18th St., Ste. 725
  N Twr.
  Denver, CO 80202
URL: http://www.trade.gov/denver-contact-us
Contact: Suzette Nickle, Director
E-mail: suzette.nickle@trade.gov
Description: Denver office also services the states of Montana and Wyoming.

47223 ■ U.S. Department of Commerce - International Trade Administration - U.S. Commercial Service - U.S. Export Assistance Center
1401 Constitution Ave. NW
  Washington, DC 20230
URL: http://www.trade.gov/country-commercial-guides/bolivia-market-entry-strategy
Linkedin: www.linkedin.com/company/u-s--department-of-commerce

47224 ■ U.S. Department of Commerce - International Trade Administration - U.S. Commercial Service - U.S. Export Assistance Center
440 Burroughs St., Ste. 390
  Detroit, MI 48202
URL: http://www.trade.gov/detroit-contact-us
Contact: Jennifer Moll, Director
E-mail: jennifer.moll@trade.gov

47225 ■ U.S. Department of Commerce - International Trade Administration - U.S. Commercial Service - U.S. Export Assistance Center
50 Front Ave. SW, Ste. 1038
  Grand Rapids, MI 49504
URL: http://www.trade.gov/Michigan-Grand-Rapids
Contact: Kendra Kuo, Director
E-mail: kendra.kuo@trade.gov

47226 ■ U.S. Department of Commerce - International Trade Administration - U.S. Commercial Service - U.S. Export Assistance Center
Foreign Trade Zone No. 9
  521 Ala Moana Blvd., No. 214
  Honolulu, HI 96813
URL: http://www.trade.gov/hawaii-honolulu
Contact: John Holman, Director
E-mail: john.holman@trade.gov
URL(s): www.trade.gov/cs
Description: Global network of trade professionals connects U.S. companies with international buyers, providing them with market intelligence, trade counseling, business matchmaking, and advocacy/commercial diplomacy support in Hawaii.

47227 ■ U.S. Department of Commerce - International Trade Administration - U.S. Commercial Service - U.S. Export Assistance Center
1919 Smith St., Ste. 10079
  Houston, TX 77002
URL: http://www.trade.gov/let-our-experts-help-0
Contact: Jason Wilson, Director
E-mail: jason.wilson@trade.gov

47228 ■ U.S. Department of Commerce - International Trade Administration - U.S. Commercial Service - U.S. Export Assistance Center
c/o Carol Moore, Director
  1230 Raymond Rd.
  Jackson, MS 39204
Ph: (601)373-0773
Co. E-mail: carol.moore@trade.gov
URL: http://www.commerce.gov/bureaus-and-offices/os/legislative-and-intergovernmental-affairs
Contact: Carole Moore, Director
E-mail: carol.moore@trade.gov
URL(s): www.trade.gov/mississippi-jackson

47229 ■ U.S. Department of Commerce - International Trade Administration - U.S. Commercial Service - U.S. Export Assistance Center
1000 Walnut St., Ste. 505
  Kansas City, MO 64106
URL: http://www.trade.gov/kansas-city-contact-us
Contact: Joshua Kaplan, Director
E-mail: joshua.kaplan@trade.gov
Description: Affiliated with the Wichita district office.

47230 ■ U.S. Department of Commerce - International Trade Administration - U.S. Commercial Service - U.S. Export Assistance Center
17 Market Sq., Ste. 201
  Knoxville, TN 37902
URL: http://www.trade.gov/tennessee-knoxville
Contact: Jennifer Woods, Director
E-mail: jennifer.woods@trade.gov
Description: Global network of trade professionals connects U.S. companies with international buyers, providing them with market intelligence, trade counseling, business matchmaking, and advocacy/commercial diplomacy support in Tennessee.

47231 ■ U.S. Department of Commerce - International Trade Administration - U.S. Commercial Service - U.S. Export Assistance Center
1401 Constitution Ave. NW
  Washington, DC 20230
URL: http://www.trade.gov/commercial-service-offices-us
Linkedin: www.linkedin.com/company/u-s--department-of-commerce
Description: Global network of trade professionals connects U.S. companies with international buyers, providing them with market intelligence, trade counseling, business matchmaking, and advocacy/commercial diplomacy support in Arkansas.

47232 ■ U.S. Department of Commerce - International Trade Administration - U.S. Commercial Service - U.S. Export Assistance Center
350 S Main St., Ste. 464
  Salt Lake City, UT 84101
URL: http://www.trade.gov/salt-lake-city-contact-us
Contact: Shelby Daiek, Director
E-mail: shelby.daiek@trade.gov
Description: Helps U.S. companies plan, develop and execute international sales strategies necessary to succeed in today's global marketplace. Developed by international trade specialists and economists, here you will find trusted market intelligence, practical advice and business tools to help you understand how to export, connect with foreign buyers, and expand operations in new markets.

47233 ■ U.S. Department of Commerce - International Trade Administration - U.S. Commercial Service - U.S. Export Assistance Center
601 W Broadway, Rm. 634B
  Louisville, KY 40202
URL: http://www.trade.gov/kentucky-louisville
Contact: Peggy Pauley, Director
E-mail: peggy.pauley@trade.gov
Description: Global network of trade professionals connects U.S. companies with international buyers, providing them with market intelligence, trade counseling, business matchmaking, and advocacy/commercial diplomacy support in Kentucky.

47234 ■ U.S. Department of Commerce - International Trade Administration - U.S. Commercial Service - U.S. Export Assistance Center
22 N Front St., Ste. 200
  Memphis, TN 38130
URL: http://www.commerce.gov/bureaus-and-offices/os/legislative-and-intergovernmental-affairs
Contact: Lilliam Baez, Director
E-mail: lilliam.baez@trade.gov
Description: Provides core research infrastructure for the social sciences to support the research, teaching, and service mission of UNC.

47235 ■ U.S. Department of Commerce - International Trade Administration - U.S. Commercial Service - U.S. Export Assistance Center
5835 Blue Lagoon Dr., Ste. 203
  Miami, FL 33126
URL: http://www.trade.gov/miami-contact-us
Contact: Eduardo Torres, Director
E-mail: eduardo.torres@trade.gov

47236 ■ U.S. Department of Commerce - International Trade Administration - U.S. Commercial Service - U.S. Export Assistance Center
213 Ct. St., Ste. 903
  Middletown, CT 06457
URL: http://www.trade.gov/middletown-contact-us
Contact: Melissa Grosso, Director
E-mail: melissa.grosso@trade.gov
Description: Affiliated with the Providence district office.

47237 ■ U.S. Department of Commerce - International Trade Administration - U.S. Commercial Service - U.S. Export Assistance Center
10437 Innovation Dr., Ste. 140
  Milwaukee, WI 53226
URL: http://www.trade.gov/wisconsin-milwaukee
Contact: Koreen Grube, Director

E-mail: koreen.grube@trade.gov

47238 ■ U.S. Department of Commerce - International Trade Administration - U.S. Commercial Service - U.S. Export Assistance Center
330 2nd Ave. S, Ste. 410
Minneapolis, MN 55401
Ph: (612)348-1638
URL: http://www.trade.gov/minnesota-minneapolis
Contact: Mathew Woodlee, Director
E-mail: mathew.woodlee@trade.gov

47239 ■ U.S. Department of Commerce - International Trade Administration - U.S. Commercial Service - U.S. Export Assistance Center
1401 Constitution Ave. NW
Washington, DC 20230
URL: http://www.trade.gov

47240 ■ U.S. Department of Commerce - International Trade Administration - U.S. Commercial Service - U.S. Export Assistance Center (USEAC)
87 State St., Rm. 205
Montpelier, VT 05601
URL: http://www.trade.gov/montpelier-contact-us
Contact: Susan Murray, Director
E-mail: susan.murray@trade.gov
Description: Global network of trade professionals connects U.S. companies with international buyers, providing them with market intelligence, trade counseling, business matchmaking, and advocacy/commercial diplomacy support in Vermont.

47241 ■ U.S. Department of Commerce - International Trade Administration - U.S. Commercial Service - U.S. Export Assistance Center
801 Broadway, Ste. C372
Nashville, TN 37203
URL: http://www.trade.gov/nashville-contact-us
Contact: Brie Knox, Director
E-mail: brie.knox@trad.gov

47242 ■ U.S. Department of Commerce - International Trade Administration - U.S. Commercial Service - U.S. Export Assistance Center
1301 Clay St., Ste. 630 N
Oakland, CA 94612
URL: http://www.trade.gov/oakland-contact-us
Contact: Rod Hirsch, Director
E-mail: rod.hirsch@trade.gov

47243 ■ U.S. Department of Commerce - International Trade Administration - U.S. Commercial Service - U.S. Export Assistance Center
301 NW 63rd St., Ste. 420
Oklahoma City, OK 73116
URL: http://www.commerce.gov/bureaus-and-offices/os/legislative-and-intergovernmental-affairs
Contact: Marcus Verner, Director
E-mail: marcus.verner@trade.gov
URL(s): www.trade.gov/cs

47244 ■ U.S. Department of Commerce - International Trade Administration - U.S. Commercial Service - U.S. Export Assistance Center (USEAC)
1616 Capitol Ave., Ste. 249
Omaha, NE 68102
URL: http://www.trade.gov/nebraska-omaha
Contact: Meredith Bond, Director
E-mail: meredith.bond@trade.gov
Description: Global network of trade professionals connects U.S. companies with international buyers, providing them with market intelligence, trade counseling, business matchmaking, and advocacy/commercial diplomacy support in Nebraska.

47245 ■ U.S. Department of Commerce - International Trade Administration - U.S. Commercial Service - U.S. Export Assistance Center
3452 Lake Lynda Dr., Ste. 185
Orlando, FL 32817
URL: http://www.trade.gov/florida-orlando
Contact: Kenneth Mouradian, Director
E-mail: kenneth.mouradian@trade.gov
Description: Global network of trade professionals connects U.S. companies with international buyers, providing them with market intelligence, trade counseling, business matchmaking, and advocacy/commercial diplomacy support in Florida.

47246 ■ U.S. Department of Commerce - International Trade Administration - U.S. Commercial Service - U.S. Export Assistance Center
1617 JFK Blvd., Ste. 1580
Philadelphia, PA 19103
URL: http://www.trade.gov/pennsylvania-philadelphia
Contact: Tony Ceballos, Director
E-mail: antonio.ceballos@trade.gov
Description: Global network of trade professionals connects U.S. companies with international buyers, providing them with market intelligence, trade counseling, business matchmaking, and advocacy/commercial diplomacy support in Pennsylvania.

47247 ■ U.S. Department of Commerce - International Trade Administration - U.S. Commercial Service - U.S. Export Assistance Center
1501 Wilson Blvd., Ste. 1225
Arlington, VA 22209
URL: http://www.trade.gov/virginia-arlington
Contact: April Redmon, Director
E-mail: april.redmon@trade.gov

47248 ■ U.S. Department of Commerce - International Trade Administration - U.S. Commercial Service - U.S. Export Assistance Center
William S Moorhead Federal Bldg., Ste. 807
1000 Liberty Ave.
Pittsburgh, PA 15222
URL: http://www.trade.gov/pennsylvania-pittsburgh
Contact: Ryan Russell, Director
E-mail: ryan.russell@trade.gov

47249 ■ U.S. Department of Commerce - International Trade Administration - U.S. Commercial Service - U.S. Export Assistance Center
1401 Constitution Ave., NW
Washington, DC 20230
URL: http://www.trade.gov/san-diego-contact-us
Contact: Aron Davidson, Director
E-mail: aron.davidson@trade.gov

47250 ■ U.S. Department of Commerce - International Trade Administration - U.S. Commercial Service - U.S. Export Assistance Center
312 Fore St., U.S. Custom House
Portland, ME 04101
URL: http://www.trade.gov/maine-portland
Contact: Jeffrey Porter, Director
E-mail: jeffrey.porter@trade.gov
Description: Affiliated with the Boston, Massachusetts, district office.

47251 ■ U.S. Department of Commerce - International Trade Administration - U.S. Commercial Service - U.S. Export Assistance Center
1 World Trade Ctr.
121 SW Salmon St., Ste. 242
Portland, OR 97204
Ph: (503)326-3001
URL: http://www.trade.gov/oregon-portland
Contact: Kellie Holloway Jarman, Director
E-mail: kellie.holloway@trade.gov

47252 ■ U.S. Department of Commerce - International Trade Administration - U.S. Commercial Service - U.S. Export Assistance Center
2 International Dr., Ste. 121
Portsmouth, NH 03801
URL: http://www.trade.gov/portsmouth-contact-us
Contact: Justin Oslowski, Director
E-mail: justin.oslowski@trade.gov
Description: Global network of trade professionals connects U.S. companies with international buyers, providing them with market intelligence, trade counseling, business matchmaking, and advocacy/commercial diplomacy support in New Hamsphire.

47253 ■ U.S. Department of Commerce - International Trade Administration - U.S. Commercial Service - U.S. Export Assistance Center
315 Iron Horse Way, Ste. 101
Providence, RI 02908
URL: http://www.trade.gov/rhode-island-providence
Contact: Keith Yatsuhashi, Director
E-mail: keith.yatsuhashi@trade.gov
Description: Affiliated with the Hartford district office.

47254 ■ U.S. Department of Commerce - International Trade Administration - U.S. Commercial Service - U.S. Export Assistance Center
400 S Las Vegas Blvd., Ste. 400
Las Vegas, NV 89101
URL: http://www.trade.gov/las-vegas-contact-us
Contact: Martin Herbst, Director
E-mail: martin.herbst@trade.gov
Description: Promotes trade and investment, and ensures fair trade through the rigorous enforcement of our trade laws and agreements.

47255 ■ U.S. Department of Commerce - International Trade Administration - U.S. Commercial Service - U.S. Export Assistance Center
1501 Wilson Blvd., Ste. 1225
Arlington, VA 22209
Ph: (202)557-4063
URL: http://www.sba.gov/local-assistance/export-trade-assistance/export-finance-managers
Contact: William Houck, Contact
E-mail: william.houck@sba.gov
Description: Global network of trade professionals connects U.S. companies with international buyers, providing them with market intelligence, trade counseling, business matchmaking, and advocacy/commercial diplomacy support in Virginia.

47256 ■ U.S. Department of Commerce - International Trade Administration - U.S. Commercial Service - U.S. Export Assistance Center
100 State St., Ste. 410
Rochester, NY 14614
URL: http://www.trade.gov/new-york-rochester
Contact: Timothy McCall, Director
E-mail: timothy.mccall@trade.gov

47257 ■ U.S. Department of Commerce - International Trade Administration - U.S. Commercial Service - U.S. Export Assistance Center
77 W Jackson Blvd., Ste. 707
Chicago, IL 60604
URL: http://www.trade.gov/chicago-contact-us
Contact: Dan Kim, Director
E-mail: dan.kim@trade.gov

47258 ■ U.S. Department of Commerce - International Trade Administration - U.S. Commercial Service - U.S. Export Assistance Center
1792 Tribute Rd., Ste. 455
Sacramento, CA 95825
URL: http://www.trade.gov/san-diego-contact-us
Contact: Aron Davidson, Director
E-mail: aron.davidson@trade.gov

47259 ■ U.S. Department of Commerce - International Trade Administration - U.S. Commercial Service - U.S. Export Assistance Center
1100 Corporate Square Dr., Ste. 242
Saint Louis, MO 63132
URL: http://www.trade.gov/st-louis-contact-us
Contact: Warren Anderson, Officer
E-mail: warren.anderson@trade.gov

47260 ■ U.S. Department of Commerce - International Trade Administration - U.S. Commercial Service - U.S. Export Assistance Center
350 S Main St., Ste. 464
Salt Lake City, UT 84101
URL: http://www.trade.gov/salt-lake-city-contact-us
Contact: Shelby Daiek, Director
E-mail: shelby.daiek@trade.gov

47261 ■ U.S. Department of Commerce - International Trade Administration - U.S. Commercial Service - U.S. Export Assistance Center
9449 Balboa Ave., Ste. 111
San Diego, CA 92123
URL: http://www.trade.gov/office/san-antonio-us-export-assistance-center
Contact: Aron Davidson, Director
E-mail: aron.davidson@trade.gov

47262 ■ U.S. Department of Commerce - International Trade Administration - U.S. Commercial Service - U.S. Export Assistance Center
9449 Balboa Ave., Ste. 111
San Diego, CA 92123
URL: http://www.trade.gov/california-san-diego
Contact: Aron Davidson, Director
E-mail: aron.davidson@trade.gov

47263 ■ U.S. Department of Commerce - International Trade Administration - U.S. Commercial Service - U.S. Export Assistance Center
290 Broadway, Ste. 1312
New York, NY 10007
URL: http://www.trade.gov/new-york-new-york
Contact: Carmela Mammas, Director
E-mail: carmela.mammas@trade.gov

47264 ■ U.S. Department of Commerce - International Trade Administration - U.S. Commercial Service - U.S. Export Assistance Center
St. 165 Centro Internacional de Mercadeo Tower II, Ste. 702
Guaynabo, PR 00968
URL: http://www.trade.gov/san-juan-contact-us
Contact: Jose F. Burgos, Director
E-mail: jose.burgos@trade.gov
Description: Global network of trade professionals connects U.S. companies with international buyers, providing them with market intelligence, trade counseling, business matchmaking, and advocacy/commercial diplomacy support in Puerto Rico.

47265 ■ U.S. Department of Commerce - International Trade Administration - U.S. Commercial Service - U.S. Export Assistance Center
2001 6th Ave., Ste. 2610
Seattle, WA 98121
URL: http://www.trade.gov/washington-seattle
Contact: Diane Mooney, Director
E-mail: diane.mooney@trade.gov

47266 ■ U.S. Department of Commerce - International Trade Administration - U.S. Commercial Service - U.S. Export Assistance Center
801 W Riverside Ave., Ste. 100
Spokane, WA 99201
URL: http://www.trade.gov/washington-spokane

Description: Global network of trade professionals connects U.S. companies with international buyers, providing them with market intelligence, trade counseling, business matchmaking, and advocacy/commercial diplomacy support in Washington.

47267 ■ U.S. Department of Commerce - International Trade Administration - U.S. Commercial Service - U.S. Export Assistance Center
700 N Greenwood Ave., Ste. 1400
Tulsa, OK 74106
Ph: (918)581-7650
URL: http://2014-2017.commerce.gov/locations/tulsa-us-export-assistance-center.html#15/36.1631/-95.9876

47268 ■ U.S. Department of Commerce - International Trade Administration - U.S. Commercial Service - U.S. Export Assistance Center
URL: http://www.commerce.gov
URL(s): www.trade.gov/cs

47269 ■ U.S. Department of Commerce - International Trade Administration - U.S. Commercial Service - U.S. Export Assistance Center
1100 Main St., 3rd Fl.
Wheeling, WV 26003
URL: http://www.trade.gov/commercial-service-offices-us
Contact: Diego Gattesco, Director
E-mail: diego.gattesco@trade.gov
Description: Global network of trade professionals connects U.S. companies with international buyers, providing them with market intelligence, trade counseling, business matchmaking, and advocacy/commercial diplomacy support in West Virginia.

47270 ■ U.S. Department of Commerce (USEAC) - International Trade Administration - U.S. Commercial Service - U.S. Export Assistance Center
300 W Douglas Ave., Ste. 850
Wichita, KS 67202
URL: http://www.trade.gov/wichita-contact-us
Contact: Andrew Anderson, Director
E-mail: andrew.anderson@trade.gov
Description: Affiliated with the Kansas City, Missouri, district office.

47271 ■ U.S. Department of Commerce - International Trade Administration - U.S. Commercial Service - U.S. Export Assistance Center
50 Front Ave. SW, Ste. 1038
Grand Rapids, MI 49504
URL: http://www.trade.gov/michigan-grand-rapids
Contact: Kendra Kuo, Director
E-mail: kendra.kuo@trade.gov
Description: Global network of trade professionals connects U.S. companies with international buyers, providing them with market intelligence, trade counseling, business matchmaking, and advocacy/commercial diplomacy support in Michigan.

INTERNATIONAL TRADE COMMISSION

47272 ■ International Trade Commission - Office of Operations
500 E St. SW
Washington, DC 20436
URL: http://www.usitc.gov/offices/operations
Contact: Catherine DeFilippo, Director

47273 ■ International Trade Commission - Office of Tariff Affairs and Trade Agreements (TATA)
500 E St. SW
Washington, DC 20436
URL: http://www.usitc.gov/offices/tata
Contact: Jennifer Rohrbach, Director

47274 ■ U.S. International Trade Commission (USITC) - Office of Economics
500 E St. SW
Washington, DC 20436
Ph: (202)205-3216
URL: http://www.usitc.gov/offices/econ
Contact: Bill Powers, Director
URL(s): www.usitc.gov/research_and_analysis/office_economics.htm

47275 ■ U.S. International Trade Commission - Office of Industries
500 E St. SW
Washington, DC 20436
Ph: (202)205-3296
URL: http://www.usitc.gov/offices/industries

47276 ■ U.S. International Trade Commission - Office of Unfair Import Investigations
500 E St. SW
Washington, DC 20436
Ph: (202)205-2560
URL: http://www.usitc.gov/offices/ouii
Contact: Margaret D. Macdonald, Director
E-mail: margaret.macdonald@usitc.gov

LIBRARY OF CONGRESS

47277 ■ Library of Congress (LOC) - Library
101 Independence Ave., SE
Washington, DC 20540
Ph: (202)707-9779
Co. E-mail: visit@loc.gov
URL: http://www.loc.gov
Contact: Carla Hayden, Librarian
Facebook: www.facebook.com/libraryofcongress
X (Twitter): x.com/librarycongress
Instagram: www.instagram.com/librarycongress
YouTube: www.youtube.com/libraryofcongress
Pinterest: www.pinterest.com/LibraryCongress
Description: Publishes on folk-life. Offers catalogs, guides, finding aids, bibliographies and discographies. Also offers videos and audio recordings and a quarterly newsletter. Reaches market through direct mail. Does not accept unsolicited manuscripts. **Scope:** American folklife. Folklife is defined as traditional songs, personal histories, special ways of speaking, childhood games, celebrations, personal and collective beliefs, recipes, decoration, etc. **Services:** Library open to the public. **Founded:** 1800. **Holdings:** 171 million items; 40 million books and other print material; 4.2 million audio materials; 74.5 million manuscripts; 5.6 million maps; 1.9 million moving images; 8.2 million items of sheet music; 17.3 million visual items.; 162,477,060 items.; 162,477,060 items including books, monographs and serials, bound newspapers, pamphlets, technical reports, audio materials, manuscripts, maps, microforms, sheet of music, photographs, posters, prints and drawings.; 3 million photographs, manuscripts, audio recordings, and moving images. **Publications:** *American Memory*; *THOMAS*; *National Jukebox*; *Library of Congress (LOC)*; *Business History: A Resource Guide*; *Patents: Business References*; *Telecommunications Industry: Sources of Information*; *National Union Catalog of Manuscript Collections (NUCMC)*; *Ethnic Recordings in America: A Neglected Heritage*; *California As I Saw It: First Person Narratives of California's Early Years, 1849-1900*; *AFC Annual reports* (Annual); *Folklife Center News*; *Library of Congress Online Catalog*; *Performing Arts Encyclopedia (PAE)*; *Prints & Photographs Online Catalog (PPOC)*; *Folklife Sourcebook*; *Traditional Music and Spoken Word Catalog*; *Veterans History Project*; *The American Folklife Center*; *Archived Web Sites*; *The Community of the Book: A Directory of Organizations and Programs*; *America Preserved: A Checklist of Historic Buildings, Structures and Sites*; *Folklife Sourcebook: A Directory of Folklife Resources in the United States*; *Quilt Collections: A Directory for the United States and Canada*; *Entrepreneur's Reference Guide to Small Business Information*; *Current Antarctic Literature* (Monthly). **Awards:** Community Collections Grant Program (An-

FEDERAL GOVERNMENT ASSISTANCE

nual); Gerald E. and Corinne L. Parsons Fund Award (Annual); American Folklife Center Volunteer Internship Program (Annual).

MINORITY BUSINESS DEVELOPMENT AGENCY

47278 ■ U.S. Department of Commerce - Minority Business Development Agency (MBDA)
1401 Constitution Ave. NW
  Washington, DC 20230
Ph: (202)482-2332
URL: http://www.mbda.gov
Contact: Richard M. Nixon, President
Facebook: www.facebook.com/USMBDA
Linkedin: www.linkedin.com/company/usmbda
X (Twitter): x.com/USMBDA
Instagram: www.instagram.com/usmbda
YouTube: www.youtube.com/channel/UCc8oT_4PDPOVnaQQQ7zBs5w
Description: Maintains contact with major corporations to identify business opportunities for minority-owned enterprises, and they utilize other federal, state, and local government agencies to identify contract opportunities and sources of financing to expand the minority business community. **Founded:** 1969. **Publications:** *North Carolina Minority Purchasing Guide.*

47279 ■ U.S. Department of Commerce - Minority Business Development Agency District Office - Miami (Florida) Business Center
970 SW 1St. Str, Ste. 406
  Miami, FL 33130
Ph: (786)515-0670
URL: http://www.mbda.gov/business-center/miami-mbda-business-center
Contact: Marie Gill, Director
E-mail: marie@mgillonline.com
Description: Department of commerce and business development agency in Miami.

47280 ■ U.S. Department of Commerce - Minority Business Development Agency - Philadelphia Regional Enterprise Center
4548 Market St.
  Philadelphia, PA 19139
Ph: (215)895-4046
URL: http://www.mbda.gov
Contact: Victoria Hosendorf, Program Director
Facebook: www.facebook.com/USMBDA
X (Twitter): x.com/USMBDA
Description: Department of e-commerce and business development center in the United States.

47281 ■ U.S. Department of Commerce - Minority Business Development Agency - San Francisco Regional Office
75 Hawthorne St., 2nd Fl., Ste. 2500
  San Francisco, CA 94105
Ph: (415)705-2300
URL: http://www.trade.gov/san-francisco-contact-us
Contact: Doug Wallace, Director
E-mail: douglas.wallace@trade.gov
Description: Department of commerce and business development agency.

NATIONAL AERONAUTICS AND SPACE ADMINISTRATION

47282 ■ National Aeronautics and Space Administration - Ames Research Center - Small Business Specialist
Moffett Field, CA 94035-1000
Ph: (650)604-4695
Fax: (650)604-0912
Co. E-mail: arc-smallbusiness@mail.nasa.gov
URL: http://osbp.nasa.gov/about-arc.html
Contact: Christine L. Munroe, Specialist
Description: To develop small businesses in high tech areas that include technology transfer and commercialization of technology. **Founded:** 1958.

47283 ■ National Aeronautics and Space Administration (NASA) - Goddard Space Flight Center - Small Business Specialist
8800 Greenbelt Rd.
  Greenbelt, MD 20771
URL: http://www.nasa.gov/centers/nssc/small-business
Contact: Jennifer D. Perez, Specialist
Description: Goddard Space Flight Center. Promotes human space flight activities.

47284 ■ National Aeronautics and Space Administration (NASA) - John C. Stennis Space Center - Small Business Specialist - Procurement Office
300 E St. SW, Ste. 5R30
  Washington, DC 20546
URL: http://www.nasa.gov/stennis/stennis-osbp

47285 ■ National Aeronautics and Space Administration (NASA) - John H. Glenn Research Center at Lewis Field - Small Business Specialist
21000 Brookpark Rd.
  Cleveland, OH 44135
URL: http://www.nasa.gov/osbp/sbs_spotlight
Contact: Program Manager, Program Manager
E-mail: smallbusiness@nasa.gov

47286 ■ National Aeronautics and Space Administration - Johnson Space Center - Small Business Specialist
300 E St. SW, Ste. 2K68
  Washington, DC 20546-0001
URL: http://osbp.nasa.gov/about-johnson.html
Contact: Robert E. Watts, Officer
E-mail: jsc-smallbusiness@mail.nasa.gov
Description: Promotes human space flight activities. **Founded:** 1958. **Educational Activities:** HMSDC Business Expo (Annual).

47287 ■ National Aeronautics and Space Administration - Langley Research Center - Small Business Specialist
Hampton, VA 23681
URL: http://www.nasa.gov/langley
Description: Aims to make revolutionary improvements to aviation, expand understanding of Earth's atmosphere and develop technology for space exploration. **Founded:** 1958.

47288 ■ National Aeronautics and Space Administration (NASA) - Marshall Space Flight Center - Small Business Specialist
300 E St. SW, Ste. 2K68
  Washington, DC 20546-0001
Ph: (202)358-2088
Fax: (202)358-3261
Co. E-mail: msfc-smallbusiness@mail.nasa.gov
URL: http://osbp.nasa.gov/about-marshall.html
Contact: David E. Brock, Contact
E-mail: david.e.brock@nasa.gov
Description: To promote the development and management of NASA programs that assist all categories of small business.

47289 ■ National Aeronautics and Space Administration (NASA) - Office of Small Business Programs (OSBP)
300 E St. SW, Ste. 1W53
  Washington, DC 20546
Ph: (202)358-2088
Co. E-mail: smallbusiness@nasa.gov
URL: http://www.nasa.gov/osbp
Contact: Glenn A. Delgado, Administrator
Facebook: www.facebook.com/NASASmallBusiness
X (Twitter): x.com/NASA_OSBP
Description: The development and management of the National Aeronautics and Space Administration's programs to assist small businesses are administered by its Office of Small and Disadvantaged Business Utilization. Services include individual counseling sessions for business owners seeking advice on how to best pursue contracting opportunities at NASA. NASA's procurement program is decentralized, with procurements planned and accomplished by field installations that also maintain small and minority business specialists. NASA's Technology Utilization Program provides information and other assistance to small business owners seeking to apply the results of NASA research and development projects to new commercial products or processes.

47290 ■ National Aeronautics and Space Administration - Resident Office--Jet Propulsion Laboratory - Small Business Specialist
300 E St. SW, Ste. 5R30
  Washington, DC 20546
URL: http://osbp.nasa.gov/contacts.html
Contact: Christine L. Munroe, Contact
E-mail: arc-smallbusiness@mail.nasa.gov
Description: Educational institution in California for jet propulsion technology. **Founded:** 1958.

47291 ■ National Aeronautics and Space Administration (NASA) - Resident Office--JPL - Small Business Specialist
300 E St. SW, Ste. 5R30
  Washington, DC 20546
URL: http://www.nasa.gov/osbp
Description: Firm engages in space research activities.

47292 ■ National Aeronautics and Space Administration (NASA) - Small Business Innovation Research Office
300 E St. SW, Ste. 5R30
  Washington, DC 20546
URL: http://www.nasa.gov/sbir_sttr
Contact: Jason L. Kessler, Executive
E-mail: jason.l.kessler@nasa.gov
Description: The NASA SBIR and STTR programs fund the research, development, and demonstration of innovative technologies that fulfill NASA needs as described in the annual Solicitations and have significant potential for successful commercialization.

47293 ■ National Aeronautics and Space Administration (STAC) - Southern Technology Applications Center
300 E St. SW, Ste. 5R30
  Washington, DC 20546
URL: http://www.nasa.gov

47294 ■ Nerac Inc.
One Technology Dr.
  Tolland, CT 06084
Ph: (860)872-7000
URL: http://www.nerac.com
Contact: Kevin Bouley, President
Linkedin: www.linkedin.com/company/nerac
X (Twitter): x.com/nerac_insights
YouTube: www.youtube.com/channel/UCu69ssLZxP5NfiVkLpmy5JQ
Description: Provider of research and advisory. **Founded:** 1966. **Publications:** "Innovation Scouting: Optics and Photonics Firms Use Scouts More Often Than Most"; "Eco-Innovation Optics and Photonics Companies Are Well Positioned To Eco-Innovate And Improve Profits"; "The Nerac Strategist," 2011; "Genetic Testing: The Future of Alzheimer's Disease Diagnostics"; "REACH: What Companies Need to Know"; "Stem Cells of the Smart Grid".

47295 ■ Northeast Homeland Security Regional Advisory Council (NERAC)
Co. E-mail: nerac@mapc.org
URL: http://nerac.us
Contact: Lauren Sacks, Program Manager
E-mail: lsacks@mapc.org
Facebook: www.facebook.com/NERAC.HS
X (Twitter): x.com/nerac_hs
Description: Regional security council.

47296 ■ REI Oklahoma (REI)
2912 Enterprise Blvd.
  Durant, OK 74701
Free: 800-658-2823
Fax: (580)920-2745
Co. E-mail: info@reiok.org
URL: http://www.reiok.org
Contact: Scott Dewald, President

Description: Distributor of Hydronic plumbing, heating equipment and supplies. **Founded:** 1964.

47297 ■ Small Business Programs Office (SBPO) - Jet Propulsion Laboratory
California Technical Institute
4800 Oak Grove Dr.
Pasadena, CA 91109
URL: http://acquisition.jpl.nasa.gov/business
Contact: Dr. Laurie Leshin, Director
Description: Seeks to connect and integrate small businesses that support space exploration, scientific discovery, and aeronautics research with the Jet Propulsion Lab. **Founded:** 1958.

47298 ■ University of New Mexico - Earth Data Analysis Center (EDAC)
1 University of New Mexico
MSC01 1110
Albuquerque, NM 87131-0001
Ph: (505)277-3622
Fax: (505)277-3614
Co. E-mail: social@edac.unm.edu
URL: http://edac.unm.edu
URL(s): rgis.unm.edu
Facebook: www.facebook.com/earthda taanalysiscenter
X (Twitter): twitter.com/edacunm
Description: Integral unit of University of New Mexico. Offers spectral and spatial data analysis. **Scope:** Retrieves, processes, and analyzes satellite and aerial data for earth resources and develops geographic information systems (GIS). Image processing and GIS activities include mineral exploration, cover type mapping, habitat mapping and modeling, and surveys of archeological locations. Photo search and retrieval services include satellite images, aerial photos, maps, digital data, LANDSAT data, and photos from Gemini, Apollo, Apollo-Soyuz, Skylab, and Space Shuttle missions. Offers national and international visiting scientist programs providing customized technical assistance and training in remote sensing and image processing. **Founded:** 1964. **Holdings:** Collection includes more than 150,000 aerial and satellite photographs. EDAC also maintains total satellite and aerial photo coverage of New Mexico on microfiche; coverage includes photos obtained from LANDSAT, Skylab, Gemini, Apollo, Space Shuttle, and conventional aerial photos. Machine-readable tapes are maintained for internal use.

NATIONAL CREDIT UNION ADMINISTRATION

47299 ■ National Credit Union Administration - Office of Small and Disadvantaged Business Utilization
1775 Duke St.
Alexandria, VA 22314-3428
Ph: (703)518-6300
Fax: (703)518-6660
Co. E-mail: boardmail@ncua.gov
URL: http://www.ncua.gov
Contact: Larry Fazio, Executive Director
Description: The National Credit Union Administration's Office of Small and Disadvantaged Business Utilization offers small businesses information and guidance on procurement procedures, how to be placed on a bidder's mailing list, and identification of both prime and subcontracting opportunities. **Publications:** United States National Credit Union Administration NCUA Quarterly; Credit Union Directory (Annual).

47300 ■ National Credit Union Administration Region I - Albany
9 Washington Sq.
Washington Ave. Ext.
Albany, NY 12205
Ph: (518)862-7400
Fax: (518)862-7420
URL: http://www.usccr.gov/files/pubs/uncsam/agency/natcred.htm

47301 ■ National Credit Union Administration Region II - Capital
1900 Duke St., Ste. 300
Alexandria, VA 22314
Ph: (703)519-4600
Co. E-mail: region2@ncua.gov
URL: http://www.ncua.gov/about/leadership
Contact: John Kutchey, Regional Director

47302 ■ National Credit Union Administration Region III - Atlanta
7000 Central Pky., Ste. 1600
Atlanta, GA 30328
Ph: (678)443-3000
Fax: (678)443-3020
URL: http://www.usccr.gov/files/pubs/uncsam/agency/natcred.htm

47303 ■ National Credit Union Administration Region IV - Austin
4807 Spicewood Springs Rd., Ste. 5200
Austin, TX 78759-8490
Ph: (512)342-5600
Fax: (512)342-5620
Co. E-mail: southernmail@ncua.gov
URL: http://www.ncua.gov/about/leadership/pages/page_region4.aspx

47304 ■ National Credit Union Administration Region V - Tempe
1230 W Washington St., Ste. 301
Tempe, AZ 85288-1249
Ph: (602)302-6000
Fax: (602)302-6024
Co. E-mail: westernmail@ncua.gov
URL: http://www.ncua.gov
Contact: Cherie Freed, Regional Director

NATIONAL LABOR RELATIONS BOARD

47305 ■ National Labor Relations Board (NLRB)
1015 Half St. SE
Washington, DC 20570-0001
Ph: (202)273-1991
Free: 844-762-6572
Co. E-mail: publicinfo@nlrb.gov
URL: http://www.nlrb.gov
Contact: Lauren McFerran, Chairman
Facebook: www.facebook.com/NLRBpage
Linkedin: www.linkedin.com/company/national-labor-relations-board
X (Twitter): x.com/nlrb
Instagram: www.instagram.com/nlrb_gc
Description: The National Labor Relations Board is vested with the power to prevent and remedy unfair labor practices committed by private sector employers and unions and to safeguard employees' rights to organize and determine whether to have unions as their bargaining representative. **Founded:** 1935.

47306 ■ National Labor Relations Board - Region 1 - Boston Regional Office
Thomas P. O'Neill Jr. Federal Building 10 Cswy. St., Rm. 1002
Boston, MA 02222-1001
Ph: (617)565-6700
Fax: (617)565-6725
URL: http://www.nlrb.gov/region/boston
Contact: Laura A. Sacks, Regional Director
Founded: 1935.

47307 ■ National Labor Relations Board - Region 2 - New York Regional Office
26 Federal Plz., Ste. 41-120
New York, NY 10278-0104
Ph: (212)264-0300
Fax: (212)264-2450
URL: http://www.nlrb.gov/about-nlrb/who-we-are/regional-offices/region-02-new-york
Contact: John D. Doyle, Jr., Regional Director
Description: Conducts elections, investigates charges of unfair labor practices, and protects the rights of workers to act together in New York.

47308 ■ National Labor Relations Board - Region 3 - Buffalo Regional Office
130 S Elmwood Ave., Ste. 630
Buffalo, NY 14202-2465
Ph: (716)551-4931
Fax: (716)551-4972
URL: http://www.nlrb.gov/about-nlrb/who-we-are/regional-offices/region-03-buffalo
Contact: Linda M. Leslie, Regional Director
Description: Conducts elections, investigates charges of unfair labor practices, and protects the rights of workers to act together in Buffalo.

47309 ■ National Labor Relations Board - Region 4 - Philadelphia Regional Office
100 E Penn Sq., Ste. 403
Philadelphia, PA 19107
Ph: (215)597-7601
Fax: (215)597-7658
URL: http://www.nlrb.gov/about-nlrb/who-we-are/regional-offices/region-04-philadelphia
Contact: Kimberly E. Andrews, Regional Director
Founded: 1935.

47310 ■ National Labor Relations Board Region 5
100 S Charles St., Ste. 600
Baltimore, MD 21201
Ph: (410)962-2822
Fax: (410)962-2198
URL: http://www.nlrb.gov/about-nlrb/who-we-are/regional-offices/region-05-baltimore
Contact: Sean R. Marshall, Regional Director
Founded: 1935.

47311 ■ National Labor Relations Board - Region 5 - Baltimore Regional Office
100 S Charles St., Ste. 600
Baltimore, MD 21201
Ph: (410)962-2822
Fax: (410)962-2198
URL: http://www.nlrb.gov/about-nlrb/who-we-are/regional-offices/region-05-baltimore
Contact: Sean R. Marshall, Regional Director

47312 ■ National Labor Relations Board - Region 6 - Pittsburgh Regional Office
1000 Liberty Ave., Rm. 904
Pittsburgh, PA 15222-4111
Ph: (412)395-4400
Fax: (412)395-5986
URL: http://www.nlrb.gov/about-nlrb/who-we-are/regional-offices/region-06-pittsburgh
Contact: Nancy Wilson, Regional Director
Description: Conducts elections, investigates charges of unfair labor practices, and protects the rights of workers to act together in Pittsburgh.

47313 ■ National Labor Relations Board - Region 7 - Detroit Regional Office
477 Michigan Ave., Rm. 05-200
Detroit, MI 48226
Ph: (313)226-3200
Fax: (313)226-2090
URL: http://www.nlrb.gov/about-nlrb/who-we-are/regional-offices/region-07-detroit
Contact: Elizabeth K. Kerwin, Regional Director

47314 ■ National Labor Relations Board - Region 8 - Cleveland Regional Office
1240 E 9th St., Ste. 1695
Cleveland, OH 44199-2086
Ph: (216)522-3715
Fax: (216)522-2418
Co. E-mail: relay.service@nlrb.gov
URL: http://www.nlrb.gov/about-nlrb/who-we-are/regional-offices/region-08-cleveland
Contact: Iva Y. Choe, Regional Director
Description: Conducts elections, investigates charges of unfair labor practices, and protects the rights of workers to act together in Cleveland.

47315 ■ National Labor Relations Board - Region 9 - Cincinnati Regional Office
550 Main St., Rm. 3-111
Cincinnati, OH 45202-3271
Ph: (513)684-3686

Fax: (513)684-3946
URL: http://www.nlrb.gov/about-nlrb/who-we-are/regional-offices/region-09-cincinnati
Contact: Matthew T. Denholm, Regional Director
Founded: 1935.

47316 ■ National Labor Relations Board - Region 10 - Atlanta Regional Office
401 W Peachtree St. NW, Ste. 472
Atlanta, GA 30308
Ph: (404)331-2896
Fax: (404)331-2858
URL: http://www.nlrb.gov/about-nlrb/who-we-are/regional-offices/region-10-atlanta
Contact: Lisa Y. Henderson, Regional Director
Founded: 1935.

47317 ■ National Labor Relations Board - Region 11 - Winston-Salem Regional Office
One W Fourth St., Ste. 710
Winston Salem, NC 27101
Ph: (336)631-5201
Fax: (336)631-5210
URL: http://www.nlrb.gov/about-nlrb/who-we-are/regional-offices/region-10-atlanta

47318 ■ National Labor Relations Board - Region 12 - Tampa Regional Office
201 E Kennedy Blvd., Ste. 530
Tampa, FL 33602-5824
Ph: (813)228-2641
Fax: (813)228-2874
URL: http://www.nlrb.gov/about-nlrb/who-we-are/regional-offices/region-12-tampa
Contact: David Cohen, Regional Director
Description: Conducts elections, investigates charges of unfair labor practices, and protects the rights of workers to act together in Tampa.

47319 ■ National Labor Relations Board - Region 13 - Chicago Regional Office
219 S Dearborn St., Ste. 808
Chicago, IL 60604-2027
Ph: (312)353-7570
Fax: (312)886-1341
URL: http://www.nlrb.gov/about-nlrb/who-we-are/regional-offices/region-13-chicago
Contact: Angie Cowan Hamada, Regional Director
Description: Conducts elections, investigates charges of unfair labor practices, and protects the rights of workers to act together in Chicago.

47320 ■ National Labor Relations Board - Region 14 - St. Louis Regional Office
1222 Spruce St., Rm. 8.302
Saint Louis, MO 63103-2829
Ph: (314)539-7770
Fax: (314)539-7794
URL: http://www.nlrb.gov/about-nlrb/who-we-are/regional-offices/region-14-st-louis
Contact: Andrea J. Wilkes, Regional Director
Founded: 1935.

47321 ■ National Labor Relations Board - Region 16 - Ft. Worth Regional Office
819 Taylor St., Rm. 8A24
Fort Worth, TX 76102-6107
Ph: (817)978-2921
Fax: (817)978-2928
URL: http://www.nlrb.gov/about-nlrb/who-we-are/regional-offices/region-16-fort-worth
Contact: Timothy L. Watson, Regional Director
Founded: 1935.

47322 ■ National Labor Relations Board - Region 17 - Overland Park Regional Office
8600 Farley St., Ste. 100
Overland Park, KS 66212-4677
Ph: (913)967-3000
Fax: (913)967-3010
URL: http://www.nlrb.gov/about-nlrb/who-we-are/regional-offices
Founded: 1935.

47323 ■ National Labor Relations Board - Region 18 - Minneapolis Regional Office
Paul D. Minneapolis Federal Office Bldg.
212 3rd Ave. S, Ste. 200
Minneapolis, MN 55401-2657
Ph: (612)348-1757
Fax: (612)348-1785
URL: http://www.nlrb.gov/about-nlrb/who-we-are/regional-offices/region-18-minneapolis
Contact: Jennifer A. Hadsall, Regional Director
Description: Conducts elections, investigates charges of unfair labor practices, and protects the rights of workers to act together in Minneapolis.
Founded: 1935.

47324 ■ National Labor Relations Board - Region 19 - Seattle Regional Office
915 2nd Ave., Rm. 2948
Seattle, WA 98174-1006
Ph: (206)220-6300
Fax: (206)220-6305
URL: http://www.nlrb.gov/about-nlrb/who-we-are/regional-offices/region-19-seattle
Contact: Ronald K. Hooks, Regional Director
Founded: 1935.

47325 ■ National Labor Relations Board - Region 20 - San Francisco Regional Office
450 Golden Gate Ave. 3rd Fl., Ste. 3112
San Francisco, CA 94102
Ph: (415)356-5130
Fax: (415)356-5156
URL: http://www.nlrb.gov/about-nlrb/who-we-are/regional-offices/region-20-san-francisco
Contact: Jill H. Coffman, Regional Director
Founded: 1935.

47326 ■ National Labor Relations Board - Region 21 - Los Angeles Regional Office
US Ct. House, Spring St., 312 N Spring St., 10th Fl.
Los Angeles, CA 90012
Ph: (213)894-5200
Fax: (213)894-2778
Co. E-mail: relay.service@nlrb.gov
URL: http://www.nlrb.gov/about-nlrb/who-we-are/regional-offices/region-21-los-angeles
Contact: William B. Cowen, Regional Director
Founded: 1935.

47327 ■ National Labor Relations Board - Region 22 - Newark Regional Office
20 Washington Pl., Fl. 5
Newark, NJ 07102-3127
Ph: (973)645-2100
Fax: (973)645-3852
URL: http://www.nlrb.gov/about-nlrb/who-we-are/regional-offices/region-22-newark
Contact: Suzanne Sullivan, Regional Director

47328 ■ National Labor Relations Board - Region 25 - Indianapolis Regional Office
575 N Pennsylvania St., Rm. 238
Indianapolis, IN 46204-1520
Ph: (317)226-7381
Fax: (317)226-5103
URL: http://www.nlrb.gov/about-nlrb/who-we-are/regional-offices/region-25-indianapolis
Contact: Patricia K. Nachand, Regional Director
Facebook: www.facebook.com/NLRBRegion25
Founded: 1935.

47329 ■ National Labor Relations Board - Region 26 - Memphis Regional Office
80 Monroe Ave., Ste. 935
Memphis, TN 38103-2400
Ph: (901)544-0019
Fax: (901)544-0008
URL: http://www.nlrb.gov/about-nlrb/who-we-are/regional-offices
Founded: 1935.

47330 ■ National Labor Relations Board - Region 27 - Denver Regional Office
1961 Stout St., Ste. 13-103
Denver, CO 80294
Ph: (303)844-3551
Fax: (303)844-6249
URL: http://www.nlrb.gov/about-nlrb/who-we-are/regional-offices/region-27-denver
Contact: Matthew S. Lomax, Regional Director
Facebook: www.facebook.com/nlrbgov
X (Twitter): x.com/nlrb_27

47331 ■ National Labor Relations Board - Region 28 - Phoenix Regional Office
2600 N Central Ave., Ste. 1400
Phoenix, AZ 85004-3099
Ph: (602)640-2160
Fax: (602)640-2178
URL: http://www.nlrb.gov/about-nlrb/who-we-are/regional-offices/region-28-phoenix
Contact: Cornele A. Overstreet, Regional Director
Founded: 1935.

47332 ■ National Labor Relations Board - Region 29 - Brooklyn Regional Office
Two Metro Tech Ctr., Ste. 5100
Brooklyn, NY 11201-3838
Ph: (718)330-7713
Fax: (718)330-7579
URL: http://www.nlrb.gov/about-nlrb/who-we-are/regional-offices/region-29-brooklyn
Contact: Teresa Poor, Regional Director
Description: Conducts elections, investigates charges of unfair labor practices, and protects the rights of workers to act together in Brooklyn.
Founded: 1935.

47333 ■ National Labor Relations Board - Region 31 - Los Angeles Regional Office
11500 W Olympic Blvd., Ste. 600
Los Angeles, CA 90064-1753
Ph: (310)235-7351
Fax: (310)235-7420
Co. E-mail: relay.service@nlrb.gov
URL: http://www.nlrb.gov/about-nlrb/who-we-are/regional-offices/region-31-los-angeles
Contact: Mori Rubin, Regional Director
Founded: 1935.

47334 ■ National Labor Relations Board - Region 32 - Oakland Regional Office
1301 Clay St., Rm. 300-N
Oakland, CA 94612-5224
Ph: (510)637-3300
Fax: (510)637-3315
URL: http://www.nlrb.gov/about-nlrb/who-we-are/regional-offices/region-32-oakland
Contact: Valerie Hardy-Mahoney, Regional Director
Facebook: www.facebook.com/NLRBOakland

47335 ■ National Labor Relations Board - Region 34 - Hartford Regional Office
450 Main St., S 410
Hartford, CT 06103-3078
Ph: (860)240-3522
Fax: (860)240-3564
URL: http://www.nlrb.gov/about-nlrb/who-we-are/regional-offices

NATIONAL SCIENCE FOUNDATION

47336 ■ National Science Foundation (OSDBU) - Office of Small and Disadvantaged Business Utilization
2415 Eisenhower Ave.
Alexandria, VA 22314
Ph: (703)292-8109
Co. E-mail: osdbu@nsf.gov
URL: http://new.nsf.gov/osdbu
Contact: Wonzie L. Gardner, Jr., Director
E-mail: wgardner@nsf.gov
Description: The National Science Foundation's Office of Small and Disadvantaged Business Utilization offers small businesses information and guidance on procurement procedures, how to be placed on a bidder's mailing list, and identification of both prime and subcontracting opportunities.

47337 ■ National Science Foundation (NSF) - Small Business Innovation Research Programs
2415 Eisenhower Ave.
　Alexandria, VA 22314
URL: http://www.nsf.gov/pubs/2022/nsf22551/nsf 22551.htm
Founded: 1950.

47338 ■ National Science Foundation - Small Business Technology Transfer Program
4201 Wilson Blvd., Ste. 1135
　Arlington, VA 22230
URL: http://seedfund.nsf.gov/solicitations
Founded: 1950.

OCCUPATIONAL SAFETY AND HEALTH ADMINISTRATION

47339 ■ United States Department of Labor - Occupational Safety and Health Administration (OSHA)
Occupational Safety & Health Administration
200 Constitution Ave. NW, Rm. No. N3626
　Washington, DC 20210
Free: 800-321-6742
URL: http://www.osha.gov
Contact: Douglas L. Parker, Assistant Secretary
X (Twitter): x.com/OSHA_DOL
Description: Miscellaneous Publishing. **Founded:** 1970.

47340 ■ U.S. Department of Labor Occupational Safety and Health Administration Office of Communications (OOC)
200 Constitution Ave. NW
　Washington, DC 20210
URL: http://www.osha.gov/contactus/byoffice

47341 ■ U.S. Department of Labor - Occupational Safety and Health Administration - Office of Small Business Assistance - Directorate of Cooperative and State Programs (DCSP)
200 Constitution Ave. NW
　Washington, DC 20210
Ph: (202)693-2200
URL: http://www.osha.gov/contactus/byoffice/dcsp
Contact: Douglas J. Kalinowski, Director
Linkedin: www.linkedin.com/company/u-s--departmen t-of-energy

OFFICE OF PERSONNEL MANAGEMENT

47342 ■ Office of Personnel Management Division for Human Capital Leadership and Merit System Accountability
1900 E St. NW
　Washington, DC 20415-1000
URL: http://www.opm.gov/about-us/fy-20 25-congressional-budget-justification-and-annual -performance-plan/organizational-framework
Founded: 1883.

47343 ■ Office of Personnel Management - Office of Small and Disadvantaged Business Utilization - Contracting Div.
1900 E St. NW
　Washington, DC 20415-1000
URL: http://www.opm.gov/about-us/doing-business -with-opm
Description: The Office of Personnel Management's Office of Small and Disadvantaged Business Utilization offers small businesses information and guidance on procurement procedures, how to be placed on a bidder's mailing list, and identification of both prime and subcontracting opportunities.

47344 ■ U.S. Office of Personnel Management (USOPM) - Library [United States Office of Personnel Management]
1900 E St. NW
　Washington, DC 20415-1000
Ph: (202)606-1800
URL: http://www.opm.gov
Contact: Kiran Ahuja, Director
Facebook: www.facebook.com/USOPM
X (Twitter): x.com/USOPM
Description: The Office of Personnel Management (OPM) administers a merit system to ensure compliance with personnel laws and regulations and assists agencies in recruiting, examining, and promoting people on the basis of their knowledge and skills, regardless of their race, religion, sex, political influence, or other non-merit factors. OPM's role is to provide guidance to agencies in operating human resources programs which effectively support their missions and to provide an array of personnel services to applicants and employees. OPM supports Government program managers in their human resources management responsibilities and provide benefits to employees, retired employees, and their survivors. Provides information on the specific requirements necessary to qualify as a border patrol agent, including education, experience, testing, language, firearms use, medical, and age. **Scope:** Human resources; personnel. **Founded:** 1978. **Holdings:** Figures not available. **Publications:** *Summer Jobs: Opportunities in the Federal Government*; *Directory of Federal Women's Program Managers* (Annual); *Union Recognition in the Federal Government* (Biennial); *Central Personnel Data File (CPDF)*. **Awards:** CyberCorps®: Scholarship For Service (Annual); The President's Award for Distinguished Federal Civilian Service (PADFCS) (Annual); Arthur S. Flemming Awards (Annual).

47345 ■ U.S. Office of Personnel Management (OSDBU) - Office of Small and Disadvantaged Business Utilization - Contracting Group
1900 E St. NW
　Washington, DC 20415
URL: http://www.opm.gov/about-us/doing-business -with-opm/small-business-program
Description: The Office of Personnel Management's Office of Small and Disadvantaged Business Utilization offers small businesses information and guidance on procurement procedures, how to be placed on a bidder's mailing list, and identification of both prime and subcontracting opportunities.

ONE STOP CAPITAL SHOP

47346 ■ CTB
2720 E Broadway Ave.
　Bismarck, ND 58501
Ph: (701)223-0707
URL: http://www.ed2go.com/ndwbc
Founded: 1999.

PATENT AND TRADEMARK OFFICE

47347 ■ U.S. Department of Commerce - U.S. Patent and Trademark Office - Office of the Chief Communications Officer
1401 Constitution Ave. NW
　Washington, DC 20230
Ph: (571)272-8400
Fax: (571)273-0340
Co. E-mail: occofeedback@uspto.gov
URL: http://www.uspto.gov/about-us/organizational -offices/office-chief-communications-officer
Contact: Paul Fucito, Press Secretary
E-mail: paul.fucito@uspto.gov
Description: The Patent and Trademark Office examines applications for patents and trademarks to determine whether an invention is patentable or if a trademark may be registered. Patents and trademarks, because of the legal rights they represent, are important to small businesses competing against larger or more established businesses. The Patent and Trademark Office maintains the Public Search Room for use by individuals wishing to identify new products, find solutions to problems, or check patents in a field of technology. The Patent and Trademark Office's Trademark Search Room is also open to the public. In addition, the office sponsors a system of Patent Depository Libraries, which brings collections of U.S. patents to within one hour commuting time of 45 percent of the U.S. population. An automated system known as CASSIS (Classification and Search Support Information System) is available in most of the libraries. CASSIS provides free, online access to the Patent and Trademark Office's classification databases to assist users in their patent searches.

47348 ■ U.S. Department of Commerce - U.S. Patent and Trademark Office - Office of the Commissioner for Patents
600 Dulany St.
　Alexandria, VA 22314
Ph: (571)272-8800
Fax: (571)273-8800
URL: http://www.uspto.gov/about-us/organizational -offices/office-commissioner-patents
Contact: Vaishali Udupa, Contact

47349 ■ U.S. Department of Commerce - U.S. Patent and Trademark Office - Office of Enrollment and Discipline (OED)
PO Box 1450
　Alexandria, VA 22313-1450
Ph: (571)272-4097
Fax: (571)273-0074
Co. E-mail: oed@uspto.gov
URL: http://www.uspto.gov/about-us/organizational -offices/office-general-counsel/office-enrollment-an d-discipline-oed
Contact: Will Covey, Director

47350 ■ U.S. Department of Commerce - United States Patent and Trademark Office - Office of Initial Patent Examination (OIPE)
PO Box 1450
　Alexandria, VA 22313-1450
URL: http://www.uspto.gov/help/patent-help
Founded: 1903.

47351 ■ U.S. Department of Commerce - United States Patent and Trademark Office - Office of Patent Cooperation Treaty (PCT)
501 Dulany St.
　Alexandria, VA 22314
URL: http://www.uspto.gov/patents/basics/interna tional-protection/patent-cooperation-treaty

47352 ■ U.S. Department of Commerce - United States Patent and Trademark Office - Office of Patent Publication
PO Box 1450
　Alexandria, VA 22313-1450
URL: http://www.uspto.gov/help/patent-help#type -browse-faqs_974

47353 ■ U.S. Department of Commerce - U.S. Patent and Trademark Office - Office of Petitions
PO Box 1450
　Alexandria, VA 22313-1450
Ph: (571)272-3282
Fax: (571)273-0025
URL: http://www.uspto.gov/about-us/organizational -offices/office-commissioner-patents/petitions

47354 ■ U.S. Department of Commerce - U.S. Patent and Trademark Office - Office of Policy and International Affairs
PO Box 1450
　Alexandria, VA 22313-1450
Ph: (571)272-9300
URL: http://www.uspto.gov/about-us/organizational -offices/office-policy-and-international-affairs
Contact: Mary Critharis, Director

47355 ■ U.S. Department of Commerce - United States Patent and Trademark Office - Office of Procurement
600 Dulany St.
　Alexandria, VA 22313
Ph: (571)272-1000
Free: 800-786-9199
Co. E-mail: usptoinfo@uspto.gov

URL: http://www.uspto.gov/about-us/organizational-offices/office-chief-financial-officer/office-procurement
Contact: Kristin Fuller, Director
E-mail: kristin.fuller@uspto.gov
Description: Continually strives to remain on the leading edge of procurement reform and current technology.

47356 ■ U.S. Department of Commerce - United States Patent and Trademark Office - Office of Public Affairs
Knox Bldg., 501 Dulany St.
  Alexandria, VA 22314
URL: http://www.uspto.gov/about-us/organizational-offices/office-chief-communications-officer
Description: Promote the Progress of Science and useful Arts, by securing for limited Times to Authors and Inventors the exclusive Right to their respective Writings and Discoveries.

47357 ■ U.S. Department of Commerce - U.S. Patent and Trademark Office - Patent Trial and Appeal Board (PTAB)
PO Box 1450
  Alexandria, VA 22313-1450
Ph: (571)272-9797
Fax: (571)273-9797
Co. E-mail: ptaboutreach@uspto.gov
URL: http://www.uspto.gov/patents/ptab

47358 ■ U.S. Department of Labor - United States Patent and Trademark Office - Office of Enrollment and Discipline (OED)
PO Box 1450
  Alexandria, VA 22313-1450
Ph: (571)272-4097
Fax: (571)273-0074
Co. E-mail: oed@uspto.gov
URL: http://www.uspto.gov/about-us/organizational-offices/office-general-counsel/office-enrollment-and-discipline-oed
Contact: Will Covey, Director

SECURITIES AND EXCHANGE COMMISSION

47359 ■ Securities and Exchange Commission - Office of Small Business Policy - Small Business Ombudsman
100 F St. NE
  Washington, DC 20549-0213
Ph: (202)551-3330
Free: 877-732-2001
Co. E-mail: ombudsman@sec.gov
URL: http://www.sec.gov/ombuds
Contact: Stacy A. Puente, Contact
Description: The Security and Exchange Commission's responsibilities under the securities laws are to protect investors and to ensure that capital markets operate in a fair and orderly manner. Nevertheless, the SEC believes that its regulations should not have the effect of inadvertently impairing capital formation by small businesses. Therefore the SEC has taken a number of steps to facilitate capital-raising by small businesses and to reduce undue regulatory burdens arising from the federal securities laws. The SEC is in a continuous process of examining other ways to further aid in accomplishing these goals. The SEC's Office of Small Business Policy, for example, directs the commission's small business rulemaking initiatives. It also reviews and comments on the impact of SEC rule proposals on smaller issuers and serves as a liaison with Congressional committees, government agencies, and other groups concerned with small business.

47360 ■ U.S. Securities and Exchange Commission-Atlanta Regional Office
950 E Paces Ferry Rd. NE, Ste. 900
  Atlanta, GA 30326
Ph: (404)842-7600
Co. E-mail: atlanta@sec.gov
URL: http://www.sec.gov/about/sec-regional-offices/atlanta-regional-office
Contact: Nekia Hackworth Jones, Regional Director

X (Twitter): x.com/Atlanta_SEC
Description: Serves Georgia, North Carolina, South Carolina, Puerto Rico, South Carolina, Tennessee, and Alabama.

47361 ■ U.S. Securities and Exchange Commission-Boston Regional Office
33 Arch St., 24th Fl.
  Boston, MA 02110
Ph: (617)573-8900
Co. E-mail: boston@sec.gov
URL: http://www.sec.gov/about/sec-regional-offices/boston-regional-office
Contact: John Dugan, Associate Director
Description: Serves Connecticut, Maine, Massachusetts, New Hampshire, Rhode Island, and Vermont.

47362 ■ U.S. Securities and Exchange Commission-Chicago Regional Office (CRO)
175 W Jackson Blvd., Ste. 1450
  Chicago, IL 60604
Ph: (312)353-7390
Co. E-mail: chicago@sec.gov
URL: http://www.sec.gov/about/sec-regional-offices/chicago-regional-office
Contact: Kathryn A. Pyszka, Regional Director
X (Twitter): x.com/Chicago_SEC
Description: Serves Illinois, Indiana, Iowa, Kentucky, Michigan, Minnesota, Missouri, Ohio, and Wisconsin. **Founded:** 2007.

47363 ■ U.S. Securities and Exchange Commission-Denver Regional Office
1961 Stout St., Ste. 1700
  Denver, CO 80294
Ph: (303)844-1000
Co. E-mail: denver@sec.gov
URL: http://www.sec.gov/about/sec-regional-offices/denver-regional-office
Contact: Jason Burt, Regional Director
Description: Serves Colorado, Kansas, Nebraska, New Mexico, North Dakota, South Dakota, and Wyoming.

47364 ■ U.S. Securities and Exchange Commission-Fort Worth Regional Office
801 Cherry St., Ste. 1900, Unit 18
  Fort Worth, TX 76102
Ph: (817)978-3821
Co. E-mail: dfw@sec.gov
URL: http://www.sec.gov/about/sec-regional-offices/fort-worth-regional-office
Contact: Eric R. Werner, Director
X (Twitter): x.com/FortWorth_SEC
Description: Serves Arkansas, Kansas, Oklahoma, Texas (except for the exam program which is administered by the Denver Regional Office).

47365 ■ U.S. Securities and Exchange Commission-Los Angeles Regional Office
444 S Flower St., Ste. 900
  Los Angeles, CA 90071
Ph: (323)965-3998
Co. E-mail: losangeles@sec.gov
URL: http://www.sec.gov/about/sec-regional-offices/los-angeles-regional-office
Contact: Katharine Zoladz, Regional Director
Description: Serves Arizona, Hawaii, Guam, Nevada, southern California (zip codes 93599 and below, except for 93200-93299).

47366 ■ U.S. Securities and Exchange Commission-Miami Regional Office
801 Brickell Ave., Ste. 1950
  Miami, FL 33131
Ph: (305)982-6300
Co. E-mail: miami@sec.gov
URL: http://www.sec.gov/regional-office/miami
Contact: Eric I. Bustillo, Regional Director
Description: Serves Florida, Mississippi, Louisiana, U.S. Virgin Islands, and Puerto Rico.

47367 ■ U.S. Securities and Exchange Commission-New York Regional Office
100 Pearl St., Ste. 20-100
  New York, NY 10004-2616

Ph: (212)336-1100
Co. E-mail: newyork@sec.gov
URL: http://www.sec.gov/about/sec-regional-offices/new-york-regional-office
Contact: Thomas P. Smith, Jr., Regional Director
X (Twitter): x.com/NewYork_SEC
Description: Serves New Jersey and New York.

47368 ■ U.S. Securities and Exchange Commission-Philadelphia Regional Office
1 Penn Center
  1617 John F. Kennedy Blvd., Ste. 520
  Philadelphia, PA 19103
Ph: (215)597-3100
Co. E-mail: philadelphia@sec.gov
URL: http://www.sec.gov/about/sec-regional-offices/philadelphia-regional-office
Contact: Nicholas P. Grippo, Regional Director
Description: Serves Delaware, the District of Columbia, Maryland, Pennsylvania, Virginia, and West Virginia.

47369 ■ U.S. Securities and Exchange Commission - Salt Lake Regional Office
351 SW Temple, Ste. 6. 100
  Salt Lake City, UT 84101
Ph: (801)524-5796
Co. E-mail: saltlake@sec.gov
URL: http://www.sec.gov/about/sec-regional-offices/salt-lake-regional-office
Description: Serves Utah. **Founded:** 1941.

47370 ■ U.S. Securities and Exchange Commission - San Francisco Regional Office
44 Montgomery St., Ste. 2800
  San Francisco, CA 94104
Ph: (415)705-2500
Co. E-mail: sanfrancisco@sec.gov
URL: http://www.sec.gov/about/sec-regional-offices/san-francisco-regional-office
Contact: Monique Winkler, Regional Director
Description: Serves Washington, Oregon, Alaska, Southern California (zip codes 93599 and below, except for 93200-93299).

SMITHSONIAN INSTITUTION

47371 ■ Smithsonian Institute Office of Equal Employment and Minority Affairs
600 Maryland Ave. SW, Capital Gallery, Ste. 7078
  Washington, DC 20560
URL: http://www.si.edu/object/archives/components/sova-sia-fa00-060-refidd1e690?destination=collection/search%3Fpage%3D41%26edan_q%3D%26edan_fq%255B0%255D%3Dtype%253A3d_package%2520OR%2520type%253Aead_collection%2520OR%2520type%253Aead_component%2520OR%2520type%253Ae
Founded: 1846.

TENNESSEE VALLEY AUTHORITY

47372 ■ Tennessee Valley Authority (TVA) - Research Library
400 W Summit Hill Dr.
  Knoxville, TN 37902
Ph: (865)632-2101
Co. E-mail: tvainfo@tva.com
URL: http://www.tva.com
Contact: Jeffrey J. Lyash, President
Facebook: www.facebook.com/TVA
X (Twitter): x.com/tvanews
Instagram: www.instagram.com/tva
YouTube: www.youtube.com/user/TVANewsVideo
Description: Firm engaged in electricity distribution, flood control, navigation and land management for the Tennessee river system. **Founded:** 1933. **Holdings:** Books; microfilm; news clippings; numerous databases. **Publications:** *Directory of Terminals on the Tennessee River Waterway* (Irregular).

47373 ■ Tennessee Valley Authority (TVA) - Minority Economic and Small Business Development
400 W Summit Hill Dr.
Knoxville, TN 37902
URL: http://www.tva.com/information/supplier-connections/diversity-alliance-program
Contact: Jeffrey J. Lyash, President

Description: The Tennessee Valley Authority maintains agency-wide Minority Economic Development initiatives that assist small minority and women-owned businesses (SMWOBs) that seek TVA business opportunities, as well as, the entire business community of the Valley. TVA's Economic Development organization provides capital, technical, and managerial assistance for SMWOBs, start-ups, retention and expansions. Assistance takes the form of revolving loan funds, public/private partnerships that administer training programs, and in-house technical assistance. Through its Procurement organizations, TVA encourages minority participation in prime and subcontracting opportunities. Its policy is to promote the full participation of SMWOBs in all of its procurement and contracting activities. Further, priority shall be given to fostering the economic development of the Valley through use of products and services of such firms located in the Valley region. TVA's commitment is to maximize participation through the development of mutually beneficial business relationships with these firms consistent with achieving the best value to TVA.

U.S. DEPARTMENT OF AGRICULTURE

47374 ■ U.S. Department of Agriculture (USDA) - Administrative Services Div. - Farmers Home Administration - Office of Small and Disadvantaged Business Utilization
1400 Independence Ave. SW
Washington, DC 20250
Ph: (202)720-7117
URL: http://www.usda.gov/da/osdbu
Contact: George A. Sears, Director

Founded: 1979.

47375 ■ U.S. Department of Agriculture - Administrative Services Division - Food and Nutrition Service - Office of Small and Disadvantaged Business Utilization Coordinator
3101 Pk. Center Dr.
Alexandria, VA 22302
Co. E-mail: foia-fns@usda.gov
URL: http://www.fns.usda.gov

Founded: 2009.

47376 ■ U.S. Department of Agriculture (APD) - Agricultural Research Service - Administrative and Financial Management - Acquisition and Property Div.
5601 Sunnyside Ave.
Beltsville, MD 20705
Ph: (301)504-1734
URL: http://www.ars.usda.gov/people-locations/people-list-offices/?modeCode=03-17-00-00
Contact: Michael Barnes, Director
E-mail: michael.barnes@usda.gov

47377 ■ U.S. Department of Agriculture (USDA) - Contracts and Procurement Branch - Office of the Inspector General - Office of Small and Disadvantaged Business Utilization Coordinator
1400 Independence Ave. SW
Washington, DC 20250
Ph: (202)720-7117
URL: http://www.usda.gov/da/osdbu
Contact: George A. Sears, Director

Founded: 1978.

47378 ■ U.S. Department of Agriculture - Departmental Management - Office of Small and Disadvantaged Business Utilization (USDA)
1400 Independence Ave. SW
Washington, DC 20250
Ph: (202)720-7117
URL: http://www.usda.gov/da/osdbu
Contact: George A. Sears, Director

Description: The USDA's Office of Small and Disadvantaged Business Utilization offers information and other services to minority-owned, women-owned, and small and disadvantaged businesses to assist them in increasing and maintaining their participation in the department's procurement and other program opportunities. The department has 18 major procurement offices, and an additional 260 offices across the country that offer procurement assistance to the small business community. These services are provided to increase the overall viability and competitiveness of businesses as part of maintaining an economically strong national industrial and commercial base. Emphasis is given to assisting firms that can contribute to revitalizing the nation's rural communities, improving the private agricultural sector's foreign trade competitiveness, and/or increasing the federal government's productivity. The department procures approximately $2 billion in products and services each year, $1 billion of which is awarded to minority-owned, women-owned, and small and disadvantaged businesses. **Founded:** 1979.

47379 ■ U.S. Department of Agriculture (USDA) - Departmental Management - Office of Small and Disadvantaged Business Utilization Coordinator
1400 Independence Ave., SW
Washington, DC 20250
Ph: (202)720-7117
URL: http://www.usda.gov/da/osdbu
Contact: Michelle E. Warren, Deputy Director
E-mail: michelle.warren@usda.gov

Founded: 1979.

47380 ■ U.S. Department of Agriculture - Food Safety and Inspection Service - Office of Administrative Services - Procurement Management Branch
5601 Sunnyside Ave.
Beltsville, MD 20705
URL: http://www.fsis.usda.gov/policy/fsis-notice/53-22

Description: Provides food safety and inspection service. **Founded:** 1862.

47381 ■ U.S. Department of Agriculture - Management Services Branch - Extension Service - Office of Small and Disadvantaged Business Utilization Coordinator
c/o Dexter L. Pearson, Director
1400 Independence Ave. SW, AG Stop 9501, Rm. 1085
Washington, DC 20250
Ph: (202)720-7117
Co. E-mail: dexter.pearson@osec.usda.gov
URL: http://www.dm.usda.gov/osdbu/index.php
Contact: George A. Sears, Director

47382 ■ U.S. Department of Agriculture (USDA) - Management Services Div. - Animal and Plant Health Inspection Service - Office of Small and Disadvantaged Business Utilization Coordinator
4700 River Rd., Unit 4
Riverdale, MD 20737
Co. E-mail: plantproducts.permits@usda.gov
URL: http://www.aphis.usda.gov/aphis/ourfocus/business-services/Acquisition_Management

Description: Focuses on agriculture inspection services. **Founded:** 1862.

47383 ■ U.S. Department of Agriculture - Management Services Div. - Farm Service Agency - Office of Small and Disadvantaged Business Utilization Coordinator
1400 Independence Ave. SW
Washington, DC 20250
Ph: (202)720-7117
URL: http://www.usda.gov/da/osdbu
Contact: Michelle E. Warren, Deputy Director

Description: Department of agriculture and services. **Founded:** 1979.

47384 ■ U.S. Department of Agriculture (USDA) - Management Services Div. - Natural Resources Conservation Service - Office of Small and Disadvantaged Business Utilization
1400 Independence Ave. SW
Washington, DC 20250
Ph: (202)720-7117
URL: http://www.usda.gov/da/osdbu
Contact: George Sears, Director
E-mail: george.sears@usda.gov

Founded: 1979.

47385 ■ U.S. Department of Agriculture (SBIR) - National Institute of Food and Agriculture - Small Business Innovation Research Program (SBIR)
U.S. Department of Agriculture (SBIR) National Institute of Food and Agriculture Small Business Innovation Research Program (SBIR)
1400 Independence Ave. SW, MS 2201
Washington, DC 20250-2201
URL: http://www.nifa.usda.gov/grants/funding-opportunities/small-business-innovation-research-small-business-technology
URL(s): www.nifa.usda.gov/small-business-innovation-research-small-business-technology-transfer-brochure

47386 ■ U.S. Department of Agriculture (USDA) - Office of Communications
c/o US Department of Agriculture
1400 Independence Ave. SW
Washington, DC 20250
URL: http://www.usda.gov/our-agency/staff-offices/office-communications-oc

Founded: 1913. **Publications:** CID Service.

47387 ■ U.S. Department of Agriculture (OPPM) - Office of Procurement and Property Management
1400 Independence Ave. SW, Mail Stop 9303
Washington, DC 20250
Ph: (202)720-7527
URL: http://www.usda.gov/da/business/procedures

47388 ■ U.S. Department of Agriculture - Rural Development Div. - Electric Program
STOP 1560, Rm. 4121-S
1400 Independence Ave. SW
Washington, DC 20250-1560
URL: http://www.rd.usda.gov/about-rd/agencies/rural-utilities-service
URL(s): www.rd.usda.gov/programs-services/electric-programs

U.S. DEPARTMENT OF COMMERCE

47389 ■ Alabama Public Library Service (APLS)
6030 Monticello Dr.
Montgomery, AL 36117
Ph: (334)213-3900
Free: 800-392-5671
URL: http://aplsws2.apls.state.al.us
Contact: Dr. Nancy C. Pack, Director
Facebook: www.facebook.com/AlabamaPublicLibraryService

Description: Services: Receiving and administering state and federal funds. **Scope:** Law; health and medicine; computer technology; travel and leisure; hobbies; handicrafts. **Services:** Interlibrary loan; library open to the public. **Founded:** 1959. **Holdings:** Books; music; periodicals; blu-ray; braille materials; audiobooks; music CDs; DVDs; e-audio; e-books; videos; maps; microforms; phonomusic; pictures; serials; software and video games; video home system; directories, encyclopedias and dictionaries. **Publications:** *Alabama Public Library Service Online Catalog*; *Alabama Public Library Service--Annual Report* (Annual).

47390 ■ Arizona State Library, Archives and Public Records Law Library
201 W Jefferson St.
Phoenix, AZ 85003
Ph: (602)506-7353
URL: http://azlibrary.gov/location/law-library-resource-center
Description: Research Library collects, preserves, and provides access to information for Arizonans about their government, their state and their world in a variety of formats. **Scope:** Arizona - local government; Federal Government; genealogy. **Services:** Library open to the public. **Holdings:** Books; maps; microfiche;periodicals; annual reports.

47391 ■ Arkansas Department of Workforce Services (ADWS)
No. 2 Capitol Mall
Little Rock, AR 72201
Ph: (501)682-2121
Fax: (501)682-8845
Co. E-mail: adws.info@arkansas.gov
URL: http://dws.arkansas.gov
Contact: Dr. Charisse Childers, Director
E-mail: charisse.childers@arkansas.gov
Facebook: www.facebook.com/Arkansas.Workforce
X (Twitter): x.com/myarknet
Founded: 1937.

47392 ■ Arkansas State Library (ASL)
900 W Capitol Ave., Ste. 100
Little Rock, AR 72204
Ph: (501)569-3123
Free: 800-340-9367
Fax: (501)569-3017
Co. E-mail: library@ualr.edu
URL: http://www.library.arkansas.gov
Contact: Amber Gregory, Contact
E-mail: amber.gregory@ade.arkansas.gov
Facebook: www.facebook.com/arkansasstatelibrary
Scope: Patent & trademark core; non-fiction circulating collection; federal documents; Arkansas collection; library science collection. **Services:** Interlibrary loan; library open to the public. **Founded:** 1979. **Subscriptions:** 2500 journals and other serials. **Publications:** *Arkansas Library Directory*; *Arkansas State Library Online Catalog*; *Arkansas Public Library Statistics* (Annual).

47393 ■ Association of Bay Area Governments (ABAG)
101 8th St.
Oakland, CA 94604-2050
Co. E-mail: info@abag.ca.gov
URL: http://abag.ca.gov
Contact: Derek Hansel, Chief Financial Officer
E-mail: dhansel@bayareametro.gov
Description: Publishes books to strengthen cooperation and coordination among local governments. **Scope:** Assists in land use planning, demographic data, and analysis; hazardous materials handling; earthquake preparedness planning; erosion control techniques. Serves all industries in California, primarily those in the San Francisco Bay Area. **Founded:** 1961. **Publications:** *ABAG Membership Directory*. **Training:** OSHA 40-Hour Certification: Hazardous Waste Operations Training, 2008; OSHA 24-Hour Certification: Hazardous Waste Operations Training, 2008; OSHA 16-Hour Supplemental: Hazardous Waste Operations Training, 2008; Offers Understanding and Using ABAG's Land Use Databases; The special conference San Francisco Bay Area Economic Forecast.

47394 ■ Association of Monterey Bay Area Governments (AMBAG)
24580 Silver Cloud Ct.
Monterey, CA 93940
Ph: (831)883-3750
Fax: (831)883-3755
Co. E-mail: info@ambag.org
URL: http://www.ambag.org
Contact: Maura F. Twomey, Director
E-mail: mtwomey@ambag.org
Facebook: www.facebook.com/ambagmb
X (Twitter): x.com/AMBAGMB
Description: Serves as a forum for discussing and making recommendations on issues of regional significance. **Founded:** 1968. **Publications:** *Central Coast Reporter* (Monthly). **Geographic Preference:** Local.

47395 ■ Boise State University (DORED) - Division of Research and Economic Development
1910 University Dr., Administration Bldg., Ste. 214
Boise, ID 83725-1135
Ph: (208)426-5732
Fax: (208)426-1048
Co. E-mail: boisestateresearch@boisestate.edu
URL: http://www.boisestate.edu/research
Contact: Nancy Glenn, Vice President
E-mail: nancyglenn@boisestate.edu

47396 ■ Brown University - Social Science Research Lab (SSRL) - Department of Sociology
Maxcy Hall
108 George St.
Providence, RI 02912
Ph: (401)863-2367
Fax: (401)863-3213
Co. E-mail: sociology@brown.edu
URL: http://www.brown.edu/academics/sociology
Contact: David Lindstrom, Director
E-mail: david_lindstrom@brown.edu
Facebook: www.facebook.com/SociologyAtBrown
X (Twitter): x.com/brownsociology
Description: Department of sociology, educates sociology. **Founded:** 1764.

47397 ■ Central Washington University Department of Sociology - Applied Social Data Center
400 E University Way
Ellensburg, WA 98926
Ph: (509)963-1305
Fax: (509)963-1308
Co. E-mail: zakellk@cwu.edu
URL: http://www.cwu.edu/sociology
Description: Provides opportunities for students to understand the conceptual and methodological tools used by sociologists to understand society.

47398 ■ Chicago Metropolitan Agency for Planning (CMAP)
433 W Van Buren St., Ste. 450
Chicago, IL 60607
Ph: (312)454-0400
Fax: (312)454-0411
Co. E-mail: info@cmap.illinois.gov
URL: http://www.cmap.illinois.gov
Contact: Erin Aleman, Executive Director
E-mail: ealeman@cmap.illinois.gov
Facebook: www.facebook.com/1CMAP
Linkedin: www.linkedin.com/company/chicago-metropolitan-agency-for-planning
X (Twitter): x.com/ONTO2050
Instagram: www.instagram.com/onto2050
YouTube: www.youtube.com/channel/UCnDGzjtkedlHgDg-O44Yq6A
Description: Publishes books on regional trends, including population, housing, employment and land use information. Prepares advisory policy plans on such issues as water quality and supply, recreation and land use. Offers newsletters and maps. Does not accept unsolicited manuscripts. Reaches market through direct mail and internet planning. **Founded:** 2005. **Publications:** *Commerce Business Daily (CBD)*. **Geographic Preference:** Local.

47399 ■ Cleveland State University - Maxine Goodman Levin College of Urban Affairs - Northern Ohio Data and Information Service (NODIS)
2121 Euclid Ave., UR 32
Cleveland, OH 44115-2214
URL: http://levin.urban.csuohio.edu/nodis
Contact: Dr. Mark J. Salling, Director
E-mail: m.salling@csuohio.edu
Description: Publishes research reports, conference proceedings, census data reports and newsletters dealing with urban issues, many of which pertain to the northeast Ohio region. Reaches market through direct mail. Does not accept unsolicited manuscripts. **Founded:** 1982.

47400 ■ Colorado Department of Local Affairs - Division of Local Government (DLG)
1313 Sherman St., Rm. 512
Denver, CO 80203
Ph: (303)864-7720
Co. E-mail: dola_dlg_helpdesk@state.co.us
URL: http://dlg.colorado.gov
Founded: 1966.

47401 ■ Colorado State University - College of Agricultural Sciences - Department of Agricultural & Resource Economics (DARE)
Nutrien Agricultural Sciences Building 267301
University Avenue Campus Delivery 1172 Colorado State University
Fort Collins, CO 80523-1172
Ph: (970)491-6325
Co. E-mail: cas_dare@colostate.edu
URL: http://agsci.colostate.edu/dare
Contact: Kathy Bruce, Coordinator
E-mail: kathy.bruce@colostate.edu

47402 ■ Connecticut Office of Policy and Management - Policy Development and Planning Division (PDPD)
c/o Claudio Gualtieri, Senior Policy Advisor - Health & Human Services Policy & Planning
450 Capitol Ave., MS No. 52ASP
Hartford, CT 06106-1379
Ph: (860)418-6268
Fax: (860)418-6495
Co. E-mail: claudio.gualtieri@ct.gov
URL: http://portal.ct.gov/opm/pdpd/pdpd/policy-development-and-planning-division
Contact: Claudio Gualtieri, Officer
E-mail: claudio.gualtieri@ct.gov
Description: Addresses health and human services issues. **Publications:** *Profiles of Regional Planning Agencies in Connecticut* (Irregular).

47403 ■ Connecticut State Library Government Information and References Services
231 Capitol Ave.
Hartford, CT 06106
Ph: (860)757-6500
URL: http://libguides.ctstatelibrary.org/GIRS/home
Holdings: Figures not available.

47404 ■ Cornell University - Cornell Institute for Social and Economic Research Data Archive (CISER)
391 Pine Tree Rd.
Ithaca, NY 14850-2820
URL: http://socialsciences.cornell.edu/computing-and-data#policies
Scope: Economic and social science; national and international organizations; emphasizes labor; political and social behavior; demography; economics; health and much more. **Services:** Archive open to those affiliated with Cornell University. **Founded:** 1982. **Holdings:** 27,000 data files (online); CD-ROMs; DVDs.

47405 ■ Delaware Economic Development Office (DEDO)
99 Kings Hwy.
Dover, DE 19901
URL: http://business.delaware.gov
Description: Aims to be responsible for attracting new investors and businesses to the State by promoting the expansion of existing industry, assisting small and minority-owned businesses, developing tourism and creating new and improved employment opportunities for all citizens of the State. **Founded:** 1981. **Geographic Preference:** State.

47406 ■ Departamento de Educacion
Ave. Tnte. Cesar Gonzalez, esq. Juan Calaf Street,
  Tres Monjitas Industrial Urb.
  Hato Rey, PR 00917
Ph: (787)759-2000
URL: http://de.pr.gov
Facebook: www.facebook.com/EDUCACIONPR
X (Twitter): x.com/EDUCACIONPR
Description: Department providing education and professional development.

47407 ■ Department of Administration - Demographic Services Center (DSC)
101 E Wilson St., 9th Fl.
  Madison, WI 53703
URL: http://doa.wi.gov/Pages/LocalGovtsGrants/Demographic_Services.aspx
Contact: Dan Barroilhet, Contact
E-mail: dan.barroilhet@wisconsin.gov

47408 ■ District of Columbia Office of Planning (SDC) - State Data Center
1100 4th St. SW, Ste. E650
  Washington, DC 20024
Ph: (202)442-7630
Fax: (202)442-7638
URL: http://www.census.gov/about/partners/sdc/member-network/district-of-columbia.htmlcolumbia.html
Contact: Joy Phillips, Contact
E-mail: joy.phillips@dc.gov
Founded: 1978.

47409 ■ Enoch Pratt Free Library
400 Cathedral St.
  Baltimore, MD 21201
Ph: (410)396-5430
Fax: (410)396-1441
URL: http://www.prattlibrary.org
Facebook: www.facebook.com/theprattlibrary
X (Twitter): x.com/prattlibrary
Description: Publishes on HL Mencken, Edgar Allan Poe, Maryland history. **Scope:** Fiction; Nonfiction. **Services:** Interlibrary loan; library open to the public. **Founded:** 1882. **Holdings:** Figures not available. **Publications:** Menckeniana: A Quarterly Review (Quarterly); Maryland State Library Online Catalog.

47410 ■ Florida State University College of Social Sciences and Public Policy - Center for Demography and Population Health (CDPH) - Library
113 Collegiate Loop
  Tallahassee, FL 32306-2160
Co. E-mail: popctr@fsu.edu
URL: http://popcenter.fsu.edu
Contact: Dr. Carl P. Schmertmann, Director
E-mail: schmertmann@fsu.edu
Facebook: www.facebook.com/fsupopcenter
X (Twitter): x.com/fsupopcenter
Description: An interdisciplinary research and academic unit within the College of Social Sciences and Public Policy at The Florida State University, a Carnegie Research I University. **Scope:** Demographic and population health, including studies on social, economic, and political consequences of population change and population aging, socialization of adolescents to norms of demographic behavior, components of growth of metropolitan areas, environmental quality and population change, mortality at the older ages, women's work patterns, and fertility. **Services:** Copying; SDI; center open to the public for reference use only. **Founded:** 1967. **Holdings:** 9700 books; 3500 bound periodical volumes; 3200 vertical files. **Subscriptions:** 100 journals and other serials. **Awards:** Serow Scholarship (Annual).

47411 ■ Georgia Institute of Technology Library - Government Information Department
266 4th St. NW
  Atlanta, GA 30332
URL: http://library.gatech.edu
Description: Aims to catalyze the discovery and creation of knowledge.

47412 ■ Hawaii Department of Business, Economic Development, and Tourism - Hawaii State Data Center
No. 1 Capitol District Bldg.
  250 S Hotel St.
  Honolulu, HI 96813
URL: http://census.hawaii.gov
Description: Assists the public in the use of census data by providing technical advice; educates the public by providing guides and sponsoring training on census data, products and tools; and maintains a network of affiliate organizations throughout the state.

47413 ■ Hawaii Department of Business, Economic Development, and Tourism - Research and Economic Analysis Div. (READ)
No. 1 Capitol District Bldg., 250 S Hotel St.
  Honolulu, HI 96813
URL: http://dbedt.hawaii.gov/economic
Contact: Dr. Eugene Tian, Chief Economist
E-mail: xtian@dbedt.hawaii.gov
Description: Integral unit of Hawaii Department of Business, Economic Development, and Tourism. **Scope:** Business, economic development, tourism. **Publications:** Construction and Hawaii's Economy; Quarterly Statistical and Economic Report (Quarterly); State of Hawaii Data Book (Semiannual); Hawaii Business Abroad (Irregular).

47414 ■ Idaho Commission for Libraries (ICfL)
325 W State St.
  Boise, ID 83702
Ph: (208)334-2150
Free: 800-458-3271
Fax: (208)334-4016
URL: http://libraries.idaho.gov
Contact: Stephanie Bailey-White, Librarian
E-mail: stephanie.bailey-white@libraries.idaho.gov
Facebook: www.facebook.com/IdahoCommissionforLibraries
X (Twitter): x.com/icflibs
Scope: Idaho government; library science; public sector management. **Services:** Interlibrary loan (limited); copying; library open to the public. **Founded:** 1901. **Holdings:** 50,000 books; 450 videotapes; state document depository. **Subscriptions:** 150 journals and other serials. **Publications:** Idaho Talking Book Catalog; Libraries Linking Idaho Database Catalog.

47415 ■ Idaho Department of Commerce (IDC)
700 W State St. fl.
  Boise, ID 83720
Ph: (208)334-2470
Free: 800-842-5858
Co. E-mail: info@commerce.idaho.gov
URL: http://commerce.idaho.gov
Contact: Tom Kealey, Director
E-mail: tom.kealey@commerce.idaho.gov
Facebook: www.facebook.com/IdahoCommerce
X (Twitter): x.com/IdahoCommerce
Instagram: www.instagram.com/visitidaho
Founded: 1958.

47416 ■ Idaho State University Business and Technology Center
Bldg. 86 1651 Alvin Ricken Dr., Rm. 107
  Pocatello, ID 83201
URL: http://www.isu.edu/businesstechnology

47417 ■ Indiana Economic Development Corp. (IEDC)
1 N Capitol Ave., Ste. 700
  Indianapolis, IN 46204
Ph: (317)232-8800
Free: 800-463-8081
Fax: (317)232-4146
Co. E-mail: iedc@iedc.in.gov
URL: http://www.iedc.in.gov
Contact: Eric Holcomb, Chairman Governor
Facebook: www.facebook.com/IndianaEDC
Linkedin: www.linkedin.com/company/indiana-economic-development-corporation
X (Twitter): x.com/Indiana_EDC

Description: Coordinates business services offered by the Department of Commerce and other agencies. Serves as a switchboard for access to those services, such as export promotion, defense procurement, minority business development, and regulatory assistance. **Founded:** 2005. **Geographic Preference:** State.

47418 ■ Indiana State Library State Data Center (SDC)
315 W Ohio St.
  Indianapolis, IN 46202
Ph: (317)232-3732
Fax: (317)232-3728
URL: http://www.in.gov/library/collections-and-services/isdc
Founded: 1978. **Holdings:** Figures not available.

47419 ■ Iowa State University - Iowa Community Indicators Program (ICIP)
260 Heady Hall
  518 Farm House Ln.
  Ames, IA 50011-1054
Ph: (515)294-2954
Fax: (515)294-0221
Co. E-mail: icip@iastate.edu
URL: http://www.icip.iastate.edu
Contact: Renea Miller, Administrative Assistant
E-mail: ramiller@iastate.edu
Founded: 2012.

47420 ■ Kansas Division of the Budget
900 SW Jackson St., Ste. 504
  Topeka, KS 66612
Ph: (785)296-2436
Fax: (785)296-0231
Co. E-mail: budget.info@ks.gov
URL: http://budget.kansas.gov
Contact: Julie Thomas, Deputy Director
E-mail: julie.thomas@ks.gov
Description: Aims to provide support for the effective and efficient management of Kansas state government.

47421 ■ Kansas State Library (KSL)
Capitol Bldg.
  300 SW 10th Ave., Rm. 312-N
  Topeka, KS 66612
Ph: (785)296-3296
Free: 800-432-3919
Co. E-mail: slk@ks.gov
URL: http://kslib.info
Contact: Tracey Boswell, Librarian, Reference
E-mail: tracey.boswell@ks.gov
Facebook: www.facebook.com/statelibraryofkansas
X (Twitter): x.com/LibraryofKS
Description: Publishes books on education. **Scope:** Local; state and federal government information. **Services:** Interlibrary loan; copying; Library open to the public. **Founded:** 1855. **Holdings:** The Kansas Library Catalog is maintained in computer-readable form. In addition, the Division maintains the OCLC cataloging input of the Kansas libraries and the Kansas Documents Catalog on magnetic tape. The State Library holdings consist of 80,000 bound volumes and subscriptions to 150 periodicals.; Books; magazine; audiobooks. **Subscriptions:** 250 journals and other serials; 10,000 periodicals (includes journals); 10 newspapers; 100,000 books. **Publications:** Kansas Library Catalog (KLC); Kansas Public Library Service: Directory & Statistics.

47422 ■ Kentucky Governor's Office for Policy and Management
200 Mero St. 5th Fl.
  Frankfort, KY 40622
Ph: (502)564-7300
URL: http://osbd.ky.gov/StaffAssignments/Pages/GOPM.aspx
Contact: Janice Tomes, Deputy Director
E-mail: janice.tomes@ky.gov

47423 ■ Library of Michigan Government Documents Service
702 W Kalamazoo St.
  Lansing, MI 48909-7507

URL: http://www.michigan.gov/libraryofmichigan/public/gment/mich-doc
Services: Public access to electronic government information available via the Internet. **Founded:** 1813. **Holdings:** maps; publications; microfiche, CD format.

47424 ■ Library of Virginia - Records Management Div.
800 E Broad St.
 Richmond, VA 23219-8000
Ph: (804)615-5784
URL: http://www.lva.virginia.gov/agencies/records
Contact: Chad Owen, Coordinator
E-mail: chad.owen@lva.virginia.gov
Services: Open to the public. **Holdings:** Books; periodicals; government publications; newspapers; architectural drawings and plans; manuscripts; archival records; maps; rare books; prints and photographs; fine arts.

47425 ■ Maine Department of Labor - Center for Workforce Research and Information (CWRI)
45 Commerce Dr., 118 SHS
 Augusta, ME 04333-0118
Ph: (207)623-7900
Fax: (207)287-2947
Co. E-mail: mdol@maine.gov
URL: http://www.maine.gov/labor/cwri
Contact: Mark McInerney, Director
E-mail: mark.mcinerney@maine.gov
Description: Publishes and disseminates labor market information. Reaches market through direct mail. Does not accept unsolicited manuscripts. **Publications:** *Directory of Maine Labor Organizations* (Annual).

47426 ■ Maine State Library (MSL)
64 State House Sta.
 Augusta, ME 04333
Ph: (207)287-5600
Fax: (207)287-5624
Co. E-mail: circulation.msl@maine.gov
URL: http://www.maine.gov/msl
Contact: James Ritter, Librarian
E-mail: james.ritter@maine.gov
Facebook: www.facebook.com/MaineStateLibrary
X (Twitter): x.com/MaineSTLibrary
YouTube: www.youtube.com/MaineStateLibrary
Scope: Genealogy. **Services:** Interlibrary loan; copying; computer classes; library open to the public; Performs searches free of charge; Virtual tours online. **Founded:** 1839. **Holdings:** 350,615 books and serial volumes; 848 audio materials; 650 video materials; 250,882 government documents. **Subscriptions:** 474 journals and other serials; 31 newspapers. **Publications:** *MaineCat*; *Status of Maine State Documents Depository Libraries*; *URSUS, the Maine State Library Catalog*.

47427 ■ Metropolitan Washington Council of Governments (COG) - Library
777 N Capitol St. NE, Ste. 300
 Washington, DC 20002
Ph: (202)962-3200
Fax: (202)962-3201
URL: http://www.mwcog.org
Contact: Nancy Navarro, President
Facebook: www.facebook.com/MWCOG
X (Twitter): x.com/MWCOG
Description: Elected officials from 22 local governments, the Maryland and Virginia state legislatures, and U.S. Congress. Unites area leaders to address major regional issues in the District of Columbia, suburban Maryland, and Northern Virginia. **Scope:** Local government. **Founded:** 1957. **Holdings:** Figures not available. **Publications:** *Metropolitan Washington Regional Directory* (Annual); *Metropolitan Washington Regional Directory*; *The Metro Washington Recycling Markets Directory*; *Directory of Local Government Purchasing Personnel* (Annual); *Directory of Special Transportation Services*.

47428 ■ Minnesota Department of Administration - Minnesota State Demographic Center
203 Administration Building 50 Sherburne Ave.
 Saint Paul, MN 55155
URL: http://mn.gov/admin/demography
Contact: Stephanie Boucher, Administrator
E-mail: stephanie.boucher@state.mn.us
X (Twitter): x.com/MN_StateData
Description: The main provider of demographic data and analysis for the state of Minnesota. **Founded:** 1939.

47429 ■ Minnesota Department of Education - Minnesota Resource Center for the Blind and Visually Impaired
400 NE Stinson Blvd.
 Minneapolis, MN 55413
Co. E-mail: mn.resource.libraries@msa.state.mn.us
URL: http://education.mn.gov/MDE/dse/sped/cat/bvi
Contact: Matt Kevan, Contact
Description: Newsletter. **Publications:** *Education and Community Services Directory* (Annual).

47430 ■ Missouri Small Business and Technology Development Centers (MO SBTDC)
540 Hitt St.Gentry Hall, Rm. 223
 Columbia, MO 65211
Ph: (573)884-1555
Co. E-mail: musbdcadmin@missouri.edu
URL: http://sbdc.missouri.edu
Contact: Leslie Fischer, Director
Facebook: www.facebook.com/MissouriSBDC
Linkedin: www.linkedin.com/company/missourisbdc
X (Twitter): x.com/MissouriSBDC
Instagram: www.instagram.com/missourisbdc
YouTube: www.youtube.com/user/mosbtdc
Founded: 1966.

47431 ■ Missouri State Library
600 W Main St.
 Jefferson City, MO 65101
Ph: (573)522-4036
Co. E-mail: mostlib@sos.mo.gov
URL: http://www.sos.mo.gov/library
Contact: Laura Kromer, Division Director
E-mail: laura.kromer@sos.mo.gov
Facebook: www.facebook.com/MissouriSOS
X (Twitter): x.com/MissouriSOS
Instagram: www.instagram.com/missourisos
YouTube: www.youtube.com/channel/UClKeWmPRNu2cpGoMotOGzgw
Description: Publishes on Missouri, statistics, genealogy, history, Missouri libraries, and Missouri government. **Scope:** Collects, tabulates, and publishes a wide variety of statistical data on the population and economy of the nation. Data are available to government and public users for the development and evaluation of economic and social programs. Activities of the Bureau include: censuses of population and housing, including decennial and annual components; quinquennial censuses of state and local governments, manufacturers, mineral industries, distributive trades, construction industries, service industries, and transportation; current surveys which provide information on many of the subjects covered in the censuses at monthly, quarterly, annual, or other intervals; compilation of current statistics on U.S. foreign trade, including data on imports, exports, and shipping; special censuses as requested and financed by state and local governments; publication of population estimates and projections; current data on population and housing characteristics; and current reports on manufacturing, retail and wholesale trade, services, construction, imports and exports, state and local government finances and employment, and other subjects. **Services:** Interlibrary loan; copying; Library open to the public. **Founded:** 1907. **Holdings:** 90,156 books; 367,000 microforms; federal and Missouri state documents. **Subscriptions:** 201 journals and other serials; 22 newspapers. **Publications:** *Governments Integrated Directory (GID)*; *Government Finance and Employment Classification Manual*; *Schedule B Export Codes*; *North American Industry Classification System (NAICS)*; *USA State and County QuickFacts*; *USA Counties™*; *American FactFinder*; *Missouri Library World* (Quarterly); *U.S. Census Bureau Reports*; *Directory of Missouri Libraries*; *New York City Housing and Vacancy Survey (NYCHVS)*; *Property Owners and Managers Survey (POMS)*; *Zip Code Business Patterns*; *Current Population Survey (CPS)* (Monthly); *Census 2000 Race and Hispanic or Latino Summary File*; *Census 2000 Redistricting Data Summary File*; *Comprehensive Housing Affordability Strategy (CHAS)*; *Congressional Districts of the United States*; *Residential Finance Survey*; *Public Use Microdata Samples (PUMS)*; *Public Use Microdata Samples for Puerto Rico (PUMS)*; *U.S. Exports History*; *U.S. Imports of Merchandise* (Monthly); *U.S. Imports History*; *U.S. Exports Commodity Classification*; *Consolidated Federal Funds Report (CFFR)*; *Survey of Income and Program Participation (SIPP)*; *Monthly Retail Trade and Food Services*; *Quarterly Financial Report for Manufacturing, Mining, Trade, and Selected Service Industries* (Quarterly); *Manufacturers' Shipments, Inventories, and Orders (M3)* (Monthly); *Projections of the Number of Households and Families in the United States: 1995 to 2010*; *International Data Base (IDB)*; *Women in Development*; *State Library of Missouri Online Catalog*; *U.S. County Business Patterns*; *County and City Data Book*; *TIGER/Line® Shapefiles*; *Alabama State and County QuickFacts*; *Alaska State and County QuickFacts*; *Arizona State and County QuickFacts*; *Arkansas State and County QuickFacts*; *California State and County QuickFacts*; *Colorado State and County QuickFacts*; *Connecticut State and County QuickFacts*; *Delaware State and County QuickFacts*; *District of Columbia State and County QuickFacts*; *Florida State and County QuickFacts*; *Georgia State and County QuickFacts*; *Hawaii State and County QuickFacts*; *Idaho State and County QuickFacts*; *Illinois State and County QuickFacts*; *Indiana State and County QuickFacts*; *Iowa State and County QuickFacts*; *Kansas State and County QuickFacts*; *Kentucky State and County QuickFacts*; *Louisiana State and County QuickFacts*; *Maine State and County QuickFacts*; *Maryland State and County QuickFacts*; *Massachusetts State and County QuickFacts*; *Michigan State and County QuickFacts*; *Minnesota State and County QuickFacts*; *Mississippi State and County QuickFacts*; *Missouri State and County QuickFacts*; *Montana State and County QuickFacts*; *Nebraska State and County QuickFacts*; *Nevada State and County QuickFacts*; *New Hampshire State and County QuickFacts*; *New Jersey State and County QuickFacts*; *New Mexico State and County QuickFacts*; *New York State and County QuickFacts*; *North Carolina State and County QuickFacts*; *North Dakota State and County QuickFacts*; *Ohio State and County QuickFacts*; *Oklahoma State and County QuickFacts*; *Oregon State and County QuickFacts*; *Pennsylvania State and County QuickFacts*; *Rhode Island State and County QuickFacts*; *South Carolina State and County QuickFacts*; *South Dakota State and County QuickFacts*; *Tennessee State and County QuickFacts*; *Texas State and County QuickFacts*; *Utah State and County QuickFacts*; *Vermont State and County QuickFacts*; *Virginia State and County QuickFacts*; *Washington State and County QuickFacts*; *West Virginia State and County QuickFacts*; *Wisconsin State and County QuickFacts*; *Wyoming State and County QuickFacts*; *Guide to Foreign Trade Statistics* (Irregular); *U.S. Exports of Merchandise*; *State and Metropolitan Area Data Book*; *1992 Economic Census CD-ROM: Volume 1, Report Series*; *New Residential Construction Index*; *New Residential Sales*; *United States International Trade in Goods and Services*; *Annual Survey of Public Pensions: State- and Locally-Administered Defined Benefit Data* (Annual); *Annual Survey of Manufactures (ASM)*.

47432 ■ Missouri State Office of Administration
State Capitol Bldg., Rm.125
 Jefferson City, MO 65102-0809
Ph: (573)751-1851
Fax: (573)751-1212
Co. E-mail: comofc@oa.mo.gov
URL: http://oa.mo.gov

Contact: Dan Haug, Director

47433 ■ Missouri State Office of Social and Economic Data Analysis (OSEDA)
201 Gentry, University of Missouri
Columbia, MO 65211
Ph: (573)882-7396
Fax: (573)884-4635
Co. E-mail: mayfieldw@missouri.edu
URL: http://www.oseda.missouri.edu
Contact: Wayne Mayfield, Director

47434 ■ Montana Department of Labor and Industry - Research and Analysis Bureau - Employment Relations Div.
301 S Pk. Ave. Fl. 5
Helena, MT 59601
Ph: (406)444-6543
Fax: (406)444-4140
URL: http://erd.dli.mt.gov
Contact: Eric Strauss, Administrator

47435 ■ Montana State Library-Digital Library Div. (MSL) - Library
1201 11th Ave.
Helena, MT 59620
URL: http://msl.mt.gov/digitallibrary
Description: Composed of programs that serve the information needs of all branches of state government, its agencies, local counterparts and individuals seeking information and materials that are not found in their local libraries. **Scope:** Geographic. **Holdings:** Figures not available.

47436 ■ Nebraska Department of Natural Resources (NeDNR)
245 Fallbrook Blvd., Ste. 201
Lincoln, NE 68521-6729
Ph: (402)471-2363
Fax: (402)471-2900
URL: http://dnr.nebraska.gov
Contact: Jesse Bradley, Director
E-mail: jesse.bradley@nebraska.gov
Facebook: www.facebook.com/nebraskadnr
X (Twitter): x.com/nebraskadnr
Scope: Soil and water resources - Nebraska, regional, national. **Services:** Library open to the public with restrictions. **Holdings:** Magnetic tape, diskettes, CD-ROM and other optical discs, and direct access files are held and updated regularly.; 4,000 books. **Subscriptions:** ; 20 journals and other serials. **Publications:** *Nebraska Natural Resources Commission Data Bank*.

47437 ■ Nebraska Library Commission (NLC)
The Atrium
1200 N St., Ste. 120
Lincoln, NE 68508-2023
Ph: (402)471-2045
Free: 800-307-2665
Fax: (402)471-2083
URL: http://nlc.nebraska.gov
Contact: Rod Wagner, Director
Description: Newsletter, Book. **Scope:** Administrative services; information technology; communication. **Services:** Interlibrary loan; copying; scanning center; library open to the public. **Founded:** 1901. **Holdings:** Audio magazines; audio books; braille; books; periodicals; DVDs. **Publications:** *Nebraska Library Directory*; *Guide to Nebraska State Agencies* (Annual); *Guide to Nebraska State Agencies: State Publications Classification and Ordering Directory* (Irregular); *Interlibrary Loan Directory for Nebraska*.

47438 ■ Nevada Department of Tourism and Cultural Affairs
401 N Carson St.
Carson City, NV 89701
Ph: (775)687-4810
URL: http://travelnevada.biz/nv-culture
Contact: Brenda Scolari, Director
URL(s): www.carsonnvmuseum.org

47439 ■ New Hampshire State Library (NHSL)
20 Pk. St.
Concord, NH 03301
Ph: (603)271-2144
URL: http://www.nhsl.dncr.nh.gov

Contact: Michael York, Librarian
E-mail: michael.c.york@dncr.nh.gov
Facebook: www.facebook.com/nhstatelibrary
X (Twitter): x.com/nhsl
Description: Publishes family histories for New Hampshire and New England. **Scope:** History; genealogy. **Services:** Interlibrary loan; Open to public. **Founded:** 1717. **Holdings:** Books; Magazines; Newspapers; Microfilms. **Publications:** *Directory of New Hampshire Libraries* (Annual); *New Hampshire Union Public Access Catalog (NHU-PAC)*; *New Hampshire Index*.

47440 ■ New Jersey Department of Labor and Workforce Development - Labor Market Information
Labor Bldg., 5th Fl.
Trenton, NJ 08625-0057
Fax: (609)633-9240
URL: http://www.nj.gov/labor/labormarketinformation
Contact: Jason Timian, Team Leader
E-mail: jason.timian@dol.nj.gov

47441 ■ New Jersey State Library U.S. Documents Collection
185 W State St.
Trenton, NJ 08608
Ph: (609)278-2640
Fax: (609)278-2646
Co. E-mail: refdesk@njstatelib.org
URL: http://www.njstatelib.org
Contact: Teri Taylor, Librarian

47442 ■ New Mexico State Library (NMSL)
1209 Camino Carlos Rey
Santa Fe, NM 87507-5166
Ph: (505)476-9702
Free: 800-876-2203
Co. E-mail: reference@state.nm.us
URL: http://www.nmstatelibrary.org
Contact: Kate Alderete, Contact
E-mail: kate.alderete@state.nm.us
Facebook: www.facebook.com/NewMexicoStateLibrary
X (Twitter): x.com/nmstatelibrary
Scope: State or federal government; southwest history and culture. **Services:** Interlibrary loan; library open to the public. **Founded:** 1929. **Holdings:** Magazines. **Publications:** *New Mexico Library Directory* (Annual).

47443 ■ New Mexico State University - College of Business - Economics, Applied Statistics and International Business Department (EASIB)
1320 E University Ave., Rm. 234
Las Cruces, NM 88003-8001
URL: http://catalogs.nmsu.edu/nmsu/business/economics-applied-statistics-international-business
Contact: Patti Benzie, Administrative Assistant
E-mail: pbenzie@nmsu.edu

47444 ■ New York State Education Department - Office of Cultural Education (OCE)
NYS Education Department
Cultural Education Ctr., Rm. 10D79
Albany, NY 12230
Ph: (518)474-5843
URL: http://www.oce.nysed.gov

47445 ■ North Dakota Department of Commerce - North Dakota Division of Community Services - Governmental/Technical Assistance
1600 E Century Ave., Ste. 6
Bismarck, ND 58503
Ph: (701)328-5300
URL: http://www.commerce.nd.gov/community-services
Description: Provides technical assistance to local governments, state agencies, and the executive branch in the areas of community and rural planning and development, policy research and development, and grant program implementation.

47446 ■ North Dakota State Library (NDSL)
604 E Blvd., Ave.
Bismarck, ND 58505-0800
Ph: (701)328-4622
Free: 800-472-2104
Fax: (701)328-2040
Co. E-mail: statelib@nd.gov
URL: http://www.library.nd.gov
Contact: Mary J. Soucie, Librarian
E-mail: msoucie@nd.gov
Facebook: www.facebook.com/NDStateLibrary
X (Twitter): x.com/NDStateLibrary
Instagram: www.instagram.com/ndstatelibrary
YouTube: www.youtube.com/channel/UCcLK-QjLcfNrA1KHhAVMsjA
Pinterest: www.pinterest.com/NDSL
Scope: Library community, state government, and north Dakota residents. **Services:** Interlibrary loan; copying; library open to the public. **Founded:** 1907. **Holdings:** Figures not available. **Publications:** *North Dakota State Library Online Catalog*.

47447 ■ Northern Arizona University - W.A. Franke College of Business
Building 81
Flagstaff, AZ 86011
Ph: (928)523-3657
Co. E-mail: fcb@nau.edu
URL: http://nau.edu/franke
Contact: Ashok Subramanian, Dean
E-mail: ashok.subramanian@nau.edu
Linkedin: www.linkedin.com/school/northern-arizona-university-the-w.-a.-franke-college-of-business
X (Twitter): x.com/WAFrankeCollege
Founded: 1899.

47448 ■ Northern Illinois University - Outreach, Engagement, and Regional Development Division - Center for Governmental Studies (CGS)
148 N 3rd St.
DeKalb, IL 60115
Ph: (815)753-1907
Co. E-mail: cgs@niu.edu
URL: http://www.cgs.niu.edu
Contact: Gregory T. Kuhn, Director
E-mail: gkuhn@niu.edu
Facebook: www.facebook.com/niu.cgs
Founded: 1969.

47449 ■ Northern Illinois University - The Regional Development Institute - Center for Governmental Studies (CGS)
1425 W Lincoln Hwy.
DeKalb, IL 60115-2828
Ph: (815)753-1907
URL: http://www.cgs.niu.edu
Contact: Gregory T. Kuhn, Director
E-mail: gkuhn@niu.edu
Facebook: www.facebook.com/people/Center-for-Governmental-Studies/100057694058290
Linkedin: www.linkedin.com/company/center-for-governmental-studies-at-northern-illinois-university
Founded: 1969.

47450 ■ Ohio Department of Job and Family Services - Ohio Labor Market Information
4020 E 5th Ave.
Columbus, OH 43219
Ph: (614)752-9494
Fax: (614)752-9627
Co. E-mail: contactlmi@jfs.ohio.gov
URL: http://ohiolmi.com

47451 ■ Ohio Development Services Agency - Office of Research
77 S High St., 28th Fl.
Columbus, OH 43215-6130
URL: http://development.ohio.gov/about-us/research

47452 ■ Oklahoma Department of Libraries (ODL) - Office of Government Information - U.S. Government Information Div.
200 NE 18th St.
Oklahoma City, OK 73105
URL: http://oklahoma.gov/libraries/odl-us-gov.html

Scope: Local history. Services: Interlibrary loan. Holdings: Papers; DVD; microfiche.; Figures not available. Publications: *Oklahoma Directory of Depositories for U.S. and State of Oklahoma Government Publications.*

47453 ■ Oregon Geographic Information Systems - Oregon Geospatial Enterprise Office (GEO)
530 Airport Rd. SE
Salem, OR 97301
Ph: (503)378-2166
Co. E-mail: gis.info@das.oregon.gov
URL: http://www.oregon.gov/GEO/pages/index.aspx
Contact: Erik Brewster, Coordinator
E-mail: erik.brewster@das.oregon.gov
Description: The Geospatial Enterprise (GEO) provides GIS coordination for state agencies. Founded: 1859.

47454 ■ Oregon Housing and Community Services Department (OHCS)
725 Summer St. NE, Ste. B
Salem, OR 97301-1266
Ph: (503)986-2000
Fax: (503)986-2020
Co. E-mail: hcs_housinginfo@oregon.gov
URL: http://www.oregon.gov/ohcs/Pages/index.aspx
Contact: Andrea Bell, Executive Director
Facebook: www.facebook.com/OregonHCS
X (Twitter): x.com/OregonHCS
YouTube: www.youtube.com/user/OHCSD
Description: Provide leadership that enables Oregonians to gain housing, become self-sufficient and achieve prosperity.

47455 ■ Oregon State Library
250 Winter St. NE
Salem, OR 97301
Ph: (503)378-4243
Fax: (503)585-8059
Co. E-mail: statelibrary.help@slo.oregon.gov
URL: http://www.oregon.gov/library/Pages/default.aspx
Contact: Jennifer Patterson, Director
Facebook: www.facebook.com/StateLibraryOR
X (Twitter): x.com/statelibraryor
Instagram: www.instagram.com/statelibraryor
YouTube: www.youtube.com/channel/UC0-kU8Gu0jS_YcnXg-b_TRA
Pinterest: www.pinterest.com/StateLibraryOR
Scope: Learning and community engagement. Services: Interlibrary loan; copying; SDI; library open to the public. Founded: 1905. Holdings: 1.4 million books and government documents; 1,871 videocassettes; 10,765 maps; clippings; pamphlets. Subscriptions: 773 journals and other serials. Publications: *Directory and Statistics of Oregon Libraries*; *Oregon State Library Online Catalog.*

47456 ■ Penn State University at Harrisburg (PSDC) - Institute of State and Regional Affairs - Pennsylvania State Data Center
777 W Harrisburg Pke.
Middletown, PA 17057-4898
Ph: (717)948-6336
Fax: (717)948-6754
Co. E-mail: pasdc@psu.edu
URL: http://pasdc.hbg.psu.edu/Default.aspx
Contact: Jennifer Shultz, Director
E-mail: jjb131@psu.edu

47457 ■ Pennsylvania State Data Center (SCO) - State Capital Office
777 W Harrisburg Pke.
Middletown, PA 17057-4898
Ph: (717)772-2710
Fax: (717)772-2683
Co. E-mail: pasdc-sco@psu.edu
URL: http://pasdc.hbg.psu.edu/Services/State-Capital-Office
Contact: Jennifer Shultz, Contact

47458 ■ Pennsylvania State University Harrisburg - Institute of State and Regional Affairs - Pennsylvania State Data Center (PASDC)
777 West Harrisburg Pke.
Middletown, PA 17057-4898
Ph: (717)948-6336
Fax: (717)948-6754
Co. E-mail: pasdc@psu.edu
URL: http://pasdc.hbg.psu.edu/Default.aspx
Contact: Jennifer Shultz, Director
E-mail: jjb131@psu.edu
X (Twitter): x.com/PASDC_PSU
Description: Publishes local demographics and policy. Also offers software. Scope: Data collection and analysis, including a decennial and economic census, population estimates and projections, migration flows, commutation patterns, housing school district data, geographic information systems, on-line systems, economic impacts of smoking, county to county migration flows, AIDS studies, and health insurance. Conducts regional workshops. Produces county data books, estimates reports, and abstracts. Founded: 1981. Educational Activities: PASDC User Conference (Annual), Demographics data and related topics.

47459 ■ Portland State University - College of Urban and Public Affairs - Population Research Center (PRC)
1800th Ave.
Portland, OR 97207-0751
Ph: (503)725-3922
Co. E-mail: askprc@pdx.edu
URL: http://www.pdx.edu/population-research
Contact: Ethan Sharygin, Director
E-mail: sharygin@pdx.edu
Description: The Population Research Center (PRC) is an interdisciplinary public service, research, and training unit for population-related data and research for the State of Oregon. Scope: Demography, including annual determination of actual population of all incorporated places and counties in the state of Oregon, development of census taking techniques, and computer programs for fertility, mortality patterns, and population forecasting. Founded: 1965. Holdings: The Center's library includes: comprehensive population and housing statistics in hard copy; historical data from previous federal censuses from 1950 to 1990; maps; publications from the U.S. Census Bureau; and current federal census data on CD-ROM. Publications: *Annual Population Estimates for Oregon, Counties and Cities* (Annual); *County Projections.* Educational Activities: Oregon State Data Center Meeting (Annual).

47460 ■ Princeton University - Firestone Library - Social Science Reference Center - Data and Statistical Services
1 Washington Rd.
Princeton, NJ 08544
Ph: (609)258-8714
Fax: (609)258-4105
Co. E-mail: data@princeton.edu
URL: http://www.census.gov/about/partners/sdc/member-network/new-jersey.html
Contact: Stacy Nemeroff, Contact
E-mail: stacyn@princeton.edu
URL(s): library.princeton.edu/dss

47461 ■ Recinto Universitario De Mayaguez - Universidad de Puerto Rico
259 Norte Blvd. Alfonso Valdes Cobian
Mayaguez, PR 00681
Ph: (787)832-4040
URL: http://www.uprm.edu/portada
Facebook: www.facebook.com/RecintoUniversitariodeMayaguez
X (Twitter): x.com/PrensaRUM
YouTube: www.youtube.com/user/videocolegio
Founded: 1911.

47462 ■ Rhode Island Commerce Corp. (RIC)
315 Iron Horse Way, Ste. 101
Providence, RI 02908
Ph: (401)278-9100
Fax: (401)273-8270
Co. E-mail: info@commerceri.com
URL: http://commerceri.com
Contact: Hilary Fagan, President
Facebook: www.facebook.com/CommerceRI
Linkedin: www.linkedin.com/company/commerce-ri
X (Twitter): x.com/CommerceRI
Instagram: www.instagram.com/ricommerce
Description: Provides site and building information to businesses expanding or relocating within the state. Also provides employee relocation assistance for out-of-state companies moving to Rhode Island. Founded: 1974. Publications: *Directory of Rhode Island Manufacturers* (Annual).

47463 ■ Rhode Island Department of Health - Center for Health Data and Analysis
3 Capitol Hill
Providence, RI 02908
URL: http://health.ri.gov/programs/detail.php?pgm_id=138
Contact: Samara Viner-Brown, Contact
E-mail: samara.viner-brown@health.ri.gov
Publications: *Rhode Island HCUP State Inpatient Database (SID).*

47464 ■ Rhode Island State Department of Revenue - Division of Municipal Finance
1 Capitol Hill, 1st Fl.
Providence, RI 02908
Ph: (401)574-9900
Fax: (401)574-9912
URL: http://municipalfinance.ri.gov
Contact: Laura Fraunfelter, Director
E-mail: laura.fraunfelter@dor.ri.gov
URL(s): dor.ri.gov/about-us/divisions/municipal-finance
Description: Publishes directories on Rhode Island and public administration. Publications: *Directory of City & Town Officials in Rhode Island.*

47465 ■ Rutgers University - Edward J. Bloustein School of Planning and Public Policy - Rutgers Regional Report/State Data Center
33 Livingston Ave.
New Brunswick, NJ 08901
URL: http://bloustein.rutgers.edu/centers/rutgers-regional-report
Description: The Rutgers Regional Report is a Coordinating Agency of the New Jersey State Data Center (New Jersey Department of Labor and Workforce Development) Network. It produces the quarterly SITAR-Rutgers Regional Report as well as a more extensive Rutgers Regional Report series.

47466 ■ Rutgers University - Office of Information Technology - Camden Computing Services
Paul Robeson Library, First Fl.
Camden, NJ 08102
Ph: (856)225-6274
Co. E-mail: help@camden.rutgers.edu
URL: http://it.camden.rutgers.edu/about/policies/service

47467 ■ Sacramento Area Council of Governments (SACOG) - Library
1415 L St., Ste. 300
Sacramento, CA 95814
Ph: (916)321-9000
Co. E-mail: contact@sacog.org
URL: http://www.sacog.org
Contact: Jay Schenirer, Chief Executive Officer
Facebook: www.facebook.com/sacog
Linkedin: www.linkedin.com/company/sacramento-area-council-of-governments
X (Twitter): x.com/SACOG
YouTube: www.youtube.com/user/SacramentoAreaCOG
Description: The Sacramento Area Council of Governments (SACOG) provides transportation planning and funding for the region, and serves as a forum for the study and resolution of regional issues. Scope: Planning; transportation planning; census. Founded: 1965. Holdings: Census community analysis; economic census; materials. Publications: *Current* (Irregular). Geographic Preference: Local.

FEDERAL GOVERNMENT ASSISTANCE

47468 ■ San Diego Association of Governments (SANDAG)
401 B St., Ste. 800
San Diego, CA 92101
Ph: (619)699-1900
Fax: (619)699-1905
URL: http://www.sandag.org
Contact: Hasan Ikhrata, Chief Executive Officer
Facebook: www.facebook.com/SANDAGregion
Linkedin: www.linkedin.com/company/sandag
X (Twitter): x.com/SANDAG
Instagram: www.instagram.com/sandagregion
YouTube: www.youtube.com/user/SANDAGREGION
Description: The San Diego Association of Governments (SANDAG) builds consensus, makes strategic plans, obtains and allocates resources, plans, engineers, and builds public transportation, and provides information on a broad range of topics pertinent to the region's quality of life. **Founded:** 1966. **Geographic Preference:** Local.

47469 ■ South Carolina State Library
1500 Senate St.
Columbia, SC 29201
Ph: (803)734-8666
Free: 888-221-4643
Fax: (803)734-8676
Co. E-mail: reference@statelibrary.sc.gov
URL: http://www.statelibrary.sc.gov
Contact: Ellen Dunn, Director
E-mail: edunn@statelibrary.sc.gov
Facebook: www.facebook.com/southcarolinastatelibrary
Linkedin: www.linkedin.com/company/south-carolina-state-library
X (Twitter): x.com/scstatelibrary
Instagram: www.instagram.com/scstatelibrary
YouTube: www.youtube.com/scstatelibrary
Scope: Technology; library development; administration/management; governance. **Services:** Interlibrary loan; copying; Library open to the public. **Founded:** 1969. **Holdings:** Figures not available. **Publications:** South Carolina State Library Online Catalog; Talking Book Services Online Catalog.

47470 ■ South Dakota Department of Health - Director of Administration
Robert Hayes Bldg.
600 E Capitol Ave.
Pierre, SD 57501-2536
Ph: (605)773-3361
Free: 800-738-2301
Fax: (605)773-5683
Co. E-mail: doh.info@state.sd.us
URL: http://doh.sd.gov
Contact: Joan Adam, Secretary
Description: The mission of the South Dakota Department of Health is to prevent disease and promote health, ensure access to needed, high-quality health care, and to efficiently manage public health resources.

47471 ■ South Dakota Department of Labor and Regulation (LMIC) - Labor Market Information Center
PO Box 4730
Aberdeen, SD 57402-4730
Ph: (605)626-2314
Free: 800-592-1881
Fax: (605)626-2322
URL: http://dlr.sd.gov/lmic
Contact: Marcia Hultman, Secretary

47472 ■ South Dakota State Library - Documents Department
800 Governors Dr.
Pierre, SD 57501-2235
URL: http://library.sd.gov

47473 ■ South Dakota State University - Department of Sociology and Rural Studies
1175 Medary Ave.
Brookings, SD 57006
URL: http://www.sdstate.edu/sdsu-archives-special-collections/south-dakota-water-resources-institute-records
Founded: 1881.

47474 ■ Southern California Association of Governments (SCAG) - Library
900 Wilshire Blvd., Ste. 1700
Los Angeles, CA 90017
Ph: (213)236-1800
Co. E-mail: contactus@scag.ca.gov
URL: http://scag.ca.gov
Contact: Jan C. Harnik, President
Facebook: www.facebook.com/scagmpo
Linkedin: www.linkedin.com/company/southern-california-association-of-governments
X (Twitter): x.com/scagnews
Instagram: www.instagram.com/scagnews
YouTube: www.youtube.com/user/SoCalAssociationGov
Description: The Association of Governments is mandated by the federal government to research and draw up plans for transportation, growth management, hazardous waste management, and air quality. Additional mandates exist at the state level. **Scope:** Local government. **Founded:** 1965. **Holdings:** Figures not available. **Publications:** Around the Region (Quarterly). **Educational Activities:** Southern California Association of Governments General Assembly (Annual). **Geographic Preference:** Local.

47475 ■ Southern Illinois University at Edwardsville - Regional Research and Development Services
PO Box 1039
Edwardsville, IL 62026
URL: http://www.siue.edu/~jfarley
Description: Student-centered educational community dedicated to communicating, expanding and integrating knowledge. In a spirit of collaboration enriched by diverse ideas.

47476 ■ State of Alaska Department of Commerce, Community and Economic Development - Division of Community and Regional Affairs (DCRA) - Serve Alaska Commission
550 W 7th Ave., Ste. 1650
Anchorage, AK 99501-3510
Ph: (907)269-6720
Fax: (907)269-5666
Co. E-mail: serve.alaska@alaska.gov
URL: http://www.commerce.alaska.gov/web/dcra/ServeAlaska.aspx
Contact: Katie Abbott, Executive Director
E-mail: katie.abbott@alaska.gov
X (Twitter): x.com/ServeAK
Description: Premier international development agency and a catalytic actor driving development results. USAID's work advances U.S. national security and economic prosperity, demonstrates American generosity, and promotes a path to recipient self-reliance and resilience.

47477 ■ State of Connecticut Department of Economic and Community Development - Research and Planning
450 Columbus Blvd., Ste. 5
Hartford, CT 06103
URL: http://portal.ct.gov/DECD/Services/About-DECD/Research-and-Publications

47478 ■ State of Illinois (OMB) - Office of Management and Budget
401 S Spring 603 Stratton Bldg.
Springfield, IL 62706
Ph: (217)782-4521
Fax: (217)524-4876
Co. E-mail: gomb@illinois.gov
URL: http://budget.illinois.gov
Contact: Alexis Sturm, Director
URL(s): www.illinois.gov/agencies/agency.gomb.html#

47479 ■ State of Kentucky - Department for Libraries and Archives
300 Coffee Tree Rd.
Frankfort, KY 40602
Ph: (502)564-8300
Linkedin: www.linkedin.com/company/kentucky-department-for-libraries-and-archives
Founded: 1936. **Holdings:** Books; magazines; journals; newspapers.

47480 ■ State Library of Florida Division of Library and Information Services
R.A. Gray Bldg.
500 S Bronough St.
Tallahassee, FL 32399-0250
Ph: (850)245-6500
Co. E-mail: info@dos.myflorida.com
URL: http://dos.myflorida.com/library-archives/about-us/about-the-state-library-of-florida
Contact: Amy L. Johnson, Director
Scope: History of Florida; genealogy. **Services:** Library open to public. **Founded:** 1968. **Holdings:** 700,000 books, magazines and newspapers; 200,000 government documents; 180,000 photographs; 2,000 maps. **Publications:** Florida Library Directory: With Statistics; State Library of Florida Online Catalog; Florida Biography Index; Florida State Agency Libraries and Resource Centers in Tallahassee (Biennial).

47481 ■ State Library of Iowa
1112 E Grand Ave.
Des Moines, IA 50319
Free: 800-248-4483
Fax: (515)281-6191
Co. E-mail: information.services@iowa.gov
URL: http://www.statelibraryofiowa.gov
Contact: Gary Krob, Coordinator
E-mail: gary.krop@iowa.gov
Facebook: www.facebook.com/StateLibraryIA
X (Twitter): x.com/StateLibraryIA
Scope: State government; public policy; law; Library science. **Services:** Interlibrary loan; copying; Library open to the public. **Founded:** 1838. **Holdings:** Figures not available. **Subscriptions:** 980 journals and other serials; 168,000 books; 14,842 microfilms. **Publications:** Iowa Library Directory (Annual); State Library of Iowa Online Catalog; Iowa Inventors Database.

47482 ■ State Library of Kansas
Capitol Bldg., Rm. 312-N
300 SW 10th Ave.
Topeka, KS 66612
Ph: (785)296-3296
Co. E-mail: infodesk@ks.gov
URL: http://kslib.info
Facebook: www.facebook.com/statelibraryofkansas
X (Twitter): x.com/LibraryofKS
Scope: Regional history. **Services:** Interlibrary loan; open to the public at librarian's discretion; copying. **Founded:** 1855. **Holdings:** Books; ebooks; audiobooks.

47483 ■ State Library of North Carolina Division of State Library (SLNC) - Library
109 E Jones St.
Raleigh, NC 27601
Ph: (919)814-6790
Fax: (919)733-1843
Co. E-mail: nclbph@ncdcr.gov
URL: http://statelibrary.ncdcr.gov
Contact: Cotina Jones, Director, Development
E-mail: cotina.jones@ncdcr.gov
Facebook: www.facebook.com/StateLibraryNC
Linkedin: www.linkedin.com/company/state-library-of-north-carolina
YouTube: www.youtube.com/user/statelibrarync
Scope: History; Culture. **Services:** Interlibrary loan; Copying. **Founded:** 1812. **Holdings:** Books; article.

47484 ■ State Library of Ohio
274 E 1st Ave.
Columbus, OH 43201
Ph: (614)644-7061
Co. E-mail: stateliboh@library.ohio.gov
URL: http://library.ohio.gov
Contact: Alan Hall, President
Facebook: www.facebook.com/StateLibraryOhio
X (Twitter): x.com/statelibohio
YouTube: www.youtube.com/channel/UCFiKVfM_fLdmNhXx7YXa70w
Pinterest: www.pinterest.com/stlibohio

FEDERAL GOVERNMENT ASSISTANCE

Scope: Management; social sciences; education; public administration; Ohio history. Services: Interlibrary loan; copying; library open to the public. Founded: 1817. Holdings: 594,072 books; 2,270 audio; 11,087 video.; 301,824 bound volumes; 444,716 microforms, and 1,546,762 federal and state government documents. Subscriptions: 490 periodicals (includes journals). Publications: *OHIO PUBLIC LIBRARY SYSTEMS* (Annual); *State Library of Ohio Online Catalog*.

47485 ■ State of Oregon Office of Economic Analysis - Department of Administrative Services (DAS)
Office of the Chief Operating Officer (DAS Director)
Executive Building, 155 Cottage St., NE
Salem, OR 97301
Ph: (503)378-3104
URL: http://www.oregon.gov/das/Pages/index.aspx
Contact: Berri Leslie, Director
E-mail: berri.l.leslie@das.oregon.gov
X (Twitter): x.com/OregonDAS
YouTube: www.youtube.com/user/DASOregon

Description: Provides objective forecasts of the state's economy, revenue, population, corrections population, and Youth Authority population. These forecasts are used to enable the governor, the legislature, state agencies, and the public to achieve their goals.

47486 ■ State of Rhode Island Office of Library and Information Services - Department of Administration
c/o Karen Mellor, Chief of Library Services,1 Capitol Hill
Providence, RI 02908
Ph: (401)574-9304
Fax: (401)574-9320
Co. E-mail: karen.mellor@olis.ri.gov
URL: http://olis.ri.gov
Contact: Karen Mellor, Officer
E-mail: karen.mellor@olis.ri.gov

Description: The Office of Library and Information Services strengthens, connects and empowers libraries to advance knowledge, connect communities and enrich the lives of all Rhode Islanders.

47487 ■ State of Vermont Agency of Commerce and Community Development - Tourism and Marketing
1 National Life Dr. 6th Fl.
Deane C. Davis Bldg.
Montpelier, VT 05620-0501
URL: http://accd.vermont.gov/tourism

47488 ■ Tennessee Department of Economic and Community Development Research Division
312 Rosa L. Parks Ave.
Nashville, TN 37243
Ph: (615)741-1888
Co. E-mail: ecd.communications.office@tn.gov
URL: http://www.tn.gov/ecd
Facebook: www.facebook.com/tnecd
Linkedin: www.linkedin.com/company/tnecd
X (Twitter): x.com/TNECD
Instagram: www.instagram.com/tnecd
YouTube: www.youtube.com/user/TNECD

Description: Department of economic and community development. Founded: 1980.

47489 ■ Texas A&M University - Department of Sociology
311 Academic Bldg.
College Station, TX 77843
Ph: (979)845-5133
Co. E-mail: sociology@tamu.edu
URL: http://liberalarts.tamu.edu/sociology
Contact: Christi Barrera, II, Officer
E-mail: christi@tamu.edu
Facebook: www.facebook.com/TAMUSOCI
X (Twitter): x.com/TAMUSoc
Instagram: www.instagram.com/TAMUSOCI
YouTube: www.youtube.com/channel/UCPbglJa7fX_rPoTclRrTucA
Founded: 1876.

47490 ■ Texas Geographic Information Office (TNRIS) - Library
1700 N Congress, Rm. B 40
Austin, TX 78701
Ph: (512)463-8337
URL: http://tnris.org
Contact: Richard Wade, Officer

Description: The state's clearinghouse and referral center for natural resources data. Provides access to more than 400 data files, approximately half of which exist in computer-compatible form. Maintains an automated Geographic Information System (GIS) and serves as a clearinghouse for digital map files of the state. Additional services include training, consulting, and referrals. Special emphasis is on statewide digital mapping and providing data services of the Texas/Mexico border region. Scope: Applications of remote sensing and geographic information systems to natural resource management, including water resource planning, land use planning, energy conservation efforts, and other resource endeavors. Conducts inventories of natural resources data and develops new capabilities for data handling to meet the needs of Texas state agencies. Provides assistance in the use of remote sensing technology and data, develops geocoding and geographic data handling systems, and enhances data analysis and presentation capabilities to include the latest in interactive graphics and visual presentation. Provides access to a wide variety of state-held data and to a number of automated natural resource databases available from federal agencies and private entities. Services: Copying; library open to the public. Founded: 1972. Holdings: Photos; paper; maps; reports. Subscriptions: 10 journals and other serials. Publications: *TNRIS Newsletter* (Quarterly). Educational Activities: GIS (Geographic Information Systems) Forum (Annual).

47491 ■ Texas State Library and Archives Commission (TSLAC)
1201 Brazos St.
Austin, TX 78701
Ph: (512)463-5455
Free: 800-252-9386
Fax: (512)936-2306
Co. E-mail: info@tsl.texas.gov
URL: http://www.tsl.texas.gov
Contact: Mark Smith, Director
Facebook: www.facebook.com/tslac
X (Twitter): x.com/tslac
Instagram: www.instagram.com/tslac
YouTube: www.youtube.com/user/TSLAC

Scope: Texas history and government, genealogy, librarianship. Services: Interlibrary loan; copying; library open to the public with restrictions. Founded: 1909. Holdings: 1.4 million books and bound periodical volumes; newspapers; journals, books; manuscripts; photographs; historical maps; microforms and tax records; CDs; DVDs; photos. Publications: *Library Catalog of Texas State Agencies*; *Texas Confederate Pension Applications*; *Texas State Archives Map Collection*; *Republic of Texas Claims*; *Texas Adjutant General Service Records 1836-1935*.

47492 ■ UMass Donahue Institute (UMDI)
100 Venture Way, Ste. 9
Hadley, MA 01035
Ph: (413)545-0001
Fax: (413)545-3420
Co. E-mail: info@donahue.umass.edu
URL: http://donahue.umass.edu
Contact: Johan Uvin, Executive Director
E-mail: juvin@donahue.umass.edu
Facebook: www.facebook.com/UMassDonahueInstitute
Linkedin: www.linkedin.com/company/umass-donahue-institute
X (Twitter): x.com/UMASSDonahue
Instagram: www.instagram.com/civicinitiative

Description: Addresses critical questions and develops innovative solutions to help organizations and agencies from both the public and private sector meet challenges, measure success, and set goals. Founded: 1970.

47493 ■ United States Census Bureau - State Data Center of Mississippi
537 Lamar Hall
University, MS 38677
Ph: (662)915-7295
Fax: (662)915-7736
Co. E-mail: cps@olemiss.edu
URL: http://sdc.olemiss.edu
Contact: Dr. John J. Green, Director
E-mail: jjgreen@olemiss.edu
URL(s): www.census.gov/about/partners/sdc/member-network/mississippi.html

Holdings: The Center maintains a collection of Census Bureau publications and all computer-readable Census Bureau data for the state of Mississippi.

47494 ■ U.S. Department of Commerce - Arizona Department of Economic Security
1717 W Jefferson
Phoenix, AZ 85007
Ph: (602)364-2860
Free: 866-362-2837
Fax: (602)364-2848
URL: http://des.az.gov
Contact: Michael Wisehart, Director

Description: Works to promote enhanced safety and well-being for Arizonans. Founded: 1972.

47495 ■ U.S. Department of Commerce - Bureau of Economic Analysis (BEA)
4600 Silver Hill Rd.
Suitland, MD 20746
Ph: (301)278-9004
Co. E-mail: customerservice@bea.gov
URL: http://www.commerce.gov/bureaus-and-offices/bea
Contact: Dr. Vipin Arora, Director
URL(s): www.bea.gov
Facebook: www.facebook.com/usbeagov
Linkedin: www.linkedin.com/company/u-s-department-of-commerce
X (Twitter): x.com/bea_news
Instagram: www.instagram.com/usbeagov
YouTube: www.youtube.com/channel/UCCP9QD1x_z__duUivA6Yb5w

Description: Guide. Publications: *High Technology Industries in Florida*.

47496 ■ U.S. Department of Commerce - Capital Region Council of Governments (CRCOG)
241 Main St., 4th Fl.
Hartford, CT 06106-5310
Ph: (860)522-2217
Fax: (860)724-1274
Co. E-mail: info@crcog.org
URL: http://crcog.org
Contact: Matt Hart, Executive Director
E-mail: mhart@crcog.org
Facebook: www.facebook.com/CapitolRegionCouncilofGovernments
Linkedin: www.linkedin.com/company/capitol-region-council-of-governments
X (Twitter): x.com/crcog1

Founded: 2005.

47497 ■ U.S. Department of Commerce - Center for Geographic Information and Analysis - Office of State Planning
PO Box 17209
Raleigh, NC 27619-7209
URL: http://it.nc.gov/about/boards-commissions/gicc/cgia
Contact: Tim Johnson, Contact
E-mail: tim.johnson@nc.gov

47498 ■ U.S. Department of Commerce - Colorado State University Libraries - Morgan Library
1201 Center Ave., Mall
Fort Collins, CO 80523-1019
URL: http://lib.colostate.edu
Facebook: www.facebook.com/csumorganlibrary

Scope: Figures not available.

47499 ■ U.S. Department of Commerce (EAD) - Department of Administration and Information - Economic Analysis Div.
2800 Central Ave.
Cheyenne, WY 82002-0060
Ph: (307)777-7504
Co. E-mail: ai-ead-info@wyo.gov
URL: http://eadiv.state.wy.us
Contact: Wenlin Liu, Officer Administrator
E-mail: wenlin.liu@wyo.gov
Description: Provide customers with quality and timely research, data, and analysis.

47500 ■ U.S. Department of Commerce - Department of Employment Security - LMEA
212 Maple Pk. Ave. SE
Olympia, WA 98507
URL: http://www.esd.wa.gov
Description: We partner to connect employers and job seekers - supporting transitions to new jobs and empowering careers. **Founded:** 1852.

47501 ■ U.S. Department of Commerce - Economic Development Administration (EDA)
1401 Constitution Ave. NW, Ste. 71014
Washington, DC 20230
URL: http://www.eda.gov
Contact: Dennis Alvord, Assistant Secretary Chief Operating Officer
Facebook: www.facebook.com/eda.commerce
Linkedin: www.linkedin.com/company/us-department-of-commerce-economic-development-administration
X (Twitter): x.com/US_EDA
Instagram: www.instagram.com/edagov
YouTube: www.youtube.com/user/EDACommerce
Founded: 1965.

47502 ■ U.S. Department of Commerce - Geographic Resources Center - University of Missouri-Columbia (GRC)
401 Ellis Library
Columbia, MO 65201
Ph: (573)882-7567
URL: http://muarchives.missouri.edu/c-rg6-s48.html
Description: The process of linking spatial data to descriptive attribute data is used extensively by planners, resource managers, biologists and a host of professionals to assist in decision making. **Founded:** 1980.

47503 ■ U.S. Department of Commerce - Georgia Department of Community Affairs - Office of Planning and Quality Growth
60 Executive Pk. S, NE
Atlanta, GA 30329
Ph: (404)679-4840
Free: 800-436-7442
URL: http://www.dca.ga.gov/local-government-assistance/planning
Contact: Christopher Nunn, Contact

47504 ■ U.S. Department of Commerce - Guam Department of Commerce
PO Box 3238
Agana, GU 96910
Ph: (671)477-4725
URL: http://2010-2014.commerce.gov/ssLINK/DEV01_005425.html

47505 ■ U.S. Department of Commerce - Headwaters Regional Development Commission (HRDC)
1320 Neilson Ave. SE
Bemidji, MN 56619-0906
Ph: (218)444-4732
Fax: (218)444-4722
Co. E-mail: hrdc@hrdc.org
URL: http://hrdc.org
Contact: Cal Larson, Chairman
Founded: 1971.

47506 ■ U.S. Department of Commerce - Illinois Department of Commerce and Economic Opportunity - Springfield Office
607 E Adams, 3rd Fl.
Springfield, IL 62701
Ph: (217)782-7500
URL: http://dceo.illinois.gov/contactus.html
Facebook: www.facebook.com/illinoisdceo
Linkedin: www.linkedin.com/company/illinoisdceo
X (Twitter): x.com/IllinoisDCEO

47507 ■ U.S. Department of Commerce - Indiana Department of Workforce Development - Research and Analysis
Indiana Government Center S, SE21110 N Senate Ave.
Indianapolis, IN 46204
URL: http://www.census.gov/about/partners/sdc/member-network/indiana.html
Contact: Charles Baer, Contact
E-mail: vseegert@dwd.in.gov
Founded: 1903.

47508 ■ U.S. Department of Commerce (IBRC) - Indiana University - Indiana Business Research Center
777 Indiana Ave., Ste. 210
Indianapolis, IN 46202
Ph: (317)274-2979
Co. E-mail: ibrc@iu.edu
URL: http://ibrc.kelley.iu.edu
Contact: Phil Powell, Executive Director
E-mail: phpowell@indiana.edu
URL(s): kelley.iu.edu/faculty-research/centers-institutes/index.html
Facebook: www.facebook.com/IUibrc
Linkedin: www.linkedin.com/company/indiana-business-research-center
X (Twitter): x.com/IUibrc
Founded: 1925.

47509 ■ U.S. Department of Commerce - L. William Seidman Research Institute - W.P. Carey School of Business
PO Box 874011
Tempe, AZ 85287-4011
Ph: (480)965-5362
Fax: (480)965-5458
Co. E-mail: wpcareyseid@asu.edu
URL: http://seidmaninstitute.com
Contact: Dr. Dennis L. Hoffman, Director
Facebook: www.facebook.com/wpcareyschool
X (Twitter): x.com/wpcareyschool
YouTube: www.youtube.com/wpcareyschool
Founded: 1985.

47510 ■ U.S. Department of Commerce - Maryland Department of Planning
401 E Pratt St.
Baltimore, MD 21202
URL: http://commerce.maryland.gov/compatibleuse
Contact: Sarah Diehl, Contact
E-mail: sarah.diehl@maryland.gov
Description: The company provides services and involves in public welfare activities. **Publications:** Maryland InfoPortal:A Digital Catalog of State Assistance Programs; Directory of Planning Agencies and Maryland APA Members (Irregular).

47511 ■ U.S. Department of Commerce - Metropolitan Council Research - Metropolitan Council Data Center
390 Robert St. N
Saint Paul, MN 55101-1805
Ph: (651)602-1000
Co. E-mail: public.info@metc.state.mn.us
URL: http://metrocouncil.org
Contact: Charles A. Zelle, Chairman
E-mail: charles.zelle@metc.state.mn.us
Description: Provides policy, planning and essential services.

47512 ■ U.S. Department of Commerce - Michigan Department of Technology, Management, & Budget - Center for Shared Solutions and Technology Partnerships - Michigan Information Center
1401 Constitution Ave. NW
Washington, DC 20230
URL: http://www.commerce.gov
Linkedin: www.linkedin.com/company/u-s--department-of-energy

47513 ■ U.S. Department of Commerce (MDA) - Mississippi Development Authority
501 N W St.
Jackson, MS 39201
Ph: (601)359-3449
Free: 800-360-3323
Co. E-mail: social@mississippi.org
URL: http://mississippi.org
Contact: Laura Hipp, Executive Director
Facebook: www.facebook.com/msdevelopmentauthority
Description: Provides assistance to the state's businesses and industries, including loans and loan guarantees to small businesses, and an outreach program. **Founded:** 1936.

47514 ■ U.S. Department of Commerce - Nebraska Governor's Policy Research and Energy Office
PO Box 95085
Bellevue, NE 68005-5085
Ph: (402)471-2867
Fax: (402)471-3064
URL: http://www.energy.gov/eere/bioenergy/state-biomass-contacts#ne

47515 ■ U.S. Department of Commerce - Nebraska Policy Research Office
c/o Erin Bottger, Policy Advisor
PO Box 94601
Lincoln, NE 68509-4601
Ph: (402)471-2853
Co. E-mail: erin.bottger@nebraska.gov
URL: http://www.census.gov/about/partners/gln/nebraska.html
Contact: Erin Bottger, Advisor
E-mail: erin.bottger@nebraska.gov
Description: Provide training and assistance; assist the bureau in achieving its mission; and foster two-way communications with the bureau on data usability, data user needs and operational issues.

47516 ■ U.S. Department of Commerce - The Nelson A. Rockefeller Institute of Government
411 State St.
Albany, NY 12203-1004
Ph: (518)445-4150
Co. E-mail: communications@rock.suny.edu
URL: http://rockinst.org
Contact: Robert Megna, President
Facebook: www.facebook.com/rockefellerinst
X (Twitter): x.com/rockefellerinst
Instagram: www.instagram.com/rockefellerinst
YouTube: www.youtube.com/user/RockefellerInstitute
Founded: 1981.

47517 ■ U.S. Department of Commerce - Office of Business Liaison
1401 Constitution Ave., NW
Washington, DC 20230
Ph: (202)482-1360
Co. E-mail: businessliaison@doc.gov
URL: http://www.commerce.gov/bureaus-and-offices/os/business-liaison
Contact: Laura O'Neill, Director
E-mail: lo'neill@doc.gov
Linkedin: www.linkedin.com/company/u-s-department-of-commerce
Description: The Department of Commerce's Office of Business Liaison seeks to develop and promote a cooperative working relationship and to assure effective communication between the department and the business community, including small businesses. The office serves as the focal point for all of the department's agencies to contact the business community. It informs the business community of department and administration resources, policies, and programs, as well as informs department and administration officials about business community interests and issues. In addition, the office promotes business involvement in departmental policymaking and program development. The office also provides business assistance to individuals and firms that need help dealing with the federal government. The Business Assistance Program provides professional staff members to give guidance on the many federal

programs; to answer inquiries concerning government policies, programs, and services; and to provide information and published materials on a variety of business topics.

47518 ■ U.S. Department of Commerce - Office of Real Property Programs (ORPP)
1401 Constitution Ave. NW
Washington, DC 20230
Ph: (202)482-5053
Co. E-mail: askorpp@doc.gov
URL: http://www.commerce.gov/ofeq/offices/office-real-property-programs
Description: Coordinates DoC implementation of Government-wide programs for the acquiring, managing, utilizing, and disposing of real property.

47519 ■ U.S. Department of Commerce - Office of Real Property Tax Services - Department of Taxation and Finance
1401 Constitution Ave. NW
Washington, DC 20230
URL: http://www.tax.ny.gov/research/property/regional/orpts.htm
URL(s): www.commerce.gov

47520 ■ U.S. Department of Commerce - Office of Small and Disadvantaged Business Utilization (OSDBU)
1401 Constitution Ave., NW
Washington, DC 20230
Ph: (202)482-1472
Co. E-mail: osdbu@doc.gov
URL: http://www.commerce.gov/bureaus-and-offices/os/cfo-asa/small-and-disadvantaged-business-utilization
Description: Is an advocacy and advisory office responsible for promoting the use of small, small disadvantaged, 8(a), women-owned, veteran-owned, service-disabled veteran-owned, and HUBZone small businesses within the U.S. Department of Commerce's (DOC) acquisition process.

47521 ■ U.S. Department of Commerce - Pennsylvania State Library
Forum Bldg., Rm. 219
333 Market St.
Lower Swatara, PA 17057
URL: http://www.census.gov/about/partners/sdc/member-network/pennsylvania.html
Contact: Kathy Hale, Contact
E-mail: kahale@pa.gov

47522 ■ U.S. Department of Commerce - Puget Sound Regional Council - Information Center
1011 W Ave., Ste. 500
Seattle, WA 98104-1035
Ph: (206)464-7090
Co. E-mail: info@psrc.org
URL: http://www.psrc.org
Contact: Josh Brown, Executive Director
E-mail: jbrown@psrc.org
Facebook: www.facebook.com/PugetSoundRegionalCouncil
Linkedin: www.linkedin.com/company/soundregion
X (Twitter): x.com/SoundRegion
Instagram: www.instagram.com/soundregion
Description: The Puget Sound Regional Council works with local government, business, and citizens to build a common vision for the region's future, expressed through three connected major activities: VISION 2040, the region's growth strategy, Destination 2030, the region's comprehensive long-range transportation plan; and Prosperity Partnership, which develops and advances the region's economic strategy. **Scope:** Population, housing, economy, transportation. **Founded:** 1991. **Holdings:** Figures not available. **Publications:** *Regional View* (Monthly). **Awards:** VISION 2040 Award (Annual). **Geographic Preference:** Local.

47523 ■ U.S. Department of Commerce - Rhode Island Department of Elementary and Secondary Education (RIDE)
255 Westminster St.
Providence, RI 02903
Ph: (401)222-4600
Co. E-mail: info@ride.ri.gov
URL: http://ride.ri.gov
Contact: Patricia Dicenso, Chairman of the Board
URL(s): www.ri.gov/government/?tags=education
Facebook: www.facebook.com/RIDeptEd
X (Twitter): x.com/RIDeptEd
Instagram: www.instagram.com/ridepted
YouTube: www.youtube.com/channel/UCI9aP7qCwsyjeWrQXbaAQGw
Description: Publishes educational materials for schools and colleges. **Founded:** 1981. **Publications:** *Rhode Island Educational Directory* (Annual).

47524 ■ U.S. Department of Commerce - U.S. Census Bureau - State Data Center Program - Texas Demographic Center (TXSDC)
1 UTSA Cir.
San Antonio, TX 78249
Ph: (210)458-6543
Fax: (210)458-6541
Co. E-mail: tdc@utsa.edu
URL: http://demographics.texas.gov
Contact: Dr. Lloyd B. Potter, Director
Facebook: www.facebook.com/TexasDemographics
Linkedin: www.linkedin.com/company/u-s-department-of-commerce
X (Twitter): x.com/TexasDemography
Instagram: www.instagram.com/texasdemographiccenter
Description: The Texas Demographic Center functions as a focal point for the production, interpretation, and distribution of demographic information for Texas. **Founded:** 1980.

47525 ■ U.S. Department of Commerce - University of North Carolina - Howard W. Odum Institute for Research in Social Science
Davis Library, 2nd Fl.
Chapel Hill, NC 27599-3355
Co. E-mail: oduminstitute@unc.edu
URL: http://www.odum.unc.edu/odum/home2.jsp
Contact: Todd Bendor, Director
E-mail: bendor@unc.edu
Facebook: www.facebook.com/OdumInstitute
YouTube: www.youtube.com/user/OdumInstitute
Description: Provides core research infrastructure for the social sciences to support the research, teaching, and service mission of UNC.

47526 ■ U.S. Department of Commerce - Urban Information Center - University of Missouri--St. Louis
240 Heinkel Bldg.
Columbia, MO 65211
Ph: (314)882-7396
Free: 888-GO2-UMSL
Fax: (314)884-4635
Co. E-mail: admissions@umsl.edu
URL: http://www.oseda.missouri.edu
Contact: Kristin Sobolik, Chancellor
Facebook: www.facebook.com/UMSL.edu
Linkedin: www.linkedin.com/school/university-of-missouri---st.-louis
Instagram: www.instagram.com/umsl

47527 ■ U.S. Department of Commerce - Utah Governor's Office of Economic Development
60 E S Temple, Ste. 300
Salt Lake City, UT 84111-1041
Ph: (801)538-8680
Co. E-mail: business@utah.gov
URL: http://business.utah.gov
Contact: Daniel Hemmert, Executive Director
E-mail: danhemmert@utah.gov
Facebook: www.facebook.com/businessutah
Linkedin: www.linkedin.com/company/businessutah
X (Twitter): x.com/businessutah
Instagram: www.instagram.com/businessutah
YouTube: www.youtube.com/channel/UC8Ombh9mGzeKq_KzKyA1oeA
Founded: 2005.

47528 ■ U.S. Department of Commerce - Virgin Islands Department of Economic Development
8000 Nisky Shopping Ctr., Ste. 620
Saint Thomas, VI 00802
Ph: (340)714-1700
Co. E-mail: info@usvieda.org
URL: http://www.usvieda.org
Contact: Kevin Rodriquez, Chairman
Facebook: www.facebook.com/usvieda
Linkedin: www.linkedin.com/company/usvieda
X (Twitter): x.com/usvi_eda
Instagram: www.instagram.com/usvieda
Description: Provide guidelines on equipment, customs (including shipping regulations and immigration travel identification), film permits, marine production, insurance coverage, and available crew.

47529 ■ U.S. Department of Commerce - Virgin Islands Economic Development Authority (VIEDA)
8000 Nisky Shopping Ctr., Ste. 620
Saint Thomas, VI 00802
Ph: (340)714-1700
Co. E-mail: info@usvieda.org
URL: http://www.usvieda.org
Contact: Wayne L. Biggs, Jr., Chief Executive Officer
Facebook: www.facebook.com/usvieda
Linkedin: www.linkedin.com/company/usvieda
X (Twitter): x.com/usvi_eda
Instagram: www.instagram.com/usvieda
Description: Responsible for the promotion and enhancement of economic development in the U.S. Virgin Islands. **Founded:** 2001.

47530 ■ U.S. Department of Commerce (VEC) - Virginia Employment Commission
PO Box 26441
Richmond, VA 23261-6441
Free: 866-832-2363
Co. E-mail: veteran.services@vec.virginia.gov
URL: http://www.vec.virginia.gov
Facebook: www.facebook.com/VirginiaEmploymentCommission
Linkedin: www.linkedin.com/company/virginia-employment-commission
X (Twitter): x.com/vaemploy
YouTube: www.youtube.com/channel/UCoJKinzHEx2TdyP50Sorn_g
Description: Employment service commission of Virginia. **Founded:** 1915.

47531 ■ U.S. Department of Commerce - West Virginia Development Office - Research and Strategic Planning Group
1900 Kanawha Blvd., E
Charleston, WV 25305
Ph: (304)558-2234
URL: https://djcs.wv.gov/orsp/Pages/default.aspx
Contact: Janet Spry, Officer
Founded: 2005.

47532 ■ U.S. Department of Commerce - West Virginia State Library Commission - Reference Library
Culture Ctr., Bldg. 9
1900 Kanawha Blvd. E
Charleston, WV 25305
URL: http://librarycommission.wv.gov/What/Pages/Reference-Library.aspx

47533 ■ United Way of Rhode Island (UWRI)
50 Valley St.
Providence, RI 02909
Ph: (401)444-0600
URL: http://www.unitedwayri.org
Contact: Cortney Nicolato, President
Facebook: www.facebook.com/LIVEUNITEDri
Linkedin: www.linkedin.com/company/united-way-of-rhode-island
X (Twitter): x.com/liveunit
Instagram: www.instagram.com/liveunitedri
YouTube: www.youtube.com/user/unitedwayri
Description: Works to mobilize the power of the community to improve the lives of people in need. **Founded:** 1926. **Geographic Preference:** State.

47534 ■ University of Alabama - Culverhouse College of Commerce and Business Administration - Center for Business and Economic Research (CBER) - Library
1500 Greensboro Ave., Ste. 1
Tuscaloosa, AL 35401
Ph: (205)348-6191
Fax: (205)348-2951
Co. E-mail: uacber@cba.ua.edu
URL: http://cber.culverhouse.ua.edu
Contact: Ahmad Ijaz, Executive Director
E-mail: aijaz@culverhouse.ua.edu
Facebook: www.facebook.com/uacber

Description: Publishes on business, economics, demography and subjects directly related to the Alabama economy. Also publishes a quarterly. Does not accept unsolicited manuscripts. Reaches market through direct mail. **Scope:** Business and economics, revenue forecasting, and employment in Alabama; estimates of population in Alabama counties; and investigations of state and regional economies. Engaged in construction and maintenance of annual econometric model for the state. **Founded:** 1930. **Holdings:** Figures not available. **Publications:** *Alabama Economic Outlook* (Annual); *Alabama Business* (Quarterly); *Alabama Business Confidence Index* (Quarterly). **Educational Activities:** Alabama Business Confidence Index (Quarterly), Online survey.; Alabama Economic Outlook Meeting (Annual), Every January.

47535 ■ University of Alaska Anchorage (UAA) - Library
3211 Providence Dr.
Anchorage, AK 99508
Ph: (907)786-1800
URL: http://www.uaa.alaska.edu
Contact: Claudia Lampman, Professor
E-mail: cblampman@alaska.edu
Facebook: www.facebook.com/UAAnchorage
Linkedin: www.linkedin.com/school/uaanchorage
X (Twitter): x.com/uaanchorage
Instagram: www.instagram.com/ua.anchorage
YouTube: www.youtube.com/user/UAAnchorage

Description: Education: Academics, opportunities for internships, research and real-world experience. **Scope:** Accounting; agriculture; astronomy; biography; economics; geographics; geology; political science. **Services:** Copying; interlibrary loan. **Founded:** 1954. **Holdings:** 728,313 titles; books; jouranals; magazines. **Publications:** *Alaska Quarterly Review* (Quarterly). **Awards:** Elaine Atwood Excellence Scholarship (Annual); Dr. Jon Baker Memorial Scholarship (Annual); UAA Michael Baring-Gould Memorial Scholarship (Annual); Mark A. Beltz Scholarship (Annual); Pat Brakke Political Science Scholarship (Annual); Edward Rolling Clinton Memorial Endowment Fund (Annual); Governor William A. Egan Award (Annual); Michael D. Ford Memorial Scholarship; Jan and Glenn Fredericks Scholarship (Annual); Ardell French Memorial Scholarship (Annual); Benjamin A. Gilman International Scholarship (Annual); Ken Gray Endowment Scholarship Fund (Annual); Muriel Hannah Scholarship in Art (Annual); Lenore and George Hedla Accounting Scholarship (Annual); Chris L. Kleinke Scholarship (Annual); Kris Knudson Memorial Scholarship (Annual); Arlene Kuhner Memorial Scholarship (Annual); Diane Olsen Memorial Scholarship (Annual); April Relyea Scholarship (Annual); Brown Schoenheit Memorial Scholarship (Annual); Eveline Schuster Memorial Award/Scholarship (Annual); Lillian Smith Scholarship for Teaching Students (Annual); Sheri Stears Education Scholarship; Sturgulewski Family Scholarship (Annual); UAA Accounting Club Scholarship (Annual); UAA Alaska Kidney Foundation Scholarship (Annual); UAA Alumni Association Scholarships (Annual); UAA College of Business and Public Policy Scholarships - American Marketing Association & F.X. Dale Tran Memorial Scholarship (Annual); Emi Chance for Aspiring Artists Scholarship (Annual); UAA Friends of the Performing Arts Scholarship (Annual); UAA GCI Scholarship (Annual); UAA Kimura Scholarship Fund for Illustration (Annual); UAA Kimura Scholarship Fund for Photography (Annual); Pignalberi Public Policy Scholarship (Annual); UAA Quanterra Scholarship (Annual); Recruitment and Retention of Alaska Natives into Nursing (RRANN) (Annual); Wells Fargo Career Scholarship (Annual); Melissa J. Wolf Accounting Scholarship (Annual).

47536 ■ University of Arizona - Eller College of Management - Economic and Business Research Center (EBRC) - Library
1130 E Helen St.
Tucson, AZ 85721-0108
Ph: (520)621-2155
Fax: (520)621-2150
Co. E-mail: ebrpublications@email.arizona.edu
URL: http://eller.arizona.edu/departments-research/centers-labs/economic-business-research
Contact: George W. Hammond, Director
E-mail: ghammond@eller.arizona.edu
Facebook: www.facebook.com/UArizonaEBRC
X (Twitter): x.com/UArizonaEBRC

Description: Integral unit of University of Arizona. **Scope:** Regional economic forecasting, economic data collection and analysis, econometric and input-output impact models, policy-analytic studies, and international economic research. Assists individuals and groups interested in Arizona economy and aids public and private organizations with their research and planning activities. **Services:** Library open to the public for reference use only. **Founded:** 1949. **Holdings:** Articles; reports. **Publications:** *Arizona Economic Indicators* (Semiannual); *Arizona Statistical Abstract*; *Arizona's Economy* (Quarterly). **Educational Activities:** Economic Outlook Luncheon (Annual), For research and development.; Economic Update Breakfast (Annual), For research and development.

47537 ■ University of California, Berkeley - UC DATA
University of California, 350 Social Sciences Bldg.
Berkeley, CA 94720-3030
URL: http://dlab.berkeley.edu/data/uc-data

Description: Provide access to a broad range of computerized social science data to faculty, staff, and students at UC Berkeley. **Founded:** 1991.

47538 ■ University of Cincinnati Institute for Policy Research (UCIPR)
2600 Clifton Ave.
Cincinnati, OH 45221
Ph: (513)556-5028
URL: http://www.uc.edu/about/ipr.html
Contact: Kimberly Downing, Director
E-mail: kim.downing@uc.edu

Description: Integral unit of University of Cincinnati. Oversees the Survey Research Center; the Southwest Ohio Regional Data Center; the Social, Behavioral, and Health Sciences Data Archive; and the Community Research Collaborative. **Scope:** Operates the omnibus Greater Cincinnati Survey and the omnibus Ohio Poll. **Founded:** 1971. **Publications:** *IPR Reports*.

47539 ■ University of Colorado at Boulder - Leeds School of Business - Business Research Division (BRD)
995 Regent Dr., 419 UCB
Boulder, CO 80309
Ph: (303)492-3307
Co. E-mail: brdinfo@colorado.edu
URL: http://www.colorado.edu/business/business-research-division#overview
Contact: Brian Lewandowski, Executive Director
E-mail: brian.lewandowski@colorado.edu

Description: Publishes directories. **Scope:** Regional and local economic impact studies, and forecasting. **Founded:** 1915. **Publications:** *Environmental Concerns: The 1999-2000 Directory of the Environmental Industry in Colorado*; *Directory of Colorado Manufacturers--Information, Science, & Technology*; *Colorado Biomedical Directory*; *Colorado Photonics Industry Directory*; *Colorado Ski Industry* (Annual); *Directory of Colorado Manufacturers with International Sales*; *Colorado Manufacturers Directory* (Annual); *Directory of Colorado High Tech Manufacturers*. **Educational Activities:** Annual Colorado Business Economic Outlook Forum (Annual), Offer exemplary teaching and training programs.

47540 ■ University of Delaware School of Public Policy & Administration
184 Graham Hall
Newark, DE 19716
Ph: (302)831-1687
Co. E-mail: bidenschool@udel.edu
URL: http://www.bidenschool.udel.edu
Contact: Amy Ellen Schwartz, Dean
E-mail: aeschwar@udel.edu

47541 ■ University of Georgia Libraries - Map & Government Information Library (MAGIL)
320 S Jackson St.
Athens, GA 30602
Ph: (706)542-0690
Co. E-mail: mapsinfo@uga.edu
URL: http://www.libs.uga.edu/magil
Contact: Sarah Causey, Librarian
E-mail: stamatki@uga.edu
X (Twitter): x.com/magil_uga

Scope: Government. **Services:** Library not open to public. **Holdings:** Cartographic materials; maps and atlases; aerial photography; Georgia city directories; U.S. government documents; Georgia state government documents; international government documents; Unites Nations publications.

47542 ■ University of Illinois at Chicago - Chicago Area Geographic Information Study (CAGIS)
1007 W Harrison
Chicago, IL 60607-7139
Ph: (312)413-3570
Fax: (312)413-3573
URL: http://www.uic.edu/apps/departments-az/search?dispatch=letter&letter=C
Contact: John Monaghan, Director
E-mail: monaghan@uic.edu

Description: Autonomous research group of the University of Illinois at Chicago housed within the Department of Geography. **Scope:** Conducts research and provides services in geographic information systems. Maintains computer mapping capabilities. Also conducts census summary processing. **Founded:** 1970.

47543 ■ University of Iowa - Public Policy Center - Iowa Social Science Research Center (ISRC)
605 E Jefferson St., Public Policy Research Bldg.
Iowa City, IA 52242
Co. E-mail: isrc-info@uiowa.edu
URL: http://ppc.uiowa.edu/isrc
Contact: Frederick Boehmke, Director
E-mail: frederick-boehmke@uiowa.edu

Description: Integral unit of Public Policy Center, University of Iowa. **Founded:** 1987.

47544 ■ University of Kansas - Institute for Policy and Social Research - Center for Research on Global Change (CRGC)
1541 Lilac Ln., 607 Blake Hall
Lawrence, KS 66045
URL: http://ipsr.ku.edu/crgc
Contact: Joane Nagel, Director
Facebook: www.facebook.com/KUIPSR
X (Twitter): x.com/ku_ipsr

Description: Publishes on business, economics and public policy in the state of Kansas. Conducts research and publishes reports. Accepts unsolicited manuscripts. **Scope:** Global change, including its social, political, economic and cultural dimensions. **Founded:** 2001. **Holdings:** Machine-readable holdings include several hundred computer tapes and CD-ROMs of census and sample data. Library holdings include 9000 bound volumes, subscriptions to 200 periodicals, and maps and microfiche. **Publications:** *Kansas Policy Review* (Periodic); *Kansas Statistical Abstract* (Annual). **Educational Activities:** Kansas Community Economic Development Conference (Annual), Features community economic development leaders, city and county government officials, and the business community to explore ways of strengthening community economic development activities in local communities.; Kansas Economic Policy Conference (Annual), Explores the economic and policy implications of solutions to current issues facing the state of Kansas.

47545 ■ University of Louisville School of Urban and Public Affairs (USI) - Urban Studies Institute
426 W Bloom St.
  Louisville, KY 40208
URL: http://urbanlouisville.org/centers-and-institutes

47546 ■ University of Louisville Urban Studies Institute (USI)
426 W Bloom St.
  Louisville, KY 40208
URL: http://urbanlouisville.org/centers-and-institutes
Contact: Dr. Matthew H. Ruther, Director
E-mail: matthew.ruther@louisville.edu
Description: Publishes research books on Kentucky and database management. Also publishes reports, produces customized print-outs from census tapes and other special services for a fee. **Scope:** Social policy and economics. **Founded:** 1976.

47547 ■ University of Maryland (DCS) - Department of Computer Science
8125 Paint Branch Dr.
  College Park, MD 20742
Ph: (301)405-2662
Fax: (301)405-6707
Co. E-mail: helpdesk@cs.umd.edu
URL: http://www.cs.umd.edu
Contact: Kate Atchison, Associate Director
E-mail: katea@umd.edu
Facebook: www.facebook.com/UMDComputerScience
Linkedin: www.linkedin.com/company/department-of-computer-science-umd
X (Twitter): x.com/umdcs
Instagram: www.instagram.com/umdcs

47548 ■ University of Missouri-Kansas City Center for Economic Information (UMKC CEI)
Haag Hall 210
  5211 Rockhill Rd.
  Kansas City, MO 64110
Ph: (816)235-2832
Fax: (816)235-2834
URL: http://cei.umkc.edu
Contact: Peter Eaton, Director
E-mail: eatonp@umkc.edu
Description: Uses information technology in support of economic decision-makers in the public and private sectors, and academic researchers. **Founded:** 1994.

47549 ■ University of Montana Bureau of Business and Economic Research (UM BBER)
Gallagher Business Bldg.
  32 Campus Dr., No. 6840
  Missoula, MT 59812-6840
Ph: (406)243-5113
Co. E-mail: bbermail@business.umt.edu
URL: http://www.bber.umt.edu
Contact: Patrick Barkey, Director
E-mail: patrick.barkey@business.umt.edu
Facebook: www.facebook.com/bbermt
X (Twitter): x.com/MontanaBBER
Description: Integral unit of School of Business Administration at University of Montana. Offers county data packages: updated economic information for Montana counties. **Scope:** Provides Montana business community with statistical data and interpretation and disseminates general information on economic conditions and prospects in the state. **Services:** Copying; library open to the public with restrictions. **Founded:** 1948. **Publications:** *Informational Brochures*; *Bureau of Business and Economic Research Monographs* (Periodic); *Montana Business Quarterly (MBQ)* (Quarterly). **Educational Activities:** Annual Economic Outlook Seminar (EOS) (Annual).

47550 ■ University of Montana School of Business Administration
Gallagher Business Bldg.
  32 Campus Dr.
  Missoula, MT 59812
URL: http://www.umt.edu/business
Founded: 1918.

47551 ■ University of Nebraska at Omaha - Center for Public Affairs Research - Nebraska State Data Center (NSDC)
108 CPACS 6001 Dodge St.
  Omaha, NE 68182
Ph: (402)554-2134
Co. E-mail: unocpar@unomaha.edu
URL: http://www.unomaha.edu/college-of-public-affairs-and-community-service/center-for-public-affairs-research/programs/nebraska-state-data-center.php
Description: Publishes on economic development, public policy, Nebraska. Reaches market through direct mail. Does not accept unsolicited manuscripts. **Founded:** 1978.

47552 ■ University of New Hampshire - Office of Biometrics
Thompson Hall, Main St.
  Durham, NH 03824
Ph: (603)862-1990
Free: 800-735-2964
Co. E-mail: social.media@unh.edu
URL: http://departments.unh.edu
Contact: James W. Dean, Jr., President
Facebook: www.facebook.com/universityofnewhampshire
Linkedin: www.linkedin.com/school/university-of-new-hampshire
X (Twitter): twitter.com/uofnh
Instagram: www.instagram.com/uofnh
YouTube: www.youtube.com/c/unh
Pinterest: www.pinterest.com/unh

47553 ■ University of New Mexico - Bureau of Business & Economic Research - Data Bank (UNM BBER)
400 Cornell Dr. NE
  Albuquerque, NM 87131
Ph: (505)277-2216
Co. E-mail: dbinfo@unm.edu
URL: http://bber.unm.edu
Contact: RaeAnn McKernan, Contact
E-mail: bber@unm.edu
Facebook: www.facebook.com/UNMBBER
Linkedin: www.linkedin.com/in/unmbber
X (Twitter): x.com/UNMBBER
Instagram: www.instagram.com/UNMBBER
YouTube: www.youtube.com/channel/UCxij5K50zix6PznCtS4pvng
Scope: National; regional; state; and local economic conditions; demography; census. **Services:** Library open to the public. **Founded:** 1967. **Holdings:** Books; reports; periodicals; CDs; sheet maps; microfilm.

47554 ■ University of New Mexico (UNM) - Bureau of Business and Economic Research - New Mexico State Data Center/Business and Industrial Data Center Program (SDC/BIDC)
University of New Mexico, Zimmerman Library B25, MSC05 3020
  Albuquerque, NM 87131-0001
URL: http://digitalrepository.unm.edu/business_economic_research
Description: The Bureau of Business and Economic Research (BBER) is the recognized expert in providing socioeconomic data and forecasting in New Mexico.

47555 ■ University of North Dakota Department of Geography and Geographic Information Science
O'Kelly Hall, Rm. 152
  221 Centennial Dr., Stop 9020
  Grand Forks, ND 58202-9020
Ph: (707)777-4246
URL: http://arts-sciences.und.edu/academics/geography
Contact: Douglas Munski, Chairman
E-mail: douglas.munski@und.edu
YouTube: www.youtube.com/channel/UCEAwl9Qks-z2v4TkEe3zllg

47556 ■ University of Northern Colorado - James A. Michener Library
14th Ave. & 20th St.
  Greeley, CO 80639
Ph: (970)351-2671
Fax: (970)351-2963
Co. E-mail: libraries@unco.edu
URL: http://www.unco.edu/library/about_us/history-info.aspx
Scope: Arts & Humanities; business; citations & bibliographies; communication; education; general studies; health sciences. **Services:** Interlibrary loan; copying; open to public. **Holdings:** 1.5 million items in book, periodical, government document, audiovisual and microforms; 900 linear feet of research notes, manuscripts, galley proofs and correspondence, notebooks, maps, photographs and slides.

47557 ■ University of Northern Iowa College of Social and Behavioral Sciences - Center for Social and Behavioral Research (CSBR)
2304 College St.
  Cedar Falls, IA 50614-0402
Ph: (319)273-2105
Fax: (319)273-3104
Co. E-mail: csbr@uni.edu
URL: http://csbr.uni.edu
Contact: Mary Losch, Director
E-mail: mary.losch@uni.edu
Description: Integral unit of College of Social and Behavioral Sciences, University of Northern Iowa, but with its own board of control. Offers consulting services. **Scope:** Geography, history, home economics, political science, psychology, sociology, anthropology, criminology, social work, and public policy, including studies on adolescents, adult education, airline passengers, airports, educational needs assessment, elderly, environmental impact assessment, highways, human services needs assessment, outdoor recreation, radio listening habits, substance abuse, and television viewing habits. Performs feasibility studies on proposed projects such as sports complexes and auditoriums. Conducts special surveys for groups, organizations, localities, regions, and social aggregates. **Founded:** 1967. **Educational Activities:** CSBR Conferences.

47558 ■ University of Oklahoma - Michael F. Price College of Business - Center for Economic & Management Research (CEMR)
307 W Brooks, Ste. 4., Adams Hall
  Rm. 4D
  Norman, OK 73019
Ph: (405)325-2931
URL: http://www.ou.edu/price/fsservices/fsit/it_handbook/introduction
Contact: Dr. Robert Dauffenbach, Director
E-mail: rdauffen@ou.edu
Description: Publishes research in human and physical resources pertinent to regional economic development. Also publishes journals, reports and periodicals. Reaches market through direct mail. Does not accept unsolicited manuscripts. **Scope:** Business and economic problems, including studies on business conditions, energy demand, utilization of human resources, economic development, and business trends in the state. **Founded:** 1928. **Holdings:** CEMR maintains a library of more than 3000 statistical publications and a computer-readable collection of time-series data. **Publications:** *Oklahoma Business Bulletin* (Quarterly); *Oklahoma Business Bulletin* (Quarterly); *Statistical Abstract of Oklahoma* (Annual).

47559 ■ University of Oregon Library - Document Center
1501 Kincaid St.
  Eugene, OR 97403-1299
URL: http://library.uoregon.edu/govdocs
Holdings: map collection; microforms; business resources; government information.

47560 ■ University of Southern Maine - Maine State Data Center - Center for Business and Economic Research (MCBER)
34 Bedford St.
Portland, ME 04104
Ph: (207)780-4181
Co. E-mail: usmcber@maine.edu
URL: http://www.mainecber.com
Description: Provides research and technical assistance to companies and organizations in Maine.

47561 ■ University of Tennessee - College of Business Administration - Boyd Center for Business and Economic Research
453 Haslam Business Bldg.
Knoxville, TN 37996-4140
Co. E-mail: utboydcenter@utk.edu
URL: http://haslam.utk.edu/boyd-center
Contact: Kira Rasmussen, Business Manager
E-mail: krasmus3@tennessee.edu
Facebook: www.facebook.com/UTBoydCenter
X (Twitter): x.com/UTBoydCenter
Founded: 1967.

47562 ■ University of Vermont - Center for Rural Studies (CRS)
206 Morrill Hall, 146 University Pl.
Burlington, VT 05405
URL: http://www.uvm.edu/crs
Contact: Dr. Jane Kolodinsky, Director
E-mail: jane.kolodinsky@uvm.edu
Description: Integral unit of College of Agriculture of University of Vermont. Data information service for Vermont communities and small businesses. **Scope:** Rural problems and related issues, particularly community development organizations, demography, appropriate technology (including computers), international rural development, natural resource based economic development, agriculture, and the environment. Activities include survey design and administration and data processing and management. **Founded:** 1980. **Publications:** *Center for Rural Studies Publication Series*; *Data briefs* (Monthly); *Rural Developments* (Semiannual). **Educational Activities:** Town officer training; Rural Sociological Society Meetings.

47563 ■ University of the Virgin Islands - Eastern Caribbean Center (ECC)
c/o Lawanda Cummings, Director
No. 2 John Brewers Bay
Saint Thomas, VI 00802
Ph: (340)693-1020
Fax: (340)693-1025
Co. E-mail: ecc@uvi.edu
URL: http://www.uvi.edu/research/eastern-caribbean-center/index.html
Contact: Dr. Lawanda Cummings, Director
E-mail: lawanda.cummings@live.uvi.edu
Description: To conduct scientific research and associated training, technology transfer and information dissemination, that is responsive to the social, economic and environmental needs of the USVI and applicable to the small islands of the Eastern Caribbean. **Scope:** Caribbean area, with emphasis on scientific surveys, demographic/ socioeconomic and GPS-mapped environmental issues of the Virgin Islands and the development issues of small-island communities. **Founded:** 1991. **Publications:** *Caribbean Perspectives* (Annual).

47564 ■ University of Virginia - Weldon Cooper Center for Public Service
2400 Old Ivy Rd.
Charlottesville, VA 22903
Ph: (434)982-5522
Fax: (434)982-5524
Co. E-mail: it@mail.institute.virginia.edu
URL: http://coopercenter.org
Contact: Paula Campbell, Business Manager
E-mail: pbc@virginia.edu
Facebook: www.facebook.com/coopercenterUVA
Linkedin: www.linkedin.com/company/weldon-cooper-center-public
X (Twitter): x.com/UVACooperCenter
Instagram: www.instagram.com/weldoncoopercenter
Description: Publishes on Virginia government, politics, public affairs, economics and demographics. Accepts unsolicited manuscripts. Reaches market through direct mail. **Scope:** Studies the economy of the state and its region, Virginia demographics, jobs and education, voting rights, local government structure and functions, and emerging trends and issues. Projects include official population estimates for Virginia; target industry studies focusing on economic development efforts in regions of the state; analysis of changing job skills in the labor force; studies on adjusted gross income, population, housing units, taxable sales, employment, and personal income; evaluation of status of minorities in the Commonwealth; staffing for statewide commissions; projections of school enrollment; and other state public policy issues. **Founded:** 1931. **Publications:** *Weldon Cooper Center for Public Service Research Reports*; *Virginia Statistical Abstract* (Biennial). **Educational Activities:** Senior Executive Institute and Management Excellence Program. **Awards:** Wallerstein Scholarship.

47565 ■ University of Washington - Center for Social Science Computation and Research (CSSCR)
PO Box 351202
Seattle, WA 98195
URL: http://www.washington.edu/research/research-centers/center-for-social-science-computation-and-research-csscr
Contact: Jerry Herting, Contact
Description: A computer resource center providing facilities and support for social science departments at the University of Washington. **Founded:** 1972.

47566 ■ University of Wisconsin - Madison (APL) - Department of Community and Environmental Sociology - Applied Population Laboratory
Agricultural Hall Rm. 316, 1450 Linden Dr.
Madison, WI 53706
URL: http://apl.wisc.edu
Contact: David Long, Director
E-mail: ddlong@wisc.edu
X (Twitter): x.com/appliedpoplab
Founded: 1960.

47567 ■ University of Wyoming - Wyoming Survey and Analysis Center (WYSAC)
1000 E University Ave., UW Office Annex, 406 S 21st St.
Laramie, WY 82071
Ph: (307)766-2189
Co. E-mail: wysac@uwyo.edu
URL: http://wysac.uwyo.edu/wysac
Contact: Bistra Anatchkova, Manager
E-mail: bistra@uwyo.edu
URL(s): acalogcatalog.uwyo.edu/content.php?catoid=4&navoid=155#wyoming-survey-analysis-center
Description: Integral unit of University of Wyoming. **Scope:** Analyses and surveys on criminal justice, substance abuse, education, environment, opinion polling, and development of database-driven Web site applications. **Founded:** 1989. **Publications:** *Research Samples Newsletter* (Occasionally); *WYSAC Technical reports* (Periodic).

47568 ■ Urban Greater DC
500 L'Enfant Plz. SW
Washington, DC 20024
URL: http://greaterdc.urban.org
Contact: Peter A. Tatian, Officer
E-mail: ptatian@urban.org

47569 ■ Utah Governor's Office of Planning & Budget
Utah State Capitol, 350 N State St., Ste. 150
Salt Lake City, UT 84114-2210
Ph: (801)538-1027
URL: http://gopb.utah.gov
Contact: Sophia DiCaro, Executive Director
E-mail: sophiadicaro@utah.gov
Description: Provides leadership for the initiatives of the Governor and meets customer information, budgeting, planning, strategy, and issue coordination needs by providing accurate and timely data, impartial analyses, and objective recommendations.

47570 ■ Vermont Department of Libraries
60 Washington St., Ste. 2
Barre, VT 05641
Ph: (802)636-0040
Free: 800-479-1711
Co. E-mail: lib.ablelibrary@vermont.gov
URL: http://libraries.vermont.gov
Contact: Tom Frank, Chairman of the Board
Facebook: www.facebook.com/VermontLib
Instagram: www.instagram.com/vermontdeptlib
YouTube: www.youtube.com/vermontlib
Description: Publishes directories. **Founded:** 1983. **Publications:** *Vermont Department of Libraries Online Catalog*; *Vermont Library Directory* (Monthly); *Vermont Legislative Directory and State Manual* (Biennial); *Legislative Directory and State Manual* (Biennial).

47571 ■ Washington State Library (WSL)
6880 Capitol Blvd., Point Plz. E
Tumwater, WA 98501
Ph: (360)704-5221
Co. E-mail: askalibrarian@sos.wa.gov
URL: http://www.sos.wa.gov/library
Contact: Sara Jones, Librarian
E-mail: sara.jones@sos.wa.gov
Facebook: www.facebook.com/WashingtonStateLibrary
X (Twitter): x.com/WAStateLib
Instagram: www.instagram.com/washingtonstatelibrary
YouTube: www.youtube.com/user/WAStateLibrary
Description: Publishes directories on library, government. **Scope:** History; genealogy; rural heritage; northwest. **Services:** Interlibrary loan; Open to public by appoinments. **Founded:** 1853. **Holdings:** Audio books; Books; Journals; DVD's; Manuscripts; Maps; Newspapers. **Publications:** *Washington State Library*; *Washington State Library Online Catalog*; *Territorial Library Collection*; *Washington Naturalization Records Database*; *Washington State Oaths of Office, 1854-2013*; *Spokane County Auditor, Birth Returns 1907-1907*; *Spokane County Auditor, Marriage Records 1880-2013*; *Classics in Washington History* (Quarterly); *Washington Cities, Counties, and Corporations*; *Washington Historical Maps*; *Washington State Constitution*; *Select Index to the Olympian and Other Regional Publications*; *Washington Territorial and State Governors*; *Women in the Washington State Legislature*; *Washington State Sanborn Maps*; *Directory of Washington Libraries* (Annual); *Washington Public Library Statistical Report* (Annual).

47572 ■ Washington State Office of Financial Management - Forecasting Div.
PO Box 43113
Olympia, WA 98504-3113
Co. E-mail: ofm.forecasting@ofm.wa.gov
URL: http://ofm.wa.gov/division-contacts/forecasting-research-division
Contact: David Schumacher, Director

47573 ■ Washington State University - School of Economics Sciences
PO Box 646210
Pullman, WA 99164-6210
URL: http://ses.wsu.edu
Contact: Thomas Dahl, Secretary
E-mail: tomdahl@wsu.edu
Description: Offers a highly rated Ph.D. program in Economics and Agricultural Economics, an M.S. degree in Applied Economics, and an undergraduate program leading to a B.S. degree that open doors to a wide variety of career paths. **Founded:** 2004.

47574 ■ Wayne State University - Center for Urban Studies (CUS) - Michigan Metropolitan Information Center (MIMIC)
5700 Cass Ave.
Detroit, MI 48202
Ph: (313)577-2208

Co. E-mail: cusinfo@wayne.edu
URL: http://www.cus.wayne.edu
Contact: Dr. Lyke Thompson, Director
E-mail: lyke@wayne.edu
Facebook: www.facebook.com/waynestateuniversity
X (Twitter): twitter.com/waynestate

Description: Integral unit of Wayne State University. Offers community education and social service program evaluations for local governments and businesses; consulting; demographic analyses; planning studies; policy surveys. **Scope:** Survey research; program evaluation; demographic analysis of population and urban economic problems; community and economic development; community indicators; community and public health; organizational capacity building; and crime trends and crime prevention. **Founded:** 1981. **Holdings:** The Center maintains census data dating back to 1930 in hardcopy and computer-readable forms. **Educational Activities:** Center for Urban Studies Conferences, On census, population, housing topics, and family issues.

47575 ■ West Virginia University College of Business and Economics - Bureau of Business and Economic Research (BBER) - Research
2161 University Ave., Ste. 450
 Morgantown, WV 26505
Ph: (304)293-7831
Co. E-mail: bebureau@mail.wvu.edu
URL: http://business.wvu.edu/research-outreach/bureau-of-business-and-economic-research
Contact: John Deskins, Director
E-mail: john.deskins@mail.wvu.edu

Description: Publishes books on studies, forecasts, county data profiles and newsletters. Does not accept unsolicited manuscripts. **Scope:** Business and economic problems, policies, and institutions, especially those related to state and local economies of West Virginia, including economic forecasts, studies on public finance, labor force and employment, demographic projections, specific industries, plant location, business management, and marketing. Conducts consumer analyses, community trade surveys, travel and tourism, and studies of national or regional scope that are significant to residents and business communities of West Virginia. **Founded:** 1940. **Holdings:** Figures not available. **Publications:** *Morgantown MSA Monitor* (Quarterly); *West Virginia Business and Economic Review* (Quarterly); *Journal of Small Business Management (JSBM)* (6/year). **Educational Activities:** Economic Outlook Conference (Annual), Obtain a detailed and reliable forecast for the national and state economies.; West Virginia Economic Outlook Conference (Annual), Obtain a detailed and reliable forecast for the national and state economies.

47576 ■ West Virginia University Health Sciences Center (OHSR) - Office of Health Services Research
Morgantown, WV
Ph: (304)293-7206
URL: http://www.hsc.wvu.edu
Contact: Robert Byrd, Contact
E-mail: kshipp@hsc.wvu.edu

Description: University of health sciences. **Founded:** 1867.

47577 ■ West Virginia University - Office of Health Services Research (OHSR)
64 Medical Center Dr.
 Morgantown, WV 26505-9190
URL: http://publichealth.wvu.edu/ohsr
Contact: Adam D. Baus, Director

Description: Organization providing public health services.

47578 ■ Western Washington University (OSR) - Office of Institutional Effectiveness
516 High St.
 Bellingham, WA 98225
URL: http://oie.wwu.edu
Contact: John Krieg, Director
E-mail: john.krieg@wwu.edu

Description: Integral unit of Western Washington University. **Scope:** Demographics. **Publications:** *Demographic Research Laboratory Working papers*.

47579 ■ Wichita State University - Center for Economic Development and Business Research (CEDBR)
1845 Fairmount, Grace Wilkie Hall, Rm. 223
 Wichita, KS 67260-0121
Ph: (316)978-3225
Fax: (316)978-3950
URL: http://www.cedbr.org
Contact: Jeremy Hill, Director

Description: Integral unit of W. Frank Barton School of Business, Wichita State University. Provides speakers and contract research. **Scope:** Collection, retrieval, and analysis of state and local demographic economic data, including construction and real estate, commerce, public utilities, and employment, for use by government and business. **Founded:** 1969. **Publications:** *Kansas Economic Indicators* (Monthly); *CEDBR Data Base*; *Kansas Economic Information* (Monthly). **Educational Activities:** Annual Kansas Economic Outlook Conference (Annual), To enhance the region's economic growth and development by conducting applied business, economic and demographic research.

U.S. DEPARTMENT OF DEFENSE

47580 ■ Department of Defense - Defense Logistics Agency Aviation - Defense Supply Center Richmond (DSCR)
6090 Strathmore Rd.
 Richmond, VA 23237
Ph: (804)279-3861
URL: http://www.dla.mil/Aviation
Founded: 1942.

47581 ■ U.S. Department of Defense (DOD) - Defense Contract Management Agency (DCMA)
Atlanta, GA
URL: http://www.dcma.mil

Description: Provides advice and information to help construct effective solicitations, identify potential risks, select the most capable contractors, and write contracts that meet the needs of our customers in DoD, Federal and allied government agencies.

47582 ■ U.S. Department of Defense - Defense Contract Management Agency (DCMA)
3901 Adams Ave., Bldg. 10500
 Fort Lee, VA 23801
URL: http://www.dcma.mil
Contact: Gregory L. Masiello, Director
Linkedin: www.linkedin.com/company/dcma
Founded: 2000.

47583 ■ U.S. Department of Defense - Defense Contract Management Agency (DCMA)
1400 Defense Pentagon
 Washington, DC 20301-1400
URL: http://www.defense.gov
Contact: David G. Bassett, Director

47584 ■ U.S. Department of Defense - Defense Contract Management Agency (DCMA)
3901 Adams Ave.
 San Diego, CA 92116
Co. E-mail: dcma.gregg-adams.hq.mbx.dcma-public-affairs@mail.mil
URL: http://www.dcma.mil
Contact: David G. Bassett, Director
Facebook: www.facebook.com/DefenseContractManagementAgency
Linkedin: www.linkedin.com/company/dcma
X (Twitter): x.com/DCMAnews

Description: DCMA directly contributes to the military readiness of the United States and its allies, and helps preserve the nation's freedom. **Founded:** 2000.

47585 ■ U.S. Department of Defense - Defense Contract Management Agency (DCMA)
3901 A Ave., Bldg. 10500
 Fort Lee, VA 23801
Co. E-mail: dcma.gregg-adams.hq.mbx.dcma-public-affairs@mail.mil
URL: http://www.dcma.mil
Contact: David G. Bassett, Director
URL(s): www.defense.gov; dcmacareers.com/index.cfm/locations/western-region-locations/dcma-santa-ana
Facebook: www.facebook.com/DefenseContractManagementAgency
Linkedin: www.linkedin.com/company/dcma
X (Twitter): x.com/DCMAnews

Description: DCMA provides advice and information to help construct effective solicitations, identify potential risks, select the most capable contractors, and write contracts that meet the needs of our customers. **Founded:** 2000.

47586 ■ U.S. Department of Defense - Defense Contract Management Agency APO East Hartford
130 Darlin St.
 East Hartford, CT 06108
Ph: (860)291-7930
URL: http://www.dcmacareers.com/index-cfm/locations/eastern-region-locations1/dcma-apo-east-hartford

47587 ■ U.S. Department of Defense - Defense Contract Management Agency Baltimore
MD
URL: http://www.dcma.mil/About/Contact-Us

Description: DCMA monitors contractors' performance and management systems to ensure that cost, product performance, and delivery schedules are in compliance with the terms and conditions of the contracts.

47588 ■ U.S. Department of Defense - Defense Contract Management Agency Garden City
605 Stewart Ave.
 Garden City, NY 11530
Ph: (516)228-5717
URL: http://www.dcmacareers.com/index-cfm/locations/eastern-region-locations1/dcma-garden-city

Description: Contributes to the military readiness of the United States and its allies, and helps preserve the nation's freedom in Garden City.

47589 ■ U.S. Department of Defense - Defense Contract Management Agency Orlando
Orlando, FL
URL: http://www.dcma.mil

Description: Contributes to the military readiness of the United States and its allies, and helps preserve the nation's freedom.

47590 ■ U.S. Department of Defense - Defense Contract Management Agency St. Louis
1222 Spruce St.
 Saint Louis, MO 63103
Ph: (314)331-5432
URL: http://www.dcmacareers.com

Description: Provides a broad range of contract-procurement management services for American army.

47591 ■ U.S. Department of Defense - Defense Contract Management Agency San Diego
7675 Dagget St.
 San Diego, CA 92111
Ph: (858)495-7401
URL: http://www.dcmacareers.com/index-cfm/locations/western-region-locations/dcma-san-diego

Description: Contributes to the military readiness of the United States and its allies, and helps preserve the nation's freedom in San Diego.

47592 ■ U.S. Department of Defense - Defense Contract Management Agency Syracuse (DCMA)
615 Erie Blvd. W
Syracuse, NY 13204-2483
Ph: (315)423-8589
URL: http://www.dcmacareers.com/index-cfm/loca tions/eastern-region-locations1/dcma-syracuse
Description: Contributes to the military readiness of the United States and its allies, and helps preserve the nation's freedom in Syracuse.

47593 ■ U.S. Department of Defense - Defense Contract Management Area Operations
URL: http://www.dcma.mil
Contact: David G. Bassett, Director

47594 ■ U.S. Department of Defense - Defense Contract Management Area Operations
Syracuse, NY
URL: http://www.dcma.mil/Contact-Us/Division_O

47595 ■ U.S. Department of Defense (DOD) - Defense Information Systems Agency (DISA)
VA
URL: http://www.disa.mil
Contact: Robert J. Skinner, Director
Facebook: www.facebook.com/USdisa
Linkedin: www.linkedin.com/company/ defenseinformationsystemsagency
Description: Engaged in information sharing and communication across the Department of Defense.
Founded: 1960.

47596 ■ U.S. Department of Defense - Defense Information Systems Agency - Office of Small Business Programs (OSBP)
URL: http://disa.mil/about/small-business

47597 ■ U.S. Department of Defense - Defense Logistics Agency - Defense Supply Center (DSCC)
401 N Yearling Ave.
Columbus, OH 43213
URL: http://www.dla.mil/Land-and-Maritime/About/ Locations/Columbus
Founded: 1962.

47598 ■ U.S. Department of Defense - Defense Logistics Agency - Defense Supply Center Philadelphia (DSCP)
700 Robbins Ave.
Philadelphia, PA 19111-5092
Ph: (215)737-7209
Co. E-mail: dscc.partssupport@dla.mil
URL: http://www.dla.mil/Land-and-Maritime/Offers/ Technical-Support/Document-Standards/Parts -Management
Description: Covers activities for GSA, Public Building Services (Philadelphia, PA), Army Corps of Engineers (Philadelphia, PA), Defense Personnel Support Center-Clothing & Textile (Philadelphia, PA), Defense Personnel Support Center-Medical (Philadelphia, PA), Defense Personnel Support Center-Subsistence (Philadelphia, PA). **Founded:** 1952.

47599 ■ U.S. Department of Defense - Defense Threat Reduction Agency - Office of Small and Disadvantaged Business Utilization
8725 John J. Kingman Hwy.
Fort Belvoir, VA 22060-6201
Ph: (703)767-7889
URL: http://www.dtra.mil/Contracts/Small-Businesses
Founded: 1946.

47600 ■ U.S. Department of Defense - Office of Small Business Programs
201 12th St., Ste. 406
Arlington, VA 22202
Ph: (703)601-3848
URL: http://www.acq.osd.mil/osbp/offices/index.shtml
Contact: Shannon Jackson, Director

Description: One of the primary objectives of the Department of Defense (DOD) is to acquire weapons and materials that fully meet qualitative, quantitative, and delivery requirements at the lowest overall cost.

47601 ■ U.S. Department of Defense (DOD) - Office of Small Business Programs (OSBP)
4800 Mark Ctr. Dr., Ste. 15G13
Alexandria, VA 22311
Ph: (571)372-6191
Co. E-mail: osd.business.defense@mail.mil
URL: http://business.defense.gov
Contact: Kasey Diaz, Director
Description: One of the primary objectives of the Department of Defense (DOD) is to acquire weapons and materials that fully meet qualitative, quantitative, and delivery requirements at the lowest overall cost. Maximum emphasis is placed on full and free competition to achieve this objective, with equal opportunity to all interested, qualified suppliers to compete for defense contracts. The Department of Defense's military departments and defense agencies have contracting offices located throughout the United States. Each department and agency has an office of the director of small and disadvantaged business utilization. They also have small business specialists at each of their procurement and contract administration offices to assist small and disadvantaged businesses, women-owned businesses, minority-owned businesses, and firms to market their products and services with the DOD. These specialists can provide information and guidance on defense procurement procedures, placement on the solicitation mailing lists, and identification of both prime and subcontract opportunities.

47602 ■ U.S. Department of Education - Office of the Deputy Secretary - Office of Small and Disadvantaged Business Utilization (OSDBU)
Potomac Ctr., Plz., Rm. 10115 550 12th St. SW
Washington, DC 20202
Ph: (202)245-6300
Co. E-mail: small.business@ed.gov
URL: http://www2.ed.gov/about/offices/list/ods/osdbu .html
Contact: Calvin Mitchell, Jr., Director
E-mail: calvin.mitchell@ed.gov
Description: The Department of Education solicits proposals for the following services and materials: management consulting; program evaluation or surveys; computer-based projects; student testing materials; plus other professional services. In addition, federal funds may be used by schools, state agencies, and other recipients for the purchase of audiovisual and other types of equipment. Inquiries should be made to the applicable organization. The department also provides various publications to aid small businesses in their dealings. These publications include A Guide to U.S. Department of Education Programs. This annual guide provides the information necessary to begin the process of applying for funding from individual federal education programs. Another publication is Doing Business With the Department of Education. This guide is designed to provide business firms, small businesses, small disadvantaged businesses, and small disadvantaged subcontractors with basic information on contracting opportunities with the Department of Education. A "Forecast of Contract Opportunities" is also available listing upcoming contracts, which is distributed by the OSDBU office. **Founded:** 1980.

47603 ■ U.S. Department of the Navy - Office of the Secretary of the Navy - Office of Small Business Programs (OSBP)
1000 Navy PentagonRm 4D652
Washington, DC 20350-2000
Ph: (202)685-6485
Co. E-mail: osbp.pao@navy.mil
URL: http://www.secnav.navy.mil/smallbusiness/ Pages/programs.aspx
Facebook: www.facebook.com/NAVYOSBP
X (Twitter): x.com/DoN_OSBP
YouTube: www.youtube.com/channel/UCulftV56j 4jspsLAvPe_XqQ

47604 ■ U.S. Missile Defense Agency (MDA)
Bldg. 245
5700 18th St.
Fort Belvoir, VA 22060-5573
Co. E-mail: mda.info@mda.mil
URL: http://www.mda.mil
Contact: Heath A. Collins, Director
Founded: 2002.

U.S. DEPARTMENT OF EDUCATION

47605 ■ U.S. Department of Education - Office of the Deputy Secretary - Office of Small and Disadvantaged Business Utilization (OSDBU)
Potomac Ctr., Plz., Rm. 10115 550 12th St. SW
Washington, DC 20202
Ph: (202)245-6300
Co. E-mail: small.business@ed.gov
URL: http://www2.ed.gov/about/offices/list/ods/osdbu .html
Contact: Calvin Mitchell, Jr., Director
E-mail: calvin.mitchell@ed.gov
Description: The Department of Education solicits proposals for the following services and materials: management consulting; program evaluation or surveys; computer-based projects; student testing materials; plus other professional services. In addition, federal funds may be used by schools, state agencies, and other recipients for the purchase of audiovisual and other types of equipment. Inquiries should be made to the applicable organization. The department also provides various publications to aid small businesses in their dealings. These publications include A Guide to U.S. Department of Education Programs. This annual guide provides the information necessary to begin the process of applying for funding from individual federal education programs. Another publication is Doing Business With the Department of Education. This guide is designed to provide business firms, small businesses, small disadvantaged businesses, and small disadvantaged subcontractors with basic information on contracting opportunities with the Department of Education. A "Forecast of Contract Opportunities" is also available listing upcoming contracts, which is distributed by the OSDBU office. **Founded:** 1980.

47606 ■ University of Delaware (UD) - Library
210 S College Ave.
Newark, DE 19716
Ph: (302)831-2792
Co. E-mail: socialmedia@udel.edu
URL: http://www.udel.edu
Contact: Dr. Dennis Assanis, President
E-mail: president@udel.edu
Facebook: www.facebook.com/udelaware
Linkedin: www.linkedin.com/school/university-of -delaware
X (Twitter): x.com/UDelaware
YouTube: www.youtube.com/user/UnivDelaware
Pinterest: www.pinterest.com/udelaware
Scope: Arts; English; Irish; American literature; history and Delawareana; horticulture; history of science and technology. **Services:** Interlibrary loan(limited); document delivery; circulation. **Founded:** 1743.
Publications: *The Review* (Monthly).

U.S. DEPARTMENT OF ENERGY

47607 ■ U.S. Department of Energy (US DOE) - Albuquerque Operations Office (AOO)
PO Box 5400
Albuquerque, NM 87185-5400
Free: 866-747-5994
Fax: (505)284-7512
URL: http://www.energy.gov/ig/field-offices
Contact: Christina H. Hamblen, Officer

47608 ■ U.S. Department of Energy - Amarillo Field Office
801 S Fillmore St., Ste. 500
Amarillo, TX 79101-3545
Ph: (806)356-1000

FEDERAL GOVERNMENT ASSISTANCE

Fax: (806)356-1041
Co. E-mail: blm_nm_comments@blm.gov
URL: http://www.blm.gov/office/amarillo-field-office
Contact: Sam Burton, Manager
Linkedin: www.linkedin.com/company/u-s--department-of-energy
Founded: 1980.

47609 ■ **U.S. Department of Energy (BPA) - Bonneville Power Administration - Library**
905 NE 11th Ave.
Portland, OR 97232
Ph: (503)230-3000
Free: 800-282-3713
Co. E-mail: communications@bpa.gov
URL: http://www.bpa.gov
Contact: John Hairston, Chief Executive Officer
E-mail: jlhairston@bpa.gov
Facebook: www.facebook.com/bonnevillepower
Linkedin: www.linkedin.com/company/bonnevillepower
X (Twitter): x.com/bonnevillepower
Instagram: www.instagram.com/bonnevillepower
YouTube: www.youtube.com/user/BonnevillePower
Scope: Economics; computer; geology; psychology; engineering; transmission; management. **Services:** Interlibrary loan; library open to the public. **Founded:** 1937. **Holdings:** Government documents; technical conference proceedings; photos; video archive.

47610 ■ **U.S. Department of Energy - Chicago Operations Office**
Forrestal Building 1000 Independence Ave. SW
Washington, DC 20585
URL: http://www.energy.gov/ea/argonne-national-laboratory

47611 ■ **U.S. Department of Energy - Denver Regional Office**
1617 Cole Blvd.
Golden, CO 80401
Ph: (720)356-1703
URL: http://www.energy.gov/ig/about-us/field-offices

47612 ■ **U.S. Department of Energy, Headquarters (DOE) - Office of Small and Disadvantaged Business Utilization**
1000 Independence Ave. SW, Rm. 5B-194
Washington, DC 20585
Ph: (202)586-7377
URL: http://www.energy.gov/osdbu/office-small-and-disadvantaged-business-utilization
Contact: Ron Pierce, Director
Facebook: www.facebook.com/DOEOSDBU
Linkedin: www.linkedin.com/company/us-department-of-energy-osdbu
Description: Provide maximum practicable opportunities in the Departments' acquisitions to all small business concerns. **Founded:** 2015.

47613 ■ **U.S. Department of Energy - National Energy Technology Laboratory (NETL)**
3610 Collins Ferry Rd.
Morgantown, WV 26505
Ph: (304)285-4764
Fax: (304)285-4403
URL: http://netl.doe.gov
Contact: Brian Anderson, Director
Facebook: www.facebook.com/NationalEnergyTechnologyLaboratory
Linkedin: www.linkedin.com/company/national-energy-technology-laboratory
X (Twitter): x.com/NETL_DOE
Instagram: www.instagram.com/netl_doe
YouTube: www.youtube.com/NETLMultimedia
Publications: *Crude Oil Analysis Database (COADB).*

47614 ■ **U.S. Department of Energy - National Nuclear Security Administration - Los Alamos Field Office**
Los Alamos, DC
Ph: (505)667-6691
Co. E-mail: nnsalosalamos@nnsa.doe.gov
URL: http://www.energy.gov/nnsa/locations
Contact: Theodore Wyka, Manager

47615 ■ **U.S. Department of Energy - Nevada Operations Office**
PO Box 98518
Las Vegas, NV 89193-8518
Ph: (702)295-0779
URL: http://www.energy.gov/ig/field-offices

47616 ■ **U.S. Department of Energy (US DOE) - Oak Ridge Operations Office (ORO)**
200 Administration Rd., Federal Bldg.
Oak Ridge, TN 37830
URL: http://www.energy.gov/ea/downloads/us-department-energy-oak-ridge-operations-office-nuclear-facility-safety-basis

47617 ■ **U.S. Department of Energy - Office of Energy Efficiency and Renewable Energy - Golden Field Office (GFO)**
15013 Denver W Pky.
Golden, CO 80401
Ph: (720)356-1800
URL: http://www.energy.gov/eere/golden-field-office-reading-room
Contact: Derek Passarelli, Director
Founded: 1992.

47618 ■ **U.S. Department of Energy - Office of Kansas City Natural Security Campus (KCNSC)**
14520 Botts Rd.
Kansas City, MO 64147
Ph: (816)488-2000
Co. E-mail: customer_inquiry@kcnsc.doe.gov
URL: http://kcnsc.doe.gov
Facebook: www.facebook.com/KansasCityNSC
X (Twitter): x.com/KCNSC
YouTube: www.youtube.com/channel/UCbXlyCeUQisL-vF8dXjjFaQ
Founded: 1949.

47619 ■ **U.S. Department of Energy - Office of Science - Argonne Site Office (ASO)**
9800 S Cass Ave.
Lemont, IL 60439-4801
Ph: (630)252-2000
URL: http://science.osti.gov/aso
Contact: Pete Siebach, Officer
E-mail: peter.siebach@science.doe.gov
URL(s): www.energy.gov/mailing-addresses-and-information-numbers-operations-field-and-site-offices

47620 ■ **U.S. Department of Energy - Office of Science - Brookhaven Site Office (BHSO)**
PO Box 5000
Upton, NY 11973
URL: http://science.osti.gov/bhso

47621 ■ **U.S. Department of Energy (DOE) - Office of Science - Fermi Site Office (FSO)**
PO Box 2000
Batavia, IL 60510
Ph: (630)840-3281
URL: http://www.energy.gov/mailing-addresses-and-information-numbers-operations-field-and-site-offices

47622 ■ **U.S. Department of Energy - Office of Science - Princeton Site Office (PSO)**
100 Stellarator Rd.
Princeton, NJ 08543
Ph: (609)243-3700
Fax: (609)243-2032
URL: http://science.osti.gov/pso
Linkedin: www.linkedin.com/company/u-s--department-of-energy
Description: Designated to oversee and manage the Management and Operating (M&O) contract for the Princeton Plasma Physics Laboratory (PPPL).

47623 ■ **U.S. Department of Energy - Pinellas Area Office**
7887 Bryan Dairy Rd., Ste. 260
Largo, FL 33777
Co. E-mail: public.affairs@lm.doe.gov
URL: http://www.energy.gov/lm/pinellas-county-florida-site
Founded: 1977.

47624 ■ **U.S. Department of Energy - Pittsburgh Energy Technology Center**
626 Cochran Mill Rd.
Pittsburgh, PA 15236-0940
Ph: (412)386-6000
URL: http://www.energy.gov/about-us/contact-us/mailing-addresses-national-laboratories-and-technology-centers
URL(s): www.energy.gov/node/4813231
Linkedin: www.linkedin.com/company/u-s--department-of-energy
Founded: 1977.

47625 ■ **U.S. Department of Energy - Pittsburgh Naval Reactors (PNR)**
PO Box 109
West Mifflin, PA 15122-0109
Ph: (412)476-7202
URL: http://www.energy.gov/contact-us/mailing-addresses-and-information-numbers-operations-field-and-site-offices

47626 ■ **U.S. Department of Energy - Princeton Plasma Physics Laboratory (PPPL)**
100 Stellarator Rd.
Princeton, NJ 08543-0451
Ph: (609)243-2000
Co. E-mail: pppl_communications@pppl.gov
URL: http://www.pppl.gov
Contact: Steven Cowley, Professor
E-mail: scowley@pppl.gov
Facebook: www.facebook.com/PPPLab
Linkedin: www.linkedin.com/company/princeton-plasma-physics-lab
X (Twitter): x.com/PPPLab
Instagram: www.instagram.com/ppplab
YouTube: www.youtube.com/PPPLab
Pinterest: www.pinterest.com/princetonplasma
Description: National, government-owned, contractor-operated research and development laboratory of the Department of Energy at Princeton University. **Scope:** Thermonuclear fusion for the purpose of developing a source of electrical energy that would be safe, economical, and environmentally acceptable. Laboratory activities have focused on understanding the physics and engineering aspects of low-density plasmas produced and confined by magnetic fields in toroidal systems. Although thermonuclear applications are the Laboratory's specialty, PPPL also conducts experimental, theoretical, and computer investigations in all branches of plasma physics. **Founded:** 1951. **Publications:** *Annual Highlights Report* (Annual); *PPPL Proceedings*; *PPPL Research reports.*

47627 ■ **U.S. Department of Energy - Richland Operations Office - Office of Organizational Effectiveness and Communications**
825 Jadwin Ave.
Richland, WA 99352
URL: http://www.energy.gov/ne/careers

47628 ■ **U.S. Department of Energy (SNL) - Sandia National Laboratories**
1515 Eubank Blvd. SE
Albuquerque, NM 87123
Ph: (505)844-8066
URL: http://www.sandia.gov
Contact: Harry Truman, President
Facebook: www.facebook.com/SandiaLabs
Linkedin: www.linkedin.com/company/sandia-national-laboratories
X (Twitter): x.com/SandiaLabs
Instagram: www.instagram.com/SandiaLabs
YouTube: www.youtube.com/c/SandiaGov
Description: Manufacturing and distributor of solutions for national security such as weapon components. **Scope:** Primary mission encompasses both traditional responsibilities, such as defense-related programs, energy and environmental programs, and DoD support projects, and emerging responsibilities, including advanced manufacturing efforts, transportation systems, information and computational sciences projects, and biomedical engineering initiatives. **Founded:** 1949. **Publications:** *Energy and Environment*; *Manufacturing Technology*; *Sandia Science*

News a four-page compilation of news releases; Testing Technology and Defense Programs. **Educational Activities:** SOLTECH (Annual).

47629 ■ U.S. Department of Energy - Schenectady Naval Reactors Office
PO Box 1069
  Schenectady, NY 12301-1069
URL: http://www.energy.gov/nnsa/naval-nuclear
  -laboratory-contract
Founded: 1977.

47630 ■ U.S. Department of Energy - Southeastern Power Administration (SEPA)
1166 Athens Tech Rd.
  Elberton, GA 30635-6711
Ph: (706)213-3800
Fax: (706)213-3884
Co. E-mail: info2@sepa.doe.gov
URL: http://www.energy.gov/sepa/southeastern
  -power-administration
Founded: 1950.

47631 ■ U.S. Department of Energy - Waste Isolation Pilot Plant - Carlsbad Field Office (CBFO)
4021 National Parks Hwy.
  Carlsbad, NM 88220
URL: http://wipp.energy.gov/cbfo-leadership.asp
Contact: Reinhard Knerr, Manager
URL(s): www.wipp.energy.gov/TribalProgram.htm

47632 ■ U.S. Department of Energy - Western Area Power Administration (WAPA)
PO Box 281213
  Lakewood, CO 80228-8213
Ph: (720)962-7000
Fax: (720)962-7200
Co. E-mail: mediarelations@wapa.gov
URL: http://www.wapa.gov/Pages/Western.aspx
Contact: Tracey A. LeBeau, Chief Executive Officer
Facebook: www.facebook.com/wapa.gov
Linkedin: www.linkedin.com/company/western-area
  -power-administration
YouTube: www.youtube.com/user/Wes
  ternAreaPower1
Description: Publishes educational information on conservation and renewable energy. **Founded:** 1977.

47633 ■ U.S. Department of the Interior - Bureau of Land Management - Amarillo Field Office
801 S Fillmore St., Ste. 500
  Amarillo, TX 79101-3545
Ph: (806)356-1000
Fax: (806)356-1041
Co. E-mail: blm_nm_comments@blm.gov
URL: http://www.blm.gov/office/amarillo-field-office
Contact: Sam Burton, Manager

U.S. DEPARTMENT OF HEALTH AND HUMAN SERVICES

47634 ■ Health Resources and Services Administration - Grants and Procurement Management Div. - Contracts Policies and Operations
5600 Fishers Ln.
  Rockville, MD 20857
Free: 877-464-4772
Co. E-mail: callcenter@hrsa.gov
URL: http://www.hrsa.gov/grants
Facebook: www.facebook.com/HRSAgov
Linkedin: www.linkedin.com/company/us-governmen
  t-department-of-health-&-human-services-hrsa
X (Twitter): x.com/HRSAgov
Instagram: www.instagram.com/hrsagov
YouTube: www.youtube.com/user/HRSAtube
Founded: 1982.

47635 ■ National Institutes of Health - Division of Contracts and Grants - Small and Disadvantaged Business Utilization Specialist
200 Independence Ave., S.W.Hubert Humphrey
  Bldg., Rm. 405D
  Washington, DC 20201
Ph: (202)690-7300
URL: http://www.hhs.gov/grants/grants-business-con
  tacts/small-business-staff/specialists/index.html
Contact: Shannon Jackson, Executive Director
Founded: 1979.

47636 ■ U.S. Department of Health and Human Services (HHS) - Division of Grants and Contracts - Small Business Specialist
200 Independence Ave., SW
  Washington, DC 20201
URL: http://www.hhs.gov/grants-contracts/small-busi
  ness-support/index.html
Contact: Natasha Boyce, Specialist
E-mail: natasha.boyce@hhs.gov
Description: To enhance and protect the health and well-being of all Americans. We fulfill that mission by providing for effective health and human services and fostering advances in medicine, public health, and social services.

47637 ■ U.S. Department of Health and Human Services (HHS) - Health Resources and Services Administration - Office of Equal Opportunity, Civil Rights and Diversity Management
c/o Anthony F. Archeval, Director
  5600 Fishers Ln., Rm. 14N192
  Parklawn Bldg.
  Rockville, MD 20857
Ph: (301)443-0171
Fax: (301)443-7898
Co. E-mail: aarcheval@hrsa.gov
URL: http://www.hhs.gov/about/agencies/asa/eeo/
  about-eeo/programs-offices/index.html
Contact: Anthony F. Archeval, Director
E-mail: aarcheval@hrsa.gov
Founded: 2002.

47638 ■ U.S. Department of Health and Human Services - Office of Equal Employment Opportunity (HHS)
c/o Reginald R. Mebane, Director
  1600 Clifton Rd. - Mailstop K-83
  Atlanta, GA 30333
Ph: (770)488-3210
Fax: (770)488-3195
Co. E-mail: rmebane@cdc.gov
URL: http://www.hhs.gov/about/agencies/asa/eeo/
  about-eeo/programs-offices/index.html
Contact: Reginald R. Mebane, Director
E-mail: rmebane@cdc.gov

47639 ■ U.S. Department of Health & Human Services - Office of Grants and Acquisition Policy and Accountability - Division of Acquisitions Management
200 Independence Ave. SW
  Washington, DC 20201
URL: http://www.hhs.gov/about/agencies/asfr/ogapa/
  acquisition/index.html

47640 ■ U.S. Department of Health and Human Services (OSDBU) - Office of Small and Disadvantaged Business Utilization (OSDBU)
200 Independence Ave. SW, Hubert Humphrey
  Building, Rm. 405D
  Washington, DC 20201
Ph: (202)690-7300
URL: http://www.hhs.gov/about/agencies/asfr/ogapa/
  osdbu/index.html
Contact: Shannon Jackson, Executive Director
E-mail: shannon.jackson@hhs.gov
Description: The procurement policy of the Department of Health and Human Services seeks to stimulate competition among potential contractors and to make awards on a competitive basis to the fullest degree consistent with quality, efficiency, and economy. It is the department's policy that small businesses, disadvantaged businesses, women-owned businesses, and labor-surplus area concerns receive a fair and equitable share of the contracts awarded. Procurement assistance is available from the HHS's Office of Small and Disadvantaged Business Utilization and from the small business specialists at each HHS regional office. **Founded:** 1979.

47641 ■ U.S. Department of Health and Human Services - Program Support Center - Small and Disadvantaged Business Utilization Specialist - Division of Acquisition (DA)
200 Independence Ave., SW
  Washington, DC 20201
URL: http://www.hhs.gov/about/agencies/asfr/ogapa/
  acquisition/index.html

47642 ■ U.S. Department of Health and Human Services - Region 1
JFK Federal Building, Rm. 2250Government Ctr
  Boston, MA 02203
Ph: (617)565-2370
URL: http://www.hhs.gov/ash/about-ash/regional-of
  fices/region-1/index.html
Contact: Betsy Rosenfeld, Administrator
E-mail: betsy.rosenfeld@hhs.gov
Description: Serves Connecticut, Maine, Massachusetts, New Hampshire, Rhode Island, and Vermont. **Founded:** 2002.

47643 ■ U.S. Department of Health and Human Services - Region 2
Jacob K. Javits Federal Bldg.
  26 Federal Plz., Ste. 3835
  New York, NY 10278
Ph: (212)264-4600
URL: http://www.hhs.gov/about/agencies/iea/regional
  -offices/region-2/index.html
Contact: Joseph Salvador Palm, Regional Director
E-mail: hhsreg2@hhs.gov
X (Twitter): x.com/HHSRegion2
Description: Serves New Jersey, New York, Puerto Rico, and the Virgin Islands.

47644 ■ U.S. Department of Health and Human Services - Region 3
150 S Independence Mall W, Ste. 436
  Philadelphia, PA 19106
Ph: (215)861-4633
Fax: (215)861-4625
Co. E-mail: region3oash@hhs.gov
URL: http://www.hhs.gov/ash/about-ash/regional-of
  fices/region-3/index.html
Contact: Dr. Dalton Paxman, Administrator
E-mail: dalton.paxman@hhs.gov
X (Twitter): x.com/hhsregion3
Description: Serves Delaware, the District of Columbia, Maryland, Pennsylvania, Virginia, and West Virginia.

47645 ■ U.S. Department of Health and Human Services - Region 4
61 Forsyth St. SW
  Atlanta, GA 30303-8909
Free: 800-368-1019
Fax: (202)619-3818
Co. E-mail: ocrmail@hhs.gov
URL: http://www.hhs.gov/ash/about-ash/regional-of
  fices/region-4/index.html
Contact: Dr. John W. Gilford, Administrator
E-mail: john.gilford@hhs.gov
Description: Serves Alabama, Florida, Georgia, Kentucky, Mississippi, North Carolina, South Carolina, and Tennessee.

47646 ■ U.S. Department of Health and Human Services - Region 5
233 N Michigan Ave., Ste. 240
  Chicago, IL 60601
Ph: (312)353-5160
Fax: (312)353-4144
URL: http://www.hhs.gov/about/agencies/iea/regional
  -offices/region-5/index.html
Contact: Mildred Hunter, Analyst
E-mail: mildred.hunter@hhs.gov
X (Twitter): x.com/hhsregion5
Description: Serves Illinois, Indiana, Michigan, Minnesota, Ohio, and Wisconsin.

47647 ■ U.S. Department of Health and Human Services - Region 6
1301 Young St., Ste. 1124
  Dallas, TX 75202
Ph: (214)767-3301

Fax: (214)767-3617
URL: http://www.hhs.gov/about/agencies/iea/regional-offices/region-6/index.html
X (Twitter): x.com/hhsregion6
Description: Serves Arkansas, Louisiana, New Mexico, Oklahoma, and Texas.

47648 ■ U.S. Department of Health and Human Services - Region 7
601 E 12th St. Rm. 353
Kansas City, MO 64106
Ph: (816)426-2821
URL: http://www.hhs.gov/ash/about-ash/regional-offices/region-7/index.html
Contact: Kimberly Davids, Administrator
E-mail: kimberly.davids@hhs.gov
X (Twitter): x.com/hhsregion7
Description: Serves Iowa, Kansas, Missouri, and Nebraska.

47649 ■ U.S. Department of Health and Human Services - Region 8
1961 Stout St., Rm. 08-148
Denver, CO 80294
Ph: (303)844-3372
Fax: (303)293-0512
Co. E-mail: hhsregion8ord@hhs.gov
URL: http://www.hhs.gov/about/agencies/iea/regional-offices/region-8/index.html
Contact: Lily Griego, Regional Director
E-mail: lily.griego@hhs.gov
X (Twitter): x.com/hhsregion8
Description: Serves Colorado, Montana, North Dakota, South Dakota, Utah, and Wyoming.

47650 ■ U.S. Department of Health and Human Services - Region 9
90 7th St., Ste. 4-500
San Francisco, CA 94103
Ph: (415)437-8500
URL: http://www.hhs.gov/about/agencies/iea/regional-offices/region-9/index.html
Contact: Jeffrey Reynoso, Director
E-mail: region9ord@hhs.gov
X (Twitter): x.com/hhsregion9
Description: Serves Arizona, California, Guam, Hawaii, Nevada, and the Trust Territory of the Pacific Islands.

47651 ■ U.S. Department of Health and Human Services - Region 10
701 5th Ave., Ste. 1600
Seattle, WA 98104
Ph: (206)615-2010
Fax: (206)615-2087
URL: http://www.hhs.gov/about/agencies/iea/regional-offices/region-10/index.html
Contact: Priya A. Helweg, Deputy Regional Director
X (Twitter): x.com/hhsregion10
Description: Serves Alaska, Idaho, Oregon, and Washington.

47652 ■ U.S. Food and Drug Administration - Division of Contracts and Grants Management - Office of Management (OM)
White Oak Bldg. 51, Rm. 5134,10903 New Hampshire Ave.
Silver Spring, MD 20903
Ph: (301)796-3300
Co. E-mail: cderomimmediateoffice@fda.hhs.gov
URL: http://www.fda.gov
Description: Government develops and implements cost effective Center management policies and programs concerning financial and human resource management and many more.

47653 ■ U.S. Food and Drug Administration - Office of Acquisitions and Grants Services - Office of Regional Operations
7500 Standish Pl.
Rockville, MD 20855
URL: http://www.fda.gov/about-fda/fda-organization/steven-solomon
Contact: Dr. Steven M. Solomon, Director
Description: Provides food and drug services.
Founded: 1848.

47654 ■ U.S. Social Security Administration - Office of Acquisitions and Grants - Small and Disadvantaged Business Utilization Specialist
c/o Leslie Ford, Director
1540 Robert M. Ball Bldg., 6401 Security Blvd.
Baltimore, MD 21244
Ph: (410)594-0111
Fax: (410)965-2965
Co. E-mail: smallbusiness@ssa.gov
URL: http://www.ssa.gov/osdbu
Contact: Leslie Ford, Director

U.S. DEPARTMENT OF HOUSING AND URBAN DEVELOPMENT

47655 ■ U.S. Department of Housing and Urban Development - Deputy Assistant Secretary for Economic Development - Grants Management Div.
451 7th St. SW
Washington, DC 20410
URL: http://www.hud.gov/program_offices/cfo/gmomgmt
Contact: Dorthera Yorkshire, Director

47656 ■ U.S. Department of Housing and Urban Development - Office of the Chief Procurement Officer (OCPO)
451 7th St. SW
Washington, DC 20410
URL: http://www.hud.gov/program_offices/cpo

47657 ■ U.S. Department of Housing and Urban Development - Office of Departmental Operations and Coordination (ODOC)
451 7th St. SW
Washington, DC 20410
URL: http://www.hud.gov/about/acronyms
Contact: Craig T. Clemmensen, Director

47658 ■ U.S. Department of Housing and Urban Development - Office of Security and Emergency Planning
451 7th St. SW
Washington, DC 20410
Ph: (202)708-1112
URL: http://www.hud.gov
Contact: Dr. Ben Carson, Sr., Secretary
Facebook: www.facebook.com/HUD
X (Twitter): x.com/hudgov
YouTube: www.youtube.com/user/HUDchannel

47659 ■ U.S. Department of Housing and Urban Development (HUD) - Office of Small and Disadvantaged Business Utilization (OSDBU)
451 7th St., Rm 2200 (SS)
Washington, DC 20410-1000
Ph: (202)402-5477
Free: 800-877-8339
Fax: (202)401-6930
Co. E-mail: smallbusiness@hud.gov
URL: http://www.hud.gov/smallbusiness
Contact: Jean Lin Pao, Director
E-mail: jean.lin.pao@hud.gov
Description: The Department of Housing and Urban Development purchases supplies and services to repair and provide housing management services for the properties it acquires, as well as to fulfill its logistical, administrative, and programmatic requirements. Private contractors, including small and disadvantaged firms, are awarded contracts based on bids that they submit to appropriate HUD offices or area managers. HUD encourages and facilitates the participation of small business firms, minority business firms, and firms located in labor-surplus areas. Activities are carried out through a network of field offices. HUD also encourages small business firms to participate in its research and demonstration programs, as the majority of competitively awarded contracts and assistance agreements have been granted to small businesses.

47660 ■ U.S. Department of Housing and Urban Development - Region 1
c/o Thomas P. O'Neill, Jr.
Federal Bldg. Rm. 370, Field Office, 10 Cswy., St.
Boston, MA 02222
Ph: (617)994-8380
URL: http://www.hudoig.gov/about-hud-oig/contacts-locations
Contact: Thomas P. O'Neill, Jr., Contact
Description: Administers field offices in Connecticut, Maine, Massachusetts, New Hampshire, Rhode Island, and Vermont.

47661 ■ U.S. Department of Housing and Urban Development - Region 2
Jacob K. Javits Federal Bldg.
26 Federal Plz., Rm. 3430
New York, NY 10278
Ph: (212)264-4174
Fax: (212)264-1400
URL: http://www.hudoig.gov/about-hud-oig/contacts-locations
Description: Administers field offices in New Jersey and New York.

47662 ■ U.S. Department of Housing and Urban Development - Region 3
100 Penn Square E
Philadelphia, PA 19107
Ph: (215)656-0500
URL: http://www.hudoig.gov/about-hud-oig/contacts-locations
Description: Administers field offices in Delaware, the District of Columbia, Maryland, Pennsylvania, Virginia, and West Virginia.

47663 ■ U.S. Department of Housing and Urban Development - Region 4
Five Points Plz. Bldg.
40 Marietta St.
Atlanta, GA 30303
Ph: (404)331-5136
Fax: (404)730-2392
URL: http://www.hud.gov/states/shared/working/r4
Description: Administers field offices in Alabama, Florida, Georgia, Kentucky, Mississippi, North Carolina, Puerto Rico, South Carolina, Tennessee, and the Virgin Islands.

47664 ■ U.S. Department of Housing and Urban Development - Region 5
77 W, Jackson Blvd.
Chicago, IL 60604
Ph: (312)913-8499
Fax: (312)353-8866
URL: http://www.hudoig.gov
Contact: Kudakwashe Ushe, Chief Information Officer
Description: Administers field offices in Illinois, Indiana, Michigan, Minnesota, Ohio, and Wisconsin.

47665 ■ U.S. Department of Housing and Urban Development - Region 6
307 W 7th St., Ste. 1000
Fort Worth, TX 76102
Ph: (817)978-5600
Fax: (202)485-9113
URL: http://www.hud.gov/program_offices/field_policy_mgt/regions
Contact: Jerlinda Banks, Director
E-mail: jerlinda.d.banks@hud.gov
Description: Administers field offices in Arkansas, Louisiana, New Mexico, Oklahoma, and Texas.

47666 ■ U.S. Department of Housing and Urban Development - Region 7
400 State Ave., Rm. 200
Kansas City, KS 66101-2406
Ph: (913)551-5462
Fax: (913)551-5469
URL: http://www.hud.gov/states/kansas/offices
Contact: Ulysses Clayborn, Administrator
E-mail: regionaladministratorkansascity@hud.gov
Description: Administers field offices in Iowa, Kansas, Missouri, and Nebraska.

47667 ■ U.S. Department of Housing and Urban Development - Region 8 (HUD)
1670 Broadway
Denver, CO 80202-4801
URL: http://www.hud.gov/states/shared/working/viiiregstaff
Description: Administers field offices in Colorado, Montana, North Dakota, South Dakota, Utah, and Wyoming.

47668 ■ U.S. Department of Housing and Urban Development - Region 9 (HUD)
One Sansome St.
San Francisco, CA 94104
Ph: (415)489-6400
Fax: (415)489-6701
URL: http://www.hudoig.gov/location/san-francisco-ca
Description: Administers field offices in the American Samoa, Arizona, California, Guam, Hawaii, and Nevada.

47669 ■ U.S. Department of Housing and Urban Development - Region 10
400 NW Gilman Blvd.
Issaquah, WA 98027
Ph: (206)220-5380
URL: http://www.hudoig.gov/about/where-were-located
Description: Administers field offices in Alaska, Idaho, Oregon, and Washington.

U.S. DEPARTMENT OF THE INTERIOR

47670 ■ Bureau of Indian Affairs - Business Utilization and Development Specialist - Aberdeen Area Office
1849 C St., NW
Washington, DC 20240
Ph: (202)208-5116
Fax: (202)208-6334
URL: http://www.bia.gov/bia

47671 ■ Bureau of Indian Affairs - Business Utilization and Development Specialist - Albuquerque Area Office
1001 Indian School Rd. NW
Albuquerque, NM 87104
Ph: (505)563-3103
Fax: (505)563-3101
URL: http://www.bia.gov/regional-offices/southwest

47672 ■ Bureau of Indian Affairs - Business Utilization and Development Specialist - Anadarko Area Office
Hwy. 281 N & Parker McKenzie Rd.
Anadarko, OK 73005
Ph: (405)247-6677
Fax: (405)247-3942
URL: http://www.bia.gov/regional-offices/southern-plains/anadarko-agency
Contact: Sidney M. Carney, Director
URL(s): www.bia.gov/as-ia/opa/online-press-release/indian-bureau-names-director-anadarko-area-office

47673 ■ Bureau of Indian Affairs - Business Utilization and Development Specialist - Billings Area Office
2021 4th Ave. N
Billings, MT 59101
Ph: (406)247-7943
Fax: (406)247-7976
URL: http://www.bia.gov/regional-offices/rocky-mountain

47674 ■ Bureau of Indian Affairs - Business Utilization and Development Specialist - Minneapolis Area Office
1849 C St., NW
Washington, DC 20240
URL: http://www.bia.gov/as-ia/opa/online-press-release/bia-minneapolis-area-director-appointed

47675 ■ Bureau of Indian Affairs - Business Utilization and Development Specialist - Muskogee Area Office
3100 W Peak Blvd.
Muskogee, OK 74401
Ph: (918)781-4600
Fax: (918)781-4604
URL: http://www.bia.gov/regional-offices/eastern-oklahoma-region

47676 ■ Bureau of Indian Affairs - Business Utilization and Development Specialist - Phoenix Area Office
2600 N Central Ave., 4th Fl.
Phoenix, AZ 85004
Ph: (602)379-6600
Fax: (602)379-4139
URL: http://www.bia.gov/regional-offices/western

47677 ■ Bureau of Indian Affairs - Business Utilization and Development Specialist - Portland Area Office
911 NE 11th Ave.
Portland, OR 97232-4169
Ph: (503)231-6702
Fax: (503)231-2201
URL: http://www.bia.gov/regional-offices/northwest

47678 ■ Bureau of Indian Affairs - Business Utilization and Development Specialist - Sacramento Area Office
2800 Cottage Way
Sacramento, CA 95825
URL: http://www.bia.gov/regional-offices/pacific

47679 ■ Bureau of Ocean Energy Management - Alaska OCS Region
3801 Centerpoint Dr., Ste. 500
Anchorage, AK 99503
Ph: (907)334-5200
URL: http://www.boem.gov/regions/alaska-ocs-region
Contact: Michael Haller, Liaison
E-mail: michael.haller@boem.gov

47680 ■ Bureau of Ocean Energy Management (POR) - Pacific OCS Region
760 Paseo Camarillo, Ste. 102
Camarillo, CA 93010
Ph: (805)384-6305
Free: 855-320-1484
URL: http://www.boem.gov/regions/pacific-ocs-region
Contact: Douglas Boren, Regional Director
E-mail: douglas.boren@boem.gov

47681 ■ National Park Service - Business Utilization and Development Specialist - Outdoor Recreation Information Center
319 Second Ave. S
Seattle, WA 98104
URL: http://www.nps.gov/klse/learn/management/seattle-area-national-park-sites.htm

47682 ■ National Park Service - Business Utilization and Development Specialist - Pacific Northwest Region
c/o Billy Shott, Regional, Director
National Pk. Service, 333 Bush St., Ste. 500
San Francisco, CA 94104-2828
Ph: (415)623-2100
URL: http://www.nps.gov/aboutus/contactinformation.htm
Contact: Billy Shott, Regional Director
Founded: 1916.

47683 ■ Office of Aircraft Services - Business Utilization and Development Specialist - Division of Contracting
c/o Kevin Fox, Regional Director
4405 Lear Ct.
Anchorage, AK 99502-1032
Ph: (907)271-3700
Fax: (907)271-4788
URL: http://www.doi.gov/aviation/akro
Contact: Kevin Fox, Regional Director

47684 ■ Office of Surface Mining Reclamation and Enforcement (OSMRE) - Appalachian Regional Office
3 Pky., Ctr.
Pittsburgh, PA 15220
URL: http://www.osmre.gov/about/offices
Contact: Thomas Shope, Regional Director

47685 ■ U.S. Department of the Interior - Bureau of Indian Affairs - Eastern Regional Office
545 Marriott Dr., Ste. 700
Nashville, TN 37214
Ph: (615)564-6500
Fax: (615)564-6701
Co. E-mail: eastern.inquiries@bia.gov
URL: http://www.bia.gov/regional-office/eastern-region
Founded: 1824.

47686 ■ U.S. Department of the Interior - Bureau of Indian Affairs - Juneau Office
709 W 9th St.
Juneau, AK 99802
Ph: (907)586-7177
Free: 800-645-8397
Fax: (907)586-7252
URL: http://www.bia.gov/regional-offices/alaska/juneau-office

47687 ■ U.S. Department of the Interior - Bureau of Indian Affairs - Navajo Regional Office
301 W Hill St.
Gallup, NM 87301
Ph: (505)863-8314
Fax: (505)863-8324
URL: http://www.bia.gov/regional-offices/navajo-region
Contact: Gregory C. Mehojah, Regional Director
Founded: 1824.

47688 ■ U.S. Department of the Interior - Bureau of Land Management - Alaska State Office
222 W 7th Ave., Ste. 13
Anchorage, AK 99513
Ph: (907)271-5960
Fax: (907)271-3684
Co. E-mail: blm_ak_akso_public_room@blm.gov
URL: http://www.blm.gov/office/alaska-state-office
Contact: Steve Cohn, Director
E-mail: blm_ak_state_director@blm.gov
Facebook: www.facebook.com/BLMAlaska
X (Twitter): x.com/BLMAlaska
YouTube: www.youtube.com/user/BLMALASKA

47689 ■ U.S. Department of the Interior - Bureau of Land Management - Arizona State Office
One N Central Ave., Ste. 800
Phoenix, AZ 85004-4427
Ph: (602)417-9200
Fax: (602)417-9556
Co. E-mail: blm_az_asoweb@blm.gov
URL: http://www.blm.gov/office/arizona-state-office
Contact: Raymond Suazo, Director
Description: Publishes directories. **Founded:** 1814.

47690 ■ U.S. Department of the Interior - Bureau of Land Management - Business Utilization and Development Specialist - Branch of Procurement Management
1849 C St. NW, Rm. 5665
Washington, DC 20240
Ph: (202)208-3801
Fax: (202)208-5242
URL: http://www.blm.gov
Contact: Michael Nedd, Assistant Director
E-mail: mnedd@blm.gov
Facebook: www.facebook.com/BLMNational
X (Twitter): x.com/BLMNational
Description: To sustain the health, diversity, and productivity of the public lands for the use and enjoyment of present and future generations. **Founded:** 1946.

47691 ■ U.S. Department of the Interior - Bureau of Land Management - California State Office
2800 Cottage Way, Ste. W1623
  Sacramento, CA 95825
Ph: (916)978-4400
Fax: (916)978-4416
Co. E-mail: blm_ca_web_so@blm.gov
URL: http://www.blm.gov/office/california-state-office
Contact: Karen Mouritsen, Director
E-mail: castatedirector@blm.gov
Facebook: www.facebook.com/blmcalifornia
X (Twitter): x.com/BLMca
Description: To sustain the health, diversity, and productivity of public lands for the use and enjoyment of present and future generations.

47692 ■ U.S. Department of the Interior - Bureau of Land Management - Colorado State Office
Denver Federal Ct., Bldg. 40
  Lakewood, CO 80225
Ph: (303)239-3600
Fax: (303)239-3933
Co. E-mail: blm_co_info@blm.gov
URL: http://www.blm.gov/office/colorado-state-office
Contact: Doug Vilsack, Director
E-mail: blm_co_statedirector@blm.gov
Facebook: www.facebook.com/BLMColorado
X (Twitter): x.com/BLM_CO
YouTube: www.youtube.com/user/BLMCOLORADO

47693 ■ U.S. Department of the Interior (BLM) - Bureau of Land Management - Eastern States Office
5275 Leesburg Pke.
  Falls Church, VA 22041
Ph: (703)558-7754
Fax: (703)558-2258
Co. E-mail: blm_es_inquiries@blm.gov
URL: http://www.blm.gov/eastern-states
Contact: Mitchell Leverette, Director

47694 ■ U.S. Department of the Interior - Bureau of Land Management - Idaho State Office
1387 S Vinnell Way
  Boise, ID 83709
Ph: (208)373-4000
Fax: (208)373-3899
Co. E-mail: blm_id_stateoffice@blm.gov
URL: http://www.blm.gov/idaho
Contact: Karen Kelleher, Director
Facebook: www.facebook.com/BLMIdaho
X (Twitter): x.com/blmidaho
YouTube: www.youtube.com/user/BLMIDAHO

47695 ■ U.S. Department of the Interior - Bureau of Land Management - Montana State Office
5001 Southgate Dr.
  Billings, MT 59101
Ph: (406)896-5004
Fax: (406)896-5298
Co. E-mail: blm_mt_so_information@blm.gov
URL: http://www.blm.gov/office/montanadakotas-state-office
Contact: Sonya Germann, Director

47696 ■ U.S. Department of the Interior - Bureau of Land Management - Nevada State Office
1340 Financial Blvd.
  Reno, NV 89502
Ph: (775)861-6500
Fax: (775)861-6606
Co. E-mail: blm_nv_nvso_web_mail@blm.gov
URL: http://www.blm.gov/office/nevada-state-office
Contact: Jon Raby, Director
Facebook: www.facebook.com/BLMNevada
X (Twitter): x.com/blmnv
YouTube: www.youtube.com/user/BLMNEVADA
Founded: 1812.

47697 ■ U.S. Department of the Interior (NMSO) - Bureau of Land Management - New Mexico State Office
301 Dinosaur Trl.
  Santa Fe, NM 87508
Ph: (505)954-2000
Fax: (505)954-2010
Co. E-mail: blm_nm_comments@blm.gov
URL: http://www.blm.gov/office/new-mexico-state-office
Contact: Melanie Barnes, Director
E-mail: blm_nm_comments@blm.gov
Facebook: www.facebook.com/BLMNewMexico
X (Twitter): x.com/BLMNewMexico
YouTube: www.youtube.com/channel/UC27T9eDfe8iM-q9-4I8fBEA

47698 ■ U.S. Department of the Interior (BLM) - Bureau of Land Management - Oregon State Office
1220 SW 3rd Ave.
  Portland, OR 97204
Ph: (503)808-6001
Fax: (503)808-6422
Co. E-mail: blm_or_so_land_office_mail@blm.gov
URL: http://www.blm.gov/office/oregonwashington-state-office
Contact: Barry Bushue, Director

47699 ■ U.S. Department of the Interior - Bureau of Land Management - Utah State Office
440 W 200 S, Ste. 500
  Salt Lake City, UT 84101
Ph: (801)539-4001
Fax: (801)539-4237
Co. E-mail: blm_ut_so_public_room@blm.gov
URL: http://www.blm.gov/office/utah-state-office
Contact: Matt Preston, Deputy Director
E-mail: mpreston@blm.gov
Founded: 2012.

47700 ■ U.S. Department of the Interior - Bureau of Land Management - Wyoming State Office
5353 Yellowstone Rd.
  Cheyenne, WY 82009
Ph: (307)775-6256
Fax: (307)775-6129
Co. E-mail: blm_wy_copywork@blm.gov
URL: http://www.blm.gov/office/wyoming-state-office
Contact: Andrew Archuleta, Director

47701 ■ U.S. Department of the Interior (GPR) - Bureau of Reclamation - Business Utilization and Development Specialist - Great Plains Region
2021 4th Ave. N
  Billings, MT 59101
URL: http://www.usbr.gov/gp

47702 ■ U.S. Department of the Interior - Bureau of Reclamation - Business Utilization and Development Specialist - Lower Colorado Region
500 Fir St.
  Boulder City, NV 89005-2403
Ph: (702)293-8421
Co. E-mail: sha-lcr-webcomments@usbr.gov
URL: http://www.usbr.gov/lc/region
Contact: Jacklynn Gould, Regional Director
Description: Provides procurement, financial assistance, and Government purchase card support for Reclamation offices in Arizona, southern Nevada and Southern California.

47703 ■ U.S. Department of the Interior - Bureau of Reclamation - Business Utilization and Development Specialist - Mid-Pacific Region
c/o Ernest Conant, Regional Director
  Region 10 Office
  Federal Office Bldg.
  2800 Cottage Way
  Sacramento, CA 95825-1898
Founded: 1942.

47704 ■ U.S. Department of the Interior (PNR) - Bureau of Reclamation - Business Utilization and Development Specialist - Pacific Northwest Region
1150 N Curtis Rd.
  Boise, ID 83706-1234
Ph: (208)378-6231
Fax: (208)378-5019
Co. E-mail: pninfo@usbr.gov
URL: http://www.usbr.gov/pn
Contact: Roland Springer, Regional Director

47705 ■ U.S. Department of the Interior - Bureau of Reclamation - Business Utilization and Development Specialist - Phoenix Area Office
6150 W Thunderbird Rd.
  Glendale, AZ 85306-4001
Ph: (623)773-6200
Fax: (623)773-6480
URL: http://www.usbr.gov/lc/phoenix
Contact: Alexander B. Smith, Manager
Description: To manage, develop, and protect water and related resources in an environmentally and economically sound manner in the interest of the American public.

47706 ■ U.S. Department of the Interior - Bureau of Reclamation - Business Utilization and Development Specialist - Upper Colorado Region
125 S State St., Rm. 8100
  Salt Lake City, UT 84138-1147
URL: http://www.usbr.gov/uc/aboutus
Contact: Wayne Pullan, Regional Director

47707 ■ U.S. Department of the Interior - Bureau of Reclamation - Management Services Office - Acquisition and Assistance Management Div. (AAMD)
c/o Diana Terrell Denver Federal Center
  6th & Kipling, Bldg. 56
  Denver, CO 80225
Ph: (303)445-2349
Co. E-mail: dterrell@usbr.gov
URL: http://www.usbr.gov/mso/aamd/index.html
Contact: Diana Terrell, Manager
E-mail: dterrell@usbr.gov

47708 ■ U.S. Department of the Interior - National Park Service - Alaska Region
c/o Sarah Creachbaum, Regional Director
  National Pk. Service, 240 W 5th Ave., Ste. 114
  Anchorage, AK 99501
Ph: (907)644-3510
URL: http://www.nps.gov/aboutus/contactinformation.htm
Contact: Sarah Creachbaum, Regional Director

47709 ■ U.S. Department of the Interior - National Park Service - Intermountain Region
PO Box 25287
  Denver, CO 80225-0287
URL: http://www.nps.gov/subjects/nationalhistoriclandmarks/contact-the-national-historic-landmarks-program-intermountain-region.htm

47710 ■ U.S. Department of the Interior - National Park Service - Midwest Region
c/o Bert Frost, Regional Director
  601 Riverfront Dr.
  Omaha, NE 68102-4226
Ph: (402)661-1736
Fax: (402)661-1982
URL: http://www.nps.gov/aboutus/contactinformation.htm
Contact: Bert Frost, Regional Director
Facebook: www.facebook.com/MidwestNationalParks
X (Twitter): x.com/MidwestNPS

47711 ■ U.S. Department of the Interior - National Park Service - National Capitol Regional Office
1100 Ohio Dr., SW
  Washington, DC 20242
Ph: (202)619-7020

URL: http://www.nps.gov/orgs/1465/whatwedo.htm

47712 ■ U.S. Department of the Interior (US DIO-NPS) - National Park Service - Northeast Region
1234 Market St., 20th Fl.
Philadelphia, PA 19107
Ph: (215)597-5814
URL: http://www.nps.gov/subjects/nationalhistoriclandmarks/contact-the-national-historic-landmarks-program-northeast-region.htm
Contact: Gay Vietzke, Regional Director

47713 ■ U.S. Department of the Interior - National Park Service - Pacific West Region
1849 C St. NW
Washington, DC 20240
URL: http://www.doi.gov/ocl/pacific-northwest-parks

47714 ■ U.S. Department of the Interior - National Park Service - Southeast Region
75 Ted Turner Dr. SW, Ste. 304
Atlanta, GA 30303-3311
Ph: (404)331-5600
URL: http://www.doi.gov/solicitor/southeast-region

47715 ■ U.S. Department of the Interior - Office of Small and Disadvantaged Business Utilization
Main Interior Bldg., Ms. 4214
1849 C St. NW
Washington, DC 20240
Ph: (202)208-3493
Fax: (202)208-7444
Co. E-mail: doi_osdbu@ios.doi.gov
URL: http://www.doi.gov/pmb/osdbu
Contact: Colleen Finnegan, Director

Description: The Department of the Interior's Small and Disadvantaged Business Program provides counseling and advice to small, women-owned, and minority-owned businesses on opportunities in the department. The program helps the bureaus and offices of the department in their efforts to increase contracting opportunities for such businesses. (This applies to direct contracting and subcontracting opportunities as well as to the Small Business Administration's programs.) For instance, the department's Bureau of Land Management sets aside certain commodities and services for procurement from small businesses. This bureau also conducts a lottery to allow the public the opportunity to purchase land. The Bureau of Indian Affairs provides technical assistance to Native American and tribal businesses on reservations for the establishment of enterprises, the preparation of economic development plans, the development of educational and residential facilities, and related undertakings. Furthermore, the department provides various publications that assist small business and small and disadvantaged business concerns with contracting opportunities. The Department of the Interior also hosts an annual Small Business Procurement Fair, which provides contact between the department's acquisition officials and small businesses.

47716 ■ U.S. Department of the Interior - Office of the Solicitor
1849 C St. NW
Washington, DC 20240
Ph: (202)208-4423
URL: http://www.doi.gov/solicitor
Contact: Robert Anderson, Contact
Founded: 1849.

47717 ■ U.S. Department of the Interior - Office of Surface Mining Reclamation and Enforcement (OSMRE) - Mid-Continent Regional Office (MCR)
501 Belle St.
Alton, IL 62002-6169
Ph: (618)463-6460
Fax: (618)463-6470
URL: http://www.osmre.gov/programs/technical-innovation-and-professional-services/training

47718 ■ U.S. Department of the Interior - Office of Surface Mining Reclamation and Enforcement - Western Regional Office
One Denver Federal Center, Ste.41
Lakewood, CO 80225

47719 ■ U.S. Fish and Wildlife Service - Alaska Region
1011 E Tudor Rd.
Anchorage, AK 99503
Ph: (907)786-3431
Co. E-mail: tewosret_vaughn@fws.gov
URL: http://www.fws.gov/about/region/alaska
Facebook: www.facebook.com/USFWSAlaska
X (Twitter): x.com/USFWSAlaska
Instagram: www.instagram.com/usfws
Description: Serves to preserve and protect wildlife in Alaska.

47720 ■ U.S. Fish and Wildlife Service - Budget and Administration Div. - Region 5 - Northeast Regional Office
300 Westgate Center Dr.
Hadley, MA 01035
Ph: (413)253-8200
URL: http://www.fws.gov/about/region/northeast
Contact: Kyla Hastie, Regional Director
Facebook: www.facebook.com/usfwsnortheast
X (Twitter): x.com/usfwsnortheast
Founded: 1940.

47721 ■ U.S. Fish and Wildlife Service (CGS) - Business Utilization and Development Specialist - Division of Contracting and General Services
1875 Century Blvd. NE, 3rd Fl.
Atlanta, GA 30345-3391
URL: http://www.fws.gov/cfm

47722 ■ U.S. Fish and Wildlife Service - Contracting & General Services Chief - Alaska Region
1011 E Tudor Rd.
Anchorage, AK 99503
Ph: (907)786-3431
URL: http://www.fws.gov/office/alaska-region-headquarters
Contact: Greg Siekaniec, Regional Director
Description: Recover endangered species; assess and conserve native fish and wildlife populations.
Founded: 1871.

47723 ■ U.S. Fish and Wildlife Service - Contracting & General Services Chief - Region 4
1875 Century Blvd.
Atlanta, GA 30345
Ph: (404)679-4000
URL: http://www.fws.gov/program/southeast-region
Contact: Mike Oetker, Regional Director
URL(s): www.fws.gov/endangered/regions/index.html
Founded: 1871.

47724 ■ U.S. Fish and Wildlife Service - Contracting & General Services Officer - Region 2
500 Gold Ave. SW
Albuquerque, NM 87103
Ph: (505)248-6911
URL: http://www.fws.gov/about/region/southwest
Contact: Amy Lueders, Regional Director
E-mail: rdlueders@fws.gov

47725 ■ U.S. Fish and Wildlife Service - Contracting Officer - Region 6
134 Union Blvd.
Lakewood, CO 80228
URL: http://www.fws.gov/about/region/mountain-prairie
Contact: Matt Hogan, Regional Director

47726 ■ U.S. Fish and Wildlife Service - Contracting & Procurement Officer - Region 3
5600 American Blvd. W, Ste. 990
Bloomington, MN 55437-1458
Ph: (612)713-5436
Co. E-mail: permitsr3mb@fws.gov
URL: http://www.fws.gov/program/migratory-bird-permit/contact-us
Founded: 1940.

47727 ■ U.S. Fish and Wildlife Service - Division of Contracting and General Services
Lake Plaza N
134 Union Blvd.
Lakewood, CO 80228-1807
URL: http://www.fws.gov/offices/directory/OfficeDetail.cfm?OrgCode=60181

47728 ■ U.S. Fish and Wildlife Service - Midwest Region (https://www.fws.gov/midwest/)
5600 American Blvd. W, Ste. 990
Bloomington, MN 55437-1458
Ph: (612)713-5360
Co. E-mail: midwestnews@fws.gov
URL: http://www.fws.gov/midwest
Contact: Charles Wooley, Regional Director
Facebook: www.facebook.com/USFWSMidwest
X (Twitter): x.com/usfwsmidwest
Founded: 1940.

47729 ■ U.S. Fish and Wildlife Service - Mountain Prairie Region
c/o Matt Hogan, Regional Director
134 Union Blvd., Ste. 400
Lakewood, CO 80225
Ph: (303)236-7920
URL: http://www.fws.gov/office/mountain-prairie-region-headquarters
Contact: Matt Hogan, Regional Director
Founded: 1956.

47730 ■ U.S. Fish and Wildlife Service - Northeast Region
300 Westgate Center Dr.
Hadley, MA 01035
Ph: (413)253-8200
URL: http://www.fws.gov/about/region/northeast
Contact: Wendi Weber, Regional Director
Facebook: www.facebook.com/usfwsnortheast
X (Twitter): x.com/usfwsnortheast
Founded: 1940.

47731 ■ U.S. Fish and Wildlife Service - Pacific Region
911 NE 11th Ave.
Portland, OR 97232
Ph: (503)231-6120
URL: http://www.fws.gov/program/pacific-region
Contact: Hugh Morrison, Regional Director
URL(s): www.fws.gov/about/region/pacific

47732 ■ U.S. Fish and Wildlife Service - Policy, Management and Budget - Great Lakes, Big Rivers Region
1 Federal Dr.
Fort Snelling, MN 55111
Ph: (612)713-5360
Fax: (612)713-5287
Co. E-mail: midwestnews@fws.gov
URL: http://www.fws.gov/wetlands/nwi/rwc3.html
Contact: Lori Nordstrom, Regional Director
E-mail: lori_nordstrom@fws.gov

47733 ■ U.S. Fish and Wildlife Service - Procurement Assistant - Region 1
911 NE 11th Ave.
Portland, OR 97232-4181
Ph: (503)231-6151
URL: http://www.fws.gov/program/endangered-species

47734 ■ U.S. Fish and Wildlife Service - Southeast Region
1875 Century Blvd.
Atlanta, GA 30345
Ph: (404)679-4000
URL: http://www.fws.gov/about/region/southeast
Contact: Martha Williams, Director
Facebook: www.facebook.com/usfwssoutheast
X (Twitter): x.com/usfwssoutheast

FEDERAL GOVERNMENT ASSISTANCE

47735 ■ U.S. Fish and Wildlife Service - Southwest Region
500 Gold Ave. SW
Albuquerque, NM 87103-1306
Ph: (505)248-6911
Fax: (505)248-6788
Co. E-mail: permitsr2es@fws.gov
URL: http://www.fws.gov/about/region/southwest
Contact: Amy Lueders, Regional Director
E-mail: rdlueders@fws.gov

47736 ■ U.S. Geological Survey - Business Utilization and Development Specialist
345 Middlefield Rd.
Menlo Park, CA 94025
Fax: (650)329-5203
Co. E-mail: askcalvo@usgs.gov
URL: http://www2.usgs.gov/contracts/USGS-SmallBus.html

47737 ■ U.S. Geological Survey - Central Region
Denver Federal Ctr., Bldg., 67
Denver, CO 80225-0046
URL: http://www.usgs.gov/media/images/central-region-management-conference
Description: Offers geologic Information about the Central Region states. Founded: 1977.

U.S. DEPARTMENT OF JUSTICE

47738 ■ Federal Bureau of Prisons - Acquisition Offices - Administration Division
320 First St., NW
Washington, DC 20534
URL: http://www.bop.gov/about/agency/org_adm.jsp
Contact: Randall C. Burleson, Assistant Director
Description: Responsible for the Bureau's financial and facility management.

47739 ■ U.S. Department of Justice - Federal Bureau of Investigation - Seattle Div.
1110 3rd Ave.
Seattle, WA 98101-2904
Ph: (206)622-0460
URL: http://www.fbi.gov/contact-us/field-offices/seattle
Founded: 1914.

47740 ■ The United States Department of Justice - Federal Bureau of Prisons - National Contracts and Policy Section
320 1st St. NW, 6th Fl.
Washington, DC 20534
Ph: (202)307-3067
URL: http://www.justice.gov/osdbu/contact-doj-representative

47741 ■ U.S. Department of Justice - Justice Management Div. - Procurement Services Staff (PSS)
Two Constitution Sq., 145 N St. NE, Ste. 8E.300
Washington, DC 20002
Ph: (202)307-2000
Fax: (202)307-1931
URL: http://www.justice.gov/jmd/procurement-services-staff
Description: Provides acquisition support to the Department's Offices, Boards and Divisions (OBDs). Founded: 1870.

47742 ■ U.S. Department of Justice - Office of Small and Disadvantaged Business Utilization
950 Pennsylvania Ave. NW
Washington, DC 20530
Ph: (202)616-0521
Fax: (202)616-1717
URL: http://www.justice.gov/osdbu
Contact: Bob Connolly, Director
Description: The Department of Justice's Office of Small and Disadvantaged Business Utilization develops and implements appropriate outreach programs aimed at heightening the awareness of the small business community to the contracting opportunities available within the department. Outreach efforts include activities such as sponsoring small business fairs and procurement conferences, and participating in trade group seminars, conventions, and other forums that promote the utilization of small businesses as contractors. The office also provides counseling and advice to inquiring small businesses regarding their possible eligibility for special consideration under preferential purchasing programs that the department employs.

47743 ■ U.S. Drug Enforcement Administration - Office of Acquisition and Relocation Management
8701 Morrissette Dr.
Springfield, VA 22152
Co. E-mail: deasmallbusinessprogram@dea.gov
URL: http://www.dea.gov/resources/doing-business-dea
Founded: 1973.

47744 ■ U.S. Federal Prisons Industries/UNICOR - Procurement Branch
PO Box 11849
Lexington, KY 40578-1849
Free: 800-827-3168
URL: http://www.unicor.gov/contracting.aspx
Contact: Linda Kerr, Officer
E-mail: lkerr@central.unicor.gov

47745 ■ U.S. Marshals Service - Procurement Policy and Oversight Team
FSD - Office of Procurement
2604 Jefferson Davis Hwy., 9th Fl. CS-3
Alexandria, VA 22301
Ph: (202)353-9126
Co. E-mail: officeof.procurementhelpdesk@usdoj.gov
URL: http://www.usmarshals.gov
Contact: Donald W. Washington, Director

U.S. DEPARTMENT OF LABOR

47746 ■ Delaware Department of Labor - Office of Occupational and Labor Market Information (OOLMI)
4425 N Market St.
Wilmington, DE 19802
URL: http://labor.delaware.gov/divisions/oolmi
Description: Provides information regarding employment levels, unemployment rates, wages and earnings, employment projections, jobs, training resources, and careers.

47747 ■ Department of Labor - Labor Market Information - Research and Statistics Div.
1001 N 23rd St.
Baton Rouge, LA 70804-9094
Fax: (225)219-7759
Co. E-mail: oois@lwc.la.gov
URL: http://www.laworks.net/PublicRelations/PR_Contacts.asp
Contact: Ava Cates, Secretary

47748 ■ Department of Labor - Workforce Information and Analysis
223 Courtland St. NE, Ste. 200
Atlanta, GA 30303
URL: http://dol.georgia.gov/view-workforce-information
Description: Collects, analyzes, and publishes a wide array of information about the state's labor market to provide a snapshot of Georgia's economy, job market, businesses, and its workforce.

47749 ■ Florida Agency of Economic Opportunity - Labor Market Statistics - State Census Data Center
111 W Madison St., Ste. 574
Tallahassee, FL 32399-6588
Ph: (850)487-1402
URL: http://www.census.gov
Description: Provides them with market intelligence, trade counseling, business matchmaking, and advocacy/commercial diplomacy support in West Virginia.

47750 ■ Georgia Department of Labor - Labor Market Information
c/o Mark Watson, Director
148 International Blvd., NE
Atlanta, GA 30303-1751
Ph: (404)232-3875
Fax: (404)232-3888
Co. E-mail: mark.watson@gdol.ga.gov
URL: http://www.bls.gov/bls/ofolist.htm
Contact: Mark Watson, Director
E-mail: mark.watson@gdol.ga.gov
Description: Collects, analyzes, and publishes a wide array of information about the state's labor market to provide a snapshot of Georgia's economy, job market, businesses, and its workforce.

47751 ■ Louisiana Workforce Commission - Media Relations
PO Box 94094
Baton Rouge, LA 70804
Ph: (225)342-3035
Co. E-mail: lwcpio@lwc.la.gov
URL: http://www.laworks.net/PublicRelations/PR_Contacts.asp

47752 ■ Louisiana Workforce Commission - Office of Management & Finance - Tax Accounting/Adjustments Unit
PO Box 94186
Baton Rouge, LA 70804-9186
Free: 833-708-2866
URL: http://www2.laworks.net/PublicRelations/PR_Contacts.asp
Founded: 1913.

47753 ■ Louisiana Workforce Commission (LMI) - Research and Statistics Division - Labor Market Information
1001 N 23rd St.
Baton Rouge, LA 70804-9094
Fax: (225)219-7759
Co. E-mail: oois@lwc.la.gov
URL: http://www.laworks.net/LaborMarketInfo/LMI_MainMenu.asp

47754 ■ U.S. Census Bureau - Florida Department of Economic Opportunity - Labor Market Statistics - State Census Data Center
107 E Madison St.
Tallahassee, FL 32399-4111
Ph: (850)245-7291
Fax: (850)245-7201
URL: http://www.census.gov/sdc/flsdc.html
Contact: Steven Dillingham, Director
Facebook: www.facebook.com/uscensusbureau
X (Twitter): twitter.com/uscensusbureau
Instagram: www.instagram.com/uscensusbureau
YouTube: www.youtube.com/user/uscensusbureau
Founded: 1902.

47755 ■ U.S. Department of Labor - Bureau of Labor Statistics (BLS)
2 Massachusetts Ave. NE
Washington, DC 20212-0001
Ph: (202)691-5200
Co. E-mail: blsdata_staff@bls.gov
URL: http://www.bls.gov
Contact: Amrit Kohli, Director
E-mail: kohli.amrit@bls.gov
X (Twitter): x.com/BLS_gov
YouTube: www.youtube.com/channel/UCijn3WBpHtx4AvSya7NER9Q
Description: The Bureau of Labor Statistics is the principal fact-finding agency for the Federal Government in the broad field of labor economics and statistics. Scope: Principal data gathering agency of the federal government for labor economics issues. Data are compiled from voluntary responses to surveys of businesses or households conducted by BLS, the Bureau of the Census (on a contract basis), or in conjunction with other cooperating state and federal agencies. Founded: 1884. Holdings: More than 230,000 summary data series are stored in the Bureau's computer-readable LABSTAT (Labor Statistics) Data Base. Publications: *Career Outlook* (Quarterly); *Occupational Earnings and Wage Trends in Metropolitan Areas*; *Occupational Outlook Hand-*

book; *Compensation and Working Conditions*; *CPI Detailed Report* (Monthly); *Employment and Earnings*; *Monthly Labor Review (MLR)*; *Bargaining Calendar* (Annual); *PPI Detailed Report* (Monthly). **Awards:** ASA/NSF/BLS Fellowships (Annual); Lawrence R. Klein Award (Annual).

47756 ■ U.S. Department of Labor - Office of Small and Disadvantaged Business Utilization (OSDBU)
200 Constitution Ave., NW
Washington, DC 20210
Free: 888-972-7332
URL: http://www.dol.gov/agencies/oasam/centers-offices/office-of-the-senior-procurement-executive/office-of-small-and-disadvantaged-business-utilization

Description: Emphasizes development of small and disadvantaged business utilization in contract and grant activities, promotes interaction with Historically Black Colleges and Universities and Hispanic and other minority colleges and universities, and has management oversight responsibility for Department of Labor advisory committees. **Founded:** 1913.

U.S. DEPARTMENT OF STATE

47757 ■ U.S. Department of State - Bureau of Diplomatic Security (DSS) - Office of Foreign Missions (OFM)
2201 C St. NW, Rm. 2236
Washington, DC 20520
Ph: (202)647-3417
URL: http://www.state.gov/ofm
Contact: Cliff Seagroves, Deputy Director Principal
Facebook: www.facebook.com/ofmdc

Description: The Office of Foreign Missions (OFM) provides the legal foundation to facilitate secure and efficient operations of U.S. missions abroad, and of foreign missions and International organizations in the United States. **Founded:** 1982.

47758 ■ U.S. Department of State Office of Civil Rights (S/OCR)
2201 C St., NW
Washington, DC 20520
Ph: (202)647-9294
Fax: (202)647-4969
Co. E-mail: socr_direct@state.gov
URL: http://www.state.gov/bureaus-offices/secretary-of-state/office-of-civil-rights
Contact: Gregory B. Smith, Director

47759 ■ U.S. Department of State Office of the Inspector General (OIG)
SA-39, 1700 N Moore St.
Arlington, VA 22209
Co. E-mail: oighotline@state.gov
URL: http://www.stateoig.gov
Contact: Diana R. Shaw, Inspector General
Linkedin: www.linkedin.com/company/stateoig
X (Twitter): x.com/StateOIG
YouTube: www.youtube.com/channel/UCBS6MoW1EPKEfEeILKXWgjw

Description: Publishes directories. NUM. **Publications:** *Telephone Directory--Department of State*; *Employees of Diplomatic Missions* (Quarterly); *U.S. Department of State Bulletin: The Official Record of U.S. Foreign Policy* (Monthly); *Handbook and Directory of Consular Services* (Biennial); *Your Trip Abroad* (Irregular). **Awards:** OIG Safe Driving Award (Annual); Leamon R. Hunt Award for Management Excellence (Annual).

47760 ■ U.S. Department of State - Office of Small and Disadvantaged Business Utilization (OSDBU)
OSDBU, SA-6, Rm. L500
Washington, DC 20522
Ph: (703)875-6822
Co. E-mail: smallbusiness@state.gov
URL: http://www.state.gov/bureaus-offices/office-of-small-and-disadvantaged-business-utilization
Contact: George Price, Director

Description: Provides to the small business community training and counseling about doing business with the Department of State in order to expand the base of small business firms selling to the Department.

U.S. DEPARTMENT OF TRANSPORTATION

47761 ■ U.S. Department of Transportation - Federal Aviation Administration - Small Business Innovative Research (SBIR)
1200 New Jersey Ave., SE
Washington, DC 20590
URL: http://www.transportation.gov/briefing-room/usdot-awards-2-million-12-small-businesses-csai-initiative

Description: Seeks to encourage the initiative of the private sector and to use small businesses as effectively as possible in meeting Federal research and development objectives.

47762 ■ U.S. Department of Transportation (USDOT) - Federal Aviation Administration - Small Business Utilization Office
1200 New Jersey Ave. SE, W56-485
Washington, DC 20590
Ph: (202)366-1930
Free: 800-532-1169
Fax: (202)366-7228
Co. E-mail: dot-osdbu@dot.gov
URL: http://www.transportation.gov/osdbu
Contact: Shelby M. Scales, Director

47763 ■ U.S. Department of Transportation - Federal Highway Administration - Central Federal Lands Highway Div.
12300 W Dakota Ave.
Lakewood, CO 80228
Co. E-mail: cfl.fhwa@dot.gov
URL: http://www.transportation.gov/procurement-office-info/fhwa-central-federal-lands-highway-division

47764 ■ U.S. Department of Transportation - Federal Highway Administration - Eastern Federal Lands Highway Div. - Small and Disadvantaged Business Utilization Liaison
1200 New Jersey Ave. SE W56-485
Washington, DC 20590
Ph: (202)366-1930
Free: 800-532-1169
Fax: (202)366-7228
URL: http://www.transportation.gov/osdbu
Contact: Shelby M. Scales, Director

47765 ■ U.S. Department of Transportation - Federal Highway Administration - Office Federal Lands Highway (FLH)
1200 New Jersey Ave. SE
Washington, DC 20590
URL: http://highways.dot.gov/federal-lands
Contact: Curtis Scott, Chief Engineer

47766 ■ U.S. Department of Transportation (WFLHD) - Federal Highway Administration - Office of Federal Lands Highway - Western Federal Lands Highway Div.
610 E 5th St.
Vancouver, WA 98661
Ph: (360)619-7700
Fax: (360)619-7846
Co. E-mail: wfl.fhwa@dot.gov
URL: http://highways.dot.gov/federal-lands/about/contacts
Contact: Kevin McLaury, Division Director

47767 ■ U.S. Department of Transportation - Federal Highway Administration - Office of Small Disadvantaged Business Utilization - Procurement Assistance Division - Small Business Specialist
1200 New Jersey Ave. SE W56-485
Washington, DC 20590
URL: http://www.transportation.gov/osdbu/procurement-assistance/talk-dot-small-business-specialist

47768 ■ U.S. Department of Transportation - John A. Volpe National Transportation Center - Office of Management Services - Contracts and Small Business Programs Branch
c/o Mary E Doherty, Director
55 Broadway
Cambridge, MA 02142
Ph: (617)494-2669
Co. E-mail: mary.doherty@dot.gov
URL: http://www.volpe.dot.gov/about-us/mary-e-doherty
Contact: Mary E. Doherty, Director, Acquisitions
E-mail: mary.doherty@dot.gov

47769 ■ U.S. Department of Transportation - John A. Volpe National Transportation Systems Center - Research and Innovative Technology Administration - Contracts and Small Business Branch
Volpe National Transportation Systems Ctr., 55 Broadway Kendall Sq.
Cambridge, MA 02142
Ph: (617)494-2669
URL: http://www.volpe.dot.gov/about-us/mary-e-doherty
Contact: Mary E. Doherty, Director
E-mail: mary.doherty@dot.gov
Linkedin: www.linkedin.com/company/volpe-the-national-transportation-systems-center
X (Twitter): x.com/VolpeUSDOT
YouTube: www.youtube.com/user/volpecenter
Founded: 1998.

47770 ■ U.S. Department of Transportation - Maritime Administration - Virtual Office of Acquisition
1200 New Jersey Ave. SE
Washington, DC 20590
URL: http://www.maritime.dot.gov/about-us/marad-business-services-products

Description: Provide you with all pertinent information regarding the agency's acquisition programs, including access to announcements/business opportunities, program-specific registration, links to applicable regulations and sites, and Questions and Answers previously asked.

47771 ■ U.S. Department of Transportation - Office of Research and Technology
1200 New Jersey Ave. SE
Washington, DC 20590
Co. E-mail: usdotresearch.info@dot.gov
URL: http://www.transportation.gov/administrations/assistant-secretary-research-and-technology/office-research-development-technology-0
Facebook: www.facebook.com/USDOTResearch
X (Twitter): x.com/Research_USDOT

47772 ■ U.S. Department of Transportation - Office of Small and Disadvantaged Business Utilization (OSDBU)
1200 New Jersey Ave. SE, W56-485
Washington, DC 20590
Ph: (202)366-1930
Free: 800-532-1169
Fax: (202)366-7228
Co. E-mail: dot-osdbu@dot.gov
URL: http://www.transportation.gov/osdbu
Contact: Shelby M. Scales, Director

Description: The DOT's Office of Small and Disadvantaged Business Utilization provides policy direction for minority, women-owned, and small and disadvantaged business enterprise participation in direct procurement and federal financial assistance activities. It also is responsible for conducting programs directed at encouraging, promoting, and assisting disadvantaged business enterprises in securing contracts, subcontracts, and projects generated by these activities. The office schedules presentations for firms to present their capabilities to the procurement and program staff and monitors all procurement activities for disadvantaged business enterprises by the department, its grantees, and recipients nationwide. All proposed procurements are reviewed for the participation of small business. When possible, specific procurements are set aside exclusively for small business competition.

47773 ■ U.S. Department of Transportation - Office of Small and Disadvantaged Business Utilization - Procurement Assistance Div.
1200 New Jersey Ave. SE
 Washington, DC 20590
Ph: (202)366-1930
Free: 800-532-1169
Fax: (202)366-7228
URL: http://www.transportation.gov/osdbu/
 procurement-assistance

47774 ■ U.S. Department of Transportation - Pipeline and Hazardous Materials Safety Administration
1200 New Jersey Ave. SE
 Washington, DC 20590
Ph: (202)366-4109
Free: 800-467-4922
Fax: (202)366-3666
URL: http://www.phmsa.dot.gov
Contact: Howard McMillan, Executive Director
Linkedin: www.linkedin.com/company/pipeline-an
 d-hazardous-materials-safety-administration
X (Twitter): x.com/PHMSA_DOT
YouTube: www.youtube.com/user/PHMSADOT
Founded: 2004.

47775 ■ U.S. Department of Transportation - St. Lawrence Seaway Development Corporation - Office of the Associate Administrator
1200 New Jersey Ave. SE W62-300
 Washington, DC 20590
URL: http://www.seaway.dot.gov/about/meet-our
 -team
Founded: 1954.

47776 ■ U.S. Department of Transportation - Small Business Specialist - Federal Transit Administration
c/o LaStar Matthews
 1200 New Jersey Ave. SE
 Washington, DC 20590
Ph: (202)366-8552
Free: 877-877-6280
Co. E-mail: lastar.matthews@dot.gov
URL: http://www.transportation.gov/osdbu/
 procurement-assistance/talk-dot-small-business
 -specialist
Contact: LaStar Matthews, Specialist
E-mail: lastar.matthews@dot.gov
URL(s): www.fta.dot.gov
Facebook: www.facebook.com/FTADOT
Linkedin: www.linkedin.com/company/dot-federal
 -transit-administration
X (Twitter): x.com/FTA_DOT
Instagram: www.instagram.com/federaltransitadminis
 tration
YouTube: www.youtube.com/channel/UC5gSHRnW
 3K_kIgD4On061sg
Founded: 1964.

47777 ■ U.S. Department of Transportation - Small Business Specialist - Office of Acquisition
c/o Barakat Shakir
 1200 New Jersey Ave. SE
 Washington, DC 20590
Ph: (202)366-1229
Co. E-mail: barakat.shakir@dot.gov
URL: http://www.transportation.gov/osdbu/
 procurement-assistance/talk-dot-small-business
 -specialist
Contact: Barakat Shakir, Contact
E-mail: barakat.shakir@dot.gov

47778 ■ U.S. Department of Transportation (FRA) - Small Business Specialist - Office of Small Disadvantaged Business Utilization - Procurement Assistance Division - Federal Railroad Administration
1200 New Jersey Ave. SE
 Washington, DC 20590
Ph: (202)493-6024
Fax: (202)493-6481
Co. E-mail: frapa@dot.gov
URL: http://railroads.dot.gov
Contact: Michael Lestingi, Executive Director
Facebook: www.facebook.com/USDOTFRA
Linkedin: www.linkedin.com/company/federal-railroa
 d-administration
X (Twitter): x.com/USDOTFRA
YouTube: www.youtube.com/user/usdotfra
Founded: 1966.

U.S. DEPARTMENT OF THE TREASURY

47779 ■ U.S. Department of Homeland Security Customs and Border Protection
1300 Pennsylvania Ave. NW
 Washington, DC 20229
Ph: (202)325-8000
URL: http://www.cbp.gov
Contact: Troy A. Miller, Commissioner
Facebook: www.facebook.com/CBPgov
Linkedin: www.linkedin.com/company/customs-an
 d-border-protection
X (Twitter): x.com/cbp
Instagram: www.instagram.com/cbpgov
YouTube: www.youtube.com/user/customsborderpro
 tect
Description: Procures search/detection equipment, data processing services, computer related services, computer programming, uniforms, construction, computer equipment, personal/household goods, repair/maintenance, administrative/general management consulting, investigative services, computer systems design, schools/instruction, security guards, and facilities support services. Provides news releases and fact sheets on border patrol initiatives.
Founded: 1924. **Publications:** *ACS Interface Development Resource Directory*.

47780 ■ U.S. Department of Homeland Security - Federal Law Enforcement Training Center (FLETC)
1131 Chapel Crossing Rd.
 Glynco, GA 31524
Ph: (912)267-2100
Co. E-mail: fletcadmissions@fletc.dhs.gov
URL: http://www.fletc.gov
Contact: Thomas J. Walters, Director
Facebook: www.facebook.com/fletc
X (Twitter): x.com/FLETC
Instagram: www.instagram.com/fletc
YouTube: www.youtube.com/c/Fe
 deralLawEnforcementTrainingCenters
Founded: 1970.

47781 ■ U.S. Department of Homeland Security - Federal Law Enforcement Training Center Glynco (FLETC)
1131 Chapel Crossing Rd.
 Brunswick, GA 31525
URL: http://www.fletc.gov
Contact: Benjamine C. Huffman, Director
Facebook: www.facebook.com/fletc
X (Twitter): x.com/FLETC
Instagram: www.instagram.com/fletc
YouTube: www.youtube.com/c/Fe
 deralLawEnforcementTrainingCenters
Founded: 1970.

47782 ■ U.S. Department of Homeland Security - U.S. Secret Service - Procurement Div.
245 Murray Dr. SW, Bldg. 410, Rm. 3523-28
 Washington, DC 20528
URL: http://www.dhs.gov/small-business-specialists
Description: Procures computer equipment, computer facilities management, passenger car leasing, software, computer systems design, telecommunications, custom computer programming, hardware manufacturing, computer repair, and janitorial services. **Founded:** 2002.

47783 ■ U.S. Department of the Treasury - Acquisition Management
1500 Pennsylvania Ave., NW
 Washington, DC 20220
URL: http://home.treasury.gov/about/offices/
 management
Founded: 1789.

47784 ■ U.S. Department of the Treasury - Alcohol and Tobacco Tax and Trade Bureau
1310 G St. NW
 Washington, DC 20005
URL: http://www.ttb.gov
Contact: Christina McMahon, Chief Counsel
Founded: 2003.

47785 ■ U.S. Department of the Treasury - Bureau of Engraving & Printing - Office of Acquisitions
14th & C St. SW, Rm. 705-A
 Washington, DC 20228
URL: http://www.moneyfactory.gov/counterfeitde
 terrence.html
Contact: Charles Strickland, Contact
Description: Directs all BEP acquisition activities including the award and administration of contracts for research and development, architectural and engineering services.

47786 ■ U.S. Department of the Treasury - Bureau of Engraving and Printing Washington
14th & C St. SW
 Washington, DC 20228
Ph: (202)874-3188
Free: 800-456-3408
Fax: (202)874-3232
Co. E-mail: moneyfactory.info@bep.gov
URL: http://www.bep.gov
Contact: Charlene Williams, Director (Acting)
Facebook: www.facebook.com/USMoneyfactory
Linkedin: www.linkedin.com/company/bureau-of-en
 graving-and-printing
X (Twitter): x.com/BEPgov
Instagram: www.instagram.com/bepgov
YouTube: www.youtube.com/user/usmoneyfactory
Founded: 1862.

47787 ■ U.S. Department of the Treasury - Bureau of the Public Debt
1500 Pennsylvania Ave., NW
 Washington, DC 20220
URL: http://home.treasury.gov/about/bureaus

47788 ■ U.S. Department of the Treasury - Chicago Financial Center
Chicago, IL
URL: http://www.irs.gov/pub/irs-utl/6209_Section%20
 6_2014.pdf

47789 ■ U.S. Department of the Treasury - Federal Law Enforcement Training Center (FLETC)
2000 Bainbridge Ave.
 North Charleston, SC 29405
Ph: (843)566-8551
URL: http://www.fletc.gov
Contact: Benjamine C. Huffman, Director
Facebook: www.facebook.com/fletc
X (Twitter): x.com/FLETC
Instagram: www.instagram.com/fletc
YouTube: www.youtube.com/c/Fe
 deralLawEnforcementTrainingCenters
Founded: 1970.

47790 ■ U.S. Department of the Treasury - Federal Law Enforcement Training Center (FLETC)
9000 Commo Rd.
 Clinton, MD 20735
Ph: (301)868-5830
URL: http://www.fletc.gov/cheltenham-maryland
Contact: Benjamine C. Huffman, Director
Facebook: www.facebook.com/fletc
X (Twitter): x.com/FLETC
Instagram: www.instagram.com/fletc

YouTube: www.youtube.com/c/Fe
deralLawEnforcementTrainingCenters
Description: Provides career-long training to law enforcement professionals to help them fulfill their responsibilities safely and proficiently. **Founded:** 1970.

47791 ■ U.S. Department of the Treasury (FLETC) - Federal Law Enforcement Training Center
1717 H St. NW, 7th Fl. No. 16
Washington, DC 20006
Ph: (202)233-0260
Fax: (202)233-0258
URL: http://www.fletc.gov
Instagram: www.instagram.com/fletc
YouTube: www.youtube.com/c/Fe
deralLawEnforcementTrainingCenters
Founded: 1970.

47792 ■ U.S. Department of the Treasury - Financial Management Service
Liberty Center Bldg. 401, 14th St., SW
Washington, DC 20227
Ph: (202)874-6950
URL: http://www.fms.treas.gov/aboutfms/index.html
Contact: Bernadine Stewart, Contact
Facebook: www.facebook.com/ustreasury
X (Twitter): twitter.com/USTreasury
Founded: 2012.

47793 ■ U.S. Department of the Treasury Internal Revenue Service - Detroit Computing Center
985 Michigan Ave.
Detroit, MI 48226
URL: http://www.emporis.com/buildings/118544/irs-detroit-computing-center-detroit-mi-usa

47794 ■ U.S. Department of the Treasury Internal Revenue Service (ECCMTB) - Enterprise Computing Center - Martinsburg
240 Murall Dr.
Kearneysville, WV 25430
URL: http://www.irs.gov/irm/part3/irm_03-030-127

47795 ■ U.S. Department of the Treasury - Internal Revenue Service - Mid-States Area
1045-NDAL, 9th Fl.
4050 Alpha Rd.
Dallas, TX 75244-4203
URL: http://home.treasury.gov/policy-issues/small-business-programs/small-and-disadvantaged-business-utilization/bureau-small-business-specialists
Contact: Hassan Villalba, Specialist
E-mail: hassan.a.villalba@irs.gov
Description: Serves Oklahoma, Texas, Arkansas, Kansas, Missouri, Illinois, Nebraska, Iowa, Wisconsin, Minnesota, North Dakota, and South Dakota. This office also supports the IRS Service Centers in Austin, TX, Kansas City, MO, and Ogden, UT.

47796 ■ U.S. Department of the Treasury (MSR) - Internal Revenue Service - Mid-States Region
c/o Anthony McCoy, Chief Procurement Officer
1045-NDAL
4050 Alpha Rd., 9th Fl.
Dallas, TX 75244-4203
Ph: (469)801-0780
URL: http://home.treasury.gov/policy-issues/small-business-programs/small-and-disadvantaged-business-utilization/bureau-small-business-specialists
Contact: Anthony McCoy, Chief Procurement Officer
Description: Serves Oklahoma, Texas, Arkansas, Kansas, Missouri, Illinois, Nebraska, Iowa, Wisconsin, Minnesota, North Dakota, and South Dakota. This office also supports the IRS Service Centers in Austin, TX, Kansas City, MO, and Ogden, UT.

47797 ■ U.S. Department of the Treasury - Internal Revenue Service Northeast Area
290 Broadway, 3rd Fl.
New York, NY 10007-1867
Ph: (212)436-1471
URL: http://home.treasury.gov/policy-issues/small-business-programs/small-and-disadvantaged-business-utilization/how-to-do-business-with-treasury
Contact: Peter Dinicola, Chief Procurement Officer
Description: Serves Maine, Massachusetts, New Hampshire, Vermont, Rhode Island, Connecticut, New York, New Jersey, Pennsylvania, Ohio, and Michigan. This office also supports the IRS Service Centers in Andover, MA, Brookhaven, NY, and Philadelphia, PA.

47798 ■ U.S. Department of the Treasury - Internal Revenue Service Salisbury
601 E Naylor Mill Rd., Unit C
Salisbury, MD 21804
Free: 844-545-5640
URL: http://www.irs.gov

47799 ■ U.S. Department of the Treasury - Kansas City Financial Center (NPCE)
PO Box 12599-0599
Kansas City, MO 64116-0599
Ph: (816)414-2340
Free: 855-868-0151
Co. E-mail: payments@fiscal.treasury.gov
URL: http://fiscal.treasury.gov/fds
Founded: 1935.

47800 ■ U.S. Department of the Treasury - Office of the Comptroller of the Currency - Central District - Chicago Field Office
425 S Financial Pl., Ste. 1700
Chicago, IL 60605
Ph: (312)360-8800
URL: http://www.occ.treas.gov/about/who-we-are/locations/central-district/index-central-district.html
Description: Serves Ohio, Illinois, Indiana, Michigan, and Wisconsin.

47801 ■ U.S. Department of the Treasury - Office of the Comptroller of the Currency - Northeastern District - Washington D.C. Field Office
c/o Tania Phillips
400 7th St. SW
Washington, DC 20219
Ph: (202)649-6510
URL: http://www.occ.treas.gov/about/who-we-are/locations/locations-list-view.html
Contact: Tania Phillips, Contact

47802 ■ U.S. Department of the Treasury - Office of the Comptroller of the Currency - Southern District - Atlanta Field Office
c/o Jason Sisack
3 Ravinia Dr., Ste. 550
Atlanta, GA 30346
Ph: (770)280-4400
URL: http://www.occ.treas.gov/about/who-we-are/locations/southern-district/index-southern-district.html
Contact: Jason Sisack, Comptroller
Description: Serves Alabama, Florida, Georgia, Kentucky, Maryland, North Carolina, South Carolina, Tennessee, Virginia, District of Columbia, Puerto Rico, and Virgin Islands.

47803 ■ U.S. Department of the Treasury - Office of the Comptroller of the Currency - Southern District - Dallas Field Office
500 N Akard St., Ste. 1600
Dallas, TX 75201
Ph: (214)720-0656
URL: http://www.occ.treas.gov/about/who-we-are/locations/south-region/index-south-region.html
Contact: Troy Thornton, Contact
Description: Serves Arkansas, Iowa, Kansas, Louisiana, Minnesota, Missouri, Mississippi, North Dakota, Nebraska, New Mexico, Oklahoma, South Dakota, and Texas.

47804 ■ U.S. Department of the Treasury - Office of the Comptroller of the Currency - Western District
c/o Kurt Raney
Independence Plz.
1050 17th St., Ste. 1500
Denver, CO 80265
Ph: (720)475-7500
URL: http://www.occ.gov/about/who-we-are/locations/west-region/index-west-region.html
Contact: Kurt Raney, Contact
Description: Serves Alaska, Arizona, California, Colorado, Hawaii, Idaho, Montana, North Dakota, New Mexico, Oregon, South Dakota, Utah, Washington, Wyoming, Guam, and Northern Mariana Islands.
Founded: 1863.

47805 ■ U.S. Department of the Treasury - Office of the Comptroller of the Currency - Western District - Santa Ana Field Office
1551 N Tustin Ave., Ste. 1050
Santa Ana, CA 92705
Ph: (714)796-4700
URL: http://www.occ.treas.gov/about/who-we-are/locations/west-region/index-west-region.html
Contact: Richard Dixon, Comptroller
Description: Serves Alaska, Arizona, California, Colorado, Hawaii, Idaho, Montana, North Dakota, New Mexico, Oregon, South Dakota, Utah, Washington, Wyoming, Guam, and Northern Mariana Islands.

47806 ■ U.S. Department of the Treasury - Office of the Procurement Executive (OPE)
1500 Pennsylvania Ave. NW
Washington, DC 20220
URL: http://home.treasury.gov/about/offices/management/procurement-executive

47807 ■ U.S. Department of the Treasury - Office of Thrift Supervision
400 7th St. SW
Washington, DC 20219
URL: http://home.treasury.gov/about/offices/public-affairs
Founded: 1789.

47808 ■ U.S. Department of the Treasury - Philadelphia Financial Center
PO Box 51318
Philadelphia, PA 19115
Free: 855-868-0151
URL: http://www.fiscal.treasury.gov/pfc

47809 ■ U.S. Department of the Treasury - Small Business and Community Development Programs - Office of Small and Disadvantaged Business Utilization
1722 I St. NW
Washington, DC 20006
URL: http://home.treasury.gov/policy-issues/small-business-programs/small-and-disadvantaged-business-utilization/office-of-small-and-disadvantaged-business-utilization
Contact: Donna Ragucci, Director
Description: The mission of the Department of the Treasury includes formulating and recommending financial, tax, and fiscal policies; serving as the financial agent for the U.S. government; enforcing various federal laws; protecting the President & Vice President of the United States; and manufacturing coins and currency. The accomplishment of this mission requires the procurement of a wide variety of commercial goods and services at an annual expenditure of approximately two billion dollars. Contracting authority has been delegated to the various bureaus of the department, and each conducts the procurement transactions necessary to carry out its respective program. The department's procurement efforts include a commitment to increase contract awards to small, minority, and women-owned business firms. **Founded:** 1789.

47810 ■ U.S. Department of the Treasury - U.S. Mint
801 9th St. NW
Washington, DC 20220
Free: 800-872-6468
Co. E-mail: inquiries@usmint.gov
URL: http://www.usmint.gov
Contact: Francis O'Hearn, Chief Information Officer Associate Director
Facebook: www.facebook.com/UnitedStatesMint
X (Twitter): x.com/usmint
Instagram: www.instagram.com/unitedstatesmint

YouTube: www.youtube.com/user/USMINT
Pinterest: www.pinterest.com/usmint
Founded: 1792.

U.S. NUCLEAR REGULATORY COMMISSION

47811 ■ **U.S. Nuclear Regulatory Commission (USNRC) - Office of Small and Disadvantaged Business Utilization/Civil Rights**
4934 Boiling Brook Pky.
Rockville, MD 20852
URL: http://www.nrc.gov/about-nrc/organization/sbcrfuncdesc.html
Contact: Vonna Ordaz, Director
Description: The Nuclear Regulatory Commission's Office of Small and Disadvantaged Business Utilization offers small businesses information and guidance on procurement procedures, how to be placed on a bidder's mailing list, and identification of both prime and subcontracting opportunities.

47812 ■ **U.S. Nuclear Regulatory Commission Region 1 (U.S. NRC Region I)**
475 Allendale Rd., Ste. 102
King of Prussia, PA 19406-1415
Ph: (610)337-5000
Free: 800-432-1156
URL: http://www.nrc.gov/about-nrc/locations/region1.html
Description: Serves Connecticut, Delaware, Maine, Maryland, Massachusetts, New Hampshire, New Jersey, New York, Pennsylvania, Rhode Island, Vermont, and Washington.

47813 ■ **U.S. Nuclear Regulatory Commission Region 2 (U.S. NRC Region II)**
Marquis One Twr.
245 Peachtree Center Ave. NE, Ste. 1200
Atlanta, GA 30303
Ph: (404)997-4000
Free: 800-577-8510
URL: http://www.nrc.gov/about-nrc/locations/region2.html
Description: Serves Alabama, Florida, Georgia, Kentucky, Mississippi, North Carolina, Puerto Rico, South Carolina, Tennessee, Virginia, Virgin Islands, and West Virginia.

47814 ■ **U.S. Nuclear Regulatory Commission Region 3 (U.S. NRC Region III)**
2443 Warrenville Rd., Ste. 210
Lisle, IL 60532-4352
Ph: (630)829-9500
Free: 800-522-3025
Fax: (630)515-1078
URL: http://www.nrc.gov/about-nrc/locations/region3.html
Description: Serves Illinois, Indiana, Iowa, Michigan, Minnesota, Missouri, Ohio, and Wisconsin.

47815 ■ **U.S. Nuclear Regulatory Commission Region 4 (U.S. NRC Region IV)**
1600 E Lamar Blvd.
Arlington, TX 76011-4511
Ph: (817)200-1100
Free: 800-952-9677
URL: http://www.nrc.gov/about-nrc/locations/region4.html
Linkedin: www.linkedin.com/company/u-s--department-of-energy
Description: Serves Alaska, Arizona, Arkansas, California, Colorado, Hawaii, Idaho, Kansas, Louisiana, Montana, Nebraska, Nevada, New Mexico, North Dakota, Oklahoma, Oregon, South Dakota, Texas, Utah, Washington, and Wyoming.

U.S. POSTAL SERVICE

47816 ■ **U.S. Postal Inspection Postal Service (USPIS) - Dangerous Mail Investigations Program**
Criminal Investigations Service Ctr.
433 W Harrison St., St3255
Chicago, IL 60699-3255
URL: http://www.uspis.gov/tips-prevention/suspicious-mail
Description: Specially trained and equipped Postal Inspectors within the Dangerous Mail Investigations (DMI) Program respond when a prohibited mailing, mail bomb or substance may cause harm to Postal Service employees, Postal Service customers, the mail, or Postal Service property.

47817 ■ **U.S. Postal Service (ITD) - Administrative Operations - Information Technology Div.**
2111 Wilson Blvd., Ste. 500
Arlington, VA 22201-3036
Free: 800-275-8777
URL: http://about.usps.com/postal-bulletin/2004/html/pb22126/a-c.html
Founded: 1775.

47818 ■ **U.S. Postal Service - Environmental and MRO Category Management Center**
7800 N Stemmons Fwy., Ste. 700
Dallas, TX 75247-4223
URL: http://about.usps.com/postal-bulletin/2009/pb22263/html/info_010.htm
Description: Serves Arizona, Louisiana, Oklahoma, and Texas.

47819 ■ **U.S. Postal Service - Intelligent Mail and Address Quality**
225 N Humphreys Blvd., Ste. 501
Memphis, TN 38188-1001
URL: http://about.usps.com/postal-bulletin/2011/pb22302/html/info_010.htm

47820 ■ **U.S. Postal Service-Memphis Purchasing Service Center (USPS)**
225 N Humphreys Blvd., Ste. 501
Memphis, TN 38188-1001
Free: 800-522-9085
Co. E-mail: postalone@email.usps.gov
URL: http://www.usps.com/postalone/contact.htm
Founded: 1775.

47821 ■ **U.S. Postal Service (USPIS) - United States Postal Inspection Service**
433 W Harrison St., Rm. 3255
Chicago, IL 60699-3255
Free: 877-876-2455
URL: http://www.uspis.gov
Contact: Gary R. Barksdale, Officer
Facebook: www.facebook.com/Postalinspectors
X (Twitter): x.com/USPISpressroom
Instagram: www.instagram.com/postalinspectors
YouTube: www.youtube.com/channel/UCSDPeYyj8pBF4BiAPlb8KMQ
Description: Offers support and protect the U.S. Postal Service and its employees, infrastructure, and customers; enforce the laws that defend the nation's mail system from illegal or dangerous use; and ensure public trust in the mail.

U.S. SMALL BUSINESS ADMINISTRATION

47822 ■ **U.S. Department of the Navy - Space and Naval Warfare Systems**
4301 Pacific Hwy.
San Diego, CA 92110-3127
Ph: (619)524-3432
URL: http://www.public.navy.mil/spawar/Pages/default.aspx
Founded: 1830.

47823 ■ **U.S. Small Business Administration (SBA)**
409 3rd St. SW
Washington, DC 20416
Ph: (202)205-6766
Free: 800-827-5722
Fax: (202)205-7064
Co. E-mail: answerdesk@sba.gov
URL: http://www.sba.gov
Facebook: www.facebook.com/SBAgov
Linkedin: www.linkedin.com/company/us-small-business-administration
X (Twitter): x.com/sbagov
Instagram: www.instagram.com/sbagov
YouTube: www.youtube.com/user/sba
Description: Continues to help small business owners and entrepreneurs pursue the american dream.
Founded: 1953. **Publications:** *Directory of Operating Small Business Investment Companies* (Semiannual); *www.BusinessLaw.gov*; *SBA Online*; *U.S. Business Advisor*. **Awards:** U.S. SBA Entrepreneurial Success Award (Annual); U.S. SBA Small Business Advocates of the Year (Annual); U.S. SBA Small Business Exporter of the Year (Annual); U.S. SBA National Small Business Person of the Year (Annual); Phoenix Award for Small Business Disaster Recovery (Annual); Phoenix Award for Outstanding Contributions to Disaster Recovery (Annual).

47824 ■ **U.S. Small Business Administration - Alabama District Office**
2 N 20th St., Ste. 325
Birmingham, AL 35203
Ph: (205)290-7101
URL: http://www.sba.gov/about-sba/sba-locations/sba-district-offices
Contact: Thomas A. Todt, Director
E-mail: thomas.todt@sba.gov

47825 ■ **U.S. Small Business Administration - Alaska District Office**
420 L St., Ste. 300
Anchorage, AK 99501
Ph: (907)271-4022
Co. E-mail: alaska8a@sba.gov
URL: http://www.sba.gov/district/alaska
Contact: Steven Brown, Director
E-mail: steven.brown@sba.gov
Founded: 1953.

47826 ■ **U.S. Small Business Administration - Albuquerque District Office**
500 Gold Ave. SW, Ste. 11301
Albuquerque, NM 87102
Ph: (505)248-8225
URL: http://www.sba.gov/district/new-mexico
Contact: John M. Garcia, Director
E-mail: john.garcia@sba.gov
Linkedin: www.linkedin.com/showcase/sbanewmexico
X (Twitter): x.com/SBA_NewMexico
Description: Offers loans, loan guarantees, contracts, counseling sessions and other forms of assistance to small businesses in Albuquerque.
Founded: 1953.

47827 ■ **U.S. Small Business Administration - Arizona District Office**
4041 N Central Ave., Ste. 1000
Phoenix, AZ 85012
Ph: (602)745-7200
Co. E-mail: arizona8a@sba.gov
URL: http://www.sba.gov/district/arizona
Contact: Robert J. Blaney, Director
E-mail: robert.blaney@sba.gov
Linkedin: www.linkedin.com/showcase/sbaarizona
X (Twitter): x.com/sba_arizona

47828 ■ **U.S. Small Business Administration - Arkansas District Office**
2120 Riverfront Dr., Ste. 1000
Little Rock, AR 72202
Ph: (501)324-7379
Co. E-mail: arkansas_do@sba.gov
URL: http://www.sba.gov/district/arkansas
Contact: Edward Haddock, Director
E-mail: edward.haddock@sba.gov

47829 ■ **U.S. Small Business Administration - Baltimore District Office**
100 S Charles St., Ste. 1201
Baltimore, MD 21201
Ph: (410)962-6195
Co. E-mail: baltimore_do@sba.gov
URL: http://www.sba.gov/district/baltimore
Contact: Stephen D. Umberger, Director
E-mail: stephen.umberger@sba.gov
X (Twitter): x.com/SBA_Baltimore
Founded: 1953.

47830 ■ U.S. Small Business Administration - Boise District Office
380 E Parkcenter Blvd., Ste. 330
Boise, ID 83706
Ph: (208)334-9004
URL: http://www.sba.gov/district/boise
Contact: Shannon Madsen, Director
E-mail: shannon.madsen@sba.gov
Founded: 1953.

47831 ■ U.S. Small Business Administration (SBA) - Buffalo District Office
130 S Elmwood Ave., Ste. 540
Buffalo, NY 14202
Ph: (716)551-4301
URL: http://www.sba.gov/district/buffalo
Contact: Franklin J. Sciortino, Director
E-mail: franklin.sciortino@sba.gov
Description: Offers SCORE counseling, advice, and information on starting a business; financial assistance for new or existing businesses through guaranteed loans made by area bank and non-bank lenders; consulting services and training events; assistance to businesses owned and controlled by socially and economically disadvantaged individuals through the Minority Enterprise Development Program; advice to women business owners; special loan programs for businesses involved in international trade; and guaranteed loans for credit-worthy veterans.

47832 ■ U.S. Small Business Administration - Buffalo District Office - Rochester Branch Office
100 State St., Rm. 410
Rochester, NY 14614
Ph: (585)263-6700
URL: http://www.sba.gov/offices/district/ny/buffalo
Contact: Franklin J. Sciortino, Director
Founded: 1953.

47833 ■ U.S. Small Business Administration - Business Information Center
2 MLK Jr. Dr., Ste. 313, Floyd W Tower
Atlanta, GA 30334-1530
Ph: (404)656-2817
URL: http://sos.ga.gov/page/first-stop-business-information-center

47834 ■ U.S. Small Business Administration - Business Information Center
380 E Parkcenter Blvd., Ste. 330
Boise, ID 83706
Ph: (208)334-9004
Co. E-mail: boise_do@sba.gov
URL: http://www.sba.gov/district/boise
Contact: Shannon Madsen, Director

47835 ■ U.S. Small Business Administration (SBA) - Business Information Center
500 W Madison St., Ste. 1150
Chicago, IL 60661
Ph: (312)353-4528
Fax: (312)886-5688
URL: http://www.sba.gov/offices/district/ga/atlanta

47836 ■ U.S. Small Business Administration - Business Information Center
721 19th St., Ste. 426
Denver, CO 80202
Ph: (303)844-2607
URL: http://www.sba.gov/district/colorado
Contact: Frances Padilla, Director
Description: Government provides educational and technical assistance to self-employed recipients and to those who want to become self employed.
Founded: 1953.

47837 ■ U.S. Small Business Administration - Business Information Center
330 N Brand Blvd., Ste. 1200
Glendale, CA 91203
URL: http://www.sba.gov/district/los-angeles
Founded: 1953.

47838 ■ U.S. Small Business Administration - Cedar Rapids Branch Office
2750 1st Ave. NE, Ste. 350
Cedar Rapids, IA 52402
Ph: (319)362-6405
URL: http://www.sba.gov/district/iowa
Contact: Jo Eckert, Branch Manager
E-mail: jo.eckert@sba.gov
Founded: 1953.

47839 ■ U.S. Small Business Administration - Charleston Branch Office
405 Capitol St., Ste. 412
Charleston, WV 25301
Ph: (304)347-5220
Fax: (304)347-5350
URL: http://www.sba.gov/district/west-virginia
Contact: Kimberly Donahue, Branch Manager
E-mail: kimberly.donahue@sba.gov
Founded: 1953.

47840 ■ U.S. Small Business Administration (SBA) - Cleveland District Office
1350 Euclid Ave., Ste. 211
Cleveland, OH 44115
Ph: (216)522-4180
URL: http://www.sba.gov/district/cleveland
Contact: John G. Turner, Director
X (Twitter): x.com/SBA_Cleveland
Founded: 1953.

47841 ■ U.S. Small Business Administration - Cleveland U.S. Export Assistance Center
1350 Euclid Ave., Ste. 211
Cleveland, OH 44115
URL: http://www.sba.gov/local-assistance/export-trade-assistance/export-finance-managers

47842 ■ U.S. Small Business Administration - Colorado District Office (CDO)
721 19th St., Ste. 426
Denver, CO 80202
Ph: (303)844-2607
URL: http://www.sba.gov/district/colorado
Contact: Frances Padilla, Director
E-mail: frances.padilla@sba.gov
Linkedin: www.linkedin.com/showcase/sbacolorado
X (Twitter): x.com/SBA_Colorado
Founded: 1953.

47843 ■ U.S. Small Business Administration - Columbus District Office
65 E State St., Ste. 1350
Columbus, OH 43215
Ph: (614)427-0407
URL: http://www.sba.gov/district/columbus
Contact: Everett M. Woodel, Jr., Director
E-mail: everett.woodel@sba.gov
Founded: 1953.

47844 ■ U.S. Small Business Administration (SBA) - Connecticut District Office
280 Trumbull St., 2nd Fl.
Hartford, CT 06103
Ph: (860)240-4700
URL: http://www.sba.gov/district/connecticut
Contact: Catherine Marx, Director
Linkedin: www.linkedin.com/showcase/sbaconnecticut
X (Twitter): x.com/SBA_Connecticut
Founded: 1953.

47845 ■ U.S. Small Business Administration - Corpus Christi Branch Office
2820 S Padre Island Dr., Ste. 108
Corpus Christi, TX 78415
Ph: (361)879-0017
URL: http://www.sba.gov/district/lower-rio-grande-valley
Contact: Monica Stuber, Branch Manager
E-mail: monica.stuber@sba.gov

47846 ■ U.S. Small Business Administration - Dallas District Office
150 Westpark Way, Ste. 130
Euless, TX 76040
Ph: (817)684-5500
Co. E-mail: dfwdo.email@sba.gov
URL: http://www.sba.gov/district/dallas-fort-worth
Contact: Herbert Austin, Director
E-mail: herbert.austin@sba.gov
Linkedin: www.linkedin.com/showcase/sbadallasfortworth
X (Twitter): x.com/SBADFW

47847 ■ U.S. Small Business Administration (SBA) - Dallas/Fort Worth District Office (DFWDO)
150 Westpark Way, Ste. 130
Euless, TX 76040
Ph: (817)684-5500
Co. E-mail: dfwdo.email@sba.gov
URL: http://www.sba.gov/district/dallas-fort-worth
Contact: Herbert Austin, Director
E-mail: herbert.austin@sba.gov
X (Twitter): x.com/SBADFW
Description: Offers SCORE counseling, advice, and information on starting a business; financial assistance for new or existing businesses through guaranteed loans made by area bank and non-bank lenders; consulting services and training events; assistance to businesses owned and controlled by socially and economically disadvantaged individuals through the Minority Enterprise Development Program; advice to women business owners; special loan programs for businesses involved in international trade; and guaranteed loans for credit-worthy veterans.

47848 ■ U.S. Small Business Administration - Delaware District Office
1105 Market St., Lobby Lvl., Ste. 02
Wilmington, DE 19801
Ph: (302)300-1935
Fax: (302)573-6060
URL: http://www.sba.gov/district/delaware
Contact: Michelle Harris, Director
E-mail: michelle.harris@sba.gov
X (Twitter): x.com/SBA_Delaware

47849 ■ U.S. Small Business Administration - Denver U.S. Export Assistance Center (USEACs)
999 18th St., Ste. 725, N Twr
Denver, CO 80202
Ph: (303)844-6623
URL: http://www.sba.gov/local-assistance/export-trade-assistance/us-export-assistance-centers
Description: Serves Wyoming, Utah, Colorado, and New Mexico. Founded: 1953.

47850 ■ U.S. Small Business Administration Des Moines District Office
210 Walnut St., Rm. 749
Des Moines, IA 50309
Ph: (515)284-4422
Co. E-mail: dmdo@sba.gov
URL: http://www.sba.gov/district/iowa
Contact: Jayne Armstrong, Director
E-mail: jayne.armstrong@sba.gov

47851 ■ U.S. Small Business Administration - Detroit District Office
477 Michigan Ave., Ste. 1819
Detroit, MI 48226
Ph: (313)226-6075
URL: http://www.sba.gov/district/michigan
Founded: 1953.

47852 ■ U.S. Small Business Administration (SBA) - Disaster Assistance Customer Service Center
130 S Elmwood Ave., Ste. 540
Buffalo, NY 14202
Free: 800-659-2955
Co. E-mail: disastercustomerservice@sba.gov
URL: http://www.sba.gov/about-sba/organization/contact-sba
Contact: Franklin J. Sciortino, Director

47853 ■ U.S. Small Business Administration - Disaster Assistance Processing & Disbursement Center
409 Thirrd St. SW, Ste. 6050
  Washington, DC 20416
Ph: (202)205-6734
URL: http://www.sba.gov/about-sba/sba-locations/headquarters-offices/office-disaster-assistance
Contact: Francisco Sanchez, Jr., Administrator

47854 ■ U.S. Small Business Administration - Disaster Office Customer Service Center (CSC)
409 3rd St., SW
  Washington, DC 20416
Free: 800-659-2955
URL: http://www.sba.gov/about-sba/organization/contact-sba

47855 ■ U.S. Small Business Administration - Disaster Offices - Disaster Field Operations Center - East (FOCE)
101 Marietta St. NW, Ste. 700
  Atlanta, GA 30303
Ph: (404)331-0333
URL: http://www.sba.gov/about-sba/sba-locations/disaster-field-operations-centers
Description: Covers regions three, four, and five.
Founded: 1953.

47856 ■ U.S. Small Business Administration - Disaster Offices - Disaster Field Operations Center - West
6501 Sylvan Rd.
  Citrus Heights, CA 95610
Ph: (916)735-1500
URL: http://www.sba.gov/about-sba/sba-locations/disaster-field-operations-centers#section-header-3
Description: Covers regions eight, nine, and ten.

47857 ■ U.S. Small Business Administration - El Paso District Office
211 N Florence St., Ste. 201, 2nd Fl.
  El Paso, TX 79901
Ph: (915)834-4600
URL: http://www.sba.gov/district/el-paso
Contact: Dante Acosta, Director
E-mail: phillip.silva@sba.gov
X (Twitter): x.com/SBA_ElPaso

47858 ■ U.S. Small Business Administration - Elmira Branch Office
400 E Church St.
  Elmira, NY 14901
Ph: (607)734-8130
URL: http://www.sba.gov/district/syracuse?page=0%2C1
Contact: Daniel Rickman, Director
Founded: 1953.

47859 ■ U.S. Small Business Administration - Fargo District Office
657 2nd Ave. N, Rm. 360
  Fargo, ND 58108
Ph: (701)239-5131
Fax: (202)481-0075
Co. E-mail: north.dakota@sba.gov
URL: http://www.sba.gov/district/north-dakota
Contact: Alan J. Haut, Director
E-mail: alan.haut@sba.gov
X (Twitter): x.com/SBA_NorthDakota
Description: Offers loans, loan guarantees, contracts, counseling sessions and other forms of assistance to small businesses in Fargo.

47860 ■ U.S. Small Business Administration (SBA) - Fresno District Office
801 R St., Ste. 201
  Fresno, CA 93721
Ph: (559)487-5791
URL: http://www.sba.gov/district/fresno
Contact: Dawn Golik, Division Director

47861 ■ U.S. Small Business Administration - Georgia District Office
233 Peachtree St. NE, Ste. 300
  Atlanta, GA 30303
Ph: (404)331-0100

URL: http://www.sba.gov/about-sba/sba-locations/sba-district-offices
Contact: Terri L. Denison, Director

47862 ■ U.S. Small Business Administration - Gulfport Branch Office
2510 14th St., Ste. 103
  Gulfport, MS 39501
Ph: (228)863-4449
URL: http://www.sba.gov/local-assistance/veterans-business-development-officers
Contact: Bridget Johnson Fells, Contact
E-mail: bridget.johnson@sba.gov
Founded: 1953.

47863 ■ U.S. Small Business Administration - Hartford District Office
280 Trumbull St., 2nd Fl.
  Hartford, CT 06103
Ph: (860)240-4700
URL: http://www.sba.gov/district/connecticut
Contact: Catherine Marx, Director
E-mail: catherine.marx@sba.gov

47864 ■ U.S. Small Business Administration (SBA) - Hawaii District Office
500 Ala Moana Blvd., Ste. 1-306
  Honolulu, HI 96813
Ph: (808)541-2990
Free: 800-659-7113
Fax: (808)541-2976
Co. E-mail: hawaiigeneral@sba.gov
URL: http://www.sba.gov/district/hawaii
Contact: T. Mark Spain, Director
E-mail: thornton.spain@sba.gov
X (Twitter): x.com/SBA_Hawaii

47865 ■ U.S. Small Business Administration Headquarters Office - Office of International Trade
409 3rd St. SW, Ste. 2400
  Washington, DC 20416
Ph: (202)205-6720
URL: http://www.sba.gov/about-sba/sba-locations/headquarters-offices/office-international-trade
Contact: Claire Ehmann, Deputy Administrator Associate
Founded: 1953.

47866 ■ U.S. Small Business Administration - Helena District Office
10 W 15th St., Ste. 1100
  Helena, MT 59626
Ph: (406)441-1081
URL: http://www.sba.gov/district/montana
Contact: Brent Donnelly, Director
E-mail: brent.donnelly@sba.gov
Description: Offers loans, loan guarantees, contracts, counseling sessions and other forms of assistance to small businesses in Helena.

47867 ■ U.S. Small Business Administration - Houston District Office
8701 S Gessner Dr., Ste. No. 1200
  Houston, TX 77074
Ph: (713)773-6500
Fax: (713)773-6550
Co. E-mail: houston@sba.gov
URL: http://www.sba.gov/district/houston
Contact: Tim Jeffcoat, Director
E-mail: timothy.jeffcoat@sba.gov

47868 ■ U.S. Small Business Administration - Illinois District Office
332 S Michigan Ave., Ste. 600
  Chicago, IL 60604
Ph: (312)353-4528
Co. E-mail: illinois.do@sba.gov
URL: http://www.sba.gov/district/illinois
Contact: Robert Steiner, Director
X (Twitter): x.com/SBA_Illinois

47869 ■ U.S. Small Business Administration - Indiana District Office
5726 Professional Cir., Ste. 100
  Indianapolis, IN 46241
Ph: (317)226-7272
URL: http://www.sba.gov/district/indiana

Contact: Stacey Poynter, Director
E-mail: stacey.poynter@sba.gov
Founded: 1953.

47870 ■ U.S. Small Business Administration - Indianapolis District Office
5726 Professional Cir., Ste. 100
  Indianapolis, IN 46241
Ph: (317)226-7272
URL: http://www.sba.gov/district/indiana
Contact: Stacey Poynter, Director
E-mail: stacey.poynter@sba.gov
X (Twitter): x.com/SBA_Indiana
Description: Offers loans, loan guarantees, contracts, counseling sessions and other forms of assistance to small businesses in Indianapolis.
Founded: 1953.

47871 ■ U.S. Small Business Administration - Jackson District Office
210 E Capitol St., Ste. 900
  Jackson, MS 39201
Ph: (601)965-4378
Fax: (601)965-5629
Co. E-mail: jacksonms@sba.gov
URL: http://www.sba.gov/district/mississippi
Contact: Janita R. Stewart, Director
E-mail: janita.stewart@sba.gov
X (Twitter): x.com/SBA_MS
Founded: 1953.

47872 ■ U.S. Small Business Administration (SBA) - Kansas City District Office
1000 Walnut St., Ste. 500
  Kansas City, MO 64106
Ph: (816)426-4900
URL: http://www.sba.gov/district/kansas-city
Contact: Michael L. Barrera, Director

47873 ■ U.S. Small Business Administration (SBA) - Kentucky District Office
600 Dr. Martin Luther King Jr. Pl., Ste. 188
  Louisville, KY 40202
Ph: (502)582-5971
Fax: (502)582-5009
Co. E-mail: ky@sba.gov
URL: http://www.sba.gov/district/kentucky
Contact: Robert Coffey, Director
E-mail: robert.coffey@sba.gov
Linkedin: www.linkedin.com/showcase/sba-kentucky-district-office
X (Twitter): x.com/SBA_Kentucky

47874 ■ U.S. Small Business Administration - The Klamath Tribes - Business Information Center
409 3rd St., SW
  Washington, DC 20416
Free: 800-827-5722
Co. E-mail: support@us-sba.atlassian.net
URL: http://www.sba.gov
Contact: Stephen Kong, Officer
Linkedin: www.linkedin.com/company/us-small-business-administration
X (Twitter): x.com/sbagov
Instagram: www.instagram.com/sbagov
YouTube: www.youtube.com/user/sba

47875 ■ U.S. Small Business Administration (SBA) - Las Vegas District Office
300 S 4th St., Ste. 400
  Las Vegas, NV 89101
Ph: (702)388-6611
Fax: (702)388-6469
Co. E-mail: nvdo@sba.gov
URL: http://www.sba.gov/district/nevada
Contact: Saul Ramos, Director
E-mail: saul.ramos@sba.gov

47876 ■ U.S. Small Business Administration - Little Rock District Office
2120 Riverfront Dr., Ste. 1000
  Little Rock, AR 72202
Ph: (501)324-7379
URL: http://www.sba.gov/district/arkansas
Contact: Adriene Brown, Director
X (Twitter): x.com/SBA_Arkansas

47877 ■ U.S. Small Business Administration - Loans & Grants - Small Business Loans - Office of Loan Programs
409 3rd St. SW
Washington, DC 20416
URL: http://www.sba.gov/funding-programs/loans

47878 ■ U.S. Small Business Administration - Los Angeles District Office
312 N Spring St.
Los Angeles, CA 90012
Ph: (213)634-3855
Co. E-mail: lado@sba.gov
URL: http://www.sba.gov/district/los-angeles
Contact: Julie Clowes, Director
Linkedin: www.linkedin.com/showcase/sbalosangeles
X (Twitter): x.com/SBA_LosAngeles

47879 ■ U.S. Small Business Administration (LRGVDO) - Lower Rio Grande Valley District Office
2422 E Tyler Ave., Ste. E
Harlingen, TX 78550
Ph: (956)427-8533
Fax: (956)427-8537
Co. E-mail: lrgvdo.email@sba.gov
URL: http://www.sba.gov/district/lower-rio-grande-valley
Contact: Angela R. Burton, Director
E-mail: angela.burton@sba.gov
X (Twitter): x.com/SBA_LRGV

47880 ■ U.S. Small Business Administration - Lubbock District Office
1205 Texas Ave., Rm. 408
Lubbock, TX 79401
Ph: (806)472-7462
URL: http://www.sba.gov/district/west-texas
Contact: Calvin O. Davis, Director
E-mail: calvin.davis@sba.gov
Description: Offers loans, loan guarantees, contracts, counseling sessions and other forms of assistance to small businesses in San Diego. **Founded:** 1953.

47881 ■ U.S. Small Business Administration (MDO) - Madison District Office
740 Regent St., Ste. 100
Madison, WI 53715
Ph: (608)441-5263
URL: http://www.sba.gov/district/wisconsin?page=0%2C1
Contact: Eric Ness, Director
E-mail: eric.ness@sba.gov

47882 ■ U.S. Small Business Administration (MDO) - Maine District Office
68 Sewall St., Rm. 512
Augusta, ME 04330
Ph: (207)622-8551
URL: http://www.sba.gov/district/maine
Contact: Diane Sturgeon, Director
E-mail: diane.sturgeon@sba.gov
X (Twitter): x.com/SBA_Maine

47883 ■ U.S. Small Business Administration - Massachusetts District Office
10 Cswy. St., Rm. 265
Boston, MA 02222
Ph: (617)565-5590
URL: http://www.sba.gov/district/massachusetts
Contact: Robert H. Nelson, Director
E-mail: rhnelson@sba.gov
X (Twitter): x.com/SBA_MA
Founded: 1953.

47884 ■ U.S. Small Business Administration - Melville Branch Office
145 Pinelawn Rd., Ste. 250 S
Melville, NY 11747
Ph: (631)249-6502
URL: http://www.sba.gov
Contact: Amaleka McCall-Brathwaite, Contact
Description: Offers loans, loan guarantees, contracts, counseling sessions and other forms of assistance to small businesses in Melville. **Founded:** 1953.

47885 ■ U.S. Small Business Administration - Miami U.S. Export Assistance Center
c/o Sandro Murtas
5835 Blue Lagoon Dr., Ste. 203
Miami, FL 33126
Ph: (727)365-6939
Co. E-mail: sandro.murtas@sba.gov
URL: http://www.sba.gov/local-assistance/find
Contact: Sandro Murtas, Contact
E-mail: sandro.murtas@sba.gov
Description: Serves Florida.

47886 ■ U.S. Small Business Administration - Michigan District Office
477 Michigan Ave., Ste. 1819
Detroit, MI 48226
Ph: (313)226-6075
URL: http://www.sba.gov/district/michigan
Contact: Laketa Henderson, Director

47887 ■ U.S. Small Business Administration (SBA) - Minneapolis District Office
330 2nd Ave. S, Ste. 430
Minneapolis, MN 55401
Ph: (612)370-2324
Fax: (202)481-0139
Co. E-mail: minnesota@sba.gov
URL: http://www.sba.gov/district/minnesota
Contact: Brian McDonald, Director
E-mail: brian.mcdonald@sba.gov
Description: Offers loans, loan guarantees, contracts, counseling sessions and other forms of assistance to small businesses in Minneapolis.

47888 ■ U.S. Small Business Administration - Minnesota District Office
330 2nd Ave. S, Ste. 430
Minneapolis, MN 55401
Ph: (612)370-2324
URL: http://www.sba.gov/district/minnesota
Contact: Brian McDonald, Director
Description: Through an extensive network of field offices and partnerships with public and private organizations, SBA delivers its services to people throughout the United States, Puerto Rico, the U. S. Virgin Islands and Guam.

47889 ■ U.S. Small Business Administration (MDO) - Montana District Office
10 W 15th St., Ste. 1100
Helena, MT 59626
Ph: (406)441-1081
URL: http://www.sba.gov/district/montana
Contact: Brent Donnelly, Director
E-mail: brent.donnelly@sba.gov
X (Twitter): x.com/sba_montana

47890 ■ U.S. Small Business Administration - Montpelier District Office
87 State St., Unit 205
Montpelier, VT 05601
Ph: (802)828-4439
URL: http://www.sba.gov/local-assistance/veterans-business-development-officers
Contact: Darcy Carter, Director
E-mail: darcy.carter@sba.gov

47891 ■ U.S. Small Business Administration (NDO) - Nebraska District Office
10675 Bedford Ave., Ste. 100
Omaha, NE 68134
Ph: (402)221-4691
Co. E-mail: nebraska.general@sba.gov
URL: http://www.sba.gov/district/nebraska
Contact: Timothy Mittan, Director
E-mail: timothy.mittan@sba.gov
Linkedin: www.linkedin.com/showcase/sbanebraska
X (Twitter): x.com/SBA_Nebraska

47892 ■ U.S. Small Business Administration - Nevada District Office
300 S 4th St., Ste. 400
Las Vegas, NV 89101
Ph: (702)388-6611
Fax: (702)388-6469
Co. E-mail: nvdo@sba.gov
URL: http://www.sba.gov/district/nevada
Contact: Saul Ramos, Director
E-mail: saul.ramos@sba.gov
Linkedin: www.linkedin.com/showcase/sbanevada
X (Twitter): x.com/SBA_Nevada

47893 ■ U.S. Small Business Administration - New Hampshire District Office
55 Pleasant St., Ste. 3101
Concord, NH 03301
Ph: (603)225-1400
Fax: (603)225-1409
Co. E-mail: newhampshire_do@sba.gov
URL: http://www.sba.gov/district/new-hampshire
Contact: Amy Bassett, Director
E-mail: amy.bassett@sba.gov
Linkedin: www.linkedin.com/showcase/sbanewhampshire
X (Twitter): x.com/SBA_NH
Founded: 1953.

47894 ■ U.S. Small Business Administration (SBA) - New Jersey District Office
2 Gateway Ctr., Ste. 1002
Newark, NJ 07102
Ph: (973)645-2434
Fax: (973)645-6265
URL: http://www.sba.gov/district/new-jersey
Contact: John M. Blackstock, Director
E-mail: john.blackstock@sba.gov
Linkedin: www.linkedin.com/showcase/sbanewjersey
X (Twitter): x.com/SBA_NewJersey

47895 ■ U.S. Small Business Administration - New York District Office
26 Federal Plz., Ste. 3100
New York, NY 10278
Ph: (212)264-4354
URL: http://www.sba.gov/district/metro-new-york
Contact: Beth L. Goldberg, Director
E-mail: beth.goldberg@sba.gov
Founded: 1953.

47896 ■ U.S. Small Business Administration - New York U.S. Export Assistance Center
290 Broadway, Rm. 1312
New York, NY 10007
URL: http://www.sba.gov/local-assistance/export-trade-assistance/us-export-assistance-centers
Contact: Abby Martinez, Contact
E-mail: abigail.martinez@sba.gov

47897 ■ U.S. Small Business Administration (SBA) - Newark District Office
2 Gateway Ctr., Ste. 1002
Newark, NJ 07102
Ph: (973)645-2434
URL: http://www.sba.gov/district/new-jersey
Contact: John M. Blackstock, Director
E-mail: john.blackstock@sba.gov
Founded: 1953.

47898 ■ U.S. Small Business Administration (NCDO) - North Carolina District Office
6302 Fairview Rd., Ste. 300
Charlotte, NC 28210
Ph: (704)344-6563
Fax: (704)344-6769
Co. E-mail: nc@sba.gov
URL: http://www.sba.gov/district/north-carolina
Contact: Michael P. Arriola, Director
E-mail: michael.arriola@sba.gov
X (Twitter): x.com/sba_nc

47899 ■ U.S. Small Business Administration - North Texas Export Assistance Center
4300 Amon Carter Blvd., Ste. 116
Fort Worth, TX 76155
URL: http://www.sba.gov/business-guide/grow-your-business/export-products
Description: Serves Oklahoma, Texas, Louisiana, and Arkansas. **Founded:** 1953.

47900 ■ U.S. Small Business Administration - North Texas U.S. Export Assistance Center
150 Westpark Way, Ste. 235
Euless, TX 76040
URL: http://www.trade.gov/dallas-fort-worth-contact-us

FEDERAL GOVERNMENT ASSISTANCE

Contact: Jessica Gordon, Director
E-mail: jessica.gordon@trade.gov
Description: Serves Oklahoma, Texas, Louisiana, and Arkansas. **Founded:** 1953.

47901 ■ U.S. Small Business Administration (SBA) - Office of 8(a) Business Development
409 3rd St. SW, Eighth Fl.
  Washington, DC 20416
Ph: (202)765-1264
Co. E-mail: 8aquestions@sba.gov
URL: http://www.sba.gov/federal-contracting/contracting-assistance-programs/8a-business-development-program
Financial Assistance: Yes

47902 ■ U.S. Small Business Administration - Office of Advocacy
409 3rd St. SW
  Washington, DC 20416
Ph: (202)205-6533
Co. E-mail: advocacy@sba.gov
URL: http://advocacy.sba.gov
Contact: Luckie Wren, Director, Administration
E-mail: luciette.wren@sba.gov
Facebook: www.facebook.com/AdvocacySBA
X (Twitter): x.com/AdvocacySBA
Description: Newsletter. **Founded:** 1976. **Publications:** *The Small Business Advocate*; *The States and Small Business: A Directory of Programs and Activities* (Irregular).

47903 ■ U.S. Small Business Administration - Office of Communications and Public Liaison
409 3rd St. SW
  Washington, DC 20416
URL: http://www.sba.gov/offices/headquarters/ocpl
Contact: Cynthia Jasso, Director (Acting)

47904 ■ U.S. Small Business Administration - Office of Entrepreneurial Development (OED)
409 Third St. SW, Ste. 6200
  Washington, DC 20416
Co. E-mail: oed@sba.gov
URL: http://www.sba.gov/about-sba/sba-locations/headquarters-offices/office-entrepreneurial-development
Contact: Mark Madrid, Administrator
Founded: 1953.

47905 ■ U.S. Small Business Administration - Office of the Inspector General
409 3rd St. SW, Ste. 7150
  Washington, DC 20416
Ph: (202)205-6586
URL: http://www.sba.gov/about-sba/oversight-advocacy/office-inspector-general
Contact: Sheldon Shoemaker, Inspector General
E-mail: sheldon.shoemaker@sba.gov
Founded: 1953.

47906 ■ U.S. Small Business Administration (SBA) - Office of International Trade
409 3rd St. SW, Ste. 2400
  Washington, DC 20416
Ph: (202)205-6720
URL: http://www.sba.gov/about-sba/sba-locations/headquarters-offices/office-international-trade
Contact: Claire Ehmann, Deputy Administrator Associate

47907 ■ U.S. Small Business Administration - Office of Minority Enterprise Development - Division of 8(a) Program Certification and Eligibility
409 3rd St. SW
  Washington, DC 20416
Free: 800-827-5722
Co. E-mail: answerdesk@sba.gov
URL: http://www.sba.gov
Contact: Jovita Carranza, Administrator

47908 ■ U.S. Small Business Administration - Office of the National Ombudsman
409 3rd St. SW
  Washington, DC 20416
Free: 888-734-3247
Co. E-mail: ombudsman@sba.gov

URL: http://www.sba.gov/about-sba/oversight-advocacy/office-national-ombudsman
Contact: Marilyn D. Landis, Contact

47909 ■ U.S. Small Business Administration - Office of Native American Affairs
409 3rd St. SW
  Washington, DC 20416
Ph: (202)205-6411
URL: http://www.sba.gov/about-sba/sba-locations/headquarters-offices/office-native-american-affairs
Contact: Jackson S. Brossy, Administrative Assistant
Description: Ensures that American Indians, Native Alaskans and Native Hawaiians seeking to create, develop and expand small businesses have full access to the necessary business development and expansion tools available through the Agency's entrepreneurial development, lending and procurement programs.

47910 ■ U.S. Small Business Administration (SBA) - Office of Small Business Development Centers (SBDC)
409 3rd St. SW, Ste. 6400
  Washington, DC 20416
Ph: (202)205-6766
URL: http://www.sba.gov/about-sba/sba-locations/headquarters-offices/office-small-business-development-centers
Contact: Bruce Purdy, Associate Administrator
Description: Although other federal agencies also provide some services to small business, the SBA's primary duties are to aid, counsel, assist, and protect the interests of small business. It ensures that small business concerns receive a fair portion of government purchases, contracts, and subcontracts, as well as fair portions of the sales of government property. The SBA grants loans to small business concerns, to state and local development companies, and to the victims of floods, other catastrophes, or certain types of economic injuries. The administration also licenses, regulates, and grants loans to small business investment companies (SBICs). A small business must meet SBA size standards to be eligible for its loans, procurement assistance, and other services. Interested small business owners should contact the nearest SBA field offices for current standards since they vary by industry and are subject to change. The SBA administers a variety of loan programs for eligible small business concerns that cannot borrow money on reasonable terms from conventional lenders without government assistance. Most of the SBA's loans are made by private lenders and then guaranteed by the SBA, which can guarantee loans up to 90 percent for a maximum of $500,000. In addition to these regular business loans, the SBA offers a variety of special loan programs, including local development company loans that are offered to groups of local citizens. The SBA licenses and regulates small business investment companies (SBICs) which provide venture capital to small businesses. SBA field officers provide counseling and other services to small business owners seeking to do business with the federal government. Procurement specialists at district offices assist in identifying the government agencies that are prospective customers, in instructing small businesses about inclusion on bidders' lists, and in obtaining drawings and specifications for specific contracts. The SBA seeks to increase small business' share of procurement through the activities of its network of procurement center representatives (PCRs), stationed at or in liaison with all federal military and civilian installations with major buying programs. The SBA's procurement assistance program sets aside suitable government purchases for competitive award to small business concerns and provides an appeal procedure when the ability of a low-bidding small firm to perform a contract is questioned. The SBA also develops subcontracting opportunities, designating the amounts to be subcontracted to small business concerns by prime contractors undertaking major federal projects. The SBA administers the Small Business Innovation Research Program, which fosters participation by small businesses in federal research and development; and provides counseling and information to small businesses through a network of resource programs. The SBA also sponsors the Small Business Development Center (SBDC) Program in conjunction with the educational community, state and local governments, the federal government, and the private sector. In each state there is one "lead" organization that sponsors each SBDC and from which a statewide director manages the program. SBDCs seek to further economic development by providing management and technical assistance to existing and prospective small businesses. The lead organizations coordinate the activities performed on behalf of small business through the participation and establishment of SBDC subcenters and satellite locations. The SBA also offers export counseling and training through its Office of International Trade or small businesses wishing to export products and materials. The SBA is authorized, under Section 8 (a) of the Small Business Act, to enter into contracts with other federal agencies for goods and services and then to subcontract the work to firms owned by socially and economically disadvantaged persons. The firms must be approved to participate in the 8(a) program by the SBA. In addition, the SBA also is authorized, under Section 7(j) of the act, to provide management and technical assistance to SBA clients and small businesses in areas of high unemployment. This program allows the SBA to contract with qualified individuals, state and local governments, educational institutions, Native American tribes, and other nonprofit institutions. The SBA seeks to increase the strength, profitability, and visibility of women-owned businesses by enhancing their access to existing government and private sector resources. Specific efforts include assisting women business owners in surviving business crises; providing SBA personnel with the appropriate skills to respond to the needs of women business owners; increasing federal marketing opportunities; negotiating an annual goal for procurement from women business owners for each federal department and agency; and collecting and analyzing data about women-owned businesses. The SBA's Office of Advocacy attempts to evaluate the impact of legislative proposals and other public policy issues on small business and represents its views before Congress, federal agencies, and state and local governments. The chief counsel also coordinates and conducts applied economic research on a wide range of small business issues, as well as serves as a source of information about the federal government for small business. The office's activities are supported by advocates located at each of the ten SBA regional offices. The SBA also publishes a variety of pamphlets and booklets about its programs and services.

47911 ■ U.S. Small Business Administration (SBA) - Office of Women's Business Ownership (OWBO)
409 Third St. SW, Ste. 6600
  Washington, DC 20416
URL: http://www.sba.gov/about-sba/sba-locations/headquarters-offices/office-womens-business-ownership
Contact: Christina Hale, Assistant Administrator
Founded: 1979.

47912 ■ U.S. Small Business Administration - Oklahoma City District Office
301 NW 6th St. 116
  Oklahoma City, OK 73102
Ph: (405)609-8000
Fax: (405)609-8990
Co. E-mail: okofferletters@sba.gov
URL: http://www.sba.gov/district/oklahoma
Contact: Fernanda Pedraza-Schmitt, Director
E-mail: fernanda.pedraza-schmitt@sba.gov
X (Twitter): x.com/SBA_Oklahoma
Description: Government agency provides small business resource guide in Oklahoma. **Founded:** 1953.

47913 ■ U.S. Small Business Administration - Omaha District Office
10675 Bedford Ave., Ste. 100
  Omaha, NE 68134
Ph: (402)221-4691

URL: http://www.sba.gov/district/nebraska
Contact: Lisa Tedesco, Deputy Director
Founded: 1953.

47914 ■ U.S. Small Business Administration - Philadelphia District Office
660 American Ave., Ste. 301
King of Prussia, PA 19406
Ph: (610)382-3062
URL: http://www.sba.gov/district/philadelphia
Contact: Steven R. Dixel, Director
Founded: 1953.

47915 ■ U.S. Small Business Administration - Philadelphia U.S. Export Assistance Center
660 American Ave., Ste. 301
King of Prussia, PA 19406
URL: http://www.sba.gov/business-guide/grow-your-business/export-products

47916 ■ U.S. Small Business Administration (SBA) - Phoenix District Office
4041 N Central Ave., Ste. 1000
Phoenix, AZ 85012
Ph: (602)745-7200
URL: http://www.sba.gov/district/arizona
Contact: Robert J. Blaney, Director
E-mail: robert.blaney@sba.gov
Founded: 1953.

47917 ■ U.S. Small Business Administration (SBA) - Pittsburgh District Office
3 Pky. Center Dr. S, Ste. 375
Pittsburgh, PA 15220
Ph: (412)395-6560
Fax: (412)395-6562
URL: http://www.sba.gov/district/pittsburgh
Contact: Dr. Kelly Hunt, Director
E-mail: kelly.hunt@sba.gov
Linkedin: www.linkedin.com/company/us-small-business-administration
X (Twitter): x.com/SBA_Pittsburgh
Instagram: www.instagram.com/sbagov

47918 ■ U.S. Small Business Administration - Portland District Office
620 SW Main St., Ste. 313
Portland, OR 97205
Ph: (503)326-2682
URL: http://www.sba.gov/district/portland
Contact: Martin Golden, Director
E-mail: martin.golden@sba.gov
Linkedin: www.linkedin.com/showcase/sbaportland
X (Twitter): x.com/SBA_PortlandOR
Founded: 1953.

47919 ■ U.S. Small Business Administration - Puerto Rico and U.S. Virgin Islands District Office
273 Ponce de Leon Ave., Ste. 510
San Juan, PR 00917
Ph: (787)766-5572
URL: http://www.sba.gov/district/puerto-rico-us-virgin-islands
Contact: Josué E. Rivera, Director
Description: Offers loans, loan guarantees, contracts, counseling sessions and other forms of assistance to small businesses in Puerto Rico and U.S. Virgin Islands.

47920 ■ U.S. Small Business Administration Region I (SBA Region I)
10 Cswy. St., Rm. 265
Boston, MA 02222
URL: http://advocacy.sba.gov/tag/region-1
Description: Supports local district offices and works to advocate economic development, growth, and competitiveness within the New England area.

47921 ■ U.S. Small Business Administration Region II
26 Federal Pl., Ste. 3100
New York, NY 10278
Ph: (212)264-4354
URL: http://www.sba.gov/district/metro-new-york
Contact: John Mallano, Director

Description: Supports local district offices and works to advocate economic development, growth, and competitiveness within the Atlantic area. **Founded:** 1953.

47922 ■ U.S. Small Business Administration Region III
660 American Ave., Ste. 301
King of Prussia, PA 19406
URL: http://advocacy.sba.gov/regional-advocates
Contact: Ngozi Bell, Contact
E-mail: ngozi.bell@sba.gov
Description: Supports local district offices and works to advocate economic development, growth, and competitiveness within the Mid-Atlantic area.
Founded: 1953.

47923 ■ U.S. Small Business Administration Region IV
233 Peachtree St. NE, Ste. 300
Atlanta, GA 30303
Ph: (404)331-0100
URL: http://www.sba.gov/sites/sbagov/files/2022-02/COVID-19%20EIDL%20TA%20STA_020320 22_Public-508.pdf
Contact: Allen Thomas, Administrator
Description: Supports local district offices and works to advocate economic development, growth, and competitiveness within the Southeast area.

47924 ■ U.S. Small Business Administration - Region IX Office
409 3rd St., SW
Washington, DC 20416
URL: http://www.sba.gov/person/elmy-bermejo
Contact: Elmy Bermejo, Administrator
Description: Supports local district offices and works to advocate economic development, growth, and competitiveness within the Pacific area.

47925 ■ U.S. Small Business Administration Region V
332 S Michigan Ave., Ste. 600
Chicago, IL 60604
URL: http://www.sba.gov/partners/lenders/cdc50 4-loan-program/rural-initiative-pilot-program
Description: Supports local district offices and works to advocate economic development, growth, and competitiveness within the Great Lakes area.

47926 ■ U.S. Small Business Administration Region VI [South Central Region]
150 W Pky., Ste. 245
Fort Worth, TX 76155
Description: Supports local district offices and works to advocate economic development, growth, and competitiveness within the South Central area.

47927 ■ U.S. Small Business Administration Region VII (SBA Region VII)
1000 Walnut St., Ste. 500
Kansas City, MO 64106
Ph: (816)426-4900
URL: http://www.sba.gov/person/mindy-brissey
Contact: Michael L. Barrera, Director
Description: Supports local district offices and works to advocate economic development, growth, and competitiveness within the Great Plains area.
Founded: 1953.

47928 ■ U.S. Small Business Administration Region VIII (SBA Region VIII)
721 19th St., Ste. 400
Denver, CO 80202
Contact: Aikta Marcoulier, Administrator
Description: Supports local district offices and works to advocate economic development, growth, and competitiveness within the Rocky Mountains area.

47929 ■ U.S. Small Business Administration Region X
2401 4th Ave., Ste. 450
Seattle, WA 98121
Ph: (206)553-7310
URL: http://www.sba.gov/district/seattle

Description: Supports local district offices and works to advocate economic development, growth, and competitiveness within Pacific Northwest area.
Founded: 1953.

47930 ■ U.S. Small Business Administration - Rhode Island District Office
380 Westminster St., Rm. 511
Providence, RI 02903
Ph: (401)528-4561
URL: http://www.sba.gov/about-sba/sba-locations/sba-district-offices
Contact: Mark S. Hayward, Director
E-mail: mark.hayward@sba.gov
X (Twitter): x.com/SBA_RhodeIsland
Founded: 1953.

47931 ■ U.S. Small Business Administration - Richmond District Office
400 N 8th St., Ste. 1150
Richmond, VA 23219
Ph: (804)771-2400
URL: http://www.sba.gov/offices/district/va/richmond
Contact: Carl B. Knoblock, Director
E-mail: carl.b.knoblock@sba.gov
X (Twitter): x.com/SBA_Virginia
Founded: 1953.

47932 ■ U.S. Small Business Administration - Sacramento Branch Office
6501 Sylvan Ave.
Citrus Heights, CA 95610
Ph: (916)735-1700
URL: http://www.sba.gov/district/sacramento
Contact: Heather Luzzi, Director
E-mail: heather.luzzi@sba.gov

47933 ■ U.S. Small Business Administration - Sacramento District Office
6501 Sylvan Ave.
Citrus Heights, CA 95610
Ph: (916)735-1700
Co. E-mail: sacramento_do@sba.gov
URL: http://www.sba.gov/district/sacramento
Contact: Heather Luzzi, Director

47934 ■ U.S. Small Business Administration - St. Croix Post of Duty
409 3rd St. SW
Washington, DC 20416
Ph: (340)718-5381
Fax: (340)718-1102
URL: http://www.sba.gov/local-resources/puerto-rico?page=5&location=christiansted-st-croix&order=field_cdc_504_loan_amount&sort=asc
Description: Offers loans, loan guarantees, contracts, counseling sessions and other forms of assistance to small businesses in St. Croix. **Founded:** 1953.

47935 ■ U.S. Small Business Administration - St. Louis District Office
1222 Spruce St., Ste. 10.103
Saint Louis, MO 63103
Ph: (314)539-6600
URL: http://www.sba.gov/district/st-louis
Contact: Maureen E. Brinkley, Director
Founded: 1953.

47936 ■ U.S. Small Business Administration - Salt Lake City District Office
125 S State St., Ste. 2227
Salt Lake City, UT 84138
Ph: (801)524-3209
Fax: (801)524-4160
Co. E-mail: utahgeneral@sba.gov
URL: http://www.sba.gov/district/utah
Contact: Marla Trollan, Director
E-mail: marla.trollan@sba.gov

47937 ■ U.S. Small Business Administration (SADO) - San Antonio District Office
615 E Houston St., Ste. 298
San Antonio, TX 78205
Ph: (210)403-5900
Fax: (210)403-5936
Co. E-mail: sado.email@sba.gov
URL: http://www.sba.gov/district/san-antonio

Contact: Mary Hernandez, Director
E-mail: mary.hernandez@sba.gov
X (Twitter): x.com/SBA_SanAntonio
Founded: 1953.

47938 ■ U.S. Small Business Administration - San Diego District Office
550 W C St., Ste. 550
San Diego, CA 92101
Ph: (619)557-7250
URL: http://www.sba.gov/district/san-diego
Contact: Ruben R. Garcia, Director
E-mail: ruben.garcia@sba.gov
Description: Offers loans, loan guarantees, contracts, counseling sessions and other forms of assistance to small businesses in San Diego. **Founded:** 1953.

47939 ■ U.S. Small Business Administration (SFDO) - San Francisco District Office
455 Market St., Ste. 600
San Francisco, CA 94105
Ph: (415)744-6820
URL: http://www.sba.gov/district/san-francisco
Contact: Chris Horton, Director
X (Twitter): x.com/SBA_SF
Founded: 1953.

47940 ■ U.S. Small Business Administration (SADO) - Santa Ana District Office
5 Hutton Centre Dr., Ste. 900
Santa Ana, CA 92707
Ph: (714)550-7420
URL: http://www.sba.gov/district/orange-county-inland-empire
Contact: J. Adalberto Quijada, Director
E-mail: adalberto.quijada@sba.gov
Founded: 1953.

47941 ■ U.S. Small Business Administration - SBA/Greater El Paso Chamber of Commerce - Business Information Center
303 N Oregon Str., Ste. 610.
El Paso, TX 79901
Ph: (915)534-0500
Co. E-mail: info@elpaso.org
URL: http://www.elpaso.org
Contact: David Jerome, President
E-mail: david@elpaso.org
Facebook: www.facebook.com/ElPasoChamber
Linkedin: www.linkedin.com/company/greater-el-paso-chamber-of-commerce
X (Twitter): x.com/EPC915
Instagram: www.instagram.com/elpasochamber
YouTube: www.youtube.com/channel/UC3U1WjPrpeluQLqoYbWULUA

47942 ■ U.S. Small Business Administration - Seattle District Office
2401 4th Ave., Ste. 450
Seattle, WA 98121
Ph: (206)553-7310
Co. E-mail: infosdo@sba.gov
URL: http://www.sba.gov/district/seattle
Contact: Kerrie Hurd, Director
E-mail: kerrie.hurd@sba.gov
X (Twitter): x.com/SBASeattle

47943 ■ U.S. Small Business Administration (SFDO) - Sioux Falls District Office
200 N Phillips Ave., Ste. L101
Sioux Falls, SD 57104
Ph: (605)330-4243
Co. E-mail: southdakota_do@sba.gov
URL: http://www.sba.gov/district/south-dakota
Contact: Jaime Wood, Director
E-mail: jaime.wood@sba.gov

47944 ■ U.S. Small Business Administration - South Carolina District Office (SCDO)
1835 Assembly St., Ste. 1425
Columbia, SC 29201
Ph: (803)765-5377
URL: http://www.sba.gov/district/south-carolina
Contact: Richard Gregg White, Director
E-mail: richard.white@sba.gov

47945 ■ U.S. Small Business Administration - South Dakota District Office
200 N Phillips Ave., Ste. L101
Sioux Falls, SD 57104
Ph: (605)330-4243
Co. E-mail: southdakota_do@sba.gov
URL: http://www.sba.gov/district/south-dakota
Contact: Jaime Wood, Director
E-mail: jaime.wood@sba.gov
Linkedin: www.linkedin.com/showcase/sbasouthdakota
X (Twitter): x.com/SBA_SouthDakota
Founded: 1953.

47946 ■ U.S. Small Business Administration (SFDO) - South Florida District Office
51 SW 1st Ave., Ste. 201
Miami, FL 33130
Ph: (305)536-5521
Fax: (305)536-5521
Co. E-mail: southflorida_do@sba.gov
URL: http://www.sba.gov/offices/district/fl/miami
Contact: Malcom Richards, Director
E-mail: jon.richards@sba.gov
Linkedin: www.linkedin.com/showcase/sbasouthflorida
X (Twitter): x.com/SBA_SouthFL
Founded: 1953.

47947 ■ U.S. Small Business Administration - Spokane Branch Office
801 W Riverside Ave., Ste. 444
Spokane, WA 99201
Ph: (509)353-2800
Co. E-mail: infosdo@sba.gov
URL: http://www.sba.gov/offices/district/wa/seattle
Contact: Joel Nania, Branch Manager
E-mail: joel.nania@sba.gov
Description: Serving Eastern Washington and Northern Idaho.

47948 ■ U.S. Small Business Administration - Springfield Branch Office
3330 Ginger Creek Rd., Ste. B
Springfield, IL 62711
Ph: (312)353-4528
Co. E-mail: illinois.do@sba.gov
URL: http://www.sba.gov/district/illinois
Contact: Robert Steiner, Director
X (Twitter): x.com/SBA_Illinois
Founded: 1953.

47949 ■ U.S. Small Business Administration - Springfield Branch Office
901 E Saint Louis St., Ste. 704
Springfield, MO 65806
Ph: (417)501-0542
URL: http://www.sba.gov/district/kansas-city
Contact: Michael L. Barrera, Director
E-mail: michael.barrera@sba.gov
Founded: 1953.

47950 ■ U.S. Small Business Administration - Syracuse District Office
224 Harrison St., Ste. 506
Syracuse, NY 13202
Ph: (315)471-9393
URL: http://www.sba.gov/district/syracuse
Contact: Jeffrey Boyce, Manager
E-mail: jeffrey.boyce@sba.gov

47951 ■ U.S. Small Business Administration - Tennessee District Office
2 International Plz. Dr., Ste. 500
Nashville, TN 37217
Ph: (615)736-5881
URL: http://www.sba.gov/district/tennessee
Contact: David Glasgow, Director
X (Twitter): x.com/SBA_Tennessee

47952 ■ U.S. Small Business Administration (US SBA) - U.S. Export Assistance Center (USEACs)
c/o David Leonard
230 Peachtree St. NW, Ste. 1725
Atlanta, GA 30303
Ph: (404)242-6373

Co. E-mail: david.leonard@sba.gov
URL: http://www.sba.gov/business-guide/grow-your-business/export-products
Contact: David Leonard, Contact
E-mail: david.leonard@sba.gov
Description: Serves Georgia, Alabama, Kentucky, Tennessee, Mississippi. **Founded:** 1953.

47953 ■ U.S. Small Business Administration (SBA) - U.S. Export Assistance Center
100 S Charles St., Ste. 1201
Baltimore, MD 21201
Ph: (410)962-6195
URL: http://www.sba.gov/district/baltimore
Contact: Stephen D. Umberger, Director
Description: Serves Maryland, Virginia, West Virginia, and District of Columbia.

47954 ■ U.S. Small Business Administration - U.S. Export Assistance Center (USEACS)
10 Cswy. St., Rm. 265
Boston, MA 02222
URL: http://www.sba.gov/business-guide/grow-your-business/export-products
Description: Serves Maine, Vermont, New Hampshire, Massachusetts, Connecticut, and Rhode Island.

47955 ■ U.S. Small Business Administration - U.S. Export Assistance Center (USEACS)
332 S Michigan Ave., Ste.600
Chicago, IL 60604
Ph: (312)353-4528
URL: http://www.sba.gov/district/illinois
Contact: Robert Steiner, Director
Description: Serves Wisconsin, Illinois, and Indiana. **Founded:** 1953.

47956 ■ U.S. Small Business Administration - U.S. Export Assistance Center (USEAC)
409 3rd St. SW
Washington, DC 20416
URL: http://www.sba.gov/local-assistance/export-trade-assistance/us-export-assistance-centers

47957 ■ U.S. Small Business Administration - U.S. Export Assistance Center (USEACs)
440 Burroughs St., Ste. 390
Detroit, MI 48226
Ph: (313)872-6794
URL: http://www.sba.gov/local-assistance/export-trade-assistance/us-export-assistance-centers
Description: Serves Michigan.

47958 ■ U.S. Small Business Administration - U.S. Export Assistance Center
2302 Martin Ct., Ste. 315
Irvine, CA 92612
Ph: (949)660-1688
URL: http://www.sba.gov/local-assistance/export-trade-assistance/us-export-assistance-centers
Description: Serves Southern California, Nevada, Arizona, and Hawaii. **Founded:** 1953.

47959 ■ U.S. Small Business Administration - U.S. Export Assistance Center
409 3rd St., SW
Washington, DC 20416
URL: http://www.sba.gov/business-guide/grow-your-business/export-products
Description: Serves Florida.

47960 ■ U.S. Small Business Administration - U.S. Export Assistance Center (USEACs)
409 3rd St., SW
Washington, DC 20416
URL: http://www.sba.gov/business-guide/grow-your-business/export-products
Description: Serves South Dakota, Nebraska, Iowa, Kansas, and Missouri.

47961 ■ U.S. Small Business Administration - U.S. Export Assistance Center
2001 6th Ave., Ste. 2600
Seattle, WA 98121
URL: http://www.sba.gov/local-assistance/export-trade-assistance/us-export-assistance-centers

47962 ■ U.S. Small Business Administration - Vermont District Office
400 Cornerstone Dr., Ste. 240
 Williston, VT 05495
Ph: (802)828-4422
URL: http://www.sba.gov/district/vermont
Contact: Darcy Carter, Director
Description: Provides millions of loans, loan guarantees, contracts, counseling sessions and other forms of assistance to small businesses.

47963 ■ U.S. Small Business Administration (SBA) - West Virginia District Office (WVDO)
320 W Pke. St., Ste. 330
 Clarksburg, WV 26301
Ph: (304)623-5631
Fax: (304)623-0023
Co. E-mail: wvinfo@sba.gov
URL: http://www.sba.gov/district/west-virginia
Contact: Karen Friel, Director
E-mail: karen.friel@sba.gov

47964 ■ U.S. Small Business Administration - Wichita District Office
220 W Douglas Ave., Ste. 450
 Wichita, KS 67202
Ph: (316)269-6616
Co. E-mail: wichita_do@sba.gov
URL: http://www.sba.gov/district/wichita
Contact: Wayne E. Bell, Director
E-mail: wayne.bell@sba.gov
X (Twitter): x.com/sba_wichita

47965 ■ U.S. Small Business Administration - Wilkes-Barre Branch Office
7 N Wilkes Barre Blvd., Ste. 4M
 Wilkes Barre, PA 18702
Ph: (610)382-3062
URL: http://www.sba.gov/district/philadelphia
Contact: Steven R. Dixel, Director
Description: Government provides agency programs and services more accessible to the northern tier of Pennsylvania and better connects the agency with the lending and small business communities that it serves.

47966 ■ U.S. Small Business Administration - Wilmington Branch Office
1105 Market St., Lobby Level, Ste. 02
 Wilmington, DE 19801
URL: http://www.sba.gov/district/delaware
Contact: Jim Provo, Contact

47967 ■ U.S. Small Business Administration (WDO) - Wisconsin District Office
310 W Wisconsin Ave., Ste. 580W
 Milwaukee, WI 53203
Ph: (414)297-3941
Co. E-mail: wisconsin@sba.gov
URL: http://www.sba.gov/district/wisconsin
Contact: Eric Ness, Director
E-mail: eric.ness@sba.gov
Linkedin: www.linkedin.com/showcase/sbawisconsin

X (Twitter): x.com/SBA_Wisconsin

47968 ■ U.S. Small Business Administration (US SBA) - Wyoming District Office (WDO)
150 E, B St., Rm. 1011
 Casper, WY 82601
Ph: (307)261-6500
URL: http://www.sba.gov/district/wyoming
Contact: Amy Lea, Director
E-mail: amy.lea@sba.gov
Description: Offers loans, loan guarantees, contracts, counseling sessions and other forms of assistance to small businesses in Wyoming.

REFERENCE WORKS

47969 ■ "$10,000 Grants Available for Women-Owned Businesses" in Small Business Trends(February 4, 2023)
URL(s): smallbiztrends.com/2023/02/latest-small-business-grants-for-women-february-2023.html
Ed: Annie Pilon. **Released:** February 04, 2023.
Description: Provides details on grants available for women-owned businesses. **Availability:** Online.

47970 ■ "The Best Small Business Government Grants in 2023" in Business News Daily (February 21, 2023)
URL(s): www.businessnewsdaily.com/15758-government-grants-for-small-businesses.html
Ed: Skye Schooley. **Released:** February 21, 2023.
Description: A discussion of small business grants available for small businesses. **Availability:** Online.

47971 ■ "Grants of Up to $20,000 Available for Building Upgrades, Startup Expenses, and More" in Small Business Trends(February 18, 2023)
URL(s): smallbiztrends.com/2023/02/grants-for-building-upgrades-startup-expenses-and-more.html
Ed: Annie Pilon. **Released:** February 18, 2023.
Description: Provides details about small business grants available. **Availability:** Online.

47972 ■ "Grants Up to $50,000 Available for Businesses across the U.S." in Small Business Trends(January 14, 2023)
URL(s): smallbiztrends.com/2023/01/latest-grants-for-businesses-america.html
Ed: Annie Pilon. **Released:** January 14, 2023.
Description: Discusses current small business grants that are open for applications. **Availability:** Online.

47973 ■ "In the News: Grants of Up To $20,000 for Small Business Improvements and More" in Small Business Trends(February 24, 2023)
URL(s): smallbiztrends.com/2023/02/small-business-news-roundup-february-24-2023.html

Released: February 24, 2023. **Description:** Provides details on grants available to assist small business with developments and repair projects. **Availability:** Online.

47974 ■ "In the News: Hundreds of Millions of Dollars Available to Small Businesses from SSBCI" in Small Business Trends(March 3, 2023)
URL(s): smallbiztrends.com/2023/03/weeklsmall-business-news-roundup-march-3-2023.html
Released: March 03, 2023. **Description:** Small businesses can apply for funding through the State Small Business Credit Initiative in order to provide help for their long-term survival. **Availability:** Online.

47975 ■ "In the News: New Pandemic Relief Grant Programs of $500 to $35K for Small Businesses" in Small Business Trends(January 27, 2023)
URL(s): smallbiztrends.com/2023/01/small-business-news-roundup-january-27-2023.html
Released: January 27, 2023. **Description:** Small businesses can benefit with funds obtained through some new pandemic relief grants. Details are discussed. **Availability:** Online.

47976 ■ "Millions in Grant Funding Available to Help Businesses with Employee Training, Storefront Improvements" in Small Business Trends(January 5, 2023)
URL(s): smallbiztrends.com/2023/01/grant-funding-for-businesses-with-employee-training.html
Ed: Annie Pilon. **Released:** January 05, 2023.
Description: Discusses some available small business grants. **Availability:** Online.

47977 ■ "Pandemic Recovery Grant Programs Launch Additional Funding Rounds" in Small Business Trends (March 11, 2023)
URL(s): smallbiztrends.com/2023/03/latest-pandemic-recovery-business-grant-programs.html
Ed: Annie Pilon. **Released:** March 11, 2023. **Description:** Some grant programs used in the COVID pandemic are relaunching in order to continue providing funds for struggling small businesses. Details about the grants are included. **Availability:** Online.

47978 ■ "Up to $2 Million in Grants Available for Dairy Businesses, Child Care Centers, and More" in Small Business Trends(February 26, 2023)
URL(s): smallbiztrends.com/2023/02/grants-for-dairy-businesses-child-care-centers.html
Ed: Annie Pilon. **Released:** February 26, 2023.
Description: Industry-specific grant programs are available. Details about the grants are given. **Availability:** Online.

Master Index

This index provides an alphabetical listing of all organizations, products, services, and other activities covered in the Descriptive Listings section of this directory. Citations include organization, product, or service name, followed by book entry number(s). Entry numbers appear in boldface type if the reference is to the organization for which information is provided and in lightface type if the reference is to a former or alternate name included within the text of a cited entry.

NUMERICS

"1 in 3 Americans Frustrated with Patient Billing, Collections" in RevCycle Intelligence (October 18, 2019) **[10889]**

"1 in 4 Food Delivery Drivers Admit to Eating Your Food" in NPR (July 30, 2019) **[6893]**, **[11692]**, **[23464]**

1-800-Got-Junk L.L.C. **[2085]**

1-800-Radiator **[33311]**

"1Q Office Vacancies Mainly Up; Class A Space Bucks Trend, Falls" in Crain's Detroit Business (Vol. 24, April 14, 2008, No. 15) **[12870]**, **[13122]**, **[13368]**, **[19154]**

"1st Black-Owned Beauty Supply Store in Nashville Made $50,000 in it's First 3 Hours of Opening!" in Soultanicals (March 4, 2019) **[1385]**, **[44856]**

1st Source Capital Corp. **[39627]**

"2 New Tools for Safeguarding Your Website: Website Backup Made Simple" in Inc. (Vol. 33, September 2011, No. 7, pp. 52) **[9089]**, **[16378]**, **[33088]**, **[33824]**

"2nd Watch Rides AWS Market Maturity to 400% Growth" in Computer Business Week (August 28, 2014, pp. 21) **[3477]**, **[3607]**, **[16379]**, **[26200]**, **[33089]**

3 Alternative Ways to Fund Your Startup **[30902]**, **[34482]**

"3 Big Trends in 2019 Indie Books, According to Publishing Startup Reedsy's CEO" in Forbes (March 4, 2019) **[1635]**

"3 Business Situations That Are Ripe for Mediation" in Small Business Trends (January 21, 2020) **[10792]**

"3 Business Terms All Self-Employed People Need to Understand" in Due (September 7, 2018) **[32983]**

3 Challenges Social Impact Startups Face Now with Paul Zelizer **[34582]**

3+ Corporation **[46731]**

3 Day Startup (3DS) **[45493]**

"3 Hard Parts of Starting a Plumbing Business" in Home Business (December 12, 2019) **[12612]**

"3 Key Growth Elements for Small Security Integrators" in Security Distributing & Marketing (Vol. 42, July 2012, No. 7, pp. 108) **[14380]**, **[17895]**, **[31150]**

"3 Lessons on Launching From 3 Young, Early-Stage Founders" in Entrepreneur (Sept. 1, 2020) **[36009]**

"3 Market Research Tips for Small Business" in Small Business Computing.com **[29483]**

"$3 Million in Repairs Prep Cobo for Auto Show" in Crain's Detroit Business (Vol. 26, January 4, 2010, No. 1, pp. 1) **[11366]**, **[15826]**, **[20717]**, **[29090]**, **[35019]**

"The 3 Pillars of Corporate Sustainability" in Investopedia (June 29, 2021) **[34263]**

"3 Proven Sustainability Practices for Small Businesses" in Hazardous Waste Experts Blog (March 3, 2015) **[23070]**, **[34264]**

"3 Questions with Andrew Tosh, CEO of GameSim Inc. - and Brother to a Star" in Orlando Business Journal (Vol. 30, April 18, 2014, No. 43, pp. 8) **[577]**, **[19466]**, **[33337]**

"3 Question for Stephen Purpura, CEO of the Big-Data Startup Context Relevant" in Puget Sound Business Journal (Vol. 35, May 23, 2014, No. 5, pp. 10) **[3473]**, **[3597]**, **[6224]**

"3 Signs Your Employees Hate Their Jobs (and What to Do About It)" in Business News Daily (March 6, 2023) **[22069]**

"3 Tattoo Studio Marketing Strategies That Are Extremely Easy to Execute" in TattooPro blog (Sept. 6, 2020) **[15286]**

"3 Things Employers Should Do Before Philadelphia's New Wage History Law Goes Into Effect" in Philadelphia Business Journal (August 18, 2020) **[35472]**

3 Things Social Entrepreneurs Do that Stop Growth **[34413]**

"3 Tips to Help Small Business Owners Calculate Payroll Taxes" in Hiscox Blog **[31624]**

"3 Tricks Criminals Use to Undermine Jewelry Store Security" in Jewelers of America (November 6, 2019) **[9971]**

"3 Types of Grants Available to Seniors" in SeniorAdvisor Blog **[33057]**

"3 Ways Entrepreneurs Can Implement Sustainable Practices in 2022" in Forbes (Jan. 30, 2022) **[23071]**

"3 Ways to Make Your Business More Customer-Centric" in Legal Zoom (February 21, 2023) **[20375]**

"Three Ways Proposed New $300M-$400M Megamall, Hotel May Change I-Drive" in Orlando Business Journal (Vol. 30, May 9, 2014, No. 46, pp. 9) **[3969]**, **[8354]**, **[32088]**

"3 Ways a Strong Brand Identity Can Lead to Greater Success for Your Small Business" in Entrepreneur (July 25, 2021) **[17427]**

The 3i Show **[17159]**

"3M Teams Up with Graphic Design Company Wrapmate" in Twin Cities Business (September 25, 2019) **[3292]**, **[31151]**

"3Par: Storing Up Value" in Barron's (Vol. 90, August 30, 2010, No. 35, pp. 30) **[3478]**, **[3691]**, **[6240]**, **[9303]**, **[19767]**, **[21773]**, **[30670]**, **[31152]**

3Pe Consulting **[42259]**

"3PL Logistics Team Enters Distribution Market" in Memphis Business Journal (Vol. 33, March 16, 2012, No. 49, pp. 1) **[20607]**

"3rd Annual 'OneMedForum NY 2012', July 11th-12th, to Spotlight JOBS Act, Crowdfunding, and Promising Areas for Healthcare Investment" in Investment Weekly (June 23, 2012) **[15827]**, **[28053]**, **[30887]**, **[31926]**, **[32704]**, **[35223]**

4 Actions Your Small Business Can Take to Make Change **[34414]**

"4 Analytics Categories to Track to Improve Your Marketing Strategy" in Forbes (October 22, 2020) **[29515]**

"The 4 Big Reasons Apps Fail" in Engrepreneur (September 3, 2019) **[16380]**

"4 Cash Flow Challenges Facing Small Business Owners Today" in Forbes (April 21, 2019) **[19705]**

The 4 Commitments to Grow Your Reach Online **[17459]**

"4 Credit Repair Company Lies — and How to Fix Your Score Without Help" in MoneyTalksNews (June 18, 2019) **[4737]**

The 4 Elements You Need to Build a Bulletproof PR Plan with Billion-Dollar Founder Suneer Madhani **[31803]**

"4 Essential Hires if You're Starting a Business in 2020" in Bplans **[26480]**, **[34483]**

4 Final Lessons of Being Boss **[19631]**

"4 Financing Options for Agriculture Business Owners" in FORA Financial (Jan. 30, 2020) **[16981]**, **[23718]**

"4 Great Resources to Simplify Hiring" in Small Business Trends(December 10, 2018) **[26481]**

"The 4 Hottest Industries to Start a Businesses in for 2020" in Bplans **[18878]**, **[34484]**

4 Key Elements of a Small Business Owner's Estate Plan **[6019]**

4 Leaf Consulting **[5064]**

4 Mistakes to Avoid When Starting a Sewing Business **[14644]**

"4 Reasons Small Businesses Need Nonbank Lenders More Than Ever" in Entrepreneur (Aug. 30, 2021) **[30903]**

4 Reasons Why Auto Repair Shops Need Business Insurance **[14544]**

"4 Rivers Smokehouse Eyes Four New Locations in Florida" in Orlando Business Journal (Vol. 29, August 10, 2012, No. 8, pp. 1) **[13894]**

"4 Signs You Hired a Bad Home Inspector" in U.S.News & World Report (August 28, 2015) **[2016]**

"4 Small-Business Communication Trends (and How They Improve Customer Experience)" in CallRail Blog (Nov. 11, 2021) **[17621]**

"4 Small Business Groups You Can Join for Free" in Nav (February 22, 2017) **[18836]**

"4 Strategies for Sustainable Businesses" in MIT Management Sloan School Ideas Made to Matter (Nov. 30, 2021) **[23072]**

"4 Tasty Ways to Work Nutrition into Your Fitness Business" in Glofox blog (February 14, 2019) **[12390]**

4 Team-Building Techniques That Work for Small Business **[22070]**

4 Things Commercial Photographers Need to Discuss with Their Small Business Clients **[12296]**

"4 Things You Need To Know About Credit Scores: What Millennials Don't Know Can Hurt Their Finances" in Black Enterprise (Vol. 45, July-August 2014, No. 1, pp. 64) **[4709]**, **[4738]**, **[4762]**, **[23719]**

"4 Tips for Managing Cash Flow in a Seasonal Business" in Entrepreneur (Dec. 9, 2017) **[32943]**

"4 Traits That Have Helped Small Businesses Survive the Pandemic" in Entrepreneur (Sept. 21, 2021) **[22470]**

"4 Types of Gym Employees Who Will Power Your Hybrid Success" in Glofox blog (October 26, 2020) **[12391]**

"4 Visa Programs That Can Help Employers Solve Their Workforce Needs" in U.S. Chamber of Commerce (Nov. 12, 2021) **[30524]**, **[35168]**

4 Ways AI Is Helping Small Businesses in Sales & Marketing **[29614]**, **[32450]**

4 Ways Small Businesses Benefit from Responsible Waste Management **[7942]**

"4 Ways You Can Safely Address and Combat Drug Addiction in the Workplace" in Inc. **[34674]**

4aBetterBusiness, Inc. **[2205]**

4Pillars Consulting Group Inc. **[6713]**

4Refuel **[33312]**

4th Generation Systems **[32690]**

"5 Automotive Tool Franchises" in Small Business Trends (February 15, 2023) **[24313]**

"5 Best Fitness Apps for Kids" in MentalUP(June 24, 2022) **[6812]**, **[12392]**

"The 5 Best Non-Traditional Funding Tactics for Your Small Business" in Yelp Business Blog (June 14, 2019) **[30904]**

The 5 Best Personal Trainer Certifications **[12393]**

5 Best Screen Printing Machines for Small Business **[14349]**

"5 Book Genre Trends We Predict for 2019" in Mythos & Ink (January 3, 2019) **[1636]**

"5 Business Lessons From Bob's Burgers" in Business News Daily (March 20, 2023) **[23589]**

"5 Business Structures: Find the Right One for Your Small Business" in Business News Daily (April 12, 2022) **[27166]**, **[34485]**

"5 Businesses You Could Start In Retirement for Under $5,000" in Forbes (Feb. 27, 2020) **[33058]**

"5 Cash Management Tactics Small Businesses Use to Become Bigger Businesses" in Entrepreneur (April 23, 2018) **[19706]**

"5 Challenges for Family-Owned Businesses" in SCORE Blog (April 16, 2018) **[23590]**

"5 Characteristics of Successful Entrepreneurs" in Investopedia (March 13, 2021) **[22471]**

5 Master Index

"5 Conversations: How to Transform Trust, Engagement and Performance at Work" **[22071]**
"5 E-Commerce Landmines You Need to Avoid" in Legal Zoom (February 15, 2023) **[11693]**
"5 E-Commerce Must-Haves That Will Save You Time and Money" in Legal Zoom (March 15, 2023) **[11694]**
"5 Effective Ways to Beat Your Competition" in business. com (Jan. 31, 2022) **[19768]**
"5 Employee Theft Prevention Strategies" by U.S. Chamber of Commerce **[22339]**
5 Entrepreneurial Skills to Master (Absolutely!) As an Entrepreneur **[22472]**
"5 Global Trends Affecting the Art Market This Fall" in Artsy (September 10, 2019) **[966]**, **[1067]**
"5 Great Corporate Wellness Program Ideas for Your Fitness Business" in Glofox blog (August 14, 2019) **[12394]**
5 Impactful Ways to Grow Your Coffee Business This Year **[3175]**
"5 Inexpensive Branding Strategies for Small Businesses" in 99designs (2016) **[17428]**
"The 5 Keys to Successful Marketing" in Massage Magazine (January 10, 2019) **[10758]**, **[29615]**
"5 Marketing Missteps That Make Cash Flow and Business Growth Stumble" in Entrepreneur (January 25, 2018) **[19707]**, **[29616]**
"5 Marketing Practices Most Landscaping Contractors Get Wrong" in Lawn & Landscape (March 2, 2017) **[10084]**
5 Marketing Tips for Dog Trainers **[12135]**
"5 Mistakes to Avoid When Choosing Your Business Entity" in Legal Zoom (March 14, 2023) **[27167]**
"5 Mistakes to Avoid When Selling Your Small Business" in The Balance Small Business (April 12, 2019) **[19218]**
5 Must Ask Questions Before You Open a Photography Studio **[12338]**
"5 Must-Have Tools for Refurbishing Wood Furniture" in The Spruce (February 2, 2019) **[7238]**
"5 Occupational Safety and Health Trends to Watch in 2020" in The Link (December 11, 2019) **[30941]**
5 Powerful Ways to Take REAL Action on DEI **[30525]**
5 Priorities for Hiring & Retaining Women in Tech **[26201]**
"5 Productivity Tools for Self-Employed Internet Entrepreneurs" in Entrepreneur (January 23, 2017) **[32984]**
"5 Reasons Small Businesses Should Adopt a CSR Strategy & How To Do It" in America's Charities (Jan. 21, 2021) **[34265]**
"5 Reasons Why E-Waste Management Is a Must for Small Businesses - And What You Can Do About It" in Credibly Blog **[7943]**
"5 Reasons Why Incubators Are So Popular" in Geekers Magazine (August 31, 2021) **[8826]**
"5 Reasons Why Right Now Is Prime Time for Women-Owned Businesses" in GoSite Blog (March 8, 2021) **[35731]**
"5 Reasons Why UX Design Is Important for Your Website in 2020" in Digital Agency Network (October 25, 2020) **[16381]**
"5 Simple Project Management Organization Tips" in Small Business Trends (August 31, 2022) **[28432]**
5 Simple Strategies to Increase Online Sales in Small Business **[32451]**
"5 Simple Ways to Pinpoint Your Brand's Target Audience" in Business.com (June 4, 2020) **[34707]**
"5 Skills Every Entrepreneur Should Have" in Investopedia (Apr 5, 2021) **[22473]**
"5-Step Guide on How to Do Market Research for Your Business" in Small Business Rainmaker Blog (November 3, 2020) **[29484]**
"5 Steps to Filing Partnership Taxes" in Legal Zoom (February 28, 2023) **[31153]**, **[34722]**
"5 Steps to Starting a Consulting Business" in Legal Zoom (March 24, 2023) **[20080]**, **[32985]**
"5 Steps for Writing an Executive Summary" in Business News Daily (February 21, 2023) **[18879]**
"5 Straightforward Ways to Go from Employed to Self-Employed" in Forbes.com(October 26, 2022) **[5307]**, **[26758]**
"5 Strategies of 'Psychological Pricing'" in Entrepreneur (July 21, 2016) **[31649]**
"5 Surprising Things an Answering Service Can Do for Your Business" in Small Business Trends (March 20, 2018) **[15558]**
"5 Sustainable Businesses in 2020 & Their Best Practices" in FlyGreen Blog (February 26, 2020) **[23073]**
"5 Things Every Fitness Founder Needs to Know About Gym Membership Sales" in Glofox blog (February 12, 2019) **[12395]**
"5 Things to Know Before Becoming a Professional Organizer" in Pro Organizer Studio Blog **[12807]**
"5 Things You Need to Know About Water Parks, But Probably Don't" in healthychildren.org (June 6, 2019) **[600]**, **[15238]**
5 Things You Need to Know Before Opening a Dispensary **[4983]**
"5 Things You Should Know About Getting a Small Business Loan: Insights From a Banking Executive to Improve Your Odds" in Black Enterprise (Vol. 44, June 2014, No. 10, pp. 20) **[28086]**
5 Things You Should Know About the Highest Paying Translation Services **[15929]**
"5 Things You Should Know If Your Bank Fails" in Black Enterprise (Vol. 41, December 2010, No. 5, pp. 29) **[6241]**, **[23720]**, **[25195]**, **[33936]**
"5 Tips to Attract New Online Customers" in Legal Zoom (March 9, 2023) **[11695]**, **[16902]**, **[29617]**
"5 Tips for Better Small Business Networking" in The Balance Small Business (October 17, 2018) **[18837]**
"5 Tips for Choosing the Right Location for Your Automotive Business" in Small Business Trends (May 9, 2018) **[14545]**
"5 Tips for Designing a Logo for Your Online Store" in Digital Agency Network (October 27, 2020) **[16382]**
"5 Tips for Hiring a Franchise Business Coach" in Entrepreneur (Aug. 10, 2017) **[24314]**
"5 Tips to Protect Your Brand on Social Media" in Legal Zoom (March 16, 2023) **[29516]**, **[29618]**
"5 Tips for Starting a Carpentry Business" in Woodworking Network (November 28, 2018) **[2634]**
"5 Tips to Stay Labor Law Compliant" in Legal Zoom (February 10, 2023) **[26482]**, **[26871]**
"5 Tips for a Top-Notch Residential Lease" in Legal Zoom (March 27, 2023) **[12871]**, **[13123]**
"5 Tutor Marketing Strategies" in TutorCruncher (Nov. 30, 2021) **[16126]**
"The 5 Types of Business Networking Organizations" in Entrepreneur (November 1, 2017) **[18838]**
5 Ways to Build Customer Relationships for Your Small Business **[20376]**
5 Ways Business Incubator Programs Can Help Your Startup Grow **[8803]**
"5 Ways to Create a Better Golf Shop" in Golf Inc. (June 19, 2017) **[7515]**
"5 Ways Entrepreneurs Learn to Manage Risk" in Entrepreneur (February 18, 2015) **[32382]**
"5 Ways a Franchise Can Grow Fast" in Entrepreneur (January 14, 2020) **[24315]**
"5 Ways to Get a Free Website for Your Small Business" in Business 2 Community (September 29, 2021) **[16383]**, **[33532]**
"5 Ways to Get More Cash Flowing Into Your Business" in Forbes (February 24, 2019) **[19708]**
"5 Ways to Motivate Small Business Staff" in ZenBusiness (Dec. 13, 2021) **[22072]**
5 Ways to Spot Small Business Fraud **[19250]**
"5 Ways To Improve Your Communication in Business and Why It's Important" in Indeed (Feb. 22, 2021) **[17622]**
"5 Ways to Use Video Marketing to Strengthen Your Small Business Branding" in Insider (Feb. 26, 2021) **[29619]**
"The 5 Worst Cash-Flow Mistakes Small-Business Owners Make" in Entrepreneur (September 25, 2015) **[19709]**
5AM Venture Management L.L.C. **[37268]**
"6 Best Accounts Receivable Software for Small Businesses" in FreshBooks Hub **[16773]**
"The 6 Best Advertising Strategies for Small Businesses" in Entrepreneur (April 20, 2016) **[31848]**
"The 6 Best Financing Options for Franchising a Business" in Entrepreneur (May 16, 2018) **[24316]**
"6 Biggest Business Insurance Risks (and How to Mitigate Them)" in Business News Daily (February 21, 2023) **[27229]**
"6 Common IRS Tax Penalties on Small Business Owners" in allBusiness **[31625]**
6 Common Scams That Target Small Businesses **[19251]**
"6 Core Competencies for Mechanical Insulation Site Foremen" in Insulation Outlook (September 1, 2019) **[8849]**
"The 6 Different Types of Lawyers for Small Businesses" in Fora Financial Blog (May 19, 2021) **[18500]**
"6 Effective Yoga Marketing Tips to Take Your Studio to the Next Level" in Glofox blog (April 2, 2019) **[12396]**, **[29620]**
"6 Goals Every Small Business Needs to Set" in inBusiness **[19467]**
6 Great Marketing Strategies Your Tattoo Studio Needs to Try **[15287]**
"The 6 Legal Steps to Closing Sale of Your Business" in ExitAdviser (August 31, 2018) **[19219]**
"6 Legalese Terms Every Franchisee Should Understand" in Entrepreneur (Aug. 3, 2017) **[24317]**
"6 Lessons from Audit Experts Who Adopted AI Early" in Journal of Accountancy (November 23, 2021) **[1742]**, **[11926]**, **[16774]**
"6 Methods to Overcome Challenges at Work" in sweetbutfearless.com(October 15, 2020) **[22073]**
"6 Powerful Sports Marketing Promotions That Are Better Than Google" in Forbes (February 6, 2014) **[15128]**, **[31849]**
6 Proven Ways to Increase Your Dry Cleaning and Laundry Business Profits **[5231]**
"6 Risk Factors You Need to Consider Before Purchasing a Franchise" in Entrepreneur (Jan. 9, 2019) **[24318]**
"The 6 Secrets That Will Help Your Hair Salon and Day Spa Succeed" in Entrepreneur (September 30, 2014) **[7859]**
"6 Steps to a Better Business Budget" in Investopedia (Jan. 6, 2020) **[17488]**
"6 Steps to Creating an Effective Gym Lead Management Process" in Glofox blog (July 23, 2019) **[12397]**
"6 Steps for Starting a Professional Organizing Business" in Metropolitan Organizing Blog (November 12, 2018) **[12821]**
"6 Tips to Find Graphic Designers for Your Small Businesses" in DesignHill (December 20, 2017) **[3293]**
"6 Tips for Growing a Waste Management Business" in Fundbox Blog (April 27, 2017) **[7944]**, **[29621]**
"6 Tips for Open-Office Etiquette" in Business News Daily (March 7, 2023) **[22074]**, **[26872]**
6 Tips That Will Increase Your Photo Studio Production **[12339]**
"6 Tips on Using Bartering Services in Your Small Business" in Tech Funnel (Jan. 6, 2020) **[17240]**
"6 Tips to Winterize Your Food Truck" in FoodTruckOperator.com (October 3, 2019) **[6963]**
"6 Top Online Consignment Shops for Selling Your Clothes" in U.S. News & World Report (February 21, 2019) **[3884]**, **[11696]**
"6 Top-Ranked Business Networking Groups on the Web" in GoDaddy (January 30, 2018) **[18839]**
6 Unbelievably Eash Ways to Grow Your Food Delivery Business **[6894]**
6 Vital Entrepreneur Skills for a Successful Small Business **[22474]**
"6 Ways Artificial Intelligence Can Transform Your Small Business" in business.com (April 10, 2020) **[29622]**, **[33937]**
"6 Ways Integrity Can Improve Your Business" in ZenBusiness (Aug. 11, 2021) **[23465]**
"6 Ways to Manage Cash Flow for Your Business" in NerdWallet (Jan. 12, 2021) **[19710]**
"6 Ways to Manage Your Small-Business Cash Flow" in NerdWallet (October 5, 2020) **[19711]**
"6 Ways to Market Your Small Business for Less Than $100" in Entrepreneur (May 30, 2019) **[34708]**
"6 Ways Playing Poker Can Help You in Business (and 2 Ways It Can't)" in Entrepreneur (Oct. 23, 2015) **[7271]**
"6 Worth-the-Price Fix-Ups" in Realtor Magazine (Vol. 44, April-May 2011, No. 44, pp. 23) **[12822]**, **[13124]**
7 AI Tools for Small Businesses Marketing **[29623]**
7 Best Free and Open Source Campground Management Software **[2509]**
"7 of the Best Market Research Tools for Small Businesses" in Groupon Merchant (January 24, 2020) **[29485]**
7 Best Mobile Business Ideas With Real Life Examples **[30454]**
"7 Best Small Business Grants in 2022" in Fit Small Business (Jan. 17, 2022) **[24937]**
"7 Best Small Business Grants in 2022" in Fit Small Business (Jan. 17, 2022) [24937]
"The 7 Best Small Business Groups for Networking" in insureon Small Business Blog (December 7, 2016) **[18840]**
"7 Businesses You Can Start With Almost No Cash" in Entrepreneur (January 5, 2017) **[34486]**
7 Deadly Marketing Mistakes **[29536]**
"7 Easy Steps to Start a Tutoring Business" in The Daily Egg (July 12, 2022) **[24287]**
"7-Eleven Considers Private Label Ice Cream" in Ice Cream Reporter (Vol. 22, December 20, 2008, No. 1, pp. 1) **[4425]**, **[8541]**, **[30671]**
7-Eleven, Inc. **[4451]**
"7 Estate Planning Tips from Entrepreneurs" in The McKenzie Law Firm website (December 3, 2015) **[6020]**
"7 Facebook Tips for Small & Medium-Sized Businesses" in Business 2 Community (October 1, 2021 **[29517]**, **[33533]**
"7 Factors of Great Office Design" in Harvard Business Review (May 20, 2016) **[31025]**
"7 Fool-Proof Tactics to Boost Class Attendance in 2019" in Glofox blog (July 17, 2019) **[12398]**
"7 Lead Generation Strategies for Gyms in Year One of Business" in Glofox blog (June 16, 2019) **[12399]**

3168 Small Business Sourcebook • 42nd Edition

7 Marketing Mistakes to Avoid [30144]
7 Mistakes Hurting Your Moving Company's Local SEO Ranking [11139]
"7 Mobile Business Ideas To Meet Customers' Post-Pandemic Needs" in Forbes (Aug. 13, 2021) [30455]
"7 Modern BBSes Worth Calling Today" in PCMag (December 26, 2017) [2120]
"7 Places to Incorporate Your Small Business Online" in Small Business Trends (March 18, 2022) [27168], [34487]
"7 Plumbing Business Management Tips to Streamline and Grow" in Service Titan Blog (November 5, 2020) [12613]
"7 Popular Marketing Techniques for Small Businesses" in Investopedia (June 16, 2020) [29486]
"7 Proven Tips for Young Entrepreneurs to Start Off Strong" in business.com (Nov. 15, 2017) [46652]
"7 Reasons to Hire a Franchise Consultant" in allBusiness [24319]
"7 Reasons to Use Cloud Based Applications for Your Tattoo Shop" in DaySmart Body Art blog (April 15, 2022) [15288]
"7 Smart Budgeting Tips for Small Business Owners" in Business News Daily (Dec. 21, 2021) [17489]
7 Smart Pricing Strategies to Attract Customers [19983]
7 Sources of Start-up Financing [30905], [34488]
"7 Statistics About Fraud Your Business Should Know in 2022" in asmag.com (July 14, 2022) [19252]
"7 Steps to Acquiring a Small Business" in Entrepreneur (Dec. 3, 2019) [19644]
7 Steps to a Multi-Million Dollar Campground [2510]
"7 Steps to Selling Your Small Business" in Investopedia (February 27, 2020) [19220]
7 Steps for Small Businesses To Hire Great Employees [26483]
7 Successful Sales Tips for Small Business Owners [32452]
"7 Tattoo Artist Tips for Taking Your Business Digital" in DaySmart Body Art blog (Feb. 15, 2022) [15289]
"7 Tax Strategies to Consider When Selling a Business" in SBA Blog (February 21, 2020) [19221]
"7 Things You Need to Know Before Becoming a Franchise Owner" in Entrepreneur (Nov. 22, 2017) [24320]
"7 Things You Need to Remember About Workplace Safety" in Bplans [30942]
7 Tips for Great Pet Boarding Business Management [12081]
"7 Tips for Hiring a More Diverse Workforce" in U.S. Chamber of Commerce (June 9, 2020) [30526]
"7 Tips for Managing Safety for a Small Business" in BasicSafe (February 24, 2016) [30943]
"7 Tips for Managing Your Business While on Vacation" in Legal Zoom (March 17, 2023) [16533], [28433]
"7 Trends Affecting the Security Technology Business" in IP SecurityWatch.com (March 2012) [2705], [3768], [14381], [26202], [30953]
7 Types of Advertising to Promote Your Small Business Effectively [31850]
"7 Useful Ways to Successfully Network with Other Small Businesses" in Fundera (July 30, 2020) [18841]
"7 Ways to Advertise Your Home-Based Small Business for Free" in Citizens General blog (Dec. 7, 2018) [16903], [26759]
"7 Ways to Build Customer Loyalty" Business News Daily (March 17, 2023) [17429]
"7 Ways a Business Incubator Can Benefit Your Online Startup" in Business News Daily (September 10, 2019) [8804]
7 Ways to Buy a Franchise When You're Short on Funds [24321]
"7 Ways Event Planners Can Navigate the Current Flower Shortage" in BizBash (September 23, 2021) [6852]
7 Ways to Find Clients for Your Professional Organizing Business [12823]
7 Ways to Get Clients for Your Professional Organizing Business [12824]
"7 Ways to Protect Your Small Business from Fraud and Cybercrime" in Merchants Insurance Group Blog (Jan. 27, 2022) [22340]
"The 7 Wonders of Tourism" in Business Journal Portland (Vol. 31, May 9, 2014, No. 10, pp. 10) [15729], [15982], [17896], [20718]
"8 Alternative Funding Options for Small Businesses" in Bplans [30906]
"8 Bed-And-Breakfasts Perfect For a Romantic Getaway" in USA Today (April 16, 2019) [1407]
"The 8 Best Online Dog Training Certification Programs of 2020" in The Spruce Pets (September 19, 2020) [12136]
"8 Best Tattoo Shop Marketing Strategies to Grow Your Business" in Appointy blog (Apr. 1, 2022) [15290]
8 DIY Laundromat Marketing Ideas that Work [10165]
8 Ideas on How to Get Landscaping Customers [10085], [29624]
"8 Important Things I've Learned in 4 Years of Freelance Writing" in Business 2 Community (October 7, 2021) [5346]
"8 Marketing Tactics to Boost Your Laundromat Business" in Safi Laundry Blog (June 24, 2022) [10166]
"The 8 Most Common Small Business Accounting Mistakes" in Bplans [16775]
"8 Motivation Tricks to Inspire Your Employees" in Small Business Trends (January 25, 2023) [22075]
"8 Online Business Ideas for Retirees" in U.S. News & World Report (Sept. 9, 2020) [33059]
"8 Practical Product and Service Ideas to Boost Gym Revenue" in Glofox blog (August 19, 2019) [12400]
"8 Pricing Strategies for Your Digital Product" in Entrepreneur (October 18, 2016) [29518], [31650]
"8 Reasons Why Small Businesses Need to Make Graphic Design a Priority" in penjji.co (December 12, 2018) [3294]
"8 Reasons You May Need to Update Your Will" in NextAvenue.com (August 22, 2019) [6021]
"8 Sustainable Business Practices - Are You Doing Your Part?" in Thriving Small Business (May 29, 2019) [23074]
"8 Tax Season Preparation Steps" in Business News Daily (March 6, 2023) [34723]
"8 Things to Try If Your Business Growth Has Stagnated" in Small Business Trends (Jan. 12, 2022) [32453]
"8 Things You Need to Set Up your Home Recording Studio" in Rolling Stone (February 6, 2019) [13652]
"8 Tips for How to Successfully Manage a Business Budget" in TravelBank Blog [17490]
"8 Unique Delivery Services" in Business News Daily (Oct. 20, 2022) [6895]
"8 Ways Employees Commit Time Theft" in Business News Daily (Nov. 19, 2021) [22341]
"8 Ways to Make Your Crowdfunding Campaign Stand Out" in Entrepreneur (June 2014) [7063], [22958]
"8 Web Development Trends Every CTO Should Expect in 2020" in Core dna (August 6, 2020) [16384]
The 8th Habit: From Effectiveness to Greatness [28272]
8VC [37269]
"9 Best Business Networking Groups for New Businesses" in Next Insurance website (Sept. 16, 2020) [18842]
"9 Competitive Benefits for Small Businesses" in CareerBuilder [17270]
"9 Grants for Black Women Entrepreneurs" by Now Corp. [30316], [35732]
"9 Low-Cost Business Ideas for Animal Lovers" in Entrepreneur (February 21, 2019) [12137]
"9 Photographers Share What They Love (and Hate) about Their Jobs" in Business News Daily (October 5, 2018) [12297]
9 Plumbing Digital Marketing Ideas for Small Business Owners [12614]
"9 Sales Promotion Ideas for Your Tutoring Business" in Smith.ai blog [16127]
9 Sales Techniques That Will Highly Increase Your Success [32454]
"9 Skills Your Trainers Need to Deliver an Incredible Online Experience" in Glofox blog (October 30, 2020) [12401]
"9 Strategies to BUILD and GROW Your Author Platform: A Step-by-Step Book Marketing Plan to Get More Exposure and Sales" [1602], [4930], [5424], [29558], [32423]
"9 Things You MUST Do Today to Grow Your Small Business" in Small Business Trends (January 22, 2021) [33534]
9 Tips to Help Your Small Business Stand Out in Customer Service [20377]
"9 Tips for Marketing Your Craft Brewery" in TripleSeat blog (August 26, 2020) [1895]
9 Ways to Improve Cash Flow for Your Moving Company [11140]
"9 Ways to Invest in Real Estate Without Buying Property in 2019" in Forbes (February 22, 2019) [13369]
9 Ways to Market Your Campground: A Guide for Campgrounds and RV Parks [2511]
9Mile Labs (9ML) [46245]
"10 Advantages of E-Commerce for Consumers & Businesses" in become Blog (July 21, 2020) [21774]
"10 B2B Marketing Strategies to Grow Your Presence" in The Blueprint (September 23, 2020) [19236], [29625]
10 Books That Changed My Business (+ Life) [24781]
"10 Bubble Tea Franchise Opportunities in 2023" in Small Business Trends (March 13, 2023) [24322]
"10 Business Apology Letter Examples" in Small Business Trends (July 15, 2021) [17623]
10 Business Skills All Entrepreneurs Need to Develop [22475]
"10 Carpet Cleaning Franchises" in Small Business Trends (March 1, 2023) [24323]
"10 Common Leadership Mistakes You're Probably Making" in Business News Daily (March 2, 2023) [22476]
"10 Competitive Advantages Small Businesses Have Over Big Companies" in ZenBusiness (Dec. 6, 2021) [19769]
"10 Dirty Little Secrets of the Commerical Photography Industry" in PetaPixel (July 24, 2019) [12298]
10 Easy Ways to Get Started with Marketing AI (Artificial Intelligence) [29626]
"10 Effective Local Advertising Ideas for Small Businesses" in LOCALiQ Blog (September 22, 2020) [31851]
"10 Effective Methods for Measuring Employee Happiness" in Small Business Trends (August 23,2022) [22076]
10 Everyday Actions to Make the Workplace More Inclusive for Women [30527], [35733]
"10 Goals You Can Set to Grow Your Small Business" in Economic Development Collaborative (Apr 29, 2021) [19468]
10 Ideas to Start Your Own Food Delivery Business [6896]
10 Ideas for Your Laundromat Grand Opening [5232]
10 Make-or-Break Career Moments: Navigate, Negotiate, and Communicate for Success [17624], [20081]
"10 Minority Grant Opportunities for Small Business in 2022" in Merchant Maverick (Nov. 30, 2021) [30317]
"10 Mobile Business Ideas You Can Take on the Road" by U.S. Chamber of Commerce (Feb. 4, 2021) [30456]
10 Most Profitable Agricultural Business Ideas in 2021 [16982]
"The 10 Most Reliable Ways to Fund a Startup" in Entrepreneur (February 20, 2019) [34489]
"10 Powerful Marketing Strategies for Designers" in JUST Creative Blog (March 9, 2020) [3295]
10 Productivity Hacks that Actually Work [24782]
"10 Reasons You Need a Digital Marketing Strategy in 2020" in Smart Insights (October 12, 2020) [27803]
"10 Retirement-Friendly Business Ideas for the Over 50's" in Due Blog (Jan. 17, 2022) [33060]
10 Sales Strategies That Small Businesses Can Use [32455]
"10 Scams That Prey on Small Businesses" in business.com (September 20, 2022) [19253]
"10 Small Business Ideas for Retirees" in U.S. Chamber of Commerce CO (Oct. 14, 2021) [33061]
10 Small Business Internet Marketing Tips [27804]
"10 Small-Business Networking Tools and Vendors to Watch in 2020" in CRN Magazine (January 20, 2020) [18843]
"10 Small Business Statistics" in Oberlo Blog (Jan. 1, 2022) [17897]
"10 Startup Tips From Affordable Franchise Coffee News" in Small Business Trends (September 12, 2017) [3176]
"10 Strategies for Estate Sale Leads" in EstateSales.org Blog [6066]
"10 Successful Young Entrepreneurs" in Investopedia (Apr 11, 2021) [36010]
"10 Surprising Areas Missed in Small Business Sustainability Programs" in Cultivating Capital [34266]
10 Surprisingly Effective Sales Techniques, Backed by Research [32456]
"10 Talents That Drive Entrepreneurial Success; Gallup Has Identified the Behaviors We Have Consistently Observed In Highly Successful Entrepreneurs" in Gallup Business Journal (May 6, 2014) [22477]
"10 Things About OSHA Small Businesses Must Know" in Small Business Trends (October 9, 2019) [30944]
"10 Things to Do Before Opening a Food Truck" in Business News Daily (February 21, 2023) [6964]
"10 Things to Do Before Opening a Salon" in Business News Daily (June 16, 2020) [7860]
10 Til 2- Part-Time Placement Service [5452]
"10 Tips for Adjusting Your Business Strategies to Meet the Demands of Modern Consumers" in Small Business Trends (January 22, 2022) [16534]
"10 Tips for Effectively Communicating with Clients, Prospects, Employees, and Other Business Stakeholders" in Small Business Trends (January 29, 2022) [17625], [28434]
"10 Tips To Help Improve Your Company's Cash Flow" in Signature Analytics Blog [19712]
10 Tips on How to Increase Sales for Your Small Business [32457]
"10 Tools for Your Genealogy Research That You Never Thought You'd Need" in Ancestral Findings [7350]
"10 Types of Business Budget to Consider at the Budget Planning Stage" in Finextra Blog (Sept. 14, 2021) [17491]
10 Unconventional Ways to Get More Moving Leads [11141], [29627]

Small Business Sourcebook • 42nd Edition 3169

10 Master Index

10 Warning Signs to Look for When Buying a Business **[19645]**
"10 Ways to Make Money Sewing" in Sew My Place (April 5, 2016) **[14645]**
"10 Ways to Make Your Small Business More Sustainable" in Looka (July 7, 2021) **[23075]**
"10 Ways to Reduce Your Fuel Costs" in Business News Daily (March 8, 2023) **[16072]**
"10 Ways to Tailor Your Marketing Strategy to Your Business" in Small Business Trends (August 15, 2020) **[29519]**, **[34709]**
"11 Accounting Tips All Small Businesses Should Know" in business.com (Feb. 3, 2022) **[16776]**
"The 11 Best Communication Tools for Business (By Category)" in DialPad Newsletter (July 27, 2021) **[17626]**
11 Best Embroidery Machines for Small Business **[14646]**
11 Best Tattoo Shop Marketing Ideas in 2022 **[15291]**
"11 Creative Craft Brewery Marketing Tips (+5 Examples)" in 2ndKitchen.com (February 27, 2020) **[1896]**
11 Diversity, Equity & Inclusion Resources for Small Businesses **[30528]**
"11 Free Ways to Get Publicity for Your Small Business" in SCORE (August 20, 2020) **[31852]**
"11 Minutes That Rocked the Sneaker World" in Business Journal Portland (Vol. 30, February 14, 2014, No. 50, pp. 8) **[3004]**, **[4585]**, **[14671]**, **[21775]**, **[31154]**
"11 Reasons Why Business Communication Is Critical to Your Company's Success" in Smarp Blog (July 9, 2020) **[17627]**
"11 Sales Techniques to Help Grow Your Small Business" in Score Blog (Sept. 9, 2021) **[32458]**
"11 Secrets of Personal Shoppers" in Mental Floss (September 15, 2017) **[12018]**
"11+ Small Business Grants for Minorities" by Now Corp. **[30318]**
"11 Things to Do Before Starting a Business" in Business News Daily (February 21, 2023) **[34490]**
"11 Tips for Starting a Successful Plumbing Business" in Design Hill Blog (July 11, 2018) **[12615]**
"11 Tips for Successful Business Networking" in ZenBusiness Blog (Aug. 11, 2021) **[18844]**
"11 Ways to Avert a Data-Storage Disaster" in Nature (2019) **[3479]**
"11 Ways to Better Manage Cash Flow in Business" in SCORE.org Blog (Nov. 5, 2020) **[19713]**
"11 Ways to Reward Hardworking Employees (and Encourage More Exemplary Behavior)" in Small Business Trends (January 15, 2023) **[22077]**
"11th Circuit: Don't Break the Law to Comply with It" in Miami Daily Business Review (October 21, 2009) **[4763]**, **[18501]**, **[25196]**
"The 12 Best POS Systems for Small Businesses: Our Top Picks for 2023" in Business News Daily (February 24, 2023) **[32089]**
"$1.2 Billion Master-Planned Community in Celina Back on Track" in Dallas Business Journal (Vol. 35, June 8, 2012, No. 39, pp. 1) **[3970]**, **[13370]**
"12 Business Networking Tips" in Business 2 Community (Jan. 27, 2021) **[18845]**
"12 Business Skills You Need to Master" in business.com (Jan. 31, 2022) **[22478]**
12 Characteristics & Personality Traits Great Entrepreneurs Share **[22479]**
"12 Facts That Show Shy Bottled Water Is One of the Biggest Scams of the Century" in Business Insider (March 20, 2019) **[1855]**
"12 Family Business Ideas—Plus Tips for Starting a Family Business" in NerdWallet (Oct. 22, 2020) **[23591]**
"12 Franchises Under 10K You Can Start in 2023" in Small Business Trends (February 2, 2023) **[24324]**
"12 Helpful Tips for Communicating Bad News to Staff and Stakeholders" in Small Business Trends (October 16, 2022) **[17628]**
12 Reasons Why Team Building Works **[22078]**
"12 Secrets to Keeping Employees Happy without a Raise" in Business News Daily (March 20, 2023) **[22079]**
"12 Simple (Yet Effective!) Ways Small Businesses Can Compete with the Big Brands" in LOCALiQ Blog (Oct. 7, 2020) **[19770]**
12-Step Checklist for Hiring Employees **[26484]**
"12 Steps to Take after Receiving Negative Feedback about Your Company Culture" in Small Business Trends (February 19, 2023) **[22080]**
12 Tips for Managing a Seasonal Business **[32944]**
12 Tools I Can't Run My Business Without **[16617]**
12 Tough Lessons Learned from Buying a Business (Plus 15-Point Checklist) **[19646]**
"12 Ways to Promote Your Freelance Graphic Design Business" in millo.com (April 2, 2020) **[3296]**
"12 Workplace Safety Tips Every Employee Should Know in 2021" in Connecteam (October 26, 2020) **[30945]**
13 B2B E-commerce Brands Unveil the Secrets to Scalable Online Success **[19237]**, **[29628]**
"13 Effective Office Design Ideas for a Small Business" in Autonomous (Mar 28, 2021) **[31026]**
"13 Small Business Legal Requirements and Tips for Launch" in Legal Zoom (February 15, 2023) **[34491]**
"13 Things You Need to Know about Freight Forwarding" in UniversalCargo (December 19, 2017) **[7027]**
"13 Ways to Screw over Your Internet Provider" in Tech Crunch (September 2, 2019) **[9090]**
"113D Filings: Investors Report to the SEC" in Barron's (Vol. 88, March 24, 2008, No. 12, pp. M13) **[6242]**, **[9304]**, **[13371]**, **[18502]**, **[18880]**, **[19469]**, **[19771]**, **[23721]**, **[25701]**, **[28435]**, **[31155]**, **[32090]**, **[32718]**
13i Capital Corp. **[39454]**
"14 Best Job Apps for Listing Your Open Positions" in Small Business Trends (January 19, 2022) **[26485]**
"14 Business Letter Templates Every Business Should Have" in Legal Zoom (February 15, 2023) **[17629]**
"14 Collaboration Tools for Small Business" in Business News Daily (Jan. 14, 2021) **[17630]**
"14 Employee Recruitment Strategies for Success" in Business News Daily (Nov. 19, 2021) **[26486]**
"14 First Class Gym Event Ideas to Boost Your Acquisition and Retention" in Glofox blog (February 8, 2019) **[12402]**
"14 Stunning Examples of Small Business Branding" in ActiveCampaign (March 7, 2018) **[17430]**
"14 Tips to Tune Up Your Self-Propelled Sprayer" in Farm Industry News (November 3, 2010) **[16983]**
"14 Types of Alternative Financing for Small Businesses" in Merchant Maverick Blog (July 13, 2021) **[30907]**
14 Viral Tattoo Marketing Content Ideas for Insta & TikTok **[15292]**
15 Advantages of Ecommerce for Small Businesses **[21776]**
"15 Amazing Small Business Owner Titles: Which One is Right for You?" in Small Business Trends (May 14, 2018) **[16535]**
"15 Business Ideas for Senior Citizens" in Seniority Live Evergreen Blog **[33062]**
"15 Entrepreneur Characteristics to Develop" on Indeed Career Guide (Apr 1, 2021) **[22480]**
15 Reasons Why the Office Matters **[31027]**
"15 Small Business Team-Building Ideas" in Constant Contact Blog (Feb. 7 2022) **[22081]**
15 Steps to Growing Your Tattooing Business **[15293]**
"16 Awesome Marketing Strategies for Small Businesses" in buildfire **[29520]**
"16 Cool Job Perks That Keep Employees Happy" in Business News Daily (March 7, 2023) **[22082]**
"16 Creative and Cheap Ways to Say 'Thank You'" in HR Specialist (Vol. 8, September 2010, No. 9, pp. 8) **[17271]**, **[22083]**, **[26873]**
"16 Great Customer Service Tips and Examples" in Small Business Trends (Aug. 12, 2021) **[20378]**
"16 Money-Making Mobile Business Ideas" in The Balance Small Business (Nov. 20, 2019) **[30457]**
16 Pros & Cons of Owning a Laundromat New Investors Need to Know **[10167]**
16-Step Legal Checklist for Startups and Small Businesses **[18881]**
16 Tips for a Happy and Productive Office Environment **[31028]**
"16 Venmo Scams to Watch Out For" in Small Business Trends (February 7, 2023) **[16536]**
"16 Ways Small Businesses Can Tackle Financial Risk Management" in Forbes (July 23, 2020) **[32383]**
"A 16-Year Housing Slump? It Could Happen" in Barron's (Vol. 88, March 17, 2008, No. 11, pp. 27) **[6243]**, **[9305]**, **[13125]**, **[13372]**, **[23722]**
"17 Employee Benefits That Are Actually Worth the Investment" in gusto Blog (Oct. 19, 2020) **[17272]**
"17 Mobile Business Ideas to Get Your Company-on-Wheels Rolling" in NerdWallet (Oct. 22, 2020) **[30458]**
"18 Best Small-Business Apps" in NerdWallet (Jan. 19, 2022) **[16777]**
"18 Online Cooking Classes for the Busy Budding Chef" in SheKnows (March 27, 2019) **[4461]**, **[11697]**
"19 Best Books for Starting a Business" in Legal Zoom (March 14, 2023) **[16537]**
20/20 HealthCare Partners (20/20 HCP) **[40653]**
"20 Advantages and Disadvantages of Outsourcing from Your Small Business" in Small Business Trends (March 11, 2021) **[20082]**, **[31112]**
"20 Beer Packaging Innovations" in TrendHunter (March 20, 2019) **[1897]**
"The 20 Best Jobs for Flexibility" in Business News Daily (March 17, 2023) **[16538]**
"20 Best Seasonal Business Ideas for Warm Weather" in NerdWallet (Oct. 22, 2020) **[32945]**
"20 Business Ideas for Stay-at-Home Parents" in Entrepreneur (May 15, 2021) **[26760]**
"20 Communication Platforms for High-Growth Companies" in Nextiva Blog **[17631]**
"20 Home Improvement Franchises" in Small Business Trends (February 21, 2023) **[24325]**
"20 Important LinkedIn Groups for Business" in Small Business Trends (May 19, 2014) **[18846]**
"20 Lessons Learnt from Owning a Tattoo Shop" in Painful Pleasures Blog (October 2, 2018) **[15294]**
20 Quick Team Building Activities for Small Business Leaders **[22084]**
"20 Small Business Ideas in the Growing Cannabis Industry" in Small Business Trends (October 9, 2016) **[4984]**
"20 Tips and Tricks for Zoom - before, during and after Meetings" in krisp(October 1, 2022) **[20379]**, **[22085]**
20 Ways to Communicate Effectively with Your Team" in Small Business Trends (November 24, 2021) **[17632]**
"21 Dance Studio Industry Stats for 2021" in Studio Director (January 28, 2021) **[4849]**
"21 Percent of Fish is Mislabeled in Restaurant and Stores" in U.S. News & World Report (March 8, 2019) **[6744]**, **[23466]**
"21 Success Tips for Young and Aspiring Entrepreneurs" in Entrepreneur **[36011]**
21 Tips for Starting & Running a Successful Christmas Tree Farm **[2931]**
"21 Ways to Market Your Business Online" in Entrepreneur (October, 26, 2016) **[27805]**
"21-Year-Old Opens Gift Shop in Midland Mall" in Midland Daily News (November 2, 2019) **[7474]**
"22 Top Recycling Tips for the Workplace That You Can Implement Today" in Recycle Coach (October 9, 2020) **[7945]**, **[13699]**
"22 Vision Statement Examples" in Small Business Trends (Nov. 22, 2021) **[19470]**
22squared Inc. **[30175]**
"23 Green Business Ideas for Eco-Minded Entrepreneurs" in Business News Daily (Dec. 21, 2021) **[23076]**
"23 Low-Budget Marketing Ideas for Small Businesses" in The WordStream Blog (September 25, 2020) **[31853]**
"23 Questions to Ask a Franchisor When You Meet Face to Face" in Entrepreneur (Feb. 6, 2019) **[24326]**
24/7 Shared Kitchen **[38823]**
"24 Fitness Marketing Strategies to Grow Your Gym or Training Business" in Maniac Marketing Blog (August 3, 2020) **[12403]**
"24 Team Building Exercises and Games Your Team Will Enjoy" in Small Business Trends (February 13, 2023) **[22086]**
"25 Best Genealogy Websites for Beginners" in Family Tree **[7351]**, **[11698]**
"The 25 Best Places to Shop for Beauty Products" in StyleCaster **[4508]**
"25 Cybersecurity Statistics Small Businesses Should Know" in Small Business Trends (December 06, 2022) **[16539]**
25 Dead Simple Landscape Marketing Ideas to Increase New Lawn Care Customers and Sales **[10086]**, **[29629]**
"25 Home Based Business Ideas That Let You Work From Home" in Shopify Blog (Jan. 6, 2022) **[26761]**
"25 LinkedIn Groups Every Entrepreneur Should Belong To" in Business News Daily (Nov. 18, 2021) **[18847]**
"25 Senior Service Business Ideas" in Small Business Trends (July 3, 2019) **[33063]**
"25 Social Media Business Ideas" in Small Business Trends(January 26, 2023) **[26762]**, **[33535]**
"25 Tasks to Do When You're a Professional Organizer With No Clients" in Organizers Connect website (Sept. 15, 2021) **[12825]**
26 Best Small Business Ideas for Graphic Designers in 2020 **[3297]**
"26 Great Business Ideas for Entrepreneurs" in Business News Daily (March 8, 2023) **[22481]**, **[34492]**
"26 Things Holding Canadians Back" in Canadian Business (Vol. 85, August 13, 2012, No. 13, pp. 27) **[16505]**, **[20719]**, **[25702]**, **[27832]**
26 Things I Wish I'd Known Before Starting My Photography Business **[12340]**
"26 Types of Insurance Your Small Business Should Consider" in Business News Daily (February 21, 2023) **[27230]**
"27 Mission Statement Examples" in Small Business Trends (February 27, 2023) **[33536]**, **[34493]**
"30 Charming Bed-and-Breakfasts Across America" in U.S. News & World Report (September 10, 2018) **[1408]**
"30 New Year Greetings for Business Owners" in Small Business Trends (September 21, 2022) **[16540]**

3170 Small Business Sourcebook • 42nd Edition

Master Index
Aaron

"30 Office Desk Plants to Brighten Your Business" in Small Business Trends(July 18, 2022) **[16541]**
30+ Small Business Ideas That Use Skills You Already Have **[26763]**
31 Days to Greeting Card Marketing Mastery **[29630]**, **[32459]**
32 Degrees Capital **[46662]**
"33 FIVERR Power Tips: Featuring Prove Ways to Boost Your Sales and Quit Your Job" [29631], **[32460]**
35 Free Small Business Classes for Business Owners **[21440]**
"39 Entrepreneur Statistics You Need to Know" in SmallBizGenius.net Blog (Feb. 4, 2022) **[17898]**
"39 Green Business Ideas for Sustainable Entrepreneurs" in Just Business (October 22, 2020) **[23077]**
"40 Creative Marijuana & Cannabis Business Ideas for 2020" in Everything But The Plant (March 9, 2020) **[4985]**
"40 Virtual Event Ideas" in Small Business Trends (February 24, 2022) **[22087]**
42 Home-Based Businesses You Can Start Today **[22482]**, **[26764]**
43North (43N) **[42828]**
"$44M Father/Son Biz Involved in Major Orlando Projects" in Orlando Business Journal (Vol. 31, July 18, 2014, No. 3, pp. 3) **[22359]**, **[23592]**, **[32719]**
"45 Green Business Ideas for Aspiring Entrepreneurs" in LegalZoom (Oct. 12, 2021) **[23078]**
45 Marketing Ideas for a Christmas Tree Farm **[2932]**
"49 Clever Mobile Business Ideas You Can Start in 2022" in Starter Story (Jan. 20, 2022) **[30459]**
"50 Best Companies for Diversity" in Black Enterprise (Vol. 38, July 2008, No. 12, pp. 12) **[24596]**, **[26487]**, **[28436]**, **[30319]**
"50 Best Home Sewing Business Ideas for 2021" in Profitable Venture Magazine **[14647]**
"50 Best Spa & Massage Small Business Ideas for 2021" in Profitable Venture Magazine **[10759]**
"50 Creative Business Ideas to Start in 2023" in Small Business Trends(February 7, 2023) **[26765]**, **[33537]**
"50+ Eye-Opening Branding Statistics" in smallbizgenius (August 2, 2019) **[17431]**
"50 Family Small Business Ideas" in Small Business Trends (July 5, 2021) **[23593]**
"50 Handmade Business Ideas to Start in 2023" in Small Business Trends(February 8, 2023) **[26766]**, **[33538]**
"50 Mobile Business Ideas to Keep You Moving in a Profitable Direction" in Small Business Trends (Apr 4, 2017) **[30460]**
"50 Small Agricultural Business Ideas" in Small Business Trends (July 5, 2021) **[16984]**
"50 Small Business Grants Available from Kevin Hart's Tequila Brand" in Small Business Trends (March 10, 2023) **[33539]**
"50 Things to Sew and Sell" in Small Business Trends (October 9, 2019) **[14648]**
"50 Unusual Pet Businesses to Start" in Small Business Trends (January 16, 2016) **[12138]**
"50 Years of Wings Big Business for Anchor Bar" in Business First of Buffalo (Vol. 30, March 7, 2014, No. 25, pp. 4) **[1312]**, **[13895]**
"56% of Employees Believe Too Many Meetings Affecting Job Performance" in Small Business Trends (August 10, 2021) **[22088]**
60 Main Street News **[45714]**
"63 Grants, Loans and Programs to Benefit Your Small Business" in CO - U.S. Chamber of Commerce (October 13, 2022) **[24938]**
"66% of Consumers Expect Free Shipping on Every Purchase" in Small Business Trends (August 10, 2021) **[7028]**
"67 Creative and Effective Ways to Get Students to Register for Dance Class" in DanceStudioOwner **[4850]**, **[18882]**
"73 Remarkable Small Business Statistics to Know" in Semrush Blog (Feb. 26, 2021) **[17899]**
"74% of Consumers Prefer Texting with Businesses if a Real Person is Texting Back" in Small Business Trends (January 26, 2023) **[17633]**
76FWD **[44378]**
"77% of Companies Expect to Encounter a Talent Shortage" in Small Business Trends (August 10, 2021) **[26488]**
"7.7% Workers' Comp Decrease Recommended in Missouri" in Insurance Journal (November 16, 2021) **[27231]**, **[41700]**
80Amps **[45937]**
"85 Amazing Food Business Ideas You Could Start in 2023" in Small Business Trends(March 2, 2023) **[6897]**, **[6965]**, **[33090]**
85 Broads **[35513]**
90 Days After My Acquisition **[33041]**
"100 Brilliant Companies" in Entrepreneur (May 2014) **[3005]**, **[11632]**, **[19324]**, **[22483]**, **[27833]**
"$100 Million Plan for Jefferson Arms" in Saint Louis Business Journal (Vol. 32, October 14, 2011, No. 7, pp. 1) **[866]**, **[3971]**, **[34724]**
"100 Percent Equipment Tax Deduction Deadline Nears" in Farm Industry News (December 1, 2010) **[16985]**, **[34725]**
"The $100 Startup: Reinvent the Way You Make a Living, Do What You Love, and Create a New Future" **[22360]**
"100+ Time Saving Tips for Small Businesses" in Small Business Trends(June 16, 2021) **[34979]**
"$100M Complex To Be Built on Purple People Bridge" in Business Courier (Vol. 27, November 12, 2010, No. 28, pp. 1) **[1313]**, **[3972]**, **[8355]**, **[13373]**, **[13896]**
"$100M Merger Stalled" in Philadelphia Business Journal (Vol. 31, February 17, 2012, No. 1, pp. 1) **[1898]**, **[18503]**, **[31156]**
101 Business Problems: Diagnosis and Remedy **[16712]**
101 Internet Businesses You Can Start from Home: How to Choose and Build Your Own Successful E-Business **[9083]**, **[18883]**, **[21757]**, **[26729]**, **[29632]**
101 Secrets to Building a Winning Business **[17900]**, **[24597]**
"101 Secrets to Running a Successful Home-Based Business" in allBusiness **[26767]**
101 Ways to Sell More of Anything to Anyone: Sales Tips for Individuals, Business Owners and Sales Professionals **[20380]**, **[32461]**
108 Ideaspace Inc. **[28939]**
"145 Restaurant Franchise Opportunities" in Small Business Trends (March 6, 2023) **[24327]**
180 Degree Capital Corp. **[42203]**
225 Keith **[44710]**
The 250 Questions Every Self-Employed Person Should Ask **[22361]**, **[24512]**
300m [30201], [31897]
"352 Media Group Opens New Tampa Web Design and Digital Marketing Office" in Entertainment Close-Up (May 2, 2011) **[16385]**, **[17901]**, **[29633]**
"$353 Million in SSBCI Funds Going to Small Businesses in 4 States" in Small Business Trends(March 1, 2023) **[24939]**, **[28087]**, **[33540]**
360Clean **[2086]**
"$400M Fiction Giant Wattpad Wants to Be Your Literary Agent" in Forbes (September 24, 2018) **[10347]**
"401(k) Keys to Stable Value" in Barron's (Vol. 88, March 10, 2008, No. 10, pp. 40) **[6244]**, **[9306]**, **[17273]**, **[23723]**, **[25197]**
.406 Ventures **[40654]**
420 Magazine **[5025]**
"The 490 Made Chevy a Bargain Player" in Automotive News (Vol. 86, October 31, 2011, No. 6488, pp. S22) **[11367]**, **[19772]**, **[19984]**, **[29091]**
500 Startups **[37537]**
"529.com Wins Outstanding Achievement in Web Development" in Investment Weekly (November 14, 2009, pp. 152) **[9091]**, **[9307]**, **[16386]**, **[23724]**, **[29634]**
"$550 Cash Rent on 330 Acres in Iowa" in Farm Industry News (November 30, 2011) **[13764]**, **[16986]**
"$560 Million Acquisition in Storage for CubeSmart" in Orlando Business Journal (Vol. 28, September 7, 2012, No. 30, pp. 1) **[12975]**, **[17902]**, **[31157]**
701 Ventures LLC **[43311]**
757 Makerspace **[45938]**
1000 Island Clayton Visitor Guide **[42509]**
1000 Islands Area Clayton Chamber of Commerce **[42510]**
"$161.9M 'Pit Stop' Fix-Up Will Create About 1,600 Jobs" in Orlando Business Journal (Vol. 26, January 22, 2010, No. 34, pp. 1) **[3973]**, **[25108]**, **[26489]**
1776 [44378]
1776 New York City **[42829]**
1871 **[39396]**
"1914 Proved to Be Key Year for Chevy" in Automotive News (Vol. 86, October 31, 2011, No. 6488, pp. S18) **[8644]**, **[11368]**, **[12926]**, **[29092]**, **[29635]**, **[31680]**, **[31854]**
1953-54 Buick Skylark Club **[11355]**
"The 2007 Black Book" in Hawaii Business (Vol. 53, December 2007, No. 6, pp. 43) **[21441]**, **[22484]**, **[28437]**
"2007 Top Colleges for Entrepreneurs" in Entrepreneur (Vol. 35, November 2007, No. 11, pp. 82) **[21293]**, **[22362]**, **[24513]**
"2009 Real Estate in Review: Median Prices Drop, Sales Up" in Bellingham Business Journal (Vol. February 2010, pp. 15) **[13126]**, **[13374]**, **[32462]**
"2010 Book of Lists" in Business Courier (Vol. 26, December 26, 2009, No. 36, pp. 1) **[8356]**, **[8883]**, **[9308]**, **[13127]**, **[13375]**, **[13897]**, **[15730]**, **[15983]**, **[21442]**, **[24598]**, **[25703]**, **[26203]**, **[27232]**, **[32463]**, **[33091]**
"2010: Important Year Ahead for Waterfront" in Bellingham Business Journal (Vol. March 2010, pp. 2) **[867]**, **[3974]**, **[5514]**, **[5797]**, **[20720]**, **[23079]**
"2011 FinOvation Awards" in Farm Industry News (January 19, 2011) **[5515]**, **[5798]**, **[11369]**, **[16987]**, **[23080]**, **[30672]**
"2011 a Record Year for New Wind Energy Installations in Canada" in CNW Group (September 26, 2011) **[5516]**, **[5799]**, **[17903]**, **[23081]**
"The 2011 Rental Readers' Choice Award Winners" in Rental Product News (Vol. 33, October 2011) **[13765]**
"2011 Report on the $9 Billion US Trade Show & Event Planning Services Industry" in Investment Weekly (January 21, 2012, pp. 47) **[15828]**, **[17904]**, **[35020]**
"2011 Tax Information of Interest" in Business Owner (Vol. 35, November-December 2011, No. 6, pp. 10) **[46]**, **[1743]**, **[15364]**, **[16778]**, **[34726]**
"2012 Department of Homeland Security Small Business Achievement Award Given to Compass for Outstanding Performance" in Information Technology Business (May 1, 2012, pp. 16) **[14382]**, **[25109]**
"2012 Outlook: ROI Still Piles on the Pressure" in Conference & Incentive Travel (March 1, 2012, pp. 14) **[11902]**, **[15829]**, **[17905]**
"2014 Promises Tech IPO Frenzy" in San Francisco Business Times (Vol. 28, January 3, 2014, No. 24, pp. 6) **[26204]**, **[31158]**, **[35319]**
"2015 Corporate Counsel Legal Pricing Guide - Mergers & Acquisitions" in Economics & Business Week (August 16, 2014, pp. 3) **[18504]**, **[19985]**, **[20721]**, **[25198]**, **[27440]**, **[31159]**
"2015 Marketing Calendar for Real Estate Pros: Own It" **[3975]**, **[11008]**, **[12872]**, **[13128]**, **[13376]**, **[13766]**, **[16387]**, **[21777]**, **[22996]**, **[32464]**
"2019 Top 100 Retailers Power Players: Consumer Electronics/Telecoms" in Stores.org (July 1, 2019) **[4382]**
"2020 Could Be a Defining Year For the Cannabis Industry" in CNN Business (January 10, 2020) **[4986]**
"Report to the Nations - 2020 Global Study on Occupational Fraud and Abuse" in Association of Certified Fraud Examiners (2020) **[19254]**
2022 Pet Sitting and Dog Walking Services Global Market Size & Growth Report with Updated Forecasts **[12263]**
"$10,000 Grants Available for Women-Owned Businesses" in Small Business Trends(February 4, 2023) **[33541]**, **[47969]**

A

A-1 Concrete Leveling Inc. **[4343]**, **[10744]**
A. Davis Grant & Co. **[8843]**
A/R/C Associates Inc. **[4304]**, **[14340]**
"A2L Servicing Best Practices" in AC & Heating Connect (October 22, 2021) **[465]**
A2Y Chamber [40852], [41077]
A.A. World Services Inc. [34668]
AAA Annual Conference Trade Show [573]
AAA Annual Meeting [117]
AAA-CPA Annual Meeting & Education Conference [118]
AAA Franchise Legal Help advice hotline **[2615]**, **[18748]**
AAAC Wildlife Removal (AAAC) **[2087]**
AAB Bulletin **[10929]**
AACC Annual Scientific Meeting & Clinical Lab Expo [32917]
AACPDM Annual Meeting **[26060]**
AACS Annual Conference [1400], [4537]
AACS Annual Convention & Expo **[1400]**, **[4537]**
AACSB Insights **[21735]**
AACSB International [21303]
AACSB-The International Association for Management Education [21303]
AAD Annual Meeting **[26061]**
AAEA Annual Meeting **[17160]**, **[17161]**
AAF Government Reports **[382]**
AAFP Family Medicine Experience (FMX) **[26062]**
AAGD ANNUAL TRADE SHOW [12906]
AAGO's annual trade show [12907]
AAID Business Bite **[26096]**
AAMCO Transmissions, LLC **[14573]**
AAMI Conference & Expo **[10868]**
AAMI eXchange [10868]
AAMI News **[10860]**
AAMI's annual conference and expo [10868]
AAMP Convention [2437]
A&W Food Services of Canada Inc. **[14113]**
A&W Restaurants Inc. **[14114]**
AAO Annual Meeting [16310]
AAOHA Convention & Trade Show **[8484]**
AAPEX Export Interest Directory: 2008 **[8685]**
AAPM&R Annual Assembly [12501]
Aaron Deitsch, F.S.A. **[17386]**

Small Business Sourcebook • 42nd Edition
3171

AASBO

Master Index

AASBO Annual Conference and Exposition **[21680]**
AASBO Conferences [21680]
Aatrix Top Pay™ **[11944]**, **[16892]**, **[17522]**
Aatrix Ultimate Payroll™ **[11945]**
AAVIN Private Equity (AAVIN) **[39810]**
AAVIN Private Equity Advisors **[39837]**
ABA Annual Convention **[24833]**
ABA Bank Marketing Conference **[6700]**, **[24222]**, **[35110]**
ABA/BMA National Conference for Community Bankers **[6701]**, **[24223]**, **[35111]**
ABA Insurance Risk Management Annual Forum **[14491]**
"Abacast, Citadel Strike Radio Ad Deal" in Business Journal Portland (Vol. 27, December 31, 2010, No. 44, pp. 3) **[227]**, **[13026]**, **[14754]**, **[29636]**, **[31160]**, **[33825]**
Abacus Benefit Consultants Inc. [17387]
"Abaddon Acquires Pukaskwa Uranium Properties in NW Ontario" in Canadian Corporate News (May 16, 2007) **[24599]**, **[31161]**, **[32720]**
ABAX of RI, Inc. **[17387]**
ABB Technology Ventures (ATV) **[43266]**
Abbeyfield Houses Society of Canada Newsletter **[8271]**, **[11527]**, **[25982]**
Abbott Nutrition Manufacturing Inc. **[11603]**
Abbott's Frozen Custard Inc. **[8605]**
ABC Annual Conference [2008]
ABC Country Restaurants Inc. **[14115]**
ABC Dialogue **[2004]**
ABC In-home Tutoring **[16154]**
ABC Inc. **[4344]**
ABC Seamless [4344]
"ABC Supply Company Finally Finds Idaho" in Idaho Business Review (September 17, 2014) **[10390]**, **[14325]**, **[17906]**, **[19773]**, **[20608]**, **[35487]**
ABC Tutors In Home Tutoring **[16155]**
ABCD: The Microcomputer Industry Association [3766]
ABCD: The Microcomputer Industry Association-- Membership Directory [3700]
Aberdare Ventures **[37270]**
Aberdeen Area Chamber of Commerce (AACC) **[44634]**
Aberdeen Chamber of Commerce (ACC) **[40364]**
Aberdeen-South Monroe Chamber of Commerce [41416]
ABF Conference and Tradeshow [1495]
ABF E-Buzz **[1492]**
ABI/INFORM **[2165]**, **[2374]**, **[6717]**, **[12919]**, **[17416]**, **[21258]**, **[26728]**, **[31899]**
abi Innovation Hub [42022]
Abilene Chamber of Commerce **[45021]**
Abilene Small Business Development Center **[44904]**, **[45482]**
Abingworth **[37714]**
ABM Continuing Education Conference and Vendor Showcase **[24465]**
"ABM Janitorial Services Receives Service Excellence Award from Jones Lang LaSalle" in Investment Weekly News (July 16, 2011, pp. 75) **[2061]**, **[33092]**
ABONAR Business Consultants Ltd. **[2206]**, **[28940]**
Aboriginal Youth Mean Business! **[46725]**
About Books (ABI) **[1604]**, **[1696]**
Abrakadoodle Remarkable Art Education **[13851]**
Abrams Valuation Group Inc. (AVGI) **[35437]**
ABRY Partners, LLC **[40655]**
ABS Capital Partners **[40424]**
ABS Consulting Training Services **[45588]**
ABS Ventures **[40656]**
ABSEL Conference **[21681]**
Absolute Best Care Nanny Agency **[11331]**
"Abstracting and Indexing Still Relevant in the Digital Age" in GreenPoint Content + Publishing (August, 2015) **[4]**
"Abt Electronics and Appliances Announces the Second Annual Earth Day Recycle Drive" in Ecology, Environment & Conservation Business (May 3, 2014, pp. 3) **[787]**, **[4383]**, **[13757]**, **[23082]**
ABWA Management L.L.C. [35530]
ACA Buyer's Guide **[2512]**
ACA International (ACA) **[4756]**
ACA International - Member Directory **[4764]**
ACA National Conference **[2528]**
"Acacia Subsidiary Acquires Patents Related to Shared Memory for Multimedia Processing from a Major Corporation" in Economics & Business Week (April 26, 2014, pp. 5) **[2706]**, **[3692]**, **[3769]**, **[4384]**, **[27986]**, **[31162]**
Academic Emergency Medicine: A Global Journal of Emergency Care (AEM) **[25983]**
Academic OneFile **[24901]**
Academie Canadienne de Medecine du Sport et de l'Exercice (ACMSE) **[12479]**
Academie Canadienne de Parodontologie [25649]
Academy of Art University Library **[3068]**
Academy of Clinical Mental Health Counselors [2594]

Academy of Dispensing Audiologists [8129]
Academy of Doctors of Audiology (ADA) **[8129]**
Academy of Family Mediators [10786]
Academy of General Practice of Pharmacy [5213]
Academy of Legal Studies in Business (ALSB) **[33934]**
Academy for Mathematics and English **[16156]**
Academy of Nutrition and Dietetics (AND) **[8080]**, **[8123]**, **[11557]**, **[11604]**, **[16518]**
Academy of Pharmacy Practice [5213]
Academy of Pharmacy Practice and Management [5213]
AcademyHealth **[25639]**
Acadia Entrepreneurshp Centre (AEC) **[46745]**
Acadiana Angels **[35257]**, **[40204]**
ACC Craft Show Baltimore **[4684]**
ACCA Annual Conference. [533]
ACCA Annual Conference and IE3 Expo **[533]**
ACCA Conference & Expo [533]
Accel **[37271]**, **[37715]**
Accel-KKR L.L.C. **[37272]**
Accel Management Company Inc. **[37273]**
Accel Partners [37271], [37715]
Acceleprise [38178]
Accelerate Okanagan **[46704]**
"AccelerateMSP Picks CEO, Drops Plan for Seed Fund" in Business Journal (Vol. 31, March 28, 2014, No. 44, pp. 7) **[7064]**
AccelerateNFC **[45494]**
The Accelerator **[42830]**
Accelerator Centre (AC) **[46812]**
Accelerator Ventures (AV) **[37274]**
AccelFoods [42833]
AccelHUB LLC **[40743]**
Access to Law Incubator (ALI) **[37538]**
Access LIVE [1952]
Access Plus Capital (APC) **[37539]**
Access Salt Lake **[45676]**
Access Venture Partners (AVP) **[37915]**
"Accessibility Is an Opportunity, Not an Obstacle" in Associations Now (May 9, 2022) **[30529]**
Accessibility Professionals Association (APA) **[3912]**
Accessible Home Health Care (AHHC) **[8279]**
Accessible Web Design: Complying with Section 508 **[33739]**
"Acciona Windpower to Supply 3-Megawatt Turbines to Prince Edward Island Energy" in Professional Close-Up (September 11, 2012) **[5517]**, **[5800]**, **[23083]**, **[31163]**
Accord CapX LLC **[39455]**
Accountants Association of Iowa (AAI) **[16728]**
"Accountants Get the Hook" in Canadian Business (Vol. 80, October 22, 2007, No. 21, pp. 19) **[47]**, **[16779]**, **[18505]**, **[23467]**
Accountant's Relief [160], [15464]
Accountants Society of Virginia [16757]
AccountantsWorld L.L.C. **[16865]**
Accounting Aid Society (AAS) **[121]**, **[40790]**
Accounting & Auditing Resource Guide **[16891]**
Accounting and Business Research (ABR) **[16888]**
Accounting Evolutions, Inc. **[122]**
Accounting and Finance Benchmarking Consortium (AFBC) **[8]**, **[6226]**
Accounting and Finance Personnel Inc. **[16866]**
Accounting & Financial Women's Alliance (AFWA) **[16729]**, **[35514]**
Accounting and Financial Women's Alliance (AFWA) **[9]**
Accounting and Financial Women's Alliance - Billings Chapter **[35515]**
Accounting and Financial Women's Alliance Birmingham **[35516]**
Accounting and Financial Women's Alliance Chicago Chapter **[35517]**
Accounting and Financial Women's Alliance - Denver Chapter **[35518]**
Accounting and Financial Women's Alliance - Flagstaff Chapter **[35519]**
Accounting and Financial Women's Alliance Houston Chapter (AFWA) **[35520]**
Accounting and Financial Women's Alliance - Mesa East Valley Chapter **[16730]**
Accounting and Financial Women's Alliance Milwaukee Chapter **[35521]**
Accounting and Financial Women's Alliance - Omaha Chapter **[35522]**
Accounting and Financial Women's Alliance Philadelphia Chapter **[35523]**
Accounting and Financial Women's Alliance - San Diego Chapter **[35524]**
Accounting and Financial Women's Alliance San Francisco Chapter **[35525]**
Accounting and Financial Women's Alliance Silicon Valley Chapter **[35526]**
Accounting and Financial Women's Alliance - Springfield Chapter **[16731]**
"Accounting Firm ATKG Adding Assurance Services Division" in San Antonio Business Journal (Vol. 28, July 11, 2014, No. 22, pp. 10) **[48]**

"Accounting Firm Weaver is Still Pursuing Growth Via Mergers" in San Antonio Business Journal (Vol. 25, January 6, 2012, No. 50, pp. 1) **[49]**, **[17907]**, **[31164]**
Accounting Group International **[123]**
"Accounting Lags Behind: Profession Trails Others in Recruiting and Retaining Minorities" in Philadelphia Business Journal (Vol. 28, June 29, 2012, No. 20, pp. 1) **[50]**, **[16780]**, **[30530]**
Accounting On Computers Inc. (AONC) **[124]**
Accounting Perspectives **[51]**
The Accounting Review **[105]**
Accounting Software Tutor Inc. **[125]**
Accounting Solutions Unlimited L.L.C. **[126]**
Accounting & Tax Database® [157], [15459]
Accounting Transition Advisors L.L.C. **[127]**
Accounting Workbook for Dummies **[16781]**
Accounting's New Guidelines: From GAAP to IFRS (Onsite) **[16759]**
Accreditation Council on Optometric Education (ACOE) **[16274]**
Accredited Gemologists Association (AGA) **[9956]**
Accredited Home Newspapers of America - Suburban Newspapers of America - Suburban Section of the National Newspaper Association - National Advertising Newspaper Association [11472]
Accrediting Commission for Cosmetology Education - National Accrediting Commission for Cosmetology Schools - Cosmetology Accrediting Commission [7854]
"Accrual vs. Cash Accounting, Explained" in Business Owner (Vol. 35, July-August 2011, No. 4, pp. 13) **[52]**, **[1744]**, **[15365]**, **[16782]**, **[23725]**
ACCS - Advanced Cisco Campus Switching (Onsite) **[21319]**
Accuitive Medical Ventures L.L.C./ AMV Partners **[38802]**
Accurate Franchising **[24471]**
AccuTrak Inventory Specialists **[28019]**
ACDA National Conference [11197], [11281]
ACDI/VOCA **[16920]**
ACE Academy **[6702]**
"ACE Agrees to Pay Out $266 Million to Investors" in Globe & Mail (February 17, 2006, pp. B1) **[6245]**, **[9309]**, **[33093]**
"ACE Aims High With Spinoff of Repair Unit" in Globe & Mail (January 31, 2007, pp. B15) **[19471]**, **[30865]**, **[33000]**
"ACE Commits $300,000 to Support Environmental Conservation Initiatives and Green Business Entrepreneurs" in Insurance Business Weekly (March 2, 2012, pp. 13) **[5518]**, **[5801]**, **[7079]**, **[23084]**
Ace DuraFlo Systems L.L.C. **[12682]**
"ACE Expands M&A Practice" in Economics & Business Week (March 22, 2014, pp. 2) **[9310]**, **[27233]**, **[31165]**
"Ace Retailers Provide Meaningful Yard Makeovers" in Hardware Retailing (November 6, 2019) **[7916]**
Acer Technology Ventures America, LLC [37390]
ACFA Bulletin **[661]**
ACFN, the ATM Franchise Business **[33313]**
Achieving Excellence in Customer Service (Onsite) **[20369]**
Achieving Leadership Success Through People (Onsite) **[28273]**
"Acing the Test" in Contractor (Vol. 57, January 2010, No. 1, pp. 32) **[5363]**, **[5519]**, **[5802]**, **[14608]**, **[14903]**, **[23085]**
"ACON Investments Acquires Igloo Products Corporation" in Economics & Business Week (April 19, 2014, pp. 6) **[29093]**, **[31166]**
Acorn Campus **[37275]**
Acorn Ventures Inc. **[46183]**
Acoustic Guitar Magazine **[11186]**, **[11272]**, **[11315]**
Acoustical Interior Construction **[4270]**
ACP Update **[1605]**
"Acquisition to Give Mylan Tax Benefits, Boost Sales" in Pittsburgh Business Times (Vol. 33, July 18, 2014, No. 53, pp. 3) **[5144]**, **[17908]**, **[27441]**, **[31167]**, **[34727]**
"Acquisitions Remain Future Growth Strategy for IMB Partners as Black Firm Achieves $1 Billion Revenue Mark" in Black Enterprise(February 6, 2023) **[9311]**
ACRE **[42831]**
"Acsys Interactive Announces Crowdsourcing Comes to the Hospital Industry" in Marketwired (August 23, 2010) **[25704]**, **[29637]**, **[30673]**
"Actian, Data Transformed and Yellowfin BI Mashup Helps Kollaras Group Reap Big Data Rewards" in Computer Business Week (August 28, 2014, pp. 22) **[3480]**, **[8357]**, **[10314]**, **[13377]**, **[27442]**
Action Consulting Association [20679], [33438]
Action for Enterprise (AFE) **[20679]**, **[33438]**
"Action: Huge Film Incentive Boost Eyed in Virginia" in Washington Business Journal (Vol. 32, January 3, 2014, No. 38, pp. 5) **[6173]**, **[24940]**
Action International [2329]
ActionCOACH **[2329]**

"Actions to Implement Three Potent Post-Crisis Strategies" in Strategy & Leadership (Vol. 38, September-October 2010, No. 5) **[17909]**, **[20722]**, **[28438]**
"Actiontec and Verizon Team Up for a Smarter Home" in Ecology,Environment & Conservation Business (November 5, 2011, pp. 3) **[2707]**, **[5520]**, **[5803]**, **[14383]**, **[23086]**, **[33094]**
Activate Venture Partners **[42710]**
Active Green + Ross **[1167]**
Active Voice **[5266]**, **[35142]**, **[46357]**
Acton-Agua Dulce Chamber of Commerce **[36718]**
Acton Area Chamber of Commerce [40603]
Acton Chamber of Commerce [36718]
The Actor's Garage **[11133]**
Acupuncture Canada **[11334]**, **[12480]**
Acupuncture Foundation of Canada Institute [11334], [12480]
Ad Age **[396]**
A.D. Banker & Co. **[27377]**
Ad Complaints Reports **[206]**
Ad Council **[207]**, **[31817]**
Ada Area Chamber of Commerce **[43730]**
Ada Chamber of Commerce [43730]
Adam & Eve Stores **[32361]**
Adams Capital Management Inc. (ACM) **[44331]**
Adams County Chamber of Commerce and Tourism **[46358]**
Adams County Genealogical Society (ACGS) **[7391]**
Adams-Friendship Chamber of Commerce [46358]
Adams Hub **[41960]**
Adams Street Partners LLC (ASP) **[39347]**
"Adapt or Die: How Local Bike Shops Are Evolving to Stay Alive" in Gear Junkie (November 16, 2018) **[1516]**
Adapting Your Marketing Strategy in the Creator Age with Kipp Bodnar **[30145]**
"Add Aquatics to Boost Business" in Pet Product News (Vol. 64, December 2010, No. 12, pp. 20) **[829]**, **[12184]**, **[17910]**, **[32091]**, **[32465]**
"Addiction in the Workplace: How Leaders Can Help Create a Path to Recovery" in Forbes (Oct. 12, 2021) **[34675]**
"Adding Partners to an LLC" in Legal Zoom (March 16, 2023) **[27169]**
Addison Chamber of Commerce and Industry (ACCI) **[39085]**
Addison County Chamber of Commerce (ACCOC) **[45715]**
Addison Industrial Association [39085]
"Addition by Subtraction in Tokyo" in Barron's (Vol. 92, August 25, 2012, No. 38, pp. 20) **[9312]**, **[27443]**, **[28439]**
Address Book for Germanic Genealogy **[7352]**
Adel-Cook County Chamber of Commerce **[38681]**
Adel Partners Chamber of Commerce **[39709]**
ADG Group (ADG) **[20147]**, **[24232]**
"Adidas' Brand Ambitions" in Business Journal Portland (Vol. 27, December 10, 2010, No. 41, pp. 1) **[14672]**, **[15084]**, **[17911]**, **[27444]**, **[29638]**, **[31681]**
Adirondack Regional Business Incubator **[42832]**
Adirondack Regional Chamber of Commerce (ARCC) **[42511]**
Adirondacks-Spectacular Region Chamber of Commerce [42512]
Adirondacks-Speculator Region Chamber of Commerce **[42512]**
ADL Consulting Services **[10190]**
Adler Pollock & Sheehan, P.C. (AP&S) **[6054]**
ADLM Annual Meeting [32917]
Administration publique du Canada [31703]
Administrative Professionals Retreat **[22034]**
Adobe 99U Conference **[33633]**
Adobe Acrobat I (Onsite) **[21320]**
Adobe Acrobat II **[33740]**
Adobe Acrobat Section 508 Accessibility (Onsite) **[25183]**, **[33741]**
Adobe After Effects I (Onsite) **[21321]**
Adobe Bridge **[33742]**
Adobe ColdFusion II (Onsite) **[33743]**
Adobe Creative Suite 5 Bootcamp Training (Onsite) **[33744]**
Adobe Fireworks II **[33745]**
Adobe Flash Media Server **[33746]**
Adobe FrameMaker I (Onsite) **[21322]**, **[33747]**
Adobe FrameMaker II (Onsite) **[21323]**
Adobe FrameMaker III: Structured **[33748]**
Adobe Illustrator I (Onsite) **[21324]**
Adobe Illustrator II (Onsite) **[21325]**
Adobe Illustrator III (Onsite) **[21326]**
Adobe InDesign CS4 Master Class for Designers Training (Onsite) **[21327]**, **[33749]**
Adobe InDesign III (Onsite) **[33750]**
Adobe InDesign with InCopy for Workgroups Training (Onsite) **[21328]**, **[33751]**

Adobe InDesign for Long Documents I (Onsite) **[33752]**
Adobe InDesign for Long Documents II (Onsite) **[33753]**
Adobe InDesign for Long Documents III (Onsite) **[33754]**
Adobe Lightroom Photo Workflow **[33755]**
Adobe Photoshop for Beginners (Onsite) **[33756]**
Adobe Photoshop Channels and Masks (Onsite) **[33757]**
Adobe Photoshop Digital Mastery I (Onsite) **[33758]**
Adobe Photoshop Digital Painting (Onsite) **[33759]**
Adobe Photoshop Extended **[33760]**
Adoption Resource Book **[25705]**, **[30866]**
ADR Institute of Canada, Inc. (ADRIC) **[10784]**
"Adrian Ellis Wears No Cape, But His Firm Protects Execs From Bad Guys" in Orlando Business Journal (Vol. 30, March 14, 2014, No. 38, pp. 3) **[14384]**, **[19472]**, **[31168]**
ADSA Annual Session [10873]
Advance Grower Solutions I Nursery/Greenhouse Accounting Software **[7654]**
Advance Realty Inc. **[13332]**
AdvanceCT (CERC) **[37981]**
Advanced Analytical Technologies Inc. **[3797]**, **[4419]**, [37277]
Advanced Auditing for In-Charge Auditors (Onsite) **[23701]**
Advanced Business Concepts **[4305]**
Advanced Business Learning Inc. (ABL) **[2207]**
Advanced Collection Strategies (Onsite) **[23702]**
Advanced Copyediting (Onsite) **[17822]**
Advanced Critical Thinking Applications Workshop (Onsite) **[19428]**
Advanced Diversity Strategies (Onsite) **[26845]**
Advanced Electric Motor/Generator/Actuator Design and Analysis for Automotive Applications (Onsite) **[29083]**
Advanced Employee Complaint Handling (Onsite) **[26846]**
"Advanced Energy Showcases Industry Leading Inverters and Energy Management Solutions at Solar Power International 2012" in Benzinga.com (September 11, 2012) **[14904]**, **[35021]**
Advanced Financial Forecasting and Modeling Workshop **[23703]**
Advanced Issues in EEO Law **[26847]**
Advanced Issues in Employee Relations **[22035]**, **[28274]**
Advanced IT Audit School (Onsite) **[28275]**
Advanced Leadership Communication Strategies (Onsite) **[17528]**
Advanced Maintenance **[33314]**
Advanced Medical Technology Association (AdvaMed) **[10817]**, **[10944]**
Advanced Network Consulting (ANC) **[30990]**, **[31056]**
Advanced PC Configuration, Troubleshooting and Data Recovery: Hands-On (Onsite) **[21329]**
"Advanced Persuasion Techniques for Top Producers, Part 2: Mental Pivots and Mental Removers" in Senior Market Advisor (Vol. 13, October 2012, No. 10, pp. 32) **[32466]**
Advanced Research Journal of Business Management (ARJBM) **[29043]**
Advanced Sales Management (Onsite) **[32437]**
Advanced Selling for Dummies **[21778]**, **[29639]**, **[32467]**
Advanced Technology Development Center [26475], [38834]
Advanced Technology Ventures (ATV) **[37276]**, **[40657]**
Advanced Textiles Expo [14660]
Advanced Training for Microsoft Excel (Onsite) **[33761]**
Advanced Writing and Editing for Government Proposals **[17823]**, **[25103]**
Advancia Corp. [46315], [46585]
"Advancing the Ball" in Inside Healthcare (Vol. 6, December 2010, No. 7, pp. 31) **[179]**, **[1023]**, **[8244]**, **[11506]**, **[17912]**, **[26490]**, **[26874]**, **[30674]**
Advancing Canadian Entrepreneurship [22456]
Advancit Capital LLC **[40658]**
Advantage **[41184]**
Advantage Business Concepts (ABC) **[2208]**
Advantage Capital **[40205]**
"Advantage Capital Partners Awarded $60 Million Allocation in New Markets Tax Credit Program" in Economics & Business Week (June 28, 2014, pp. 7) **[24941]**, **[34728]**, **[35320]**
Advantage Group International **[20148]**, **[20541]**
"Advantage Tutoring Center Helps Students of All Levels" in Bellingham Business Journal (Vol. February 2010, pp. 16) **[16114]**, **[21443]**, **[23594]**
"The Advantage: Why Organizational Health Trumps Everything Else in Business (J-B Lencioni Series)" **[16542]**, **[19774]**, **[22089]**
Advantages of Small Business and the Economy **[20723]**
Advent International Corporation **[40659]**, **[42711]**
Advent-Morro Equity Partners **[46642]**
"Adventure Capital" in Austin Business Journal (Vol. 34, June 20, 2014, No. 18, pp. 4) **[26162]**, **[35224]**

Adventure Cycling Association **[1511]**
Adventure Cyclist **[1531]**
Adventure Pet **[12105]**
Adventure Travel Trade Association (ATTA) **[15720]**, **[15964]**
"Adventures at Hydronicahh" in Contractor (Vol. 56, September 2009, No. 9, pp. 52) **[466]**, **[3976]**, **[5521]**, **[5804]**, **[14905]**, **[23087]**
Advertising Age **[396]**
"Advertising Agencies" in Black Enterprise (Vol. 44, June 2014, No. 10, pp. 81) **[228]**
Advertising Agencies Industry in the US - Market Research report **[377]**, **[16909]**
Advertising Compliance Service **[383]**
Advertising in Gaming - US - 2021 **[378]**, **[16270]**, **[16910]**
The Advertising and Marketing Independent Network [214], [29569], [31825]
"Advertising May Take a Big Hit in Southwest/AirTran Merger" in Baltimore Business Journal (Vol. 28, October 1, 2010, No. 21, pp. 1) **[229]**, **[19325]**
Advertising Men's League of New York **[208]**, **[31818]**
Advertising Photographers of America **[213]**, **[12287]**
Advertising Production Club of New York (APC-NY) **[3281]**
The Advertising Research Foundation (ARF) **[397]**, **[10707]**, **[31819]**
Advertising Research (Onsite) **[21330]**, **[29577]**
Advertising Standards Canada (ASC) **[209]**
Advertising Women of New York (AWNY) **[225]**, **[31844]**
"Advertising Your Tutor Business - How to Land More Students?" in Superprof blog (Oct. 10, 2020) **[16128]**
"Advice at Entrepreneurs Event: Make Fast Decisions, See Trends" in Crain's Detroit Business (Vol. 30, July 28, 2014, No. 30, pp. 4) **[11370]**, **[15830]**, **[22485]**, **[35022]**
Advising the Small Business **[10222]**, **[33695]**
Advisor **[1507]**, **[15555]**, **[16323]**
"Advisory Firm Launches Own Foundation" in Financial Advisor (November 1, 2019) **[6246]**
Advisory Management Services Inc. **[10492]**, **[20149]**, **[22308]**, **[28941]**
ADVOCAP Inc. Business Development Center **[46557]**
The Advocate **[45022]**
ADVOCIS **[6227]**
Adweek **[384]**
A.E. Schwartz and Associates **[27121]**
AECB News [1626]
AECOM **[561]**, **[2822]**, **[6005]**
AECOM Technology Corp. [561], [2822], [6005]
AEMA-ARRA-ISSA Annual Meeting **[1559]**
Aerobics and Fitness Association of America (AFAA) **[12368]**
"Aeronautics Seeking New HQ Site" in The Business Journal-Milwaukee (Vol. 25, September 5, 2008, No. 50, pp. 1) **[18884]**, **[19155]**, **[29094]**, **[33338]**
Aesthetics International Association (AIA) **[7900]**
AF Ventures **[42833]**
AFA Annual Meeting **[24224]**
AFC Enterprises Inc. [14232]
Affiliated Car Rental L.C. **[13852]**
Affiliated Warehouse Companies (AWC) **[12966]**
Affinity Health Canada **[8280]**
Affirmative Action Plan Workshop (Onsite) **[26848]**
Affirmative Action Register [14981], [14990], [26711], [30627]
Affordable-Sensible [13852]
Affton Chamber of Commerce **[41513]**
AFP ICONs **[7176]**, **[35112]**
The AFP International Conference [7176], [35112]
"Africa Rising" in Harvard Business Review (Vol. 86, September 2008, No. 9, pp. 36) **[230]**, **[1637]**, **[1810]**, **[8686]**, **[27445]**, **[29640]**
African American Chamber of Commerce (AACC) **[43401]**
African-American Chamber of Commerce [42513]
African-American Chamber of Commerce of Pennsylvania, New Jersey and Delaware (AACC) **[44167]**
African-American Chamber of Commerce of Philadelphia [44167]
African American Chamber of Commerce of Westchester and Rockland Counties **[42513]**
African American Entrepreneurs Association (AAEA) **[30237]**
African Americans in Business and Entrepreneurship: A Resource Guide **[1378]**, **[24279]**, **[27979]**, **[29510]**, **[30444]**, **[33709]**
"After 4 Decades, Claypool's Moving On" in Philadelphia Business Journal (Vol. 33, June 27, 2014, No. 20, pp. 8) **[868]**, **[20724]**
"After $4M Funding, ThisClicks CEO Talks What's Next" in Business Journal (Vol. 31, January 10, 2014, No. 33, pp. 7) **[7065]**, **[26163]**, **[30665]**

"After Recession, Texas Cities Lead National Recovery" in Dallas Business Journal (Vol. 37, June 27, 2014, No. 42, pp. 28) [13129], [20725], [26491]
Ag-Bio Centre [46889]
"Ag Firms Harvest Revenue Growth" in The Business Journal-Serving Metropolitan Kansas City (Vol. 26, July 18, 2008, No. 45, pp. 1) [6247], [9313], [16988], [17913], [23726]
AG PRO EXPO [17176]
"AG Warns Slots MBE Plan Risky" in Boston Business Journal (Vol. 29, May 27, 2011, No. 3, pp. 1) [7272], [18506], [25110], [25199], [30320], [35734]
"Agana To Bottle Rain for Whole Foods" in Austin Business Journal (Vol. 32, March 30, 2012, No. 4, pp. 1) [1856], [5522], [5805], [7719], [8003], [23088]
Age Advantage Home Care Franchising Inc. [11534]
AgeLine® [193]
Agency of Commerce and Community Development - Department of Economic Development [45709]
"The Agency Model Is Bent But Not Broken" in Advertising Age (Vol. 79, July 7, 2008, No. 26, pp. 17) [231], [18885], [19473], [29641]
Agency Sales Magazine [10581]
"The Agency-Selection Process Needs Fixing Now" in Advertising Age (Vol. 79, July 7, 2008, No. 26, pp. 18) [232], [18886], [19474], [29642]
Agent and Representative [10581]
"Agfa To Debut New: M-Press Leopard" in American Printer (Vol. 128, June 1, 2011, No. 6) [3298], [12723], [16182], [30954]
Aggie Angel Network (AAN) [45427]
Aggregate Capital Partners L.L.C. [45744]
Agile Alliance (AA) [3760]
Agilent Technologies Campus [37951]
Agilent Technologies, Inc. [3797], [4419], [37277]
Agiletic Law Group [10493]
Agility Computer Network Services L.L.C. [30991], [31057]
Aging Excellence [188]
Aging Life Care Association (ALCA) [11491]
Aging and Working in the New Economy: Changing Career Structures in Small IT Firms [26205], [26875]
Aging2 [40100]
AGN North America (AGN-NA) [10]
AGORA Partnerships [38176]
Agoura-Las Virgenes Chamber of Commerce [36917]
Agoura - Oak Park - Las Virgenes Chamber of Commerce [36917]
Agpro Inc. [17184]
"AgraQuest Deal Signals Growth for Biopesticide Makers" in Sacramento Business Journal (Vol. 29, July 13, 2012, No. 20, pp. 1) [16989], [23089], [29095]
Agri-Business Consultants Inc. [17185]
Agri-Energy Roundtable (AER) [16921]
Agri Marketing Conference [17162]
Agribusiness: An International Journal [17140]
AgriBusiness Association of Kentucky (ABAK) [16922], [39985]
Agribusiness Council (ABC) [16923]
Agribusiness Development Partners [17186]
Agribusiness Incubator Program [38886]
"Agribusiness and Value Chains" in The World Bank [16990]
"Agricharts Launches New Mobile App for Ag Market" in Farm Industry News (December 1, 2011) [2708], [3693], [16991], [26206]
AGRICOLA Database [17203]
Agricultural Bankers Conference [6705], [24229], [35130]
"Agricultural Community Implements Green Technologies, Building Team" in Contractor (Vol. 56, September 2009, No. 9, pp. 5) [3977], [5523], [5806], [13130], [13378], [23090]
Agricultural Consulting Services, Inc. (ACS) [17187]
Agricultural Cooperative Development International [16920]
Agricultural Engineering Associates (AEA) [17188]
Agricultural Groups Concerned About Resources and the Environment [16935]
Agricultural & Industrial Manufacturers Representatives Association [17036]
Agricultural Investment Associates, Inc. [17189]
Agricultural Online Access [17203]
Agricultural Publications Summit [17163]
Agricultural Relations Council (ARC) [12922]
Agricultural Utilization Research Institute (AURI) [17226]
"Agriculture Law 'Infoline' Available for Maryland Farmers" in Ecology, Environment & Conservation Business (June 21, 2014, pp. 3) [16992], [18507]
AgriInstitute [17227]
Agritech Sprouts Start-Ups [16993], [26207]
Agritech Startups, Innovations & Facts [16994], [26208]
Agrivalue Processing Business Incubator (APBI) [46664]
AGTS, Inc. Business English and Grammar Review (Onsite) [17824]

Agvise Laboratories Inc. [17190]
AHA Annual Convention [8486]
"The AHA Moment" in Hispanic Business (December 2010) [233], [10636], [19775], [30321], [35735]
AHA News: American Hospital Association News [25984]
AHCA/NCAL Annual Convention and Exposition [11531]
AHEAD Human Resources Inc. [5453], [15654]
"Ahead of the Trend: What Will the World Map Look Like in Five Years?" in Pet Product News (Vol. 66, September 2012, No. 9, pp. S1) [11342], [12185], [20381]
AHR Expo [534]
AHR Expo: International Air-Conditioning, Heating, Refrigerating Exposition [534]
Ahwatukee Foothills Chamber of Commerce (AFCC) [36306]
AI Academy Experts Discuss AI for Small Business and Content Marketing [29643]
AI for Creatives: Navigating the Ethics of Technology with Tasha L. Harrison [23555]
AI for Marketing: A CMO's Guide [29644]
AiAdertising, Inc. [3658]
AIB International [1240]
AIB Library [3362]
AIBMR Life Sciences, Inc. [11605]
AIC Annual Meeting (Meeting) [982]
AICPA Advanced Personal Financial Planning (PFP) Conference [24225]
AICPA & CIMA Personal Financial Planning Summit [24225]
Aid to Artisans (ATA) [4578]
AIDS International [31918]
AIDS Partnership Michigan [20597]
AIDS Research and Human Retroviruses [10930]
AIIP Annual Conference [3443]
AIIP's Symposium [3443]
Aiken Area SBDC [44499]
Aiken Area Small Business Development Center [44499]
Aiken Chamber of Commerce [44547]
Aikido Pharma Inc. [22028], [35449]
"Ailing Economy Nibbling at Tech-Sector Jobs" in Puget Sound Business Journal (Vol. 29, November 7, 2008, No. 29, pp. 1) [20726], [24514], [26164]
AIM Associates [31058]
AIM Mail Centers [10981]
AIMR Membership Directory [9407]
Aims Community College [37957]
AIMS International [593]
Ainsley Ideas Inc. [8067]
Ainsworth Area Chamber of Commerce [41834]
Ainsworth Area Chamber of Commerce and North Central Development Center (NCDC) [41834]
"Air Canada Boss Gains $3.5-Million in Options" in Globe & Mail (January 19, 2007, pp. B5) [6248], [9314]
"Air Canada to Slash 600 Non-Union Jobs" in Globe & Mail (February 11, 2006, pp. B3) [18887], [19475], [28440], [33095], [35169]
"Air Canada's Flight Plan for 777s Excludes India" in Globe & Mail (March 28, 2007, pp. B5) [19476], [33096]
Air Comm Corp. (ACC) [31599]
Air Conditioning Contractors of America Association (ACCA) [450]
Air Conditioning Contractors of America--Membership Directory [467]
Air-Conditioning, Heating, and Refrigeration Institute (AHRI) [451], [14897]
Air Conditioning, Heating & Refrigeration News--HVACR Directory and Source Guide [36194]
Air Conditioning & Refrigeration (Onsite) [19429], [21331]
Air Conditioning and Refrigeration (Onsite) [2052]
Air Industries and Transport Association of Canada [411]
Air Line Pilots Association International - Canada (ALPA) [410]
Air Medical Journal (AMJ) [435], [25985]
Air Transport Association of Canada (ATAC) [411]
Air & Waste Management Association (A&WMA) [7977]
Air & Waste Management Association Annual Conference & Exhibition (ACE) [23440]
Airbnb for Dummies [766], [12873], [13131], [13767]
"Aircraft Maker May Land in Austin" in Austin Business Journal (Vol. 31, April 15, 2011, No. 6, pp. 1) [3978], [19156], [29096], [33339]
Aircraft Owners and Pilots Association (AOPA) [412]
Aircraft Technical Publishers [449]
Aire-Master of America Inc. [2088]
Aire Serv Heating & Air Conditioning Inc. [546]
Airline Without a Pilot: Lessons in Leadership [28441]
Airlines for America (A4A) [413], [7062]
"Airlines Show Reality 'Behind the Scenes" in Dallas Business Journal (Vol. 35, March 23, 2012, No. 28, pp. 1) [19326], [20382]

"Airmall Mulls I-95 Travel Plazas Bid" in Baltimore Business Journal (Vol. 29, September 2, 2011, No. 17, pp. 3) [13898], [19157], [19327], [25111]
"Airport Adds More Detroit Flavor; Local Brands Bolster Metro Dining, Retail" in Crain's Detroit Business (Vol. 30, July 28, 2014, No. 30, pp. 3) [1899], [2540], [15004], [19328], [31933]
Airport Area Chamber of Commerce [38687]
Airport Directory--Minnesota [429]
Airport Minority Advisory Council (AMAC) [414], [30238], [35527]
Aitkin Area Chamber of Commerce (AACC) [41185]
AJAX Development I (Onsite) [33762]
AJAX Development II (Onsite) [33763]
Ajo District Chamber of Commerce [36307]
Akin Gump Investment Partners 2000 L.P. [45428]
Akron Bar Association (ABA) [43642]
Akron Chamber of Commerce [44318]
Akron Global Business Accelerator [43650]
Akron Regional Development Board [43479]
Akron Small Business Development Centers [43347]
ALA Annual Conference & Expo [18741]
ALA Conference [5418], [18741]
"ALA: Hot Topics for Librarianship" in Information Today (Vol. 28, September 2011, No. 8, pp. 17) [1638], [15831], [30675], [33938], [35023]
Alabama A & M University - J.F. Drake Memorial Learning Resources Center [2415], [11850]
Alabama Association of REALTORS (AAR) [13076]
Alabama Business [36196]
Alabama Business Confidence Index [36197]
Alabama Business Incubation Network [33439]
Alabama Department of Commerce - Enterprise Business Incubator [36168]
Alabama Department of Economic and Community Affairs (ADECA) - Community and Economic Development Programs [36063], [46926]
Alabama Department of Finance - Division of Purchasing [36164]
Alabama Department of Transportation (ALDOT) [1175], [5111], [10292], [15528]
Alabama Gulf Coast Area Chamber of Commerce [36098]
Alabama International Trade Center (AITC) [36064]
Alabama Launchpad [36065]
Alabama Law Institute (ALI) [34233]
Alabama Legislature House of Representatives - House Commerce and Small Business Committee [36193]
Alabama Limited Partnership Law [34233]
Alabama Microenterprise Network (AMEN) [36040]
Alabama Public Library Service (APLS) [47389]
Alabama Small Business Development Center Network (ASBDC) [36165]
Alabama Small Business Development Consortium, Lead Office (ASBDC) [36048]
Alabama State Black Chamber of Commerce (ASBCC) [36077]
Alabama State House of Representatives - House Commerce Committee [36193]
Alabama State University Small Business Development Center (ASU SBDC) [36049]
Alabama Technology Network (ATN) [36066]
Alachua Chamber of Commerce [38320]
Alamance County Area Chamber of Commerce [43078]
Alameda Business Library [2375], [2416]
Alameda Chamber of Commerce [36719]
Alameda County Small Business Development Center (ACSBDC) [36559]
Alamo Angels [45429]
"Alamo Beer Tapping Into New Momentum on East Side" in San Antonio Business Journal (Vol. 28, July 4, 2014, No. 21, pp. 7) [1314], [1900]
Alamo Chamber of Commerce [45023]
Alamo City Black Chamber of Commerce (ACBCC) [45024]
Alamogordo Chamber of Commerce (ACC) [42299]
Alamogordo Small Business Development Center [42272]
Alamosa County Chamber of Commerce (ACCC) [37813]
Alan Biller and Associates [6708]
Alantra [40660]
Alaska Business Development Center Inc. (ABDC) [33643], [36254]
Alaska Business Monthly [36256]
Alaska Business Monthly [36255]
Alaska Department of Commerce, Community, and Economic Development (DCCED) [36212]
Alaska Department of Labor [46927]
Alaska Department of Labor and Workforce Development - Research and Analysis [46927]
Alaska Dietary Managers Association [11560]
Alaska Marine Safety Education Association (AMSEA) [10627]

Alaska Small Business Development Center Anchorage [36210]
Alaska Small Business Development Center Fairbanks (ASBDC) [36205]
Alaska Small Business Development Center Homer [36206]
Alaska Small Business Development Center Juneau (ASBDC) [36207]
Alaska Small Business Development Center Ketchikan (SBDC) [36208]
Alaska Small Business Development Center Soldotna (ASBDC) [36209]
Alaska Small Business Development Center State Office (ASBDC) [36210]
Alaska Small Business Development Center Wasilla (ASBDC) [36211]
Alaska State Chamber of Commerce [36218]
Alaska Venture Partners, LLC [36257]
Albany Area Chamber of Commerce (AACC) [43935]
Albany Area Chamber of Commerce - Georgia [38682]
Albany Business Review [42988]
Albany Center for Economic Success (ACES) [42834]
Albany Chamber of Commerce [41186], [43936]
Albany Medical College - Schaffer Library of Health Sciences [1038]
Albany Park Chamber of Commerce [39086]
Albany Small Business Development Center [42390]
Albany Texas Chamber of Commerce [45025]
Albemarie County Chamber of Commerce [45845]
"Albemarle to Invest $1.3B, Create 300-Plus Jobs with New Chester County Facility" in The Business Journals (March 22, 2023) [29097]
Albert Lea-Freeborn County Chamber of Commerce (ALFCCOC) [41187]
Alberta Agriculture and Forestry-Crop Diversification Centre South Library [17204]
Alberta Agriculture and Rural Development - Crop Diversification Centre South (CDCS) [8168]
Alberta Band Association Music Lending Library (ABA) [11290]
"Alberta Carbon Capture Strategy Falters: Alberta's Favoured Emissions-Control Plan is Falling Apart" in Canadian Business (Vol. 85, June 11, 2012, No. 10, pp. 13) [5524], [23091], [25200]
Alberta Enterprise Fund (AE) [46683]
"Alberta: Help Wanted, Badly" in Globe & Mail (March 11, 2006, pp. B5) [20727], [24600]
Alberta Securities Commission (ASC) [9945], [18791], [24510]
Alberta Small Business Resources [46657]
"Alberta Star Begins Phase 2 Drilling On Its Eldorado & Contact Lake IOCG & Uranium Projects" in Canadian Corporate News (May 16, 2007) [25201], [30867], [31934], [35321]
Alberta Womens Entrepreneurs (AWE) [46661]
Albion Chamber of Commerce (ACC) [41835]
Albion Economic Development Corp. [41072]
Album VC [45657]
Albuquerque Business First [42361]
"Albuquerque Entrepreneurs Selected As Top Participants in USHCC Foundation Green Builds Business Program" in Marketing Weekly News (April 21, 2012) [5525], [5807], [22486], [23092]
Albuquerque Small Business Development Center [42273]
Albuquerque South Valley Small Business Development Center [42274]
Albuquerque Technical-Vocational Institute [42358]
The Alchemist Accelerator (AA) [37540]
"Alcoa: 'Going Where No Materials Scientist Has Gone Before'" in Pittsburgh Business Times (Vol. 33, July 18, 2014, No. 53, pp. 5) [23093], [29098], [31169], [32721]
"Alcoa's Quebec Deal Keeps Smelters Running" in Pittsburgh Business Times (Vol. 33, February 28, 2014, No. 33, pp. 3) [11371], [29099], [31170]
Alcohol Beverage Legislative Council [10310]
Alcohol Research Group Library [34693]
Alcoholic Beverage Industry [1371], [10342]
Alcoholics Anonymous World Services, Inc. (A.A.) [34668]
Alden & Associates Marketing Research (AA-MR) [30176]
Aldrich & Cox Inc. (A&C) [17388]
"Ale for One, One for Ale: DC's Beer Industry Collects Behind a New Brewers' Guild" in Washington Business Journal (Vol. 33, August 15, 2014, No. 17, pp. 6) [1901]
Aleria Opens Groundbreaking One-Year Inclusion Program for Small Businesses [30531]
Alerion Capital Group [36420]
Alert! [10681]
Alert [36720]

"Alex Gomez on Leaving Medical School to Launch a Startup" in South Florida Business Journal (Vol. 34, May 9, 2014, No. 42, pp. 19) [9287], [10813], [22363], [35225]
Alex James: Slowing Down Fast Fashion [3006], [23094]
Alexander Associates [30992]
Alexander Business Investment Consultants Inc. [30177]
Alexander City Chamber of Commerce (ACCC) [36078]
Alexander Technique International (ATI) [11335]
Alexandria Bay Chamber of Commerce [42514]
Alexandria Center for Life Science [42835]
Alexandria Chamber of Commerce (ACC) [45826]
Alexandria Lakes Area Chamber of Commerce [41188]
Alexandria Lakes Area Visitor and Livability Guide [41189]
Alexandria Launch Labs [42836]
Alexandria Small Business Development Center (ASBDC) [45767]
Alexandria Technical College (ATC) [41357]
"The Alfond Inn: a Small Hotel that Packs a Punch" in Orlando Business Journal (Vol. 30, January 24, 2014, No. 31, pp. 6) [8358], [20383]
Alfred Swenson Pao-Chi Chang Architects [11649]
Alfred University - Inamori School of Engineering - Center for Glass Research (CGR) [7506]
Alger County Chamber of Commerce [40849]
Algoma Area Chamber of Commerce [46359]
"Algoma Resolves Hedge Fund Fight" in Globe & Mail (March 8, 2006, pp. B1) [6249], [9315], [33001]
Algona Area Chamber of Commerce [39710]
Algonquin - Lake in the Hills Chamber of Commerce [39087]
Alhambra Chamber of Commerce [36721]
Aliceville Area Chamber of Commerce (AACC) [36079]
Aliens Art Private Limited [15342]
Aliens Tattoo [15342]
Alive [25986]
AlixPartners LLP [22353]
"All Aboard!" Austin Business Journal (Vol. 32, April 27, 2012, No. 8, pp. A1) [13379], [15511]
All About Honeymoons [16034]
"All About The Benjamins" in Canadian Business (Vol. 81, September 29, 2008, No. 16, pp. 92) [3979], [8687], [9092], [9316], [13380], [18508], [19255], [26209], [27446], [31171]
All America Karate Federation [10711]
All American Grooming Show [12102]
All American Pet Resorts [12106]
All American Specialty Restaurants, Inc. [8606]
A All Animal Control [2087]
"All Eyes On Iris" in Canadian Business (Vol. 81, July 22, 2008, No. 12-13, pp. 20) [6250], [9317], [19477], [23727], [25202], [33939]
"All Fired Up!" in Small Business Opportunities (November 2008) [12527], [13899], [18888], [19478], [21444], [24328]
"All Hail: How Taxi Companies Stay Competitive in an Evolving Marketplace" in SmartcitiesDive (March 28, 2019) [11699], [15512], [21779]
All Handwriting Services, LLC [7908]
"All In The Family: Weston Undergoes a Shakeup" in Canadian Business (Vol. 79, September 22, 2006, No. 19, pp. 75) [17914], [23595], [24601]
All-Industry Research Advisory Council [9013]
All Money Is Not Created Equal: How Entrepreneurs Can Crack the Code to Getting the Right Funding for Their Startup [34494]
All Nations Flag Co., Inc. [3275]
All Night Auto Repair [14574]
"All-Star Advice 2010" in Black Enterprise (Vol. 41, October 2010, No. 3, pp. 97) [4765], [6251], [8884], [9318], [13132], [13381], [20242], [27234], [34729]
"All-Star Execs: Top CEO: Gordon Nixon" in Canadian Business (Vol. 80, November 24, 2008, No. 22, pp. 9) [6252], [19776], [25203], [27447]
All Star Franchising L.L.C. [5110]
"All Things Being Equitable" in Associations now (May 9, 2022) [30532]
"All the Things Your Wedding DJ Can Do (Besides Play Music)" in WeddingWire (July 20, 2018) [4962]
"All Those Applications, and Phone Users Just Want to Talk" in Advertising Age (Vol. 79, August 11, 2008, No. 31, pp. 18) [2709], [9093], [14755], [17634], [24329], [26210]
"All the Trimmings" in Green Industry Pro (Vol. 23, March 2011, No. 3, pp. 29) [7612], [10050], [10087], [10225], [33097]
All Tune and Lube (ATL) [13001], [14575]
"All You Need to Know About Selecting a SaaS Design Platform" in Digital Agency Network (September 11, 2020) [16388]
Alla Breve [11187]
Allan Savory Center for Holistic Management [5788]

Alle Kiski Strong Chamber of Commerce [44168]
Allegan Area Chamber of Commerce (AACC) [40850]
Allegany County Chamber of Commerce (ACCC) [40365]
Alleghany County Chamber of Commerce (ACCC) [43079]
Alleghany Highlands Chamber of Commerce [45827]
Alleghany Highlands Chamber of Commerce & Tourism [45827]
Alleghany Highlands Economic Development Corp. - Business Assistance Program [45939]
Allegheny Valley Chamber of Commerce [44168]
Allegis Capital L.L.C. / Media Technology Ventures [37278]
Allegra Marketing - Print - Mail [17816]
Allegra Partners/Lawrence, Smith & Horey [42712]
Allen County Business Directory [43402]
Allen County Public Library - Business and Technology Department [32071]
Allen Economic Development Group (AEDG) [43643]
Allen-Fairview Chamber of Commerce [45026]
Allen Market Place (AMP) [41073]
Allen Sapp Gallery (ASG) [988]
Allentown-Lehigh County Chamber of Commerce [44228]
Allergy/Asthma Information Association (AAIA) [551]
Alliance [43403]
Alliance of American Insurers [8857], [9003]
Alliance for American Manufacturing (AAM) [29067]
Alliance of Angels (AA) [46184]
Alliance of Area Business Publications--Membership Directory [24775]
Alliance of Area Business Publishers (AABP) [11951], [38116]
Alliance Area Chamber of Commerce (AACC) [43404]
Alliance for Audited Media (AAM) [11952]
Alliance of Canadian Cinema Television and Radio Artists (ACTRA) [13013], [15566]
Alliance Chamber of Commerce [41836]
Alliance for Children and Television [15632]
Alliance for Community Media (ACM) [2474]
Alliance Cost Containment L.L.C. (ACC) [2330]
Alliance Des Arts Mediatiques Independants [6164]
Alliance Franchise Brands LLC (AFB) [17816]
Alliance for Higher Education (45561]
The Alliance Management Group Inc. [2209], [10494], [20150], [28942]
Alliance Management International Ltd. [2210], [10495], [17882], [20151], [28943]
"The Alliance: Managing Talent in the Networked Age" [22090], [28442]
L'Alliance Medias Jeunesse [15632]
Alliance Newsletter [38164]
Alliance for Nonprofit Management [31670]
"Alliance Offers to Help Italian Workers Settle In" in Crain's Detroit Business (Vol. 25, June 15, 2009, No. 24, pp. 21) [27448], [34267]
Alliance for Pharmacy Compounding (IACP) [5124]
Alliance of Professional Tattooists, Inc. (APT) [15280]
Alliance Small Business Development Center [36560]
Alliance Tattoo Supply [15320]
Alliance for Women in Media (AWM) [31820]
AllianceBernstein Holding L.P. [9946]
Allied Beauty Association (ABA) [7851]
"Allied Brands Loses Baskin-Robbins Franchise Down Under" in Ice Cream Reporter (Vol. 23, November 20, 2010, No. 12, pp. 2) [8542], [24330], [27449], [29645]
"Allied Brokers of Texas Looking to Fill Private Lending Gap" in San Antonio Business Journal (Vol. 26, March 23, 2012, No. 8, pp. 1) [17915], [19643], [22364], [28054], [32999]
Allied Farm Equipment Manufacturers Association [10047]
Allos Ventures [39668]
AllOver Media Inc. (AOM) [389]
"Allowing Ethanol Tax Incentive to Expire Would Risk Jobs, RFA's Dinneen Says" in Farm Industry News (November 3, 2010) [5526], [5808], [16995], [23095], [34730]
Alloy Development Company (HCDC) [43644]
Alloy Development Co. [43644]
Alloy Digest [32852]
Allsop Venture Partners / AAVIN [39811]
"ALLSTAR Chauffeured Services Celebrates 25 Years of Growth" in Chauffeur Driven (November 12, 2019) [10278]
Allstate Private Equity [39348]
Allstream Business Inc. [3444]
Allsup, L.L.C. [28944]
Allworth Press [42996]
Alma Area Chamber of Commerce [40919]
Alma/Bacon County Chamber of Commerce [38683]
Alma Chamber of Commerce (ACC) [36432]
Almaz Capital [37279]

"Almost Like Home" in Pet Product News (Vol. 66, September 2012, No. 9, pp. S18) **[8004]**, **[12186]**, **[20384]**
ALOA Security Expo **[10360]**
ALOA Security Professionals Association, Inc. (ALOA) **[10350]**
Aloha Hotels and Resorts **[8498]**, **[24494]**
Aloha USA **[16157]**
Alpaca Breeders of the Rockies (ABR) **[623]**
Alpena Community College (ACC) **[41126]**
Alpha Business Communications (ABC) **[3779]**
Alpha Capital Partners Ltd. **[35438]**, **[39349]**
Alpha Legal Forms & More Inc. **[2331]**, **[2396]**
Alpha Loft **[42022]**
AlphaGraphics Inc. (AG) **[12773]**
AlphaLab Gear **[44379]**
"Alpharetta Seeding Startups To Encourage Job Growth" in Atlanta Business Chronicle(June 20, 2014, pp. 3A) **[21445]**, **[24515]**, **[25204]**, **[27207]**, **[27235]**, **[28055]**, **[35226]**
Alpine Chamber of Commerce **[36722]**
Alpine Chamber of Commerce (ACC) **[45027]**
Alpine County Chamber of Commerce (ACCC) **[36723]**
Alpine County Chamber of Commerce and Visitor Information Center [36723]
Alpine County Small Business Development Center **[36561]**
Alpine and Mountain Empire Chamber of Commerce [36722]
ALSA Architecture L.L.C. **[927]**
Alsb Annual Conference **[18742]**
Alsip Chamber of Commerce **[39088]**
Alsop Louie Partners (ALP) **[37716]**
"Alstom Launches the ECO 122 - 2.7MW Wind Turbine for Low Wind Sites" in CNW Group (September 28, 2011) **[5527]**, **[5809]**, **[23096]**, **[29100]**
Alta Mere **[2567]**
Alta Partners **[37280]**
Alta Ventures (AV) **[45691]**
Altadena Chamber of Commerce (ACC) **[36724]**
Altarum Institute **[41074]**
Altavista Area Chamber of Commerce (AACC) **[45828]**
"Altegrity Acquires John D. Cohen, Inc." in November 19, 2009, pp. 14) **[2177]**, **[14385]**, **[20083]**, **[31172]**
"Altera Ranks Among Top 25 Greenest Companies in U.S." in Ecology, Environment & Conservation Business (August 9, 2014, pp. 2) **[5528]**, **[5810]**, **[7946]**, **[23097]**
"Alternate Financing Options For Startups" in Inc42 (Aug. 29, 2020) **[30908]**
The Alternative Board (TAB) **[2332]**
"Alternative Energy Calls for Alternative Marketing" in Indoor Comfort Marketing (Vol. 70, June 2011, No. 6, pp. 8) **[468]**, **[5529]**, **[5811]**, **[14906]**, **[23098]**, **[29646]**, **[33940]**
"Alternative Energy Is a Major Topic at Agritechnica 2011" in Farm Industry News (November 16, 2011) **[5530]**, **[5812]**, **[16996]**, **[23099]**
Alternative Energy Resources Organization (AERO) **[14898]**, **[14962]**
"Alternative Financing for a Small Business" in Chron **[30909]**
"Alternative Fuels Take Center Stage at Houston Auto Show" in Houston Business Journal (Vol. 44, January 31, 2014, No. 39, pp. 8) **[5531]**, **[5813]**, **[11372]**, **[15832]**, **[23100]**, **[29101]**, **[30676]**, **[35024]**
"Alternative Lending: Best Lenders and Loan Options" in Fundera (Dec. 20, 2021) **[30910]**
Alternative Services Inc. (ASI) **[2211]**, **[20152]**, **[26080]**
"Alterra Acquiring Sugarbush Resort in Vermont" in Travel Weekly (November 13, 2019) **[8359]**
"Although a Chain, Claim Jumper is a Good Addition to Downtown" in Sacramento Business Journal (Vol. 30, January 10, 2014, No. 46, pp. 4) **[13900]**
Alticor Inc. Corporate Library **[30664]**
Altira Group L.L.C. **[37916]**
Altitude Accelerator **[46813]**
Altitude Ventures (AV) **[44868]**
Altoona Area Chamber of Commerce (AACC) **[39711]**
Altoona Blair County Development Corporation (ABCD Corp.) **[44380]**
Altos Ventures **[37281]**
Alturas Chamber of Commerce **[36725]**
Altus Chamber of Commerce **[43731]**
"Altus Jobs Founders' Unique Operating System Generates Success" in Orlando Business Journal (Vol. 30, April 11, 2014, No. 42, pp. 3) **[6102]**, **[22091]**, **[22487]**
Aluminum Extruders Council (AEC) **[10416]**
Aluminum Wares Association [8172]
Alva Chamber of Commerce **[43732]**
Alvana Business Consulting Inc. **[28945]**
Alvin-Manvel Area Chamber of Commerce **[45028]**
"Always Two Sides to a Chip: Sounding Off on the Issues" in South Florida Business Journal (Vol. 34, January 10, 2014, No. 25, pp. 14) **[7273]**

Alzheimer Disease Center and Related Neuropsychiatric Disorders [10941]
"Am I Self-Employed or Small Business Owner? What the Heck Am I?" (September, 27, 2016), www.mariettemartinez.com. **[32986]**
AMA Customer Service Excellence: How to Win and Keep Customers **[20370]**
AMA Developing Your Personal Brand and Professional Image **[22036]**
AMA Effective Technical Writing (Onsite) **[17529]**
AMA Export/Import Procedures and Documentation (Onsite) **[23704]**
AMA Fixed Asset Accounting (Onsite) **[16760]**
AMA Fundamentals of Cost Accounting (Onsite) **[16761]**
AMA Fundamentals of Finance and Accounting for Administrative Professionals (Onsite) **[16762]**
AMA Greater Productivity Through Improved Work Processes: A Guide for Administrative Professionals (Onsite) **[22037]**
The AMA Handbook of Project Management **[22488]**, **[28443]**
AMA How to Sharpen Your Business Writing Skills (Onsite) **[17825]**
AMA Improving Your Project Management Skills: The Basics for Success **[28276]**
AMA Leading Virtual Teams **[28277]**
AMA Making the Transition to Management (Onsite) **[28278]**
AMA Making the Transition from Staff Member to Supervisor (Onsite) **[28279]**
AMA Management Skills for Administrative Professionals **[28280]**
AMA Managing Chaos: Dynamic Time Management, Recall, Reading, and Stress Management Skills for Administrative Professionals (Onsite) **[28281]**
AMA Managing Emotions in the Workplace: Strategies for Success (Onsite) **[17530]**
AMA Managing a World-Class IT Department (Onsite) **[28282]**
AMA Master Organizational Politics, Influence and Alliances (Onsite) **[28283]**
AMA Partnering with Your Boss: Strategic Skills for Administrative Professionals **[22038]**
AMA Principles of Professional Selling **[32438]**
AMA Project Management for Administrative Professionals (Onsite) **[28284]**
AMA Recruiting, Interviewing and Selecting Employees (Onsite) **[26849]**
AMA Responding to Conflict: Strategies for Improved Communication **[17531]**
AMA Strategies for Developing Effective Presentation Skills (Onsite) **[17532]**
AMA Successful Meeting Planning (Onsite) **[17533]**
AMA Successful Product Management (Onsite) **[29578]**
AMA Technical Project Management (Onsite) **[28285]**
AMA Territory and Time Management for Salespeople (Onsite) **[32439]**
AMA The Voice of Leadership: How Leaders Inspire, Influence, and Achieve Results (Onsite) **[28286]**
AMA Winter Academic Conference [21700]
Amador County Chamber of Commerce [36726]
Amador County Chamber of Commerce and Visitors Bureau **[36726]**
Amador County Small Business Development Center **[36562]**
Amalgamated Printers' Association (APA) **[12714]**
Amarillo Chamber of Commerce (ACC) **[45029]**
AMA's 2-Day Business Writing Workshop (Live Online) **[17826]**
AMA's 5-Day MBA Workshop **[28287]**
AMA's Advanced Course in Strategic Marketing (Onsite) **[29579]**
AMA's Advanced Executive Leadership Program (Onsite) **[28288]**
AMA's Advanced Financial Forecasting and Modeling Workshop (Onsite) **[19430]**
AMA's Comprehensive Budgeting Workshop **[16763]**
AMA's Comprehensive Project Management Workshop (Onsite) **[28289]**
AMA's Course on Mergers and Acquisitions (Onsite) **[31149]**
AMA's Finance Workshop for Nonfinancial Executives (Onsite) **[23705]**
AMA's Insurance and Risk Management Workshop (Onsite) **[27228]**
AMA's Leading with Emotional Intelligence (Onsite) **[28290]**
AMA's Myers-Briggs Type Indicator (MBTI) Certification Program **[22039]**
AMA's PMP Exam Prep Express (Onsite) **[21332]**
Amato's **[14116]**
"Amazing Apple Does It Again" in Barron's (Vol. 92, September 15, 2012, No. 38, pp. 26) **[2710]**, **[28444]**, **[29647]**

"Amazon Beats Best Buy As Top Electronics Retailer" in RetailDive (April 17, 2018) **[4385]**, **[11700]**
"Amazon to End Its Restaurant Delivery Service" in The New York Times (June 11, 2019) **[6898]**, **[11701]**
"Amazon Hits Back at Bloomberg Report About Small Suppliers Purge" in Fast Company (May 28, 2019) **[10010]**, **[11702]**
"Amazon Is Poised to Unleash a Long-Feared Purge of Small Suppliers" in Bloomberg (May 28, 2019) **[10011]**, **[11703]**
"Amazon Launches Free Creator University with Guides for Affiliates and Influencers" in Small Business Trends(February 9, 2023) **[11704]**
"Amazon Launches a Personal Shopper Service That Sends Monthly Curated Clothing Boxes" in The Verge (July 31, 2019) **[11705]**, **[12019]**, **[21780]**
"Amazon Makes Inroads Selling Medical Supplies to the Sick" in The Wall Street Journal (November 29, 2018) **[10945]**, **[11706]**
"Amazon Selling Secrets: How to Make an Extra $1K - $10K a Month Selling Your Own Products on Amazon" **[11679]**, **[21758]**
"Amazon Targets Denton-Based Sally Beauty's Professional Salon Customers" in The Dallas Morning News (June 24, 2019) **[1386]**, **[11707]**
"Amazon Was Supposed to Have Crushed Bookstores. So Why Are Indie Bookshops Booming in D.C.?" in wamu.org (July 6, 2017) **[1811]**
"Amazon Will Regret Building Private Label Brands" in Marketplace Pulse (September 25, 2019) **[11708]**, **[12803]**
"Amazon's Booze Business in Jeopardy with Investigation into Fake LA Liquor Store" in Vinepair (August 20, 2019) **[10315]**, **[11709]**
"Amazon's Top Doctor on Why Air Quality Is the Biggest Workplace Health Challenge of This Century" in CNBC (October 22, 2021) **[554]**
Ambassadors Impact Network **[45430]**
AmBex Venture Partners LLC **[37717]**
"Ambitious Horse Center Is In the Works for Southeastern Idaho" in Idaho Business Review (August 25, 2014) **[3980]**, **[8317]**, **[8360]**, **[16997]**, **[25706]**, **[32092]**
Ambler Growth Strategy Consultants Inc. **[2212]**, **[20153]**, **[31921]**
Ambridge Area Chamber of Commerce (AACC) **[44169]**
Ambridge Regional Chamber of Commerce [44169]
Ambulance Association of Pennsylvania (AAP) **[566]**
Ambulance Services: Leadership and Management Perspectives **[570]**
AMC Institute (AMCI) **[1047]**
AMC Networks Inc. **[14348]**
"Amcon Distributing Expands Into Northwest Arkansas" in Arkansas Business (Vol. 26, November 9, 2009, No. 45, pp. 13) **[4426]**, **[17916]**, **[20609]**, **[31173]**
AMDA - Dedicated to Long Term Care Medicine [11492]
AMDA - The Society for Post-Acute and Long-Term Care Medicine (AMDA) **[11492]**
Ameren Corporation **[35970]**
"America's Top 40 Wealth Management Firms" in Barron's (Vol. 92, September 17, 2012, No. 38, pp. 28) **[6253]**, **[9319]**, **[23728]**
American Academy of Advertising (AAA) **[210]**, **[31821]**
American Academy of Attorney-CPAs (AAA-CPA) **[11]**
American Academy of Implant Dentistry Annual Meeting **[10869]**, **[10959]**
American Academy of Optometry (AAO) **[16275]**, **[16315]**
American Academy of Optometry Foundation (AOF) **[16276]**
American Academy of Philately [3213]
American Academy of Physical Medicine and Rehabilitation Annual Assembly **[12501]**
American Academy of Procedural Coders [29566], [35528]
American Academy of Professional Coders (AAPC) **[29566]**, **[35528]**
American Accounting Association (AAA) **[12]**
American Accounting Association Annual Meeting **[117]**
American Advertising Federation (AAF) **[211]**, **[31822]**
"American Airlines Works to Keep Its Brand Aloft" in Dallas Business Journal (Vol. 35, May 18, 2012, No. 36, pp. 1) **[8645]**, **[19329]**, **[27450]**, **[35170]**
American Alfalfa Processors Association [16925]
American Alliance Against Violence [7840]
American Alternative Medical Association (AAMA) **[12481]**
American Amateur Karate Federation (AAKF) **[10711]**
American Amateur Racquetball Association [12389], [15675]
American Ambulance Association (AAA) **[567]**
American Ambulance Association Annual Conference and Trade Show **[573]**

American Amusement Machine Association (AAMA) **[575]**
American Animal Hospital Association (AAHA) **[673]**
American Apparel Contractors Association--Directory of Contractors [3058]
American Apparel Contractors Association--Directory for Sourcing American Made Apparel [3058]
American Apparel and Footwear Association (AAFA) **[2843]**, **[10301]**
American Apparel Producers' Network--Directory for Sourcing American Made Apparel [3058]
American Apparel Producers' Network--Directory for Sourcing Apparel [3058]
"American Apparel: When Dov Cries" in *Canadian Business (Vol. 83, June 15, 2010, No. 10, pp. 71)* **[3007]**, **[3089]**, **[4766]**, **[20243]**, **[20385]**, **[23729]**
American Arbitration Association (AAA) **[10785]**
American Assembly of Collegiate Schools of Business [21303]
American Association for Access, Equity and Diversity (AAAED) **[30499]**
American Association of Advertising Agencies (AAAA) **[212]**, **[31823]**
American Association for Aerosol Research (AAAR) **[32710]**
American Association for Affirmative Action [30499]
American Association of Attorney-Certified Public Accountants Annual Meeting and Educational Conference **[118]**
American Association of Bioanalysts (AAB) **[10899]**
American Association of Biological Anthropologists [32711]
American Association for Budget and Program Analysis (AABPA) **[17485]**
American Association of Business Networking (ABN) **[18799]**
American Association of Candy Technologists (AACT) **[2534]**
American Association of Certified Wedding Planners (AACWP) **[6080]**
American Association of Cleaning Professionals (AACP) **[2963]**
American Association for Clinical Chemistry Annual Meeting **[32917]**
American Association of Clinical Laboratory Supervisors and Administrators [10908]
American Association of Colleges of Pharmacy (AACP) **[5125]**
American Association of Commercial Collectors [4759]
American Association of Cosmetology Schools (AACS) **[7852]**
American Association of Counseling and Development [2588]
American Association of Exporters and Importers (AAEI) **[8677]**, **[27391]**
American Association of Feline Practitioners (AAFP) **[674]**
American Association of Finance & Accounting, Inc. (AAFA) **[16732]**
American Association of Fund-Raising Counsel Membership Directory [7115]
American Association of Fundraising Counsel [7077]
American Association of Group Workers [25681]
American Association of Handwriting Analysts (AAHA) **[7901]**, **[7909]**
American Association of Homes for the Aging [11501]
American Association of Homes and Services for the Aging [11501]
American Association for Horsemanship Safety (AAHS) **[8299]**
American Association of Industrial Editors [17526], [17821]
American Association of Industrial Editors International Council of Industrial Editors [17526], [17821]
American Association of Inside Sales Professionals (AAISP) **[32426]**
American Association of Insurance Management Consultants (AAIMCo) **[8854]**
American Association of Insurance Services (AAIS) **[8855]**
American Association for Laboratory Accreditation (A2LA) **[10900]**
American Association for Laboratory Animal Science Conference & Exhibits **[10934]**
The American Association of Language Specialists (TAALS) **[15922]**
American Association of Meat Processors (AAMP) **[2425]**
American Association of Medical Record Librarians [10887], [10973]
American Association of Medical Social Workers [25681]
American Association for Medical Transcription [10967]
American Association of Minority Enterprise Small Business Investment Companies [9350], [30272], [35285]

American Association of Nurserymen [7604], [10045]
American Association of Nursing Homes [1021], [11494], [25641]
American Association of Nutritional Consultants (AANC) **[11558]**
American Association of Occupational Health Nurses, Inc. (AAOHN) **[1039]**
American Association of Oriental Healing Arts [10754]
American Association of Pharmacy Technicians (AAPT) **[5126]**
American Association of Physical Anthropologists (AABA) **[32711]**
American Association of Professional Bridal Consultants [1959]
American Association of Psychiatric Social Workers [25681]
American Association of Radon Scientists and Technologists (AARST) **[13068]**
American Association of Social Workers [25681]
American Association of State Climatologists (AASC) **[32712]**
American Association of Swine Practitioners [675]
American Association of Swine Veterinarians (AASV) **[675]**
American Association of University Instructors in Accounting [12]
American Association of University Teachers of Insurance [8858]
American Association of Wildlife Veterinarians (AAWV) **[676]**
American Association of Zoo Veterinarians (AAZV) **[677]**
American Audiology Society [8130]
American Auditory Society (AAS) **[8130]**
American Automobile Association, Inc. (AAA) **[5112]**, **[11469]**
American Automotive Leasing Association (AALA) **[1148]**, **[11356]**
American Bakers Association (ABA) **[1206]**, **[1241]**
American Ballet Competition [4847]
American Banker: Charting the Future of Financial Services (AB) **[11101]**
American Banker: The Financial Services Daily [11101]
American Bar Association Legal Guide for Small Business: Everything You Need to Know About Small Business, from Start-up to Employment to Financing and Selling **[18509]**, **[23730]**, **[24516]**, **[26876]**, **[28088]**, **[33002]**
American Bee Journal **[1457]**, **[1493]**
American Beekeeping Federation (ABF) **[1428]**
American Beekeeping Federation Conference & Tradeshow **[1495]**
American Beekeeping Federation Newsletter [1492]
American Beverage Association (ABA) **[3865]**, **[14300]**
American Beverage Institute (ABI) **[1886]**
American Beverage Licensees (ABL) **[10310]**
American Board of Bioanalysis (ABB) **[10901]**
American Board of Bioanalysts [10901]
American Board on Counseling Services [2593]
American Board of Funeral Service Education (ABFSE) **[7192]**
American Board of Opticianry (ABO) **[16277]**
American Board of Opticianry [16290]
American Board on Professional Standards in Vocational Counseling [2593]
American Boat Builders & Repairers Association (ABBRA) **[10585]**
American Boat & Yacht Council (ABYC) **[10586]**
American Boat and Yacht Council--Membership Directory (Internet only) [10597]
American Book Producers Association (ABPA) **[1606]**, **[5267]**
American Book Publishers Council [1607]
American Border Leicester Association (ABLA) **[624]**
American Bottlers of Carbonated Beverages [3865], [14300]
American Bowling Congress - United States Seniors Bowling Association [1875]
American Brahmousin Council (ABC) **[625]**, **[16924]**
American Branding Association (ABA) **[17424]**
American Breweriana Association Inc. (ABA) **[1887]**
American Business Advisors Inc. (ABA) **[10496]**
American Business Association (ABA) **[33440]**
American Business Communication Association [17525], [17820]
American Business Dynamics Corp. **[18458]**, **[28946]**
American Business Law Association [33934]
American Business Law Journal (ABLJ) **[18763]**
American Business Women's Association (ABWA) **[35529]**
American Business Women's Association (ABWA) **[35530]**
American Business Women's Association - Big Sky Chapter **[35531]**

American Business Women's Association Cavalier Chapter **[35532]**
American Business Women's Association - Columbia Triad Chapter **[35533]**
American Business Women's Association Convention **[35914]**
American Business Women's Association - Coral Springs Charter Chapter **[35534]**
American Business Women's Association - DC Charter Chapter (ABWA DC) **[35535]**
American Business Women's Association - Denver Downtown Chapter **[35536]**
American Business Women's Association - Dynamic Connections Chapter **[35537]**
American Business Women's Association - Greenspoint Chapter **[35538]**
American Business Women's Association - Heart of the Piedmont Chapter (ABWA-HOP) **[35539]**
American Business Women's Association - Indianapolis Charter Chapter **[35540]**
American Business Women's Association - La Capitale Chapter **[35541]**
American Business Women's Association - La Luz Chapter **[35542]**
American Business Women's Association - Maryland Capital Chapter **[35543]**
American Business Women's Association - Mo-Kan Chapter **[35544]**
American Business Women's Association - Na Kilohana 'O Wahine Chapter **[35545]**
American Business Women's Association - New York City Chapter **[35546]**
American Business Women's Association - Novi Oaks Charter Chapter **[35547]**
American Business Women's Association - Nutmeg Chapter **[35548]**
American Business Women's Association - Palm Desert Trendsetter Chapter **[35549]**
American Business Women's Association - Pathfinder Chapter **[35550]**
American Business Women's Association - Quincy Charter Chapter **[35551]**
American Business Women's Association - Reno Tahoe Express Network **[35552]**
American Business Women's Association - River Region Chapter **[35553]**
American Business Women's Association - Rochester Charter Chapter **[35554]**
American Business Women's Association - Singing River Charter Chapter **[35555]**
American Business Women's Association - Smoky Mountain Sevier Chapter **[35556]**
American Business Women's Association - Territorial Charter Chapter (TCC ABWA) **[35557]**
American Business Women's Association - Tu'Ya Chapter **[35558]**
American Business Women's Association - West Des Moines Charter Chapter **[35559]**
American Business Writing Association [17525], [17820]
American Camp Association (ACA) **[2501]**, **[2533]**
American Camping Association [2501], [2533]
American Camping Association Conference & Exhibits **[2529]**
American-Canadian Genealogical Society (ACGS) **[7392]**
American Cannabis Company Inc. **[5065]**
American Car Rental Association (ACRA) **[1149]**
American Cat Fanciers Association (ACFA) **[626]**
American Cemetery Association [7198]
American Ceramic Society Bulletin **[4611]**
American Chain of Warehouses (ACWI) **[12967]**
American Chapter, International Real Estate Federation [13089]
American Cheese Society (ACS) **[14999]**
"American Chemistry Council Launches Flagship Blog" in *Ecology,Environment & Conservation Business (October 29, 2011, pp. 5)* **[5532]**, **[5814]**, **[14386]**, **[19777]**, **[21781]**, **[23101]**, **[25205]**, **[26877]**, **[27834]**
American Choral Directors Association National Conference **[11197]**, **[11281]**
American Christmas Tree Association (ACTA) **[2951]**
American Christmas Tree Journal **[2950]**
American City and County **[31701]**
American Cleaning Institute (ACI) **[2964]**
American Clinical Laboratory Association (ACLA) **[10902]**
American Coatings Association (ACA) **[11854]**, **[11871]**
American Collectors Association [4764]
American Collectors Association [4756]
American Collectors Associations--Membership Roster [4764]
American College of Apothecaries (ACA) **[5127]**
American College of Apothecaries Research & Education Foundation - Research & Education Resource Center **[26102]**

American College of Clinical Pharmacy (ACCP) [25640]
American College of Health Care Administrators (ACHCA) [196], [1020], [11493], [11538]
American College of Nursing Home Administrators [196], [1020], [11493], [11538]
American College Public Relations Association [7184]
American Commercial Collectors Association [4759]
American Compensation Association [19732]
American Composites Manufacturers Association (ACMA) [29068]
American Concrete Institute (ACI) [3913]
American Concrete Institute Nebraska Chapter [41812]
American Concrete Pavement Association (ACPA) [1545]
American Conference on Crystal Growth and Epitaxy (ACCGE) [32918]
American Conservatory of Music - Robert R. McCormick Memorial Library [11205]
American Convention of Meat Processors and Suppliers' Tradeshow [2437]
American Corn Millers' Federation [16962]
American Corn Millers Federation Export Institute [16962]
American Council for Construction Education (ACCE) [3914]
American Council on Exercise (ACE) [12369]
American Council of Life Insurers (ACLI) [8856]
American Council on Public Relations [12924], [31744]
American Counseling Association (ACA) [2588]
American Countertrade Association [27412]
American Court and Commercial Newspapers, Inc. (ACCN) [11953]
American Craft [4668]
American Craft Council (ACC) [4579], [4638], [4652], [4689]
American Craft Show [4684]
American Crafts Council [4579], [4638], [4652], [4689]
American Craftsmen's Council [4579], [4638], [4652], [4689]
American Culinary Federation (ACF) [4456]
American Custom Gunmakers Guild (ACGG) [7827]
American Dance Guild (ADG) [4834]
American Dance Therapy Association (ADTA) [4835]
American Defense Institute (ADI) [32937]
The American Demand for Office Furniture and Anticipated Trends [11672]
American Dental Association Annual Convention [10870]
American Dental Association Annual Session & Technical Exhibition [10870]
American Dental Hygienists' Association Convention [10871]
American Dental Trade Association [10819]
American Dietetic Association [8080], [8123], [11557], [11604], [16518]
American Disc Jockey Association (ADJA) [4959]
American Documentation Institute [8827]
American Dog Breeders Association (ADBA) [627]
American Down Association [1569], [8173], [9021]
American Driver Education Association [5098]
American Driver and Safety Education Association [5098]
American Driver and Traffic Safety Education Association (ADTSEA) [5098]
American Driving Society (ADS) [8300]
American Economic Development Council [20700]
American Educational Publishers Institute [1607]
American Electrology Association (AEA) [7845]
American Electrolysis Association [7845]
American English Academy (AEA) [2213], [17799], [17883], [20154], [21701]
American English College [2213], [17799], [17883], [20154], [21701]
American Enterprise Association [25630]
American Enterprise Institute (AEI) [25630]
American Enterprise Institute for Public Policy Research and National Legal Center for the Public Interest [25630]
American Envelope Manufacturers Association [11659]
American Express Kabbage Inc. [11007]
"American Express Provides $1 Million in Grants to Restaurants across the U.S." in *Small Business Trends*(March 4, 2023) [13901]
"American Farmland Trust Profiles In Stewardship, How California Farmers and Ranchers are Producing a Better Business" in *Ecology, Environment & Conservation Business* (January 4, 2014, pp. 2) [16998], [23102]
"American Farmland Trust, The Culinary Institute of America, Fabulous Beekman Boys Hold Special Event to Raise Awareness in Culinary Students" in *Ecology, Environment & Conservation Business* (April 19, 2014, pp. 3) [4462], [6174], [16999]
American Federation for Clinical Research [10940]
American Federation for Medical Research (AFMR) [10940]

American Federation of State County and Municipal Employees (AFSCME) [31671]
American Federation of Teachers (AFT) [16177]
American Feed Industry Association (AFIA) [16925]
American Feed Manufacturers Association [16925]
American Fence Association (AFA) [3915]
American Film Institute (AFI) [2475], [11135]
American Finance Association (AFA) [23694]
American Financial Services Association (AFSA) [4732]
American Fisheries Society (AFS) [6760]
American Fisheries Society Annual Meeting [6791]
American Fishing Tackle Manufacturers Association [1228]
American Floorcovering Association [6827]
American Fly Fishing Trade Association (AFFTA) [1227]
American Formalwear Association [3087]
American Foundation for Management Research [10474], [28251]
American Foundation for Pharmaceutical Education (AFPE) [5128]
American Franchisee Association (AFA) [24304]
American-French Genealogical Society (AFGS) [7393]
American Fur Council (AFC) [7226], [7232]
American Fur Industry [7226], [7232]
American Gaming Association (AGA) [7257]
American Gem Trade Association (AGTA) [9957]
American Guild of Appraisers (AGA) [804]
American Hair Loss Council (AHLC) [7846]
American Handwriting Analysis Foundation (AHAF) [7902]
American Harp Society National Conference [11198]
American Hatpin Society (AHS) [728], [3210], [9958]
American Health Care Association (AHCA) [1021], [11494], [25641]
American Health Care Association Annual Convention and Exposition [11531]
American Health Information Management Association (AHIMA) [10887], [10973]
American Hellenic Institute (AHI) [27392]
American Herb Association (AHA) [8148], [8158]
American Herbal Products Association (AHPA) [8149]
American Hereford Association (AHA) [16926]
American Holistic Health Association (AHHA) [11336]
American Home Furnishings Alliance (AHFA) [8192]
American Home Laundry Manufacturers Association [785]
American Home Lighting Association [5408]
American Honey Producers Association (AHPA) [1429]
American Horse Council (AHC) [8301]
American Horse Council--Horse Industry Directory [8318]
American Horse Publications (AHP) [8302]
American Horse Shows Association [8314]
American Horse Shows Association Inc. [8314]
American Horticultural Society (AHS) [6878], [7601], [7655], [10140]
American Hospital Association (AHA) [8233], [11495]
American Hospital Directory [10937], [10963]
American Hotel Foundation [8341]
American Hotel and Lodging Association (AHLA) [8340], [8525], [16044]
American Hotel & Lodging Educational Foundation (AHLEF) [8341]
American House Cleaners Association (AHCA) [2965]
American Hydrangea Society (AHS) [7602]
American Imported Automobile Dealers Association [11357]
American Importers Association [8677], [27391]
American Independent Business Alliance (AMIBA) [26754]
"*American Indian College Fund to Support Environmental Science and Sustainability Programs, Fellowships, and Internships*" in *Ecology, Environment & Conservation Business (April 12, 2014, pp. 21)* [5533], [7080], [17000], [21446], [32722]
American Indian Sciences and Engineering Society (AISES) [2589], [30500]
American Indonesian Chamber of Commerce (AICC) [27393]
American Industrial Hygiene Foundation [35975]
American Infrastructure Funds LLC [37282]
American Institute of Baking (AIB) [1306]
American Institute for Biosocial and Medical Research (AIBMR) [11605]
American Institute of Certified Public Accountants (AICPA) [13]
American Institute of Commemorative Art (AICA) [7193]
American Institute of Constructors (AIC) [3916]
American Institute of Constructors and Constructor Certification Commission [3916]
American Institute for Economic Research (AIER) [15481]
American Institute of Employment Counseling [5437], [15637]

American Institute of Fishery Research Biologists (AIFRB) [6761]
American Institute of Floral Designers (AIFD) [6846]
American Institute of Food Distribution Information and Research Center [1305], [2697], [3866], [4929], [6945], [7711], [7824], [14304], [15069]
American Institute of Graphic Arts (AIGA) [3282], [12715]
American Institute of the History of Pharmacy (AIHP) [5129]
American Institute of Inspectors (AII) [2010]
American Institute of Kitchen Dealers [8200], [9027]
American Institute of Landscape Architects [10071], [10141]
American Institute of Laundering [5226], [5264], [5265]
American Institute of Mortgage Brokers [10999]
American Institute of Musical Studies (AIMS) [11252]
American Institute of Organbuilders (AIO) [11307]
American Institute of Real Estate Appraisers [805], [828]
American Institute of Small Business (AISB) [41366]
American Institute of Supply Associations [12608]
American Institute of Travel Trailer and Camper Manufacturers [13671]
American Institute of Wood Engineering [10412]
American Intercontinental University Library [3069], [9071]
American International Automobile Dealers Association (AIADA) [11357]
American Inventors, Entrepreneurs, and Business Visionaries [22941]
American-Israel Chamber of Commerce, Southeast Region [27406]
American Jersey Cattle Association (AJCA) [16927]
American Jewelers Protective Association [9966]
American Jewish Historical Society (AJHS) [7394]
American Journal of Agricultural Economics (AJAE) [17141]
American Journal of Clinical Nutrition (AJCN) [11581]
American Journal of Economics and Business Administration [24851]
American Journal of EEG Technology [26036]
American Journal of Electroneurodiagnostic Technology: Journal of the American Society of Electroneurodiagnostic Technologists, Inc [26036]
American Journal of Infection Control (AJIC) (AJIC) [25987]
American Journal of Small Business [8822], [33626]
American Journal of Veterinary Research (AJVR) [701]
American Junior Brahman Association (AJBA) [16928]
American Junior Golf Association (AJGA) [7507]
American Junior Shorthorn Association (AJSA) [16929]
American Kennel Club (AKC) [628]
American Kennel Club Library (AKC Library) [666], [12159]
American Kenpo Karate International (AKKI) [10712]
American Land Title Association (ALTA) [13077]
American Laundry News [10187]
American Law Institute (ALI) [15482]
American Lawn Applicator [10127], [10254]
American Leak Detection Inc. (ALD) [12683]
American Lighting Association (ALA) [5408]
American Lock Collectors Association [10357]
American Lumber Standard Committee, Incorporated (ALSC) [10373]
American Lutheran Publicity Bureau (ALPB) [31824]
American Machine Tool Distributors' Association [29072]
American Managed Behavioral Healthcare Association [25644]
American Managed Care Pharmacy Association [5142]
American Management Association (AMA) [10474], [28251]
American Manufacturers of Toilet Articles [1383], [1579], [4507]
American Marketing Association (AMA) [10633], [27801], [29567]
American Marketing Association Foundation (AMAF) [29568]
American Massage Therapy Association (AMTA) [10753]
American Massage and Therapy Association [10753]
American Massage Therapy Association National Convention [10779]
American Meat Institute [2428]
American Medical Directors Association [11492]
American Medical Record Association [10887], [10973]
American Medical Technologists (AMT) [10903]
American Medical Technologists Convention [10935]
American Metal Stamping Association [10420]
American Mobile Retail Association (AMRA) [30451]
American Montessori Society (AMS) [2864]
American Motorcyclist Association (AMA) [11106]
American Museum of Magic - Lund Memorial Library [4690]
American Music [11273]

American Music Teacher **[11188]**
American Musical Instrument Society (AMIS) **[11308]**
American Mustang and Burro Association (AMBA) **[8326]**
American Mutual Alliance [8857], [9003]
American Mutual Insurance Alliance [8857], [9003]
American Mutual Life Association (AMLA) **[17258]**
American National Standards Committee Z39 [1627]
American Needlepoint Guild (ANG) **[14642]**
American Nightlife Association (ANA) **[1310]**
American Numismatic Association (ANA) **[3211]**
American Numismatic Society (ANS) **[3212]**, **[3254]**, **[3262]**
American Nursery and Landscape Association [7604], [10045]
American Nurses Association (ANA) **[1040]**
American Nursing Home Association [1021], [11494], [25641]
American Nutrition Association (ANA) **[11559]**
American Oat Association [16962]
American Olive Oil Association [16963]
American Optical Association [16278], [16316]
American Optometric Association (AOA) **[16278]**, **[16316]**
American Optometric Student Association (AOSA) **[16279]**
American Organization for Bodywork Therapies of Asia (AOBTA) **[10754]**
American Organization of Nurse Executives Annual Meeting and Exposition (AONE) **[26063]**
American Oriental Bodywork Therapy Association [10754]
American Paint Manufacturers Association [11854], [11871]
American Painting Contractor--Buyers' Guide **[11877]**
American Painting Contractor--Tool & Equipment Catalog Issue [11877]
American Payroll Association (APA) **[11923]**, **[31623]**
American Payroll Association Annual Congress **[11941]**
American Personal Chef Association [4457]
American Personal and Private Chef Association (APPCA) **[4457]**
American Personnel and Guidance Association [2588]
American Pet Products Association (APPA) **[832]**, **[12179]**
American Pet Products Manufacturers Association [832], [12179]
American Pet Society [835], [12183]
American Pharmaceutical Association [5213]
American Pharmacy [5199]
American Philatelic Congress (APC) **[3213]**
American Philatelic Society (APS) **[3214]**, **[3255]**
American Photographic Artists (APA) [213], **[12287]**
American Physical Therapy Association (APTA) **[12482]**, **[12504]**
American Physical Therapy Association - Academy of Orthopaedic Physical Therapy (APTA AOPT) **[12483]**
American Physical Therapy Association Annual Conference [12502]
American Plywood Association [10375]
American Polled Hereford Association [16926]
American Polygraph Association--Member Directory (Internet only) **[12795]**
American Poolplayers Association [1542], [12684]
American Printer: The Graphic Arts Managers Magazine **[12765]**
American Productivity & Quality Center (APQC) **[34958]**
American Property Casualty Insurance Association (APCIA) **[8857]**, **[9003]**
American Prospect Research Association [7076]
American Prosperity Group (APG) **[6053]**
American Psychological Association (APA) **[25642]**
American Public Health Association Public Health Expo **[26064]**, **[35113]**
American Public Policy Association [17485]
American Public Relations Association [12924], [31744]
American Public Transportation Association (APTA) **[15505]**
American Purchasing Society (APS) **[31904]**
The American Quarter Horse Journal **[15205]**
American Ramp Systems **[12450]**
American Real Estate Society (ARES) **[13078]**
American Real Estate Society Annual Meeting **[772]**, **[35114]**
American Real Estate Society Conference [772], [35114]
American Real Estate Society Meeting [772], [35114]
American Real Estate and Urban Economics Association (AREUEA) **[13079]**
American Recreational Equipment Association [593]
American Reflexology Certification Board (ARCB) **[11337]**
American Rental Association (ARA) **[13760]**
American Rental Association Annual Convention and Rental Trade Show **[13849]**

American Research Journal of Business and Management (ARJBM) **[24852]**
American Restaurant Institute [6890], [13886]
American Restoration Services **[2089]**
American Retail Federation [3088], [32082]
The American Review of Public Administration (ARPA) **[31702]**
American Rifleman [853]
American Risk and Insurance Association (ARIA) **[8858]**
American River College (ARC) **[37653]**
American Saddlebred Museum - Library **[8327]**
American Salers **[662]**
American School Band Directors Association (ASBDA) **[11256]**
American School Health Association National School Health Conference **[26065]**, **[35115]**
American Seed Research Foundation (ASRF) **[17228]**
American Seed Trade Association (ASTA) **[7603]**, **[10044]**
American Seniors Housing Association (ASHA) **[11496]**
American Sewing Guild (ASG) **[4653]**, **[14643]**
American Shiatsu Association [10754]
The American Small Business Coalition, LLC (ASBC) **[40344]**
American Small Business League (ASBL) **[36599]**
American Small Manufacturers Coalition (ASMC) **[29069]**
American Society of Agricultural Consultants (ASAC) **[16930]**
American Society for the Alexander Technique (AMSAT) **[4836]**
American Society of Association Executives (ASAE) **[30501]**
American Society of Bakery Engineers [1242]
American Society of Baking (ASB) **[1242]**
American Society of Bariatric Physicians [16502]
American Society for Clinical Laboratory Science (ASCLS) **[10904]**
American Society for Clinical Pathology (ASCP) **[10905]**
American Society of CLU and ChFC [8881]
American Society of Consultant Pharmacists (ASCP) **[5130]**
American Society of Consultant Pharmacists Annual Meeting and Exhibition **[5203]**
American Society of Consulting Arborists (ASCA) **[10070]**
American Society of Corporate Secretaries [16224]
American Society of Hand Therapists (ASHT) **[10755]**
American Society of Health-System Pharmacists (ASHP) **[5131]**
American Society for Healthcare Risk Management Convention **[26066]**
American Society of Heating, Refrigerating and Air-Conditioning Engineers (ASHRAE) **[452]**
American Society of Heating, Refrigerating and Air-Conditioning Engineers Research Program (ASHRAE) **[549]**
American Society of Heating, Refrigerating, and Air Conditioning Engineers Winter Conference [535]
American Society of Indexers [1]
American Society for Indexing (ASI) **[1]**
American Society for Information Science [8827]
American Society for Information Science and Technology (ASIS&T) **[8827]**
American Society of Inspectors of Plumbing and Sanitary Engineering [12607]
American Society of Insurance Management [8879]
American Society of Interior Designers (ASID) **[9018]**
American Society of Inventors (ASI) **[27827]**
American Society of Journalists and Authors (ASJA) **[5268]**
American Society of Journalists and Authors Newsletter [5333]
American Society of Landscape Architects (ASLA) **[10071]**, **[10141]**
American Society of Magazine Editors (ASME) **[11954]**
American Society of Magazine Photographers [11955], [12288]
American Society of Media Photographers (ASMP) **[11955]**, **[12288]**
American Society of Pension Professionals and Actuaries (ASPPA) **[17259]**
American Society for Pharmacy Law (ASPL) **[5132]**
American Society of Photographers (ASP) **[12289]**
American Society of Piano Technicians [11313]
American Society of Plumbing Engineers (ASPE) **[12606]**
American Society of Professional Estimators (ASPE) **[3917]**
American Society of Professional Organizers (ASPO) **[12816]**
American Society for Public Administration (ASPA) **[31672]**
American Society of Real Estate Counselors [13086]

American Society of Sanitary Engineering (ASSE) **[12607]**
American Society of Superintendents of Training Schools for Nurses [8242]
American Society of Training Directors [2376], [3544], [10568], [21305], [21740], [26836], [27164]
American Society of Travel Agents (ASTA) **[15965]**
American Society of Women Accountants - San Diego Chapter No. 17 [35524]
American Society of Women Accountants, Silicon Valley Chapter No. 103 [35526]
American Solar Energy Society (ASES) **[14899]**
American Soybean Association (ASA) **[16931]**
"Americans Spend $16.9 Billion on Target Shooting" in *Shooting Illustrated (September 9, 2018)* **[847]**
American Sportfishing Association (ASA) **[1228]**
American Sports Builders Association (ASBA) **[3918]**, **[12370]**, **[15664]**
American Staffing Association (ASA) **[5431]**, **[15635]**
American Stamp Dealers Association (ASDA) **[3215]**
American String Teachers Association (ASTA) **[11162]**
American Subcontractors Association (ASA) **[11872]**, **[14318]**
American Suffolk Horse Association (ASHA) **[8328]**
American Supply Association (ASA) **[12608]**
American Supply Association--Member Directory **[469]**, **[12675]**
American Suzuki Journal (ASJ) **[11189]**
American Tamil Entrepreneurs Association (ATEA) **[30239]**
American Tarot Association (ATA) **[11338]**
American Taxation Association (ATA) **[14]**, **[15350]**, **[34720]**
American Taxicab Association [15508]
American Tennis Association (ATA) **[15665]**
American Tennis Federation [15670]
American Tennis Industry Federation [15670]
American Title Association [13077]
American Trade Association for Cannabis & Hemp (ATACH) **[4965]**
American Translators Association (ATA) **[15923]**
American Translators Association Annual Conference **[15954]**
American Translators Association--Membership Directory **[15930]**
American Transplant Congress (ATC) **[32919]**
American Transportation Research Institute (ATRI) **[16112]**
American Truck Historical Society (ATHS) **[16111]**
American Trucking Association Management Conference & Exhibition (ACE MCE) **[16102]**
American Trucking Associations (ATA) **[16051]**
American University - College of Arts and Sciences - School of Education - National Center for Health Fitness (NCHF) **[10897]**
American-Uzbekistan Chamber of Commerce (AUCC) **[27394]**
American Veteran Owned Business Association (aVOBa) **[33441]**
American Veterinary Medical Association (AVMA) **[678]**
American Veterinary Medical Association Annual Convention **[707]**
American Viewpoint Society [34446]
American Walnut Manufacturers Association (AWMA) **[10374]**
American Warehouse Association [12969]
American Warehousemen's Association [12969]
American Waterpark Association [599]
"American Water's Ed Vallejo Chosen for 2012 Minority Business Leader Awards" in *Manufacturing Close-Up (July 30, 2012)* **[9320]**, **[23731]**, **[28445]**, **[30533]**
American Welding Society (AWS) **[3919]**
American Wholesale Marketers Association [2535], [15692]
American Window Cleaner Magazine: The Voice of the Professional Window Cleaner **[2079]**
American Window Covering Manufacturers Association [1571], [9031]
American Woman's Society of Certified Public Accountants (AWSCPA) **[15]**
American Women in Radio and Television [31820]
American Youth Horse Council (AYHC) **[8303]**
AmeriCandy Retail Interactive Kiosk (AIRK) **[2554]**
AmericanHort **[7604]**, **[10045]**
"The Americans Are Coming" in *The Economist (Vol. 390, January 3, 2009, No. 8612, pp. 44)* **[15931]**, **[17635]**, **[20084]**, **[21447]**, **[27451]**
Americans for Better Care [11499]
Americans for Safe Access (ASA) **[4966]**
"Americans Spend Billions on Takeout. But Food Delivery Apps Are Still a Terrible Business" in *Barron's (November 15, 2019)* **[10978]**, **[11710]**
"America's Best Executive Recruiting Firms" in *Forbes (March 27, 2019)* **[6103]**

America's Central Port [39397]
America's Health Insurance Plans (AHIP) [27216]
America's Little Switzerland [46360]
Americas MLM Consultants [45590]
"America's Oldest Art Supply Store Closes After 111 Years" in ArtnetNews (August 29, 2016) [1015]
America's Pharmacist: The Voice of the Community Pharmacists [5197]
America's Public Television Stations (APTS) [15567]
"America's Rural Radio Stations Are Vanishing - and Taking the Country's Soul with Them" in The Guardian (June 6, 2019) [13027]
America's SBDC [33442]
America's SBDC Conference [33634]
America's SBDC Iowa for Mid Iowa [39672]
America's SBDC Iowa at Southeastern Community College [39673]
America's SBDC at North Iowa Area Community College [39674]
America's SBDC Washington Aberdeen (WSBDC) [45999]
America's Small Business Development Center (ASBDC) [33442]
America's Supermarket Showcase [7807]
America's Swimming Pool Co. [15248]
AmeriCorps (CNCS) [46952]
Americus-Sumter County Chamber of Commerce [38684]
Amerimark Capital Corp. (ACC) [45431]
AmeriSpec Inspection Service [2030]
AmeriStamp Expo (ASE) [3251]
Ameriwest Business Consultants Inc. (ABCI) [19126], [19637]
Ames Center for Animal Health [721]
Ames Chamber of Commerce (ACC) [39712]
Amgen Inc. [5211], [37283]
Amgen Ventures [37284]
Amherst Area Chamber of Commerce (AACC) [40556]
Amherst Chamber of Commerce (ACC) [42515]
Amherst County Chamber of Commerce (ACCC) [45829]
AMIA Annual Symposium [10872]
AMIA Fall Symposium [10872]
Amidzad Partners Co. [37285]
AMIN Worldwide [214], [29569], [31825]
"Amistee Air Duct Acquires Ducts R Us, Looks at 2nd Competitor" in Crain's Detroit Business (Vol. 35, September 1, 2014, No. 35, pp. 5) [555], [19778], [31174]
Amory-North Monroe Chamber of Commerce and Development Council [41417]
Amoskeag Business Incubator [42022]
Ampersand Capital Partners [40661]
Ampersand Ventures Management Corp. [40662]
Amplifier Advisors [45979]
Amplify [14853]
Amplify LA [37718]
Amplio Strategies (AS) [10497]
"Ampm Focus Has BP Working Overtime" in Crain's Chicago Business (April 28, 2008) [234], [4427], [8688], [24331], [27452], [29648], [31855]
Amref Health Africa, USA [26103]
AmSpirit Business Connections [2397]
AMT--Member Product Directory [10425]
Amusement Consultants Ltd. [591], [617], [10498]
Amusement Expo International (AEI) [590]
Amusement Industry Manufacturers and Suppliers International (AIMS) [593]
Amusement & Music Operators Association (AMOA) [576]
The Amusement Park: 900 Years of Thrills and Spills, and the Dreamers and Schemers Who Built Them [601]
ANA Business Marketing [29570]
ANA Nonprofit Federation (DMANF) [1048]
Anaconda Chamber of Commerce [41747]
Anacortes Chamber of Commerce (ACC) [46045]
Anago Franchising Inc. [2090]
Anaheim Business Advocate [36727]
Anaheim Chamber of Commerce [36728]
Anahuac Area Chamber of Commerce (AACC) [45030]
"Analysis of the U.S. Residential Solar Power Market" in PR Newswire (September 19, 2012) [14907], [17917], [24942]
"Analysts Expect American Airlines Bankruptcy to Raise Ticket Prices" in Dallas Business Journal (Vol. 35, February 17, 2012, No. 23, pp. 1) [19330], [19986]
"Analysts: Intel Site May Be Last Major U.S.-Built Fab" in Business Journal-Serving Phoenix and the Valley of the Sun (October 18, 2007) [3981], [26211], [29102], [33941]
Analytics without Overwhelm with Aby Blum Sudds [30146]
Analytics Ventures (AV) [37286]

Anamosa Area Chamber of Commerce [39713]
The Anatomical Record: Advances in Integrative Anatomy and Evolutionary Biology [32853]
"The Anatomy of a High Potential" in Business Strategy Review (Vol. 21, Autumn 2010, No. 3, pp. 52) [19779], [22092], [26878], [28446]
Anchor Advisors Ltd. [33644]
Anchor Bay Chamber of Commerce (ABCC) [40851]
Anchor Point Chamber of Commerce [36219]
Anchorage Chamber of Commerce [36220]
Anchorspace [40320]
"And Now, Goodbye: Consumer Response To Sponsor Exit" in International Journal of Advertising (Vol. 31, February 2012, No. 1, pp. 39) [10637], [31175]
Anderson Area Chamber of Commerce [44535]
Anderson Area Chamber of Commerce (AACC) [43405]
Anderson Area Medical Center [5212], [11539]
Anderson County Chamber of Commerce (ACCC) [44711]
Anderson County Chamber of Commerce (ACCOC) [40015]
Anderson Kill P.C. [27381]
"Anderson Pitches Liberty Towne Place" in Business Courier (Vol. 27, June 18, 2010, No. 7, pp. 1) [3982], [13133], [13382], [15085], [32093]
Anderson Valley Chamber of Commerce [36729]
Andrade Business Consultants L.L.C. [10499]
Andreessen Horowitz (AH) [37287]
Andrew Barile Consulting Corporation Inc. [35439]
Andrews Chamber of Commerce [43080]
"Android Users Can Now Manage Life On-the-Go With New AboutOne Family Organizer Companion Application" in PR Newswire (August 1, 2012) [2711], [12826], [33826]
Andrology [32854]
ANDY OnCall (AOC) [4345]
Andy Warhol Museum Archives Study Center [989], [11206], [11291]
Anesthesia Business Consultants L.L.C. (ABC) [26081]
Angel Capital Association (ACA) [35258]
Angel Fire Chamber of Commerce [42300]
Angel Forum - Vancouver [46694]
"Angel Investing Network Launches" in Washington Business Journal (Vol. 31, August 31, 2012, No. 19, pp. 1) [22365], [31138], [35227]
Angel Investor Forum (AIF) [37970]
"Angel Investors Across Texas Collaborate" in Austin Business Journal (Vol. 31, May 20, 2011, No. 11, pp. 1) [24517], [28089], [30911], [31176]
Angel One Network [46776]
Angel Round Capital Fund, LP (ARC) [42713]
The Angel Roundtable (ART) [44821]
Angel Venture Forum (AVF) [40481]
Angela Henderson Consulting [36645]
Angelina College Procurement Assistance Center (ACPAC) [45483]
Angelina College Small Business Development Center [44905]
Angelina County Chamber of Commerce [45262]
Angelo State University Small Business Development Center [44906]
AngelPad [42837]
The Angels' Forum (TAF) [37707]
Anges Québec [46884]
Angier Chamber of Commerce [43081]
"Angiotech to Buy Top Medical Devices Company" in Globe & Mail (February 1, 2006, pp. B1) [5145], [31177], [32723]
Angiuli Katkin and Gentile L.L.P. (A & G) [18749]
Angola Area Chamber of Commerce (AACC) [39513]
Angwin Community Council [36730]
Anheuser-Busch Companies, LLC (ABC) [1372], [1954]
Animal Free Dairy: Making Cheese without Cows with Irina Gerry [23420]
Animal Health Institute (AHI) [679]
Animal Ink [15344]
Animal Medical Center (AMC) [714]
Ankeny Area Chamber of Commerce [39714]
AnMed Health Medical Center [5212], [11539]
Ann Arbor Angels (A2A) [41037]
Ann Arbor Area Chamber of Commerce [40852], [41077]
"Ann Arbor Google's Growth Dips: Few Worried about High-tech Firm's Future" in Crain's Detroit Business (Vol. 25, June 8, 2009, No. 23, pp. 3) [17918], [21782], [26212]
Ann Arbor SPARK Business Accelerator [41075]
Ann Arbor SPARK Regional Incubator Network (SRIN) [41076]
Ann Arbor/Ypsilanti Regional Chamber [40852], [41077]
Ann Welsh Communications Inc. [17800]
Anna-Jonesboro Area Chamber of Commerce [43591]
Anna Maria Island Chamber of Commerce [38321]
Annals & Magazine of Natural History [32896]

Annals of the Missouri Botanical Garden [7640]
Annandale Chamber of Commerce (ACC) [45830]
Annandale Community Directory [45831]
Annapolis and Anne Arundel County Chamber of Commerce, Inc. [40366]
Annapolis Capital [46685]
"Annapolis Seeks City Market Vendors" in Boston Business Journal (Vol. 29, June 10, 2011, No. 5, pp. 3) [869], [10012], [25112]
Anna's Commercial Kitchen [44381]
Anne Arundel Economic Development Corporation (AAEDC) [40439]
Anne Arundel Trade Council [40366]
Annex Brands, Inc. [3395]
Annie Halenbake Ross Library - Special Collections [7395]
Anniston SCORE [36068]
Annual ARNOVA Conference [26067], [35116]
Annual Conference [21681]
Annual Conference & Solutions Expo [24226]
Annual Convention [16343]
Annual Convention & Trade Show [16345]
Annual Credit Congress & Expo [20364]
"The Annual Entitlement Lecture Medicare Elephantiasis" in Barron's (March 31, 2008) [6254], [8885], [9321], [17274], [23732], [24943], [25707], [27236], [34731]
Annual Heckerling Institute on Estate Planning [6052]
Annual IAIP Convention [8996], [35915]
Annual Meeting of the American Academy of Ophthalmology [16310]
Annual Meeting of the Business History Conference [24837]
Annual Meeting of the Southeastern Psychological Association [26077]
Annual National Convention & Tradeshow [13850]
Annual National Leadership Conference [21683]
Annual Progressive Detroit Boat Show [1234], [10619], [15117]
Annual SAE International® Brake Colloquium & Exhibition [1123]
Annual Session of the American Dental Society of Anesthesiology [10873]
Annual convention and trade show [1884]
"Annual Small Business Growth Reaches Record High, Data Shows" in The Ascent (Sept. 16, 2021) [17919]
Annual Spring Conference [772], [821], [35114]
Anoka Area Chamber of Commerce (AACC) [41190]
"Another California Firm Moving to Austin" in Austin Business Journal (Vol. 31, May 6, 2011, No. 9, pp. 1) [8646], [12927], [13134], [13383], [19158], [21783], [33340]
"Another Determinant of Entrepreneurship: The Belief in Witchcraft and Entrepreneurship" in International Journal of Entrepreneurship and Small Business (Vol. 10, July 6, 2010) [22489], [27453], [30534]
Ansir Cowork [37541]
Ansir Innovation Center [37541]
Anson County Chamber of Commerce (ACCC) [43082]
"Answers About Commercial Wind Farms Could Come from Downstate" in Erie Times-News (September 27, 2011) [5534], [5815], [23103]
Antares Capital Corp. [35440]
"Anthem Becomes First to Penalize Small-Business Employees for Smoking" in Denver Business Journal (Vol. 64, August 17, 2012, No. 13, pp. 1) [8886], [16543], [25708], [27237]
Anthem Venture Partners (AVP) [37288]
Anthony Chamber of Commerce [39858]
Anthony Curtis' Las Vegas Advisor [7318]
Anthony Valletta on How to Gain Loyalty Instead of Frequency at Your Restaurant [14049]
Anthropological Literature [7389]
Antioch Chamber of Commerce [36731]
Antioch Chamber of Commerce and Industry (ACCI) [39089]
Antiquarian Booksellers Association of America (ABAA) [1800]
Antiquarian Booksellers' Association of America, Inc. [1800]
Antiquarian Booksellers' Association of Canada (ABAC) [729], [1801]
Antique Automobile Club of America (AACA) [11117]
Antique Bottle & Glass Collector [744], [3272], [4669]
Antique and Decorative Arts League [732]
Antique Wireless Association [15564]
Antiques and the Arts Weekly [745]
Antiques & Collectibles Insurance Group [730]
Antiques and Collectibles National Association (ACNA) [730]
Antler - USA [42838]
"Anxiety Saps Vigor of Small Businesses" in Barron's (Vol. 92, September 15, 2012, No. 38, pp. 36) [20244], [20728], [33542]

Anytime Fitness LLC [12451]
AOPA Aviation Summit - Aircraft Owners and Pilots Association [437]
"APA Creates 2020 Form W-4 Webpage. Sample Letter to Explain Changes" in American Payroll Association (November 14, 2019) [11927]
APA: The Engineered Wood Association [10375]
Apache Junction Chamber of Commerce [36308]
Apalachicola Bay Chamber of Commerce (ABCC) [38322]
"Apartment Action: A Renewal in Rentals" in Barron's (Vol. 88, March 17, 2008, No. 11, pp. 17) [3983], [12874], [13135], [13384], [17920]
Apartment Association of Greater Dallas Annual Trade Show [12906]
Apartment Association of Greater Orlando Tradeshow [12907]
Apartment Association of Metro Denver Seminar and Trade Show [12908]
Apartment Management Magazine [770]
"Apartment Tower in River North Fetches More Than $90 Million" in Crain's Chicago Business (Vol. 34, October 24, 2011, No. 42, pp. 17) [6255], [9322], [13136], [13385], [13768], [33003]
"Apartments Head to Schilling Farms: $48 Million Investment Includes Office, Retail Space" in Memphis Business Journal (Vol. 34, August 17, 2012, No. 18, pp. 1) [3984], [13769]
Apax Partners of New York [42714]
APC Commercial Kitchen [37542]
ApEx [2690], [6931], [8113], [8485], [14088], [35117]
APEX Accelerator (MN PTAC) [41345]
APEX Accelerator of Alabama (PTAC) [36166]
Apex Brasil [38550]
Apex Chamber of Commerce [43083]
Apex Innovations Inc. [10500], [20155], [28947]
APhA Academy of Pharmacy Practice and Management (APhA-APPM) [5213]
APHON Conference & Exhibit [10874]
API Security [32395]
Apiary Inspectors of America (AIA) [1430]
Apopka Area Chamber of Commerce [38323]
"App Brings Real-Time Personal Security, Company Says" in Philadelphia Business Journal (Vol. 33, July 4, 2014, No. 21, pp. 11) [2712], [3694], [14387], [26213]
"App Helps Consumers Spot Suspicious Charges" in Black Enterprise (Vol. 44, June 2014, No. 10, pp. 34) [4767], [20245], [21784]
"App Maker Thinks He Has the Ticket: But Denver Is Balking At Alternative To Parking Fines" in Denver Business Journal (Vol. 65, April 25, 2014, No. 50, pp. A10) [2713], [25113], [26214]
APPA Business & Financial Conference [24834]
APPA Customer Connections Conference [24835]
Appalachia-Science in the Public Interest (ASPI) [5762]
The Appalachian Center for Economic Networks, Inc. (ACEnet) [43645]
Appalachian Development Alliance (ADA) [40093]
Apparel Retailers of America [3088], [32082]
Appian Ventures [37917]
Apple Auto Glass [7500]
Apple Tree Partners (ATP) [42715]
Apple Valley Chamber of Commerce [41191]
Apple Valley Chamber of Commerce [36920]
Applebee's International Inc. [14117]
Applebee's Restaurants LLC [14117]
Applegate Inc. [8607]
"Apples, Decoded: WSU Scientist Unraveling the Fruit's Genetics" in Puget Sound Business Journal (Vol. 29, September 5, 2008, No. 20) [17001], [25114], [31935], [32724]
Appleton Chamber of Commerce [46411]
Appliance Design [801]
Appliance Parts Distributors Association (APDA) [784]
Appliance Parts Jobbers Association [784]
Appliance Repair Industry in the US - Market Research Report [797]
Application Development Trends Magazine (ADT) [3670]
Application Systems Development Audit and Security [26184]
"Applications for Law School Drop" in Philadelphia Business Journal (Vol. 28, June 8, 2012, No. 17, pp. 1) [18510], [21448]
Applications of Marketing Research (Onsite) [29580]
Applied Arts Magazine [3341], [12311]
Applied Business and Entrepreneurship Association International (ABEAI) [22449]
Applied Business Technologies Corp. [3445]
Applied Engineering in Agriculture [32855]
Applied Fire Protection Engineering, Inc. [2021]
Applied Materials, Inc. [37289]
Applied Personnel Research (APR) [20592]
Applied Process Engineering Laboratory (APEL) [46211]

Applied Ventures LLC (AV) [37290]
"Apply These 3 Techniques to Address Addiction in the Workplace" in Small Business Trends (Dec. 21, 2020) [34676]
"Applying to Colleges? Consultants Can Demystify the Process" in Palm Beach Post (September 3, 2011) [20085], [21449]
Applying Diversity Management to Innovation, Decision Making, Complex Problem Solving and Business Results (Onsite) [26850]
"The Appraisal Industry at the Crossroads of Change and Re-Invention" in MBA Insights (October 8, 2019) [812]
Appraisal Institute Annual Conference [821]
Appraisal Institute Education and Relief Foundation (AI) [805], [828]
Appraisal Institute Education Trust [805], [828]
Appraisers Association of America (AAA) [731], [806]
Appraisers Association of America--Membership Directory [738], [813]
The Appraisers Standard [819], [2019]
"The Apprentice Entrepreneur" [22490]
"Apprenticeship: Earn While You Learn" in Occupational Outlook Quarterly (Vol. 54, Fall 2010, No. 3, pp. 24) [21450], [26492], [26879], [35171]
"Apps For Anybody With an Idea" in Advertising Age (Vol. 79, October 17, 2008, No. 39, pp. 29) [2714], [9094], [14756], [26215], [33827]
APRA Big R Show [1122]
Apricot Lane (ALB) [6148]
"April is National Home Inspection Month" in Internet Wire (April 27, 2012) [2017]
APTA Magazine [12496], [25988]
Aptos Chamber of Commerce [36732]
AQSG Seminar [4705], [35118]
AQUA--Buyers' Guide Issue [15241]
AQUA Magazine: The Business Magazine for Spa and Pool Professionals [15243]
Aquaculture Magazine [6788]
Aquarium and Zoo Facilities Association (AZFA) [833]
Aquatic Biology Laboratory [16359]
Aquatic Control Inc. [6792]
Aquatic Exercise Association (AEA) [12371]
"Aquatic Medications Engender Good Health" in Pet Product News (Vol. 64, November 2010, No. 11, pp. 47) [830], [12187], [21451], [29103], [32094]
ARA Show [13849]
Arab American Business Women's Council (AABWC) [30240], [35560]
Arab Chamber of Commerce [36080]
Arabian Horse Association (AHA) [8329]
Arabian Journal of Business and Management Review (AJBMR) [24853]
ARAMARK Business & Industry, LLC [2214]
"Aramark Rolls Out Ballpark Food Truck" in Nation's Restaurant News (Vol. 45, August 8, 2011, No. 16, pp. 4) [6966], [13902]
Aransas Pass Chamber of Commerce [45031]
Arapahoe Chamber of Commerce [41837]
Arba Group [37708]
Arbitrators and Mediators Institute of Canada [10784]
Arbor Partners L.L.C. [41038]
ArborBridge [16147]
The Arboretum at Flagstaff - Transition Zone Horticultural Institute Library [10142]
Arboretum Ventures [41039]
Arc Flash Electrical Safety NFPA 70E [5356]
Arc Flash Protection & Electrical Safety 70E [5356], [19431], [21333]
The Arc News [25989]
Arcade Area Chamber of Commerce [42516]
Arcadia Academy of Music [11204]
Arcadia California [36733]
Arcadia Chamber of Commerce (ACC) [36734]
Arcata Chamber of Commerce (AACC) [36735]
ARCEO Executive Office Program [38551]
Arch Franchise Consultants [2335], [24472]
Arch Venture Partners L.P. [39350]
Archadeck [2647]
Archbold Area Chamber of Commerce [43406]
Archdale-Trinity Chamber of Commerce (ATCC) [43084]
Archer Venture Capital, LLC (AVC) [37719]
Archery Lane Operators Association [844]
Archery Range And Retailers' Organization, A Cooperative Association (ARRO) [844]
Architecting A Company of Owners: Company Culture By Design [33543]
"Architect's Designs for Proposed Underwater Tennis Court Look Unreal" in Bleacher Report (May 16, 2015) [836], [15676]
"Architects On Track for Ambitious Depot Renovation" in Sacramento Business Journal (Vol. 29, September 21, 2012, No. 30, pp. 1) [870], [3985]
Architectural Alliance [31059]

Architectural Digest (AD) [9055]
Architectural Engineering Institute of ASCE (AEI) [10723]
Architectural Glass and Metal Contractors Association (AGMCA) [3920]
Architectural Research Consultants Inc. (ARC) [33428]
Architectural Woodwork Institute (AWI) [2630]
"Architecture Panel Pushes Bozzuto" in Baltimore Business Journal (Vol. 31, March 21, 2014, No. 47, pp. 4) [871], [3986], [31178]
Archives of Environmental Health [25990]
Archives of Environmental & Occupational Health: An International Journal [25990]
Arco/Butte Business Incubation Center [38950]
Arcola Chamber of Commerce [39090]
Arctaris Royalty Partners [40663]
Arcturus Capital [37291]
The Arcview Group [37292]
Ardea Consulting [5748]
"Arden Fair Stops Using Parking Lot Solar Panels" in Sacramento Business Journal (Vol. 31, April 18, 2014, No. 8) [14908]
ARDITO Information and Research Inc. [19979], [25616], [31600]
Ardmore Chamber of Commerce [43733]
"Are Accelerators Worth It?" in Inc. [8789], [8805]
"Are Apartment Finder Services a Scam?" in Spark Rental (April 19, 2017) [767]
"Are Business Ethics Important for Profitability?" in Investopedia (May 27, 2021) [23468]
"Are Nutrient-Content Claims Always Effective? Match-Up Effects Between Product Type and Claim Type in Food Advertising" in International Journal of Advertising (Vol. 31, May 2012, No. 2, pp. 421) [235], [10638]
"Are Offline Pushes Important to E-Commerce?" in DM News (Vol. 31, September 14, 2009, No. 23, pp. 10) [236], [9095], [21785], [29649]
"Are Prepaid Legal Services Worthwhile?" in Contractor (Vol. 56, December 2009, No. 12, pp. 31) [8887], [17275], [27238]
"Are Vehicle Inspections Really About Safety?" in The Zebra (July 18, 2016) [2569]
Are You Cut Out to Run a Kennel or Pet Boarding Business? [12082]
"Are You an Electrical Contractor or a Consultant?" in ecmag.com (February 13, 2018) [5364]
"Are You Ignoring Trends That Could Shake Up Your Business?" in Harvard Business Review (Vol. 88, July-August 2010, No. 7-8, pp. 124) [17921], [29650], [33942]
"Are You Interested in Becoming a Professional Organizer?" in Peace of Mind Blog (January 26, 2020) [12827]
"Are You Micromanaging Your Company's Financial Tasks?" in allBusiness [23733], [31626]
"Are You Overinsured? Some Policies May Not Offer Much Additional Benefit" in Black Enterprise (Vol. 38, March 1, 2008, No. 8, pp. 126) [8888], [27239]
"Are You Ready for Dow 20,000?" in Barron's (Vol. 88, March 24, 2008, No. 12, pp. 26) [6256], [9323], [20729], [23734]
"Are You Ready for a Four-Day Workweek?" in Business News Daily (March 22, 2023) [16544]
"Are You Ready To Do It Yourself? Discipline and Self-Study Can Help You Profit From Online Trading" in Black Enterprise (February 1, 2008) [9324], [21786], [23735]
"Are You Ready for a Transformation?" in Women Entrepreneur (November 28, 2008) [18889], [19479], [29651], [30677], [35736]
"Are You Rich? How Much of a Nest Egg Do You Need to Join the True Elite" in Barron's (Vol. 88, March 10, 2008, No. 10, pp. 27) [20730], [24602]
"Are You Using Fitness Content Marketing to Grow Your Business?" in Glofox blog (May 19, 2019) [12404]
"Are You a Young Canadian Entrepreneur Looking for Recognition?" in CNW Group (November 10, 2010) [27835], [34268], [36012]
"Are Your Goals Hitting the Right Target?" in Business Strategy Review (Vol. 21, Autumn 2010, No. 3, pp. 46) [18890], [19331]
Area Development Partnership (ADP) [41382]
Area Guide [40260]
Area Guide to Manchester and the Mountains [45716]
"Area Small Businesses Enjoy Benefits of Bartering Group" in News-Herald (August 22, 2010) [17241], [24332], [31179]
"Arena Football League Sees S.A. as Crucial Market" in San Antonio Business Journal (Vol. 28, August 1, 2014, No. 25, pp. 6) [9325], [15129]
ARES Annual Conference [772], [35114]
ARES Annual Meeting [772], [35114]
"Areva Diversifies Further Into Wind" in Wall Street Journal Eastern Edition (November 29, 2011, pp. B7) [3987], [5535], [5816], [23104], [27454]

Argentum   **Master Index**

Argentum **[175]**, **[1022]**, **[11497]**
The Argentum Group **[42716]**
Argona Partners **[39661]**
Argos Multilingual (USA) **[15955]**
Argos Software I ABECAS Insight **[16893]**, **[17523]**
Argus Business Solutions **[9278]**
The Argus Group **[31601]**
Ariel Southeast Angel Partners (ASAP) **[35259]**, **[38803]**
Ariel Ventures L.L.C. (AV) **[43646]**
Arithmetic, Numeracy, Literacy & Imagination: A Research Guide **[16894]**
Arizona Association of Realtors (AAR) **[13080]**
Arizona Business Alliance (ABA) **[36258]**
Arizona Business Brokers Association (AZBBA) **[2128]**
Arizona Business Incubation Association **[33443]**
Arizona Business and Professional Women (Arizona BPW) **[35561]**
Arizona Business Travel Association (AZBTA) **[19287]**
Arizona Center for Innovation **[36412]**
Arizona Chamber of Commerce and Industry **[36309]**
Arizona City Chamber of Commerce (AZC) **[36310]**
Arizona Department of Economic Security **[47494]**
Arizona Dispensaries Association (ADA) **[4967]**
Arizona Hispanic Chamber of Commerce (AZHCC) **[36311]**
Arizona Minority Business Development Agency **[36378]**
Arizona Native American Business Development Center - National Center for American Indian Enterprise Development Center (NCAIED) **[36379]**
Arizona Small Business Association (ASBA) **[36259]**
Arizona Small Business Development Center **[36265]**
Arizona State Library, Archives and Public Records Law Library **[47390]**
Arizona State University Architectural and Environmental Design Library **[1575]**, **[14963]**
Arizona State University Architectural and Environmental Design Library - Solar Energy Collection **[14964]**
Arizona State University - CAPS Research **[31915]**
Arizona State University - Child Development Laboratory (CDL) **[2915]**
Arizona State University - Child Study Laboratory (CSL) **[2916]**
Arizona State University Department of Economics - W. P. Carey School of Business (CEESP) - Center for Environmental Economics and Sustainability Policy **[17229]**
Arizona State University SkySong **[36410]**
Arizona State University (ASU) - W. P. Carey School of Business - Center for Competitiveness and Prosperity Research **[36419]**
Arizona State University - W.P. Carey School of Business - JPMorgan Chase Economic Outlook Center **[21263]**
Arizona Tech Investors (ATI) **[36381]**
Arizona Western College Small Business Development Center (AZSBDC) **[36266]**
The ARK Challenge **[36511]**
Ark City Chamber **[39859]**
Arkadelphia Area Chamber of Commerce **[36433]**
Arkadelphia Chamber of Commerce **[36433]**
Arkansas APEX Accelerator (APAC) **[36508]**, **[36509]**
"Arkansas Attorney General Sues Collection Agency" in *PaymentsSource* (July 18, 2012) **[4768]**, **[18511]**, **[20246]**, **[25206]**
Arkansas Business **[36518]**
Arkansas Business and Professional Women (AR/BPW) **[35562]**
Arkansas Business Publishing Group **[36519]**
Arkansas Capital Corporation **[36507]**
Arkansas City Area Chamber of Commerce **[39859]**
Arkansas Department of Workforce Services (ADWS) **[47391]**
Arkansas Economic Development Commission (AEDC) **[36506]**
Arkansas Employment Security Department - Research and Analysis Section - Department of Workforce Services **[47391]**
Arkansas Hospitality Association Convention & Exhibition **[8486]**
Arkansas Procurement Assistance Center **[36508]**, **[36509]**
Arkansas Procurement Technical Assistance Center - Satellite Office **[36510]**
"Arkansas Receives EPA Grant to Tackle Hazardous Waste" in *Waste Today* (November 6, 2019) **[7947]**
Arkansas Small Business Development Center, Lead Office **[36425]**
Arkansas Small Business and Technology Development Center - Lead Center (ASBTDC) **[36425]**
Arkansas Small Business and Technology Development Center Monticello (ASBTDC) **[36426]**
Arkansas Small Business and Technology Development Center University of Arkansas, Fayetteville **[36427]**
Arkansas State Chamber of Commerce (ASCC) **[36434]**

Arkansas State Library (ASL) **[47392]**
Arkansas State University Small Business and Technology Development Center (ASU SBTDC) **[36428]**
Arlington Chamber of Commerce **[40557]**, **[45832]**
Arlington Chamber of Commerce (ACC) **[45032]**
Arlington Heights Chamber of Commerce (AHCC) **[39091]**
Arlington Hispanic Chamber of Commerce (AHCC) **[45033]**
The Arlingtonian **[45833]**
ARMA Canada Region **[8828]**
ARMA InfoCon **[28937]**
ARMA International's InfoCon [28937]
Armed Forces Judo Association [10716]
Armory Square Ventures (ASV) **[42717]**
Armour Research Foundation [30858]
Armstrong County Chamber of Commerce [44168]
"Army Surplus Store Rebuilding Again" in *Spokesman-Review* (November 17, 2010) **[3988]**, **[32095]**
Arnheim & Neely Inc. **[13610]**
Arnold Business Advisors L.L.C. **[24473]**
Arnold Chamber of Commerce **[41514]**
Arnold & Porter Kaye Scholer LLP **[18792]**, **[34955]**
Arnold S. Goldin & Associates Inc. **[128]**, **[6709]**, **[10501]**, **[16867]**, **[20156]**, **[28948]**
Arnold Sanow, MBA, CSP **[30178]**
Around Alhambra **[36736]**
Array Healthcare Facilities Solutions **[31060]**
Arrowhead Center, New Mexico State University **[42344]**
Arsenal Growth **[38614]**
"Arsenic in Some Bottled Water Brands at Unsafe Levels, Consumer Reports Say" in *Consumer Reports* (June 28, 2019) **[1857]**
Art and Antique Dealers League of America (AADLA) [732]
"The Art of Appreciation" in *Business Horizons* (November-December 2007, pp. 441) **[22093]**, **[28447]**
Art of Business **[7884]**
"The Art and Business of Motivational Speaking: Your Guide" in *Inc.* (Volume 32, December 2010, No. 10, pp. 124) **[14507]**, **[17636]**
Art Business News **[984]**
The Art of Business Valuation: Accurately Valuing a Small Business **[16545]**
"The Art of Calligraphy" in *The Guardian* (February 19, 2010) **[2480]**
Art Center College of Design - James Lemont Fogg Memorial Library **[3361]**
The Art of Coaching Employees to Excel (Onsite) **[28291]**
Art and Craft Materials Institute [1013]
Art and Creative Materials Institute (ACMI) **[1013]**
Art Dealers Association of America, Inc. (ADAA) **[961]**
Art Dealers Industry in the US - Market Research Report **[976]**
"Art & Design in Cannabis Packaging" in *Cannabis Business Executive* (August 6, 2020) **[4987]**
"Art Gallery Business Plan Template" in *GrowThink* **[967]**
Art Gallery of Greater Victoria (AGGV) **[990]**
Art Index™ **[3358]**, **[11656]**
Art Institute of Boston at Lesley University Library **[3362]**
"Art Institute of Chicago Goes Green" in *Contractor* (Vol. 56, July 2009, No. 7, pp. 1) **[470]**, **[5536]**, **[5817]**, **[17922]**, **[23105]**
Art Munin Consulting **[21702]**
"Art of the Online Deal" in *Farm Industry News* (March 25, 2011) **[17002]**, **[21787]**, **[32468]**
"The Art of Rapid, Hands-On Execution Innovation" in *Strategy and Leadership* (Vol. 39, March-April 2011, No. 2, pp. 28) **[27836]**, **[30678]**
The Art and Science of Running a Car Dealership **[11373]**
Art on Screen Database™ **[985]**, **[3359]**, **[4635]**
The Art of Social Impact Storytelling with Tamika Bickham **[30147]**
"The Art of War for Women" in *Hawaii Business* (Vol. 54, July 2008, No. 1, pp. 23) **[2178]**, **[22491]**, **[24603]**, **[28448]**, **[35025]**
The Art of War for Women: Sun Tzu's Ultimate Guide to Winning Without Confrontation **[35737]**
Artemis Inc. **[824]**
Artesia Chamber of Commerce [42320]
Arthur K. Williams Microbusiness Enterprise Center **[38824]**
Arthur P. Gould & Co. **[42718]**
Arthur Ventures (AV) **[41329]**
"Articles of Incorporation: What New Business Owners Should Know" in *Business News Daily* (February 28, 2023) **[27170]**
Artiman Management LLC **[37293]**
Artisan Exchange (AE) **[44382]**
Artist Incubation Inc. **[43848]**
Artists Managers Guild [10345], [15255]

ARTnews Magazine **[977]**
Arts Council of New Orleans - Arts Business Program **[40212]**
"Artscape Looks for Last Big Donations" in *Baltimore Business Journal* (Vol. 32, July 11, 2014, No. 10, pp. 4) **[4586]**, **[4851]**, **[7081]**, **[29652]**
Aruba Tanning Franchise **[15266]**
Arvada Chamber of Commerce (ACC) **[37814]**
"Arvada Coffee Shop Wants To Be a Model for Employers" in *Denver Business Journal* (Vol. 66, May 30, 2014, No. 2, pp. A5) **[7545]**, **[34269]**
Arvin Chamber of Commerce **[36737]**
"As Capital Gains Tax Hike Looms, Baltimore's Merger Activity Percolates" in *Baltimore Business Journal* (Vol. 28, August 27, 2010, No. 16, pp. 1) **[6257]**, **[9326]**, **[20731]**, **[31180]**, **[33943]**, **[34732]**
"As Comic Book Industry Grows, Smaller Publishers Learn to Adapt" in *The New York Times* (May 8, 2019) **[3266]**, **[31181]**
"As Costs Skyrocket, More U.S. Cities Stop Recycling" in *The New York Times* (March 16, 2019) **[13700]**, **[23106]**
"As the Sports-Betting Industry Transforms, Entrepreneurs May Find It Hard to Get in on Gambling Profits -- but Related Businesses Will Thrive" in *Entrepreneur* (May 21, 2018) **[7274]**
"As the Supply Chain Slows, Demand for Aftermarket Equipment Takes Off" in *Restaurant Business* (November 17, 2021) **[2668]**, **[13903]**
"As Talent War Escalates, Law Firms Fear Business Pros Getting Poached" in *The American Lawyer* (November 23, 2021) **[10217]**
"As Technology Changes, So Must African American Business" in *Black Enterprise* (Vol. 41, August 2010, No. 1, pp. 61) **[19780]**, **[21788]**, **[26216]**, **[30322]**, **[33944]**
"As Traditional Web Site Adoption Slows, Facebook and Other Social Networks Become Key Platforms for Home-Based Business Promotional and Commercial Activity Online" in *Marketing Weekly News* (June 16, 2012) **[237]**, **[2715]**, **[9096]**, **[26768]**, **[29653]**
"As Windows 8 Looms, Tech Investors Hold Their Breath" in *Barron's* (Vol. 92, July 23, 2012, No. 30, pp. 22) **[3695]**, **[9327]**, **[14757]**, **[26217]**, **[30679]**, **[33828]**
As You Sow Foundation (AYS) **[34255]**
ASAE Annual Meeting & Exposition **[1054]**
ASAE: The Center for Association Leadership **[1049]**
ASAE: The Center for Association Leadership Knowledge Center **[1057]**
Asbury Park Chamber of Commerce (APCC) **[42099]**
Ascension Chamber of Commerce **[40149]**
Ascension Ventures (AV) **[41657]**
Ascent Innovation **[44670]**
Ascent Venture Partners **[40664]**
ASCP Annual Meeting & Exhibition [5203]
ASCR International [31918]
Ash Creek Capital Advisors LLC **[38086]**
Ashburn Turner County Chamber of Commerce **[38685]**
Ashe County Chamber of Commerce **[43085]**
Asheboro/Randolph Chamber of Commerce **[43086]**
Asheville Area Chamber of Commerce **[43087]**
Asheville-Buncombe Technical Community College - Small Business Center (SBC) **[43238]**
Ashford Business Association (ABA) **[37971]**
Ashland Alliance **[40016]**
Ashland Area Chamber of Commerce (AACC) **[43407]**, **[46361]**
Ashland Chamber of Commerce **[39860]**, **[43937]**
Ashland Chamber News **[43938]**
Ashland Community & Technical College - The Entrepreneur Center **[40101]**
Ashland Group L.P. **[7177]**, **[12952]**
Ashland Small Business Development Center (SBDC AU) **[43348]**
Ashoka Innovators for the Public **[33444]**
ASHRAE Winter Conference **[535]**
Ashtabula Area Chamber of Commerce [43408]
Ashtabula County Chamber of Commerce **[43408]**
ASI Annual Conference **[6]**
ASI Show Orlando 2022 - Advertising Specialty Institute **[16914]**
"Asia Breathes a Sigh of Relief" in *Business Week* (September 22, 2008, No. 4100, pp. 32) **[6258]**, **[9328]**, **[11009]**, **[20247]**, **[20732]**, **[23736]**, **[27455]**, **[28090]**
Asia Pacific Foundation of Canada [20696]
Asian American Hotel Owners Association (AAHOA) **[8342]**
Asian American Hotel Owners Association Convention & Trade Show [8484]
Asian American Journalists Association (AAJA) **[5269]**, **[30241]**
Asian American Writers Workshop (AAWW) **[5270]**

Asian Chamber of Commerce **[36312]**
Asian Chamber of Commerce Serving Arizona/Grand Canyon State [36312]
Asian Chamber of Texas (ACT) **[45034]**
Asian Chao/Maki of Japan/Chao Cajun **[14118]**
ASIAN, Inc. **[37262]**
Asian/Pacific Islander American Chamber of Commerce and Entrepreneurship (ACE) **[30310]**
Asian Women in Business (AWIB) **[30242]**, **[35563]**
ASIS International (ASIS) **[14368]**
The ASJA Weekly **[5333]**
"Ask Inc.: Managing and Real Estate to Build Value" in *Inc. (December 2007, pp. 83-84)* **[13137]**, **[13386]**, **[26493]**, **[28022]**, **[30535]**
Ask NELMA Newsletter **[10401]**
Asking for What You Want, Slack Early Days **[34583]**
Asociación Interamericana de Contabilidad [32]
Asociacion Nacional de Periodistas Hispanos [5292]
Asotin Chamber of Commerce **[46046]**
ASP-America's Swimming Pool Co. **[15248]**
Aspen Chamber Resort Association (ACRA) **[37815]**
Aspen Network for Developing Entrepreneurs (ANDE) **[38155]**
ASPEN Nutrition Science & Practice Conference **[11587]**
Asphalt Association [1546]
Asphalt Consultants L.L.C. **[1560]**
Asphalt Contractor **[1558]**
Asphalt Emulsion Manufacturers Association--Membership Directory **[1550]**
Asphalt Institute **[1546]**
Asphalt Paving Technologists **[1551]**
Asphalt Recycling & Reclaiming Association--Membership Directory **[1552]**
Asphalt Roofing Industry Bureau [14319]
Asphalt Roofing Manufacturers Association (ARMA) **[14319]**
Asphalt Tile Institute [6826]
Asphalt and Vinyl Asbestos Tile Institute [6826]
Aspire Business Development Inc. **[2215]**, **[10502]**, **[28949]**
Aspiring Lodging Professional Conference **[8487]**
ASQ Quality Management Journal [28918]
Assabet Valley Chamber of Commerce **[40558]**
Assertive Communication - Essential Skills for Successful Women (Onsite) **[17534]**
Assertive Management (Onsite) **[22040]**, **[28292]**
Assertiveness Skills: Communicating With Authority and Impact (Onsite) **[17535]**
Assertiveness Skills for Managers and Supervisors (Onsite) **[28293]**
Assertiveness Training for Managers **[17536]**
Assertiveness Training for Managers (Onsite) **[28294]**
Assertiveness Training (Onsite) **[21334]**
Assertiveness Training for Women in Business **[17537]**
Assertiveness Training for Women in Business Canada **[17538]**
"Assess Your DEI Maturity to Determine What's Next" in *Associations Now (May 9, 2022)* **[30536]**
"Assessing the Health of Independent Bookshops" in *The New York Times (February 25, 2015)* **[1812]**
Asset Management Company Venture Capital (AMV) **[37294]**
Asset Management Ventures (AMV) **[37720]**
Assets conference [823]
Assets Protection Inc. (API) **[22354]**
Assist-2-Sell **[13333]**
"Assisted Living Facility Faces Bankruptcy and Care Issues" in *South Florida Business Journal (Vol. 33, August 17, 2012, No. 3, pp. 1)* **[1024]**, **[13387]**, **[18512]**
Associated Bakers of America [1245]
Associated Bodywork & Massage Professionals (ABMP) **[10756]**
Associated Builders and Contractors Convention **[4293]**
Associated Builders and Contractors, Inc. (ABC) **[3921]**
Associated Camera Clubs of America [2492], [12291], [12334]
Associated Coffee Industries of America [3173], [7541]
Associated Court and Commercial Newspapers [11953]
Associated Credit Bureaus [4757]
Associated Designers of Canada (ADC) **[3283]**
Associated Enterprises, Ltd. **[10503]**
Associated Equipment Distributors--Membership Directory **[20610]**
Associated General Contractors of America (AGC) **[3922]**
Associated General Contractors of North Dakota (AGCND) **[43269]**
Associated Independent Electrical Contractors of America [5351]
Associated Industries of Maine [40291]
Associated Landscape Contractors of America and Professional Lawn Care Association of America [10080]

Associated Locksmiths of America [10350]
Associated Management Services, Inc. (AMSI) **[10504]**
Associated Management Systems Inc. **[2156]**, **[31602]**
Associated Manufacturers of Toilet Articles [1383], [1579], [4507]
Associated Medical Services (AMS) **[25643]**
Associated Minority Contractors of America [30287]
Associated Pipe Organ Builders of America (APOBA) **[11309]**
Associated Press Broadcast Services (AP) **[13014]**, **[15568]**
Associated Professional Massage Therapists and Allied Health Practitioners International [10756]
Associated Professional Massage Therapists and Bodyworkers [10756]
Associated Retail Bakers of America [1245]
Associated Retail Confectioners of North America [2539]
Associated Retail Confectioners of the U.S. [2539]
Associated Schools of Construction (ASC) **[3923]**
Associated Tavern Owners of America [10310]
Associated Writing Programs [5272]
Associated Writing Programs Catalogue of Writing Programs [5308]
Association for Accessible Medicines (AAM) **[5133]**
Association for Accounting Administration [28]
Association of Accounting Administrators [28]
Association of Accredited Small Business Consultants (AASBC) **[33646]**
Association to Advance Collegiate Schools of Business (AACSB) **[21303]**
Association for the Advancement of Medical Instrumentation (AAMI) **[10818]**
Association of African Entrepreneurs-USA, Inc. (AAE-USA) **[30243]**
The Association Agenda **[1050]**
Association nationale des distributeurs aux petites surfaces alimentaires **[20599]**
Association of Alternate Postal Systems (AAPS) **[3390]**
Association of Alternative Newsmedia (AAN) **[11956]**
Association of Alternative Newsweeklies [11956]
The Association of American Literary Agents (AAR) **[10344]**
Association of American Publishers (AAP) **[1607]**
Association of American Stock Exchange Firms [9299]
Association of American University Presses (AAUP) **[1608]**
Association of American University Presses--Directory **[1639]**
Association of America's Public Television Stations [15567]
Association of Applied IPM Ecologists (AAIE) **[12037]**
Association of Area Business Publications [11951], [38116]
Association of Area Business Publications--Advertising Rates [24775]
Association of Area Business Publications--Directory of Members [24775]
Association of Area Business Publications--Membership Directory [24775]
Association of Arts Administration Educators (AAAE) **[21304]**
Association of Average Adjusters of the United States and Canada (AAAUS) **[27217]**
Association des eleveurs Ayrshire du Canada **[629]**
Association of Bay Area Governments (ABAG) **[47393]**
Association for Behavioral Health and Wellness (ABHW) **[25644]**
Association of Better Computer Dealers [3766]
Association of Black Social Workers (ABSW) **[25645]**
Association of Black Women Physicians (ABWP) **[25646]**
Association of Brewers and Brewers' Association of America [1890]
Association of Bridal Consultants (ABC) **[1959]**
Association for Business Communication (ABC) **[17525]**, **[17820]**
Association for Business Simulation and Experiential Learning (ABSEL) Conference [21681]
Association du transport aérien du Canada [411]
L'Association des architects paysagistes du Canada [10074]
L'Association internationale de la gestion du personnel - Canada [26841]
Association of Canadian Academic Healthcare Organizations [25674]
Association of Canadian Orchestras [11234]
Association of Canadian Publishers (ACP) **[1609]**
Association of Canadian Search, Employment and Staffing Services [2590]
Association of Canadian Travel Agencies (ACTA) **[15721]**, **[15966]**
Association of Canadian Venture Capital Companies [35267]
Association Canadienne des Aliements de Sante [7995], [8088], [11561]

Association Canadienne de la Boulangerie [1243]
Association Canadienne du Capital de Risque et d'Investissement [35267]
Association Canadienne des Compagnies d'Assurance Mutuelles (ACCAM) **[8859]**
Association Canadienne du Comptables d'Assurance [20]
Association Canadienne de la Construction [3926]
L'Association Canadienne des Createurs Professionnels de L'Image [3287], [12290]
Association Canadienne D'Alarme Incendie (CFAA) **[14369]**
Association Canadienne d'Articles de Sport [15077]
Association Canadienne d'Auto Distribution (ACAD) **[16246]**
Association Canadienne De Terrazzo, Tuile et Marbre (ACTTM) **[6821]**
Association Canadienne d'Equitation Therapeutique [8304]
Association Canadienne de Dermatologie [25653]
Association Canadienne D'Etudes Cinematographiques (ACEC) **[6156]**
L'Association Canadienne d'Études Fiscales [21], [15351], [15484]
L'Association Canadienne des Distributeurs de Produits Chimiques [20606]
Association Canadienne des Entrepreneur Electriciens (ACEE) **[5350]**
Association Canadienne des Entrepreneurs en Couverture (ACEC) **[14320]**
L'Association Canadienne des Experts Independants [8861]
Association Canadienne des Femmes Cadres et Entrepreneurs [35588]
Association Canadienne des Foires et Expositions (ACFE) **[594]**
Association Canadienne de la Franchise **[24305]**
Association Canadienne de Gestion Environnementale [2047], [5075]
Association Canadienne des Industries du Recyclage (ACIR) **[13684]**
L'Association Canadienne des Journalistes [5276], [11959]
Association Canadienne de l'enseigne [226]
L'Association Canadienne de L'immeuble [13083]
Association Canadienne de l'industrie des Plastiques [29076]
L'Association Canadienne Marchands Numismatiques **[3216]**
Association Canadienne de la Medecine du Travail et de l'Environnement (OEMAC) **[25647]**
Association Canadienne des Medecins Veterinaires [683]
L'Association Canadienne des Optometristes [16284]
Association Canadienne des Pilotes de Ligne Internationale [410]
Association Canadienne des Professeurs de Comptabilite [18]
Association Canadienne de Protection Medicale [25658]
Association Canadienne des Radiodiffuseurs (ACR) **[13015]**, **[15569]**
L'Association Canadienne des Relations Industrielles (CIRA) **[35143]**
Association Canadienne des Ressources Hydriques (ACRH) **[23023]**
Association Canadienne des Restaurateurs et des Services Alimentaires [2667], [3834], [4483], [4879], [6892], [8091], [13890], [14308]
Association Canadienne de Sante Publique [25663]
Association Canadienne de Science Economique des Affaires [20686]
L'Association Canadienne de la Securite [14370]
Association Canadienne de Soins e a Domicile (ACSSD) **[8234]**
Association Canadienne des Thérapeutes du Sport (CATA) **[12484]**
Association Canadienne de Traitement d'Images et de Reconnaissance des Formes **[3418]**, **[3599]**
Association Canadienne du Vehicule Recreatif [13670]
Association Candienne des Pepinieristes et des Paysagistes [7605], [10073]
Association for Car and Truck Rental Independents and Franchisees [1149]
Association of Casualty Accountants and Statisticians [8882]
Association of Catholic Publishers (ACP) **[1610]**
Association of Certified Public Accountant Examiners [37]
Association of Change Management Professionals (ACMP) **[28252]**
Association of Chartered Accountants in the United States [23]
Association for Childhood Education Annual International Study Conference & Exhibition [2891]
Association for Childhood Education International [2867]

Association for Childhood Education International Annual International Conference & Exhibition **[2891]**
Association of Clean Water Administrators (ACWA) **[23024]**
Association of Club Catering Professionals (ACCP) **[2663]**
Association for the Coaching and Tutoring Profession **[16122]**
Association of Cocoa and Chocolate Manufacturers of the U.S. [2536]
Association of College Professors of Textiles and Clothing--Membership Directory [3034]
Association of Collegiate Schools of Nursing [8242]
Association of Commercial Finance Companies of New York [28080], [35307]
Association of Commercial Real Estate Professionals (ACRP) **[13081]**
Association for Computer Educators [3422], [3546]
Association of Computer Engineers and Technicians (ACET) **[3761]**
Association for Computing Machinery (ACM) **[3762]**
Association for Computing Machinery Stonehill College **[40780]**
Association for Conflict Resolution (ACR) **[10786]**
Association of Consulting Engineering Companies - Canada (ACEC) **[2169]**
Association for Convention Operations Management [15819]
Association of Cooking Schools [4458]
Association for Corporate Growth - Toronto Chapter (ACG) **[2170]**, **[17891]**, **[28253]**
Association of Credit Card Investigators [4760]
Association of Credit and Collections Professionals [4756]
Association of Cytogenetic Technologists [32714]
Association des courtiers d'assurances du Canada [8868]
Association des Designers Canadiens [3283]
Association of Destination Management Executives [15967]
Association of Destination Management Executives International (ADMEI) **[15967]**
Association d'information sur l'allergie et l'asthme [551]
Association for Early Learning Leaders (AELL) **[2865]**
Association of Energy Engineers (AEE) **[32713]**
Association for Enterprise Information (AFEI) **[24585]**
Association for Enterprise Integration [24585]
Association for Enterprise Opportunity (AEO) **[33445]**, **[34475]**
Association for Entrepreneurship USA (AFEUSA) **[22972]**, **[34476]**
Association of Environmental and Resource Economists (AERE) **[23025]**
Association of Equipment Manufacturers (AEM) **[29070]**
Association of Executive Recruiting Consultants [5432]
Association of Executive Search Consultants [5432]
Association of Executive Search and Leadership Consultants (AESC) **[5432]**
Association canadienne des importateurs et exportateurs [20698]
Association of Fashion and Image Consultants [8643]
Association Féline Canadienne (AFC) **[630]**
Association of Finance and Insurance Professionals (AFIP) **[27218]**
Association for Financial Professionals (AFP) **[23695]**
Association for Financial Technology Spring Summit **[24227]**
Association of Fitness Studios [12373]
Association des Fonderies Canadiennes (AFC) **[10417]**
Association of Food Distributors [13878]
Association of Food Industries (AFI) **[13878]**
Association For Bridge Construction And Design (ABCD) **[3924]**
Association of Forensic Document Examiners (AFDE) **[7903]**
Association of Free Community Papers (AFCP) **[31826]**
Association of Fund Raisers and Direct Sellers [7072]
Association of Fund-Raising Distributors and Suppliers (AFRDS) **[7072]**
Association of Fundraising Professionals (AFP) **[7073]**
Association of Fundraising Professionals Advancement Northwest **[45993]**
Association of Fundraising Professionals Alabama Chapter **[36041]**
Association of Fundraising Professionals Aloha Chapter **[38858]**
Association of Fundraising Professionals Berks Regional Chapter **[44082]**
Association of Fundraising Professionals Bluegrass Chapter **[39986]**
Association of Fundraising Professionals California Valley Chapter (AFP-CV) **[36525]**
Association of Fundraising Professionals California, Yosemite Chapter **[36526]**

Association of Fundraising Professionals Central Virginia Chapter **[45757]**
Association of Fundraising Professionals Chicago Chapter (AFP Chicago) **[38964]**
Association of Fundraising Professionals Colorado Chapter **[37772]**
Association of Fundraising Professionals East Central Illinois Chapter (AFPECI) **[38965]**
Association of Fundraising Professionals East Texas Chapter **[44875]**
Association of Fundraising Professionals - Edmonton and Area Chapter **[7074]**, **[46653]**
Association of Fundraising Professionals Fairfield County Connecticut Chapter (FCC) **[37972]**
Association of Fundraising Professionals Greater Arizona Chapter (AFP) **[36260]**
Association of Fundraising Professionals Greater Atlanta Chapter **[38619]**
Association of Fundraising Professionals Greater Baton Rouge Chapter **[40119]**
Association of Fundraising Professionals Greater Cincinnati Chapter **[43328]**
Association of Fundraising Professionals Greater Cleveland Chapter (AFPGC) **[43329]**
Association of Fundraising Professionals - Greater Detroit **[40791]**
Association of Fundraising Professionals Greater Los Angeles Chapter (AFP-GLAC) **[36527]**
Association of Fundraising Professionals Greater Louisville Chapter **[39987]**
Association of Fundraising Professionals Greater Madison Chapter **[46309]**
Association of Fundraising Professionals - Greater Milwaukee Chapter [7075]
Association of Fundraising Professionals - Greater New York Chapter [42369]
Association of Fundraising Professionals Greater Philadelphia Chapter **[44083]**
Association of Fundraising Professionals Greater San Fernando Valley Chapter (AFPGSFV) **[36528]**
Association of Fundraising Professionals IN, Michiana Chapter **[39464]**
Association of Fundraising Professionals Indiana Chapter (AFP-IC) **[39465]**
Association of Fundraising Professionals Las Vegas Chapter **[41905]**
Association of Fundraising Professionals Long Island Chapter (AFPLI) **[42368]**
Association of Fundraising Professionals Maryland Chapter **[40330]**
Association of Fundraising Professionals Miami Chapter **[38197]**
Association of Fundraising Professionals - Miami-Dade County Chapter [38197]
Association of Fundraising Professionals Minnesota Chapter **[41146]**
Association of Fundraising Professionals Montana Chapter (AFP MT) **[41715]**
Association of Fundraising Professionals Nashville Chapter **[44675]**
Association of Fundraising Professionals New Jersey Chapter (AFP-NJ) **[42029]**
Association of Fundraising Professionals New Mexico Chapter (AFPNM) **[42269]**
Association of Fundraising Professionals New York City Chapter (AFPNY) **[42369]**
Association of Fundraising Professionals New York, Finger Lakes Chapter **[42370]**
Association of Fundraising Professionals - North Central Ohio Chapter [43330]
Association of Fundraising Professionals Northeast Ohio Chapter (AFPNEO) **[43330]**
Association of Fundraising Professionals Northern New England Chapter (AFP NNE) **[45696]**
Association of Fundraising Professionals - Nova Scotia Chapter (AFP) **[46744]**
Association of Fundraising Professionals NY, Mid-Hudson Valley Chapter (AFPMHV) **[42371]**
Association of Fundraising Professionals Orange County Chapter (AFPOC) **[36529]**
Association of Fundraising Professionals - Oregon Chapter [43901]
Association of Fundraising Professionals Oregon & SW Washington Chapter **[43901]**
Association of Fundraising Professionals Rhode Island Chapter (AFP-RI) **[44449]**
Association of Fundraising Professionals St. Louis Regional Chapter **[41459]**
Association of Fundraising Professionals San Antonio Chapter **[44876]**
Association of Fundraising Professionals San Diego Chapter (AFPSD) **[36530]**
Association of Fundraising Professionals Santa Barbara/Ventura Counties Chapter **[36531]**

Association of Fundraising Professionals Sierra Chapter **[41906]**
Association of Fundraising Professionals Silicon Valley Chapter **[36532]**
Association of Fundraising Professionals South Carolina Lowcountry Chapter **[44494]**
Association of Fundraising Professionals Southeastern Wisconsin Chapter **[7075]**
Association of Fundraising Professionals Southern Arizona **[36261]**
Association of Fundraising Professionals Southern Minnesota Chapter **[41147]**
Association of Fundraising Professionals Treasure Coast Chapter **[38198]**
Association of Fundraising Professionals Washington DC Metro Area Chapter **[38149]**
Association of Fundraising Professionals West Michigan Chapter (AFPWM) **[40792]**
Association of Fundraising Professionals Western New York Chapter (AFP WNY) **[42372]**
Association of Fundraising Professionals Western North Carolina Chapter (AFP-WNC) **[43031]**
Association of Genetic Technologists (AGT) **[32714]**
Association canadienne de gerontologie [25650]
Association of Golf Merchandisers (AGM) **[7508]**, **[15075]**
Association for Health Services Research [25639]
Association for Healthcare Documentation Integrity (AHDI) **[10967]**
Association of Hispanic Advertising Agencies [16901]
The Association of Hispanic MBAs & Business Professionals [30303]
Association of Home Appliance Manufacturers (AHAM) **[785]**
Association of Home-Based Women Entrepreneurs [35635]
Association of Image Consultants [8643]
Association of Image Consultants International (AICI) **[8643]**
Association des biens Immobiliers du Canada [13112], [13366]
Association of Independent Commercial Producers (AICP) **[31827]**
Association of Independent Information Professionals (AIIP) **[3763]**
Association of Independent Mailing Equipment Dealers [11658], [16528]
Association of Independent Manufacturers'/Representatives, Inc. (AIM/R) **[12609]**
Association of Independent Mortgage Experts (AIME) **[10997]**
Association of Industry Manufacturers Representatives [12609]
Association for Information Media and Equipment (AIME) **[6157]**
Association of Information Technology Professionals [3766]
Association of International Certified Public Accountants (AICPA) **[16733]**
Association of International Photography Art Dealers (AIPAD) **[962]**
Association for Investment Management and Research [9290]
Association for Investment Management & Research-- Membership Directory [9407]
Association of Jewish Aging Services (AJAS) **[11498]**
Association of Kentucky Fried Chicken Franchisees Annual Convention **[24466]**
Association of Latino Professionals for America (ALPFA) **[30502]**
Association canadienne sur la qualite de l'eau [23026]
Association de la Librairie Ancienne du Canada [729], [1801]
L'Association canadienne des sciences de l'information [8829]
Association of Local Air Pollution Control Officials [23040]
Association of Management Consultants [10475]
Association for the Management of Organization Design [28263]
Association of Manpower Franchise Owners (AMFO) **[15636]**
Association for Manufacturing Excellence (AME) **[29071]**
Association for Manufacturing Technology (AMT) **[29072]**
Association of Marketing and Communication Professionals (AMCP) **[10634]**
Association of Media Producers [6159]
Association Medicale Canadienne (AMC) **[25648]**
Association of Metropolitan Planning Organizations (AMPO) **[31673]**
Association of Metropolitan Sewerage Agencies [23041]
Association of Millwork Distributors [2633]
Association of Monterey Bay Area Governments (AMBAG) **[47394]**

Association of Moving Image Archivists (AMIA) **[6158]**
Association for Multicultural Counseling and Development (AMCD) **[30503]**
Association of Municipal Recycling Coordinators [5491], [13689], [23039]
Association of National Advertisers (ANA) **[215]**, **[31828]**
Association Nationale des Enterprises en Recrutement et Placement de Personnel (ACSESS) **[2590]**
Association of Network Marketing Professionals (ANMP) **[30661]**
Association for Non-White Concerns in Personnel and Guidance [30503]
Association of Nutrition and Foodservice Professionals (ANFP) **[11560]**
Association of Occupational Health Professionals in Healthcare (AOHP) **[30940]**
Association canadienne des infirmieres en oncologie [8235]
Association des Opticiens du Canada (AOC) **[16280]**
Association canadienne de la paie [11925], [16743]
Association Pharmaciens Du Canada (APhC) **[5134]**
Association for PRINT Technologies **[12716]**
Association of Printing and Data Solutions Professionals (APDSP) **[4486]**
Association of Private Postal Systems [3390]
Association des Produits Forestiers du Canada (APFC) **[29073]**
Association for Professional Broadcasting Education [15571]
Association of Professional Canadian Consultants (APCC) **[3419]**, **[20075]**
Association of Professional Computer Consultants [3419], [20075]
Association of Professional Genealogists Directory **[7353]**
Association of Professional Insurance Women (APIW) **[27219]**
Association of Professional Landscape Designers (APLD) **[10046]**, **[10072]**
Association of Professional Organizers [12818]
Association of Professional Placement Agencies and Consultants [2590]
Association of Professional Recruiters of Canada (APRC) **[6101]**
Association of Professional Researchers for Advancement (APRA) **[7076]**
Association of Professionals [18799]
Association canadienne des employés professionnels [35146]
Association of Progressive Rental Organizations (APRO) **[13761]**
Association of Promotion Marketing Agencies Worldwide [32429]
Association of Proposal Management Professionals (APMP) **[4931]**, **[20076]**
Association for Public Broadcasting [15567]
Association for Public Policy Analysis and Management (APPAM) **[31740]**
Association of Public Television Stations [15567]
Association of Publishers' Representatives [31838]
Association of Publishers for Special Sales (APSS) **[1611]**, **[4932]**
Association canadienne de médecine physique et de réaptation [12485]
Association of Regulatory Boards of Optometry (ARBO) **[16281]**
Association of Reptilian and Amphibian Veterinarians (ARAV) **[680]**
Association for Research on Nonprofit Organizations and Voluntary Action Annual Conference [26067], [35116]
Association of Residential Cleaning Services International (ARCSI) **[2966]**
Association of Retail Travel Agents (ARTA) **[15968]**
Association Royale de Numismatique du Canada (ARNC) **[3217]**
Association of Schools and Colleges of Optometry (ASCO) **[16282]**
Association of Sewing and Design Professionals (ASDP) **[2999]**
Association of Shareware Professionals [3764]
Association of Small Business Development Centers [33442]
Association of Software Professionals (ASP) **[3764]**
The Association of Specialists in Cleaning and Restoration [4828], [16230]
Association of Specialists in Cleaning and Restoration [31918]
Association of State and Interstate Water Pollution Control Administrators [23024]
Association of Stock Exchange Firms [14379]
Association of Strategic Alliance Professionals (ASAP) **[28254]**
Association for Strategic Planning [18871]

Association for the Study of Community Organization [25681]
Association for Suppliers of Printing and Publishing and Converting Technologies [12716]
Association for Suppliers of Printing and Publishing Technologies - National Printing Equipment and Supply Association [12716]
Association of Talent Agents (ATA) **[10345]**, **[15255]**
Association for Talent Development (ATD) **[2376]**, **[3544]**, **[10568]**, **[21305]**, **[21740]**, **[26836]**, **[27164]**
Association of Teachers of Technical Writing (ATTW) **[5271]**
Association for Technology in Music Instruction (ATMI) **[11163]**
Association of TeleServices International (ATSI) **[15556]**, **[16324]**
Association des Traducteurs et Interpretes Judiciaires (ATIJ) **[15924]**
Association des Traducteurs et Traductrices Littéraires du Canada (ATTLC) **[15925]**
Association des Transports du Canada [15509]
The Association of Union Constructors (TAUC) **[3925]**
Association of University Interior Designers (AUID) **[9019]**
Association of Vacation Home Rental Managers [12869]
Association of Vision Science Librarians (AVSL) **[16283]**
Association of Visual Communicators [6165]
Association of Visual Language Interpreters of Canada (AVLIC) **[15926]**
Association of Visual Science Librarians [16283]
Association of the Wall and Ceiling Industries International [10724]
Association of the Wall and Ceiling Industry (AWCI) **[10724]**
Association of Water Technologies Annual Convention & Exposition [16343]
Association for Wedding Professionals International (AFWPI) **[1960]**
Association of Wisconsin Cleaning Contractors [2968]
Association of Women Business Owners [35635]
Association for Women in Communications (AWC) **[35564]**
Association for Women in Computing (AWC) **[3600]**
Association of Women in the Metal Industries (AWMI) **[29074]**
Association for Women in Science (AWIS) **[35565]**
Association of Women's Business Centers (AWBC) **[35566]**
Association of Writers & Writing Programs (AWP) **[5272]**
Associations Canada **[1056]**
Associations Now (May 9, 2022) "How Metrics Can Improve the Quality of Your DEI Initiatives" in [30574]
Associations Plus Inc. **[35014]**
Assumption Area Chamber of Commerce **[40150]**
ASTD [2376], [3544], [10568], [21305], [21740], [26836], [27164]
ASTD Buyer's Guide [21452]
Astia **[35701]**
ASTM Phase I & Phase II Environmental Site Assessment Processes (Onsite) [23059], **[25184]**
Astoria-Warrenton Area Chamber of Commerce (AWACC) **[43939]**
Asynchronous Learning Networks [21318]
At-A-Glance **[36313]**
"At the Drugstore, the Nurse Will See You Now" in Globe & Mail (April 13, 2007, pp. B1) **[5146]**, **[19781]**, **[26494]**
"At-Home Tax Prep Trend Likely to Grow After Pandemic's Boost" in Bloomberg Tax (July 10, 2020) **[15366]**, **[16783]**, **[34733]**
A.T. Kearney Inc. [2421]
"At Last - Local Job Growth Picks Up" in Sacramento Business Journal (Vol. 30, February 21, 2014, No. 52, pp. 3) **[20733]**
ATA Annual Conference [15954]
ATA Directory of Translators and Interpreters (Online) **[15932]**
ATA Management Conference & Exhibition [16102]
ATA Translation Services Directory [15932]
"AT&T Spend Nears $2 Billion in California With Minority, Women and Disabled Veteran-Owned Businesses in 2011" in Engineering Business Journal (March 21, 2012) **[2716]**, **[30323]**, **[32972]**, **[35738]**
Atascadero Chamber of Commerce **[36738]**
Atchison Area Chamber of Commerce (AACC) **[39861]**
Atchison Public Library (APL) **[7396]**
ATD Buyer's Guide (Internet only) **[21452]**
ATD Convention & Expo **[16103]**
ATEA National Conference **[32920]**, **[35119]**
Atel Capital Group **[37295]**
ATHENA Foundation [22450], [35567]
ATHENA International **[22450]**, **[35567]**
Athens Area Chamber of Commerce **[44712]**

Athens Area Chamber of Commerce (AACC) **[38686]**
Athens Chamber of Commerce **[45035]**
"Athletes Face Wins and Losses After Pro Sports" in The Business Journal - Serving Phoenix and the Valley of the Sun (Vol. 29, September 21, 2008, No. 3, pp. 1) **[13138]**, **[13388]**, **[20734]**, **[33544]**, **[33945]**, **[34270]**
Athletic Business--Buyers Guide Issue **[12405]**
Athletic Business--Professional Directory Section **[15130]**
Athletic Equipment Managers Association (AEMA) **[15076]**
Athletic Goods Manufacturers Association [15082]
Athletic Purchasing & Facilities Buyers Guide [12405]
Atiyah's Accidents, Compensation and the Law **[18513]**, **[20735]**, **[26880]**
ATL Airport Chamber, Inc. **[38687]**
Atlanta Agent Magazine **[13346]**
Atlanta Area Chamber of Commerce **[40853]**
Atlanta Area Chamber of Commerce (AACC) **[45036]**
"Atlanta BeltLine Inc. Could Leave Underground Atlanta" in Atlanta Business Chronicle (July 11, 2014, pp. 14A) **[19159]**
Atlanta Boat Show **[10617]**
Atlanta Botanical Garden (ABG) **[7656]**
Atlanta Bread Company International **[1287]**
Atlanta Business Chronicle (ABC) **[38849]**
Atlanta Business League (ABL) **[30244]**
Atlanta-Fulton Public Library - Learning and Career Center **[8138]**
Atlanta-Fulton Public Library - Learning Center Library [8138]
The Atlanta Small Business Monthly **[38850]**
Atlanta Technology Angels (ATA) **[35260]**, **[38804]**
Atlanta Tribune **[30432]**
Atlanta Urban League [38801]
"Top 25 Engineering Firms" in South Florida Business Journal (Vol. 34, February 14, 2014, No. 30, pp. 12) **[16546]**, **[27837]**
Atlantic Area Chamber of Commerce (AACC) **[39715]**
Atlantic Boating Almanac **[2831]**
Atlantic Boating & Fishing Almanac [2831]
Atlantic Cape Community College Procurement Technical Assistance Center (PTAC) **[42226]**
Atlantic Cape Community College - William Spangler Library **[4475]**
Atlantic City Boat Show **[10618]**
Atlantic City Free Public Library - Alfred M. Heston Collection **[7337]**
Atlantic City Regional Chamber of Commerce [42127]
Atlantic City Sub Shops Inc. **[4890]**
Atlantic Coast Exposition **[3202]**, **[16267]**
Atlantic Institute for Market Studies (AIMS) **[21264]**
Atlantic Management Company, Inc. **[31603]**
Atlantic Provinces Economic Council (APEC) **[21265]**
Atlantic Salmon Association [6762]
Atlantic Salmon Federation (ASF) **[6762]**
Atlantic Technology Centre (ATC) **[46880]**
Atlantic Windshield Repair Inc. **[7501]**
Atlena **[37664]**
Atmore Area Chamber of Commerce (AACC) **[36081]**
Atomic **[37296]**
"Attention Businesswomen! International Trade Isn't Just for Large Businesses" in Minority Business Entrepreneur (Vol. 39, Fall, 2022, No. 4, pp. 56-57) **[35739]**
"Attention, Shoppers Take a Deep Breath: Why It Pays to Help Customers Relax" in Inc. (Vol. 33, November 2011, No. 9, pp. 26) **[20386]**, **[32096]**
"Attention Songwriters: Protect Your Valuable Assets with a Copyright" in Legal Zoom (March 24, 2023) **[11259]**, **[27838]**
"Attorney Panel Tackles Contract Questions" in Agency Sales Magazine (Vol. 39, September-October 2009, No. 9, pp. 8) **[15833]**, **[18514]**, **[29104]**, **[35026]**
"Attracting Veteran-Franchisees To Your System" in Franchising World (Vol. 42, November 2010, No. 11, pp. 53) **[24333]**, **[33946]**, **[34271]**
Atwater Chamber of Commerce **[36739]**
Atwood Chamber of Commerce (ACC) **[39862]**
AtWork Group **[15655]**
AtWork Personnel Services [14995]
Au Bas de l'Echelle **[3284]**
Au Gres Area Chamber of Commerce **[40854]**
Au Pair in America (APIA) **[11324]**
"Au Revoir Or Goodbye?" in Barron's (Vol. 88, July 14, 2008, No. 28, pp. 5) **[6259]**, **[9329]**, **[11010]**, **[13139]**, **[20248]**, **[20736]**, **[23737]**, **[25207]**, **[27456]**, **[28091]**
Aub bas de l'echelle...pas pour toujours **[3285]**
"Aubry & Kale Walch, Herbivorous Butcher" in Business Journal (Vol. 32, August 29, 2014, No. 14, pp. 6) **[2424]**, **[7990]**, **[8145]**, **[23577]**
Auburn Area Chamber of Commerce (AACC) **[46047]**
Auburn Business Incubator (ABI) **[36169]**
Auburn Chamber of Commerce **[41838]**

Auburn Master Index

Auburn Chamber of Commerce (ACC) **[36740]**
Auburn Journal **[21255]**
Auburn Research and Technologoy Foundation (ARTF) **[36170]**
Auburn University - Alabama Agricultural Experiment Station - Department of Fisheries and Allied Aquacultures [6800]
Auburn University - Alabama Agricultural Experiment Station - Ornamental Horticulture Research Center (OHRC) **[7694]**
Auburn University Alabama Agricultural Experiment Station - School of Fisheries, Aquaculture and Aquatic Sciences (FAAS) **[6800]**
Auburn University - Charles Allen Cary Veterinary Medical Library **[715]**
Auburn University - College of Agriculture - School of Fisheries, Aquaculture and Aquatic Sciences - International Center for Aquaculture and Aquatic Environments (ICAAE) **[843]**, **[6795]**
Auburn University - Government and Economic Development Institute (GEDI) **[15483]**
Auburn University - National Center for Asphalt Technology (NCAT) **[1564]**
Auburn University Small Business Development Center **[36050]**
Auburndale Chamber of Commerce **[38324]**
"Auction Company Grows with Much Smaller Sites" in Automotive News (Vol. 86, October 31, 2011, No. 6488, pp. 23) **[1058]**, **[3885]**, **[11374]**, **[17923]**, **[23596]**
Auction Marketing Institute [1065], [6065]
Auctioneer **[1085]**
"Auctions and Bidding: A Guide for Computer Scientists" in ACM Computing Surveys (Vol. 43, Summer 2011, No. 2, pp. 10) **[1068]**, **[3424]**, **[3608]**, **[16389]**, **[19987]**, **[20737]**, **[21789]**, **[31936]**, **[32725]**
Audatex Collision Estimating Database **[14603]**
Audio Engineering Society, Inc. (AES) **[13644]**
Audiovisual and Integrated Experience Association (AVIXA) **[6159]**
"Audit: Bad Billing System Costs Glens Falls Hospital $38 Million in Revenue" in The Post Star (March 7, 2019) **[3803]**, **[25709]**
Audit Bureau of Circulations [11952]
Auditing: A Journal of Practice & Theory **[106]**
"Auditing the Auditors" in Barron's (Vol. 92, September 17, 2012, No. 38, pp. 16) **[53]**, **[16784]**, **[25208]**
Auditing Business Application Systems (Onsite) **[26185]**, **[33764]**
Auditing the Manufacturing Process (Onsite) **[19432]**
Auditing Networked Computers (Onsite) **[26186]**
Auditing Outsourced Operations (Onsite) **[31111]**
Auditing and Securing Oracle Databases (Onsite) **[26187]**
Audubon Business and Technology Center **[42839]**
Augment Ventures (AV) **[41140]**
August Capital **[37297]**
Augusta Chamber of Commerce [40287]
The Augusta Chronicle **[38688]**
Augusta Metro Chamber of Commerce (AMCC) **[38689]**
Augusta SCORE **[40248]**
Augusta University Life Sciences Business Development Center (LSBDC) **[38825]**
Aullwood Audubon Center and Farm **[6006]**
Auntie Anne's LLC **[15055]**
Aurora Area Chamber and Development (AACD) **[41839]**
Aurora Chamber of Commerce **[37816]**, **[43409]**
Aurora Chamber of Commerce [43940]
Aurora Colony Visitors Association (ACVA) **[43940]**
Aurora Management Partners Inc. **[2216]**, **[10505]**, **[20157]**, **[24233]**, **[28950]**, **[30846]**, **[33647]**
Aurora Missouri Chamber of Commerce **[41515]**
Aussie Pet Mobile Inc. (APM) **[12107]**
"Austin, Aggies and Innovation" in Austin Business Journal (Vol. 32, April 6, 2012, No. 5, pp. A1) **[21294]**, **[22366]**, **[31927]**, **[32705]**, **[35228]**
"Austin: An Oil and Gas Hub? When Drillers Want an Office, This Is the Place" in Austin Business Journal (Vol. 32, April 13, 2012, No. 6, pp. 1) **[33341]**
Austin Area Chamber of Commerce **[41192]**
"Austin-Based Insuraprise Growing Fast" in Austin Business Journal (Vol. 31, April 22, 2011, No. 7, pp. 1) **[8889]**, **[17924]**, **[26495]**, **[27240]**, **[32469]**, **[33342]**
Austin Business Journal **[45583]**
Austin Business Travel Association (ABTA) **[19288]**, **[44877]**
"Austin to Buy $1.1B of Wind Power from Two" in Austin Business Journal (Vol. 31, August 19, 2011, No. 24, pp. A1) **[5537]**, **[5818]**, **[23107]**
Austin Chamber of Commerce [45172]
Austin Grill (AG) **[14119]**
"Austin Group-Buying Site Hones In on Hispanics" in Austin Business Journal (Vol. 31, July 1, 2011, No. 17, pp. 1) **[21790]**, **[31182]**, **[32097]**
"Austin Ponders Annexing Formula One Racetrack" in Austin Business Journal (Vol. 31, July 8, 2011, No. 18, pp. 1) **[3989]**, **[25209]**, **[33343]**, **[34734]**
"Austin Realtors Cozy Up To Trulia" in Austin Business Journal (Vol. 34, May 9, 2014, No. 12, pp. 6) **[3481]**, **[13140]**, **[13389]**, **[31183]**
Austin Technology Incubator (ATI) **[45495]**
Austin Ventures L.P. (AV) **[45432]**
"Austin on Verge of Losing 7,500 Jobs" in Austin Business Journal (Vol. 31, May 6, 2011, No. 9, pp. 1) **[20738]**, **[25210]**, **[26881]**
"Austin Welcomes New Program for Entrepreneurs" in Austin Business JournalInc. (Vol. 29, February 12, 2010, No. 29, pp. 1) **[22367]**, **[24518]**, **[24930]**, **[35229]**
Austin Womens Chamber of Commerce of Texas [45414]
Australian Trade and Investment Commission (AUSTRADE) **[27395]**
Austrian Trade Commissions in the United States (ATCUSC) **[27396]**
Austrian Trade Commissions in the United States and Canada [27396]
Authorship **[5334]**
Auto Appraisal Network Inc. (AAN) **[826]**
"Auto Asphyxiation" in Canadian Business (Vol. 85, August 13, 2012, No. 13, pp. 38) **[11375]**, **[17925]**, **[20739]**, **[29105]**, **[33947]**
"Auto Bankruptcies Could Weaken Defense" in Crain's Detroit Business (Vol. 25, June 8, 2009, No. 23, pp. 1) **[1095]**, **[11376]**, **[14388]**, **[25115]**, **[29106]**
Auto Care Association **[14529]**
Auto Dealer **[11457]**
Auto Dealers CPAs **[16]**, **[16734]**
"Auto Glass Shortage Requires Creativity to Persevere" in Autobody News (October 20, 2021) **[1185]**, **[7491]**
Auto International Association [1091]
"Auto Loan Demand On the Upswing" in Memphis Business Journal (Vol. 34, May 25, 2012, No. 6, pp. 1) **[11377]**, **[28092]**
Auto Painters Association **[1132]**
Auto Parts Stores Industry in the US - Market Research Report **[1114]**
"Auto Repair Shop Financing" in Small Business Funding **[14546]**
Auto Service Excellence [14538]
"Auto Show Aims to Electrify" in Crain's Detroit Business (Vol. 26, January 11, 2010, No. 2, pp. 1) **[11378]**, **[15834]**, **[20740]**, **[23108]**, **[27839]**, **[29107]**, **[35027]**
Auto Suppliers Benchmarking Association (ASBA) **[1087]**, **[18870]**
Auto Windshield Repair Services Industry in the US - Market Research Report **[1190]**, **[7497]**
AutoInc. **[405]**
"Automaker Foundations Run Leaner" in Crain's Detroit Business (Vol. 26, January 11, 2010, No. 2, pp. 1) **[18891]**, **[19480]**, **[23109]**, **[29108]**, **[29654]**, **[34272]**
Automate Your Business Plan **[19150]**
"Automated Kiosks Ease Downtown Parking Pain" in America's Intelligence Wire (September 19, 2012) **[10013]**
Automated Laundromat Services Market Forecasts to 2028 **[10181]**
Automatic Merchandiser--Blue Book Buyer's Guide Issue **[3195]**, **[16249]**
Automatic Merchandiser: The Monthly Management Magazine for Vending and OCS Professionals **[3199]**, **[16266]**
Automatic Transmission Rebuilders Association (ATRA) **[1184]**
Automation Alley **[41078]**
Automotive Aftermarket Suppliers Association (AASA) - Brake Manufacturers Council (BMC) **[1088]**
Automotive Cooling Journal [14562]
Automotive Fleet **[1164]**
Automotive Fleet and Leasing Association (AFLA) **[1150]**
Automotive Glazing Materials (Onsite) **[25185]**, **[29084]**
Automotive Lighting (Onsite) **[25186]**, **[29085]**
Automotive Maintenance and Repair Association (AMRA) **[14530]**
Automotive Oil Change Association (AOCA) **[12997]**
Automotive Rebuilder [14563]
Automotive Service Association (ASA) **[402]**, **[1089]**, **[14531]**, **[14604]**
Automotive Service Association - Midwest (MWACA) **[14532]**
Automotive Service Association of Missouri/Kansas [14532]
Automotive Service Councils [402], [1089], [14531], [14604]
Automotive Technology & Digital Retailing **[26470]**
Automotive Warehouse Distributors Association (AWDA) **[1090]**
Autonomous (Mar 28, 2021); "13 Effective Office Design Ideas for a Small Business" in [31026]
"Autonomous Vehicles and the Future of Auto Repair" in Ratchet + Wrench (October 3, 2018) **[14547]**
AutoWeek **[11458]**
"AutoZone Revs Up Sales With Focus on Commercial Market" in Memphis Business Journal (Vol. 35, January 24, 2014, No. 42, pp. 4) **[1096]**, **[17926]**, **[32098]**
Autry Technology Center **[43832]**
Autry Technology Center Business Incubator **[43849]**
"Autumn Rat Control Essential for Poultry Units" in Poultry World (Vol. 165, September 2011, No. 9, pp. 32) **[12040]**, **[17003]**
"Auxilium Drug's New Use: Putting the Squeeze On Cellulite" in Philadelphia Business Journal (Vol. 30, September 16, 2011, No. 31, pp. 1) **[5147]**, **[27840]**, **[30680]**, **[31937]**, **[33004]**
"AV Concept Expands Into Green Energy Storage" in Wireless News (January 25, 2010) **[20611]**, **[23110]**, **[27457]**, **[29109]**, **[31184]**
Ava Area Chamber of Commerce (AACC) **[41516]**
AVAC Group **[46686]**
"Avalon Advisors Opens Alamo City Office" in San Antonio Business Journal (Vol. 28, April 18, 2014, No. 10, pp. 7) **[6260]**, **[9330]**, **[17927]**
Avalon Chamber of Commerce **[42100]**
Avalon Ventures LLC **[37298]**
"Avanti Hosts 19th Annual User's Conference in Washington, DC" in American Printer (Vol. 128, July 1, 2011, No. 7) **[3299]**, **[3696]**, **[12724]**, **[15835]**, **[16183]**, **[35028]**
Aventi Group L.L.C. **[30179]**
"The Average Salary of Auto Repair Owners" in Chron (June 29, 2018) **[14548]**
Average Small Business Travel **[19332]**
Avery, Cooper & Co. **[129]**, **[16868]**, **[28951]**
"Aviat Networks Partners With AT&T Government Solutions for Department of Homeland Security Business" in Entertainment Close-Up August 13, 2012 **[14389]**, **[25116]**, **[26218]**
Aviation Medical Bulletin **[436]**
Avinde **[45496]**
Avis Budget Group, Inc. (ABG) **[8499]**, **[14120]**
Avita & Associates **[30426]**, **[35919]**
AVITAS Inc. **[441]**
"Avoid the Stress of Traffic and Pollution with House Call Doctor Los Angeles" in Ecology, Environment & Conservation Business (May 24, 2014) **[23111]**, **[25710]**, **[30461]**
"Avoid a Tablet Generation Gap" in American Printer (Vol. 128, July 1, 2011, No. 7) **[3300]**, **[12725]**, **[16184]**
"Avoid These 5 Common Business Plan Mistakes" in Legal Zoom (March 21, 2023) **[18892]**
"Avoid These Common Pitfalls in Order to Run a Profitable Screen Printing Business" in Printa Blog (August 8, 2013) **[14350]**
"Avoid the Traps That Can Destroy Family Businesses: An Emerging Set of Best Practices Can Turn the Age-Old Problem of Generational Succession Into an Opportunity To Thrive" in Harvard Business Review (Vol. 90, January-February 2012, No.1, pp. 25) **[18893]**, **[19481]**, **[23597]**
Avoiding Business Failure by Improving Cash Flow **[19714]**
Avon Chamber of Commerce (ACOC) **[38027]**, **[39514]**
Avon Park Chamber of Commerce (APCC) **[38325]**
Avrio Capital [46684]
Avrio Subdebt Inc. **[46684]**
AVS International Symposium & Exhibition **[32921]**
"AVT Featured on TD Waterhouse Market News Website and in Vending Times Magazine" in Benzinga.com (August 17, 2011) **[16250]**, **[31856]**
"AVT Launches New ExpressPay Vending Systems" in Benzinga.com (July 13, 2011) **[16251]**, **[33948]**
"avVaa World Health Care Products Rolls Out Internet Marketing Program" in Health and Beauty Close-Up (September 18, 2009) **[238]**, **[1387]**, **[9097]**, **[16390]**, **[20612]**, **[28449]**, **[29655]**, **[32470]**
Award Magazine: Architecture, Construction, Interior Design **[9056]**
"Award Win Highlights Slingsby's Green Credentials" in Ecology,Environment & Conservation Business (August 20, 2011, pp. 3) **[5538]**, **[5819]**, **[7475]**, **[7699]**, **[23112]**
Aweida Venture Partners (AVP) **[37918]**
Awesome Inc. **[40102]**
AWFS Vegas **[7246]**
AWP's Guide to Writing Programs **[5308]**
AWRA Annual Conference **[16342]**
AWT Annual Convention & Exposition **[16343]**
AWT Private Investments **[42204]**
AWWA Annual Conference & Exposition **[16344]**
AWWA'S Annual Conference & Expo [16344]
Axcel Innovation **[45980]**
The Axelrod Group Inc. **[22309]**
Ayden Chamber of Commerce **[43088]**

3186 Small Business Sourcebook • 42nd Edition

Ayrshire Breeders' Association of Canada [629]
AZ TechCelerator [36385]
"Azaya Therapeutics Taking Big Steps" in San Antonio Business Journal (Vol. 28, March 28, 2014, No. 7, pp. 8) [5148], [7082], [17928], [25211]
Azle Area Chamber of Commerce (AACC) [45037]
Aztec Chamber of Commerce [42301]
Azure Capital Partners [37299]
Azure Magazine [920], [978]
Azusa Chamber of Commerce [36741]

B

B-More Kitchen [40440]
"B-N Pawn Shop Auctions Off Jimmy Hoffa's Rifle" in Pantagraph (September 14, 2010) [1069], [11915]
B2B Marketing: 10 Key Differences from Consumer Marketing [19238], [29656]
"B2B Marketing: How to Grow Your Business" in Evinex (November 2, 2020) [19239], [29657]
"B2B vs. B2C Marketing: What's the Difference in Marketing to the Business Market?" in Catalyst (January 3, 2019) [19240], [29658]
BA Venture Partners [37482]
Babies 'N' Bells Inc. [12774]
"BABs in Bond Land" in Barron's (Vol. 89, July 6, 2009, No. 27, pp. 14) [3990], [6261], [9331], [20741], [23738], [24944], [34735]
Babson College - Arthur M. Blank Center for Entrepreneurship [31622], [40744]
Babson College - Center for Entrepreneurial Studies [31622], [40744]
"Baby Boomers Look to Senior Concierge Services to Raise Income" in The New York Times (May 19, 2017) [3869], [25711]
"Baby Fashion Accessories Market to Witness Steady Expansion During 2019 to 2025" in The Chicago Sentinel (October 30, 2019) [6123]
Baby Power / Forever Kids (BPFK) [2893]
"Baby's Room Franchisee Files Bankruptcy" in Crain's Detroit Business (Vol. 25, June 22, 2009, No. 25, pp. 15) [1192], [23739], [24334]
Back to Business Buckeye [36351]
Back on the Career Track: A Guide for Stay-At-Home Moms Who Want to Return to Work [33949], [35740]
"Back In the Black, Maryland Zoo Upgrades" in Baltimore Business Journal (Vol. 32, July 25, 2014, No. 12, pp. 4) [7083], [23740]
"Back Off on ABM Legislation, Banks Warn MPs" in Globe & Mail (April 20, 2007, pp. B1) [25212], [26219]
"Back in the Race. New Fund Manager Has Whipped Sentinel International Equity Back into Shape" in Barron's (Vol. 88, March 17, 2008, No. 11, pp. 43) [6262], [9332], [18894], [20742], [23741], [27458], [28450]
Back Stage/Shoot Commercial Production Directory [6208]
"Back-Tested ETFs Draw Assets, Flub Returns" in Barron's (Vol. 92, July 23, 2012, No. 30, pp. 26) [3482], [6263], [9333], [23742]
"Back To the Roots Puts a Hold On Bad Phone Music" in San Francisco Business Times (Vol. 28, February 21, 2014, No. 31, pp. 3) [837], [6778]
"Backer Christmas Trade Show Preview" in Pet Product News (Vol. 66, September 2012, No. 9, pp. 12) [12188], [29110], [35029]
Backflow Prevention Journal [16338]
Backstage Capital [30245], [35261], [37721]
Backstage Guide to Real Estate: Produce Passive Income, Write Your Own Story, and Direct Your Dollars Toward Positive Change [13390]
"Backtalk with Terrie M. Williams" in Black Enterprise (Vol. 38, December 2007, No. 5, pp. 204) [20086], [22492], [25712], [31745], [34273], [35741]
The Backyard Beekeeper [1458]
Bad Ass Coffee Co. [14361]
"Bad Loans Start Piling Up" in Crain's New York Business (Vol. 24, January 6, 2008, No. 1, pp. 2) [6264], [9334], [11011], [20249], [23743], [28093]
"Bad Paper" in Canadian Business (Vol. 80, November 19, 2007, No. 23, pp. 34) [6265], [9335], [25213]
"Bad Reviews Can Boost Sales. Here's Why" in Harvard Business Review (Vol. 90, April 2012, No. 4, pp. 28) [1640], [1813], [5309], [32471]
"Bad Web Design Isn't Just Annoying--It Costs You" Entrepreneur NEXT (July 14, 2020) [16391]
Bagadocia Music Lending Library (BMLL) [11207], [11292]
Bagel Stores Industry in the US - Market Research Report [1212]
Bahama Buck's Franchise Corp. [8608]
Bahama Buck's Original Shaved Ice [8608]
Bahr International Inc. [10506], [20158], [28952]
Baileys Harbor Community Association (BHCA) [46362]

Bain Capital Ventures (BCV) [37300]
Bain & Company, Inc. [31604]
Bainbridge Chamber of Commerce [42517]
Bainbridge-Decatur County Chamber of Commerce [38690]
Bainbridge Island Chamber of Commerce (BICC) [46048]
Baird Capital [46588]
Baird Chamber of Commerce (BCC) [45038]
Bake [1213]
Baker Botts, L.L.P. Law Library [13351]
Baker Capital [42719]
Baker Chamber of Commerce and Agriculture [41748]
Baker College - Owosso Campus [41127]
Baker County Chamber of Commerce [38326]
Baker County Unlimited Chamber of Commerce (BCCC) [43941]
Baker & McKenzie - Library [15465]
Baker Scott & Co. [13051], [15620]
"Bakeries Turn to Automation to Tackle Warehouse Woes" in BakingBusiness.com (November 18, 2021) [1246]
Baker's Journal [11957]
Bakersfield Downtown Business Association (DBA) [33446]
Baking Association of Canada (BAC) [1243]
Baking Buyer [1213]
Baking & Snack [1214], [1276]
Baking/Snack Directory & Buyer's Guide [1211]
"Baking Up a Bigger Lance" in Charlotte Business Journal (Vol. 25, December 3, 2010, No. 37, pp. 1) [7720], [9336], [29111], [31185]
"Bakugan Battle Brawlers From Spin Master: A Marketing 50 Case Study" in Advertising Age (Vol. 79, November 17, 2008, No. 43, pp. S2) [15786], [29659]
The Balanced Pet Sitter: What You Wish You Knew Before Starting Your Pet Care Business [12281]
"Balancing Freedom of Speech with the Right to Privacy: How to Legally Cope with the Funeral Protest Problem" in Pace Law Review (Fall 2007) [7205], [18515]
"Balancing Risk and Return in a Customer Portfolio" in Journal of Marketing (Vol. 75, May 2011, No. 3, pp. 1) [23744], [29660]
Balch & Bingham LLP (B&B) [2417]
Balch Springs Chamber of Commerce [45039]
Bald Knob Area Chamber of Commerce [36435]
Bald Knob Chamber of Commerce [36435]
"Baldor Specialty Foods, Bronx Brewery Release Beer to Benefit Brownsville Community Center" in Brewbound (September 18, 2019) [1315], [1902], [15005]
Baldwin Chamber of Commerce (BCC) [42518]
Baldwin City Chamber of Commerce [39863]
"Baldwin Connelly Partnership Splits" in Business Journal Serving Greater Tampa Bay (Vol. 30, November 19, 2010, No. 48, pp. 1) [8890], [17929], [19482], [27241], [31186]
Baldwin County Business Incubator [36171]
Baldwin Park Chamber of Commerce (BOC) [42519]
Ball State University - Bureau of Business Research [21266]
Ball State University - Center for Business and Economic Research (CBER) [21266]
Ball State University - Center for Energy Research/ Education/Service (CERES) [14965], [14970]
Ball State University - Center for Organizational Resources (CORe) [30856]
Ball State University Entrepreneurship Center [39655]
Ball State University - Human Performance Laboratory (HPL) [12509]
Ball State University-Small Business Entrepreneurship Program [39656]
Ballard Alliance (BCC) [46049]
Ballard Chamber of Commerce [46049]
Ballast Point Ventures (BPV) [38615]
Ballet Schools Industry in the US - Market Research Report [4857]
Ballinger Chamber of Commerce [45040]
Ballistic Missile Defense Organization [47604]
"Ballpark Sales Tax Extension Could Fund New Arena" in Milwaukee Business Journal (Vol. 27, January 29, 2010, No. 18, pp. A1) [15131], [25214], [32099], [34736]
Baltimore Angels [40482]
"Baltimore-Area Businesses Still on the Mend 10 Years After 9/11" in Baltimore Business Journal (Vol. 29, September 9, 2011, No. 18, pp. 1) [14390], [18895], [20743]
"Baltimore-Area Hospital Tower Projects Could Add Hundreds of New Jobs" in Baltimore Business Journal (Vol. 28, June 25, 2010, No. 7, pp. 1) [3991], [25713], [26496], [26882]
"Baltimore Businesses Put Cash Behind Bernstein" in Baltimore Business Journal (Vol. 28, August 20, 2010, No. 15, pp. 1) [7084], [18516], [25215]

Baltimore City Chamber of Commerce [40367]
Baltimore City Small Business Resource Center (SBRC) [40335]
"Baltimore Commercial Real Estate Foreclosures Continue to Rise" in Baltimore Business Journal (Vol. 28, October 1, 2010, No. 21, pp. 1) [11012], [13141], [13391], [28094]
Baltimore County Chamber of Commerce (BCCC) [40368]
Baltimore County Small Business Development Center [40336]
"Baltimore Dealers Fear Shortages in Car Supply" in Boston Business Journal (Vol. 29, May 13, 2011, No. 1, pp. 1) [1097], [11379], [11856], [11878]
"Baltimore Developer Caves Valley Partners Bids for $750M Social Security Project - County Tract Pitched for Data Center" in Baltimore Business Journal (Vol. 28, July 23, 2010, No. 11, pp. 1) [3483], [3992], [31682]
"Baltimore Entrepreneur Develops an Event-Themed Wish List App" in Baltimore Business Journal (Vol. 32, July 25, 2014, No. 12, pp. 7) [7476], [11711], [22493]
"Baltimore Eyeing Tax Breaks for New Arena" in Boston Business Journal (Vol. 29, June 3, 2011, No. 4, pp. 1) [3993], [8361], [15132], [24945], [28095], [34737]
"Baltimore GM Plant Moves Forward" in Baltimore Business Journal (Vol. 32, July 4, 2014, No. 9, pp. 18) [22094], [29112]
"Baltimore Grand Prix Didn't Fill Up City Hotels" in Baltimore Business Journal (Vol. 29, September 16, 2011, No. 19, pp. 1) [15133]
"Baltimore Grand Prix Week Schedule Filling Up With Galas, Nonprofit Fundraisers" in Baltimore Business Journal (Vol. 29, July 22, 2011, No. 11, pp. 1) [7085], [15134], [29661], [33098]
Baltimore Museum of Art (BMA) [3363]
"Baltimore Ravens Back to Business as NFL Lockout Ends" in Baltimore Business Journal (Vol. 29, July 29, 2011, No. 12, pp. 1) [239], [15135], [21791], [29662], [33099]
Baltimore Regional, National Association of Women Business Owners [35637]
"Baltimore Rejects Plans for Waxter Site" in Baltimore Business Journal (Vol. 30, May 25, 2012, No. 3, pp. 1) [3994], [25216]
"Baltimore Restaurants Banking on Andretti Name" in Baltimore Business Journal (Vol. 30, May 18, 2012, No. 2, pp. 1) [8362], [13904], [15136]
"Baltimore Shopping Centers Go On the Block as Sellers See Demand" in Baltimore Business Journal (Vol. 29, September 2, 2011, No. 17, pp. 1) [7721], [13392], [32100]
"Baltimore Vendors Brave Heat, Red Tape to Eke Out a Living: Working the Streets" in Baltimore Business Journal (Vol. 28, July 30, 2010, No. 12, pp. 1) [3836], [6899], [16252], [27841]
"Baltimore's Burger Market Sizzling with Newcomers" in Boston Business Journal (Vol. 29, June 10, 2011, No. 5, pp. 1) [4880], [13905], [17930], [33950]
"Baltimore's Businesses: Equipment Tax Breaks Help, But Money Still Tight: Weighing the Write-Off" in Baltimore Business Journal (Vol. 28, September 10, 2010, No. 18, pp. 1) [20744], [24946], [29113], [34738]
"Baltimore's Businesses, Latest Stats Show Growth may be an Aberration: Recovery a Ruse?" in Baltimore Business Journal (Vol. 28, August 6, 2010, No. 13, pp. 1) [20745], [24947], [29114], [32472]
"Baltimore's Co-Working Spaces Introduces New Kind of Cubicle Culture" in Baltimore Business Journal (Vol. 29, August 19, 2011, No. 15, pp. 1) [5310], [22494], [31029], [33100], [33951]
"Baltimore's Hilton Convention Headquarters Hotel Still Losing Money" in Baltimore Business Journal (Vol. 28, October 15, 2010, No. 23, pp. 1) [8363], [35030]
"Baltimore's Hispanic Businesses Try to Drum Up Cash to Battle Crime Spree" in Baltimore Business Journal (Vol. 28, September 3, 2010, No. 17) [18517], [30324], [33344]
"Baltimore's Steamed Crab Prices Reach New Highs: Paying the Price" in Baltimore Business Journal (Vol. 28, July 9, 2010, No. 9, pp. 1) [6745], [6779], [13906], [19988]
BaMa [30246]
Bama Technology Incubator [36181]
Bamboo Detroit [41079]
"Ban Threatens Soda Fountain: Mayor's Size Limit Could Crimp Sales, Change Bottling" in Crain's New York Business (Vol. 28, July 30, 2012, No. 31, pp. 6) [25217]
Band of Angels [37301]
Bandana's Bar-B-Q [14121]
"B&B Bicycles Named Best Bicycle Shop" in Focus Daily News (July 28, 2019) [1517]

"B&B Hopes to Appeal to Fiat Execs" in Crain's Detroit Business (Vol. 25, June 15, 2009, No. 24, pp. 21) [1409], [15731], [15984], [28451]
Bandera County Texas Chamber of Commerce [45041]
Bandon Chamber of Commerce (BCC) [43942]
"Bangles, BMWs Elbow Out Delis and Discount Shops" in Crain's New York Business (Vol. 24, January 13, 2008, No. 2, pp. 35) [12875], [13142], [13393], [32101], [33545]
Bangor Regional Chamber of Commerce (BRCC) [40261]
"Bank of America Fights To Keep Top Spot in Mobile Banking" in Charlotte Business Journal (Vol. 27, June 15, 2012, No. 13, pp. 1) [2717], [9098], [19782], [22997], [23745], [30462]
"Bank Buys May Heat Up In Birmingham" in Birmingham Business Journal (Vol. 31, May 9, 2014, No. 19, pp. 8) [6266], [9337], [19647], [20746], [31187]
Bank of Nova Scotia Archives [6726]
"Bank On It: New Year, New Estate Plan" in Hawaii Business (Vol. 53, February 2008, No. 8, pp. 54) [6022], [6267], [17276], [18896], [23746], [24604], [34739]
Bankers Capital Corp. (BCC) [45433]
Bankers Small Business Community Development Corp. [36600]
"Banking on Cord Blood" in Business Journal-Serving Phoenix & the Valley of the Sun (Vol. 31, September 10, 2010, No. 1, pp. 1) [25714], [31938], [32726], [34274]
"Banking Sector To See Moderate Growth in 2014" in Houston Business Journal (Vol. 44, January 3, 2014, No. 35, pp. 5) [17931], [20747], [23747]
"The Bankrate Double Play, Bankrate Is Having Its Best Quarter Yet" in Barron's (Vol. 88, March 24, 2008, No. 12, pp. 27) [6268], [9099], [9338], [16392], [21792], [23748], [31188]
"Bankruptcies" in Crain's Detroit Business (Vol. 24, March 24, 2008, No. 12, pp. 6) [3995], [7722], [7831], [11380], [12726], [14977], [18518], [24605], [25715], [29114], [33101]
"Bankruptcies" in Crain's Detroit Business (Vol. 26, January 11, 2010, No. 2, pp. 7) [18519], [20748]
Bankruptcy for Small Business [18520], [23749], [24606]
"Banks Continue March Out of Bad-Loan Numbers: Total Loans Up, Non-Performing Loans Decline" in Memphis Business Journal (Vol. 34, August 24, 2012, No. 19, pp. 1) [13143], [23750], [28096]
Banks County Chamber of Commerce (BCCC) [38691]
"Banks Looking to Lend, Compete to Make Small-Business Loans" in Puget Sound Business Journal (Vol. 33, August 17, 2012, No. 17, pp. 1) [10426], [17932], [28097]
"Banks, Retailers Squabble Over Fees" in Baltimore Business Journal (Vol. 28, June 18, 2010, No. 6, pp. 1) [4769], [20250], [23751], [25218], [32102]
"BankUnited, Banco do Brasil Lead Local Lenders" in South Florida Business Journal (Vol. 35, September 12, 2014, No. 7, pp. 5) [17933], [28098]
Banning Chamber of Commerce [36742]
Banquet Managers Guild [2665], [6083]
Banyan Ventures [45658]
"Baptist Hatching Health Care Plan" in Memphis Business Journal (Vol. 34, June 15, 2012, No. 9, pp. 1) [25716]
"Baptist Health System Plans to Expand Stone Oak-Area Hospital: $32 Million Project Will Add Two Floors, 100 Beds" in San Antonio Business Journal (Vol. 26, May 25, 2012, No. 17, pp. 1) [17934], [25717], [26497]
BAPTurnkey [130]
Bar-B-Cutie SmokeHouse [14122]
Bar Convent Brooklyn [1365], [14089]
Bar Harbor Chamber of Commerce (BHCC) [40262]
Bar Harbor Visitors' Guide [40263]
The Bar Register of Preeminent Lawyers™ [18784]
Baraboo Area Chamber of Commerce (BCC) [46363]
Barada Associates Inc. [26726]
"Barbarians Set Bar Low With Lowly Canadian Telco" in Globe & Mail (March 31, 2007, pp. B1) [6269], [9339], [31189], [33102]
Barber Shops Industry in the US - Market Research Report [7879]
"Barbering Is an Art" in The New York Times (May 4, 2018) [7861]
Barbershop Elevates Marketing to Support Expansion [7862]
"Barbershops Are Back and Bucking Retail Trends" in Forbes (July 6, 2017) [7863]
Barberton Community Development Corporation (BCDC) [43647]
"Bargain Hunting In Vietnam" in Barron's (Vol. 88, July 14, 2008, No. 28, pp. M6) [6270], [9340], [17935], [20749], [23752], [27459]
Bargaining With Vendors and Suppliers (Onsite) [17539]

Bark Busters [12152]
Bark Busters Home Dog Training [12153]
"Bark Up The Right Tree" in Small Business Opportunities (Winter 2009) [12083], [12255], [17936], [18897], [19483], [20750], [24335]
Barkefellers [12108]
"Barnes Shakes Up Sara Lee Exec Suite" in Crain's Chicago Business (Vol. 31, April 21, 2008, No. 16, pp. 1) [18898], [28452], [29115]
Barnesville Area Chamber of Commerce [43410]
Barnesville-Lamar County Chamber of Commerce [38692]
Barnie's Coffee and Tea Company Inc. [7571]
Baroda Ventures [37302]
"Barriers to Small Business Creations in Canada" in International Journal of Entrepreneurship and Small Business [22495], [24519]
Barrington Area Chamber of Commerce (BACC) [39092]
Barrington Partners [40665]
Barron's [2148], [6718], [9915], [9938], [11102]
The Barrow [44056]
Barrow County Chamber of Commerce (BCCC) [38693]
Barry County Area Chamber of Commerce [40855]
Barry University The Entrepreneurial Institute [38253]
Bars & Nightclubs Industry in the US - Market Research Report [1356]
"Bars, Restaurants to Change Game for Baltimore Grand Prix Patrons" in Baltimore Business Journal (Vol. 29, July 22, 2011, No. 11, pp. 1) [1316], [13907], [15137]
"Bars See Green, Neighbors In Red Over Strolls" in Baltimore Business Journal (Vol. 31, February 28, 2014, No. 44, pp. 7) [1317]
"Barshop Leading 'Paradigm Shift' In Aging Research" in San Antonio Business Journal (Vol. 28, September 12, 2014, No. 31, pp. 4) [5149], [21453], [24947], [31939]
"BARS+TONE Achieves Green Business Certification by the City and County of San Francisco" in Benzinga. com (April 26, 2012) [5539], [5820], [6175], [23113]
Barstow Area Chamber of Commerce (BACC) [36743]
"Barter: A Strategic Tool for the New Economy" in Zen Business (Aug. 11, 2021) [17242]
"Barter Exchanges and How They Work" in The Balance Small Business (Aug 2, 2019) [17243]
"Barter in Small Business" in Business Practical Knowledge [17244]
The Barter System - Is It for You? [17245]
"Bartering is Local Club's Stock in Trade" in Pueblo Chieftain (September 6, 2010) [17246], [20751]
"Bartering Trades on Talents" in Reading Eagle (June 20, 2010) [17247], [17937], [20752], [31190], [33103], [33952]
Bartlesville Regional Chamber of Commerce (BRCC) [43734]
Bartlett Area Chamber of Commerce (BACC) [44713]
Bartlett Chamber of Commerce [39093]
Barton Area Chamber of Commerce [45717]
Barton County Chamber of Commerce [41517]
Barton County Historical Society (BCHS) [7397]
Bartow Board of Trade [38387]
Baruch College Lawrence N. Field Center for Entrepreneurship [42391]
Basalt Chamber of Commerce [37817]
Base Ventures [30247], [37722]
BaseCamp Ventures [42205]
Baseline Intelligence [6219], [15627], [24277]
"Baseline Metrics CEOs Need for Online Brand Oversight" in South Florida Business Journal (Vol. 34, May 23, 2014, No. 44, pp. 16) [8647], [14758], [20387], [21793], [31746], [33829]
BaselineFT's In Production Database [6219], [15627], [24277]
Basic Business Essentials: Concepts and Tools [24854]
Basic Electricity for the Non Electrician [2053]
Basic Electricity for the Non Electrician (Onsite) [19433], [21335]
Basic Fundamentals of Modern Tattoo [15345]
Basic Problem Solving Techniques (Onsite) [21336], [22041]
"The Basics of Branding" in Entrepreneur [17432]
Basics of Commercial Contracting (Onsite) [21337]
The Basics of Employee Benefits [17277]
Basics of Government Contract Administration (Onsite) [17827], [25104]
The Basics of Human Resource Law (Onsite) [18481]
"Basics Market Expands Beyond Portland's City Limits" in Grocery Dive (November 4, 2019) [7723]
Basics of Time Management Workshop (Onsite) [34966]
Basin Business [43943]
"Baskin-Robbins" in Ice Cream Reporter (Vol. 23, November 20, 2010, No. 12, pp. 7) [8543], [30681]
"Baskin-Robbins Expanding in China and U.S." in Ice Cream Reporter (Vol. 21, August 20, 2008, No. 9, pp. 1) [8544], [17938], [27460]

Baskin-Robbins L.L.C. [8609]
"Baskin-Robbins: New in U.S., Old in Japan" in Ice Cream Reporter (Vol. 23, August 20, 2010, No. 9, pp. 2) [8545], [17939], [24336], [27461]
"Baskin-Robbins Reopens in New Orleans" in Ice Cream Reporter (Vol. 23, September 20, 2010, No. 10, pp. 3) [8546], [17940]
"Baskin-Robbins Tests New Upscale Concept" in Ice Cream Reporter (Vol. 21, September 20, 2008, No. 10, pp. 1) [8547], [13908], [17941]
Bass Lake Chamber of Commerce [36744]
"Bass Pro Shops Plans Megastore for Rocklin" in Sacramento Business Journal (Vol. 51, February 14, 2014, No. 51, pp. 4) [15086], [32103], [33345]
Bastrop Chamber of Commerce (BCC) [45042]
Bastyr University Library [11350], [11606]
Batavia Chamber of Commerce (BCC) [39094]
Bates International Motor Home Rental Systems Inc. [1168]
Batesville Area Chamber of Commerce [39515]
Batesville Area Chamber of Commerce (BACC) [36436]
Bath Area Chamber of Commerce [40307], [44268]
Bath County Chamber of Commerce (BCCC) [45834]
Bath Fitter [8224]
Bath Saver Inc. [8224]
Baton Rouge Area SCORE [40134]
Baton Rouge Black Chamber of Commerce (BRBCC) [40151]
"Battelle Given Keys to CompeteColumbus" in Business First-Columbus (October 15, 2007, pp. 1) [12876]
"Battered Loblaw Makes Deep Job Cuts" in Globe & Mail (January 25, 2007) [7724], [19484]
"Battered U.S. Auto Makers in Grip of Deeper Sales Slump" in Globe & Mail (April 4, 2007, pp. B1) [6271], [9341], [11381], [29116]
Batteries Plus Bulbs [1129]
Batteries Plus L.L.C. [1129]
Batterson Venture Capital L.L.C. [39381]
Battery Ventures L.P. [37303]
Battle Creek Area Chamber of Commerce [40856]
Battle Ground--North Clark County Directory [46050]
Baudette-Lake of the Woods Chamber of Commerce [41193]
"Baupost Group Pours Money into Charlotte Real Estate Projects" in Charlotte Business Journal (Vol. 25, December 3, 2010, No. 37, pp. 1) [6272], [9342], [13144], [13394], [23753]
Baxley-Appling County Chamber of Commerce [38694]
Baxter Springs Chamber of Commerce [39864]
Baxter & Woodman Inc. [7972]
Bay Area Business Travel Association (BABTA) [19289], [36533]
Bay Area Chamber of Commerce (BACC) [40857], [43944]
Bay Area Independent Publishers Association (BAIPA) [1612], [5273]
Bay Area Kitchen Rental (BAKR) [37543]
Bay Area Legal Incubator (BALI) [37544]
Bay Biz [38327]
Bay Biz Magazine [38328]
Bay City Capital LLC [37304]
Bay County Chamber of Commerce (BCCC) [38329]
Bay Minette Chamber of Commerce [36141]
Bay Partners [37305]
Bayer Center for Nonprofit Management (BCNM) [28953]
Bayfield Chamber of Commerce [46364]
Baylink LLC [37545]
Baylor Angel Network (BAN) [45434]
Baylor College of Medicine - Center for Medical Ethics and Health Policy [26104]
"Baylor Turns Around Carrollton Hospital" in Dallas Business Journal (Vol. 35, June 15, 2012, No. 40, pp. 1) [20388], [25718]
Baylor University - Center for Private Enterprise [22951]
Baylor University - Crouch Fine Arts Library (CFAL) [11208]
Baylor University - Hankamer School of Business - Center for Business and Economic Research [21267]
Baylor University John F. Baugh Center for Entrepreneurship & Free Enterprise [45575]
Baymont Inn & Suites [8500]
Bayou La Batre Area Chamber of Commerce [36082]
Bayou La Batre Chamber of Commerce [36082]
Baytown Chamber of Commerce (BCC) [45043]
"BayTSP, NTT Data Corp. Enter Into Reseller Pact to Market Online IP Monitoring" in Professional Services Close-Up (Sept. 11, 2009) [9100], [14759], [21794], [27462], [29663], [32473], [33830]
Bayview Chamber of Commerce [38905]
The BBB Bulletin [39855]
"BBB Business Tip: Top 10 Scams Targeting Small Businesses" in Better Business Bureau website (April 12, 2022) [19256]

BBB Great West + Pacific [36217], [37810], [38870], [38904], [41746], [43934], [46043], [46596]
BBB of Midwest Plains [39856]
BBB of Midwest Plains - Lincoln [41832]
BBB of Midwest Plains - Omaha [41833]
BBB of Midwest Plains - Wichita Falls [39857], [41511]
"BBB Reworks Logo, Grading System" in Crain's Cleveland Business (Vol. 28, October 8, 2007, No. 40, pp. 5) [29664], [31747], [31857]
BBB Serving Manitoba & N.W. Ontario [46724]
"BBB Tips: 7 Tips for Hiring a Cleaning Service" in International Association of Better Business Bureaus (April 28, 2020) [2969], [26498]
BBB Wise Giving Alliance [19249]
BBLM Architects PC [31061]
BC Innovation Council (BCIC) [24586]
BC Tech Association [3420], [3601], [3765]
BC Technology Industry Association - Centre4Growth [46713]
BCA Billiard & Home Leisure Expo [1541]
BCA-Credit Information [13016], [15570]
BCA Expo [1541]
BCB [32856]
"BCE Mulls Radical Changes With Industry Under Pressure" in Globe & Mail (March 30, 2007, pp. B1) [17942], [18899], [19485], [31191]
BCM Technologies Inc. [45435]
BD Technologies and Innovation (BDTI) [42230]
BD Ventures / Becton, Dickinson and Co. [42206]
BDA Morneau Shepell [34685]
"BDC Launches New Online Business Advice Centre" in Marketwired (July 13, 2010) [2179], [6273], [9343], [20087], [21795], [22496], [23754], [24520]
BDO FMA LLC [131]
BDPA Information Technology Thought Leaders [3602]
"Be a Better Manager: Live Abroad" in Harvard Business Review (Vol. 88, September 2010, No. 9, pp. 24) [22497], [27463], [28453], [30537], [30682]
Be a Brilliant Business Writer: Write Well, Write Fast, and Whip the Competition [5311], [17637], [17854], [19783], [22095]
Be Cause Business Resources Inc. [24234], [28954]
"Be Nice at Work - Everybody's Watching" in Puget Sound Business Journal (Vol. 34, April 4, 2014, No. 51, pp. 10) [22096]
BE NKY Growth Partnership [40103]
Be a Profitable Badass Small Business Owner: 5 Mistakes Small Business Owners Make [16618]
Be a Profitable Badass Small Business Owner: 7 Key Pillars of a Strong Business Foundation [16619]
Be a Profitable Badass Small Business Owner: Are You a Profitable Business Owner? [24199]
Be a Profitable Badass Small Business Owner: Do You Need Goals to Have a Successful Small Business Owner? [19632]
Be a Profitable Badass Small Business Owner: Is It Time to Shut Down Your Small Business? [33042]
Be a Profitable Badass Small Business Owner: Two Calculations to Know in Your Small Business [24200]
"Be Safe: CSE Requires a Series of Steps" in Contractor (Vol. 56, October 2009, No. 10, pp. 40) [12616], [35939]
Be the SOLution: Building Community and Sharing Resources with Megan Bott [23421]
"Be Wary of Dual-Flush Conversion Kits" in Contractor (Vol. 56, September 2009, No. 9, pp. 66) [471], [3996], [5540], [14609], [23114]
"Be Wary of Legal Advice on Internet, Lawyers Warn" in Crain's Detroit Business (Vol. 24, September 22, 2008, No. 38, pp. 16) [9101], [16393], [18521], [33953]
Beachwood Business Development Center [43411], [43648]
Beachwood Chamber of Commerce (BCC) [43411], [43648]
The Beacon [39516]
Beacon Angels [35262], [40666]
Beacon Management-Management Consultants [2217], [10507], [19127], [20159], [22936], [24235], [28955]
Bean Association [13878]
Bear Lake Rendezvous Chamber of Commerce (BLRCC) [45625]
"The Bear Stearns-JPMorgan Deal - Rhymes with Steal - Of A Lifetime" in Barron's (Vol. 88, March 24, 2008, No. 12, pp. 24) [6274], [9344], [23755], [28099], [31192]
The Bearclaw Coffee Co. [7572]
BearCom Building Services Inc. [5080]
Beardstown Chamber of Commerce (BCC) [39095]
"The Bear's Back" in Barron's (Vol. 88, July 7, 2008, No. 27, pp. 17) [6275], [9345], [20753], [23756]
"Beat the Buck: Bartering Tips from In-The-Know Authors" in (June 23, 2010) [17248], [23757], [31193]
Beatrice Area Chamber of Commerce (BCC) [41840]

Beatty Nevada Chamber of Commerce [41928]
Beaufort Area SBDC [44500]
Beaufort Area Small Business Development Center [44500]
Beaufort Regional Chamber of Commerce [44536]
Beaumont Chamber of Commerce [36745]
Beaumont Chamber of Commerce (BCC) [45044]
"Beaumont Outsources Purchasing as Route to Supply Cost Savings" in Crain's Detroit Business (Vol. 25, June 1, 2009, No. 22) [10946], [23758], [31113]
"The Beauty of Banking's Big Ugly" in Barron's (Vol. 89, July 27, 2009, No. 30, pp. 31) [6276], [9346], [20754], [23759], [28100]
The Beauty Industry Report (BIR) [7882]
Beauty Salon Industry Analysis [7864]
Beauty Supply Outlet [1402]
Beaver County Chamber of Commerce (BCCC) [44170]
Beaver Dam Area Chamber of Commerce (BDACC) [46365]
Beaver Dam Chamber of Commerce [46365]
Beaver Street Enterprise Center (BSEC) [38552]
The Beaverbrook Art Gallery [991]
Beaverhead Chamber of Commerce [41749]
Beaverton Area Chamber of Commerce (BACC) [43945]
"Because 10 Million Zumba Lovers Can't Be Wrong" in Inc. (Volume 32, December 2010, No. 10, pp. 106) [12406], [22498], [31194]
"Because Kids Need To Be Heard: Tina Wells: Buzz Marketing Group: Voorhees, New Jersey" in Inc. (Volume 32, December 2010) [1641], [10639], [29665], [35742]
Beckett and Raeder Inc. (BRI) [928]
Beckley - Raleigh County Chamber of Commerce (BRCCC) [46262]
Beckman Laser Institute Photonics Incubator [37546]
"Become a Franchise Owner in 5 Easy Steps" in Entrepreneur (June 19, 2020) [24288]
Become a Personal Shopper for Seniors [12020]
"Become a Personal Shopper: Step-by-Step Career Guide" in Study.com (March 4, 2020) [12021]
Become a World Class Assistant (Onsite) [28295]
Become Your Own Boss in 12 Months: A Month-by-Month Guide to a Business that Works [18859], [24521]
Becoming Better Together, LLC (BBT) [30630]
Becoming and Event Planner [6085]
"Bed and Breakfast Among Planned Uses for New Bohemia Properties" in Gazette (January 30, 2012) [872], [1410], [33954]
Bed & Breakfast & Hostel Accommodations Industry in the US - Market Research Report [1426], [8470]
"Bed and Breakfast Inspired by 'The Waltons' Set to Open in Virginia" in WSLS.com (October 10, 2019) [1411]
Bed & Mattress Stores Industry in the US - Market Research Report [8214]
"Bedandbreakfast.eu: Bed & Breakfast Emerging in Europe" in Travel & Leisure Close-Up (January 11, 2012) [1412], [17943], [27464]
"Bedbugs Are Here, But Help Is At Hand" in Register-Guard (June 26, 2011) [12041]
Bedford Area Chamber of Commerce [39517]
Bedford Area Chamber of Commerce [45835]
Bedford Banner [40559]
Bedford Capital Corp. [42720]
Bedford Capital Ltd. [46777]
Bedford Chamber of Commerce [40560]
Bedford Chamber of Commerce (BACC) [45835]
Bedford County Chamber of Commerce [44171]
Bedford Hills Chamber of Commerce [42520]
Bedrock Capital [42721]
BedTimes: The Business Journal for the Sleep Products Industry [8228]
Bee County Chamber of Commerce [45045]
Bee-Craft Consult [1496]
Bee Culture [1459]
"Bee Mindful: NY Lawmakers Want to Preserve, Relocate Pesky Hives" in TimesUnion (October 10, 2019) [1460], [25219]
Bee2Bee Honey Collective [1497]
Beech Mountain Chamber of Commerce [43089]
Beech-Nut Nutrition Corp. [11607]
Beecher Chamber of Commerce [39096]
Beechtree Capita,l LLC [36421]
Beecken Petty O'Keefe & Co. (BPOC) [39351]
Beef O'Bradys Family Sports Pubs [14123]
Beehive Venture Capital [46869]
BeeHively Group [1498]
The Beekeeper's Bible: Bees, Honey, Recipes & Other Home Uses [1461]
The Beekeeper's Handbook [1462]
The Beekeepers of Indiana [1431]
The Beekeeper's Problem Solver [1463]

"Beekeepers Seek to Save Honeybees From a Colony-Invading Pest" in Smithsonian (September 30, 2019) [1464]
"Beekeeping 101: Should You Raise Honey Bees? The Pros and Cons of Keeping Bees" in The Old Farmer's Almanac (July 24, 2019) [1465]
Beekeeping: For Beginners and Backyard Business People [1466]
Beekeeping For Beginners: How to Raise Your First Bee Colonies [1467]
Beekeeping For Dummies [1468]
Beekeeping: Growing a Backyard Business with Bees [1469]
Beekeeping Industry in the US - Market Research Report [1490]
Beekeeping: Planning, Managing, and Keeping Bees [1470]
Beekeeping: The Business, Care, and Specifics of Handling Bees [1471]
Beekeeping: The Techniques, Benefits, and Drawbacks of Beekeeping Explained [1472]
Beekeeping: The Ultimate Beginner's Guide to Learn Managing Bees [1473]
Beekeeping: Understanding the Opportunities and Dangers of Keeping Bees [1474]
Beekeeping in the US - Industry Market Research Report [1491]
"Beep Fruit Drink Makes Comeback: Prodded by Fans, a Maritime Dairy Brings Back Retro Drink Beep" in Canadian Business (Vol. 85, August 13, 2012, No. 13, pp. 9) [17004], [20389], [29666]
Beer Associates, L.L.C. [14104]
Beer Canada [1888], [1955]
Beer Cans and Brewery Collectibles Magazine [3273]
Beer Distributors Secretaries of America [35485]
Beer Institute [1889]
Beer-Wells Real Estate Services Inc. [12914]
"Beermakers Are Experimenting With New - and Sustainable - Six-Pack Designs" in Fortune (September 2, 2019) [1903]
"Bees & Beekeeping: Past & Present" in American Bee Journal (November 1, 2021) [1475]
Bees in the D [1432]
Before & After: How to Design Cool Stuff [3342]
"Before Happiness: The 5 Hidden Keys to Achieving Success, Spreading Happiness, and Sustaining Positive Change" [22097], [28454]
Beginning Beekeeping: Everything You Need to Make Your Hive Thrive! [1476]
"Begslist.org Launches Crowdfunding On Its Website" in Computer Business Week (August 2, 2012) [22959], [28056], [30888], [35230]
Behavioral and Neural Biology [32904]
Behavioral Research in Accounting [107]
"Behind the Numbers: When It Comes to Earnings, Look for Quality, Not Just Quantity" in Black Enterprise (Vol. 38, July 2008, pp. 35) [6277], [9347], [17944], [23760]
"Being All a-Twitter" in Canadian Business (Vol. 81, December 8, 2008, No. 21, pp. 22) [240], [9102], [14760], [21796], [29667], [32474], [33831]
Being Realistic about Social Enterprise Growth [34415]
Belfast Area Chamber of Commerce (BACC) [40264]
Belgrade Chamber of Commerce (BCC) [41750]
Belhaven Community Chamber of Commerce [43090]
Bell County Chamber of Commerce [40017]
Bell Springs Publishing [37699]
Bell Techlogics [30993], [31062]
"The Bell Tolls for Thee" in Canadian Business (Vol. 81, March 3, 2008, No. 3, pp. 36) [21454], [26220], [26499], [33104]
Bellacino's Pizza and Grinders Inc. [12539]
Bellaire Chamber of Commerce [40858]
Bellaire/Southwest Houston Chamber of Commerce [45214]
Bellbrook-Sugarcreek Area Chamber of Commerce (BSACoC) [43412]
Belle Capital [41040]
Belle Glade Chamber of Commerce [38330]
Belle Impact Fund, LP [41041]
Belle Plaine Area Chamber of Commerce [39865]
Bellefonte Area Chamber of Commerce [44172]
Bellefonte Intervalley Area Chamber of Commerce (BIACC) [44172]
Belleville Area Chamber of Commerce (BACC) [40859]
Belleville Chamber of Commerce [39866]
Belleville Chamber of Commerce and Main Street [39866]
Belleville Economic Progress [39183]
Bellevue Area Chamber of Commerce [43413]
Bellevue Chamber of Commerce [46051]
"Bellevue Collection Collects 4 New Towers" in Puget Sound Business Journal (Vol. 35, May 16, 2014, No. 4, pp. 4) [8364], [12877], [13395]

Bellevue Master Index

Bellevue Harpeth Chamber of Commerce (BHCC) **[44714]**
Bellingham Angel Investors (BAI) **[35263]**, **[46185]**
"Bellingham Boatbuilder Norstar Yachts Maintains Family Tradition" in Bellingham Business Journal (Vol. February 2010, pp. 12) **[10598]**, **[19160]**, **[23598]**, **[29117]**
Bellingham/Whatcom Chamber of Commerce and Industry **[46052]**
Bellville Chamber of Commerce **[45046]**
Belmond Area Chamber of Commerce **[39716]**
Belmont-Central Chamber of Commerce (BCCC) **[39097]**
Belmont Chamber of Commerce **[36746]**
Belmont University Center for Entrepreneurship **[44854]**
Beloit Area Chamber of Commerce (BACC) **[39867]**
Belpre Area Chamber of Commerce (BACC) **[43414]**
Belron Canada Inc. (BCI) **[7502]**, **[10563]**
Belton Area Chamber of Commerce **[45047]**
Belton Chamber of Commerce (BCOC) **[41518]**
Belvidere Area Chamber of Commerce (BACC) **[39098]**
Belvidere Chamber of Commerce [39098]
Belzoni-Humphreys Development Foundation (BHDF) **[41383]**
Bemidji Area Chamber of Commerce (BACC) **[41194]**
Ben Franklin Technology Partners (BFTP) **[44332]**
Ben Franklin TechVentures (BFTV) **[44383]**
"Ben Hulse" in Canadian Business (Vol. 85, August 13, 2012, No. 13, pp. 55) **[3301]**, **[15138]**, **[31858]**
"Ben & Jerry's Changing Some 'All Natural' Labels" in Ice Cream Reporter (Vol. 23, October 20, 2010, No. 11, pp. 1) **[8005]**, **[8548]**
Ben & Jerry's Homemade, Inc. **[8610]**
"Ben & Jerry's Introduces 'Green' Freezer" in Ice Cream Reporter (Vol. 21, October 20, 2008, No. 11, pp. 1) **[5821]**, **[8549]**
Benaroya Capital Co. **[46186]**
Benaroya Research Institute at Virginia Mason (BRI) **[26105]**
Bench-Strength Mail Associates **[46856]**
Benchmark **[37306]**
Benchmark Capital **[37307]**
The Benchmark Co. **[13052]**, **[15621]**
"Benchmark Makes Granduca Entrance" in Houston Business Journal (Vol. 40, January 8, 2010, No. 35, pp. 2) **[8365]**, **[10480]**, **[17945]**, **[32973]**, **[33105]**
The Benchmarking Network, Inc. (TBN) **[20542]**
Bend Area Chamber of Commerce [43947]
Bend Chamber Business **[43946]**
Bend Chamber of Commerce (BCC) **[43947]**
The Benefit Capital Companies, Inc. (BCC) **[41954]**
Benefit Communications Inc. (BCI) **[17389]**
Benefit Partners Inc. **[17390]**, **[27122]**
"Benefits of Bartering" in Mail Tribune (November 22, 2010) **[17249]**, **[31195]**
Benefits Law Journal **[17381]**
Benefits Quarterly **[17382]**
Benetech Inc. **[17391]**
Bengston Business Forms Inc. **[2381]**
Benham REO Group **[13334]**
Benhamou Global Ventures (BGV) **[37308]**
Benicia Chamber of Commerce [36747]
Benicia Chamber of Commerce and Visitors' Center **[36747]**
Benihana Inc. [14221]
Benjamin Rose Library **[197]**
Bennington Area Chamber of Commerce (BACC) **[45718]**
Bennington County Industrial Corp. (BCIC) **[45746]**
Benson Area Chamber of Commerce (BACC) **[43091]**
Benson Chamber of Commerce [36314]
Benson/San Pedro Valley Chamber of Commerce **[36314]**
Bent County Chamber of Commerce **[37818]**
Bentley Miller Lights Inc. (BML) **[15622]**
Benton Area Chamber of Commerce **[36437]**
Benton Business Incubator **[46558]**
Benton City Chamber of Commerce **[46053]**
Benton County/Camden Chamber of Commerce **[44715]**
Benton-West City Area Chamber of Commerce **[39099]**
Bentonville-Bella Vista Chamber of Commerce **[36438]**
Benzie County Chamber of Commerce **[40860]**
BEQ [23571]
Berea, Ohio Chamber of Commerce **[43415]**
Beresford Chamber of Commerce (BCC) **[44635]**
Bergen Community College (BCC) **[42251]**
Bergen Community College Regional Accelerator **[42231]**
Bergen Small Business Development Center **[42034]**
Berkeley Chamber of Commerce **[36748]**
Berkeley County Chamber of Commerce [36748]
Berkeley International Capital Corp. [37309]
Berkeley Springs Chamber of Commerce [46263]
Berkeley Springs - Morgan County Chamber of Commerce (BSMCCC) **[46263]**
Berkeley VC International LLC (BICC) **[37309]**
Berkeley Ventures **[37547]**
Berklee College of Music - Stan Getz Library **[11209]**
Berkley Area Chamber of Commerce **[40861]**
Berkshire Botanical Garden (BBG) **[7657]**
Berlin Chamber of Commerce (BCC) **[40369]**
Berne Chamber of Commerce (BCC) **[39518]**
Bernie Shaeffer's Option Advisor **[9916]**
"Bernier Open to Telecom Changes" in Globe & Mail (March 22, 2006, pp. B1) **[25220]**, **[26221]**, **[33106]**
Berrien County Chamber of Commerce **[38695]**
Berry College Entrepreneurial Program **[38842]**
Berrybrook Farm Natural Food Pantry **[8075]**
Bertelsmann Digital Media Investments Inc. (BDMI) **[42722]**
"Bertha's Birth Stirs Juice" in Barron's (Vol. 88, July 14, 2008, No. 28, pp. M11) **[6278]**, **[7725]**, **[9348]**, **[17005]**, **[20755]**, **[23761]**
Berthel Fisher & Company Planning Inc. (BFCP) **[39812]**
Berthoud Area Chamber of Commerce **[37819]**
Berwyn Development Corp. (BCD) **[39100]**
Bessemer Area Chamber of Commerce (BACC) **[36083]**
Bessemer Business Incubation System (BBIS) **[36172]**
Bessemer Venture Partners (BVP) **[37310]**, **[37723]**, **[42723]**
Bessemer Venture Partners (BVP) **[40667]**
"Best Accounting Software for Small Business" in The Balance Small Business (Dec. 8, 2021) **[16785]**
"The Best (and Worst) Parts of Starting a Pet Grooming Business" in The Balance Small Business (July 28, 2019) **[12084]**
"Best April Fools' Day Brand Pranks" in Business News Daily (March 21, 2023) **[17433]**
"Best Baby Clothing Stores of 2019" in Babylist (January 1, 2019) **[2844]**, **[11712]**
"The Best Bar in N.J. is a Semi-Swanky Cocktail Lounge That Serves Some of the Best Food in the Region" in NJ.com (June 27. 2019) **[1318]**, **[42258]**
"The Best Bars in America, 2019" in Esquire (June 6, 2019) **[1319]**
"Best of the Best: 20 Business-to-Business Examples to Check Out" in Disruptive Advertising (March 17, 2020) **[19241]**, **[29668]**
Best Books for Kids and Teens (BBKT) **[1613]**
"Best of Breed" in Barron's (Vol. 92, September 17, 2012, No. 38, pp. 24) **[9349]**, **[18900]**
"The Best Business Accounting Software Services of 2023" in Business News Daily (March 9, 2023) **[16786]**, **[33832]**
"Best Business Books of All Time" in Small Business Trends(November 23, 2020) **[16547]**
Best Business Ideas for Aging Population - 60 TOP Ideas **[33064]**
"Best Business Loans for 2023" in Business News Daily (February 24, 2023) **[20251]**
"The Best Business Translation Services" in Business News Daily (January 23, 2019) **[15933]**
"The Best in Business Travel" in Entrepreneur (May 2014) **[8366]**, **[15985]**, **[16394]**, **[19333]**
"Best Businesses for Retirees to Start" in ZenBusiness Blog (Aug. 11, 2021) **[33065]**
"The Best Candy Store in Every State" in Insider (August 9, 2019) **[2541]**
Best Cannabis Marketing Guide **[4988]**, **[29669]**
"Best Cash Flow Generators" in Canadian Business (Vol. 82, Summer 2009, No. 8, pp. 40) **[6279]**, **[9350]**, **[17946]**, **[19334]**, **[23762]**
"Best Credit Card Processing Companies of 2023" in Business News Daily (February 24,2023) **[4710]**
Best Credit and Collections Software for Small Businesses **[20252]**
"Best CRM Software of 2023" in Business News Daily (February 28, 2023) **[20390]**
"Best Days and Weekends to Shop for Clothing" in U.S. News and World Report (April 23, 2018) **[3090]**, **[11713]**, **[32946]**
"Best Desktop Publishing Software of 2019" in Top Ten Reviews (January 8, 2019) **[4936]**
Best Distribution Channels for Small Businesses **[20613]**
"The Best-Dressed Windows and How to Get Them" in The New York Times (August 6, 2019) **[16522]**
"The Best Five-Month Run Since 1938" in Barron's (Vol. 89, August 3, 2009, No. 31, pp. M3) **[6280]**, **[9351]**, **[15582]**, **[23763]**
"Best Foot Forward" in Canadian Business (Vol. 80, October 22, 2007, No. 21, pp. 115) **[2180]**, **[20088]**, **[21455]**
"Best Free PowerShell Training Resources" in Business News Daily (March 16, 2023) **[3609]**
"The Best Grants for Women-Owned Businesses" in Nav Blog (June 2, 2022) **[35743]**
"Best In Show" in Pet Product News (Vol. 64, November 2010, No. 11, pp. 20) **[689]**, **[11333]**, **[12189]**, **[20391]**
"Best Internet Marketing Services for Small Businesses--2020" in Inc. **[27806]**
"Best iPhone Apps to Manage Your Business Contacts" in Business News Daily (February 21, 2023) **[33833]**
"Best Layoff Practices: Can You Lay Off and Hire at the Same Time?" in Business News Daily (March 7, 2023) **[26500]**, **[26883]**
"The Best Marketing Strategy for Private Tutors and Tutoring Centers" in Bookshelf PH blog (March 30, 2022) **[16129]**
"The Best Online Fax Services of 2023" in Business News Daily (March 17, 2023) **[17638]**
"Best Online Stores for Personal Electronics" in Money Crashers **[4386]**, **[11714]**
"The Best Option for All" in American Executive (Vol. 7, September 2009, No. 5, pp. 170) **[4739]**, **[4770]**, **[17278]**, **[18901]**, **[20253]**
"The Best Organic Marketing Strategies for Small Business" in TechRadar (Jan. 6, 2022) **[29670]**
"Best Payroll Services for 2023" in Business News Daily (March 6, 2023) **[11928]**
"Best Payroll Software for Small Businesses" in NerdWallet (April 9, 2018) **[11929]**, **[31627]**
The Best Phone Systems for Small Business **[17639]**
"Best Places to Work; No. 2 Tasty Catering Inc." in Crain's Chicago Business (Vole 35, April 2, 2012, No. 14, pp. 18) **[2669]**, **[11903]**, **[22499]**
"Best Practices: Developing a Rewards Program" in Franchising World (Vol. 42, September 2010, No. 9, pp. 13) **[17279]**, **[24337]**
Best Practices in Java Programming: Hands-On (Onsite) **[21338]**
"Best Practices for Labeling Infused Products" in Cannabis Business Executive (May 1, 2020) **[4989]**
Best Practices for Managing Inventories and Cycle Counts (Onsite) **[27988]**
Best Practices for the Multi-project Manager **[28296]**
Best Practices for Safe Food Delivery, Take Out **[6900]**
"Best (Professional) Foot Forward: Effective Marketing Strategies for any Phase of Your Career" in Black Enterprise (Vol. 44, June 2014, No. 10, pp. 44) **[26501]**, **[26884]**, **[28455]**
"The Best Roller Skates, According to Roller Skaters" in New York Magazine (August 9, 2019) **[14719]**
Best in Show Consulting L.L.C. **[12104]**
Best Small Business Credit Cards for Travel Rewards 2020 **[19335]**
"The Best Small Business Government Grants in 2022" in Business News Daily (Dec. 20, 2021) **[24948]**
"The Best Small Business Government Grants in 2023" in Business News Daily (February 21, 2023) **[47970]**
Best Small Business Ideas for Bike Shops **[1518]**
The Best Small Business Podcast: Co-Opetition - Growing Your Small Business with Unexpected Competitive Alliances **[19974]**
The Best Small Business Podcast: Decision Velocity - How to Make Tough Decisions **[24783]**
The Best Small Business Podcast: The Best Time for a Tech Refresh **[33925]**
The Best Small Business Show: 4 Critical Pre-Sale Tools You Ned to Get More Clients **[32677]**
The Best Small Business Show: 4 Easy Ways to Stand Out **[24784]**
The Best Small Business Show: 4 Steps to Dramatically Increase Your Profits **[24201]**
The Best Small Business Show: 4 Things to Keep in Mind When Starting Your Own Business **[16620]**
The Best Small Business Show: Are You Entrepreneurship Material? **[22877]**
The Best Small Business Show: Boost Your Video Presence **[30148]**
The Best Small Business Show: Brand Awareness - Collaboration Is Key **[17460]**
The Best Small Business Show: Business Fears - What Do You Do If You Lose Your Biggest Client? **[24785]**
The Best Small Business Show: Business Fears - What Happens If You Get Sick? **[24786]**
The Best Small Business Show: Business Fears - What If You Lose Your Best Employee? **[27097]**
The Best Small Business Show: Business Fears - What If Your Industry Is Slowly Going Out of Business? **[24787]**
The Best Small Business Show: Choose the Right Product Mix to Get the Best Clients **[24788]**
The Best Small Business Show: Closing the Sale - You're Doing It All Wrong **[32678]**
The Best Small Business Show: Content Is King - Delivering on Your Company's Message **[17461]**
The Best Small Business Show: Delighting Your Customers - Taking the Customer Experience to the Next Level **[20537]**
The Best Small Business Show: Enhancing Your Lead Generation **[16621]**, **[30149]**
The Best Small Business Show: Finding Your Best Clients **[24789]**

3190 Small Business Sourcebook • 42nd Edition

Master Index Better

The Best Small Business Show: Fortified Bytes - Cybersecurity on a Small Business Budget **[16622]**
The Best Small Business Show: Friction - The Expectation of Seamless Customer Experiences **[20538]**
The Best Small Business Show: Go Back 10 Years - What Would You Do Differently? **[24790]**
The Best Small Business Show: How to Better Communicate with Your Audience **[24791]**
The Best Small Business Show: How to Gain a Competitive Advantage Over Your Competition **[19975]**
The Best Small Business Show: How to Hire Your First Employee **[16623]**
The Best Small Business Show: If You Own a Business, You're a Salesperson **[22878]**
The Best Small Business Show: Increasing Your Brand Awareness **[17462]**
The Best Small Business Show: Is Your Business Becoming Obsolete? **[24792]**
The Best Small Business Show: Keeping a Watchful Eye on Your Vendors **[24793]**
The Best Small Business Show: Make Friends with Your Business Financials **[24202]**
The Best Small Business Show: Mangers with Empathy Are the Best Leaders **[27098]**
The Best Small Business Show: Organize Your Business with SDR Methods **[24794]**
The Best Small Business Show: Pricing Your Company Out of Business - When to Stop Raising Prices **[31660]**
The Best Small Business Show: Raise Your Rates without Losing Customers **[31661]**
The Best Small Business Show: Securing Success - Why Insurance Matters for Your Small Business **[27362]**
The Best Small Business Show: Six Books That Will Explode Your Business **[16624]**
The Best Small Business Show: Take Charge of Your Brand CV **[17463]**
The Best Small Business Show: The Best Ways to Network and Grow Your Business **[24795]**
The Best Small Business Show: They're Fooling You - The Entrepreneurship Myth **[22879]**
The Best Small Business Show: Top 4 Business Books You Should Be Reading **[24796]**
The Best Small Business Show: Top 4 Business Tools You Should Be Using **[24797]**
The Best Small Business Show: We All Can Fail - It's What You Do After **[24798]**
The Best Small Business Show: What to Do When Technology Fails You **[33926]**
The Best Small Business Show: When Major Shifts Need to Happen in Your Business **[24799]**
The Best Small Business Show: Why Did You Lose that Client? **[24800]**
The Best Small Business Show: Why Getting Started Is More Important than Succeeding **[24801]**
"The Best Tattoo Machines for Beginners" in DaySmart Body Art blog (Oct. 4, 2022) **[15295]**
"The Best Text Message Marketing Services of 2023" in Business News Daily (March 22, 2023) **[17640]**, **[29671]**
"The Best Time and Attendance Software of 2023" in Business News Daily (March 9, 2023) **[33834]**
"Best Turnaround Stocks" in Canadian Business (Vol. 81, Summer 2008, No. 9, pp. 65) **[6281]**, **[9352]**, **[17947]**, **[20254]**, **[20756]**, **[23764]**, **[28101]**, **[29118]**
"Best UI & UX Design Agencies for Startups and Small Businesses in 2020" in Digital Agency Network (July 26, 2020) **[16395]**
"Best Value Stocks" in Canadian Business (Vol. 81, Summer 2008, No. 9, pp. 63) **[6282]**, **[9353]**, **[17948]**, **[20757]**, **[23765]**
The Best Video Conferencing Equipment for 2022 **[31030]**
"Best Web Design of 2020 (So Far) - And What We Can Learn From It" in DesignRush (October 2, 2020) **[16396]**
Best's Review **[8986]**
Best's Statement File - Life/Health - United States **[2166]**
Betamore **[40441]**
Betaworks Studio L.L.C. **[43014]**
"BETC Backers Plot Future" in Business Journal Portland (Vol. 27, December 10, 2010, No. 41, pp. 1) **[5541]**, **[5822]**, **[23115]**, **[24949]**, **[25221]**, **[26502]**, **[26885]**, **[29119]**, **[34740]**
Bethany-Fenwick Area Chamber of Commerce **[38131]**
Bethel Area Chamber of Commerce (BACC) **[40265]**
Bethel Chamber of Commerce **[38028]**
Bethel Island Chamber of Commerce **[36749]**
Bethesda-Chevy Chase Chamber of Commerce [40387]
"Bethesda Firm Aims to Revitalize Hat Chain Lids" in Washington Business Journal (March 15, 2019) **[7934]**, **[20392]**, **[31196]**
Bethlehem Chamber of Commerce **[42521]**
Bethlehem Chamber of Commerce [41985]
Bethlehem Visitors Center **[41985]**
"Betsey Johnson Falls Out of Fashion" in Canadian Business (Vol. 85, June 11, 2012, No. 10, pp. 14) **[3008]**, **[3091]**, **[23766]**
"Better than Advertised: Chip Plant Beats Expectations" in Business Review Albany (Vol. 41, June 27, 2014, No. 14, pp. 4) **[3697]**, **[3997]**, **[20758]**, **[26503]**, **[29120]**, **[31940]**
Better Business Bureau [39510], [45825]
Better Business Bureau of Abilene **[45010]**
Better Business Bureau of Akron **[43394]**
Better Business Bureau of Alaska, Oregon and Western Washington [36217], [37810], [38870], [38904], [41746], [43934], [46043], [46596]
Better Business Bureau of Amarillo, Texas **[45011]**
Better Business Bureau of Arkansas **[36431]**
Better Business Bureau of Asheville/Western North Carolina **[43075]**
Better Business Bureau of Atlantic Provinces **[46733]**, **[46742]**, **[46746]**, **[46879]**
Better Business Bureau, Birmingham [36075]
Better Business Bureau, Catawba and Lincoln Counties [43077]
Better Business Bureau of Central California **[36711]**
Better Business Bureau of Central Canada **[46723]**, **[46749]**, **[46769]**, **[46915]**
Better Business Bureau of Central East Texas (BBB CET) **[45012]**
Better Business Bureau of Central and Eastern Iowa [39708]
Better Business Bureau of Central and Eastern Kentucky **[40013]**
Better Business Bureau of Central Florida **[38316]**
Better Business Bureau of Central Georgia [38679]
Better Business Bureau of Central Illinois **[39083]**
Better Business Bureau of Central Indiana **[39510]**
Better Business Bureau of Central Louisiana [40144]
Better Business Bureau of Central Louisiana and the Ark-La-Tex **[40144]**
Better Business Bureau of Central New England [40554]
Better Business Bureau Central and Northern Alberta **[46659]**
Better Business Bureau - Central, Northern and Western Arizona **[36304]**
Better Business Bureau of Central Ohio **[43395]**
Better Business Bureau of Central Oklahoma **[43728]**
Better Business Bureau of Central Virginia **[45822]**
Better Business Bureau of Chicago and Northern Illinois **[39084]**
Better Business Bureau of the Coastal Bend [45013]
Better Business Bureau of Coastal Carolina **[44532]**
Better Business Bureau of Coastal Empire [38317]
Better Business Bureau of Connecticut **[38026]**
Better Business Bureau Corpus Christi **[45013]**
Better Business Bureau of Dayton/Miami Valley **[43396]**
Better Business Bureau of Delaware **[38130]**
Better Business Bureau of Denver/Boulder **[37809]**
Better Business Bureau of Detroit and Eastern Michigan **[40846]**
Better Business Bureau of Eastern Missouri and Southern Illinois **[41509]**
Better Business Bureau of Eastern North Carolina **[43076]**
Better Business Bureau Education Foundation of the Heart of Texas [45015]
Better Business Bureau of the Golden Gate and Northern California [36714]
Better Business Bureau Great West + Pacific **[36217]**, **[37810]**, **[38870]**, **[38904]**, **[41746]**, **[43934]**, **[46043]**, **[46596]**
Better Business Bureau - Greater Cleveland **[43397]**
Better Business Bureau of Greater East Tennessee **[44706]**
Better Business Bureau of Greater Hampton Roads **[45823]**
Better Business Bureau of Greater Houston and South Texas **[45014]**
Better Business Bureau of Greater Iowa - Quad Cities and Siouxland Region **[39708]**
Better Business Bureau of Greater Kansas City **[41510]**
Better Business Bureau of Greater Maryland **[40363]**
Better Business Bureau of Greater Toronto Area (BBB) **[46770]**
Better Business Bureau serving the Heart of Texas **[45015]**
Better Business Bureau of the Inland Northwest **[46044]**
Better Business Bureau of Los Angeles and Silicon Valley (BBBLASV) **[36712]**
Better Business Bureau of Louisville, Southern Indiana and Western Kentucky **[40014]**
Better Business Bureau of Mahoning Valley **[43398]**
Better Business Bureau of Mainland British Columbia (BBB) **[46692]**
Better Business Bureau of Manitoba [46724]
Better Business Bureau of Manitoba and Nortwest Ontario **[46724]**
Better Business Bureau of Metro Atlanta, Athens and Northeast Georgia **[38678]**
Better Business Bureau of Metropolitan New York **[42505]**
Better Business Bureau of the Mid-South **[44707]**
Better Business Bureau of Middle Tennessee **[44708]**
Better Business Bureau of Midwest Plains **[39856]**
Better Business Bureau of Midwest Plains - Lincoln **[41832]**
Better Business Bureau of Midwest Plains - Omaha **[41833]**
Better Business Bureau of Midwest Plains - Wichita Falls **[39857]**, **[41511]**
Better Business Bureau of Minnesota and North Dakota (BBB) **[41183]**
Better Business Bureau of Mississippi **[41381]**
Better Business Bureau of New Hampshire **[41984]**
Better Business Bureau of New Jersey (BBB) **[42098]**
Better Business Bureau of New York - Long Island Office **[42506]**
Better Business Bureau of New York - Mid-Hudson Region Office **[42507]**
Better Business Bureau of Newfoundland and Labrador [46733], [46742], [46746], [46879]
Better Business Bureau of North Alabama **[36074]**
Better Business Bureau of North Central Texas **[45016]**
Better Business Bureau of Northeast California **[36713]**
Better Business Bureau of Northeast Florida and the Southeast Atlantic **[38317]**
Better Business Bureau of Northeast Louisiana **[40145]**
Better Business Bureau of Northern Colorado and Wyoming **[37811]**
Better Business Bureau of Northern Indiana **[39511]**
Better Business Bureau of Northwest Florida **[38318]**
Better Business Bureau - Northwest and West Central Ohio and Southeast Michigan **[40847]**, **[43399]**
Better Business Bureau, Oregon/Western Washington [36217], [37810], [38870], [38904], [41746], [43934], [46043], [46596]
Better Business Bureau of Ottawa [46771]
Better Business Bureau, Phoenix [36304]
Better Business Bureau of St. Paul [41183]
Better Business Bureau of San Angelo **[45017]**
Better Business Bureau of San Antonio, TX **[45018]**
Better Business Bureau of San Mateo County **[36714]**
Better Business Bureau Serving Acadiana **[40146]**
Better Business Bureau Serving Central, Coastal, Southwest Texas & Permian Basin - Austin Office **[45019]**
Better Business Bureau Serving Central & South Alabama - Birmingham Office **[36075]**
Better Business Bureau Serving Central and South Alabama - Mobile Office **[36076]**
Better Business Bureau Serving Central South Carolina and Charleston Area **[44533]**
Better Business Bureau Serving Central and Western Massachusetts and Northeastern Connecticut **[40554]**
Better Business Bureau Serving Eastern Massachusetts, Maine, Rhode Island and Vermont (BBB) **[40555]**
Better Business Bureau Serving Eastern Massachusetts, Maine and Vermont [40555]
Better Business Bureau Serving Eastern, Northern Ontario and the Outaouais **[46771]**
Better Business Bureau Serving the Fall Line Corridor, Inc. **[38679]**
Better Business Bureau Serving Metro Washington DC and Eastern Pennsylvania **[38163]**
Better Business Bureau Serving New Mexico and Southwestern Colorado **[42298]**
Better Business Bureau Serving Southern Alberta & East Kootenay (BBB) **[46660]**
Better Business Bureau of Serving Southern Arizona (BBB) **[36305]**
Better Business Bureau Serving Utah **[45624]**
Better Business Bureau of South Alabama [36076]
Better Business Bureau of South Central Louisiana **[40147]**
Better Business Bureau of South Central Ontario **[46772]**
Better Business Bureau of South Jersey [42098]
Better Business Bureau Southeast Atlantic [38317]
Better Business Bureau of Southeast Tennessee and Northwest Georgia **[44709]**
Better Business Bureau of Southeast Texas **[45020]**
Better Business Bureau of Southern Alberta [46660]
Better Business Bureau of Southern Colorado, Inc. **[37812]**
Better Business Bureau of Southern Nevada **[41927]**
Better Business Bureau of Southern Piedmont **[43077]**
Better Business Bureau of the Southland [36716]
Better Business Bureau of Southwest Louisiana **[40148]**

Master Index

Small Business Sourcebook • 42nd Edition 3191

Better Business Bureau of Southwest Missouri [41512]
Better Business Bureau of Tri-Counties [36715]
Better Business Bureau of Upstate New York (BBB) [42508]
Better Business Bureau of Upstate South Carolina [44534]
Better Business Bureau of Vancouver Island (BBB) [46693]
Better Business Bureau of West Central Ohio [40847], [43399]
Better Business Bureau of West Florida [38319]
Better Business Bureau of West Georgia - East Alabama [38680]
Better Business Bureau of Western Michigan [40848]
Better Business Bureau of Western Ontario (BBB) [46773]
Better Business Bureau of Western Pennsylvania (BBB) [44166]
Better Business Bureau of Western Virginia [45824]
Better Business Bureau, Wichita Falls [45016]
Better Business Bureau of Wisconsin [46356]
Better Business Bureau · Wise Giving Alliance [19249]
Better Business Writing [17886]
"A Better-For-You Grocery Pops Up in NYC" in Supermarket News (September 20, 2019) [8006]
Better Hiring Strategies for Your Small Business with Dana Kaye [27099]
Better Investing [2149]
"Better Made's Better Idea: Diversify Despite Rising Costs" in Crain's Detroit Business (Vol. 24, September 22, 2008, No. 38, pp. 18) [7726], [17949], [18902], [19486], [20759], [29121], [30683], [32475]
"Better ROI Or Your Money Back, Says Buzz Agency" in Advertising Age (Vol. 79, July 14, 2008, No. 7, pp. 1) [241], [29672], [31748], [31859]
A Better Solution Inc. (ABS) [8281]
"Better Than New Runs on Tried-and-True Model" in Bellingham Business Journal (Vol. February 2010, pp. 16) [242], [3092], [6124], [23599], [29673], [32104]
"'Better Together:' OCO LPA Executives Discuss Recent Merger" in San Antonio Business Journal (Vol. 28, July 4, 2014, No. 21, pp. 8) [873], [3998], [13145], [13396]
"A Better Way to Tax U.S. Businesses" in (Vol. 90, July-August 2012, No. 7-8, pp. 134) [6283], [9354], [15367], [23767], [27465], [34741]
Betterway Books [43697]
"Betting Big, Winning Big: Interview With Bruce Berkowitz, CEO of Fairholme Capital Management" in Barron's (Vol. 88, March 17, 2008, No. 11, pp. 49) [6284], [9355], [23768]
"Betting on a Happy Ending" in Barron's (Vol. 88, July 7, 2008, No. 27, pp. 14) [6285], [9356], [15583], [23769]
"Betting On Spec" in San Antonio Business Journal (Vol. 28, April 25, 2014, No. 11, pp. 4) [13146], [13397], [33346]
"Betting On Volatile Materials" in Barron's (Vol. 88, July 14, 2008, No. 28, pp. M11) [6286], [8689], [9357], [20760], [23770], [27466], [29122]
"Between the Lines: Intangible Assets" in Canadian Business (Vol. 79, July 17, 2006, No. 14-15, pp. 17) [6287], [9358], [17950], [19487]
Between Rounds Bakery Sandwich Cafe [1218]
Beulah Chamber of Commerce (BCC) [43286]
Beveridge and Diamond P.C. [5763]
Beverly Hills Chamber of Commerce [36750]
Beverly Hyman Ph.D. & Associates (BHA) [17801]
Beverly Kay Laundry Consulting and Training Services [10191]
Bevill State Business Incubator Center [36173]
Bevinco [1370], [10341], [28020]
"Beware the Amateur Gunsmith" in Ammoland (January 30, 2019) [7832]
"Beware this Chinese Export" in Barron's (Vol. 90, August 30, 2010, No. 35, pp. 21) [6288], [8690], [9359], [27467], [31197]
"Beware of Credit 'Repair' Companies, Consumer Watchdogs Say" in The New York Times (May 10 2019) [4740], [23469]
"Beware of E15 Gasoline" in Rental Product News (Vol. 33, October 2011) [5542], [5823], [13770], [23116], [25222]
"Beware the Hotspot: How You're Vulnerable" in Philadelphia Business Journal (Vol. 33, June 13, 2014, No. 18, pp. 7) [9103], [14391]
"Beware of Rotting Money" in Barron's (Vol. 89, July 13, 2009, No. 28, pp. 31) [6289], [9360], [20761], [23771], [25223]
Bexley Area Chamber of Commerce (BACC) [43416]
Beyer Business Solutions Inc. [3780]
Beyond Booked Solid: Your Business, Your Life, Your Way-It's All Inside [17951], [20393], [33107]
"Beyond Bootstrapping" in Inc. (Vol. 36, September 2014, No. 7, pp. 64) [22368], [23691], [28057]

"Beyond the Food Truck: 10 Unique Mobile Businesses" in Entrepreneur (June 6, 2013) [30463]
"Beyond Green – Ways to Make Your Business More Sustainable in 2022" in Success Consciousness [23117]
"Beyond Grits: The Many Varieties of Southern Cuisine" in Women In Business (Vol. 62, June 2010, No. 2, pp. 14) [4463], [13909]
"Beyond Meat (R) Completes Largest Financing Round to Date" in Ecology, Environment & Conservation Business (August 16, 2014, pp. 4) [5543], [5824], [8007], [9361], [23118], [29123]
"Beyond Microsoft and Yahoo!: Some M&A Prospects" in Barron's (Vol. 88, March 17, 2008, No. 11, pp. 39) [6290], [9362], [14761], [23772], [26222], [31198], [33835]
"Beyond Repair" in Business First Buffalo (Vol. 28, March 23, 2012, No. 27, pp. 1) [8245], [25719], [34742]
Beyond Venture Capital: 4 Alternative Financing Strategies [30912]
"Beyond Zipcar: Collaborative Consumption" in Harvard Business Review (Vol. 88, October 2010, No. 10, pp. 30) [27993], [31199]
BGP - Configuring BGP on Cisco Routers (Onsite) [26188]
BIA/Kelsey [22027], [30180]
"Biblical Secrets to Business Success" [20394], [22098], [22500], [23470]
Bibliography of the History of Art [986]
Bicycle Stamps Club (BSC) [3218]
Biddeford Saco Chamber of Commerce and Industry (BSCCI) [40266]
"Bidding On Airport Terminal is Big Job In Itself" in Wichita Business Journal (Vol. 27, February 10, 2012, No. 6, pp. 1) [3999], [19336]
Bienenstock Furniture Library (BFL) [7253], [9072]
"Bienvenido, Mercadito" in Washington Business Journal (Vol. 33, September 12, 2014, No. 21, pp. 8) [13910], [23600], [31200]
Big 2Go (B2G) [28956], [30631]
Big Apple Bagels (BAB) [1219], [14124]
Big Basin Capital [37724]
Big Bear Chamber of Commerce [36751]
Big Bend Community College (BBCC) [46229]
Big Bend Region Minority & Small Business Development Center [44907]
Big Bend Small Business Development Center [44907]
"Big Bling: Signet Acquires Zales Corporation" in Dallas Business Journal (Vol. 37, June 6, 2014, No. 39, pp. 6) [9972], [31201]
"Big Data at Work: Dispelling the Myths, Uncovering the Opportunities" [3484], [3610], [20395]
"Big Deals With More To Come" in Business Journal Portland (Vol. 30, January 24, 2014, No. 47, pp. 14) [28102], [31202]
"A Big Dream That 'Was Going Nowhere'" in Globe & Mail (February 4, 2006, pp. B4) [18903], [19488], [30684]
The Big Enough Approach to Entrepreneurship with Lee LeFever [22880]
"Big Gains Brewing at Anheuser-Busch InBev" in Barron's (Vol. 90, August 30, 2010, No. 35, pp. 34) [1320], [1904], [6291], [9363], [31203]
Big I Michigan [27220]
"The Big Idea: No, Management Is Not a Profession" in Harvard Business Review (Vol. 88, July-August 2010, No. 7-8, pp. 52) [21456], [24607], [28456]
"The Big Idea: The Case for Professional Boards" in Harvard Business Review (Vol. 88, December 2010, No. 12, pp. 50) [24608], [28457]
"The Big Idea: The Judgment Deficit" in Harvard Business Review (Vol. 88, September 2010, No. 9, pp. 44) [6292], [9364], [20762], [23773]
Big Lake Chamber of Commerce [45048]
Big Lake Chamber of Commerce (BLCC) [41195]
Big O Tires Inc. [14576], [15688]
"Big Oil: Picks and Pans" in Canadian Business (Vol. 79, August 14, 2006, No. 16-17, pp. 67) [6293], [9365], [20763]
The Big Payback: The History of the Business of Hip-Hop [11260], [13653], [22501], [30538], [31204], [32105], [35488]
Big Picture Framing [12709]
The Big Pitch: Professional, Concise, and Attention-Grabbing with Billion-Dollar Funder Suneera Madhan [17464]
Big Rapids Chamber of Commerce [40972]
Big Red Ventures [43015]
Big Sky Economic Development (BSED) [41728], [41802]
Big Spring Area Chamber of Commerce (BSACC) [45049]
Big Stone Lake Area Chamber of Commerce (BSLACC) [41196]

The Big Switch: Rewiring the World, from Edison to Google [3485], [21797], [26223], [33955]
"Big Tax Breaks for Small Businesses" in Legal Zoom (March 23, 2023) [16548], [34743]
Big Town Hero (BTH) [1220], [4891]
"Big Trouble at Sony Ericsson" in Barron's (Vol. 88, March 24, 2008, No. 12, pp. M9) [2718], [6294], [9366], [23774], [31205], [32476], [33108], [34744]
Biga & Associates Inc. [20228]
Bigel Institute for Health Policy [26107]
Bigfork Area Chamber of Commerce (BACC) [41751]
A Bigger Bottom Line LLC [1781], [16869]
"Biggest Caribbean Resort Operator Seeks to Get 'IPO Ready'" in Bloomberg (September 3, 2019) [8367]
"'Biggest Loser' Adds Bit of Muscle to Local Economy" in Crain's Detroit Business (Vol. 26, January 4, 2010, No. 1, pp. 1) [12407], [15584], [20764], [33546]
Bijan International Inc. [27123]
"Bike Company Sharing More Than Pedal Power: Long Beach To Get Some of Bike Nation's Profits; L.A. Might, Too" in Los Angeles Business Journal (Vol. 34, September 3, 2012, No. 36, pp. 12) [1519], [10014]
"'Bill Feinberg on Building the Model of Success - 'Strive for 100 Percent Satisfaction'" in South Florida Business Journal (Vol. 34, June 27, 2014, No. 49, pp. 13) [4000], [22502], [34275]
"Bill to Roll Back Banking Regulations Faces Tough Odds" in San Antonio Business Journal (Vol. 28, April 18, 2014, No. 10, pp. 6) [23775], [25224]
Billboard Connection (BC) [390]
Billiard and Bowling Institute of America (BBIA) [1533], [1870]
Billiard Congress of America (BCA) [1534]
Billiards Digest [1540]
Billings Area Chamber of Commerce [41752]
Billings SCORE [41736]
Billings Small Business Development Center [41718]
A Billion-Dollar CEO's #1 Fundraiisng Tip [24203]
"Billion-Dollar Impact: Nonprofit Sector is Economic Powerhouse" in Business First Buffalo (November 12, 2007, pp. 1) [24609], [34276]
"Bills Raise Blues Debate: An Unfair Edge or Level Playing Field?" in Crain's Detroit Business (Vol. 24, January 21, 2008, No. 3) [8891], [17280], [25225], [27242], [34745]
"Bills Would Regulate Mortgage Loan Officers" in Crain's Detroit Business (Vol. 24, February 25, 2008, No. 8, pp. 9) [11013], [13147], [13398], [18522], [25226]
Biloxi Chamber of Commerce [41384]
Biltmore Ventures [36422]
"BIM: What to Watch Out For" in Contractor (Vol. 57, February 2010, No. 2, pp. 28) [18523], [28458]
"BIM and You: Know Its Benefits and Risks" in Contractor (Vol. 57, January 2010, No. 1, pp. 46) [4001], [5365], [12617], [14610], [18524]
Bimen Business Consultants Ltd. [2218]
Binding Industries of America [1715]
Binding Industries Association (BIA) [1715]
Binding Industries Association of America [1715]
Binghamton Small Business Development Center (SBDC) [42392]
Binghamton University - Southern Tier High Technology Incubator (STHTI) [42840]
Binghamton University - Start-Up Suite [42841]
Bio-Integral Resource Center (BIRC) [12069]
Bio-Technical Resources L.P. (BTR) [1953], [2219], [20160], [32927]
BioAdvance [44333]
BioBM Consulting Inc. [44433]
BioChem Technology Inc. [2220], [20161], [32928]
Biochemistry and Cell Biology [32856]
"Biodiesel Poised to Regain Growth" in Farm Industry News (January 21, 2011) [5544], [5825], [17006], [17952], [23119], [30685], [33956], [34746]
BioEnterprise [43649]
BioGenerator (BG) [41658]
BioHealth Innovation Inc. (BHI) [40442]
"Bioheat - Alternative for Fueling Equipment" in Indoor Comfort Marketing (Vol. 70, May 2011, No. 5, pp. 14) [472], [5545], [5826], [23120], [29674], [33957]
BioHouston [45497]
BioInnovations Gateway (BIG) [45677]
Biological Control [12050]
Biomanufacturing Tech Hubs [32915]
Biomedical Instrumentation & Technology (BI&T) [10861]
Biomedical Management Resources (BMR) [19128], [28957], [31605], [33648]
Biomedical Research Foundation (BRF) [40213]
Biomedical Science Consulting Company, Inc. [2221], [2382], [10508], [20162], [26082]
BioPed Footcare Centres [10884]
Biopolymers [32857]
BioQUEST Library [5755]

"BioRASI Aims to Fill Larger HQ With More Jobs" in South Florida Business Journal (Vol. 34, April 11, 2014, N. 38, pp. 4) [26504], [31941], [32727]
BioSciCon, Inc. [2221], [2382], [10508], [20162], [26082]
"Bioscience Hiring Flat in Florida" in South Florida Business Journal (Vol. 34, July 4, 2014, No. 50, pp. 8) [26505], [31942], [32728]
BioSource Consulting [43900]
BioSquare [40745]
BioStar Capital [41042]
"Biotech Reels In $120M for 1Q" in Philadelphia Business Journal (Vol. 31, March 30, 2012, No. 7, pp. 1) [9367], [10912], [26224], [35322]
Biotechnology Advances: Research Reviews [32858]
Biotechnology & Bioengineering [32859]
Biotechnology Commercialization Center (BCC) [45498]
"Biotechnology Wants a Lead Role" in Business North Carolina (Vol. 28, March 2008, No. 3, pp. 14) [25720], [26225], [31943], [32729]
"Biotechs Are Using Back Door to Go Public" in Boston Business Journal (Vol. 31, May 27, 2011, No. 18, pp. 1) [9368], [26226], [31206], [33958]
"Biovail Hits SAC With $4.6 Billion Suit" in Globe & Mail (February 23, 2006, pp. B1) [9369], [18525], [23471]
BioVentures [36512]
BioVentures Investors [40668]
Birch Bay Chamber of Commerce [46054]
Birch Hill Equity Partners [46778]
Birch Run Area Chamber of Commerce [40862]
Birch Run Chamber of Commerce [40862]
Birchfield Jacobs Foodsystems Inc. [2222], [8117], [20163]
Birchmere Ventures [44334]
"Birdcage Optimization" in Pet Product News (Vol. 64, November 2010, No. 11, pp. 54) [12160], [29124], [32106], [33959]
Birenbaum & Associates [34683]
Birmingham Angels [41043]
Birmingham-Bloomfield Chamber of Commerce (BBCC) [40863]
Birmingham Botanical Gardens Library [7658], [10143]
Birmingham Business Alliance (BBA) [36084]
Birmingham Business Journal Inc. (BBJ) [36198]
Birmingham Business Resource Center (BBRC) [36158]
"Birmingham Tech Firms Eye Growth in 2014" in Birmingham Business Journal (Vol. 31, January 10, 2014, No. 2, pp. 4) [17953], [26227], [26506]
"Birmingham's Turf War" in Birmingham Business Journal (Vol. 31, January 24, 2014, No. 4, pp. 4) [19784], [24950], [34747]
Bishop Area Chamber of Commerce and Visitors Bureau [36752]
Bishop Chamber of Commerce [36752]
Bishop, Texas Chamber of Commerce [45050]
Bismarck Area Chamber of Commerce [43287]
Bismarck-Mandan Chamber of Commerce [43287]
Bison Capital Asset Management [37311]
"Bitcoin 'Killer App' Or the Currency of the Future?" in Providence Business News (Vol. 28, January 6, 2014, No. 40, pp. 1) [3486], [3611], [14762], [21798], [22503], [26228], [33836]
Bitner Goodman [30181], [31810]
Bitner Group, Inc. [30181], [31810]
Bitterroot Valley Chamber of Commerce [41753]
"Bitumen Oilsands: Slick Science" in Canadian Business (Vol. 81, September 15, 2008, No. 14-15, pp. 55) [5546], [5827], [23121], [27842], [30868], [32730]
Bixby Metro Chamber of Commerce [43735]
Bixler Consulting Group [8674]
The Biz Insider [38331]
"Biz Pays Tribute: Franchise Helps Owners Grieve and Honor Their Beloved Pets" in Small Business Opportunities (November 2007) [12130], [24289]
Biz Virtuoso Consulting [42977]
BizBest Media Corp. [37700]
BizEd: The Leading Voice of Business Education [21735]
BizLink [38029]
BizStarts [46582]
BizTech [2411], [3671]
BizVoice [39519]
BizWorks [45940]
BizWorks Enterprise Center [45941]
BJME [11190]
"BK Menu Gives Casual Dining Reason to Worry" in Advertising Age (Vol. 79, November 17, 2008, No. 43, pp. 12) [13911], [17954], [19785], [19989], [24338], [29675], [30686]
BKR International (BKR) [17]
"Blach Builds on Teamwork" in Silicon Valley/San Jose Business Journal (Vol. 30, August 24, 2012, No. 22, pp. 1) [4002], [17955], [22099]
The Black Business Alliance (BBA) [30311]

Black Business Association (BBA) [30248], [36753]
Black Business Investment Fund (BBIF) [30427], [33649]
Black Business News [30433]
"Black Business Owners Are Up 38% in U.S. From Pre-Covid Levels" in Bloomberg (September 15, 2021) [30325]
Black Business and Professional Association (BBPA) [30249]
Black Career Women's Network (BCWN) [30250], [35568]
Black Chamber of Arizona (BCAZ) [36315]
Black Chamber of Commerce of Greater Kansas City (BCCGKC) [41519]
Black Chamber of Commerce of Lake County (BCCCL) [39101]
Black Chamber of Commerce - Permian Basin [45305]
Black Connect [30251]
Black Consumers: Digital Trends & Impact of COVID-19 One Year Later - US - April 2021 [11827], [29500]
Black Data Processing Associates (BDPA) [3602]
Black Diamond Ventures [37725]
Black Enterprise [30412], [30434]
Black Entrepreneurs [30252]
Black EOE Journal [30435]
"Black Gold: Jobs Aplenty" in Canadian Business (Vol. 79, August 14, 2006, No. 16-17, pp. 57) [26507], [27814], [28459], [29125], [33109]
Black Hawk College, Quad-Cities Campus [39441]
Black Hills Business Development Center [44670]
Black Innovation Alliance (BIA) [30253]
Black Mountain-Swannanoa Chamber of Commerce [43092]
"Black-Owned Businesses See Largest Surge in 25 Years Amidst Pandemic, Social Uprisings" in The Black Wall Street Times (July 14, 2021) [30326]
"Black-Owned Company Signed $334 Million Deal with Houston's William P. Hobby Airport" in Black Enterprise(February 10, 2023) [427], [13912], [24339]
"Black Pot Entrepreneurs Fight for Piece of Washington's Very White Marijuana Industry" in Crosscut (February 13, 2020) [4990]
Black Sheep Business Consulting Corp. (BSBCON) [2223]
Black Tennis Magazine: Tennis [15677]
"Black Travelers, an Untapped Market with Tremendous Buying Power" in Host Agency Reviews(February 18, 2022) [15732], [15986]
"Black-Woman Owned Tech Company Introduces First Two-Part Charging System Portable Device" in Minority Business Entrepreneur (February 2, 2022) [30327], [35744]
Black Women Business Owners of America (BWBO) [30254], [35569]
"BlackBerry 10 Unlikely to Save RIM. RIM Has Few Options. Staying the Course Isn't One of Them" in Canadian Business (Vol. 85, July 16, 2012, No. 11-12, pp. 12) [2719], [3487], [3612], [14392], [19489], [19786], [30687]
blackbox [37548]
BlackBusiness.org Blog [30436]
Blackmon Roberts Group Inc. (BRG) [17802], [21703]
BlackRiver Busines Capital [45436]
Blacksburg Regional Chamber of Commerce [45883]
"Blackstone to Acquire Ancestry.com for $4.7 Billion" in Reuters (August 5, 2020) [7354]
Blackstone Chamber of Commerce [45836]
"Blackstone Set to Sell Stake" in Globe & Mail (March 17, 2007, pp. B6) [6295], [9370], [18904], [19490], [31207]
Blackstone Valley Chamber of Commerce (BVCC) [40561]
Blackstone Valley Chamber of Commerce [44478]
"Blackstone's Outlook Still Tough" in Barron's (Vol. 88, March 17, 2008, No. 11, pp. 19) [6296], [9371], [23776], [31208]
"Blackwater Is LEED Golden for Port of Portland Building" in Contractor (Vol. 56, October 2009, No. 10, pp. 3) [5547], [5828], [16332], [23122]
Blackwell Area Chamber of Commerce [43736]
Blade Fire Labs [37549]
Blaine Community Chamber of Commerce [46055]
The Blaine Group, Inc. [33051]
Blair Business Mirror [44173]
Blair County Chamber of Commerce [44174]
Blairsville - Union County Chamber of Commerce (BUCCC) [38696]
Blakely-Early County Chamber of Commerce [38697]
Blanco Chamber of Commerce [45051]
Blanding Small Business Development Center [45604]
Blanding Visitor Center [45626]
Blankinship & Associates Inc. [10509], [20164], [27124], [28958]
Blanton-Peale Graduate Institute [26106]

Blanton-Peale Institute and Counseling Center [26106]
"Blatstein's North Broad St. Casino Plan in for Fight" in Philadelphia Business Journal (Vol. 28, April 20, 2012, No. 10, pp. 1) [7275]
Blaze Fast-Fire'd Pizza [12540], [14125]
"Blaze Pizza Adds Nine Franchise Groups" in FastCasual.com (September 2, 2014) [12524], [13861], [19491], [24290]
Blaze Pizza, LLC [12540], [14125]
"The Blazers' Money Maker" in Business Journal Portland (Vol. 31, April 18, 2014, No. 7, pp. 4) [15139], [28460]
"Blazing Trails Placing One Foot in Front of the Other" in Minority Business Entrepreneur (Vol. 39, Fall, 2022, No. 4, pp. 42-44) [14673]
Blenz Coffee [3205], [14126], [15056]
Blimpie Subs & Salads [14127]
Blind Brokers Network [16525]
Blind Man of America [1572]
"Blindspot: Hidden Biases of Good People" [20560], [22504], [28461]
Bling Capital [38612]
Blinn College Small Business Development Center [44908]
Blissfield Area Chamber of Commerce [40864]
Blissfield DDA/Main Street [40864]
Blissymbolics Communication International (BCI) [3603]
"Blog Buzz Heralds Arrival of iPhone 2.0" in Advertising Age (Vol. 79, June 9, 2008, No. 40, pp. 8) [2720], [9104], [14763], [17641], [24340], [26229]
"Blood Diamonds are Forever" in Canadian Business (Vol. 83, August 17, 2010, No. 13-14, pp. 59) [18526], [23472], [27468]
Blood Sweat & Script [15346]
"Bloody Monday for Bear?" in Barron's (Vol. 88, March 17, 2008, No. 11, pp. M14) [6297], [9372], [23777]
Bloomberg Beta [37312]
Bloomberg BNA [35971]
Bloomberg Industry Group [35971]
Bloomer Chamber of Commerce [46366]
Bloomfield Chamber of Commerce [46302]
Bloomfield Chamber of Commerce (BCC) [38030]
Bloomfield Chamber of Commerce [42193]
Bloomingdale Chamber of Commerce (BCC) [39102]
"Bloomington Police to Buy 24-Hour Electronic Kiosk With Federal Grant" in Herald-Times (September 5, 2012) [10015], [25117], [25227]
Bloomington SCORE [39508]
Bloomsburg Area Chamber of Commerce [44197]
Blount County Chamber of Commerce [44716]
Blount-Oneonta Chamber of Commerce (BO) [36085]
Blowing Rock Chamber of Commerce (BRCC) [43093]
Blu Venture Investors [45917]
"Blue Bell Breaks Ground in South Carolina" in Ice Cream Reporter (Vol. 23, August 20, 2010, No. 9, pp. 3) [8550], [17956], [20614]
"Blue Bell Touts Non-Shrinkage" in Ice Cream Reporter (Vol. 21, July 20, 2008, No. 8, pp. 1) [243], [8551], [29676]
Blue Book Marketing Research Services Directory [29677]
Blue Chip Cookies [1221], [1288]
Blue Chip Venture Co. [43619]
"Blue-Collar Broker Ranks in Nation's Elite" in Boston Business Journal (Vol. 31, July 15, 2011, No. 25, pp. 1) [6298], [9373]
"Blue Cross to Put Kiosk in Mall" in News & Observer (November 9, 2010) [8892], [10016], [25721], [27243], [29678], [30688]
Blue Garnet Associates L.L.C. [19638], [28959]
Blue Heron Capital [45988]
Blue Hill Peninsula Chamber of Commerce (BHPCoC) [40267]
"Blue Hill Tavern to Host Baltimore's First Cupcake Camp" in Daily Record (August 10, 2011) [1247], [29679], [33960]
Blue Island Area Chamber of Commerce and Industry [39103]
Blue Knights International Convention [11114]
Blue Knights International Law Enforcement Motorcycle Club Convention [11114]
Blue Mountain Community College Small Business Development Center (SBDC) [43907]
Blue Ribbon Coalition [13669]
Blue Ridge Food Ventures (BRFV) [43239]
Blue Ridge Labs (BRL) [42842]
Blue Rock Capital [38141]
Blue Springs Chamber of Commerce [41520]
Blue Startups [38885]
BlueCar Partners [42724]
Bluegrass Angels (BGA) [35264], [40094]
Bluegrass Community & Technical College Learning Resource Center (BCTC) [31020]

Bluegrass Small Business Development Center [39990]
Blueprint Health [42843]
BlueRibbon Coalition (BRC) [13669]
Bluestem Captial Company, LLC [44668]
BlueTree Allied Angels [44335]
Bluffton Chamber of Commerce [39619]
Blumberg Capital Ventures [37313]
Blytheville Area Chamber of Commerce [36465]
Blytheville-Gosnell Area Chamber of Commerce [36465]
BMBRI [1892]
BMO Nesbitt Burns Inc. [9947]
BMR Bathmaster Reglazing Ltd. [12690]
"BMW Revs Up for a Rebound" in Barron's (Vol. 89, July 13, 2009, No. 28, pp. M7) [6299], [9374], [11382], [23778], [29126], [32477]
BNA Income Tax Planner [159], [15461]
BNI Accelerator [46719]
BNI Indiana [39466]
BNI Minnesota & Northern Wisconsin [41148]
BNI New Hampshire [41967]
BNI Northeast Texas [44880]
BNI Northern Alabama [36043]
BNI Northern Indiana [39467]
BNI Ohio [43335]
BNI OK East [43701]
BNi Publications Inc. [4356]
BNI Southwest Florida [38199]
BNI Vermont [45697]
BNI West Virginia [46248]
BNI Western Pennsylvania [44084]
"Boar Market: Penny-Wise Consumers Favoring Pork" in Crain's Chicago Business (Vol. 31, April 14, 2008, No. 15, pp. 4) [6300], [9375], [22505], [23779]
The Board Book: An Insider's Guide for Directors and Trustees [23473], [24610], [28462]
Board for Certification of Genealogists (BCG) [7343]
Board of Cooperative Educational Services - Adult and Continuing Education (BOCES) [42964]
Board of Hospitals and Homes of The Methodist Church [25696]
Board of Schools of the ASCP [10911]
Board of Schools of Medical Technology [10911]
Board of Trade [44175]
Board of Trade Association [40617]
"Boards That Lead: When to Take Charge, When to Partner, and When to Stay Out of the Way" [23474], [28463]
Boat Owners Association of the United States [2826], [10587]
"Boat Sales Sputter as Cash-Strapped Buyers Drift Away" in Puget Sound Business Journal (Vol. 29, August 15, 2008, No. 17, pp. 1) [10599], [20765]
Boating Magazine [10612]
Boating Writers International (BWI) [5274]
BoatUS [2826], [10587]
"Boatyard Expansion 8-Year Odyssey" in Providence Business News (Vol. 28, March 31, 2014, No. 52, p. 1) [5548], [10600], [19492], [23123], [25228]
Boaz Chamber of Commerce (BCC) [36086]
Bob Bly [386], [5345]
Bob Pike's Train-the-Trainer Boot Camp (Onsite) [26851]
"Bob's Discount Furniture Moving into Harford County, Region" in Baltimore Business Journal (Vol. 27, January 22, 2010, No. 38, pp. 1) [8175], [8202], [13771], [20615], [26508], [32107], [33347]
Boca Grande Area Chamber of Commerce [38332]
Boca Raton West Chamber of Commerce [38388]
BOCES Putnam/Northern Westchester - BOCES Professional Library [2912]
"Bodovino Is a World Leader in Self-Service Wine Tasting" in Idaho Business Review (September 8, 2014) [10578], [15006], [16253], [27469], [32108]
Body Language [1117]
"The Body Shop: What Went Wrong?" in BBC (February 9, 2017) [1580]
BodyShop Business [14561]
Boeing Company - Integrated Defense Systems - Business Information Center [445]
"Boeing Moving 1,000 Washington Engineering Jobs to California" in Business Journal Portland (Vol. 31, April 11, 2014, No. 6) [17957], [19161], [29127]
"Boeing Partnership to Preserve Thousands of Acres of Threatened Wetlands in South Carolina" in Ecology, Environment & Conservation Business (August 2, 2014, pp. 3) [5549], [23124], [24951], [31209]
"BofA Goes for Small Business" in Austin Business Journal (Vol. 31, July 22, 2011, No. 20, pp. A1) [23780], [28103]
"BofA May Part With U.S. Trust" in Boston Business Journal (Vol. 31, May 20, 2011, No. 17, pp. 1) [6301], [9376], [23781], [33005]
"BofA Will Reach the Top with Countrywide Deal" in Business North Carolina (Vol. 28, March 2008, No. 3, pp. 36) [6302], [9377], [11014], [31210]

Bogalusa Chamber of Commerce [40152]
"The Bogleheads' Guide to Investing" [6303], [9378], [23782], [34748]
Boiler Operation, Maintenance and Safety [2054]
Boiler Operation, Maintenance & Safety (Onsite) [19434], [21339]
Boise Angel Alliance (BAA) [35265], [38948]
Boise Metro Chamber of Commerce (BMCC) [38906]
Boise State University (DORED) - Division of Research and Economic Development [47395]
Bojangles' Famous Chicken 'n Biscuits [1289], [14128]
Bojangles', Inc. [1289], [14128]
Bold Endeavors: How Our Government Built America, and Why It Must Rebuild Now [24952], [25229]
Bolingbrook Area Chamber of Commerce (BACC) [39104]
Bolingbrook Chamber of Commerce and Industry [39104]
Bolivar Area Chamber of Commerce [41521]
Bolivar Peninsula Chamber of Commerce (BPCOC) [45052]
Bollinger Band Letter [9917]
Bolt Innovation Management [40784]
BOMA [13629]
"Bombardier Deja Vu" in Canadian Business (Vol. 83, August 17, 2010, No. 13-14, pp. 28) [19787], [25118], [27470]
"Bombardier Wins Chinese Rail Deal" in Globe & Mail (March 20, 2006, pp. B1) [24611], [33110]
Bon Appetit: America's Food and Entertaining Magazine [4473]
Bonaventure Capital (BC) [36160]
"Bond Hill Cinema Site To See New Life" in Business Courier (Vol. 27, October 29, 2010, No. 26, pp. 1) [4003], [11489], [19162], [21457], [30539], [32109], [33348]
"Bonds v. Stocks: Who's Right About Recession?" in Barron's (Vol. 90, August 23, 2010, No. 34, pp. M3) [6304], [9379], [20766], [23783], [31211]
"Bonefish Grill Debuts New Cocktail to Benefit Conservation Foundation" in Ecology, Environment & Conservation Business (May 17, 2014, pp. 5) [7086], [13913], [23125]
Bonfire Ventures [37314]
Bonham Area Chamber of Commerce and Economic Development (BACC) [45053]
Bonham Economic Development Corporation [45053]
Bonita Springs Area Chamber of Commerce [38506]
"Bonnaroo 2012: Food Truck Oasis Returns With 9 Delicious Trucks" in International Business Times (June 4, 2012) [3837], [29680], [30464]
Bonner Business Center (BBC) [38949]
Bonner Springs/Edwardsville Area Chamber of Commerce [39868]
Bonney Lake Chamber of Commerce [46056]
Bonnie Bee and Company [1499]
Bonsall Chamber of Commerce [36754]
Bonus of America [2091]
Bonus Building Care [2091]
"Bonuses In Bad Times: In a Recession, How Should a Supermarket Chain Acknowledge Its Employees' Extra Effort?" in Harvard Business Review (Vol. 90, July 2012, No. 7-8, pp. 153). [7727], [17281]
"The Book of Battery Manufacturing" [29128]
Book Business [1850]
Book Club of California [1728]
Book Industry Study Group (BISG) [1614], [1802]
"Book Industry Supply Chain Delays to Impact Holiday Season" in American Booksellers Association (August 19, 2021) [1642], [1814], [16073]
Book Manufacturers Institute, Inc. (BMI) [1615], [1716]
"The Book On Indigo" in Canadian Business (Vol. 81, July 22, 2008, No. 12-13, pp. 29) [1643], [1815], [6305], [9380], [11261], [17958], [23784]
Book and Periodical Council (BPC) [1616], [11958]
Book and Periodical Development Council [1616], [11958]
Book Publishers Directory [1669], [1836], [5321]
"Book Publishing is Growing" in Information Today (Vol. 28, October 2011, No. 9, pp. 10) [1644], [1816], [17959]
Book Publishing Industry in the US - Market Research Report [1684]
Book Review Index (BRI) [1705]
"Book Sales Are Up This Year Over Last Year, and Physical Books Are Thriving" in Quartz (December 28, 2018) [1817]
Book Stores Industry in the US - Market Research Report [1841]
"Book Yourself Solid: The Fastest, Easiest, and Most Reliable System for Getting More Clients Than You Can Handle" [21799], [29681], [30689], [32478], [33111]
"Bookbinder Restores Pages From the Past" in The Dallas Morning News (February 24, 2012) [1719]

"A Bookbinding Bonanza" in The Harvard Gazette (September 22, 2014) [1720]
BookExpo [1846]
BookExpo America [1846]
Bookhaven Press L.L.C. [44439]
Bookkeeping: A Beginner's Guide to Accounting and Bookkeeping for Small Businesses [1736]
Bookkeeping for Creatives with Alisha Thomas [4624]
"Bookkeeping For Dummies" [1745], [23785]
"Bookkeeping Options for Time-Starved Startups" in Legal Zoom (February 21, 2023) [1746], [16787], [34495]
Bookkeeping Practices for Digital Marketers [16788], [29682]
Bookman's Price Index: A Guide to the Values of Rare and Other Out of Print Books [3267]
"Bookstores Find Growth as 'Anchors of Authenticity'" in The New York Times (June 23, 2019) [1818]
"Bookworms, Rejoice: Shakespeare & Co. Returns to the Upper West Side" in News 1 NY (November 28, 2018) [1819]
"Boom and Bust in the Book Biz" in Canadian Business (Vol. 83, August 17, 2010, No. 13-14, pp. 16) [1820], [5425], [11715], [21800], [31212], [32110], [32479]
"Boom has Tech Grads Mulling Their Options" in Globe & Mail (March 14, 2006, pp. B1) [9105], [16397], [17960], [26230], [26509]
"Boom Times for Cannabis Businesses as Californians, in a Pandemic Fog, Isolate Indoors" in Los Angeles Times (April 18, 2020) [4991]
"Boomers' Spending Hurts Retirement" in Employee Benefit News (Vol. 25, November 1, 2011, No. 14, pp. 18) [6306], [9381], [17282], [23786]
Boomtown Accelerator [37931]
Boone Area Chamber of Commerce (BACC) [43094]
Boone County Chamber of Commerce [39520]
Boone Hospital Center Medical Library [8295]
Booneville Development Corporation - South Logan County Chamber of Commerce [36439]
Boonville Area Chamber of Commerce [41522], [42522]
Booster Juice Inc. [8076]
"The Booth and Beyond: Art Fair Design and the Viewing Experience" in Entrepreneur (September 2014) [15836], [35031]
Boothbay Harbor Region Chamber of Commerce [40268]
Bootstrap Dallas [45499]
BootstrapLabs [37315]
"Bootstrapping or Equity Funding: Which Is Better for Your Business?" in Business News Daily (February 21, 2023) [34496]
Booz Allen Hamilton - Research Services and Information Center [17205]
"Border Boletin: UA to Take Lie-Detector Kiosk to Poland" in Arizona Daily Star (September 14, 2010) [10017], [14393], [18527], [19337], [26231], [27471], [30540], [31213], [31944], [32731]
Borealis Ventures [42028]
Borger Chamber of Commerce (BCC) [45054]
Born to Organize: Everything You Need to Know About a Career As a Professional Organizer [12828]
Boron Chamber of Commerce [36755]
Borough of Cresson Chamber of Commerce [44204]
Borrego Springs Chamber of Commerce [36756]
"Borrow Baby Couture Launch Rocks Fasion World - Provides Couture Fashion for Girls" in Benzinga.com (June 18, 2012) [1193], [2845], [3009], [11716], [32111]
Borrowing Brilliance: The Six Steps to Business Innovation by Building on the Ideas of Others [27843], [30690], [31945], [32732]
Boscobel Chamber of Commerce [46367]
"Bose Seeking Expansion Options in Framingham" in Boston Business Journal (Vol. 34, June 13, 2014, No. 19, pp. 15) [4387], [13148], [13399], [17961], [29129], [33349]
Boss Project [2322]
Bossier Chamber of Commerce (BCC) [40153]
Boston Architectural Center - Alfred Shaw and Edward Durell Stone Library [4360], [14966]
Boston Business Journal [40775]
Boston Business Journal (BBJ) [40774]
"Boston Cab Association Gets 2012 Green Business Award" in Professional Close-Up (April 28, 2012) [5550], [5829], [15513], [23126]
Boston Cannabis Convention [5051]
Boston College - Boston College Business Institute (BLI) [33725]
Boston College (BC) - Carroll School of Management - Center for Corporate Citizenship (CCC) [31903]
Boston Consulting Group - Chicago Information and Research Group [2418]
Boston Consulting Group, Inc. (BCG) [13611]
Boston Financial & Equity Corp. (BFEC) [40669]

Boston Harbor Angels [40485]
Boston International Antiquarian Book Fair [1847]
Boston Millennia Partners (BMP) [40670]
Boston Pizza [14129]
Boston Pizza International Inc. [14129]
Boston Public Library - Kirstein Business Library [30231], [33713]
Boston Public Library - Kirstein Business Library & Innovation Center [30231], [33713]
Boston SCORE [40506]
Boston Seed Capital [40671]
Boston Tattoo Convention [15339]
Boston University - Center for Finance, Law and Policy [6733]
Boston University Department of Electrical & Computer Engineering - Multimedia Communications Laboratory (MCL) [3542]
Boston University - Frederick S. Pardee Management Library [29047]
Boston University (BU) - Institute for Economic Development (IED) [33726]
Boston University - Institute for Technology Entrepreneurship and Commercialization (ITEC) [22952]
Boston's The Gourmet Pizza [12541], [14130]
Botetourt Chamber of Commerce [45837]
The Bottled Water Market [1864]
Bottled Water Reporter [1865]
"Bottom-Fishing and Speed-Dating in India-How Investors Feel About the Indian Market" in Barron's (Vol. 88, March 24, 2008, No. 12, pp. M12) [6307], [8691], [9382], [15837], [17962], [20767], [23787], [27472], [35032]
"The Bottom Line" in Retail Merchandiser (Vol. 51, July-August 2011, No. 4, pp. 60) [3010], [6125], [10302], [32112]
Bottom Line [42303]
The Bottom Line [41197], [42523]
Bottom Line Service System [14299]
Bottom-Line Training: Performance-Based Results [22100], [22506], [28464]
"Bottom's Up: This Real-Estate Rout May Be Short-Lived" in Barron's (Vol. 88, July 14, 2008, No. 28, pp. 25) [11015], [13149], [13400], [20768]
Boulder Chamber (BC) [37820]
Boulder Chamber of Commerce [37820]
Boulder City Chamber of Commerce [41929]
Boulder Junction Chamber of Commerce [46368]
Boulder Small Business Development Center (SBDC) [37781]
Boulder Ventures Ltd. [40425]
Bounce Innovation Hub [43650]
"Bouncing Back" in Orlando Business Journal (Vol. 29, September 7, 2012, No. 12, pp. 1) [28104]
"Boundaries for Leaders (Enhanced Edition): Results, Relationships, and Being Ridiculously In Charge" [20396], [22101], [23475], [28465]
"Bountiful Barrels: Where to Find $140 Trillion" in Barron's (Vol. 88, July 14, 2008, No. 28, pp. 40) [6308], [8692], [9383], [17963], [23788], [27473], [33112]
Bouse Chamber of Commerce [36316]
Bowie Business Innovation Center (BIC) [40443]
Bowie Chamber of Commerce [45055]
The Bowker Annual [1661], [1830], [11987]
The Bowker Annual: Library and Book Trade Almanac [1661], [1830], [11987]
Bowl Canada [1871]
Bowl Expo [1884]
Bowlers Journal International (BJI) [1882]
Bowling Green [40018]
Bowling Green Area Chamber of Commerce [40019]
Bowling Green Chamber of Commerce [41523]
Bowling Green Community College of Western Kentucky University [40112]
Bowling Green and South Central Kentucky [40018]
Bowling Green State University (ML BSSA) - Music Library and Sound Recordings Archives [13665]
Bowling Proprietors Association of America (BPAA) [1872]
Bowling Proprietors Association of America International Bowl Expo [1883]
Bowling Proprietors' Association of Canada [1871]
Bowling Writers Association of America [5284]
Bowling Writers Association of America and National Women Bowling Writers Association [5284]
Bowman Area Chamber of Commerce [43288]
"Bowman Funeral Directors Building New, Larger Facility in Garden City" in Idaho Business Review (March 13, 2014) [4004], [7206]
The Bowser Database [9918]
The Bowser Directory of Small Stocks [9918]
Boxador [37316]
BoxGroup [42725]
Boxing Gyms & Clubs Industry in the US - Market Research Report [12443]

The Boyd Company Inc. [19211]
Boyne Area Chamber of Commerce [40865]
Boynton Beach Business Monthly [38333]
Bozeman Area Chamber of Commerce (BACC) [41754]
Bozeman Business and Professional Women (BPW) [35570]
Bozeman Small Business Development Center [41719]
Bozeman Technology Incubator [41806]
BPA National Leadership Conference [21683]
BPW BC and Yukon [46688]
BPW Canada [35589]
BPW Montreal [46883]
BR Venture Fund [43015]
"Bracing for a Bear of a Week" in Barron's (Vol. 88, March 17, 2008, No. 11, pp. 24) [6309], [9384], [20255], [20769], [23789], [28105]
"Bracing for More Layoffs: This Week's Oil and Gas Jobs News" in Sacramento Business Journal (Vol. 28, September 30, 2011, No. 31, pp. 1) [20770], [26886]
"Braden Cadenelli - Brining Sustainable Practices to the Food Industry" [23422]
Bradford Area Chamber of Commerce (BACC) [44175]
Bradford & Bigelow Inc. [40777]
Bradford Regional Chamber of Commerce [38472]
Bradford's International Directory of Marketing Research Agencies [10640], [28466], [29683]
Bradley County Chamber of Commerce [36440]
Bradley Regional Chamber of Commerce [38031]
Bradley University - Foster College of Business - Center for Business and Economic Research (CBER) [34234]
Brady [7840]
Brady Campaign to Prevent Gun Violence [7840]
Brady Chamber of Commerce [45056]
Brady/McCulloch County Chamber of Commerce [45056]
Braemar Energy Ventures [42726]
Brain, Behavior, and Immunity [32860]
Brainerd Lakes Area Chambers of Commerce [41198]
"BrainScripts for Sales Success: 21 Hidden Principles of Consumer Psychology for Winning New Customers" [32480]
Brainstorm Ventures [37726]
Braintree Business Development Center [43651]
BRAKE [1123]
The Brake Colloquium [1123]
Brake Colloquium & Exhibition [1123]
Brake Masters [14577]
Brake System Parts Manufacturers Council [1088]
Branch County Area Chamber of Commerce [40895]
Branch Venture Group [40672]
Branches and Twigs Genealogical Society Collection [7398]
"Branching Out: Towards a Trait-based Understanding of Fungal Ecology" in Canadian Business (Vol. 79, July 17, 2006, No. 14-15, pp. 41) [17964], [20256], [29684]
"Brand, Branding and Small Businesses" in The Economic Times (Sept. 2, 2021) [17434]
Brand Knew (BK) [37550]
Brand New Matter (BNM) [38114]
"Brand Police Keep the Lines Distinct at GM" in Automotive News (Vol. 86, October 31, 2011, No. 6488, pp. 3) [11383], [29685]
"Brand Storytelling Becomes a Booming Business" in Entrepreneur (April 2012) [9084], [16364], [24522], [27819], [29686]
"Branded Entertainment: Dealmaking Strategies & Techniques for Industry Professionals" [244], [2447], [13028], [15585], [31214]
Brandeis University - Center for Youth and Communities (CYC) [10006], [14997]
Brandeis University - Schneider Institutes for Health Policy (SIHP) [26107]
The Brandery [43652]
Branding Basics for Small Business [17423]
:Branding in a Diverse Universe: Serving Both Sides of the Buy/Sell" in Minority Business Entrepreneur (March 14, 2023) [17435]
"Branding Spree" in Pet Product News (Vol. 66, September 2012, No. 9, pp. 40) [12190], [14394], [17965], [29130], [30691]
"Branding Your Way" in Canadian Business (Vol. 80, February 12, 2007, No. 4, pp. 31) [245], [9106], [26232], [29687], [31749], [33961]
Brandon Area Chamber of Commerce (BACC) [45719]
Brandon Chamber of Commerce [45719]
"Brands' Mass Appeal" in ADWEEK (Vol. 51, June 14, 2010, No. 24) [246], [21801], [29688], [30692]
Brandywine Business Advisory L.L.C. (BBA) [2224]
Branford Chamber of Commerce [38073]
Branson-Lakes Area Chamber of Commerce (BLACC) [41524]
Brass Gas Stop Institute [12611]
Brattleboro Area Chamber of Commerce (BACC) [45720]
"A Brave New World — Working From Home" in Innovation & Tech Today (October 8, 2021) [26834]

"Braves' Parking Pitch Fails to Connect With Property Owners" in Atlanta Business Chronicle (June 27, 2014, pp. 1) [1553], [4005], [15140]
Brawley Chamber of Commerce [36757]
Brawley Chamber of Commerce and Economic Development Commission [36757]
Brazil-Canada Chamber of Commerce (BCCC) [20680]
Brazil Interactive Media Inc. [5065]
Brazilian-American Chamber of Commerce (BACC) [27397]
Brazilian Government Trade Bureau of the Consulate General of Brazil in New York [27398]
"Brazil's New King of Food" in Barron's (Vol. 89, July 13, 2009, No. 28, pp. 28) [8693], [9385], [17007], [20771], [27474], [31215]
Brazos Valley Small Business Development Center (BVSBDC) [44909]
Brazosport College Small Business Development Center [44910]
Brea Chamber of Commerce (BCC) [36758]
Breadeaux Pizza [12542]
Breadsmith [1222], [1290]
Break the Rules!: The Six Counter-Conventional Mindsets of Entrepreneurs That Can Help Anyone Change the World [22507]
Breakaway Ventures (BV) [40673]
"Breaking Bad: Rid Yourself of Negative Habits" in Black Enterprise (Vol. 40, July 2010, No. 12, pp. 104) [22102], [26887]
"Breaking Bad? This New Everett Pool Hall Can Help Your Shot" in HeraldNet (August 5. 2019) [1535]
"Breaking Barriers" in Baltimore Business Journal (Vol. 30, June 29, 2012, No. 8, pp. 1) [17524], [22369], [25175], [30236]
Breaking into Business Consulting: Upleveling in the Impact Space with Paul Zelizer [20138]
Breaking Down the 4 Types of Corporate Social Responsibility [34277]
"Breaking Down Walls - 2 Kinds" in Puget Sound Business Journal (Vol. 35, August 22, 2014, No. 18, pp. 9) [18905], [29131]
Breaking the Hustle-to-Burnout Pipeline with Doreen Vanderhart [24802]
"Breaking Through" in Inc. (January 2008, pp. 90-93) [17966], [22508]
"Breaking with Tradition, Foundations Seek Out Diverse Asset Managers" in Crain's Chicago Business (October 15, 2021) [9386], [30328]
"Breaking from Tradition Techstyle" in Providence Business News (Vol. 28, March 17, 2014, No. 50, pp. 1) [14909], [19788], [21458], [26233]
"Breaking Up: How Will It Affect Your Residence Permit?" in Canadian Business (Vol. 80, March 12, 2007, No. 6, pp. 34) [18528], [31216]
Breakthrough: How to Build a Million Dollar Business by Helping Others Succeed [22370], [26730]
"Breast Surgery Breakthrough Propels Palo Alto Startup AirXpanders" in Silicon Valley/San Jose Business Journal (Vol. 30, June 22, 2012, No. 13, pp. 1) [10823], [25722]
Breaux Bridge Area Chamber of Commerce [40154]
Breckenridge Chamber of Commerce [45057]
Breckenridge Resort Chamber of Commerce (BRC) [37821]
Brecksville Chamber of Commerce (BCC) [43417]
Breen & Associates Inc. [2022], [4306]
Breese Chamber of Commerce [39105]
Bremen Area Chamber of Commerce [43418]
Bremerton Area Chamber of Commerce (BACC) [46057]
Brenda Spencer [929]
"Brent Leary on Partnering with Amazon for the Last Mile" in Small Business Trends (September 20, 2022) [7029], [20616]
Brentwood-Baldwin-Whitehall Chamber of Commerce (BBWCC) [44176]
Brentwood Business Owners Association (BBOA) [33447]
Brentwood Chamber of Commerce [36759]
Brentwood Venture Capital [37317]
Brevard - Transylvania Chamber of Commerce [43095]
Brevity: Your AI Pitch Coach [35408]
Brewers Association (BA) [1890]
Brewers Association of Canada [1888], [1955]
Brewers Association of Maryland (BAM) [1891]
"Brewers Association: US Craft Brewing Industry Contributes $79 Billion to US Economy" in Brewbound (September 30, 2019) [1905]
Brewers Hill Hub [40444]
Brewery Tours Industry in the US - Market Research Report [1357], [1944]
Brewing and Malting Barley Research Institute [1892]
"Brewing Up a Brand" in Canadian Business (Vol. 80, February 26, 2007, No. 5, pp. 68) [247], [29689]

Brewing Master Index

Brewing Up a Business: Adventures in Beer from the Founder of Dogfish Head Craft Brewery **[1885]**, **[22371]**, **[24523]**
"Brewpub and Taproom Safety Tips" in Brewers Association (October 6, 2020) **[1906]**
Brewster Chamber of Commerce **[42524]**
Breyer Capital **[37318]**
Brian Kathenes Autographs & Collectibles **[825]**
"Briarcliff Office Building Fills Up Fast" in The Business Journal-Serving Metropolitan Kansas City (Vol. 26, Sept. 5, 2008, pp. 1) **[12878]**, **[13401]**, **[17967]**, **[18906]**, **[20772]**
Brick Industry Association (BIA) **[10725]**, **[10748]**
Brick Industry Association--Membership Directory (Internet only) **[10735]**
Brick Township Chamber of Commerce **[42101]**
The BrickKicker **[2031]**, **[4346]**, **[13335]**
Bridal Association of America (BAOA) **[1961]**
"Bridal Chain Files for Bankruptcy, Leaving Brides Frantic Over Gowns" in Charlotte Business Journal (July 17, 2017) **[1964]**
Bridal Guide **[2005]**
The Bridge **[38334]**, **[41199]**
Bridge Business and Property Brokers Inc. **[1366]**
Bridgeport Area Chamber of Commerce (BACC) **[45058]**
Bridgeport Chamber of Commerce **[36760]**
Bridgeport Innovation Center (BIC) **[38106]**
Bridgeport Regional Business Council (BRBC) **[38032]**
Bridgeton Area Chamber of Commerce (BACC) **[42102]**
Bridgeview Chamber of Commerce [39106]
Bridgeview Chamber of Commerce & Industry **[39106]**
Bridgewood Consultants **[35441]**
Bridgeworks Enterprise Center (BEC) **[44384]**
"Bridging the Academic-Practitioner Divide in Marketing Decision Models" in Journal of Marketing (Vol. 75, July 2011, No. 4, pp. 196) **[21459]**, **[29690]**
"Bridging the Bay" in Business Journal Serving Greater Tampa Bay (Vol. 30, November 5, 2010, No. 46, pp. 1) **[1554]**, **[4006]**
"Bridging Diverging Perspectives and Repairing Damaged Relationships in the Aftermath of Workplace Transgressions" in Business Ethics Quarterly (Vol. 24, July 2014, No. 3, pp. 443) **[18529]**, **[23476]**
Bridging the Divide Between Funders and Founders with Sarah Sterling **[35409]**
"Bridging the Talent Gap Through Partnership and Innovation" in Canadian Business (Vol. 81, October 27, 2008, No. 18, pp. 88) **[21460]**, **[27844]**, **[31217]**
"Bridging the Worlds" in Academy of Management Journal (Vol. 50, No. 5, October 1, 2007, pp. 1043) **[1645]**, **[26888]**, **[28023]**, **[31946]**, **[32733]**
"Brief: Janitorial Company Must Pay Back Wages" in Buffalo News (September 24, 2011) **[2062]**, **[18530]**, **[22103]**, **[26889]**, **[33113]**, **[35172]**
"Brief: Make a Bigger Impact by Saying Less" **[17642]**, **[22509]**, **[28467]**
"BRIEF: Montana Street Pawn Shop Closing Doors" in Montana Standard (November 6, 2010) **[11916]**, **[13772]**, **[20773]**
"BRIEF: New In-Home Senior Care Provider Opens In Longmont" in America's Intelligence Wire (September 19, 2012) **[8246]**
Briefings **[39869]**
"Briefly: Physician Groups Unite" in Crain's Detroit Business (Vol. 25, June 15, 2009, No. 24, pp. 18) **[6310]**, **[9387]**, **[31218]**
Brigantine Beach Chamber of Commerce **[42103]**
Briggs Chamber of Commerce [38945]
Brigham City Area Chamber of Commerce **[45627]**
Brigham Young University Family History Library (BYU) **[7399]**
Brigham Young University - Human Performance Research Center (HPRC) **[12510]**
"A Bright Spot: Industrial Space in Demand Again" in Sacramento Business Journal (Vol. 28, October 21, 2011, No. 34, pp. 1) **[13150]**, **[13402]**, **[29132]**, **[33350]**
Brightpoint Community College (JTCC) **[45975]**
Brightspark Financial, Inc. **[46779]**
Brightspark Ventures [46779]
BrightStar Healthcare **[8282]**
Brightstone Capital **[43008]**
Brillion Area Chamber of Commerce **[46369]**
Brimfield Area Chamber of Commerce (BACC) **[43419]**
"Bring Out the Best in Your Team" in Harvard Business Review Vol. 92, September 2014, No. 9, pp. 26) **[22104]**, **[28024]**
"Bringing Charities More Bang for Their Buck" in Crain's Chicago Business (Vol. 34, May 23, 2011, No. 21, pp. 31) **[2063]**, **[3011]**, **[3093]**, **[7087]**, **[11662]**, **[29133]**, **[34278]**
"Bringing Healthcare Home" in Austin Business Journal (Vol. 34, June 6, 2014, No. 16, pp. B13) **[14764]**, **[17968]**, **[20397]**, **[33837]**
"Bringing Manufacturing Concerns to Springfield" in Crain's Chicago Business (Vol. 31, March 31, 2008, No. 13, pp. 6) **[22510]**, **[25230]**, **[28468]**, **[29134]**
Brink & Associates Inc. **[10688]**
Brinkley Chamber of Commerce **[36441]**
Brisbane Chamber of Commerce **[36761]**
"Brisk Activity in North Fulton Office Market" in Atlanta Business Chronicle (July 11, 2014, pp. 2B) **[13151]**, **[13403]**, **[20774]**, **[25723]**, **[26234]**
Bristol Chamber of Commerce [44717]
Bristol County Chamber of Commerce [44469]
Bristol County Chamber of Commerce, Inc. **[40562]**
Bristol Tennessee/Virginia Chamber of Commerce **[44717]**
"Brite-Strike Tactical Launches New Internet Marketing Initiatives" in Marketwired (September 15, 2009) **[2181]**, **[9107]**, **[11717]**, **[21802]**, **[29691]**, **[32481]**
British American Chamber of Commerce of Central Florida **[38335]**
British Canadian Chamber of Trade and Commerce (BCCTC) **[20681]**
British Columbia Genealogical Society (BCGS) **[7400]**
British Columbia Institute of Technology (BCIT) - Aerospace and Technology Campus Library **[446]**
British Columbia Land Surveyors Foundation - Anna Papove Memorial Library **[15233]**
British Columbia Technology Industries Association [3420], [3601], [3765]
British Journal of Music Education **[11190]**
British Trade Office at Consulate-General **[27399]**
BritishAmerican Business Inc. of New York and London (BAB) **[27400]**
Britt Chamber of Commerce (BCC) **[39717]**
Broad Universe (BU) **[5275]**
Broadcast Advertising Bureau [13024], [13065], [31842]
Broadcast Cable Credit Association (BCCA) **[13016]**, **[15570]**
Broadcast Credit Association [13016], [15570]
Broadcast Education Association (BEA) **[15571]**
Broadcaster **[15617]**
Broadsword Solutions Corp. (BSC) **[3659]**
BroadVision, Inc. **[19639]**, **[28960]**
Broadway-Timberville Chamber of Commerce **[45838]**
Brockport Small Business Development Center **[42393]**
Brodhead Chamber of Commerce **[46370]**
Broken Arrow Chamber of Commerce **[43737]**
Broken Bow Chamber of Commerce **[41841]**, **[43738]**
"Brokerages Seek a Foothold in Charlotte Real Estate Market" in Charlotte Business Journal (Vol. 25, October 15, 2010, No. 30, pp. 1) **[13152]**, **[13404]**, **[33351]**
Bromont Science Park **[46890]**
Bronx Business Tech Incubator **[42844]**
Bronx Chamber of Commerce (BCC) **[42525]**
Bronx Cookspace **[42845]**
Bronx Small Business Development Center **[42394]**
Bronxville Chamber of Commerce **[42526]**
Brook Venture Partners **[40674]**
Brookdale Community College **[42252]**
"Brookfield Asset Management: A Perfect Predator" in Canadian Business (Vol. 83, July 20, 2010, No. 11-12, pp. 50) **[9388]**, **[13153]**, **[13405]**
Brookfield Chamber of Commerce **[41525]**
Brookfield Chamber of Commerce (BCC) **[39107]**
Brookfield Chamber of Commerce [46419]
Brookgreen Gardens **[7659]**
Brookhaven - Lincoln County Chamber of Commerce **[41385]**
Brookings Area Chamber of Commerce and Convention Bureau **[44636]**
Brookings-Harbor Chamber of Commerce **[43948]**
Brookings Innovation Center [44672]
Brookline Chamber of Commerce **[40563]**
Brooklyn Area Chamber of Commerce (BACOC) **[46371]**
Brooklyn Botanic Garden (BBG) **[7660]**
Brooklyn Botanic Garden Library [7660]
"Brooklyn-Bred Business Owner Starts Student-Entrepreneur Grant in Immigrant Parents' Names" in Entrepreneur (March 3, 2021) **[36013]**
Brooklyn Bridge Ventures (BBV) **[42727]**
Brooklyn Chamber of Commerce (BCC) **[42527]**
Brooklyn Fashion + Design Accelerator (BF+DA) **[42846]**
Brooklyn FoodWorks **[42847]**
Brooklyn - Irish Hills Chamber of Commerce **[40866]**
Brooklyn Museum **[3070]**
Brooklyn Public Library Business & Career Center **[161]**, **[15466]**
Brookstone Venture Capital **[36382]**
Brookville Area Chamber of Commerce (BACC) **[44177]**
The Broome Chamber [42581]
Broome County Chamber of Commerce [42581]
Broome County Industrial Development Agency (BCIDA) **[42848]**
Broome County Public Library - J. Donald Ahearn Business Resource Center **[24907]**
Broomfield Chamber of Commerce **[37822]**
The Broomfielder **[37823]**
"Brought To You By the Letter 'W'" in Washington Business Journal (Vol. 33, August 29, 2014, No. 19, pp. 6) **[874]**, **[4007]**, **[8368]**, **[13914]**
Broward County Office of Economic and Small Business Development (OESBD) **[38254]**
Brown and Caldwell **[7978]**
George Brown College of Applied Arts & Technology - Archives [3074], [6152]
Brown County Chamber of Commerce **[39521]**
Brown County Culinary Kitchen (BCCK) **[46559]**
Brown Forum for Enterprise **[44456]**
"Brown Lab Image of R.I. Innovation" in Providence Business News (Vol. 28, February 24, 2014, No. 47, pp. 1) **[10913]**, **[21461]**, **[31947]**, **[32734]**
Brown University - Center for Gerontology and Health Care Research (CGHR) **[203]**
Brown University - Institute at Brown for Environment & Society (IBES) **[7979]**, **[13753]**
Brown University - Orwig Music Library **[11210]**
Brown University - Social Science Research Lab (SSRL) - Department of Sociology **[47396]**
Brown University - Watson Institute for International Studies **[26108]**
"Brown's Goal: 1,300 New Apartments and Condos" in Business First of Buffalo (Vol. 30, February 28, 2014, No. 24, pp. 6) **[4008]**, **[13154]**, **[13406]**, **[13773]**, **[20775]**
Brown's Tree Farm **[2952]**
Brownsburg Chamber of Commerce **[39522]**
Brownsville Chamber of Commerce (BCOC) **[45059]**
Brownwood Area Chamber of Commerce (BCC) **[45060]**
"Brownwood Hotel & Spa to Open in Central Fla." in Travel Weekly (November 13, 2019) **[8369]**
Bruce Community Futures Development Corporation (CFDC) **[46760]**
Bruce D. Wyman Co. **[28961]**
"Bruce Lee's Martial Arts Studio Has Reopened in Chinatown" in Los Angeles Magazine (October 22, 2019) **[10721]**
Bruegger's Enterprises **[1223]**
Brunswick Area Chamber of Commerce (BACC) **[41526]**
Brunswick Chamber of Commerce [41526]
Brunswick County Chamber of Commerce **[43096]**
Brunswick-Golden Isles Chamber of Commerce (BGICC) **[38698]**
Brush Area Chamber of Commerce **[37824]**
Brush Valley Buyer's Guide **[44178]**
Bruster's Real Ice Cream Inc. **[8611]**
Bryan Area Chamber of Commerce **[43420]**
"Bryan Berg, Target Corp., Senior Vice President, Region 1" in Hawaii Business (Vol. 53, March 2008, No. 9, pp. 28) **[20776]**, **[24612]**, **[33547]**
Bryan Cave L.L.P., Law Library **[5764]**, **[18793]**, **[25629]**
Bryan Media Corp. **[33650]**
Bryant Chamber of Commerce (BCC) **[36442]**
Bryant and Stratton Business Institute - Syracuse Campus [42966]
Bryant and Stratton College - Buffalo Campus **[42965]**
Bryant & Stratton College - Parma Campus **[43685]**
Bryant and Stratton College - Syracuse Campus **[42966]**
BS-Free Service Business Show: 5 Places to Cut the BS in Your Service Business **[33296]**
BS-Free Service Business Show: 5 Questions Every Micro Agency Owner Needs to Ask **[16625]**
BS-Free Service Business Show: Agency or Solo: What's Right for You? **[16626]**
BS-Free Service Business Show: Antidote to Overwhelm and Overwork When You Work with Clients **[28921]**
BS-Free Service Business Show: Awkward Client Situations: What to Do When Things Get Sticky **[33297]**
BS-Free Service Business Show: Best-Case Scenario Productivity vs. Reality: The Missing Margin **[35008]**
BS-Free Service Business Show: BS-Free Sustainability for Service Businesses **[33298]**
BS-Free Service Business Show: Building a Business by Blending Products and Services with Zoe Linda **[16627]**
BS-Free Service Business Show: Consumer Caution: Understanding the Risks of Payment Plans in Online Business **[27815]**
BS-Free Service Business Show: Covering Your Ass: Planning for the Unexpected with Julee Yokoyama **[33299]**
BS-Free Service Business Show: Creatives, Coaches, and Consultants: The Key Differences Between Different Types of Service Businesses **[33300]**
BS-Free Service Business Show: Ethics over Easy: Succeed without the Shady Shortcuts **[23556]**
BS-Free Service Business Show: Exits and Evolutions: Change Is the Only Constant **[24803]**
BS-Free Service Business Show: Exits and Evolutions: Navigating Change in Your Service Business **[16628]**

3196 Small Business Sourcebook • 42nd Edition

BS-Free Service Business Show: From Solo to Agency and Back Again with Jules Taggart **[34466]**
BS-Free Service Business Show: Keeping Your Business Simple and Sustainable (A Check-In) **[16629]**
BS-Free Service Business Show: Leadership Fundamentals for a Successful Agency **[16630]**
BS-Free Service Business Show: Making the Math "Math" for Your Service Business **[24204]**
BS-Free Service Business Show: Mindful Marketing: Andréa Jones Shares Her Social Media Evolution **[29537]**
BS-Free Service Business Show: Myths of the Microagency **[33301]**
BS-Free Service Business Show: Practical Pricing for Service Business Owners **[31662]**
BS-Free Service Business Show: Pricing Survival Guide for a Messed-Up Economy **[24205]**
BS-Free Service Business Show: Putting Sell the Strategy into Action **[33302]**
BS-Free Service Business Show: Sell the Strategy: Stepping Up Your Service Business **[33303]**
BS-Free Service Business Show: Staying Solo: Ditching Busy Work for Systems **[16631]**
BS-Free Service Business Show: Staying Solo: Rethinking Planning to Focus on Seasons **[16632]**
BS-Free Service Business Show: Staying Solo: Using Strategy to Break the Income Ceiling **[16633]**
BS-Free Service Business Show: Staying Solo: What Every One-Person Business Should Know **[34467]**
BS-Free Service Business Show: Staying Solo: What Support Do You Really Need? **[16634]**
BS-Free Service Business Show: Staying Solo: Your Framework for a Simple, Sustainable Service Business **[16635]**
BS-Free Service Business Show: Stop Selling, Start Solving: For Solopreneurs Who Hate Sleazy Sales **[32679]**
BS-Free Service Business Show: The Art of Reinvention with AdeOla Fadumiye **[16636]**
BS-Free Service Business Show: The Cult of Scale (and Why Sustainability Is More Important) **[33304]**
BS-Free Service Business Show: The Different Types of Support for Entrepreneurs **[16637]**
BS-Free Service Business Show: The Growth Path for Micro Agency Owners **[16638]**
BS-Free Service Business Show: The Power of Retainer Clients **[16639]**
BS-Free Service Business Show: The Real Cost of Bad Boundaries with Clients **[16640]**
BS-Free Service Business Show: The Real Cost of Content Creation **[16641]**
BS-Free Service Business Show: The Real Cost of Creating an Agency **[24206]**
BS-Free Service Business Show: The Real Cost of Growing a Service Business **[18438]**
BS-Free Service Business Show: The Real Cost of Tech and Tools for Solopreneurs **[16642]**
BS-Free Service Business Show: The Rise of Trauma-Informed Coaching **[33305]**
BS-Free Service Business Show: The State of "Ethical" Business 2024 **[23557]**
BS-Free Service Business Show: The State of Ethical Marketing and Online Business for 2023 **[33306]**
BS-Free Service Business Show: The Summer Slowdown **[16643]**
BS-Free Service Business Show: The Top 10 Awkward Client Moments (and How to Avoid Them) **[33307]**
BS-Free Service Business Show: What No One Tells You About Running a Micro Agency **[16644]**
BS-Free Service Business Show: Your Guide to Marketing a Service Based Business **[29538]**
"Bubble Trouble? Many Experts Say Seattle Housing Market Is Headed for a Fall" in Puget Sound Business Journal (Vol. 34, April 18, 2014, No. 53, pp. 4) **[13155]**, **[13407]**, **[19990]**, **[27475]**, **[33962]**
BUC Book--The Statistically Authenticated Used Boat Price Guide [10601]
BUC Used Boat Price Guide **[10601]**
Buchanan Area Chamber of Commerce (BACC) **[40867]**
"The Buck Stops Here" in Canadian Business (Vol. 81, November 10, 2008, No. 19, pp. 25) **[8648]**, **[12928]**, **[22511]**, **[28469]**, **[29692]**, **[31860]**
Buck or Two Plus! [32362]
A Buck or Two Stores Ltd. **[32362]**
Buckeye Lake Region Chamber of Commerce **[43421]**
Buckeye Valley Chamber of Commerce **[36317]**
"Buckhead Image Consultant Takes Time to Know Clients" in Northside Neighbor (August 4, 2017) **[8649]**
Buckingham Chamber of Commerce **[45839]**
Buckingham County Chamber of Commerce [45839]
Buckley Chamber of Commerce **[46058]**
Bucknell University Entrepreneurs Incubator (BUEI) **[44385]**
Bucknell University Small Business Development Center (SBDC) **[44092]**
Buckner Chamber of Commerce **[41527]**
Buck's Pizza Franchising Corporation, Inc. **[12543]**
Bucyrus Area Chamber of Commerce (BACC) **[43422]**
Buda Area Chamber of Commerce (BACC) **[45061]**
Budd Lake Chamber of Commerce [42167]
Budget Blinds, LLC (BB) **[1573]**
Budget Brake and Muffler Distributors Ltd. (https://budgetbrake.com/company/contact-us/) **[1169]**
Budgeting for Publications **[16764]**
"Budgeting vs. Forecasting: What's the Difference Between the Two?" in FreshBooks Hub **[16789]**, **[17492]**
Buena Park Map **[36762]**
Buena Venture Associates L.P. (BVA) **[45437]**
Buena Vista Chamber of Commerce **[37825]**
Buffalo Area Chamber of Commerce **[41528]**
Buffalo Area Chamber of Commerce (BACC) **[41200]**
Buffalo, Barrels, & Bourbon: The Story of How Buffalo Trace Distillery Became The World's Most Awarded Distillery **[1907]**, **[17436]**
Buffalo Business First **[42989]**
Buffalo Chamber of Commerce **[45062]**
Buffalo Chamber of Commerce [46597]
Buffalo & Erie County Public Library-Business, Science & Technology **[16896]**, **[18465]**, **[27382]**
Buffalo Grove Chamber of Commerce [39108]
Buffalo Grove Lincolnshire Chamber of Commerce (BGLCC) **[39108]**
Buffalo Niagara Partnership (BNP) **[42528]**
Buffalo Philly's - Wings, Cheesesteaks N' More **[14131]**
Buffalo State College Small Business Development Center (SBDC) **[42395]**
Buffalo Wild Wings Grill & Bar [14132]
Buffalo Wild Wings Inc. **[14132]**
Buffalo Wild Wings & Weck [14132]
Buffalo Wings & Rings L.L.C. **[14133]**
Buffalo, Wyoming Chamber of Commerce **[46597]**
Buhl Chamber of Commerce **[38907]**
"Buhler Versatile Launches Next Generation of Equipment" in Farm Industry News (November 23, 2011) **[17008]**, **[27476]**, **[29135]**
"Buick Prices Verano Below Rival Luxury Compacts" in Automotive News (Vol. 86, October 31, 2011, No. 6488, pp. 10) **[11384]**, **[19991]**, **[29136]**
Build, Buy or Franchise? The Best Way to Jumpstart Your Entrepreneurial Journey with Tim Vogel **[16645]**
Build Diversity, Equity and Inclusion in the Workplace **[30541]**
"Build Your Business Through Networking" in U.S. Small Business Administration website (Nov. 16, 2018) **[18848]**
Build Your Own Beekeeping Equipment **[1477]**
"Build Your Own Shooting Range" in RealTree (June 26, 2018) **[848]**
"Builder Confidence Boost Highest in Nearly 10 Years" in Small Business Trends(February 17, 2023) **[4009]**
"Builder Confidence Continues Cautious Increase" in Small Business Trends (March 16, 2023). **[2018]**, **[4010]**
Builder Incubator **[2015]**
Builder: The Magazine of the National Association of Home Builders **[4271]**
"Builders Aim to Cut Costs: Pushing Changes to Regain Share of Residential Market; Seek Council's Help" in Crain's New York Business **[4011]**, **[9389]**, **[17283]**, **[19789]**, **[19992]**, **[25231]**, **[35173]**
"Builder's Bankruptcy Fans Fears" in Crain's Cleveland Business (Vol. 28, October 22, 2007, No. 42, pp. 1) **[4012]**, **[13156]**, **[13408]**, **[20777]**
"Builder's Comeback Highlights Uptick in Demand for New Homes" in Boston Business Journal (Vol. 29, June 3, 2011, No. 4, pp. 1) **[4013]**, **[13157]**
Builders Hardware Manufacturers Association (BHMA) **[7910]**
"Builders: Land Prices Up, Bank Lending Down" in Orlando Business Journal (Vol. 30, January 31, 2014, No. 32, pp. 5) **[4014]**, **[13158]**, **[13409]**, **[28106]**
Building Applications with Microsoft Access 2007: Hands-On (Onsite) **[21340]**
Building Better Work Relationships: New Techniques for Results-oriented Communication **[22042]**
"Building Black-Owned Bigger" in Crain's Chicago Business (November 11, 2021) **[22512]**, **[30329]**
Building Brick by Brick with Torrey C Butler **[22881]**
Building Business & Apartment Management (BBAM) **[771]**
"Building a Business Website: A Small Business Guide" in Business News Daily (March 7, 2023) **[16398]**
Building a Community **[30416]**, **[34416]**
Building a Community of Climate Entrepreneurs in New Mexico with Wart Hendon **[23423]**
Building Conservation Associates Inc. (BCA) **[930]**
Building and Construction Trades Department - Canadian Office **[35144]**
"Building an Estate Sale Business by Franchising a Name and Brand" in The New York Times (May 4, 2016) **[6067]**, **[24341]**
"Building Fast-Growing Companies" in South Florida Business Journal (Vol. 35, September 19, 2014, No. 8, pp. 16) **[4015]**, **[17969]**, **[23790]**
Building a Global SaaS Company **[34584]**
Building a High Tech Marketing Agency **[30150]**
"Building Inclusive Markets in Rural Bangladesh: How Intermediaries Work Institutional Voids" in Academy of Management Journal (Vol. 55, August 1, 2012, No. 4, pp. 819) **[27477]**
Building a More Diverse and Inclusive Culture **[30542]**
Building Owners and Managers Association International (BOMA) **[13629]**
Building Owners and Managers Association International Annual Convention **[12909]**
Building the Perfect Scorecard to Achieve DE&I Goals **[30543]**
"Building a Portfolio, BRIC by BRIC" in Barron's (Vol. 92, August 25, 2012, No. 38, pp. M8) **[9390]**, **[20778]**, **[27478]**
Building a Positive, Motivated and Cooperative Team (Onsite) **[28297]**
"Building the Right Culture Can Add Huge Value" in South Florida Business Journal (Vol. 34, May 9, 2014, No. 42, pp. 20) **[22105]**, **[23791]**
Building a Secure Startup **[32396]**
Building Service Contractors Association International (BSCAI) **[2046]**
Building Socially Beneficial Companies Leveraging AI with Prashant Samant **[34417]**
Building Stone Institute [10732]
Building a Strategy Focused Organization (Onsite) **[19435]**
Building a Successful Business Analysis Work Plan **[28298]**
"Building a Sustainable Business" developed by the Minnesota Institute for Sustainable Agriculture; published by Sustainable Agriculture Research and Education. **[17009]**, **[18907]**
"Building Targeted for Marriott in Violation" in Business Journal-Milwaukee (Vol. 28, December 24, 2010, No. 12, pp. A1) **[4016]**, **[8370]**, **[14395]**, **[25232]**
Building Up Women, Building Communities **[35896]**
Building Wealth in China: 36 True Stories of Chinese Millionaires and How They Made Their Fortunes **[8694]**, **[22513]**, **[27479]**
Building a Wellness Business That Lasts: How to Make a Great Living Doing What You Love **[1375]**, **[6813]**, **[10760]**
"Building a Workforce" in Business Journal Milwaukee (Vol. 29, July 27, 2012, No. 44, pp. 1) **[24953]**, **[26510]**, **[30544]**
"Building a Workplace Harassment Policy That Keeps You and Your Employees Safe" in Legal Zoom (March 9, 2023) **[26890]**
Building XML Web Services with Java- Hands-On (Onsite) **[22979]**
Building XML Web Services with .NET: Hands-On (Onsite) **[22980]**
BUILDING.CO **[38553]**
The BuildingGreen Report **[4272]**
"Buildings to Flank Broken Spoke: Legendary Country Dance Hall To Be Surrounded But Won't Be Touched" in Austin Business Journal (Vol. 32, April 13, 2012, No. 6, pp. 1) **[4017]**, **[13774]**, **[13915]**, **[32113]**
BuildingSMART Alliance [4376]
BuildingStars International **[2092]**
Buildng an Event Strategy that Connects with Your Community **[6100]**
"Built For Growth" in Canadian Business (Vol. 87, July 2014, No. 7, pp. 50) **[17970]**, **[33114]**
Built to Last: Successful Habits of Visionary Companies **[22514]**, **[24613]**
Built to Sell: Creating a Business That Can Thrive Without You **[16549]**
Bulk Barn Foods Ltd. **[15057]**
"A Bull Market in Finger-Pointing" in Barron's (Vol. 88, March 10, 2008, No. 10, pp. 9) **[6311]**, **[9391]**, **[11016]**, **[20257]**, **[20779]**, **[23792]**
Bull Shoals Lake White River Chamber of Commerce **[36443]**
Bulldog Angel Network! (BAN) **[35266]**, **[41438]**
The Bulletin of the Association for Business Communication [17817]
Bulletin of the Business Historical Society [24857]
Bullhead Area Chamber of Commerce **[36318]**
"Bullied Into Legislation" in Philadelphia Business Journal (Vol. 33, February 21, 2014, No. 2, pp. 4) **[20561]**, **[25233]**
"Bullish Alert: A Brave Market Call" in Barron's (Vol. 92, July 23, 2012, No. 30, pp. 12) **[6312]**, **[9392]**, **[17971]**

Small Business Sourcebook • 42nd Edition 3197

Bullitt County Chamber of Commerce [40020]
Bullpen Capital [37319]
Bulverde Spring Branch Area Chamber of Commerce (BSBACOC) [45063]
Bunker Hill Community College [40768]
Burbank Chamber of Commerce [36763]
Bureau d'Assurance du Canada [8869]
Bureau of Envelope Manufacturers of America [11659]
Bureau of Indian Affairs - Business Utilization and Development Specialist - Aberdeen Area Office [47670]
Bureau of Indian Affairs - Business Utilization and Development Specialist - Albuquerque Area Office [47671]
Bureau of Indian Affairs - Business Utilization and Development Specialist - Anadarko Area Office [47672]
Bureau of Indian Affairs - Business Utilization and Development Specialist - Billings Area Office [47673]
Bureau of Indian Affairs - Business Utilization and Development Specialist - Minneapolis Area Office [47674]
Bureau of Indian Affairs - Business Utilization and Development Specialist - Muskogee Area Office [47675]
Bureau of Indian Affairs - Business Utilization and Development Specialist - Phoenix Area Office [47676]
Bureau of Indian Affairs - Business Utilization and Development Specialist - Portland Area Office [47677]
Bureau of Indian Affairs - Business Utilization and Development Specialist - Sacramento Area Office [47678]
Bureau of Land Management - Alaska State Office [47688]
Bureau of Land Management - California State Office [47691]
Bureau of Land Management - Colorado State Office [47692]
Bureau of Land Management - Idaho State Office [47694]
Bureau of Land Management - Montana State Office [47695]
Bureau of Land Management - Nevada State Office [47696]
Bureau of Land Management - New Mexico State Office [47697]
Bureau of Land Management - Utah State Office [47699]
Bureau of Land Management - Wyoming State Office [47700]
Bureau of Ocean Energy Management - Alaska OCS Region [47679]
Bureau of Ocean Energy Management (POR) - Pacific OCS Region [47680]
Bureau of Ocean Energy Management, Regulation and Enforcement - Alaska OCS Region [47679]
Bureau of Ocean Energy Management, Regulation and Enforcement - Pacific OCS Region [47680]
Bureau of Reclamation - Business Utilization and Development Specialist - Great Plains Region [47701]
Bureau of Reclamation - Business Utilization and Development Specialist - Lower Colorado Region [47702]
Bureau of Reclamation - Business Utilization and Development Specialist - Mid-Pacific Region [47703]
Bureau of Reclamation - Business Utilization and Development Specialist - Pacific Northwest Region [47704]
Bureau of Reclamation - Business Utilization and Development Specialist - Phoenix Area Office [47705]
Bureau of Reclamation - Business Utilization and Development Specialist - Upper Colorado Region [47706]
Burger King Corporation (BKC) [14134]
"Burger King Moves Forward on Commitment to Electric Vehicles" in Bizwomen (March 27, 2023) [1156], [13916]
Burkburnett Chamber of Commerce [45064]
Burke County Chamber of Commerce [43097]
Burleson Area Chamber of Commerce (BACC) [45065]
Burleson County Chamber of Commerce - Caldwell Office [45066]
Burley Chamber of Commerce [38930]
Burlingame Business [36764]
Burlingame Chamber of Commerce [36765]
Burlington Area Chamber of Commerce (BACC) [46372]
Burlington Chamber of Commerce (BCC) [46059]
Burlington County Chamber of Commerce [42104]
Burlington County College [42256]
Burlington County Regional Chamber of Commerce (BCRCC) [42104]
Burlington Mercer Chamber of Commerce [42105]
Burnet Chamber of Commerce [45067]
Burney Basin Chamber of Commerce [36766]
Burney Chamber of Commerce [36766]
"A Burning Issue: Lives Are at Stake Every Day" in Contractor (Vol. 56, October 2009, No. 10, pp. 29) [4018], [12618], [27845]

Burnsville Chamber of Commerce [41201]
The Burson Center [38826]
Burwell Chamber of Commerce [41842]
Buset & Partners [9004], [13352], [13630]
Bushnell Chamber of Commerce [39109]
Business [36767], [36768], [38699], [38700], [39110]
Business Advancement Inc. (BAI) [2225]
"Business Adventures by John Brooks - A 30-Minute Instaread Summay: Twelve Classic Tales from the World of Wall Street" [6313], [9393]
Business Advisory Centre of Northumberland (BECN) [46842]
Business Advisory Council [2377]
Business Advisory Group (BAG) [46843]
The Business Advocate [36319]
Business Alabama [36199]
Business America [827], [2159]
Business Analysis for Dummies [17972]
Business Analysis Essentials (Onsite) [28299], [33765]
Business Angel Minority Association [30246]
Business Answers International Inc. (BAI) [28962]
The Business of Antiques [727], [1059]
Business As a Force for Good and Impact Leadership with Catherine Bell [28244]
Business Automation Associates Inc. [3446]
Business Automation Specialists of Minnesota Inc. (BASM) [2226]
Business Barometer [20682], [24587], [26755], [33448], [43423]
Business of Beauty: A Resource Guide [1379], [4546]
Business Benefits, Inc. (BBI) [17392], [24236]
Business Black Belt: Develop the Strength, Flexibility and Agility to Run Your Company [6314], [20089], [21462], [22515], [23793], [26891], [28470], [29693], [32482]
Business Books International [38117]
"Business Books for Women" in Small Business Trends(October 31, 2022) [16550], [35745]
Business Boutique [35916]
Business Breakthroughs Inc. [3447]
Business of Brides Annual Conference [2008]
Business Brief [41202]
"Business Briefs: Alcoholic Beverage Manufacturing Is Big Business In Idaho" in Idaho Business Review (August 19, 2014) [1908], [15007], [17973], [29137]
Business Broadcast [43424]
Business Brokers of Florida (BBF) [2129], [38200]
Business Brokers Hawaii L.L.C. (BBH) [2157]
Business Browser North America [27794]
Business Browser U.S. [27794]
"Business Builders: Tradeshow Attendance Incentives Add Up" in Pet Product News (Vol. 64, December 2010, No. 12, pp. 14) [12161], [15838], [17284], [19338], [32114], [34749], [35033]
The Business Bulletin [40021]
Business to Business [42529]
The Business to Business Marketer [19247]
Business Bytes [43425]
Business Call [40022]
"The Business Case for Diversity May Be Backfiring, a New Study Shows" in Forbes (June 20, 2022) [30545]
The Business Center (TBC) [27125], [44386]
Business Central [41203]
Business Centre [31606]
Business Coach L.L.C. [28963]
Business & Commercial Law Journal [18764]
Business Communication Consultants Inc. [17803]
Business Communication Quarterly [17817]
Business Communication Solutions L.L.C. (BCS) [17804]
Business and Community [41529]
Business Computer Consultants, Inc. (BCCI) [16870]
Business Computer Report [33924]
Business Confidant [38604]
The Business Connection [36769]
Business Connections [40868], [46060]
Business Consultants Network Inc. (NYBC) [2227]
Business Consulting: Insane But True Facts About Consulting [2182]
Business Consulting Services [2228], [20165]
Business Consumer Alliance (BCA) [36716]
Business Control Systems L.P. (BCS) [15651], [15652], [15653]
Business Conversation for Sales and Service (Onsite) [17540], [22043]
Business Conversation Skills for the Multilingual Professional (Onsite) [17541]
Business Council (BC) [2377]
Business Council of Georgia [38733]
Business Council on National Issues [20688]
Business Council of New York State Conference [24836]
Business Council of Westchester (BCW) [42530]
Business Courier [43692]
The Business of Craft with Abby Glassenberg [4625]
Business Credit: The Publication for Credit and Finance Professionals [20366]

Business Culture Consultants [21704]
Business & Decision USA [3448]
Business Development Advisors Inc. (BDA) [30182]
Business Development Association of Orange County (BDA/OC) [36534]
Business Development Bank of Canada (BDC) [11105]
Business Development Board of Martin County (BDBMC) [38201]
Business Development Centre (BDC) [45942]
Business Development Corporation for a Greater Massena (BDC) [42373]
Business Development Corporation of the Northern Panhandle [46247]
Business Development Div. - Wisconsin Department of Commerce [46337], [46546]
Business Development for Dummies [17974]
Business Development Group Inc. (BDG) [19129], [22310]
The Business Development Incubator at New Jersey City University (BDI) [42232]
Business Development International Corp. [2229]
Business Development International Inc. (BDII) [10510]
"Business Diary" in Crain's Detroit Business (Vol. 24, October 6, 2008, No. 40, pp. 23) [17975], [18531], [20780], [24614], [30693], [31219], [33115], [33431], [33548]
Business Directory [26769], [36320], [36321], [36322], [36770], [36771], [36772], [36773], [36774], [36775], [36776], [36777], [36778], [36779], [36780], [36781], [36782], [38336], [38337], [38701], [39111], [39112], [39718], [40869], [40870], [40871], [40872], [41204], [42304], [43098], [43099], [43100], [43426], [43949], [44637], [45068], [45840], [46061], [46373], [46374], [46598]
Business Directory of Bedford [43427]
Business Directory and Buyer's Guide [42106]
Business Directory/Buyer's Guide [42531]
Business Directory and Buying Guide [40873]
Business Directory and Community Guide [36783]
Business Directory and Map [42107]
Business and Economic Review [24855]
Business Economics: Designed to Serve the Needs of People Who Use Economics in Their Work [21256]
Business Education Forum: Official Publication of the National Business Education Association [21736]
"The Business End of Staying in Business" in Contractor (Vol. 56, September 2009, No. 9, pp. 51) [6315], [12619], [33549]
Business Engineering [10511]
Business Enterprise Centre (BEC) [46844]
Business Enterprise Mapping Inc. (BEM) [2230]
Business Equipment Manufacturers Association [3689], [11660]
Business Ethics Journal Review (BEJR) [23570]
Business Ethics Quarterly [23571]
Business Ethics: The Magazine of Corporate Responsibility [23553], [34412]
"Business Execs Await Walker's Tax Cut Plan" in Business Journal-Milwaukee (Vol. 28, December 17, 2010, No. 11, pp. A1) [23794], [34750]
Business Extravaganza [21682]
Business Facilities: The Location Advisor [33430]
Business Facilities: The Source for Corporate Site Selectors [21247], [33425]
The Business Factory [45500]
Business Fairy Tales [22516], [23477], [24615]
Business Farmer [17200]
Business Financial Consultants Inc. (BFC) [16871]
"Business Financing Tips for Hispanic Small Business Owners" in Legal Zoom (February 13, 2023) [30330]
Business First of Buffalo: Western New York's Business Newspaper [42990]
Business Focus [36784]
Business Forecast Systems Inc. [2231]
Business Franchise Guide [24509]
Business Freedom Index [24616]
Business & Government Continuity Services Inc. [2232]
Business and Government Strategies International (BGSI) [21252]
Business Grammar & Proofreading (Onsite) [17828]
"Business Grants from Papaya Available to Women Small Business Owners" in Small Business Trends (March 9, 2023) [35746]
The Business Group [28964], [33651]
Business Guide and Business Relocation [38908]
"A Business Guide to Diversity, Equity, and Inclusion" in U.S. Chamber of Commerce (Sept. 14, 2021) [30546]
"Business Guide and Employment Role" [5467], [20781], [23795], [26892], [28471]
Business History [24856]
Business History: A Resource Guide [2413]
Business History Conference Meeting [24837]
Business History Review [24857]

Business Horizons [24858]
"Business Ideas for Teens - 30 Teen Business Ideas" in *TRUiC* (Feb. 4, 2022) [36014]
Business Improvement Architects (BIA) [2233], [10512], [20166], [21705], [28965], [30183]
"Business Incubator" in *HowDo* [8806]
Business Incubator Association of New York State (BIANYS) [33512]
Business Incubator at Breanu University (BIBU) [38827]
Business Incubator Center (BIC) [37932]
Business Incubator Center Kitchen (BIC) [37933]
Business Incubator: The Ultimate Step-By-Step Guide [8807], [30913]
Business Industrial Network (BIN) [29465]
Business and Industry [44179]
Business and Industry Advisory Committee to the OECD (BIAC) [27401]
Business and Industry Directory [43101], [43511]
Business Information Group Inc. (BIG) [3781]
Business Information Review (BIR) [24859]
Business Innovation Group (BIG) [38828]
Business Insider [36785]
Business and Institutional Furniture Manufacturer's Association (BIFMA) [11629]
Business Insurance [8987], [17417], [25991], [27380]
Business Insurance Consultants Inc. (BIC) [27372]
Business Insurance for Tattoo Parlors [15296]
"Business Insurance: When You Need It and When You Don't" in *Legal Zoom* (March 23, 2023) [27244]
Business Interiors [11646]
Business Jet Traveler [19420]
The Business Journal Serving San Jose and Silicon Valley [37697]
Business Know-How: An Operational Guide for Home-Based and Micro-Sized Businesses with Limited Budgets [24617], [26770]
Business and Labor History: Primary Sources at the Library of Congress [2414], [19151]
The Business Law Center on WestlawNext [18743], [24237]
Business Law Journal (BLJ) [18765]
Business Law Monographs [18766]
Business Law Section of the Florida Bar [18477], [38202]
Business Law Today (BLT) [18767]
The Business Lawyer [18768]
"Business Leaders Share Their Predictions about the Lasting Impact of COVID-19" in *Legal Zoom* (February 21, 2023) [26893]
Business Learning Center (BLC) [16872]
Business and Legal Forms for Authors and Self-Publishers [5347]
Business Logic Incorporated [30994]
"Business Looks for Results in Congress" in *Baltimore Business Journal* (Vol. 28, November 5, 2010, No. 26, pp. 1) [18532], [24618], [24954], [25234], [26511]
Business Management Consultants [10513], [28966]
Business Management for Entrepreneurs [22517], [28472]
Business Management for Tropical Dairy Farmers [17010], [23796], [28473]
Business Marketing Association Carolinas Chapter [43032]
Business Marketing Association Chicago Chapter [38966]
Business Marketing Association Houston Chapter (BMAHOU) [44878]
Business Marketing Association Milwaukee Chapter [46310]
Business Marketing Association - National Industrial Advertisers Association - Association of Industrial Advertisers [29570]
Business Marketing Association Northern California Chapter [36535]
Business Marketing Association Southern California Chapter (SoCal BMA) [36536]
Business Marketing Consultants (BMC) [31607]
Business Matters [36786]
"The Business of Medicine: Maintaining a Healthy Bottom Line" in *Black Enterprise* (Vol. 41, October 2010, No. 3, pp. 60) [25235], [25724]
Business Meeting & Event Planning for Dummies [17643]
Business Methods Corp. (BMC) [17520]
Business Modeling and Integration Domain Task Force (BMIDTF) [28255]
Business Month [38708]
Business Monthly [41205]
Business in Nebraska [41901]
Business Network International Alaska [36202]
Business Network International - Austin, Dallas, Fort Worth, San Antonio (BNI) [44879]
Business Network International, Buffalo Region [42374]

Business Network International Central Alabama and Southwest Georgia [36042]
Business Network International, Central Ohio/Greater Columbus Area [43331]
Business Network International, Central and Southern Illinois [38967]
Business Network International, Central West Florida (BNI WCF) [38203]
Business Network International, Columbia Area [44495]
Business Network International Connecticut [37973]
Business Network International, Dallas/Ft. Worth Area [44879]
Business Network International Denver Metro [37773]
Business Network International, Eastern Ohio/Greater Akron Area [43332]
Business Network International - Eugene Metro [43902]
Business Network International, Greater Albany/Rochester/Syracuse [42377]
Business Network International, Greater Boston Region [40486]
Business Network International Hawaii [38859]
Business Network International Heartland--Nebraska, Wyoming, South Dakota, Western Iowa [39669], [41813], [44621], [46589]
Business Network International Inc. (BNI) [18800], [33449]
Business Network International Indiana [39466]
Business Network International Iowa [39670]
Business Network International Louisiana [40120]
Business Network International Maryland - East - BNI 4 Shore [40331]
Business Network International, Maryland and Washington D.C. [40331]
Business Network International Miami Dade [38204]
Business Network International Michigan [40793]
Business Network International Mid America [38968], [41460]
Business Network International - Mid-South (BNI) [44676]
Business Network International, Middle Tennessee [44677]
Business Network International Minnesota & Northern Wisconsin (BNI MN) [41148]
Business Network International New Hampshire [41967]
Business Network International, New Mexico [42270]
Business Network International New York [42375]
Business Network International, Northeast Ohio/Greater Cleveland Area [43333]
Business Network International Northeast Texas [44880]
Business Network International Northern Alabama [36043]
Business Network International, Northern Arizona (BNI) [36262]
Business Network International Northern Indiana [39467]
Business Network International, Northwest Ohio [43334]
Business Network International Ohio [43335]
Business Network International Oklahoma-East [43701]
Business Network International, Reno Area [41907]
Business Network International Shenandoah Valley [45758]
Business Network International - South Central and South Texas [44881]
Business Network International South East Tennessee [44678]
Business Network International - Southern Alabama [36044]
Business Network International - Southwest Kentucky Northern Ohio (BNI) [39988]
Business Network International - Staten Island Area [42376]
Business Network International Upstate New York [42377]
Business Network International Vermont [45697]
Business Network International - West Texas [44882]
Business Network International West Virginia [46248]
Business Network International Western Pennsylvania (BNI-WPA) [44084]
Business Network International Wisconsin South & Upper Peninsula Michigan [40794], [46311]
Business Networks Inc. [46729]
Business New Brunswick [46732]
Business News [36444], [40874], [43950]
Business News and Views [46062]
Business NH Magazine [42027]
Business North Carolina (BNC) [43260]
Business, Occupations, Professions, & Vocations in the Bible [24619], [34279]
Business Online [38338]
Business Opportunities for People Who Sew at Home [14649]
Business Opportunity Expo [30169]
Business Opportunity Fair [24838]
Business Oregon - Global Strategy Section [43919]

Business Organizations with Tax Planning [34947]
Business Outlook [41530]
Business Ownership Strategies L.L.C. (BOS) [33652]
"Business Partnership Agreement Writing Guide" in *Business News Daily* (February 21, 2023) [34497]
Business People Magazine [39663]
Business Performance Associates Inc. (BPA) [2234]
Business Performance Improvement Consortium L.L.C. (BPI) [10514], [28967]
Business Performance Improvement Consortium L.L.C. [10515]
Business Periodicals Index [2994], [24902]
Business Periodicals Index Retrospective™: 1913-1982 [2994], [24902]
Business Perspective [39870]
Business by Phone Inc. [15552]
The Business Place Ltd. [31608], [35442]
Business Plan [45069]
Business Plan Basics [18872], [33517], [35702]
Business Plan Writing Help Center [18908]
Business Planning Consultants, Inc. [19130]
Business Planning Inc. (BPI) [2383], [17393]
Business Plans for Dummies [18909]
Business Plans Handbook [18910]
Business Plans Kit for Dummies [18911], [24620]
Business Plans That Work: A Guide for Small Business [18912], [24621]
Business Process Analysis [28300]
Business Process Consulting Group (BPCG) [2235], [29466]
Business Process Management Initiative and Object Management Group [28255]
Business Process Reengineering for Competitive Advantage (Onsite) [21341]
Business and Professional Chamber of Commerce of McCloud [37019]
Business and Professional Communication: A Practical Guide to Workplace Effectiveness [14312]
Business and Professional Communication Quarterly (BPCQ) [17817]
Business and Professional Directory [39112]
Business and Professional Women of Boulder (BPWB) [35571]
Business and Professional Women of Charlotte County [35572]
Business and Professional Women - Concord [35593]
Business and Professional Women - Fayetteville [35573]
Business and Professional Women - Granite Falls [35574]
Business and Professional Women/Jupiter [35575]
Business and Professional Women Michigan (BPW/Michigan) [35576]
Business and Professional Women of North Carolina (BPW-NC) [35577]
Business and Professional Women of Raleigh [35578]
Business and Professional Women/St. Petersburg-Pinellas [35579]
Business and Professional Women Tallahassee [35580]
Business and Professional Women of Tennessee (BPWTN) [35581]
Business and Professional Women Valley Sunset District [35582]
Business and Professional Women/Vermont (BPW/VT) [35583]
Business and Professional Women of Washington State (BPW/WA) [35584]
Business and Professional Women - West St. Tammany [35674]
Business and Professional Women's Club of Canonsburg [35585]
Business and Professional Women's Club of the Lehigh Valley [35586]
Business and Professional Women's Foundation (BPW) [35930]
Business Professionals of America (BPA) [21306]
Business Professionals of America National Leadership Conference [21683]
Business Psychology and Organizational Behaviour [16551], [17644], [23478]
Business and Quality Process Management L.L.C. (BQPM) [2236]
Business Referral Guide [45070]
The Business Research Lab [27126]
Business Research Services, Inc. (BRS) [10689]
Business Resource Consulting L.L.C. (BRC) [27127]
Business Resource Directory [36787], [45071]
Business Resource Group Inc. [28968]
Business Review [43951]
"Business for Sale: Pocket Change?" in *Inc.* (Vol. 30, December 2008, No. 12, pp. 28) [1532], [10979], [33006]
"Business Scams 101: Common Schemes and How to Avoid Them" in *business.com* (Sept. 20, 2022) [19257]

"Business Sidestepped Trouble" in Denver Business Journal (Vol. 65, May 9, 2014, No. 52, pp. A8) [25236], [34751]
Business for Social Responsibility (BSR) [34256]
Business & Society [24860]
Business Software Alliance (BSA) [14747], [33738]
Business Software Association [14747], [33738]
Business Source® Alumni Edition [24903]
Business Spotlight Inc. [2237]
Business Staffing Inc. [27128]
"Business Stands Firm for Reform: Battle Over 2011 Budget Expected" in Crain's Detroit Business (Vol. 26, January 4, 2010, No. 1, pp. 3) [17493], [20782], [33963], [34752]
"Business Succession Planning From an Estate Planner's Perspective" in New Jersey Law Review (December 7, 2007) [18913], [23601]
Business Sweden [27402]
Business Systems Consultants Inc. (BSCI) [3449]
Business Systems Consulting (BSC) [35443]
Business Talk [40875]
"Business Tax Complaints Prompt Action" in Sacramento Business Journal (Vol. 28, July 29, 2011, No. 22, pp. 1) [25237], [34753]
Business Team (BT) [2158], [19703], [31609], [33052]
"Business Team Building Activities" in Chron [22106]
Business Tech, Ltd. (BTA) [3782]
Business Technology Associates [3450]
Business Technology Associates [3782]
Business Technology Association (BTA) [11658], [16528]
Business Technology Center (BTC) [45501]
Business Technology Center of Los Angeles County (BTC) [37551]
Business Technology Consultants, Inc. [3451]
Business Technology Group Inc. (BTG) [26727]
Business and Technology Institute Small Business Development Center [39841]
Business Technology Partners L.L.P. [3452]
The Business Times [37962]
"Business Tips on Spending Smart in Tough Times" in Legal Zoom (March 27, 2023) [18914]
Business-to-Business Marketing 2023 [10641], [29487], [29694]
Business Today (Princeton, New Jersey) [24861]
"Business Travel Can be a Trip if Structured Right" in Globe & Mail (February 3, 2007, pp. B11) [19339], [24622]
Business Travel News [19418]
Business Traveller Middle East [16023]
Business Update [37690], [37691], [43261], [45584]
Business as Usual [1581], [4509], [20090], [22518], [34280], [35747]
Business Utilization and Development Specialist - Branch of Procurement Management [47690]
Business Valuation Inc. (BVI) [24238]
Business Ventures Corp. [20543], [28969]
Business View [36087], [36788]
Business Visions L.L.C. [19131]
Business and Visitors Guide [40876]
Business Warrior: Strategy for Entrepreneurs [19790], [22519], [24623], [26894], [28474], [29695], [32483]
Business Watch [38339]
Business Week Magazine [33624]
Business Wire [3537], [3564], [3794], [6719], [9939], [11103]
"Business Wisdom from the Mountaintops" in Canadian Business (Vol. 83, October 12, 2010, No. 17, pp. 91) [19340], [28475]
"Business Without Borders: All For One, None for All?" in Canadian Business (Vol. 83, October 12, 2010, No. 17, pp. 60) [8695], [19791], [25238], [27480], [31220]
Business Works of Ohio L.L.C. [3453]
Business Writing for Administrative Professionals [17829]
Business Writing and Grammar Skills Made Easy and Fun! (Onsite) [17830]
Business Writing & Grammar Skills (Onsite) [17831]
Business Writing and Grammar Skills (Onsite) [17832]
Business Writing for the Multilingual Professional [17833]
business.com (Feb. 1, 2022); "Small Business Guide to Alternative Lending" in [30935]
business.com (Jan. 7, 2020); "How to Design a Workspace That Improves Productivity" in [31040]
"Businesses Encouraged to Imagine the Possibilities With Meeting Planner Package" in Internet Wire (May 23, 2012) [8371], [11904], [15839]
"Businesses Fret Over Crime Wave" in Philadelphia Business Journal (Vol. 31, February 10, 2012, No. 52, pp. 1) [7088], [14396]
"Businesses Owned by Women Grow Twice as Fast" in Business News Daily (Sept. 23, 2019) [35748]
BusinessLink [21257]
BusinessMedia [30184]
"BusinessOnLine Launches New Web-Based Search Engine Optimization Tool: First Link Checker for Google" in Marketwired (October 19, 2009) [9108], [14765], [16399], [29696], [33838]

BusinessPlanWorld.com [19132]
BusinessWoman [35925]
"But Is It Legal? Dogs in the Office" in Legal Zoom (March 21, 2023) [26895]
"Butane Heated Pressure Washer Offers Diverse Cleaning Options" in Product News Network (March 8, 2011) [2064], [12695], [33116]
Butler Area Chamber of Commerce [44180]
Butler County Chamber of Commerce (BCCC) [44181]
Butte Business Center [38950]
Butte College SBDC [36563]
Butte College Small Business Development Center [36563]
Butte SCORE [41737]
Butte-Silver Bow Chamber of Commerce [41755]
Butterflies in Progress L.L.C. [35444]
Buttonwillow Chamber of Commerce [36789]
Buy an Existing Business or Franchise [19648]
"Buy the Pants, Save the Planet?" in Globe & Mail (February 5, 2007, pp. B1) [3094], [23127], [29697]
Buyer's Guide [44182]
Buyer's Guide and Membership Directory [43428]
Buyer's Guide of Used Machine Tools & Metal Working Equipment Dealers [10446]
"Buyers Shouldn't Bank on Cheaper Fresh Atlantic Cod" in IntraFish (November 2, 2019) [6746]
"Buying a Food Truck: Advice, Insight on Customization, Design and Decor" in FoodTruckOperator.com (March 9, 2020) [6967]
Buying and Running a Guesthouse or Small Hotel [1413], [8372]
"Buying a Short Sale Property: A Guide to Understanding the Short Sale Process and How to Profit From Short Sale" [11017], [13159]
Buyology: Truth and Lies About Why We Buy [2721], [11385], [29138], [29698]
"Buyout Rumors Have Rackspace Back in the News" in San Antonio Business Journal (Vol. 28, September 12, 2014, No. 31, pp. 6) [3488], [9109], [19649], [21803], [31221]
Buzz [43429]
The Buzz [15969]
"Buzz Kill" in Canadian Business (Vol. 83, August 17, 2010, No. 13-14, pp. 24) [1478], [17011]
BVM Capital Partners LLC [40206]
BW-3 [14132]
bwTech@UMBC Research and Technology Park [40445]
Byline [36790]
ByrneMRG Corp. [2238], [10516], [20167], [28970], [30847]
Byron Area Chamber of Commerce [39113]
Byte & Mortar [41080]
BYU Idaho [38954]

C

"C-Class Could Boost Auto Suppliers" in Birmingham Business Journal (Vol. 31, June 27, 2014, No. 26, pp. 10) [1098], [11386], [20783], [29139]
"C. Fla. Notches $5B in Real Estate Property Sales in Last 12 Months" in Orlando Business Journal (Vol. 31, July 4, 2014, No. 1, pp. 4) [875], [4019], [13160], [13410], [20784]
C Programming: Hands-On (Onsite) [21342], [33766]
C++ Programming for Non-C Programmers (Onsite) [21343]
C. W Post Campus of Long Island University - Long Island University [42970]
CAA News [979]
"Cabela's Plans Outpost Strategy for Smaller Markets" in Pet Product News (Vol. 66, April 2012, No. 4, pp. 21) [10018], [15087], [32115]
"Caber Engineering Helps to Reduce Canada's Carbon Footprint" in Ecology,Environment & Conservation Business (July 16, 2011, pp. 7) [5551], [5830], [23128]
"Cabi to Develop Major Retail Project" in South Florida Business Journal (Vol. 32, July 6, 2012, No. 50, pp. 1) [4020], [13411], [27481], [32116]
Cabinet & Vanity Manufacturing Industry in the US - Market Research Report [2642]
Cable Area Chamber of Commerce (CACC) [46375]
Cable and Telecommunications: A Marketing Society [2442], [15572]
Cable Television Administration and Marketing Society [2442], [15572]
"Cable TV News Viewership Slows in July, Fox News Keeps Lead" in MediaPost (August 1, 2019) [2448]
Cabot Chamber of Commerce [36445]
Cache Chamber of Commerce (CCC) [45628]
Cactus Car Wash [2584]
CADA Newsline [11358]
"CADD Microsystems Launches the CADD Community, Partners with Global eTraining to Provide Online, On-Demand Training for Autodesk Software" in Computer Business Week (August 28, 2014, pp. 24) [14766], [21463], [21804], [31222], [33839]

Cadillac Area Business Magazine [40877]
Cadillac Area Chamber of Commerce (CACC) [40878]
"Cadillac Tower Largest to Start in a Decade" in Globe & Mail (March 28, 2006, pp. B5) [4021], [17976], [18915]
Cadiz-Trigg County Chamber of Commerce [40023]
Cadott Chamber of Commerce [46376]
Cadott Community Association [46376]
Cadwalader, Wickersham & Taft Library [562], [5765]
"Caesars Deals a New Reality" in Memphis Business Journal (No. 35, April 4, 2014, No. 52, pp. 4) [7276], [33007]
Cafe Ala Carte [3206], [7573]
Café Association du Canada (CAC) [7540]
Café Dépôt [7574]
Caffeinated Capital [37320]
CAG Conference [21684]
CAG Family Conference [21684]
Cahokia Area Chamber of Commerce (CCC) [39114]
CAHPERD State Conference [4861], [12447]
CahrConference [27117]
CAIA Association (CAIAA) [23696]
Cairo Chamber of Commerce [42532]
Cal/EPA [5738], [23417]
Calabasas Chamber of Commerce [36791]
Calais Regional Chamber of Commerce [40302]
Calaveras County Chamber of Commerce (CCCC) [36792]
Calaveras County Small Business Development Center [36564]
Calbiotech [37552]
Caldwell Chamber of Commerce [38909]
Caldwell Community College and Technical Institute-Small Business Center [43255]
Caldwell County Chamber of Commerce (CCCC) [43102]
"Calendar" in Crain's Detroit Business (Vol. 24, March 10, 2008, No. 10, pp. 21) [8696], [14508], [15840], [20785], [22520], [23129], [27482], [29699], [30331], [34754], [35034], [35749]
Calendar of Events [42533], [44183], [45721]
Calhoun City Chamber of Commerce (CCCC) [41386]
Calhoun County Chamber of Commerce (CCCOC) [36088]
Caliche Ltd. [35959]
Caliente Chamber of Commerce [41930]
California Apparel News [2857]
California Association of Business Brokers (CABB) [2130], [36537]
California Association of Collectors Annual Conference [20363]
California Association for Health, Physical Education, Recreation, and Dance State Conference [4861], [12447]
California Association of Pet Professionals [835], [12183]
California Association of Realtors (CAR) [13082]
California Botanic Garden (CALBG) [7661]
California Builder & Engineer [4273]
California Business Bank (CBB) [28082], [37321]
California Business Incubation Alliance (CBIA) [37553]
California Canning Peach Association (CCPA) [16932]
California Chamber of Commerce [41531]
California Chamber of Commerce (CCC) [36793]
California Chamber of Commerce - Southern California Office [36793]
California Clean Energy Fund (CalCEF) [37322]
California Closet Company Inc. (CC) [11655], [11675], [12854], [31106]
California Coast Venture Forum (CCVF) [37665]
California Collectors Association Annual Conference and Expo [20363]
California College of the Arts Libraries - Meyer Library [3364], [4639], [4691]
California Conference for Women [35587]
California Council for the Social Studies Conference [21685]
California Department of Conservation - Division of Recycling - Resource Center [7980], [13748]
California Department of Finance (SCDC) - State Census Data Center [46928]
California Department of General Services - Office of Small Business and Disabled Veteran Business Enterprise Services [36601]
California Department of General Services - Office of Small Business and DVBE Services - Small & Minority Business [37263]
California Department of Housing and Community Development Housing Resource Center [12920]
California Department of Pesticide Regulation Library (DPR) [12064]
California Department of Resources Recycling and Recovery Library [13749]
California Environmental Protection Agency (CalEPA) [563]

California Film Commission (CFC) - Location Resource Center Library **[6220]**
"California Forces Pet Stores to Sell Only Dogs and Cats from Shelters" in The New York Times (January 2, 2019) **[12191]**, **[25239]**
California Fresno Small Business Development Center, Lead Office **[36565]**
"The California Fur Ban and What It Means for You" in The New York Times (October 14, 2019) **[7234]**, **[25240]**
California Grape Grower [15045]
California HR Conference **[27117]**
California Institute for Energy Efficiency [550]
California Institute for Quantitative Biosciences [37615]
California Institute for Rural Studies (CIRS) **[17230]**
California Israel Chamber of Commerce (CICC) **[36794]**
California Land Surveyors Association Conference **[15230]**
California Los Angeles Region Small Business Development Center, Lead Office **[36566]**
California Office of Small Business Certification and Resources [36601]
California Optometric Association OptoWest **[16311]**
"California has a Plan B for Enacting Health Care Reform" in Sacramento Business Journal (Vol. 29, May 18, 2012, No. 12, pp. 1) **[18533]**, **[25725]**
California Polytechnic State University - Robert F. Kennedy Library - Government Documents and Map Department - Diablo Canyon Power Plant Depository Library **[2419]**
California Procurement Technical Assistance Center - The Federal Technology Center (FTC) **[37535]**
California Procurement Technical Assistance Center - San Diego Contracting Opportunities Center (SDCOC) **[37536]**
California Public Health Foundation [10942]
California Real Estate Services Division Library **[4361]**
"California Restaurant Association Sues to Block Berkeley, Calif., Natural Gas Ban" in Nation's Restaurant News (November 22, 2019) **[13917]**, **[33117]**
California San Diego Small Business Development Center, Lead Office **[36602]**
California Society of Etchers [3286]
California Society of Printmakers (CSP) **[3286]**
California State Department of Motor Vehicles - Licensing Operations Division - Research and Development Branch - Traffic Safety Research Library **[1176]**, **[5113]**, **[10293]**, **[15529]**
California State Polytechnic University, Pomona College of Environmental Design - John T. Lyle Center for Regenerative Studies **[14971]**
California State Polytechnic University, Pomona - Don B. Huntley College of Agriculture - Apparel Technology & Research Center (ATRC) **[29474]**
California State Polytechnic University - W.K. Kellogg Arabian Horse Library (WKKAHL) **[8330]**
California State University, Fresno - Center for Agricultural Business [17231]
California State University, Fresno - Institute for Food and Agriculture (IFA) **[17231]**
California State University, Long Beach College of Health and Human Services - Graduate Center for Public Policy and Administration (GCPPA) **[31719]**
California State University, Los Angeles - Edmund G. Brown Institute for Public Affairs **[26109]**
California State University Press **[37701]**
California Technology Ventures L.L.C. (CTV) **[37323]**
California University of Pennsylvania - Louis L. Manderino Library - Special Collections **[748]**, **[992]**, **[11211]**, **[11293]**
California Vehicle Leasing Association [1152]
"California vs. Freelance Writers" in National Review (October 22, 2019) **[5312]**, **[25241]**, **[26771]**
"California Water Treatment Facility Turns to Solar Power" in Chemical Business Newsbase (September 11, 2012) **[13701]**, **[14910]**, **[29140]**, **[31683]**, **[35323]**
"California Wines Nab 64 Percent of U.S. Sales" in Sacramento Business Journal (Vol. 31, April 25, 2014, No. 9) **[15008]**, **[17012]**, **[17977]**
"California's Largest Recycling Business Closes, 750 Laid Off" in U.S. News & World Report (August 5, 2019) **[13702]**
CALISO Consulting L.L.C. **[33653]**
"Calista Sells Rural Newspapers" in Alaska Business Monthly (Vol. 27, October 2011, No. 10, pp. 8) **[11974]**, **[12727]**, **[19650]**, **[33008]**
Calistoga Chamber of Commerce (CCC) **[36795]**
"The Call of the City" in Puget Sound Business Journal (Vol. 35, September 5, 2014, No. 20, pp. 16) **[27846]**, **[32117]**, **[33352]**
Call and Contact Center Expo USA **[20540]**
"Call for Superblock Jobs Tie-In Lacks Baltimore Backing" in Baltimore Business Journal (Vol. 30, June 1, 2012, No. 4, pp. 1) **[25242]**, **[26512]**, **[34755]**
Callaway Chamber of Commerce (CCC) **[41532]**
"Calling All Creatives, Innovators, 'Expats': Detroit Is Hopping In September" in Crain's Detroit Business (Vol. 30, September 1, 2014, No. 35, pp. 6) **[14509]**, **[20786]**, **[27847]**
Calmac Manufacturing Corp. **[540]**
"Calpine Gets Ready to Light It Up" in Barron's (Vol. 92, July 23, 2012, No. 30, pp. 15) **[5552]**, **[5831]**, **[6316]**, **[9394]**, **[17978]**
CALTRUX **[16093]**
Calvert Chamber of Commerce **[45072]**
Calvert County Chamber of Commerce (CCCC) **[40370]**
Calvert Social Venture Partners L.P. **[45918]**
Cam Supply Inc. **[15321]**
Camara de Comercio Latina de los EEUU [27421]
Cámara De Comercio De Puerto Rico **[46638]**
Camara En Accion **[46639]**
Camas-Washougal Chamber of Commerce **[46063]**
Cambria Chamber of Commerce **[36796]**
The Cambria Group **[45438]**
Cambridge Area Chamber of Commerce (CCC) **[43430]**
Cambridge Area Chamber of Commerce [41280]
Cambridge Area Chamber of Commerce Visitors and Convention Bureau [43430]
Cambridge Capital Management Corp. **[39628]**
Cambridge Chamber of Commerce (CCC) **[40564]**, **[46774]**
Cambridge Innovation Center (CIC) **[40746]**
Cambridge Public Library - Audio-Visual Department **[11212]**
Cambridge Quarterly of Healthcare Ethics **[25992]**
Cambridge Samsung Partners L.L.C. (CSP) **[44043]**
Cambridge Seven Associates Inc. **[31063]**
Camden Area Chamber of Commerce (CACC) **[42534]**
Camden County Chamber of Commerce **[38702]**
Camden County Regional Chamber of Commerce **[42108]**
Camdenton Area Chamber of Commerce **[41533]**
"Cameco to Supply Reactors With Recycled Nukem Warheads" in Canadian Business (Vol. 85, August 13, 2012, No. 13, pp. 10) **[6317]**, **[9395]**, **[27483]**, **[31223]**
Camelot Therapeutic Horsemanship - Camelot Library **[8331]**
Camelot Venture Group (CVG) **[35464]**
Camera de Comercio Espana - Estados Unidos [27430]
Camera Stores Industry in the US - Market Research Report **[2498]**
Cameron Area Chamber of Commerce **[41534]**
Cameron Chamber of Commerce **[45073]**
Cameron University - Center for Emerging Technology and Entrepreneurial Studies (CU) **[43850]**
Camilla Chamber of Commerce **[38703]**
Camille's Sidewalk Cafe **[3860]**, **[4892]**
Camp Bow Wow Franchising, Inc. (CBW) **[12109]**
Camp Horsemanship Association [8305]
Camp Inc. [3681], [43673]
Camp Run-A-Mutt (CRAM) **[12110]**
"Campaign Ads Lucrative for Denver's TV Stations" in Denver Business Journal (Vol. 64, September 7, 2012, No. 16, pp. 1) **[248]**, **[15586]**
"Campaign Launches to Educate Hispanics on Tax Preparation" in Economics Week (February 3, 2012, pp. 35) **[7089]**, **[15368]**, **[30547]**, **[34281]**
Campaign Solutions **[12953]**
"Campaigner Survey: 46 Percent of Small Businesses Use Email Marketing" in Wireless News (November 21, 2009) **[9110]**, **[17855]**, **[17979]**, **[21805]**, **[29700]**, **[33964]**
Campbell Chamber of Commerce (CCC) **[36797]**
"Campbell Clinic in Expansion Mode: Plans to Triple Size of Surgery Center, Add Employees" in Memphis Business Journal (Vol. 34, August 24, 2012, No. 19, pp. 1) **[17980]**, **[25726]**, **[26513]**
Campbell Connection **[36798]**
Campbell County Chamber of Commerce **[46599]**
Campbell County Chamber of Commerce (CCCC) **[44718]**
Campbell Soup Company Research Information Center **[11608]**
Campbellsville - Taylor County Chamber of Commerce **[40024]**
Campgrounds & RV Parks Industry in the US - Market Research Report **[2525]**
Camping Magazine **[2526]**
Camping Magazine--Buyer's Guide Issue [2512]
CAMUS International **[29075]**
CAN BE Innovation Center [44392]
Can Clean **[4829]**
"Can Day Care Help a Child Succeed in School?" in VeryWellFamily (September 30, 2019) **[2877]**
"Can Fashion Designs Be Copyrighted?" in Legal Zoom (March 27, 2023) **[27848]**
"Can He Win the Patent Game?" in Globe & Mail (February 20, 2006, pp. B1) **[18534]**, **[22521]**, **[27849]**, **[28476]**
"Can I Have More Than One LLC?" in Legal Zoom (February 17, 2023) **[27171]**
"Can Online Legal Services Really Help Your Business?" in Business News Daily (February 21, 2021) **[10218]**
"Can People Collaborate Effectively While Working Remotely? Vint Cerf, Co-Creator of the Internet, On How Employees Can Work Together More Productively In An Age When Many Can Work Almost Anywhere" in Gallup Business Journal (March 13, 2014) **[9111]**, **[22107]**
"Can Slow and Steady Win the Eco-Devo Race?" in Birmingham Business Journal (Vol. 31, June 6, 2014, No. 23, pp. 8) **[20787]**, **[26235]**
"Can Tech Industry Share Wealth?" in Puget Sound Business Journal (Vol. 35, May 23, 2014, No. 5, pp. 10) **[20788]**, **[26236]**, **[35035]**
"Can We Afford Sustainable Business?" in MIT Sloan Management Review (Sept. 8, 2021) **[34282]**
"Can We Talk?" in Canadian Business (Vol. 79, September 11, 2006, No. 18, pp. 131) **[17645]**, **[24624]**
"Can You Cook Food from Home and Sell As a Delivery Business" in Marketing Food Online Blog (Jan. 24, 2022) **[6901]**
"Can You Hear Them Now?" in Hawaii Business (Vol. 54, August 2008, No. 2, pp. 48) **[2722]**, **[17981]**, **[26237]**, **[32484]**, **[33118]**
"Can You Make a Million Bucks in the House Cleaning Business?" in Cleaning Business Today (July 13, 2016) **[2970]**, **[17982]**, **[18916]**
"Can You Make a Profit and Be Socially Responsible?" in Business.com (April 8, 2020) **[34283]**
"Can You Overcome Fear of Public Speaking? Y.E.S." in Idaho Business Review (August 22, 2014) **[17646]**
"Can You Really Manage Engagement Without Managers? Zappos May Soon Find Out, as the Online Retailer is Eliminating the Traditional Manager Role" in Gallup Business Journal (April 24, 2014) **[11718]**, **[28477]**
"Can You Say $1 Million? A Language-Learning Start-Up Is Hoping That Investors Can" in Inc. (Vol. 33, November 2011, No. 9, pp. 116) **[15920]**, **[16400]**, **[21295]**, **[28107]**, **[30914]**
Canaan **[37324]**
Canaan Partners **[38087]**
"Canada in 2020 Energy: Mr. Clean" in Canadian Business (Vol. 81, October 27, 2008, No. 18, pp. 74) **[5553]**, **[5832]**, **[23130]**, **[35324]**
Canada Agriculture and Agri-Food - Dairy and Swine Research and Development Centre Lennoxville - Canadian Agriculture Library **[17206]**
Canada Bread Company, Limited **[1224]**
Canada Business Network **[46721]**
The Canada Co. **[17191]**
Canada Earth Energy Association [5505]
Canada-Finland Chamber of Commerce (CFCC) **[20683]**
Canada Fitness Survey [12375], [12478]
Canada Hippique [8306]
Canada-India Business Council (C-IBC) **[20684]**
Canada Industrial Innovation Centre [22451], [30857]
"Canada Joins TPP Free Trade Talks" in Canadian Business (Vol. 85, August 13, 2012, No. 13, pp. 7) **[8697]**, **[25243]**, **[27484]**, **[31224]**
Canada National Committee of the International Association on Water Pollution Research and Control [23026]
Canada National Research Council - CISTI Institute for Research in Construction Branch **[4362]**
"Canada Nears European Trade Treaty" in Globe & Mail (February 5, 2007, pp. B1) **[20789]**, **[25244]**, **[27485]**
"Canada, Not China, Is Partner In Our Economic Prosperity" in Crain's Chicago Business (Vol. 31, April 14, 2008, No. 15, pp. 14) **[8698]**, **[17983]**, **[20790]**, **[27486]**
Canada Numismatica **[3238]**, **[3274]**
Canada Office of the Auditor General Knowledge Centre Library **[162]**
Canada-Pakistan Business Council (CPBC) **[20685]**
Canada School of Public Service Library **[29048]**
"Canada Seeks Collection Agency To Pursue $129M In Fines" in PaymentsSource (August 21, 2012) **[4771]**, **[20258]**, **[25119]**, **[25245]**
"Canada Tops Again in G7: Study" in Globe & Mail (March 22, 2006, pp. B8) **[20791]**, **[24625]**
Canada-United States Business Association (CUSBA) **[27403]**
"Canada's Largest Bakery Officially Opened Today" in Ecology,Environment & Conservation Business (October 15, 2011, pp. 7) **[1248]**, **[4022]**, **[5554]**, **[5833]**, **[23131]**
"Canada's New Government Introduces Amendments to Deny Work Permits to Foreign Strippers" in Marketwired (May 16, 2007) **[1321]**, **[25246]**
Canadawide Financial Corporation Ltd. (CFCL) **[46845]**
Canadian Aboriginal and Minority Supplier Council (CAMSC) **[46775]**

Small Business Sourcebook • 42nd Edition **3201**

Canadian Academic Accounting Association (CAAA) [18]
Canadian Academy of Periodontology (CAP) [25649]
Canadian Academy of Recording Arts and Sciences (CARAS) [13645]
Canadian Academy of Sport and Exercise Medicine [12479]
Canadian Accounting Perspectives [51]
Canadian Accredited Independent Schools (CAIS) [21307]
Canadian Administrative Housekeepers' Association [2047], [5075]
Canadian Aerophilatelic Society (CAS) [3219]
Canadian Aerophilatelist [3220]
Canadian Agricultural Engineering [16933]
Canadian American Business Council (CABC) [27404]
Canadian Angus Association [2170], [17891], [28253]
Canadian Apparel Directory [3095], [10307]
Canadian Apparel Manufacturer--Buyers' Guide Issue [3095], [10307]
Canadian Association of Aquarium Clubs (CAOAC) [834]
Canadian Association of Broadcasters [13015], [15569]
Canadian Association for Business Economics (CABE) [20686]
Canadian Association for Distance Education [21310]
Canadian Association of Environmental Management (CAEM) [2047], [5075]
Canadian Association of Fairs and Exhibitions [594]
Canadian Association of Gerontology (CAG) [25650]
Canadian Association for Health, Physical Education and Recreation [12383]
Canadian Association for Health, Physical Education, Recreation and Dance [12383]
Canadian Association of Home and Property Inspectors (CAHPI) [2011]
Canadian Association of Importers and Exporters [20698]
Canadian Association of Independent Schools [21307]
Canadian Association for Information Science (CAIS) [8829]
Canadian Association of Insolvency and Restructuring Professionals (CAIRP) [6228]
Canadian Association of International Development Consultants [2171], [20077]
Canadian Association of International Development Professionals (CAIDP) [2171], [20077]
Canadian Association of Journalists (CAJ) [5276], [11959]
Canadian Association of Labour Media (CALM) [35145]
Canadian Association of Landscape Architecture [10074]
Canadian Association of Message Exchange Inc. [1508], [15557], [16325]
Canadian Association of Message Exchanges [1508], [15557], [16325]
Canadian Association of Mutual Insurance Companies [8859]
Canadian Association of Nurses in Oncology (CANO) [8235]
Canadian Association of Optometrists (CAO) [16284]
Canadian Association of Photographers and Illustrators in Communications [3287], [12290]
Canadian Association of Physical Medicine & Rehabilitation (CAPMR) [12485]
Canadian Association of Professional Employees (CAPE) [35146]
Canadian Association of Professional Image Creators (CAPIC) [3287], [12290]
Canadian Association of Professional Speakers (CAPS) [35445]
Canadian Association of Recycling Industries [13684]
Canadian Association of Token Collectors (CATC) [3263]
Canadian Association on Water Quality (CAWQ) [23026]
Canadian Association of Women Executives and Entrepreneurs (CAWEE) [35588]
Canadian Automatic Merchandising Association [16246]
"Canadian Banks Too Timid in China, Beijing Tells Flaherty" in Globe & Mail (January 22, 2007, pp. B1) [6318], [9396]
Canadian Biosystems Engineering [16933]
Canadian Board of Marine Underwriters (CBMU) [8860]
Canadian Bookbinders and Book Artists Guild (CBBAG) [1729]
Canadian Broadcasting Corporation - Reference Library/ Image Research Library [13060]
Canadian Business Aircraft Operators [415]
Canadian Business Aviation Association (CBAA) [415]
Canadian Business Aviation Association Convention and Exhibition [438]
Canadian Call Management Association (CAM-X) [1508], [15557], [16325]
Canadian Camping Association (CCA) [2502]
Canadian Cancer Society [25690]
Canadian Cardiovascular Society (CCS) [25651]
Canadian Carwash Association (CCA) [2579]
Canadian Cat Association [630]

Canadian Centre for Architecture (CCA) [861]
Canadian Chamber of Commerce [20687]
Canadian Chemical Engineering Conference [32922]
Canadian Chemistry Conference and Exhibition [32923]
Canadian Children's Book Centre (CCBC) [1617]
Canadian Children's Book News [1618]
Canadian Coin News [3239]
Canadian College of Health Leaders (CCHL) [25652]
Canadian College of Health Service Executives [25652]
Canadian Committee on Irrigation and Drainage [23023]
Canadian Community Newspapers Association [11970]
Canadian Construction Association (CCA) [3926]
Canadian Consulting Engineer [2172]
Canadian Contractor [11960]
Canadian Cooperative Wool Growers Magazine: Livestock Supply Catalogue [7231]
Canadian Copyright Institute (CCI) [1619], [5277], [11961]
Canadian Cosmetic, Toiletry and Fragrance Association [4503]
Canadian Council for Aboriginal Business [20692]
Canadian Council of Chief Executives [20688]
Canadian Council of Land Surveyors [15217]
Canadian Council for Small Business and Entrepreneurship (CCSBE) [33450]
Canadian Crafts Council [4701]
Canadian Crafts Federation (CCF) [4701]
Canadian Credit Institute Educational Foundation [6234]
Canadian Decorating Products Association [9029], [11873]
Canadian Dermatology Association (CDA) [25653]
Canadian Disc Jockey Association (CDJA) [4960], [13017]
Canadian Educational Standards Institute [21307]
Canadian Electrical Contractors Association [5350]
Canadian Environmental Defence Fund [5487]
Canadian Environmental Law Association (CELA) [5477]
Canadian Environmental Network [5478], [13685], [23027]
Canadian Equestrian Federation [8306]
Canadian Family Physician (CFP) [25654]
Canadian Federation of Business and Professional Women (CFBPWC) [35589]
Canadian Federation of Business and Professional Women British Columbia and Yukon [46688]
Canadian Federation of Business and Professional Women Montreal (BPW) [46883]
Canadian Federation of Independent Business (CFIB) [20689], [22950], [24588], [26756], [33451]
Canadian Federation of Music Teachers' Associations (CFMTA) [11164]
Canadian Federation of University Women (CFUW) [21308]
Canadian Fire Alarm Association [14369]
Canadian Fitness and Lifestyle Research Institute [12375], [12478]
Canadian Foundation for Dietetic Research [11566]
Canadian Foundation for Dispute Resolution [10784]
Canadian Foundry Association [10417]
Canadian Franchise Association [24305]
Canadian Fur Trade Development Institute [7227], [7233]
Canadian Gemmological Association (CGA) [9959]
Canadian German Chamber of Industry and Commerce. Inc [20702]
Canadian Good Roads Association [15509]
Canadian Grain Commission Library (CGC) [17207]
Canadian Health Coalition [25666]
Canadian Health Food Association (CHFA) [7995], [8088], [11561]
Canadian Healthcare Association [25674]
Canadian Home Builders Association (CHBA) [3927]
Canadian Home Care Association [8234]
The Canadian Home Inspector [2012]
"Canadian Hydronics Businesses Promote 'Beautiful Heat'" in Indoor Comfort Marketing (Vol. 70, September 2011, No. 9, pp. 10) [473], [5555], [5834], [23132], [27487], [29701], [33965]
Canadian Image Processing and Pattern Recognition Society [3418], [3599]
Canadian Importers Association [20698]
Canadian Independent Adjusters Association (CIAA) [8861]
Canadian Independent Music Association (CIMA) [13646]
Canadian Independent Record Production Association [13646]
Canadian Industrial Relations Association [35143]
Canadian Innovation Centre (CIC) [22451], [30857]
Canadian Innovation Centre Resource Centre (CIC) [33727], [46865]
Canadian Institute of Financial Planning (CIFP) [6229]
Canadian Institute of Gemmology (CIG) [9960]
Canadian Institute of Management (CIM) [28256]

Canadian Institute of Plumbing and Heating (CIPH) [7911]
Canadian Institute of Public and Private Real Estate Companies [13112], [13366]
Canadian Institute of Quantity Surveyors (CIQS) [19], [1737]
Canadian Institute of Steel Construction (CISC) [3928]
Canadian Insurance Accountants Association (CIAA) [20]
Canadian International Trade Tribunal Library [27796]
Canadian Investor Relations Institute (CIRI) [6230]
Canadian Jewellers Association (CJA) [9961]
Canadian Journal on Aging (CJA) [25655]
Canadian Journal of Biochemistry [32856]
The Canadian Journal of Cardiology [25656]
Canadian Journal of Chemistry [32861]
Canadian Journal of Comparative Medicine/Veterinary Science [681]
Canadian Journal of Dietetic Practice and Research [11562], [25993]
Canadian Journal of Information and Library Science [8830]
Canadian Journal of Learning and Technology [21309]
Canadian Journal of Medical Laboratory Science (CJLMS) [10906]
Canadian Journal of Medical Technology [10906]
Canadian Journal of Ophthalmology (CJO) [16285]
Canadian Journal of Optometry [16286]
The Canadian Journal of Psychiatry (CJP) [25657]
Canadian Journal of Public Health [25994]
Canadian Journal of Veterinary Research (CJVR) [681]
Canadian Kendo Federation (CKF) [10713]
Canadian Kennel Club (CKC) [631]
Canadian Labour Congress (CLC) [20690], [35147], [35215]
Canadian Library Handbook [8836]
Canadian Library Yearbook [8836]
Canadian Life and Health Insurance Association Inc. (CLHIA) [8862]
Canadian Management Centre (CMC) [28257]
The Canadian Manager [28258]
Canadian Manufacturing Technology Show [29459]
Canadian Marketing Association (CMA) [216]
Canadian Meat Council (CMC) [2426]
Canadian Media Guild (CMG) [35148]
Canadian Media Producers Association (CMPA) [6160]
Canadian Media Production Association [6160]
Canadian Medical Association [25648]
Canadian Medical Protective Association (CMPA) [25658]
Canadian Mental Health Association (CMHA) [25659]
Canadian MoneySaver [15431]
The Canadian Music Teacher [11165]
The Canadian Music Teacher: Canada Music Week Edition [11166]
Canadian National Exhibition (CNE) [15816]
Canadian Netherlands Business and Professional Association Inc. [20697]
Canadian Network for Innovation in Education (CNIE) [21310]
Canadian Network of Toxicology Centres (CNTC) [5479]
Canadian Numismatic Association [3217]
Canadian Numismatic Association Library [3261]
Canadian Numismatic Research Society (CNRS) [3221]
Canadian Nursery Landscape Association (CNLA) [7605], [10073]
Canadian Nursery Trades Association [7605], [10073]
Canadian Nurses Foundation (CNF) [8236]
Canadian Nutrition Society (CNS) [11563]
Canadian Oncology Nursing Journal [8237]
Canadian Ophthalmological Society (COS) [16287]
Canadian Paediatric Society (CPS) [25660]
Canadian Paediatric Society - News Bulletin [25669]
Canadian Pain Society (CPS) [25661]
Canadian Parks and Wilderness Society [5503]
Canadian Patent Reporter Plus (CPR) [27975]
"Canadian Patients Give Detroit Hospitals a Boost" in Crain's Detroit Business (Vol. 24, April 14, 2008, No. 15, pp. 10) [17984], [25727], [27488]
Canadian Payroll Association [11925], [16743]
"Canadian Pet Charities Won't Go Hungry" in Pet Product News (Vol. 66, September 2012, No. 9, pp. 15) [7090], [12192], [29141], [34284]
Canadian Pharmaceutical Journal [5135]
Canadian Pharmacists Association [5134]
Canadian Pharmacists Journal (CPJ) [5135]
The Canadian Philatelist [3222]
Canadian Physical Education Association [12383]
Canadian Plastic Bag Association [29076]
Canadian Plastics Industry Association (CPIA) [29076]
Canadian Poolplayers Association (CPA) [1542], [12684]
Canadian Property Valuation [820]
Canadian Protector Company Ltd. [42771]
Canadian Psychiatric Association (CPA) [25662]

Master Index CarBiz

Master Index

Canadian Public Administration (CPA) **[31703]**
Canadian Public Health Association (CPHA) **[25663]**
Canadian Public Personnel Management Association [26841]
Canadian Public Relations Society (CPRS) **[12923]**
Canadian Publishers' Council (CPC) **[1620]**
Canadian Pulp and Paper Association [29073]
The Canadian Real Estate Association (CREA) **[13083]**
Canadian Real Estate Association Annual Conference and Trade Show **[773]**, **[35120]**
Canadian Recording Industry Association [13649]
Canadian Recreational Vehicle Association (CRVA) **[13670]**
Canadian Resort Development Association [8343]
Canadian Resort & Travel Association (CVOA) **[8343]**
Canadian Restaurant and Foodservices Association [2667], [3834], [4483], [4879], [6892], [8091], [13890], [14308]
Canadian Restaurant & Foodservices Association Resource Centre [2667], [3834], [4483], [4879], [6892], [8091], [13890], [14308]
Canadian Roofing Contractors Association [14320]
Canadian Rose Society (CRS) **[6847]**
Canadian School of Natural Nutrition (CSNN) **[21715]**
Canadian Scientific Pollution and Environment Control Society [5506], [13695], [23052]
Canadian Securities Institute [9292]
Canadian Security Association (CANASA) **[14370]**
Canadian ShareOwner Investments Inc [9302]
Canadian Ski Museum Archives **[14743]**
Canadian Small Business Kit for Dummies **[18535]**, **[22372]**, **[22522]**, **[24524]**, **[24626]**, **[27387]**, **[34756]**
Canadian Society of Association Executives (CSAE) **[1051]**
Canadian Society of Cinematographers--Directory **[6176]**
Canadian Society for Clinical Investigation [25691]
Canadian Society of Environmental Biologists [5504]
Canadian Society of Gastroenterology Nurses and Associates [8243]
Canadian Society of Landscape Architects (CSLA) **[10074]**
Canadian Society for Medical Laboratory Science (CSMLS) **[10907]**, **[10939]**
Canadian Society of Professional Event Planners [14505]
Canadian Society for the Study of Diseases of Children [25660]
"Canadian Solar Expands Into Puerto Rico With Planned 26MW Solar Power Plant Installation" in Benzinga.com (October 2, 2012) **[14911]**, **[17985]**, **[27489]**
Canadian Sporting Goods Association (CSGA) **[15077]**
Canadian Stamp News **[3240]**
Canadian Tax Foundation (CTF) **[21]**, **[15351]**, **[15484]**
Canadian Tax Journal **[22]**, **[15352]**
Canadian Teachers Federation (CTF) **[35149]**
Canadian Telecommunications Association (CWTA) **[2700]**
Canadian Therapeutic Riding Association (CanTRA) **[8304]**
Canadian Thoroughbred Horse Society (CTHS) **[632]**
Canadian Tire Corporation, Limited **[15689]**
Canadian Tourism Research Institute (CTRI) **[15722]**, **[15970]**
Canadian Translators Terminologists and Interpreters Council (CTTIC) **[15927]**
Canadian Trucking Alliance (CTA) **[16052]**
Canadian Union of Professional and Technical Employees [35146]
Canadian Union of Public Employees [35157]
Canadian University Music Society [11178]
Canadian University Press (CUP) **[11962]**
Canadian Valley Technology Center (CVTECH) **[43879]**
Canadian Venture Capital and Private Equity Association (CVCA) **[35267]**
Canadian Veterinary Journal (CVJ) **[682]**, **[702]**
Canadian Veterinary Medical Association (CVMA) **[683]**
Canadian Water Resources Association [23023]
Canadian Water Resources Journal **[23028]**
Canadian Welding Bureau (CWB) **[10418]**
Canadian Wilderness **[5480]**
"Canadian Wind Farm Sued Due to Negative Health Effects" in PC Magazine Online (September 22, 2011) **[5556]**, **[5835]**, **[18536]**, **[23133]**, **[25728]**
"Canadian Wine to Ship Across Provincial Borders: Let the Wine Flow Freely. Feds To Allow Shipments Inside Canada" in Canadian Business (Vol. 85, August 13, 2012, No. 13, pp. 8) **[10316]**, **[25247]**, **[32485]**
Canadian Wireless Telecommunications Association [2700]
The Canadian Writers Foundation [5288]
"The Canadians Are Coming!" in Canadian Business (Vol. 80, October 22, 2007, No. 21, pp. 15) **[6319]**, **[9397]**, **[27490]**, **[31225]**
Canal Partners LLC [36382]
Canal Winchester Area Chamber of Commerce (CWACC) **[43431]**
Canal Winchester Area Chamber of Commerce Newsletter **[43432]**
Canastota Bee-Journal **[12002]**
Canby Area Chamber of Commerce **[41206]**, **[43952]**
"Cancer-Fighting Entrepreneurs" in Austin Business Journal (Vol. 31, August 5, 2011, No. 22, pp. 1) **[21464]**, **[26514]**, **[31948]**, **[32735]**
"Cancer Genome Project Will Put San Antonio In Research Spotlight" in San Antonio Business Journal (Vol. 25, January 27, 2012, No. 53, pp. 1) **[25729]**, **[31949]**, **[32736]**
"Cancer Survivor Becomes Marathoner, Author" in Business Journal-Serving Phoenix & the Valley of the Sun (Vol. 30, August 20, 2010, No. 50, pp. 1) **[1646]**, **[12408]**, **[25730]**, **[35750]**
"Candidates Won't Bash Fed; Rate Cuts Bash Savers" in Barron's (Vol. 88, March 24, 2008, No. 12, pp. 31) **[6320]**, **[9398]**, **[20792]**, **[23797]**, **[25248]**
"Candor, Criticism, Teamwork" in Harvard Business Review (Vol. 90, January-February 2012, No.1-2, pp. 40) **[17647]**, **[22108]**
Candy Bouquet International (CBI) **[2555]**
Candy Industry Buyer's Guide **[2542]**
Candy Industry: The Global Magazine of Chocolate Confectionery **[2550]**
Canine Campus **[12111]**
"Canine Cuisine: AKC Tips for a Healthful Diet" in Seattle Times (September 13, 2008, pp. D9) **[8008]**, **[12193]**
Canine Dimensions **[12154]**
Canine Journal **[12077]**
Canna Advisors **[5066]**
Cannabis Business Association **[4968]**
Cannabis Business Solutions, Inc. (CBS) **[4969]**, **[38533]**
Cannabis Business Times (CBT) **[5035]**
"Cannabis Company Basics: Compliance Is Key" in Cannabis Business Executive (October 29, 2020) **[4992]**
Cannabis Culture Magazine **[5036]**
Cannabis Equipment & Accessory Stores Industry in the US - Market Research Report **[5028]**
"Cannabis Financing: Cannabis Equipment Financing Options in 2020" in Nav (October 21, 2020) **[4993]**
Cannabis Industry and Conference Expo **[5052]**
"Cannabis Industry Growth Potential for 2021" in Business News Daily (September 16, 2020) **[4994]**
"Cannabis Industry Job Growth Up 50 Percent" in Green Market Report (October 20, 2020) **[4995]**
Cannabis Industry Journal **[5029]**
"Cannabis Industry Recruiting Best Practices" in Cannabis Business Executive (November 3, 2020) **[4996]**
Cannabis Marketing Association (CMA) **[4970]**
Cannabis Now **[5037]**
Cannabis & Tech Today **[5038]**
Cannabis in the US **[5030]**
"Cannabis at Work: How Employers Are Reacting to the Legalization of Marijuana" in Business News Daily (June 10, 2020) **[34677]**
Cannon Beach Chamber of Commerce (CBCC) **[43953]**
Cannon Falls Area Chamber of Commerce **[41207]**
Canola Digest **[17142]**
Cañon City Chamber of Commerce [37895]
Canopy **[37934]**
Cantey & Company Inc. **[13612]**
Canton Area Chamber of Commerce (CACC) **[39115]**
Canton Chamber of Commerce **[44638]**
Canton Chamber of Commerce (CCC) **[40879]**, **[42535]**
Canton Regional Chamber of Commerce (CRCC) **[43433]**
Canton Regional SCORE **[43373]**
Canton Small Business Development Center **[42396]**
Canton Texas Chamber of Commerce (CTCC) **[45074]**
"CanWEA Unveils WindVision for BC: 5,250 MW of Wind Energy by 2025" in CNW Group (October 4, 2011) **[5557]**, **[5836]**, **[17986]**, **[23134]**, **[25249]**
"CanWest Plotting Buyback of Newspaper Income Trust" in Globe & Mail (February 7, 2007, pp. B1) **[19493]**, **[19651]**, **[33009]**
Canyon Chamber of Commerce (CCC) **[45075]**
Canyon Creek Capital **[37325]**
Cap-It International Inc. **[12806]**
Capacity Consulting **[42978]**
CapActix Business Solutions **[16873]**
Cape Ann Chamber of Commerce **[40565]**
Cape Cod Canal Region Chamber of Commerce **[40566]**
Cape Cod and the Islands SCORE **[40507]**
Cape Cod SCORE [40507]
Cape Coral Chamber of Commerce **[38340]**
Cape Fear Small Business and Technology Development Center **[43041]**
Cape Girardeau Area Chamber of Commerce **[41535]**
Cape Kennedy Area Chamber of Commerce [38355]
Cape May County Chamber of Commerce **[42109]**
Cape Vincent **[42536]**
Cape Vincent Chamber of Commerce **[42537]**
Capital Across America,L.P. **[44822]**
Capital Angel Network (CAN) **[46780]**
Capital Area Guide **[40269]**
Capital Balance L.L.C. **[132]**
Capital Business Solutions (CBS) **[2239]**
"Capital Coming Into City, but Local Money Lags" in Pittsburgh Business Times (Vol. 33, March 21, 2014, No. 36, pp. 4) **[9399]**, **[26238]**, **[35325]**
Capital and Exit Strategies for Impact Founders with Miyoko Schinner **[34418]**
Capital Factory **[45502]**
Capital For Business Inc. (CFB) **[41659]**
Capital Growth Inc. (CGI) **[40483]**
Capital Innovators (CI) **[41669]**
Capital Insights L.L.C. (CI) **[36383]**
"Capital Is a Good Bet as HQ Site, Report Says" in Sacramento Business Journal (Vol. 29, August 17, 2012, No. 25, pp. 1) **[20091]**, **[33353]**
Capital Kitchens **[45503]**
"Capital Metro May Soon Seek Contractor" in Austin Business Journal (Vol. 31, June 10, 2011, No. 14, pp. 1) **[4023]**, **[10279]**, **[25120]**, **[25250]**
Capital Midwest Fund (CMF) **[46547]**
The Capital Network Inc. **[45439]**
"Capital One and Count Me In for Women's Economic Independence to Launch Program to Support Women Veteran-Owned Small Businesses Across the U.S." in Investment Weekly News (June 23, 2012, pp. 210) **[21465]**, **[35751]**
"Capital One Expanding Campus in Plano" in Dallas Business Journal (Vol. 35, April 20, 2012, No. 2, pp. 1) **[4024]**, **[6321]**, **[26515]**
"Capital Position: M&I Acquisition Opens the Door for Rivals to Gain Market Share" in Business Journal-Milwaukee (Vol. 28, December 24, 2010, No. 12, pp. A1) **[9400]**, **[19652]**, **[19792]**, **[26516]**, **[26896]**, **[28108]**, **[31226]**
Capital Project Management Inc. (CPMI) **[4307]**
Capital Region Minority Supplier Development Council (CRMSDC) **[30255]**, **[40421]**
Capital Region SBDC **[36567]**
Capital Southwest Corporation (CSWC) **[45440]**
Capital + Support: Helping Native Entrepreneurs Thrive with Garry McBerryhill **[30628]**
Capitalism for Kids: Growing Up to Be Your Own Boss **[36015]**
"Capitalizing On Our Intellectual Capital" in Harvard Business Review (Vol. 90, May 2012, No. 5, pp. 42) **[21466]**, **[27491]**, **[28025]**, **[31227]**
Capitol Conference **[27365]**
Capitol Hill Association of Merchants and Professionals (CHAMPS) **[38165]**
"Capitol Ideas: Regions to Lansing: Focus on Taxes, Reform, Keeping Talent" in Crain's Detroit Business (Vol. 24, October 6, 2008) **[20793]**, **[24627]**, **[25251]**, **[26517]**, **[33550]**, **[33966]**
Capitol Services **[25617]**, **[37666]**
Capitola **[36799]**
Capitola Chamber of Commerce [36800]
Capitola-Soquel Chamber of Commerce **[36800]**
Capria Ventures LLC **[46187]**
Capsity **[37554]**
Capstone Communications Group **[30185]**
Capstone Community Action **[45743]**
CapStone Holdings, Inc. **[38616]**
Capt. Submarine **[4893]**
"Captain Planet" in (Vol. 90, June 2012, No. 6, pp. 112) **[18917]**, **[19494]**, **[20794]**, **[21467]**, **[28478]**, **[34285]**
"Capturing Generation Y: Ready, Set, Transform" in Credit Union Times (Vol. 21, July 14, 2010, No. 27, pp. 20) **[6322]**, **[9401]**, **[21806]**, **[23798]**, **[29702]**, **[33967]**
CapX Partners [39455]
"Car Audio Is Second-Fastest-Declining Profession in U.S." in CEPro (March 30, 2017) **[2565]**
Car Body Shops Industry in the US - Market Research Report **[1186]**
"Car Dealer Closings: Immoral, Slow-Death" in Crain's Detroit Business (Vol. 25, June 8, 2009, No. 23) **[11387]**, **[29142]**, **[35752]**
Car and Driver **[11459]**
"Car Parts Stocks are Down and for Once It's Not About Amazon" in Barron's (April 25, 2019) **[1099]**
Car Rental Industry in the US - Market Research Report **[1161]**
Car and Truck Renting and Leasing Association of Alabama [1155]
Car Wash & Auto Detailing Industry in the US - Market Research Report **[1134]**, **[2581]**
Car Wash to Cash Flow with Sean Oatney **[24446]**
Car-X Associates Corp. **[14578]**
"CarBiz Inc. Speaking At NABD" in Marketwired (May 14, 2007) **[11388]**, **[14767]**, **[15841]**, **[20092]**, **[35036]**

Small Business Sourcebook • 42nd Edition 3203

"Carbon Capture and Storage: Grave Concerns" in Canadian Business (Vol. 81, July 21 2008, No. 11, pp. 25) [18918], [20093], [23135], [25252], [33119], [33968], [34757]
Carbon County Chamber of Commerce (CCCC) [45629]
Carbondale Area Chamber of Commerce [44218]
Carbondale Chamber of Commerce (CCC) [39116]
Carbondale Chamber of Commerce [37826]
Carbondale Community Chamber of Commerce [37826]
Carbondale Technology Transfer Center (CTTC) [44387]
Cardiac Carr Co. [2894]
Cardiff-by-the-Sea Chamber of Commerce [36801]
Cardinal Partners / Cardinal Health Partners [42207]
Care.com, Inc. [12247]
The Career Development Quarterly (CDQ) [2610]
Career Dimensions Inc. [2613]
Career Directors International (CDI) [2591]
"Career Guidance Helps Students Figure Out Their Paths" in EdSource (May 26, 2015) [2597]
The Career Guide--Dun's Employment Opportunities Directory [5439]
Career Information Center [9994]
Career Planning and Adult Development Network (CPADN) [2592], [5433]
"The Career Shift from Employed to Independent" in Entrepreneur (October 27, 2017) [32987]
Careers in Focus--Business [2617]
Careers in Focus--Business Managers [2618]
Careers for Homebodies & Other Independent Souls [22523], [26772]
"Careers in Organic Food Production" in Occupational Outlook Quarterly (Vol. 54, Fall 2010, No. 3, pp. 3) [8009], [8092], [17013]
Careers for Self-Starters and Other Entrepreneurial Types [4646], [22373], [24525]
Careers USA, Inc. [5454], [15656]
CareerTech [43720], [43837]
CareMinders Home Care Inc. [189]
CARES Directory: Social and Health Services in the Greater New York Area [25731]
Carey Area Chamber of Commerce [43434]
CARF Newsletter [217]
CARF Update [218]
Cargill, Incorporated [17208]
The Caribbean American Chamber of Commerce & Industry Inc. (CACCI) [30256]
Caribbean - Central American Action (CCAA) [19290]
Caribbean/Central American Action [19290]
Caribbean/Latin American Action [19290]
"Caribou Coffee Kick-Starts Spring Planting with New Grounds for Your Ground Program in Time for Earth Day" in Ecology, Environment and Conservation Business (May 3, 2014, pp. 5) [7546], [23136], [32118]
Caribou Information Book [40270]
Caribou Information Book and Chamber of Commerce & Industry Membership Directory: Caribou Map and Guide (Maine) [40270]
"Caring Concern" in Small Business Opportunities (September 2010) [173], [8230], [26731]
Caring Senior Service [190]
Carleton University - Carleton Research Unit on Innovation, Science, and Environment (CRUISE) [31720]
Carlinville Community Chamber of Commerce [39117]
Carl's Jr. Restaurants LLC [14135]
Carlsbad Business Journal [36802]
Carlsbad Chamber of Commerce (CCC) [36803]
Carlsbad Small Business Development Center [42275]
Carlson Communications Corp. (CC) [12318]
Carmel Business Association [39591]
Carmel Chamber of Commerce [39591]
Carmi Chamber of Commerce (CCC) [39118]
Carmichael Chamber of Commerce (CCC) [36804]
Carnegie Library of Pittsburgh Downtown & Business [16897], [24281], [29049], [30232], [33714]
Carnegie Library of Pittsburgh - Music Department [993], [4559]
Carnegie Mellon University - Hunt Institute for Botanical Documentation Library [8159]
Carnegie Mellon University - Software Engineering Institute (SEI) [14892]
Carnegie Mellon University-Special Collections [12784], [16215]
Carnegie Mellon University - Tepper School of Business - Donald H. Jones Center for Entrepreneurship [44388]
"Carnival Cruise Lines Hosts First-Ever Wedding at Charleston's Annual 10K Cooper River Bridge Run" in Benzinga.com (April 4, 2011) [1965]
Caro Chamber of Commerce [40880]
Carol Stream Chamber of Commerce [39119]
Carolina Angel Network (CAN) [43217]
Carolina Foothills Chamber of Commerce [43103]
Carolinas Association of Chamber of Commerce Executives (CACCE) [43104], [44537]

Carolinas - Virginia Business Brokers Association (CVBBA) [2131], [43033]
Carolinas-Virginia Minority Supplier Development Council [45915]
"The Carpenter: A Story About the Greatest Success Strategies of All" [15141], [19495], [28479], [32486]
Carpenters Industry in the US - Market Research Report [2643]
"Carpenters Picket to Highlight Wage Theft Laws; Contractors Targeted Dispute Claims" in Twin Cities Pioneer Press (August 2, 2019) [2635]
Carpet Cleaning Industry in the US - Market Research Report [2982]
Carpet and Rug Institute (CRI) [6822]
Carpinteria Valley, Member Directory and Visitors Guide [36805]
Carrie Morey Founder and CE O of Callie's Hot Little Biscuit [14050]
Carrington Area Chamber of Commerce [43289]
"Carrington Co. LLC Revolutionizes the Hot Tea Market with First-Ever, Organic Tea in Eco-Friendly Packaging" in Ecology, Environment & Conservation Business (May 3, 2014, pp. 6) [7547], [8010], [13703], [23137]
Carrington Convention and Visitors Bureau [43289]
Carrizozo Chamber of Commerce [42305]
Carroll Chamber of Commerce (CCC) [39719]
Carroll County Chamber of Commerce [38704], [44719]
Carroll County Chamber of Commerce (CCCC) [40371]
Carroll County Chamber of Commerce Membership Directory and Buyer's Guide [40372]
"Cars Get Stuck at U.S. Garages for Weeks in Spare-Parts Shortage" in Bloomberg (October 16, 2021) [1100]
Carson Chamber of Commerce (CCC) [36806]
Carson City Area Chamber of Commerce [41931]
Carson City Nevada Small Business Development Center [41909]
Carson Valley Chamber of Commerce [41932]
Carson Valley Chamber of Commerce and Visitors Authority [41932]
CARSTAR Automotive Canada Inc. [1138]
Carter & Tani Attorneys at Law [2616], [18754]
Carteret County Chamber of Commerce (CCCC) [43105]
Cartersville-Bartow County Chamber of Commerce (CBC) [38705]
Carterville Chamber of Commerce [39120]
Cartesian Holdings, LLC [2240], [28971]
Cartesian, Inc. [2240], [28971]
Carthage Area Chamber of Commerce [42538]
Carthage Area Chamber of Commerce (CACC) [39121]
Carthage Chamber of Commerce (CCC) [41536]
Carthage Chamber of Commerce [39121]
Cartoon Cuts [1367], [7885]
Cartoonists Northwest (CNW) [3264]
Cartridge Express [12775]
Cartridge World [12776]
Carvel Franchisor SPV LLC [3861], [8612]
Carvel Ice Cream [3861], [8612]
"Carvel Offers Franchisee Discount" in Ice Cream Reporter (Vol. 21, August 20, 2008, No. 9, pp. 2) [8552], [24342]
Carver Peterson Consulting [33654]
"Carving Passion, Talent Help Couple Craft Business on Wood-Rich Land" in Crain's Cleveland Business (October 8, 2007) [4587], [22524], [23602]
Cary Chamber of Commerce [43106]
Cary Grove Area Chamber of Commerce [39122]
Caryl Baker Visage (CBV) [4539]
CAS Annual Meeting [10875]
Casabona Ventures LLC [42208]
Cascade Angels Fund [44044]
Cascade Chamber of Commerce (CCC) [38910]
Cascade Policy Institute [15485]
Cascade Seed Fund [44044]
"Cascades Awarded 'Innovative Product of the Year' and 'Environmental Strategy of the Year' by Pulp & Paper International PPI" in Ecology, Environment & Conservation Business (January 4, 2014, pp. 4) [13704], [23138]
Cascading Style Sheets CSS for Web Page Development (Onsite) [22981]
Cascading Style Sheets II [33767]
Case Books/CASE [7184]
"The Case of the Deflated IPO" in Boston Business Journal (Vol. 29, June 24, 2011, No. 7, pp. 1) [6323], [9402], [20795], [33120]
Case Handyman and Remodeling Services LLC [4347], [10745]
"Case IH Announces Strategy to Meet 2014 Clean Air Standards" in Farm Industry News (September 15, 2011) [5558], [5837], [17014], [23139], [25253]
Case In Point, Inc. (CIP) [12801]
Case Master: Thoughtful Cases for Competitive Future Consultants [10481], [20094]

"The Case for Thousand Dollar Wallpaper" in Architectural Digest (February 22, 2017) [11857]
"The Case for Treating the Sex Trade As an Industry" in Canadian Business (Vol. 83, October 12, 2010, No. 17, pp. 9) [18537], [23479], [25254]
Case Western Reserve University (CMLA) - Cleveland Health Sciences Library [11609]
Case Western Reserve University Department of Biology - Skeletal Research Center (SRC) [12511]
Case Western Reserve University - Elderly Care Research Center (ECRC) [204]
CaseBase: Case Studies in Global Business [27786]
"Cash for Appliances Targets HVAC Products, Water Heaters" in Contractor (Vol. 56, October 2009, No. 10, pp. 1) [474], [788], [5559], [5838], [20796], [23140], [24955]
"Cash Deals Are King, But Don't Reign Supreme In Birmingham" in Birmingham Business Journal (Vol. 31, May 16, 2014, No. 20, pp. 6) [11018], [13161], [13412], [33969]
"Cash Flow Analysis for Small Business Owners" in The Balance Small Business (April 13, 2020) [27807]
"Cash Flow: The Reason 82% of Small Businesses Fail" in Preferred CFO (June 8, 2020) [19715]
"Cash-Heavy Biovail on the Prowl for Deals" in Globe & Mail (March 24, 2006, pp. B1) [17987], [31228]
Cash In a Flash [17988], [22525], [23799]
"Cash for Kiosks: EcoATM Pulls in Series B Funding" in San Diego Business Journal (Vol. 33, May 7, 2012, No. 19, pp. 10) [2723], [10019], [13705], [35326]
Cash Management Practitioners Association [23695]
Cash Plus Inc. (CP) [2839], [15446], [34946]
"Cash Rents Reach Sky-High Levels" in Farm Industry News (November 23, 2011) [13775], [17015], [19993]
Cashiers Area Chamber of Commerce [43107]
"Cashing In: Gleaning an Education from Our Economic State" in Agency Sales Magazine (Vol. 39, August 2009, No. 8, pp. 22) [20398], [20797], [24628]
Cashmere Chamber of Commerce [46064]
Casino Chip and Gaming Token Collectors Club (CC&GTCC) [7258]
Casino Direct Marketing Association (CDMA) [7259]
Casino Gaming in the United States: A Research Guide [7277]
The Casino Institute [7321]
Casino Life [7331]
Casino Player Magazine [7332]
"Casinos In Pitch Battle" in Philadelphia Business Journal (Vol. 28, July 20, 2012, No. 23, pp. 1) [7278], [17989], [19793], [29703], [34758]
Casket and Funeral Supply Association of America (CFSA) [7194]
Casket & Funeral Supply Association of America Newsletter [7217]
Casket Manufacturers Association of America [7194]
Casper Area Chamber of Commerce (CACC) [46600]
Cass City Chamber of Commerce [40881]
Cassville Area Chamber of Commerce [41537]
Cassway/Albert Ltd. [11650], [31064]
Castle Rock Chamber of Commerce (CRCC) [37827]
Castro Valley/Eden Area Chamber of Commerce [36807]
Castroville Chamber of Commerce [45076]
Caswell County Chamber of Commerce [43108]
Cat Fanciers' Association (CFA) [633]
Cat Fanciers' Association--Yearbook [645]
Cat Fanciers' Federation (CFF) [634]
Catalina Island Chamber of Commerce [36808]
Catalina Island Chamber of Commerce & Visitors Bureau [36808]
Catalog of Funeral Home & Cemetery Supplies [7211]
Catalog of Funeral Home Supplies [7211]
Cataloging and Indexing [17203]
The Catalyst Center for Business & Entrepreneurship [36195]
Catalyst Connection [44389]
The Catalyst Group Inc. [45441]
Catalyst Health Ventures (CHV) [40675]
Catalyst Innovation Center [36513]
Catalyst Law Institute [44058]
Catamount Ventures [37326]
Catapult Capital LLC [37327]
Catapult Chicago [39396]
Catawba County Chamber of Commerce [43109]
The Catbird Seat [43851]
"Catch Up To Your Dream Retirement" in Canadian Business (Vol. 85, July 16, 2012, No. 11-12, pp. 46) [17285], [23800]
"Catch the Wind Announces Filing of Injunction Against Air Data Systems LLC and Philip Rogers" in CNW Group (September 30, 2011) [5560], [5839], [18538], [23141], [26239]
"Catch the Wind to Hold Investor Update Conference Call on October 18, 2011" in CNW Group (October 4, 2011) [5561], [5840], [9403], [23142], [26240], [29143]

"The Caterer Interview - Patrick Harbour and Nathan Jones" in Caterer & Hotelkeeper (October 28, 2011, No. 288) **[2670]**, **[18919]**, **[22526]**, **[33121]**
Caterers Industry in the US - Market Research Report **[2685]**
"Caterpillar to Expand Research, Production in China" in Chicago Tribune (August 27, 2008) **[17990]**, **[27492]**, **[29144]**, **[31950]**, **[32737]**
Catholic Book Publishers Association [1610]
Catholic Cemetery Conference (CCC) **[7195]**
"Catholic Charities USA Releases 4th Quarter Snapshot Survey Showing Agencies Save Americans in Need More Than $7 Million per Year through Tax Preparation Assistance" in Investment Weekly News (March 31, 2012, pp. 231) **[15369]**, **[34286]**
Catholic Health Alliance (CHAC) **[25664]**
Catholic University of America - Music Library **[11213]**
Catoosa County Chamber of Commerce **[38706]**
Catterton Partners **[38088]**
"Cautions on Loans with Your Business" in Business Owner (Vol. 35, July-August 2011, No. 4, pp. 5) **[54]**, **[1747]**, **[16790]**, **[23801]**, **[28109]**, **[34759]**
"Cautions on Negotiating Business and Personal Contracts" in Business Owner (Vol. 35, March-April 2011, No. 2, pp. 12) **[18539]**
CAV Angels **[45919]**
Cava Capital **[38089]**
Cavalier Area Chamber of Commerce **[43290]**
Cave City Area Chamber of Commerce **[40025]**
"CAW Hopes to Beat Xstrata Deadline" in Globe & Mail (January 30, 2007, pp. B3) **[11389]**, **[29145]**, **[35174]**
Cayenne Consulting (CC) **[37667]**
Cayucos Chamber of Commerce **[36809]**
Cayuga County Chamber of Commerce (CCCOC) **[42539]**
Cayuga Venture Fund (CVF) **[43016]**
CBA: The Association for Christian Retail (CBA) **[1803]**
CBAA Convention and Exhibition [438]
"CBC Eyes Partners for TV Downloads" in Globe & Mail (February 9, 2006, pp. B1) **[15587]**, **[20617]**, **[26241]**, **[31229]**
CBC/Radio Canada Maritimes - Halifax Broadcast Centre **[15628]**
CBI [6819]
CBIZ, Inc. **[133]**, **[2241]**, **[10517]**, **[16874]**, **[20168]**, **[24239]**, **[28972]**
CBRC Incubator Kitchen (CBRC) **[45678]**
CBS News Reference Library **[13061]**
"CBS Radio Group Seeks New Space for Growing Event, Online Business" in Dallas Business Journal (Vol. 35, June 15, 2012, No. 40, pp. 1) **[11719]**, **[13029]**
CCH ProSystem fx Tax™ **[18785]**, **[25628]**, **[34949]**
CCH Protos™ [18785], [25628], [34949]
CCH Tax Protos™ [18785], [25628], [34949]
CCSS Annual Conference [21685]
CD Computing News [30143]
CD Tradepost Inc. **[3415]**
CDC Small Business Finance Corp. (CDCSBF) **[36568]**
CDER Small Business and Industry Assistance (SBIA) **[40345]**
CDM Smith Inc. **[16348]**
C.D.S. Building Movers **[19212]**
C.E. Marquardt Lighting Design **[31065]**
"CE2 Carbon Capital and Dogwood Carbon Solutions Partner with Missouri Landowners to Generate High Quality Carbon Offsets from 300,000 Acres of Forest" in Nanotechnolgy Business Journal (January 25, 2010) **[5562]**, **[5841]**, **[23143]**, **[31230]**
Cecchetti Council of America (CCA) **[4837]**
Cecil County Chamber of Commerce **[40373]**
Cedar City Area Chamber of Commerce **[45630]**
Cedar City Small Business Development Center **[45605]**
Cedar Creek Lake Area Chamber of Commerce (CCLACC) **[45077]**
"Cedar Fair to Solicit Bids for Geauga Lake" in Crain's Cleveland Business (Vol. 28, October 8, 2007, No. 40, pp. 1) **[602]**, **[13162]**, **[13413]**
Cedar Hill Chamber of Commerce **[45078]**
Cedar Key Chamber of Commerce (CKACOC) **[38341]**
Cedar Park Chamber of Commerce and Tourism **[45079]**
Cedar Rapids Area Chamber of Commerce [39720]
Cedar Rapids Metro Economic Alliance **[39720]**
Cedar Ventures LLC **[38805]**
Cedarburg Chamber of Commerce (CCC) **[46377]**
Cedaredge Area Chamber of Commerce **[37828]**
CEF Consultants Ltd. **[6793]**
CEI Ventures Inc. **[40314]**
The CEI Women's Business Center (WBC) **[40313]**
Ceilings and Interior Systems Construction Association (CISCA) **[3929]**, **[10726]**
Ceilings and Interior Systems Contractors Association [3929], [10726]

"Celebrate Holiday Spirit With Sparkling Sales" in Pet Product News (Vol. 66, September 2012, No. 9, pp. 48) **[12194]**, **[16523]**, **[29704]**, **[32947]**
"Celebrate Innovation, No Matter Where It Occurs" in Harvard Business Review (Vol. 90, April 2012, No. 4, pp. 36) **[3096]**, **[12409]**, **[12493]**, **[25732]**, **[30694]**
"Celebrate Self Improvement Month with These Tips and Resources for Entrepreneurs" in Small Business Trends (September 2, 2022) **[22527]**
"Celebrate Success. Embrace Innovation" in Black Enterprise (Vol. 37, February 2007, No. 7, pp. 145) **[15842]**, **[20798]**, **[22109]**, **[22528]**, **[30332]**, **[33551]**, **[35037]**, **[35753]**
"Celebrating America, Scoop by Frosty Scoop" in The New York Times (July 2, 2019) **[8553]**
Celina Area Chamber of Commerce [43435]
Celina-Mercer County Chamber of Commerce **[43435]**
Cell Motility and the Cytoskeleton [32867]
Cell Phone Recycling Industry in the US - Market Research Report **[2813]**, **[13734]**
Cellular Telecommunications Industry Association Annual Meeting and Exposition [2821]
Celtic House Venture Partners **[46781]**
"Cemex Paves a Global Road to Solid Growth" in Barron's (Vol. 88, March 10, 2008, No. 10, pp. 24) **[6324]**, **[8699]**, **[9404]**, **[17991]**, **[23802]**, **[27493]**, **[29146]**
Cen-Tex Hispanic Chamber of Commerce (CTHCC) **[45080]**
Cen-Tex Hispanic Chamber of Commerce of Waco [45080]
Cendana Capital **[37328]**
Cendant Corp. [8499], [14120]
"Cengage Learning Makes Boston Its Headquarters" in Boston Business Journal (Vol. 34, April 25, 2014, No. 12, pp. 6) **[1647]**, **[19163]**, **[21468]**
Census Processing Center [36201]
The Centech Group, Inc. **[3783]**
Centenary College Small Business Development Center (SBDC) **[42035]**
Centennial Chamber of Commerce [37898]
Centennial College Centre of Entrepreneurship **[46814]**
Centennial Investors (CI) **[41713]**
Centennial Ventures **[37919]**
Center for Advanced Purchasing Studies [31915]
Center for Alzheimer's Disease and Related Disorders [10941]
Center for American Entrepreneurship (CAE) **[17892]**
Center for Applied Ethics [34448]
Center for Asian American Media (CAAM) **[6161]**
Center for Auto Safety (CAS) **[408]**
Center for Book Arts (CBA) **[1717]**
Center for the Book in the Library of Congress (LOC) **[1621]**
Center for Business Ethics [34450]
Center for Business Research [36419]
Center for Construction and Environment [23460]
Center for Coordination Science [3567]
Center for Corporate Community Relations [31903]
Center for Creative Leadership (CCL) **[34959]**
Center for Cultural Innovation Arts Project Incubator (CCI) **[37555]**
Center for Economic Development [21279], [21290]
Center for Economic Development Research and Assistance [42294]
Center for Economic Research [21262], [47575]
Center for Electric Power [5407]
Center for Emerging Entrepreneurial Development [44851]
Center for Emerging Technologies (CET) **[41670]**
Center for Emerging Technology and Entrepreneurial Studies at Cameron University (CETES CU) **[43852]**
Center for Entrepreneurial Innovation (CEI) **[36386]**
Center for Entrepreneurial Studies [22955], [31622], [40744]
Center for Entrepreneurial Studies and Development, Inc. (CESD) **[21741]**
Center for Entrepreneurship & Business Innovation (CEBI) **[43686]**
The Center for Entrepreneurship at Wichita State University (WSU) **[39969]**
Center for Environmental Information (CEI) **[5792]**, **[6007]**
Center for Environmental Research (CER) **[5786]**
Center for Evaluative Clinical Sciences [26113]
Center of Excellence in Energy Efficiency (C3E) **[46909]**
Center for Exhibition Industry Research (CEIR) **[15817]**, **[29571]**
Center For Advanced Professional Studies (CAPS) **[39970]**
Center For Health, Environment and Justice (CHEJ) **[7981]**
Center for Health Care Leadership and Strategy [26145]
Center for Health Care Strategies Inc. (CHCS) **[11552]**

Center for Health Policy Analysis and Research [26107]
Center for Health and Safety Studies [5122]
Center for Health Services Research [26152]
Center for Holistic Management [5788]
Center for Human Resources [10006], [14997]
Center for Immunity Enhancement in Domestic Animals [721]
Center for Industrial Services (CIS) **[44828]**
Center for Innovation at Arlington **[45504]**
Center for Innovation - Ina Mae Rude Entrepreneur Center **[43315]**
Center for Innovative Technology [45987]
Center for International Business [27799]
Center for International Business Education and Research [27799]
Center for International Private Enterprise (CIPE) **[25098]**
Center for Interuniversity Research in Quantitative Economics (CIREQ) **[21268]**
Center for Lifestyle Enhancement-Columbia Medical Center of Plano **[2242]**, **[11594]**, **[16511]**, **[20169]**, **[26083]**
Center for Local Government Administration [31736]
Center for Local Tax Research [21269]
Center for Micro-Entrepreneurial Training **[22452]**
Center for Occupational Research and Development (CORD) **[21742]**
The Center for Organizational Excellence, Inc. (COE) **[2243]**, **[10518]**, **[20170]**, **[27129]**, **[28973]**
Center for Particulate Control in Process Equipment [564]
Center on Philanthropy [7190]
Center for Physical and Motor Fitness [12520]
Center for Policy Research (CPR) **[10808]**
Center for Public Leadership Studies [26144]
Center for Real Estate and Urban Economic Studies [13643]
Center for Regenerative Studies [14971]
Center for Rehabilitation Technology [12514]
Center for Renewable Resources [14900]
Center for Research in Disease Prevention [34703]
Center for Risk Management and Insurance Research [26117]
Center for Safety and Traffic Education [5122]
Center for Small Town Research and Design [958]
Center for Social Innovation (CSI) **[42849]**
Center for the Study of Economics (CSE) **[21269]**
Center for the Study of Languages [21754]
Center for the Study of Population [47410]
Center for the Study of Social Policy (CSSP) **[26110]**
Center for the Study of Welfare Policy [26110]
"The Center of Success: Author Explores How Confidence Can Take You Further" in Black Enterprise (Vol. 38, March 1, 2008, No. 8) **[14510]**, **[22529]**, **[28480]**
The Center for Technical Communication [386], [5345]
The Center for Technology, Enterprise & Development Business Incubator **[38554]**
Center for Transportation Research [1567]
Center for Urban Entrepreneurship (CUE) **[42850]**
Center for Urban and Environmental Research and Services [47475]
Center for Urban and Industrial Pest Management [12072]
Center for Vocational Education [9993]
Center for Women and Enterprise Administrative Offices & Eastern Massachusetts Center - Boston **[40650]**
Center for Youth Development [10006], [14997]
Center4 **[42851]**
CenterPoint Venture **[45442]**
"Centerra Caught in Kyrgyzstan Dispute" in Globe & Mail (April 19, 2007, pp. B5) **[18920]**, **[24629]**, **[25121]**
CenterState Corporation for Economic Opportunity (CENTERSTATE CEO) **[42540]**
Centerville Area Chamber of Commerce **[39721]**
Centerville Chamber of Commerce **[45081]**
Central Arizona College Small Business Development Center (CAC) **[36267]**
Central Baldwin Chamber of Commerce (CBCC) **[36089]**
Central Bark Doggy Day Care **[12268]**
Central Bradford County Chamber of Commerce (CBCCC) **[44184]**
Central Bucks Chamber of Commerce (CBCC) **[44185]**
Central California Hispanic Chamber of Commerce (CCHCC) **[36810]**
Central California Small Business Development Center Fresno **[36569]**
Central City Area Chamber of Commerce **[41843]**
Central Coast Small Business Development Center [36588]
Central Coast Venture Forum [37665]
Central Committee on Lumber Standards [10373]
Central Connecticut State University - Institute of Technology and Business Development (ITBD) **[38107]**

Central Delaware Chamber of Commerce (CDCC) [38132]
Central Fairfax Chamber of Commerce (CFCC) [45841]
Central Fayette Chamber of Business and Industry [44209]
"Central Florida Real Estate Values to Level Out this Year" in Orlando Business Journal (Vol. 29, June 15, 2012, No. 54, pp. 1) [13163], [34760]
Central Fort Bend Chamber Alliance (CFBC) [45082]
"Central Freight Lines Relocates Irving Terminal" in Dallas Business Journal (Vol. 35, March 2, 2012, No. 25, pp. 1) [7030], [16074], [19164]
Central Hillsborough county Chamber of Commerce [38414]
Central Illinois Angels Inc. (CIA) [39456]
Central Indiana Small Business Development Center (CISBDC) [39470]
Central Institute for the Deaf (CID) [8139]
Central Jersey SCORE [42051]
Central Kitchen [43656]
Central Lake Area Chamber of Commerce [40882]
Central Lakes College (CLC) [41358]
Central Lakes College Small Business Development Center [41152]
Central Louisiana Business Incubator [40214]
Central Louisiana Chamber of Commerce [40155]
Central Michigan University Research Corp. (CMURC) [41081]
Central Minnesota SCORE [41165]
Central Minnesota Small Business Development Center [41153]
Central New Mexico Community College (CNM) [42358]
The Central New York Business Journal (CNYBJ) [42991]
Central & North Florida Business Travel Association (CNFBTA) [19291], [38205]
Central Oklahoma Business And Job Development Corp. [43853], [43880]
Central Oklahoma Technology Center [43881]
Central Oregon SCORE [43927]
Central Palm Beach County Chamber of Commerce [38342]
Central Park Tutors [16148]
Central Pennsylvania Chamber of Commerce [44186]
Central Pennsylvania College (CPC) [44428]
Central Point Area Chamber of Commerce [43954]
Central Point Chamber of Commerce [43954]
Central Rhode Island Chamber of Commerce [44467]
Central and South Texas Minority Business Council [30305]
Central State University - International Center for Water Resources Management (ICWRM) [16353]
Central Supply Association [12608]
Central Technology Center [43881]
Central Texas Angel Network (CTAN) [44883]
Central Utah SCORE [45615]
"Central Valley Local Fund II Has $110M to Invest" in Sacramento Business Journal (Vol. 29, May 25, 2012, No. 13, pp. 1) [27494], [35327]
Central Valley SCORE [36605]
Central Vermont Chamber of Commerce [45722]
Central Vermont Community Action Council [45743]
Central Virginia Procurement Technical Assistance Center [45929]
Central Virginia Small Business Development Center (CV SBDC) [45768]
Central Washington SCORE [46023], [46065]
Central Washington University Department of Sociology - Applied Social Data Center [47397]
Central Wisconsin SCORE [46338]
Centrale des Syndicats du Quebec (CSQ) [35150]
Centralia Area Chamber of Commerce (CACC) [41538]
Centralia-Chehalis Chamber of Commerce [46066]
Centre for Addiction and Mental Health Library [34688]
Centre Canadien d'Architecture [861]
Centre Canadien d'Architecture - Bibliotheque [861]
Centre de Commerce Mondial Montréal [20691]
Centre County Industrial Development Corp. (CCIDC) [44390]
Centre d'Action Écologique [5484], [13756], [23030]
Centre d'Enterprises et d'Innovation de Montreal (CEIM) [46891]
Centre d'Étude des Niveaux de Vie [21270]
Centre Harbor-Moultonboro Chamber of Commerce [42009]
Centre International de Criminologie Comparée (CICC) [22357]
Centre International d'Étude sur le Je et les Comportements à Risque Chez les Jeunes [7341]
Centre International pour l'Entreprise Privée [25098]
Centre for Investigative Journalism [5276], [11959]
Centre de Recherches pour le Développement International (CRDI) [26111]

Centre for Social Innovation (CSI) [46815]
Centre for the Study of Living Standards (CSLS) [21270]
Centre for Women in Business (CWB) [35590]
CentreStone Ventures [46730]
Centricap [38090]
Centro de Investigacion sobre Obesidad [16520]
Centum Financial Group Inc. [11100]
"Centurion Signs Egypt Deal With Shell" in Globe & Mail (March 21, 2006, pp. B5) [29147], [31231]
Century 21 Canada L.P. (C21) [13336]
Century Business Solutions [14869]
Century City Chamber of Commerce [36811]
Century Tax & Bookkeeping Services [14869]
CEO Advisors [2244], [20171], [33655], [38534]
"The CEO of Anglo American On Getting Serious About Safety" in (Vol. 90, June 2012, No. 6, pp. 43) [21469], [28481], [35940]
CEO Focus [36387]
"CEO Forecast: With Cloudy Economy, Executives Turn to Government Contracting" in Hispanic Business (January-February 2009, pp. 34, 36) [5563], [5842], [20799], [22530], [23144], [25122], [25733], [26242], [28482], [30333]
"The CEO of General Electric On Sparking an American Manufacturing Renewal" in Harvard Business Review (Vol. 90, March 2012, No. 3, pp. 43) [26897], [29148], [35175]
"CEO Pay: Best Bang for Buck" in Philadelphia Business Journal (Vol. 30, September 30, 2011, No. 33, pp. 1) [17286], [26898], [28483]
"CEO Pay: The Details" in Crain's Detroit Business (Vol. 25, June 22, 2009, No. 25) [9405], [17287], [26899], [28484]
"The CEO Poll: Fuel for Thought II Canadian Business Leaders on Energy Policy" in Canadian Business (Vol. 81, September 15, 2008, No. 14-15, pp. 12) [5564], [5843], [14912], [20800], [23145], [25255], [29149], [30869], [33122], [33970]
"The CEO Poll: Potash Sale Must Be Blocked" in Canadian Business (Vol. 83, October 12, 2010, No. 17, pp. 24) [17016], [25256], [27495], [28485], [33010]
"The CEO Poll: Split on Migrant Workers" in Canadian Business (Vol. 83, September 14, 2010, No. 15, pp. 23) [25257], [26518], [26900], [28486], [30548]
"CEO Putting Rubber to Road at Lanxess Corporation" in Pittsburgh Business Times (Vol. 33, May 2, 2014, No. 42, pp. 4) [15682], [27496], [29063]
"The CEO of TJX On How To Train First-Class Buyers" in Harvard Business Review (Vol. 92, May 2014, No. 5, pp. 45) [3097], [27994], [32119]
"The CEO of Williams-Sonoma on Blending Instinct with Analysis" in Harvard Business Review (Vol. 92, September 2014, No. 9, pp. 41) [9032], [20399], [29705], [32120]
"The CEO's Role in DEI Success" in Associations Now (May 9, 2022) [30549]
"CEOs Decry Budget Taxation Change" in Globe & Mail (April 2, 2007, pp. B1) [27497], [28487], [34761]
"CEOs Gone Wild" in Canadian Business (Vol. 79, August 14, 2006, No. 16-17, pp. 15) [9406], [28488], [29150]
"CEOs Keep Bringing Home the Perks" in Baltimore Business Journal (Vol. 30, May 18, 2012, No. 2, pp. 1) [7917], [19733], [28489], [31232]
"CEOs With Headsets" in Harvard Business Review (Vol. 88, September 2010, No. 9, pp. 21) [19734], [28490]
Ceramics Monthly [4612], [4670]
Cereal Chemistry [32862]
Ceres Chamber of Commerce [36812]
Ceridian Corp. [41347]
Ceridian HCM, Inc. [41347]
Ceridian Small Business Solutions Div. [42046]
Cerritos Regional Chamber of Commerce [36813]
Cerritos Regional Chamber of Commerce Business Directory [36814]
"Certain Predicts 2012 as Breakthrough Year for Events" in Internet Wire (January 5, 2012) [15843], [17992], [33840], [35038]
CertaPro Painters Ltd. [2093], [11887]
"Certification Experts Germanischer Lloyd Wind Energy Assist NaiKun's Offshore Wind Project" in Marketwired (May 14, 2007) [20095], [23146], [26243], [28491], [33123]
Certified Ethical Hacker (Onsite) [21344]
"Certified Technicians can Increase Bottom Line" in Contractor (Vol. 56, September 2009, No. 9, pp. 37) [475], [20400], [33124]
CertiRestore Certified Furniture Restoration [7247]
Cervin [37329]
CES Business Consultants [2245]
CF Services Group Inc. [17394]
CFA Institute [9290]
CFA Institute--Membership Directory [9407]

CFA Institute Research Foundation [6734]
CFA Research Foundation [6734]
CFA Society New York (CFANY) [9291]
CFDA Fashion Incubator [42852]
CFDA Foundation [3000], [6122]
CFI Group USA L.L.C. [20172], [22311], [27130], [28974]
CFMA Building Profits [4274]
CFO Tools Inc. [37668]
"CFOs Walk a Tightrope When Picking Consultants" in The Wall Street Journal (July 26, 2016) [10482], [20096], [28492]
CFOs2Go [37669]
CFR: Title 13. Business Credit and Assistance [20801], [23803], [24630], [24956], [25258]
"CGB Purchases Illinois Grain-Fertilizer Firm" in Farm Industry News (December 2, 2011) [9408], [17017], [19653]
CHA-Association for Horsemanship Safety and Education [8305]
CHA - Certified Horsemanship Association (CHA) [8305]
CHA Create and Connect Conference and Trade Show [4630], [4685], [15807]
Chabot College (CC) [37654]
Chadler Solutions [17395]
Chadron Area Chamber of Commerce [41844]
Chadron - Dawes County Area Chamber of Commerce (CDCCC) [41844]
Chadron State College - Nebraska Business Development Center (NBDC) [19152]
"Chafee Eyes Tax On Travel Sites" in Providence Business News (Vol. 28, March 24, 2014, No. 51, pp. 1) [8373], [15733], [15987], [21807], [25259], [31233], [34762]
Chagrin Valley Chamber of Commerce (CVCC) [43436]
Chain Drug Marketing Association (CDMA) [5136]
"The Challenger Sale: Taking Control of the Customer Conversation" [32487]
"Challenges Await Quad in Going Public" in Milwaukee Business Journal (Vol. 27, January 29, 2010, No. 18, pp. A1) [3302], [9409], [12728], [19794], [28493], [31234]
"Challenges, Responses and Available Resources: Success in Rural Small Businesses" in Journal of Small Business and Entrepreneurship (Vol. 23, Winter 2010, No. 1) [20802], [22531], [28494], [33354]
Chama Valley Chamber of Commerce [42306]
Chamber [37829], [40156]
The Chamber [40374], [41208]
Chamber 630 [39123]
Chamber in Action [46639]
The Chamber Advantage [41986], [44639]
The Chamber Business Incubator [37556]
Chamber of Business and Industry of Centre County (CBICC) [44187], [44391]
Chamber Business Line [41539]
The Chamber Charge [43955]
Chamber Chat [39124]
Chamber Chatter [41387], [41540], [44188]
Chamber Check [39523]
The Chamber Comments [45842]
Chamber of Commerce of the Attleboro Area [40637]
Chamber of Commerce of Auburn and Cayuga County [42539]
Chamber of Commerce of the Bellmores [42541]
Chamber of Commerce of the Borough of Queens [42653]
Chamber of Commerce in Broadview Heights [43437]
Chamber of Commerce Business Directory [40375]
Chamber of Commerce Davie County [43123]
Chamber of Commerce Directory [39718]
Chamber of Commerce of Eastern Connecticut [38033]
Chamber of Commerce of Fargo Moorhead [41229]
Chamber of Commerce of Frederick County (CCFC) [40376]
Chamber of Commerce of Greater Augusta [38689]
Chamber of Commerce of Greater Bay Shore [42542]
Chamber of Commerce of Greater Cape May [42110]
Chamber of Commerce for Greater Milford (CCGM) [38133]
Chamber of Commerce of the Greater Ronkonkoma [42543]
Chamber of Commerce of Greater West Chester (CCGWC) [44189]
Chamber of Commerce of Harrison County [39524]
Chamber of Commerce Hawaii (COCHi) [38866], [38871]
Chamber of Commerce of Huntsville/Madison County [36090]
Chamber of Commerce of Independence [39906]
Chamber of Commerce of Lafourche and the Bayou Region [40157]
Chamber of Commerce of the Mastics and Shirley [42544]

Chamber of Commerce of Metropolitan Montreal - Info
  Entrepreneurs [33728], [46907]
Chamber of Commerce of the Mid-Ohio Valley (MOV)
  [46264]
Chamber of Commerce Mountain View [36815]
Chamber of Commerce News [43438]
The Chamber of Commerce News [41209]
Chamber of Commerce Newsletter [46601]
Chamber of Commerce of Newtown (CCN) [38034]
Chamber of Commerce, Northern Palm Beaches
  Chamber of Commerce [38476]
Chamber of Commerce of Northwest Connecticut
  [38035]
Chamber of Commerce of Okeechobee County [38343]
Chamber of Commerce of the Palm Beaches [38344]
The Chamber of Commerce Serving Lexington, Rock-
  bridge County, and Buena Vista [45843]
Chamber of Commerce Serving Old Bridge, Sayreville
  and South Amboy [42111]
Chamber of Commerce of the Shoals [36151]
Chamber of Commerce Southern New Jersey (CCSNJ)
  [42112]
Chamber of Commerce of Southwestern Madison County
  (SWMC) [39125]
Chamber of Commerce of Speculator, Lake Pleasant and
  Piseco [42512]
Chamber of Commerce of the Tonawandas [42545]
Chamber of Commerce of Ulster County [42693]
The Chamber of Commerce of Walker County [36091]
Chamber of Commerce of West Alabama [36092]
Chamber of Commerce of the Willistons (CCW) [42546]
Chamber of Commerce - Windham Region [38036]
The Chamber Communicator [36816], [43125]
Chamber Connection [36817], [38345], [40026], [40027],
  [40158], [43110], [43291]
The Chamber Connection [37830]
Chamber Connections [40271]
Chamber Courier [39126]
Chamber, Daytona Beach and Halifax Area [38364]
Chamber Dialogue [44640], [45083]
Chamber Directory [38037], [38337], [40883], [43439]
Chamber E-Central [44190]
Chamber Edge [41210]
Chamber Focus [36118]
The Chamber of Gadsden/Etowah County [36093]
Chamber at a Glance [45084]
The Chamber of Grand Haven, Spring Lake, Ferrysburg
  [40884]
Chamber In Motion [38707]
Chamber Information Booklet [42113]
Chamber Insider [38346]
Chamber Insight [40159]
Chamber-Main Street Sac City [39722]
Chamber of Manitowoc County [46378]
Chamber of Medford - Jackson County [43956]
Chamber Member Directory [40885]
Chamber Membership [41541]
Chamber Membership Directory [41211]
Chamber Membership Directory and Business Resource
  Guide [36818]
The Chamber Network [43957]
CHAMBER NEWS [46067]
Chamber News [36221], [36819], [36820], [38708],
  [40377], [40886], [41212], [41388], [41542], [41578],
  [41756], [43958], [44641], [44721], [44722], [46379]
The Chamber News [44720], [46380]
Chamber News Updates [40160]
Chamber Newsletter [36094], [40028], [41543], [41845]
Chamber Newsletters [36821]
Chamber Notes [43440]
The Chamber Outlook [39871]
Chamber Page in the Versailles Republican [39525]
The Chamber page lake powell [36352]
Chamber Report [36822]
The Chamber Report [40029], [40567], [45085]
Chamber Review [38347], [39127], [46381]
Chamber Scene [39526]
Chamber Serving the Broomfield Area [37822]
Chamber South (CS) [38348]
Chamber of Southern Saratoga County (CSSC) [42547]
Chamber Southwest Louisiana (SWLA) [40161]
The Chamber Speaks [40568]
The Chamber for Superior & Douglas County [46382]
The Chamber Today [45086]
Chamber Trends [38349]
Chamber Update [40887], [41213]
Chamber Vision [42548]
The Chamber Vision [39872]
Chamber Voice [42307], [43110]
Chamber Works [40378], [45087]
ChamberChat [42308]
Chamberfax [42114]
ChamberGram [42549]

Chambergram [39128]
Chamberlain-Oacoma Area Chamber of Commerce
  [44642]
Chamberline [44191]
ChamberLink [38709]
ChamberRVA [45844]
Chambers Ltd. [9065]
Chamber's Profile [43959]
The Chamberview [44643]
ChamberWest [45631]
ChamberWorks [43960]
Chambre de Commerce Brésil-Canada [20680]
"Chameleonic or Consistent? A Multilevel Investigation of
  Emotional Labor Variability and Self-Monitoring" in
  Academy of Management Journal (Vol. 55, August 1,
  2012, No. 4, pp. 905) [22110], [28495]
"Chameloeonic or Consistent? A Multilevel Investigation
  of Emotional Labor Variability and Self-Monitoring" in
  Academy of Management Journal (Vol. 55, August
  2012, No. 4, pp. 905) [22111], [28496]
Champaign County Black Chamber of Commerce
  (CCBCC) [39129]
Champaign County Chamber of Commerce [39130],
  [43441]
Champion Networks L.L.C. [30995], [31066]
Champlain College BYOBiz [45751]
Champlain College Center for Innovation &
  Entrepreneurship (CIE) [45751]
Chandler Area Chamber of Commerce (CACOC) [43739]
Chandler Chamber of Commerce [36323]
Chandler Innovations [36388]
"Chandrashekar LSP on How to Deal with Inflation" in
  Small Business Trends (August 9, 2022) [33971]
"The Change Foundation Awards Northumberland Com-
  munity Partnership $3 Million Project To Improve
  Seniors' Healthcare Transitions and Use Patient Input
  to Drive Redesign" in CNW Group (June 5, 2012)
  [7091], [25734], [31235]
"Change Is in the Air" in Agency Sales Magazine (Vol.
  39, August 2009, No. 8, pp. 30) [15844], [20803],
  [29151], [35039]
"A Change Would Do You Good" in Canadian Business
  (Vol. 80, November 19, 2007, No. 23, pp. 15) [3012],
  [3098], [6126], [27498], [29152], [31114]
"Changes Sought to Health Law" in Baltimore Business
  Journal (Vol. 28, July 30, 2010, No. 12, pp. 1) [8893],
  [18540], [25260], [25735], [27245]
Changing Course [2611]
"The Changing Face of the U.S. Consumer" in Advertis-
  ing Age (Vol. 79, July 7, 2008, No. 26, pp. 1) [17993],
  [29706], [31750]
"Changing Prescriptions" in Business North Carolina (Vol.
  28, March 2008, No. 3, pp. 52) [5150], [20401],
  [23603]
"Changing the Rules of the Accounting Game" in
  Canadian Business (Vol. 81, December 8, 2008, No.
  21, pp. 19) [55], [1748], [15370], [16791], [25261],
  [27499]
Chanute Area Chamber of Commerce & Office of Tour-
  ism [39873]
Chapel Hill-Carrboro Business Directory [43111]
Chapel Hill - Carrboro Chamber of Commerce [43112]
Chapman University - A. Gary Anderson Center for
  Economic Research (ACER) [21271]
Chapman University - Albert Schweitzer Institute [11214]
Chappell Chamber of Commerce [41846]
"Characteristics of Great Salespeople" in Agency Sales
  Magazine (Vol. 39, November 2009, No. 10, pp. 40)
  [19795], [28497], [32488]
Chardon Area Chamber of Commerce (CACC) [43442]
"Charged Up for Sales" in Charlotte Business Journal
  (Vol. 25, October 15, 2010, No. 30, pp. 1) [5565],
  [5844], [11390], [23147], [26519], [29153], [32489]
Chariton Area Chamber/Main Street [39723]
Chariton Chamber of Commerce [39723]
Chariton Chamber and Development Corp. [39723]
Charleroi Chamber of Commerce [44263]
Charles A. Krueger [16875], [24240]
Charles County Chamber of Commerce (CCCOC)
  [40379]
Charles Darwin University - Palmerston Campus Library
  [24908]
Charles River Regional Chamber [40609]
Charles River Ventures (CRV) [37330]
Charles Village Exchange [40446]
Charles W. Gould Business Incubator (GBI) [44599]
Charleston Angel Partners (CA) [35268], [44590]
Charleston Area Alliance [46265]
Charleston Area Chamber of Commerce (CACC) [39131]
Charleston Chamber of Commerce [41544]
Charleston Metro Chamber of Commerce (CMCC)
  [44538]
Charleston Regional Business Journal [44615]

Charleston Regional Chamber of Commerce [46265]
Charleston Regional Chamber of Commerce and
  Development [46265]
Charleston Small Business Development Center [44501]
Charleston Trident Chamber of Commerce [44538]
Charlestown Chamber of Commerce [44468]
Charlevoix Area Chamber of Commerce [40888]
Charlotte Business Journal (CBJ) [43263]
Charlotte Business Journal [43262]
Charlotte Chamber of Commerce [43113]
Charlotte County Chamber of Commerce [38350]
"Charlotte Pipe Launches Satirical Campaign" in
  Contractor (Vol. 57, January 2010, No. 1, pp. 6) [249],
  [8700], [9112], [12620], [17648], [27500], [29707]
Charlotte Regional Business Alliance [43113]
Charlottesville - Albemarle County Chamber of Com-
  merce [45845]
Charlottesville Angel Network (CAN) [35269], [45920]
Charlottesville Regional Chamber of Commerce (CRCC)
  [45845]
The Charlwood Pacific Group (CPG) [13626]
Charo Chicken Systems Inc. [14136]
Charolais Journal [663]
Charp Associates Inc. [35960]
"The Chart that Organized the 20th Century" in Harvard
  Business Review (Vol. 92, September 2014, No. 9, pp.
  32) [7031]
Charter Life Sciences (CLS) [37331]
Charter School Business Management (CSBM) [21706]
Chartered Accountants Worldwide Network USA
  (ACAUS) [23]
Chartered Alternative Investment Analyst Association
  [23696]
Chartered Institute of Logistics and Transport in North
  America (CILTNA) [15506]
Chartered Institute of Transport in North America [15506]
Chartered Management Co. [2246], [10519], [20173],
  [24241], [28975], [33656]
Chartered Professional Accountants of Canada (CPA
  CANADA) [24], [1738], [15353]
Chase County Historical Society & Museum Library
  [7401]
"Chasing Credit" in Canadian Business (Vol. 81,
  November 10, 2008, No. 19, pp. 59) [20259], [20804],
  [23804], [28110], [30915]
Chatham Area Chamber of Commerce (CACC) [39132]
Chatham Chamber of Commerce [40569]
Chatham Chamber of Commerce [39132]
Chatham County United Chamber of Commerce
  (CCUCC) [43114]
Chatham County United Chamber of Commerce and
  Travel and Tourism Office [43114]
The Chatham Group Inc. (CG) [10690]
Chatsworth Chamber of Commerce [36823]
Chatsworth-Murray County Chamber of Commerce
  [38710]
Chatsworth Porter Ranch Chamber of Commerce
  (CPRCOC) [36823]
CHATT Foundation [44837]
Chattanooga Area Chamber of Commerce [44723]
Chattanooga Kitchen [44837]
Chattanooga Renaissance Fund (CRF) [44866]
Chattanooga State Community College (CSCC) [44855]
Chattanooga State Community College Small Business
  Development Center [44838]
Chattanooga State Technical Community College [44855]
Chattanooga State Technical Institute [44855]
Chatters Salon [1403], [7886]
Chattooga County Chamber of Commerce [38711]
Chautauqua County Chamber of Commerce [42550]
"Cheap Deposits Fuel Bank Profits" in Boston Business
  Journal (Vol. 31, July 29, 2011, No. 27, pp. 1) [20805],
  [23805]
"Cheap Tubing Risk to Local Jobs, Execs Caution" in
  Pittsburgh Business Times (Vol. 33, May 23, 2014, No.
  45, pp. 4) [8701], [25262], [27501]
Cheatham County Chamber of Commerce [44724]
Cheba Hut Toasted Subs [4894]
Cheboygan Area Chamber of Commerce (CACC)
  [40889]
"Check It Out! The Professional Beauty Association
  Launches New Website" in Modern Salon (November
  11, 2019) [7865], [11720]
"Check Out How a Nurse Made Millions with Her Etsy
  Business" in Small Business Trends(February 22,
  2023) [11721], [26773]
"Check Out the Top 20 Commercial Users of Solar
  Power" in Electrical Wholesaling (Vol. 93, October 1,
  2012, No. 10) [14913]
Checkers - Rally's [14137]
"A Checklist for Maintaining Your Corporate Veil" in Legal
  Zoom (March 13, 2023) [27172]
The Checklist Manifesto: How to Get Things Right
  [18921], [22532], [28498]

CheckMark Software Inc. [134], [14870], [16876], [33929]
Checotah Chamber of Commerce [43740]
Chedd's Gourmet Grilled Cheese [4895]
Cheeburger Cheeburger Restaurants, Inc. [14138]
Cheektowaga Chamber of Commerce (CCC) [42551]
Cheekwood Botanical Gardens Library [7662]
"Cheese Is Now Idaho's Largest Export" in Idaho Business Review (August 28, 2014) [8702], [17018]
Cheese Market News: The Weekly Newspaper of the Nation's Cheese and Dairy-Deli Business [15066]
The Cheese Reporter [15039]
CheeseCon [7808]
Chef David Viana Chef/Partner of Heirloom Kitchen [14051]
"Chef Revelations - Derek Johnstone" in Caterer & Hotelkeeper (October 28, 2011, No. 288) [2671], [8374]
Chef Yia Vang Chef/Owner of Hilltribe Restaurant Group [14052]
Chef's Workshop [36174]
Chefscape [45943]
Chehalem Valley Chamber of Commerce [43961]
Chelsea Area Chamber of Commerce (CACC) [40890]
"Chem-Dry Carpet Cleaning Franchise on Pace for 120 New Locations In 2014" in Internet Wire (September 16, 2014) [16226], [24291], [33082]
ChemDry Canada Ltd. (CDC) [16233], [33315]
Chemeketa Community College Small Business Development Center (SBDC) [43908]
Chemical Alliance Zone Inc. (CAZ) [46300]
Chemical Angel Network [37332]
The Chemical Educator [21677]
Chemical Engineering Research and Design (ChERD) [32863]
Chemical and Petroleum Engineering [32864]
Chemical Waste Transportation Institute [7941]
ChemStation International Inc. [2094]
Chemung County Chamber of Commerce [42552]
The Chemunicator [20600]
Cheney Chamber of Commerce [39874]
Cheney Chamber of Commerce [46174]
Cherokee [43218]
Cherokee Chamber of Commerce [39724]
Cherokee Chamber of Commerce (CCC) [43115]
Cherokee County Chamber of Commerce [38712]
Cherokee County Chamber of Commerce (CCCC) [43116]
Cherokee County Chamber of Commerce (CCCoC) [36095]
Cherry Tree Investments Inc. [41330]
Cherrystone Angel Group [44493]
Cherryville Chamber of Commerce EDC [43117]
Chesaning Chamber of Commerce (CCC) [40891]
Chesapeake Bay Maritime Museum - Howard I. Chapelle Memorial Library [10628]
"Chesapeake Beach Resort and Spa Announces Dream Waterfront Wedding Giveaway" in Benzinga.com (October 29, 2011) [1966], [29708]
"Chesapeake Firm Regains Veteran-Owned Status" in Virginian-Pilot (August 21, 2012) [25123], [25263]
Chesapeake Gateway Chamber of Commerce [40380]
Cheshire Chamber of Commerce (CCC) [38038]
Chester County Chamber of Business and Industry (CCCBI) [44192]
Chester County Chamber of Commerce (CCCC) [44539]
Chesterfield Chamber of Commerce (CCC) [41545]
Chesterfield County Chamber of Commerce [45846]
Chesterland Chamber of Commerce (CCC) [43443]
Chesters International, LLC [14139]
Chetek Area Chamber of Commerce [46383]
Chetek Chamber of Commerce [46383]
"Chew On This: Soul Fans to 'Chews' Games' First Play" in Philadelphia Business Journal (Vol. 30, September 30, 2011, No. 33, pp. 3) [15142], [29709], [31236]
Chewelah Chamber of Commerce [46068]
Cheyenne County Chamber of Commerce (CCCC) [41847]
Cheyenne - Roger Mills Chamber of Commerce and Tourism [43741]
Cheyenne SCORE [46594]
CHFA East Tradeshow [8066]
CHFA NOW Toronto [8066]
Chicago Area Gay and Lesbian Chamber of Commerce [39225]
Chicago Association of Commerce and Industry [39134]
Chicago Association of Realtors (CAR) [13084]
Chicago Build [925], [4294], [13326]
Chicago Business [39449]
Chicago Business Travel Association (CBTA) [19292], [38969]
Chicago Chinatown Chamber of Commerce [39133]
Chicago Home and Garden [7641], [9057]

Chicago Metropolitan Agency for Planning (CMAP) [47398]
Chicago Minority Business Opportunity Center [39345]
Chicago Minority Supplier Development Council (MSDC) [39346]
Chicago Public Library Central Library - Business/Science/Technology Division [2620], [27980], [29050], [30233], [31021], [33715]
Chicago Public Library - Visual & Performing Arts Division - Music Information Center [3416], [11215], [11294]
"Chicago Public Schools District Builds Green" in Contractor (Vol. 56, October 2009, No. 10, pp. 5) [476], [556], [4025], [5366], [23148]
Chicago SCORES [39005]
"Chicago Senior Care Acquires The Clare at Water Tower" in Investment Weekly News (April 29, 2012, pp. 168) [25736], [31237]
Chicago Shoe Market [14692], [32350]
Chicago State University Office of Continuing Education [39442]
Chicago Technology Park (CTP) [39398]
Chicagoland Chamber of Commerce (CCOC) [39134]
Chickasha Chamber of Commerce [43742]
Chicken Connection Franchise Corp. [14140]
Chicken Delight [12544], [14141]
Chico Chamber of Commerce [36824]
Chico SCORE [36606]
Chicopee Chamber of Commerce [40580]
Chief Marketing Officer Council [29572]
Child Care Bridges [2888]
Child Care Millionaire: Secrets to Building a Profitable 7 or 8 Figure Child Care Business [2878]
Child Welfare: Journal of Policy, Practice, and Program (CWJ) [2889]
Child Welfare League of America (CWLA) [2866]
Child and Youth Services [25995]
"Child-Care Policy and the Labor Supply of Mothers with Young Children: A Natural Experiment from Canada" in University of Chicago Press (Vol. 26, July 2008, No. 3) [2879], [18541], [33972]
Childersburg Chamber of Commerce [36114]
Childhood Education International (ACEI) [2867]
Children's Book Insider [5335]
Children's Book Insider Newsletter [5335]
Children's Books in Print [1648], [1821]
Children's Defense Fund (CDF) [2868]
Children's Defense Fund of the Washington Research Project [2868]
"Children's Hospital to Grow" in Austin Business Journal (Vol. 31, July 22, 2011, No. 20, pp. A1) [4026], [17994], [25737]
Children's Lighthouse Franchise Co. (CLFC) [1202], [2895], [8225]
Children's Orchard (CO) [2859], [3167]
Children's Psychological Health Center, Inc. (CPHC) [2247], [20174], [26084]
Children's Voice [25996]
Childress Chamber of Commerce [45088]
Chilean and American Chamber of Commerce of Greater Philadelphia (CACCGP) [44193]
Chilled Water Systems (Onsite) [19436], [21345]
Chillicothe Area Chamber of Commerce (CACC) [41546]
Chillicothe Chamber of Commerce [39135]
Chillicothe Ross Chamber of Commerce (CRCC) [43444]
Chilton Chamber of Commerce [46384]
Chilton County Chamber of Commerce [36096]
Chilton Food Innovation Center (CFIC) [36175]
Chimney Sweep Guild [2919]
"The China Connection" in Crain's Chicago Business (Vol. 31, March 24, 2008, No. 12, pp. 26) [20806], [21470], [21808], [27502]
The China Painter [4613]
"The China Syndrome" in Canadian Business (Vol. 79, July 17, 2006, No. 14-15, pp. 25) [17995], [24631], [31115]
"China Vs the World: Whose Technology Is It?" in Harvard Business Review (Vol. 88, December 2010, No. 12, pp. 94) [8703], [18542], [25264], [26244], [27503], [31238]
China's Rational Entrepreneurs: The Development of the New Private Business Sector [22533], [24632], [27504]
"China's Slowing Growth Could Benefit the Global Economy; An Expert On China's Economy Says the Country Is Seeing an Upside to Slowing Down" in Gallup Business Journal (April 8, 2014) [20807], [27505]
"China's Super Consumers: What 1 Billion Customers Want and How to Sell It to Them" [27506]
"China's Transition to Green Energy Systems: The Economics of Home Solar Water Heaters and Their Popularization in Dezhou City" in Energy Policy (Vol. 39, October 2011, No. 10, pp. 5909-5919) [5566], [5845], [14914], [23149], [25265], [27507]

"China's ZTE in Hunt for Partners" in Globe & Mail (February 27, 2006, pp. B1) [17996], [18922], [31239]
Chinatown Chamber of Commerce [39133]
ChinaVest [37727]
Chincoteague Chamber of Commerce [45847]
"A Chinese Approach to Management: A Generation of Entrepreneurs Is Writing Its Own Rules" in Harvard Business Review (Vol. 92, September 2014, No. 9, pp. 103) [27850], [29154], [30695]
Chinese Entrepreneur Association (CEA) [22453]
"Chinese Coal Giant Shifts Focus with ECA Pact" in Pittsburgh Business Times (Vol. 33, January 10, 2014, No. 26, pp. 3) [27508], [31240]
Chino Valley Area Chamber of Commerce (CVACC) [36324]
Chino Valley Chamber of Commerce (CVCC) [36825]
Chip Chats [4614]
"Chip Heath: Get Over Your Fear of Change" in Canadian Business (Vol. 83, June 15, 2010, No. 10, pp. 38) [18923], [20808], [28499]
"Chipotle Mexican Grill Adds Alexa for Reorders of Favorite Meals" in Nation's Restaurant News (November 21, 2019) [11722], [13918], [21809]
Chippewa Falls Area Chamber of Commerce (CFACC) [46385]
Chippewa Innovation Center (CVIC) [46560]
Chippewa Valley Angel Investors Network, LLC (CVAIN) [35270], [46548]
"The Chips Are In" in Business Journal-Portland (Vol. 24, November 2, 2007, No. 35, pp. 1) [26245], [35328]
Chisholm Area Chamber of Commerce [41214]
CHL Medical Partners [38091]
Chloride Chamber of Commerce (CCC) [36325]
Chocolate Manufacturers Association of the U.S.A. [2536]
Choctaw Chamber of Commerce [43743]
Choice Coaching and Consulting [27131]
Choice Hotels Canada Inc. [8501]
Choice Hotels International Inc. [8502]
Choose a Business Structure [32404]
Choose Marshall [40970]
Choosing the Best Massage Business Structure [10761]
"Choosing a Location for Your Retail Business: Pros and Cons of Brick and Mortar vs. Online" in business.com (Apr 8, 2020) [30465]
Choosing the Right Business Entity [16713]
"Choosing the Right CRM Software for Your Business" in Small Business Trends (August 23, 2022) [20402]
Choosing the Right Legal Form of Business: The Complete Guide to Becoming a Sole Proprietor, Partnership, LLC, or Corporation [18543], [27173], [32405], [34457]
"Choosing the Right Small Business Software for Collecting Payments" in Business 2 Community (October 4, 2021) [11930], [33841]
"Choosing the United States: In Contests to Attract High-Value Business Activities, the U.S. Is Losing out More than It Should" in Harvard Business Review (Vol. 90, March 2012, No. 3, pp. 80) [19796], [31116]
"Chopping Option Added to Calmer Corn Head Kits" in Farm Industry News (January 16, 2011) [17019], [30696]
Christian Booksellers Association [1803]
Christian Booksellers Association International Convention [1848]
Christian Camp and Conference Association (CCCA) [2503]
Christian County Chamber of Commerce [40030]
Christian Entrepreneurs Association (CEA) [22454]
Christie's Chips [34585]
Christmas Decor Inc. [2927], [2958]
"Christmas Tree Farmers Rapidly Abandoning the Industry" in York Dispatch (Dec. 4, 2019) [2933]
"Christmas Trees Are a Big Small Business" in Business News Daily (June 29, 2022) [2934]
"Christmas Trees Keep Giving in St. Louis Area" in St. Louis Post-Dispatch (January 11, 2012 [2935], [13706], [23150], [25266]
The Chronicle of Philanthropy [7173]
Chrysalis Ventures [40095]
Chrysalix Venture Capital [46695]
"Chrysler Unions Set Up Roadblocks to Private Equity" in Globe & Mail (March 20, 2007, pp. B3) [29155], [35176]
"Chuck E. Cheese's CEO to Retire" in Dallas Business Journal (Vol. 37, March 28, 2014, No. 29, pp. 6) [12528], [19496], [28500]
"Chuck's Big Chance" in Barron's (Vol. 89, July 13, 2009, No. 28, pp. L3) [6325], [9410], [23806], [30697]
Chugiak-Eagle River Business & Service Directory [36222]
Chugiak-Eagle River Chamber of Commerce [36223]
Chula Vista Chamber of Commerce [36826]

Churchill County Chamber of Commerce [41936]
Churchill County Nevada Small Business Development Center [41910]
Church's Fried Chicken Inc. [14142]
ChurchSpace: Airbnb for Churches [34586]
Churro; Navajosa [640]
"Chuy's Ready to Serve New Markets" in *Austin Business Journal* (Vol. 31, June 17, 2011, No. 15, pp. 1) [13919], [17997], [19165], [33355]
Chyten Educational Services [16158]
"CIBC Spends $1.1 Billion on Caribbean Expansion" in *Globe & Mail* (March 14, 2006, pp. B1) [6326], [9411], [17998], [18924], [31241]
Cicco & Associates Inc. [10520], [30186]
CiCi Enterprises, LP [12545], [14143]
CiCi's Pizza [12545], [14143]
CID Capital (CID) [39629]
Cigar Aficionado [15708]
Cimarron Capital Partners LLC [43828]
Cimarron Chamber of Commerce [42309]
CIMTEC [46816]
Cincinnati Better Business Bureau [43400]
"Cincinnati Business Committee's Tom Williams: Future is Now" in *Business Courier* (Vol. 27, August 13, 2010, No. 15, pp. 1) [8704], [19797], [20809], [21471], [25267], [31684]
Cincinnati Business Courier [12011]
Cincinnati Business Courier [43693]
"Cincinnati Consults Executives on Police Chief Hire" in *Business Courier* (Vol. 27, August 27, 2010, No. 17, pp. 1) [25268], [26520], [26901], [28501], [31685]
"Cincinnati Hospitals Feel Pain from Slow Economy" in *Business Courier* (Vol. 27, September 3, 2010, No. 18, pp. 1) [4772], [20260], [20810], [23807], [25738], [28111]
"Cincinnati Hospitals Mandate Flu Shots" in *Business Courier* (Vol. 27, November 19, 2010, No. 29, pp. 1) [25739], [26902]
"Cincinnati Hospitals Wage War on 'Bounce-Backs'" in *Business Courier* (Vol. 27, July 30, 2010, No. 13, pp. 1)* [8894], [24957], [25269], [25740], [27246]
"Cincinnati Museum Center to Exhibit New Look" in *Business Courier* (Vol. 24, February 21, 2008, No. 46, pp. 1) [4027], [13414], [18925]
"Cincinnati Reds Hit Ratings Homer" in *Business Courier* (Vol. 27, July 30, 2010, No. 13, pp. 1) [2449], [13030], [15143], [15588]
Cincinnati USA Regional Chamber [43445]
Cincinnati USA Regional Chamber - Minority Business Accelerator (MBA) [43615], [43653]
"Cincinnati's Minority Business Accelerator Welcomes First Hispanic Firms" in *Business Courier* (Vol. 27, August 13, 2010, No. 15, pp. 1) [10088], [30334]
CincyTech [43654]
Cini-Little International Inc. [2691], [8495], [14105]
Cinnzeo [1291]
Cintrifuse [43655]
Circle Chamber of Commerce and Agriculture [41757]
Circle K Arizona [4452]
"Cirrus Logic: Too Much Apple?" in *Austin Business Journal* (Vol. 32, April 6, 2012, No. 5, pp. A1) [3698], [5412], [19654]
Cisco Chamber of Commerce (CCC) [45089]
Cisco Networking Introduction: Hands-On (Onsite) [22982]
CISM Journal ACSGC [15228]
CIT Group / Venture Capital [42209]
"CIT Serves as Sole Lead Arranger on $27.2 Million Financing for Texas Assisted Living Facilities" in *Senior Living News* (September 13, 2019) [1025]
"Citadel EFT (CDFT) Contracts With New Search Engine Optimization (SEO) and Banner Ad Web Marketing Companies" in *Internet Wire* (August 8, 2012) [250], [4711], [9113], [10461], [11723], [16401], [29710], [31242], [32121]
"Citadel Hires Three Lehman Execs" in *Chicago Tribune* (October 2, 2008) [6327], [9412], [18926], [19497], [19798], [23808], [26521], [28502]
"Citi Ruling Could Chill SEC, Street Legal Pacts" in *Wall Street Journal Eastern Edition* (November 29, 2011, pp. C1) [6328], [9413], [11019], [18544], [23480], [23809]
Cities from the Arabian Desert: The Building of Jubail and Yambu in Saudi Arabia [24633], [25270], [27509], [33973]
"Cities Work to Attract Small Biz: Officials Review 'Hoops' and Master Plans" in *Crain's Detroit Business* (Vol. 25, June 8, 2009, No. 23, pp. 20) [19166], [33356]
"CitiMortgage to Hire Hundreds in Dallas-Fort Worth" in *Dallas Business Journal* (Vol. 35, April 20, 2012, No. 32, pp. 1) [11020], [26522]
Citizen Kitchens [44839]

Citizen's Association [39152]
Citizens Budget Commission (CBC) [31721]
Citizens Clearinghouse for Hazardous Waste [7981]
Citizens for Tax Justice (CTJ) [15486]
Citizens Utility Board of Wisconsin (CUB) [46312]
Citizenship Educational Service [34446]
"Citrus Bowl Construction Bids Going Out This Year" in *Orlando Business Journal* (Vol. 29, June 29, 2012, No. 2, pp. 1) [876], [4028], [15144]
Citrus County Chamber of Commerce - Crystal River [38351]
Citrus Heights Chamber of Commerce [36827]
"City Board Tweaks Internet Cafe Ordinance" in *Ocala Star-Banner* (July 19, 2011) [7548], [13920], [25271]
"City Buys Aspen Mini Storage, Expanding Lumberyard Property" in *Aspen Daily News* (October 9, 2019) [10391]
City of Cleveland Office of Equal Opportunities (OEO) [43616]
City of Coachella [37557]
City College of City University of New York - Art Visual Resources Library [951], [9073]
City College of San Francisco (CCSF) - Culinary Arts and Hospitality Studies - Alice Statler Library [2695], [4476], [8124], [8526], [14301]
City of Corpus Christi Development Services Department [45418]
City of Corpus Christi Economic Development Division [45418]
"City, County May Kill VC Tax" in *Business Journal-Portland* (Vol. 24, October 12, 2007, No. 33, pp. 1) [19167], [34763], [35329]
City of Flagstaff Economic Development Department [36389]
City of Jackson Economic Development Division - Equal Business Opportunity Office [41434]
City Kitchen [2692]
City of Las Cruces - Economic Development Office [42345]
City Light [43017]
City Looks [7887]
"City May Aid Pop-Up Stores Downtown" in *Austin Business Journal* (Vol. 31, August 19, 2011, No. 24, pp. A1) [25272], [32122], [32948]
The City of Oilton [43744]
"City-Owned Buildings Get an Injection of Solar Power" in *America's Intelligence Wire* (September 11, 2012) [4029], [14915], [31686]
City of Peoria Economic Development Services Department [36390]
City of Phoenix [36268]
City Publications [391]
City and Regional Magazine Association (CRMA) [11963]
City of Ridgeland Chamber of Commerce [41389]
City of San Antonio Finance Department - Purchasing Div. [45484]
City of San Luis Economic Development Commission [36391]
"City Seeks More Minorities" in *Austin Business Journal Inc.* (Vol. 28, November 7, 2008, No. 34, pp. A1) [4030], [25124], [30335], [33125], [35754]
City of South Houston Chamber of Commerce [45090]
City Wide Maintenance Company Inc. [2095]
City Wok [14144]
CityDesk [38555]
Citygate Network [26100]
Cityside Ventures (CSV) [41044]
Civil + Structural Engineer [4275], [15227]
"A Civilian Cybersecurity Center for D.C.?" in *Washington Business Journal* (Vol. 32, March 7, 2014, No. 47, pp. 5) [14397], [25125]
CKO Kickboxing [12452]
Clackamas Community College Small Business Development Center [43909]
Claggett Wolfe Associates (CWA) [37670]
Claiborne Chamber of Commerce [40162]
Claiborne County Chamber of Commerce [44725]
CLAIMS® Direct Database [27976]
"Clairol Taps Hair Color Influencers for First Ad Campaign in Five Years" in *Bizwomen* (March 24, 2023) [29521]
Clairvest Group Inc. [46782]
Clallam Bay - Sekiu Chamber of Commerce [46069]
Clare Area Chamber of Commerce [40892]
Claremont Creek Ventures (CCV) [37728]
Claremore Chamber of Commerce [43745]
Clarence Chamber of Commerce [42553]
"Clarence Firm Gets OK To Make Tobacco Products" in *Business First of Buffalo* (Vol. 30, March 14, 2014, No. 26, pp. 3) [15696], [25273], [31243], [34764]
Clarendon County Chamber of Commerce (CCCC) [44540]
Clarinda Association of Business and Industry [39725]

Clarinda Chamber of Commerce [39725]
Clarinda Economic Development Corporation (CEDC) [39725]
Clarion Area Chamber of Business and Industry [44194]
Clarion Capital Corp. [42728]
Clarion University Small Business Development Center (SBDC) [44093]
Claritas Capital [44823]
CLark County Chamber of Commerce [39590]
Clark University - George Perkins Marsh Institute - Center for Technology, Environment, and Development (CENTED) [6015]
Clarke County Chamber of Commerce [41390]
Clarkesville-Habersham County Library [7402]
Clarkesville Lake Country Chamber of Commerce [45848]
Clarksburg Area Chamber of Commerce [46271]
Clarksdale - Coahoma County Chamber of Commerce and Industry Foundation (CCCCCIF) [41391]
Clarkston Area Chamber of Commerce [40893]
Clarkston Chamber of Commerce [46121]
Clarksville Area Chamber of Commerce [44726]
Clarksville Chamber of Commerce [45331]
Clarksville-Johnson County Chamber of Commerce [36446]
"The Clash of the Cultures: Investment vs. Speculation" [6329], [9414], [25274]
"Clash of the Titans" in *Canadian Business* (Vol. 80, March 12, 2007, No. 6, pp. 27) [6330], [9415], [19799], [26246], [27851]
"Clash of the Titans" in *San Francisco Business Times* (Vol. 28, February 7, 2014, No. 29, pp. 4) [7092], [17999], [19800], [25741]
Class 101 [16159]
Classes to Consider Taking When Starting a Business [21472]
"The Classless Workplace: The Digerati and the New Spirit of Technocapitalism" in *WorkingUSA* (Vol. 11, June 2008, No. 2, pp. 181) [22534], [23481], [24634], [26903]
Clatskanie Chamber of Commerce [43962]
Claxton-Evans County Chamber of Commerce [38713]
Clay Center Area Chamber of Commerce [39875]
Clay County Chamber of Commerce [38352], [43118]
Clay County Chamber of Commerce - Alabama [36097]
Clay County Partnership Chamber of Commerce [44727]
Clayton Chamber of Commerce (CCC) [41547], [43119]
Clayton Chamber of Commerce [42510]
Clayton County Chamber of Commerce [38714]
Clayton State University - College of Business - Small Business Development Center [38636]
Clayton-Union County Chamber of Commerce [42310]
Cle Elum-Roslyn Chamber of Commerce [46070]
Clean Energy Incubator (CEI) [45505]
Clean Energy Trends: Driving Innovation [23424]
Clean Energy Venture Group (CEVG) [40676]
Clean First Time Inc. [10564]
Clean and Happy Windows [2096]
Clean Living Specialists Inc. [2097]
Clean Show [5250]
The Clean Tech Center (TTG) [42853]
"Clean-Tech Focus Sparks Growth" in *Philadelphia Business Journal* (Vol. 28, January 15, 2010, No. 48, pp. 1) [5567], [5846], [18000], [20811], [23151], [31244]
The Cleaning Authority (TCA) [2098], [5081]
Cleaning Business: Published for Self-Employed Cleaning Professionals [2992]
Cleaning Consultant Services Inc. (CCS) [2084], [2099], [5079], [5082], [10565], [16232], [46240]
Cleaning Management Institute (CMI) [2048]
Cleaning & Restoration [4828], [16230]
Cleaning and Restoration Association (CRA) [2967]
"Cleaning Service Companies in Oklahoma Find Green Market Niche" in *Journal Record* (April 19, 2012) [2043], [35501]
Cleanlots: America's Simplest Business, A Parking Lot Litter Removal Business You Can Be Proud Of [2962]
CleanNet USA, Inc. [2100]
CleanStart [37558]
The Cleantech Open [37559]
"Cleanup to Polish Plating Company's Bottom Line" in *Crain's Cleveland Business* (Vol. 28, October 29, 2007, No. 43, pp. 4) [18927], [24958], [28112], [29156]
Clear Business, Technical, and E-mail Writing [17834]
Clear Lake Area Chamber of Commerce (CLACC) [39726]
Clear Lake Chamber Newsletter [36828]
Clear Light Books [20669]
Clear Light Publishing [20669]
Clearfield Chamber of Commerce [44195]
Clearstone Venture Partners / Idealab! Capital Partners [37333]
Clearview Business Solutions Inc. [16877]

Clearwater Navigator **[5739]**
"*Clearwire Struggling, Banks on Deals with Competitors*" in *Puget Sound Business Journal* (Vol. 33, August 24, 2012, No. 18, pp. 1) **[2724]**, **[19801]**, **[23810]**, **[28503]**, **[31245]**
Cleburne Chamber of Commerce **[45091]**
Clemson Area Chamber of Commerce (CACC) **[44541]**
Clemson Area SBDC [44502]
Clemson Area Small Business Development Center **[44502]**
Clemson Regional Small Business Development Center (SBDC) **[44503]**
Clemson Small Business Development Center **[44504]**, **[44595]**
Clemson University-College of Health, Education & Human Development-Learning Resource Center **[11540]**
Clermont Area Chamber of Commerce [38502]
Clermont Chamber of Commerce (CCC) **[43446]**
Cleveland Area Chamber of Commerce **[45092]**
Cleveland-Bolivar County Chamber of Commerce (CBCCC) **[41392]**
Cleveland Botanical Garden - Eleanor Squire Library **[7663]**, **[8160]**, **[10144]**
Cleveland Bradley Business Incubator (CBBI) **[44840]**
Cleveland/Bradley Chamber of Commerce **[44728]**
Cleveland Chamber of Commerce **[46386]**
Cleveland County Chamber of Commerce **[43120]**
Cleveland Culinary Launch Kitchen **[43656]**
Cleveland FES Center **[12512]**
Cleveland Institute of Art (CIA) **[3365]**, **[4640]**
Cleveland Institute of Music (CIM) **[11216]**
Cleveland-Marshall Solo Practice Incubator **[43657]**
Cleveland Public Library Literature Department **[1706]**, **[5348]**, **[16216]**
Cleveland Public Library - Science and Technology Department **[667]**
Cleveland State University - Maxine Goodman Levin College of Urban Affairs - Northern Ohio Data and Information Service (NODIS) **[47399]**
Clevenger Associates (CA) **[8496]**, **[14106]**
Clewiston Chamber of Commerce **[38353]**
"*Click Your Chicken*" in *Canadian Business* (Vol. 87, October 2014, No. 10, pp. 11) **[13921]**, **[17020]**, **[21810]**
"*ClickFuel Unveils Internet Marketing Tools for Small Businesses*" in *Marketwired* (October 19, 2009) **[9114]**, **[14768]**, **[18001]**, **[21811]**, **[29711]**, **[33842]**, **[33974]**
Clicking Through: A Survival Guide for Bringing Your Company Online **[9115]**, **[16402]**, **[18545]**, **[21812]**, **[27852]**
"*Clicks Vs. Bricks*" in *Birmingham Business Journal* (Vol. 31, April 25, 2014, No. 17, pp. 4) **[11724]**, **[19802]**, **[32123]**, **[34765]**
ClickZ **[29509]**
The Client Lifecycle **[16646]**
Clifton Chamber of Commerce **[45093]**
Clifton Chamber of Commerce and the Passaic Valley Chamber of Commerce **[42171]**
Clifton-Passaic Regional Chamber of Commerce [42171]
Clifton Springs Area Chamber of Commerce (CSCOC) **[42554]**
"'*Climate Positive Now' a Welcome Message of Sustainability*" in *Woodworking Network* (November 19, 2021) **[2636]**, **[8203]**, **[23152]**
Climatic Test Techniques (Onsite) **[23060]**
"*Climbing the Wall of Worry, Two Steps at a Time*" in *Barron's* (Vol. 89, July 13, 2009, No. 28, pp. L16) **[6331]**, **[9416]**, **[23811]**
Clinical Gerontologist: The Journal of Aging and Mental Health **[187]**, **[11528]**
Clinical and Investigative Medicine (CIM) **[25665]**
Clinical Laboratory Management Association (CLMA) **[10908]**
Clinical Laboratory Management Association KnowledgeLab [10936]
Clinical Laboratory News **[25997]**
Clinical and Laboratory Standards Institute (CLSI) **[10909]**
Clinical Pharmacology™ **[5209]**
Clintar Groundskeeping Services **[2101]**, **[10135]**, **[10264]**
Clinton **[41548]**
Clinton Area Chamber of Commerce **[41549]**
Clinton Area Chamber of Commerce (CACC) **[39727]**
Clinton Area Chamber of Commerce [39136]
Clinton Area Chamber of Commerce and Tourism Bureau **[39136]**
Clinton Chamber of Commerce **[36447]**, **[38039]**, **[41393]**, **[43746]**
Clinton Chamber of Commerce (CCC) **[42555]**
Clinton County Chamber of Commerce **[39527]**, **[40894]**
Clinton County Chamber of Commerce **[44196]**, **[44711]**
Clinton County Economic Partnership (CCEP) **[44196]**

Clinton-Sampson Chamber of Commerce (CACC) **[43121]**
Clintonville Area Chamber of Commerce **[46387]**
CLIX **[2896]**
CLMA KnowledgeLab **[10936]**
"*Clock Ticks On Columbia Sussex Debt*" in *Business Courier* (Vol. 27, July 30, 2010, No. 13, pp. 1) **[4773]**, **[8375]**, **[20261]**, **[23812]**, **[28113]**
Cloquet Area Chamber of Commerce (CACC) **[41215]**
"*Close the Deal: The Sandler Sales Institute's 7 Step System for Successful Selling*" **[32490]**
"*Closed Minds and Open Skies*" in *Barron's* (Vol. 88, March 10, 2008, No. 10, pp. 50) **[8705]**, **[20812]**, **[27510]**, **[29157]**, **[31117]**
Closet Factory **[12855]**
Closets by Design Franchising **[12856]**
Closets and Storage Concepts **[12857]**
"*Closures Pop Cork on Wine Bar Sector Consolidation*" in *Houston Business Journal* (Vol. 40, January 22, 2010, No. 37, pp. A2) **[1322]**, **[15009]**, **[19803]**, **[31246]**
Clothes Mentor (CM) **[6149]**
Clothing Poverty: The Hidden World of Fast Fashion and Second-Hand Clothes **[3013]**, **[23153]**
Cloud 9 **[3660]**
"*Cloud City: An Industry - and a Region - On the Rise*" in *Puget Sound Business Journal* (Vol. 34, February 28, 2014, No. 46, pp. 4) **[3489]**, **[3613]**, **[14769]**, **[21813]**, **[26247]**, **[33357]**, **[33843]**, **[33975]**
"*Cloud Computing for a Crowd*" in *CIO* (Vol. 24, October 2, 2010, No. 1, pp. 16) **[18002]**, **[22112]**, **[26904]**, **[29712]**, **[30698]**
Cloud Computing Technologies (CCT) **[14871]**
Cloud Sherpas **[14890]**
Cloud Storage Made Easy: Securely Backup and Share Your Files **[3490]**
Cloud[8]Sixteen, Inc. **[3661]**
CloudBees Inc. **[14872]**
Cloudblue Technologies Inc. [3664]
CloudCommerce, Inc. [3658]
Cloudcroft Chamber of Commerce (CCC) **[42311]**
Cloudera, Inc. **[14873]**
Cloudflare Inc. **[16497]**
Cloudium.Net **[14874]**
Cloudmark Inc. **[14875]**
Cloudnexa **[14876]**
CloudNine **[14877]**
"*Clouds in the Forecast*" in *Information Today* (Vol. 28, September 2011, No. 8, pp. 10) **[3491]**, **[3699]**, **[14770]**, **[33844]**, **[33976]**
CloudSmartz **[3662]**
"*Cloudy Future for VMware?*" in *Barron's* (Vol. 90, September 13, 2010, No. 37, pp. 21) **[3492]**, **[3614]**, **[9417]**, **[19804]**, **[21814]**
Cloverdale Chamber of Commerce **[36829]**
Clovis Chamber of Commerce **[36830]**
Clovis Chamber of Commerce and Economic Development [42312]
Clovis/Curry County Chamber of Commerce **[42312]**
Clovis Small Business Development Center **[42276]**
Clown Club of America [11892]
Clowns of America [11892]
Clowns of America International (COAI) **[11892]**
CLSA Annual Conference [15230]
Club Business International (CBI) **[6819]**
Club Canin Canadien [631]
Club Managers Association of America Conference and Expo **[28938]**
Club Scientific, LLC **[21716]**
Club SciKidz **[16160]**
Club Z! In-Home Tutoring **[16161]**
Club Z! Tutoring Services **[16162]**
Clubnet Solutions Inc. **[10521]**, **[33657]**
"*Clusters Last Stand?*" in *Canadian Electronics* (Vol. 23, February 2008, No. 1, pp. 6) **[4388]**, **[15845]**, **[25275]**, **[26248]**, **[27853]**, **[35040]**
Clydesdale Ventures LLC **[37334]**
CM Equity Partners L.P. (CMEP) **[42729]**
Cm It Solutions **[3582]**
CMC Communicating Up, Down and Across the Organization **[17835]**
CMC Confronting the Tough Stuff: Turning Managerial Challenges into Positive Results **[28301]**
CMC Developing Executive Leadership **[28302]**
CMC How to Communicate with Diplomacy, Tact and Credibility **[17836]**
CMC Leadership and Team Development for Managerial Success **[22044]**
CMC Process Management: Applying Process Mapping to Analyze and Improve Your Operation **[28303]**
CMC Stepping Up to Leadership **[28304]**
CMC The Project Planning Workshop **[21346]**
CMC's Course on Financial Analysis **[16765]**

CMIT Solutions Inc. **[3561]**, **[26824]**
"*The CMO of Consequence*" in *Business Strategy Review* (Vol. 21, Autumn 2010, No. 3, pp. 42) **[28504]**, **[29713]**, **[31951]**, **[32738]**
CMO Council **[29572]**
"*CMO Nicholson Exits Pepsi as Share Declines*" in *Advertising Age* (Vol. 79, July 7, 2008, No. 26, pp. 4) **[251]**, **[9418]**, **[28505]**, **[29158]**, **[29714]**
CMPX: Canadian Mechanical & Plumbing Exposition (CMPX) **[12679]**
CMS National Conference [11199], [11282]
"*CN Aims for Regional Pacts to Halt Labor Row*" in *Globe & Mail* (April 17, 2007, pp. B2) **[30870]**, **[35177]**
The CN Journal **[3223]**
CNLA Newsbrief **[7606]**, **[10075]**
"*CNL's James Seneff Jr. Reveals 7 Ways to Grow Your Firm, Even in Down Times*" in *Orlando Business Journal* (Vol. 30, May 16, 2014, No. 47, pp. 3) **[13164]**, **[13415]**
CNY Biotech Accelerator (CNYBAC) **[42854]**
The CO-OP **[40447]**
"*Co-Op Launches Revolving Loan Program for Farmers*" in *Bellingham Business Journal* (Vol. February 2010, pp. 3) **[5568]**, **[5847]**, **[17021]**, **[23154]**, **[28114]**
"*Co-Working a Hit in Seattle Market*" in *Puget Sound Business Journal* (Vol. 34, March 14, 2014, No. 48, pp. 8) **[11633]**, **[19805]**, **[31247]**, **[33977]**
"*Co-Working Space by Day, Cocktail Lounge by Night*" in *OakPark.com* (July 16, 2019) **[1323]**, **[3838]**
Coachella Valley Small Business Development Center **[36570]**
Coaching: A Strategic Tool for Effective Leadership **[28305]**
Coaching and Counseling for Outstanding Job Performance **[28306]**
Coaching & Mentoring for Dummies **[28506]**
Coaching, Mentoring & Team-Building Skills (Onsite) **[28307]**
Coaching and Teambuilding Skills for Managers and Supervisors (Onsite) **[22045]**
CoachMeFit **[12453]**
Coady International Institute **[32420]**
Coahoma County Business Development Center **[41446]**
"*Coal Train Crush Feared*" in *Puget Sound Business Journal* (Vol. 33, July 6, 2012, No. 11, pp. 1) **[7032]**, **[8706]**, **[23155]**
Coalition Canadienne de la Santé **[25666]**
Coalition for Common Sense in Government Procurement [25101]
Coalition of Franchisee Associations, Inc. (CFA) **[24306]**
Coalition for Government Procurement (CGP) **[25101]**
Coalition of Handcrafted Entrepreneurs (COHE) **[4499]**, **[4654]**
Coalition of Independent Music Stores (CIMS) **[3409]**
Coalition to Promote Independent Entrepreneurs **[32982]**
Coalition for Scenic Beauty [31843]
Coalition for Service Industries (CSI) **[33086]**
Coalition for Tattoo Safety **[15281]**
Coast Capital Partners **[44620]**
Coast Capital Savings Venture Connection **[46711]**
Coastal Alabama Business Chamber **[36098]**
Coastal Bend Business Innovation Center (CBBIC) **[45506]**
Coastal Capital Partners **[40782]**
Coastal Carolina SCORE **[43051]**
Coastal Chamber of Commerce [42000]
Coastlines **[38354]**
Cobb Chamber of Commerce **[38715]**
"*Cobblers Face Extinction — and Are Busier Than Ever*" in *U.S. News & World Report* (March 23, 2019) **[14663]**
The Coca-Cola Company **[1373]**, **[1869]**, **[6944]**
"*The Coca-Cola Company and Rise Up Crowdfunding LLC Launch Equity Crowdfunding Resource for Women and Minority-Owned Small Business*" in *Minority Business Entrepreneur* (March 7, 2023) **[35330]**
"*Coca-Cola FEMSA, Family Dollar, Other Dividend Payers On a Roll*" in *Benzinga.com* (June 21, 2012) **[7728]**, **[8376]**, **[9116]**, **[9419]**, **[18003]**, **[19341]**, **[29159]**
Cocciardi & Associates Inc. **[35961]**
Cocke County Partnership/Chamber of Commerce **[44729]**
Cocktails Magazine **[1361]**, **[1948]**
Cocoa Beach Area Chamber of Commerce [38355]
Cocoa Beach Regional Chamber of Commerce (CBRCC) **[38355]**
Coconino Community College Small Business Development Center **[36269]**
Coconut Grove Chamber of Commerce (CGCC) **[38356]**
"*The Code-Cracker: Prominent Researcher at Miami Part of Federal Effort to Solve Protein Structures*" in *Business Courier* (Vol. 24, January 10, 2008, No. 40, pp. 1) **[29160]**, **[30699]**, **[32739]**

"Code Name: Inventors: Go from Golden Idea to Agent of Invention" in Black Enterprise (Vol. 41, November 2010, No. 4, pp. 78) [7918], [22535], [27854]
Cody Country Chamber of Commerce [46602]
Coeur d'Alene Area Chamber of Commerce [38911]
Coeur d'Alene Chamber of Commerce [38911]
Coffee Association of Canada [7540]
The Coffee Beanery Ltd. (CB) [3207], [7575]
"Coffee Breaks Don't Boost Productivity After All" in Harvard Business Review (Vol. 90, May 2012, No. 5, pp. 34) [22113], [26905], [28507]
Coffee Business Technology [3177]
Coffee News [7576], [11480]
Coffee Perks [6933]
"A Coffee Shop Owner's Guide to Handling Food & Dairy Allergies" in Perfect Daily Grind (November 1, 2019) [7549], [35941]
"Coffee Shop Startup Costs" in Cardconnect.com [3178]
Coffee & Snack Shops Industry in the US - Market Research Report [1274], [3196]
Coffee Time Donuts Inc. [1292], [4896], [7577]
Coffey County Chamber of Commerce [39876]
Coffeyville Area Chamber of Commerce (CCC) [39877]
Coffeyville Community College (CCC) [39979]
Cognetics Corp. [14878]
"Cogs in R.I. Manufacturing Machine" in Providence Business News (Vol. 28, January 27, 2014, No. 43, pp. 1) [10427], [10579], [20618], [29161]
Cogswell College Library [35972]
Cogswell Polytechnical College [35972]
Cohasset Chamber of Commerce [40570]
Cohesion Consulting L.L.C. [1697]
Coin Laundries - Road to Financial Independence: A Complete Guide to Starting and Operating Profitable Self-Service Laundries [5224], [24526]
Coin Laundry Association (CLA) [5225]
Coin-O-Matic [10192]
"Coin Toss? A Real Cartoon Caper" in Barron's (Vol. 92, September 17, 2012, No. 38, pp. 17) [1070], [29715]
Coin World: World's 1 Publication for Coin Collectors [3241]
Coins Magazine [3242]
"Coinstar, Inc. and Seattle's Best Coffee Sign Exclusive Agreement to Roll Out Thousands of the New Rubi Kiosks in Grocery, Drug and Mass Channels" in Marketing Weekly News (June 23 2012, pp. 77) [3179], [5151], [7550], [7729], [10020], [31248], [32124]
Coit Cleaning and Restoration [559], [1574], [16234]
Coit Services Inc. [559], [1574], [16234]
Cokato Chamber of Commerce (CCC) [41216]
CoLab [40448]
Colbert/Ball Tax Service [15447]
Colburn & Guyette Consulting Partners Inc. [5252]
Colby Area Chamber of Commerce [39878]
Colby College - Bixler Art and Music Library [994]
Colby - Thomas County Chamber of Commerce [39878]
Cold Spring Area Chamber of Commerce [42556]
Cold Stone Creamery Inc. [8613]
"Cold Stone Creamery Offers New Eight-Layer Ice Cream Cakes" in Ice Cream Reporter (Vol. 23, October 20, 2010, No. 11, pp. 2) [1249], [8554], [30700]
"Cold Stone in Licensing Agreement with Turin Chocolates" in Ice Cream Reporter (Vol. 22, December 20, 2008, No. 1, pp. 2) [2543], [8555], [30701], [31249]
Coldspring Chamber of Commerce [45094]
Coldspring/San Jacinto County Chamber of Commerce (CCC) [45094]
Coldwater Area Chamber of Commerce (CCC) [40895]
Coldwell Banker Commercial Reliant Realty [13613]
Cole Financial Service Inc. [22312], [27132]
Cole & Goyette Architects & Planners Inc. [31067]
Cole, Warren and Long Inc. [31610]
Coleman County Chamber of Commerce, Agriculture and Tourist Bureau [45095]
Coleman Foundation, Inc. [35271]
Colfax Chamber of Commerce [36831]
Colgate-Palmolive Company [1600], [4547]
Collab [42855]
The Collaborative CFO Workgroups [35272], [41331]
Collaborative Leadership Skills [28308]
Collaborative Leadership Skills (Onsite) [28308]
CollabTech Incubator [38829]
"Collateral Damage" in Business Courier (Vol. 26, October 16, 2009, No. 25, pp. 1) [4031], [18546], [25276], [26906], [35178]
The Collection [42115]
"Collection Agency Issues Whitepaper on Legal and Ethical Methods of Collecting on Overdue Accounts" in Marketwired (July 20, 2009) [4741], [4774], [18547], [20262], [25277], [33978]
Collection-Master [4822]

Collections Laws [18482]
Collective [30632]
The Collective 12 | 12 [46665]
The Collective Kitchen [44057]
Collector: The Official Publication of the ACA International [4820]
The Collectors Club (CC) [3256]
Collectors Club of Chicago (CCC) [3257]
The Collectors Club Philatelist (CCP) [3243]
College Bookstore Association [1808]
College Canadien des Leaders en Sante [25652]
College of the Canyons Small Business Development Center (COC SBDC) [36571]
College of DuPage Center for Entrepreneurship - Illinois Procurement Technical Assistance Center (PTAC) [39387]
College of Eastern Idaho (CEI) [38955]
College of Family Physicians of Canada - Ontario Chapter (CFPC) [25667]
College Hunks Hauling Junk Inc. [33316]
College des Medecins de Famille du Canada [25667]
College Music Society National Conference [11199], [11282]
College of Optometrists in Vision Development (COVD) [16288]
College Placement Council [2626], [5436]
College of Southern Idaho School of Vo-Tech Education [38956]
College of Southern Idaho Small Business Development Center [38898]
College of Southern Maryland - Southern Maryland Studies Center (SMSC) [7461]
College of Staten Island Small Business Development Center [42397]
College Stores Research & Educational Foundation [1808]
College of William and Mary - Center for Archaeological Research (W&MCAR) [954]
College of William and Mary - Mason School of Business - McLeod Business Library [24909]
Collegiate Entrepreneurs' Organization (CEO) [22973]
Colleyville Area Chamber of Commerce (CACC) [45096]
The Collide Village (CV) [45507]
Colliers International [13614]
"Colliers Shifts Its Brokerage Home" in Charlotte Business Journal (Vol. 25, November 5, 2010, No. 33, pp. 1) [13165], [13416], [31250]
Collierville Area Chamber of Commerce [44730]
Collierville Magazine [44731]
Collin County Black Chamber of Commerce (CCBCC) [45097]
Collin County Genealogical Society Library (CCGS) [7403]
Collin Small Business Development Center [44911]
Collins Area Chamber of Commerce [41396]
Collinsville Chamber of Commerce [39137], [43747]
"Collision Centers See Business Boom" in Atlanta Business Chronicle (February 7, 2014, pp. 3A) [14549], [27247]
Coloma Area Chamber of Commerce [40896]
Coloma-Watervliet Area Chamber of Commerce (CWACC) [40896]
Colombian American Association (CAA) [27405]
Colombian-American Chamber of Commerce [27405]
"Colombia's Green Coffee Company Earns RA Certification for All It's Farms" in Daily Coffee News (November 26, 2021) [3180], [7551]
Colonial Beach Chamber of Commerce (CBCC) [45849]
Colonial Compliance Systems, Inc. [20670]
Colonial Heights Chamber of Commerce (CHCC) [45850]
Colonial Technology Development Co. [33658]
Colonie Chamber of Commerce [42557]
The Colony Chamber of Commerce [45098]
Color-Glo International [14661]
Color Me Mine Franchising Inc. [4706]
"The Color of Success: ELC Focuses On Making Diversity Work" in Black Enterprise (Vol. 41, December 2010, No. 5, pp. 59) [28508], [30550]
Color World Housepainting Inc. [11888]
Colorado Association of REALTORS (CAR) [13085]
Colorado Business Association (CBA) [37774]
Colorado Business Incubation Association [33452]
Colorado Business Women (CBW) [35591]
Colorado Calligraphers' Guild Newsletter [2483]
Colorado City Area Chamber of Commerce [45099]
"Colorado Companies Adjust as Drought Boosts Food Prices" in Denver Business Journal (Vol. 64, August 17, 2012, No. 13, pp. 1) [19994], [24959]
"Colorado Could Set Record for Oil Production" in Denver Business Journal (Vol. 64, August 24, 2012, No. 14, pp. 1) [25278]
Colorado Department of Local Affairs - Division of Local Government (DLG) [47400]

Colorado Economic Demographic Information System [777]
Colorado Leads [4971]
Colorado Mountain College - Alpine Campus Library [8527], [34229]
Colorado Northwestern Community College (CNCC) [37958]
Colorado Office of Economic Development and International Trade - Colorado International Trade Office [37800]
Colorado Office of Economic Development and International Trade - Minority Business Office [37913]
Colorado Office of Economic Development and International Trade (SBDC) - Small Business Development Center [37801]
Colorado Procurement Technical Assistance Center - Denver Small Business Development Procurement Center (SBDC) [37930]
Colorado River Valley Chamber (RACC) [37831]
Colorado RV Adventure Travel Show [15774]
Colorado Small Business Development Center (CSBDC) [37782]
Colorado Springs Business Journal (CSBJ) [37963]
Colorado Springs Pioneers Museum - Starsmore Center For Local History (SCLH) [7462]
Colorado Springs Small Business Development Center [37783]
Colorado State University - College of Agricultural Sciences - Department of Agricultural & Resource Economics (DARE) [47401]
Colorado State University College of Liberal Arts - Center for Research on Writing and Communication Technologies [17887]
Colorado State University Department of Health and Exercise Science - Human Performance Clinical Research Laboratory (HPCRL) [12513]
Colorado State University - Industrial Assessment Center (IAC) [23457]
"Colorado Statehouse Races Key for Business" in Denver Business Journal (Vol. 64, August 31, 2012, No. 15, pp. 1) [20813], [25279], [26523]
Colorado Technical University, Inc. (CTU) [3468]
Colorado Women's Leadership Coalition [35591]
"Colorado's Ag Industry Grows Despite Flooding" in Denver Business Journal (Vol. 65, January 10, 2014, No. 35, pp. A6) [8707], [17022]
"Colorado's Hollywood Wager" in Denver Business Journal (Vol. 65, April 25, 2014, No. 50, pp. A4) [6177], [24960]
"Colorado's Oldest Craft Brewery is Downsizing, Ending Distribution and Laying Off 21 Employees" in The Denver Post (October 10, 2019) [1909], [15010]
ColorAll Technologies (CA) [14579]
ColorComm: Women of Color in Communications [30257], [35592]
Colors on Parade [1139]
A Colossal Failure of Common Sense: The Inside Story of the Collapse of Lehman Brothers [6332], [9420], [20814]
Colquitt - Miller County Chamber of Commerce (CMCCOC) [38716]
"The Colt Effect" in Hawaii Business (Vol. 53, January 2008, No. 7, pp. 30) [15145], [20815], [21473]
Colt Ventures (CV) [45593]
Colton Chamber of Commerce [36832]
Columbia Chamber of Commerce [41550]
Columbia City Area Chamber of Commerce [39621]
Columbia City Commercial Club [39621]
Columbia County Chamber of Commerce [42558]
Columbia Gorge Community College Small Business Development Center [43910]
Columbia Montour Chamber of Commerce [44197]
Columbia Montour Chamber of Commerce and Berwick Area Chamber of Commerce [44197]
Columbia Regional Business Report [44616]
Columbia River Inter-Tribal Fish Commission (CRITFC) [6796]
Columbia Technology Incubator [44600]
Columbia University - Center for Social Policy and Practice in the Workplace [34698]
Columbia University College of Physicians and Surgeons - Institute of Human Nutrition (IHN) [11625]
Columbia University - College of Physicians and Surgeons - New York Nutrition and Obesity Research Center (NYNORC) [16520]
Columbia University - Columbia Business School - Columbia Institute for Tele-Information (CITI) [15554]
Columbia University - Industrial Social Welfare Center [34698]
Columbiana Area Chamber of Commerce (CACC) [43447]
"Columbia's JPB Raising $175M to Acquire Companies, Real Estate" in Boston Business Journal (Vol. 29, May 27, 2011, No. 3, pp. 1) [9421], [13166], [13417], [33126], [35331]

Columbus Master Index

Columbus Area Chamber of Commerce (CACC) **[41848]**
Columbus Area Chamber of Commerce, Inc. (CACC) **[39528]**
Columbus Bar Association (CBA) **[43658]**
Columbus Business First **[43694]**
Columbus Chamber [43448]
Columbus Chamber of Commerce (CCC) **[43448]**
Columbus Chamber of Commerce [38737], [41794]
Columbus Chamber of Commerce and Tourism (GWCC) **[43122]**
Columbus SCORE **[43374]**
Columbus State University Regional Technology Incubator [38831]
The Columbus Times **[20590]**, **[30413]**, **[30626]**
Columbus Top Startups **[43690]**
"Column: Good Decisions. Bad Outcomes" in Harvard Business Review (Vol. 88, December 2010, No. 12, pp. 40) **[17288]**, **[22114]**, **[28509]**
The Column Group (TCG) **[37729]**
"Column: It's Time to Take Full Responsibility" in Harvard Business Review (Vol. 88, October 2010, No. 10, pp. 42) **[1749]**, **[8650]**, **[12929]**, **[15371]**, **[23482]**, **[28510]**, **[31751]**
"Column: Redefining Failure" in Harvard Business Review (Vol. 88, September 2010, No. 9, pp. 34) **[24635]**, **[28511]**
"Column: To Win, Create What's Scarce" in Harvard Business Review (Vol. 88, November 2010, No. 11, pp. 46) **[24636]**, **[30702]**
"Column: Want People to Save? Force Them" in Harvard Business Review (Vol. 88, September 2010, No. 9, pp. 36) **[6333]**, **[9422]**, **[23813]**, **[25280]**, **[27511]**
"Column: What 17th-Century Pirates Can Teach Us About Job Design" in Harvard Business Review (Vol. 88, October 2010, No. 10, pp. 44) **[26907]**, **[28512]**
"Column: Work Pray Love" in Harvard Business Review (Vol. 88, December 2010, No. 12, pp. 38) **[22115]**, **[28513]**
Colville Chamber of Commerce **[46071]**
Comanche Chamber of Commerce [45100]
Comanche Chamber of Commerce & Agriculture **[45100]**
"Combating Reverse Ageism as a Young Entrepreneur" in Entrepreneur (Sept. 11, 2018) **[36016]**
"Combo Dorm-Field House Built to Attain LEED Gold" in Contractor (Vol. 56, September 2009, No. 9, pp. 1) **[477]**, **[4032]**, **[5569]**, **[23156]**
Combustion Group (CG) **[42233]**
"Comcast Corp. Enters Home Security Business" in Record (May 27, 2012) **[2450]**, **[14398]**
"Comcast Launches New Home Security Service, Developed in Portland" in The Oregonian (June 7, 2011) **[2451]**, **[2725]**, **[9117]**, **[14399]**
Comcast Ventures **[37335]**
"Come Together: A Thematic Collection of Times Articles, Essays, Maps and More About Creating Community" in Pet Product News (Vol. 64, December 2010, No. 12, pp. 28) **[12162]**, **[20403]**, **[29716]**, **[32125]**, **[32491]**
Comenius University - Faculty of Management Library **[29051]**
Comer & Associates L.L.C. (CA) **[2248]**, **[20175]**, **[28976]**, **[30187]**, **[30848]**, **[33659]**
Comet Cleaners **[5253]**
Comfort Chamber of Commerce **[45101]**
Comfort Keepers **[8283]**
Comfort Keepers-Canada **[8284]**
Comic Shop: The Retail Mavericks Who Gave Us a New Geek Culture **[3268]**, **[33979]**
"Comics Retailers Hope to Rebound in 2018" in Publishers Weekly (February 9, 2018) **[3269]**, **[33980]**
"Coming: Cheaper Oil and a Stronger Buck" in Barron's (Vol. 88, March 24, 2008, No. 12, pp. 53) **[6334]**, **[8708]**, **[9423]**, **[20816]**, **[23814]**, **[27512]**
"Coming Soon: Bailouts of Fannie and Freddie" in Barron's (Vol. 88, July 14, 2008, No. 28, pp. 14) **[6335]**, **[9424]**, **[11021]**, **[13167]**, **[20263]**, **[20817]**, **[23815]**, **[24961]**, **[25281]**, **[28115]**
"Coming Soon: Electric Tractors" in Farm Industry News (November 21, 2011) **[5570]**, **[5848]**, **[17023]**, **[23157]**, **[29162]**, **[30703]**
"Coming: The End of Fiat Money" in Barron's (Vol. 92, July 23, 2012, No. 30, pp. 32) **[6336]**, **[9425]**, **[20818]**, **[23816]**, **[27513]**
"Coming Through When It Matters Most: How Great Teams Do Their Best Work Under Pressure" in Harvard Business Review (Vol. 90, April 2012, No. 4, pp. 82) **[22116]**, **[30704]**
Comite Consultatif Economique et Industriel aupres de l'O.C.D.E. [27401]
"A Comment on 'Balancing Risk and Return in a Customer Portfolio" in Journal of Marketing (Vol. 75, May 2011, No. 3, pp. 18) **[23817]**, **[29717]**
"Commentary. Economic Trends for Small Business" in Small Business Economic Trends (April 2008, pp. 3) **[20819]**, **[24637]**, **[33981]**
Commerce Business Daily Online [25172]
Commerce Chamber of Commerce (CCC) **[45102]**
Commerce Connection **[39138]**
Commerce Industrial Council Chamber of Commerce **[36833]**
"Commercial Builders Take It on the Chin" in Crain's Chicago Business (Vol. 31, April 28, 2008, No. 17, pp. 16) **[4033]**, **[8377]**, **[13418]**, **[25742]**, **[32126]**
Commercial Carrier Journal **[15527]**, **[16094]**
Commercial Cost Control Inc. (CCC) **[4308]**
Commercial Finance Association [28080], [35307]
Commercial Food Equipment Service Agencies of America [13879]
Commercial Food Equipment Service Association (CFESA) **[13879]**
Commercial, Industrial and Institutional Roofing Materials Guide [14329]
Commercial Investment Journal [13313], [13600]
Commercial Investment Real Estate Magazine (CIRE) **[13313]**, **[13600]**
Commercial Kitchen Fort Myers (CKFM) **[38556]**
"Commercial Loans Ready for Refinance: High Number of Mortgages Creates Buying Opportunities" in Memphis Business Journal (Vol. 34, June 22, 2012, No. 10, pp. 1) **[11022]**, **[28116]**
Commercial Low-Slope Roofing Materials Guide [14329]
"Commercial Real Estate Brokers See Steady Growth In 2014" in Sacramento Business Journal (Vol. 30, January 10, 2014, No. 46, pp. 3) **[13168]**, **[13419]**, **[20820]**
"Commercial Real Estate Developers" in Business Review Albany (Vol. 41, August 8, 2014, No. 20, pp. 8) **[4034]**, **[13420]**
Commercial Real Estate Development Association [13361]
Commercial Real Estate Investing for Dummies **[12879]**
"Commercial Real Estate May Be Cooling, While Residential Clamors to Meet Demand" in Houston Business Journal (Vol. 44, January 3, 2014, No. 35, pp. 6) **[4035]**, **[13169]**, **[13421]**, **[20821]**, **[27995]**
"Commercial Water Efficiency Initiatives Announced" in Contractor (Vol. 56, November 2009, No. 11, pp. 5) **[12621]**, **[14611]**, **[18004]**, **[23158]**, **[31952]**
Commercialization Center for Innovative Technologies (CCIT) **[42234]**
Commission Europeenne du Tourisme [15971], [19294]
"Commissioner Wants to Expand Private Market for Insurance" in South Florida Business Journal (Vol. 32, June 8, 2012, No. 46, pp. 1) **[27248]**
A Commitment to Training and Employment for Women (ACTEW) **[21311]**
Committee for the Caribbean [19290]
Committee of National Security Companies [14376]
CommNexus San Diego [37568]
Commodity Classic **[17164]**
"Commodity Speculation: Over the Top?" in Barron's (Vol. 89, July 13, 2009, No. 28, pp. 22) **[6337]**, **[9426]**, **[23818]**, **[25282]**
"Common Cash Flow Problems Facing Small Businesses and How to Solve Them" FreshBooks Blog (June 2020) **[19716]**
Common Financial Mistakes Entrepreneurs Make and Hot to Avoid Them **[24207]**
"Common Franchisee Mistakes—and How to Avoid Them" in FranchiseWire(July 28, 2020) **[24343]**
Common Ground **[39139]**
Common Kitchen (CK) **[40449]**
Common Mistakes Family-Owned Businesses Make **[23604]**
Common Sense Pest Control Quarterly **[12051]**
Common Wealth Development (CWD) **[46333]**
Common Wealth Kitchen Incubator **[43659]**
The Commons Law Center **[44058]**
Commonwealth Capital Ventures **[40677]**
Commonwealth Dispensary Association (CDA) **[4972]**
"CommScope and Comsearch to Showcase Innovative Wind Power Solutions at WINDPOWER 2012 in Atlanta" in Benzinga.com (May 31, 2012) **[5571]**, **[5849]**, **[23159]**, **[26249]**, **[35041]**
Communicating for America (CA) **[16934]**
Communicating Change **[17542]**
Communicating with Confidence (Onsite) **[17543]**
Communicating Effectively in Your Corporate Culture (Onsite) **[17544]**
"Communicating Nutrition Research" in Today's Dietitian (Vol. 20, May 2018, No. 5, p. 38) **[11572]**
"Communicating With Your Loved Ones in Long-Term Care Facilities During Disaster Situations" in Senior Living News (October 4, 2019) **[1026]**
Communication and Interpersonal Skills: A Seminar for IT and Technical Professionals (Onsite) **[17545]**
Communication and Interpersonal Skills for IT & Technical Professionals **[17546]**
Communication Skills: Results Through Collaboration (Onsite) **[17547]**, **[17548]**
Communication Skills for Women **[17549]**
"Communication Strategies for Enhancing Perceived Fit in the CSR Sponsorship Context" in International Journal of Advertising (Vol. 31, February 2012, No. 1, pp. 133) **[8651]**, **[10642]**, **[34287]**
"Communication Technology and Inclusion Will Shape the Future of Remote Work" in Business News Daily (March 6, 2023) **[22117]**
Communications Market Association [2701]
Communications Marketing Association (CMA) **[2701]**
"Communications and Power Industries Awarded $6 Million to Support Apache Helicopter" in Defense & Aerospace Business (August 13, 2014, pp. 11) **[25126]**, **[29163]**
Communications Workers of America Canada (CWA) **[5278]**, **[35151]**
Communicator **[39140]**
The Communicator **[38357]**, **[43449]**
Communique **[36099]**
Communispond Inc. **[17805]**
Communitech Hub **[46817]**
Communitech Rev **[46818]**
Community Affairs Program - Chicago Regional Office [47037]
Community Association for New Business Entrepreneurship (CAN BE) **[44392]**
Community Building vs. Traditional Marketing **[17465]**
Community Business Partnership (CBP) **[45944]**
Community College of Allegheny County - North Campus (CCAC) **[44429]**
Community College Business Officers (CCBO) **[21312]**
Community College of Southern Nevada-Cheyenne Campus (CSN) **[41962]**
"Community Commitment Safeguards Franchising Industry" in Franchising World (Vol. 42, November 2010, No. 11, pp. 38) **[24344]**, **[34288]**
Community Development Foundation (CDF) **[41394]**
Community Development Partnership (CDP) **[41395]**
Community Economic Development Centre [21281]
Community Futures Development Corporation of Greater Trail - Kootenay Regional Business Library **[24910]**
Community Futures Nicola Valley (CFNV) **[46690]**
Community Futures Tawatinaw **[46658]**
Community Futures Ventures **[46917]**
Community Futures Wood Buffalo (CFWB) **[46666]**
Community Guide (Crystal Lake) **[39143]**
Community Guide **[36834]**, **[39141]**, **[39142]**, **[41551]**
Community Guide and Business Directory **[39144]**
Community Guide and Membership Directory **[36835]**
Community Guide and Shopping, Dining, Lodging Guide, and a Street Map **[39145]**
Community Health Nurses Association of Canada [25677]
Community and Hospital Infection Control Association - Canada [25676]
Community Law Practice Incubator (CLPI) **[37560]**
Community Legal Aid SoCal (LEAP) **[37561]**
Community LendingWorks (CLW) **[28083]**
Community Profile **[46388]**
Community Profile and Business Directory [40871]
Community Radio News **[13046]**
Community Therapy Services Inc. (CTS) **[12505]**
Community and Visitor Guide **[36836]**
CommunityConnective, LLC **[30633]**
"Companies Founded by Amazing Young Entrepreneurs" in Business News Daily (Sept. 8, 2019) **[36017]**
"Companies Must Innovate, Regardless of Economy" in Crain's Detroit Business (Vol. 25, June 1, 2009, No. 22, pp. M007) **[18005]**, **[20822]**, **[27855]**
"Companies Must Set Goals for Diversity" in Crain's Detroit Business (Vol. 24, April 14, 2008, No. 15, pp. 16) **[18928]**, **[24638]**, **[35179]**
"Companies Operating at Sea Must Embrace Conservation and Sustainability — And Not Wait to Be Forced Into It" in The Conversation (Oct. 21, 2021) **[34289]**
"Companies Press Ottawa to End CN Labor Dispute" in Globe & Mail (April 16, 2007, pp. B1) **[24962]**, **[35180]**
"The Companies We Love" in Canadian Business (Vol. 85, September 17, 2012, No. 14, pp. 43) **[24639]**
"Company Hopes To Pack Profits With Self-Storage" in Crain's Detroit Business (Vol. 24, February 18, 2008, No. 7, pp. 15) **[12976]**, **[18006]**
The Company Lab (CO.LAB) **[44841]**
"Company Severs Ties with Chiquita, Starts Own Brand" in Business Journal-Serving Phoenix and the Valley of the Sun (October 4, 2007) **[17024]**, **[30705]**, **[31251]**
"A Company's Good Deeds Can Make Consumers Think Its Products Are Safer" in The Conversation (Feb. 26, 2020) **[34290]**
Compare the Best Customer Service Software **[20404]**
"A Comparison of Adverse Impact Levels Based on Top-Down, Multisource, and Assessment Center Data: Promoting Diversity and Reducing Legal Challenges" in Human Resource Management (Vol. 51,May- June 2012, No. 3, pp. 313-341) **[20562]**, **[26908]**, **[30551]**

3212 Small Business Sourcebook • 42nd Edition

Master Index Conquering
Master Index

Compass **[43450]**
"Compassion Fatigue in the Time of COVID-19" in AACC (November 1, 2021) **[10914]**
"Compelling Opportunities for Investors in Emerging Markets" in Barron's (Vol. 88, March 10, 2008, No. 10, pp. 39) **[6338]**, **[8709]**, **[9427]**, **[16075]**, **[23819]**, **[29164]**, **[33127]**
"Competing in the Growing Quick Lube Market" in Ratchet + Wrench (July 5, 2018) **[12998]**
"Competing on Talent Analytics" in Harvard Business Review (Vol. 88, October 2010, No. 10, pp. 52) **[19806]**, **[26909]**, **[28514]**
Competition and Financials - Back of the Napkin to Business Plan in 11 Slides with Brandon White **[16647]**
"Competition Is Fierce For Hospital Rankings" in Dallas Business Journal (Vol. 35, July 20, 2012, No. 45, pp. 1) **[19807]**, **[25743]**
"Competition Qualms Overblown: Inco" in Globe & Mail (February 15, 2006, pp. B1) **[19808]**, **[31252]**
Competitive Edge Inc. **[21707]**, **[22313]**
Competitive Enterprise Institute (CEI) **[15487]**
"Competitive Pricing Strategy" in Chron (Jan. 25, 2019) **[19995]**
Competitive Pricing Strategy – See How Products Are Priced **[19996]**
The Competitive Pricing Strategy Guide (Covers B2B and B2C Businesses) **[19997]**
"Competitive Pricing: What It Is and How to Use It for Your Business" in QuickBooks Blog (May 31, 2020) **[19998]**
"Competitor Based Pricing Strategy: Competition Based Pricing for SAAS" in ProfitWell Blog (Sept. 6, 2021) **[19999]**
"Competitors Eye Whole Foods" in Sacramento Business Journal (Vol. 31, August 8, 2014, No. 24, pp. 6) **[7730]**, **[8011]**, **[19809]**
Compleat Business Solutions **[2249]**
"Complementary Strengths Fuel Research Duo's Success" in Providence Business News (Vol. 29, June 2, 2014, No. 9, pp. 22) **[5152]**, **[25744]**, **[31953]**, **[32740]**
The Complete Course on Interviewing People (Onsite) **[26852]**
"Complete Discovery Source, Inc. (CDS) Receives Minority Owned Business Certification" in Marketwired (December 14, 2010) **[21815]**, **[25127]**, **[25283]**, **[30336]**, **[33128]**
Complete Employee Handbook: A Step-by-Step Guide to Create a Custom Handbook That Protects Both the Employer and the Employee **[18548]**, **[26910]**
The Complete Guide to Building a Photography Studio **[12341]**
The Complete Guide to Buying a Business **[18549]**, **[19655]**, **[28117]**, **[33011]**, **[34766]**
A Complete Guide to Commercial Photography **[12299]**
The Complete Guide to Google Adwords: Secrets, Techniques, and Strategies You Can Learn to Make Millions **[252]**, **[9118]**, **[11725]**, **[16403]**, **[21816]**, **[29718]**, **[32492]**
The Complete Guide to Modern Massage: Step-by-Step Massage Basics and Techniques from Around the World **[10762]**
Complete Guide to Public Employment **[14978]**
The Complete Guide to Selling on Amazon: Tips and Tricks for Profitable Sales **[11726]**
The Complete Guide to Selling a Business **[19656]**, **[19810]**, **[33012]**
"The Complete Guide to Starting a Business" in Legal Zoom (March 15, 2023) **[27174]**, **[34498]**
The Complete Guide to Successful Event Planning **[11905]**, **[14511]**
The Complete Idiot's Guide to Beekeeping **[1479]**
The Complete Idiot's Guide to Starting an eBay® Business **[1060]**, **[4775]**, **[11680]**, **[20000]**, **[20264]**, **[21759]**, **[24527]**
"A Complete Marketing Plan for the Photography Studio I Just Got Beautiful Portraits From" in The Better Marketing Brief (April 7, 2020) **[12342]**
Complete Weddings + Events **[11896]**
Compliance Consultants **[25618]**
Composites Fabricators Association [29068]
Compost Council of Canada [23029]
Composting News **[5740]**, **[13737]**, **[17143]**, **[23418]**
Composting & Organics Recycling Conference **[13742]**
Compoundings **[29450]**
Comprehensive 5-Day Training Program For Energy Managers (Onsite) **[23061]**
"The Comprehensive Business Case for Sustainability" in Harvard Business Review (October 21, 2016) **[23160]**, **[34291]**
Comprehensive Email Marketing Strategies Seminar (Onsite) **[29581]**
The Comprehensive Financial Planning System, Inc. (CFPS) **[6714]**
"A Comprehensive Guide to Branding for Small Businesses" in Small Biz Ahead Blog (Feb. 4, 2022) **[17437]**
"A Comprehensive Guide on How to Start a Packaging Business" in Home Business (August 3, 2022) **[26774]**
Comprehensive Guide to Leather Repair and Restoration **[7239]**
Comprehensive Integrated Payroll System **[11946]**
The Comprehensive Project Management Workshop (Onsite) **[28309]**
Comprehensive Proofreading (Onsite) **[17550]**
CompTIA **[3766]**
Compton Chamber of Commerce **[36837]**
Compuchild **[3168]**, **[3562]**, **[15810]**
Computer Animation & Virtual Worlds **[32865]**
Computer Assisted Language Instruction Consortium (CALICO) **[3545]**
Computer Assisted Language, Learning and Instruction Consortium [3545]
Computer and Business Equipment Manufacturers Association [3689], [11660]
Computer and Communications Industry Association (CCIA) **[3767]**
Computer Connections Inc. **[30996]**, **[31068]**
Computer Database **[3538]**, **[3565]**, **[3675]**, **[3756]**, **[3795]**
Computer Forensics and Incident Response: Hands-On - Analyzing Windows-Based Systems (Onsite) **[26189]**
Computer Industry Association [3767]
Computer Industry Council [3766]
Computer and Information Technology Institute [3569]
Computer Modules, Inc. [33930]
Computer Renaissance **[3753]**
Computer and Robot Vision (CRV) **[3421]**, **[3604]**
"Computer Science for All: Can Schools Pull It Off?" in Education Week (February 19, 2018) **[3549]**, **[21474]**
Computer Science Education **[3554]**
Computer Stores Industry in the US - Market Research Report **[3746]**
Computer Troubleshooters Midtown East, NY **[3583]**
Computerized Investing **[2150]**
Computers in Libraries **[3559]**
ComputerTalk for the Pharmacist--Buyers Guide **[5153]**
Computerworld **[3539]**, **[3566]**, **[3796]**
Computerworld Canada [11964]
Computing Canada **[11964]**
Computing Reviews (CR) **[3653]**
Computing in Science and Engineering (CiSE) **[32866]**
Computing Technology Industry Association [3766]
Computing Technology Industry Association--Membership Directory **[3700]**
COMsciences Inc. **[17806]**, **[31896]**
Comstock's: Business Insight for California's Capital Region **[37692]**
ComtronicSystems Debtmaster: Debt Collection Software **[4823]**
"Con Roundup: Novi Eyed for $11 Million, 100-Bed Medilodge" in Crain's Detroit Business (Vol. 25, June 1, 2009, No. 22, pp. M032) **[4036]**, **[11507]**, **[25745]**, **[33358]**
"Con-Way Development Back in High Gear" in Business Journal Portland (Vol. 27, November 5, 2010, No. 36, pp. 1) **[7033]**, **[13170]**, **[13422]**, **[16076]**
Concentrated Course in Construction Contracts (Onsite) **[18483]**
Concession Profession **[3839]**
Concord Associates Co. **[3347]**, **[4493]**
Concord-Cabarrus BPW [35593]
Concord-Cabarrus Business and Professional Women **[35593]**
Concord Chamber of Commerce **[40571]**
Concord Chamber of Commerce [36916]
Concord Free Public Library Music Collection **[11217]**
Concordia Area Chamber of Commerce **[39879]**
Concordia Chamber Of Commerce, Inc. **[40163]**
Concordia University - Centre for Building Studies [4375]
Concordia University - Department of Building, Civil and Environmental Engineering (BCEE) **[4375]**
Concordia University - Department of Civil Engineering [4375]
Concrete Chamber of Commerce **[46072]**
"Concrete Company Makes Lasting Impression in Valley" in Silicon Valley/San Jose Business Journal (Vol. 30, August 10, 2012, No. 20, pp. 1) **[4037]**, **[23605]**
Concrete Foundations Association (CFA) **[3930]**
Concrete Paver Institute [10731], [10750], [10751]
Concrete Raising of America, Inc. **[10746]**
Concurrency and Computation: Practice and Experience, [14855], [32900]
Conde Nast Publications Library and Information Services **[3071]**, **[3170]**, **[6151]**, **[9074]**
"Condos Becoming FHA No-Lending Zones" in Providence Business News (Vol. 29, June 2, 2014, No. 9, pp. 7) **[11023]**, **[24963]**, **[25284]**, **[28118]**
"Conducting Effective Reference Checks For Your Food Truck" in Mobile-Cuisine.com (2020) **[6968]**, **[26524]**, **[30466]**
Conducting Employee Performance Evaluations (Onsite) **[28310]**
"Conducting Market Research" in Entrepreneur Press **[29488]**, **[34710]**
"Cones and Cues Closes After Decades-Long Run" in The Monroe News (August 24, 2019) **[1536]**
CONEXPO-CON/AGG **[4295]**
Conexx: America Israel Business Connector **[27406]**
Confederation of National Trade Unions [35152]
Confédération des Syndicats Nationaux (CSN) **[35152]**
The Conference Board (TCB) **[29059]**
"Conference Calendar" in Marketing to Women (Vol. 21, April 2008, No. 4, pp. 7) **[14512]**, **[15846]**, **[22536]**, **[28515]**, **[29719]**, **[35042]**, **[35755]**
Conference for Community Bankers [6701], [24223], [35111]
Conference of Consulting Actuaries (CCA) **[8863]**
The Conference on Customer Service (Onsite) **[20371]**
Conference on Landscape Architecture **[10130]**
"Conference Networking Tips" in Women In Business (Vol. 66, Summer 2014, No. 1, pp. 14) **[14513]**, **[15847]**, **[35756]**
The Conference on Social Media (Onsite) **[19437]**
"Conference To Aid Minority Business Ties" in Tulsa World (July 24, 2012) **[15848]**, **[30337]**, **[35043]**
Conferences for Women [35587]
"Conferencing Takes on High-Tech Futuristic Feel" in Crain's Cleveland Business (Vol. 28, October 29, 2007, No. 43, pp. 17) **[17649]**, **[17856]**, **[26250]**
Confidante Consulting **[10522]**, **[34663]**
Conflict Communications **[17551]**
Conflict Management Skills for Women (Onsite) **[17552]**
Conflict Resolution Education Network [10786]
Conflict Resolution for the Helping Professions: Negotiation, Mediation, Advocacy, Facilitation, and Restorative Justice **[10793]**
"Congestion Relief: The Land Use Alternative" in Canadian Business (Vol. 80, February 12, 2007, No. 4, pp. 31) **[19342]**, **[26251]**, **[31954]**
"Congress Ponders Annuity Trusts" in National Underwriter Life & Health (Vol. 114, June 21, 2010, No. 12, pp. 10) **[24964]**, **[33982]**, **[34767]**
"Congress Targets Online Ad Tracking" in Inc. (Vol. 33, November 2011, No. 9, pp. 30) **[253]**, **[25285]**
"Congresswoman Aimed at Improving Small Business Exports" in Small Business Trends (September 23, 2022) **[16552]**
Conifer Chamber of Commerce **[37832]**
Conneaut Area Chamber of Commerce **[43451]**
Connect with SmartBook: Online Access for Canadian Entrepreneurship and Small Business Management **[22537]**, **[27514]**, **[28516]**
"Connect the Thoughts" in Canadian Business (Vol. 81, October 27, 2008, No. 18, pp. 8) **[6339]**, **[9428]**
Connected International Meeting Professionals Association (CIMPA) **[14502]**
Connecticut Beekeepers Association (CBA) **[1433]**
Connecticut Business Incubator Network (CBIN) **[33513]**
Connecticut Business and Industry Association (CBIA) **[38040]**
Connecticut Center for Advanced Technology, Inc. (CCAT) **[38108]**
Connecticut Economic Resource Center [37981]
Connecticut Innovations Inc. (CI) **[38092]**
Connecticut Judicial Branch - Putnam Law Library **[6055]**
Connecticut Office of Policy and Management - Policy Development and Planning Division (PDPD) **[47402]**
Connecticut Pharmacists Association (CPA) - Academy of Medical Marijuana Dispensaries **[4973]**, **[37974]**
Connecticut Procurement Technical Assistance Center (CT PTAC) **[38104]**
Connecticut Procurement Technical Assistance Center (CTSBDC) - Small Business Development Procurement Center **[38105]**
Connecticut River Valley Chamber of Commerce (CRVCC) **[38041]**
Connecticut Small Business Development Center (CTSBDC) **[37980]**
Connecticut Society of Genealogist Library (CSG Literary) **[7404]**
Connecticut State Library Government Information and References Services **[47403]**
Connecticut State Library History and Genealogy Unit **[7405]**
The Connecting Source **[45103]**
Connection **[38358]**
Connections Magazine **[45104]**
Connetic Ventures **[40118]**
Connwood Foresters Inc. **[2953]**
"Conquering the Seven Summits of Sales: From Everest to Every Business, Achieving Peak Performance" **[19498]**, **[22118]**, **[32493]**, **[34980]**

Small Business Sourcebook • 42nd Edition 3213

Conquering | Master Index

Conquering Your Management Challenges: Advanced Management Skills for Supervisors (Onsite) **[28311]**
Conrad Area Chamber of Commerce **[41758]**
Conrad Chamber of Commerce [41758]
Conroe Chamber of Commerce - Greater Conroe Chamber of Commerce [45105]
Conroe/Lake Conroe Chamber of Commerce **[45105]**
"Conscious Capitalism: Liberating the Heroic Spirit of Business" **[7034]**, **[8012]**, **[9119]**, **[9429]**, **[20405]**, **[22119]**, **[23161]**, **[34292]**, **[35489]**
Conseil Canadien pour le Commerce Autochtone (CCAB) **[20692]**
Conseil Canadien du Compost **[23029]**
Conseil Canadien de la Fourrure (CCF) **[7227]**, **[7233]**
Conseil de Commerce Canada-Inde [20684]
Conseil Des Affaires Canado-Americanes [27404]
Conseil Économique des Provinces de l'Atlantique [21265]
Conseil National d'Éthique en Recherche chez l'humain (NCEHR) **[23461]**
Conseil des Viandes du Canada [2426]
"The Consequences of Tardiness" in Modern Machine Shop (Vol. 84, August 2011, No. 3, pp. 34) **[10428]**, **[22120]**, **[26911]**, **[28517]**
Conservatoire de Musique de Quebec Bibliotheque **[11218]**, **[11295]**
"Consignment Shop Blends Business With a Giving Spirit" in Gazette (January 17, 2012) **[3886]**, **[7093]**, **[15088]**, **[34293]**
"Consignment Shop Offers Children's Clothes, Products" in Frederick News-Post (August 19, 2010) **[1194]**, **[1822]**, **[2846]**, **[3014]**, **[3099]**, **[3887]**, **[6127]**, **[15787]**
"Consignment Shop Opens In Spring Township To Serve Hard-To-Find Sizes" in Reading Eagle (June 16, 2012) **[3100]**, **[3888]**, **[35757]**, **[36018]**
"Consignment Shops Form Friendly Alliance in Eagle Plaza" in Mail Tribune (August 7, 2012) **[2847]**, **[3101]**, **[3889]**
"Consignment Shops Use Web To Help Sell Used Clothing" in Chattanooga Times/Free Press (March 17, 2012) **[3890]**, **[18007]**, **[33983]**
"ConsignPro Elevates Nature of Consignment Business, Encourages Designer Resale" in Internet Wire (May 15, 2012) **[3015]**, **[3102]**, **[3891]**, **[32127]**, **[33984]**
Consortium for Entrepreneurship Education **[21313]**
"Constant Contact Launches Marketing Podcast for Small Business" in Small Business Trends (March 10, 2023) **[29522]**, **[29720]**
Construct The Present (CTP) **[30634]**
"Construction" in Inc. (Vol. 36, September 2014, No. 7, pp. 166) **[4038]**, **[18008]**
Construction Briefings **[4276]**
Construction Business Owner (CBO) **[4357]**
Construction Canada **[2013]**, **[3931]**
Construction Consultants Library (ccl) **[14342]**
Construction Contracting **[3968]**
Construction Contracts Law Report **[4277]**
The Construction Economist **[25]**, **[1739]**
Construction Executive: The Magazine for the Business of Construction (CE) **[4278]**
Construction Experts Inc. (CEI) **[4309]**
Construction Financial Management Association (CFMA) **[3932]**
Construction Industries Associations [29070]
Construction Industry CPAs/Consultants Association (CICPAC) **[26]**, **[16735]**
Construction Industry Manufacturers Association [29070]
Construction Interface Services Inc. **[4310]**
Construction Litigation Reporter **[4279]**
Construction Management Association of America (CMAA) **[3933]**
Construction Owners Association of America (COAA) **[3934]**
Construction Specifications Canada (CSC) **[2014]**, **[3935]**
Construction Specifications Institute (CSI) **[3936]**
The Construction Specifier **[2020]**, **[4280]**
Construction Testing Inc. (CTI) **[4311]**
Constructor: The Construction Management Magazine **[4281]**
Construire **[4282]**
ConsulAgr Inc. **[17192]**
"Consultant Helps Brides Choose the Best Dress for the Special Day" in The Oakland Press (February 18, 2019) **[1967]**
Consultants & Consulting Organizations Directory (CCOD) **[5572]**, **[10483]**, **[20097]**
Consultative Selling Skills Training **[29582]**
"The Consulting Business Booms Just as Consultants Disappear" in Bloomberg (July 29, 2021) **[2183]**, **[20098]**
The Consulting CEO **[33660]**
Consulting & Conciliation Service (CCS) **[2250]**, **[10523]**, **[10805]**, **[20176]**, **[27133]**, **[28977]**
Consulting to Family Businesses: Contracting, Assessment, and Implementation **[23606]**
"Consulting Firm Goes Shopping" in Crain's Chicago Business (Vol. 31, April 28, 2008, No. 17, pp. 45) **[8895]**, **[17289]**, **[20099]**, **[25746]**, **[27249]**, **[28518]**, **[31253]**
The Consulting Source, Inc. **[20177]**
Consulting Success: The Proven Guide to Start, Run and Grow a Successful Consulting Business **[10484]**, **[20100]**
Consumer Behavior **[20406]**, **[29721]**, **[32128]**, **[32494]**
Consumer Brands Association (CBA) **[7708]**
"Consumer Contagion? A Bleak Earnings View" in Barron's (Vol. 88, March 10, 2008, No. 10, pp. 15) **[6340]**, **[9430]**, **[18009]**, **[20823]**, **[23820]**
Consumer Credit Industry Association (CCIA) **[8864]**
Consumer Data Industry Association (CDIA) **[4757]**
Consumer Electronics & Appliances Rental Industry in the US - Market Research Report **[798]**, **[4412]**, **[13843]**
Consumer Electronics Vision [1120], [2566]
Consumer Guide **[36717]**
Consumer Healthcare Products Association (CHPA) **[25668]**
Consumer InSite **[194]**, **[1174]**, **[4636]**, **[11536]**
Consumer Products Division of the National Electrical Manufacturers Association [785]
"Consumer Startup Hub Set for Downtown" in Atlanta Business Chronicle (June 13, 2014, pp. 3A) **[2726]**, **[9085]**, **[21760]**, **[27208]**, **[33330]**
"Consumer Tastes Are Redefining Convenience Retail" in Food Business News (July 2, 2019) **[4428]**, **[8013]**
"Consumer Trust in E-Commerce Web Sites: a Meta-Study" in ACM Computing Surveys (Vol. 43, Fall 2011, No. 3, pp. 14) **[3425]**, **[3615]**, **[14400]**, **[21817]**
"Consumers Are Buying and Using CBD Products Incorrectly" in CBD Today (October 26, 2020) **[4997]**
"Consumers Are Still Wary; Here's How To Win Them. The Great Recession Has Left Consumers Worried About Their Financial Future. But the Right Strategies Can Engage Leery Spenders" in Gallup Business Journal (June 24, 2014) **[20824]**, **[23821]**, **[32495]**
"Consumers Like Green, But Not Mandates" in Business Journal-Milwaukee (Vol. 28, December 10, 2010, No. 10, pp. A1) **[789]**, **[5573]**, **[5850]**, **[11391]**, **[23162]**, **[33985]**
"Consumers Love Food Delivery. Restaurants and Grocers Hate It." in The Wall Street Journal (March 9. 2019) **[6902]**, **[11727]**
"Consumers Seek to Redo Rate Structure: Smaller Biz Paid Big Rates" in Crain's Detroit Business (Vol. 25, June 22, 2009) **[20001]**, **[23822]**
"Consumers Turned Off? Not at Best Buy" in Barron's (Vol. 88, March 24, 2008, No. 12, pp. 29) **[4389]**, **[6341]**, **[9431]**, **[18010]**, **[23823]**, **[26252]**
"Consumers Want to Learn More About Green Business Efforts Despite Deep Doubt" in Benzinga.com (May 1, 2012) **[5574]**, **[5851]**, **[23163]**, **[31955]**
"Consumers Who Saw a Food Truck This Summer" in Nation's Restaurant News (Vol. 45, September 26, 2011, No. 20, pp. 8) **[6969]**, **[33986]**
ConTACt **[38359]**
Contact Lens Manufacturers Association (CLMA) **[16289]**
Contact Lens Manufacturers Association--Member Directory **[16297]**
"Contagious: Why Things Catch On" **[254]**, **[17650]**, **[21818]**, **[29722]**
Contempo Nails **[11323]**
Contemporary Accounting Research **[27]**
Content Delivery and Security Association (CDSA) **[6162]**, **[13647]**
Content Delivery and Storage Association [6162], [13647]
Content Rich: Writing Your Way to Wealth on the Web **[16404]**, **[21819]**, **[27856]**, **[29723]**, **[32496]**
The Content Sales Funnel - Creating an Effective Social Media Content Strategy Series **[17425]**, **[32440]**, **[33518]**, **[35703]**
Content That Drives Sales Across Pinterest and Instagram, Session #1 **[29583]**, **[33519]**, **[35704]**
Content That Drives Sales Across Pinterest and Instragram, Session #2 **[29584]**, **[33520]**, **[35705]**
"Contextual Intelligence: Despite 30 Years of Experimentation and Study, We are Only Starting to Understand that Some Managerial Knowledge is Universal and Some is Specific to a Market or a Culture" in Harvard Business Review (Vol. 92, September 2014, No. 9, pp. 58) **[28026]**, **[28519]**
Continental Advertising Agency Network [214], [29569], [31825]
Continental Appraisal Co. **[13615]**
Continental Association of CPA Firms [10]
Continental Association of Funeral and Memorial Societies--Directory of Member Societies [7209]
Continental Film Business Solutions (CFPC) **[6216]**
"Contingent Offers: Weighing the Risk" in Crain's Chicago Business (Vol. 31, April 21, 2008, No. 16, pp. 48) **[11024]**, **[13171]**, **[13423]**
"Continuant's Big Win: A Lawsuit That Seemed Like a Lifetime" in Puget Sound Business Journal (Vol. 34, April 11, 2014, No. 52, pp. 4) **[18550]**, **[29165]**
"Continuing Education Courses Every Business Owner Should Consider" in Legal Zoom (February 22, 2023) **[21475]**
"Continuously Monitoring Workers' Comp Can Limit Costs" in Crain's Cleveland Business (Vol. 28, October 8, 2007, No. 40, pp. 21) **[8896]**, **[18929]**, **[27250]**
"ContiTech Celebrates 100 Years" in American Printer (Vol. 128, July 1, 2011, No. 7) **[3303]**, **[12729]**, **[16185]**, **[29166]**
Contour Venture Partners **[42730]**
Contra Costa Small Business Development Center (CCSBDC) **[36572]**
Contract Cleaning Services **[2983]**
The Contract Mistakes Small Business Owners Make **[18551]**
Contracting Profits **[2080]**
"Contractor Backlog Dip Signals New Uncertainty" in Washington Business Journal (Vol. 31, August 3, 2012, No. 15, pp. 1) **[25128]**
Contractor Connection **[529]**, **[12677]**, **[14640]**
"Contractors Can't Do It Alone, PHCC's Pfeffer Says" in Contractor (Vol. 56, October 2009, No. 10, pp. 3) **[478]**, **[12622]**, **[35181]**
"Contractors Debate Maximizing Green Opportunities, Education" in Contractor (Vol. 56, November 2009, No. 11, pp. 3) **[4039]**, **[21476]**, **[23164]**, **[32497]**
"Contractors Must be Lead Certified" in Contractor (Vol. 57, February 2010, No. 2, pp. 3) **[4040]**, **[11858]**, **[11879]**, **[25286]**
Controllers Institute Research Foundation [1794]
Controllership Foundation [1794]
"Controversial Bill Could Raise Rates for Homeowners" in Orlando Business Journal (Vol. 26, January 22, 2010, No. 34, pp. 1) **[8897]**, **[25287]**, **[27251]**
Convenience Distribution Association (CDA) **[2535]**, **[15692]**
Convenience Distribution: AWMA's Magazine for Candy, Tobacco, Grocery, Foodservice and General Merchandiser Marketers **[2551]**, **[15709]**
Convenience Distribution Marketplace **[4449]**
"Convenience Store Deal for Cardtronics" in American Banker (Vol. 174, July 28, 2009, No. 143, pp. 12) **[4429]**, **[29724]**, **[33987]**
"Convenience Store Expanding" in Clovis News Journal (November 9, 2010) **[4041]**, **[4430]**, **[32129]**
"Convenience Store Owners Will Request New Zoning Once More" in Daily Republic (November 1, 2010) **[4431]**, **[14550]**, **[32130]**
Convenience Stores Industry in the US - Market Research Report **[4421]**
"Convention Budgeting Best Practices" in Franchising World (Vol. 42, November 2010, No. 11, pp. 11) **[15849]**, **[24345]**, **[35044]**
"Convention Ctr. Rehab To Impact Hotels, Eateries" in Silicon Valley/San Jose Business Journal (Vol. 30, May 18, 2012, No. 8, pp. 1) **[877]**, **[4042]**, **[8378]**, **[13922]**, **[15850]**, **[35045]**
Convention & Expo [16863], [30425]
"Convergence Collaboration: Revising Revenue Recognition" in Management Accounting Quarterly (Vol. 12, Spring 2011, No. 3, pp. 18) **[56]**, **[1750]**, **[15372]**, **[16792]**, **[25288]**
"Conversation Starters for the Holiday" in Barron's (Vol. 89, July 6, 2009, No. 27, pp. 7) **[6342]**, **[9432]**, **[20825]**, **[23824]**, **[25747]**
"A Conversation with: Renea Butler" in Crain's Detroit Business (Vol. 25, June 8, 2009, No. 23, pp. 12) **[13172]**, **[13424]**, **[20826]**, **[26912]**, **[35758]**
"A Conversation With: Ron Gantner, Jones Lang LaSalle" in Crain's Detroit Business (Vol. 24, October 6, 2008, No. 40, pp. 9) **[6343]**, **[9433]**, **[12880]**, **[13173]**, **[13425]**, **[20101]**, **[20265]**, **[20827]**, **[23825]**, **[28119]**
"Conversations with Customers" in Business Journal Serving Greater Tampa Bay (Vol. 31, December 31, 2010, No. 1, pp. 1) **[9120]**, **[16405]**, **[17651]**, **[20407]**, **[21820]**, **[29725]**
"Conversations Need to Yield Actions Measured in Dollars" in Advertising Age (Vol. 79, July 7, 2008, No. 26, pp. 18) **[255]**, **[26253]**, **[29726]**, **[31861]**
Conversion Tactics that Win **[32680]**
"Convert New Customers to Long Term Accounts" in Indoor Comfort Marketing (Vol. 70, February 2011, No. 2, pp. 22) **[5575]**, **[5852]**, **[20408]**, **[23165]**, **[29727]**
"Convictions Under the Fisheries Act" in Marketwired (May 16, 2007) **[1231]**, **[6747]**, **[25289]**
Conway Area Chamber of Commerce (CACC) **[36448]**, **[44542]**

3214 Small Business Sourcebook • 42nd Edition

Conyers-Rockdale Chamber of Commerce [38717]
Cook Chamber of Commerce [41217]
Cooke & Bake Center LLC [42856]
The Cookery [43240]
Cookeville Area-Putnam County Chamber of Commerce [44732]
Cookie Cutters Haircuts for Kids [7888]
Cookies in Bloom, Inc. [7471]
Cooking Classes Industry in the US - Market Research Report [4472]
Cooking for Profit [2686], [4474], [8108], [14042]
"Cooking With Celeb Chef Jet Tila" in Dallas Business Journal (Vol. 37, June 6, 2014, No. 39, pp. 6) [8379], [13923], [19499]
CookSpring Shared Kitchen [39636]
The Cookware & Bakeware Alliance (CMA) [8172]
"Cool on Chicago Office Properties" in Crain's Chicago Business (Vol. 31, March 31, 2008, No. 13, pp. 16) [6344], [9434], [12881], [13174], [13426]
Cool Daddy's [11897], [13853]
Cooling Journal [14562]
Cooling Technology Institute (CTI) [16354]
Cooper Institute (CI) [12477]
Cooper Institute for Aerobics Research [12477]
The Cooperative Business Journal [24862]
Cooperative Food Distributors of America [4424], [7715]
The Cooperator Expo [12910], [13327]
Cooperstown Chamber of Commerce (CCC) [42559]
Coopersville Area Chamber of Commerce [40897]
Coordinating Council for Handicapped Children [2263], [20187], [26087]
The Coordinating and Development Corporation Division of Entrepreneurial Development (CDC) [40215]
"Cope with Unforseen Challenges at BrandSmart 2023" in Small Business Trends(March 4, 2023) [17438]
"Coping With a Shrinking Planet" in Agency Sales Magazine (Vol. 39, December 2009, No. 11, pp. 46) [8710], [18011], [20828], [27515], [29167], [32498]
Coppell Chamber of Commerce [45106]
Copper Basin Chamber of Commerce (CBCC) [36326]
Copper Basin-Fannin Chamber of Commerce [38731]
Copperas Cove Chamber of Commerce & Visitors Bureau [45107]
Copperas Cove Economic Development Corp. (CCEDC) [45508]
"Copy Karachi?" in Barron's (Vol. 88, June 30, 2008, No. 26, pp. 5) [6345], [9435], [23826], [27516], [29168]
"Copyright Clearance Center (CCC) Partnered with cSubs" in Information Today (Vol. 28, November 2011, No. 10, pp. 14) [1649], [1823], [11975], [21821], [27857], [31254]
Copyright Clearance Center Inc. (CCC) [4487]
"The Copyright Evolution" in Information Today (Vol. 28, November 2011, No. 10, pp. 1) [17652], [21822], [27858], [29728]
Coqual [30504]
Coquille Chamber of Commerce and Visitor Information Center [43963]
Cora Breakfast and Lunch [14145]
Coral Gables Chamber of Commerce (CGCC) [38360]
Coral Group [41332]
Coral Springs Chamber of Commerce [38361]
Corbeil Appliances [802]
Cordele-Crisp Chamber of Commerce [38718]
Cordova Chamber of Commerce [36224]
Core Capital Partners [38171]
Core: Leadership, Infrastructure, Futures [8831]
Core Money Engine [44434]
CoreCard Corporation [38830]
COREL WTA Tour [15669]
CoreNetwork Fund [43699]
Corigin Ventures [42731]
Coriolis Ventures [42732]
CorLyst L.L.C. [40450]
"Corn Belt Farmland Prices Hit Record Levels" in Farm Industry News (December 1, 2011) [17025], [20002]
Cornell Feline Health Center (FHC) [684], [719]
Cornell Hospitality Quarterly (CHQ) [8474], [14043]
The Cornell Hotel and Restaurant Administration Quarterly [8474], [14043]
Cornell SC Johnson College of Business [8497], [14107]
Cornell University - Bailey Hortorium Library [7664]
Cornell University - Baker Institute for Animal Health [720]
Cornell University - Cornell Cooperative Extension - New York State Integrated Pest Management Program [12070]
Cornell University - Cornell Institute for Social and Economic Research Data Archive (CiSER) [47404]
Cornell University - Cornell Waste Management Institute (CWMI) [13754]
Cornell University Institute of Biotechnology (CIB) [42857]

Cornell University - International Studies in Planning Concentration [955], [31722]
Cornell University - Johnson Graduate School of Management Library [32419]
Cornell University - The Nestlé Library [8528], [14302]
Cornell University - School of Industrial and Labor Relations - Martin P. Catherwood Library [35973]
"Corner Bakery Readies Its Recipes for Growth" in Dallas Business Journal (Vol. 35, February 17, 2012, No. 23, pp. 1) [1250], [7552], [18012], [24346]
Cornerstone Angels [39352]
"Cornerstone Seeks Investors for Hedge Fund" in Baltimore Business Journal (Vol. 32, June 20, 2014, No. 7, pp. 10) [6346], [7094], [9288], [23827], [31255]
Corning Area Chamber of Commerce [36449]
Corning Area Chamber of Commerce (CACC) [42560]
Corning District Chamber of Commerce (CCC) [36838]
Corona Chamber of Commerce [36839]
Corona del Mar Chamber of Commerce (CDMCC) [36840]
Coronado Chamber of Commerce [36841]
"Coronavirus Pandemic Upends the Dry Cleaning Industry" in NPR.org (March 31, 2021) [5233], [30338]
"Coronavirus Relief Bill Gives Small Businesses More Time to Cover Payroll Taxes" in CNBC (March 27, 2020) [34241]
Corporate Affiliations [24640]
Corporate Annual Reports at the Library of Congress [18463]
"Corporate Canada Eyes Retiree Health Benefit Cuts" in Globe & Mail (March 8, 2006, pp. B3) [17290], [24641], [25748]
Corporate Cash Management (onsite) [23706]
Corporate Caterers [2693]
Corporate Consulting, Inc. [2251], [10524], [20178], [24242], [28978], [33661]
Corporate Design [11646]
Corporate Entrepreneurship & Innovation [19811], [22538], [24642]
"Corporate Event Management Best Practices: 2020 Guide" in The Bizzabo Blog (January 9, 2020) [6086], [18930], [29729]
"Corporate Governance Reforms in China and India: Challenges and Opportunities" in Business Horizons (January-February 2008) [27517], [28520]
Corporate Impact [28979]
Corporate & Incentive Travel (C&IT) [15916], [16024]
"Corporate Park Retrofits for Water Savings" in Contractor (Vol. 56, October 2009, No. 10, pp. 5) [4043], [12623], [14612], [16333], [23166]
Corporate Radar: Tracking the Forces That Are Shaping Your Business [14401], [23167], [24643]
Corporate Report [41701]
Corporate Report Kansas City [41701]
"Corporate Responsibility" in Professional Services Close-Up (July 2, 2010) [5576], [5853], [7095], [22121], [22539], [23168], [23483], [23828], [24965], [26913], [28521], [34294]
Corporate Social Responsibility (CSR): A Resource Guide [23454], [34445]
"Corporate Social Responsibility Is Not Only Ethical, But Also A Modern Business Tool" in Forbes (Apr 5, 2021) [34295]
"Corporate Social Responsibility in Today's Socially and Politically Active World" in Reworked (Apr 2, 2021) [34296]
"Corporate Social Responsibility and Trade Unions: Perspectives Across Europe" [27518], [34297], [35182]
Corporate Travel Management for Small Businesses [19343]
"Corporate Travel Planners is Geared Up for More Growth" in San Antonio Business Journal (Vol. 26, September 7, 2012, No. 32, pp. 1) [15988], [18013], [19344]
Corporation des Associations de Detaillants d'Automobiles (CADA) [11359]
"Corporation, Be Good! The Story of Corporate Social Responsibility" in Business and Society (December 2007, pp. 479-485) [20829], [34298]
Corporation for Enterprise Development [20709], [23018]
Corporation for National and Community Service Department of AmeriCorps [46953]
Corporation for National and Community Service Field Liaison [46952]
Corporation for National and Community Service Office of Learn and Serve [46954]
"The Corporation and Private Politics" in Journal of Business Strategy (Vol. 35, May-June 2014, No. 3, pp. 59-62) [31752], [34299]
Corpus Christi Black Chamber of Commerce (CCBCC) [45108]
Corpus Christi Hispanic Chamber of Commerce [45109]
"Corrales Site of New Senior Living/Care Complex" in America's Intelligence Wire (August 13, 2012) [4044], [8247], [10089], [12410], [13924], [25749]

Correlation Ventures (VC) [37336]
Corridor Angel Investors [39813]
Corridor Business Journal (CBJ) [39835]
Corry Area Chamber of Commerce [44198]
Corry Redevelopment Authority [44393]
Corsa Ventures [45594]
Corsicana/Navarro County Chamber of Commerce [45110]
Corte Madera Chamber of Commerce [36842]
Cortez Area Chamber of Commerce (CACC) [37833]
Cortland County Business Development Corp. [33453]
Cortland County Chamber of Commerce [42561]
"Corus Eases Off Ailing Condo Market" in Crain's Chicago Business (April 28, 2008) [4045], [6347], [8380], [9436], [13427], [23829], [28120]
Corvallis Chamber of Commerce [43964]
Coshocton Area Chamber of Commerce [43452]
Coshocton Chamber of Commerce [43452]
Coshocton County Chamber of Commerce [43452]
Cosmetic Career Women [4500]
Cosmetic Executive Women (CEW) [4500]
Cosmetic Industry Buyers and Suppliers (CIBS) [1380], [1577], [4501]
Cosmetic Ingredient Review (CIR) [4502]
Cosmetic, Toiletry and Fragrance Association [1383], [1579], [4507]
Cosmetics Alliance Canada (CAC) [4503]
"Cosmetics Are a Case Study for Embracing Diversity in Marketing" in Forbes (October 17, 2019) [4510], [10643]
Cosmetics & Toiletries--Cosmetic Bench Reference [1582]
Cosmetics & Toiletries--Cosmetic Materials Directory Issue [1582]
Cosmetics & Toiletries: The International Magazine of Cosmetic Technology [1398], [1594], [4529]
"Cost of Creating Health Insurance Exchange in Md. 'Largely Unknown'" in Baltimore Business Journal (Vol. 28, September 3, 2010, No. 17, pp. 1) [8898], [19812], [20003], [23830], [25750], [27252]
"Cost Cuts Lead Dealers to Record Profits" in Globe & Mail (March 24, 2006, pp. B3) [6348], [9437], [18014]
Cost Cutters Family Hair Care [7889]
"Cost of Md.'s Business Banking May Soon Go Up" in Baltimore Business Journal (Vol. 28, October 29, 2010, No. 25, pp. 1) [4712], [4776], [20266], [23831]
"Cost to Open a Laundromat" in ZenBusiness [10157]
"Cost Remains Top Factor In Considering Green Technology" in Canadian Sailings (June 30, 2008) [5854], [8711], [20102], [23169], [27519], [32741]
Cost Still the Main Hurdle for Small Business Employers Looking to Expand Benefits [17291]
Costa Mesa Chamber of Commerce [36843]
CoStaff Services L.L.C. [27134]
Costella Kirsch (CK) [37713]
The Costs, Benefits and Dangers of Pressure Washing [12696]
The Costs and Benefits of Running a Mobile Business [30467]
"Costs to Starting and Operating an Apartment Locating Business" in Brokersponsorship (June 13, 2018) [765]
Costume Society of America (CSA) [4551]
Cotati Chamber of Commerce [36844]
Cotati Promotion Club [36844]
COTC Technologies Inc. [3454], [3784], [10525], [20179]
Cote Capital [42733]
Cottage Grove Area Chamber of Commerce [41218], [43965]
CottageCare Canada (CC) [5083]
CottageCare Inc. (CC) [5084]
Cotter Chamber of Commerce [36450]
Cotter Gassville Chamber of Commerce [36450]
Cottonwood Chamber of Commerce [36845]
Cottonwood Technology Funds (CTF) [42365]
"The Couch in the Corner Office: Surveying the Landscape of the CEO Psyche" in Inc. (January 2008, pp. 33-34) [2184], [10485], [28522]
Coudersport Area Chamber of Commerce [44199]
Cougar Capital (CC) [45659]
"Could Bond OK Bring Back the Charlotte Housing Battle?" in Charlotte Business Journal (Vol. 25, November 5, 2010, No. 33, pp. 1) [4046], [13175], [13428]
"Could UNC Charlotte Be Home to Future Med School?" in Charlotte Business Journal (Vol. 25, July 23, 2010, No. 18, pp. 1) [21477], [25751], [33359]
Coulee City Chamber of Commerce [46073]
Council for Advancement and Support of Education (CASE) [7184]
Council of the Americas (CoA) [27407]
Council Bluffs Area Chamber of Commerce (CBACC) [39728]

Council Master Index

Council Bluffs Chamber of Commerce [39728]
Council Capital **[44867]**
Council Chamber of Commerce (CCC) **[38912]**
Council of Development Finance Agencies (CDFA) **[20693]**, **[35273]**
Council of the District of Columbia (CDC) **[38183]**
Council on Employee Benefit Plans [17260], [19727]
Council on Employee Benefits (CEB) **[17260]**, **[19727]**
Council for Entrepreneurial Development (CED) **[43043]**
Council of Fashion Designers of America [3000], [6122]
Council on Foreign Relations (CFR) **[31723]**
Council on Foundations Resource Center (COF) **[7185]**
Council on Hotel, Restaurant and Institutional Education [4459], [8350]
Council of Industrial Development Bond Issuers [20693], [35273]
Council of Insurance Agents and Brokers (CIAB) **[8865]**
Council for Inter-American Cooperation [8679]
Council for Interior Design Accreditation (CIDA) **[9020]**
Council of International Investigators (CII) **[12786]**
Council for Latin America [27407]
"Council OKs Curtis Park Tax-Credit Plan" in Sacramento Business Journal (Vol. 31, June 13, 2014, No. 16, pp. 3) **[13429]**, **[34768]**
Council on Optometric Education [16274]
Council of PR Firms **[31741]**
Council of Protocol Executives (COPE) **[15818]**
Council of Real Estate Brokerage Managers [11005]
Council for Research in Music Education (CRME) **[11253]**
Council on the Safe Transportation of Hazardous Articles [7939]
Council on Safe Transportation of Hazardous Articles, Inc. (COSTHA) **[7939]**
Council of Sales Promotion Agencies [32429]
Council of Small Business Executives (COSBE) **[46334]**
Council for Supplier Diversity (CSD) **[30258]**
Council for Urban Economic Development [20974]
Council for Urban Economic Development [20700]
"Councilman Addresses Union Harassment Accusations" in Philadelphia Business Journal (Vol. 33, March 28, 2014, No. 7, pp. 7) **[4047]**, **[18552]**, **[35183]**
Counselors of Real Estate (CRE) **[13086]**
"Counterfeits Plague Many Collectibles" in Coin World (September 16, 2019) **[3235]**, **[27520]**
Counterman **[1118]**, **[32675]**
"Counting on Cornhole: Popular Bean Bag Game Brings Crowds to Bars" in Baltimore Business Journal (Vol. 29, July 15, 2011, No. 10, pp. 1) **[1324]**, **[15788]**, **[29730]**, **[32499]**
"Counting Crabs: Supply Dips, Putting Crimp on Memorial Day Feast" in Boston Business Journal (Vol. 29, June 3, 2011, No. 4, pp. 1) **[6748]**, **[6780]**, **[13925]**
"Counting on Engagement at Ernst & Young" in Workforce Management (Vol. 88, November 16, 2009, No. 12, pp. 25) **[18015]**, **[20103]**, **[20830]**, **[22122]**, **[35184]**
Country Dance and Song Society (CDSS) **[4838]**
Country Dance and Song Society of America - Country Dance Society of America [4838]
Country Dance and Song Society--Newsletter **[4858]**
Country Inns and Suites by Carlson **[8503]**
Country Radio Broadcasters Inc. (CRB) **[13018]**
Country Radio Seminar (CRS) **[13049]**
Country Roads Angel Network (CRAN) **[46295]**
Country Sampler **[9058]**
Country Style **[7578]**
Counts Benefit Services Inc. **[17396]**
County Guide [44241]
"The Coup Is Over, the Execution Begins" in Canadian Business (Vol. 85, June 11, 2012, No. 10, pp. 9) **[9438]**, **[28523]**, **[31256]**
Coupeville Chamber of Commerce (CCC) **[46074]**
"Couple Hopes to Lead Schlotzsky's Twin Cities Revival" in Business Journal (Vol. 31, January 17, 2014, No. 34, pp. 4) **[13926]**, **[19500]**, **[23832]**, **[24347]**, **[33360]**
"Coupons.com Sees Growth In the Bargain" in Silicon Valley/San Jose Business Journal (Vol. 30, June 8, 2012, No. 11, pp. 1) **[18016]**
Couri Hatchery Student Business Incubator **[42858]**
"Courier 250 Companies Hope to Rebound From 2009" in Business Courier (Vol. 27, July 16, 2010, No. 11, pp. 1) **[7096]**, **[18017]**, **[20831]**, **[32500]**
"Court Reporting: More Than Just Typing Fast" in Huseby (March 4, 2019) **[16225]**
Court Square Law Project **[42859]**
Courtiers Indenpendants en Securite Financiere [8866]
CourtSide Consulting **[30635]**
Coushatta-Red River Chamber of Commerce **[40164]**
Cousins Subs **[4897]**, **[14146]**
Coustic-Glo [2108]
"Covario Recognized for Second Year in a Row as OMMA Award Finalist for Online Advertising Creativity in Both SEO and SEM" in Internet Wire (August 29, 2012) **[256]**, **[9121]**, **[16406]**, **[29731]**
CoVenture **[42734]**
"Battle-Tested Vestas Shrugs Off Ill Winds" in Business Journal Portland (Vol. 30, January 31, 2014, No. 48, pp. 4) **[5577]**, **[18018]**, **[19813]**, **[34769]**
"Campus CEOs: Young and the Restless" in Business Journal Portland (Vol. 30, February 21, 2014, No. 50, pp. 4) **[21296]**, **[22374]**, **[35998]**
"Cover Story: Minnesota Firms Plug Into Solar" in Business Journal (Vol. 31, April 25, 2014, No. 48, pp. 10) **[14916]**, **[23170]**
"Cover Your Assets: An Insurance Primer for Small Businesses" in Business News Daily (March 15, 2023) **[27253]**
Coverall Health-Based Cleaning System **[2102]**
"Covered California Adds Dental Benefits" in Sacramento Business Journal (Vol. 31, August 29, 2014, No. 27, pp. 8) **[17292]**, **[25752]**, **[27254]**
"COVID-19 Small Business Resources & Federal Government Programs" by SBE Council (Jan. 23, 2022) **[24966]**
Covina Chamber of Commerce **[36846]**
Covington County Chamber of Commerce **[41396]**
Covington County Economic Development Center (CCEDC) **[36176]**
Cowboy Technology Investors **[43829]**
Coweta Chamber of Commerce **[43748]**
CoWharf **[41082]**
Cowork Tahoe **[37562]**
Cowork Tampa **[38557]**
"Coworking Spaces Can Be Ideal for Entrepreneurs" in The Balance Small Business (January 2, 2020) **[31031]**
Cowtown Angels **[45443]**
Cox Graae + Spack Architects (CGS) **[931]**
"Cox Opens Norfolk Mall Kiosk; Wireless Service Not Ready" in Virginian-Pilot (September 20, 2010) **[2727]**, **[9122]**, **[10021]**
The Coxe Group Inc. **[10691]**
Coyote Canyon **[7579]**
CP Franchising L.L.C. (CP) **[16035]**
CPA Auto Dealer Consultants Association [16], [16734]
CPA Firm Management Association (CAFMA) **[28]**
The CPA Journal (Certified Public Accountants) **[108]**
The CPA Journal **[16889]**
CPA Magazine **[16890]**
CPA Manufacturing Services Association [34], [16738]
"CPI, Coal Lead Local Stock Decline" in Saint Louis Business Journal (Vol. 32, October 14, 2011, No. 7, pp. 1) **[6349]**, **[9439]**, **[20832]**
"CPI Corp. Acquires Assets of Bella Pictures" in Benzinga.com (January 28, 2011) **[1968]**, **[9440]**, **[12300]**, **[12343]**, **[33129]**
CPMA Annual Convention & Trade Show [17165]
CPMA Convention and Tradeshow **[17165]**
"CPR-CN Deal to Ease Vancouver Logjam" in Globe & Mail (January 27, 2006, pp. B4) **[8712]**, **[27521]**, **[33130]**
CPR Services **[26092]**
CPS News **[25669]**
CQIB The Life Sciences Incubator **[46892]**
"CR Magazine Taps ITT As a 'Best Corporate Citizen' in Government Contracting" in Profesisonal Services Close-Up (July 30, 2010) **[23484]**, **[24967]**, **[34300]**
Cracker Jack Collectors Association (CJCA) **[733]**, **[3224]**
"Cracking the Code on Anti-Discrimination Policies for Your Small Business" in Small Business Trends (Nov. 5, 2017) **[20563]**
Cracking New Accounts: High Pay-Off Prospecting (Onsite) **[32441]**
"Cradle of Commerce" in San Antonio Business Journal (Vol. 28, August 29, 2014, No. 29, pp. 4) **[878]**, **[15734]**
"CradlePoint Is Adding Workers, Seeking More Space" in Idaho Business Review (September 3, 2014) **[14402]**, **[14771]**, **[18019]**, **[19814]**, **[21823]**, **[26254]**, **[26525]**, **[33845]**
The Cradlerock Group **[22314]**
"Craft Beers without the Buzz: Brewing New Options for the 'Sober Curious'" in NPR (June 20, 2019) **[1910]**
"Craft Brewers Want 20 Percent of U.S. Market" in Denver Business Journal (Vol. 65, April 18, 2014, No. 49, pp. A8) **[1325]**, **[1911]**, **[19501]**
"Craft Businesses That Make (the MOST) Money" in Made Urban (April 12, 2018) **[4588]**, **[4656]**, **[20004]**, **[33552]**
Craft Council of Newfoundland and Labrador (CCNL) **[4692]**
Craft Horizons [4668]
"Craft-Spirits Maker Brings Art of Distilling to SoFlo Area" in San Antonio Business Journal (Vol. 28, March 7, 2014, No. 4, pp. 5) **[1912]**, **[18020]**
Craft Ventures **[37337]**
Craft3 **[44045]**, **[46188]**
Crafted **[4589]**
Craftideas **[4615]**, **[4671]**
Crafts 'n things [4615], [4671]
The Crafts Report [4634]
The Crafts Report--Shows & Fairs Column [4594], [4658]
Craig Chamber of Commerce **[37834]**
Craigdarroch Castle **[995]**, **[9075]**
Crain Communications Inc. **[11470]**
Crain's Chicago Business **[39450]**
Crain's Cleveland Business **[43695]**
Crain's Detroit Business **[41135]**
Crain's Indianapolis **[39664]**
"Crain's Makes Ad Sales, Custom Marketing Appointments" in Crain's Chicago Business (Vol. 34, October 24, 2011, No. 42, pp. 13) **[257]**, **[11976]**, **[26526]**, **[29732]**
Crain's New York Business **[42992]**
Crain's Philadelphia **[44436]**
"Crain's Picks Top '08 Stocks" in Crain's New York Business (Vol. 24, January 6, 2008, No. 1, pp. 3) **[6350]**, **[9441]**, **[23833]**
Cranberry Coast Chamber of Commerce [46176]
Cranberry Country Chamber of Commerce (CCCC) **[40572]**
Crandon Area Chamber of Commerce [46408]
Cranford Chamber of Commerce **[42116]**
"Craning for Workers: Seattle Is Full of Cranes, but Not Enough Operators" in Puget Sound Business Journal (Vol. 35, August 15, 2014, No. 17, pp. 4) **[4048]**, **[18021]**, **[21478]**, **[26527]**
"A Crash Course in Global Relations" in Canadian Business (Vol. 87, July 2014, No. 7, pp. 77) **[15934]**, **[21479]**, **[27522]**
"Crash Landing? Serious Signal Flashing" in Barron's (Vol. 88, July 7, 2008, No. 27, pp. 11) **[6351]**, **[9442]**, **[20833]**, **[23834]**
Crash Proof 2.0: How to Profit From the Economic Collapse **[6352]**, **[9443]**, **[20834]**, **[23835]**
Crater Small Business Development Center of Longwood University **[45769]**
Craters & Freighters **[11158]**
Crawford Area Chamber of Commerce (CACC) **[37835]**
Crawfordsville & Montgomery County Chamber of Commerce (CMCCC) **[39529]**
Crawley Ventures **[37966]**
Crayon, Water Color and Craft Institute [1013]
"'Crazy' Or Not, Baltimore-Area Restaurateurs Are Finding Ways to Open New Eateries" in Baltimore Business Journal (Vol. 28, October 8, 2010) **[13862]**, **[20835]**
"Crazy Tax Deductions That Are Actually Legal" in Business News Daily (March 2, 2023) **[34770]**
Create a Successful Product with Your Invention Idea with Kevin Mako **[27971]**
Create Your Own Employee Handbook: A Legal & Practical Guide for Employers **[17293]**, **[26914]**
"Creating Health-Tech Opportunity" in Providence Business News (Vol. 29, April 14, 2014, No. 2, pp. 1) **[25753]**, **[26255]**
"Creating the Perfect Lead Magnet" in Small Business Trends(November 29, 2022) **[32501]**, **[33553]**
Creating a Positive, High-Energy Workplace (Onsite) **[27438]**
"Creating a Safety Culture in a Small Business Environment" in OH&S (July 7, 2020) **[30946]**
Creating a Step-by-Step Small Biz Wholesale Plan **[35495]**
"Creating Sustainable Performance: If You Give Your Employees the Chance To Learn and Grow, They'll Thrive - And So Will Your Organization" in Harvard Business Review (Vol. 90, January-February 2012, No. 1-2, pp. 92) **[22123]**
Creative Associates International Inc. **[30997]**
Creative Business Consultants Inc. **[3806]**
"Creative Cluster Paints Business Success" in Business Journal Serving Greater Tampa Bay (Vol. 30, October 29, 2010, No. 45, pp. 1) **[968]**, **[1016]**
Creative Colors International (CCI) **[16235]**
Creative Company Inc. **[16498]**, **[30188]**
Creative Concepts International, Inc. (CCI) **[20544]**
"Creative Cost-Cutting Ideas for Small Businesses" in Legal Zoom (March 9, 2023) **[18931]**
Creative Destruction Lab (CDL) **[46667]**
"Creative In-Sourcing Boosts Franchisee Performance" in Franchising World (Vol. 42, September 2010, No. 9, pp. 16) **[23836]**, **[24348]**, **[26915]**
The Creative Leadership Workshop [28312]
Creative Leadership Workshop for Managers, Supervisors, and Team Leaders **[28312]**
Creative Office Solutions for Small Businesses **[31032]**
Creative Organizing **[31069]**
Creative Problem Solving and Strategic Thinking (Onsite) **[21347]**, **[26853]**

3216 Small Business Sourcebook • 42nd Edition

Creative: The Magazine of Promotion and Marketing [16524]
Creative Ways to Cut and Control Costs [23707]
Creative World School Franchising [2897]
"Creativity, Inc.: Overcoming the Unseen Forces That Stand in the Way of True Inspiration" [6178], [22124], [28524]
Creativity and Innovation: Breaking New Ground..Without Breaking the Bank [18022], [19815], [22540]
"Credit Card Issuers vs. Networks — What's the Difference?" in *Credit Card Insider* (October 21, 2019) [4713]
"Credit Conditions Improve for Small Businesses" in *Small Business Economic Trends* (February 2008, pp. 12) [4714], [4742], [4777], [20267], [23837], [28121], [33988]
Credit Counselors, Surveyors & Appraisers Industry in the US - Market Research Report [818], [4753], [15226]
"The Credit Crisis Continues to Take Victims" in *Barron's* (Vol. 88, March 10, 2008, No. 10, pp. M12) [6353], [9444], [11025], [20268], [20836], [23838], [28122]
Credit Professionals International (CPI) [4733], [4758]
Credit Repair Business: 2 Manuscripts How to Fix Your Credit from Poor to Excellent and Raising Your Credit Score to 720+ [4743], [20269]
Credit Repair Services Business Book: Secrets to Start-up, Finance, market, How to Fix Credit & Make Massive Money Right Now! [4729]
"Credit Reporting Agencies Face Pressure from Skeptical U.S. Congress" in *Reuters* (February 26, 2019) [4778]
Credit Research Foundation (CRF) [1793], [4734]
"Credit Unions Buck Trend, Lend Millions More" in *Saint Louis Business Journal* (Vol. 32, September 9, 2011, No. 2, pp. 1) [28123], [33989]
"Credit Unions Seek to Raise Lending for Small Business" in *Denver Business Journal* (Vol. 64, September 28, 2012, No. 64, pp. 1) [20270], [25290], [28124]
Credit Women - International [4733], [4758]
Credit Women's Breakfast Clubs of North America [4733], [4758]
Credo Ventures [37338]
Creede and Mineral County Chamber of Commerce [37836]
Cremation Association of America [7196]
Cremation Association of North America (CANA) [7196]
"Cremation Popularity On the Rise" in *Memphis Business Journal* (Vol. 34, April 13, 2012, No. 53, pp. 1) [7207], [33990]
Cremationist of North America [7196]
Crepemaker [14147]
"Crescent to Add Two Restaurants" in *Memphis Business Journal* (Vol. 33, April 6, 2012, No. 52, pp. 1) [12882], [13927]
Crescent City/Del Norte County Chamber of Commerce [36847]
Crescent Wines [15058]
Crescenta Valley Chamber of Commerce (CVCC) [36848]
Cresson Area Chamber of Commerce [44204]
The Crestcom International L.L.C. [2334]
Crested Butte Chamber of Commerce [37837]
Crested Butte/Mount Crested Butte Chamber of Commerce [37837]
Crestline Chamber of Commerce [43474]
Crestline Resorts Chamber of Commerce [43474]
Creston Chamber of Commerce (CCC) [39729]
Crestview Area Chamber of Commerce (CACC) [38362]
Creswell Chamber of Commerce [43966]
Crete Area Chamber of Commerce [39146]
Crete Chamber of Commerce [41849]
Creve Coeur - Olivette Chamber of Commerce [41552]
"Crew Training Changes Tactics" in *Memphis Business Journal* (Vol. 33, March 16, 2012, No. 49, pp. 1) [17653], [21480], [22125]
Crewe - Burkeville Chamber of Commerce [45851]
"Crime and Punishment" in *Canadian Business* (Vol. 81, December 24, 2007, No. 1, pp. 21) [9445], [15220], [18553], [23485]
Crime Writers of Canada (CWC) [5279]
Criminal Justice [12800]
Cripple Creek and Victor Chamber of Commerce [37838]
Crisfield Area Chamber of Commerce [40381]
Criterium Engineers [2335]
"The Critical Need to Reinvent Management" in *Business Strategy Review* (Vol. 21, Spring 2010, No. 1, pp. 4) [28525], [33991]
Critical Thinking: A New Paradigm for Peak Performance (Onsite) [28313]
Critical Thinking and Out-of-the-Box Problem Solving (Onsite) [17553]
Critical Thinking Skills-Strategic Planning in Action (Onsite) [21348]
Critical Thinking Workshop [19428]
Criticism & Discipline Skills for Managers and Supervisors (Onsite) [22046], [28314]
"Critics Target Bribery Law" in *Wall Street Journal Eastern Edition* (November 28, 2011, pp. B1) [18554], [23486], [27523]
Crittenden County Chamber of Commerce, Inc. [40031]
Crittenden Directory of Real Estate Financing [13176]
Critter Control, Inc. [12058]
CRO Engineering Ltd. [19133]
Croatian Genealogical & Heraldic Society Library [7406]
Crock A Doodle [4632], [26825]
Crocker Ventures (CV) [45660]
Crockett Area Chamber of Commerce [45111]
Crockett County Chamber of Commerce [44733]
Croft & Bender LP (C&B) [38806]
Crookston Area Chamber of Commerce [41219]
Crookston Chamber and Visitors Bureau [41219]
"Crop Insurance Harvest Prices in 2011" in *Farm Industry News* (November 9, 2011) [8899], [17026], [27255]
CropCircle Kitchen [40747]
Cropsey and Associates Inc. [932]
Crosbie & Company Inc. [46783]
Crosby-Huffman Chamber of Commerce (CHCC) [45112]
"Cross Atlantic Commodities Launches National Internet Marketing Programs" in *Manufacturing Close-Up* (September 8, 2009) [1388], [9123], [28526], [29733]
Cross Country Ski Areas of America - National Ski Touring Operators' Association [14727]
Cross Country Ski Areas Association (CCSAA) [14727]
Cross Country Skier: The Journal of Nordic Skiing [14740]
Cross County Chamber of Commerce and Economic Development Corp. (CCCEDC) [36451]
Cross-Cultural Dance Resources, Inc. (CCDR) [4839]
Cross Timbers Procurement Center (CTPC) [45485]
CrossCoin Ventures, LLC [37339]
Crosscut Ventures Management LLC [37340]
Crossett Area Chamber of Commerce (CACC) [36452]
Crossing the Chasm: Marketing and Selling Disruptive Products to Mainstream Customers [9124], [21824], [26256], [29734], [32502]
Crosslink Capital (CC) [35446], [37341]
Crossmedia451 Inc. [30189]
"Crossover Skills Give Upholsterers Business Opportunities in Many Markets" in *Specialty Fabrics Review* (August 1, 2017) [16228]
The CrossRoads Institute [45945]
Crossroads Regional Chamber of Commerce [39530]
CrossSphere: the Global Association for Packaged Travel [15725], [15974]
Crossville-Cumberland County Chamber of Commerce [44734]
Croton-Hardy Business Alliance [40999]
"Crouching Tigers Spring to Life" in *Globe & Mail* (April 14, 2007, pp. B1) [17294], [20837], [31257]
Crouser & Associates Inc. [28980], [30190]
"Crouser Releases Offline UV Coating Price Report" in *American Printer* (Vol. 128, June 1, 2011, No. 6) [3304], [12730], [16186], [20005], [30955]
"Crowd Control" in *Washington Business Journal* (Vol. 33, August 15, 2014, No. 17, pp. 8) [7097], [21825], [25291]
"Crowdfund Your Way to Millions: LeVar Burton's Kickstarter Campaign Raises $1 Million In Less Than 12 Hours" in *Black Enterprise* (Vol. 45, July-August 2014, No. 1, pp. 61) [7098], [21826]
"Crowdfunding Author Thinks Google Will Beat Facebook to the Punch on InvestP2P Acquisition" in *GlobeNewswire* (July 17, 2012) [22998], [28125], [30916], [31258], [35332]
"Crowdfunding Becomes Relevant for Medical Start-Ups as TCB Medical Launches Campaign On Idiegogo to Bring Life-Saving Epinephrine Key to Market" in *PR Newswire* (July 31, 2012) [10814], [28058], [30889], [35231]
"Crowdfunding Comes to Science's Aid as Budgets, Grants Face Squeeze" in *Economic Times* (July 10, 2012) [7099], [31956], [32742]
"CrowdFunding Made Simple Conference at University of Utah Ignites Ecosystem of Entrepreneurs and Investors" in *Economics Week* (June 29, 2012) [7100], [22375], [22999], [25292], [28126], [30890], [35333], [45687]
"CrowdFunding Platform, START.ac, Announces It Is Expanding Its International Scope From the US, Canada and the UK to 36 Countries Including Australia, India, Israel, Italy and Africa" in *Benzinga.com* (July 11, 2012) [17893], [22960], [27388], [28059], [30891], [35232]
"Crowdfunding Site Targets Jan. Launch" in *Crain's Detroit Business* (July 9, 2012) [22961], [30892], [35233]
"Crowdsourcing the Law" in *LJN's Legal Tech Newsletter* (October 1, 2010) [18555], [30706]
"Crowdsourcing their Way into One Big Mess" in *Brandweek* (Vol. 51, October 25, 2010, No. 38, pp. 26) [3103], [6128], [21827], [29735], [30707], [32131]
Crowe Horwath [16878], [34944]
Crowe Horwath International [16878], [34944]
Crowell Chamber of Commerce [45113]
Crown Trophy Inc. [5473]
CRS Library [6847]
"CRTC Signals CHUM Deal Will Get Nod" in *Globe & Mail* (May 2, 2007, pp. B3) [15589], [31259]
"Crucible: A New Will to Win" in *Harvard Business Review* (Vol. 88, September 2010, No. 9, pp. 110) [18932], [28527]
"Crucible: Battling Back from Betrayal" in *Harvard Business Review* (Vol. 88, December 2010, No. 12, pp. 130) [57], [1751], [13707], [16793], [18023], [18556], [23487], [26528], [26916], [27524], [27996], [28528]
"Crucible: Losing the Top Job - And Winning It Back" in *Harvard Business Review* (Vol. 88, October 2010, No. 10, pp. 136) [13928], [22541], [26529], [26917], [28529]
"Crude Awakening" in *Canadian Business* (Vol. 81, October 27, 2008, No. 18, pp. 14) [5578], [5855], [20838], [23171], [33992]
Crude Oil: Sampling, Testing, and Evaluation (Onsite) [23062]
Crudup-Ward Women's Business Center (CWAC) [41435]
Cruise Holidays [16036]
Cruise Planners [16035]
Cruise Travel--Cruise Calendar Section: The Worldwide Cruise Vacation Magazine [15735]
CruiseOne [16037]
The Cruising Club Fractional Boat Ownership [2835]
CRV [37342]
"Crystal Hotel Resumes Construction" in *Business Journal Portland* (Vol. 27, December 31, 2010, No. 44, pp. 1) [1326], [1913], [4049], [8381]
Crystal Internet Venture Fund L.P. [43620]
Crystal Lake Chamber of Commerce [39147]
Crystal River - Nature Coast Chamber of Commerce [38351]
C.S. Simons Consulting L.L.C. [24849]
"CSE: Contractors Are Always Responsible" in *Contractor* (Vol. 56, November 2009, No. 11, pp. 34) [12624], [31033], [35942]
CSI Business Incubator [38951]
CSI Global Education [9292]
CSI Kick Start [38616]
CSI Tech Incubator [42860]
CSP Associates Inc. [33662]
CSRA Business League Inc. [30259]
CTAM: Cable and Telecommunications Association for Marketing (CTAM) [2442], [15572]
CTAM, The Marketing Society for the Cable and Telecommunications Industry [2442], [15572]
CTB [47346]
CTIA - The Wireless Association [2702]
CTMA View [29077]
"CTV's CHUM Proposal Gets Chilly Reception" in *Globe & Mail* (May 1, 2007, pp. B1) [15590], [25293], [31260]
Cuba Chamber of Commerce [41553]
Cuban American National Council (CNC) [30260]
Cuban National Planning Council [30260]
CUC International, Inc [8499], [14120]
"The Cudgel of Samson: How the Government Once Used 'Jawboning' to Fight Inflation" in *Barron's* (Vol. 88, March 24, 2008, No. 12, pp. 62) [20839], [24968], [25294]
Cue Ball Capital [40678]
Cuero Chamber of Commerce, Agriculture, & Visitor's Center [45114]
Cuesta College - Business & Entrepreneurship Center (BEC) [37563]
Culbertson Chamber of Commerce [41759]
Culinary Careers: How to Get Your Dream Job in Food with Advice from Top Culinary Professionals [2659], [4873], [13863]
The Culinary Cooperative [46212]
Culinary Institute of America - Conrad N. Hilton Library [2696], [4477], [14303]
Culinary Kitchen & Beyond L.L.C. [45509]
"Culinary School Puts a Food Truck on the Road" in *St. Louis Post-Dispatch* (March 21, 2012) [3819], [6949], [21481], [30446]
The Culinary Studio [41083]
Culligan International Co. [16347]
Cullman Area Chamber of Commerce (CACC) [36100]
Cullman County Chamber of Commerce [36100]
Culpeper County Chamber of Commerce [45852]
"The Cult of Ralph: Chrysler's Ralph Gilles" in *Canadian Business* (Vol. 79, September 22, 2006, No. 19, pp. 90) [28530], [29169]

Cultivation Capital **[41660]**
"Cultural Change That Sticks: Start With What's Already Working" in (Vol. 90, July-August 2012, No. 7-8, pp. 110) **[19502]**, **[19816]**
"Cultural Due Diligence" in Canadian Business (Vol. 80, April 23, 2007, No. 9, pp. 60) **[22126]**, **[26530]**, **[35185]**
"Culturally Incongruent Messages In International Advertising" in International Journal of Advertising (Vol. 31, May 2012, No. 2, pp. 355) **[258]**, **[30552]**
Culture Cipher Consulting **[30636]**
"Culture Club: Effective Corporate Cultures" in Canadian Business (Vol. 79, October 9, 2006, No. 20, pp. 115) **[22127]**, **[24644]**, **[28531]**
"A Culture of Ethical Behavior Is Essential to Business Success" in Business News Daily (Aug. 30, 2021) **[23488]**
The Culture High **[5049]**
Culture Marketing Council [16901]
Culture Solutions Group **[2252]**, **[30637]**
Culver Chamber of Commerce **[39531]**
Culver City Business Directory **[36849]**
Culver City Chamber of Commerce **[36850]**
Culvers Frozen Custard **[8614]**
Cumberland Business Incubator (CBI) **[44842]**
Cumberland Chamber of Commerce (CCC) **[46389]**
Cumberland County Chamber of Commerce **[40032]**
Cumming-Forsyth County Chamber of Commerce **[38719]**
"Cummins Is a Engine of Growth" in Barron's (Vol. 88, July 14, 2008, No. 28, pp. 43) **[5154]**, **[6354]**, **[9446]**, **[18024]**, **[19817]**, **[23839]**
Cunningham Enterprise Center at Columbus State University **[38831]**
CUNY Startup Accelerator **[42861]**
CUNY SustainableWorks **[42862]**
"Cupcake Maker Explains Tricks of the Trade" in Chattanooga Times/Free Press (September 6, 2011) **[1251]**, **[35759]**
Cupertino Business News **[36851]**
Cupertino Chamber of Commerce **[36852]**
"Curbing the Debt Collector" in Business Journal-Portland (Vol. 24, October 5, 2007, No. 32, pp. 1) **[4715]**, **[4744]**, **[4779]**, **[20271]**, **[25295]**
Currency Internationalization: Global Experiences and Implications for the Renminbi **[6355]**, **[8713]**, **[9447]**, **[23840]**, **[27525]**, **[33993]**
Current Blackjack News (CBJN) **[7319]**
Curtis Institute of Music (CIM) - Milton L. Rock Resource Center **[11219]**
Curves For Women, Inc. [16512]
Curves International, Inc. [16512]
Cushing Chamber of Commerce and Industry **[43749]**
Custer Area Chamber of Commerce and Visitors Bureau **[44644]**
"Custom Fit" in Canadian Business (Vol. 80, November 19, 2007, No. 23, pp. 42) **[26531]**, **[26918]**, **[28532]**
Custom Forestry Inc. **[17193]**
Custom Payroll **[11947]**
"Custom Picture Framing Is Too Expensive — and Framebridge Has a Fix for That" in Forbes (January 4, 2019) **[11728]**, **[12705]**, **[21828]**
Custom Tailors and Designers Association (CTDA) **[3001]**
"Customer Data Represents Huge Opportunities and Challenges: My, What Big Data You Have" in Canadian Business (Vol. 85, August 13, 2012, No. 13, pp. 14) **[3493]**, **[3616]**, **[20409]**
Customer Focused Telephone Techniques (Onsite) **[17554]**
"The Customer Is Always Right Even When He's Wrong" in Contractor (Vol. 57, February 2010, No. 2, pp. 12) **[5367]**, **[12625]**, **[14613]**, **[20410]**, **[31753]**
"Customer Loyalty: Making Your Program Excel" in Franchising World (Vol. 42, August 2010, No. 8, pp. 47) **[18025]**, **[20411]**, **[24349]**
Customer Perspectives **[10692]**, **[30191]**
"Customer Preferences Control Skid Steer Choices" in Rental Product News (Vol. 33, June 2011) **[13776]**, **[20412]**
"Customer Retention is Proportionate to Employee Retention" in Green Industry Pro (Vol. 23, September 2011) **[7613]**, **[10090]**, **[10226]**, **[20413]**, **[22128]**, **[28533]**, **[33131]**
"The Customer Rules: The 39 Essential Rules for Delivering Sensational Service" **[20414]**
Customer Satisfaction and Loyalty Research (Onsite) **[20372]**
"Customer Service Guide for Small Business" in The Balance Small Business (June 25, 2019) **[20415]**
Customer Service for Small Business Owners: Everything You Need to Know **[20416]**
"Customer Service Solutions for Small Businesses" in Business News Daily (Dec. 3, 2021) **[20417]**

Customer Service That Wows! (Onsite) **[20373]**
"Customers Will Pay More For Less" in (Vol. 90, June 2012, No. 6, pp. 30) **[20006]**, **[32503]**
"Customized Before Custom Was Cool" in Green Industry Pro (July 2011) **[5579]**, **[5856]**, **[7614]**, **[10091]**, **[10227]**, **[22542]**, **[23172]**, **[33132]**
Customized Logistics and Delivery Association (CLDA) **[10976]**
"Customizing a Job Application Template to Fit Your Business" in Legal Zoom (February 15, 2023) **[26532]**
Customs Brokers and Forwarders Association of America [2139], [7024]
Customs Clerks Association of the Port of New York [2139], [7024]
Cut Bank Area Chamber of Commerce **[41760]**
"The Cutest Houston-Made Kids' Clothes Will Soon Come in Mom Versions" in Houstonia (August 7, 2019) **[2848]**, **[11729]**, **[35760]**
Cutlass Capital LLC **[40679]**
Cutter Business Technology Journal [14853]
Cutter IT Journal [14853]
"Cutting Credit Card Processing Costs for Your Small Business" in Hawaii Business (Vol. 53, March 2008, No. 9, pp. 56) **[18026]**, **[20272]**, **[24645]**
"Cutting Health Care Costs: the 3-Legged Stool" in HR Specialist (Vol. 8, September 2010, No. 9, pp. 1) **[8900]**, **[17295]**, **[26919]**, **[27256]**
Cutting Horse Chatter **[15206]**
"Cutting the Power: A New Trend in Jewelry Store Burglaries" in Jewelers of America (July 8, 2019) **[9973]**
Cutting Tool Manufacturers of America [10424]
Cutting Tool Manufacturers Association [10424]
Cuyahoga Community College (Tri-C) **[43687]**
Cuyahoga Falls Chamber of Commerce (CFCC) **[43453]**
CVMA Source Guide and Directory **[685]**
CVTC Applied Technology Center (CVTC) **[46561]**
C.W. Downer & Co. [40660]
CWB Group [10418]
CWCBExpo **[5053]**
CWI: Credit Professionals [4733], [4758]
Cy-Fair Houston Chamber of Commerce (CFHCC) **[45115]**
"A Cyber Breach: More Likely Than a Fire" in Philadelphia Business Journal (Vol. 33, June 13, 2014, No. 18, pp. 6) **[3494]**, **[14403]**, **[31957]**
Cyber Incubator **[40451]**
"Cyber Thanksgiving Online Shopping a Growing Tradition" in Marketing Weekly News (December 12, 2009, pp. 137) **[9125]**, **[11730]**, **[16407]**, **[21829]**, **[29736]**, **[32132]**, **[32504]**
"The Cybersecurity Shortage Is Real, and Women May Be the Solution" in BizTech (August 4, 2021) **[3792]**, **[14499]**
Cybersecurity for Small Business **[19258]**
"Cyberwise" in Black Enterprise (Vol. 40, July 2010, No. 12, pp. 48) **[34981]**
Cycad Group **[37730]**
Cycle Capital Management (CCM) **[46908]**
cycle news **[11113]**
Cylburn Arboretum Association Library **[7665]**
"Cynergy Data May Pick Memphis for HQ Move" in Memphis Business Journal (Vol. 33, February 10, 2012, No. 44, pp. 1) **[3495]**, **[19168]**
Cynthia Wong Founder of Life Raft Treats **[35496]**
Cynthiana-Harrison County Chamber of Commerce **[40033]**
Cypress Chamber of Commerce **[36853]**
Cypress College (CC) **[37655]**
Cytoskeleton **[32867]**
Czechoslovak Genealogical Society [7344]
Czechoslovak Genealogical Society International (CGSI) **[7344]**

D

"D-Link Enhances Small Business Professional Security Solutions with New Outdoor Bullet Cameras Featuring Cloud Services Support and Wide Dynamic Range Sensor" in PR Newswire September 10, 2012 **[14404]**
D Pet Hotels **[12112]**
The Da Vinci Group Inc. **[12954]**
DAAP Library [3082]
Dace Ventures **[40680]**
Dadeville Area Chamber of Commerce **[36101]**
Daedalus Ventures Ltd. **[28981]**
DAG Ventures **[37343]**
Dahlonega-Lumpkin County Chamber of Commerce [38720]
Dahlonega Lumpkin County Chamber of Commerce & Visitors Bureau **[38720]**
Daily Brief **[11481]**, **[12014]**
Daily Business Review **[42993]**

Daily Pilot **[36854]**
Daily Record (Parsippany, New Jersey) **[13601]**
The Daily Record: Business **[40479]**
The Daily Times **[44735]**
"DaimlerChrysler Bears Down on Smart" in Globe & Mail (March 27, 2006, pp. B11) **[18933]**, **[29170]**
Daingerfield Chamber of Commerce (DCC) **[45116]**
Dairy Management Inc. (DMI) **[8538]**
"Dairy Queen Aims to Blitz Blizzberry" in Ice Cream Reporter (Vol. 23, August 20, 2010, No. 9, pp. 1) **[8556]**, **[18557]**
Dairy Queen Canada (DQ) **[8615]**, **[14148]**
"Dairy Queen Ends Effort Against Yogubliz" in Ice Cream Reporter (Vol. 23, November 20, 2010, No. 12, pp. 1) **[8557]**, **[19818]**
Dakota County Regional Chamber of Commerce **[41220]**
Dakota Venture Group (DVG) **[43327]**
Dale Hollow-Clay County Chamber of Commerce **[44727]**
Dalhart Area Chamber of Commerce (DACC) **[45117]**
Dalhousie University - Faculty of Medicine - Department of Community Health and Epidemiology - Health Data Nova Scotia (HDNS) **[26112]**
Dallas Angel Network (DAN) **[35274]**, **[45444]**
Dallas Area Chamber of Commerce (DACC) **[43967]**
Dallas Black Chamber of Commerce (DBCC) **[45118]**
Dallas Business Journal **[45585]**
The Dallas Entrepreneur Center (DEC) **[45510]**
Dallas Fort Worth Business Travel Association (DFWBTA) **[19293]**, **[44884]**
Dallas/Fort Worth Chapter of the American Marketing Association (AMA DFW) **[44885]**
Dallas/Fort Worth Minority Business Development Council (D/FW MSDC) **[45419]**
Dallas/Fort Worth Minority Supplier Development Council [45419]
"Dallas Law Firms Play Big Role in State's M&A Deals" in Dallas Business Journal (Vol. 37, July 18, 2014, No. 45, pp. 9) **[18558]**, **[31261]**
Dallas Regional Minority Purchasing Council [45419]
Dallas Small Business Development Center **[44912]**
"Dallas Top-Performing City for Small Business Growth" in Dallas Business Journal (Vol. 37, July 11, 2014, No. 44, pp. 13) **[20840]**, **[26533]**, **[33329]**
Daly City Business Center **[37564]**
Daly City/Colma Chamber of Commerce **[36855]**
Damariscotta Region Chamber of Commerce (DRCC) **[40272]**
Dan River Business Development Center (DRBDC) **[45946]**
Dana Point Chamber of Commerce (DPCC) **[36856]**
"Danaher to Acquire Tectronix for $2.8 Billion" in Canadian Electronics (Vol. 22, November-December 2007, No. 7, pp. 1) **[9448]**, **[26257]**, **[29171]**, **[31262]**
Danbury Chamber of Commerce [38046]
Dance Affiliates [4847]
Dance Educators of America (DEA) **[4840]**
Dance Films Association (DFA) **[4864]**
Dance International **[4859]**
Dance Magazine **[4860]**
Dance Magazine College Guide **[4852]**
Dance Notation Bureau (DNB) **[4841]**
Dance Teachers Guild [4834]
D'Angelo Grilled Sandwiches **[14149]**
"The Danger of Doing Nothing" in Harvard Business Review (Vol. 90, April 2012, No. 4, pp. 38) **[19819]**, **[20841]**, **[25296]**
"The Danger from Within: The Biggest Threat to Your Cybersecurity May Be an Employee or a Vendor" in Harvard Business Review (Vol. 92, September 2014, No. 9, pp. 94) **[14405]**, **[22342]**, **[28534]**
Dangerous Goods Advisory Council (DGAC) **[7940]**
Dangerous Goods Council, Inc. (DGC) **[7973]**
Daniel Bloom and Associates Inc. (DBAI) **[19213]**, **[21708]**, **[25619]**
The Danielle Adams Publishing Co. **[44440]**
Daniels County Chamber of Commerce and Agriculture **[41761]**
Danish American Chamber of Commerce (DACC) **[27408]**
Danish American Trade Council [27408]
Danish Luncheon Club of New York [27408]
Dansville Chamber of Commerce (DCC) **[42562]**
DANTH Inc. **[933]**
Danville Area Chamber of Commerce **[36857]**
Danville Area Chamber of Commerce and Visitor Center [45853]
Danville-Boyle County Chamber of Commerce **[40034]**
Danville Pittsylvania County Chamber of Commerce [45853]
Darien Chamber of Commerce (DCC) **[38042]**
Darien Chamber of Commerce and Industry [38042]
Darien-McIntosh Chamber of Commerce **[38721]**
Darke County Chamber of Commerce **[43454]**

Master Index Definitive

Darke County Historical Society (DCHS) **[7407]**
DART: British Columbia Statute Service on Internet **[18786]**
Dartmouth College - Dartmouth Entrepreneurial Network (DEN) **[42023]**
Dartmouth College - Geisel School of Medicine - Dartmouth Institute for Health Policy and Clinical Practice **[26113]**
Dartmouth Regional Technology Center (DRTC) **[42024]**
"The Darwinian Workplace: New Technology Is Helping Employers Systematically Shift More Work To Their Best Employees" in Harvard Business Review (Vol. 90, May 2012, No. 5, pp. 25) **[17296]**, **[19820]**, **[22129]**, **[28535]**
Data Analysis for EEO Professionals (Onsite) **[18484]**
Data Analysis for Marketing Research: The Fundamentals (Onsite) **[29585]**
The Data Base for Advances in Information Systems **[8837]**
"Data Center Operators are Finding San Antonio has the Right Stuff" in San Antonio Business Journal (Vol. 28, February 28, 2014, No. 3, pp. 4) **[3496]**, **[3617]**, **[33361]**
Data Center World **[3778]**
Data Conversion Laboratory (DCL) **[14879]**
"Data Deep Dive: Supporting and Hiring Individuals with Disabilities and Neurodivergence" in U.S. Chamber of Commerce (Aug. 25, 2022) **[26534]**, **[30553]**
Data Doctors **[3584]**, **[3754]**
Data Elite **[37344]**
Data Hoarding Business Hazards **[32397]**
"Data: Nearly 80% of Black Entrepreneurs Believe They Run Thriving Businesses, Yet Gaining Access to Capital Still a Hurdle" in Black Enterprise(February 24, 2023) **[18027]**, **[22543]**, **[28127]**
Data Point Capital **[40681]**
Data Processing Management Association [3766]
"Data Security is No. 1 Compliance Concern" in HRMagazine (Vol. 53, October 2008, No. 10, pp. 32) **[3497]**, **[14406]**
Data Strategy: How to Profit from a World of Big Data, Analytics and Artificial Intelligence **[33554]**
Database Design for Web Development **[22983]**
Datasets at the Library of Congress: A Research Guide **[18858]**
Daugherty Business Solutions **[2253]**
Davenport Chamber of Commerce **[43750]**
Davenport Chamber of Commerce (DCC) **[46075]**
Davenport University - Thomas F. Reed, Jr. Memorial Library **[10974]**, **[15778]**, **[16045]**
"David Bugs Developer Goliaths" in Denver Business Journal (Vol. 64, August 17, 2012, No. 13, pp. 1) **[879]**, **[13430]**, **[33994]**
David Foulquier Chef/Owner We All Gotta Eat! **[14053]**
David G. Schantz **[2384]**, **[10526]**, **[20180]**, **[28982]**
David Hall's Inside View **[3244]**
David Johnston Research + Technology Park **[46819]**
David L. Ward and Associates Inc. **[35015]**
"David Leonhardt on Hiring a Copywriter for Your Small Business" in Small Business Trends(October 18, 2022) **[5313]**, **[17654]**, **[33555]**
"David Maus Debuting New Dealership" in Orlando Business Journal (Vol. 26, February 5, 2010, No. 36, pp. 1) **[11352]**, **[26535]**, **[31263]**
"David Robinson Column" in Buffalo News (October 2, 2011) **[5580]**, **[5857]**, **[23173]**
Davie-Cooper City Chamber of Commerce (DCCC) **[38363]**
Davie County Chamber of Commerce **[43123]**
Davis Chamber of Commerce **[36858]**, **[45632]**
"Davis Family Expands Cable Empire" in St. Louis Business Journal (Vol. 32, June 15, 2012, No. 43, pp. 1) **[2452]**, **[18028]**, **[23607]**, **[28536]**, **[31264]**
Davis, Tuttle Venture Partners (DTVP) **[43830]**
Dawes Arboretum Library **[7666]**
Dawson County Chamber of Commerce **[38722]**
Dawson Springs Chamber of Commerce **[40035]**
"Day-Care Center Owner to Argue Against Liquor Store Opening Nearby" in Chicago Tribune (March 13, 2008) **[2880]**, **[10317]**, **[18559]**, **[21482]**
"Day Care Directors Are Playing Doctor, and Parents Suffer" in The New York Times (September 16, 2019) **[2881]**, **[25754]**
A Day to Cherish Wedding Videos **[2398]**, **[12319]**
"A Day Late and a Dollar Short" in Indoor Comfort Marketing (Vol. 70, March 2011, No. 3, pp. 30) **[479]**, **[5581]**, **[5858]**, **[9449]**, **[23174]**, **[29737]**, **[33995]**
"A Day in the Life of an Albany Pool Hall" in Spotlightnews.com (April 4, 2018) **[1537]**
"The Day That Apple Called" in Business Journal Portland (Vol. 31, March 28, 2014, No. 4, pp. 9) **[1650]**, **[3701]**
Dayforce **[41347]**
Days Inns Canada **[2336]**
Days Inns Worldwide Inc. **[8504]**
Daytime Broadcasters Association [13021], [13063], [15575]
Dayton Area Chamber of Commerce **[41933]**
Dayton Area Chamber of Commerce (DACC) **[43455]**
Dayton Area Chamber of Commerce Economic Development Division [43455]
Dayton Auto Show **[406]**
Dayton Business Journal **[43696]**
Dayton Chamber of Commerce **[44736]**
Dayton Chamber of Commerce (DCC) **[46076]**
Daytona Beach Area Chamber of Commerce [38364]
Daytona Regional Chamber of Commerce **[38364]**
Dazbog Coffee Co. **[7580]**
DBL Partners **[37731]**
DC Chamber of Commerce (DCCC) **[38166]**
DCL News **[2122]**, **[3439]**, **[3555]**, **[3749]**, **[14854]**
DDB Worldwide Communications Group LLC **[398]**
De Anza College (DAC) **[37656]**
De Bellas & Co. **[2254]**, **[9928]**
De Dutch Pannekoek House Restaurants **[14150]**
De Forest Area Chamber of Commerce **[46390]**
De Leon Chamber of Commerce and Agriculture **[45119]**
De Queen/Sevier County Chamber of Commerce **[36453]**
Dead on Arrival: How the Anti-Business Backlash is Destroying Entrepreneurship in America and What We Can Still Do About It! **[22544]**, **[24646]**, **[25297]**
Deadwood Chamber of Commerce and Visitors' Bureau **[44645]**
Deaf Smith County Chamber of Commerce (DSCC) **[45120]**
"Deal Braces Cramer for Growth Run" in The Business Journal-Serving Metropolitan Kansas City (Vol. 26, July 4, 2008, No. 43, pp. 1) **[6356]**, **[9450]**, **[18029]**, **[20619]**, **[23841]**, **[31265]**
"Deal Made for Pontiac Home of Film Studio" in Crain's Detroit Business (Vol. 25, June 1, 2009, No. 22, pp. 3) **[6179]**, **[21483]**, **[33362]**
"Dealer Gets a Lift with Acquisitions at Year's End" in Crain's Detroit Business (Vol. 26, January 11, 2010, No. 2, pp. 3) **[11392]**, **[16077]**, **[18030]**, **[26536]**, **[29172]**, **[31266]**
"Dealers Leasing Changes Name, Hopes to Stoke National Growth" in Wichita Business Journal (Vol. 27, January 27, 2012, No. 4, pp. 1) **[13777]**, **[23842]**
Dealing with Competing Demands **[21349]**
"Dealing With Problem Estate Sale Customers" in EstateSales.org Blog **[6068]**
"Deals Dip In Florida Amid Squabbles Over Price" in South Florida Business Journal (Vol. 34, May 30, 2014, No. 45, pp. 4) **[9451]**, **[25755]**, **[26258]**
Dean College **[40769]**
"Dean Foods: Uh Oh. Here Comes Wal-Mart" in Ice Cream Reporter (Vol. 23, September 20, 2010, No. 10, pp. 8) **[8558]**, **[27997]**, **[28537]**, **[31958]**, **[32743]**
Dean L. Hubbard Center for Innovation and Entrepreneurship **[41671]**
Dearborn Area Chamber of Commerce (DACC) **[40898]**
Dearborn County Chamber of Commerce (DCC) **[39532]**
Dearborn Real Estate Education **[46586]**
"Death by 1,000 Clicks: Where Electronic Health Records Went Wrong" in Kaiser Health News (March 18, 2019) **[3804]**, **[25756]**, **[34301]**
"The Death of the Local Bike Shop" in Outside (November 2, 2016) **[1520]**, **[11731]**
"Death of the PC" in Canadian Business (Vol. 83, October 12, 2010, No. 17, pp. 44) **[2728]**, **[3702]**, **[19821]**, **[30708]**, **[30956]**, **[33996]**
"Death Spiral" in Business Journal Serving Greater Tampa Bay (Vol. 30, October 29, 2010, No. 45, pp. 1) **[4780]**, **[9452]**, **[20273]**, **[25298]**, **[28128]**, **[31267]**
Debra F. Latimer Nutrition and Diabetes Associates L.L.C. **[11595]**
"Debt-Collection Agency to Lay Off 368 in Hampton Center" in Virginian-Pilot (December 4, 2010) **[4781]**, **[20274]**, **[26537]**, **[26920]**, **[31118]**, **[33133]**
Debugit Computer Services **[3585]**
Decatur Chamber of Commerce (DCC) **[45121]**
Decatur Chamber of Commerce (DCC) **[39533]**
Decatur Chamber of Commerce [36102]
Decatur County Area Chamber of Commerce **[39880]**
Decatur County Chamber of Commerce (DCCC) **[44737]**
Decatur Genealogical Society (DGS) **[7408]**
Decatur-Morgan County Chamber of Commerce (DCC) **[36102]**
Decatur-Morgan County Entrepreneurial Center **[36051]**, **[36177]**
Decatur SCORE **[39006]**
"December is National Write a Business Plan Month" in Small Business Trends(December 2, 2022) **[18934]**
"A Decent Proposal" in Hawaii Business (Vol. 53, March 2008, No. 9, pp. 52) **[4590]**, **[18031]**, **[29173]**
"Decent Termination: A Moral Case for Severance Pay" in Business Ethics Quarterly (Vol. 24, April 2014, No. 2, pp. 203) **[17297]**, **[23489]**
Dechert LLP Library **[9948]**
Deck Renewal Systems USA L.L.C. **[4831]**
Deck the Walls **[9067]**, **[12710]**
"Declutter Your Office by Updating Your Personal Tech" in Entrepreneur (May 2014) **[11634]**
Deco [9064]
"Decoding Demand Opportunities" in Business Strategy Review (Vol. 21, Spring 2010, No. 1, pp. 64) **[10644]**, **[29738]**
Decor & You Inc. **[9068]**
Decorah Area Chamber of Commerce (DACC) **[39730]**
"Decorated Marine Sues Contractor" in Wall Street Journal Eastern Edition (November 29, 2011, pp. A4) **[4050]**, **[18560]**, **[25129]**, **[26538]**
Decorating Den Interiors (DDI) **[12032]**, **[26826]**
Decorating Elves (DE) **[2399]**
Decorating Retailer--Buyers Guide Issue [11861], [11883]
Decorative Arts Digest [4619]
Decorative Arts Painting [4619]
Decorative Hardware Association (DHA) **[10376]**, **[10415]**
"Dedge Rejects Inflation Concerns" in Globe & Mail (January 26, 2007, pp. B3) **[20842]**, **[24647]**
Dedicated to Helping Serious and Committed Entrepreneurs with Jay Rodgers **[22882]**
Deduct It! Lower Your Small Business Taxes **[58]**, **[1752]**, **[15373]**, **[16794]**, **[34771]**
"Deep Dive: Does Your Food Truck Operation Need a Commissary Kitchen?" in FoodTruckOperator.com (March 16, 2020) **[6970]**
"Deep in the Heart of Drought" in Green Industry Pro (Vol. 23, October 2011) **[7615]**, **[10092]**, **[10228]**, **[33134]**
"Deep Thoughts: Getting Employees to Think Better Requires a Bit of Creative Thinking Itself" in Canadian Business (March 17, 2008) **[19503]**, **[21484]**, **[22130]**, **[33556]**
Deer Isle - Stonington Chamber of Commerce **[40273]**
Deer Isle-Stonington Historical Society (DISHS) **[10629]**
Deer Park Area Chamber of Commerce [46077]
Deer Park Chamber of Commerce **[45122]**, **[46077]**
Deer and Turkey Expos [15207]
"Deere to Open Technology Center in Germany" in Chicago Tribune (September 3, 2008) **[17027]**, **[18032]**, **[18935]**, **[27526]**, **[29174]**, **[32744]**
Deerfield, Bannockburn, Riverwoods Chamber of Commerce (DBR) **[39148]**
Deerfield Chamber of Commerce [39148]
"Defend Your Research: Commercials Make Us Like TV More" in Harvard Business Review (Vol. 88, October 2010, No. 10, pp. 36) **[259]**, **[2453]**, **[15591]**, **[29739]**
"Defend Your Research: I Can Make Your Brain Look Like Mine" in Harvard Business Review (Vol. 88, December 2010, No. 12, pp. 32) **[17655]**, **[17857]**
"Defend Your Research: It's Not "Unprofessional" to Gossip at Work" in Harvard Business Review (Vol. 88, September 2010, No. 9, pp. 28) **[22131]**, **[28538]**
"Defend Your Research: People Often Trust Eloquence More Than Honesty" in Harvard Business Review (Vol. 88, November 2010, No. 11, pp. 36) **[17656]**, **[17858]**, **[23490]**, **[25299]**
"Defend Your Research: The Early Bird Really Does Get the Worm" in Harvard Business Review (Vol. 88, July-August 2010, No. 7-8, pp. 30) **[22545]**, **[28539]**, **[34982]**
"Defendants in Ponzi Case Seek Relief from Court" in Denver Business Journal (Vol. 64, September 7, 2012, No. 16, pp. 1) **[9453]**, **[18561]**
Defending Our Plant Everywhere [5039]
Defending Windows Networks (Onsite) **[21350]**
"Defense Budget Ax May Not Come Down So Hard on Maryland" in Baltimore Business Journal (Vol. 28, August 20, 2010, No. 15, pp. 1) **[14407]**, **[24969]**, **[25300]**
Defense Contract Management Agency [47581], [47582]
Defense Contract Management Command [47581], [47582], [47584], [47585]
Defense Information Systems Agency, Continental United States (DISA CONUS) **[39388]**
"Defense Mobile Joins Forces with RadioShack to launch New Military Focuses Mobile Service this Fall" in Defense & Aerospace Business (September 10, 2014, pp. 7) **[2729]**, **[4390]**, **[31268]**, **[34302]**
"Defer Tax with Installment Sale Election" in Business Owner (Vol. 35, September-October 2011, No. 5, pp. 12) **[15374]**, **[33013]**, **[34772]**
Defiance Area Chamber of Commerce **[43456]**
"Define a Target Market for Your Small Business" in Nolo **[34711]**
"The Definitive Office Supplies Checklist for Small Businesses" in Small Business Trends(January 27, 2023) **[11663]**, **[16553]**

Small Business Sourcebook • 42nd Edition 3219

Defta Master Index

Defta Partners **[37345]**
"DEI Gets Real" in Harvard Business Review (Jan-Feb 2022) **[30554]**
DEI International L.L.C. **[26827]**, **[32700]**
D.E.I. Management Group Inc. **[30192]**, **[32691]**
DEI & You Consulting **[30638]**
DeKalb Chamber of Commerce **[39149]**
Del Mar College Small Business Development Center **[44913]**
Del Mar Regional Chamber of Commerce [37148]
"Del Mar's Free Carpentry Classes to Expand in Corpus Christi" in Corpus Christi Business News (September 6, 2019) **[2637]**
Del Norte Chamber of Commerce (DNCC) **[37839]**
Del Rio Chamber of Commerce (DRCC) **[45123]**
Delafield Chamber of Commerce (DCC) **[46391]**
DeLand Area Chamber of Commerce (DACC) **[38365]**
Delano Area Chamber of Commerce (DACC) **[41221]**
Delano Chamber of Commerce **[36859]**
Delavan - Delavan Lake Area Chamber of Commerce **[46392]**
Delaware Area Chamber of Commerce **[43457]**
Delaware Association of Realtors (DAR) **[13087]**
Delaware County Chamber of Commerce **[44200]**
Delaware County Chamber of Commerce [43457]
Delaware County Community College (DCCC) **[44430]**
Delaware Crossing Investor Group (DCIG) **[44441]**
Delaware Department of Labor - Office of Occupational and Labor Market Information (OOLMI) **[47746]**
Delaware Department of Natural Resources and Environmental Control - Division of Waste and Hazardous Substances (DWHS) **[46955]**
Delaware Economic Development Office (DEDO) **[47405]**
Delaware Kitchen Share **[38142]**
Delaware River Towns Chamber of Commerce & Visitors Bureau **[42117]**
Delaware Small Business Development Center (DSBDC) **[38124]**, **[38125]**
Delaware State Chamber of Commerce (DSCC) **[38134]**
Delaware State Museums Division of Historical and Cultural Affairs - Johnson Victrola Museum Collection **[13666]**
Delaware Technology Park Inc. (DTP) **[38143]**
"Delaware Valley Floral Group Opens Long Island Distribution Center" in The Produce News (October 9, 2019) **[6853]**
Delaware Valley University - Joseph Krauskopf Memorial Library **[17209]**
Delegation: The Most Rewarding, Frustrating . . . Awesome Part of Running Your Business **[28540]**
Delivering Knock Your Socks Off Service **[24648]**, **[33135]**
"Delivering the Milk" in Barron's (Vol. 92, July 23, 2012, No. 30, pp. M7) **[9454]**, **[14408]**, **[17028]**, **[18033]**, **[27527]**
The Delmarva Farmer: The Agribusiness Newspaper of the Mid-Atlantic Region **[17201]**
Deloitte Services LLP Information Center **[1787]**
Deloitte & Touche - Library **[163]**, **[15467]**
Deloitte & Touche - Research Center **[1788]**
Delos Payment Systems, Inc. [38830]
"Delphi Latest In Fight Over Offshore Tax Shelters" in Crain's Detroit Business (Vol. 30, July 7, 2014, No. 27, pp. 1) **[3703]**, **[11393]**, **[29175]**, **[34773]**
Delphi Ventures **[37346]**
Delphos Area Chamber of Commerce **[43458]**
Delta Alpha Publishing Ltd. **[41136]**
Delta Area Chamber of Commerce (DACC) **[45633]**
Delta Area Chamber of Commerce, Inc. **[37840]**
Delta Center for Economic Development (DCED) **[36514]**
Delta Chamber of Commerce **[43459]**
Delta Contract Procurement Center, Inc [41443]
Delta County Area Chamber of Commerce **[40899]**
Delta County Chamber of Commerce (DCCC) **[40900]**
Delta Cuisine Commercial Kitchen and Business Incubator **[36515]**
Delta Junction Chamber of Commerce **[36226]**
Delta Junction Chamber of Commerce **[36225]**
Delta Properties **[46562]**
"Delta Rebrands Its Business Travel Tools Package" in Small Business Trends (September 5, 2022) **[428]**
Delta Systems **[22315]**
Deltatee Enterprises Ltd. **[46668]**
D.E.M. Allen & Associates Ltd. (DEMA) **[13053]**, **[15623]**
"DEM Says River Needs Cleanup" in Providence Business News (Vol. 28, January 6, 2014, No. 40, pp. 1) **[5582]**, **[5859]**, **[7948]**, **[23175]**, **[25130]**, **[25301]**
DeMers Programming Media Consultants **[13054]**, **[15624]**
Deming-Luna County Chamber of Commerce **[42313]**
Demographic Research Laboratory [47578]
Demographics **[44543]**
Demokratizatsiya: The Journal of Post-Soviet Democratization **[31704]**
Demolition Annual Convention & Expo [4300]
Demopolis Area Chamber of Commerce (DACC) **[36103]**
Demotte Chamber of Commerce **[39534]**
"Denali Asks Consumers to Name Next Moose Tracks Flavor" in Ice Cream Reporter (Vol. 23, August 20, 2010, No. 9, pp. 4) **[8559]**, **[29740]**
Denali Chamber of Commerce **[36227]**
Denison Area Chamber of Commerce (DACC) **[45124]**
Denison Consulting **[28983]**
DenMark Business Solutions Inc. **[2255]**
Dennis G. Glore Inc. (DGG) **[618]**
Denny's Corporation **[14151]**
Dent Doctor **[14580]**
Dental Manufacturers of America [10819]
Dental Trade Alliance (DTA) **[10819]**
The Dentist's Choice, Inc. (TDC) **[11598]**, **[26093]**
Denton Angels **[35275]**, **[45445]**
Denton Chamber of Commerce (DCC) **[45125]**
"Denton to Consider Texas' First Fracking Ban" in Dallas Business Journal (Vol. 37, July 11, 2014, No. 44, pp. 12) **[18562]**, **[23176]**
Denton County Small Business Development Center **[44914]**
"Denver Airport Picks New Contractors As It Struggles to Conclude Previous Relationship" in ConstructionDive (October 14, 2019) **[4051]**, **[19822]**
Denver Botanic Gardens **[7667]**
Denver Business Journal (DBJ) **[37964]**
Denver Design Incubator (DDI) **[37935]**
Denver Metro Chamber of Commerce (DMCC) **[37841]**
Denver Metro Chamber of Commerce - Small Business Development Center (SBDC) **[37802]**
Denver Metro Small Business Development Center **[37784]**
Departamento de Educacion **[47406]**
Department of Administration - Demographic Services Center (DSC) **[47407]**
Department of Business Education of the National Education Association [21316]
Department of Defense - Defense Logistics Agency Aviation - Defense Supply Center Richmond (DSCR) **[47580]**
Department of Defense - Defense Logistics Agency - Defense General Supply Center [47580]
Department of Defense - Defense Logistics Agency - Defense Supply Center Richmond [47580]
Department of Defense - Defense Supply Agency - Defense General Supply Center [47580]
Department of Economic & Community Development - Office of Business and Economic Development **[37982]**
Department of Economic & Community Development - Office of Business and Industry Development [37982]
Department of Environmental Quality [46975], [47014]
Department of Labor - Labor Market Information - Research and Statistics Div. **[47747]**
Department of Labor - Workforce Information and Analysis **[47748]**
Department Stores and Shoe Retailer Directory **[32133]**
DePaul University Coleman Entrepreneurship Center **[39399]**
Deploying Intrusion Detection Systems: Hands-On (Onsite) **[21351]**, **[26190]**
Deploying Microsoft Windows Vista Business Desktops (Onsite) **[33768]**
Deploying Virtual Server and Workstation Technology: Hands-On (Onsite) **[21352]**
Deposit Chamber of Commerce **[42563]**
DER Kitchen **[6957]**, **[44601]**
Derby Chamber of Commerce (DCC) **[39881]**
Derivative Integrated Solutions **[30193]**
Dermott Area Chamber of Commerce (DACC) **[36454]**
Dermott Chamber of Commerce [36454]
Derrick Hayes Founder & CEO of Big Dave's Cheesesteaks **[14054]**
Des Moines Area Community College - Urban Campus (DMACC) **[39830]**
Des Moines Art Center Library **[3366]**
Des Moines SCORE **[39692]**
Des Plaines Chamber of Commerce and Industry **[39150]**
"Describing the Entrepreneurial Profile: The Entrepreneurial Aptitude Test (TAI)" in International Journal of Entrepreneurship and Small Business (Vol. 11, November 1, 2010) **[22546]**, **[31959]**
Desert Hot Springs Chamber of Commerce **[36860]**
Deshler Chamber of Commerce **[43460]**
"Design '07 (Fashion): Haute Flyers" in Canadian Business (Vol. 80, November 19, 2007, No. 23, pp. 68) **[3016]**, **[3104]**, **[6129]**, **[18034]**
"Design '07 (Housing): Prince of the City" in Canadian Business (Vol. 80, November 19, 2007, No. 23, pp. 62) **[4052]**, **[13177]**, **[13431]**
"Design program in Athletic Footwear" in Occupational Outlook Quarterly (Vol. 55, Fall 2011, No. 3, pp. 21) **[2598]**, **[3017]**, **[14674]**, **[15089]**, **[21485]**
"Design Center Shows Quality of Digital Paper" in American Printer (Vol. 128, June 1, 2011, No. 6) **[3305]**, **[12731]**, **[16187]**, **[33846]**
"Design Challenge Seeks to Expand Access" in Philadelphia Business Journal (Vol. 33, April 25, 2014, No. 11, pp. 7) **[19823]**, **[25757]**, **[32134]**
Design Collective Inc. (DCI) **[31070]**
Design Core Detroit (DC3) **[41084]**
Design Cost Data: Cost Estimating Magazine for Design and Construction **[4283]**
Design that Drives: Software Development Requirements **[14858]**
Design Financial Inc. **[35447]**
Design Management Institute (DMI) **[16501]**
Design and Page Layout Skills (Onsite) **[31847]**
Design Professionals of Canada (GDC) **[3288]**
Design Reviews for Effective Product Development (Onsite) **[18873]**
Design Your Own Home **[9069]**
"Designed to Deceive: How Gambling Distorts Reality and Hooks Your Brain" in The Conversation (August 13, 2018) **[7279]**
The Designer's Guide to Marketing and Pricing: How to Win Clients and What to Charge Them **[3018]**, **[20007]**, **[29741]**
Designing and Building Great Web Pages: Hands-On (Onsite) **[21353]**, **[33769]**
Designing Effective Questionnaires: A Step By Step Workshop **[29586]**
"Designing an Office Around Your Company's Goals How Eventbrite Learned That a Workspace Becomes Much More Than an Office Once Your Team Weighs In" in Inc. (Vol. 36, September 2014, No. 7, pp. 122) **[11635]**, **[11732]**, **[33136]**, **[35761]**
"Designing Solutions Around Customer Network Identity Goals" in Journal of Marketing (Vol. 75, March 2011, No. 2, pp. 36) **[20418]**, **[29742]**
Designing Websites for Every Audience **[9126]**, **[16408]**, **[21830]**
"Designing Women? Apparel Apparatchic at Kmart" in Barron's (Vol. 88, March 17, 2008, No. 11, pp. 16) **[260]**, **[3105]**, **[9127]**, **[16409]**, **[20419]**, **[29743]**, **[32135]**
Desjardins Venture Capital **[46910]**
"Deskside Story: As the Latest Buzzword Suggests, PR Firms Are Happy To Drop By" in Inc. (December 2007, pp. 70, 73) **[8652]**, **[12930]**, **[29744]**, **[32505]**
"Desmarais Makes Move into U.S." in Globe & Mail (February 2, 2007, pp. B1) **[19504]**, **[31269]**
Desmond-Fish Library **[6797]**
DeSoto Chamber of Commerce (DCC) **[45126]**
DeSoto County Chamber of Commerce **[38366]**
"Despite Economic Upheaval Generation Y is Still Feeling Green: RSA Canada Survey" in CNW Group (October 28, 2010) **[5583]**, **[5860]**, **[20843]**, **[23177]**, **[33997]**
"Despite FDA Approval, Heart Test No Boom for BG Medical" in Boston Business Journal (Vol. 31, June 17, 2011, No. 21, pp. 1) **[9455]**, **[10824]**, **[25758]**, **[29176]**
"Despite Higher Prices, Organic Food Gains" in MMR (Vol. 29, February 20, 2012, No. 4, pp. 39) **[8014]**, **[17029]**, **[18035]**
Destin Area Chamber of Commerce **[38367]**
Destination Flagstaff **[36327]**
Destination Guide **[46393]**
Destination Moosehead Lake (DML) **[40274]**
"Destination Wedding Giveaway: A Custom Instagram Book" in Benzinga.com (October 29, 2011) **[1969]**, **[29745]**
"Detecting and Combating Employee Theft" in Wolters Kluwer Expert Insights (Mar 20, 2020) **[22343]**, **[32384]**
"Determining Your Food Truck Employee Needs" in Mobile-Cuisine.com (September 8, 2020) **[6971]**, **[22132]**, **[26539]**
Determining Your Small Business Break Even Point **[16795]**
Deterring Social Engineering Attacks: Resisting Human Deception (Onsite) **[26191]**
Detroit Association for Business Economics (DABE) **[40795]**
Detroit Association of Realtors **[13088]**
Detroit Auto Show [11463]
Detroit Boat Show **[1234]**, **[10619]**, **[15117]**
Detroit Chinese Business Association (DCBA) **[30261]**
Detroit Creative Corridor Center [41084]
"Detroit Deli Named Among Best Sandwidh Shops in America" in Click On Detroit (July 23, 2019) **[4881]**
Detroit Economic Club (DEC) **[33454]**
Detroit Hives (DH) **[1434]**
"Detroit Hosts Conferences on Green Building, IT, Finance" in Crain's Detroit Business (Vol. 25, June 1, 2009, No. 22, pp. 9) **[5584]**, **[5861]**, **[6357]**, **[15851]**, **[23178]**, **[26259]**, **[30339]**, **[35046]**

3220 Small Business Sourcebook • 42nd Edition

Detroit Kitchen Connect (DKC) **[41085]**
Detroit Lakes Regional Chamber of Commerce **[41222]**
"Detroit Pawn Shop to be Reality TV Venue" in UPI NewsTrack (July 10, 2010) **[11917]**
"Detroit Pistons, Corporate Sponsors Support Small Businesses Through Grants and Promotions" in Small Business Trends(December 3, 2022) **[33557]**
Detroit Public Library [41139]
Detroit Public Library Business, Science and Technology Department **[41139]**
Detroit Regional Chamber (DRC) **[40901]**
"Detroit Residential Market Slows; Bright Spots Emerge" in Crain's Detroit Business (Vol. 24, October 6, 2008, No. 40, pp. 11) **[4053], [11026], [12883], [13178], [13432], [18036], [20844], [24970]**
Detroit SCORE **[40822]**
Detroit Tooling Association [10423]
Detroit Top Startups **[34587]**
Detroit Treasury Management Association [40798]
Detroiter **[40902]**
"Develop the Finance and Accounting Skills Every Entrepreneur Needs" in Entrepreneur (Feb. 9, 2022) **[16796]**
"Developer Backs Out of Major Bastrop Project" in Austin Business JournalInc. (Vol. 28, December 19, 2008, No. 40, pp. 1) **[13179], [13433], [32136]**
"Developer Plans to Build Verizon Store in Woodstock" in Northwest Herald (July 20, 2019) **[2730]**
"Developer To Use New Owasso Senior Care Center as Template for More Services, Expansion" in Journal Record (May 23, 2012) **[1027], [4054], [25759]**
"Developer Tries to Bring Homes to Buda" in Austin Business JournalInc. (Vol. 28, December 26, 2008, No. 41, pp. 1) **[4055], [13180], [13434], [13708]**
"Developers Accommodate Need for Rooms" in Puget Sound Business Journal (Vol. 35, September 19, 2014, No. 22, pp. 8) **[4056], [8382], [9456]**
"Developers Give Big to Stephanie Rawlings-Blake Bid for Mayor" in Baltimore Business Journal (Vol. 29, August 26, 2011, No. 16, pp. 1) **[4057], [13181], [13435], [31687]**
"Developers Give City Dwellings a Modern Spin" in Crain's Cleveland Business (Vol. 28, November 5, 2007, No. 44, pp. 18) **[4058], [13182], [13436]**
"Developers Move Forward Along Seattle's Waterfront" in Puget Sound Business Journal (Vol. 35, July 25, 2014, No. 14, pp. 4) **[4059], [13183], [13437]**
"Developers Poised to Pull Trigers" in Boston Business Journal (Vol. 30, November 12, 2010, No. 42, pp. 1) **[4060], [13184], [13438], [13778], [18037]**
"Developers Tout Benefits of Federal Tax Breaks" in Business First of Buffalo (Vol. 30, March 14, 2014, No. 26, pp. 4) **[880], [4061], [13439], [24971], [34774]**
DeveloperTown **[39637]**
Developing AJAX Web Applications: Hands-On - Enhancing the Web User Experience (Onsite) **[22984]**
Developing a Balanced Scorecard for Business & Government **[19438]**
Developing Dynamic Presentation Skills **[17555]**
Developing Effective Business Conversation Skills (Onsite) **[17556]**
Developing Effective Communications Skills (Onsite) **[17557]**
Developing Effective Software Estimation Techniques (Onsite) **[21354], [33770]**
Developing Effective Training **[21355]**
Developing High-Performance SQL Server Databases: Hands-On Onsite Meeting **[26192]**
Developing Into a Powerful Leader (Onsite) **[28315]**
"Developing the Next Generation of Rosies" in Employee Benefit News (Vol. 25, November 1, 2011, No. 14, pp. 36) **[26921], [28541], [35762]**
Developing Procedures, Policies and Documentation (Onsite) **[17837]**
"Developing a Small Business Educational Program for Growing Rural Businesses" in Journal of Small Business Strategy (Vol. 31, December 1, 2021, No. 4, 50-56) **[22547], [34499]**
Developing SQL Queries for SQL Server: Hands-On (Onsite) **[21356], [33771]**
Developing Web E-Commerce Applications **[21772]**
Developing a Web Site: Hands-On (Onsite) **[22985]**
Developing Your Analytical Skills: How to Research and Present Information (Onsite) **[19439]**
Developing Your Emotional Intelligence (Onsite) **[28316]**
Developments in Business Simulation and Experiential Exercises [32933]
Developments in Business Simulation and Experiential Learning **[32933]**
DevelopWell **[28984], [34664], [35920]**
Devices & Diagnostics Letter [10862]
Devils Lake Area Chamber of Commerce **[43292]**
"The Devolution of Home-Electronics Stores" in Philadelphia Business Journal (Vol. 28, June 8, 2012, No. 17, pp. 1) **[4391], [19824], [20008], [32137], [33998]**
Devon North Town Business and Professional Association [39335]
Devries & Associates, P.C. **[31611], [33053]**
DeVry University, Chicago Campus Library **[3592]**
DeVry University, Columbus Campus Library **[3593]**
DeVry University - James E. Lovan Library **[3594]**
DeVry University Library **[3469]**
DeVry University Library Services **[3595]**
Dewar Sloan L.L.C. **[33663]**
"DeWind Delivering Turbines to Texas Wind Farm" in Professional Services Close-Up (September 25, 2011) **[5585], [5862], [23179], [29177]**
DeWitt Area Chamber of Commerce (DACC) **[40903]**
Dexter Chamber of Commerce (DCC) **[41554]**
"Dexter Gauntlett Gauges the Wind" in Business Journal Portland (Vol. 30, January 31, 2014, No. 48, pp. 6) **[5586], [26540], [29178]**
DFJ Frontier **[35465]**
DFJ Mercury Venture Partners [45459]
DFW Capital Partners Inc. **[42735]**
DFW Excellerator **[45511]**
"DFW Inventors Psyched for New, Local Patent Office" in Dallas Business Journal (Vol. 35, August 3, 2012, No. 47, pp. 1) **[27859]**
"DHR Hires Carr for Sports Group" in Crain's Detroit Business (Vol. 25, June 8, 2009, No. 23, pp. 5) **[6104], [15146], [28542]**
"DIA Contract Sets a Record for Denver Minority, Woman-Owned Business" in Denver Business Journal (Vol. 65, February 21, 2014, No. 41) **[4062], [8383], [25131], [30340], [33137], [35763]**
Diagnostic & Medical Laboratories Industry in the US - Market Research Report **[10915]**
Dialogue on Diversity **[20694]**
Dialogue Magazine **[11924], [16736]**
Diamond Council of America (DCA) **[9962]**
Diamond State Ventures (DSV) **[36523]**
Diamondhead Ventures L.P. **[37347]**
D'Iberville-St. Martin Chamber of Commerce **[41397]**
Dickenson County Chamber of Commerce **[45854]**
Dickey's Barbecue Pit **[14152]**
Dickinson Area Chamber of Commerce (DACC) **[43293]**
Dickinson and Wheelock P.C. (D&W) **[18750]**
Dickinson's FDA Review **[25610]**
"Dick's Sporting Goods Distances Itself further from Firearms" in USA Today (October 6, 2019) **[7833], [15090]**
Dickson County Chamber of Commerce **[44738]**
Dictionary of Finance, Investment and Banking **[6358], [9457], [23843]**
Dictionary of Real Estate Terms **[6359], [8901], [11027], [13185], [13440], [13779], [18563], [27257]**
Die Casting Engineer (DCE) **[10450]**
Dierks Chamber of Commerce (DCC) **[36455]**
Diet Center **[16513]**
Dietary Managers Association [11560]
"Dietetic Technicians Bring Nutrition To the Table" in Occupational Outlook Quarterly (Vol. 58, Summer 2014, No. 2, pp. 26) **[11573]**
Dietetics in Health Care Communities (DHCC) **[11564]**
Dietitians of Canada **[11565]**
The Difference Between Good and Great Supervisors **[28317]**
"The Difference Between Management and Project Management" in Contractor (Vol. 57, February 2010, No. 2, pp. 30) **[59], [17494], [28543]**
"The Difference Between a DBA, Sole Proprietor, Corporation and LLC" in Small Business Trends (June 9, 2022) **[27175]**
"A Different Kind of Lender Can Get You the Loan You Need" in Small Business Trends(December 26, 2022) **[33558]**
Different Thinking **[33559]**
Different Twist Pretzel Co. **[3862]**
Digest **[39731]**
"Digging Dallas-Fort Worth: How Top 10 Major Construction Projects Will Change North Texas" in Dallas Business Journal (Vol. 37, May 23, 2014, No. 37, pp. 4) **[881], [4063], [8204], [8902]**
"Digging Deep for Gold: David Iben, Manager, Nuveen Tradewinds Value Opportunities Fund" in Barron's (Vol. 88, March 24, 2008, No. 12, pp. 49) **[6360], [9458], [22548], [23844]**
"Digital Duplication" in Crain's Cleveland Business (Vol. 28, October 1, 2007, No. 39, pp. 3) **[18038], [18936], [26260], [31270]**
Digital Harvest Capital **[42863]**
Digital Leisure Inc. (DL) **[46857]**
"Digital Marketing 101" in PlanetLaundry (Nov. 2, 2021) **[10168]**
"Digital Marketing in 2020 - 7 Reasons Why Small Businesses Need It" in Marketo Blog. **[29523], [34712]**
Digital Marketing for Christmas Tree Farms: 4 Online Growth Strategies **[2936]**
Digital Marketing for Dummies **[29746]**
"Digital Marketing: Integrating Strategy and Tactics with Values, A Guidebook for Executives, Managers, and Students" **[21831], [23000], [26261], [28544], [29747], [30957]**
"Digital Marketing Trends for Gyms in 2019" in Glofox blog (July 26, 2019) **[12411], [29748]**
Digital Media Center (DMC) **[37565]**
"Digital New Ventures: Assessing the Benefits of Digitalization in Entrepreneurship" in Journal of Small Business Strategy (May 27, 2020) **[33696]**
Digital Photography Techniques (Onsite) **[21357]**
"Digital-Physical Mashups: To Consumers, the Real and Virtual Worlds Are One. The Same Should Go For Your Company" in Harvard Business Review (Vol. 92, September 2014, No. 9, pp. 84) **[20009], [20420], [21486], [28545]**
"Digital Power Management and the PMBus" in Canadian Electronics (Vol. 23, June-July 2008, No. 4, pp. 8) **[4392], [26262], [29179], [30709]**
Digital Printing Industry in the US - Market Research Report **[11828], [12763]**
"Digital Printing Walks the Plank" in American Printer (Vol. 128, August 1, 2011, No. 8) **[3306], [12732], [16188], [29180]**
"Digital Publishers Team Up to Compete for More Video Ad Dollars" in The Wall Street Journal (September 23, 2019) **[261]**
"Digital Realty Routes $50 Million for Data Center Improvements" in St.Louis Business Journal (Vol. 33, September 14, 2012, No. 3, pp. 1) **[3498], [13186]**
Digital Scanning for Production **[33772]**
digitalundivided **[30262], [35276], [35594]**
Dilbert and the Cubicle vs the Open Office **[31034]**
Dimmit County Chamber of Commerce **[45127]**
Dine Brands Global, Inc. **[14153]**
DineEquity Inc. [14153]
The Ding King Training Institute Inc. **[1140]**
"Dining Notes: The Salty Fig is Jacksonville's Newest Food Truck" in Florida Times-Union (July 13, 2012) **[3820], [6950], [23578], [30494]**
Dinuba Chamber of Commerce **[36861]**
Dippin' Dots Franchising, L.L.C. (DDF) **[8616]**
"Direct Care Workforce: LeadingAge Applauds New Legislation" in LeadingAge (September 24, 2019) **[1028]**
Direct Link **[14493]**
Direct Marketing Association Annual Conference & Exhibition **[10471]**
Direct Marketing Association of Detroit (DMAD) **[29573]**
Direct Marketing to Business - Fall **[30170]**
"Direct Recovery Associates Debt Collection Agency Beats Industry Record" in Internet Wire (June 24, 2010) **[4782], [18564], [20275], [27528]**
"Direct Sales Evolving to 'Hi-Touch, Hi-Tech' Approach" in Providence Business News (Vol. 29, June 2, 2014, No. 9, pp. 4) **[32506]**
Direct Selling Association (DSA) **[32427]**
Direct Selling Education Foundation (DSEF) **[32428]**
Direct-to-Consumer Retailing - US - January 2021 **[32334]**
Direct-to-Retail (DTR) Strategies that Win **[17466]**
"Direct to Your Mailbox" in Silicon Valley/San Jose Business Journal (Vol. 30, August 10, 2012, No. 20, pp. 1) **[29749]**
DirectBuy **[32363]**
Direction for Business **[41850]**
Directions **[5107]**
The Director: Official Publication of the National Funeral Directors Association **[7218]**
Directors Guild of America--Member Directory **[6180]**
Directors Guild of Canada [6167]
"Directors May Revise HCA Collection Agency Regulations" in Standard-Speaker (May 20, 2012) **[4783], [20276], [25302]**
Directory of Apparel Specialty Stores **[2849], [3106]**
Directory of Bonded Collectors [4764]
Directory and Community Guide **[39151]**
Directory of Contract Service Firms [14979]
Directory of Contract Staffing Firms **[14979]**
Directory of Corporate Affiliations/U.S. Public [24640]
Directory of Department Stores [32133]
Directory of Drug Store & HBC Chains [5155]
Directory of Foodservice Distributors [2684], [7790], [14038]
Directory of Freight Forwarders and Custom House Brokers **[7035]**
Directory of Ingredients, Equipment and Packaging **[2544]**
Directory of International and Regional Organizations Conducting Standards-Related Activities **[10916]**
Directory of Libraries in Canada [8836]
Directory of Listed Plumbing Products **[12626]**

Small Business Sourcebook • 42nd Edition **3221**

Directory Master Index

The Directory of Mail Order Catalogs **[10462]**
Directory of Office Building Properties [45282]
Directory of Plumbing Research Recommendations [12626]
Directory of Professional Genealogists and Related Services [7353]
Directory of Small Press/Magazine Editors & Publishers **[1651]**, **[11977]**
The Directory of Venture Capital & Private Equity Firms **[6361]**, **[9459]**, **[35334]**
"Dirty Schools the Norm Since Privatizing Custodians: Principals" in Chicago Reporter (September 8, 2014) **[2065]**
Disa Conus - Defense Information Systems Agency [39388]
Disability Income Concepts Inc. (DIC) **[35448]**
"Disabled Inventors: Necessity Is the Mother of Invention" in Legal Zoom (March 27, 2023) **[27860]**
"Disagree With Your Client? 11 Ways to Find a Positive and Effective Solution" in Small Business Trends (August 21, 2022) **[28546]**
"Disappearing Act" in Globe & Mail (April 21, 2007, pp. B1) **[6362]**, **[9460]**
"The Disappearing Chimney Sweeps of Paris" in The New York Times (February 18, 2019) **[2920]**
Disaster Kleenup International (DKI) **[4832]**
Disaster Recovery Planning: Ensuring Business Continuity (Onsite) **[18874]**, **[26193]**
"Discipline In Your Business" in South Florida Business Journal (Vol. 34, June 6, 2014, No. 46, pp. 10) **[17657]**, **[19505]**, **[19735]**, **[22133]**
Disciplined Entrepreneurship Workbook **[22549]**, **[34500]**
"The Discomfort Zone: How Leaders Turn Difficult Conversations Into Breakthroughs" **[17658]**, **[22134]**
"Discount Beers Take Fizz Out Of Molson" in Globe & Mail (February 10, 2006, pp. B3) **[1327]**, **[6363]**, **[9461]**, **[10318]**, **[29181]**
Discount Sport Nutrition (DSN) **[11599]**, **[32364]**
Discover Boating Miami International Boat Show [10623]
Discover the Chamber **[39732]**
Discover the New "I Wrote a Book" and How to Grow Your Brand with Carolina Flores **[17467]**
Discover the Power of Crystal Reports **[16766]**
"Discover the Wedding Location of Your Dreams" in Benzinga.com (December 24, 2011) **[1970]**, **[8384]**
Discovering Your Brand Identity **[17426]**, **[33521]**, **[35706]**
Discovery **[43461]**
Discovery Capital **[46696]**
Discovery Center FABLAB **[46319]**
"Discovery Communications: Don't Sell, But Don't Buy" in Workforce Management (Vol. 88, December 14, 2009, No. 13, pp. 17) **[8903]**, **[17298]**, **[25760]**, **[27258]**
Discovery Foundation **[46705]**
Discovery Guide **[41223]**
"Discovery Networks" in Brandweek (Vol. 49, April 21, 2008, No. 16, pp. SR9) **[262]**, **[6181]**, **[15592]**, **[18039]**, **[28547]**, **[29750]**, **[32507]**
Discovery Parks [46714]
"Discrete Wavelet Transform-Based Time Series Analysis and Mining" in ACM Computing Surveys (Vol. 43, Summer 2011, No. 2, pp. 6) **[3426]**, **[3499]**, **[3618]**
Discrimination and Sexual Harassment Policies **[20564]**
"Disguised Age Bias at the Revel Casino?" in Philadelphia Business Journal (Vol. 31, February 17, 2012, No. 1, pp. 1) **[8385]**, **[20565]**
"Dish Network to Buy EchoStar's Broadcast Satellite Business" in The Wall Street Journal (May 20, 2019) **[14344]**, **[31271]**
"Dish's Charlie Ergen Sees Nothing Good in Comcast-Time Warner Merger" in Denver Business Journal (Vol. 65, February 21, 2014, No. 41) **[2454]**, **[9128]**, **[31272]**
"Disney's High Hopes for Duffy" in Canadian Business (Vol. 83, October 12, 2010, No. 17, pp. 14) **[15789]**, **[19825]**, **[27529]**, **[30710]**
"Dispelling Rocky Mountain Myths Key to Wellness" in Employee Benefit News (Vol. 25, November 1, 2011, No. 14, pp. 12) **[21487]**, **[25761]**, **[26922]**
"Disrupt Yourself: Four Principles for Finding the Career Path You Really Want" in Harvard Business Review (Vol. 90, July-August 2012, No. 7-8, pp. 147). **[22550]**, **[28548]**
Disrupting Male-Dominated Fields **[35897]**
"The Disruptive Future of Interior Design Is Here" in Inc. (July 14, 2017) **[9033]**
"Disruptive Innovators: Commonground is Transforming the Advertising Landscape by Living at the Intersection of Culture, Creativity, Content, and Technology" in Black Enterprise (Vol. 44, June 2014, No. 10, pp. 82) **[263]**, **[29751]**, **[30555]**, **[31273]**
Disruptors for Good: Biofuel Cells and the Future of Sustainable Batteries **[23425]**
Disruptors for Good: Building a Unicorn Tech Company and the Importance of a Co-Founder **[34588]**
Disruptors for Good: Creating an Entrepreneurial Blueprint for the Next Generation of Farmers **[17156]**, **[34419]**
Disruptors for Good: Innovative Approach to Upskilling Overlooked and Hidden Talent **[27100]**, **[34420]**
Disruptors for Good: Regenerative Farming, Ethical Supply Chains, and Future of Plastic Bottles **[23426]**, **[34421]**
Distilled Spirits Council of the United States (DISCUS) **[1311]**, **[1374]**, **[10343]**
The Distinct Advantage (Onsite) **[32442]**
"Distributed Data Management Using mapReduce" in ACM Computing Surveys (Vol. 46, Fall 2014, No. 3, pp. 31) **[3500]**, **[3619]**
"Distribution 101 for Entrepreneurs" on Score.org (June 21, 2019) **[20620]**
Distribution Business Management Association (DBMA) **[20601]**
Distribution Center Management **[20666]**
"Distribution Dilemma: Standard Process of Tariff Revisions Across States Can Make Discoms Viable" in Best's Review (Vol. 113, September 2012, No. 5, pp. 15) **[8904]**, **[27259]**, **[32508]**
Distribution Research and Education Foundation [20603], [20675], [35483]
District of Columbia Office of the Deputy Mayor Planning and Economic Development (DMPED) **[38160]**
District of Columbia Office of Planning (SDC) - State Data Center **[47408]**
District of Columbia Small Business Development Center (DCSBDC) **[33455]**, **[38150]**
District of Columbia Small Business Development Center at University of District of Columbia (DC SBDC) **[38156]**
"Disunion in the House: the Steep Price We Pay" in Philadelphia Business Journal (Vol. 33, March 28, 2014, No. 7, pp. 4) **[4064]**, **[18565]**, **[26541]**, **[35186]**
Disuptors for Good: Finding Ethical and Sustainable Manufacturers and Suppliers **[34422]**
"Ditch the Discount: 10 Incentives to Drive Sales and Earn New Customers" in Small Business Trends (Jan. 30, 2022) **[32509]**
"Ditch the Pet Store! MindJolt SGN and The Humane Society of the United States Unleash Fluff Friends Rescue" in Benzinga.com (January 4, 2012) **[578]**, **[690]**, **[7101]**, **[14772]**, **[34303]**
"Ditch the Rental Car: A New Way to Arrive in Style" in Inc. (Vol. 33, September 2011, No. 7, pp. 54) **[11108]**, **[13780]**, **[24350]**
Dittrick Medical History Center (DMHC) **[8161]**
Divas Doing Business: What the Guidebooks Don't Tell You About Being A Woman Entrepreneur **[22551]**, **[35764]**
Diverse & Engaged **[30639]**
Diverse Strategies (DSI) **[37671]**
Diversified Health Resources Inc. **[2256]**, **[11533]**, **[20181]**, **[26085]**
Diversified Product Supplier (DPS) **[15322]**
Diversifying Your Business Revenue **[17468]**
Diversity Awareness (Onsite) **[30522]**
"Diversity in Business Awards: Minority Businessperson of the Year and Diversity Corporation of the Year Finalists" in ColoradoBiz (Vol. 30, July 2012, No. 7, pp. 32) **[20421]**, **[30341]**, **[30556]**, **[34304]**
The Diversity Code: Unlock the Secrets to Making Differences Work in the Real World **[18566]**, **[25303]**, **[26923]**, **[28549]**, **[30557]**
Diversity, Equity, and Inclusion in the Workplace in 2022: Best Practices **[30342]**, **[30558]**
Diversity and Inclusion (D&I) **[30410]**, **[30624]**
Diversity and Inclusion Matters: Tactics and Tools to Inspire Equity and Game-Changing Performance **[26924]**
Diversity Information Resources, Inc. (DIR) **[30263]**
"Diversity Knocks" in Canadian Business (Vol. 83, October 12, 2010, No. 17, pp. 62) **[27530]**, **[30559]**
Diversity Services Group **[30640]**
DiversityInc **[30437]**
Divine Wisdom at Work: 10 Universal Principles for Enlightened Entrepreneurs **[22552]**, **[24649]**
Diving Equipment and Marketing Association (DEMA) **[15236]**
"Diving Into Internet Marketing" in American Agent and Broker (Vol. 81, December 2009, No. 12, pp. 24) **[9129]**, **[19826]**, **[29752]**
Division for Small Business - Business Service Ombudsman [42421]
Dixie Business Center (DBC) **[40216]**
Dixie County Chamber of Commerce **[38368]**
Dixon Chamber of Commerce [39152]
Dixon Chamber of Commerce & Main Street **[39152]**
Dixon District Chamber of Commerce **[36862]**
DJ Times: The International Magazine for the Professional Mobile and Club DJ **[4964]**
DJT Consulting Group L.L.C. **[20593]**, **[27135]**
DLA Piper LLP US Library **[5766]**
DMA Nonprofit Federation [1048]
"DMW Gets MBE Certification" in Wireless News (July 29, 2012) **[3620]**, **[5587]**, **[15221]**, **[20104]**, **[30343]**, **[35765]**
DN Capital **[37348]**
DN Partners L.L.C. **[39353]**
DNA: A Journal of Molecular Biology [32868]
DNA and Cell Biology **[32868]**
"DNERO & Bits of Stock Team Up to Offer Wealth-Building Rewards to Hispanic Market" in Minority Business Entrepreneur (March 7, 2022) **[9462]**, **[30344]**
"Do Check-Cashing Services Provide a Banking Alternative?" in The Simple Dollar (March 11, 2019) **[2836]**
"Do Coin Shops Have a Future?" in Numismatic News (June 1, 2015) **[3236]**, **[9130]**
*"Do Cool Sh*t: Quit Your Day Job, Start Your Own Business, and Live Happily Ever After"* **[2995]**, **[11556]**, **[12525]**, **[18040]**, **[22376]**, **[26165]**, **[27820]**, **[35502]**
"Do Fair Value Adjustments Influence Dividend Policy?" in Accounting and Business Research (Vol. 41, Spring 2011, No. 2, pp. 51) **[60]**, **[1753]**, **[15375]**, **[16797]**
"Do It Best Celebrates New Products, Expands Paint Options at 2019 Fall Market" in Hardware Retailing (October 21, 2019) **[7919]**
"Do-It-Yourself Portfolio Management" in Barron's (Vol. 89, July 13, 2009, No. 28, pp. 25) **[6364]**, **[9131]**, **[9463]**, **[16410]**, **[21832]**, **[23845]**
"Do Private Tutors Require Insurance?" in Superprof blog (Oct. 10, 2020) **[16130]**
Do Professional Organizers Need Insurance? **[12829]**
"Do the Right Thing" in Contractor (Vol. 56, December 2009, No. 12, pp. 16) **[480]**, **[12627]**, **[33138]**
"Do Small Businesses Need NDAs?" in Legal Zoom (March 27, 2023) **[16554]**
"Do Social Deal Sites Really Work? A Theme Park Chain Considers Whether the Boost In Ticket Sales Is Worth the Trouble" in Harvard Business Review (Vol. 90, May 2012, No. 5, pp. 139) **[603]**, **[20422]**, **[29753]**, **[32510]**
"Do You Have A Retirement Parachute?" in Barron's (Vol. 88, July 7, 2008, No. 27, pp. 32) **[17299]**, **[18937]**, **[20845]**, **[26542]**
Do You Have a Marketing Problem? **[24804]**
Do You Have Too Many Services or Offers? **[24805]**
Do You Need a License to Start a Tutoring Business? **[16115]**
"Do You Need to Reinvent Your Managers?" in Rental Product News (Vol. 33, June 2011) **[13781]**, **[28550]**
"Do You Own a Small Business? Here's How to Control Your Social Security and Medicare Tax Bills" in MarketWatch (May 21, 2019) **[34242]**
Doc Green's Gourmet Salad and Sandwich Bar **[4898]**
Dockery House Publishing Inc. **[45589]**
"Docs Might Hold Cure for Baltimore-Area Real Estate, Banks" in Baltimore Business Journal (Vol. 28, November 5, 2010, No. 26, pp. 1) **[4065]**, **[11028]**, **[13187]**, **[13441]**, **[13782]**, **[25762]**, **[33999]**
"The Doctor Is In" in Canadian Business (Vol. 80, February 12, 2007, No. 4, pp. 38) **[30711]**, **[32745]**
"Doctor: J & J Alerted in '06 to Procedure Risks" in Pittsburgh Business Times (Vol. 33, June 6, 2014, No. 47, pp. 4) **[10825]**, **[10917]**, **[25304]**, **[25763]**
"Dr. Melanie Brown" in Women in Business (Vol. 65, Winter 2013, No. 3, pp. 40) **[26263]**, **[35766]**
"Doctor Shortage Continues to Plague Region" in Business First of Buffalo (Vol. 30, April 11, 2014, No. 30, pp. 6) **[25305]**, **[25764]**, **[27260]**
Dr. Vinyl and Associates Ltd. **[1141]**, **[14581]**
Doctor's Associates, Inc. [4922], [8121]
Doctors Management L.L.C. (DM) **[26086]**
The Doctors Touch **[14582]**
"Doctors Try 1st CRISPR Editing in the Body for Blindness" in Associated Press (March 4, 2020) **[25765]**
Document Management Industries Association [11661]
Document Preparation Services Industry in the US - Market Research Report **[2380]**, **[4944]**, **[14317]**
Document Strategy Forum **[10684]**
Documentaristes du Canada **[6163]**
Documentary Organization of Canada [6163]
"DocuSign Raises $85 Million for Electronic Signatures" in San Francisco Business Times (Vol. 28, March 7, 2014, No. 33, pp. 6) **[18041]**, **[21833]**, **[27531]**, **[31274]**
Dodge City Area Chamber of Commerce, Inc. (DCACC) **[39882]**
"Dodge Frets Over Flood of Fast Money" in Globe & Mail (May 2, 2007, pp. B1) **[18042]**, **[24650]**
Dodgeville Area Chamber of Commerce **[46394]**
doejo **[39400]**
"Does America Really Need Manufacturing? Yes, When Production Is Closely Tied to Innovation" in Harvard Business Review (Vol. 90, March 2012, No. 3, pp. 94) **[29182]**, **[30712]**, **[31960]**, **[32746]**

3222 Small Business Sourcebook • 42nd Edition

Master Index Dream

"Does Branding Really Matter for a Small Business?" in Forbes (June 10, 2021) **[17439]**
"Does Diversity Pay Dividends?" in Canadian Business (Vol. 87, October 2014, No. 10, pp. 89) **[6365]**, **[9464]**, **[35767]**
"Does Farming Drive Fish Disease?" in The Scientist (April 19, 2017) **[6781]**
"Does the Gig Economy Have a Future in Grocery Stores?" in Grocery Dive (November 7, 2019) **[7731]**, **[11733]**, **[31134]**
"Does the Hierarchical Position of the Buyer Make a Difference? The Influence of Perceived Adaptive Selling on Customer Satisfaction and Loyalty in a Business-To-Business Context" in Journal of Business & Industrial Marketing (Vol. 29, June 2014, No. 5) **[20423]**, **[32511]**
"Does It Make Financial Sense to Hire a Cleaning Service?" in U.S. News & World Report (March 7 2016) **[5076]**
"Does Rudeness Really Matter? The Effects of Rudeness on Task Performance and Helpfulness" in Academy of Management Journal (Vol. 50, No. 5, October 1, 2007, pp. 1181) **[17659]**, **[22135]**, **[28551]**
"Does Spray Tanning Have Side Effects?" in U.S. News & World Report (July 8, 2019) **[15259]**, **[31961]**
"Does Staples Rebranding Foretell the Fall of Another Retailer to Private Equity?" in Forbes (April 10, 2019) **[11664]**
"Does Your Business Really Need a Facebook Page?" in Legal Zoom (March 22, 2023) **[29524]**, **[29754]**
"Does Your Dog Need Obedience School?" in WebMD **[12139]**
"Does Your Home-Based Business Need Business Insurance?" in Legal Zoom (March 22, 2023) **[26775]**, **[27261]**, **[32988]**
"Does Your Home or Building Need Radon Testing?" in U.S. News & World Report (February 24, 2016) **[13069]**, **[25306]**
"Does Your Website Violate Copyright Law? in Legal Zoom (March 27, 2023) **[16411]**, **[27861]**
"Dog Behaviors Like Aggression and Fearfulness are Linked to Breed Genetics" in Science News (October 1, 2019) **[646]**
"Dog Days and Stimulus Fatigue" in Barron's (Vol. 92, August 25, 2012, No. 38, pp. M10) **[4784]**, **[9465]**, **[20277]**, **[25307]**
The Dog Gurus **[12266]**
D.O.G. Hotels [12113]
"Dog Marketplace: Pet Waste Products Pick Up Sales" in Pet Product News (Vol. 66, September 2012, No. 9, pp. 58) **[5588]**, **[5863]**, **[12195]**, **[23180]**, **[29183]**, **[30713]**
Dog Miami Beach LLC **[12113]**
Dog Obedience School Business Plan **[12140]**
The Dog Stop **[12114]**, **[12155]**
Dog Walking Services in the US - Industry Market Research Report **[12264]**
The Dog Wizard **[12156]**
Dog Wizard Academy [12156]
Dog World: Active Dogs, Active People **[12234]**
Doggies Gone Wild **[12115]**
Dogs Love Running! Inc. **[12269]**
Dogs Rule Resort **[12116]**
"The Dogs of TSX" in Canadian Business (Vol. 81, Summer 2008, No. 9, pp. 77) **[6366]**, **[9466]**, **[18043]**, **[18938]**, **[20846]**, **[23846]**
Dogtopia **[12117]**
"'Doing Business As': How to Register a DBA Name" in Business News Daily (February 21, 2023) **[27176]**
Doing Business in Memphis **[44864]**
Doing Business in Memphis: A Directory of Business and Industry (Tennessee) **[44860]**
Doing Company Research: A Resource Guide **[18464]**
"DOL Stiffens Child Labor Penalties" in HR Specialist (Vol. 8, September 2010, No. 9, pp. 2) **[18567]**, **[25308]**, **[26925]**
Dolan Springs Information **[36328]**
Doll Capital Management (DCM) **[37349]**
Dollar Castle Inc. **[2648]**
"A Dollar, a Dream, and a Cup of Joe" in Business Review Albany (Vol. 41, July 25, 2014, No. 18, pp. 6) **[4432]**, **[7280]**
"Dollar General Selects GSI Commerce to Launch Its eCommerce Business" in Benzinga.com (October 29, 2011) **[1071]**, **[21834]**, **[29755]**, **[32138]**, **[33139]**
Dollar Rent A Car **[1170]**
"Dollar Store Growth Presents New Challenge to Larger Mass Retailers" in Pet Product News (Vol. 66, August 2012, No. 8, pp. 4) **[19827]**, **[20010]**, **[32139]**
"Dollar Thrifty Adds Franchises" in Journal Record (December 7, 2010) **[13783]**, **[18044]**, **[24351]**
Dollar Thrifty Automotive Group Canada Inc. **[13854]**
"Dollar Tree Store to Open Mid-July in Shelby Mall" in La Crosse Tribune (June 20, 2010) **[18045]**, **[32140]**
Dolores Chamber of Commerce **[37842]**
Domain Associates L.L.C. **[42210]**
Dominari Holdings Inc. **[22028]**, **[35449]**
"Dominion Electric Supply Inks Lease at Ashburn Crossing Business Park" in Loudoun Times-Mirror (August 1, 2019) **[5413]**
Dominion Energy Innovation Center (DEIC) **[45947]**
Dominion Resources Innovation Center **[45948]**
Domino's Pizza of Canada Ltace. **[12546]**
Domino's Pizza, Inc. **[12547]**
Don Phin, Esq. **[18744]**, **[20545]**, **[21709]**, **[28985]**, **[30194]**, **[33664]**, **[35962]**
Don Ryan Center for Innovation (DRCI) **[44602]**
"Don't Do Your Business Taxes Before Reading This" in Small Business Trends(February 7, 2023) **[34775]**
Don't Hire a Franchise Consultant if You See These Warning Signs! **[24352]**
"Don't Let Your Small Business Fall Victim to These Four Scams" in Forbes (August 16, 2022) **[19259]**
Donaldsonville Chamber of Commerce **[40165]**
Donalsonville/Seminole County Chamber of Commerce **[38723]**
Doniphan Chamber of Commerce and Economic Development Council [41621]
Doniphan County Chamber of Commerce (DCCC) **[39883]**
Donnelly Area Chamber of Commerce **[38913]**
"Don't Ask To Get Married Before Courting Your Prospect" in South Florida Business Journal (Vol. 34, June 13, 2014, No. 47, pp. 21) **[17660]**, **[32512]**
"Don't Bet Against The House" in Barron's (Vol. 88, July 14, 2008, No. 28, pp. 20) **[6367]**, **[9467]**, **[20847]**, **[23847]**, **[27532]**
"The Don't Do Lists" in Inc. (Vol. 33, October 2011, No. 8, pp. 65) **[17661]**, **[22136]**, **[22553]**, **[32513]**
"Don't Do This!" in Planet Laundry (January 30, 2015) **[5234]**
"Don't Fear the Phone" in Senior Market Advisor (Vol. 13, October 2012, No. 10, pp. 50) **[6368]**, **[9468]**, **[34983]**
"Don't Hang Up On FairPoint" in Barron's (Vol. 88, July 7, 2008, No. 27, pp. M5) **[2731]**, **[6369]**, **[9469]**, **[23848]**, **[33140]**
"Don't' Hate the Cable Guy" in Saint Louis Business Journal (Vol. 31, August 5, 2011, No. 50, pp. 1) **[2455]**, **[2732]**, **[9132]**, **[15561]**, **[15593]**, **[20424]**, **[28552]**, **[33141]**
"Don't Leave Employees on the Outside Looking In" in Canadian Business (Vol. 83, July 20, 2010, No. 11-12, pp. 13) **[17662]**, **[22137]**, **[28553]**
"Don't Let the Bed Bugs Bite" in Yuma Sun (April 22, 2011) **[12042]**
"Don't Quit When The Road Gets Bumpy" in Women Entrepreneur (November 25, 2008) **[18939]**, **[19506]**, **[20278]**, **[20848]**, **[22554]**, **[24651]**, **[35768]**
Don't Run Out Off Cash! Manage Your Accounts Receivable (A/R) Properly **[16798]**
"Don't Shoot the Messenger: A Wake-Up Call For Academics" in Academy of Management Journal (Vol. 50, No. 5, October 1, 2007, pp. 1020) **[21488]**, **[28554]**
"Don't Tweak Your Supply Chain - Rethink It End to End" in Harvard Business Review (Vol. 88, October 2010, No. 10, pp. 62) **[3107]**, **[27533]**, **[27998]**
"The Doodle Revolution: Unlock the Power to Think Differently" **[22555]**, **[28555]**
DoodyCalls **[33317]**
Dooley's Inc. **[1368]**, **[1543]**
Dooly County Chamber of Commerce **[38724]**
"The Doomsday Scenario" in Conde Nast Portfolio (Vol. 2, June 2008, No. 6, pp. 91) **[11394]**, **[20621]**, **[20849]**, **[29184]**
Door County Visitor Bureau (DCVB) **[46395]**
Door and Hardware Institute Annual Convention and Exposition **[7929]**
Door-To-Door Dry Cleaning **[5254]**
DoorDash Inc. **[6934]**
Dope Magazine **[5039]**
Dorchester Chamber of Commerce **[40382]**
Dorchester County Economic Development Department (DCED) **[40452]**
Dorchester County Economic Development Office - Eastern Shore Innovation Center (ESIC) **[40453]**
"Doria Camaraza on the Best Advice She's Ever Received 'Leave Your Ego at the Door'" in South Florida Business Journal (Vol. 34, June 20, 2014, No. 43, pp. 13) **[4716]**, **[22138]**, **[28556]**
Dorset Capital L.L.C. **[37350]**
Dorsey & Whitney L.L.P. **[24495]**
Dot Edu Ventures **[37351]**
DOT Hazardous Materials Training (Onsite) **[23063]**, **[25187]**
Dotcal: The Calendar Wars **[35410]**
Dothan Area Chamber of Commerce (DACC) **[36104]**
"Doubtful Donors" in Canadian Business (Vol. 81, December 8, 2008, No. 21, pp. 8) **[20850]**, **[34305]**
Doug Zeif Founder & CEO of Next Hospitality Advisors **[8483]**
"Dougherty: AuthenTec Embedded Security Business Building Momentum" in Benzinga.com (March 5, 2012) **[14409]**, **[26264]**
Douglas - Coffee County Chamber of Commerce **[38725]**
Douglas County Chamber of Commerce **[38726]**
Douglass Chamber of Commerce (DCC) **[39884]**
Dove Cleaners and Cadet Cleaners **[5255]**
Dover Area Chamber of Commerce (DACC) **[36456]**
Dover Small Business Development Center **[38126]**
"Dow AgroSciences Buys Wheat-Breeding Firm in Pacific Northwest" in Farm Industry News (July 29, 2011) **[17030]**, **[19657]**, **[31962]**, **[32747]**
"Dow Champions Innovative Energy Solutions for Auto Industry at NAIAS" in Business of Global Warming (January 25, 2010, pp. 7) **[5589]**, **[5864]**, **[15852]**, **[23181]**, **[27534]**, **[29185]**, **[31275]**, **[35047]**
Dow Jones Business and Financial Weekly [6718], [9938], [11102]
Dow Theory Forecasts **[2151]**
Dow Venture Capital **[41141]**
Down Beat: Jazz, Blues & Beyond **[11191]**, **[11274]**
"Down on the Boardwalk" in Retail Merchandiser (Vol. 51, September-October 2011, No. 5, pp. 56) **[15790]**, **[29756]**, **[31754]**
"Down a 'Peg' in Canadian Business (Vol. 79, September 25, 2006, No. 19, pp. 41) **[20851]**, **[24652]**
"Down the Tracks, a Whistle Is a-Blowin" in Barron's (Vol. 89, July 27, 2009, No. 30, pp. 36) **[8714]**, **[20852]**, **[24972]**, **[25309]**
Downeast Maine SCORE **[40249]**
Downers Grove Area Chamber of Commerce and Industry [39123]
Downey Business **[36863]**
Downey Chamber of Commerce (DCC) **[36864]**
"The Downfall of Trustify" in PInow.com (November 11, 2019) **[11734]**, **[12796]**, **[23491]**
"The Downfall of the Virtual Assistant (So Far)" in ComputerWorld (June 20, 2019) **[3870]**, **[11735]**
Downingtown-Thorndale Regional Chamber of Commerce (DTRCC) **[44201]**
"Downtown Bank Got High Marks for Irwin Purchase, Is Looking For More" in Business Courier (Vol. 27, September 3, 2010, No. 18, pp. 1) **[6370]**, **[9470]**, **[19658]**, **[23849]**, **[31276]**
"Downtown: Grunnah Trades Homes for a Shot at Warehouse District" in Austin Business Journal (Vol. 34, February 28, 2014, No. 2, pp. 8) **[1328]**, **[9034]**
Downtown Idea Exchange **[921]**
"Downtown Light Rail Plans Up in the Air" in Business Journal Serving Greater Tampa Bay (Vol. 30, October 22, 2010, No. 44, pp. 1) **[1555]**, **[4066]**
Downtown Market Incubator Kitchen **[41086]**
Downtown Windsor Business Accelerator **[46820]**
Downtown Works **[37566]**
"Downtowns Must Court Young, CEOs for Cities President Says" in Crain's Detroit Business (Vol. 24, October 6, 2008, No. 40, pp. 18) **[15853]**, **[21489]**, **[26543]**, **[28557]**, **[35048]**
"Downturn Tests HCL's Pledge to Employees" in Workforce Management (Vol. 88, November 16, 2009, No. 12, pp. 23) **[20853]**, **[22139]**, **[26265]**, **[26926]**, **[28558]**, **[35187]**
"Dox Choice Joins Growing Medical Records Industry" in Memphis Business Journal (Vol. 34, April 13, 2012, No. 53, pp. 1) **[10968]**, **[24973]**
Doyle Dane Bernbach [398]
"Doyle: Domino's New Pizza Seasoned with Straight Talk" in Crain's Detroit Business (Vol. 26, January 11, 2010, No. 2, pp. 8) **[264]**, **[12529]**, **[18940]**, **[19507]**, **[29757]**
"Dozens 'Come Alive' in Downtown Chicago" in Green Industry Pro (July 2011) **[7616]**, **[10093]**, **[10229]**, **[21490]**, **[29758]**, **[32514]**, **[33142]**
DPR Construction **[36392]**
DPRA Inc. **[17194]**
"Draft Recommendations Call for Making National Park Campgrounds More Accommodating" in National Parks Traveler (October 13, 2019) **[2513]**
Dragon Magazine [4672]
DragonVenture **[37672]**, **[37732]**
Drama Kids International, Inc. (DKI) **[21717]**
Draper & Associates **[4312]**
Draper Associates (DA) **[37352]**
Draper Fisher Jurvetson [37507]
Draper International **[37353]**
Draper Triangle Ventures **[44336]**
Dream Dinners Inc. **[4707]**
Dream Kitchen **[39401]**
"Dream On" in Barron's (Vol. 89, July 27, 2009, No. 30, pp. 21) **[17495]**, **[20854]**, **[24974]**

Small Business Sourcebook • 42nd Edition 3223

"Dream Town Launches Organic Food Delivery for Its Employees" in Internet Wire (June 28, 2012) [8015], [11029], [22140]
DreamBuilder [22945], [33710], [35928]
Dreamit Ventures [30264], [42864]
DreamMaker Bath & Kitchen [2649]
Dresner Capital Resources Inc. [39354]
Dresner Partners [39354]
"Dress Professionally Cool for Summer" in Women In Business (Vol. 62, June 2010, No. 2, pp. 38) [3108], [35769]
"Dressbarn Announces First Round of Closings for June and July. Is Yours on the List?" in USA Today (June 21, 2019) [3109]
Dressd: Red Carpet or Red Ocean? [35411]
Drew County Chamber of Commerce [36482]
DRI Capital Inc. [46784]
DRI Consulting Inc. (DRIC) [2385], [10527], [19134], [20182], [28986]
DRI Healthcare [46784]
Dried Fruit Association of New York [13878]
"Drilling Deep and Flying High" in Barron's (Vol. 88, June 30, 2008, No. 26, pp. 34) [6371], [9471], [18046], [23850], [27535], [29186], [33143]
"Drink Up!" in (Vol. 92, July 23, 2012, No. 30, pp. 19) [7553], [7732], [8016], [8093], [34000]
"Drinking Buddies: S.F.'s New Round of Barkeeps" in San Francisco Business Times (Vol. 28, January 17, 2014, No. 26, pp. 4) [1329], [18047], [20855]
Drinking Water & Backflow Prevention [16338]
The Driving Book: Everything New Drivers Need to Know but Don't Know to Ask [5100]
Driving Innovation: Proven Processes, Tools and Strategies for Growth (Onsite) [28318]
"Driving Passion" in Small Business Opportunities (April 2008) [7516], [22556]
Driving With No Brakes: How a Bunch of Hooligans Built the Best Travel Company in the World [15736], [15989], [22557], [28559], [31277]
Driving With a Teenage Brain: A State Trooper's Notes on How to Stay Alive [5101]
"Drop in the Bucket Makes a lot of Waves" in Globe & Mail (March 22, 2007, pp. B1) [20011], [23182], [29187]
"Drought Takes Toll on Farmers, Restaurants" in Saint Louis Business Journal (Vol. 31, August 12, 2011, No. 51, pp. 1) [13929], [17031]
DRS Corp. [35450]
"Drug, Seed Firms Offer Antidote For Inflation" in Crain's Chicago Business (Vol. 31, April 21, 2008, No. 16, pp. 4) [6372], [9472], [20856], [23851]
Drug Store & HBC Chain Leads Databases [5155]
Drug Store and HBC Chains Leads [5155]
"Drug Trial Halt at YM Sets Stage for Selloff" in Globe & Mail (January 31, 2007, pp. B3) [6373], [9473], [32748]
Drug Wholesalers Association [5138]
"Drugs and Alcohol in the Workplace?" in Wallace Welch & Willingham Wellness Blog (Jan. 15, 2021) [34678]
Drummondville Economic Development Corp. (SDED) [46893]
Drumright Chamber of Commerce [43751]
Dry Cleaners Industry in the US - Market Research Report [5245]
"Dry Cleaners, Seeking New Ways to Survive, Take Inspiration from Restaurants and Retail" in Chicago Tribune (March 24, 2017) [5235], [18941]
Drycleaning and Laundry Institute International (DLI) [5226], [5264], [5265]
DSAA Annual Conference [5109]
DSF [10684]
DSP: Digital Signal Processing (Onsite) [26194]
"DT Interpreting VideoHub Service Expanding" in Internet Wire (March 26, 2012) [15935], [25766]
DTAH [934]
"DTE Energy Foundation Expands 'Greening' Programs at Michigan Festivals" in Ecology, Environment & Conservation Business (June 28, 2014, pp. 3) [13709], [23183]
DTS Language Services Inc. [15956]
Du Bois Area Chamber of Commerce [44222]
Du Quoin Chamber of Commerce [39153]
Dual News [5108]
Duarte Business [36865]
Duarte Chamber of Commerce [36866]
Duarte View [36867]
Dublin Chamber of Commerce [36868]
Dublin Entrepreneurial Center (DEC) [43660]
Dublin - Laurens County Chamber of Commerce [38727]
Dubois Chamber of Commerce [46603]
Dubuque Area Chamber of Commerce [39733]
Dubuque Area SCORE [39693]
"Ducati Returns to Production: "We Are Ready to Go" - Domenicali" in Ultimate Motorcycling (April 28. 2020) [11109]

Duchesne County Chamber of Commerce (DCACC) [45634]
"Ducking the New Health-Care Taxes" in Barron's (Vol. 92, September 15, 2012, No. 38, pp. 34) [15376], [23852], [25767], [27262], [34776]
Duct Tape Marketing: The World's Most Practical Small Business Marketing Guide [265], [18048], [29759]
Ductmedic [560]
Duke Angel Network [43219]
Duke Capital Partners (DCP) [43219]
Duke University Hospital Outpatient Department - Duke Eye Center [16319]
Dulles Regional Chamber of Commerce (DRCC) [45855]
Duluth Area Chamber of Commerce (DACC) [41224]
Dumac Economic Development Corporation (EDC) [44956]
Dumas Chamber of Commerce [36457]
Dumas/Moore County Chamber of Commerce and Visitors Center [45128]
"Dumb Financial Mistakes Business Owners Make and How to Avoid Them" in Small Business Trends(February 20, 2023) [23853], [33560]
The Dun & Bradstreet Companies of Canada ULC [46858]
Duncan Center for Business Development [43854]
Duncan Chamber of Commerce and Industry [43752]
Duncanville Chamber of Commerce (DCC) [45129]
Dundee Venture Capital [41904]
Dunedin Chamber of Commerce [38369]
Duneland Chamber of Commerce [39535]
Duneland Today [39536]
Dungeons & Dragon Magazine (D&D) [4672]
Dunham Tavern Museum Library [749]
"Dunkin' Donuts Franchise Looking Possible for 2011" in Messenger-Inquirer (January 2, 2010) [1252], [18049], [24353]
Dunn Area Chamber of Commerce (DACC) [43124]
Dunn Bros Coffee [7581]
Dunnellon Area Chamber of Commerce [38370]
Dunnellon Chamber & Business Association (DCBA) [38370]
"Dunnellon Welcomes Internet Cafe Jobs" in Ocala Star-Banner (August 18, 2011) [7554], [13930]
Dunrath Capital [39457]
Dunsmuir Chamber of Commerce [36869]
DuPont Pioneer - Library Resources Group [17210]
The duPont Registry: A Buyer's Gallery of Fine Boats [8185], [8219], [13314]
The duPont Registry: A Buyer's Gallery of Fine Homes [10613]
"DuPont's Pioneer Hi-Bred, Evogene to Develop Rust-Resistant Soybean Varieties" in Farm Industry News (November 22, 2011) [17032], [30714], [31278], [31963], [32749]
Duquesne Business Law Journal [18769]
Duquesne University Small Business Development Center [44094]
Duraclean International Inc. [16236]
Durango Area Chamber Resort Association [37843]
Durango Chamber of Commerce [37843]
DurangoSpace [37936]
Durham SCORE [43052]
"Duro Bag to Expand, Add 130 Jobs" in Business Courier (Vol. 27, August 6, 2010, No. 14, pp. 1) [18050], [25310], [26544], [29188], [34777]
DURO vitres d'autos [7503]
Durum Wheat Institute [16962]
Dutchess County Regional Chamber of Commerce [42564]
Dutchess SCORE [42422]
"The Duty of Wealth: Canadian Business Leaders on Nepotism and Philanthropy" in Canadian Business (Vol. 80, Winter 2007, No. 24) [15222], [22558], [23608]
DVEO Computer Modules [33930]
Dyersburg-Dyer County Chamber of Commerce [44739]
Dyersville Area Chamber of Commerce (DACC) [39734]
"The Dynamic DUO" in Canadian Electronics (Vol. 23, February 2008, No. 1, pp. 24) [22141], [29189], [31035]
"Dynamic Duo: Payouts Rise at General Dynamics, Steel Dynamics" in Barron's (Vol. 88, March 10, 2008, No. 10, pp. 45) [6374], [9474], [18051], [23854], [29190]
Dynamic Listening Skills for Successful Communication (Onsite) [17558]
The Dynamic Small Business Manager [24653], [28560]
Dynamic Web Development I [33773]
Dynamic Web Development II [33774]
"Dynamically Integrating Knowledge in Teams: Transforming Resources Into Performance" in Academy of Management Journal (Vol. 55, August 1, 2012, No. 4, pp. 998) [22142], [28027], [28561]

E

E-biz [44202]
E-Book Publishing Industry in the US - Market Research Report [1685], [11829]

"E-Cards Are Back, Thanks to the Pandemic" in The New York Times (June 22, 2021) [7700], [11736]
The E-Center [36051], [36177]
E. Central Illinois (ECI) SCORE [39007]
"E-Commerce Jewelry Startup Gemvara Won't Pursue Retail Store in Boston" in Boston Business Journal (Vol. 34, March 14, 2014, No. 6) [9954], [11681], [35503]
E-Commerce for Small Business: Starting Out [21835]
"E-Commerce's Impact on Small Business in the Age of COVID-19" in The National Law Review (Feb. 22, 2021) [21836]
E-Communicator [43125]
E! Entertainment Television L.L.C. [37354]
E-mail and Business Writing [17838]
The E-Mail and Business Writing Workshop (Onsite) [17839]
"E-Medical Records Save Money, Time in Ann Arbor" in Crain's Detroit Business (Vol. 24, January 21, 2008, No. 3, pp. 6) [3501], [8905], [25768], [27263]
The E-Myth Enterprise: How to Turn a Great Idea into a Thriving Business [22377], [24528]
E-Newsletter [39154]
E-The Environmental Magazine [5741]
E8 [46189]
Eagle Chamber of Commerce [37844]
Eagle Grove Area Chamber of Commerce [39735]
Eagle Nest Chamber of Commerce (ENCC) [42314]
Eagle Pass Chamber of Commerce (EPCC) [45130]
"Eagle River's Only Music Store Is Closing up Shop" in U.S. News & World Report (June 15, 2019) [11262]
Eagle Rock Chamber of Commerce [36870]
Eagle Strategy Group, LLC. [42260]
Eagle Venture Fund (EVF) [45446]
Eaglerider Motorcycle Rental [1171]
"Eagles Add Sponsors to Nest" in Orlando Business Journal (Vol. 28, August 24, 2012, No. 28, pp. 1) [15147], [29760]
"Eagles Measure Suite Success" in Philadelphia Business Journal (Vol. 30, September 9, 2011, No. 30, pp. 1) [14773], [15148], [29761], [33847]
EagleShotz [12320]
Earl of Sandwich L.L.C. [4899]
Early Music America (EMA) [11257]
"Early Spring Halts Drilling Season" in Globe & Mail (March 14, 2007, pp. B14) [20857], [29191], [32949]
"Early-Stage Biomed Firm Seeks Funds for First Device" in San Antonio Business Journal (Vol. 28, March 7, 2014, No. 4, pp. 6) [7102], [10826]
Early Stage Partners (ESP) [43621]
Early Startup Reality Checks [34589]
Earth Day Canada (EDC) [5481]
Earth Elements Entrepreneurs' Kitchen (E3K) [43855]
Earth Energy Society of Canada [5505]
Earth Island Journal: An International Environmental News Magazine [5742]
Earth and Mineral Sciences [32869]
Earthquake Intensity Database, 1638-1985 [5756]
EarthSave Canada [5482], [13686]
Earthsave Foundation [5793]
EarthSave International [5793]
Earthshots™ [12324], [12360]
Earthworm Inc. [13755]
"Easier Options Orders" in Barron's (Vol. 92, August 25, 2012, No. 35, pp. 28) [9475], [11737], [23855]
"Easing the Global (and Costly) Problem of Workplace Stress; Stress Is Reportedly the Leading Cause of Long-Term Sickness for Workers Around the World. But Relief Is In Sight" in Gallup Business Journal (March 27, 2014) [22143], [25769]
East Alabama Chamber of Commerce [36105]
East Baton Rouge Parish Library (EBRPL) [24911]
East Bay Chamber of Commerce (EBCC) [44469]
East Bay Small Business Development Center [36559]
East Boston Chamber of Commerce (EBCC) [40573]
East Brunswick Regional Chamber of Commerce (EBRCC) [42118]
East Central Community College Small Business Development Center (SBDC) [41370]
East Central Indiana Small Business Development Center (SBDC) [39471]
East Central Ohio SCORE [43375]
East Central University Small Business Development Center [43708]
East of Chicago Pizza Co. [12548]
"East Coast Solar" in Contractor (Vol. 57, February 2010, No. 2, pp. 17) [4067], [5368], [5590], [5865], [14917], [21491], [23184], [31964]
East Coast Subs [4900]
East County Regional Chamber of Commerce [37150]
East Georgia State College (EGSC) [38843]
East Granby Chamber of Commerce [38031]
East Greenwich Chamber of Commerce (EGCC) [44470]

East Hampton Chamber of Commerce (EHCC) **[42565]**
East Haven Chamber of Commerce (EHCC) **[38043]**
East Jordan Area Chamber of Commerce (EJACC) **[40904]**
East Lake County Chamber of Commerce **[38371]**
East Lee County Chamber of Commerce **[38372]**
East Liberty Quarter Chamber of Commerce (ELQCC) **[44203]**
East Los Angeles Chamber of Commerce **[36871]**
East Manhattan Chamber of Commerce [42632]
East Orange Chamber of Commerce (EOCC) **[42119]**
East Orange Chamber of Commerce [38374]
East Oranger **[38373]**
East Orlando Chamber of Commerce (EOCC) **[38374]**
East Peoria Business Directory **[39155]**
East Peoria Chamber of Commerce **[39156]**
East Peoria Chamber of Commerce and Tourism [39156]
East Prairie Chamber of Commerce **[41555]**
East Providence Area Chamber of Commerce (EPACC) **[44471]**
East St. Tammany Chamber of Commerce **[40166]**
East Side Business Center L.L.C. (ESBC) **[42865]**
East Side Mario's **[14154]**
"East-Side Real Estate Forum Detours To Grand Rapids" in *Crain's Detroit Business* (Vol. 24, October 6, 2008, No. 40, pp. 17) **[11030]**, **[12884]**, **[13188]**, **[13442]**, **[15854]**, **[35049]**
East Stroudsburg University Business Accelerator (ESU) **[44394]**
East Tennessee State University College of Business and Technology - Bureau of Business and Economic Research **[21272]**
East Tennessee State University (ETSU) - Innovation Lab **[44843]**
East Tennessee State University - Tennessee Small Business Development Center (TSBDC) **[34235]**
East Troy Area Chamber of Commerce **[46396]**
Eastchester Tuckahoe Chamber of Commerce **[42566]**
Eastern Apicultural Society [1435]
Eastern Apicultural Society of North America (EAS) [1435]
Eastern Arizona College (EAC) **[36413]**
Eastern Arizona College Small Business Development Center (EAC SBDC) **[36270]**
Eastern Cambria County Chamber of Commerce **[44204]**
Eastern Idaho Technical College [38955]
Eastern Iowa Small Business Development Center **[39675]**
Eastern Kentucky University Business and Technology Accelerator (EKU) **[40104]**
Eastern Kentucky University - Center for Economic Development, Entrepreneurship and Technology (CEDET) **[40105]**
Eastern Kentucky University Small Business Development Center (EKU SBDC) **[39991]**
Eastern Laboratory Service Associates **[17195]**
Eastern Lake County Chamber of Commerce **[43462]**
Eastern Madera County Chamber of Commerce [37057]
Eastern Maine Development Corp. (EMDC) **[40317]**
"Eastern Market's New Bite?" in *Washington Business Journal* (Vol. 33, August 8, 2014, No. 16, pp. 6) **[3840]**, **[7733]**, **[13784]**, **[23856]**
Eastern Maumee Bay Chamber of Commerce **[43463]**
Eastern Monmouth Area Chamber of Commerce (EMACC) **[42120]**
Eastern Montgomery County Chamber of Commerce (EMCCC) **[44205]**
Eastern New Mexico University-Roswell (ENMU-Roswell) **[42359]**
Eastern New York Angels (ENYA) **[42736]**
Eastern Oklahoma County Technology Center (EOCTC) **[43856]**
Eastern Panhandle Small Business Development Center **[46250]**
Eastern Panhandle Technology Innovation Center (EPTIC) **[46301]**
Eastern Plumas Chamber of Commerce [37006]
Eastern Point Consulting Group Inc. **[2257]**, **[20183]**, **[20594]**, **[22316]**, **[27136]**, **[30663]**
Eastern Region [47075]
Eastern Shore Chamber of Commerce (ESCC) **[36106]**
Eastern Shore of Virginia Chamber of Commerce (ESVA) **[45856]**
Eastern Ski Representatives Association [14728]
Eastern States Office [47693]
Eastern West Virginia Community & Technical College - Entrepreneurship Incubator **[46302]**
Eastern Winter Sports Reps Association (EWSRA) **[14728]**
Eastham Chamber of Commerce on Cape Cod **[40574]**
Eastland Chamber of Commerce **[45131]**
Eastman - Dodge County Chamber of Commerce **[38728]**

Easton Capital **[43018]**
Easton Hunt Capital Partners L.P. **[42737]**
Eastpointe - Roseville Chamber of Commerce (EACC) **[40905]**
Eastport Area Chamber of Commerce (EACC) **[40275]**
Eastside Partners **[36161]**
Eastward Capital Partners LLC (ECP) **[40682]**
EasyChair Media **[12009]**
EatingWell **[11582]**
Eaton - Preble County Chamber of Commerce (PCCC) **[43464]**
Eatonton-Putnam County Chamber of Commerce **[38729]**
EatsPlace **[38177]**
Eau Claire Area Chamber of Commerce **[46397]**
eBay Business the Smart Way **[1061]**, **[3879]**, **[11682]**, **[16412]**, **[21761]**, **[27999]**, **[32515]**
The eBay Business Start-Up Kit: With 100s of Live Links to All the Information & Tools You Need **[1062]**, **[2127]**, **[3880]**, **[11683]**, **[21762]**, **[32516]**
EBay Income: How ANYONE of Any Age, Location, and/or Background Can Build a Highly Profitable Online Business with eBay **[266]**, **[1063]**, **[4785]**, **[9133]**, **[11684]**, **[15377]**, **[16413]**, **[16799]**, **[18860]**, **[20012]**, **[20279]**, **[21837]**, **[27536]**, **[29762]**, **[32073]**, **[32517]**, **[34778]**
Eblast Newsletter **[36872]**
eCenter@LindenPointe **[44395]**
"Eclectic Reading" in *Business Strategy Review* (Vol. 23, Spring 2012, No. 1, pp. 68) **[10645]**, **[17663]**, **[29763]**, **[30560]**
ECnow.com Inc. **[35451]**
Eco Barons: The New Heroes of Environmental Activism **[5591]**, **[5866]**, **[22559]**, **[23185]**
The Eco Laundry Co. **[10200]**
"Eco-Preneuring" in *Small Business Opportunities* (Feb. 6, 2012) **[1858]**, **[4511]**, **[15737]**, **[15990]**, **[17033]**, **[29764]**
"Eco Smart Home Will Showcase Green Technology" in *Contractor* (Vol. 56, September 2009, No. 9, pp. 3) **[481]**, **[4068]**, **[5592]**, **[5867]**, **[14918]**
eCoast Angel Network **[42019]**
EcoElectron Ventures **[37355]**
EcoFarm Conference **[17166]**
Ecojustice Canada **[5483]**
Ecology Action Centre (EAC) **[5484]**, **[13756]**, **[23030]**
eCommerce Behaviors: Gen Z vs. Millennials: Incl Impact of Covid-19 - US - June 2020 **[11830]**
eCompanies L.L.C. **[37356]**
Econo Lube N' Tune Inc. **[13002]**, **[14583]**
Economic Alliance Snohomish County (EASC) **[46078]**, **[46203]**
Economic Community Development Institute (ECDI) **[43661]**
"Economic Crisis and Accounting Evolution" in *Accounting and Business Research* (Vol. 41, Summer 2011, No. 3, pp. 2159) **[61]**, **[1754]**, **[15378]**, **[16800]**, **[20858]**
"Economic Development: 105 CEOs Depart in July" in *South Florida Business Journal* (Vol. 35, August 15, 2014, No. 3, pp. 5) **[28562]**, **[34001]**
Economic Development Administration--Annual Report **[20859]**
Economic Development Alliance of Jefferson County **[36516]**
Economic Development Alliance of St. Clair County **[41059]**
Economic Development Alliance of Southeast Alberta **[46679]**
Economic Development Association of Skagit County **[46207]**
Economic Development Center of St. Charles County Missouri (EDC) **[41672]**
Economic Development Corporation of Lea County (EDCLC) **[42346]**
Economic Development Corporation of Weslaco (EDC-Weslaco) **[45512]**
Economic Development & Industrial Corporation of Lynn - Office of Economic Development **[40748]**
Economic Development Lethbridge (EDL) **[46669]**
Economic Development Partnership of Monroe County **[41417]**
"Economic Distance and the Survival of Foreign Direct Investments" in *Academy of Management Journal* (Vol. 50, No. 5, October 1, 2007, pp. 1156) **[9476]**, **[20860]**, **[27537]**
Economic Freedom and the American Dream **[20861]**, **[22560]**, **[28563]**
Economic Growth Business Incubator (EGBI) **[45513]**
"Economic Impact of the Arts: $125 Million" in *Memphis Business Journal* (Vol. 34, June 22, 2012, No. 10, pp. 1) **[969]**, **[7103]**
"Economic Loss Rule and Franchise Attorneys" in *Franchise Law Journal* (Vol. 27, Winter 2008, No. 3, pp. 192) **[18568]**, **[24354]**

"Economic Outlook 2009: In Search of New Tools and Initiatives" in *Hispanic Business* (January-February 2009, pp. 30, 32) **[18942]**, **[20862]**, **[34002]**
"Economic Recovery Prognosis: Four More Years" in *Barron's* (Vol. 89, July 13, 2009, No. 28, pp. 11) **[6375]**, **[9477]**, **[20863]**, **[23857]**
Economic Report **[36873]**
Economic Research and Development Centre [21268]
"Economic Trends for Small Business" in *Small Business Economic Trends* (April 2008, pp. 1) **[4717]**, **[4745]**, **[4786]**, **[20280]**, **[20864]**, **[28000]**, **[32518]**, **[34003]**
"An Economic Warning Sign: RV Shipments are Slipping" in *The Wall Street Journal* (August 19, 2019) **[13674]**
"The Economics of Christmas Trees" in *The Hustle* (Dec. 5, 2020) **[2937]**
The Economics of Integrity: From Dairy Farmers to Toyota, How Wealth Is Built on Trust and What That Means for Our Future **[23492]**, **[24654]**, **[31279]**
"Economics: The User's Guide" **[20865]**, **[27538]**
"The Economics of Well-Being: Have We Found a Better Gauge of Success Than GDP?" in *Harvard Business Review* (Vol. 90, January-February 2012, No.1-2, pp. 78) **[20866]**, **[21492]**
The Economist Intelligence Unit Limited (EIU) **[8787]**
"Economists Warn Against Smart Cap" in *Orlando Business Journal* (Vol. 29, September 21, 2012, No. 14, pp. 1) **[20867]**, **[25311]**, **[34779]**
"Economy: The Case for a Bright Future" in *Canadian Business* (Vol. 83, July 20, 2010, No. 11-12, pp. 58) **[26266]**, **[27862]**
Ecosystem Ventures **[37733]**
"Ecovative Moves Beyond Packaging" in *Business Review Albany* (Vol. 41, August 1, 2014, No. 19, pp. 12) **[3391]**, **[23186]**, **[30715]**
ECRI Institute **[10886]**, **[10964]**
Ed Doherty Founder of One Degree Coaching **[20139]**
Edelson Technology Partners (ETP) **[42211]**
Eden Business Incubator **[45514]**
Eden Chamber of Commerce **[43126]**
Eden Prairie Chamber of Commerce (EPC) **[41225]**
Edenton-Chowan Chamber of Commerce **[43127]**
EDexpo **[15547]**
"EDF Ventures Dissolves Fund, Begins Anew On Investment" in *Crain's Detroit Business* (Vol. 24, February 25, 2008, No. 8, pp. 14) **[28129]**, **[35335]**
The EDGE **[36178]**
The Edge Entrepreneurship Center **[36179]**
EDGE Incubator and Accelerator **[36180]**
EDGE Labs **[36181]**
Edge Marketing **[135]**
Edgerton Area Chamber of Commerce (EACC) **[43465]**
"Edible Endeavors" in *Black Enterprise* (March 1, 2008) **[2672]**, **[30345]**, **[35770]**
Edinboro University - Baron-Forness Library Special Collections **[996]**, **[11220]**, **[11296]**
Edinburg Chamber of Commerce (ECC) **[45132]**
Edinburgh Napier University - Craiglockhart Campus Library **[16898]**
Edison Business Incubator **[40749]**
Edison Chamber of Commerce (ECC) **[42121]**
Edison Partners **[42212]**
Editorial Code and Data Inc. (ECDI) **[1698]**, **[4947]**, **[11478]**
"Editorial: Find Private Money for FutureGen Plant" in *Crain's Chicago Business* (Vol. 34, September 12, 2011, No. 37, pp. 18) **[5593]**, **[5868]**, **[23187]**, **[28130]**
Editorial Freelancers Association (EFA) **[5280]**
Editorial Freelancers Association--Membership Directory **[5314]**
"Editorial: It's Not Perfect; But Illinois a Good Home for Business" in *Crain's Chicago Business* (Vol. 34, October 24, 2011, No. 42, pp. 18) **[18052]**, **[24529]**, **[33363]**, **[34780]**
Editorial Skills for Non-Editors (Onsite) **[17559]**
Editors Association of Canada (EAC) **[5281]**, **[35153]**
Edmond Area Chamber of Commerce **[43753]**
Edmonds Small Business Development Center (SBDC) **[46000]**
Edmonton Chamber of Commerce (ECC) **[20695]**
Edmonton Economic Development [46671]
Edmonton - Metcalfe County Chamber of Commerce **[40036]**
Edmonton Unlimited (EU) **[46670]**
Edo Japan **[14155]**
EDS Leadership Summit [4414]
EDspaces **[15548]**
"An Educated Play on China" in *Barron's* (Vol. 88, June 30, 2008, No. 26, pp. M6) **[6376]**, **[9478]**, **[16131]**, **[18053]**, **[21493]**, **[23858]**, **[27539]**
Education Conference **[15245]**
Education Development Center Inc. (EDC) **[2258]**, **[20184]**, **[32929]**
"The Education of Jack Bogle" in *Philadelphia Business Journal* (Vol. 33, April 4, 2014, No. 8, pp. 4) **[6377]**, **[9479]**

"*Education Required to Be a Photographer*" in Chron (July 24, 2018) **[12301]**
Educational Conference **[21686]**
Educational Dealer: The Magazine for the School Supply Industry **[15545]**
Educational Equity Center [10007]
Educational Equity Concepts/Academy for Educational Development [10007]
The Educational Foundation for Women in Accounting (EFWA) **[29]**, **[35595]**
Educational Outfitters Group L.L.C. **[2860]**
Educational Technology Magazine: Magazine for Managers of Change in Education **[3556]**
Educational Trust of the American Hospital Association [26118]
"*Educator Makes It Her Business to Bring Books Back to Life*" in U.S. News & World Report (January 27, 2019) **[1721]**
Edward-Dean Museum & Gardens Art Reference Library **[7254]**
Edwards County Chamber of Commerce (ECCC) **[45133]**
Edwardsburg Area Chamber of Commerce **[40906]**
Edwardsville/Glen Carbon Chamber of Commerce **[39157]**
EEI Communications Active Server Pages I **[16369]**
EEI Communications Adobe Acrobat 9 for Legal Professionals **[33775]**
EEI Communications Adobe After Effects II (Onsite) **[33776]**
EEI Communications Adobe Captivate 3 **[17560]**, **[33777]**
EEI Communications Adobe ColdFusion I **[16370]**
EEI Communications Adobe Director I **[21358]**
EEI Communications Adobe Director II **[21359]**
EEI Communications Adobe Dreamweaver I (Onsite) **[16371]**
EEI Communications Adobe Dreamweaver II (Onsite) **[16372]**
EEI Communications Adobe Dreamweaver III (Onsite) **[16373]**
EEI Communications Adobe Fireworks I **[16374]**
EEI Communications Adobe Flash I (Onsite) **[21360]**
EEI Communications Adobe Flash II (Onsite) **[21361]**
EEI Communications Adobe Flash III (Onsite) **[33778]**
EEI Communications Adobe Flex I - Developing Rich Internet Client Applications **[33779]**
EEI Communications Adobe Flex II - Data and Communications **[33780]**
EEI Communications Adobe Flex III - Building Dashboard Applications **[33781]**
EEI Communications Adobe GoLive **[16375]**
EEI Communications Adobe InDesign I (Onsite) **[21362]**
EEI Communications Adobe InDesign II (Onsite) **[21363]**
EEI Communications Adobe Photoshop I (Onsite) **[21364]**
EEI Communications Adobe Photoshop II (Onsite) **[21365]**
EEI Communications Adobe Photoshop III: Tips and Tricks (Onsite) **[21366]**
EEI Communications Adobe Premiere I (Onsite) **[21367]**
EEI Communications Advanced Editing **[17561]**
EEI Communications Advanced Grammar Roundtable (Onsite) **[21368]**
EEI Communications Apple DVD Studio Pro I (Onsite) **[33782]**
EEI Communications Apple Final Cut Pro Bootcamp (Onsite) **[33783]**
EEI Communications Apple Final Cut Pro I (Onsite) **[33784]**
EEI Communications Apple Final Cut Pro II (Onsite) **[33785]**
EEI Communications Apple Motion I (Onsite) **[33786]**
EEI Communications ASP.NET with VB.NET and C I (Onsite) **[33787]**
EEI Communications ASP.NET with VB.NET and C II **[33788]**
EEI Communications ASP.NET with VB.NET C III **[33789]**
EEI Communications Becoming a Publications Manager **[4933]**
EEI Communications Cascading Style Sheets (CSS) I **[16376]**
EEI Communications Copywriting I (Onsite) **[5302]**
EEI Communications Copywriting II (Onsite) **[5303]**
EEI Communications Creating Successful Newsletters **[11473]**
EEI Communications Design for Presentations **[14506]**
EEI Communications Design for Print **[4934]**
EEI Communications Designing for Diversity **[17562]**
EEI Communications Digital Video Production for Streaming and DVD (Onsite) **[33790]**
EEI Communications Earned Value Management Systems (EVMS) for Project Managers **[28319]**

EEI Communications Effective Briefings **[17563]**
EEI Communications Effective Business Writing (Onsite) **[17564]**
EEI Communications Effective Presentation Techniques: Public Speaking **[17565]**
EEI Communications Enhanced and Video Podcasts (Onsite) **[33791]**
EEI Communications Intensive Introduction to Copyediting (Onsite) **[29587]**
EEI Communications Intensive Review of Grammar (Onsite) **[5304]**
EEI Communications Internet Marketing **[22986]**
EEI Communications Introduction to Information Design **[17566]**
EEI Communications Introduction to Project Management (Onsite) **[28320]**
EEI Communications Introduction to Soundtrack Pro **[26195]**
EEI Communications Introduction to Windows **[21369]**
EEI Communications JavaScript for Non-Programmers **[16377]**
EEI Communications Macromedia Authorware I **[21370]**
EEI Communications Managing the Publications Department **[1632]**
EEI Communications Microsoft Access 2007 - I (Onsite) **[21371]**
EEI Communications Microsoft Access 2007 - II (Onsite) **[21372]**
EEI Communications Microsoft PowerPoint 2007 - I (Onsite) **[21373]**
EEI Communications Microsoft Word 2007 - I (Onsite) **[21374]**
EEI Communications Microsoft Word 2007 - II (Onsite) **[21375]**
EEI Communications Microsoft Word 2007 - III (Onsite) **[21376]**
EEI Communications Production Techniques and Technology **[1633]**
EEI Communications Professional Design Techniques with Adobe Creative Suite 4 (CS4) **[33792]**
EEI Communications Project Management for Streaming DVD, and Multimedia **[28321]**
EEI Communications Quality Control in Publications **[1634]**
EEI Communications QuarkXPress I **[21377]**
EEI Communications QuarkXPress II **[21378]**
EEI Communications QuarkXPress III **[21379]**
EEI Communications Scientific Editing (Onsite) **[5305]**
EEI Communications Strategies of Effective Writing (Onsite) **[17567]**
EEI Communications Substantive Editing I (Onsite) **[17568]**
EEI Communications Substantive Editing III **[17840]**
EEI Communications Technical Writing (Onsite) **[17569]**
EEI Communications The Designing Editor **[5306]**
EEI Communications Visual Thinking II: Color Theory **[4935]**
EEI Communications Web Design **[22987]**
EEI Communications Web Design with Adobe Dreamweaver and Photoshop (Onsite) **[33793]**
EEI Communications Writing News (Onsite) **[11474]**
EEI Communications Writing the Perfect Business E-Mail (Onsite) **[17841]**, **[21380]**
EEI Communications Writing for the Web I (Onsite) **[22988]**
EEI Communications Writing for the Web II (Onsite) **[17570]**, **[33794]**
EEI Communications (X)HTML and CSS I (Onsite) **[22989]**
EEI Communications (X)HTML and CSS II (Onsite) **[22990]**
EEI Communications (X)HTML and CSS III (Onsite) **[22991]**
"*EEOC Issues Enforcement Guidance Addressing Pregnancy-Related Disabilities*" in Idaho Business Review (August 18, 2014) **[20566]**, **[25312]**
EF Marburger Fine Flooring **[31071]**
"*The Effect of 3-D Product Visualization on the Strength of Brand Attitude*" in International Journal of Advertising (Vol. 31, May 2012, No. 2, pp. 377) **[267]**, **[10646]**, **[29765]**
"*The Effect of Corporate Governance on Firm's Credit Ratings: Further Evidence Using Governance Score in the United States*" in Accounting and Finance (Vol. 52, June 2012, No. 2, pp. 291) **[9480]**, **[20281]**, **[28564]**
Effective Business Writing **[17842]**
Effective Business Writing seminar [17842]
Effective Communication and Motivation (Onsite) **[17571]**, **[22047]**
Effective Compensation Inc. (ECI) **[2259]**, **[20185]**, **[24243]**, **[27137]**
Effective Executive Speaking (Onsite) **[17572]**
The Effective Facilitator **[22048]**

The Effective Facilitator: Maximizing Involvement and Results **[22049]**
Effective Meeting Management (Onsite) **[28322]**
Effective Negotiating **[17573]**, **[28323]**
"*Effective Networking*" in Women in Business (Vol. 64, Summer 2012, No. 2, pp. 50) **[15855]**, **[17664]**, **[35050]**, **[35771]**
"*Effective Organizing for the Home Business*" in Gaebler Ventures Resources for Entrepreneurs **[26776]**
Effective Project Communications, Negotiations and Conflict (Onsite) **[22050]**, **[28324]**
Effective Sales Tactics for Small Businesses **[32519]**
Effective Technical Writing (Onsite) **[17843]**
Effective Time Management: Prioritizing for Success (Onsite) **[34967]**
Effective Training Techniques for Group Leaders (Onsite) **[21381]**, **[28325]**
"*Effective Use of Field Time*" in Agency Sales Magazine (Vol. 39, July 2009, No. 7, pp. 40) **[29192]**, **[31755]**, **[32520]**
"*The Effectiveness of Advertising That Leverages Sponsorship and Cause-Related Marketing: A Contingency Model*" in International Journal of Advertising (Vol. 31, May 2012, No. 2, pp. 317) **[268]**, **[10647]**, **[29766]**
"*The Effectiveness of Regulatory (In)Congruent Ads: The Moderating Role of an Ad's Rational Versus Emotional Tone*", in International Journal of Advertising (Vol. 31, May 2012, No. 2, pp. 397) **[269]**
Effectiveness Resource Group Inc. **[2260]**, **[20186]**, **[31922]**
"*Effects of a Lack of Ethics on a Business Environment*" in Chron (March 11, 2019) **[23493]**
"*The Effects of Perceived Corporate Social Responsibility on Employee Attitudes*" in Business Ethics Quarterly (Vol. 24, April 2014, No. 2, pp. 165) **[22144]**, **[34306]**
Effingham Chamber of Commerce and Industry **[39158]**
Effingham County Chamber of Commerce **[38730]**
"*Effort Is Growing to Offer Healthier Choices in Vending Machines*" in Philadelphia Inquirer (July 29, 2011) **[8017]**, **[8094]**, **[16254]**, **[34004]**
"*Egg Fight: The Yolk's on the Shorts*" in Barron's (Vol. 88, July 7, 2008, No. 27, pp. 20) **[6378]**, **[7734]**, **[9481]**, **[17034]**, **[20622]**, **[20868]**, **[23859]**
EGL Ventures **[38807]**
EIFS Industry Members Association (EIMA) **[8845]**
EIGERlab **[39402]**
"*Eight Bucks an Hour*" in South Florida Business Journal (Vol. 34, July 11, 2014, No. 51, pp. 13) **[22561]**, **[31280]**, **[32521]**
"*Eight Cannabis Leaders Discuss Emerging Trends in the Industry Going Forward: 2020*" in Forbes (May 6, 2020) **[4998]**
"*Eight Common Loan Scams – Don't Fall for Them*" in Small Business Trends (February 8, 2023) **[16555]**
Eight Sheet Outdoor Advertising Association [31835]
"*Eight Tips For Leaders On Protecting the Team*" in Puget Sound Business Journal (Vol. 35, August 22, 2014, No. 18, pp. 13) **[14410]**, **[22145]**, **[28565]**
Einstein Bros. Bagels **[1225]**
Eisenhower Foundation for the Prevention of Violence [30276]
El Cajon Chamber of Commerce [37150]
El Camino College Small Business Development Center **[36573]**
El Camino Hospital **[1041]**, **[8296]**
El Camino Hospital Auxiliary [1041], [8296]
El Campo Chamber of Commerce and Agriculture **[45134]**
El Centro Chamber of Commerce and Visitors Bureau **[36874]**
The El Cerrito Chamber of Commerce (ECCC) **[36875]**
El Dorado Chamber of Commerce (EDCC) **[36458]**, **[39885]**
El Dorado County Chamber of Commerce **[36876]**
El Dorado Hills Chamber of Commerce **[36877]**
El Dorado Springs Chamber of Commerce **[41556]**
El Dorado Ventures **[37357]**
El Pajjaro Community Development Corp. **[37567]**
El Paso Chamber of Commerce **[45135]**
El Paso Community College (EPCC) **[45576]**
El Paso Community College Small Business Development Center **[44915]**
El Paso Hispanic Chamber of Commerce (EPHCC) **[45136]**
El Paso Minority Business Development Center **[45420]**
El Pollo Loco, Inc. **[14156]**
El Reno Chamber of Commerce and Development Corp. **[43754]**
El Segundo Chamber of Commerce **[36878]**
El Sobrante Chamber of Commerce **[36879]**
eLab **[42967]**
eLab Ventures **[41045]**

Master Index Employee
Master Index

"Elanco Challenges Bayer's Advantage, K9 Advantix Ad Claims" in Pet Product News (Vol. 64, November 2010, No. 11, pp. 11) **[270]**, **[672]**, **[12196]**, **[19828]**, **[21838]**, **[25313]**, **[29767]**
ELAP Family Law Fellowship (ELAP) **[46213]**
"Elastic Path Software Joins Canada in G20 Young Entrepreneur Summit" in Marketwire (June 14, 2010) **[14774]**, **[27540]**, **[33848]**, **[36019]**
"Elder Care Costs Surge" in National Underwriter Life & Health (Vol. 114, November 8, 2020, No. 21, pp. 25) **[180]**, **[1029]**, **[8248]**, **[8906]**, **[11508]**, **[23860]**, **[27264]**
"Elder Care, Rx Drug Reforms Top Zoeller's Agenda" in Times (December 21, 2010) **[181]**, **[1030]**, **[5156]**, **[8249]**, **[11509]**, **[25314]**
"Elder-Care Seminar to Teach Ways to Avoid Falls" in Virginian-Pilot (November 25, 2010) **[182]**, **[1031]**, **[8250]**, **[11510]**
Elderly Living and Learning Facility (ELLF) [202], [11551]
Eldon Area Chamber of Commerce (ECC) **[41557]**
Eldora Area Chamber of Commerce (EACC) **[39736]**
"Election Futures are a Smart Idea" in Canadian Business (Vol. 85, June 11, 2012, No. 10, pp. 18) **[9482]**, **[25315]**
Electra Chamber of Commerce **[45137]**
Electric Machines and Power Systems [32870]
Electric Motors, Drives and Control Circuits **[2055]**
Electric Power Components and Systems **[32870]**
Electric Supply Jobbers Association [5352]
Electrical Contractor **[5395]**
Electrical Engineering in Japan (EEJ) **[32871]**
Electrical Ladder Drawings, Schematics & Diagrams (Onsite) **[5357]**, **[19440]**, **[21382]**
Electrical Safety Workshop **[5398]**
Electrical Troubleshooting & Preventive Maintenance (Onsite) **[5358]**, **[21383]**
Electrical Wholesaling **[5396]**
"Electrician Tools – Your List for Starting a Business" in Small Business Trends (January 25, 2023) **[5369]**
Electrogists International [5353]
"Electrolux Feeding Economy: Contracts for Local Firms at $64 Million; Supplier Bids Up Next" in Memphis Business Journal (Vol. 34, June 22, 2012, No. 10, pp. 1) **[4069]**, **[29193]**
"Electrolux Nears Product Testing" in Memphis Business Journal (Vol. 34, September 21, 2012, No. 23, pp. 1) **[26545]**, **[29194]**
Electrolysis Society of America [7847]
Electronic Commerce **[2733]**, **[9134]**, **[14411]**, **[16414]**, **[17665]**, **[20869]**, **[21839]**, **[26267]**, **[27541]**, **[29768]**, **[30716]**, **[32522]**, **[34005]**
Electronic & Computer Repair Services Industry in the US - Market Research Report **[3579]**
Electronic Distribution Show **[4414]**
Electronic Editing (Onsite) **[21384]**
Electronic International Journal for Time Use Research [2175], [10477]
Electronic Literature Organization (ELO) **[5423]**
Electronic Media [2472], [13048]
Electronic Privacy Information Center (EPIC) **[14371]**
Electronic Security Association (ESA) **[14372]**
Electronic Solutions Co. (ESC) **[30998]**
Electronic Tax Filers [15454]
"Electronics Assembly" in Canadian Electronics (Vol. 23, February 2008, No. 1, pp. 12) **[26268]**, **[29195]**, **[30717]**
Electronics for Imaging, Inc. (EFI) **[37358]**
Electronics Manufacturers Association of BC [3420], [3601], [3765]
"Electronics Recyclers Poised to Grow" in Austin Business Journal (Vol. 31, July 22, 2011, No. 20, pp. A1) **[4393]**, **[13710]**
Electronics Representatives Association (ERA) **[4380]**
Electronics Technicians Association International (ETA) **[14343]**, **[15559]**
Element 8 [46189]
Element Partners **[44337]**
Element Tattoo Supply **[15323]**
Elements Massage [10781]
Elements Therapeutic Massage L.L.C. **[10781]**
"Eleni Reed: C&W Gets Green Star" in Crain's New York Business (Vol. 24, January 6, 2008, No. 1, pp. 25) **[13189]**, **[23188]**
Elephant Butte Chamber of Commerce **[42315]**
ELEVATE [10256]
Elevate Ventures **[39630]**
Elevate Your Social Media Marketing and Presence for Engagement and Growth **[29512]**, **[33522]**, **[35707]**
Elevated Entrepreneurship: A Female Entrepreneur's Perspective with Michelle Pippin **[35898]**
Elevated Entrepreneurship: Alan Stein Jr.: Improving Your Entrepreneurial Game **[24208]**
Elevated Entrepreneurship: Amber Hurdle: The Science of Recruiting Well **[26712]**
Elevated Entrepreneurship: Art as a Business with Jessica Abel **[4626]**
Elevated Entrepreneurship: Ashley Alderson: Connecting in the Chaos **[16648]**
Elevated Entrepreneurship: Creating More by Doing Less with Kate Northrup **[35009]**
Elevated Entrepreneurship: David Wood: Navigating Tough Conversations **[17789]**
Elevated Entrepreneurship: Experiences of Running a Family-Owned Business with Chris Prefontaine **[23690]**
Elevated Entrepreneurship: Geoff Woods: Finding Your One Thing **[16649]**
Elevated Entrepreneurship: Gino Wickman: The Six Essential Traits for Entrepreneurship **[22883]**
Elevated Entrepreneurship: Rural Entrepreneurship with Jessi Roberts **[32345]**
Elevated Entrepreneurship: Ryan Langford: The Entrepreneurial Family **[23674]**
"Elevating the Vital Role of the Custodian" in Cleaning & Maintenance Management (June 1, 2015) **[2066]**
Elgin Area Chamber of Commerce (EACC) **[39159]**
Elgin Business Resource Centre (EBRC) **[46821]**
"Eliminating All of Your Estate Tax Burden" in Contractor (Vol. 57, January 2010, No. 1, pp. 48) **[6023]**, **[34781]**
eLink Design **[40114]**
eLink Ventures, LLC **[40096]**
Elite Entrepreneur Organization **[22455]**
Elixir Enterprises LLC **[45515]**
Elixir Kitchen Space [45515]
Elizabeth Area Chamber of Commerce (EACOC) **[37845]**
Elizabeth Capen **[19135]**, **[30195]**
Elizabeth Chamber of Commerce **[39160]**
Elizabeth City Area Chamber of Commerce **[43128]**
Elizabethton - Carter County Chamber of Commerce **[44740]**
Elizabethtown Small Business Development Center [39993]
Elizabethtown-White Lake Area Chamber of Commerce **[43129]**
Elk City Chamber of Commerce **[43755]**
Elk Grove Chamber of Commerce **[36880]**
Elk Rapids Area Chamber of Commerce (ERACC) **[40907]**
Elk River Area Chamber of Commerce (ERACC) **[41226]**
Elkader Area Chamber of Commerce (EACC) **[39737]**
Elkader Chamber of Commerce [39737]
"Elkhart Education Foundation to Open Supply Store for Teachers" in The Elkart Truth (June 5, 2019) **[15540]**, **[21494]**
Elkhart Lake Area Chamber of Commerce **[46398]**
Elkhorn Area Chamber of Commerce & Tourism Center, Inc. (EACC) **[46399]**
Elkins-Randolph County Chamber of Commerce [46285]
Elko Area Chamber of Commerce **[41934]**
Elko Directory **[41935]**
Elko Nevada Small Business Development Center **[41911]**
Elkton Chamber and Alliance **[40383]**
Ellen Yin Founder and Co-Owner of High Street Hospitality Group **[14055]**
Ellensburg Chamber of Commerce [46114]
Ellenville Area Chamber of Commerce [42567]
Ellenville / Wawarsing Chamber of Commerce (EWCOC) **[42567]**
Ellevate Network [35513]
Ellianos Coffee Co. **[7582]**
Ellicottville Chamber of Commerce **[42568]**
Ellington Chamber of Commerce **[41558]**
Ellinwood Chamber of Commerce **[39886]**
Ellsworth Area Chamber of Commerce **[40276]**
Ellsworth Area Chamber of Commerce (EACC) **[46400]**
Ellsworth-Kanopolis Area Chamber of Commerce **[39887]**
Ellwood City Area Chamber of Commerce **[44206]**
Elm Street Ventures (ESV) **[38093]**
Elma Chamber of Commerce **[46079]**
Elmer's Genealogy Library [7421]
Elmhurst Chamber of Commerce and Industry **[39161]**
Elmhurst Community **[39162]**
"Elon Musk's Solar Firm Is Nearly Doubling Its Massachusetts Workforce" in Boston Business Journal (Vol. 34, May 30, 2014, No. 17, pp. 3) **[5594]**, **[5869]**, **[14919]**, **[23189]**, **[26546]**
Eloy Chamber of Commerce (ECC) **[36329]**
Elroy Area Advancement Corporation [46401]
Elroy Area Chamber of Commerce **[46401]**
Ely Chamber of Commerce (ECC) **[41227]**
Ely Nevada Small Business Development Center **[41912]**
EM Microelectronic-US Inc. **[30999]**
"Emack & Bolio's Founder Blames Brookline Store Closure on Rising Rents" in Ice Cream Reporter (Vol. 23, October 20, 2010, No. 11, pp. 8) **[8560]**, **[20425]**, **[29769]**, **[32523]**
Email Innovations Summit **[10685]**, **[29506]**, **[29555]**, **[30171]**
"Email Marketing: Still the Most Powerful Tool to Take Your Business to the Next Level" in Forbes (October 26, 2020) **[29525]**
The Ember Company **[42866]**
EMBOLDEN Action LLC **[30641]**
Embrace the Pace **[39537]**
Embrase Business Consulting **[46902]**
Embroiderers' Guild of America (EGA) **[4655]**
EmbroidMe [32365]
Embroidme [3169]
"Embry-Riddle Aeronautical University Opening Alliance Campus" in Dallas Business Journal (Vol. 35, May 25, 2012, No. 37, pp. 1) **[21495]**
EMDA Member Directory [17036]
Emerald Lotus Massage & Spa [1404]
Emerald Technology Ventures Inc. **[46785]**
Emerge Memphis **[44844]**
Emerge Natural Sales Solutions **[8068]**, **[32692]**
Emerge2 Digital Inc. **[33665]**, **[46846]**
Emergence Capital Partners (ECP) **[37359]**
"The Emergence of Governance In an Open Source Community" in Academy of Management Journal (Vol. 50, No. 5, October 1, 2007, pp. 1079) **[14775]**, **[28566]**, **[33849]**
"Emergency Cannabis Small Business Health and Safety Act - A Legislative Update" in Cannabis Industry Journal (May 4, 2020) **[4999]**
Emergency Care Research Institute [10886], [10964]
Emergency Medical Services Magazine--Buyers Guide Issue: The Journal of Emergency Care, Rescue and Transportation **[10947]**
Emergent Incubator **[45516]**
Emerging Business Online: Global Markets and the Power of B2B Internet Marketing **[9135]**, **[16415]**, **[17666]**, **[21840]**, **[27542]**, **[29770]**, **[34006]**
"The Emerging Capital Market for Nonprofits" in Harvard Business Review (Vol. 88, October 2010, No. 10, pp. 110) **[6379]**, **[7104]**, **[9483]**, **[29771]**, **[35336]**
Emerging Enterprise Center (EEC) **[38144]**
"Emerging Equals" in Business Strategy Review (Vol. 25, Summer 2014, No. 2, pp. 38) **[20567]**, **[30561]**
"Emerging Tech Companies in One State Can Now Apply for Matching Business Grants" in Small Business Trends (November 5, 2022) **[33561]**
Emerging Technology Centers (ETC) **[40454]**
Emerging Technology Partners LLC (ETP) **[37734]**
Emily Eldh Owner of The Muffin Drop **[36036]**
Emily Griffith Opportunity School [37959]
Emily Griffith Technical College (EGTC) **[37959]**
"Emissions: Cloudy Skies" in Canadian Business (Vol. 81, October 27, 2008, No. 18, pp. 101) **[5595]**, **[5870]**, **[23190]**, **[25316]**
Emmanuel College - Cardinal Cushing Library **[997]**, **[5214]**
Emmetsburg Chamber of Commerce (ECC) **[39738]**
"Emotional Brand Attachment and Brand Personality: The Relative Importance of the Actual and the Ideal Self" in Journal of Marketing (Vol. 75, July 2011, No. 4, pp. 35) **[29772]**, **[31756]**, **[31862]**
"Empathy: An Entrepreneur's Killer App" in Women Entrepreneur (February 3, 2009) **[20870]**, **[22562]**, **[26547]**, **[28567]**, **[35188]**
"Empathy, Engagement the 'Secret Sauce' for Post-Pandemic Leadership Success" in Minority Business Entrepreneur (October 11, 2022) **[28568]**
"Empathy, Engagement the 'Secret Sauce' for Post-Pandemic Leadership Success" in Minority Business Entrepreneur (Vol. 39, Fall, 2022, No. 4, pp. 48-49) **[22146]**
"The Emperor Strikes Back" in Canadian Business (Vol. 80, March 26, 2007, No. 7, pp. 48) **[6380]**, **[9484]**, **[18054]**, **[18943]**
Empire Angels **[42738]**
Empire Building Diagnostics Inc. (EBD) **[4313]**
Empire Business Brokers **[2160]**
Empire College School of Business **[37657]**
Empire State Development-Division for Small Business-Procurement Assistance Program (ESD) **[42819]**
Empire State Development - Minority and Women's Business Development Division (DMWBD) **[42705]**
Empire State Honey Producers Association **[1436]**
Employee Benefit Plan Review **[17383]**, **[27095]**
Employee Benefit Research Institute (EBRI) **[15488]**, **[17261]**, **[17397]**, **[19728]**
Employee Benefits Infosource™ [17418]
"Employee Benefits Requirements As a Small Business Owner" in WeWork (Jan. 13, 2021) **[17300]**
"The Employee Brand: Is Yours an All-Star?" in Business Horizons (September-October 2007, pp. 423) **[22147]**, **[29773]**
Employee Development Systems Inc. (EDSI) **[22317]**

Small Business Sourcebook • 42nd Edition 3227

Employee **Master Index**

Employee Management for Small Business **[22563]**, **[26927]**, **[28569]**
"Employee Theft: Identify & Prevent Fraud Embezzlement & Pilfering" in ZenBusiness (Aug. 11, 2021) **[22344]**, **[32385]**
"Employee Training and Development Is the Biggest HR Focus Area in 2019" in Payscale (January 7. 2019) **[9995]**
"Employee vs. Independent Contractor: What Employers Need to Know" in Legal Zoom (March 24, 2023) **[5429]**, **[26548]**, **[32989]**
"Employees Change Clothes at Work? Heed New Pay Rules" in HR Specialist (Vol. 8, September 2010, No. 9, pp. 1) **[18569]**, **[26928]**
"Employees Want Genuine Corporate Social Responsibility, Not Greenwashing" in The Conversation (Jan. 29, 2020) **[34307]**
"Employer Costs for Employee Compensation - June 2020" in Bureau of Labor Statistics (September 17, 2020) **[35473]**
"Employer Guide to Tax Credits for Hiring Employees With Disabilities" in U.S. Chamber of Commerce (Aug. 25, 2022) **[26549]**, **[30562]**
"Employer Jobless Tax Could Rise" in Sacramento Business Journal (Vol. 28, May 27, 2011, No. 13, pp. 1) **[8907]**, **[24975]**, **[27265]**, **[34782]**
Employer Legal Forms Simplified **[62]**, **[11931]**, **[15379]**, **[16801]**, **[18570]**, **[26929]**
Employers Council on Flexible Compensation (ECFC) **[17262]**, **[19729]**
Employers Directory [39773]
Employers Group (EG) **[34960]**
"Employers See Workers' Comp Rates Rising" in Sacramento Business Journal (Vol. 28, April 8, 2011, No. 6, pp. 1) **[18571]**, **[25770]**, **[34007]**, **[35943]**
Employing Bookbinders of American [1615], [1716]
Employment Agencies Protective Association [5437], [15637]
Employment Discrimination Law Update (Onsite) **[18485]**, **[20558]**
Employment & Recruiting Agencies Industry in the US - Market Report **[5430]**, **[15648]**
"Employment and Unemployment Among Youth - Summer 2010" in Montly Labor Review (Vol. 133, September 2010, No. 9, pp. 2) **[26550]**, **[26930]**
Emporia Area Chamber of Commerce [39888]
Emporia Area Chamber and Visitors Bureau **[39888]**
Emporia Chamber of Commerce and Convention and Visitors Bureau [39888]
Emporia-Greensville Chamber of Commerce **[45857]**
"Empowered" in Harvard Business Review (Vol. 88, July-August 2010, No. 7-8, pp. 94) **[8653]**, **[9136]**, **[12931]**, **[19345]**, **[20426]**, **[21841]**, **[22148]**, **[28570]**, **[31757]**, **[31863]**
EmpowerHome Team **[33666]**
"Empreinte Enters the Activewear Market with IN-PULSE" in The Lingerie Journal (November 5, 2019) **[3019]**, **[10303]**
Empress Chili **[14157]**
"Empty Lots Could Be Full of Promise" in San Francisco Business Times (Vol. 28, March 14, 2014, No. 34, pp. 4) **[4070]**, **[13190]**, **[13443]**, **[25317]**
"Empty Office Blues" in Business Journal Portland (Vol. 26, December 4, 2009, No. 39, pp. 1) **[13444]**, **[13785]**, **[31281]**
"EMU, Spark Plan Business Incubator for Ypsilanti" in Crain's Detroit Business (Vol. 23, October 15, 2007, No. 42, pp. 3) **[21496]**, **[31965]**, **[32750]**, **[35234]**
Enablis **[46894]**
Enactus **[41673]**
Enactus Canada **[22456]**
Enbede Co. **[16499]**
"EnCana Axes Spending on Gas Wells" in Globe & Mail (February 16, 2006, pp. B1) **[6381]**, **[9485]**, **[18944]**, **[19508]**, **[29196]**
Encinitas Chamber of Commerce (ECC) **[36881]**
Encino Chamber of Commerce **[36882]**
Encore Business Solutions Inc. **[3455]**
"Encore Container, Manufacturer of Plastic Drums and IBC Totes, Leads the Way in Environmental Sustainability" in Ecology, Environment & Conservation Business (January 25, 2014, pp. 33) **[13711]**, **[23191]**, **[29197]**
"Encore on Cue: Migratory Hopes More Venues, Artists Take Note of Its Kiosks That Offer Concert Recordings to Fans Immediately After Shows" in Los Angeles Business Journal (Vol. 34, May 28, 2012, No. 22, pp. 5) **[10022]**, **[11263]**
"Encouraging Study in Critical Languages" in Occupational Outlook Quarterly (Vol. 55, Summer 2011, No. 2, pp. 23) **[2599]**, **[14412]**, **[15936]**, **[21497]**, **[24976]**, **[26931]**
Encyclopedia of Associations: National Organizations of the U.S. **[1053]**
Encyclopedia of Small Business **[22564]**, **[24655]**
Encyclopedia of Social Work **[26932]**
"End of the Beginning" in Canadian Business (Vol. 81, November 10, 2008, No. 19, pp. 17) **[4718]**, **[4746]**, **[4787]**, **[6382]**, **[9486]**, **[20282]**, **[20871]**, **[25318]**, **[27543]**
"The End of Clock-Punching" in Canadian Business (Vol. 83, September 14, 2010, No. 15, pp. 96) **[2185]**, **[22149]**, **[25319]**, **[26933]**, **[34984]**
"End of an Era" in Barron's (Vol. 88, July 7, 2008, No. 27, pp. 3) **[6383]**, **[9487]**, **[20872]**, **[23861]**, **[26551]**
The End of the Golden Age of Online Business with Erica Courdae & Tasha L. Harrison **[27816]**
"The End of RIM" in Canadian Business (Vol. 85, August 13, 2012, No. 13, pp. 22) **[21498]**, **[26269]**, **[27544]**
"The End of Solution Sales: The Old Playbook No Longer Works. Star Salespeople Now Seek To Upend the Customer's Current Approach to Doing Business" in Harvard Business Review (Vol. 90, July-August 2012, No. 7-8, pp. 60) **[32524]**
Endeavor Capital Management **[40683]**
Endeavor Center **[43662]**
"Endeca Gears Up for Likely IPO Bid" in Boston Business Journal (Vol. 31, July 1, 2011, No. 23, pp. 1) **[9137]**, **[9488]**, **[18055]**, **[21842]**, **[31282]**
Endorphin Advisors **[30196]**
"Endowments for Colleges Hit Hard in '09' in Milwaukee Business Journal (Vol. 27, February 12, 2010, No. 20, pp. A1) **[7105]**, **[20873]**, **[21499]**
"The Enduring Popularity of Microsoft Word" in TMCNet.com (November 26, 2018) **[16529]**
Energetics Technology Center (ETC) **[40455]**
Energy Auditing 101: Identifying Cost Saving Opportunities in Plants & Buildings (Onsite) **[23064]**
"Energy Boom Spurring Manufacturing Growth" in Pittsburgh Business Times (Vol. 33, May 2, 2014, No. 42, pp. 7) **[18056]**, **[26270]**, **[29198]**
"Energy Consulting Company to Expand" in Austin Business JournalInc. (Vol. 28, November 7, 2008, No. 34, pp. A1) **[5596]**, **[5871]**, **[18057]**, **[23192]**
"Energy Efficiency Ordinance Softened" in Austin Business JournalInc. (Vol. 28, October 3, 2008, No. 29) **[5597]**, **[5872]**, **[13191]**, **[23193]**, **[25320]**
Energy Efficient Building Association [3937]
Energy and Environmental Building Alliance (EEBA) **[3937]**
"Energy Exec Bankrolls Big-Budget UT Film" in Austin Business Journal (Vol. 34, June 6, 2014, No. 16, pp. A8) **[6182]**, **[15149]**, **[21500]**
"Energy Firms Face Stricter Definitions" in Globe & Mail (March 26, 2007, pp. B3) **[6384]**, **[9489]**, **[25321]**, **[29199]**
"ENERGY: Georgia Power to Buy More Solar: Customer Bills Will Not Be Affected By Renewable Energy Plan, Utility Says" in Atlanta Journal-Constitution (September 27, 2012, pp. A13) **[14920]**, **[19829]**
Energy Management and Controls Society [32713]
"Energy MPLs: Pipeline to Profits" in Barron's (Vol. 89, July 27, 2009, No. 30, pp. 9) **[6385]**, **[9490]**, **[23862]**, **[33144]**
"Energy Slide Slows 4th-Quarter Profits" in Globe & Mail (April 13, 2007, pp. B9) **[9491]**, **[24656]**, **[29200]**
"Bartering Takes Businesses Back to Basics" in Buffalo News (July 9, 2010) **[2146]**, **[17250]**, **[18058]**, **[29774]**, **[31283]**
Enertech Capital /Enertech Capital Partners L.P. **[44338]**
Engage Annual Conference [24226]
"Engage Employees to Embed DEI Across Your Association" in Assocations Now (May 9, 2022) **[30563]**
Engine Builder **[14563]**
Engine Professional **[14564]**
Engineered Lighting Products, Inc. (ELP) **[31072]**
"Engineering Business Success: Essential Lessons In Building A Thriving Company" **[22565]**
Engineering Contractors Association (ECA) **[3938]**
Engineering Harmonics Inc. **[13055]**, **[13662]**
Engineering Research Center [40474]
Engineering and Technical Consultants Inc. (ETC) **[4314]**
Englewood Area Chamber of Commerce [38375]
Englewood-Cape Haze Area Chamber of Commerce [38375]
Englewood Chamber of Commerce (ECC) **[42122]**
Englewood Florida Chamber of Commerce **[38375]**
"Enhancing Brand Image Via Sponsorship: Strength of Association Effects" in International Journal of Advertising (Vol. 31, February 2012, No. 1, pp. 113) **[8654]**, **[10648]**
Enhancing Your Management Skills (Onsite) **[22051]**, **[28326]**
Enhancing Your People Skills **[17574]**, **[22052]**
Enid/Northwest Oklahoma SCORE **[43724]**
Enlaso Corp. [15955]
Ennis Area Chamber of Commerce **[41762]**
Ennis Chamber of Commerce **[45138]**
Ennis Chamber of Commerce [41762]
The Ennovation Center **[41674]**
Enoch Pratt Free Library **[47409]**
E.nopi [21718]
"Enriching the Ecosystem: A Four-Point Plan for Linking Innovation, Enterprises, and Jobs" in Harvard Business Review (Vol. 90, March 2012, No. 3, pp. 140) **[5598]**, **[5873]**, **[21501]**, **[23194]**, **[26552]**, **[28028]**, **[30718]**, **[31284]**
"Entenmann's Brings Back Classic Packaging after Rampant Customer Complaints" in Small Business Trends (March 12, 2023) **[1253]**, **[17440]**
Enterprise Center of Johnson County (ECJC) **[39971]**
The Enterprise Center in Johnson County (ECJC) **[39972]**
Enterprise Center at Plymouth (ECP) **[42025]**
Enterprise Center at Salem State College [40750]
Enterprise Center at Salem State University (SSU) **[40750]**
Enterprise Chamber of Commerce **[36107]**
Enterprise Development Corporation of South Florida **[38558]**
Enterprise Florida Inc.-Marketing And Development Div. (EFI) **[38255]**
Enterprise Greater Moncton [46731]
"Enterprise Holdings Hires More Than 4,000 Military Veterans Since Joining 100,000 Jobs Mission Coalition" in Defense & Aerospace Business (September 3, 2014, pp. 9) **[1157]**, **[13786]**, **[34308]**
Enterprise and Small Business: Principles, Practice and Policy **[22566]**, **[24657]**
Enterprise & Society: The International Journal of Business History **[24863]**
EnterpriseWorks **[39403]**
EnterpriseWorks Chicago (EWC) **[39404]**
Enterprising Women: The Magazine for Women Business Owners **[35926]**
Entertainment Media Ventures (EMV) **[37735]**
Entertainment Merchants Association (EMA) **[14748]**
Entertainment Operators of America [4846]
Entertainment Software Association (ESA) **[14749]**
Entree **[16025]**
The Entrepreneur **[43466]**
Entrepreneur; "21 Success Tips for Young and Aspiring Entrepreneurs" in [36011]
Entrepreneur (Aug. 30, 2021); "4 Reasons Small Businesses Need Nonbank Lenders More Than Ever" in [30903]
The Entrepreneur Authority L.L.C. **[24307]**
The Entrepreneur Center **[40106]**
Entrepreneur Center of Central Texas **[45517]**
Entrepreneur Centers of North Dakota [47346]
Entrepreneur Franchise 500 Ranking **[24355]**
Entrepreneur Inc. **[33697]**
Entrepreneur (Jan. 17, 2021); "How to Lead Kids Down a Path to Entrepreneurship in 2021" in [36024]
Entrepreneur Magazine **[8821]**, **[33625]**
Entrepreneur Magazine's Ultimate Guide to Buying or Selling a Business **[18945]**, **[19659]**, **[24356]**, **[33014]**
Entrepreneur Media Inc. **[33698]**
The Entrepreneur Next Door: Discover the Secrets to Financial Independence **[22567]**, **[24658]**
Entrepreneur Press [33698]
"Entrepreneur Quiz: Is Starting a Business Right for You?" in Small Business Trends (October 17, 2019) **[22568]**
"The Entrepreneur Salary: How Much Should You Pay Yourself?" in NerdWallet (Oct. 30, 2020) **[19736]**
"Entrepreneur Says Spirituality Has Been a Key to Her Success" in Business First Columbus (Vol. 25, October 17, 2008, No. 8, pp. 1) **[8176]**, **[8205]**, **[9035]**, **[22569]**, **[35772]**
The Entrepreneur Space (ES) **[42867]**
Entrepreneurial Development Center Inc. (EDC) **[39817]**
Entrepreneurial and Education Center **[46563]**
Entrepreneurial Finance **[17496]**, **[22570]**, **[23863]**, **[32406]**, **[34458]**
Entrepreneurial Management Institute [22952]
Entrepreneurial Marketing: How to Develop Customer Demand **[10649]**
"Entrepreneurial Orientation and Firm Performance: The Unique Impact of Innovativeness, Proactiveness, and Risk-taking" in Journal of Small Business and Entrepreneurship (Vol. 23, Winter 2010, No. 1) **[18946]**, **[19509]**, **[22571]**, **[27863]**, **[28571]**, **[31966]**, **[32751]**
"Entrepreneurial passion: A systematic review and research opportunities" in Journal of Small Business Strategy (August 11, 2021) **[22942]**
Entrepreneurial Small Business **[22572]**, **[23864]**, **[24659]**
"'Entrepreneurial Spirit' Leads Executives to Form New Tower Company" in South Florida Business Journal (Vol. 34, February 21, 2014, No. 31, pp. 6) **[2699]**, **[7066]**, **[28245]**, **[33015]**

3228 **Small Business Sourcebook • 42nd Edition**

"Entrepreneurial StrengthsFinder" **[22378]**
Entrepreneurial Studies Center [23019]
Entrepreneurial Thought Leaders: A New Approach to the Great Outdoors **[34590]**
Entrepreneurial Thought Leaders: Behind the Scenes of a Mega-Unicorn **[34591]**
Entrepreneurial Thought Leaders: Breaking the Venture Capital Mold **[35412]**
Entrepreneurial Thought Leaders: Build, Don't Break **[34423]**
Entrepreneurial Thought Leaders: Building Biotech to Last **[34592]**
Entrepreneurial Thought Leaders: Building Startups, Fast and Slow **[34593]**
Entrepreneurial Thought Leaders: Building from Values **[22884]**
Entrepreneurial Thought Leaders: Career Advice from a VC Pro **[35413]**
Entrepreneurial Thought Leaders: Clara Shih (Salesforce AI) - What No One Tells You About Entrepreneurship **[22885]**
Entrepreneurial Thought Leaders: Cody Coleman (Coactive AI) - Starting from 'Why' **[34594]**
Entrepreneurial Thought Leaders: David Allemann (On) - Exploration in Sports Technology **[34595]**
Entrepreneurial Thought Leaders: Derisking Biotech **[34424]**
Entrepreneurial Thought Leaders: Developing a Founder's Mindset **[34596]**
Entrepreneurial Thought Leaders: Diverse Businesses Are Better Businesses **[34425]**
Entrepreneurial Thought Leaders: Driving Innovation **[34597]**
Entrepreneurial Thought Leaders: Engineering Green Materials **[23427]**
Entrepreneurial Thought Leaders: Entrepreneurship Education Is About More than Startup Creation **[34598]**
Entrepreneurial Thought Leaders: Ernestine Fu (Brave Capital) - Taking Action for Startup Success **[34599]**
Entrepreneurial Thought Leaders: Ethical Crypto Innovation **[23558]**
Entrepreneurial Thought Leaders: Finding Deeper Purpose **[34426]**
Entrepreneurial Thought Leaders: Finding Fulfillment in Entrepreneurship **[22886]**
Entrepreneurial Thought Leaders: Fixing Tech's Gender Gap **[34427]**
Entrepreneurial Thought Leaders: From Customer to Co-CEO **[22887]**
Entrepreneurial Thought Leaders: Garry Tan (Y Combinator) - Unconventional Advice for Founders **[34600]**
Entrepreneurial Thought Leaders: How to Build an Ethical Company **[23559]**
Entrepreneurial Thought Leaders: Innovating Accessibly **[34428]**
Entrepreneurial Thought Leaders: Innovating for Social Impact **[34601]**
Entrepreneurial Thought Leaders: Innovation in Ed-Tech and Biotech **[34602]**
Entrepreneurial Thought Leaders: Investing at the Cutting Edge **[35414]**
Entrepreneurial Thought Leaders: Kathleen Eisenhardt (Stanford) - Strategy for New Companies **[34603]**
Entrepreneurial Thought Leaders: Lessons from a Stanford Success **[22888]**
Entrepreneurial Thought Leaders: Making Entrepreneurship More Inclusive **[34604]**
Entrepreneurial Thought Leaders: Maria Barrera (Clayful) - Mental Health Tech, Mentally Healthy Startups **[34605]**
Entrepreneurial Thought Leaders: Marketing for Entrepreneurs **[30151]**
Entrepreneurial Thought Leaders: New Angel Investing **[35415]**
Entrepreneurial Thought Leaders: OpenAI **[23560]**
Entrepreneurial Thought Leaders: Opportunities in Climate Tech **[23428]**
Entrepreneurial Thought Leaders: Problem-Solving for a Unique Market **[34606]**
Entrepreneurial Thought Leaders: Qasar Younis (Applied Intuition) - Radically Pragmatic Insights **[34607]**
Entrepreneurial Thought Leaders: Responsible AI Innovation **[23561]**
Entrepreneurial Thought Leaders: Ruthless Empathy **[34429]**
Entrepreneurial Thought Leaders: Sam Altman (OpenAI) - The Possibilities of AI **[34608]**
Entrepreneurial Thought Leaders: Scaling Operations and People **[18439]**
Entrepreneurial Thought Leaders: Scaling with Resilience **[34609]**
Entrepreneurial Thought Leaders: Scaling Sustainable Fashion **[34610]**

Entrepreneurial Thought Leaders: Seizing Global Success **[22889]**
Entrepreneurial Thought Leaders: Serial Co-Founders **[34611]**
Entrepreneurial Thought Leaders: Sharon Prince (Grace Farms Foundation) - Designing from Values **[22890]**
Entrepreneurial Thought Leaders: Shiza Shahid (Our Place) - A Meaningful Entrepreneurial Path **[22891]**
Entrepreneurial Thought Leaders: Solving for Infrastructure **[32916]**
Entrepreneurial Thought Leaders: The Biodesign Innovation Process **[24806]**
Entrepreneurial Thought Leaders: The Power of Scrappiness **[22892]**
Entrepreneurial Thought Leaders: The Truth about Entrepreneurship **[22893]**
Entrepreneurial Thought Leaders: Transforming Digital Healthcare **[34430]**
Entrepreneurial Thought Leaders: Weathering a Storm **[24807]**
Entrepreneurial Thought Leaders: What Investors Want **[34612]**
Entrepreneurial Thought Leaders: What is Responsible Innovation? **[34431]**
Entrepreneurial Thought Leaders: Why Startups Fail **[34613]**
Entrepreneurial Thought Leaders: World Positive Investing **[35416]**
The Entrepreneur's Almanac: Fascinating Figures, Fundamentals and Facts You Need to Run and Grow Your Business **[22573]**
The Entrepreneurs Center (TEC) **[43663]**
Entrepreneurs of Color Magazine [30438]
Entrepreneurs in Community Lawyering (ECL) **[45518]**
"*Entrepreneurs Conference Recap: the Business Revolution: Start Focusing On a Growth Strategy For Your Company*" in Black Enterprise (Vol. 45, July-August, 2014, No. 1, pp. 17) **[15856]**, **[19510]**, **[35051]**
Entrepreneur's EDGE **[43336]**
The Entrepreneur's Edge: Finding Money, Making Money, Keeping Money **[22574]**, **[23865]**, **[24530]**
Entrepreneurs Forum [44085]
Entrepreneurs Forum of Greater Philadelphia (EFGP) **[44085]**
Entrepreneurs Foundation of Central Texas **[44886]**
Entrepreneurs Foundation of Colorado [37777]
Entrepreneurs Foundation of Hawaii (EFH) **[38860]**
"*Entrepreneurs and Gamblers: Shared Traits*" in Entrepreneur (Sept. 8, 2017) **[7281]**, **[22575]**
Entrepreneur's Information Sourcebook **[22379]**, **[33432]**
Entrepreneurs Organization (EO) **[33456]**, **[36003]**, **[45949]**
Entrepreneurs' Organization At Large - U.S. Central Chapter (EO) **[22457]**
Entrepreneurs' Organization - Atlanta Chapter (EO) **[38620]**
Entrepreneurs' Organization - Austin Chapter (EO) **[44887]**
Entrepreneurs' Organization - Baltimore Chapter (EO Baltimore) **[40332]**
Entrepreneurs' Organization - Birmingham Chapter (EO) **[36045]**
Entrepreneurs' Organization - Boston Chapter (EO) **[40487]**
Entrepreneurs' Organization - Bryan-College Station (EO) **[44888]**
Entrepreneurs' Organization - Capital District New York (EO) **[42378]**
Entrepreneurs' Organization - Charleston Chapter (EO) **[44496]**
Entrepreneurs' Organization - Charlotte Chapter (EO) **[43034]**
Entrepreneurs' Organization - Chicago Chapter (EO) **[38970]**
Entrepreneurs' Organization - Cincinnati Chapter (EO) **[43337]**
Entrepreneurs' Organization - Cleveland Chapter (EO) **[43338]**
Entrepreneurs' Organization - Columbus Chapter (EO) **[43339]**
Entrepreneurs' Organization - Connecticut Chapter (EO) **[37975]**
Entrepreneurs' Organization - Dallas Chapter (EO) **[44889]**
Entrepreneurs' Organization - Detroit Chapter (EO) **[40796]**
Entrepreneurs' Organization - Fort Worth Chapter (EO) **[44890]**
Entrepreneurs' Organization - Houston Chapter (EO) **[44891]**
Entrepreneurs' Organization - Indianapolis Chapter (EO) **[39468]**
Entrepreneurs' Organization - Iowa Chapter (EO) **[39671]**

Entrepreneurs' Organization - Kansas City Chapter (EO) **[41461]**
Entrepreneurs' Organization - Knoxville Chapter **[44679]**
Entrepreneurs' Organization - Louisiana Chapter (EO) **[40121]**
Entrepreneurs' Organization - Minnesota Chapter **[41149]**
Entrepreneurs' Organization - Nashville Chapter **[44680]**
Entrepreneurs' Organization - Nebraska Chapter (EO) **[41814]**
Entrepreneurs' Organization - New Jersey Chapter (EO) **[42030]**
Entrepreneurs' Organization - New York Chapter (EO) **[22458]**
Entrepreneurs' Organization - New York Long Island Chapter (EO) **[42379]**
Entrepreneurs' Organization - Oklahoma City Chapter (EO) **[43702]**
Entrepreneurs' Organization - Pittsburgh Chapter (EO) **[44086]**
Entrepreneurs' Organization - Raleigh Durham Chapter **[43130]**
Entrepreneurs' Organization - Richmond Chapter (EO) **[45759]**
Entrepreneurs' Organization - St. Louis Chapter **[41462]**
Entrepreneurs' Organization - San Antonio Chapter (EO) **[44892]**
Entrepreneurs' Organization - South Florida Chapter (EO) **[38206]**
Entrepreneurs' Organization - Southeast Virginia Chapter (EO) **[45760]**
Entrepreneurs' Organization - Tampa Bay Chapter (EO) **[38207]**
Entrepreneurs' Organization - Tulsa Chapter (EO) **[43703]**
Entrepreneurs' Organization - Washington, DC Chapter (EO DC) **[38151]**
Entrepreneurs' Organization - West Michigan Chapter (EO) **[40797]**
Entrepreneurs' Organization - Western New York Chapter (EO) **[42380]**
Entrepreneurs' Organization - Wisconsin Chapter (EO) **[46313]**
Entrepreneur's Reference Guide to Small Business Information **[22946]**
Entrepreneurs Roundtable Accelerator (ERA) **[42868]**
"*Entrepreneurs: Search Party*" in Business Strategy Review (Vol. 21, Autumn 2010, No. 3, pp. 30) **[19346]**, **[22380]**, **[24531]**, **[28060]**
Entrepreneur's Showcase: Market Research for Small Businesses and the Woman Entrepreneur's Guide to Financing a Business **[29489]**
The Entrepreneur's Source (TES) **[2161]**
The Entrepreneur's Space (ES) **[42869]**
"*Entrepreneurs Take Different Paths, but Arrive at Same Place*" in Business Journal Portland (Vol. 30, February 14, 2014, No. 50, pp. 6) **[22381]**, **[35999]**
Entrepreneurship **[18861]**, **[18947]**, **[22382]**, **[22576]**, **[28061]**, **[29559]**
Entrepreneurship: A Process Perspective **[18059]**, **[18572]**, **[18948]**, **[22577]**, **[24660]**
Entrepreneurship: A Small Business Approach **[22578]**, **[24532]**
Entrepreneurship and the Creation of Small Firms: Empirical Studies of New Ventures **[22383]**, **[24533]**
Entrepreneurship Development Institute (EDI) **[38559]**
Entrepreneurship for Dummies **[22579]**, **[33562]**, **[34501]**
Entrepreneurship and Ethics: Ethics in Venture Capital **[23562]**
Entrepreneurship and Ethics: Facing a Crisis with Principles **[23563]**
Entrepreneurship and Ethics: Teaching Ethical Entrepreneurship **[23564]**
Entrepreneurship and Ethics: The Ethics of Emerging Technologies **[23565]**
Entrepreneurship and Ethics: Theranos Whistleblower Erika Cheung on Incentivizing Ethics **[23566]**
The Entrepreneurship Institute (TEI) **[22974]**, **[33457]**
Entrepreneurship Laval (EL) **[46903]**
"*Entrepreneurship and Service Innovation*" in Journal of Business & Industrial Marketing (Vol. 29, July 2014, No. 6) **[22580]**, **[27864]**, **[33145]**
Entrepreneurship and Small Business Development in the Former Soviet Bloc **[22581]**, **[24661]**, **[27545]**
Entrepreneurship: Successfully Launching New Ventures **[22384]**, **[24534]**
Entrepreneurship Theory and Practice (ETP) **[8822]**, **[33626]**
Entrepreneurship: Theory, Process, and Practice **[22582]**, **[24662]**
The Entrust Group **[35461]**
Enumclaw Chamber of Commerce (EACC) **[46080]**
Envar Services Inc. **[25620]**

Envelope Manufacturers Association (EMA) [11659]
Envelope Manufacturers Association of America [11659]
Envest Capital Partners [45921]
Envest Private Equity [45921]
Enviro Business Guide [5485], [13687], [23031]
EnviroBusiness Inc. (EBI) [5749]
"Environment Consulting Service Market Incredible Possibilities, Growth Analysis and Forecast to 2024" in *Tech Mag (October 28, 2019)* [5599], [10650]
Environment Systems and Decisions [5757]
Environmental Assessment Services Inc. [25621], [35963]
Environmental Bankers Association (EBA) [23456]
Environmental Building News [4272]
Environmental Business Consultants (EBC) [5750], [28987]
Environmental Business Council of New England (EBCNE) [5486], [5794]
Environmental Business International Inc. (EBI) [2261]
Environmental Compliance Alert [5743]
Environmental Consulting Industry in the US - Market Research Report [5737], [23413]
Environmental Defence [5487]
Environmental Design Research Association (EDRA) [23032]
Environmental & Energy Technology Council of Maine (E2TECH) [23033]
Environmental Engineering Science [7971]
Environmental & Engineering Services Inc. (EESI) [541], [4315], [5400]
Environmental Entrepreneurs (E2) [23034]
Environmental Entrepreneurs Mountain West Chapter [23035]
Environmental Entrepreneurs Northern California Chapter [23036]
Environmental Entrepreneurs Southern California San Diego Chapter [36538]
The Environmental Factor Inc. (EFI) [10265]
Environmental Guide to the Internet [5600], [5874], [23195]
Environmental Industry Associations [7941]
Environmental Law Reporter [5758]
Environmental Management Consultants, Inc. (EMC) [25622]
Environmental Monitoring Inc. (EMI) [25623]
Environmental News Network (ENN) [5744]
Environmental Protection Agency - Region 1 (EPA Region 1) [46956]
Environmental Protection Agency - Region 2 (EPA Region 2) [46957]
Environmental Protection Agency - Region 5 (EPA Region 5) [46958]
Environmental Protection Agency - Region 7 (EPA) [46959]
Environmental Protection Agency State Superfund Office - Commission of Environmental Quality - Hazardous and Solid Waste Div. - Superfund and Emergency Response Section [46960]
Environmental Protection Agency State Superfund Office - Department of Ecology - Waste Management Program - Investigations and Cleanup Program [46961]
Environmental Protection Agency State Superfund Office - Department of Energy and Environmental Protection - Small Business Assistance [46962]
Environmental Protection Agency State Superfund Office (DSWM) - Department of Environment and Conservation - Division of Solid Waste Management [46963]
Environmental Protection Agency State Superfund Office (DENR) - Department of Environment and Natural Resources [46964]
Environmental Protection Agency State Superfund Office - Department of Environment and Natural Resources - Waste Management Program [46965]
Environmental Protection Agency State Superfund Office - Department of the Environment - Recycling in Maryland [46966]
Environmental Protection Agency State Superfund Office - Department of Environmental Conservation - Division of Air Quality [46967]
Environmental Protection Agency State Superfund Office - Department of Environmental Conservation - Division of Environmental Remediation [46968]
Environmental Protection Agency State Superfund Office - Department of Environmental Management - Waste Management [46969]
Environmental Protection Agency State Superfund Office - Department of Environmental Protection - Bureau of Waste and Recycling [46970]
Environmental Protection Agency State Superfund Office - Department of Environmental Protection - Division of Waste Management [46971]
Environmental Protection Agency State Superfund Office - Department of Environmental Protection - Hazardous Waste Management Div. [46972]
Environmental Protection Agency State Superfund Office - Department of Environmental Protection - Office of the Commissioner [46973]
Environmental Protection Agency State Superfund Office - Department of Environmental Protection - Small Business Assistance [46974]
Environmental Protection Agency State Superfund Office - Department of Environmental Quality (DEQ) [46975]
Environmental Protection Agency State Superfund Office (MDEQ) - Department of Environmental Quality [46976]
Environmental Protection Agency State Superfund Office - Department of Environmental Quality - Air and Waste Management Div. [46977]
Environmental Protection Agency State Superfund Office (DAQ) - Department of Environmental Quality - Division of Air Quality [46978]
Environmental Protection Agency State Superfund Office (ECSI) - Department of Environmental Quality - Environmental Cleanup Site Information [46979]
Environmental Protection Agency State Superfund Office - Department of Environmental Quality (DEQ) - Land Protection Div. (LPD) [46980]
Environmental Protection Agency State Superfund Office (EPA) - Department of Environmental Quality - Office of Waste and Water Quality [46981]
Environmental Protection Agency State Superfund Office - Department of Environmental Quality - Waste Programs Div. [46982]
Environmental Protection Agency State Superfund Office - Department of Environmental Services - Commissioners Office [46983]
Environmental Protection Agency State Superfund Office - Department of Health and Environment - Bureau of Waste Management - Storage Tank Section [46984]
Environmental Protection Agency State Superfund Office (DHEC) - Department of Health and Environmental Control [46985]
Environmental Protection Agency State Superfund Office - Department of Health - Waste Management Div. [46986]
Environmental Protection Agency State Superfund Office - Department of Natural Resources - Environmental Protection Div. - Land Protection Branch - Solid Waste Management Program [46987]
Environmental Protection Agency State Superfund Office - Department of Natural Resources - Hazardous Waste Management Program [46988]
Environmental Protection Agency State Superfund Office - Department of Natural Resources Waste Management - Air Quality Bureau - Water Supply Section [46989]
Environmental Protection Agency State Superfund Office - Department of Public Health and Environment - Hazardous Materials and Waste Management Div. (HMWMD) [46990]
Environmental Protection Agency State Superfund Office - Environmental Protection Agency [46991]
Environmental Protection Agency State Superfund Office - Environmental Protection Agency - Bureau of Land - Pollution Prevention [46992]
Environmental Protection Agency State Superfund Office - Pollution Control Agency - Groundwater & Solid Waste Div. [46993]
Environmental Protection Agency State Superfund Office - Water Commission - Hazardous and Solid Waste Division - Superfund and Emergency Response Section [46994]
Environmental Quality Management [13738]
Environmental Sciences & Pollution Management [5759]
Environmental Support Network Inc. (ESN) [25624], [35964]
"Environmental Working Group Names Whole Foods Market (R) Leading National Retailer for 'Green' Sunscreen" in *Ecology, Environment & Conservation Business (June 14, 2014, pp. 5)* [8018], [15260], [23196], [32141]
The Environmentalist [5757]
ENvironnement JEUnesse (ENJEU) [5488]
EnviroSpect Inc. [6004]
EOC Technology Center (EOCTC) [43882]
Eos Partners, L.P. [42739]
"EOTech Product Improves Holographic Gun Sights" in *Crain's Detroit Business (Vol. 24, February 4, 2008, No. 5, pp. 9)* [7834], [14413], [25132], [26271]
"EPA Announces Funding for Gulf of Mexico Waterway Cleanup" in *Waste Today (September 24, 2019)* [7949]
"EPA Finalizes WaterSense for Homes" in *Contractor (Vol. 57, January 2010, No. 1, pp. 70)* [4071], [5601], [5875], [12628], [23197], [34008]
"EPA Grants E15 Waiver for 2001-2006 Vehicles" in *Farm Industry News (January 21, 2011)* [5602], [5876], [17035], [23198], [25322], [34783]
"EPA Removes New York Scrap Dealer from Superfund List" in *Waste Today (October 30, 2019)* [7950], [25323]
"EPA Removes Strasburg Landfill from National Priorities List" in *Waste Today (September 6, 2019)* [7951], [25324]
"EPA to Tighten Energy Star Standards for 2011" in *Contractor (Vol. 56, September 2009, No. 9, pp. 6)* [482], [4072], [5370], [23199]
"EPAM May End the IPO Dry Spell" in *Philadelphia Business Journal (Vol. 31, February 3, 2012, No. 51, pp. 1)* [9492], [31285]
Epcon Communities [4348]
Ephraim Small Business Development Center (SBDC) [45606]
Ephrata Area Chamber of Commerce [44270]
Ephrata Chamber of Commerce (ECC) [46081]
Epic Ventures [45692]
Epidarex Capital [40426]
Epilepsie Canada [25670]
Epilepsy Canada (EC) [25670]
Epstein Becker and Green, P.C. (EBG) [15468]
"Equal Weighting's Heavy Allure" in *Barron's (Vol. 92, July 23, 2012, No. 30, pp. 27)* [6386], [9493], [18060], [23866]
Equine Canada (EC) [8306]
Equipment Leasing and Finance Association (ELFA) [13762]
Equipment Manufacturers Institute [29070]
Equipment Marketing and Distribution Association-- Membership Directory [17036]
The Equipment Needed for a T-shirt Business [14351]
"An Equitable Workforce" in *Business Journal Portland (Vol. 31, May 2, 2014, No. 9, pp. 10)* [30564], [34309]
Equitrend Capital, LLC [45447]
"Equity Crowdfunding Platform Initial Crowd Offering, Inc. Closes Equity Financing with Third-Party Investor" in *GlobeNewswire (July 18, 2012)* [16416], [18061], [23001], [29775], [30917], [35337]
"Equity 'Crowdfunding' Platform, RelayFund, Launched by Michigan Investor Group" in *Economics Week (July 20, 2012)* [7106], [22962], [25325], [28062], [30893], [35235]
Equity & Results Consulting LLC [30642]
Equity-South Advisors L.L.C. [38808]
Erbert & Gerbert's Sandwich Shops [4901]
"eResearch Issues Initiating Report on Aldershot Resources Ltd." in *Marketwired (May 14, 2007)* [18062], [30871], [31286], [32752]
Erick Chamber of Commerce [43756]
Erie Area Chamber of Commerce [44207]
Erie Chamber of Commerce [37846]
Erie Community College - City Campus [42968]
Erie Insurance Group Corporate Library [9005]
Erie Regional Chamber and Growth Partnership (ERCGP) [44207]
Erie Technology Incubator (ETI) [44396]
ERISA Industry Committee (ERIC) [17263]
ERM - West Inc. Library [5767]
Ernst & Young Center for Business Knowledge [164], [15469]
Ernst & Young Library [165], [11948], [15470]
Ernst & Young LLP Center for Business Knowledge [3676]
Ernst & Young L.L.P., Center for Business Knowledge [166], [15471]
Error Analysis Inc. [31073], [35965]
"Escada Bought by US Private Equity Firm Regent" in *Fashion Network (October 30, 2019)* [6130]
Escalent Inc. [10708]
Escalon Chamber of Commerce [36883]
Escape from Cubicle Nation: From Corporate Prisoner to Thriving Entrepreneur [22385], [24535]
Escape Enterprises Ltd. [14158]
"Escape from Iron Mountain" in *Barron's (Vol. 92, September 17, 2012, No. 38, pp. 23)* [9494], [13445]
Escapees Magazine [13681]
Escondido Chamber [36884]
Escondido Chamber of Commerce [36884]
"Esencia Estate to Host 'The Esencia Experience for Upscale Wedding Planners' to Re-Introduce the Estate as a Premier Wedding Venue" in *Benzinga.com (October 29, 2011)* [1971]
eShipping [7059]
"ESolar Partners With Penglai on Landmark Solar Thermal Agreement for China" in *Business of Global Warming (January 25, 2010, pp. 8)* [5603], [5877], [14921], [23200], [27546], [31287]
Espanola Valley Chamber of Commerce (EVCC) [42316]
Esparto Regional Chamber of Commerce [36885]
Espionage Research Institute [28988]
Espionage Research Institute International (ERII) [28988]
The Essential Entrepreneur: What It Takes to Start, Scale, and Sell a Successful Business [19222], [22583], [34502]

Master Index Evolving

Essential Facilitation Workshop **[28327]**
Essential Oil Manufacturing Industry in the US - Market Research Report **[11344]**
"Essential Releases Record First Quarter Results" in Marketwired (May 14, 2007) **[6387]**, **[9495]**, **[18063]**, **[23867]**
Essential Skills of Dynamic Public Speaking (Onsite) **[17575]**
Essential Skills for the First-Time Manager or Supervisor (Onsite) **[22053]**
Essential Time Management & Organizational Skills (Onsite) **[34968]**
EssentialNet Solutions **[31000]**, **[31074]**
The Essentials of Cash Flow Forecasting **[23708]**
The Essentials of Collections Law (Onsite) **[18486]**
The Essentials of Communicating With Diplomacy and Professionalism (Onsite) **[17576]**
The Essentials of Communication and Collaboration (Onsite) **[17577]**
The Essentials of HR Law **[26854]**, [26855]
The Essentials of Human Resources Law **[26855]**
The Essentials Of Crystal Reports (Onsite) **[33795]**
Essentials for Personnel and HR Assistants (Onsite) **[26856]**
Essentials of Project Management for the Nonproject Manager **[28328]**
Essex & Drake Fund Raising Counsel **[7178]**
"Essex Leases Space for Largest Retail Store" in Memphis Business Journal (Vol. 34, September 28, 2012, No. 24, pp. 1) **[26553]**, **[32142]**
Essex - Middle River Chamber of Commerce [40380]
Essex - Middle River - White Marsh Chamber of Commerce [40380]
Essex Woodlands Health Ventures/Woodlands Venture **[45448]**
Estacada Chamber of Commerce **[43968]**
Estacada - Clackamas River Area Chamber of Commerce [43968]
Estate Planning for Dummies **[6024]**
"Estate Planning for an Owner-Dependent Business" in Entrepreneur **[6025]**
Estate Planning Review--The Journal **[6051]**
Estate Planning for the Savvy Client: What You Need to Know Before You Meet with Your Lawyer **[6026]**
"Estate Planning for Small Business Owners in 8 Steps" in Fundera (October 28, 2020) **[6027]**
"Estate Planning Suggestions for Small Business Owners" in Stouffer Legal website (February 18, 2020) **[6028]**
"Estate Planning Tips for Food and Beverage Entrepreneurs" in Nutter Uncommon Law (March 9, 2020) **[6029]**, **[13931]**
"Estate Planning With Partnerships: Important New Considerations" in Stites & Harbison PLLC website (February 15, 2016) **[6030]**
"Estate Sale Company Guide to Building an Online Presence" in EstateSales.org Blog **[6069]**
"Estate Sale Contracts Guide" in EstateSales.org Blog **[6070]**
"Estate Tax Problems may Soon Disappear" in Contractor (Vol. 56, September 2009, No. 9, pp. 60) **[6031]**, **[18573]**, **[34784]**
Estero **[38376]**
Estero Chamber of Commerce **[38377]**
Estes Park Area Chamber of Commerce [37847]
Estes Park Chamber Resort Association [37847]
Estes Park Resort **[37847]**
Estherville Area Chamber of Commerce **[39739]**
Estherville Chamber of Commerce [39739]
Estill County 21st Century, Inc. **[40037]**
Estill Development Alliance [40037]
ETA International [14343], [15559]
Eternal Tattoo Supply (ETS) **[15324]**
"Etextbook Space Heats Up" in Information Today (Vol. 28, November 2011, No. 10, pp. 10) **[1652]**, **[2734]**, **[3704]**, **[21502]**, **[21843]**
"Etextbooks: Coming of Age" in Information Today (Vol. 28, September 2011, No. 8, pp. 1) **[1653]**, **[21503]**, **[21844]**
"ETF Process May be Tweaked" in Austin Business JournalInc. (Vol. 28, December 26, 2008, No. 41, pp. 3) **[24977]**, **[26166]**, **[28063]**
"ETF Score Card" in Barron's (Vol. 89, July 13, 2009, No. 28, pp. 51) **[6388]**, **[9496]**, **[23868]**
Ethical Hacking and Countermeasures: Hands-On - Preventing Network and System Breaches (Onsite) **[26196]**
Ethical Pitfalls for Professional Organizers **[12830]**, **[23494]**
Ethics Centre CA Library **[23572]**
Ethics and Compliance Initiative (ECI) **[34446]**
Ethics and Compliance Officer Association [34446]
"The Ethics of Price Discrimination" in Business Ethics Quarterly (Vol. 21, October 2011, No. 4, pp. 633) **[20013]**, **[20568]**, **[23495]**
Ethics Research Center [34446]
Ethics Resources **[23554]**
Ethics and a Successful Small Business: Can You Have Both? **[23496]**
Ethnic and Multicultural Information Exchange Round Table of the American Library Association (EMIERT) **[30505]**
Ethnic NewsWatch: A History™ **[12015]**
ethology [36406]
Etowah Area Chamber of Commerce **[44741]**
"Etsy Alternatives for Crafty Entrepreneurs" in Business News Daily (February 21, 2023) **[4591]**, **[11738]**
"Etsy: Etsy Business for Beginners! Master Etsy and Build a Profitable Business In No Time" **[2996]**, **[4573]**, **[8171]**, **[11685]**, **[14309]**, **[26732]**
"Etsy Says Payment Delays from SVB Collapse are Resolved" in Small Business Trends (March 17, 2023) **[11932]**, **[16556]**
"Etsy Sellers Experience Payment Delays after Silicon Valley Bank Collapse" in Small Business Trends (March 11, 2023) **[11739]**
Euclid Chamber of Commerce (ECC) **[43467]**
Eufaula Area Chamber of Commerce **[43757]**
Eugene Area Chamber of Commerce **[43969]**
Eugene O'Neill Theater Center - Liebling-Wood Library - Monte Cristo Cottage Collection **[4560]**
Eunice Chamber of Commerce **[40167]**
Eureka Area Chamber of Commerce (EACC) **[41763]**
Eureka Chamber of Commerce **[41559]**
Eureka Chamber of Commerce [36918]
The Eureka Chamber Review **[36886]**
Eureka Loft **[36393]**
Eureka, The California Career Information System Library **[2621]**
European-American Business Council [27431]
European-American Chamber of Commerce in Washington, DC [27431]
European Travel Commission (ETC) **[15971]**, **[19294]**
"Europe's Meltdown" in Canadian Business (Vol. 83, June 15, 2010, No. 10, pp. 76) **[6389]**, **[8715]**, **[9497]**, **[27547]**
Eustis Area Chamber of Commerce [38446]
Eutaw Area Chamber of Commerce **[36108]**
"Evaluate Your Process and Do It Better" in Modern Machine Shop (Vol. 84, October 2011, No. 5, pp. 34) **[10429]**, **[19830]**, **[29201]**
"Evaluating the 1996-2006 Employment Projections" in Montly Labor Review (Vol. 133, September 2010, No. 9, pp. 33) **[20874]**, **[25326]**, **[26554]**, **[26934]**
Evaluation & the Health Professions **[25998]**
Evangelical Christian Publishers Association (ECPA) **[1622]**
Evangelical Lutheran Good Samaritan Society (ELGSS) **[11541]**
Evanston Chamber of Commerce (ECC) **[39163]**
Evanston Community Guide **[39164]**
Evansville Area Chamber of Commerce and Tourism **[46402]**
Evansville Regional Economic Partnership, Inc. (EREP) **[39638]**
"Even Money on Recession" in Barron's (Vol. 88, March 10, 2008, No. 10, pp. M9) **[20875]**, **[24663]**, **[26555]**
Event Management: For Tourism, Cultural, Business and Sporting Events **[6087]**
"Event Planning Guide 2020" in Cvent Blog (August 27, 2019) **[6088]**, **[18949]**
Event Planning and Management: Principles, Planning and Practice **[6078]**
"The Event Planning Recipe for Success" in Entrepreneur **[6089]**, **[18950]**
"Event-Planning Startup Extends Its Reach" in Indianapolis Business Journal (Vol. 33, June 18, 2012, No. 16, pp. 2A) **[1957]**, **[11900]**, **[14500]**, **[15814]**
The Event Planning Toolkit: Your Guide to Organizing Extraordinary Meetings and Events **[6090]**
"Event Postponement and Cancellation Guide" Cvent (May 15, 2020) **[6091]**, **[29776]**
"Event-Related Advertising and the Special Case of Sponsorship-Linked Advertising" in International Journal of Advertising (Vol. 31, February 2012, No. 1, pp. 15) **[271]**
Event Service Professionals Association (ESPA) **[15819]**
The Event - Specialty Coffee Association of America **[3203]**
"Event Will Highlight Underappreciated Rose Wines" in Sacramento Business Journal (Vol. 31, July 18, 2014, No. 21, pp. 4) **[15011]**, **[35052]**
Eventi Capital Partners (ECP) **[46868]**
Events Calendar - Community **[36887]**
"Events, Improved Economy Mean Full Hotels in Silicon Valley" in Silicon Valley/San Jose Business Journal (Vol. 30, September 28, 2012, No. 27, pp. 1) **[8386]**, **[15857]**, **[20876]**, **[35053]**
e.ventures [37385]
Everett Chamber of Commerce [46078], [46203]
Everett Community College (EvCC) - Small Business Accelerator **[46214]**
"Everett Hospice Planned" in Puget Sound Business Journal (Vol. 29, September 26, 2008, No. 23, pp. 1) **[4073]**, **[25771]**
Evergreen **[37848]**
Evergreen Area Chamber of Commerce (EACC) **[37849]**
Evergreen Business Capital (EBC) **[28084]**
Evergreen Climate Innovations **[8790]**, **[34479]**
Evergreen/Conecuh Chamber of Commerce **[36109]**
Evergreen - Conecuh County Area Chamber of Commerce [36109]
Evergreen - Conecuh County Chamber of Commerce [36109]
Evergreen Freedom Foundation [26115]
Evergreen Park Chamber of Commerce (EPCC) **[39165]**
Every Airbnb Host's Tax Guide **[8387]**, **[13787]**
"Every Business Needs a Succession Plan: Here's How to Get Started" in Legal Zoom (February 13, 2023) **[18951]**
Every Californian's Guide to Estate Planning **[6032]**, **[34785]**
Every Monday **[38378]**
"Everybody Wants To Save the World: But When You Start a Charity Overseas, Good Intentions Often Go Awry" in Inc. (December 2007) **[27548]**, **[34310]**
Everyday Leadership: You Will Make A Difference **[28572]**
"Everyone Has a Story Inspired by Chevrolet" in Automotive News (Vol. 86, October 31, 2011, No. 6488, pp. S003) **[272]**, **[11395]**, **[29202]**
"Everyone Is Not a Demographic: A Guide to Target Markets for Small Businesses" in WordStream (February 26, 2020) **[34713]**
"Everyone Out of the Pool" in Barron's (Vol. 89, July 20, 2009, No. 29, pp. 18) **[6390]**, **[9498]**, **[13192]**, **[13446]**, **[15239]**, **[23869]**
"Everything Food Truck Operators Need to Know About the Mobile POS" in FoodTruckOperator.com (July 13, 2020) **[6972]**
Everything is Possible: Life and Business Lessons from a Self-Made Billionaire and the Founder of Slim-Fast **[11574]**, **[16506]**, **[22584]**
"Everything Small Business Owners Need to Know About Drug Testing" in allBusiness **[34679]**
The Everything Store: Jeff Bezos and the Age of Amazon **[1824]**, **[11740]**, **[20014]**, **[21845]**, **[23002]**
"Everything You Ever Wondered About Hiring a Virtual Assistant (and More)" in HubSpot **[3871]**
"Everything You Need to Know About Credit Card Issuers" in Experian.com (March 27, 2018) **[4719]**
"Everything You Need to Know About Owning a Mobile Business" in Million Mile Secrets (May 3, 2019) **[30468]**
"Everything You Need to Know About...Bartering" in Courier Workshop Newsletter (Oct. 28, 2021) **[17251]**
"Evidence-Based Management and the Marketplace For Ideas" in Academy of Management Journal (Vol. 50, No. 5, October 2007, pp. 1009) **[26935]**, **[28573]**
"Evigence and Jarja Floral Partner to Create a Monitoring Device That Measures Flower Freshness" in Garden Center (October 21, 2019) **[7617]**
"EVMS Gets Grant to Train Providers for Elder Care" in Virginian-Pilot (October 29, 2010) **[183]**, **[1032]**, **[8251]**, **[11511]**, **[21504]**
"The Evolution of Cannabis Advertising" in Cannabis Business Executive (June 15, 2020) **[5000]**
"The Evolution of Carolyn Elman" in Women In Business (Vol. 62, September 2010, No. 3, pp. 11) **[28574]**, **[35773]**
"Evolution of the Cookie" in Women in Business (Vol. 65, Winter 2013, No. 3, pp. 10) **[1254]**
"The Evolution of the Laws of Software Evolution: a Discussion Based On a Systematic Literature Review" in ACM Computing Surveys (Vol. 46, Summer 2014, No. 2, pp. 28) **[14776]**, **[18574]**, **[33850]**
"The Evolution of Self-Regulation in Food Advertising: an Analysis of CARU Cases from 2000-2012" in International Journal of Advertising (Vol. 31, May 2012, No. 2, pp. 257) **[273]**, **[10651]**, **[29777]**
"Evolutionary Psychology in the Business Sciences" **[274]**, **[11636]**, **[16557]**, **[17667]**, **[19831]**, **[21846]**, **[22585]**, **[23497]**, **[27865]**, **[29778]**
"Evolve Bank Ramps Up Staff for SBA Lending" in Memphis Business Journal (Vol. 33, February 24, 2012, No. 46, pp. 1) **[24978]**, **[28131]**
Evolving eCommerce: Vitamins, Minerals & Supplements: Incl Impact of COVID-19 - US - December 2020 **[5193]**, **[11831]**
Evolving and Pivoting Your Business with Kathleen Shannon **[24808]**

Master Index

Small Business Sourcebook • 42nd Edition 3231

Evolving Master Index

"Evolving from Practice to Enterprise" in Financial Advisor (November 1, 2019) **[6033]**, **[6391]**, **[23870]**
EvoNexus **[37568]**
Evos **[8119]**
"New Hotels, Offices Eyed Near SJC" in Silicon Valley/San Jose Business Journal (Vol. 30, June 8, 2012, No. 11, pp. 1) **[8388]**, **[32143]**
eWomen Network Conference **[35917]**
eWomenNetwork **[35596]**
eWomenNetwork - Birmingham Chapter **[18801]**, **[35597]**
eWomenNetwork - Boca Raton Chapter **[18802]**, **[35598]**
eWomenNetwork - Calabasas Chapter **[18803]**, **[35599]**
eWomenNetwork - Colorado Springs Chapter **[18804]**, **[35600]**
eWomenNetwork - Denver Chapter **[18805]**, **[35601]**
eWomenNetwork - Ft. Lauderdale Chapter **[18806]**, **[35602]**
eWomenNetwork - Fresno Chapter **[18807]**, **[35603]**
eWomenNetwork - Greater Hartford Chapter **[18808]**, **[35604]**
eWomenNetwork - Jacksonville Chapter **[18809]**, **[35605]**
eWomenNetwork - Ladera Heights Chapter **[18810]**, **[35606]**
eWomenNetwork - Los Angeles Chapter **[18811]**, **[35607]**
eWomenNetwork - Miami Chapter **[18812]**, **[35608]**
eWomenNetwork - Palo Alto Chapter **[18813]**, **[35609]**
eWomenNetwork - Phoenix/Scottsdale Chapter **[18814]**, **[35610]**
eWomenNetwork - Sacramento Chapter **[18815]**, **[35611]**
eWomenNetwork - San Diego Chapter **[18816]**, **[35612]**
eWomenNetwork - San Jose Chapter **[18817]**, **[35613]**
eWomenNetwork - Tucson Chapter **[18818]**, **[35614]**
eWomenNetwork - Washington D.C. Metro Chapter **[18819]**, **[35615]**
eWomenNetwork - Wilmington Chapter **[18820]**, **[35616]**
"Ex-Im Bank Accepts $105 Million in Financing for Aquarium in Brazil" in Travel & Leisure Close-Up (October 8, 2012) **[838]**, **[8716]**, **[27549]**, **[28132]**
"Ex-Medical Student Stages Career In Event Planning: Barcelona Owner Makes Inroads with Luxury Car Dealerships" in Los Angeles Business Journal (Vol. 34, June 18, 2012, No. 25, pp. 10) **[11396]**, **[12197]**, **[15858]**, **[18064]**, **[22586]**, **[29779]**, **[35054]**
"Ex-MetLife Lenders Align With Illinois Mortgage Group" in Wichita Business Journal (Vol. 27, January 27, 2012, No. 4, pp. 1) **[11031]**
"Ex-MP? Ex-con? Exactly!" in Canadian Business (Vol. 83, October 12, 2010, No. 17, pp. 16) **[1654]**, **[6183]**
"Ex-NFL Players' Game Plan: 2 New Nissan Dealerships" in Crain's Detroit Business (Vol. 30, July 28, 2014, No. 30, pp. 1) **[11353]**, **[15150]**, **[33331]**
"An Examination of Rural and Female-Led Firms: A Resource Approach" in Journal of Small Business Strategy (Vol. 31, December 1, 2021, No. 4, 20-39) **[35774]**
"Examining the Real Costs of Remote Work" in Small Business Trends (September 11, 2022) **[22150]**
"Examples of Barter Transactions?" in Investopedia (May 5, 2021) **[17252]**
"Examples of Social Responsibility Strategies" in Chron (November 9, 2018) **[34311]**
Excelerate Health Ventures (EHV) **[43220]**
Excelerate Labs [39437]
Excell Technology Partners **[43019]**
Excelling as A Manager or Supervisor (Onsite) **[28329]**
Excelling as a Highly Effective Team Leader (Onsite) **[28330]**
Excelsior Springs Area Chamber of Commerce **[41560]**
Exceptional Business Writing and Goof-Proof Grammar **[17844]**
Exceptional Children (EC) **[16145]**
Exceptional Management Skills **[28331]**
Exceptional Presentation Training **[17578]**
Exceptional Service, Exceptional Profit: The Secrets of Building a Five-Star Customer Service Organization **[8389]**, **[18065]**, **[20427]**, **[33146]**
Executive **[41851]**
Executive Analytics & Design Inc. **[3456]**
"Executive Compensation: Both Eyes on the Prize" in Canadian Business (Vol. 83, September 14, 2010, No. 15, pp. 42) **[17301]**, **[19737]**, **[25327]**, **[26936]**, **[28575]**
"Executive Decision: Damn the Profit Margins, Sleeman Declares War on Buck-a-Beer Foes" in Globe & Mail (January 28, 2006, pp. B3) **[1330]**, **[10319]**, **[18952]**, **[19511]**, **[29203]**
"Executive Decision: To Make Inroads Against RIM, Palm Steals Its Strategy" in Globe & Mail (March 25, 2006, pp. B3) **[2735]**, **[18066]**, **[18953]**, **[30719]**, **[31288]**
"Executive Decision: XM Mulls Betting the Bank in Competitive Game of Subscriber Growth" in Globe & Mail (March 18, 2006, pp. B3) **[13031]**, **[19832]**, **[26272]**, **[29780]**, **[33147]**
Executive Excellence Publishing [45690]
The Executive Group **[27138]**
The Executive Leadership Council (ELC) **[30265]**
Executive Management Services Inc. (EMS) **[22355]**
Executive Office Link **[44397]**
Executive Office of the President - Office of Management and Budget - Administrator of the Small Business Administration **[47017]**
Executive Office of the President - Office of Management and Budget - Office of Federal Procurement Policy **[47018]**
Executive Office of the President (SBA) - Office of Management and Budget - Small Business Administration **[47019]**
"Executive Presence: The Missing Link Between Merit and Success" **[17668]**, **[28576]**
"Executive Summary: Codeines and Coding" in Business Strategy Review (Vol. 23, Spring 2012, No. 1, pp. 82) **[22151]**, **[25772]**
"Executive Summary: How Smart Firms Create Productive Ties" in Business Strategy Review (Vol. 23, Spring 2012, No. 1, pp. 83) **[9499]**, **[22587]**
"Executive Training" in Black Enterprise (Vol. 37, December 2006, No. 5, pp. 70) **[18954]**, **[21505]**
The Exempt Organization Tax Review (EOTR) **[15432]**
Exer-Safety Association [12372]
Exercise Safety Association (ESA) **[12372]**
Exeter Area Chamber of Commerce (EACC) **[41987]**
Exeter Board of Trade [36888]
Exeter Chamber of Commerce **[36888]**
Exhibit Builder **[35109]**
Exhibit Designers and Producers Association (EDPA) **[15820]**, **[35018]**
Exhibition Services and Contractors Association [15821]
Exovations **[2650]**
"Expanding Distribution Channels" in business.com (Feb. 2, 2022) **[20623]**
"Expanding the Entrepreneur Class" in Harvard Business Review (Vol. 90, July-August 2012, No. 7-8, pp. 40) **[21506]**, **[22588]**
"Expanding Middleby's Food Processing Biz" in Crain's Chicago Business (Vol. 31, April 21, 2008, No. 16, pp. 6) **[18067]**, **[18955]**, **[19512]**, **[22589]**, **[29204]**, **[31289]**
Expansion Venture Capital (EVC) **[42740]**
"Expatriate Knowledge Transfer, Subsidiary Absorptive Capacity, and Subsidiary Performance" in Academy of Management Journal (Vol. 55, August 1, 2012, No. 4, pp. 927) **[28029]**, **[30565]**
"Expect Action on Health Care and the Economy" in Contractor (Vol. 57, January 2010, No. 1, pp. 30) **[483]**, **[6034]**, **[12629]**, **[25328]**, **[25773]**, **[34786]**
Expedia CruiseShip Centers **[16038]**
"Expedia Tells Hotels Adding Resort Fees Will Lower Your Listings on Its Pages" in Skift (November 14, 2019) **[8390]**, **[11741]**
Expense Control Systems Inc. **[32979]**
Expense Reduction Analysts Inc. (ERA) **[2337]**
Experience Conference & Exhibition **[2991]**
Experience Sedona Guide **[36330]**
Experiential Marketing Summit **[10686]**
Experimental Heat Transfer **[32872]**
"Experts Discuss New Tax Rules in Webinar to Help Farmers With Year-End Tax Planning" in Farm Industry News (November 22, 2011) **[17037]**, **[34787]**
"Experts: Orlando Great Fit for Cars Land" in Orlando Business Journal (Vol. 29, September 7, 2012, No. 12, pp. 1) **[604]**
"Experts Share How to Create Company Culture That Gets Results" in Small Business Trends (October 29, 2022) **[22152]**, **[26937]**, **[28577]**
"Experts Sound Off On Top Legal Trends" in Birmingham Business Journal (Vol. 31, January 17, 2014, No. 3, pp. 4) **[9138]**, **[18575]**, **[25774]**
"Experts Strive to Educate on Proper Pet Diets" in Pet Product News (Vol. 64, November 2010, No. 11, pp. 40) **[691]**, **[11575]**, **[12163]**, **[20428]**, **[21507]**, **[29205]**, **[32144]**, **[34009]**
Expetec Technology Services **[3586]**
"Expiring Tax Deals Pose Challenges" in Providence Business News (Vol. 29, May 5, 2014, No. 5, pp. 1) **[34788]**
"Explainer: The Rules for Shooting on Film Sets" in The Conversation (January 25, 2017) **[6184]**, **[35944]**
"Explaining Organizational Responsiveness to Work-Life Balance Issues: the Role of Business Strategy and High-Performance Work Systems" in Human Resource Management (Vol. 51,May- June 2012, No. 3, pp. 407-432) **[22153]**, **[26938]**
"An Exploratory Study of Executive Factors That Lead To Technology Adoption in Small Businesses" Journal of Small Business Strategy (May 27, 2020) **[33699]**
Explore Edmonton **[46671]**
Explore Waterford **[46403]**
Exploring E-Commerce **[21847]**
"Exploring Supportive and Developmental Career Management Through Business Strategies and Coaching" in Human Resource Management (Vol. 51, January-February 2012, No. 1, pp. 99-120) **[21508]**, **[26939]**, **[28578]**
Expo Marketplace [24839]
Export Advertising Association [221], [399], [31832]
Export Council of Norway [27416]
Export-Import Bank of the United States (EXIM) **[47020]**
Export-Import Bank of the United States (EXIM) - Global Business Development **[47021]**
Export-Import Bank of the United States - Midwest Regional Office - Chicago Regional Office - U.S. Export Assistance Center (USEAC) **[47022]**
Export-Import Bank of the United States - Southwest Regional Office - Houston Regional Office **[47023]**
"Export Opportunity" in Business Journal-Portland (Vol. 24, October 12, 2007, No. 33, pp. 1) **[8717]**, **[20877]**, **[27550]**
The Export Practitioner **[8782]**
"Exporting Portlandia: Unconventional Brands Carry a Taste of Portland Across U.S." in Business Journal Portland (Vol. 30, January 17, 2014, No. 46, pp. 4) **[8655]**, **[13932]**, **[31758]**
Exposition Nationale Canadienne [15816]
Exposition Services & Contractors Association (ESCA) **[15821]**
Express Employment Professionals [5455], [6115], [15657]
Express Oil Change [13003]
Express Oil Change & Tire Engineers (ETE) **[13003]**
Express Services, Inc. **[5455]**, **[6115]**, **[15657]**
ExSeed Marketing **[16525]**
Exterior Insulation Manufacturers Association [8845]
Exton Region Chamber of Commerce (ERCC) **[44208]**
"Extortion: How Politicians Extract Your Money, Buy Votes, and Line Their Own Pockets" **[7107]**, **[18576]**, **[23498]**, **[25329]**, **[28133]**
"Extra Rehab Time Boosts M-B's Off-Lease Profits" in Automotive News (Vol. 86, October 31, 2011, No. 6488, pp. 22) **[11397]**, **[13788]**, **[23871]**, **[29206]**
"Extreme Amenities" in Puget Sound Business Journal (Vol. 35, May 9, 2014, No. 3, pp. 4) **[4074]**, **[13789]**, **[34010]**
"Extreme Negotiations" in Harvard Business Review (Vol. 88, November 2010, No. 11, pp. 66) **[17669]**, **[17859]**, **[28579]**
The Extreme Pita **[14159]**
Extreme Pizza Inc [12571]
"Extreme Temperatures May Pose Risks to Some Mail-Order Meds" in NPR (January 7, 2019) **[10463]**, **[10948]**, **[11742]**
Extreme Venture Partners (EVP) **[46870]**
"Exxon Mobil Campus 'Clearly Happening'" in Houston Business Journal (Vol. 40, January 15, 2010, No. 36, pp. 1) **[13447]**, **[19169]**
Eye Level Learning Centers **[21718]**
"Eye in the Sky: A Look at Security Tech from All Angles" in Bellingham Business Journal (October 2008, pp. 23) **[10354]**, **[14414]**
Eyecare Business: Retail Strategies for Profitable Dispensing **[16305]**
"Eyes to the Sky" in Canadian Business (Vol. 80, March 26, 2007, No. 7, pp. 33) **[13193]**, **[13448]**, **[18068]**
EYESthere **[14494]**
Eyewitness **[16306]**
EZ Compliance, Inc. [20670]

F

F-O-R-T-U-N-E Personnel Consultants (FPC) **[6116]**
F-Prime **[40684]**
F & S Political Risk Letter [27782]
FA Technology Ventures [40685]
F.A. Technology Ventures Corp. (FATV) **[40685]**
Fabricare **[5247]**
Fabricare Canada **[5248]**
FABRICARE - Great Western Exhibit **[5251]**
Fabricating Machinery Association [10419]
Fabricating Manufacturers Association [10419]
The Fabricator **[10451]**
Fabricators and Manufacturers Association, International (FMA) **[10419]**
"Fabricator's Toolroom Becomes Captive CNC Machine Shop" in Modern Machine Shop (November 3, 2019) **[10430]**
FACC Chicago Chapter [39170]
FACC Dallas/Fort Worth Chapter [45153]
"Face Time: Fastenal founder Bob Kierlin and CEO Will Oberton" in Business Journal (Vol. 31, January 31, 2014, No. 36, pp. 9) **[19833]**, **[21509]**, **[26556]**

3232 Small Business Sourcebook • 42nd Edition

Master Index **Farmington-Wilton**

Master Index

"Facebook: A Promotional Budget's Best Friend" in Women Entrepreneur (February 1, 2009) **[17497], [17670], [17860], [20878], [29781], [34011]**
The Facebook Effect: The Inside Story of the Company That Is Connecting the World **[9139], [11978], [16417], [17671], [18069], [21848], [22590], [34012]**
"Facebook, Google, LinkedIn Line Up In Patent Case Before Supreme Court" in San Francisco Business Times (Vol. 28, March 28, 2014, No. 36) **[9140], [18577], [21849], [27866]**
"Facebook IPO Buyers Deserved To Lose" in Canadian Business (Vol. 85, July 16, 2012, No. 11-12, pp. 16) **[9141], [9500], [31290]**
"The Facebook IPO Hype Meter" in Canadian Business (Vol. 85, June 11, 2012, No. 10, pp. 74) **[9142], [9501], [31291]**
"Facebook Launches Online Dating Service in US" in Financial Times (September 5, 2019) **[3812], [11743]**
Facebook Marketing: Leveraging Facebook's Features for Your Marketing Campaigns **[21850], [29782], [31759]**
"Facebook Marketplace vs. the Competition for E-Commerce Businesses" in Business News Daily (March 20, 2023) **[11744]**
"Facebook Purchased Push Pop Press" in Information Today (Vol. 28, October 2011, No. 9, pp. 12) **[1655], [3705], [19660], [21851]**
Facelogic **[1404]**
"The Faces Behind the Nation's Largest Instrument Repair Shop" in The Frederick News-Post (July 6, 2016) **[11314]**
Faces Cosmetics **[4540]**
"Faces: Q&A with Kevin Huyck, Chef/Owner of R.A. MacSammy's Food Truck Specializing in Mac and Cheese" in Saint Paul Pioneer Press (March 28, 2012) **[3821], [6973], [13864], [18070], [22386]**
"Faces: Q&A With Katie Johnson, Co-Owner of Bloomy's Roast Beef Food Truck" in Saint Paul Pioneer Press (June 13, 2012) **[3822], [6951], [18862], [30447], [31139]**
"Facials for Fido? Retail: Kriser's Pet Store Grows With High-End Pet Products Market" in San Fernando Valley Business Journal (Vol. 17, February 20, 2012, No. 4, pp. 1) **[8019], [12085], [12198], [32145]**
"Facilitating and Rewarding Creativity During New Product Development" in Journal of Marketing (Vol. 75, July 2011, No. 4, pp. 53) **[17302], [21510], [22154], [27867], [30720]**
Facilitating Sustainable Innovation through Collaboration: A Multi-Stakeholder Perspective **[27551], [27868]**
Facilitation Skills (Onsite) **[28332]**
Facilitative Leadership® [28333]
Facilitative Leadership® Workshop **[28333]**
The Facilitator **[17788], [35894]**
Facilities Maintenance Expo **[2081]**
Facilities Management for Business Incubators: Practical Advice and Information for Design, Construction and Management of 21st Century Business Incubation Facilities **[8808]**
Facilities Management (Onsite) **[28334]**
Facility Executive **[11646]**
Facility Kitchens **[41087]**
Facility Logix **[40477]**
"Factors to Consider When Opening a New Location for Your Salon" in Millennium Systems International (November 11, 2019) **[7866]**
The Factory **[41088]**
FAF Membership Directory [9407]
FAH Conference and Business Exposition [10876]
FAH Public Policy Conference and Business Exposition **[10876]**
"Fail Forward's Ashley Good on How to Screw Up in the Best Possible Way" in Canadian Business (Vol. 87, October 2014, No. 10, pp. 47) **[2186], [20105]**
"A Failed Promise: A Dream Job Gone..or Just Delayed?" in Restaurant Business (Vol. 107, September 2008, No. 9, pp. 34) **[4464], [13933], [22591]**
"The Failure Detector Abstraction" in ACM Computing Surveys (Vol. 43, Summer 2011, No. 2, pp. 9) **[3427], [3502], [3621]**
Failure Is Your Trampoline to Success with Rich Moyer **[16650]**
"Fair or Foul? Ballparks and their Impact on Urban Revitalization" in Real Estate Review (Vol. 41, Spring 2012, No. 1, pp. 15) **[882], [15151]**
Fair Haven Area Chamber of Commerce (FHACC) **[42569]**
Fair Lawn Chamber of Commerce (FL) **[42123]**
"Fair and Lovely: Building an Integrated Model to Examine How Peer Influence Mediates the Effects of Skin-Lightening Advertisements On College Women In Singapore" in International Journal of Advertising (Vol. 31, February 2012, No. 1, pp. 189) **[275], [4512], [10652]**
Fair Oaks Business Directory **[36889]**
Fair Oaks Chamber of Commerce **[36890]**
Fair Shake Environmental Legal Services **[44398]**
Fairbanks Historical Society [45343]
Fairborn Area Chamber of Commerce (FACC) **[43468]**
Fairbury Chamber of Commerce **[39166], [41852]**
Fairfax County Chamber of Commerce [45886]
Fairfield Area Chamber of Commerce (FACC) **[39740]**
Fairfield Chamber of Commerce **[38044], [43469]**
Fairfield Chamber of Commerce (FCC) **[45139]**
Fairfield Chamber of Commerce [39186]
Fairfield County Chamber of Commerce (FCCC) **[44544]**
Fairleigh Dickinson University Rothman Institute of Innovation & Entrepreneurship **[42253]**
Fairmont Area Chamber of Commerce **[41228]**
"Fairness First" in Canadian Business (Vol. 80, April 23, 2007, No. 9, pp. 45) **[19738], [34312], [35189]**
Fairview Area Chamber of Commerce **[44742]**
Fairview Chamber of Commerce **[43758]**
Fairview Heights Chamber of Commerce [39248]
Fairview Technology Center (FTC) **[44845]**
"Falcons' Blank Kicking Off 'Westside Works' Job Training Program" in Atlanta Business Chronicle (May 30, 2014, pp. 6A) **[4075], [7108], [21511], [26557], [34313]**
"Fall Fever" in Canadian Business (Vol. 81, October 13, 2008, No. 17, pp. S12) **[3020], [3110], [6131]**
Fall River Area Chamber of Commerce and Industry, Inc. [40562]
Fallbrook Chamber of Commerce **[36891]**
Fallbrook's Chamber of Commerce Newsletter **[36892]**
Falling Behind: How Rising Inequality Harms the Middle Class **[20879], [24664]**
"Falling Local Executive Pay Could Suggest a Trend" in Tampa Bay Business Journal (Vol. 30, January 15, 2010, No. 4, pp. 1) **[9502], [17303], [23872], [26940], [28580], [34013]**
"Falling Markets' Nastiest Habit" in Barron's (Vol. 88, July 7, 2008, No. 27, pp. 7) **[6392], [9503], [20880], [23873]**
"Falling Share Prices Will Convince Big Oil Producers to Pay Up to Drill" in Globe & Mail (April 21, 2007, pp. B1) **[6393], [9504]**
"Falling Through the Cracks of Vision Care" in U.S. News & World Report (May 15, 2018) **[16298], [25775]**
Fallon Chamber of Commerce **[41936]**
Falls Chamber of Commerce **[46404]**
Falls City Area Chamber of Commerce (FCACC) **[41853]**
Falmouth Chamber of Commerce (FCC) **[40575]**
Famaco Publishers L.L.C. **[38611]**
Famiglia-DeBartolo L.L.C. [12549]
A Familiarization of Drivetrain Components (Onsite) **[29086]**
Family Business **[20881], [23609], [28581]**
Family Business Coalition (FBC) **[23583]**
Family Business Institute Inc. (FBI) **[2262], [2386], [10528], [23680], [28989]**
Family Business Models: Practical Solutions for the Family Business **[23610], [28582]**
Family Business Network **[23681]**
"Family Business Research: A Strategic Reflection" in International Journal of Entrepreneurship and Small Business (Vol. 12, December 3, 2010, No. 1) **[23611], [31967], [32753], [34014]**
Family Business Review: Journal of the Family Firm Institute (FBR) **[23687]**
Family Business USA **[23682]**
Family Campers and RVers (FCRV) **[2504]**
"Family Child Care Record-Keeping Guide, Ninth Edition (Redleaf Business Series)" **[1755], [2882], [15380], [25330], [26777], [34789]**
"Family Dollar Plans to Sell Alcohol at 1,000 Stores" in The New York Times (June 1, 2019) **[10320]**
"Family Dollar Reaches Preliminary Class Action Settlement" in Benzinga.com (September 12, 2012) **[18578], [22155], [32146]**
"Family Feud: Pawn Shop Empire Stalls with Transition to Second Generation" in Billings Gazette (December 19, 2010) **[11918], [18956], [23612]**
Family Financial Centers (FFC) **[2840]**
Family Firm Institute (FFI) **[23584]**
Family Firm Institute, Inc. - North Texas Study Group **[44893]**
Family Firm Institute - Midwest Study Group (FFI-MWC) **[38971]**
Family Health International [10007]
"Family Human Capital and the Championing of Innovation in Small Firms" in Journal of Small Business Strategy (November 19, 2021) **[23688]**
Family Office Association **[23585]**
Family-Owned Businesses **[23613]**
"Family-Owned Train Service Offers a Ride for Your Raft" in Idaho Business Review (June 11, 2014) **[15738], [23614]**
Family Resource Center on Disabilities (FRCD) **[2263], [20187], [26087]**
"Family Takes Wind Turbine Companies to Court Over Gag Clauses on Health Effects of Turbines" in CNW Group (September 12, 2011) **[5604], [5878], [18579], [23201], [25776]**
"The Family Tools" in Canadian Business (Vol. 80, March 26, 2007, No. 7, pp. 14) **[22592], [23615]**
Family Tree Home Business - Genealogy & Ancestry **[7355]**
The Family Tree Problem Solver: Tried-and-True Tactics for Tracing Elusive Ancestors **[7356]**
Family Trusts: A Guide for Beneficiaries, Trustees, Trust Protectors, and Trust Creators **[6035]**
Family Veterinary Care of Oakdale **[28990]**
Family Wars **[23616]**
"A Family's Fortune" in Canadian Business (Vol. 80, Winter 2007, No. 24, pp. 103) **[13032], [15250], [17253], [23617]**
Famous Famiglia **[12549]**
"Famous For Its Bookies, New Jersey Keeps a Different Type Of Bookmaker in Business" in Northjersey.com (April 16, 2018) **[1722]**
Fancy Food Show **[7809]**
Fandom Directory (Science fiction, fantasy, comics) **[3270]**
Fannin County Chamber of Commerce **[38731]**
Fannin-Polk Chamber of Commerce [38731]
Fanning, Fanning & Associates Inc. **[542], [4316]**
Fantastic Flagler Visitor, Newcomer & Resident Guide **[38379]**
Fantastic Sams Cut & Color [7890]
Fantastic Sams Hair Salons [7890]
Fantastic Sams International Corporation (FSIC) **[7890]**
Fantasy Sports & Gaming Association (FSTA) **[7260]**
Fantasy Sports Trade Association [7260]
"Fantasy in the Workplace" in Orlando Business Journal (Vol. 28, September 7, 2012, No. 30, pp. 1) **[15152], [34985]**
"Far Out: Satellite Radio Finds New Way to Tally Listeners" in Globe & Mail (March 14, 2007, pp. B14) **[276], [13033], [26273], [29783]**
Fard Engineers Inc. **[4317]**
Fargo Chamber of Commerce [41229]
Fargo Moorhead West Fargo Chamber of Commerce **[41229]**
Fargo Small Business Development Center - North Dakota State University (NDSU) **[43313]**
Faribault Area Chamber of Commerce and Tourism **[41230]**
Farm Bureau News **[17144]**
Farm Credit Administration - Office of Equal Employment Opportunity [47024]
Farm Credit Administration (FCA) - Office of Equal Employment Opportunity and Inclusion **[47024]**
Farm Credit Administration Office of Equal Employment Opportunity and Inclusion (EEO) **[47025]**
Farm Credit Administration Office of Inspector General (FCA OIG) **[47026]**
Farm Credit Administration Office of Management Services **[47027]**
Farm Credit Administration - Office of Management Services - Office of Procurement **[47028]**
Farm Equipment Manufacturers Association (FEMA) **[10047]**
Farm & Food Care [16935]
Farm and Food Care Ontario **[16935]**
"Farm to Fork: The Pros and Cons for Foodservice" in FoodTruckOperator.com (August 5, 2019) **[6974]**
Farm Industry News **[17145]**
Farm Science Review **[17167]**
"Farm to Table Distribution Getting Boost" in Philadelphia Business Journal (Vol. 28, May 11, 2012, No. 13, pp. 1) **[13934], [17038]**
Farmer Boys Food, Inc. **[6935], [14160]**
Farmers Branch Chamber of Commerce **[45140]**
Farmersville Chamber of Commerce (FCC) **[45141]**
Farmerville Chamber of Commerce [40196]
"Farming Starts in December; High-Priced Embryos" in Farm Industry News (November 29, 2011) **[17039], [32950]**
Farmingdale Small Business Development Center **[42398]**
Farmingdale State College Broad Hollow Bioscience Park (BHBP) **[42870]**
Farmington Chamber of Commerce (FCC) **[42317]**
Farmington/Farmington Hills Chamber of Commerce [40925]
Farmington Regional Chamber of Commerce (FRC) **[41561]**
Farmington River Watershed Association (FRWA) **[5768]**
Farmington Small Business Development Center **[42277]**
Farmington-Wilton Chamber of Commerce [40278]

Small Business Sourcebook • 42nd Edition **3233**

Farmville Area Chamber of Commerce [45858]
Farmville Chamber of Commerce (FCC) [45858]
The Farnsworth Group (TFG) [30197]
Farwell Area Chamber of Commerce (FACC) [40908]
Farwest Show [7649]
Fashion Calendar [3021]
Fashion Industry: A Resource Guide [6150]
Fashion Institute of Design and Merchandising (FIDM) [1204], [3072], [3171], [7936]
Fashion Institute of Design & Merchandising - Cyril Magnin Resource and Research Center [1204], [3072], [3171], [7936]
Fashion Institute of Design & Merchandising (FIDM) - Orange County Library [3073], [4561], [7937]
Fashion Tech Consortium Advanced Accelerator [42871]
"Fashionistas Weigh in on the Super-Thin" in Charlotte Observer (February 7, 2007) [3022], [3111], [10992]
Fashionopolis: The Price of Fast Fashion and the Future of Clothes [3023], [23202]
Fasken Martineau DuMoulin L.L.P., Toronto Library [6056]
"Fast 50: HNM Global Logistics" in Orlando Business Journal (Vol. 30, June 27, 2014, No. 53, pp. 8) [7036], [27552]
Fast-Fix Jewelry and Watch Repairs [9989]
Fast Forward [34477]
"Fast-Growing Companies Stepped Up Pace in 2011" in Sacramento Business Journal (Vol. 29, July 6, 2012, No. 19, pp. 1) [4076], [18071], [20882]
"Fast-Growing Envision Joins Billion-Dollar Club" in Sacramento Business Journal (Vol. 29, March 9, 2012, No. 2, pp. 1) [5157], [20015]
"Fast-Growing Office Pride Franchise Targets Louisville For Expansion" in Internet Wire (September 9, 2014) [2044], [19513], [24292], [33083]
Fast-teks On-site Computer Services [3587], [30495]
"Fast Times for the US Residential Solar Market" in Greentech Media (November 21, 2019) [14922]
Faster Cheaper Better [18072], [19834], [20016], [27553]
Fastframe USA Inc. [12711]
Fastline [17146]
Fastline--Indiana Farm Edition [17147]
Fastline--Kentucky Farm Edition [17148]
Fastline--Mid-South Farm Edition [17149]
Fastline--Missouri Farm Edition [17150]
Fastline--Oklahoma Farm Edition [17151]
Fastline--Tennessee Farm Edition [17152]
Fastline --Texas Farm Edition [17153]
Fastline--Wisconsin Farm Edition [17154]
Fastrackids International, Ltd. [21719]
FastSigns International Inc. [14708]
"The Fatal Bias" in Business Strategy Review (Vol. 25, Summer 2014, No. 2, pp. 34) [23874], [28583]
Fatty Acid Producers' Council [2964]
FAU Tech Runway [38560]
"Faulkner Pest Service Has Been Providing Quality Pest Control Solutions for 23 Years" in OfficialSpin (September 30, 2011) [12043]
Fauquier County Chamber of Commerce [45859]
"Faux Down Below" in Entrepreneur (May 2014) [839], [4077], [15739]
"The Favorite In the Casino, Racino Race" in Business Review Albany (Vol. 41, July 25, 2014, No. 18, pp. 7) [7282], [19835], [25331]
Fayette Area Chamber of Commerce [36110]
Fayette Center for Manufacturing and Innovation [36182]
Fayette Chamber of Commerce [44209]
Fayette County Chamber of Commerce [43470], [44210]
Fayette County Chamber of Commerce (FCCC) [46266]
Fayetteville Business Center [43241]
Fayetteville Chamber of Commerce (FCC) [36459]
Fayetteville - Lincoln County Chamber of Commerce [44743]
Fayetteville Regional Chamber [43135]
Fazoli's System Management [14161]
FCA Venture Partners (FCA) [44869]
"FCC Adopts New Media Ownership Rules" in Black Enterprise (Vol. 38, March 1, 2008, No. 8, pp. 26) [11979], [25332], [30346], [31292]
"The FCC Has Fined Robocallers $208 Million. It's Collected $6,790" in The Wall Street Journal (March 28, 2019) [15549], [25333]
FDA [4550], [11621]
FDA Food Code [1427], [8122]
FDA Newsletter [11460]
FDA Week [5198], [25611], [25999]
FDAnews Device Daily Bulletin [10862]
FDAnews Drug Daily Bulletin [4530]
FDL SHRM [46405]
FDLAC [46405]
"Fear of the Unknown Muted Impact of Baltimore Grand Prix" in Baltimore Business Journal (Vol. 29, September 9, 2011, No. 18, pp. 3) [8391], [10023], [13935], [15153]

"Fearless Leaders: Sharpen Your Focus: How the New Science of Mindfulness Can Help You Reclaim Your Confidence" [22593], [28584]
Featherlite Exhibits [35139]
"February Hot for Mutual Fund Sales" in Globe & Mail (March 3, 2006, pp. B10) [6394], [9505], [23875]
"The Fed Still Has Ammunition" in Barron's (Vol. 90, August 30, 2010, No. 35, pp. M9) [6395], [9506], [20883], [24979]
"Fed Tackles Bear of a Crisis" in Barron's (Vol. 88, March 17, 2008, No. 11, pp. M10) [6396], [9507], [20884], [23876], [24980]
FedBizOpps [25172]
FedDev Ontario [46761]
"Federal Bailout, Three Years Later" in Business Owner (Vol. 35, September-October 2011, No. 5, pp. 6) [6397], [9508], [20885], [24981]
Federal Bar Association (FBA) [10214]
"Federal Buildings to Achieve Zero-Net Energy by 2030" in Contractor (Vol. 56, December 2009, No. 12, pp. 5) [4078], [5371], [5605], [12630], [23203]
Federal Bureau of Prisons - Acquisition Offices - Administration Division [47738]
Federal Business Development Bank [11105]
Federal Career Opportunities [14987]
Federal Communications Commission (FCC) - Consumer Inquiries and Complaints Div. [47029]
Federal Communications Commission (FCC-EB) - Enforcement Bureau [47030]
Federal Communications Commission - Homeland Security Policy Council [47043]
Federal Communications Commission - Office of Communications Business Opportunities (OCBO) [47031]
Federal Communications Commission - Office of General Counsel - Administrative Law Div. [47032]
Federal Communications Commission (OMR) - Office of Media Relations [47033]
Federal Communications Commission (FCC/OWD) - Office of Workplace Diversity [47034]
Federal Communications Commission - Wireless Telecommunications Bureau (WTB) [47035]
Federal Deposit Insurance Corporation (FDIC) - Boston Area Office [47036]
Federal Deposit Insurance Corporation (CRO) - Chicago Regional Office [47037]
Federal Deposit Insurance Corporation - Kansas City Regional Office [47038]
Federal Deposit Insurance Corporation - New York Regional Office [47039]
Federal Deposit Insurance Corporation (FDIC) - Office of Diversity and Economic Opportunity - Minority and Women Outreach Program - Northeast Service Center [47040]
Federal Deposit Insurance Corporation - Office of Diversity and Economic Opportunity - Minority and Women Outreach Program - Southwest Service Center [47041]
Federal Deposit Insurance Corporation (FDIC) - San Francisco Regional Office [47042]
"Federal Employees Turn to Pawnshops Amid Shutdown's Financial Pinch" in The New York Times (January 19, 2019) [11919]
"Federal Employer Identification Number (FEIN): How to Get One" in Business News Daily (February 28, 2023) [27177], [34503], [34790]
"Federal Financial Assistance for Small Businesses" on Benefits.gov (Mar 31, 2021) [24982]
"The Federal Government Is Making a New Investment in Women-Owned Small Businesses" in The 19th (Dec. 7, 2021) [35775]
"Federal Grants for Women: Multiple Grants for Entrepreneurs" by Now Corp. [35776]
Federal Home Loan Mortgage Corporation (FHLMC) [47071]
Federal Home Loan Mortgage Corporation - Southeast Region [47072]
Federal Home Loan Mortgage Corporation - Southwest Region [47073]
Federal Home Loan Mortgage Corporation - Western Region [47074]
Federal Income Taxation of Corporations and Shareholders [15456], [34950]
Federal Income Taxation of S Corporations [32418], [34951]
Federal Mediation and Conciliation Service - Eastern Region - Cleveland, Ohio Regional Office [47075]
Federal Mediation and Conciliation Service - Office of Procurement [47076]
Federal Mediation and Conciliation Service (FMCS) - Office of Procurement and Operational Support [47076]
Federal Mediation and Conciliation Service Office of Public Affairs [47077]
Federal Mediation and Conciliation Service - Western Region [47078]

Federal Mediation and Conciliation Service - Western Region - Minneapolis, Minnesota Sub-Regional Office [47079]
Federal Research Service Report [14987]
"Federal Support for Small Business Owners and Independent Contractors Impacted by COVID-19" by The American Speech-Language-Hearing Association (Apr 2, 2021) [24983]
Federal Taxes Weekly Alert [15457], [34952]
Federal Trade Commission (FTC) - Bureau of Consumer Protection [47082]
Federal Trade Commission (FTC) - Denver Regional Office [47083]
Federal Trade Commission - East Central Region (ECR) [47084]
Federal Trade Commission - Midwest Region [47085]
Federal Trade Commission - Northeast Region [47086]
Federal Trade Commission - Northwest Region [47087]
Federal Trade Commission (FTC OIG) - Office of Inspector General [47088]
Federal Trade Commission (FTC) - Procurement and General Services Div. [47089]
Federal Trade Commission - Southeast Region [47090]
Federal Trade Commission - Southwest Region [47091]
Federal Trade Commission - Western Region [47092]
Federal Trade Commission - Western Region [47093]
Federated Employers [34960]
Federation of American Hospitals Conference and Business Exposition [10876]
Federation of American Scientists (FAS) [32715]
Federation of BC Writers (FBCW) [5282]
Federation of Canadian Naturalists [5494]
Fédération Canadienne des Épiciers Indépendants (FCEI) [7709]
Fédération Canadienne de l'Entreprise Indépendante [20689], [22950], [24588], [26756], [33451]
Federation Canadienne des Professeurs de Musique [11164]
Fédération canadienne des métiers d'art [4701]
Federation of Employee Benefit Association [17260], [19727]
Fédération canadienne des enseignantes et des enseignants [35149]
Federation of International Trade Associations (FITA) [27409]
Federation of Ontario Naturalists [5494]
Federation of Societies for Coathings Technology [11854], [11871]
Federation of Societies for Coatings Technology [11854], [11871]
Federation of Societies for Paint Technology [11854], [11871]
Federation des Travailleurs et Travailleuses du Quebec - Centre de Documentation [35216]
Fedration canadienne des enseignantes et des enseignants [35149]
"Feds Battling to Put the Brakes on Ambulance Billing Fraud" in Philadelphia Business Journal (Vol. 33, April 25, 2014, No. 11, pp. 4) [571], [18580], [20283]
"Feds Finalize I-9 Form Rules Allowing Electronic Storage" in HR Specialist (Vol. 8, September 2010, No. 9, pp. 5) [63], [1756], [11933], [15381], [18581], [21852], [25334], [26941]
"Feds to Pay University Hospital $20M" in Business Courier (Vol. 27, July 23, 2010, No. 12, pp. 3) [18582], [21512], [24984], [25777], [34791]
Feed-Lot [664]
"Feeding the Elephants While Searching for Greener Pastures" in American Printer (Vol. 128, July 1, 2011, No. 7) [3307], [12733], [16189]
"Feeding the Elephants While Searching for Greener Pastures" in Inc. (Volume 32, December 2010, No. 10, pp. 34) [20886], [27869], [30721], [31968], [32754]
"Fees Come Down; Markets Come Down More" in Barron's (Vol. 89, July 13, 2009, No. 28, pp. L8) [6398], [9509], [23877]
"Feet on the Street: Reps Are Ready to Hit the Ground Running" in Agency Sales Magazine (Vol. 39, July 2009, No. 7, pp. 12) [20429], [29207], [32525]
Felicis Ventures [37360]
"FEMA Postpones Switch to New Risk-Based Flood Insurance Rating Until 2021" in Insurance Journal (November 8, 2019) [8908], [27266]
Female Entrepreneur Association (FEA) [35617]
Female Entrepreneurship in East and South-East Asia: Opportunities and Challenges [22594], [27554], [35777]
Female Small Business Owners Embrace Equity of International Women's Day [35899]
Fennimore Area Chamber of Commerce [46406]
Fenox Venture Capital [37736]
Fenton Area Chamber of Commerce (FACC) [41562]
Fenton Regional Chamber of Commerce [40909]

Fentress County Chamber of Commerce [44744]
Fenwick & West LLP Law Library [9949], [15472]
Fergus Falls Area Chamber of Commerce (FFACC) [41231]
Ferndale Chamber of Commerce (FCC) [46082]
Fernley Chamber of Commerce [41937]
Ferrum College - Blue Ridge Heritage Archive [4693]
Ferry County Business Resource Center [46001]
Fertility Weekly [26000]
Fetch! Pet Care [12270]
"A Few Points of Contention" in Barron's (Vol. 88, July 14, 2008, No. 28, pp. 3) [6399], [9510], [17040], [20887], [23878], [24985], [25335], [33148]
ff Asset Management LLC [42741]
ff Venture Capital [42741]
FGWA Convention & Trade Show [16345]
FHCA Annual Conference [26068]
FHCA Annual Conference & Trade Show [26068]
FHI 360 [10007]
FHL Capital Corp. [36162]
FIABCI-USA [13089]
Fiber Fuels Institute [23044]
Fiberglass Fabrication Association [29068]
Fibrenew [1142]
Fidelity Investor [6694]
Fidelity National Property and Casualty Group [151], [16886], [24267]
Fiducial Century Small Business Solutions Inc. [42417]
Field Spaniel Society of America (FSSA) [635]
"Fieldbrook Foods Acquired By Private Equity Firm" in Ice Cream Reporter (Vol. 23, October 20, 2010, No. 11, pp. 1) [8561], [9511], [31293]
Fierce Leadership [22595], [28585]
Fife Milton Edgewood Chamber of Commerce (FME) [46083]
Fifth Estate [6002]
"Fifth Third Spinoff Eyes More Space" in Business Courier (Vol. 27, July 16, 2010, No. 11, pp. 1) [9512], [13194], [13449], [18073], [23879], [31294], [33149], [33364]
Fifth Wall Ventures [35466]
"Fifty Comic Stores That Have Closed Since January 2017" in Bleeding Cool (January 19, 2018) [3271], [34015]
Fifty-Forty-Ten-News [42399]
"Fifty Percent of Global Online Retail Visits Were to Amazon, eBay and Alibaba in June 2011" in Benzinga.com (October 29, 2011) [1072], [21853], [32147], [34016]
Figaro's Pizza [12550]
"Fight Ensues Over Irreplaceable Princess Diana Gowns" in Tampa Bay Business Journal (Vol. 30, January 15, 2010, No. 4, pp. 1) [3024], [4788], [7109], [18583], [20284], [28134], [35338]
"Fight Over Casino Funds Limits Kitty for MEDC" in Crain's Detroit Business (Vol. 24, January 21, 2008, No. 3, pp. 3) [7283], [20888]
"Fighting for Civil Rights Tourism" in Memphis Business Journal (Vol. 33, March 2, 2012, No. 47, pp. 1) [15740], [15991], [19836], [30347]
"Fighting The Good Fight - Against Hate" in Inc. (Vol. 33, October 2011, No. 8, pp. 8) [21513], [28586]
"The File On..Jenne Distributors" in Crain's Cleveland Business (Vol. 28, October 8, 2007, No. 40, pp. 26) [17672], [18074]
Filene Research Institute (FRI) [6735]
Filipino Chamber of Commerce [30266]
"Filling the Business Gap" in Hispanic Business (December 2010) [20889], [26558], [26942], [30348], [30566], [35778]
"Filling the Gap" in Canadian Business (Vol. 80, March 12, 2007, No. 6, pp. 62) [18075], [22596], [32148]
Film Comment [11130]
Film Journal--Equipment, Concessions, & Services Guide Issue [11122]
Film Journal International--Equipment, Concessions & Services Guide (Internet only) [11122]
Film Studies Association of Canada [6156]
Film and Tape Directory [6208]
FIN Capital [35467]
Final Mile Forum and Expo [20667]
"Finally, New Life For Old IBM Offices" in Austin Business Journal (Vol. 34, June 6, 2014, No. 16, pp. A4) [883], [4079], [9036], [31295]
"Finally! Windsor Gets a New Bridge" in Canadian Business (Vol. 85, August 21, 2012, No. 14, pp. 20) [25336], [27555]
Finance & Accounting: How to Keep Your Books and Manage Your Finances with an MBA, a CPA, or a Ph.D [64], [1757], [16802], [23880]
Financial & Accounting Concepts, Statements & Terminology: 2 Day (Onsite) [23709]
Financial Analysts Federation [9290]

Financial Analysts Research Foundation [6734]
"Financial Benefits of an Eco-Friendly Business" in Green Business Bureau (June 17, 2019) [23204]
Financial Concepts & Tools for Business Managers [24275]
Financial Executives Research Foundation (FERF) [1794]
"The Financial Illiteracy Problem Among Small Business Owners" in Small Business Trends (September 12, 2022) [16558]
Financial Managers Society (FMS) [6231]
Financial Planning & Analysis and Performance Management [6036], [6400], [23881]
Financial Planning Association (FPA) [6232]
Financial Planning Standards Council [46751]
Financial Solutions Inc. [13056], [15625]
"Financial Stability: Fraud, Confidence, and the Wealth of Nations" [6401], [9513], [20890], [23882]
Financial Statement Analysis (Onsite) [23710]
"Financial Woes Continue to Plague Nearly Half of Women Small Business Owners" in bizwomen (Oct. 8, 2021) [35779]
Financial Women's Association (FWA) [23697], [35618]
Financial Women's Association of New York (FWA) [6233]
FinancialAdvisors.com (FA) [24244]
Financing Your Small Business [6402], [9514], [28135], [31296], [35339]
Finaventures [37361]
Find. Build. Sell.: How I Turned a $100 Backyard Bar into a $100 Million Pub Empire [1331], [22597]
"Find a Customer To Validate Your Idea" in South Florida Business Journal (Vol. 34, May 2, 2014, No. 41, pp. 15) [22387], [26167], [35236], [35504]
FINDERBINDER--Oklahoma (Media) [2471]
FinderBinder/SourceBook Directories [1703]
"Finding Competitive Advantage in Adversity" in Harvard Business Review (Vol. 88, November 2010, No. 11, pp. 102) [19837], [20891], [31297]
Side Hustle to Small Business: Finding Your Balance as an Entrepreneur [14056]
"Finding Life Behind the Numbers" in Crain's Chicago Business (Vol. 31, March 24, 2008, No. 12, pp. 25) [21514], [27556]
Finding a Mentor Who Thinks Holistically with Paul Zelizer [8824]
"Finding the Right Resources to Get Started Overseas" in Pittsburgh Business Times (Vol. 33, January 3, 2014, No. 25, pp. 4) [18076], [27557]
Finding a Product Market Fit [17469]
"Finding the Right Accountant for Your Small Business" Business News Daily (February 21, 2023) [65], [16803], [34504]
"Finding Startup Success in a Challenging Market" in Food Business News (October 5, 2020) [34505]
"Finding a Way to Continue Growing" in Green Industry Pro (Vol. 23, March 2011, No. 3, pp. 31) [7618], [10094], [10230], [18077], [19838], [33150]
Finding Your Niche Market [29539]
"Finding Your Place in the World: Global Diversity Has Become a Corporate Catchphrase" in Black Enterprise (November 2007) [27558], [30567]
Findlay-Hancock County Chamber of Commerce [43471]
Fine Details Inc. [2585]
Fine Hardwood Veneer Association [10376], [10415]
Fine Hardwood Veneer Association/American Walnut Manufacturers Association [10376]
Fine Hardwoods American Walnut Association [10374]
Fine Ink Studios Corp. [15343]
"A Fine Time for Timber" in Barron's (Vol. 92, August 25, 2012, No. 38, pp. 18) [9515], [10392], [13450], [20892]
"Fine Wine, Poor Returns" in Barron's (Vol. 92, September 17, 2012, No. 38, pp. 11) [6403], [9516], [15012], [23883], [34792]
The Finer Points of a Laundromat Business Plan [10169]
"Fines Can't Snuff Out Hookah Sales" in Providence Business News (Vol. 28, March 3, 2014, No. 48, pp. 1) [1332], [13936], [15697], [18584]
Finishing Contractors Association International (FCA) [3939]
"Finishing High School Leads to Better Employment Prospects" in Occupational Outlook Quarterly (Vol. 55, Summer 2011, No. 2, pp. 36) [2600], [21515]
Finistere Ventures Inc. (FV) [37737]
Finnegan, Henderson, Farabow, Garrett & Dunner, LLP [27981]
Finney County Genealogical Society Library [7409]
Finnish American Chamber of Commerce (FACC) [27410]
"FinOvation 2009" in Farm Industry News (Vol. 42, January 1, 2009, No. 1) [17041], [27870], [30722], [32755]
Fintech: Financial Technology Research Guide [6725]

FinTech Innovation Lab [42872]
Fiorello H. LaGuardia Community College of the City University of New York - Division of Adult and Continuing Education - Center for Corporate Education [42969]
"Fire Destroys Surplus Store, Sets Off Live Rounds Near Jacksonville NAS" in Florida Times-Union (December 5, 2010) [7835], [32149]
"Fire Your Agent? Not Yet. Hollywood Writers and Talent Agencies Extend Talks" in The New York Times (April 7, 2019) [15257], [35190]
Firearm Laws for Businesses and Their Customers [849]
Firearms News [7838]
Firelands Historical Society Library [7410]
FirePower Capital [46786]
Firkin Group of Pubs [6936], [14162]
"Firm Raises City's Largest VC Fund In 3 Years" in Dallas Business Journal (Vol. 35, July 20, 2012, No. 45, pp. 1) [26274], [35340]
"Firm Restricts Cellphone Use While Driving" in Globe & Mail (January 30, 2006, pp. B3) [2736], [25337]
"The Firm: The Story of McKinsey and Its Secret Influence on American Business" [2187], [21516]
"Firms Bet On Games To Hike Wellness" in Business Journal (Vol. 30, June 1, 2012, No. 1, pp. 1) [2737], [14777], [17304], [19839], [25778], [33151], [33851]
"Firms Start Increasing their Space" in Philadelphia Business Journal (Vol. 31, March 23, 2012, No. 6, pp. 1) [12885], [18078], [20893]
"Firms Sue Doracon to Recoup More Than $1M in Unpaid Bills" in Baltimore Business Journal (Vol. 28, July 9, 2010, No. 9, pp. 1) [4080], [4789], [8909], [10736], [13790], [18585], [20285], [27267]
"First Airport Location for Paciugo Gelato" in Ice Cream Reporter (Vol. 23, October 20, 2010, No. 11, pp. 2) [8562], [19347]
First Analysis Securities Corp. (FASC) [39355]
First Ascent Ventures (FAV) [46787]
First Capital Group (FCG) [45449]
First Choice Haircutters, Ltd. (FCH) [7891]
First Flight Venture Center (FFVC) [43242]
"First Food Truck Festival Features Enticing Fare, Frustrating Waits" in Saint Paul Pioneer Press (August 6, 2012) [3841], [6975], [30469], [34017]
First Health Review Inc. [17398]
"First Impressions of Robotic Farming Systems" in Farm Industry News (September 30, 2011) [17042], [26275], [29208]
First Liberty Institute (FLI) [15489]
"First Look at Downtown's JW Marriott" in Houston Business Journal (Vol. 45, June 27, 2014, No. 7, pp. 10A) [4081], [8392], [12412]
"First Mariner Bank's New Ads No Passing Fancy" in Baltimore Business Journal (Vol. 29, September 16, 2011, No. 19, pp. 1) [277], [23884]
"First, the Merger: Then, The Culture Clash. How To Fix the Little Things That Can Tear a Company Apart" in Inc. (January 2008) [278], [884], [9037], [9517], [14701], [31298]
First Monday [38380]
First Round Capital [44339]
"First Solar Signs Power Purchase Agreements with Pacific Gas and Electric Company for 72 Megawatts" in Benzinga.com (September 11, 2012) [14923], [31299]
First State Innovation (FSI) [38122]
First Strike Management Consulting Inc. (FSMC) [2387], [10529], [20188], [28991], [33667]
"First Sustainability Standard for Household Portable and Floor Care Appliances Developed to Identify Environmentally Responsible Products" in Ecology, Environment & Conservation Business (September 13, 2014, pp. 39) [790], [5606], [5879], [6828], [23205], [25338], [29209], [32150]
"First Suzlon S97 Turbines Arrive in North America for Installation" in PR Newswire (September 28, 2011) [5607], [5880], [23206], [29210]
"First-Time Landlord: Your Guide to Renting Out a Single-Family Home" [13073], [13358], [13758], [18586], [25339]
"First Venture Reports Proprietary Yeasts Further Reduce Ethyl Carbamate in Sake" in Canadian Corporate News (May 16, 2007) [10321], [23207], [32756]
First Watch Restaurants, Inc. [14163]
"First Woman To Lead Builders Group" in Philadelphia Business Journal (Vol. 32, January 31, 2014, No. 51, pp. 8) [885], [4082], [34793], [35780]
FirstGrowthVC [42956]
FirstMark [42742]
FirstMark Capital [42743]
"FirstMerit's Top Executive Turns Around Credit Quality" in Crain's Cleveland Business (Vol. 28, October 15, 2007, No. 41, pp. 3) [6404], [18079], [19514], [20286], [23885], [26559]

FirstMile Ventures [37920]
FirstService Brands, Inc. [33318]
"FIS-Metavante Deal Paying Off for Many" in Business Journal-Milwaukee (Vol. 28, December 17, 2010, No. 11, pp. A1) [6405], [7110], [9518], [19170], [19661], [26276], [34314]
Fiscal Agents - Financial Information Service - Research Department Library [6727]
"Fiscal Cliff Notes" in Barron's (Vol. 92, September 15, 2012, No. 38, pp. 27) [6406], [9519], [17673], [20894], [23886]
Fiscal Management Associates L.L.C. [131]
Fischer Kraker Miscelli Inc. [1782]
Fish Bytes [44646]
Fish Window Cleaning Services Inc. [2103]
Fish Wrapper [44647]
"Fishbrain Launches in-App Fishing Tackle Shop" in Fishing Tackle Retailer (October 10, 2019) [1232], [11745]
Fisheries Museum of the Atlantic Library [6798]
Fisheries of the United States [6782]
Fishers Chamber of Commerce [39591]
Fishing Tackle Retailer (FTR) [1233]
FIT Business Innovation Center [38561]
Fit Zone for Women [12454]
The Fitness Business Association (AFS) [12373]
"The Fitness Marketing Guide for the Modern Fitness Founder" in Glofox blog (March 20, 2019) [12413], [29784]
Fitzsimons BioBusiness Incubator [37937]
Fitzsimons Innovation Campus (FIC) [37938]
Fitzsimons Innovation Community [37941]
Fitzsimons Innovation Company (FIC) [37939]
Fitzsimons Life Science District [37940]
Fitzsimons Redevelopment Authority (FRA) [37941]
FIU Hospitality Review [8476]
"Five Area Businesses Win State Tax Breaks" in Crain's Detroit Business (Vol. 25, June 22, 2009, No. 25, pp. 9) [24986], [34794]
Five CEO Tips for Succeeding through an Economic Bust [24209]
"Five Distinct Divisions, One Collective Focus" in Green Industry Pro (Vol. 23, October 2011) [7619], [10095], [10231], [29785], [32526], [33152]
"Five Easy Ways to Fail: Nothing Like a Weak Team Or An Unrealistic Schedule To Start a Project Off Right" in Inc. (November 2007, pp. 85-87) [14778], [33852]
Five Elms Capital [41714]
"Five Essential Finance and Accounting Strategies for Small Businesses" in Forbes (July 9, 2021) [16804]
Five Guys Burgers and Fries [14164]
Five Guys Enterprises, LLC [14164]
"Five Lessons in Entrepreneurship from the Worlds of Trading and Gambling" in Entrepreneur (Aug. 21, 2017) [7284], [22598]
"Five Myths About Bed and Breakfasts" and USA Today (December 29, 2015) [1414]
"Five Myths About Child Care" in The Washington Post (November 5, 2021) [2883]
"Five New Scientists Bring Danforth Center $16 Million" in Saint Louis Business Journal (Vol. 32, October 7, 2011, No. 6, pp. 1) [21517], [24987], [31969], [32757]
"Five Reasons Why the Gap Fell Out of Fashion" in Globe & Mail (January 27, 2007, pp. B4) [3112], [19840], [29211], [32151]
"Five Tips for Killer Landing Pages" in Retirement Advisor (Vol. 13, October 2012, No. 10, pp. 27) [6407], [9520], [16418]
"Five Ways to Make RTK Pay" in Farm Industry News (March 25, 2011) [17043], [34018]
"Fix-It Careers: Jobs in Repair" in Occupational Outlook Quarterly (Vol. 54, Fall 2010, No. 3, pp. 26) [484], [14551], [33153]
"Fixing Up the Area: Leo Piatz Opens General Repair Business" in The Dickinson Press (November 16, 2010) [16916], [33084]
FJ Labs [42744]
Flagler County Chamber of Commerce [38381]
Flagship [40576]
Flagship Enterprise Center (FEC) [39639]
Flagship Pioneering [40686]
Flagship Technologies, Inc. [14888], [33668]
Flagship Ventures [40686]
Flagstaff Chamber of Commerce [36331]
The Flame Broiler Inc. [14165]
Flamers Grill-Charbroiled Hamburgers and Chicken [14166]
Flamingo-A-Friend Inc. [33319]
Flashpoint (FP) [38847]
FlashStarts [43664]
Flat Rate Realty (FR) [13337]
Flat River Area Chamber of Commerce [41611]
"Flat or Slight Decline Seen for Nortel 2007 Revenue" in Globe & Mail (March 17, 2007, pp. B3) [19515], [33154]

Flatonia Chamber of Commerce (FCC) [45142]
Flavour and Fragrance Journal [1595]
The Flaw of Averages: Why We Underestimate Risk in the Face of Uncertainty [66], [5608], [5881], [9521], [16805], [23208], [23887], [25340], [25779]
"A Flawed Yardstick for Banks" in Barron's (Vol. 88, July 14, 2008, No. 28, pp. M6) [6408], [9522], [11032], [20287], [20895], [23888]
Fledge LLC [46215]
"Fledgling Brands May Take the Fall With Steve & Barry's" in Advertising Age (Vol. 79, July 7, 2008, No. 26, pp. 6) [3025], [3113], [15091], [27871], [32152]
Fleet Equipment [16095]
Fleming County Chamber of Commerce (FCCC) [40038]
Fletcher Spaght Ventures (FSV) [40687]
Flett Research Ltd. [2264], [20189], [32930]
Flex-Plan Services Inc. [17406]
FLEXO [12766]
FLEXO: Converting Technology [12766]
Flexographic Technical Association (FTA) [12717]
Flight Safety Foundation (FSF) [416], [447]
"Flights of Fancy" in Crain's Chicago Business (Vol. 31, April 21, 2008, No. 16, pp. 27) [19348], [19841], [33155]
Flint Food Works [41089]
"Flint Group Raises Prices of Offset Inks in EMEA" in American Printer (Vol. 128, August 1, 2011, No. 8) [3308], [12734], [16190], [20017]
Flippin Chamber of Commerce [36460]
Float Small Business [43920]
"A Flood of New Construction: Will You Tap into the $400B Seawall Pipeline?" in ConstructionDive (October 16, 2019) [4083], [18957]
Floodgate [37362]
Floor Covering Installation Contractors Association (FCICA) [6823]
Floor Covering Product Resource Guide [6829], [9038]
Floor Covering Weekly [6835]
Floor Coverings International Ltd. [6839]
Floor Trends [6836], [16231]
Floorguard Inc. [12858]
FloraCulture International (FCI) [7642]
"Floral-Design Kiosk Business Blossoming" in Colorado Springs Business Journal (September 24, 2010) [6854], [7735], [10024], [22599], [26778], [35781]
Florence Area Chamber of Commerce (FACC) [43970]
Florence Area Small Business Development Center (SBDC) [44505], [44603]
Florence Chamber of Commerce [37850]
Florence Crittenton Association of American [2866]
Florence-Darlington Technical College (FDTC) [44611]
Floresville Chamber of Commerce [45143]
Florida A&M University (FAMU) - Frederick S. Humphries Science Research Center Library [10975], [12506]
Florida A&M University - Small Business Development Center (SBDC) [38216]
Florida Accounting and Business Expo [16861]
Florida Agency of Economic Opportunity - Labor Market Statistics - State Census Data Center [47749]
Florida Agency for Workforce Innovation - Labor Market Statistics - State Census Data Center [46930]
Florida Ambulance Association (FAA) [568]
Florida APEX Accelerator (PTAC) [38541]
Florida Association of Realtors [13090]
Florida Atlantic Research and Development Authority (FARDA) [38562]
Florida Atlantic University - Technology Business Incubator [38563]
Florida Bar Convention [10221], [38603]
Florida Black Business Investment Board (BBIF) [38529]
Florida Buildings & Facilities Maintenance Show [12911]
Florida Business Development Corporation (FBDC) [38256]
Florida Business Incubation Association (FBIA) [33458]
Florida Business Travel Association, Gulf Coast Chapter [19296]
Florida Business Travel Association - South Florida Chapter (FBTA) [19295]
Florida Chamber of Commerce (FCC) [38382]
Florida Chapter of the Data Management Association [38208]
Florida Citrus Show [17168]
Florida Department of Agriculture and Consumer Services - Division of Plant Industry Library [1504]
Florida Department of Economic Opportunity - Labor Market Information - Florida Census Data Center [46929]
Florida Department of Economic Opportunity - Labor Market Statistics Center - Florida Census Data Center [46930]
Florida Department of Management Services - Agency Purchasing [38542]
"Florida Fast 100: D&D Construction Services" in South Florida Business Journal (Vol. 35, September 19, 2014, No. 8, pp. 16) [4084], [8393], [13195], [13451], [13937], [20896]

Florida Gulf Coast University-Florida Procurement Technical Assistance Center (PTAC) [38543]
"Florida Harvest Power Converting Organic Biz Waste to Electricity" in Orlando Business Journal (Vol. 30, March 21, 2014, No. 39, pp. 3) [5882], [17044]
Florida Health Care Association Conference [26068]
"Florida Hospital Planning $104.1M in Expansions" in Orlando Business Journal (Vol. 29, June 8, 2012, No. 53, pp. 1) [4085], [15640], [25780]
"Florida Hospital, UCF Affiliation in Danger?" in Orlando Business Journal (Vol. 29, September 21, 2012, No. 29, pp. 1) [19842], [21518], [25781], [31300]
Florida Keys Community College [38598]
Florida Medical Entomology Laboratory Library [12073]
Florida Pest Management Association Convention and Exposition [12056]
Florida Pharmacy Association Annual Meeting and Convention [5204]
Florida Procurement Center Representatives (FI PCR) [38544]
The Florida Procurement Technical Assistance Center (PTAC) [38545]
Florida Procurement Technical Assistance Center [38541]
Florida Procurement Technical Assistance Center-University of South Florida-Pinellas Park [38546]
Florida Realtors [13090]
Florida RV Supershow [1124], [35121]
Florida SBDC at Indian River State College, Fort Pierce [38217]
Florida SBDC at USF: Counties of Sarasota and Manatee [38218]
Florida Small Business Development Center at Daytona State College (FSBDC) [38219]
Florida Small Business Development Center at Eastern Florida State College Melbourne (FSBDC) [38220]
Florida Small Business Development Center Network (FSBDCN) [38221]
Florida Small Business Development Center at Seminole Community College (FSBDC) [38222]
Florida Small Business Development Center at South Florida State College [38223]
Florida Small Business Development Center at the University of Central Florida (FSBDC) [38224]
Florida Small Business Development Center at the University of West Florida (FSBDC) [38225]
Florida Solar Energy Center Research Library (FSEC) [14967]
Florida State Minority Supplier Development Council (FSMSDC) [38530]
Florida State University - Career Center Library [2622]
Florida State University College of Business - Jim Moran Institute for Global Entrepreneurship [38564]
Florida State University College of Music - Center for Music Research (CMR) [11254]
Florida State University College of Social Sciences and Public Policy - Center for Demography and Population Health (CDPH) [47410]
Florida State University - Florida Center for Public Management (FCPM) [31724]
Florida State University - Panama Branch Library [24912]
Florida State University - Special Collections [8162]
Florida TaxWatch (FTW) [15490]
Florida Trend [2412]
Florida Tropical Fish Farms Association (FTFFA) [6763]
Florida Veterinary Medical Association Annual Meeting [708]
"Florida's Housing Gloom May Add To Woes of National City" in Crain's Cleveland Business (Vol. 28, October 29, 2007, No. 43, pp. 1) [6409], [9523], [20288], [23889], [31301]
FloridaWest [38565]
Florissant Valley Chamber of Commerce [41566]
Florists Industry in the US - Market Research Report [6865]
Florists' Review Magazine [6867]
Flow Ventures [46904]
"Flower Confidential" in Business Horizons (Vol. 51, January-February 2008, No. 1, pp. 73) [6855]
Flower Mound Chamber of Commerce [45144]
"Flower Power" in Garden Center (November 4, 2019) [6856], [7620]
Flowerama [6875]
Flowers Canada (FC) [6848], [7607]
Floyd County [40039]
Floyd County Chamber of Commerce [45860]
Floyd County Chamber of Commerce [39590]
Fluff & Fold 101 [10191]
Fluke Venture Partners (FVP) [46190]
"Flurry of Activity from Restaurant Groups as Industry Strengthens" in Wichita Business Journal (Vol. 27, February 17, 2012, No. 7, pp. 1) [886], [4086], [13938], [18080], [24357], [28587]

Master Index **Former**

Master Index

Flushing Area Chamber of Commerce (FACC) **[40910]**
Fluvanna County Chamber of Commerce (FCCC) **[45861]**
Flybridge Capital Partners **[42745]**
Flying Biscuit **[14167]**
"Flying Colors for All American Label" in Memphis Business Journal (Vol. 34, June 1, 2012, No. 7, pp. 1) **[18081]**, **[19171]**
"Flying Discounted Skies" in Barron's (Vol. 92, September 17, 2012, No. 38, pp. 20) **[19349]**, **[20018]**
"Flying the Unfriendly Skies" in Crain's Chicago Business (Vol. 31, April 21, 2008, No. 16, pp. 26) **[19350]**, **[27559]**, **[33156]**, **[34019]**
Flying Wedge Pizza Co. **[12551]**
Flywheel Ventures **[42342]**
FMF [20667]
FMI Connect [20668]
FMI Midwinter Executive Conference **[30172]**
The FMI Show **[20668]**
FMLA Compliance (Onsite) **[26857]**
FMS [6231]
FMS Forum **[6703]**, **[24228]**
FMS Forum Annual Conference [6703], [24228]
Focal Point Business Coaching **[2338]**
FocalPoint Business Coaching **[10530]**
Focus on Autism and Other Developmental Disabilities **[26001]**
Focus on the Family (FOTF) **[23586]**
Focus Group Moderator Training (Onsite) **[29588]**, **[29589]**
Focus On Your Business Inc. **[16879]**
"'Focusing On the Moment" in Dallas Business Journal (Vol. 37, June 27, 2014, No. 42, pp. 4) **[19351]**, **[19516]**, **[25341]**, **[30723]**, **[31302]**
Foit-Albert Associates, Architecture, Engineering and Surveying, P.C. **[2023]**
Foliage Design Systems (FDS) **[12603]**
Foliage Service by Concepts **[12602]**
Folkston/Charlton County Chamber of Commerce [38770]
"Follow the Numbers: It's the Best Way To Spot Problems Before They Become Life-Threatening" in Inc. (January 2008, pp. 63-64) **[18863]**, **[32424]**
"Following the Signs" in Minority Business Entrepreneur (Vol. 39, Fall, 2022, No. 4, pp. 22-26) **[28588]**
Folsom Chamber of Commerce **[36893]**
Fond du Lac Area Association of Commerce (FDLAAC) **[46407]**
Fond du Lac Area Chamber of Commerce [46407]
Fondation Canadienne de la Recherche en Diététique (CFDR) **[11566]**
Fondation Scolaire de l'Institut Canadien du Credit **[6234]**
*FONE*Data* **[15553]**
Fontana Chamber of Commerce **[36894]**
Fontinalis Partners (FP) **[41046]**
The Food & Beverage International **[7799]**, **[15040]**
Food Brokers Association [13878]
Food Business Incubator [44839]
Food Carryout and Delivery in the U.S. **[6927]**
Food and Dairy Expo [6932]
Food Delivery Tales: True Stories about Delivering Restaurant Food **[6903]**
The Food & Drug Letter [4530]
The Food Industry Association **[6958]**, **[7996]**
Food Industry Association Executives (FIAE) **[7710]**
Food Institute (FI) **[1305]**, **[2697]**, **[3866]**, **[4929]**, **[6945]**, **[7711]**, **[7824]**, **[14304]**, **[15069]**
The Food Institute **[7800]**
Food Institute Report [7800]
The Food Lab (TFL) **[45519]**
Food Marketing Institute (FMI) **[4422]**, **[7712]**
Food Marketing Institute Annual Business Conference **[16104]**
Food Marketing Institute Information Service (FMI) **[6946]**
"Food as Nature Intended" in Pet Product News (Vol. 64, November 2010, No. 11, pp. 30) **[692]**, **[11576]**, **[12164]**, **[32153]**, **[34020]**
Food Northwest Process & Packaging Expo **[7810]**, **[14090]**
Food Nutrition Conference Expo (FNCE) **[11588]**
Food Processing Suppliers Association (FPSA) **[8539]**
Food Service Equipment Industry [13880]
Food Shippers of America Annual Logistics Conference **[16105]**
Food Trade News **[7801]**
Food Truck Association of Georgia (FTAG) **[6959]**
Food Truck Business: Complete Guide for Beginners. How to Start, Manage & Grow YOUR OWN Food Truck Business **[3823]**, **[6952]**
"Food Truck Group Backs Proposed Regulations" in Buffalo News (January 18, 2012) **[3842]**, **[6976]**, **[25342]**, **[30470]**
"The Food Truck Handbook: Start, Grow, and Succeed in the Mobile Food Business" **[3824]**, **[6953]**, **[16255]**, **[18864]**, **[19843]**, **[22388]**, **[30448]**, **[32971]**, **[33332]**
"Food-Truck Learnings Travel Indoors" in Nation's Restaurant News (Vol. 45, June 27, 2011, No. 13, pp. 3) **[6977]**, **[13939]**
Food Truck Strategy: Simple Steps to Launch Your Own Food Truck **[6978]**
"Food Truck Supplies 101: A Handy Checklist" in FoodTruckOperator.com (August 16, 2017) **[6979]**
"Food Truck Weddings Gain Popularity, Buck Tradition" in Tampa Tribune (June 24, 2012) **[1972]**, **[3843]**, **[6980]**, **[30471]**, **[34021]**
"Food Trucks Savor Rebirth in City" in Providence Business News (Vol. 27, April 16, 2012, No. 2, pp. 1) **[3844]**, **[6981]**, **[18082]**, **[30472]**, **[44490]**
Food Trucks in the US - Industry Market Research Report **[7020]**
FOOD-X **[42873]**
FoodFutureCo (FFC) **[42874]**
"The Foodie Generation Grows Up" in Business Review Albany (Vol. 41, August 8, 2014, No. 20, pp. 4) **[13940]**, **[34022]**
"Foods for Thought" in Pet Product News (Vol. 64, December 2010, No. 12, pp. 16) **[831]**, **[12199]**, **[29212]**, **[30724]**, **[34023]**
Foodservice Consultants Society International--Membership Directory **[2673]**
Foodservice Equipment Distributors Association (FEDA) **[13880]**
Foodservice and Hospitality Magazine **[8109]**
Foodservice and Lodging Institute [6890], [13886]
Foodservice and Packaging Institute (FPI) **[6888]**
Foodworks Culinary Center **[37569]**
Fooling Some of the People All of the Time **[6410]**, **[9524]**, **[23890]**
Foot Solutions, Inc. **[12033]**
"Footage Shows Workers Concerned About Hard Rock New Orleans Before Deadly Collapse" in Construction-Dive (October 18, 2019) **[4087]**, **[35945]**
Foothill Entrepreneur Center (FEC) **[37570]**
Foothill Ventures **[37363]**
Foothills Business Incubator **[46672]**
Footwear Distributors and Retailers of America (FDRA) **[14667]**
Footwear Retailers of America [14667]
"For 2020, Expect Biggest Commercial Insurance Hikes in Years: Willis Towers Watson" in Insurance Journal (November 15, 2019) **[8910]**, **[27268]**
"For Allegiance Capital, Oil and Gas are Hot" in Dallas Business Journal (Vol. 37, May 30, 2014, No. 38, pp. 8) **[19662]**, **[31303]**
"For Apple, It's Showtime Again" in Barron's (Vol. 90, August 30, 2010, No. 35, pp. 29) **[2456]**, **[2738]**, **[3706]**, **[15562]**, **[21854]**, **[26277]**, **[30725]**, **[30958]**, **[31036]**
"For Buffett Fans, the Price Is Right" in Barron's (Vol. 89, July 13, 2009, No. 28, pp. 17) **[6411]**, **[9525]**, **[23891]**
"For Gilead, Growth Beyond AIDS" in Barron's (Vol. 88, June 30, 2008, No. 26, pp. 18) **[6412]**, **[9526]**, **[18083]**, **[23892]**, **[25782]**, **[32527]**, **[32758]**
"For Giving Us a Way To Say Yes To Solar: Lynn Jurich and Edward Fenster" in Inc. (Volume 32, December 2010, No. 10, pp. 110) **[5609]**, **[5883]**, **[14924]**, **[22600]**, **[23209]**, **[31304]**, **[35782]**
"For His Bigness of Heart: Larry O'Toole: Gentle Giant Moving, Somerville, Massachusetts" in Inc. (Volume 32, December 2010) **[11142]**, **[20019]**, **[22601]**
"For Janus Motorcycles, Building Bikes by Hand Is the Only Way" in Gear Patrol (November 11, 2019) **[11110]**
"For National Frozen Yogurt Month, Get a Spoonful of These Tasty Franchises" in Entrepreneur (June 9, 2016) **[8563]**
"For One Homebuilder, It's Pretty Easy Being Green, Even in Houston" in Houston Business Journal (Vol. 44, April 11, 2014, No. 49, pp. 7) **[4088]**, **[5610]**, **[5884]**, **[13452]**, **[23210]**
"For-Profit Medical School Ramping Up for Business" in Sacramento Business Journal (Vol. 30, February 21, 2014, No. 52, pp. 6) **[5158]**, **[21519]**, **[25783]**
"For Retailers, the Smartphone is Future of Store Experience" in The Associated Press (December 12, 2018) **[2739]**
"For Tax Preparation Agencies, Inbound Consumer Calls Trend Higher in January than April" in Marketing Weekly News (May 5, 2012) **[279]**, **[10653]**, **[15382]**, **[29786]**
"For Tech Companies, Holding Onto Prized Patents Can Be Expensive" in Puget Sound Business Journal (Vol. 33, May 18, 2012, No. 4, pp. 1) **[3707]**, **[18587]**, **[27872]**
Forbes **[24776]**
Forbes (Aug. 25, 2021) "The Rise Of Franchise Consultants As A Result Of The Pandemic" in [24404]
Forbes Small Giants: 25 Companies that-believe-smaller-is-better **[24665]**
Forbes--Up-and-Comers Class Issue [24665]
"Ford Canada's Edsel of a Year: Revenue Plummets 24 Percent in '05" in Globe & Mail (February 2, 2006, pp. B1) **[6413]**, **[9527]**, **[20897]**, **[29213]**
"Ford: Down, Not Out, and Still a Buy" in Barron's (Vol. 92, July 23, 2012, No. 30, pp. 14) **[6414]**, **[9528]**, **[11398]**, **[18084]**, **[20898]**, **[23893]**, **[29214]**
Ford, Lincoln, Mercury Minority Dealers Association [11360], [30267]
Ford Minority Dealers Association (FMDA) **[11360]**, **[30267]**
Ford Motor Minority Dealers Association [11360], [30267]
Fordham University - Fordham Foundry **[42875]**
Fordyce Chamber of Commerce (FCC) **[36461]**
Forecast **[1843]**
The Foreclosure of America: Life Inside Countrywide Home Loans and the Selling of the American Dream **[11033]**, **[13196]**, **[13453]**
"Foreign Flavor of U.S. Innovation: Report Makes New Case for Immigration Reform" in Silicon Valley/San Jose Business Journal (Vol. 30, July 20, 2012, No. 17, pp. 1) **[27873]**, **[30568]**
Foreign Military Sales (Onsite) **[27439]**
Foreign Pharmacy Graduate Examination Commission [5137]
Foreign Pharmacy Graduate Examination Committee (FPGEC) **[5137]**
Forensic Photoshop (Onsite) **[21385]**, **[33796]**
Forerunner Ventures **[37364]**
"ForeSee Finds Satisfaction On Web Sites, Bottom Line" in Crain's Detroit Business (Vol. 24, February 25, 2008, No. 8, pp. 3) **[9143]**, **[15223]**, **[16419]**, **[18085]**, **[21855]**, **[27560]**
Foresight Capital **[37365]**
Forest City Tree Protection Company Inc. **[10258]**
Forest County Chamber of Commerce **[46408]**
Forest Grove/Cornelius Chamber of Commerce **[43971]**
Forest Lake Area Chamber of Commerce (FLACC) **[41232]**
Forest Park Chamber of Commerce [39167]
Forest Park Chamber of Commerce and Development (FPC) **[39167]**
"Forest Park Medical Center to Double Operations" in Dallas Business Journal (Vol. 35, April 13, 2012, No. 31, pp. 1) **[18086]**, **[25784]**
Forest Products Association of Canada [29073]
Foresthill Divide Chamber of Commerce **[36895]**
Forge **[45950]**
The Forge **[43857]**
"Forget the Pretzels and Soda, Shoppers Are Scooping Up Flowers and Salads at Convenience Stores" in CNBC.com (April 6, 2019) **[4433]**, **[18087]**
"Forget Retirement: Senior Citizens are Founding Small Businesses, and Research Shows More of Them are Likely to Succeed Than Young Entrepreneurs" in Business Insider (August 12, 2019) **[33066]**
"Forget Your Pants, Calvin Klein Wants Into Your Bedroom" in Globe & Mail (March 31, 2007, pp. B4) **[3114]**, **[8206]**, **[32154]**
Fork Food Lab (FFL) **[40321]**
Forks Chamber of Commerce (FCC) **[46084]**
Formal Wear & Costume Rental Industry in the US - Market Research Report **[4556]**, **[13844]**
"Former Boxer Lou Savarese Fits Into New Business Role" in Houston Business Journal (Vol. 40, January 8, 2010, No. 35, pp. 1) **[12364]**, **[22389]**
"Former Collection Agency CFO Sentenced" in PaymentsSource (April 24, 2012) **[4790]**, **[18588]**, **[20289]**
"Former Dell Exec Turns Entrepreneur, Buys Travel Agency" in Austin Business Journal (Vol. 34, May 9, 2014, No. 12, pp. 9) **[15963]**, **[22602]**, **[35783]**
"Former NFL Player Tackles a New Restaurant Concept" in Inc. (Vol. 33, September 2011, No. 7, pp. 32) **[13941]**, **[23618]**
"Former Owner of Spartanburg Tax Preparation Business Pleads Guilty to Fraud in Multi-Million Dollar Scheme" in Internet Wire (January 26, 2012) **[15383]**, **[33853]**
"Former Prov. Mayor Sees Potential in Newport Grand" in Providence Business News (Vol. 29, July 21, 2014, No. 16, pp. 4) **[887]**, **[7285]**, **[19663]**, **[25343]**
"Former Robinhood Employees Launch Parafin, a Finance Startup for Small Business" in The Wall Street Journal (September 29, 2021) **[19717]**, **[34506]**, **[35341]**
"Former Schaefer & Strohminger Dealerships to Hit Auction Block" in Baltimore Business Journal (Vol. 28, September 10, 2010) **[1073]**, **[11399]**, **[13197]**, **[13454]**
"Former Tech Execs Want to Tap Building Trend in Austin" in Austin Business Journal (Vol. 31, May 13, 2011, No. 10, pp. A1) **[4089]**, **[5611]**, **[5885]**, **[7037]**, **[23211]**, **[33365]**, **[34315]**

Small Business Sourcebook • 42nd Edition **3237**

"Former WCVB Anchor Bianca De la Garza Discusses the Launch of Her New Media Venture" in Boston Business Journal (Vol. 34, June 6, 2014, No. 18, pp. 4) **[2441]**, **[15565]**, **[22390]**, **[35505]**
"The Formula for Growth: Through a Mixture of Vision and Partnerships, Leon Richardson has ChemicoMays in Expansion Mode" in Black Enterprise (Vol. 44, June 2014, No. 10, pp. 66) **[4434]**, **[22603]**, **[28589]**
"Formula One Makes Room(s) for Aspiring Entrepreneur in Austin" in Austin Business Journal (Vol. 31, July 1, 2011, No. 17, pp. 1) **[3309]**, **[8394]**, **[15992]**, **[21856]**
"Formula for Success: Dispelling the Age-Old Myths" in Agency Sales Magazine (Vol. 39, July 2009, No. 7, pp. 26) **[22604]**, **[32528]**
"Formulating Policy With a Parallel Organization" in Strategy & Leadership (Vol. 38, September-October 2010, No. 5, pp. 33-38) **[18088]**, **[18958]**, **[28590]**
Forney Area Chamber of Commerce **[45145]**
Forrest City Area Chamber of Commerce **[36462]**
Forsyth Area Chamber of Commerce **[41563]**
Forsyth-Monroe County Chamber of Commerce **[38732]**
Fort Atkinson Area Chamber of Commerce (FAACC) **[46409]**
Fort Bend Chamber of Commerce (FBCC) **[45146]**
Fort Bend Forward **[45147]**
Fort Benton Chamber of Commerce **[41764]**
Fort Bragg - Mendocino Coast Chamber of Commerce **[36896]**
Fort Collins Area Chamber of Commerce **[37851]**
Fort Davis Chamber of Commerce **[45148]**
Fort Edward Chamber of Commerce **[42570]**
Fort Fairfield Chamber of Commerce **[40277]**
Fort Gibson Chamber of Commerce **[43759]**
Fort Lauderdale / Broward, National Association of Women Business Owners [38215]
"Fort Lauderdale Hotel's Service, Facilities Honored at 'Bride's Choice' by WeddingWire" in Internet Wire (February 10, 2012) **[1973]**, **[29787]**
Fort Lauderdale International Boat Show **[10620]**
"Fort Lauderdale Startup Wants You To 'Join the Club" in South Florida Business Journal (Vol. 35, September 19, 2014, No. 8, pp. 14) **[16365]**
Fort Lee Regional Chamber of Commerce (FLRCC) **[42124]**
Fort Lewis College - Office of Business and Economic Research (OBER) **[21273]**
Fort Lewis College - Office of Economic Analysis and Business Research [21273]
Fort Madison Area Chamber of Commerce **[39741]**
Fort Morgan Area Chamber of Commerce (FMACC) **[37852]**
Fort Morgan Small Business Development Center [37791]
Fort Payne Chamber of Commerce **[36111]**
Ft. Pierce/St. Lucie County Chamber of Commerce [38493]
Fort Scott Area Chamber of Commerce (FSACC) **[39889]**
Fort Smith Regional Chamber of Commerce **[36463]**
Fort Stockton Chamber of Commerce **[45149]**
Fort Sumner Chamber of Commerce **[42318]**
Fort Walton Beach Chamber of Commerce - Greater Ft. Walton Beach Chamber of Commerce [38396]
Fort Wayne's Woman's Bureau - Women's Enterprise **[39622]**
Fort Worth Business Assistance Center (BAC) **[45520]**
Fort Worth Chamber of Commerce **[45150]**
Fort Worth Metropolitan Black Chamber of Commerce (FWMBCC) **[45151]**
Fortuna Chamber of Commerce (FCC) **[36897]**
Fortune **[24777]**
Fortune Magazine [24777]
FORUM **[6235]**
Forum Business Advisors **[2265]**
Forum Publishing Co. **[42997]**
Forum for State Health Policy Leadership **[26114]**
Forum Ventures **[38178]**
Forum for Women Entrepreneurs (FWE) **[35619]**
Forward Janesville, Inc. (FJI) **[46410]**
"Forward Motion" in Green Industry Pro (July 2011) **[7621]**, **[10096]**, **[10232]**, **[19844]**, **[20430]**, **[21520]**, **[22156]**, **[23894]**, **[33157]**
Forward Ventures **[37366]**
"Fossil Fuel, Renewable Fuel Shares Expected to Flip Flop" in Farm Industry News (April 29, 2011) **[5612]**, **[5886]**, **[17045]**, **[20020]**, **[23212]**
Foster City Chamber of Commerce **[36898]**
Fostoria Area Chamber of Commerce **[43472]**
The Fostoria Glass Society of America, Inc. (FGSA) **[734]**, **[3225]**
Foundation Aiding the Elderly (FATE) **[11499]**
Foundation Asie Pacifique du Canada **[20696]**
Foundation Capital **[37367]**

Foundation Center Cleveland Library **[7186]**
Foundation Center, Washington, DC Library **[7187]**
Foundation Focus **[8238]**
Foundation for Interior Design Education Research [9020]
Foundation for Leading Teams (Onsite) **[28335]**
Foundation of the National Student Nurses Association (FNSNA) **[25671]**
Foundation for Physical Therapy (FPT) **[12486]**
A Foundation for Trust with Diversity, Equity, and Inclusion **[30411]**, **[30625]**
Foundation of the Wall and Ceiling Industry (FWCI) **[4363]**, **[10749]**
The Foundations of Female Entrepreneurship: Enterprise, Home and Household in London, c. 1800-1870 **[22605]**, **[35784]**
"The Foundations of Supplier Engagement; Companies' Relationships With Their Suppliers Are Vital To Their Success. Here Are the Fundamental Ways Businesses Can Measure and Manage Those Relationships" in Gallup Business Journal (June 26, 2014) **[27561]**, **[32974]**
Founder Collective (FC) **[40785]**
Founder Institute (FI) **[37571]**
Founder Labs (F) **[42876]**
Founder Work-Life Balance **[35010]**
FounderFuel **[46895]**
Founders' Co-op **[46191]**
Founders Embassy (FE) **[37572]**
Founders Factory New York (FF) **[42877]**
Founders First Capital Partners (FFCP) **[30268]**, **[35277]**, **[35620]**, **[37738]**
Founders Fund **[37368]**
Founders Network **[35278]**, **[37369]**
Founders Space **[37573]**
"Founding Family Acquires Airport Marriott" in Crain's Cleveland Business (Vol. 28, November 5, 2007, No. 44, pp. 3) **[8395]**, **[18959]**, **[19517]**
Foundry **[37370]**
Foundry Group **[37921]**
Fountain Healthcare Partners **[42746]**
Fountain Hills Chamber of Commerce **[36332]**
Fountain Valley Chamber of Commerce **[36899]**
Fountain Valley Chamber of Commerce (FVCC) **[37853]**
"The Four Cheapest Plays in Emerging Markets" in Barron's (Vol. 89, July 27, 2009, No. 30, pp. 34) **[6415]**, **[9529]**, **[23895]**, **[27562]**
"Four Common Hiring Mistakes Small Businesses Should Avoid in This Unprecedented Labor Market" in The Business Journals (Sept. 29, 2021) **[26560]**
Four Corners Management Systems (FCMS) **[37961]**
"Four Exhibition Considerations" in American Printer (Vol. 128, August 1, 2011, No. 8) **[3310]**, **[12735]**, **[15859]**, **[16191]**, **[35055]**
Four Flags Area Chamber of Commerce [40927]
"Four Lessons in Adaptive Leadership" in Harvard Business Review (Vol. 88, November 2010, No. 11, pp. 86) **[22606]**, **[28591]**
Four Lessons from COVID-19 for the Future of Christmas Tree Marketing **[2938]**
The Four Steps to the Epiphany: Successful Strategies for Products that Win **[17441]**, **[29788]**, **[32529]**
"Four Tactics Young Tech Entrepreneurs Should Keep In Mind to Ensure the Long-Term Success of Their Startups" in Entrepreneur (May 3, 2021) **[36020]**
"Four Ways to Fix Banks: A Wall Street Veteran Suggests How To Cut Through the Industry's Complexity" in (Vol. 90, June 2012, No. 6, pp. 106) **[17305]**, **[23896]**, **[25344]**, **[28592]**
"Four Ways Hospitals Can Reduce Patient Readmissions; Hospitals Have a Powerful Financial Incentive to Reduce Readmissions. Here Are the Most Effective Strategies" in Gallup Business Journal (July 2, 2014) **[23897]**, **[25785]**
Fox Cities Chamber of Commerce and Industry (FCC) **[46411]**
Fox Cities SCORE **[46339]**
Fox and Fiddle Corp. **[14168]**
Fox Fire Safety, Inc. **[35966]**
Fox Lake Chamber of Commerce **[46412]**
Fox Lake/Richmond/Spring Grove Area Chamber of Commerce (FLRSGAC) **[39168]**
Foxhound Bee Company **[1500]**
Fox's Pizza Den, Inc. **[12552]**
FP Canada **[46751]**
FPA Annual Meeting and Convention [5204]
FPA Journal of Financial Planning **[6695]**
FPC/F-O-R-T-U-N-E Personnel Consultants (FPC) **[6117]**
FPC National [6116]
"A Framework for Conceptual Contributions in Marketing" in Journal of Marketing (Vol. 75, July 2011, No. 4, pp. 136) **[280]**, **[29789]**
Framing and Art Centre **[12712]**

"France Telecom Takes Minitel Offline" in Canadian Business (Vol. 85, August 13, 2012, No. 13, pp. 12) **[2378]**, **[2740]**, **[12736]**, **[25133]**, **[33158]**
Franchise Architects **[24474]**
Franchise Basics **[24358]**
Franchise Brokers Association (FBA) **[2132]**, **[24308]**
Franchise Business Systems Inc. (FBS) **[16880]**, **[24475]**
The Franchise Company Inc. [33318]
Franchise Compliance Inc. **[2339]**
The Franchise Consulting Company (FCC) **[24476]**
Franchise Consulting Group (FCG) **[2266]**, **[24477]**
Franchise Development International **[2340]**, **[20229]**, **[24496]**
Franchise Developments Inc. **[2341]**, **[20230]**, **[24478]**, **[24497]**
Franchise Foundations (FF) **[2342]**, **[20231]**, **[24498]**
Franchise Law Team **[18751]**
The Franchise Maker **[2343]**
Franchise Marketing Systems **[2344]**, **[24479]**
Franchise Opportunity Consultants **[2345]**
Franchise Search Inc. **[2346]**, **[2400]**, **[24499]**
Franchise Selection Specialists Inc. **[2347]**
The Franchise Show **[24467]**
Franchise Specialists **[2348]**, **[24480]**
Franchise Specialists Inc. **[2349]**, **[20232]**, **[24500]**
"Franchise vs. Startup: Which Way to Go" in Investopedia (July 14, 2020) **[24359]**
FranchiseCanada **[24309]**
"Franchisee to Add 10 New Applebee's" in Memphis Business Journal (Vol. 34, June 8, 2012, No. 8, pp. 1) **[13942]**, **[19664]**, **[24360]**
The Franchisee Handbook **[24361]**
"Franchisee to Smash Way Into Orlando's Better Burger Race" in Orlando Business Journal (Vol. 30, January 31, 2014, No. 32, pp. 3) **[13865]**, **[24293]**
FranchiseKnowHow L.L.C. **[2350]**
FranchiseMart **[2351]**, **[24501]**
"Franchises with an Eye on Chicago" in Crain's Chicago Business (Vol. 34, March 14, 2011, No. 11, pp. 20) **[1576]**, **[2862]**, **[4874]**, **[5072]**, **[11851]**, **[11868]**, **[13866]**, **[21297]**, **[24362]**, **[33366]**
Franchises on Fire with Lance Graulich **[24447]**
Franchising 101: Buy It or Build It with Josh Minturn **[24448]**
Franchising - The Better Path to Business Ownershp with Jon Ostenson **[24449]**
"Franchising: The Importance Of Great Systems within the System" in Small Business Trends (November 25, 2013) **[24363]**
Franchising World **[24445]**
FranChoice Inc. **[24502]**
Francis Marion University - James A. Rogers Library Special Collections **[7841]**
Francis Tuttle Technology Center (Rockwell Campus) **[43883]**
Franconia Notch Regional Chamber of Commerce **[41988]**
Frank Lloyd Wright Trust Restoration Resource Center **[956]**
Frankenmuth Chamber of Commerce [40911]
Frankenmuth Chamber of Commerce and Convention and Visitors Bureau **[40911]**
Frankfort Area Chamber of Commerce **[40040]**
Frankfort Area Chamber of Commerce [40912]
Frankfort Chamber of Commerce **[39169]**
Frankfort - Elberta Area Chamber of Commerce **[40912]**
Frankfort-Franklin County Chamber of Commerce [40040]
Franklin Area Chamber of Commerce (FACC) **[44211]**
Franklin Business Incubator **[45951]**
Franklin Chamber of Commerce (FCC) **[39538]**
Franklin County Chamber of Commerce **[36112]**, **[40278]**
Franklin County Chamber of Commerce (FCCC) **[40577]**
Franklin County Chamber of Commerce (FCCoC) **[44745]**
Franklin County Regional Chamber of Commerce (FCRCC) **[45723]**
Franklin-Sarrett Publishers L.L.C. (FSP) **[38852]**
Franklin-Simpson Chamber of Commerce **[40041]**
Franklin-Southampton Area Chamber of Commerce **[45862]**
Franklin Southampton Economic Development (FSEDI) **[45952]**
FranNet (FN) **[24481]**
FranServe, Inc. **[2352]**
FranSource International Inc. **[24482]**
Fransurvey.com **[10705]**
Franz Schneider & Associates L.L.C. **[33669]**
Fraser Institute (FI) **[15491]**
"Fraser and Neave Acquires King's Creameries" in Ice Cream Reporter (Vol. 23, November 20, 2010, No. 12, pp. 1) **[8564]**, **[9530]**, **[20624]**, **[29215]**, **[31305]**
Frazier & Company / Frazier Healthcare and Technology Ventures **[46192]**

FRCH Design Worldwide [31090]
FRCH Nelson [31090]
Freakonomics: A Rogue Economist Explores the Hidden Side of Everything [20899]
Fred Astaire Dance Studios Inc. (FADS) [4862]
Fred J. Robinson & Associates Inc. [10259]
Fred Pryor Seminars & CareerTrack Business Writing for Results [17845]
Fred Pryor Seminars & CareerTrack Collections Law (Onsite) [23711], [25188]
Fred Pryor Seminars & CareerTrack Creative Leadership for Managers, Supervisors, and Team Leaders [28336]
Fred Pryor Seminars & CareerTrack How to Manage Inventories and Cycle Counts [27989], [34969]
Fred Pryor Seminars & CareerTrack Managing Multiple Priorities, Projects, and Deadlines [34970]
Fred Pryor Seminars & CareerTrack OSHA Compliance [35935]
Fred Pryor Seminars & CareerTrack Records Retention and Destruction (Onsite) [17846], [25189]
Fred Pryor Seminars & CareerTrack The Exceptional Assistant [22054]
Fred Pryor Seminars Mistake-Free Grammar & Proofreading [17579]
"Fred Weber CEO Tom Dunne: Sales Talks Confidential" in Saint Louis Business Journal (Vol. 32, September 23, 2011, No. 4, pp. 1) [4090], [33016]
Freddie Mac [47071], [47072], [47074]
Frederic Remington Area Historical Society Library [7411]
Frederick Chamber of Commerce and Industry [43760]
Frederick Innovative Technology Center (FITCI) [40456]
Fredericksburg Chamber of Commerce [45152]
Fredericksburg Regional Chamber of Commerce (FRCC) [45863]
Fredericton Appraisal Associates Ltd. [13616]
Fredonia Area Chamber of Commerce [39890]
Fredonia Chamber of Commerce [39890]
"Fred's Launches New Concept" in Memphis Business Journal (Vol. 34, No. 21, September 07, 2012, pp. 1) [5159], [32155]
"Free Fall" in Canadian Business (Vol. 79, September 11, 2006, No. 18, pp. 28) [6185], [18089], [19518]
"Free File Alliance & IRS Launch 10th Year of Free Online Tax Preparation Services for Millions of Americans" in Economics Week (February 3, 2012, pp. 82) [15384], [24988], [31306], [33854], [34316]
Free Library of Philadelphia - Art Department [3367]
Free Library of Philadelphia-Social Science & History Department [1707], [16217]
Free Market Foundation [15489]
Free Publicity Is Advertising for Your Small Business [31864]
Free Software Foundation, Inc. (FSF) [14750]
"Free Speech Vs. Privacy in Data Mining" in Information Today (Vol. 28, September 2011, No. 8, pp. 22) [3428], [3503], [18589], [21857], [25345], [29790]
Free: The Future of a Radical Price [20021], [29791]
Free University Network [3548]
"Free Versus Paid Apps—when Upgrades Make Sense for Small Businesses" in Legal Zoom (February 15, 2023) [16559]
Freedom Chamber of Commerce [43761]
Freedom Foundation [26115]
Freedom Leaf [5040]
Freelance Editorial Association [5280]
"Freelance Writer Creates LI Bridal Blog" in Long Island Business News (September 10, 2010) [1974], [4937], [5315]
Freelance Writer's Report (FWR) [5336]
The Freelancer [5337]
Freelancers Union (FU) [34455]
Freely Accessible Business Journals [4281]
Freeport Merchants Association [40279]
FreeportUSA [40279]
Freese & Associates Inc. (F&A) [2267], [10531], [20190], [28992], [30198]
Freestyle Capital [37371]
Freight Carriers Association of Canada (FCA) [16053]
Fremont Area Chamber of Commerce (FACC) [41854], [46413]
Fremont Business Review [36900]
Fremont Chamber of Commerce (FCC) [36901]
Fremont Chamber of Commerce Membership Directory and Guide [36902]
Fremont County Business Development Corporation [37942]
Fremont and Dodge County Convention and Visitors Bureau [41854]
Fremont Economic Development Corp. (FEDC) [37942]
French-American Chamber of Commerce (FACC) [27411], [44212]
French American Chamber of Commerce Chicago (FACC-Chicago) [39170]

French-American Chamber of Commerce Dallas/Fort Worth (FACC DFW) [45153]
French - American Chamber of Commerce - Gulf Coast Chapter (GC) [40168]
French-American Chamber of Commerce Houston Chapter [45154]
French - American Chamber of Commerce - Louisiana Chapter [40168]
French-American Chamber of Commerce, Michigan Chapter [40913]
French-American Chamber of Commerce in the United States [27411]
French-American Chamber of Commerce in the United States Inc. [27411]
French-Canadian Genealogical Society of Connecticut (FCGSC) [7412]
French Chamber of Commerce in the United States [27411]
French and French-Canadian Family Research [7357]
French Lick West Baden Chamber of Commerce [39539]
Fresh Coat [13004]
"Fresh Off its IPO, HomeStreet Bank is Now the No. 2 Mortgage Lender in King County" in Puget Sound Business Journal (Vol. 33, June 15, 2012, No. 8, pp. 3) [11034], [25346]
Fresh Produce Association of the Americas (FPAA) [16936]
FreshBerry Natural Frozen Yogurt [8617]
FreshBooks Hub; *"6 Best Accounts Receivable Software for Small Businesses"* in [16773]
"The Freshest Ideas Are in Small Grocery Stores" in The New York Times (July 31, 2018) [7736], [23213]
FreshTracks Capital [45755]
Fresno CDFI [37539]
Fresno Chamber of Commerce [36919]
"Friday the 13th, a 'Tattoo Holiday'" in The New York Times (July 13, 2018) [15297], [31865]
"Friedland's Next Frontier: Drilling for Oil in Iraq" in Globe & Mail (April 20, 2007, pp. B1) [31307], [33159]
Friedman, Rosenwasser & Goldbaum P.A. (FRG) [18752]
A Friend of the Family [17399]
Friendly Computers [3588]
"'Friendly Fraud' Is on the Rise, and Small Business Owners May Bear the Brunt of the Impact" in Select (Jan. 28, 2021) [19260]
"Friendly Ice Cream Corporation" in Ice Cream Reporter (Vol. 23, August 20, 2010, No. 9, pp. 8) [8565], [21858], [28593], [29792]
Friends of the Earth (FOE) [38185]
Friends of the Western Philatelic Library (FWPL) [3258]
"Friends With (Health) Benefits" in Canadian Business (Vol. 87, July 2014, No. 7, pp. 32) [22157]
Friendswood Chamber of Commerce [45155]
Frio Canyon Chamber of Commerce [45156]
Friona Chamber of Commerce and Agriculture [45157]
Frisco Chamber of Commerce (FCC) [45158]
From 50 to 500: Mastering the Unique Leadership Challenges of Growing Small Companies [33563]
"From American Icon to Global Juggernaut" in Automotive News (Vol. 86, October 31, 2011, No. 6488, pp. S003) [11400], [27563], [29216]
"From the Battlefield to the Boardroom" in Business Horizons (Vol. 51, March-April 2008, No. 2, pp. 79) [22607], [28030], [28594]
"From the Business of Language to the Language of Business: The Future of Translation Worldwide" in D!gitalist Magazine (May 17, 2018) [15937]
"From Chelsea Machine Shop to Nobel Prize" in Crain's Detroit Business (Vol. 30, October 13, 2014, No. 41, pp. 35) [10431], [10827], [31970], [32759]
"From Common To Uncommon Knowledge: Foundations of Firm-Specific Use of Knowledge as a Resource" in Academy of Management Journal (Vol. 55, April 1, 2012, No. 2, pp. 421) [19845], [28031]
From Concept To Consumer: How to Turn Ideas Into Money [19846], [20022], [20625], [27874], [29793], [30726]
"From Craft Biz To Wholesale Giant" in Women Entrepreneur (January 19, 2009) [4592], [18090], [18960], [19519], [29794], [32156], [33564], [35490], [35785]
"From Economy to Luxury, What Matters Most to Hotel Guests; To Win More Repeat Customers, Hotels Must Create a Tailored Guest Experience" in Gallup Business Journal (September 5, 2014) [8396], [20431]
"From the Editors: Plagiarism Policies and Screening at AMJ" in Academy of Management Journal (Vol. 55, August 2012, No. 4, pp. 749) [5316], [18590], [23499], [28595]
"From Fat to Fit" in Canadian Business (Vol. 79, September 22, 2006, No. 19, pp. 100) [12414], [18091], [34024]

From Idea to Exit: Lessons from a Podcast Host with Chris Hutchins [24809]
"From Malls to Steel Plants" in Crain's Chicago Business (Vol. 31, April 28, 2008, No. 17, pp. 30) [4091], [18092], [27564], [31308]
"From the Moon to Malibu" in Canadian Business (Vol. 87, July 2014, No. 7, pp. 106) [5613], [11401]
"From New York to Park Avenue: Red Carpet Fashion at a Discount" in Orlando Business Journal (Vol. 30, February 14, 2014, No. 34, pp. 3) [3115], [9974], [32157], [35786]
"From Rapper to Fashion Designer, Philly 12-Year-Old Builds Brand Using Instagram" in WHYY (December 19, 2018) [3026], [22608]
From Sales Guy to Tech Founder [34614]
"From Scarcity to Plenty" in Inc. (Vol. 36, March 2014, No. 2, pp. 76) [5887], [7737], [8020], [13712], [23214]
From Side Hustle to Small Business: Samantha Besnoff, Your Financial Maven [35900]
Front Royal - Warren County Chamber of Commerce [45864]
Front Street Capital (FSC) [43267]
"Frontage Labs Moves, Plans to Hire 100" in Philadelphia Business Journal (Vol. 28, July 13, 2012, No. 22, pp. 1) [5160], [19172], [26561]
Frontenac Co. [39356]
Frontier Angels (FA) [35279], [41801]
Frontier Capital L.L.C. [43221]
Frontier Growth [43221]
Frontier Publications Inc. [12010]
Frontier Venture Capital [35465]
Frontiers of Health Services Management [26002]
Frost Research Center for Data and Research [15235]
Frostproof Chamber of Commerce [38383]
Frosty Bites Inc. [8629]
"'Frozen' Assets: Refrigeration Goes High Tech as Hussmann Invests $7 Million in Global Hub" in St. Louis Business Journal (Vol. 33, September 21, 2012, No. 4, pp. 1) [485], [4435], [7738], [26278], [32158], [35342]
"Frozen Dessert Year in Review.." in Ice Cream Reporter (Vol. 22, January 20, 2009, No. 2, pp. 1) [8566], [18093]
Frozen Food Factbook and Directory [7756]
Frozen Food Locker Institute [2425]
Frozen Ropes Training Centers [21720]
Fruit and Vegetable Truck Rate Report [16096]
Fruita Area Chamber of Commerce (FACC) [37854]
FruitFlowers/Incredibly Edible Delites [7472]
Fruits & Passion [1597]
"FSU's OGZEB Is Test Bed for Sustainable Technology" in Contractor (Vol. 56, October 2009, No. 10, pp. 1) [5372], [5614], [5888], [14925], [23251], [32760]
"FTC Sues Owner of Online Dating Service Match.com For Using Fake Love Interest Ads to Trick Consumers into Paying for a Match.com Subscription" in Federal Trade Commission (September 25, 2019) [3813], [11746], [23500]
FTV Management Company LP [37372]
Fuchsia Flash [10120]
Fuddruckers Inc. [1293], [14169]
"Fuel Costs Curb Food Truck Trend" in Tampa Tribune (March 26, 2012) [3845], [6982], [20023], [20900], [23898], [30473]
"Fuel King: The Most Fuel-Efficient Tractor of the Decade is the John Deere 8295R" in Farm Industry News (November 10, 2011) [5615], [5889], [17046], [23216], [29217]
"Fuel-Tax Proposal May Be Conversation Starter" in Sacramento Business Journal (Vol. 31, February 28, 2014, No. 1, pp. 6) [34795]
"Fujifilm Invites Printers to Take the 'Onset Challenge'" in American Printer (Vol. 128, August 1, 2011, No. 8) [3311], [12737], [16192]
Fujitsu Microelectronics Inc. [3757], [4420]
Fujitsu Semiconductor America Inc. (FMI) [3757], [4420]
Fulfillment Management Association [29482]
"Full-Court Press for Apple" in Barron's (Vol. 88, March 24, 2008, No. 12, pp. 47) [6416], [9531], [18591], [23899], [26279], [27875], [29218]
"Full Speed Ahead: How to Get the Most Out of Your Company Vehicles" in Entrepreneur (Vol. 37, October 2009, No. 10, pp. 78) [11402], [11747], [19352]
"Full Speed Ahead?" in San Antonio Business Journal (Vol. 28, May 9, 2014, No. 13, pp. 4) [10280], [15514], [18592], [25347]
Full Voice [2268], [2388], [6217], [17807], [20191], [21710]
Fullerton Chamber of Commerce [37051]
Fully Promoted [32365]
Fully Promoted (FP) [3169]
Fulton Area Chamber of Commerce [41532]
Fulton Chamber of Commerce [39171]
Fulton County Chamber of Commerce and Tourism [44213]

Fulton Master Index

Fulton County Regional Chamber of Commerce and Industry **[42571]**
Functional Gage Design (Onsite) **[21386]**
Fund for Arksans Future II **[36522]**
Fund for Renewable Energy and the Environment [14900]
Fundamental Selling Techniques for the New or Prospective Salesperson Level I (Onsite) **[32443]**
Fundamentals of Carbon Reduction (Onsite) **[23065]**
"The Fundamentals of Contract Management" in Business News Daily (February 21, 2023) **[28596]**
Fundamentals of Employee Benefits (Onsite) **[26858]**
Fundamentals of Human Resources Management **[26859]**
Fundamentals of Information Security (Onsite) **[26197]**
Fundamentals of Marketing: Your Action Plan for Success **[29590]**, **[29591]**
Fundamentals of Project Management **[28337]**
Fundamentals of Purchasing **[31908]**
Fundamentals of Purchasing for the New Buyer (Onsite) **[31909]**
Fundamentals of Successful Project Management (Onsite) **[28338]**
"Funders Fuel Explosion of Biotech Activity" in Puget Sound Business Journal (Vol. 35, July 11, 2014, No. 12, pp. 3A) **[7111]**, **[25348]**, **[26280]**, **[31309]**, **[35343]**
FundersClub **[37373]**
Funding Circle Limited (FCL) **[30269]**
"Funding Drought Stalls Biotech Incubators" in Saint Louis Business Journal (Vol. 31, July 29, 2011, No. 49, pp. 1) **[4092]**, **[8809]**, **[31971]**, **[32761]**, **[35344]**
"The Funding Is Out There!: Access the Cash You Need to Impact Your Business" **[7112]**, **[30918]**
"Funds "Friend" Facebook" in Barron's (Vol. 89, July 27, 2009, No. 30, pp. 30) **[6417]**, **[9532]**, **[23900]**, **[25349]**, **[26281]**, **[29795]**, **[32530]**
"The Funeral As We Know It Is Becoming a Relic — Just in Time for a Death Boom" in The Washington Post (April 15, 2019) **[7208]**
Funeral Consumers Alliance (FCA) **[7197]**, **[7223]**
Funeral Consumers Alliance **[7209]**
"Funeral Directors Get Creative As Boomers Near Great Beyond" in Advertising Age (Vol. 79, October 13, 2008, No. 38, pp. 30) **[281]**, **[7210]**, **[18094]**, **[20901]**, **[23217]**, **[29796]**
Funeral Home & Cemetery Directory--Buyer's Guide **[7211]**
Funeral and Memorial Societies of America [7209]
"Funeral Picketing Laws and Free Speech" in Kansas Law Review (Vol. 55, April 2007, No. 3, pp. 575-627) **[7212]**, **[18593]**
"Funky Footwear: Walk This Way" in Barron's (Vol. 90, August 23, 2010, No. 34, pp. 13) **[9533]**, **[14675]**, **[18095]**, **[29219]**
Fuquay-Varina Chamber of Commerce (FVACC) **[43131]**
Fuquay - Varina Chamber of Commerce [43131]
"Fur Centre Stakes Former Byron Cade Spot in Clayton" in St. Louis Business Journal (Vol. 33, August 10, 2012, No. 51, pp. 1) **[7235]**, **[10364]**, **[19173]**
Fur Council of Canada [7227], [7233]
"Fur Farms Still Unfashionably Cruel, Critics Say" in National Geographic (August 17, 2016) **[7228]**
"Fur Helped Build the City. Now Its Sale May Be Banned." in The New York Times (May 16, 2019) **[7229]**, **[7236]**, **[25350]**
Fur Information Council of America [7226], [7232]
Furniture Executive **[8220]**
Furniture Factories Marketing Association of the South [8193]
Furniture Library Association Library [7253], [9072]
"Furniture Making May Come Back--Literally" in Business North Carolina (Vol. 28, March 2008, No. 3, pp. 32) **[1758]**, **[8207]**, **[10393]**, **[27565]**, **[29220]**, **[34025]**
Furniture Medic of Canada **[7248]**
Furniture Medic L.P. **[7249]**
Furniture Rental Association of America [8196], [13763]
Furniture Repair & Reupholstery Industry in the US - Market Research Report **[7245]**
"Furniture Restoration and Design Firm Holds Grand Opening in Dunbar" in Charleston Gazette-Mail (July 18, 2019) **[7240]**, **[35787]**
"Furniture Retailers Start to Feel Tariff Pain More Acutely" in The Wall Street Journal (November 11, 2019) **[8208]**, **[8718]**
Furniture Today: The Weekly Business Newspaper of the Furniture Industry **[8221]**
Fuse Capital **[44591]**
The Future of AI Marketing for Small Businesses **[29797]**
"Future Autoworkers will Need Broader Skills" in Crain's Detroit Business (Vol. 25, June 8, 2009, No. 23, pp. 13) **[11403]**, **[21521]**, **[26943]**, **[29221]**, **[34026]**
Future of Business Journalism: Why It Matters for Wall Street and Main Street **[33565]**
"Future of Convention and Visitors Bureau In Question" in Houston Business Journal (Vol. 44, April 4, 2014, No. 48, pp. 10) **[15860]**, **[31310]**, **[35056]**
"Future of Diversity: Cultural Inclusion Is a Business Imperative" in Black Enterprise (Vol. 41, August 2010, No. 1, pp. 75) **[27566]**, **[30569]**, **[34027]**
"The Future of Fish Farming May Be Indoors" in Scientific American (September 17, 2018) **[6783]**
"The Future of Foodservice Equipment" in Convenience-StoreNews (November 24, 2021) **[4436]**
"Future Fuzzy at Former Pemco Plant" in Baltimore Business Journal (Vol. 32, July 25, 2014, No. 12, pp. 10) **[13455]**, **[25351]**, **[32159]**
"The Future Is Another Country; Higher Education" in The Economist (Vol. 390, January 3, 2009, No. 8612, pp. 43) **[15938]**, **[16132]**, **[20902]**, **[21522]**, **[26562]**, **[27567]**, **[34028]**
"The Future Of Outsourcing—And How To Outsource The Right Way" in Forbes(October 21, 2022) **[31119]**
"The Future of Private Equity" in Canadian Business (Vol. 80, March 26, 2007, No. 7, pp. 19) **[6418]**, **[9534]**, **[19847]**, **[20903]**
"The Future of Satellite TV is Unclear" in MediaPost (March 6, 2019) **[14345]**
"Future of the Street" in Barron's (Vol. 88, June 30, 2008, No. 26, pp. 27) **[6419]**, **[9535]**, **[23901]**
"The Future of Work" in Black Enterprise (Vol. 41, August 2010, No. 1, pp. 65) **[21859]**, **[24666]**, **[26282]**, **[26944]**, **[27568]**, **[29798]**, **[31120]**, **[33160]**, **[34029]**
"The Future of Work" in Business Strategy Review (Vol. 21, Autumn 2010, No. 3, pp. 16) **[24667]**, **[26283]**, **[26945]**, **[27569]**, **[28597]**, **[31972]**, **[32762]**, **[34030]**
"FutureDash Launches IndieGoGo Crowdfunding Campaign for the EnergyBuddy Home Energy Monitoring System" in Benzinga.com (June 21, 2012) **[23003]**, **[29799]**, **[30727]**
Futures and Options Expo **[6704]**, **[9927]**
"Futures Shock for the CME" in Crain's Chicago Business (Vol. 31, November 10, 2008, No. 45, pp. 8) **[6420]**, **[9536]**, **[20904]**, **[23902]**, **[25352]**, **[31311]**, **[34031]**
Fuzziwig's Candy Factory, Inc. **[8618]**
FYI [45104]

G

G-51 Capital L.L.C. **[45450]**
G-Force **[35154]**
"G20 Young Entrepreneur Alliance Signs Charter Outlining Commitment to Entrepreneurship" in Marketwire (November 10, 2010) **[27570]**, **[36021]**
G20 Young Entrepreneurs' Alliance (G20 YEA) **[22975]**, **[33459]**
G51 **[45451]**
"Ga. PMA Launches Online Education Program" in Contractor (Vol. 56, October 2009, No. 10, pp. 8) **[9144]**, **[12631]**, **[14614]**, **[21523]**
Gabelli Multimedia Partners **[42747]**
Gabriel Venture Partners **[37374]**
"Gabrielle Union Providing $75K in Business Grants to Black Women Owned Companies" in Small Business Trends (March 14, 2023) **[30349]**, **[35788]**
"Gadget Makers Aim for New Chapter in Reading" in Crain's Cleveland Business (Vol. 28, October 22, 2007, No. 42, pp. 20) **[1825]**, **[26284]**, **[30728]**
"Gadget of the Week: the Age of iPhoneography" in Barron's (Vol. 92, August 25, 2012, No. 35, pp. 28) **[970]**, **[2741]**
"Gadget of the Week: Easy as a Snap" in Barron's (Vol. 90, September 13, 2010, No. 37, pp. 35) **[2493]**, **[33161]**
"Gadget of the Week: Espresso Book Machine" in Barron's (Vol. 92, September 15, 2012, No. 38, pp. 27) **[1656]**, **[1723]**
Gadsden County Chamber of Commerce **[38384]**
Gadsden-Etowah Chamber of Commerce [36093]
Gahanna Area Chamber of Commerce (GACC) **[43473]**
"Gain the 'Come Alive Outside' Selling Edge" in Green Industry Pro (July 2011) **[7622]**, **[10097]**, **[10233]**, **[22158]**, **[29800]**, **[32531]**, **[33162]**
Gainesville Area Chamber of Commerce **[38385]**
Gainesville Technology Enterprise Center (GTEC) **[38566]**
Gainesville Technology Entrepreneurship Center (GTEC) **[38567]**
Gaithersburg-Germantown Chamber of Commerce (GGCC) **[40384]**
Galax - Carroll - Grayson Chamber of Commerce [45906]
Gale Business: Entrepreneurship (GB:E) **[24904]**
Galen Partners (GP) **[38094]**
Galena Area Chamber of Commerce (GACC) **[39172]**
Galesburg Area Chamber of Commerce **[39173]**
Galesville Area Chamber of Commerce (GACC) **[46414]**
Galion Area Chamber of Commerce [43474]
Galion-Crestline Area Chamber of Commerce **[43474]**
Gallagher Benefit Services Inc. **[17400]**
Gallatin Chamber of Commerce **[44746]**
Gallaudet University Press **[38186]**
Galleria Chamber of Commerce [45216]
Gallia County Chamber of Commerce **[43475]**
Galt Area Chamber of Commerce [36903]
Galt District Chamber of Commerce (GCC) **[36903]**
Galvanize **[37943]**
Galveston Chamber of Commerce **[45159]**
Galveston County Small Business Development Center **[44916]**
"Galveston Invests In Future as Major Cruise Destination" in Houston Business Journal (Vol. 44, February 28, 2014, No. 43, pp. 4) **[888]**, **[4093]**, **[15741]**, **[15993]**, **[19848]**
GAMA EXPO [15808]
GAMA Trade Show **[15808]**
Gamblers Anonymous (GA) **[7261]**
Gamblers Anonymous International Service Office [7261]
Gamblers Anonymous Publishing Inc. [7261]
Gambling Consulting Expert **[7322]**
"Gambling Firms See $7B to $8B Sports Betting Market by 2025" in The Chicago Tribune (November 5, 2019) **[7286]**
"Game Changing" in Business Strategy Review (Vol. 23, Spring 2012, No. 1, pp. 26) **[2457]**, **[15154]**, **[15594]**, **[28598]**
Game Developers' Conference (GDC) **[3752]**, **[14868]**, **[35122]**
"Game On at Jordan's New Spot" in Crain's Chicago Business (Vol. 34, October 24, 2011, No. 42, pp. 34) **[13943]**, **[15155]**, **[22609]**
"Game On: When Work Becomes Play" in Canadian Business (Vol. 80, February 12, 2007, No. 4, pp. 15) **[14779]**, **[18961]**, **[26285]**, **[30729]**
"The Game of Operation" in Crain's Chicago Business (Vol. 31, April 28, 2008, No. 17, pp. 26) **[10828]**, **[18096]**, **[29222]**
"Game Plan: The Business of Bingo" in Canadian Business (Vol. 79, September 11, 2006, No. 18, pp. 50) **[14780]**, **[18962]**, **[26286]**
"Gamesa Office Closing Part of Political Reality" in Pittsburgh Business Times (Vol. 33, February 7, 2014, No. 30, pp. 6) **[27571]**, **[29223]**, **[34796]**
"Gaming Infrastructure Paves Ready Path for Manufacturing" in Memphis Business Journal (No. 35, February 14, 2014, No. 45, pp. 4) **[7287]**, **[20905]**, **[27572]**, **[29224]**, **[31760]**
Gaming Means (Small) Business: How Casinos Boost Local Economies **[7288]**
Gamma Investors LLC **[44340]**
Gangplank **[36394]**
Ganjapreneur **[5001]**, **[5026]**
"Gannett Looks to Spare Journalists' Jobs after Big Newspaper Merger" in The Wall Street Journal (November 19, 2019) **[11980]**, **[31312]**
Gannon University Small Business Development Center (GUSBDC) **[44095]**
Garagetek **[2651]**, **[12859]**
Garberville Redway Area Chamber of Commerce [37201]
"Garden Bargains: Restaurant Cut Costs With Homegrown Foods" in Washington Business Journal (Vol. 33, August 22, 2014, No. 18, pp. 6) **[8095]**, **[13944]**, **[23903]**
Garden Center Products & Supplies: Professional Purchasing Guide for Garden Centers **[7643]**
Garden City Area Chamber of Commerce (GCACC) **[39891]**
Garden City Chamber of Commerce (GCCC) **[42572]**
Garden Grove Chamber of Commerce (GGCC) **[36904]**
Garden Railways **[4673]**
Gardena Valley Chamber of Commerce (GVCC) **[36905]**
Gardena Valley Chamber of Commerce Membership directory **[36906]**
The Gardener Inc. **[10136]**
Gardens for All [7609], [7678]
Gardiner Chamber of Commerce **[41765]**
Gardiner Roberts L.L.P., Library **[34956]**
Gardner Chamber of Commerce [39892], [40581]
Gardner Edgerton Chamber of Commerce **[39892]**
Garfield County Chamber of Commerce [41766]
Garfield County Chamber of Commerce and Agriculture **[41766]**
Garfield Park Conservatory Alliance - Garfield Park Conservatory **[6879]**, **[7668]**, **[10145]**
Garland Chamber of Commerce **[45160]**
Garlic Jim's Famous Gourmet Pizza **[12553]**
Garner Chamber of Commerce (GCC) **[39742]**, **[43132]**
Garnett Area Chamber of Commerce (GACC) **[39893]**
Garrard County Chamber of Commerce (GCCOC) **[40042]**

3240 Small Business Sourcebook • 42nd Edition

Garrett County Chamber of Commerce [40385]
Garrettsville Area Chamber of Commerce [43476]
Garrettsville - Hiram Area Chamber of Commerce [43476]
Gartner IRC [2124], [9282]
"Gartner Says Global Smartphone Sales Declined 6.8% in Third Quarter of 2021" in Gartner.com (November 23, 2021) [2742]
Gary Chamber of Commerce (GCC) [39540]
Gary Crunkleton Owner of The Crunkleton [1363]
Gary Steffy Lighting Design Inc. (GSLD) [31075]
"Gas Supplies Low Heading Into Summer Season" in Globe & Mail (April 13, 2007, pp. B6) [20906], [29225]
GASDA-Newsletter [14565]
Gasoline and Automotive Service Dealers Association (GASDA) [14533]
Gasoline Merchants [14533]
Gasoline: Specifications, Testing, and Technology (Onsite) [23066]
Gate Group USA Inc. [3348]
Gates, Hudson & Associates Inc. [12915]
Gatesville Area Chamber of Commerce (GCC) [45161]
Gatesville Chamber of Commerce [45161]
Gateway [37574]
Gateway Incubator, LLC [37575]
Gateway News [40169]
Gateway Regional Chamber of Commerce [42125]
Gathering of Angels (GOA) [44870]
Gatlinburg Chamber of Commerce [44747]
Gavin Kaysen Chef and Founder of Soigné Hospitality Group [14057]
"Gay Gordon-Byrne on Protecting the Right to Repair" in Small Business Trends (September 27, 2022) [25353]
Gaylord - Otsego County Chamber of Commerce [40914]
Gazelle Lab [38568]
GBTA, Silicon Valley Chapter [19318]
GBTA Tampa Bay Chapter, Inc. [19296]
GCI Capital [46871]
GCSAA Conference and Trade Show [7536]
GCSAA Education Conference [7535]
GDC Total Business Solutions (GDC-TBS) [29467]
"GE Announces New Projects, Technology Milestone and New Service Program at AWEA Windpower 2012" in News Bites US (June 6, 2012) [5616], [5890], [23218]
"GE Milestone: 1,000th Wind Turbine Installed in Canada" in CNW Group (October 4, 2011) [5617], [5891], [18097], [23219], [29226]
Geekers Magazine [14889]
Geeks On The Way [3589]
Gefinor Capital [42748]
"Geico and the USO of Metropolitan Washington Have Teamed Up to Provide Military Troops with a New 'Home Away From Home'" in Best's Review (Vol. 113, September 2012, No. 5, pp. 13) [8911], [19353], [24989], [31313]
Geisinger Medical Center (GMC) [8081], [8125], [11351], [11610]
Gem County Chamber of Commerce (GCCC) [38914]
GEM Health Care Services [8285]
Gemini Investors [40688]
Gemist: The Crown Jewel of Venture [35417]
Gemological Institute of America (GIA) [9991]
"Gen Z-Led Executive Communications and Strategic Engagement Agency Launches in DC" in Minority Business Entrepreneur (March 17, 2023) [2188], [17674], [30350]
"Gen Z May Value Ownership More than Millennials Do" inRealtor Magazine (November 22, 2019) [13198]
Genacast Ventures [43020]
"Gender Pay Gap Remains Stagnant" in bizwomen (September 22, 2020) [35474]
"The Gender Wage Gap: What Local Firms Plan To Do About It" in Orlando Business Journal (Vol. 30, May 2, 2014, No. 45, pp. 4) [21524], [34032]
Genealogical Journal of Jefferson County, New York [7376]
Genealogical Periodical Annual Index: Key to the Genealogical Literature [7358]
The Genealogist's Address Book [7359]
"A Genealogy Business Is About Family" in Extra Income Over 55 [7360]
gener8tor [46564]
"General Brock's Lessons for Modern CEOs" in Canadian Business (Vol. 85, June 11, 2012, No. 10, pp. 17) [22610]
General Business Consultants Inc. (GBC) [20671]
General Catalyst Partners / General Catalyst Group L.L.C. [40689]
"General Clark Stresses Ethanol's Role In National Security At AgConnect" in Farm Industry News (January 11, 2011) [14415], [17047]
"General Dynamics Secures U.S. Navy Contract" in Travel & Leisure Close-Up (October 8, 2012) [10602], [25134]

"General Electric Touts Going Green for Business Fleet Services" in America's Intelligence Wire (June 1, 2012) [5618], [5892], [11404], [13791], [23220], [29227]
General Engineering Laboratories Inc. Library (GEL) [5769], [6008]
General Merchandise Distributors Council [20602]
General Mills, Inc. [10709], [11611]
General Practice Section of APhA [5213]
General Services Administration - Chicago Business Service Center [47094]
General Services Administration - Denver Business Service Center [47095]
General Services Administration - Ft. Worth Business Service Center [47096]
General Services Administration - Kansas City Business Service Center [47097]
General Services Administration - New York Business Service Center [47098]
General Services Administration - Northwest Arctic Region [47099]
General Services Administration (GSA) - Office of Electronic Government and Technology [47100]
General Services Administration - Office of Global Supply - Logistics Operations Ctr. [47101]
General Services Administration (GSA) - Office of Small Business Utilization [47102]
General Services Administration - Washington, DC, Business Services Center [47103]
"Generalizing Newcomers' Relational and Organizational Identifications: Processes and Prototypicality" in Academy of Management Journal (Vol. 55, August 1, 2012, No. 4, pp. 949) [22159], [28599]
"Generation Entrepreneur" in Business Strategy Review (Vol. 25, Summer 2014, No. 2, pp. 41) [22611]
"Generation Gap: TV Sports Audience Growing Older" in San Francisco Business Times (Vol. 28, January 10, 2014, No. 25, pp. 4) [4094]
Generation Hustle: Young entrepreneurs got creative during the pandemic [36022]
Generation Partners [38095]
"Generation Y - An Opportunity for a Fresh Financial Start" in (September 11, 2010, pp. 241) [6421], [9537], [23904]
"Generation Y Chooses the Mobile Web" in PR Newswire (November 24, 2010) [2743], [9145], [21860], [34033]
"Generation Y Driving Portland Multifamily" in Daily Journal of Commerce, Portland (October 29, 2010) [4095], [13199], [13456], [13792], [34034]
"Generation Y: Engaging the Invincibles" in Employee Benefit News (Vol. 25, November 1, 2011, No. 14, pp. 22) [25786], [26946]
Generator at One [46822]
Generators & Emergency Power (Onsite) [19441], [21387]
Generators and Emergency Power (Onsite) [5359]
Generic Pharmaceutical Association [5133]
Generic Pharmaceutical Industry Association [5133]
Genesee County Chamber of Commerce [42573]
Genesee County Metropolitan Planning Commission (GCMPC) [41060]
Genesis Business Centers Ltd. [41348]
Genesis Centre [46743]
Genesis Medical Center - Illini Campus - Perlmutter Library of the Health Sciences [11542]
Genesis Park LP [45452]
Genesis Society [42998]
Genesys Capital [46788]
Genesys Partners Inc. [42749]
"Genetic Counselor" in Occupational Outlook Quarterly (Vol. 55, Summer 2011, No. 2, pp. 34) [2601], [25787]
Genetic Data Analysis for Plant and Animal Breeding [647]
"GeneTree.com Unveils New Family Consultation Service in Interpreting Genealogical DNA Data" in Benzinga.com (February 2, 2012) [10918], [15939], [31973], [32763]
Geneva Area Chamber of Commerce [42574]
Geneva Area Chamber of Commerce (GACC) [43477]
Geneva Chamber of Commerce (GCC) [39174]
Geneva Enterprise Development Center (GEDC) [42878]
Geneva on the Lake Chamber of Commerce [43478]
Geneva Venture Partners [37673]
Genghis Grill - The Mongolian Stir Fry [14170]
"Geo-Location Technology Linking Stores, Shoppers" in Providence Business News (Vol. 29, May 5, 2014, No. 5, pp. 1) [9975], [17675], [21861]
GeoCanada [5505]
Geocosmic Journal [11345]
"GeoEye CEO Sees Investors In His Future: Matt O'Connell Eyeing Intel Startup Post-Sale" in Washington Business Journal (Vol. 31, September 14, 2012, No. 21, pp. 1) [14364], [19849], [26168], [31314]

Geographical Center of North America Chamber of Commerce (GCNACC) [43294]
Geologic Hazards Photos [5760]
Geomatica [15228]
Geometres professionnels du Canada [15217]
Geometric Dimensioning and Tolerancing, Level 1 (Onsite) [17580]
Geomicrobiology Journal [32873]
Geopath [219], [31829]
George Brown College Archives [3074], [6152]
George Eastman House [12361]
George Eastman House Interactive Catalog [12325]
George Eastman Museum [12361]
George Mason University (GMU) - Mason Enterprise Center (MEC) [45953]
George Washington University - Elliott School of International Affairs - Institute for International Science and Technology Policy (IISTP) [31725]
George Washington University - Milken Institute School of Public Health - Jacobs Institute of Women's Health (JIWH) [26116]
George West Chamber of Commerce [45162]
Georgetown Chamber of Commerce [45163]
Georgetown County Chamber of Commerce (GCCC) [44545]
Georgetown SBDC [38125]
Georgetown-Scott County Chamber of Commerce [40043]
Georgetown University - Maternal and Child Health Library (NCEMCH) [2913]
Georgia Agribusiness Council (GAC) [16937], [38621]
Georgia Association of Business Brokers (GABB) [2133], [38622]
Georgia Association of Realtors (GAR) [13091]
Georgia Beekeepers Association (GBA) [1437]
Georgia BioBusiness Center (GBBC) [38832]
Georgia Business Travel Association, Inc. (GBTA) [19297]
Georgia Chamber of Commerce (GCC) [38733]
Georgia Department of Community Affairs - Business and Financial Assistance Div. [38647]
Georgia Department of Economic Development - Entrepreneur and Small Business Office [38648]
Georgia Department of Labor - Labor Market Information [47750]
Georgia Highlands College - Floyd Campus (GHC) [38844]
Georgia Hispanic Chamber of Commerce (GHCC) [38734]
Georgia Hispanic Chamber of Commerce Business Development Center [38833]
Georgia House of Representatives [38846]
Georgia Institute of Technology - Advanced Technology Development Center (ATDC) [26475], [38834]
Georgia Institute of Technology College of Architecture - Center for Assistive Technology and Environmental Access (CATEA) [12514]
Georgia Institute of Technology Enterprise Innovation Institute [27798]
Georgia Institute of Technology Library - Government Information Department [47411]
"Georgia Looking to Expand Film Industry Tax Credits" in Atlanta Business Chronicle (June 27, 2014, pp. 3A) [6186], [18098], [24990], [34797]
Georgia Manufacturing Organization [38733]
Georgia Minority Supplier Development Council (GMSDC) [38799]
Georgia Regents University Life Sciences Business Development Center [38825]
Georgia Southern University - Bureau of Business Research and Economic Development [21274]
Georgia Southern University - Center for Business Analytics and Economic Research (CBAER) [21274]
Georgia Southern University - College of Business Administration - Small Business Development Center [38629]
Georgia Southern University Small Business Development Center (UGA SBDC) [38630]
Georgia Southwestern State University School of Business Administration - Center for Business and Economic Development (CBED) [38853]
Georgia State University - Center for Insurance Research [26117]
Georgia State University - Center for Risk Management and Insurance Research [26117]
Georgia State University - J. Mack Robinson College of Business - Economic Forecasting Center (EFC) [21275]
Georgia State University - J. Mack Robinson College of Business - Small Business Development Center (SBDC) [25173], [38631]
Georgia Tech Enterprise Innovation Institute (EI2) [27798]

Georgia Master Index

Georgia Tech Minority Business Development Agency Business Center (MBDA) **[38800]**
Georgia Tech Procurement Assistance Center Albany Office (GTPAC) **[38816]**
Georgia Tech Procurement Assistance Center Augusta Office (GTPAC) **[38817]**
Georgia Tech Procurement Assistance Center Carrollton Office (GTPAC) **[38818]**
Georgia Tech Procurement Assistance Center Columbus Office (GTPAC) **[38819]**
Georgia Tech Procurement Assistance Center (EII) - Enterprise Innovation Institute **[38820]**
Georgia Tech Procurement Assistance Center Gainesville Office (GTPAC) **[38821]**
Georgia Tech Procurement Assistance Center Savannah Office (GTPAC) **[38822]**
Georgia Wildlife Federation Conservation Library (GWF) **[5770]**
Georgian Angel Network (GAN) **[46789]**
GeoVerde Corp. **[37674]**
German American Chamber of Commerce - Philadelphia (GACC) **[44214]**
"German Firm Ifm Electronic to Open Second Local Unit" in Philadelphia Business Journal (Vol. 28, July 20, 2012, No. 23, pp. 1) **[4394]**, **[19174]**, **[29228]**, **[30730]**
German-Texan Heritage Society (GTHS) **[7413]**
"German Win Through Sharing" in Canadian Business (Vol. 83, September 14, 2010, No. 15, pp. 16) **[14781]**, **[20907]**, **[25354]**, **[27573]**, **[27876]**, **[28032]**, **[33855]**
"Germans Win Solar Decathlon Again" in Contractor (Vol. 56, November 2009, No. 11, pp. 1) **[4096]**, **[5619]**, **[5893]**, **[14926]**, **[23221]**
Germantown Area Chamber of Commerce (GACC) **[44748]**, **[46415]**
Germantown Chamber of Commerce [40384], [44748]
Germantown Innovation Center **[40457]**
Germantown Magazine **[44749]**
Gestion TechnoCap Inc. **[46885]**
Get Clients Now!: A 28-Day Marketing Program for Professionals, Consultants, and Coaches **[20106]**, **[29801]**
Get a Financial Life: Personal Finance in Your Twenties and Thirties **[6037]**, **[6422]**, **[23905]**
"Get the Financial Risk-Management Skills You Need to Navigate Uncertain Times" in Entrepreneur (August 21, 2020) **[32386]**
Get Lost in the AWSM Sauce **[35418]**
"Get Off The Rollercoaster" in Michigan Vue (Vol. 13, July-August 2008, No. 4, pp. 19) **[6423]**, **[9538]**, **[18963]**, **[20908]**, **[23906]**
"Get On the Shelf: Selling Your Product In Retail Stores" in Black Enterprise (Vol. 44, February 2014, No. 6, pp. 18) **[23619]**, **[30351]**, **[32160]**
"Get Online Quick in the Office Or in the Field" in Contractor (Vol. 56, October 2009, No. 10, pp. 47) **[486]**, **[4097]**, **[5373]**, **[12632]**, **[16420]**, **[28600]**
"Get the Picture: 8 Instagram Tips for Small Businesses" in Legal Zoom (March 21, 2023) **[29526]**, **[29802]**
"Get Prepared for New Employee Free Choice Act" in HRMagazine (Vol. 53, December 2008, No. 12, pp. 22) **[18594]**, **[25355]**, **[26947]**, **[35191]**
"Get Stuffed: Which Animals Challenge Taxidermists the Most?" in LiveScience (April 27, 2019) **[15538]**
Get Your Business to Work!: 7 Steps to Earning More, Working Less and Living the Life You Want **[18099]**, **[19520]**, **[22612]**, **[24668]**
Get Your Climate Startup Funded with a Great Pitch Deck with Zoë Dove-Many **[34615]**
Get Your Ducks in a Row: The Baby Boomers Guide to Estate Planning **[6038]**
"Getting the Bioheat Word Out" in Indoor Comfort Marketing (Vol. 70, September 2011, No. 9, pp. 32) **[487]**, **[5620]**, **[5894]**, **[23222]**, **[29803]**, **[34035]**
Getting Cash Out of Your Business **[16714]**
"Getting Drowned Out by the Brainstorm" in Canadian Business (Vol. 83, June 15, 2010, No. 10, pp. 91) **[17676]**, **[22160]**, **[28601]**
"Getting Emotional Over Microsoft's Minecraft" in Puget Sound Business Journal (Vol. 35, September 19, 2014, No. 22, pp. 7) **[579]**, **[3708]**, **[19665]**, **[31315]**
Getting Expert Advice When Starting a Farm Business **[17048]**
"Getting Green Certification for Your Products" in Legal Zoom (March 22, 2023) **[23223]**
"Getting In on the Ground Floor With World-Class Companies" in Barron's (Vol. 89, July 27, 2009, No. 30, pp. 32) **[6424]**, **[9539]**, **[20909]**, **[23907]**
"Getting Inventive With..Ed Spellman" in Crain's Cleveland Business (Vol. 28, October 22, 2007, No. 42, pp. 18) **[22613]**, **[27877]**, **[29229]**, **[30731]**
Getting More: How to Negotiate to Achieve Your Goals in the Real World **[17677]**, **[32532]**
"Getting More Out of Retirement" in Agency Sales Magazine (Vol. 39, November 2009, No. 10, pp. 48) **[67]**, **[6425]**, **[9540]**, **[15385]**, **[23908]**, **[34798]**
Getting Paid on Past Due Invoices **[1777]**
Getting to Product Market Fit, Harvard MBA vs Startup Experience **[30838]**
Getting Results Without Authority **[28339]**
"Getting Rid of Global Glitches: Choosing Software For Trade Compliance" in Black Enterprise (Vol. 41, September 2010, No. 2, pp. 48) **[8719]**, **[14782]**, **[25356]**, **[27574]**, **[33856]**
Getting Started in Federal Contracting: A Guide through the Federal Procurement Maze **[25135]**
"Getting Started With Business Incubators" in Entrepreneur **[8810]**
"Getting to 'Us" in Harvard Business Review (Vol. 92, September 2014, No. 9, pp. 38) **[22161]**, **[28602]**
"Getting the Word Out" in Modern Machine Shop (Vol. 84, September 2011, No. 4, pp. 16) **[10432]**, **[27878]**, **[29230]**, **[30732]**
Getting to Yes: Negotiating Agreement Without Giving In **[17678]**, **[28603]**
Getty Conservation Institute (GCI) **[957]**
The Getty Provenance Index® Databases **[987]**
Gettysburg Adams Chamber of Commerce **[44215]**
Gettysburg-Adams County Area Chamber of Commerce [44215]
Geyserville Chamber of Commerce (GCC) **[36907]**
GGV Capital **[37375]**
GHT Ltd. **[543]**, **[4318]**, **[5401]**, **[12681]**
GIA Kitchen **[41349]**
"Giant Garages Could Rise Up in Downtown Cincinnati" in Business Courier (Vol. 27, October 22, 2010, No. 25, pp. 1) **[1556]**, **[4098]**, **[7289]**, **[9541]**, **[31316]**
Giant Tiger/Tigre Geant (GT) **[32366]**
Gibson Area Chamber of Commerce **[39175]**
Gibson Chamber of Commerce [39175]
Giddings Area Chamber of Commerce (GACC) **[45164]**
Giddings Chamber of Commerce [45164]
Gideon Hixon Fund **[37376]**
"Gifford's Tops in Chocolate" in Ice Cream Reporter (Vol. 21, August 20, 2008, No. 9, pp. 3) **[8567]**
"Gift Baskets News and Trends" in Bespokebrow (June 15, 2018) **[7467]**
Gift from Farm Credit Groups Supports Rural Entrepreneurship **[17049]**
"A Gift From Interactive Brokers" in Barron's (Vol. 92, July 23, 2012, No. 30, pp. M11) **[6426]**, **[9542]**, **[23909]**
Gifts & Decorative Accessories **[7470]**, **[7485]**, **[8186]**, **[15813]**
Gifts and Decorative Accessories--Buyers Guide and Directory (New England) **[7477]**
Gig Harbor Chamber of Commerce [46085]
Gig Harbor Peninsula Area Chamber of Commerce **[46085]**
"The Gig's Up for Freelancers" in The Wall Street Journal (October 27, 2019) **[5317]**, **[25357]**, **[26779]**
Gilbert Chamber of Commerce (GCC) **[36333]**
Gilchrist County Chamber of Commerce **[38386]**
Giles County Chamber of Tourism & Commerce **[44750]**
Gilmer County Chamber of Commerce **[38735]**
Gilroy **[36908]**
Gilroy Chamber of Commerce (GCC) **[36909]**
Gilroy Chamber of Commerce and Visitors Bureau [36909]
"Gilt Groupe's CEO On Building a Team of A Players" in Harvard Business Review (Vol. 90, January-February 2012, No.1-2, pp. 43) **[22162]**, **[26563]**, **[26948]**
Gimbel Associates **[31001]**
Girard Area Industrial Development Corp. - Model Works Industrial Commons **[44399]**
Girl Develop It (gdi) **[3663]**
"Girls Will Gossip: Psst! Buzz About Target" in Barron's (Vol. 89, July 27, 2009, No. 30, pp. 15) **[3116]**, **[29804]**, **[32161]**, **[32533]**
GitHub, Inc. **[14880]**
"GIV Mobile Announces New Partnership with American Forests, the Oldest National Nonprofit Conservation Organization in the Country" in Ecology, Environment & Conservation Business (January 25, 2014, pp. 34) **[2744]**, **[7113]**, **[17050]**, **[23224]**, **[31317]**
Giving **[34317]**
"Giving Biotech Startups a Hand" in Philadelphia Business Journal (Vol. 28, January 8, 2010, No. 47, pp. 1) **[21525]**, **[25788]**, **[26169]**, **[31974]**, **[32764]**, **[33163]**
"Giving In a New Age" in Denver Business Journal (Vol. 65, January 17, 2014, No. 36, pp. A4) **[7114]**, **[34036]**, **[34318]**
The Giving Institute (GI) **[7077]**
Giving Institute Membership Directory **[7115]**
Glacial Hills Food Center (GHFC) **[39973]**
Glades Crop Care, Inc. (GCC) **[31002]**
Gladewater Chamber of Commerce (GCC) **[45165]**
Gladstone Equestrian Association (GEA) **[8307]**
Glamour Shots Licensing Inc. (GS) **[12355]**
Glasco Chamber of Commerce [39894]
Glasco Chamber Pride (GCP) **[39894]**
Glascow Chamber of Commerce Newsletter **[41767]**
Glasgow Area Chamber of Commerce and Agriculture **[41768]**
Glasgow-Barren County Chamber of Commerce (GBCCC) **[40044]**
Glass Magazine: The Voice of the Flat Glass and Metals Industry **[7498]**
Glass Paperweight Foundation **[735]**, **[3226]**
Glass Patterns Quarterly (GPQ) **[4674]**
GlaxoSmithKline - USA (GSK) **[5215]**
Gleams **[16307]**
Glen Cove Chamber of Commerce **[42575]**
Glen Ellyn Chamber of Commerce (GECOC) **[39176]**
Glen Rose/Somervell County Chamber of Commerce **[45166]**
Glencoe Area Chamber of Commerce **[41233]**
Glendale Business **[36910]**
Glendale Chamber of Commerce (GCC) **[36334]**, **[36911]**
Glendale Public Library - Special Collections Room **[668]**
Glendive Chamber of Commerce and Agriculture (GCCA) **[41769]**
Glendora Chamber of Commerce **[36912]**
"Glenmede at Liberty To Show Off Space" in Philadelphia Business Journal (Vol. 32, January 24, 2014, No. 50, pp. 8) **[889]**, **[4099]**, **[11637]**, **[13457]**, **[22163]**
Glenns Ferry Chamber of Commerce (GFCC) **[38915]**
Glenrock Chamber of Commerce **[46604]**
Glenview Chamber of Commerce **[39177]**
Glenwood Chamber of Commerce [41235]
Glenwood Chamber of Commerce Newsletter **[41234]**
Glenwood Lakes Area Chamber of Commerce (GACC) **[41235]**
"A Glimpse Into the Thriving Business of Family History" in Deseret News (April 9, 2014) **[7361]**
GLMV Chamber of Commerce **[39178]**
Global Accelerator Network (GAN) **[37944]**
Global Business Cleaning Services Market Growth (Status and Outlook) 2022-2028 **[2984]**
Global Business Law Review **[18770]**
Global Business Review **[29044]**
Global Business Solutions L.L.C. **[3785]**
"Global Business Speaks English: Why You Need a Language Strategy Now" in Harvard Business Review (Vol. 90, May 2012, No. 5, pp. 116) **[17679]**, **[19521]**, **[21526]**, **[27575]**, **[30570]**
Global Business Travel Association (GBTA) **[19298]**
Global Business Travel Association - Chicago Chapter [19292], [38969]
Global Business Travel Association - Kansas City Chapter [19303]
Global Business Travel Association - Michigan Chapter [40803]
Global Business Travel Association - South Florida Chapter [19295]
Global Business Travel Association - Upstate New York Chapter **[19299]**, **[42381]**
Global Business Travel Association - Wisconsin Chapter [19323]
Global Cardiovascular Innovation Center (GCIC) **[43665]**
Global Casting Magazine **[10452]**
Global Change and Environmental Quality Program [6018]
Global Cold Chain Alliance (GCCA) **[12968]**
Global Color Tattoo Ink Market Growth 2022-2028 **[15338]**
Global Competencies for Diversity Leaders (Onsite) **[28340]**
Global Cosmetic Industry: The Business Magazine for the Global Beauty Industry (GCI) **[4545]**
Global Custodian **[6696]**
Global Digital Food Delivery Market Size & Share to 2027 **[6928]**
Global E-Commerce: Impacts of National Environment and Policy **[21862]**, **[27576]**
"Global Economy: The World Tomorrow" in Canadian Business (Vol. 81, December 19, 2007, No. 1, pp. 35) **[18100]**, **[20910]**, **[27577]**
Global Entrepreneurship Institute (GEI) **[37576]**
Global Entrepreneurship Network (GEN) **[22459]**
Global Entrepreneurship Research Association **[22460]**
Global Environment Fund (GEF) **[40427]**
"The Global Environment Movement is Bjorn Again" in Canadian Business (Vol. 83, September 14, 2010, No. 15, pp. 11) **[5621]**, **[5895]**, **[23225]**, **[27578]**
"Global Environmental Consulting Market Set to Surge" in Environmental Analyst (May 14, 2021) **[5622]**, **[23226]**
Global Food Trucks Services Market Growth (Status and Outlook) 2022-2028 **[7021]**
Global Gaming Business Magazine **[7333]**

Master Index CustomWire

Master Index

Global Healthy Cleaning Services Market Growth (Status and Outlook) 2022-2028 **[2985]**
Global Industrial Cleaning Services Market 2022-2026 **[2986]**
Global Industrial Cooperation Association (GICA) **[27412]**
Global Insurance Accelerator (GIA) **[39818]**
Global Investment Magazine: The Journal of Money Management, Trading and Global Asset Services **[9919]**
Global Laundromat Payment System Market 2022 by Company, Regions, Type and Application, Forecast to 2028 **[10182]**
Global Laundromat Payment System Market Growth (Status and Outlook) 2022-2028 **[10183]**
Global Market Development Center (GMDC) **[20602]**
Global Offset and Countertrade Association [27412]
"Global Organic Food" in Investment Weekly News (January 21, 2012, pp. 272) **[8021]**, **[10654]**, **[17051]**, **[18101]**, **[19850]**, **[34037]**
Global Promotional Sourcing Inc. (GPS) **[7323]**
Global Recruiters Network - GRN (GRN) **[2353]**
"Global Retail Chains' Revenues Inched Up 1% Last Year" in Sporting Goods Intelligence (November, 2021) **[15092]**
Global Secure Training [7974]
"Global Steel Makers Circle Stelco" in Globe & Mail (April 19, 2007, pp. B3) **[6427]**, **[9543]**, **[29231]**, **[31318]**
"The Global Talent Hunt" in Business Strategy Review (Vol. 21, Spring 2010, No. 1, pp. 78) **[20911]**, **[26949]**, **[27579]**, **[28604]**, **[34319]**
Global Technology Transfer L.L.C. **[2269]**, **[10532]**, **[20192]**, **[24245]**, **[28993]**, **[30849]**, **[33670]**
Global Tire Expo/SEMA Show **[15687]**
Global Vision Capital Corp. **[46716]**
GlobalEdgeMarkets (GEM) **[42979]**
"Globalization: Canada Tomorrow" in Canadian Business (Vol. 80, October 8, 2007, No. 20, pp. 14) **[20912]**, **[21527]**, **[22614]**, **[26287]**, **[34038]**
GlobalNET Corp. **[31003]**, **[31076]**
"The Globe: A Cautionary Tale for Emerging Market Giants" in Harvard Business Review (Vol. 88, September 2010, No. 9, pp. 99) **[18102]**, **[22615]**, **[27580]**, **[28605]**, **[30571]**
GLOBE: Conference and Exhibition on Business and the Environment **[5747]**, **[6003]**, **[13743]**
"The Globe: How to Conquer New Markets With Old Skills" in Harvard Business Review (Vol. 88, November 2010, No. 11, pp. 118) **[27581]**, **[29805]**, **[31319]**
"The Globe: Let Emerging Market Customers Be Your Teachers" in Harvard Business Review (Vol. 88, December 2010, No. 12, pp. 115) **[20432]**, **[27582]**, **[29806]**, **[32162]**, **[32534]**
Globe-Miami Regional Chamber of Commerce **[36335]**
"The Globe: Singapore Airlines' Balancing Act" in Harvard Business Review (Vol. 88, July-August 2010, No. 7-8, pp. 145) **[19354]**, **[23910]**, **[26288]**, **[27879]**
Globespan Capital Partners, Inc. **[40690]**
"Globus Plans First Phila.-Area Biotech IPO Since 2010" in Philadelphia Business Journal (Vol. 28, April 20, 2012, No. 10, pp. 1) **[9544]**, **[10829]**
Gloria Jean's Coffees USA **[7583]**
"Glossary of Health Benefit Terms" in HRMagazine (Vol. 53, August 2008, No. 8, pp. 78) **[17306]**, **[25789]**, **[26950]**
Gloucester County Chamber of Commerce (GLOCO) **[42126]**
Glouston Capital Partners (GCP) **[40691]**
Glycerine and Fatty Acid Producers Association [2964]
Glycerine and Oleochemicals Association [2964]
Glycerine Producers Association [2964]
Glynn Capital Management (GCM) **[37377]**
Glynn Law Offices **[28994]**
"GM Canada Revved Up Over Camaro" in Globe & Mail (February 17, 2006, pp. B4) **[29232]**, **[29807]**, **[30733]**
"GM Scores High Marks For Its Use of Solar Power" in Blade (September 13, 2012) **[11405]**, **[14927]**, **[29233]**
GM Ventures **[41142]**
"GMREB/Analysis of the Resale Market-First Quarter 2007: Year Off to a Great Start" in Marketwired (May 14, 2007) **[13200]**, **[13458]**
"GM's Decision to Boot Dealer Prompts Sale" in Baltimore Business Journal (Vol. 27, November 6, 2009, No. 26, pp. 1) **[4100]**, **[7739]**, **[11406]**, **[13459]**, **[24364]**, **[29234]**, **[32163]**
"GM's Mortgage Unit Deal Brings in $9 Billion" in Globe & Mail (March 24, 2006, pp. B3) **[11035]**, **[13201]**, **[13460]**, **[31320]**
"GM's Volt Woes Cast Shadow on E-Cars" in Wall Street Journal Eastern Edition (November 28, 2011, pp. B1) **[5623]**, **[5896]**, **[11407]**, **[14416]**, **[23227]**, **[25358]**, **[29235]**
GNC Holdings, Inc. **[11600]**
"GNC Reaches 'A Pivotal Moment" in Pittsburgh Business Times (Vol. 34, August 15, 2014, No. 4, pp. 4) **[11577]**, **[12415]**, **[31321]**, **[32164]**
"Go Back to Basics to Maximize Skid Steer ROI" in Rental Product News (Vol. 33, October 2011) **[13793]**
"Go Beyond Visionary. Be a Leader: Having a Grand Vision Isn't Enough to Build Your Business. You Have to Take the Reins and Actually Run Your Startup" in Inc. (Vol. 36, February 2014, No. 1, pp. 43) **[22616]**
Go Business Plans **[2270]**
The Go-Giver: A Little Story About a Powerful Business Idea **[22617]**, **[24669]**, **[34320]**
"Go Green Or Go Home" in Black Enterprise (Vol. 41, August 2010, No. 1, pp. 53) **[5624]**, **[5897]**, **[20913]**, **[22618]**, **[23228]**, **[30352]**
Go Put Your Strengths to Work **[22164]**, **[28606]**
"Go Team! Why Building a Cohesive Organization Is a Necessary Exercise" in Black Enterprise (Vol. 38, February 2008, No. 7, pp. 66) **[22165]**, **[28607]**
Go Westerly **[44472]**
GoAhead Ventures **[37378]**
The GOALS Institute (TGI) **[36416]**
"Goals for Small Business Owners" in Chron **[19522]**
Go.Be. **[40217]**
GoBeyond Investing **[38535]**
Godfather's Pizza Inc. **[12554]**
Godfrey Memorial Library (GML) **[7414]**
GoFarm Hawaii **[38886]**
Goin' Postal **[2401]**
Going to Extremes: How Like Minds Unite and Divide **[22619]**, **[24670]**
"Going Green: How Can Craft Brewers Improve Sustainability" in Beverage Daily (April 23, 2019) **[1914]**
Going Solo: Developing a Home-Based Consulting Business from the Ground Up **[17889]**, **[18865]**, **[20070]**, **[26733]**, **[29560]**
"Going Western with a Touch of Style" in Women In Business (Vol. 63, Summer 2011, No. 2, pp. 8) **[3027]**, **[6132]**
Gold Beach Chamber of Commerce **[43972]**
Gold Beach Chamber of Commerce Annual Business Directory **[43973]**
"Goldbelt Inc.: Targeting Shareholder Development" in Alaska Business Monthly (Vol. 27, October 2011, No. 10, pp. 108) **[10394]**, **[13202]**, **[13461]**, **[15742]**, **[15994]**, **[25136]**
Goldcoast Angel Investors **[35280]**, **[38536]**
The Golden 120 Seconds of Every Sales Call: A Fresh Innovative Look at the Sales Process **[17680]**, **[32535]**
Golden Angels Investors **[35468]**
Golden Chick [14172]
Golden Corral Corporation **[14171]**
Golden Franchising Corporation **[14172]**
Golden Gate Better Business Bureau [36714]
Golden Gate University - University Library **[2420]**
Golden Griddle Family Restaurants **[14173]**
A Golden Opportunity in Crisis? Decoding Agri-Tech Post Pandemic **[17052]**, **[26289]**
Golden Seeds (GS) **[42750]**
"Golden Spoon Accelerates Expansion Here and Abroad" in Ice Cream Reporter (Vol. 22, December 20, 2008, No. 1, pp. 2) **[8568]**, **[18103]**, **[24365]**, **[27583]**
Goldenwest Business Advisory Services **[10533]**
Goldey Beacom College - J. Wilbur Hirons Library **[3470]**
"Goldfarb Lighting & Electric to Close Charleston Showroom" in Charleston Gazette-Mail (July 11, 2019) **[5414]**
"Goldfingers" in Canadian Business (Vol. 81, Summer 2008, No. 9, pp. 31) **[30872]**, **[31322]**
Goldhaber Research Associates L.L.C. (GRA) **[10693]**
Goldman Associates, Inc. (GAI) **[13617]**
Gold's Gym International Inc. **[12455]**
Goldstein And Associates **[136]**
Goleta Entrepreneurial Magnet (GEM) **[37577]**
Golf **[7533]**
"Golf Club Plan Raises Hackles" in Philadelphia Business Journal (Vol. 31, April 6, 2012, No. 8, pp. 1) **[7517]**, **[12886]**
Golf Course Superintendents Association of America Golf Industry Show **[7536]**
Golf Digest **[7534]**
Golf Etc. **[15125]**
Golf Industry Show [7536]
Golf Magazine [7533]
Golf Range Association of America (GRAA) **[7509]**
Golf USA Inc. **[7538]**
"Golfsmith Goes On Offensive" in Austin Business Journal (Vol. 32, April 27, 2012, No. 8, pp. A1) **[7518]**, **[29808]**
Goliad Chamber of Commerce **[45167]**
Golub Capital **[39357]**
Gonzales Chamber of Commerce **[45168]**
Goochland County Chamber of Commerce **[45865]**
The Good Acre (TGA) **[41350]**
"Good and Bad Effects of Competition for Large and Small Businesses" in ToughNickel (June 16, 2020) **[19851]**
"A Good Book Is Worth a Thousand Blogs" in Barron's (Vol. 88, July 14, 2008, No. 28, pp. 42) **[1657]**, **[1826]**, **[6428]**, **[9545]**, **[20914]**, **[22620]**, **[23911]**
"Good for Business: Houston is a Hot Spot for Economic Growth" in Black Enterprise (Vol. 37, October 2006, No. 3, pp. 216) **[19175]**, **[20915]**, **[25790]**, **[32765]**, **[33367]**
"Good Companies Launch More New Products" in Harvard Business Review (Vol. 90, April 2012, No. 4, pp. 28) **[30734]**, **[34039]**, **[34321]**
Good Earth Coffee House **[7584]**
Good Food Consulting **[8069]**
"Good Going, Partners" in Barron's (Vol. 89, July 27, 2009, No. 30, pp. M8) **[6429]**, **[9546]**, **[23912]**, **[33164]**
Good Green Guide for Small Businesses: How to Change the Way Your Business Works for the Better **[5625]**, **[5898]**, **[23229]**
Good Locations for a Tattoo Business **[15298]**
Good News for 'Green' Brews: Consumers Say They'll Pay More for Sustainable Beer **[1915]**
"Good News If You Buy Organic Food — It's Getting Cheaper" in MarketWatch (January 24, 2019) **[8022]**
"Good Questions and the Basics of Selling" in Agency Sales Magazine (Vol. 39, September-October 2009, No. 9, pp. 14) **[20433]**, **[31761]**, **[32536]**
Good Samaritan Society [11541]
"A Good Sign for Commercial Real Estate?" in Austin Business JournalInc. (Vol. 29, December 18, 2009, No. 41, pp. 1) **[9547]**, **[11036]**, **[13203]**, **[13462]**, **[18104]**, **[20916]**
"A Good Step, But There's a Long Way to Go" in Business Week (September 22, 2008, No. 4100, pp. 10) **[6430]**, **[9548]**, **[11037]**, **[20290]**, **[20917]**, **[23913]**, **[24991]**, **[25359]**, **[28136]**
Good Work Network [40217]
Goodbye Graffiti Inc. **[2104]**
Goodcents Deli Fresh Subs [4911]
GoodCompany Ventures **[44400]**
Goodlettsville Area Chamber of Commerce **[44751]**
Goodmans Library **[6057]**
"Goodwill Haunts Local Companies" in Crain's Chicago Business (Apr. 28, 2008) **[9549]**, **[20291]**, **[20918]**, **[28137]**, **[28608]**, **[31323]**, **[34799]**
"Goodwill, the Original Thrift Store, Goes Digital" in The Business of Fashion (June 11, 2019) **[3117]**, **[11748]**
"Goodyear Extends Exclusive Deal to Supply NASCAR's Tires" in Charlotte Observer (February 4, 2007) **[15156]**, **[15683]**
"Google 'Drive' May Run Over Some Local Cloud Competitors" in Silicon Valley/San Jose Business Journal (Vol. 29, February 17, 2012, No. 47, pp. 1) **[3504]**, **[9146]**, **[19852]**
"Google Gets Creepy" in Canadian Business (Vol. 85, September 17, 2012, No. 14, pp. 28) **[282]**, **[9147]**, **[14417]**, **[16421]**
"Google Places a Call to Bargain Hunters" in Advertising Age (Vol. 79, September 29, 2008, No. 36, pp. 13) **[2745]**, **[9148]**, **[14783]**, **[21863]**, **[26290]**, **[29809]**
Google Ventures [35281], [37739]
"Google's Next Stop: Below 350?" in Barron's (Vol. 88, March 10, 2008, No. 10, pp. 17) **[6431]**, **[9149]**, **[9550]**, **[16422]**, **[21864]**, **[23914]**, **[26291]**
Gopher Angels **[41333]**
Gordon Chamber of Commerce **[41855]**
Gordon County Chamber of Commerce **[38736]**
Goren & Associates Inc. **[27139]**
Gorillas Can Dance: Lessons from Microsoft and Other Corporations on Partnering with Startups **[34507]**
Goshen Chamber of Commerce **[39541]**
Goshen County Chamber of Commerce **[46605]**
"Got Skills? Think Manufacturing" in Occupational Outlook Quarterly (Vol. 58, Summer 2014, No. 2, pp. 28) **[10433]**, **[18105]**, **[29236]**
"Got to be Smarter than the Average Bear" in Contractor (Vol. 56, September 2009, No. 9, pp. 82) **[4101]**, **[5899]**, **[12633]**, **[14615]**, **[14928]**, **[23230]**
Gotcha Covered Inc. **[16526]**
Gotham Gal Ventures (GGV) **[42751]**
Gotham Ventures **[42752]**
Gothenburg Area Chamber of Commerce **[41856]**
The Gottesman Libraries at Teachers College **[11612]**
Gottscheer Heritage and Genealogy Association Inc. (GHGA) **[7345]**
Gourmet News **[15041]**
GovCon Club [40344]
Goventure: Live the Life of an Entrepreneur **[22621]**, **[24671]**
"Government Assistance in Business" in Chron (July 28, 2020) **[24992]**
Government Contract Accounting (Onsite) **[16767]**, **[25105]**
Government Contract Assistance Program [44051]
CustomWire **[15215]**

Small Business Sourcebook • 42nd Edition 3243

Government of the District of Columbia (DSLBD) - Department of Small and Local Business Development **[38161]**, **[38169]**
Government National Mortgage Association, Ginnie Mae Procurement and Contracts (GNMA) **[47080]**
Government National Mortgage Association - Procurement Management Div. **[47081]**
Government Proposal Writing Basics **[17847]**, **[25106]**
Government Recreation and Fitness **[26003]**
Governor's of Business and Ecnomoic Development **[36603]**
"Governor Candidates Differ on Oregon's Green Streak" in Business Journal Portland (Vol. 27, October 22, 2010, No. 34, pp. 1) **[5626]**, **[5900]**, **[20919]**, **[23231]**, **[25360]**, **[31688]**, **[34800]**
Governors Highway Safety Association (GHSA) **[5099]**
Gowanda Area Chamber of Commerce (GACC) **[42576]**
"Gowns Ready to Go" in Houston Chronicle (June 3, 2010) **[1975]**, **[3028]**, **[3118]**
GPD P.C. **[544]**
GradePower Learning **[16163]**
Gradient Corp. **[6009]**
Graduate Pain Research Foundation [10886], [10964]
Graduate Women in Business [35666]
"Graduates to the TSX in 2008" in Canadian Business (Vol. 81, Summer 2008, No. 9, pp. 79) **[6432]**, **[9551]**, **[18106]**, **[23915]**, **[35345]**
Graduating Engineer & Computer Careers **[14989]**
Grafton Area Chamber of Commerce **[43295]**
Grafton Area Chamber of Commerce (GACC) **[46416]**
Graham County Chamber of Commerce **[36336]**
"Grainger Show Highlights Building Green, Economic Recovery" in Contractor (Vol. 57, February 2010, No. 2, pp. 3) **[4102]**, **[5374]**, **[5627]**, **[5901]**, **[14616]**, **[15861]**, **[20920]**, **[23232]**, **[35057]**
Granada Hills Chamber of Commerce **[36913]**
Granby Chamber of Commerce (GCC) **[37855]**, **[38045]**
"Grand Action Makes Grand Changes in Grand Rapids" in Crain's Detroit Business (Vol. 25, June 1, 2009, No. 22, pp. M012) **[15862]**, **[18107]**, **[24672]**, **[35058]**
Grand Blanc Chamber of Commerce (GBCC) **[40915]**
Grand Canyon Chamber of Commerce **[36337]**
Grand Canyon Minority Supplier Development Council [36380]
Grand Central Tech (GCT) **[42879]**
Grand Circus Detroit (GCD) **[41090]**
Grand Corridor Chamber of Commerce (GCCC) **[39179]**
Grand Coulee Dam Area Chamber of Commerce (GCDACC) **[46086]**
Grand Forks Chamber of Commerce (GFCC) **[43296]**
Grand Forks SCORE **[43279]**
Grand Island Area Chamber of Commerce (GIACC) **[41857]**
Grand Island Chamber of Commerce (GICC) **[42577]**
Grand Junction Area Chamber of Commerce **[37856]**
Grand Junction SCORE **[37803]**
Grand Junction Small Business Development Center (SBDC) **[37785]**
Grand Lake Area Chamber of Commerce **[37857]**
Grand Ledge Chamber of Commerce (GLACC) **[40916]**
Grand Marais Chamber of Commerce **[41236]**
The Grand Palms Tanning Resort **[15267]**
Grand Prairie Chamber of Commerce **[45169]**
Grand Rapids Area Chamber of Commerce **[40917]**
Grand Rapids Area Chamber of Commerce (GRACC) **[41237]**
Grand Rapids Association of Realtors [13092]
Grand Rapids Public Library - Furniture Design Collection **[7255]**
Grand Rental Station [13858]
Grand Rivers Chamber of Commerce and Tourism Commission [40045]
Grand Rivers Tourism Commission **[40045]**
The Grand Strander **[44546]**
Grand Terrace Area Chamber of Commerce **[36914]**
Grand Valley Business Times [37962]
Grand Valley State University - College of Liberal Arts and Sciences - Robert B. Annis Water Resources Institute (AWRI) **[16355]**
Grand Valley State University - The Michigan Small Business Development Center (SBDC) **[29475]**, **[41033]**
Grand Valley State University - Water Resources Institute [16355]
GrandBanks Capital **[40786]**
A Grande Finale Franchise L.L.C. **[7585]**
Grandview Chamber of Commerce **[46087]**
Grandville/Jenison Chamber of Commerce (GJCC) **[40918]**
Grandy's L.L.C. **[14174]**
Granger Chamber of Commerce **[46088]**
Grangeville Chamber of Commerce **[38916]**
Granite Falls Area Chamber of Commerce (GFACC) **[41238]**

Granite Falls Area Chamber of Commerce - Convention and Visitors Bureau [41238]
Granite Global Ventures [37375]
Granite Transformations **[2652]**, **[12860]**
Granite Ventures LLC **[37380]**
Granite Ventures LLC (GV) **[37379]**
Grant Area Chamber of Commerce [40999]
Grant County Chamber of Commerce **[46267]**
Grant County Chamber of Commerce (GCCC) **[36464]**, **[39895]**, **[40046]**, **[43974]**
"Grant Program Boosting Biomedical Research" in Providence Business News (Vol. 28, February 24, 2014, No. 47, pp. 3) **[7116]**, **[21528]**, **[25137]**, **[31975]**, **[32766]**
Grant Thornton L.L.P. **[34945]**
"Grant Could Help Schools Harness Wind" in Dallas Business Journal (Vol. 37, April 11, 2014, No. 31, pp. 8) **[5628]**, **[21529]**, **[24993]**, **[26292]**, **[31976]**
GRANTS [26098]
Grants Pass - Josephine County Chamber of Commerce **[43975]**
"Grants for Senior Citizens Starting a Business" in BizFluent (December 31, 2018) **[33067]**
"Grants of Up to $20,000 Available for Building Upgrades, Startup Expenses, and More" in Small Business Trends(February 18, 2023) **[33566]**, **[47971]**
"Grants Up to $50,000 Available for Businesses across the U.S." in Small Business Trends(January 14, 2023) **[47972]**
Grantsburg Chamber of Commerce **[46417]**
GrantSelect™ **[26098]**
Granville County Chamber of Commerce (GCCC) **[43133]**
Grapevine Chamber of Commerce **[45170]**
Graphic Communications Association [12718], [16368]
Graphic Communicator **[3343]**
"Graphic Design for Small Businesses: Fake It 'Til You Make It" in WSI (February 26, 2020) **[3312]**
Graphic Designers Industry in the US - Market Research Report **[7595]**
The Graphic Monthly **[3344]**
Graphic Monthly--Estimators' & Buyers' Guide Issue (Canada) **[3313]**
"Graphic Tech Acquires First U.S. :M-Press Tiger with Inline Screen Printing" in American Printer (Vol. 128, June 1, 2011, No. 6) **[3314]**, **[9552]**, **[12738]**, **[16193]**, **[19666]**, **[31324]**
Graphics of the Americas **[3345]**, **[12771]**, **[16214]**
Graphics Canada **[3346]**
Graphics Canada Expo [3346]
Grass!365, Inc **[10137]**
Gratiot Area Chamber of Commerce (GACC) **[40919]**
"A Grave Situation" in Chronicle of Higher Education (Vol. 54, November 30, 2007, No. 14) **[7213]**
Gravure Association of the Americas, Inc. (GAA) **[12785]**
"Gray Matters: An Aging Workforce Has Mass. Companies Scrambling to Deal with 'Silver Tsunami'" in Austin Business Journal (Vol. 34, May 30, 2014, No. 15, pp. 8) **[13204]**, **[23620]**
Grayhawk Capital **[36423]**
Grayling Regional Chamber of Commerce (GRCC) **[40920]**
Grays Harbor Chamber of Commerce **[46089]**
Grayslake Area Chamber of Commerce **[39180]**
Grayson Area Chamber of Commerce (GACC) **[40047]**
Grayson Foundation **[8337]**
Grayson-Jockey Club Research Foundation (GJCRF) **[8337]**
Grayson Small Business Development Center (Grayson SBDC) **[44917]**
Grayville Chamber of Commerce (GCC) **[39181]**
"Grazing Tables Are Suddenly Everywhere —And Nobody Knows How to Use Them" in The Wall Street Journal (October 14, 2019) **[2674]**
Grease Monkey International Inc. **[13005]**
The Great American Franchise Expo **[24468]**
Great Bend Chamber of Commerce [39896]
Great Bend Chamber of Commerce & Economic Development (GBCF) **[39896]**
"Great Breakroom Snacks for Your Business" in Small Business Trends(May 7, 2023) **[16560]**
The Great Canadian Bagel Ltd. **[14175]**
Great Canadian Dollar Store (1993) Ltd. **[32367]**
"Great Canadian's President Folds His Cards" in Globe & Mail (February 21, 2006, pp. B4) **[580]**, **[18964]**, **[28609]**
Great Clips Inc. **[7892]**
"The Great Concierge Debate: Digital or Personal?" in The New York Times (October 20, 2017) **[3872]**, **[11749]**
"The Great Deformation: The Corruption of Capitalism in America" **[20921]**, **[25361]**
"The Great Fall of China" in Canadian Business (Vol. 85, June 11, 2012, No. 10, pp. 26) **[9553]**, **[13205]**, **[20922]**, **[27584]**

"The Great Fall: Here Comes The Humpty Dumpty Economy" in Barron's (Vol. 88, March 10, 2008, No. 10, pp. 5) **[6433]**, **[9554]**, **[20292]**, **[20923]**, **[23916]**, **[26564]**
Great Falls Area Chamber of Commerce **[41770]**
Great Falls Regional Chamber of Commerce (GFRC) **[45724]**
Great Falls SCORE **[41738]**
Great Falls Small Business Development Center **[41720]**
The Great Frame Up Inc. (TFGU) **[12713]**
Great Harvest Franchising Inc. **[1294]**
Great Hill Equity Partners L.L.C. **[40692]**
Great Lakes Angels **[41047]**
Great Lakes Association for Financial Professionals (GLAFP) **[40798]**
Great Lakes Booksellers Association [1804]
Great Lakes Floral & Event Expo **[6870]**
Great Lakes Ice Cream and Fast Food Trade Show **[4450]**, **[7811]**
Great Lakes Independent Booksellers Association (GLiBA) **[1804]**
Great Lakes Innovation and Development Enterprise (GLIDE) **[43666]**
"The Great Moderation" in Canadian Business (Vol. 80, February 12, 2007, No. 4, pp. 25) **[6434]**, **[9555]**, **[20924]**
Great Neck Chamber of Commerce **[42578]**
"Great News for the Dead: The Funeral Industry Is Being Disrupted" in The Economist (April 14, 2018) **[7214]**, **[11750]**
Great Northern Catskills Chamber of Commerce [42609]
Great Oaks Venture Capital **[42753]**
Great Opportunities in Non-Food Franchising with Jon Ostenson: An EOFire Classic from 2021 **[24450]**
Great Plains Indian Gaming Association **[7262]**
Great Plains Technology Center (GPTC) **[43833]**, **[43884]**
Great Plains Technology Center Business Incubator **[43858]**
Great Plains Technology Center - Economic Development Center **[43859]**
Great Point Partners, LLC (GPP) **[38096]**
Great Steak **[14176]**
Great Valley Regional Chamber of Commerce (GVRCC) **[44216]**
Great Wraps! (GW) **[14177]**
Greater Abbeville-Vermilion Chamber of Commerce [40197]
Greater Aiken Chamber of Commerce **[44547]**
Greater Akron Chamber (GAC) **[43479]**
Greater Albion Chamber of Commerce **[40921]**
Greater Albuquerque Chamber of Commerce **[42319]**
Greater Alleghany Highlands Chamber of Commerce [45827]
Greater Angleton Chamber of Commerce **[45171]**
Greater Apex Area Chamber of Commerce [43083]
Greater Artesia Chamber of Commerce **[42320]**
Greater Artesia Chamber of Commerce and Visitors Center [42320]
Greater Atlantic City Chamber (GACC) **[42127]**
Greater Augusta Regional Chamber of Commerce (GARCC) **[45866]**
Greater Aurora Chamber of Commerce (GACC) **[39182]**
Greater Austin Chamber of Commerce (GACC) **[45172]**
Greater Austin Hispanic Chamber of Commerce (GAHCC) **[45173]**
Greater Bakersfield Chamber of Commerce **[36915]**
Greater Baldwinsville Chamber of Commerce **[42579]**
Greater Baltimore Chamber of Commerce (GBCC) **[40386]**
Greater Baltimore SCORE **[40351]**
Greater Bartow Chamber of Commerce (GBCC) **[38387]**
Greater Bath Area Chamber of Commerce **[42580]**
Greater Beaufort Chamber of Commerce [44536]
Greater Belen Chamber of Commerce **[42321]**
Greater Belleville Chamber of Commerce **[39183]**
Greater Beloit Association [46418]
Greater Beloit Chamber of Commerce (GBCC) **[46418]**
Greater Bethel Chamber of Commerce [40265]
Greater Bethesda-Chevy Chase Chamber of Commerce **[40387]**
Greater Beverly Chamber of Commerce (GBCC) **[40578]**
Greater Binghamton Chamber of Commerce **[42581]**
Greater Binghamton SCORE **[42423]**
Greater Blackfoot Area Chamber of Commerce **[38917]**
Greater Blacksburg Chamber of Commerce [45883]
The Greater Bloomington Chamber of Commerce **[39542]**
Greater Blytheville Area Chamber of Commerce (BGCC) **[36465]**
Greater Boca Raton Chamber of Commerce (GBRCC) **[38388]**
Greater Boerne Chamber of Commerce **[45174]**

Greater Bonners Ferry Chamber of Commerce (GBFCC) [38918]
Greater Bordentown Chamber of Commerce [42105]
Greater Boston Chamber of Commerce (GBCC) [40579]
Greater Bottineau Area Chamber of Commerce (GBACC) [43297]
Greater Bowie Chamber of Commerce (GBCC) [40388]
Greater Brandon Chamber of Commerce (GBCC) [38389]
Greater Breckinridge County Chamber of Commerce [40048]
Greater Brewton Area Chamber of Commerce (GBACC) [36113]
Greater Bridgton Lakes Region Chamber of Commerce (GBLRCC) [40280]
Greater Brockport Chamber of Commerce (GBCC) [42582]
Greater Brookfield Chamber of Commerce (GBCC) [46419]
Greater Buckeye Lake Chamber of Commerce [43421]
Greater BucksMont Chamber of Commerce (GBMCC) [44217]
Greater Buena Vista Area Chamber of Commerce [37825]
Greater Carbondale Chamber of Commerce [44218]
Greater Carlisle Area Chamber of Commerce [44219]
Greater Casa Grande Chamber of Commerce [36338]
Greater Cayce West Columbia Chamber of Commerce [44548]
Greater Cazenovia Area Chamber of Commerce (GCACC) [42583]
Greater Cedar Valley Chamber of Commerce-Cedar Falls [39743]
Greater Centralia Chamber of Commerce [39184]
Greater scottsville CHamber of commerce (SCCC) [45867]
Greater Chambersburg Chamber of Commerce (GCCC) [44220]
Greater Cheraw Chamber of Commerce (GCCC) [44549]
Greater Cherry Hill Chamber of Commerce [42108]
Greater Chesterfield Chamber of Commerce, Inc. [44550]
Greater Cheyenne Chamber of Commerce [46606]
Greater Chico Chamber of Commerce [36824]
Greater Chicopee Chamber of Commerce [40580]
Greater Chiefland Area Chamber of Commerce [38390]
Greater Cincinnati Chamber of Commerce [43445]
Greater Cincinnati and Northern Kentucky African American Chamber of Commerce [43480]
Greater Clare Area Chamber of Commerce [40892]
Greater Claremont Chamber of Commerce (GCCC) [41989]
Greater Cleveland Chamber of Commerce (GCCC) [45175]
Greater Colorado Venture Fund (GCVF) [37965]
Greater Columbia Chamber of Commerce (GCCC) [44551]
Greater Columbus Area Chamber of Commerce [43448]
Greater Columbus Chamber of Commerce [43448]
Greater Columbus Georgia Chamber of Commerce [38737]
Greater Concord Chamber of Commerce [36916]
Greater Conejo Valley Chamber of Commerce (GCVCC) [36917]
Greater Connellsville Chamber of Commerce [44221]
Greater Conroe/Lake Conroe Area Chamber of Commerce [45105]
Greater Coosa Valley Chamber of Commerce (CCC) [36114]
Greater Copper Valley Chamber of Commerce [36228]
Greater Cranston Chamber of Commerce (GCCC) [44473]
Greater Crofton Chamber of Commerce (GCCC) [40389]
Greater Croswell - Lexington Chamber of Commerce [40922]
Greater Cumberland Chamber of Commerce [40365]
Greater Cumberland County Chamber of Commerce [44734]
Greater Dade City Chamber of Commerce [38391]
Greater Dade-South Miami Chamber of Commerce [38348]
Greater Dallas Asian American Chamber of Commerce [45034]
Greater Dalton Chamber of Commerce (GDCC) [38738]
Greater Danbury Chamber of Commerce (GDCC) [38046]
Greater Dania Beach Chamber of Commerce [38392]
Greater Danville Chamber of Commerce [39543]
Greater DC Metro Chapter of GBTA (NVBTA) [19300], [45761]
Greater Decatur Chamber of Commerce [39185]
Greater Del Mar Chamber of Commerce [37148]
Greater Delray Beach Chamber of Commerce [38393]

Greater Derry Chamber of Commerce [41990]
Greater Derry Londonderry Chamber of Commerce [41990]
Greater Des Moines Partnership (DSM) [39744]
Greater Dover Chamber of Commerce (GDCC) [41991]
Greater Dowagiac Area Chamber of Commerce [40923]
Greater DuBois Chamber of Commerce (DCC) [44222]
Greater Dunedin Chamber of Commerce [38369]
Greater Durand Area Chamber of Commerce [40924]
Greater Durham Chamber of Commerce (DCC) [43134]
Greater Easley Chamber of Commerce (GECC) [44552]
Greater East Aurora Chamber of Commerce (GEACC) [42584]
Greater Eatonville Chamber of Commerce [46090]
Greater Edmonds Chamber of Commerce (ECC) [46091]
Greater El Paso Chamber of Commerce (GEPCC) [45176]
Greater Elgin Chamber of Commerce (ECC) [45177]
Greater Elizabeth Chamber of Commerce (GECC) [42128]
Greater Elkhart County Chamber of Commerce (GECC) [39544]
Greater Elkin - Jonesville - Chamber of Commerce [43212]
Greater Elkton Chamber of Commerce [40383]
Greater Englewood Chamber of Commerce [37858]
Greater Enid Chamber of Commerce [43762]
Greater Eureka Chamber of Commerce [36918]
Greater Eureka Springs Chamber of Commerce [36466]
Greater Eustis Area Chamber of Commerce [38446]
Greater Fairbanks Chamber of Commerce (GFCC) [36229]
Greater Fairfield Area Chamber of Commerce [39186]
Greater Farmington Area Chamber of Commerce (GFACC) [40925]
Greater Fayette County Chamber of Commerce [39187]
Greater Fayetteville Chamber [43135]
Greater Federal Way Chamber of Commerce [46092]
Greater Florence Chamber of Commerce [44553]
Greater Fort Dodge Growth Alliance (GFDGA) [39745]
Greater Fort Kent Area Chamber of Commerce (GFKCC) [40281]
Greater Fort Lauderdale Chamber of Commerce (GFLCC) [38394]
Greater Fort Myers Chamber of Commerce (GFMCC) [38395]
Greater Fort Walton Beach Chamber of Commerce (FWB) [38396]
Greater Fort Wayne Chamber of Commerce [39545]
Greater Franklin County Chamber of Commerce [43136]
Greater Fresno Area Chamber of Commerce [36919]
Greater Gardendale Chamber of Commerce [36115]
Greater Gardner Chamber of Commerce (GGCC) [40581]
Greater Gary Chamber of Commerce [39540]
Greater Gibson County Area Chamber of Commerce [44752]
Greater Glassboro Chamber of Commerce (GCC) [42129]
Greater Glenside Chamber of Commerce [44223]
Greater Golden Chamber of Commerce [37859]
Greater Golden Chamber of Commerce Network [37860]
Greater Goldendale Area Chamber of Commerce [46093]
Greater Gonzales Chamber of Commerce [40149]
Greater Gouverneur Chamber of Commerce [42585]
Greater Greenbrier Chamber of Commerce [46268]
Greater Greencastle Chamber of Commerce [39546]
Greater Greenville Chamber of Commerce (GCC) [44554]
Greater Greenwich Chamber of Commerce (GGCC) [42586]
Greater Greer Chamber of Commerce [44555]
Greater Hall Chamber of Commerce (GHCC) [38739]
Greater Hamilton Chamber of Commerce (GHCC) [43481]
Greater Hammond Chamber of Commerce [40170]
Greater Hammonton Chamber of Commerce [42130]
Greater Haralson County Chamber of Commerce [38740]
Greater Harlem Chamber of Commerce (GHCC) [42587]
Greater Hartsville Chamber of Commerce [44556]
Greater Hatboro Chamber of Commerce (GHCC) [44224]
Greater Havelock Area Chamber of Commerce [43144]
Greater Haverhill Chamber of Commerce [40582]
Greater Havre De Grace Chamber of Commerce [40394]
Greater Hawkins Chamber of Commerce [45202]
Greater Hazleton Business Innovation Center [44402]
Greater Hazleton Business and Innovation Center [44401]
Greater Hazleton Chamber of Commerce [44225]
Greater Healy-Denali Chamber of Commerce [36227]

Greater Heights Area Chamber of Commerce (GHACC) [45178]
The Greater Helen Area Chamber of Commerce, Inc. [38741]
Greater Hermiston Chamber of Commerce (GHCC) [43976]
Greater Hernando County Chamber of Commerce (GHCCC) [38397]
Greater Hewitt Chamber of Commerce (GHCC) [45179]
Greater High Desert Chamber of Commerce (GHDCC) [36920]
Greater Hillsborough Chamber of Commerce [41992]
Greater Hollywood Chamber of Commerce (GHCC) [38398]
Greater Holyoke Chamber of Commerce (GHC) [40583]
Greater Homestead/Florida City Chamber of Commerce [38501]
Greater Hot Springs Chamber of Commerce (GHSCC) [36467]
Greater Houlton Chamber of Commerce (HCC) [40282]
Greater Houston Chamber of Commerce [45180]
Greater Houston Partnership (GHP) [45180]
Greater Hudson Chamber of Commerce (GHCC) [41993]
Greater Huntington Park Area Chamber of Commerce [36921]
Greater Hyannis Area Chamber of Commerce [40584]
Greater International Falls Chamber of Commerce [41247]
Greater Irving - Las Colinas Chamber of Commerce [45181]
Greater Irwin Area Chamber of Commerce [44271]
Greater Issaquah Chamber of Commerce (GICC) [46094]
Greater Jackson Chamber of Commerce (GJCC) [41398]
Greater Jackson Chamber Partnership (GJCP) [41399]
The Greater Jackson County Chamber of Commerce [36139]
Greater Johnstown/Cambria County Chamber of Commerce [44226]
Greater Kansas City Chamber of Commerce [41564]
Greater Keller Chamber of Commerce [45182]
Greater Kellogg Chamber of Commerce [38923]
Greater Kenai Chamber of Commerce [36237]
Greater Ketchikan Chamber of Commerce (GKCC) [36230]
Greater Key West Chamber of Commerce [38441]
Greater Killeen Chamber of Commerce (GKCC) [45183]
Greater Kingston Community Chamber of Commerce [46095]
Greater Kirkland Chamber of Commerce (GKCC) [46096]
Greater Knox Area Chamber of Commerce [39608]
Greater Knoxville Chamber of Commerce [44769]
Greater Kokomo Economic Development Alliance [39547]
Greater La Porte Chamber of Commerce [39568]
Greater Laconia-Weirs Beach Chamber of Commerce and Greater Franklin Chamber of Commerce [42005]
Greater Lafayette Chamber of Commerce [40183]
Greater Lake City Chamber of Commerce [44557]
Greater Lake Placid Chamber of Commerce [38399]
Greater Lake Stevens Chamber of Commerce [46097]
Greater Lake Worth Chamber of Commerce [38342]
Greater Lakeport Chamber of Commerce [36976]
Greater Lambertville - New Hope Chamber of Commerce [42117]
Greater Las Cruces Chamber of Commerce (GLCCC) [42322]
Greater Latrobe-Laurel Valley Regional Chamber of Commerce [44227]
Greater Lava Hot Springs Chamber of Commerce [38928]
Greater Lawrence Chamber of Commerce [40600]
Greater Lawrence County Area Chamber of Commerce (GLCACC) [43482]
Greater Leadville Area Chamber of Commerce [37877]
Greater Lebanon Chamber of Commerce [42015]
Greater Lehigh Acres Chamber of Commerce [38372]
Greater Lehigh Valley Chamber of Commerce [44228]
Greater Liverpool Chamber of Commerce (GLC) [42588]
Greater Logan County Area Chamber of Commerce [43516]
Greater Logan County Area Convention and Tourist Bureau [43516]
Greater Londonderry Business and Professional Women [35621]
Greater Long Branch Chamber of Commerce (GLBCC) [42131]
Greater Lorain Chamber of Commerce [43518]
Greater Louisville Inc. - the Metro Chamber of Commerce (GLI) [40049]
Greater Louisville - The Metro Chamber [40049]
Greater Lowell Chamber of Commerce (GLCC) [40585]

Greater Lynchburg Chamber of Commerce [45879]
Greater Lynn Chamber of Commerce (LACC) **[40586]**
The Greater Mackinaw Area Chamber of Commerce **[40926]**
Greater Mackinaw Area Chamber of Commerce [40963]
Greater Macon Chamber of Commerce (GMCC) **[38742]**
Greater Madawaska Chamber of Commerce [40303]
Greater Madison Area Chamber of Commerce **[44648]**
Greater Madison Chamber of Commerce (GMCC) **[46420]**
Greater Mahopac-Carmel Chamber of Commerce **[42589]**
Greater Manchester Chamber of Commerce (GMCC) **[38047], [41994]**
Greater Mankato Business Accelerator **[41351]**
Greater Mansfield Area Chamber of Commerce [44259]
Greater Maple Valley - Black Diamond Chamber of Commerce **[46098]**
Greater Marathon Chamber of Commerce (GMCC) **[38400]**
Greater Marshall Chamber of Commerce [45269]
Greater Martinsville Chamber of Commerce **[39548]**
Greater Marysville - Tulalip Chamber of Commerce **[46099]**
Greater Maryville Chamber of Commerce **[41565]**
Greater Massena Chamber of Commerce **[42590]**
Greater Mauldin Chamber of Commerce **[44558]**
Greater Mauston Area Chamber of Commerce (GMACC) **[46421]**
Greater Medina Chamber of Commerce (GMCC) **[43483]**
Greater Memphis Chamber **[44753]**
Greater Menomonie Area Chamber of Commerce [46456]
Greater Meriden Chamber of Commerce [38060]
Greater Miami Chamber of Commerce (GMCC) **[38401]**
Greater Miami Chamber Membership Directory **[38402]**
Greater Miami Shores Chamber of Commerce **[38403]**
Greater Midwest Lenders Association (GMLA) **[28077]**
Greater Millville Chamber of Commerce (GMCC) **[42132]**
Greater Minden Chamber (GMC) **[40171]**
Greater Mission Chamber of Commerce (GMCC) **[45184]**
Greater Monticello Chamber of Commerce & White County Visitors Bureau **[39549]**
Greater Mount Airy Chamber of Commerce **[43137]**
Greater Mulberry Chamber of Commerce (GMCC) **[38404]**
Greater Muscatine Chamber of Commerce and Industry (GMCCI) **[39746]**
Greater Muskogee Area Chamber of Commerce (GMCC) **[43763]**
Greater Nags Head Chamber of Commerce [43179]
The Greater Naples Chamber of Commerce (GNCC) **[38405]**
Greater Nashua Chamber of Commerce (GNCC) **[41995]**
Greater Nassau County Chamber of Commerce **[38406]**
Greater New Braunfels Chamber of Commerce **[45185]**
Greater New Britain Chamber of Commerce (GNBCC) **[38048]**
Greater New England Minority Supplier Development Council Massachusetts Office (GNEMSDC) **[40651]**
Greater New Haven Chamber of Commerce (GNHCC) **[38049]**
Greater New Milford Chamber of Commerce (GNMCC) **[38050]**
Greater New York Chamber of Commerce (GNYCC) **[42591]**
Greater Newark Chamber of Commerce **[42592]**
Greater Newburyport Chamber of Commerce and Industry **[40587]**
Greater Newport Chamber of Commerce (GNCC) **[43977]**
Greater Newport Chamber of Commerce (NCCC) **[44474]**
Greater Niles Chamber of Commerce **[40927]**
Greater North County Chamber of Commerce **[41566]**
Greater North Dakota Chamber (GNDC) **[43298]**
Greater North Fulton Chamber of Commerce (GNFCC) **[38743]**
Greater North Miami Beach Chamber of Commerce **[38407]**
Greater North Syracuse Chamber of Commerce **[42593]**
Greater Northampton Chamber of Commerce (GNCC) **[40588]**
Greater Northeast Philadelphia Chamber of Commerce (GNPCC) **[44229]**
Greater Norwalk Chamber of Commerce **[38051]**
Greater Oak Harbor Chamber of Commerce (GOHCC) **[46100]**
Greater Ogdensburg Chamber of Commerce **[42594]**
Greater Oklahoma City Chamber of Commerce **[43764]**
Greater Oklahoma City Hispanic Chamber of Commerce **[43765]**

Greater Olean Area Chamber of Commerce (GOACC) **[42595]**
Greater Omaha Chamber of Commerce **[41858]**
Greater Oneida Chamber of Commerce **[42596]**
Greater Ontario Business Council (GOBC) **[36922]**
Greater Orange City Area Chamber of Commerce [38523]
Greater Ossining Chamber of Commerce **[42597]**
Greater Ossipee Area Chamber of Commerce (GOACC) **[41996]**
Greater Oswego-Fulton Chamber of Commerce (GOFCC) **[42598]**
The Greater Othello Chamber of Commerce **[46101]**
Greater Oviedo Chamber of Commerce [38480]
Greater Oviedo Chamber of Commerce Business Library **[33716], [34230]**
Greater Owensboro Chamber of Commerce **[40050]**
Greater Palm Harbor Area Chamber of Commerce (GPHACC) **[38408]**
Greater Palmer Chamber of Commerce (GPCC) **[36231]**
Greater Pampa Area Chamber of Commerce **[45186]**
Greater Pasco Area Chamber of Commerce **[46102]**
Greater Patchogue Chamber of Commerce **[42599]**
Greater Paterson Chamber of Commerce (GPCC) **[42133]**
Greater Pensacola Chamber **[38409]**
Greater Pflugerville Chamber of Commerce (GPCC) **[45187]**
Greater Philadelphia Chamber of Commerce (GPCC) **[44230]**
Greater Phoenix Black Chamber of Commerce [36315]
Greater Phoenix Chamber of Commerce **[36339]**
Greater Picayune Area Chamber of Commerce **[41400]**
Greater Pickens Chamber of Commerce (GPCC) **[44559]**
Greater Piedmont Area Chamber of Commerce [41613]
Greater Pine Island Chamber of Commerce (GPICC) **[38410]**
Greater Pittsburgh Chamber of Commerce **[44231]**
Greater Pittston Chamber of Commerce (GP) **[44232]**
Greater Plant City Chamber of Commerce **[38411]**
Greater Plantation Chamber of Commerce (GPCC) **[38412]**
Greater Pocatello Chamber of Commerce [38934]
Greater Pocono Chamber of Commerce (GPCC) **[44233]**
Greater Point Pleasant Area Chamber of Commerce [42180]
Greater Pointe Coupee Chamber of Commerce **[40172]**
Greater Pompano Beach Chamber of Commerce **[38413]**
Greater Poplar Bluff Area Chamber of Commerce **[41567]**
Greater Port Arthur Chamber of Commerce [45322]
Greater Port Jefferson Chamber of Commerce **[42600]**
Greater Portage Area Chamber of Commerce [46492]
Greater Porterville Chamber of Commerce [37104]
Greater Portland Chamber of Commerce [40299]
Greater Portsmouth Chamber of Commerce (GPCC) **[41997]**
Greater Poulsbo Chamber of Commerce (GPCC) **[46103]**
Greater Powell Area Chamber of Commerce **[43484]**
Greater Prairie Business Consulting **[33671]**
Greater Preston Idaho Business Association **[38919]**
Greater Princeton Area Chamber of Commerce (GPACC) **[46422]**
Greater Providence Chamber of Commerce (GPCC) **[44475]**
Greater Pueblo Chamber of Commerce (GPCC) **[37861]**
Greater Quitman Area Chamber of Commerce **[45188]**
Greater Raleigh Chamber of Commerce (GRCC) **[43138]**
Greater Redding Chamber of Commerce **[36923]**
Greater Redmond Chamber of Commerce [46137]
Greater Regional Alliance of REALTORS (GRAR) **[13092]**
Greater Reston Chamber of Commerce (GRCC) **[45868]**
Greater Richmond Chamber of Commerce [45844]
Greater Richmond Small Business Development Center (GRSBDC) **[45770]**
Greater Riverside Chambers of Commerce (GRCC) **[36924]**
Greater Riverview Chamber of Commerce (GRCC) **[38414]**
Greater Rochester Chamber of Commerce (GRCC) **[41998]**
Greater Rochester Chamber of Commerce, Women's Council **[42601]**
Greater Rochester SCORE **[42424]**
Greater Romeo-Washington Chamber of Commerce **[40928]**
Greater Romulus Chamber of Commerce (GRCC) **[40929]**
Greater Rugby Area Chamber of Commerce [43294]
Greater Rumford Chamber of Commerce [40301]

Greater Rupert Area Chamber of Commerce [38930]
Greater St. Charles County Chamber of Commerce **[41568]**
Greater San Antonio Chamber of Commerce **[45189]**
Greater San Diego Business Development Council [30258]
Greater San Diego Chamber of Commerce [37151]
Greater San Fernando Valley Chamber of Commerce **[36925]**
Greater Sandpoint Chamber of Commerce (GSCC) **[38920]**
Greater Sanford Chamber of Commerce [38415]
The Greater Sanford Regional Chamber of Commerce **[38415]**
Greater Santa Ana Chamber of Commerce [37168]
Greater Sarasota Chamber of Commerce (GSCC) **[38416]**
Greater Saratoga Chamber of Commerce [42666]
Greater Schulenburg Chamber of Commerce **[45190]**
Greater Scott County Chamber of Commerce **[39550]**
Greater Scranton Chamber of Commerce **[44234]**
Greater Seaford Chamber of Commerce **[42602]**
Greater Seattle Chamber of Commerce **[46104]**
Greater Sebring Chamber of Commerce (GSCC) **[38417]**
Greater Seffner Area Chamber of Commerce **[38418]**
Greater Seffner-Mango Chamber of Commerce [38418]
Greater Seminole Area Chamber of Commerce **[38419]**
Greater Seminole County Chamber of Commerce [38419]
Greater Seneca Chamber of Commerce [44577]
Greater Severna Park and Arnold Chamber of Commerce (GSPACC) **[40390]**
Greater Severna Park Chamber of Commerce [40390]
Greater Seymour Chamber of Commerce (GSCC) **[39551]**
Greater Shelby County Chamber of Commerce **[36116]**
Greater Shelbyville Chamber of Commerce **[39188]**
Greater Sherman Oaks Chamber of Commerce **[36926]**
Greater Shreveport Chamber of Commerce [40190]
Greater Silver Spring Chamber of Commerce (GSSCC) **[40391]**
Greater Sitka Chamber of Commerce (GSCC) **[36232]**
Greater Sleepy Hollow Tarrytown Chamber of Commerce **[42603]**
Greater Slidell Area Chamber of Commerce [40166]
Greater Smithfield-Selma Area Chamber of Commerce [43197]
Greater Smithtown Chamber of Commerce **[42604]**
Greater Somersworth Chamber of Commerce (GSCC) **[41999]**
Greater South Haven Area Chamber of Commerce [41011]
Greater Southington Chamber of Commerce **[38052]**
Greater Southwest Houston Chamber of Commerce [45214]
Greater Spokane Incorporated (GSI) **[46105], [46204]**
Greater Spring Lake Area Chamber of Commerce **[42134]**
Greater Springfield Chamber of Commerce (GSCC) **[39189]**
Greater Sterling Development Corp. (GSDC) **[39405]**
Greater Stillwater Chamber of Commerce **[41239]**
Greater Stockton Chamber of Commerce (GSCC) **[36927]**
Greater Summerville - Chamber of Commerce [44560]
Greater Summerville/Dorchester County Chamber of Commerce **[44560]**
Greater Sumter Chamber of Commerc [44561]
Greater Sumter Chamber of Commerce **[44561]**
Greater Sunrise Chamber of Commerce **[38420]**
Greater Susquehanna Keystone Innovation Zone (GSKIZ) **[44403]**
Greater Susquehanna Valley Chamber of Commerce (GSVCC) **[44235]**
Greater Sycamore Chamber of Commerce [39317]
Greater Syracuse Business Development Corp. (GSBDC) **[42400]**
Greater Talladega Area and Lincoln Chamber of Commerce **[36117]**
Greater Talladega and Lincoln Area Chamber of Commerce Newsletter **[36118]**
Greater Tallahassee Chamber of Commerce **[38421]**
Greater Tallassee Area Chamber of Commerce (TCC) **[36119]**
Greater Tampa Chamber of Commerce [38508]
Greater Tarpon Springs Chamber of Commerce [38509]
Greater Tattnall Chamber of Commerce **[38744]**
Greater Taylor Chamber of Commerce & Visitors Center **[45191]**
Greater Tehachapi Chamber of Commerce (GTCC) **[36928]**
Greater Temple Terrace Chamber of Commerce [38513]
Greater Tomah Area Chamber of Commerce **[46423]**

Greater Tomball Area Chamber of Commerce [45192]
Greater Toms River Chamber of Commerce (GTRCC) [42135]
Greater Topeka Chamber of Commerce [39897]
Greater Topsail Area Chamber of Commerce and Tourism [43139]
Greater Town and Country Area Chamber of Commerce [38512]
Greater Trinidad Chamber of Commerce [36929]
Greater Twin Falls Area Chamber of Commerce [38946]
Greater Ukiah Chamber of Commerce (GUCC) [36930]
Greater Union Grove Area Chamber of Commerce (GUGACC) [46424]
Greater University Chamber of Commerce [46170]
Greater Utica Chamber of Commerce [42605]
Greater Valley Area Chamber of Commerce (GVACC) [36120]
Greater Valley Business and Resource Guide [38053]
Greater Valley Chamber of Commerce (GVCC) [38054]
Greater Valparaiso Chamber of Commerce (GVCC) [39552]
Greater Van Buren Chamber of Commerce [40283]
Greater Vancouver Chamber of Commerce (GVCC) [46106]
Greater Ventura Chamber of Commerce [37232]
Greater Vernon Chamber of Commerce [40173]
Greater Vidalia Chamber [38745]
Greater Vienna Chamber of Commerce [45907]
Greater Vineland Chamber of Commerce (GVCC) [42136]
Greater Wabash Valley SCORE [39488]
Greater Waco Chamber of Commerce (GWCC) [45193]
Greater Warminster Chamber of Commerce [44217]
Greater Warrensburg Area Chamber of Commerce [41569]
Greater Warrensburg Area Chamber of Commerce and Visitors Center [41569]
Greater Warsaw Chamber of Commerce [42606]
Greater Wasilla Chamber of Commerce (GWCC) [36233]
Greater Watertown - North Country Chamber of Commerce (GWNC) [42607]
Greater Waunakee Area Chamber of Commerce [46530]
Greater Waynesboro Chamber of Commerce [44236]
Greater Wayzata Area Chamber of Commerce [41240]
Greater Weiser Area Chamber of Commerce [38947]
Greater West Bloomfield Chamber of Commerce [40930]
Greater West Plains Area Chamber of Commerce [41570]
Greater West Shore Area Chamber of Commerce [44320]
Greater Westerly-Pawcatuck Area Chamber of Commerce [44479]
Greater Westfield Area Chamber of Commerce (GWACC) [42137]
Greater Westhampton Chamber of Commerce [42608]
Greater Whiteville Chamber of Commerce [43122]
Greater Wildwood Chamber of Commerce (GWCOC) [42138]
Greater Williamsburg Chamber and Tourism Alliance [45869]
Greater Wilmington Chamber of Commerce [43140]
Greater Windham Chamber of Commerce [40305]
Greater Winter Haven Chamber of Commerce [38422]
Greater Woodinville Chamber of Commerce [46107]
Greater Woodland Park Chamber of Commerce [37862]
Greater Woonsocket Chamber of Commerce [44478]
Greater Yakima Chamber of Commerce (GYCC) [46108]
Greater York Area Chamber of Commerce [41859]
Greater Yuba City/Marysville Chamber of Commerce [37260]
Greater Zionsville Chamber of Commerce [39553]
GreatPoint Ventures (GPV) [37381]
Greco Pizza Donair [12555]
Greek Food and Wine Institute (GFWI) [15000]
Greeley Chamber of Commerce [37863]
Greeley County Historical Society Library [7415]
Greeley and Hansen L.L.C. [16349]
Greeley/Weld Small Business Development Center [37791]
Greeleychamber.com [37864]
Greely Area Chamber of Commerce [37863]
Green Bay Area Chamber of Commerce (GBACC) [46425]
Green Bay SCORE [46340]
"Green Business Owners Share Secrets of Success In This Business Guide" in PRNewsChannel.com (March 1, 2012) [5629], [5902], [23233]
"Green Business Plan Competition" in Chemical & Engineering News (Vol. 90, July 9, 2012, No. 28, pp. 34) [5630], [5903], [11852], [11869], [23234]
Green Business: Sources of Information [23455]
Green Chamber of Commerce [43485]
"Green and Clean" in Retail Merchandiser (Vol. 51, July-August 2011, No. 4, pp. 56) [4437], [5631], [5904], [7740], [23235], [32165]

"Green Clean Machine" in Small Business Opportunities (Winter 2010) [5073], [18108], [23021], [26734]
"Green Cleaning - It's Your Business" in Cleaning Business Today (April 3, 2019) [2971], [23236]
"Green Collar: Green Buildings Support Job Creation, Workforce Transformation and Economic Recovery" in Environmental Design and Construction (Vol. 15, July 2012, No. 7, pp. 31) [890], [4103], [5632], [5905], [18109], [23237]
Green Data Centers and Internet Business [2817], [9274]
Green Entrepreneur [5041]
Green Exchange [23037]
Green Garage [41091]
The Green Guide for Business: The Ultimate Environment for Businesses of All Sizes [5633], [5906], [13713], [23238]
Green Hotels Association (GHA) [8344], [23038]
"Green Housing for the Rest of Us" in Inc. (November 2007, pp. 128-129) [13206], [13463], [23239]
"Green Ideas for Making Your Business Environmentally Sustainable" in The Balance Small Business (February 10, 2020) [23240]
Green Industry Conference [10256]
"The Green Industry Jobs Gap" in Green Industry Pro (Vol. 23, October 2011) [7623], [10098], [10234], [26565], [26951], [33165]
Green Industry PRO [10250]
Green Industry Pros [10250]
"Green It Like You Mean It" in Special Events Magazine (Vol. 28, February 1, 2009, No. 2) [2850], [3119], [5634], [5907], [11893], [11906], [23241]
Green Lake Area Chamber of Commerce (GLACC) [46424]
"Green Light" in The Business Journal-Portland (Vol. 25, July 11, 2008, No. 18, pp. 1) [5635], [5908], [14929], [18110], [23242], [26566]
"Green Manufacturer Scouts Sites in Greater Cincinnati" in Business Courier (Vol. 27, July 23, 2010, No. 12, pp. 1) [5636], [5909], [23243], [29237], [33368]
"Green Peak Innovations to Open First of Planned 30 Marijuana Stores This Week in Bay City" in Crain's Detroit Business(July 8, 2019) [5002], [10949]
Green Profit Magazine [6868], [7644]
Green Rhino Pixelbooks [9929]
Green River Chamber of Commerce [46607]
"Green Rules To Drive Innovation: Charging for Carbon Can Inspire Conservation, Fuel Competition, and Enhance Competitiveness" in Harvard Business Review (Vol. 90, March 2012, No. 3, pp. 120) [5637], [5910], [23244], [24994], [26223], [31919]
Green Rush Consulting (GRC) [5067]
Green Rush Daily [5069]
Green Seal (GS) [6016]
Green Technologies and Business Practices: An IT Approach [23449]
"The Green Trap" in Canadian Business (Vol. 80, April 9, 2007, No. 8, pp. 19) [6435], [9556], [23245]
Green Worker Cooperatives (GWC) [42880]
Green2Gold [34480]
Greenbaum Marketing Communications [3355]
Greenbrier County Convention & Visitors Bureau [46268]
Greenbrier Valley Visitors Guide [46269]
Greencastle-Antrim Chamber of Commerce [44237]
Greencastle Chamber of Commerce [39546]
Greendale Chamber of Commerce [46427]
Greene County Chamber of Commerce [38746], [44238]
Greene County Chamber of Commerce (GCCC) [42609]
Greene County Partnership (GCP) [44754]
"Greene Street Consignment May Be the Most Happening Area Company You've Never Heard Of" in Philadelphia Inquirer (April 20, 2012) [3892], [34322], [35789]
"Greener Pastures" in Canadian Business (Vol. 80, February 12, 2007, No. 4, pp. 69) [9557], [35346]
Greenfield Area Chamber of Commerce [39554]
Greenfield Chamber/Main Street and Development Office [39747]
GreenHouse [44604]
"Greenhouse Announces Reverse Merger With Custom Q, Inc." in Investment Weekly (January 30, 2010, pp. 338) [5638], [5911], [14930], [23246], [31325]
Greenhouse Capital Partners [37382]
Greenhouse Growing [7624]
Greenhouse Management [5042], [6869], [7645]
Greening Your Small Business: How to Improve Your Bottom Line, Grow Your Brand, Satisfy Your Customers and Save the Planet [5639], [5912], [13714], [17307], [18111], [19355], [19853], [20434], [23247], [29810], [30959]
"A Greenish Light for Financial-Sector Funds" in Barron's (Vol. 88, March 24, 2008, No. 12, pp. 52) [6436], [9558], [23917]

Greenlight Business Solutions L.L.C. [20193]
"Greenlight's Mission: Poach California" in Business Journal Portland (Vol. 26, December 11, 2009, No. 40, pp. 1) [18112], [19176], [33369]
Greenmont Capital Partners [37967]
Greensboro [43141]
Greensboro Area Chamber of Commerce [43142]
Greensburg Chamber of Commerce [39555]
Greensburg Decatur County Chamber of Commerce (GDC) [39555]
Greenstone Economic Development Corporoation (GEDC) [46762]
"GreenTech Gears Up for Production" in Memphis Business Journal (Vol. 33, April 6, 2012, No. 52, pp. 1) [1101], [4104], [5640], [5913], [23248], [29238]
Greentown Labs Inc. [40751]
Greenvale Chamber of Commerce [42610]
Greenvale Chamber of Commerce Inc. [42610]
Greenville Area Chamber of Commerce (GACC) [40931], [44239]
Greenville Area Economic Development Corporation - McNeilly Business Center [44404]
Greenville Area Small Business Development Center [44504], [44595]
Greenville Business Magazine (GBM) [44617]
Greenville Chamber of Commerce [39190], [45194]
Greenville Chamber of Commerce - Minority Business Accelerator (MBA) [44589], [44605]
Greenville - Pitt County Chamber of Commerce (GPCCC) [43143]
Greenville Technical College - Northwest Campus (GTC) [44612]
Greenwich Chamber of Commerce (GCC) [38055]
Greenwich Village-Chelsea Chamber of Commerce (GVCCC) [42611]
Greenwood Area Chamber of Commerce [44562]
Greenwood Area Small Business Development Center [44506]
Greenwood Consulting Group (GCGI) [38569]
Greenwood-Leflore Chamber of Commerce (GLCC) [41401]
Greers Ferry Area Chamber of Commerce [36468]
Greeting Card Association (GCA) [7697]
"Greeting Card Companies Need a Sympathy Card: CVS, Walmart Poised to Cut Back" in USA Today (March 26, 2019) [7701]
"Greg Lueck: Glass Blowing" in Inc. (Volume 32, December 2010, No. 10, pp. 36) [4593], [4657], [20107], [26293]
Greg Root Partner at Defined Hospitality [14058]
"'Gregory Cunningham on Taking on Farm Credit of Florida'" in South Florida Business Journal (Vol. 34, July 18, 2014, No. 52, pp. 11) [17053], [20293], [25363], [28610]
Grenada Area Chamber of Commerce [41402]
Gresham Area Chamber of Commerce (GACC) [43978]
"Grey Power: On Target" in Canadian Business (Vol. 81, July 22, 2008, No. 12-13, pp. 45) [3814], [9150], [16423], [29811], [33068], [33166], [34040]
Grey Worldwide Information Center [31900]
Greybull Area Chamber of Commerce [46608]
Greycroft Partners (GP) [43009], [43012]
Greylock Management Corporation [37383]
Greylock Partners [37383]
Gridley Area Chamber of Commerce [36931]
The Gridlock Economy: How Too Much Ownership Wrecks Markets, Stops Innovation, and Costs Lives [20925], [24673], [27880]
Griffin-Spalding Chamber of Commerce [38747]
Griffiss Institute - Cyber Research Institute (CRI) [42881]
Grimes County Chamber of Commerce [45294]
Grinnell Area Chamber of Commerce [39748]
Grinnell College - Burling Library - Listening Room [11221], [11297]
Grinnell College - Burling Library Media Room [11221], [11297]
"A Gripping Read: Bargains & Noble" in Barron's (Vol. 88, March 17, 2008, No. 11, pp. 20) [1827], [6437], [9559], [23918]
"Grocers Fight Food Stamp Plan" in Philadelphia Business Journal (Vol. 30, January 20, 2012, No. 49, pp. 1) [7741], [24995]
Grocery Manufacturers of America [7708]
Groceryshop [7812]
Grolier Club of New York Library [1708], [1730], [1852], [16218]
"Groomers Eye Profit Growth Through Services" in Pet Product News (Vol. 64, December 2010, No. 12, pp. 26) [12074], [18113], [21530], [33167], [34041]
"Grooming Your Online Persona" in Women In Business (Vol. 62, June 2010, No. 2, pp. 36) [17681], [17861], [21865], [26952], [28611], [35790]
Grotech Ventures [40428]

Groucho's Master Index

Groucho's Deli **[4902]**
"Ground Forces: Insurance Companies Should Help Agents to Build the Skills and Relationships that Translate Into More Business" in Best's Review (Vol. 113, September 2012, No. 5, pp. 25) **[8912]**, **[20926]**, **[21531]**, **[27269]**
"Ground Readied for Construction of $4.5 Million Senior Care Center in Crown Point" in Times (August 9, 2012) **[1033]**, **[4105]**, **[11512]**
The Groundbreaking Impact of Technology on Brand Market Research for Small Businesses **[29490]**
"Grounded Condo Development Poised for Construction Takeoff" in Memphis Business Journal (Vol. 35, February 7, 2014, No. 44, pp. 4) **[4106]**, **[20927]**, **[28138]**
The GroundFloor **[45521]**
"'Groundhog Day' B&B Likely Will Be Converted Into One In Real Life" in Chicago Tribune (October 21, 2008) **[891]**, **[1415]**, **[4107]**, **[18965]**, **[19356]**, **[19523]**, **[23621]**, **[29812]**, **[33567]**
The Grounds Guys **[10138]**
"Grounds for Success" in Canadian Business (Vol. 87, July 2014, No. 7, pp. 73) **[3181]**, **[18114]**, **[19854]**
Groundswell: Winning in a World Transformed by Social Technologies **[9151]**, **[17682]**, **[21866]**, **[26294]**, **[28612]**, **[29813]**, **[31762]**, **[31866]**, **[34042]**, **[34323]**
Groundwork Coffee Co [1297], [3208]
"Group Thinking" in Business Strategy Review (Vol. 23, Spring 2012, No. 1, pp. 48) **[17683]**, **[21532]**, **[28613]**, **[31977]**
Groupe DGE International Inc. **[5751]**
"Groups Seek Donations to Recycle Christmas Trees" in The Register-Guard (January 7, 2012, pp. B11) **[2939]**, **[13715]**, **[23249]**
Grove Area Chamber of Commerce (GACC) **[43766]**
Grove City Area Chamber of Commerce **[44240]**
Grove City Area Chamber of Commerce (GCACC) **[43486]**
Grove Street Advisors L.L.C. **[40693]**
Groveport-Madison Area Chamber of Commerce [43573]
Grow Benzie Inc. **[41092]**
Grow Cedar Valley (GCVAC) **[39749]**
Grow Utah Ventures **[45679]**
Grow VC Group **[43010]**
Grow Your Business Through Government Contracting **[25107]**, **[33523]**, **[35708]**
Grower Direct Fresh Cut Flowers Inc. **[6876]**, **[7653]**
Growing Business Handbook **[18461]**
The Growing Business Handbook: Inspiration and Advice from Successful Entrepreneurs and Fast Growing UK Companies **[18115]**, **[22622]**, **[28614]**
Growing Christmas Trees **[2940]**
"A Growing Concern" in Canadian Business (Vol. 79, October 9, 2006, No. 20, pp. 90) **[18116]**, **[23250]**, **[24674]**
"A Growing Dilemma" in Crain's Cleveland Business (Vol. 28, October 8, 2007, No. 40, pp. 19) **[18117]**, **[18966]**, **[33568]**
"Growing Encryptics Trades Frisco for Austin" in Austin Business Journal (Vol. 34, April 25, 2014, No. 10, pp. A8) **[14784]**, **[19177]**, **[26567]**, **[33857]**
"Growing Expectations" in Financial Advisor (November 1, 2019) **[6039]**, **[6438]**, **[23919]**
"Growing Field" in Crain's Detroit Business (Vol. 26, January 11, 2010, No. 2, pp. 3) **[18118]**, **[20928]**, **[24996]**, **[28139]**, **[32767]**, **[35347]**
"Growing Food and Protecting Nature Don't Have to Conflict – Here's How They Can Work Together" in The Conversation (March 9, 2021) **[17054]**
"Growing Grocer" in Washington Business Journal (Vol. 32, March 21, 2014, No. 49, pp. 6) **[7742]**, **[18119]**
"Growing Number of Angel Investors Filling the Void" in Dallas Business Journal (Vol. 35, August 24, 2012, No. 50, pp. 1) **[35348]**
Growth Alliance for Greater Evansville (GAGE) **[39480]**
"Growth Back on CIBC's Agenda" in Globe & Mail (March 3, 2006, pp. B1) **[6439]**, **[9560]**, **[18120]**, **[23920]**
The Growth Coach **[2354]**
"Growth at E Solutions Part of 'Opportunistic' Data Center Market" in Tampa Bay Business Journal (Vol. 30, January 29, 2010, No. 6, pp. 1) **[3505]**, **[3622]**, **[18121]**, **[33168]**
"Growth in Fits and Starts" in Canadian Business (Vol. 83, July 20, 2010, No. 11-12, pp. 18) **[13207]**, **[13464]**, **[20929]**, **[29239]**
"Growth of Free Dailies Dropping" in Globe & Mail (March 24, 2007, pp. B7) **[9152]**, **[11981]**, **[16424]**
"The Growth Opportunity That Lies Next Door: How Will the Logic of Globalization Change for Corporations from Countries such as India, China, Indonesia, Brazil, and Turkey if the Growth Opportunities..." in (Vol. 90, July-August 2012, No. 7-8, pp. 141) **[4513]**, **[18122]**, **[27585]**
"Growth in Sleepy Perryville Hinges on Success of New Casino" in Baltimore Business Journal (Vol. 28, November 19, 2010, No. 28, pp. 1) **[7290]**, **[33370]**
Growthink (GT) **[37675]**
GrowthPoint Technology Partners **[37676]**
GrowthWorks **[46697]**
Grubhub Inc. **[6937]**
Grundy Center Chamber of Commerce and Development **[39750]**
Gruver Chamber of Commerce **[45195]**
GSA Business **[44618]**
GSA Business Report **[44619]**
GSC Associates Inc. **[31004]**
GSD Capital, LLC **[45661]**
"GSK Creating Pathways From Academia to Industry" in Philadelphia Business Journal (Vol. 33, March 7, 2014, No. 4, pp. 8) **[5161]**, **[21533]**, **[30735]**, **[30919]**, **[31326]**, **[31978]**, **[32768]**
GSR Ventures **[37384]**
GSVlabs [37607]
GTCR L.L.C. **[39358]**
"GTI Licenses TMC to Cannon Boiler Works" in Contractor (Vol. 56, December 2009, No. 12, pp. 6) **[27881]**, **[29240]**
Guam Chamber of Commerce (GCC) **[27413]**, **[46630]**
Guam Small Business Development Center **[46628]**
Guardsman Furniture Professionals **[7250]**
Guerrilla Marketing Goes Green: Winning Strategies to Improve Your Profits and Your Planet **[5641]**, **[5914]**, **[18123]**, **[20435]**, **[23251]**, **[23501]**, **[29814]**
"Guidance On Career Guidance for Offender Reentry" in Occupational Outlook Quarterly (Vol. 54, Fall 2010, No. 3, pp. 24) **[26568]**, **[26953]**
Guide **[40589]**
The Guide **[38423]**
Guide Book **[40284]**
A Guide to Business Ethics: How to Navigate Ethical Issues in Small Business **[23502]**
A Guide to College Programs in Hospitality and Tourism [15743]
A Guide to College Programs in Hospitality and Tourism--A Directory of CHRIE Member Colleges and Universities [15743]
A Guide to College Programs in Hospitality, Tourism, & Culinary Arts **[15743]**
"A Guide to Different Heat Types in Roasting Equipment" in Perfect Daily Grind (October 4, 2019) **[7555]**
"Guide to Estate Planning for Small Businesses" in Phillips & Blow Law website **[6040]**
A Guide to Federal Sector Equal Employment Opportunity (EEO) Law and Practice **[18787]**
Guide to Government **[42612]**
The Guide to Graduate Environmental Programs **[5513]**
Guide to Hospitality and Tourism Education: A Directory of CHRIE Member Colleges and Universities [15743]
"A Guide to Managing Estate Sale Company Reviews" in EstateSales.org Blog **[6071]**
Guide to Marketing Your Plumbing Business **[12634]**
A Guide to Merit Systems Protection Board (MSPB) Law and Practice **[18788]**
Guide to the Palm Beaches **[38424]**
A Guide to the Project Management Body of Knowledge **[24675]**, **[28615]**
Guide to the Rio Grande Valley **[45196]**
Guide to Somerset County **[44241]**
"A Guide to Starting a Driveway Paving Business" in Home Business (September 27, 2022) **[4108]**, **[26780]**
"Guide to Starting a Flower Delivery Business" in Home Business (Home Business (September 6, 2022) **[6857]**, **[26781]**
"A Guide to Starting a Food Truck Business" in Home Business (June 30, 2022) **[6983]**, **[26782]**
"Guide to Starting Your Own Roofing Business" in Home Business (May 24, 2022) **[14326]**, **[26783]**
The Guide to a Successful Clean Eating Food Delivery Service **[6881]**
A Guide to Trademarks and Brand Names for the Decorating Products Industry [11861], [11883]
Guide to Venture Capital & Private Equity Firms **[33569]**
Guild of American Papercutters (GAP) **[4580]**
Guild of Book Workers (GBW) **[1718]**, **[1731]**
Guild of Book Workers Newsletter **[1688]**, **[1726]**, **[2484]**, **[12767]**
Guild of BookWorkers--Study Opportunities List **[1724]**
Guild of Professional Paperhangers [11875]
Guild Publishing **[46587]**
Guilderland Chamber of Commerce (GCC) **[42613]**
Guilford Chamber of Commerce [38073]
"Guilford County Introduces $20 Million Grant Program for Small Businesses" in Triad Business Journal (June 4, 2020) **[35475]**
Guitar Stores Industry in the US - Market Research Report **[11268]**
Gulf Beaches on Sand Key Chamber of Commerce [38507]
Gulf Breeze Area Chamber of Commerce **[38425]**
Gulf County Chamber of Commerce **[38426]**
Gun Owners of America (GOA) **[7828]**
Gunnison County Chamber of Commerce (GCCC) **[37865]**
Guns & Ammo **[854]**
Guntersville Chamber of Commerce [36130]
Gustine Chamber of Commerce **[36932]**
Guthrie Center Chamber of Commerce (GCCC) **[39751]**
Guthrie Chamber of Commerce **[43767]**
Guthrie Theater Foundation - Staff Reference Library **[4562]**
The Gutter Guys **[29472]**, **[33320]**
Guysborough Historical Society **[7416]**
GV Management Company, LLC **[35281]**, **[37739]**
Gwinnett Chamber of Commerce **[38748]**
"Gym Insurance: Cost, Coverage & Providers" in Fit Small Business (September 15, 2020) **[12416]**
Gymboree Play & Music **[2898]**

H

"Haagen-Dazs Recruits Shop Owners through Facebook" in Ice Cream Reporter (Vol. 23, November 20, 2010, No. 12, pp. 1) **[8569]**, **[21867]**, **[24366]**
Haas Wheat & Partners L.P. **[31612]**
Habersham County Chamber of Commerce **[38749]**
"Habitat, Home Depot Expand Building Program" in Contractor (Vol. 56, September 2009, No. 9, pp. 16) **[4109]**, **[5642]**, **[18124]**, **[23252]**
Hacienda Business Park Owners Association **[33460]**
HackCville [45950]
Hackensack Chamber of Commerce [42139]
Hackensack Regional Chamber of Commerce (HRCC) **[42139]**
Hackers/Founders Utah **[45693]**
Hackettstown Area Living Magazine **[42140]**
Haddington Ventures, L.L.C. (HV) **[45592]**
Hagerman Valley Chamber of Commerce (HVCC) **[38921]**
Hagerstown-Washington County Chamber of Commerce (HWCCC) **[40392]**
HAI Foundation [417]
HAI HELI-EXPO **[439]**
Hailey Chamber of Commerce **[38922]**
"Hailey Is Getting an Indoor Ice Rink" in Idaho Business Review (August 27, 2014) **[7117]**, **[14720]**
"Hain Celestial Acquires Greek Gods Yogurt" in Ice Cream Reporter (Vol. 23, July 20, 2010, No. 8, pp. 1) **[8023]**, **[8096]**, **[8570]**, **[9561]**, **[31327]**
Haines Chamber of Commerce **[36234]**
Haines City Chamber of Commerce [38475]
Hair & Nail Salons Industry in the US - Market Research Report **[7880]**, **[11322]**
Halcyon **[38179]**
Haleyville Area Chamber of Commerce **[36121]**
"Half of Canadian Firms to Boost Marketing Budgets" in Globe & Mail (January 22, 2007, pp. B1) **[283]**, **[29815]**, **[31867]**
"Half Empty or Half Full" in Crain's Chicago Business (Vol. 31, March 24, 2008, No. 12, pp. 4) **[8024]**, **[9562]**, **[17055]**
Half Moon Bay Coastside Chamber of Commerce and Visitors Bureau **[36933]**
"Half a World Away" in Tampa Bay Business Journal (Vol. 30, December 4, 2009, No. 50, pp. 1) **[10603]**, **[15863]**, **[24997]**, **[25138]**, **[27586]**, **[35059]**
Haliburton County Development Corp. (HCDC) **[46823]**
Halifax County Chamber of Commerce **[45870]**
Hall Center for Law and Health [26121]
Hallden Business Services **[16881]**
Hallettsville Chamber of Commerce **[45197]**
Hallettsville Chamber of Commerce and Agriculture [45197]
Hallmark Cards, Inc. **[3368]**, **[7487]**, **[7707]**
Halloween Express **[4558]**
"Halloween Pop-Up Stores, Explained" in Vox (October 29, 2018) **[4553]**
"Halls Give Hospital Drive $11 Million Infusion" in The Business Journal-Serving Metropolitan Kansas City (Vol. 26, July 18, 2008) **[7478]**, **[7702]**, **[18125]**, **[22623]**, **[23622]**, **[25791]**, **[28616]**, **[29241]**, **[34324]**
The Halo Effect: And the Eight Other Business Delusions That Deceive Managers **[22624]**, **[28617]**
Halstead Architects **[935]**
Halstead Chamber of Commerce (HCC) **[39898]**
Hamburg Chamber of Commerce [42678]
Hamburger Mary's Bar & Grille **[14178]**
Hamden Business Incubator **[38109]**
Hamden Regional Chamber of Commerce **[38056]**
Hamilton Chamber of Commerce (HCC) **[45198]**

3248 Small Business Sourcebook • 42nd Edition

Hamilton County Business Center [43644]
Hamilton County Business Development Center [44847]
Hamilton County Chamber of Commerce [39191]
Hamilton County Development Co. [43644]
The Hamilton Mill (HM) [43667]
Hamilton/Morrisville Tribune [12003]
Hamilton North Chamber of Commerce [39589]
Hamilton Technology Centre (HTC) [46824]
Hammon Chamber of Commerce [39221], [39570]
Hammond INnovation Center (HIC) [39640]
Hammonton Information Guide [42141]
Hampshire Area Chamber of Commerce [39192]
Hampshire Chamber of Commerce [39192]
Hampshire County Chamber of Commerce [46270]
Hampton Area Chamber of Commerce (HACC) [42000]
Hampton Bays Chamber of Commerce (HBCC) [42614]
Hampton County Chamber of Commerce [44563]
Hampton Roads Chamber of Commerce [45871]
Hampton Roads Chamber of Commerce - Headquarters [45871]
Hampton Roads Small Business Development Center (SBDC) [45771]
Hampton Roads Small Business Development Center Eastern Shore [45772]
Hampton Roads Small Business Development Center Franklin [45773]
Hampton Roads Small Business Development Center Smithfield [45774]
Hampton Roads Small Business Development Center Suffolk [45775]
Hampton Roads Small Business Development Center Williamsburg [45776]
Hampton Roads Virginia Procurement Technical Assistance Center [45930]
Hampton University Business Incubator [45954]
Hana Kitchens (HK) [38887]
HanaHaus [37578]
Hancock County Chamber of Commerce [40051]
Hancock County Chamber of Commerce (HCCC) [41403]
Hancock & Estabrook Law Library [6058]
Hand and Stone Massage and Facial Spa [10782]
Handbag, Luggage & Accessory Stores Industry in the US - Market Research Report [10368]
"Handbag Revenues Climbing Back to Pre-pandemic Times" in WWD (October 6, 2021) [10365]
Handbook of Business Finance [16715]
Handbook of Research on Business Social Networking: Organizational, Managerial, and Technological Dimensions [18856]
Handbook of Research on E-Business Standards and Protocols: Documents, Data and Advanced Web Technologies [22030]
"Handbook of Research on Marketing and Social Corporate Responsibility" [29816], [34325]
Handbook of Research in Mobile Business: Technical, Methodological, and Social Perspectives [30498]
Handbook of Research on Serious Games as Educational, Business and Research Tools [21737]
Handbook of Research on Virtual Workplaces and the New Nature of Business Practices [24595]
Handcrafted Soap & Cosmetic Guild Conference [4538]
Handgun Control, Inc. [7840]
Handle: The Uncut Pitch [34616]
"Handleman Liquidation Leaves Questions For Shareholders" in Crain's Detroit Business (Vol. 24, October 6, 2008, No. 40, pp. 4) [6440], [9563], [11264], [18967], [19524], [20626], [23921]
The Handler Group Inc. [17808], [17884], [30199]
"H&M Offers a Dress for Less" in Canadian Business (Vol. 83, September 14, 2010, No. 15, pp. 20) [3029], [3120], [6133], [20024], [20930], [27587], [29242], [32166], [34043]
Handmade Business [4634]
Handmade Business--Show List [4594], [4658]
"H&R Block Launches One-of-a-Kind Tax Preparation Solution: Block Live" in Investment Weekly News (February 4, 2012, pp. 384) [15386], [23004]
Hands-On Business and Report Writing: The Art of Persuasion (Onsite) [17848]
Hands-On PLCs: Operation, Installation, Maintenance and Troubleshooting [5360]
Hands-On UNIX and Linux Tools and Utilities (Onsite) [21388]
HandsDown: The Accelerator Pitch [35419]
Handweavers Guild of America, Inc. (HGA) [4581]
Handwriting Analysis Plain & Simple: The Only Book You'll Ever Need [7905]
Handwriting Psychology: Personality Reflected in Handwriting [7906]
Handyman Connection [4349], [5402], [12685]
Handyman-Network Franchise Systems LLC [2402]
Handypro [4416]

Hanford-Freund & Co. [12916]
Hangtown Electric, Inc. [5403]
Hannacroix Creek Books Inc. [38118]
Hannah Grimes Center for Entrepreneurship [42026]
Hannibal Area Chamber of Commerce [41571]
Hannibal Chamber of Commerce [41571]
Hannoush Jewelers, Inc. [9990]
Hanover Area Chamber of Commerce (HACC) [42001], [44242]
Hanover Association of Business and Chamber of Commerce--Business Directory [45981]
Hanover Association of Businesses and Chamber of Commerce [45872]
Hanover Chamber of Commerce [40590]
Hansen Honey Farm LLC [1501]
"Hansen Mechanical Performs Boiler Upgrade at Zoo" in Contractor (Vol. 57, February 2010, No. 2, pp. 7) [5375], [14617], [34326]
"Hanson's to Widen Marketing Window; Company Plans Mall Kiosks, to Attend Events" in Crain's Detroit Business (Vol. 28, May 28, 2012, No. 22, pp. 3) [4110], [7492], [10025], [14327], [29817]
The Haoagen-Dazs Shoppe Company Inc. [8619]
Happy About Joint-Venturing: The 8 Key Critical Factors of Success [22625], [24676], [31328]
Happy & Healthy Products, Inc. (H&H) [8620]
Happy Joe's Pizza and Ice Cream [8621], [12556]
Happy Tails Dog Spa [12118]
"Happy Trails: RV Franchiser Gives Road Traveling Enthusiasts a Lift" in Black Enterprise (Vol. 38, July 2008, No. 12, pp. 47) [15744], [15995], [18126], [24367], [29818], [30353]
Harassment Prevention and Appropriate Behaviors in the Workplace (Onsite) [18487], [20559]
Harbert Management Corp. (HMC) [36163]
Harbert Venture Partners L.L.C. [45922]
Harbinger Ventures [37968]
Harbor Beach Chamber of Commerce [40932]
Harbor City Chamber of Commerce [37002]
Harbor City/Harbor Gateway Chamber of Commerce [37002]
Harbor Country Chamber of Commerce [40933]
Harbor Country Guide [40934]
The Harbor Entrepreneur Center [44606]
Harbor Insider [46109]
Harbor Light Capital Partners, LLC (HLCP) [42020]
Harbor Springs Area Chamber of Commerce (HSCC) [40935]
HarbourVest Partners, LLC [40694]
"The Hard Thing About Hard Things: Building a Business When There Are No Easy Answers" [9564], [19667], [23922], [26295], [28246], [33017]
"Hard Times Are 'In the Rearview Mirror' for Local Construction Industry" in San Antonio Business Journal (Vol. 28, March 14, 2014, No. 5, pp. 10) [4111], [18127]
"Hard-To-Read Fonts Promote Better Recall" in Harvard Business Review (Vol. 90, April 2012, No. 4, pp. 32) [1658], [12739]
Hardee County Chamber of Commerce (HCCC) [38427]
Hardee's Restaurants L.L.C. [14179]
Hardeman County Chamber of Commerce [44755]
HARDI Annual Conference [536]
Hardin Area Chamber of Commerce and Agriculture [41771]
Hardin County Chamber and Business Alliance (HCCBA) [43487]
Hardin County Chamber of Commerce (HCCC) [40052]
Hardin-Simmons University (HSU) - Rupert and Pauline Richardson Library [998]
Hardin-Simmons University - Smith Music Library [11222], [11298]
Hardware Manufacturers Statistical Association [7910]
Hardware Stores Industry in the US - Market Research Report [7926]
Hardwick Area Chamber of Commerce [45726]
Hardwood Distributor's Association (HDA) [10377]
Hardwood Manufacturers Association (HMA) [10378]
Hardwood Plywood Institute [10376], [10415]
Hardwood Plywood Manufacturers Association [10376], [10415]
Hardwood Plywood and Veneer Association [10376], [10415]
Hardy Stevenson and Associates Ltd. [2271], [3457]
Harford County Chamber of Commerce (HCCC) [40393]
Harford County Maryland Small Business Development Center [40342]
Harker Heights Chamber of Commerce [45199]
Harlem Biospace (Hb) [42882]
Harlem Capital Partners (HCP) [30270], [35282], [43021]
"Harleysville Eyes Growth After Nationwide Deal" in Philadelphia Business Journal (Vol. 30, October 7, 2011, No. 34, pp. 1) [8913], [9565], [18128], [19668], [27270], [31329], [33018]

Harlingen Area Chamber of Commerce (HACC) [45200]
Harlingen Economic Development Corp. [45522]
Harmonica Happenings [11275]
Harmony [5489]
Harmony Foundation [5489]
Harmony's Community Kitchen [41352]
"Harness the Internet to Boost Equipment Sales" in Indoor Comfort Marketing (Vol. 70, July 2011, No. 7, pp. 24) [488], [21868], [29819], [32537]
Harness Racing Museum and Hall of Fame [8332]
Harnessing Gen Z in the Workplace: 5 Strategies for Impact Leaders [22298]
Harney County Chamber of Commerce (HCCC) [43979]
Harold L. Kestenbaum, Esq. [18753]
Harold L. Kestenbaum P.C. (HLK) [10694], [24483]
Harper County Genealogical Society Library (HCGS) [7417]
"Harpoon Brewery Wins Boston Green Business Award for Sustainability and EnerNOC Energy Management Programs" in Investment Weekly News (May 12, 2012, No. 543) [1916], [5643], [5915], [23253]
"Harrah's Tunica Shutting Down In June" in Memphis Business Journal (No. 35, March 28, 2014, No. 51, pp. 3) [7291], [8397]
Harris County Chamber of Commerce [38750]
Harris and Harris Group Inc. [42203]
Harris Research Inc. (HRI) [16237]
"The Harris Teeter Grocery Chain Has Started a New Ice Cream Club for Shoppers" in Ice Cream Reporter (Vol. 21, July 20, 2008) [7743], [8571], [29820]
Harrisburg Area Chamber of Commerce [44243]
Harrisburg Regional Chamber of Commerce [44244]
Harrisburg Regional Chamber of Commerce & CREDC (HACC) [44243]
Harrisburg Regional Chamber & CREDC [44244]
Harrison Area Chamber of Commerce (HCC) [40936]
Harrison Chamber of Commerce (HCC) [36469]
Harrison County Chamber of Commerce (HCCC) [46271]
Harrisonburg-Rockingham Chamber of Commerce (HRCC) [45873]
Harrisonville Area Chamber of Commerce (HACC) [41572]
Hart County Chamber of Commerce [38751], [40053]
Hart - Silver Lake Mears Chamber of Commerce [41010]
Hartford Area Chamber of Commerce (HACC) [44649], [45725]
Hartford Despatch International [19214]
The Hartford Financial Services Group Loss Control Library [35974]
Hartington Area Chamber of Commerce [41860]
Hartland Area Chamber of Commerce [46428]
Hartley Chamber of Commerce [39752]
Hartness Library System [17211]
Hartselle Area Chamber of Commerce [36122]
Hartselle Chamber of Commerce [36122]
Hartshorne Chamber of Commerce [43768]
Hartsville - Trousdale County Chamber of Commerce [44756]
Harvard Area Chamber of Commerce [39193]
Harvard Business Review (HBR) [24864]
Harvard University - A. Alfred Taubman Center for State and Local Government [31726]
Harvard University - Botany Libraries [7669]
Harvard University - Harvard Negotiation Project (HNP) [10809]
Harvard University - John F. Kennedy School of Government - Belfer Center for Science and International Affairs - Environment and Natural Resources Program (ENRP) [5787]
Harvard University - Joint Center for Housing Studies (JCHS) [779]
Harvard University - School of Medicine - Massachusetts Eye and Ear Library [10965]
"Harvest Cafe Builds Strong Following for Healthy Foodservice" in Supermarket News (September 5, 2019) [8025]
Harvest Partners Inc. [42754]
"Harvesting the Royal Oak" in Barron's (Vol. 92, September 17, 2012, No. 38, pp. 18) [9976], [29243]
Harvey A. Meier Co. (HAM) [2272], [10534], [20194], [27140]
Harvey Area Chamber of Commerce (HACC) [39194]
"Harvey Mackay: How to Stop the Fear of Success From Holding You Back" in South Florida Business Journal (Vol. 34, May 30, 2014, No. 45, pp. 20) [22626]
Harvey's [14180]
Harwich Chamber of Commerce (HCC) [40591]
The Harwood Institute for Public Innovation [12955]
"Has Daylight Savings Time Fuelled Gasoline Consumption?" in Globe & Mail (April 18, 2007, pp. B1) [20931], [25364]
"Has Microsoft Found a Way to Get at Yahoo?" in Advertising Age (Vol. 79, July 7, 2008, No. 26, pp. 4) [6441], [9153], [9566], [16425], [18968], [23923], [26296], [31330]

Haskell **Master Index**

Haskell Chamber of Commerce **[45201]**
The Hassayampa Alert **[36340]**
"Hasslochers Welcome Home a San Antonio Tradition" in San Antonio Business Journal (Vol. 28, July 25, 2014, No. 24, pp. 8) **[13945]**, **[20436]**
Hastings Area Chamber of Commerce (HACC) **[41861]**
Hastings Area Chamber of Commerce and Tourism Bureau **[41241]**
Hastings Business Law Journal [18782]
Hatch **[45955]**
Hatch Properierty Ltd. **[4319]**
"HatchedIt.com Social Organizer for Families Launches New Phone App at BlogHer '12" in PR Newswire (August 3, 2012) **[2746]**, **[12831]**, **[33858]**
The Hatchery **[42883]**
"Hatching Twitter: A True Story of Money, Power, Friendship, and Betrayal" **[21869]**, **[22627]**, **[31331]**, **[31763]**
Hatfield Chamber of Commerce **[44245]**
Hatteras Venture Partners **[43222]**
Havana Area Chamber of Commerce **[39195]**
"Have a Seasonal Business? 4 Tips for Year-Round Profitability" in Business News Daily (Feb. 14, 2022) **[32951]**
Havelock Chamber of Commerce **[43144]**
Haviland Collectors International Foundation (HCIF) **[3265]**
"Having a Head for Security Means Being In the Know: Security Print Explored" in Print Week (July 4, 2012) **[12740]**, **[14418]**
Havre Area Chamber of Commerce (HACC) **[41772]**
Havre de Grace Chamber of Commerce **[40394]**
Havre Small Business Development Center (SBDC) **[41721]**
Hawaii Angels **[38897]**
Hawaii Buildings, Facilities, and Property Management Expo **[2082]**, **[38895]**
Hawaii Business **[38896]**
Hawaii Department of Business, Economic Development, and Tourism - Hawaii State Data Center **[47412]**
Hawaii Department of Business, Economic Development, and Tourism - Research and Economic Analysis Div. (READ) **[21276]**, **[47413]**
Hawaii Department of Business, Economic Development and Tourism - Strategic Marketing & Support **[38867]**
Hawaii Department of Planning and Economic Development [21276], [47413]
Hawaii Island Chamber of Commerce (HICC) **[38872]**
Hawaii Island Portuguese Chamber of Commerce (HIPCC) **[38873]**
Hawaii Korean Chamber of Commerce (HKCC) **[38874]**
"Hawaii Rides Retail Strength Into New Year" in Pacific Business News (Vol. 51, January 17, 2014, No. 48, pp. 3) **[13208]**, **[13465]**, **[32167]**
Hawaii SBDc - O'ahu **[38862]**
Hawaii Senate Committee on Commerce and Consumer Protection [38893]
Hawaii Senate Committee on Water and Land [38894]
Hawaii Senate Consumer Protection Committee [38893]
Hawaii Senate Water and Land Use Planning Committee [38894]
Hawaii Small Business Development Center Lead Office **[38863]**
Hawaii State Department of Health - Environmental Health Administration - Environmental Management Division (EMD) **[46995]**
Hawaii State Legislature - House Committee on Labor & Public Employment **[38892]**
Hawaii State Legislature - Senate Committee on Commerce, Consumer Protection, and Health **[38893]**
Hawaii State Legislature - Senate Committee on Water, Land, and Agriculture **[38894]**
Hawaii Technology Development Corporation (HDTC) **[38888]**
"The Hawaiian Philosophy Making Craft Beer More Sustainable" in Vinepair (October 3, 2019) **[1917]**
Hawarden Area Partnership for Progress [39753]
Hawarden Chamber and Economic Development Inc. **[39753]**
Hawkins Area Chamber of Commerce **[45202]**
Hawkinsville-Pulaski Chamber of Commerce [38752]
Hawkinsville-Pulaski County Chamber of Commerce **[38752]**
Hawthorne Area Chamber of Commerce **[38428]**
Hawthorne Chamber of Commerce (HCC) **[42142]**
HAX Boost **[37579]**
Haxtun Chamber of Commerce **[37866]**
"Hayes Lemmerz Reports Some Good News Despite Losses" in Crain's Detroit Business (Vol. 24, April 14, 2008, No. 15, pp. 4) **[18129]**, **[28140]**, **[29244]**
Haynes Associates L.L.C. **[22356]**, **[34684]**
Hays Area Chamber of Commerce **[39899]**
Haystack Mountain School of Crafts Library **[4641]**, **[4694]**, **[11487]**
Haysville Chamber of Commerce **[39900]**
Hayward Area Chamber of Commerce (HACC) **[46429]**
Haywood County Chamber of Commerce **[43145]**
Hazardous Materials Advisory Committee [7940]
Hazardous Materials Advisory Council [7940]
Hazardous Waste Management: The Complete Course **[23067]**, **[25190]**
Hazardous Waste Management: The Complete Course (Onsite) **[25191]**
"Hazardous Waste Management - Types, Regulations, & How Different Businesses Can Handle It" in OH&S (August 31, 2020) **[7952]**
Hazelden Betty Ford Foundation **[34689]**
Hazelden Foundation [34689]
Hazen Chamber of Commerce **[43299]**
Haztrain Inc. **[7974]**
"HBC Enlists IBM to Help Dress Up Its On-Line Shopping" in Globe & Mail (February 7, 2006, pp. B3) **[9154]**, **[28618]**, **[29821]**, **[32168]**
"HBC Sells Credit Card Division" in Globe & Mail (February 8, 2006, pp. B1) **[20294]**, **[31332]**
HBK Incubates (HBK) **[42884]**
"HBR Case Study: Play It Safe or Take a Stand?" in Harvard Business Review (Vol. 88, November 2010, No. 11, pp. 139) **[28619]**, **[30736]**, **[35791]**
"HBR Case Study: Setting Up Shop in a Political Hot Spot" in Harvard Business Review (Vol. 88, October 2010, No. 10, pp. 141) **[25365]**, **[27588]**
"HBR Case Study: When the Longtime Star Fades" in Harvard Business Review (Vol. 88, September 2010, No. 9, pp. 117) **[13654]**, **[22166]**, **[28620]**
HBR Ideacast: A Roadmap for Today's Entrepreneurs **[22894]**
HBR Ideacast: Algorithms Won't Solve All Your Pricing Problems **[31663]**
HBR Ideacast: An Astronaut's Advice on High-Stakes Collaboration **[28922]**
HBR Ideacast: Disruption Isn't the Only Path to Innovation **[18440]**
HBR Ideacast: Fast Casual Food Pioneer Ron Shaich Explains How to Find a Niche - and then Scale **[14059]**
HBR Ideacast: Here's How Managers Can Rediscover Their Joy at Work **[28923]**
HBR Ideacast: Lessons from a Turnaround Expert **[28924]**
HBR Ideacast: People with Disabilities Are an Untapped Talent Pool **[26713]**
HBR Ideacast: Rethinking Growth at All Costs **[18441]**
HBR Ideacast: Tech at Work: How to Get the Most Out of Digital Collaboration Tools **[32978]**
HBR Ideacast: The Growing "Do Good" Economy **[34451]**
HBR Ideacast: The Ins and Outs of the Influencer Industry **[29540]**
HBR Ideacast: The Real Reasons Employees Quit - and How to Retain Them **[27101]**
HBR Ideacast: The VC Fund Closing Equity Gaps - and Making Money **[35420]**
HBR Ideacast: What Venture Capitalists Can Teach Companies about Decision-Making **[32398]**
HBR Ideacast: Why Entrepreneurs Don't Need Venture Capital to Scale **[34617]**
HBR Ideacast: Why Some Startups Fail to Scale **[34618]**
HBR Ideacast: Why You Need to Stress Test Your Strategies (and Tactics) **[28925]**
HBR Ideacast: You're Overlooking a Source of Diversity: Age **[27102]**
"The HBR Interview: "We Had to Own the Mistakes"" in Harvard Business Review (Vol. 88, July-August 2010, No. 7-8, pp. 108) **[7556]**, **[8656]**, **[12932]**, **[19357]**, **[20437]**, **[27589]**, **[31764]**, **[31868]**
"HBSDealer Stock Watch: In the FAST Lane" in Chain Store Age (Vol. 85, November 2009, No. 11, pp. 44) **[4438]**, **[26297]**
HD [8475], [9059], [14044]
HDR Inc. **[9076]**
"He Fixes the Cracked Spines of Books, Without an Understudy" in The New York Times (January 6, 2017) **[1725]**
"Headington Lures High-End Retailers to Downtown Dallas" in Dallas Business Journal (Vol. 35, July 6, 2012, No. 43, pp. 1) **[8398]**, **[32169]**
Headland Area Chamber of Commerce (HCC) **[36123]**
Headline **[37385]**
Headquarters for Ghost Investigations [11340]
"Headwinds From the New Sod Slow Aer Lingus" in Barron's (Vol. 88, March 10, 2008, No. 10, pp. M6) **[284]**, **[6442]**, **[8720]**, **[9567]**, **[20295]**, **[20932]**, **[23924]**, **[27590]**, **[29822]**, **[33169]**
Healdsburg Chamber of Commerce [36934]
Healdsburg Chamber of Commerce and Visitors Bureau **[36934]**
"Healing Power from Medical Waste" in Memphis Business Journal (Vol. 33, March 30, 2012, No. 51, pp. 1) **[7953]**, [18130], [25792]
Healing Touch Professional Association (HTPA) **[11339]**
Health Affairs **[26004]**
"Health Care Briefs: Survey Says Most Approve of Donating Used Pacemakers to Medically Underserved" in Crain's Detroit Business (Vol. 25, June 1, 2009) **[10830]**, **[10950]**, **[13716]**, **[25793]**, **[34327]**
"Health Care of the Future" in Business Journal Serving Greater Tampa Bay (Vol. 30, November 19, 2010, No. 48, pp. 1) **[8914]**, **[24998]**, **[25366]**, **[25794]**, **[27271]**, **[31333]**
"Health-Care Highway" in Saint Louis Business Journal (Vol. 32, October 14, 2011, No. 7, pp. 1) **[4112]**, **[21870]**, **[25795]**
"Health care: Medicare Inc." in Canadian Business (Vol. 80, October 8, 2007, No. 20, pp. 160) **[19855]**, **[20933]**, **[25796]**
Health Care for Women International: Official Journal of the International Council on Women's Health Issues **[26005]**
"Health Centers Plan Expansion: $3M from D.C. Expected; Uninsured a Target" in Crain's Detroit Business (Vol. 25, June 15, 2009, No. 24, pp. 3) **[4113]**, **[8915]**, **[18131]**, **[24999]**, **[25797]**, **[27272]**
"Health and the City: How Close Is Too Close in Trademarks?" in Legal Zoom (March 27, 2023) **[27882]**
"Health Clinic Expansion Fuels Debate Over Care In Massachusetts" in Boston Business Journal (Vol. 34, June 27, 2014, No. 21, pp. 9) **[5162]**, **[19856]**, **[25798]**, **[32170]**
Health Fitness Corp. (HF) **[28995]**
Health Food & Beverage Group [8067]
"Health Giants Throw Support Behind Sports Centers" in Pittsburgh Business Times (Vol. 34, July 25, 2014, No. 1, pp. 8) **[15157]**, **[25799]**
Health and Healing Wisdom; PPNF [8083], [11617]
Health Industries Association [10817], [10944]
Health Industry Distributors Association (HIDA) **[10820]**, **[11500]**
Health Industry Manufacturers Association [10817], [10944]
Health Information Resource Center (HIRC) **[7997]**, **[25672]**
Health Insurance Specialists Inc. (HISI) **[17401]**, **[27373]**
"Health IT Regulations Generate Static Among Providers" in Philadelphia Business Journal (Vol. 28, January 29, 2010, No. 50, pp. 1) **[3506]**, **[3623]**, **[8916]**, **[25367]**, **[25800]**, **[27273]**
The Health Lab **[25698]**
Health Management Systems Inc. **[3807]**
Health and Medical Care Archive **[8294]**
Health Policy Center [26107]
Health Progress **[26006]**
"Health Reform Could Expand HSA-Based Plans" in Workforce Management (Vol. 88, December 14, 2009, No. 13, pp. 6) **[8917]**, **[25368]**, **[25801]**, **[27274]**
"Health Reform: How to Make it Cheaper" in Business Courier (Vol. 26, December 11, 2009, No. 33, pp. 1) **[8918]**, **[25369]**, **[25802]**, **[27275]**
Health Research and Educational Trust (HRET) **[26118]**
Health Research and Educational Trust of New Jersey (HRET) **[26119]**
Health Resources and Services Administration - Grants and Procurement Management Div. - Contracts Policies and Operations **[47634]**
Health and Safety Science Abstracts **[26007]**
"Health Science Center's Capital Campaign Will Boost Local Research" in San Antonio Business Journal (Vol. 28, March 14, 2014, No. 5, pp. 8) **[7118]**, **[21534]**, **[25803]**, **[31979]**, **[32769]**
Health Science: Living Well Into the Future **[26008]**
Health Services Research and Development Center [26123]
Health Systems Research Inc. [41074]
Health & Wellness InSite **[195]**, **[11537]**, **[11602]**, **[21739]**, **[26099]**, **[27977]**
Health Wildcatters (HW) **[45523]**
Healthbox L.L.C. **[39447]**
Healthcare Businesswomen's Association (HBA) **[35622]**
Healthcare Distribution Alliance (HDA) **[5138]**
Healthcare Distribution Management Association [5138]
Healthcare Executive **[26009]**
"Healthcare Facilities Increasingly Embracing Dynamic Glass to Benefit Patients" in Ecology, Environment & Conservation Business (May 24, 2014) **[892]**, **[4114]**, **[7493]**, **[11638]**, **[25804]**
Healthcare Financial Management Association (HFMA) **[30]**, **[23698]**
Healthcare Management Forum **[25673]**
Healthcare Ventures L.L.C. / Healthcare Investments **[40695]**
HealthCareCAN **[25674]**
HealthChoice **[17402]**
"Healthful, Organic Food is the Name of the Game at Renee's" in AZ Daily Star (May 10, 2012) **[8097]**, **[13946]**, **[23623]**

3250 **Small Business Sourcebook • 42nd Edition**

Healthscope Inc. [19136]
"Healthy Dose of New Vitality" in Business Courier (Vol. 24, February 28, 2008, No. 47, pp. 1) [5163], [18132], [25805]
"Healthy Fast Food Acquires Rights to U-Swirl Yogurt" in Ice Cream Reporter (Vol. 21, October 20, 2008, No. 11, pp. 5) [8026], [8098], [8572], [31334]
Healthy Food Factory [38570]
"Healthy Foods Drive Dining Choices" in National Restaurant Association (July 25, 2017) [8099], [23254]
"Healthy Start for Medical Kiosks; Lions Kick in $20K" in Crain's Detroit Business" (Vol. 28, June 11, 2012, No. 24, pp. 18) [7119], [10026], [15158], [21535], [25806]
"Healthy Workers = A Healthy Company" in Minority Business Entrepreneur (Vol. 39, Fall, 2022, No. 4, pp. 18-19) [22167]
HEAR Center [8131]
Hearing Aid Industry Conference [8132], [10821]
"Hearing Damage Leads to Settlement" in Register-Guard (August 13, 2011) [12044], [18595], [25807]
Hearing Education Through Auditory Research Foundation [8131]
Hearing Industries Association (HIA) [8132], [10821]
Hearne Chamber of Commerce [45203]
Heart: Building a Great Brand in the Digital Age [2189], [4115], [9039], [17056], [22628], [33170]
Heart of Catskill Association - Catskill Chamber of Commerce [42609]
"The Heart of Health Village: innovation Is Key, and to Get It, Florida Hospital Is Wooing Disruptors, Millenials" in Orlando Business Journal (Vol. 30, May 16, 2014, No. 47, pp. 4) [10919], [25808], [31980], [32770]
"Heart Hospitals Ranked for Mortality Rates" in Philadelphia Business Journal (Vol. 30, September 2, 2011, No. 29, pp. 1) [10831], [25000], [25809]
Heart and Lung: The Journal of Cardiopulmonary and Acute Care [26010]
Heart of Oklahoma Chamber of Commerce [43769]
"A Heart for Software; Led by Its Upbeat CEO, Menlo Spreads Joy of Technology" in Crain's Detroit Business (Vol. 30, October 13, 2014, No. 41, pp. 1) [14785], [22168], [28621], [33859]
Heart of the Valley Chamber of Commerce [46430]
Heart of Vermont Chamber of Commerce (HVCC) [45726]
The Heartbeat [45204]
"Heartbleed Headache Will Pound For Years" in Puget Sound Business Journal (Vol. 34, April 18, 2014, No. 53, pp. 7) [3709], [14419], [14786]
Heartland Apicultural Society (HAS) [1438]
Heartland Institute (HI) [5771], [26120]
Heartland Real Estate Business [13347]
Heartland Travel Showcase [15775]
HeartMath Institute (HMI) [30506]
"Heat Brings Out Flavor, Not Visitors to Missouri Wineries" in Saint Louis Business Journal (Vol. 31, August 12, 2011, No. 51, pp. 1) [15013]
"The Heat Is On" in Crain's Chicago Business (Vol. 31, April 28, 2008, No. 17, pp. 4) [6443], [9568], [23925], [31335], [33171]
Heating & Air-Conditioning Contractors Industry in the US - Market Research Report [527]
Heating and Piping and Air Conditioning Contractors National Association [459]
Heating/Piping/Air Conditioning Engineering: The Magazine of Mechanical Systems Engineering (HPAC) (HPAC) [530]
Heating and Piping Contractors National Association [459]
Heating, Refrigeration and Air Conditioning Institute of Canada (HRAI) [453]
Heavenly Gold Card [7183]
Heaven's Best Carpet & Upholstery Cleaning [16238]
Heavy Duty Distribution [14568]
"Heavy Duty: The Case Against Packing Lightly" in Crain's Chicago Business (Vol. 31, April 21, 2008, No. 16, pp. 29) [19358], [24677], [27591], [28622], [32538], [34986]
Heavy Duty Trucking (HDT) [16097]
Heavy Equipment Guide [4284], [13846]
Heber Chamber of Commerce [36341]
Heber-Overgaard Chamber of Commerce [36341]
Heber Springs Area Chamber of Commerce [36470]
Heber Springs Chamber of Commerce [36470]
Heber Valley Chamber of Commerce [45636]
Heber Valley Chamber of Commerce Member Directory [45635]
Heber Valley Chamber of Commerce and Visitor Center (HVCC) [45636]
HEC Montreal - Groupe de Recherche en Systemes d'Information (GReSI) [3798]
HEC Montreal - Information Systems Research Group [3798]

"Hedge Funds for the Average Joe" in Canadian Business (Vol. 85, August 13, 2012, No. 13, pp. 51) [6444], [9569], [23926]
"Hedge Funds Prevail In Merger" in Baltimore Business Journal (Vol. 31, March 21, 2014, No. 47, pp. 8) [3121], [9570], [31336], [32171]
Hedgewood Inc. [46790]
Heidelberg Graphics (HG) [1699], [11479], [12007]
Heights-Hillcrest Regional Chamber of Commerce (HRCC) [43488]
Helena Area Chamber of Commerce (HACC) [41773]
Helena Small Business Development Center [41722]
Helicopter Association International (HAI) [417]
Helicopter Foundation International [417]
Helix Center Biotech Incubator [41675]
Hellenic-American Chamber of Commerce (HACC) [27414]
Hellgate Press [44081]
"Hello, and Goodbye" in Entrepreneur (June 2014) [6105], [19739], [23503], [26569]
Help Business Services Inc. [30200]
Help Desk Institute (HDI) [20368]
Help-U-Sell Real Estate [13338]
"Help Wanted: 100 Hospital IT Workers" in Business Courier (Vol. 27, October 8, 2010, No. 23, pp. 1) [3507], [3624], [10969], [25001], [25810]
"Help Wanted: Only the Best Need Apply" in Pet Product News (Vol. 66, April 2012, No. 4, pp. 24) [12200], [20438], [26570]
"Helping Apple Go Wearable" in Austin Business Journal (Vol. 34, July 4, 2014, No. 20, pp. 13) [3030], [3710], [27592], [30737], [31121]
"Helping Customers Fight Pet Waste" in Pet Product News (Vol. 64, November 2010, No. 11, pp. 52) [12165], [18133], [21871], [23255], [29245], [29823], [32539], [34044]
Helping Sellers Expand Their Brands [17470]
"Helping Teenagers to Be Safer Drivers" in The New York Times (November 26, 2018) [5102]
Hemet/San Jacinto Valley Chamber of Commerce [36935]
Hemmler + Camayd Architects [936]
Hemp Connoisseur [5070]
Henderson Area Chamber of Commerce [45205]
Henderson Business Resource Center (HBRC) [41961]
Henderson Chamber of Commerce (HCC) [41938]
Henderson Chester County Chamber of Commerce [44757]
Henderson County Chamber of Commerce (HCCC) [44758]
Henderson-Vance County Chamber of Commerce [43146]
Hendersonville Area Chamber of Commerce (HACC) [44759]
The Hendersonville Information Guide [43147]
"Hennelly Aims to Increase Building Work in Great Lakes Region for Ryan Cos." in Crain's Chicago Business (Vol. 34, May 23, 2011, No. 21, pp. 6) [4116], [8657], [12933], [28623], [31869]
Henningson Engineering Company [9076]
Henrietta and Clay County Chamber of Commerce (HCCC) [45206]
Henry Area Chamber of Commerce [38753]
Henry County Chamber of Commerce [43489]
"Henry Mintzberg: Still the Zealous Skeptic and Scold" in Strategy and Leadership (Vol. 39, March-April 2011, No. 2, pp. 4) [21536], [28624], [34045]
Henryetta Chamber of Commerce [43770]
Heppner Chamber of Commerce [43980]
"Her Aim Is True" in Senior Market Advisor (Vol. 13, October 2012, No. 10, pp. 40) [6445], [9571], [35792]
Herald Business Journal (HBJ) [46237]
Herb Growing and Marketing Network (HGMN) [8150]
Herb Research Foundation (HRF) [8151], [8169]
Herb Society of America (HSA) [8152]
Herb Society of America--Business Member Directory [8154]
Herb Society of America--Membership Directory and By-laws [8154]
Hercules Chamber of Commerce [36936]
"Here Are the Data Brokers Quietly Buying and Selling Your Personal Information" in Fast Company (March 2, 2019) [8834]
"Here Are the Right Ways to Dispose of Your Spa's Hazardous Waste" in American Spa (March 25, 2019) [7867], [7954]
Here Are the Top 7 Cash Flow Mistakes That Can Cripple Your Small Business [19718]
Here is Houston [45207]
Here Is a Brilliant Startup Idea of Online Office Food Ordering & Delivery Business [6904]
"Here's How Movie Theaters Will Survive the Next 10 Years: Exhibitors Speak Out" in IndieWire (June 28, 2019) [11123]

"Here's How an Old School Arcade Survives in the 21st Century" in Vice (September 9, 2016) [581]
"Here's How You Boycott Amazon" in Puget Sound Business Journal (Vol. 35, June 13, 2014, No. 8, pp. 12) [11751], [21872], [32172], [34328]
"Here's One Market Amazon Can't Easily Crack: Car Parts" in CNN (November 29, 2018) [1102], [11752]
"Here's What the New Overtime Rule Means for Your Business" in Entrepreneur (September 7, 2016) [35476]
"Here's Why I Went Broke as a Used Car Dealer" in AutoTrader (February, 2017) [11408]
"Here's Why Just 15% of Pennsylvania Small Businesses Plan To Add Staff" in Philadelphia Business Journal (November 7, 2019) [35477]
"Here's Why Your Family's Christmas Tree Is So Expensive" in USA Today (November 30, 2018) [2941], [32952]
Heritage Corridor Business Alliance (HCBAQ) [39196]
The Heritage Foundation Asian Studies Center [8788]
Heritage Rose Foundation (HRF) [6849]
Hermann Area Chamber of Commerce (HACC) [41573]
Hermantown Chamber of Commerce [41242]
Hermiston Small Business Development Center [43911]
Hermosa Beach Chamber of Commerce [36937]
Hermosa Beach Chamber of Commerce and Visitors Bureau [36937]
Hernando Area Chamber of Commerce [41404]
Hernando Main Street Chamber of Commerce [41404]
Herndon Chamber of Commerce [45855]
Hero Certified Burgers [14181]
Heron Capital Equity Partners [39631]
Herrin Chamber of Commerce [39197]
Herscher Chamber of Commerce [39198]
"Hertz-Tesla Deal Signals Broad Shift to EVs for Rental-Car Companies" in The Wall Street Journal (November 27, 2021) [1158]
Hesston Community Chamber of Commerce [39901]
Hester Painting & Decorating [11889]
Hettinger Area Chamber of Commerce [43300]
Hewitt Architects [11651]
Hewitt Development Enterprises (HDE) [2273], [10535], [19137], [20195], [24246], [28996], [29468], [30850], [33672]
Hewlett-Packard Co. [18794]
"Hey, Bike Shops: Stop Treating Cusotmers Like Garbage" in Bicycling (June 12, 2019) [1521], [20439]
"Hey, You Can't Do That" in Green Industry Pro (Vol. 23, September 2011) [5644], [5916], [7625], [10051], [10099], [10235], [23256], [29246], [30738], [33172]
The Hezner Corp. [11652]
HHS Accelerator (HHSA) [42885]
"Hi-Fi Cocktail Bars Aren't Just for Tokyo Anymore" in Bloomberg (April 11, 2019) [1333]
Hialeah Chamber of Commerce and Industries (HCC&I) [38429]
Hibbing Area Chamber of Commerce [41243]
Hibbing Chamber of Commerce [41243]
Hickman County Chamber of Commerce [44760]
Hickory Dickory Decks (HDD) [4350]
Hickory Hills Chamber [39201]
Hickory Nut Gorge Chamber of Commerce [43148]
"Hickory Unemployment Stays Steady" in Charlotte Observer (February 2, 2007) [26571], [26954]
Hicksville Chamber of Commerce (HCC) [42615]
"The Hidden Advantages of Quiet Bosses" in Harvard Business Review (Vol. 88, December 2010, No. 12, pp. 28) [22169], [28625], [31981]
H.I.G. Biohealth Partners [38617]
"H.I.G. Capital Announces Acquisition of Next Generation Vending" in Benzinga.com (October 29, 2011) [6446], [9572], [16256], [33173]
Higginsville Chamber of Commerce (HCC) [41574]
"High Anxiety" in Canadian Business (Vol. 80, November 19, 2007, No. 23, pp. 11) [20025], [20934], [32173]
High County Venture, LLC (HCV) [37922]
High Desert Hispanic Chamber of Commerce (HDHCC) [36938]
"High-End Blunders" in Crain's Chicago Business (Vol. 31, April 21, 2008, No. 16, pp. 54) [13209], [13466], [20935]
"High Energy: Gaurdie Banister Joins Aera As President and CEO" in Black Enterprise (Vol. 38, July 2008, No. 12, pp. 30) [18134], [18969], [19525], [23257], [28626], [32771]
High Ground Tree Farm [2954]
High-Impact Decision Making (Onsite) [28341]
"The High-Intensity Entrepreneur" in Harvard Business Review (Vol. 88, September 2010, No. 9, pp. 74) [18135], [20936], [22629], [27593]
High Performance Business Writing [17581]
High Plains Technology Center (HPTC) [43885]
High Point Chamber of Commerce (HPCC) [43149]

High Point Market Authority (HPMKT) **[8193]**
"The High Price of Fast Fashion" in The Wall Street Journal (August 29, 2019) **[3031]**, **[23258]**
High Probability Selling (HPS) **[32693]**
High Springs Chamber of Commerce (HSCC) **[38430]**
High Street Capital (HSC) **[39359]**
"High-Tech Job-Apalooza!" in Orlando Business Journal (Vol. 26, January 15, 2010, No. 33, pp. 1) **[25139]**, **[26298]**, **[26572]**, **[26955]**, **[34801]**
The High-Tech News **[3580]**, **[15563]**
High Tech Rochester [42909]
High Technology Development Corp. [38888]
High Times **[5043]**
High Times: Voice of the Counter Culture [5043]
"High Touch Expands, Purchases Dallas Firms" in Wichita Business Journal (Vol. 27, February 3, 2012, No. 5, pp. 1) **[3508]**, **[18136]**, **[31337]**
High Touch - High Tech (HTHT) **[9936]**
"High-Yield Turns Into Road Kill" in Barron's (Vol. 88, July 7, 2008, No. 27, pp. M7) **[6447]**, **[9573]**, **[11409]**, **[20937]**, **[23927]**, **[29247]**
HighBar Partners **[37386]**
"Higher-Ed Finally in Session" in Business Journal Portland (Vol. 30, February 7, 2014, No. 49, pp. 4) **[21537]**, **[25370]**
"Higher Freight Rates Keep CPR Rolling in Profit" in Globe & Mail (February 1, 2006, pp. B3) **[6448]**, **[9574]**, **[18970]**, **[33174]**
"Higher Payouts Should Be In the Cards" in Barron's (Vol. 92, July 23, 2012, No. 30, pp. 14) **[4720]**, **[6449]**, **[9575]**, **[23928]**
Higher Yields Cannabis Consulting **[5068]**
"Highest-Paid Public Company CEO" in San Antonio Business Journal (Vol. 28, June 27, 2014, No. 20, pp. 6) **[19740]**
Highland Area Chamber of Commerce (HCOC) **[36939]**
Highland Capital Partners **[40696]**
The Highland Center **[45956]**
Highland Chamber of Commerce **[39199]**
Highland County Chamber of Commerce (HCCC) **[43490]**
Highland Park Chamber of Commerce (HPCC) **[39200]**
"Highland Row Joins Fray of Development Around U of M" in Memphis Business Journal (No. 35, February 14, 2014, No. 45, pp. 7) **[4117]**, **[13467]**
HighlandGriffith Chamber of Commerce **[39556]**
Highlands Area Chamber of Commerce **[43150]**
Highlands Chamber of Commerce [43150]
Highline **[46872]**
Highline Community College Small Business Development Center **[46002]**
"Highly Effective Cybersecurity Practices That Require Little to No Investment" in Minority Business Entrepreneur (Vol. 39, Fall, 2022, No. 4, pp. 40-41) **[16561]**
"Highmark-Owned Glasses Chain Eyeing Phila. Expansion" in Philadelphia Business Journal (Vol. 28, May 18, 2012, No. 14, pp. 1) **[16299]**, **[26573]**, **[32174]**
Highpointers Annual Convention **[15118]**
Highway Safety Directions [5107]
Highway1 **[37580]**
"Hike in Md.'s Alcohol Tax May Be Hard For Lawmakers to Swallow" in Baltimore Business Journal (Vol. 28, November 19, 2010, No. 28) **[1334]**, **[10322]**, **[18596]**, **[25371]**, **[34802]**
HilBren Computing Services LLC. (HCS) **[11098]**
Hilbren Consulting Services Inc. [11098]
Hildebrandt Tattoo Equipment **[15325]**
Hill International, Inc. **[4364]**
Hillcrest Venture Partners **[37740]**
Hilliard Area Chamber of Commerce (HACC) **[43491]**
Hillman Area Chamber of Commerce **[40937]**
Hills Chamber of Commerce **[39201]**
Hillsboro Chamber of Commerce (HCC) **[45208]**
Hillsborough Area Chamber of Commerce [43151]
Hillsborough/Orange County Chamber of Commerce **[43151]**
Hillwood Estate, Museum & Gardens Art Research Library **[999]**, **[9077]**
Hilton Head Area Small Business Development Center **[44507]**
Hilton Head Island-Bluffton Chamber of Commerce **[44564]**
HIMSS Annual Conference & Exhibition (HIMSS) **[26011]**
HIMSS Global Health Conference & Exhibition [26011]
Hinckley, Allen and Snyder L.L.P. **[6059]**
Hinesville-Liberty County Chamber of Commerce [38758]
Hinge Capital, LLC **[37387]**
Hinsdale Chamber of Commerce **[39202]**
Hinsdale Community Directory (Illinois) **[39203]**
"Hire Education: An Emerging Cohort" in Canadian Business (Vol. 79, September 11, 2006, No. 18, pp. 114) **[21538]**, **[24678]**, **[26574]**
"Hire Interstate Movers Without Getting Scammed" in The New York Times (May 8, 2018) **[11143]**
Hire and Manage Employees **[26575]**
"The Hiring Handbook: Tips & Tactics to Attract Top Tier Talent" **[26576]**, **[26956]**
Hiring Mistakes Small Business Owners Make and How to Avoid Them **[26577]**
Hiring & Retaining Great Security Officers **[14420]**, **[28627]**
"Hiring Unpaid Interns: Failing To Comply With Labor Laws Can Lead to Legal Trouble" in Black Enterprise (Vol. 44, June 2014, No. 10, pp. 22) **[21539]**, **[25372]**, **[26578]**
"His Brother's Keeper: A Mentor Learns the True Meaning of Leadership" in Black Enterprise (Vol. 37, December 2006, No. 5, pp. 69) **[21540]**, **[22630]**, **[28628]**
"His Record, Not Polls, Is What Matters" in Bangor Daily News (October 13, 2010) **[25002]**, **[34046]**, **[34717]**
"Hispanic Business 100 Influentials" in Hispanic Business (October 2009, pp. 22) **[25373]**, **[30354]**
Hispanic Chamber Cincinnati USA (HCCUSA) **[43492]**
Hispanic Chamber of Commerce of Austin [45173]
Hispanic Chamber of Commerce of Denver [37867]
Hispanic Chamber of Commerce of Metro Denver **[37867]**
Hispanic Chamber of Commerce of Sonoma County (HCCSC) **[36940]**
Hispanic Chamber News **[45209]**
Hispanic Economic Development Corp. (HEDC) **[41676]**
Hispanic Lawyers Association of Illinois (HLAI) **[10215]**
Hispanic Marketing Council (HMC) **[16901]**
Hispanic Metropolitan Chamber (HMC) **[43981]**
Hispanic Public Relations Association (HPRA) **[30507]**, **[31742]**
Hispanics Avanzando Hispanics [43492]
Hispanics: Digital Trends & Impact of COVID-19 One Year Later - US - April 2021 **[10680]**, **[11832]**, **[29501]**, **[32335]**
Hispano Chamber of Commerce de Las Cruces [42324]
Hispano Chamber of Doña Ana County [42324]
Historic Annapolis (HA) **[7463]**
Historic Annapolis Foundation [7463]
Historic Exterior Paint Colors Consulting **[937]**, **[4320]**, **[11886]**
"Historic Is Hot, But Challenging, in Bham" in Birmingham Business Journal (Vol. 31, August 1, 2014, No. 31, pp. 10) **[893]**, **[4118]**, **[25374]**, **[34047]**
Historic Silver Valley Chamber of Commerce **[38923]**
Historic Walking Tour **[36941]**
Historic Wallace Chamber of Commerce **[38924]**
History of Accounting: A Resource Guide **[16895]**
"A History of Neglect: Health Care for Blacks and Mill Workers in the Twentieth-Century South" in Canadian Business (Vol. 79, September 11, 2006, No. 18, pp. 21) **[9576]**, **[19261]**, **[25375]**
"History Partners with Tour Guide Associations to Promote Members" in Breaking Travel News (November 8, 2019) **[15745]**, **[31338]**
"Hit the Green: Golf Technology" in Canadian Business (Vol. 79, August 14, 2006, No. 16-17, pp. 73) **[7519]**, **[18971]**, **[19526]**, **[20296]**
"Hitting Bottom? Several Banks and Brokerages Are Ready to Pop Up for Air" in Barron's (Vol. 88, March 24, 2008, No. 12, pp. 21) **[6450]**, **[9577]**, **[20938]**, **[23929]**, **[25376]**
"Hitting the Green" in Canadian Business (Vol. 81, July 22, 2008, No. 12-13, pp. 34) **[7520]**, **[15093]**, **[15159]**, **[15595]**, **[29824]**
HiveLights **[1494]**
HLM Venture Partners **[40697]**
HLW International L.L.P. **[11653]**
HME News: The Business Newspaper for Home Medical Equipment Providers **[10885]**
HMSDC Business Expo **[24839]**
HMSDC Hybrid Business EXPO [24839]
Ho-Lee-Chow **[8120]**
Ho Math & Chess Learning Centre **[21721]**
HO2 Partners **[45453]**
Hobart Chamber of Commerce **[39557]**
Hobbs Chamber of Commerce (HCC) **[42323]**
Hobby Greenhouse Association (HGA) **[7608]**
Hobby Merchandiser **[4675]**
Hobby Merchandiser Annual Trade Directory **[4659]**
Hobbytown USA (H) **[4686]**
Hobe Sound Chamber of Commerce **[38431]**
Hodgeman County Culinary Incubator **[39974]**
Hoffman Estates Chamber of Commerce (HECC) **[39204]**
Hofstra Journal of International Business and Law (JIBL) **[18771]**
Hogi Yogi **[8622]**
Hohenwald-Lewis County Chamber of Commerce **[44761]**
Hoisington Chamber of Commerce (HCC) **[39902]**
Hoisington Koegler Group Inc. (HKGI) **[938]**
Holcomb Gallagher Adams Advertising Inc. **[30201]**, **[31897]**
"Hold the McJobs: Canada's High-End Employment Boom" in Globe & Mail (February 17, 2006, pp. B1) **[20939]**, **[26579]**
Holden Arboretum [7670]
Holden Area Chamber of Commerce [40639]
Holden Chamber of Commerce **[41575]**
Holden Chamber of Commerce [40639]
Holden Forests & Gardens **[7670]**
Holdenville Chamber of Commerce (HCC) **[43771]**
Holding Capital Group Inc. (HCG) **[42755]**
Holdrege Area Chamber of Commerce (HACC) **[41862]**
"Holiday Bloom: Event Designer Collin Abraham Heightens Glamour With Florals" in Black Enterprise (Vol. 41, November 2010, No. 4) **[6858]**, **[11907]**
"Holiday Sales Look Uncertain for Microsoft and PC Sellers" in Puget Sound Business Journal (Vol. 29, November 28, 2008, No. 32) **[3711]**, **[14787]**, **[20940]**, **[32175]**, **[33860]**
"Holiday Shopping Meets Social Media" in Employee Benefit News (Vol. 25, December 1, 2011, No. 15) **[17308]**, **[22170]**, **[32176]**, **[32953]**
Holiday Showcase **[1055]**
Holistic Entrepreneur Association (HEA) **[8089]**
Holistic Management International (HMI) **[5788]**
Holland Area Chamber of Commerce [40976]
Holland House Canada (CNBPA) **[20697]**
Holland - Springfield Chamber of Commerce **[43493]**
"Hollander 95 Business Park Project Getting Bigger" in Baltimore Business Journal (Vol. 29, September 23, 2011, No. 20, pp. 1) **[4119]**, **[11038]**, **[13468]**, **[18137]**
Hollingsworth & Associates **[15443]**, **[24247]**
Hollister Chamber of Commerce [37145]
Holly Area Chamber of Commerce **[40938]**
Holly Springs Chamber of Commerce **[43152]**
"Hollywood Baskets To Gift Nominees For the 2012 Teen Choice Awards July 22nd" in PR Newswire (July 16, 2012) **[7468]**, **[35793]**
Hollywood Chamber of Commerce **[36942]**
Holman Centre **[46881]**
Holmes County Chamber of Commerce **[43494]**
Holston Business Development Center (HBDC) **[44846]**
Holton Chamber of Commerce [39903]
Holton/Jackson County Chamber of Commerce **[39903]**
Holtville Chamber of Commerce **[36943]**
Holyoke Chamber of Commerce **[37868]**
"Home-Based Business Advantages and Disadvantages" in The Balance Small Business (Apr 16, 2021) **[26784]**
Home Based Business Association [36259]
Home-Based Working Moms (HBWM) **[26757]**
Home Builders Network (HBN) **[4321]**
"Home Business Ideas: 40 Remote Jobs to Explore in 2022" in NerdWallet (Jan. 7, 2021) **[26785]**
Home Business Magazine **[26786]**
Home Business Tax Deductions: Keep What You Earn **[15387]**, **[26787]**, **[34803]**
Home Care Assistance Corp. [8291]
Home Care and Hospice Conference and Expo [8276]
Home Cleaning Services **[2987]**
Home Decor Retailing: Incl Impact of COVID-19 - US - April 2020 **[8184]**, **[8215]**
"Home Depot Co-Founder Ken Langone Talks About Business" in Atlanta Business Chronicle (April 11, 2014) **[7920]**, **[22631]**
"Home Developers Buy 9 Acres in Lakewood" in Dallas Business Journal (Vol. 35, August 10, 2012, No. 48, pp. 1) **[4120]**, **[13210]**, **[31339]**
"Home Elder Care: Buyer, Beware; Scant Background Checks of Aides Often Leave Frail Elderly Vulnerable, Researchers Say" in Consumer Health News (July 12, 2012) **[8252]**
Home Fashion Products Association (HFPA) **[1569]**, **[8173]**, **[9021]**
Home Furnishings Association (HFA) **[8194]**
Home Furnishings Independents Association [8194]
Home Health Care And Residential Nursing Care Services Market Covering Nursing Care Facilities; Home Health Care Providers; Retirement Communities; Orphanages & Group Homes; Global Summary 2022 **[8269]**
Home Health Care Management & Practice (HHCMP) **[8272]**, **[26012]**
Home Health Care Services Quarterly **[1037]**, **[8273]**, **[26013]**
"Home Health Franchise Expands Across S. Fla." in South Florida Business Journal (Vol. 34, January 24, 2014, No. 27, pp. 5) **[8253]**, **[18138]**, **[35794]**
Home Health Line **[8274]**
Home Healthcare Now **[8275]**
Home Healthcare Nurse: The Journal for the Home Care and Hospice Professional [8275]

3252 Small Business Sourcebook • 42nd Edition

Master Index Housecleaning

Master Index

Home Helpers **[8286]**
"Home Improvement Service Chain Had to Fix Its Own House" in Crain's Detroit Business (Vol. 30, October 13, 2014, No. 41, pp. 15) **[2638]**, **[4121]**, **[18139]**, **[24368]**, **[33175]**
Home Instead Inc. **[11535]**
Home Instead Senior Care [11535]
"Home Instead Senior Care Awards National Salute to Senior Service Honoree" in Professional Services Close-Up (June 8, 2012) **[8254]**, **[34329]**
"Home Instead Senior Care Introduces Post-Discharge Care Initiative; Aims to Reduce Hospital Readmissions Among Seniors" in Benzinga.com (September 18, 2012) **[8255]**, **[25811]**
"Home Instead Senior Care of Seacoast and Southern New Hampshire" inNew Hampshire Business Review (Vol. 34, April 6, 2012, No. 7, pp. 45) **[8256]**, **[21541]**, **[25812]**
"Home Price Trends from a Financial Perspective" in Real Estate Review (Vol. 41, Spring 2012, No. 1, pp. 5) **[4122]**, **[11039]**
"Home Prices Sag" in Crain's Chicago Business (Vol. 31, April 28, 2008, No. 17, pp. 3) **[4123]**, **[11040]**, **[13211]**, **[13469]**, **[20941]**
"Home Security Systems That Are Fast, Easy and Totally Not Creepy" in The Wall Street Journal (August 26, 2018) **[11753]**, **[14421]**
The Home Shop Machinist **[4616]**
The Home Star Group **[4322]**
"Home Sweet (Second) Home" in Baltimore Business Journal (Vol. 30, May 25, 2012, No. 3, pp. 1) **[13212]**, **[20942]**, **[34048]**
"Home, Sweet Shipping Container" in Washington Business Journal (Vol. 33, July 18, 2014, No. 13, pp. 4) **[4124]**, **[25377]**, **[34049]**
Home Ventilating Institute (HVI) **[454]**
Home Ventilating Institute Division of the Air Movement Control Association [454]
Home Video Studio (HVS) **[6218]**, **[26828]**
"Home: Where the Money Is" in Small Business Opportunities (May 1, 2008) **[8231]**, **[24294]**
"Homebuilder Confidence Buried Under Snow" in Birmingham Business Journal (Vol. 31, February 21, 2014, No. 8, pp. 7) **[4125]**, **[13213]**, **[13470]**
"Homebuilders Continue to be Our Nemesis" in Contractor (Vol. 56, July 2009, No. 7, pp. 50) **[4126]**, **[6451]**, **[9578]**, **[14618]**, **[23930]**
"Homebuilding Numbers Going Up" in Memphis Business Journal (Vol. 33, January 27, 2012, No. 42, pp. 1) **[4127]**
"Homebuilding Thrives on Lot Prices" in Memphis Business Journal (Vol. 33, February 24, 2012, No. 46, pp. 1) **[4128]**, **[13214]**, **[20943]**
Homer, Alaska Chamber of Commerce **[36235]**
Homerville - Clinch County Chamber of Commerce **[38754]**
"Homes, Not Bars, Stay Well Tended" in Advertising Age (Vol. 79, January 28, 2008, No. 4, pp. 8) **[1335]**, **[10323]**, **[13947]**, **[15014]**, **[20944]**
The Hometeam Inspection Services Inc. **[2032]**
HomeVestors of America, Inc. **[13627]**
Homewatch CareGivers (HWCG) **[191]**
Homewood Area Chamber of Commerce (HACC) **[36124]**
Homewood Chamber of Commerce (HCC) **[36125]**
Hominy Area Chamber of Commerce **[43772]**
Homosassa Springs Area Chamber of Commerce [38351]
Hondo Area Chamber of Commerce (HACC) **[45210]**
Hondo Chamber of Commerce [45210]
Honest-1 Auto Care Inc. **[14584]**
The Honey Baked Ham Company L.L.C. (HBH) **[7823]**, **[14182]**, **[15059]**
Honey Bee Biology and Beekeeping **[1480]**
Honey Grove Chamber of Commerce (HGCC) **[45211]**
Honeysuckle Nectary Apiary and Gardens LLC **[1502]**
Hong Kong Trade Development Council (HKTDC) **[27415]**
"Hong Kong's Boom in IPOs" in Barron's (Vol. 89, July 13, 2009, No. 28, pp. M7) **[6452]**, **[9579]**, **[23931]**, **[27594]**, **[31340]**
Honolulu Japanese Chamber of Commerce (HJCC) **[38875]**
Honolulu Japanese Junior Chamber of Commerce (HJJCC) **[38876]**
Honolulu Minority Business Enterprise Center **[38883]**
The Hood Kitchen Space **[37581]**
Hood River County Chamber of Commerce (HRCCC) **[43982]**
"Hoop Culture Opens Showroom, Expands Reach Globally" in Orlando Business Journal (Vol. 30, February 28, 2014, No. 36, pp. 3) **[3122]**, **[11754]**, **[15094]**, **[15160]**, **[23005]**, **[27595]**, **[32177]**, **[35491]**
The Hoosier Genealogist [7386]
Hoosier Heartland Small Business Development Center **[39472]**
Hoosier Horse Fair and Expo (HHF&E) **[8325]**
Hoover Area Chamber of Commerce **[36126]**
Hoover Institution [15492]
Hoover Institution on War, Revolution and Peace **[15492]**
Hoover's Vision **[19527]**, **[22632]**, **[24679]**, **[34050]**
Hoover's Vision: Original Thinking for Business Success **[19528]**, **[22633]**
Hope College - Carl Frost Center for Social Science Research [15235]
"Hope Grows for a Muscular Dystrophy Drug" in Barron's (Vol. 92, August 25, 2012, No. 35, pp. 35) **[5164]**, **[9580]**, **[26299]**, **[30739]**, **[31982]**, **[32772]**
Hope-Hempstead County Chamber of Commerce **[36471]**
Hope & Main **[44487]**
Hopen Life Science Ventures **[41143]**
Hopewell-Prince George Chamber of Commerce (HPGCC) **[45874]**
Hopkins County Chamber of Commerce (HCCC) **[45212]**
Hopkins County Regional Chamber of Commerce **[40054]**
"Hopkins' Security, Reputation Face Challenges in Wake of Slaying" in Baltimore Business Journal (Vol. 28, August 6, 2010, No. 13) **[8658]**, **[12934]**, **[14422]**, **[21542]**, **[31765]**, **[31870]**, **[31983]**, **[32773]**
"Hopkins, University of Maryland, Baltimore Worry Reduced NIH Budget Will Impact Research" in Baltimore Business Journal (Vol. 29, August 19, 2011, No. 15, pp. 1) **[19857]**, **[25003]**, **[25813]**, **[31984]**, **[32774]**
Hopkinsville-Christian County Chamber of Commerce [40030]
Hopkinsville Small Business Development Center **[39992]**
Horicon Chamber of Commerce (HCC) **[46431]**
The Horizon **[37869]**
Horizon Consulting Services **[19138]**
Horizon Ventures **[37388]**
The Horn Book Magazine: About Books for Children and Young Adults **[1689]**
Horn Lake Chamber of Commerce (HLCC) **[41405]**
Horror Writers of America [5283]
Horror Writers Association (HWA) **[5283]**
Horse Industry Directory **[8318]**
"Horse Race: Putting the App in Apple" in Inc. (Vol. 30, November 2008, No. 11) **[2747]**, **[14788]**, **[21873]**, **[26300]**, **[30960]**, **[33861]**
"Horse Racing Industry Cries Foul Over Budget Switch" in Philadelphia Business Journal (Vol. 31, March 23, 2012, No. 6, pp. 1) **[7292]**, **[8319]**, **[25378]**
"Horseback Riding on the Beach, in Brooklyn. Seriously." in The New York Times (August 14, 2019) **[8320]**
Horsemanship Safety Association [8299]
Horseshoe Bend Area Chamber of Commerce (HBACC) **[36472]**
Horticultural Research Institute (HRI) **[7695]**
The Horticultural Society of New York **[8163]**, **[10146]**
Horticulture Research Center [10273]
Horton Chamber of Commerce (HCC) **[39904]**
"Hospital Communication Goes Mobile" in Providence Business News (Vol. 29, July 7, 2014, No. 14, pp. 12) **[10890]**, **[21874]**, **[25814]**, **[31341]**
Hospital, Institution and Educational Food Service Society [11560]
Hospital Progress [26006]
Hospital Research and Educational Trust [26118]
"Hospital Revenue Healthier in 2009" in Orlando Business Journal (Vol. 26, February 5, 2010, No. 36, pp. 1) **[9581]**, **[18140]**, **[23932]**, **[25815]**
Hospital Topics **[26014]**
Hospitality Design **[8475]**, **[9059]**, **[14044]**
Hospitality Financial and Technology Professionals (HFTP) **[8345]**
Hospitality Review **[8476]**
Hospitality Sales and Marketing Association International (HSMAI) **[8346]**
Hospitality Sales and Marketing Association International Research Library (HSMAI) **[8529]**
"Hospitals Say Medicaid Expansion is Critical" in Dallas Business Journal (Vol. 35, August 3, 2012, No. 47, pp. 1) **[8919]**, **[25379]**, **[25816]**, **[27276]**
"Hospitals Singing OB Blues" in Philadelphia Business Journal (Vol. 31, April 6, 2012, No. 8, pp. 1) **[25817]**
"Hospitals Try to Buy Smarter" in Crain's Detroit Business (Vol. 25, June 1, 2009, No. 22, pp. M025) **[10832]**, **[10951]**, **[23933]**, **[25818]**
"Hospitals Up the Ante for Medical Transcription Tools as Vendors Modernize with Automation, Voice Recognition" in Healthcare IT News (July 17, 2018) **[10970]**
"Hospitals Vying to Buy Physician Associates LLC" in Orlando Business Journal (Vol. 29, August 31, 2012, No. 11, pp. 1) **[19669]**, **[25819]**, **[27277]**
"Hospitals Waste Billions of Dollars in Medical Supplies" in U.S. News & World Report (March 9, 2017) **[10833]**, **[10891]**, **[10952]**
"Host" **[26957]**, **[28629]**
"Host Your Dream Wedding at the Minneapolis Marriott Southwest" in Benzinga.com (June 6, 2011) **[1976]**, **[8399]**
"Hostel or Not? Shared Rooms Pop Up in Traditional Hotels" in Skift (November 12, 2019) **[8400]**
"Hostess Names $10,000 Grand Prize Winner of its 'CupCake Jackpot' Promotion" in Entertainment Close-Up (August 19, 2011) **[1255]**, **[19858]**, **[29825]**
"Hosts Provide Vital Services Helping Maintain Lake Mitchell Campground" in The Daily Republic (August 28, 2019) **[2514]**
Hot Dog on a Leash **[12157]**
Hot to Not be Invisible (10 Ways to Get Discovered) **[30152]**
"Hot Real Estate Market Means Hard Work for Investors" in Business Journal Portland (Vol. 31, March 21, 2014, No. 3, pp. 14) **[12887]**, **[13471]**, **[13794]**
Hot Springs Area Chamber of Commerce **[44650]**
"Hot to Use Instagram Stories for Your Fitness Business" in Glofox blog (July 13, 2019) **[12417]**, **[29826]**
Hotchkiss Community Chamber of Commerce (HCCC) **[37870]**
hotDesks **[40458]**
"Hotel Boom Coming to the Palm Beaches" in Travel Weekly (November 14, 2019) **[8401]**
Hotel Brokers International (HBI) **[8347]**
Hotel Business **[8477]**
"Hotel Confidential" in Canadian Business (Vol. 80, Winter 2007, No. 24, pp. 91) **[8402]**, **[9582]**
"Hotel Could Move Into Former Movie Studio Site in Allen Park" in Crain's Detroit Business (Vol. 35, September 1, 2014, No. 35, pp. 17) **[8403]**, **[13472]**
Hotel Electronic Distribution Association [8348]
Hotel Electronic Distribution Network Association (HEDNA) **[8348]**
"Hotel Expected to Jump Start Downtown Revitalization" in Houston Business Journal (Vol. 44, March 28, 2014, No. 47, pp. 10) **[4129]**, **[8404]**
The Hotel Experience (HX) **[8488]**, **[14091]**
"Hotel Industry: Getting Better All the Time" in Orlando Business Journal (Vol. 28, May 18, 2012, No. 50, pp. 1) **[8405]**, **[15996]**
Hotel Management **[8478]**
Hotel & Motel Management [8478]
"Hotel Pitched by Mortenson Would Be Among First Of Its Kind in U.S." in Business Journal (Vol. 31, February 14, 2014, No. 38, pp. 10) **[4130]**, **[8406]**
Hotel Sales and Marketing Association International [8346]
Hotel & Travel Index [15770]
"Hotel Woes Reflect Area Struggle" in Business Journal Serving Greater Tampa Bay (Vol. 30, December 3, 2010, No. 50, pp. 1) **[4131]**, **[8407]**, **[11041]**, **[20945]**, **[31689]**
Hotelier **[8479]**
HOTELS **[8480]**, **[14045]**
"Hotels Get a Fill-Up: Fee Helps Bring Back Hot Rod Tour, Replace Biz Travel" in Crain's Detroit Business (Vol. 25, June 1, 2009, No. 22, pp. 1) **[8408]**, **[15746]**, **[19359]**
"Hotels' Healthy Finish in '07" in Crain's Chicago Business (Vol. 31, March 24, 2008, No. 12, pp. 16) **[8409]**, **[19360]**, **[20946]**
"Hotels Make Wallcoverings a Sticking Trend" in Hotel News Now (April 17, 2019) **[8410]**, **[9040]**, **[11859]**
Hotels & Motels Industry in the US - Market Research Report **[8471]**
"Hotels Up the Ante in Bid to Lure Visitors" in Sacramento Business Journal (Vol. 29, June 1, 2012, No. 14, pp. 1) **[8411]**, **[15864]**, **[15997]**, **[29827]**, **[35060]**
"Hottest Culinary School Vacations" in TravelChannel.com **[4465]**, **[15747]**
Hotwire Development L.L.C. **[36395]**
Houghton Lake Chamber of Commerce (HLCC) **[40939]**
Houghton Mifflin Company - School Division Research Center **[1709]**
Houma-Terrebonne Chamber of Commerce (HTCC) **[40174]**
Hounds Town USA **[12119]**
Hour Cucina L.L.C. **[38571]**
Hour Kitchen **[45524]**
House Beautiful **[9060]**
House of Bread, Inc. **[1295]**
House Doctors Handyman Service **[2653]**
"House Subcommittee to Hear from Small Business Owners on Right to Repair" in Small Business Trends (September 13, 2022) **[16562]**
Housecleaning Business: Organize Your Business - Get Clients and Referrals - Set Rates and Services **[5074]**, **[5645]**, **[5917]**, **[19859]**, **[20440]**, **[21875]**, **[23259]**, **[26788]**, **[28001]**

Small Business Sourcebook • 42nd Edition 3253

Housemaster, Home Inspections, Done Right [2033]
HouseWall Garage System [12861]
Housewarmers, LLC [16521]
"Housing Agency Says Lending on Rise" in Providence Business News (Vol. 29, June 30, 2014, No. 13, pp. 5) [11042]
The Housing Boom and Bust [13215], [13473]
"Housing Markets Still Struggling" in Montana Business Quarterly (Vol. 49, Spring 2011, No. 1, pp. 17) [13216], [13474], [20947], [34051]
"Housing Slide Picks Up Speed" in Crain's Chicago Business (Vol. 31, April 19, 2008, No. 16, pp. 2) [489], [4132], [5376], [10737], [11043], [13217], [13475], [14328], [20108]
"Housing Stats Contradicting" in Memphis Business Journal (Vol. 34, July 20, 2012, No. 14, pp. 1) [11044], [13795]
Houston Angel Network (HAN) [45454]
Houston Area Chamber of Commerce (HACC) [41244]
Houston Business Development, Inc. (HBDI) [44957]
Houston Business Journal (HBJ) [12012]
Houston Chamber of Commerce (HCC) [41576]
Houston Chamber of Commerce [41244], [45180]
"Houston Doctors Buy In to Medical Timeshares" in Houston Business Journal (Vol. 40, December 11, 2009, No. 31, pp. 1) [13796], [25820], [31342], [34052]
The Houston Ear Research Foundation [8141]
Houston Exponential (HTC) [45525]
"Houston Firm To Build World's Largest Plant of Its Kind" in Houston Business Journal (Vol. 44, April 25, 2014, No. 51, pp. 4A) [4133], [8721]
Houston Insurance Day [27366]
Houston Intellectual Property Law Association (HIPLA) [10216]
Houston Intercontinental Chamber of Commerce (HICC) [45213]
"Houston Law Firms Plan Rate Bumps" in Houston Business Journal (Vol. 40, December 25, 2009, No. 33, pp. 1) [18597], [20026]
Houston Metropolitan Chamber of Commerce [45214]
Houston Minority Business Council [45421]
Houston Minority Supplier Development Council (HMSDC) [45421]
Houston Museum of Decorative Arts Library [750]
Houston Northwest Chamber of Commerce (HNWCC) [45215]
Houston Private Equity Association (HPEA) [44894]
Houston Public Library (HPL) - Clayton Library Center for Genealogical Research [7418]
"Houston Tech Company Eyes California for HQ Move" in Houston Business Journal (Vol. 45, July 18, 2014, No. 10, pp. 10A) [19178], [26301], [33371], [35349]
Houston Technology Center [45525]
"Houston (Texas) Computer Repair Adds U-Haul Rentals" in Benzinga.com (March 29, 2012) [3575], [13797], [33176]
Houston Venture Capital Association [44894]
Houston Ventures (HV) [45595]
Houston West Chamber of Commerce (HWCC) [45216]
"How 15 People in Their 20s Built Million-Dollar Businesses" in Entrepreneur (Aug. 24, 2021) [36023]
"How to Accept Mobile Credit Card Payment" in Business News Daily (March 6, 2023) [20297]
"How Accountants Break the Bad News about Tax Refunds: with Chocolate and Tissues" in The Wall Street Journal (March 4, 2019) [15388], [16806], [34804]
How to Acquire Venture Capital Funding with Paul Jarrett [35421]
"How to Address a Negative Review on Social Media" in Archery Business (December 11, 2018) [850], [20441]
How ADHD Can Hinder and Help Entrepreneurs with Dave Delaney [22895]
"How to Advertise a Tutoring Business" in Chron [16133]
"How to Advertise Your Tutoring Services: The Complete Guide to Tutor Advertising" in Appointy blog (Jan. 22, 2021) [16134]
"How Agritech Startups Are Boosting Agricultural Economy by Employing AI and Data Science - Expert Explains" in Zee Business (Nov. 12, 2021) [17057], [26302]
"How AI Tools at Mailchimp Could Help Market Smaller Businesses" in Adweek (November 13, 2020) [29828]
"How Anger Poisons Decision Making" in Harvard Business Review (Vol. 88, September 2010, No. 9, pp. 26) [17684], [28630]
"How Are Digital Marketplaces Affecting the Wholesale Model?" in Business of Home (November 5, 2019) [8177], [8209], [11755], [35492]
"How Artificial Intelligence Can Help Small Businesses" in Bplans Blog [29829], [32540], [34053]
"How to Attract Clients for Your Residential and Office Cleaning Business" in Chron (March 12, 2019) [2972], [29491], [29830]

"How to Avoid Double Taxation with an S Corporation" in Small Business Trends (May 22, 2017) [27178], [34805]
"How to Avoid Leave-Related Lawsuits" in Employee Benefit News (Vol. 25, December 1, 2011, No. 15, pp. 12) [8920], [17309], [18598], [26958], [27278]
"How to Avoid the Most Common and Costliest Mistakes in Retirement Portfolio Investing" in Barron's (Vol. 88, March 10, 2008, No. 10, pp. 30) [6453], [9583], [17310], [23934]
How to Avoid the Pitfalls that Make You Hate Your Business with Eric Bandholz [16651]
"How to Avoid Quiet Quitting and Lead a Successful Small Business Team" in Small Business Trends (February 4, 2023) [22171]
"How to Avoid a Tax Audit: 7 Tips for Small Business Owners" in Legal Zoom (March 2, 2023) [34806]
How to Avoid the Top 3 Things that Take Entrepreneurs Out of the Game with Shawn Stevenson [22896]
"How B2B Bartering Can Boost Your Small Business" in KC Source Link Blog (Aug. 24, 2016) [17254]
"How Bad Is It?" in Hawaii Business (Vol. 54, July 2008, No. 1, pp. 35) [5646], [8722], [20948], [23260], [27596]
"How Baltimore's Largest Private Companies Weathered the Recession's Punch; Top Private Companies" in Baltimore Business Journal (Vol. 28, August 27, 2010, No. 16, pp. 1) [8723], [18141], [20949], [25004], [27597]
How to Bargain & Negotiate with Vendors and Suppliers [19982], [31910]
"How BBQ Can Be Birmingham's Secret Sauce" in Birmingham Business Journal (Vol. 31, May 9, 2014, No. 19, pp. 4) [13948], [15998], [18142], [24369]
How to Be the Ambassador of Your Own Brand with Talyn Rahman-Figueroa [17471]
How to Be a Dynamic Trainer (Onsite) [22055]
"How to Be Environmentally Sustainable As a Small to Medium Size Business" in noissue.com (August 8, 2018) [23261]
How to Be a Highly Successful Team Leader (Onsite) [22056], [28342], [28343]
How to Be an Outstanding Communicator (Onsite) [17582]
"How to Beat the Pros" in Canadian Business (Vol. 81, Summer 2008, No. 9, pp. 59) [6454], [9584], [20950], [23935]
"How to Become a Dog Trainer" in American Kennel Club website (March 12, 2020) [12141]
"How to Become a Licensed Dog Breeder?" in BreedingBusiness.com (October 23, 2018) [648]
"How to Become a Professional Genealogist" in How to Become a Professional Genealogist (October 10, 2018) [7362]
How to Become a Professional Organizer [12832]
"How to Become a Professional Wedding Planner" in The Spruce (October 3, 2019) [6092], [34508]
"How Beer Brewers Are Embracing Sustainability" in SevenFiftyDaily (May 11, 2020) [1918]
"How to Boost Your Business with These Customer Service Tips" in Simply Business (Dec. 23, 2020) [20442]
"How to Boost Your Small Business Marketing Efforts With AI" in Forbes (June 28, 2019) [29831]
"How to Brand-Crash the Olympics" in Canadian Business (Vol. 85, August 13, 2012, No. 13, pp. 18) [285], [15161], [29832]
How to Break into Freelance Web Design and Build Reliable Monthly Recurring Revenue with John Wooten [16495]
How to Break Into the Commercial Photography Business [12302]
How to Build an Appraisal Service Business: The Only Book You Need to Launch, Grow & Succeed [803]
How to Build a Busines with No Employees with Ian Blair [26714]
"How to Build Business Credit in 7 Steps" in NerdWallet (Dec. 14, 2021) [20298]
How to Build a Business Others Want to Buy [18972], [19223]
"How to Build a Cannabis Brand That Consumers Trust" in Cannabis Business Executive (June 1, 2020) [5003]
How to Build a Gentle Business [24810]
"How to Build a Great Employee Benefits Package" in Business News Daily (February 21, 2023) [22172], [26959], [27279]
How to Build a Regenerative Business with Helen Tremethick [34432]
How to Build a Winning Sales Team: Tips and Strategies [22173], [32541]
How to Build Your Business Without Social Media with Rebecca Tracey [29541]
How to Build Your First Photography Studio [12344]

How to Build Your Startup's Waitlist [29542]
The How of Business: 7 Start-Up Mistakes [34619]
The How of Business: Adam Siegel - Fashion Resale Business [3161], [3908]
The How of Business: Amy Rasdal - Consulting Business [20140]
The How of Business: Andrea Hoffer - Hire Higher [26715]
The How of Business: Annual Strategic Plan [19108]
The How of Business: Are You Ready to Be Your Own Boss? [33927]
The How of Business: Bryan Park - Starting a Flooring Business [6838]
The How of Business: Budgeting Fundamentals for Small Business [17517]
The How of Business: Caity Cronkhite - Better Writing Better Service [17790]
The How of Business: Candace Nelson - Sweet Success [1278]
The How of Business: Cash Flow Management [19725]
The How of Business: Christy Foley - Conflict Resolution [18735]
The How of Business: Coffee Shop Business Talk with Chris Deferio [7570]
The How of Business: Courtney Reum - Shortcut Your Startup [34620]
The How of Business: Creating a Business That Can Thrive Without You [33043]
The How of Business: Dan Perry - Handyman Business Startup [8229]
The How of Business: Daniel Feliciano - Transforming the Laundry Industry [10188]
The How of Business: Danya Shakfeh - Legal Considerations of Buying a Business [18736], [19701]
The How of Business: David Barnett - Selling Your Business [33044]
The How of Business: David Siegel - Avoiding Partnership Disputes [31590]
The How of Business: Debra Corey - Employee Recognition [22299]
The How of Business: Delegation [16652]
The How of Business: Donata Kalneinate - Legal Insights [16653]
The How of Business: Dyan Jahraus - Etsy Business [4627]
The How of Business: Earsa Jackson - Franchise Attorney [24451]
The How of Business: Email Marketing [30153]
The How of Business: Employee Development Program for Small Business [22300]
The How of Business: Entrepreneurial Leap - Finding the Right Business for You [22897]
The How of Business: Entrepreneurial Leap - Your Nightmare or Dream [19109]
The How of Business: Entrepreneurship Skills with Dan Sullivan [22898]
The How of Business: Erika Tyburski - Health Tech Startup [34621]
The How of Business: Financial Projections for Small Business Startup [24210]
The How of Business: From Idea to Fashion Product with Zack Hurley [3062]
The How of Business: Funding Your Small Business Startup [35422]
The How of Business: Giuseppe Grammatico - Small Business Franchises [24452]
The How of Business: Goal Setting & Time Management [35011]
The How of Business: Growing a Lawncare Business with Bryan Clayton [10255]
The How of Business: Henrik Johansson - Product Development [30839]
"How a Business Incubator Is Different from an Accelerator Program" in Denton Record-Chronicle (Aug. 16, 2022) [27210]
"How Business Intelligence Can Affect Bottomline" in Canadian Electronics (Vol. 23, February 2008, No. 1, pp. 6) [14423], [28033]
The How of Business: Is Your Business Model Broken? [19110]
The How of Business: Is Your Small Business Competitive? [19976]
The How of Business: Is Your Small Business Scalable? [18442]
The How of Business: Ivy Walker - Risk Management [32399]
The How of Business: Jane Allen - Entrepreneur's Lifecycle [33628]
The How of Business: Jessica Rhodes - Home-Based Business [26821]
The How of Business: John Morlan - Risk Management [32400]
The How of Business: Justine Lackey - Selling Her Small Business [33045]

The How of Business: Kelly Roach - Principles for Success **[33629]**
The How of Business: Kevin Ring - Workers' Compensation Insurance **[27363]**, **[35958]**
The How of Business: Kizzy Parks - Government Contracts **[25171]**
The How of Business: Kristina Schlegel - Make Bake **[30840]**
The How of Business: Kurt Wilkin - Hire Better **[26716]**
The How of Business: Laundromats with Keith Leimbach **[10189]**
The How of Business: LeRoy Wilkerson - Health Insurance Business **[8995]**, **[27364]**
The How of Business: Managing Hourly-Wage Employees **[27103]**
The How of Business: Matt Chiappetta - Year-End Tax Considerations **[16854]**, **[34935]**
The How of Business: Matt Grech-Smith - Swingers Crazy Golf **[1364]**, **[10988]**
The How of Business: Matt Ruedlinger - Launching a Small Business **[16654]**
The How of Business: Matt Tierney - Employee Retention **[27104]**
The How of Business: Megan Bennett - Public Relations **[31804]**
The How of Business: Mickie Kennedy - Press Releases **[17791]**
The How of Business: Mike Finger - Is Your Business Sellable **[33046]**
The How of Business: Nick Neonakis - Franchises **[24453]**
The How of Business: Overcoming Decision Paralysis **[24811]**
The How of Business: Pam Lopez - Travel Consulting Business **[16031]**
The How of Business: Pat Flynn & Matt Gartland - Entrepreneurships & Partnerships **[31591]**
The How of Business: Patrick Lange - Buying an HVAC Business **[532]**
The How of Business: Peter Mehit - Business Planning **[19111]**
The How of Business: Prepare for Successful Partnership **[31592]**
The How of Business: Pricing Fundamentals **[31664]**
The How of Business: Randy Long - Business Exit **[16655]**
The How of Business: Ray Drew - SBA Loans **[28236]**
The How of Business: Ready to Be Your Own Boss? **[34622]**
The How of Business: Rebecca Ryan - Strategic Foresight **[19112]**
The How of Business: Roger Beaudoin - Growing Restaurant Profits **[14060]**
The How of Business: Sales Fundamentals **[32681]**
The How of Business: Sara Waskow - Franchising **[24454]**
The How of Business: Scott Krone - Self-Storage Business **[11156]**
The How of Business: Shahara Wright - Legal and Business Growth Strategies **[16656]**
The How of Business: Six Stages of Successful Employee On-Boarding **[27105]**
The How of Business: Six Startup Myths **[34623]**
The How of Business: Small Business Culture **[19633]**
The How of Business: Small Business Failure **[16657]**
The How of Business: Small Business Ideation **[33630]**
The How of Business: Small Business Ownership Readiness Assessment **[16658]**
The How of Business: Small Business Plans **[19113]**
The How of Business: Starting a Franchise Business **[24455]**
The How of Business: Steve Alexander - Buying and Growing a Small Business **[33631]**
The How of Business: Steve Hoffman - Surviving a Start-Up **[16659]**
The How of Business: Stratis Morfogen - Culinary Entrepreneurship **[14061]**
The How of Business: Taking Your Entrepreneurial Leap with Gino Wickman **[22899]**
The How of Business: Thad Price - Hriing Front-Line Workers **[26717]**
The How of Business: The 6 Essential Traits of Successful Entrepreneurs **[22900]**
The How of Business: Three Benefits of Franchising **[24456]**
The How of Business: Top 5 Reasons Small Businesses Fail **[16660]**
The How of Business: Top 10 Productivity Tools **[35012]**
The How of Business: Trademarks and Copyrights with Andrea Sager **[27972]**
The How of Business: Travis Reiter - Employee Background Checks **[26718]**
The How of Business: Variable Compensation Plans **[19762]**
The How of Business: Wade Swikle - Starting a Moving Business **[11157]**
The How of Business: Walid Azami - Entrepreneurship for Creatives **[22901]**
The How of Business: William Warren - The Conquering Creative **[4628]**
"How Businesses Can Do Well by Doing Good" in U.S. News & World Report (Aug. 17, 2021) **[34330]**
"How Busy Executives Manage to Live a Balanced Life" in Influencive(March 20, 2019) **[18143]**, **[21543]**, **[34987]**
"How to Buy a Business" in Small Business Trends (May 11, 2021) **[19224]**
"How to Buy a Business: Everything You Need to Know" in NerdWallet (Oct. 22, 2020) **[19670]**
"How to Buy a Business or Franchise" in Guidant (Nov. 25, 2021) **[19671]**
"How to Buy a Company With Someone Else's Money" in Small Business Trends(January 23, 2023) **[19672]**
How to Buy and Sell Antiques **[739]**
"How to Buy a Small Business" in Funding Circle (March 27, 2020) **[19673]**
"How to Buy Small Business Insurance" in Business News Daily (February 21, 2023) **[27280]**
"How to Calculate Start Up Costs for a Laundromat" in Chron (March 19, 2019) **[10158]**
"How Can Small Business Owners Reduce Social Security and Medicare Taxes?" in Schroedel, Scullin & Bestic (May 14, 2019) **[34243]**
"How the CEO of Keap Grew His Company from Startup to $120 Million" in Small Business Trends(November 21,2022) **[34509]**
"How to Change a Corporation to an LLC without Dissolving the Corporation" in Legal Zoom (March 16, 2023) **[27179]**
"How Charlotte's Pilot Program for Incentives Could Boost Small Businesses, Workers' Skills" in Charlotte Business Journal (February 11, 2020) **[35478]**
"How to Choose the Best Digital Marketing Agency for Your Business in 2020" in Single Grain **[27808]**
"How to Choose the Best Driving School for Your Teen" in Drivingguide.com (September 24, 2018) **[5103]**, **[27281]**
"How to Choose the Best Workspace for Your Startup?" in Small Business Trends (Sept. 18, 2019) **[31037]**
"How to Choose Board Members for Your Company" in Legal Zoom (March 27, 2023) **[18973]**
"How to Choose a Pricing Strategy for Your Small Business" in Intuit Quickbooks (June 20, 2019) **[31651]**
"How to Choose a Professional Web Design Agency" in Business 2 Community (October 21, 2021) **[16500]**
"How to Choose the Right Food Truck Oven" in FoodTruckOperator.com (August 4, 2017) **[6984]**
"How Church Street Exchange May Bring Retail, 350 Jobs" in Orlando Business Journal (Vol. 30, February 28, 2014, No. 36, pp. 10) **[26303]**, **[32178]**, **[33372]**
"How to Claim a Google Business Profile" in Business 2 Community (October 22, 2021) **[30229]**, **[34228]**
"How Coffee Producers Can Adapt to Climate Change" in Perfect Daily Grind (November 7, 2019) **[3182]**, **[7557]**, **[23262]**
How to Collect Accounts Receivable **[20374]**
"How to get Commercial Cleaning Clients without Appearing Desperate" in Marketing Systems by Design (July 3, 2019) **[2973]**, **[29833]**
How to Communicate with Tact & Professionalism **[17583]**
"How Concierge Roles Are Changing in an Internet Age" in Hotel News Now (July 9, 2018) **[3873]**, **[11756]**
"How to Conduct a Financial Stress Test for Small Business Owners" in Legal Zoom (November 10, 2022) **[16563]**, **[23936]**
"How to Conduct a Functional Magnetic Resonance (fMRI) Study in Social Science Research" in MIS Quarterly (Vol. 36, September 2012, No. 3, pp. 811) **[10834]**, **[25821]**, **[31985]**
"How to Conduct a Market Analysis for Your Business" in Business News Daily (February 21, 2023) **[10655]**
"How to Conduct Primary Market Research for Your Small Business" in FindLaw (October 7, 2019) **[29492]**
"How to Conduct Thorough Market Research for Your Startup or Small Business" SalesForce Resource Center **[29493]**
How to Conduct Your Own Energy Audit (Onsite) **[19442]**, **[21389]**
"How Contractors Can Survive a Downturn" in ConstructionDive (October 21, 2019) **[4134]**, **[18974]**
"How CoolBrands' Thrills Turned to Chills" in Globe & Mail (January 25, 2007, pp. B1) **[6455]**, **[9585]**, **[29248]**
"How to Copyright a Website" in Small Business Trends (November 16, 2021) **[16426]**
"How to Cover Unexpected Costs for a New Massage Business" in Awebtoknow.com (August 26, 2019) **[10763]**
"How COVID-19 Has Changed Customer Behavior, and How Businesses Can Respond" in Legal Zoom (February 22, 2023) **[11757]**, **[20443]**
"How to Create an Auto Repair Shop Business Plan" in The Bottom Line (January 9, 2020) **[14552]**, **[18975]**
How to Create Branding You LOVE with Hollie Arnett **[17472]**
"How to Create a Business Budget for Your Small Business" in NerdWallet (Oct. 30, 2020) **[17498]**
"How to Create a Communication Plan for Your Small Business" in Camino Financial Blog (Dec. 23, 2021) **[17685]**
"How to Create a Great Employee Referral Program" in Business News Daily (March 8, 2023) **[26580]**
How to Create a Healthy Company Culture in Your Small Business with Dana Kaye **[22301]**
"How to Create a Home-Based Business Without a Product or Service" in Entrepreneur (July 31, 2021) **[26789]**
"How to Create a Landscaping Business Website" in GoDaddy (May 19, 2020) **[10100]**, **[29834]**
"How to Create an LLC" in Small Business Trends (June 29, 2021) **[27180]**, **[34510]**
"How to Create a Manifesto That Will Help You Achieve Your Goals in 2022 and Beyond" in Entrepreneur (Dec. 22, 2021) **[19529]**
"How to Create the Perfect Brand Image for Your Business" in Small Business Rainmaker (November 5, 2020) **[17442]**
How to Create a Personable Brand with Megan Dowd **[17473]**
"How to Create a Social Media Budget for Every Size of Business" in Hootsuite Blog (Aug. 31, 2021) **[17499]**
"How to Create Superfans for Your Small Business" in Small Business Trends(January 30, 2023) **[17443]**
"How to Create a Unique and Memorable Brand Identity in 2020" in Crowdspring (January 9, 2020) **[17444]**
"How to Create a Workspace That Improves Productivity" in Business News Daily (January 10, 2020) **[31038]**
"How Creative Workspace Design Encourages Productivity" in Mindspace (September 3, 2019) **[31039]**
"How to Deal" in Canadian Business (Vol. 81, November 10, 2008, No. 19, pp. 36) **[6456]**, **[9586]**
How to Deal with Unacceptable Employee Behavior **[28344]**
"How to Deal With Small Business Debt" in The Balance Small Business (Jan. 26, 2022) **[20299]**
"How the Death of Voicemail is Changing the Way We Connect" in Phys.org (May 16, 2018) **[16327]**
"How Deep Listening Will Boost Your Small Business" in Small Business Trends (march 20, 2023) **[33570]**
How to Deliver Presentations with Ease & Confidence **[17584]**
How to Design Eye-Catching Brochures, Newspapers, Ads, Reports **[17585]**
"How to Design a Workspace That Improves Productivity" in business.com (Jan. 7, 2020) **[31040]**
"How to Design Your Office for Improved Productivity and Purpose" in WeWork (October 10, 2019) **[31042]**
How to Design Your Office for Improved Productivity and Purpose **[31041]**
How to Detect and Deter Fraud in a Small Business **[19262]**
"How to Detect and Prevent Employee Fraud" in Contractor (Vol. 56, October 2009, No. 10, pp. 57) **[14619]**, **[22345]**
"How Detroit Built Its Marquee Auto Show" in Crain's Detroit Business (Vol. 30, January 6, 2014, No. 1, pp. 17) **[11410]**, **[15865]**, **[18144]**, **[29835]**, **[35061]**
"How to Develop an Active Sales Program" in Green Industry Pro (Vol. 23, September 2011) **[7626]**, **[10101]**, **[10236]**, **[20951]**, **[29836]**, **[32542]**, **[33177]**
How to Develop and Administer a Budget (Onsite) **[16768]**
"How to Dissolve a Business Partnership" in Legal Zoom (February 28, 2023) **[31343]**
How to Dissolve a Business Partnership Through Mediation **[10794]**
How Diversity, Equity, and Inclusion Can Help Corporate America Thrive **[30355]**, **[30572]**
"How to Divorce Your Office Spouse" in Canadian Business (Vol. 83, June 15, 2010, No. 10, pp. 74) **[22174]**
How to Do Everything: Genealogy **[7363]**
"How Do I Do My Own Payroll and Payroll Taxes?" in The Balance Small Business (May 24, 2020) **[31628]**
"How Do I Get a License for a Moving Company?" in Chron (March 4, 2019) **[11144]**
"How Do I Get New Massage Clients?" in Massage Business Blueprint Blog (July 23, 2020) **[10764]**
"How to Do Market Research for Small Business: 8 Affordable Market Research Techniques" in ActiveCampaign (December 15, 2017) **[29494]**
"How to Do Market Research for Your Small Business" in Fit Small Business (October 23, 2019) **[29495]**

Small Business Sourcebook • 42nd Edition **3255**

"How Do Small Businesses Approach the Budgeting Process?" in Clutch (May 12, 2021) [17500]
How Do Tattoo Artists Get Paid? [15299]
"How Do You Measure Your PR's Return On Investment?" in Puget Sound Business Journal (Vol. 34, March 21, 2014, No. 49, pp. 9) [8659], [12935], [29837], [31766]
"How Does Plant Leasing Work?" in Natura (July, 2013) [9041], [12600]
"How Does the Process of Mediation Work?" in The Balance Small Business (June 24, 2019) [10795]
"How to Dominate in Residential Maintenance" in Green Industry Pro (Vol. 23, October 2011) [7627], [10102], [10237], [29838], [32543], [33178]
How to Drive Safely: 49 Expert Tips, Tricks, and Advice for New, Teen Drivers [5104]
How to Effectively Manage Multiple Locations (Onsite) [28345]
How to Effectively Supervise People: Fundamentals of Leading With Success! (Onsite) [28346]
"How Employees' Strengths Make Your Company Stronger; Employees Who Use Their Strengths Are More Engaged, Perform Better, Are Less Likely To Leave -- and Boost Your Bottom Line" in Gallup Business Journal (February 20, 2014) [22175], [28631]
How Entrepreneurs Are Scaling Disruptive Consumer Businesses with Steve Berg [16661]
How Entrepreneurs Can Motivate Workers [22176]
How to Excel at Managing and Supervising People (Onsite) [28347]
"How Exports Could Save America" in Barron's (Vol. 89, July 20, 2009, No. 29, pp. 15) [8724], [18145], [20952], [27598]
How are Family-Owned Businesses Different Than Other Businesses? [23624]
"How Far Have Women Come?" in Women in Business (Vol. 64, Fall 2012, No. 3, pp. 13) [35795]
"How Federal Interest Rates Are Affecting Small Business Loans" in Small Business Trends (October 11, 2022) [33571]
"How to File for a Business Tax Extension" in Legal Zoom (February 28, 2023) [34807]
"How to Find the Best CRM for Your Franchise" in Entrepreneur (Oct. 25, 2019) [24370]
How to Find Cannabis Investors [5004]
"How to Find a Factory to Manufacture Your Product" in Business News Daily (February 21, 2023) [29249]
"How to Find a Good Estate Planner" in NextAvenue.com (September 10, 2019) [6041]
"How to Find the Perfect Business Name" in Business News Daily (March 17, 2023) [18976]
"How to Find a Startup Lawyer: The Ultimate Guide" in NerdWallet (May 7, 2021) [18599]
"How to Find Your Business Niche" in Business News Daily (February 21, 2023) [34511]
How to Find Your Purpose with Jessica Huie [35901]
How to Find Your Zone of Genius to Grow Your Impact and Income with Cait Scudder: An EOFire Classic from 2021 [16662]
How to Finish (Part 3 of 3) [24812]
"How Foreigners Could Disrupt U.S. Markets" in Barron's (Vol. 90, September 13, 2010, No. 37, pp. 30) [6457], [9587], [14424], [27599]
How to Form Your Own California Corporation [24536], [34452]
"How the Founder of Grubhub Built a $7 Billion Business" in Small Business Trends (November 7, 2022) [34512]
"How to Franchise a Professional Service Business" in Chron [24371]
"How to Franchise a Startup: 5 Tips for Success" in Business News Daily (Dec. 30, 2020) [24372]
"How to Franchise Your Business" in Small Business Trends (October 18, 2022) [24373]
How to Franchise Your Business: 7 Steps for Small Businesses [24374]
How to Franchise Your Small Business with Dr. Tom DuFore [24457]
How to Fund a Business - Info for Seniors [33069]
How to Gather and Document User Requirements (Onsite) [28348]
"How to Get an Animal Boarding License" in DailyPuppy (March 8, 2018) [12086]
How to Get Diversity and Inclusion Right in 2022 [30356], [30573]
How to Get Funder After the Banks Have Told You No with Brett Denton: An EOFire Classeic from 2021 [30939]
"How to Get Government Contracts" in Small Business Trends (January 14, 2022) [16364]
"How to Get Laundry Equipment Financing in 24 Hours or Less" in Laundrylux Blog [10170]
"How to Get More Clients for Your Cleaning Business" in insureon Small Business Blog (January 6, 2020) [2974], [29839]

How to Get More Organized (Onsite) [28349]
"How to Get More Students for Your Online Tutoring Business" in ClassIn blog (Jan. 17, 2022) [16135]
"How to Get the Most Value From a Career Counselor" in Time (November 17, 2014) [2602]
"How to Get in on the Online Gambling Craze" in Entrepreneur (August 29, 2022) [7293]
How to Get PR Coverage for Your Small Business with Melinda Jackson [31805]
"How to Get Professional Product Photography on a Small Business Budget" in 99 Designs [12303]
How to Get Rapid Visibility [29543]
How to Get Rich [582], [3712], [11982], [19860], [20027], [22634]
"How to Get Started in Commercial Photography" in Photography Spark (April 27, 2019) [12304]
How to Get Started (Part 1 of 3) [24813]
"How to Get a Workplace Wellness Program for Your Office" in Entrepreneurs (June 2014) [22177], [25822], [27282], [28632]
"How to Go from Tattoo Artist to Boss" in DaySmart Body Art blog (Sept. 2, 2022) [15300]
"How Good Advice 'Online' Can Attract Customers" in Indoor Comfort Marketing (Vol. 70, August 2011, No. 8, pp. 20) [490], [20444], [21876], [29840], [32544]
"How Great Leaders Think: The Art of Reframing" [22178], [22635], [28633]
"How Green Is The Valley?" in Barron's (Vol. 88, July 4, 2008, No. 28, pp. 13) [5647], [5918], [14931], [23263], [25005], [31986], [32775], [33572]
"How Growers Buy" in Farm Industry News (Vol. 42, January 1, 2009, No. 1) [17058], [20445], [32179], [33179], [34054]
"How the Growth Outliers Do It: Few Companies Manage To Prosper Over the Long Term. Those That Do Are Both More Stable and More Innovative Than Their Competition" in Harvard Business Review (Vol. 90, January-February 2012, No.1-2, pp. 110) [18146], [19530]
How to Handle Competition in Business: 10 Tips to Beat Competition [19861]
How to Handle Conflict and Confrontation (Onsite) [28350]
"How to Handle a Public Relations Crisis" in Legal Zoom (February 14, 2023) [31767]
"How Hard Could It Be? The Four Pillars of Organic Growth" in Inc. (January 2008, pp. 69-70) [18147], [26960], [31768]
"How Has Cincinnati's City Golf Privatization Played?" in Business Courier (Vol. 27, September 10, 2010, No. 19, pp. 1) [7521], [20028], [28634]
"How to Heal a Broken Legg" in Barron's (Vol. 92, September 17, 2012, No. 38, pp. 18) [26581], [28635]
"How Healthcare Managers Can Improve Outcomes and Patient Care; They Can Start With These Five Steps for Turning their Organization's Employee Engagement Results Into Clinical Improvements" in Gallup Business Journal (August 7, 2014) [25823], [28636]
"How Healthcare Organizations Can Help Improve Social Risk Interventions" in RevCycle Intelligence (February 6, 2023) [25824]
"How to Help Your Kid Start a (Legal) Business" in Business News Daily (February 21, 2023) [34513]
"How Hierarchy Can Hurt Strategy Execution" in Harvard Business Review (Vol. 88, July-August 2010, No. 7-8, pp. 74) [19361], [28637]
"How High Can Soybeans Fly?" in Barron's (Vol. 88, March 10, 2008, No. 10, pp. M14) [6458], [8725], [9588], [17059], [18148], [23937], [27600]
"How Hispanic Small Businesses Are Using Supplier Diversity Programs to Secure Contracts" in Legal Zoom (February 17, 2023) [30357]
"How I Became a Serial Entrepreneur" in Baltimore Business Journal (Vol. 31, April 18, 2014, No. 51, pp. 26) [7120], [9589], [21544], [22636], [35796]
How I Built My Small Business: Chelsea Bay Dennis - Creating a Sustainable Career as a Graphic Designer [7596]
How I Built My Small Business: Danielle Connor - A Successful Local Coffee Shop Can Make How Much? Retrograde Coffee Roasters Reveals Secrets [3200]
How I Built My Small Business: Duran Morley - No College? No Problem. 17-Year-Old Started VanSpeed Instead [36037]
How I Built My Small Business: Eric Henry - Crafting an Eco-Friendly Clothing Empire with TS Designs and the Fight Against Fashion's Waste Crisis [3063]
How I Built My Small Business: How to Start and Run an Osteopathic Practice with All Words Health with Dr. Arlene Dijamco [26058]
How I Built My Small Business: Loren Vandegrift - Insights from Business Exits Broker on Sales, Values, and Trends [2155]

How I Built My Small Business: Naomi Crawford - Discover Lunchette's Hidden Secrets to a Thriving Sustainable Food Business [14062]
How I Built My Small Business: Ross Jacobson - Behind the Scenes: Navigating Hollywood as an Indie Producer with 3311 Productions [6214]
How I Built This: A Climate-Resilient Ancient Grain with Pierre Thiam of Yoléle [17157]
How I Built This: Achieving Greater Things with Adam Grant [22902]
How I Built This: Advice Line with Andrew Abraham of Orgain [30154]
How I Built This: Advice Line with Ariel Kaye of Parachute Home [18443]
How I Built This: Advice Line with Boston Beer Company [30841]
How I Built This: Advice Line with Brett Schulman of CAVA [18855]
How I Built This: Advice Line with Fawn Weaver of Uncle Nearest Premium Whiskey [17474]
How I Built This: Advice Line with Gary Erickson of Clif Bar [30155]
How I Built This: Advice Line: Growing Beyond Your Niche [34624]
How I Built This: Advice Line with Holly Thaggard of Supergoop! [17475]
How I Built This: Advice Line with Jeff Raider of Harry's [18444]
How I Built This: Advice Line with Joe Kudla of Vuori [6143]
How I Built This: Advice Line with Leah Solivan of Taskrabbit [26471]
How I Built This: Advice Line with Mark Ramadan of Sir Kensington's [34625]
How I Built This: Advice Line with Maureen Kelly of Tarte Cosmetics [29544]
How I Built This: Advice Line with Randy Goldberg of Bombas [17476]
How I Built This: Advice Line: Reaching New Customers [30156]
How I Built This: Advice Line with Sadie Lincoln of barre3 [34626]
How I Built This: Advice Line with Sarah Kauss of S'well [19977]
How I Built This: Advice Line with Scott and Ally Svenson of MOD Pizza [18445]
How I Built This: Advice Line with Tom Rinks of Sun Bum [17477]
How I Built This: Advice Line with Tony Lamb of Kona Ice [16663]
How I Built This: Alamo Drafthouse Cinema: Tim and Karrie League [11131]
How I Built This: ARRAY: Filmmaker Ava DuVernay [6215]
How I Built This: Audible: Don Katz [14859]
How I Built This: Barefoot Wine: Bonnie Harvey and Michael Houlihan [33047]
How I Built This: Burt's Bees: Roxanne Quimby [4532]
How I Built This: Casper: Philip Krim [27817]
How I Built This: Complexly: Hank and John Green [16271]
How I Built This: Creating a Creative Community with Tina Roth-Eisenberg of CreativeMornings [22903]
How I Built This: Dang Foods: Vincent and Andrew Kitirattragam [15046]
How I Built This: Dave's Hot Chicken: Arman Oganesyan [14063]
How I Built This: Dutch Bros. Coffee: Travis Boersma [3201]
How I Built This: Food52: Amanda Hesser [22026]
How I Built This: Freshpet: Scott Morris [12235]
How I Built This: Goodreads: Otis and Elizabeth Chandler [14860]
How I Built This: Grindr: Joel Simkhai [14861]
How I Built This: Halo Top Ice Cream: Justin Woolverton [15047]
How I Built This: Harry's Razors: Andy Katz-Mayfield and Jeff Raider [4533]
How I Built This: Headspace: Andy Puddicombe and Rich Person [14862]
How I Built This: Herschel Supply Co.: Jamie and Lyndon Cormack [6144]
How I Built This: Hinge: Justin McLeod [3818]
How I Built This: Leatherman Tool Group: Tim Leatherman [22904]
How I Built This: Less Competition, More Creation with Renée Mauborgne [19978]
How I Built This: Lily's Sweets: Cynthia Tice [34627]
How I Built This: Mary's Gone Crackers: Mary Waldner [15048]
How I Built This: Merge Records: Laura Ballance and Mac McCaughan [13659]
How I Built This: Mielle Organics: Monique Rodriguez [4534]

Master Index How

Master Index

How I Built This: M.M. LaFleur: Sarah LaFleur **[3064]**
How I Built This: MOD Pizza & Seattle Coffee Company: Scott and Ally Svenson **[14064]**
How I Built This: Orangetheory Fitness: Ellen Latham **[6814]**
How I Built This: Orgain: Andrew Abraham **[15049]**
How I Built This: Osprey Packs: Mike Pfotenhauer **[15116]**
How I Built This: Paperless Post: James and Alexa Hirschfeld **[11843]**
How I Built This: Politico & Axios: Jim VandeHei **[12006]**
How I Built This: Poshmark: Manish Chandra **[32346]**
How I Built This: Reclaiming Food Waste with Jasmine Crowe-Houston of Goodr **[34433]**
How I Built This: Reimagining Seafood Production with Aryé Elfenbein and Justin Kolbeck of Wildtype **[23429]**
How I Built This: Robert Reffkin: Compass **[14863]**
How I Built This: Spikeball: Chris Ruder **[17478]**
How I Built This: Spin Master/PAW Patrol: Ronnen Harary **[15804]**
How I Built This: Stacy's Pita Chips: Stacy Madison **[15050]**
How I Built This: Stasher and Modern Twist: Kat Nouri **[23430]**
How I Built This: Suitsupply: Fokke de Jone **[3065]**
How I Built This: Sun Bum: Tom Rinks **[17479]**
How I Built This: Tapping the Heat Beneath Your Feet with Kathy Hannun of Dandelion Energy **[23431]**
How I Built This: Tarte Cosmetics: Maureen Kelly **[4535]**
How I Built This: Tate's Bake Shop: Kathleen King **[1279]**
How I Built This: The Cronut and Dominique Ansel Bakery **[1280]**
How I Built This: The Lip Bar (TLB): Melissa Butler **[4536]**
How I Built This: The Tetris Company: Henk Rogers **[14864]**
How I Built This: Twilio: Jeff Lawson **[14865]**
How I Built This: Unlocking the Renewable Energy Revolution with Ramay Swaminathan of Malta Inc. **[23432]**
How I Built This: Vuori: Joe Kudla **[3066]**
How I Built This: What It Really Takes to Build a Food Business: Part 1 **[30842]**
How I Built This: What It Really Takes to Build a Food Business: Part 2 **[30843]**
How I Built This: When Your Dinner is Printed with Eshchar Ben-Shitrit of Redefine Meat **[23433]**
How I Built This: Xero Shoes: Steven Sashen and Lena Phoenix **[22905]**
How I Built This: Yasso: Amanda Klane and Drew Harrington **[15051]**
"How I Did It: Best Buy's CEO On Learning to Love Social Media" in Harvard Business Review (Vol. 88, December 2010, No. 12, pp. 43) **[4395]**, **[11758]**, **[21877]**, **[29841]**, **[31871]**, **[32180]**
"How I Did It: Bobbi Brown, Founder and CEO, Bobbi Brown Cosmetics" in Inc. (November 2007, pp. 110-112) **[1583]**, **[4514]**, **[35797]**
"How I Did It: Jack Ma, Alibaba.com" in Inc. (January 2008, pp. 94-102) **[10765]**, **[21878]**, **[22637]**, **[31344]**
"How I Did It: Mel Zuckerman, Chairman, Canyon Ranch" in Inc. (December 2007, pp. 140-142) **[4135]**, **[12418]**, **[22638]**
"How I Did It: Timberland's CEO On Standing Up to 65,000 Angry Activists" in Harvard Business Review (Vol. 88, September 2010, No. 9, pp. 39) **[3123]**, **[5648]**, **[5919]**, **[8660]**, **[12936]**, **[23264]**, **[31345]**, **[31769]**, **[31872]**
"How I Did It: Xerox's Former CEO On Why Succession Shouldn't Be a Horse Race" in Harvard Business Review (Vol. 88, October 2010, No. 10, pp. 47) **[18977]**, **[19862]**, **[28638]**
"How I Did It: Zappos's CEO on Going to Extremes for Customers" in Harvard Business Review (Vol. 88, July-August 2010, No. 7-8, pp. 41) **[14676]**, **[20446]**, **[29842]**
How I Made It: 40 Successful Entrepreneurs Reveal How They Made Millions **[22391]**, **[24537]**
"How I Make $10K/Month Selling Printable Sewing Patterns from My Fashion Blog" in Starter Story Website (July 26, 2020) **[14650]**
"How I... Operate a Food Truck on the Streets of Honolulu" in Pacific Business News (Vol. 21, July 18, 2014, No. 21, pp. 19) **[1256]**, **[3846]**, **[6985]**, **[35798]**
How to Implement Effective Internal Controls **[23712]**
"How Important Are Small Businesses to Local Economies?" in Chron (Oct. 15, 2018) **[20953]**
"How to Improve Your Mobile Marketing" in Contractor (Vol. 56, October 2009, No. 10, pp. 54) **[286]**, **[12635]**, **[29843]**
"How Innovative Is Michigan? Index Aims To Keep Track" in Crain's Detroit Business (Vol. 24, February 4, 2008, No. 5, pp. 1) **[24680]**, **[27883]**
"How Instagram's Influencers Changed the Model Industry" in BBC News (April 3, 2021) **[10993]**
"How to Invest in Self-Storage Real Estate" in U.S. News & World Report (August 12, 2019) **[12977]**
"How Investors React When Women Join Boards" in Harvard Business Review (Vol. 88, July-August 2010, No. 7-8, pp. 24) **[9590]**, **[28639]**, **[35799]**
"How to Issue a 1099 to an LLC" in Legal Zoom (February 23, 2023) **[34808]**
"How Ivanah Thomas Founded a $5 Million Business - While Working Nights" in Orlando Business Journal (Vol. 30, April 18, 2014, No. 43, pp. 3) **[8257]**, **[22639]**, **[35800]**
How to Keep Going (Part 2 of 3) **[24814]**
"How to Keep Your Sales from Running Out of Gas" in Agency Sales Magazine (Vol. 39, July 2009, No. 7, pp. 30) **[18978]**, **[19531]**, **[32545]**
"How to Keep Your Top Employees" in Archery Business (December 14, 2018) **[851]**, **[26961]**, **[33573]**
"How to Know if You Really Classify as a Small Business" in Business News Daily (February 21, 2023) **[16565]**
How to Land Your First Client, Part 1 **[29513]**, **[35709]**
How to Launch Your Venture with 0% Funding and Profit by Helping Others with Leo Kanell **[28237]**
How Laundromat Owners Can Maximize Profit Margins **[5236]**
"How to Lead Kids Down a Path to Entrepreneurship in 2021" in Entrepreneur (Jan. 17, 2021) **[36024]**
"How to Legally Hire an Intern" in Legal Zoom (March 16, 2023) **[26582]**, **[26962]**
"How to Legally Start a Business in Auto Repair" in Chron (March 4, 2019) **[14553]**
How to Legally Terminate Employees With Attitude Problems (Onsite) **[18488]**
"How to get an LLC" in Legal Zoom (October 27, 2022) **[27181]**
"How Low Will Market for Antiques Actually Go?" in The New York Times (March 3, 2018) **[740]**
How to Make Big Money in Your Own Small Business: Unexpected Rules Every Small Business Owner Needs to Know **[18149]**, **[18979]**, **[19863]**, **[20029]**, **[20109]**, **[22392]**, **[23938]**, **[24538]**, **[24681]**, **[29844]**, **[31043]**
"How to Make Business Plans during Unpredictable Times" in Legal Zoom (February 22, 2023) **[18980]**
"How to Make the Business World Sane Again" in Small Business Trends (October 17, 2022) **[16566]**
"How to Make a Deal In Uncertain Economic Times" in Small Business Trends (November 14, 2022) **[33574]**
"How to Make my House Cleaning Service Business Unique" in A Janitor's Story **[2975]**, **[18981]**
"How to Make a Mailing List in Gmail for Business Use" in Small Business Trends (February 8, 2023) **[17686]**
"How to Make Money in Retirement: A Guide to Turning a Hobby into a Side Business" in business.com (Sept. 7, 2022) **[33070]**
How to Make Money Running a Barbershop **[7868]**
How to Make Money in the Sewing Business **[14651]**
How to Make Money with Social Media: An Insider's Guide to Using New and Emerging Media to Grow Your Business **[9155]**, **[16427]**, **[17687]**, **[18150]**, **[21879]**, **[22640]**, **[28640]**, **[29845]**, **[32546]**
"How to Make Remote Team Collaboration More Successful" in Blog.vantagecircle.com(January 3, 2023) **[22179]**
"How to Make Third-Party Delivery Work For You in Any Market" in PMG Pizza Magazine (May 2019) **[6905]**
How to Make Your Brand Stand Out with Zuza Hicks **[17480]**
"How to Make Your Coffee Shop More Accessible" in Perfect Daily Grind (August 12, 2019) **[7558]**, **[35946]**
How to Manage Conflict and Confrontation **[17586]**
How to Manage Emotions and Excel Under Pressure (Onsite) **[28351]**
How to Manage an Information Security Program (Onsite) **[18489]**, **[33797]**
"How to Manage and Motivate a Remote Workforce during a Crisis" in Legal Zoom (February 17, 2023) **[22180]**
"How to Manage the New Expectations of the Younger Workforce" in Entrepreneur (March 21, 2023) **[22181]**, **[26963]**
How to Manage & Organize Accounts Payable **[23713]**
"How to Manage Successful Crowdsourcing Projects" in eWeek (September 29, 2010) **[20447]**, **[21880]**, **[29846]**, **[30740]**
"How to Manage Your Debt as a Startup" in Legal Zoom (February 17, 2023) **[34514]**
"How to Manage Your Small Business Payroll Taxes the Easy Way" in Sage Advice Blog (Nov. 8, 2021) **[31629]**
"How Managers Become Leaders: The Seven Seismic Shifts of Perspective and Responsibility" in Harvard Business Review (Vol. 90, June 2012, No. 6, pp. 64) **[28641]**
"How Many Direct Reports? Senior Leaders, Always Pressed For Time, Are Nonetheless Broadening Their Span of Control" in Harvard Business Review (Vol. 90, April 2012, No. 4, pp. 112) **[28642]**, **[34055]**, **[34988]**
How to Market Your Business **[29847]**
"How to Market Your Dry Cleaning Business When Business Is Slow" in Kreussler Inc. Blog (April 7, 2020) **[5237]**
How to Market Your Graphic Designs **[3315]**
"How Marketers Can Tap the Web" in Sales and Marketing Management (November 12, 2009) **[9156]**, **[16428]**, **[29848]**, **[34056]**
"How to Master Cold Calling (Scripts Included)" in Business News Daily (February 21, 2023) **[17688]**
How to Master the Financial Fundamentals with Adam Kroener **[24211]**
How to Master Your Monthly Bookkeeping **[1778]**
"How to Maximize Your Investment Income" in Contractor (Vol. 56, December 2009, No. 12, pp. 33) **[8921]**, **[9591]**, **[27283]**, **[34809]**
How the Media Industry SHOULD Work for Growing Businesses and Entrepreneurs with Omar Hamdi **[31806]**
"How Metrics Can Improve the Quality of Your DEI Initiatives" in Associations Now (May 9, 2022) **[30574]**
"How Millionaire Mentor Cedric Nash Went from a $36,000 Salary to $90M in Annual Business Revenue" in Black Enterprise(February 7, 2023) **[6459]**, **[23939]**
"How Mini Sessions Can Make a Big Impact for Your Photography Studio" in H+H Color Lab Blog (December 15, 2016) **[12345]**
"How a Mobile CRM Benefits Your Business" in Business News Daily (February 21, 2023) **[20448]**
"How Mobile Devices Can Be Used in Food Truck Hiring" in Mobile-Cuisine.com (September, 23, 2020) **[6986]**, **[26583]**, **[30474]**
How to Monetize Partnerships **[31593]**
"How the Mortgage Market Is Opening Up to Brokers" in Entrepreneur (October 9, 2019) **[11045]**
"How Much Do Electricians Make?" in Small Business Trends (March 8, 2023) **[5377]**
How Much Do Tattoo Parlors Make? (And the Most Popular Tattoo Days of the Year) **[15301]**
"How Much Does it Cost to Incorporate in Each State?" in Business News Daily (June 7, 2016) **[27182]**, **[34515]**
"How Much Does It Cost to Be a Dog Breeder" in BreedingBusiness.com (October 7, 2017) **[649]**
"How Much Does It Cost to Open a Laundromat?" in NerdWallet (Oct. 18, 2020) **[10159]**
How Much Does It Cost to Start a Tattoo Parlor Business? **[15273]**
"How Much Does It Cost to Start a Tattoo Parlor?" in Chron **[15274]**
"How Much Does It Cost to Start a Tutoring Business?" in Starter Story (Oct. 20, 2022) **[16116]**
"How Much For a Magic Bullet?" in San Francisco Business Times (Vol. 28, April 25, 2014, No. 40, pp. 4) **[5165]**, **[20030]**, **[31987]**
"How Much Inequality Is Necessary for Growth?" in Harvard Business Review (Vol. 90, January-February 2012, No.1-2, pp. 28) **[18151]**, **[20954]**
"How Much Money Do Beauty Salon Owners Make?" in Chron (March 8, 2019) **[7869]**
How Much Money Do Dog Breeders Make Monthly/Yearly **[650]**
How Much Money Do Professional Organizers Make Annually? **[12833]**
How Much Money Does a Christmas Tree Farm Make? A Breakdown **[2942]**
"How Much Profit is Enough?" in Automotive News (Vol. 86, October 31, 2011, No. 6488, pp. 12) **[11411]**, **[20031]**, **[29250]**, **[35192]**
"How New Angels Can Get Their Wings" in Business Journal Portland (Vol. 30, February 28, 2014, No. 52, pp. 6) **[9289]**
"How Newsletter Innovations Are Driving Publisher Revenue" in What's New in Publishing (June 6, 2019) **[11475]**
"How Not to Raise Bank Capital" in Barron's (Vol. 88, June 30, 2008, No. 26, pp. M6) **[6460]**, **[9592]**, **[23940]**, **[27601]**
"How One Company Joins Corporate Public Relations and Community Engagement" in Denver Business Journal (Vol. 65, January 17, 2014, No. 36, pp. A6) **[7121]**, **[12937]**, **[31346]**, **[31770]**, **[34331]**, **[35801]**
How to Open a Brewpub or Microbrewery **[1919]**
How to Open a Financially Successful Bakery: With a Companion CD-ROM **[1237]**
"How to Open a Laundry & Dry Cleaning Business" in Chron (February 12, 2019) **[5238]**
How to Open and Operate a Bed & Breakfast **[1416]**, **[8412]**

Small Business Sourcebook • 42nd Edition 3257

How to Open and Operate a Financially Successful Bookstore on Amazon and Other Web Sites: With Companion CD-ROM [1799], [9157], [11686], [16429], [21881], [32074], [32547]
"How to Open and Operate a Financially Successful Florist and Floral Business Online and Off" [6845], [11687], [18470], [20367], [21763], [29561], [32075], [32425], [34810]
How to Open & Operate a Financially Successful Landscaping, Nursery, or Lawn Service Business: With Companion CD-ROM [7600], [10067], [10223], [26735]
How to Open a Plumbing Business [12636]
"How to Open a Private Medical Practice, Step by Step" in Business News Daily (February 28, 2023) [25825], [34516]
"How to Optimize a Food truck Drive-Thru Service" in FoodTruckOperator.com (June 15, 2020) [6987]
How to Optimize Your Small Business Delivery Services [6906], [33575]
"How to Organize Business Expenses: 7 Important Tips" in Legal Zoom (February 17, 2023) [18982]
How to Organize and Run a Small Business [16716]
How to Organize Your Small Business Office/Workspace [31044]
"How Our Picks Beat The Bear" in Barron's (Vol. 88, July 14, 2008, No. 28, pp. 18) [6461], [9593], [20955], [23941], [29251], [33180]
"How to Outfit Your Startup with Technology" in Small Business Trends (May 30, 2019) [31045]
How to Outsource Graphic Design (and Grow Your Business) [3316]
"How to Overcome Startup Fears and Move Forward with Your Business Goals" in Legal Zoom (February 21, 2023) [34517]
"How to Pay Yourself from Your Small Business" in Legal Zoom (February 10, 2023) [16567], [31630], [34811]
How to Pay Zero Taxes: Your Guide to Every Tax Break the IRS Allows [15389], [25140], [34812]
How to Persuade and Influence People: Powerful Techniques to Get your Own Way More Often [17689], [22641]
"How to Pick Gifts that Match Your Brand" in Small Business Trends [17445]
"How to Pick the Right Accelerator" in Inc. [8791], [8811]
How to Pitch Your Business for PR Opportunities with Lucy Werner [31807]
"How to Place Property in an LLC" in Legal Zoom (February 17, 2023) [27183]
"How to Play the Tech Mergers" in Barron's (Vol. 90, August 30, 2010, No. 35, pp. 18) [2748], [3509], [3713], [9594], [26304], [30741], [31347]
"How Plumbing Facebook Groups Have Changed the Industry" in Plumber (November 20, 2019) [11759], [12637]
How Poppi Disrupted the Soda Industry: A Conversation with Steve Clements and Allison Ellsworth [17481]
How Poppi Disrupted the Soda Industry: A Conversation with Stevie Clements and Allison Ellsworth [17482]
How to Present Online: A Skills-Based Workshop [17587]
"How to Prevent Fear, Uncertainty and Doubt from Derailing Your Retirement Plan" in Minority Business Entrepreneur (Vol. 39, Fall, 2022, No. 4, pp. 36-37) [9595]
"How to Prevent Sexual Harassment in Your Workplace" in Legal Zoom (March 15, 2023) [26964]
How to Price Commercial Photography [12305]
How to Price Products - 7 Competitive Pricing Strategies to Make a Profit [20032], [21882]
"How to Price Your Small Business Products or Services" excerpt in dummies [31652]
"How Profitable Are Add-On Airline Fees?" in Canadian Business (Vol. 85, September 17, 2012, No. 14, pp. 82) [19362], [20033]
"How Profitable Is a Laundromat Business?" in Laundry Solutions Company (January 23, 2016) [5239]
"How to Protect Your Small Business Against Fraud" in Entrepreneur (Jan. 14, 2021) [19263]
How to Protect Your Small Business from Fraud [19264]
How to Protect Yourself: Small Business Scams [19265]
"How to Purchase an Existing Business" in LegalZoom (Nov. 2, 2021) [19674]
"How to Purchase a Laundromat Franchise" in Chron (Apr. 5, 2019) [10171]
"How to Put on a Successful Gym Grand Opening" in Glofox blog (June 10, 2019) [12419]
"How Quitting Tobacco Reshaped CVS: Q&A with CEO Larry Merlo" in USA Today (September 14, 2019) [5166], [15698], [25826]
How to Read and Understand Financial Statements (Onsite) [23714]
"How to (Realistically) Start an Online Ecommerce Busines That Actually Grows in 2019" in Big Commerce [4704], [10656], [11760], [18152]
"How to Recover from a Bad Business Decision" in Legal Zoom (February 15, 2023) [18983]
"How to Register and Trademark a Brand Name" in Business News Daily (February 21, 2023) [17446], [27884]
"Handling New Health Insurance Regulations" in Baltimore Business Journal (Vol. 31, April 25, 2014, No. 52, pp. 25) [8922], [17311], [25827], [27284], [31988]
"How to Remove a Member from an LLC" in Legal Zoom (March 16, 2023) [27184]
"How to Report a Scam" in Small Business Trends (March 6, 2023) [16568]
"How to Resolve Business Disputes with Arbitration or Mediation" in The Balance Small Business (February 28, 2020) [10796]
"How to Retain Generation Y Employees?" in Journal of Small Business Strategy (March 4, 2021) [22334]
"How to Retain That 'Small Business' Feel as Your Company Grows" in Small Business Trends (December 9, 2021) [16569], [22182]
"How to Retire: Do's and Don'ts" in Canadian Business (Vol. 79, July 17, 2006, No. 14-15, pp. 29) [6462], [9596], [17312], [23942]
"How to Reuse Or Recycle Your Old Tech: eWaste Is on the Rise but You Can Help Combat It By Using Old PCs and Electronics in Different Ways" in PC Magazine (Vol. 31, February 2012, No. 2, pp. 108) [2749], [3714], [5649], [13717], [23265]
"How Risk Management Can Make Marijuana Businesses Bulletproof (or at Least Bullet Resistant)" in Green Market Report (May 3, 2019) [5005], [32387]
"How to Run a Promotion without Running from the Law" in Legal Zoom (March 28, 2023) [29849], [32548]
How to Run Your Business Like a Girl: Successful Strategies from Entrepreneurial Women Who Made It Happen [22642], [24682], [35802]
"How to Run Your Own Coffee Shop" in Investopedia (December 2, 2019) [3183]
"How to Save More and Worry Less at Tax Time" in Canadian Business (Vol. 85, August 13, 2012, No. 13, pp. 33) [6463], [23943]
"How to Scale Your Business and Stay Sane in the Process" in Legal Zoom (February 22, 2023) [18153]
How to Scale Your Consulting Business [20141]
"How to Sell a Business" in Small Business Trends (May 4, 2021) [19225]
"How to Sell, Donate, or Recycle Your Stuff" in The New York Times (January 11, 2019) [3893], [13718]
"How to Sell Your Company for More" in Small Business Trends (October 17, 2022) [19226]
"How to Service Your Own Computer: 7 Easy Things Computer Repair Places Do" in How-To Geek (November 12, 2018) [3576]
"How to Set Salaries" in Entrepreneur [35479]
How to Set Up a Commercial Photography Business [12306]
How to Set Up a Delivery Service for Your Restaurant [6907]
"How to Set Up an Effective Home Office" in Women Entrepreneur (August 22, 2008) [26790], [31046], [35803]
How to Set Up an Employee Benefits Program in 6 Steps [17313]
How to Set Up a Small Business Customer Service Call Center [20449]
"How to Set Up Your Physical Office" in The Hartford Business Owner's Playbook [31047]
"How Sharing Sent Record Sales Soaring" in Business Strategy Review (Vol. 25, Summer 2014, No. 2, pp. 7) [11265], [27885]
"How Small Business Can Motivate Employees" on StartupBros website [22183]
"How Small Business Can Negotiate with Landlords and Vendors during a Crisis" in Legal Zoom (March 9, 2023) [16570]
"How Small Businesses Can Fund Their Ransomware Protection" in BizTech (October 7, 2021) [3467]
"How Small Businesses Can Make a Big Environmental Impact" in Sustainability Times (May 28, 2021) [23266]
"How Small Businesses Can Manage Hazardous Waste: A Guide" in MultiBriefs: Exclusive (August 28, 2020) [7955]
"How Small Businesses Can Overcome Common Cash Flow Challenges" in Williston Herald (Aug. 27, 2021) [19719]
"How Small Businesses Can Protect Themselves against Counterfeiters" in Legal Zoom (February 15, 2023) [17447], [19266]
"How Small Businesses Can Stand Out From Their Competition" in Linchpin SEO (Jan. 13, 2022) [19864]
"How Small Businesses Should Adapt Their Customer Communication This Year" in Forbes (Apr 14, 2021) [17690]
How Small Businesses Should Approach Mediation [10797]
"How Small, Independent Hotels Are Using Tech to Be More Competitive" in Skift (November 11, 2019) [8413], [11761]
"How Social Security Works for Business Owners" in Due (March 29, 2018) [34244]
"How Some Cannabis Brands Plan on Breaking Up Vertical Integration" in Marijuana Venture (October 14, 2020) [5006]
"How South Florida Can Revive a Flagging Sector" in South Florida Business Journal (Vol. 34, April 4, 2014, No. 37, pp. 10) [8414], [13949], [15866], [20956], [33373], [35062]
"How to Spot Employee Theft and What You Can Do About It" in Insperity Blog [22346]
"How to Spot Secondary Revenue Streams for Your Business" in Legal Zoom (February 21, 2023) [18984]
"How to Spot and Then Avoid Getting Caught Out by Scams Targeting Businesses" in Business Companion website (May 2022) [19267]
How to Start a $24K/Month Laundromat Business [10160]
How to Start a Bankruptcy Forms Processing Service [4730], [4755], [18600], [20239], [23692], [31122]
"How to Start a Bike Shop" in Outspokin' [1522]
"How to Start a Brewery in 6 Steps" in JustBusiness (October 22, 2020) [1920]
How to Start a Brewery Business [1921]
How to Start a Brewery Business in 2020: The Complete 9 Step Guide [1922]
"How to Start Budget Planning for Your Business" in Business.com (Jan. 25, 2022) [17501]
"How to Start a Business: A Step-by-Step Guide" in Business News Daily (February 23, 2023) [34518]
"How to Start a Business Breeding Dogs" in Chron (July 19, 2017) [651]
"How to Start a Business with No Money" in Legal Zoom (March 14, 2023) [34519]
"How to Start a Business with a Partner" in Legal Zoom (March 14, 2023) [27185], [34520]
"How to Start a Car Dealership Business in 9 Simple Steps" in Starting Business (September 4, 2020) [11412]
"How to Start a Car Shop From the Ground Up" in Chron (April 9, 2019) [14554]
"How to Start a Christmas Tree Farm" in AG America Lending Blog (June 21, 2022) [2944]
"How to Start a Christmas Tree Farm" in Part-Time Money (March 29, 2022) [2943]
How to Start a Christmas Tree Farm Business in 23 Steps [2945]
How to Start a Clean Eating Food Delivery Business [6882]
"How to Start a Cleaning Business" in Entrepreneur (June 14, 2003) [2976], [18985], [34521]
How to Start a Cleaning Business [2977]
"How to Start a Cleaning Business in 7 Steps" in JustBusiness (September 15, 2020) [2978], [18986], [34522]
How to Start a Coffee Shop in a Small Town [3184]
"How to Start a Coin-Operated Laundry" in Entrepreneur (February 15, 2019) [5240]
"How to Start a Consulting Business: Determining Your Rates" in Entrepreneur (March 10, 2020) [20110], [31653]
"How to Start a Delivery Service" in How to Start an LLC [6883]
How to Start a Distribution Business in 9 Steps [20627]
"How to Start a Dog Boarding Business" in Entrepreneur (February 18, 2020) [12088]
"How to Start a Dog Boarding Business" in The Balance Careers (August 9, 2019) [12087]
How to Start a Dog Breeding Business at Home in 23 Steps [652]
How to Start a Dog Breeding Business: The Complete Guide [653]
"How to Start a Dog Grooming Business" in 123 Pet Software Blog (October 2, 2020) [12089]
"How to Start a Dog Training Business" in The Balance Careers (October 31, 2019) [12142]
"How to Start a Dog Training Business: A Complete Guide" in K9 of Mine website (September 19, 2019) [12143]
"How to Start an Electrician Business" in Small Business Trends(March 1, 2023) [5378]
"How to Start an Event Planning Business from Home" in EventMB (April 30, 2020) [6093], [34523]
How to Start a Faux Painting or Mural Business [287], [4574], [11853], [11870]
How to Start a Food Delivery Business [6908]
"How to Start a Food Delivery Business in 2022" in Circuit Blog (July 28, 2022) [6884]

3258 Small Business Sourcebook • 42nd Edition

Master Index How

How to Start a Food Delivery Business in Four Steps [6909]
How to Start a Food Delivery Business From Home [6910]
"How to Start a Food Delivery Service (with Templates)" in Paperform Blog (Aug. 11, 2022) [6885]
How to Start a Food Truck Business in 2020 [6988], [34524]
"How to Start a Genealogy Business" in The Balance Small Business (June 25, 2019) [7364]
"How to Start and Grow a Successful Dog Training Business" in Dog Matters (April 12, 2018) [12144]
"How to Start a Hazardous Waste Disposal Business" in Gaebler Ventures [7956]
How to Start a Home-Based Catering Business [2660]
How to Start a Home-Based Consulting Business: Define Your Specialty Build a Client Base Make Yourself Indispensable [2167], [5475], [10473], [20071], [26736]
How to Start a Home-based Craft Business [4575], [4647], [18987], [26737]
How to Start a Home-Based Event Planning Business [14501], [15815], [26738]
How to Start a Home-Based Landscaping Business [10068], [21883], [26739], [29850]
How to Start a Home-Based Mail Order Business [10460], [20677], [21764], [24539], [26740], [29562]
How to Start a Home-Based Online Retail Business [21765], [26741], [32076]
How to Start a Home-Based Personal Chef Business [2661], [26742]
How to Start a Home-Based Professional Organizing Business [12808], [26743]
How to Start a Home-Based Senior Care Business [184], [8923], [10281], [12022], [15515], [25828], [26791], [27285]
How to Start a Home-Based Senior Care Business: Develop a Winning Business Plan [11490], [20034], [23504], [26584], [26744], [29851]
"How to Start a Home-Based Tax Preparation Business" in Home Business (June 3, 2022) [15390], [26792]
How to Start a Home-Based Web Design Business [16366], [26745]
How to Start a Home-Based Web Design Business, 4th Edition [16367], [26746]
"How to Start an Insanely Successful Personal Training Business" in Small Business Trends (January 11, 2017) [12420]
How to Start an Internal Communications Department [17691]
How to Start an Internet Sales Business Without Making the Government Mad [68], [1759], [9086], [16807], [21766], [24540], [27886], [34813]
"How to Start a Landscaping or Lawn Care Business" in JustBusiness (October 22, 2020) [10103]
How to Start a Laundromat [10161]
How to Start a Laundromat. A Simple Step-by-Step Guide [10162]
How to Start a Laundromat Business [10208]
How to Start a Laundromat Business With Little to No Money [10163]
"How to Start a Medical Marijuana Dispensary Business in 2020" in Crowdspring (January 12, 2020) [5007]
"How to Start a Minority-Owned Business" in NerdWallet (Oct. 22, 2020) [30358]
"How to Start a Mobile Business" in The Zebra (July 12, 2021) [30475]
"How to Start a Mobile Business - On the Way to Small Business Success" in Next (Aug. 14, 2018) [30476]
How to Start a Moving Company [11145]
"How to Start a Moving Company Business" in Chron (April 24, 2019) [11146]
How to Start a Moving Company Without Alot of Money [11147]
How to Start My Own Picture Studio Store [12346]
"How to Start My Own Sewing Business" in Chron (February 12, 2019) [14652]
How to Start, Operate and Market a Freelance Notary Signing Agent Business [11046], [18471], [24541]
"How to Start a Personal Grocery Shopping Business" in ToughNickel (May 28, 2020) [12023]
"How to Start a Personal Shopper Business" in The Balance Small Business (November 17, 2019) [12024]
"How to Start a Personal Training Business From Home" in The Balance Small Business (December 8, 2019) [12421]
"How to Start a Pet Grooming Business" in Starting Your Business website (November 15, 2020) [12090]
"How to Start a Photography Business" in Photography Spark (July 3, 2020) [12347]
How to Start a Plumbing Business: A Step-by-Step Guide to Set You Up for Success [12638]
"How to Start a Private Tutoring Business" in Chron (March 11, 2019) [16117]
"How to Start a Professional Organizer Business" in My-Corporation blog [12809]
"How to Start a Professional Organizing Business" in LiveAbout website (Nov. 16, 2019) [12810]
How to Start a Professional Organizing Business [12811]
How to Start a Professional Organizing Business in 30 Days [12812]
"How to Start a Profitable Home Tutoring Business" in Zen Business [16118]
How to Start a Publishing Company: Turn Your Passion into Profit Using This Comprehensive Publishing Business Blueprint [1659]
"How to Start a Restaurant Delivery Service Business" in Chron (Feb. 4, 2019) [6886]
How to Start and Run Your Own Corporation: S-Corporations For Small Business Owners [17314], [18601], [18988], [22643], [24542], [26965], [28141], [32403], [33374], [34453], [34814], [35350]
How to Start a Screen Printing Business [14352]
"How to Start a Shirt-Printing Business" in Chron (April 30, 2019) [14353]
How to Start a Small Business in Canada: Your Road Map to Financial Freedom [23944], [24543]
"How to Start a Small Gym Business" in Chron (March 8, 2019) [12422]
How to Start a Successful Campground Business [2515]
"How to Start a Successful Coffee Shop" in The Balance Small Business (December 5, 2019) [3185]
"How to Start a Successful Moving Company Business" in MyMovingReviews.com (June 3, 2020) [11148]
"How to Start a Tattoo Business – Equipment You Need" in Tycoon Story (Oct. 16, 2020) [15275]
"How to Start a Tattoo Business and Make Money" in TattooPro Blog (Apr. 8, 2021) [15276]
How to Start a Tattoo Parlor [15277]
"How to Start a Tattoo Shop" in Chron (March 8, 2019) [15302]
How to Start a Tattoo Studio [15278]
How to Start a Thriving Drive-Thru Coffee Shop [3186]
"How to Start a Tree Farm" in Small Business Trends (Dec. 18, 2019) [2946]
"How to Start a Tutoring Business" in Care.com (July 26, 2021) [16120]
"How to Start a Tutoring Business" in NerdWallet (Sept. 10, 2020) [16119]
"How to Start a Wedding Planning Business" in Startup Jungle [6094], [34525]
"How to Start a Wholesale Distribution Business" in Entrepreneur [20628]
How to Start Your Dog Boarding Business: What to Know about Dogs, Kennels, and the Business [12091]
"How to Start Your Home Business in 2023" in Home Business (September 22, 2022) [26793]
"How to Start Your Own Graphic Design Business: Step-by-Step" in JUST Creative Blog (December 17, 2018) [3317]
"How to Start Your Own Massage Therapy Business" in Chron (March 4, 2019) [10766]
How to Start Your Own Tailoring Ship Business: A Beginner's Guide [15251]
How to Start Your Very Own Cleaning Business: Houses and Apartments Plus Much More [2979]
How to Succeed As a Lifestyle Entrepreneur [22644], [24683]
How to Succeed as an Entrepreneur in Dance and Arts with Roger Lee [22906]
"How to Successfully Launch a New Business during Tough Economic Times" in Business News Daily (March 6, 2023) [34526]
How to Supervise People (Onsite) [28352]
"How to Survive This Mess" in Crain's Chicago Business (Vol. 31, April 14, 2008, No. 15, pp. 18) [21545], [22645], [34057]
"How to Survive Your First Month of Self-Employment" in Due (February 1, 2019) [32990]
How to Sustain Profitability in Uncertain Times with Paul Zelizer [24212]
"How Sweet It Will Be" in Barron's (Vol. 89, July 13, 2009, No. 28, pp. M13) [6464], [9597], [17060], [23945]
How Tech Debt Hurts Your Small Business with Corey Winter [16664]
"How Technology Has Changed News Photography over 40 Years" in The New York Times (September 27, 2017) [12307]
"How Technology Is Shaping and Reshaping CBD Industry" in The Union Journal (October 23, 2020) [5008]
"How to Tell If Wood Furniture Is Worth Refinishing" in DIY Network [7241]
"How Tender Green Turns Top Chefs Into Fast-Food Cooks: a Quick-Serve Chain Lures Kitchen Starts by Treating Them Like Entrepreneurs" in Inc. (Vol. 36, March 2014, No. 2, pp. 28) [13950], [22646], [31348]
"How These 12 Small Business Advertising Ideas Can Drive Traffic & ROI" in LYFE Marketing (October 15, 2019) [31873]
"How To: Advertising Your Food Truck Without Spending a Dime" in FoodTruckOperator.com (March 26, 2020) [6989]
How To Balance Empathy and Accountability with Maria Ross [28926]
"How To Be a Twitter Ninja" in Canadian Business (Vol. 87, October 2014, No. 10, pp. 51) [12938], [17692], [21884], [31771]
"How To: Creating a Profitable Food Truck Patio Space" in FoodTruckOperator.com (September 14, 2020) [6990]
"How To Detect a Liar (Even One as Big as Bernie Madoff)" in South Florida Business Journal (Vol. 34, May 2, 2014, No. 41, pp. 16) [23505]
"How To Disaster-Proof Your Business" in Inc. (Vol. 33, September 2011, No. 7, pp. 38) [14425], [18989], [33181]
"How To Earn Loyalty From Millenials" in Birmingham Business Journal (Vol. 31, February 28, 2014, No. 9, pp. 16) [22184], [28643]
"How To Find More Customers and Clients with Webinars, Seminars and Workshops" [14514], [15867], [29852], [35063]
"How To Find Reputable Credit Repair Services" in U.S. News & World Report (October 24,2019) [4747]
How To Gather And Use Data For Business Analysis [33576]
"How To Get a Loan the Web 2.0 Way" in Black Enterprise (Vol. 41, December 2010, No. 5, pp. 23) [21885], [28142], [30920], [34058]
"How To: Getting More Yelp Reviews" in FoodTruckOperator.com (October 5, 2020) [6991]
A How-To Guide for Creating a Business Budget [17502]
"How to... Harness Green Power" in The Caterer (July 20, 2012, No. 325) [1417], [5650], [5920], [8415], [13951], [23267], [23625], [31349]
"How To Help New Leaders Succeed" in Birmingham Business Journal (Vol. 31, January 31, 2014, No. 5, pp. 9) [28644]
How To!: How to Follow Your Small Business Dream [12101]
"How To Identify Leadership Potential: Development and Testing of a Consensus Model" in Human Resource Management (Vol. 51,May- June 2012, No. 3, pp. 361-385) [28645]
"How To: Launching a Food Truck Catering Business" in FoodTruckOperator.com (October 5, 2020) [6911], [6992]
"How To Live To Be 100: John E. Green Co. Grows Through Diversification" in Crain's Detroit Business (February 18, 2008) [18154], [24684], [31772], [31874]
"How To Make Finance Work: The U.S. Financial Sector Has Boomed, But That Hasn't Always Been Good News For the Rest of the Economy" in Harvard Business Review (Vol. 90, March 2012, No. 3, pp. 104) [13218], [13476], [18155], [20957]
"How To Make the Most of Digital Music" in Birmingham Business Journal (Vol. 31, May 23, 2014, No. 21, pp. 10) [30961]
"How To Manage Cash Flow" in Inc. [19720]
"How To: Manage Your Cash Better" in Inc. (Volume 32, December 2010, No. 10, pp. 69) [69], [1760], [15391], [16808], [23946], [25380]
"How To Manage Your Chain of Command" in Birmingham Business Journal (Vol. 31, June 27, 2014, No. 26, pp. 12) [28646]
"How To Overcome the Jitters and Not Choke" in South Florida Business Journal (Vol. 34, July 25, 2014, No. 53, pp. 10) [22647]
"How To Pirate-Proof a Freighter" in Canadian Business (Vol. 85, June 28, 2012, No. 11-12, pp. 20) [7038], [14426]
"How To Prevent Cyber Crime At Your Biz" in Birmingham Business Journal (Vol. 31, March 14, 2014, No. 11, pp. 10) [14427], [21546]
"How To: Preventing Cross-Contamination in the Food Truck Environment" in FoodTruckOperator.com (November 2, 2020) [6993]
"How To Reduce the Risk of Discrimination" in Idaho Business Review (September 11, 2014) [20569], [25381], [26585], [26966]
"How To Set Up and Structure Multiple Businesses" in Small Business Trends (May 21, 2013) [27186], [34527]
"How To Spark Up a Medical Marijuana Firm in Florida - and Not Get Burned in the Process" in Orlando Business Journal (Vol. 30, March 21, 2014, No. 39, pp. 6) [5009], [10920], [25382], [25829]
"How To Win the Fed's New Game" in Barron's (Vol. 92, September 17, 2012, No. 38, pp. M10) [6465], [9598], [25383]

Small Business Sourcebook • 42nd Edition 3259

"How To Win In Emerging Markets: Lessons From Japan" in Harvard Business Review (Vol. 90, May 2012, No. 5, pp. 126) **[18156]**, **[27602]**, **[28647]**, **[31350]**
"How-To Workshops in St. Charles Teach Sewing, Styles" in St. Louis Post-Dispatch (September 14, 2010) **[14653]**, **[21886]**, **[23626]**, **[34059]**
"How to Transition Your Brick and Mortar Business to an Online Entity" in Legal Zoom (February 22, 2023) **[11762]**
How to Translate Your Passion into Purpose **[16665]**
How to Trust a Coach Again (After You Have Been Burned) **[16666]**
"How to Turn Employee Conflict Into a Positive, Productive Force" in HR Specialist (Vol. 8, September 2010, No. 9, pp. 6) **[22185]**, **[26967]**, **[28648]**
"How to Turn Your Idea Into a Product (and Launch It!)" in Business News Daily (February 21, 2023) **[27887]**, **[34528]**
"How a Tutoring Service Helps Students With Learning Deficits" in AZEDNEWS (May 3, 2022) **[16136]**
How Two Sisters Scaled Vintage Lockers into a Thriving Global Brand with Mustard Made Founders Becca and Jess Stern **[29545]**
"How to Use Dual Process Theory to Promote Your Cannabis Brand" in Cannabis Business Executive (September 8, 2020) **[5010]**
"How to Use Flexible Staffing Models to Solve Staffing Challenges" in Forbes (November 17, 2021) **[14980]**
How to Use the Internet to Advertise, Promote, and Market Your Business or Web Site: With Little or No Money **[288]**, **[9158]**, **[11688]**, **[16430]**, **[21887]**, **[23947]**, **[29853]**, **[32077]**
How to Use QuickBooks **[16769]**
"How to Value Your Startup Business for Equity Financing" in Legal Zoom (March 21, 2023) **[35351]**
"How to Vet Franchisors and Predict Your ROI on a Franchise Business" in Entrepreneur (Jan. 30, 2019) **[24375]**
"How Vietnamese Americans Took Over the Nails Business: A Documentary" in NPR (May 19, 2019) **[11319]**
"How and When Should You Take on a Business Partner?" in Legal Zoom (February 15, 2023) **[31351]**
How: Why How We Do Anything Means Everything **[22648]**, **[24685]**
"How and Why To Get BBB Accreditation" in Small Business Trends (August 9, 2021) **[34529]**
"How Will Home Office Tax Deductions Change When Everyone Is Working Remotely?" in Legal Zoom (February 21, 2023) **[34815]**
"How Will Small Businesses Address Cleanliness and Decontamination in a Post-Coronavirus World" in Legal Zoom (February 21, 2023) **[16571]**
"How Will The Startups Created in 2020 Be Different From Startups Build Before?" in Protocol (June 27, 2020) **[34530]**
"How to Withhold Payroll Taxes for Your Small Business" in SurePayroll (March 14, 2018) **[31631]**, **[34245]**
How Women Are Rethinking the Tattoo Parlor **[15303]**, **[35804]**
How to Work Most Effectively with Your Boss (Onsite) **[17588]**
How to Work With Difficult, Demanding, and Inconsiderate People (Onsite) **[17589]**
"How to Write a Business Plan" in Small Business Trends (November 11, 2021) **[18993]**
How to Write a Business Plan **[18990]**, **[18991]**, **[18992]**, **[19865]**, **[24686]**, **[31989]**
"How to Write a Business Proposal" in Business News Daily (February 23, 2023) **[18994]**
How to Write Effective Policies and Procedures (Onsite) **[17849]**
"How to Write a Good Vision Statement" in Cascade Blog (Jan. 24, 2022) **[19532]**
How to Write a Great Business Plan for Your Small Business in 60 Minutes or Less **[18995]**, **[20300]**, **[23948]**, **[24687]**, **[28649]**, **[29854]**
"How to Write a Job Applicant Rejection Letter" in Legal Zoom (February 15, 2023) **[26586]**
How to Write a Killer Marketing Plan (Onsite) **[29592]**
How to Write the Perfect Resume: Stand Out, Land Interviews, and Get the Job You Want **[14313]**
"How to Write a Policy on Substance Abuse in the Workplace" in Workest (Mar 15, 2021) **[34680]**
"How Yamana CEO First Struck Gold With Desert Sun" in Globe & Mail (February 27, 2006, pp. B3) **[28650]**, **[31352]**
"How Young Professionals Can Position Themselves for Board Membership: 4 Quick Tips to Get You Started" in Black Enterprise (Vol. 45, July-August 2014, No. 1, pp. 46) **[7122]**, **[27603]**, **[28651]**
How Your Small Business Can Benefit from E-Commerce **[21888]**
"How Your Stories of Failure Create Better Business Success" in Forbes(March 1, 2023) **[22649]**
"How Your Team Can Work Four Days a Week and Get More Done" in Small Business Trends (November 8, 2021) **[28652]**
Howard County Chamber of Commerce (HCCC) **[40395]**
Howard County Small Business Development Center **[40337]**
Howard Johnson International Inc. **[8505]**
Howard L. Zimmerman Architects, P.C. (HLZA) **[939]**
Howard University - School of Business Library (HUSBL) **[1789]**
Howe Area Chamber of Commerce **[45217]**
Howell Area Chamber of Commerce (HACC) **[40940]**
Howell Chamber of Commerce **[42143]**
Howick Associates **[20546]**
"Howl-o-ween" in Decatur Daily (October 25, 2011) **[6912]**, **[12201]**, **[34332]**
HP Inc. **[18794]**
HR Administration and the Law (Onsite) **[26860]**
HR Advice.com **[27141]**
HR Answers Inc. (HRA) **[27142]**
HR Business Solutions **[27143]**
The HR Dept. **[27144]**
HR Journal **[46272]**
HR People + Strategy [26844], [34964]
HR Policy Association (HRPA) **[26837]**
HRD Press Inc. **[40778]**
HSMAI's National MEET **[15918]**
HSPA Annual Conference [26069]
HSPA Annual Conference & Exp [26069]
Hub Angels Investment Group LLC **[40698]**
Hub Collaborative **[45526]**
Hub of Human Innovation **[45527]**
Huber Heights Chamber of Commerce **[43495]**
"Huberman Failing to Keep CTA on Track" in Crain's Chicago Business (Vol. 31, April 21, 2008, No. 16, pp. 22) **[19363]**, **[28653]**, **[33182]**, **[35947]**
HUBZone Contractors National Council **[33461]**
HUBZone Council [33461]
Huck Bouma Pc. Attorneys at Law **[2616]**, **[18754]**
Huddle House, Inc. (HHI) **[14183]**
Hudson Area Chamber of Commerce (HACC) **[43496]**
Hudson Area Chamber of Commerce and Tourism Bureau **[46432]**
Hudson Chamber of Commerce [40558]
Hudson County Chamber of Commerce (HCCC) **[42144]**
Hudson and Maynard Area Chamber of Commerce [40558]
Hudson Valley Center for Innovation **[42886]**
Hudson Valley Gateway Chamber of Commerce **[42616]**
Hudson Valley Startup Fund (HVSF) **[35283]**, **[42756]**
Hudsonville Area Chamber of Commerce (HACC) **[40941]**
Hueytown Chamber of Commerce **[36127]**
"Huge Fight Over Tiny Apartments" in Puget Sound Business Journal (Vol. 35, September 12, 2014, No. 21, pp. 8) **[4136]**, **[25384]**
Huguenot Society of America (HSA) **[7419]**
Huguenot Society of South Carolina **[7420]**
HuHot Mongolian Grills, LLC **[14184]**
"Human Activity Analysis: a Review" in ACM Computing Surveys (Vol. 43, Fall 2011, No. 3, pp. 16) **[3429]**, **[3625]**, **[31990]**, **[32776]**
The Human Bean Drive Thru (THB) **[7586]**
Human Capital Research Corp. (HCRC) **[24248]**
"Human Capital: When Change Means Terminating an Employee" in Black Enterprise (Vol. 41, November 2010, No. 4, pp. 40) **[18602]**, **[20570]**, **[26968]**
"'Human Error' Cited for Deadly Google Seattle Crane Collapse, 3 Firms Fined $107K" in ConstructionDive (October 21, 2019) **[4137]**, **[35948]**
"The Human Factor" in Canadian Business (Vol. 80, October 8, 2007, No. 20, pp. 22) **[20958]**, **[24688]**, **[25385]**, **[34060]**
Human Factors and Ergonomics in Manufacturing & Service Industries **[27096]**, **[28916]**, **[29451]**
Human Factors and Ergonomics Society Bulletin **[11647]**
Human Mutation: Variation, Informatics, and Disease **[32874]**
Human Resource Executive Health & Benefits Leadership Conference **[27118]**
"Human Resource Management: Challenges for Graduate Education" in Business Horizons (Vol. 51, March-April 2008, No. 2, pp. 151) **[21547]**, **[26969]**, **[28654]**
Human Resource Management: Functions, Applications, and Skill Development **[26970]**
Human Resource Planning Society [26844], [34964]
Human Resource Solutions, Inc. **[30643]**
Human Resource Specialties, Inc. (HRS) **[10536]**, **[20196]**, **[27145]**, **[28997]**
Human Resources for Anyone with Newly Assigned HR Responsibilities **[26861]**
Human Resources & Benefits Administration Industry in the US - Market Research Report **[17380]**, **[27094]**
Human Resources Kit for Dummies **[26971]**
Human Resources and the Law (Onsite) **[18490]**, **[26862]**
Human Resources for Professionals Who've Recently Assumed HR Responsibilities (Onsite) **[26864]**
Human Resources for Professionals who've Recently Assumed HR Responsibilities (Onsite) **[26863]**
Human Resources Research Organization (HumRRO) **[10008]**, **[26838]**
"Humana Planning Pa. HMO" in Philadelphia Business Journal (Vol. 28, August 10, 2012, No. 26, pp. 1) **[8924]**, **[27286]**
"Humana Seeks Higher Stake in Memphis Market" in Memphis Business Journal (Vol. 33, February 17, 2012, No. 45, pp. 1) **[8925]**, **[25830]**, **[27287]**, **[31353]**
Humane News **[703]**
Humanergy Inc. **[41137]**
Humanics ErgoSystems Inc. **[31077]**, **[35967]**
Humanities Full Text™ **[4637]**
Humble Area Chamber of Commerce [45245]
Humble Ventures **[30271]**, **[35284]**, **[35623]**, **[38193]**
Humboldt Chamber of Commerce **[44762]**
Humboldt County Chamber of Commerce **[41939]**
Humboldt & Dakota City Chamber of Commerce **[39754]**
Hummingbird's Incubator Kitchen **[44059]**
Humphreys County Area Chamber of Commerce **[44763]**
Humpty's Restaurants International Inc. **[14185]**
"Hundreds of Complaints Flood in about New York Store Signs, but from Whom?" in The New York Times (December 11, 2018) **[14702]**
The Hungry Heart **[11601]**
Hungry Howie's Pizza Inc. **[12557]**
"Hunhu Healthcare Gets Some Mayo Help" in Business Journal (Vol. 32, August 29, 2014, No. 14, pp. 4) **[21889]**, **[25831]**, **[27888]**, **[30477]**
Hunt-Scanlon Corporation **[38119]**
Hunt-Scanlon Publishing [38119]
"Hunt Valley Towne Center Gears Up for Growth; Ray Lewis Project Scrapped" in Baltimore Business Journal (Vol. 30, May 11, 2012, No. 1, pp. 1) **[768]**, **[1877]**, **[4138]**, **[13477]**, **[32181]**
Hunter Arts Publishing **[37702]**
Hunter Museum of American Art Library **[751]**
Hunterdon County Chamber of Commerce **[42145]**
Hunterdon Historical Newsletter [7377]
Hunterdon Historical Record **[7377]**
"Hunter Capital's Malone Relishes Role of Renovator" in Puget Sound Business Journal (Vol. 35, June 13, 2014, No. 8, pp. 9) **[894]**, **[4139]**, **[13478]**
Huntington Beach Chamber of Commerce **[36944]**
Huntington County Chamber of Commerce **[39558]**
Huntington Learning Centers Inc. **[16164]**
Huntington Regional Area Chamber of Commerce [46273]
Huntington Regional Chamber of Commerce (HRCC) **[46273]**
Huntington SCORE **[46258]**
Huntington Township Chamber of Commerce (HTCC) **[42617]**
Huntley Area Chamber of Commerce **[39205]**
Huntsville Area Technology and Business Complex (HA/tch) - Business Incubator Program **[45528]**
Huntsville Association of Small Businesses in Advanced Technology (HASBAT) **[36052]**
Huntsville Madison County Chamber **[36128]**
Huron Chamber of Commerce (HCC) **[43497]**
Huron River Ventures (HRV) **[41048]**
Huron Township Chamber of Commerce (HTCC) **[40942]**
Huron Valley Area Chamber of Commerce [40943]
Huron Valley Chamber of Commerce (HVCC) **[40943]**
Hurricane Valley Chamber of Commerce (HVCC) **[45637]**
Hurst - Euless - Bedford Chamber of Commerce (HEBCC) **[45218]**
"Husband-Wife Team Opens Somali Interpreting Business in Willmar, Minn." in West Central Tribune (May 22, 2012) **[15940]**, **[23627]**, **[27604]**
"Husky Proceeds on Heavy-Oil Expansion" in Globe & Mail (March 21, 2006, pp. B1) **[18157]**, **[18996]**, **[19533]**, **[29252]**
Hussian College **[43688]**
Hutar Growth Management Institute (HGMI) **[28998]**
Hutchinson Area Chamber of Commerce, Convention and Visitors Bureau [41245]
Hutchinson Area Chamber of Commerce and Tourism **[41245]**
Hutchinson/Reno County Chamber of Commerce **[39905]**
Hutchinson SCORE **[39848]**
Hutchison Forestry Inc. **[2955]**
Hutto Chamber of Commerce **[45219]**

3260 Small Business Sourcebook • 42nd Edition

Huxford Genealogical Society, Inc. - Huxford Library [7421]
Huxford Genealogical Society, Inc. - Huxford-Spear Genealogical Library [7421]
HVAC Controls and Air Distribution (Onsite) [2056]
HVAC Electrical Controls & Air Distribution (Onsite) [19443], [21390]
"HVAC/R Evolution" in Indoor Comfort Marketing (Vol. 70, March 2011, No. 3, pp. 14) [491], [34061]
"HVHC's Impact on SA Could Grow as it Pursues Big Expansion" in San Antonio Business Journal (Vol. 28, June 20, 2014, No. 19, pp. 8) [16300], [32182]
Hyannis Area Chamber of Commerce [40584]
"Hyannis Mercedes Franchise Sold" in Cape Cod Times (December 2, 2010) [11413], [24376]
"Hyatt Joins Other Big Hotel Chains by Pledging to Eliminate Small Plastic Bottles" in Skift (November 12, 2019) [8416], [23268]
Hybrid Business Advisors [2274]
Hyde Park Angels (HPA) [39458]
Hyde Park Chamber of Commerce [42618]
Hyde Park Venture Partners (HPVP) [39459]
Hydro Energy Businesses in the World [23450]
HyettPalma Inc. [21253]
The Hysen Group [14108]
"Hyundai Enters Minivan Market" in Globe & Mail (February 15, 2006, pp. B7) [11414], [29253], [29855]

I

I-94 West Chamber of Commerce [41246]
"I Brake for Yard Sales: And Flea Markets, Thrift Shops, Auctions, and the Occasional Dumpster" [1074], [3894], [8178], [9042], [32549]
I-Business Network L.L.C. [16882]
I Can't Believe I Get Paid to Do This [22650], [28655]
I-Hatch Ventures L.L.C. [42757]
"I Hate My Hearing Aids. What Do I Do?" in Healthy Hearing (November 12, 2019) [8134], [25832]
"I Hear You're Interested In A..." in Inc. (January 2008, pp. 40-43) [10657], [21890], [29856], [32550]
I Just Started My Small Business—Do I Need Payroll Software? [11934], [31632]
"I Love L.A." in Canadian Business (Vol. 81, December 8, 2008, No. 21, pp. S22) [1336]
I Love You More Than My Dog [20450], [29857], [31875]
i/o ventures [37709]
"I Quit My Day Job 4 Months Ago to Become a Freelance Writer. Here's What My Family of 4 Spends in a Typical Week" in Business Insider (October 14, 2019) [5318], [17503], [26794]
"I Tried to Live Off Women-Owned Businesses. Turns Out, Men Still Run Everything" in Time (July 22, 2021) [35805]
I2BF Global Investments Ltd. [42758]
i2E Inc. [43860]
i3 [1120], [2566]
i3 Advanced Technology Incubator [37582]
i9 Sports [15212]
IA Ventures [42759]
IAAPA Expo [615]
IABC Atlanta [38623]
IABC/Calgary [46654]
IABC New Jersey [42031]
IABC Omaha [41815]
IABC Oregon-Columbia [43906]
IABC World Conference [17797]
IAFE Convention & Trade Show [616], [3859], [11485], [15258], [15919]
IAFE Trade Show [616], [3859], [11485], [15258], [15919]
IAHCSMM Annual Conference & Expo [26069]
IAHI, the Owners' Association [8349]
IAIP Annual International Convention [8996], [35915]
"iAM Scientist Launches To Provide a Crowdfunding Platform for Science, Technology, and Medicine" in Benzinga.com (July 31, 2012) [28064], [31991], [32777], [35237]
"IAPMO GTC Debates Supplement" in Contractor (Vol. 56, September 2009, No. 9, pp. 3) [5651], [12639], [14620], [23269]
"IAPMO GTC Votes to Limit Showers to 2.0-GPM" in Contractor (Vol. 56, September 2009, No. 9, pp. 1) [4140], [5652], [12640], [14621], [23270]
IAPMO Research and Testing Inc. [455], [15237]
"IAPMO Seeks Group Participants" in Contractor (Vol. 56, September 2009, No. 9, pp. 37) [492], [14622]
IASA Annual Conferences [16862]
IBAC Update [418], [19301]
iBeeHub Incubator [42887]
Iberville Chamber of Commerce [40175]
IBEX Show [10621]

IBIMA Business Review (IBIMABR) [24865]
IBM Corporation - IBM Knowledge Center [3677], [14891]
IBM Corporation - Library/Information Resource Center [3677], [14891]
IBM Global Services - Business Continuity and Resiliency Services [3458]
IBM Journal of Research and Development [32875]
IBM PartnerWorld [45529]
IBMA Business Conference [11283]
IBMA WOB [11283]
IBMA World of Bluegrass [11283]
"IBM's Best-Kept Secret: It's Huge in Software Too" in Canadian Business (Vol. 79, September 25, 2006, No. 19, pp. 19) [18158], [26305], [28586]
"IBR Breakfast Series: Idaho's Dairy Industry Quietly Grows" in Idaho Business Review (August 15, 2014) [17061], [27605], [30742]
IBT International [29002]
IBWA Annual Business Conference and Trade Show [1866]
IBWA Convention & Tradeshow [1866]
IBWA Trade Show [1866]
ICA Annual Conference [21687]
ICA Annual Education Conference [27369]
The ICAO Journal [419]
ICBA Conference & PRIMEtime [1849]
"ICC Works on Prescriptive Green Construction Code" in Contractor (Vol. 56, October 2009, No. 10, pp. 1) [4141], [12888], [13479], [23271], [34062]
ICCFA Annual Convention & Exposition [7220]
"An Ice Boost in Revenue; Wings Score With Expanded Corporate Sales" in Crain's Detroit Business (Vol. 25, June 1, 2009, No. 22) [289], [15095], [15162], [18159], [29858], [32551]
Ice Glen Associates LLC [40773]
Ice Skating Institute [14716]
Ice Sports Industry (ISI) [14716]
Iceberg Ventures [40097]
ICG Magazine [6212], [12312]
ICMG Annual Meeting [27367]
Icon Ventures [37389]
"Iconic Boise Skateboard Shop to Close" in Idaho Business Review (August 19, 2014) [11763], [14737], [19866], [23949], [28002], [29859], [31354], [32183], [35806]
iD Ventures America, LLC [37390]
Idabel Chamber of Commerce [43773]
Idabel Chamber of Commerce and Agriculture [43773]
Idaho Business Review (IBR) [38961]
Idaho Commission for Libraries (ICfL) [47414]
Idaho Department of Commerce (IDC) [38960], [47415]
Idaho Department of Environmental Quality - Waste Management and Remediation Division - Hazardous Waste [46996]
Idaho Innovation Center Inc. (IIC) [38952]
Idaho Small Business Development Center State Office (SBDC) [38899]
Idaho State University Business and Technology Center [47416]
Idaho State University College of Technology (ISU) [38957]
IDDBA Show [1217], [1283], [4888], [15052]
Idea Age Consulting [40478]
The Idea Center (IC) [38599]
IDEA Fund Partners [43268]
IDEA Health and Fitness Association [12374]
Idea Labs Consulting [45579]
IDEA: The Association for Fitness Professionals [12374]
IDEA, The Health and Fitness Source [12374]
IDEAg Dakotafest [17169]
Ideal Image Development Corporation [4541]
Idealab [37391]
Idealliance [12718], [16368]
Ideas To Go Inc. (ITG) [387]
"Ideas at Work: Sparkling Innovation" in Business Strategy Review (Vol. 21, Summer 2010, No. 2, pp. 07) [10658], [27606], [27889], [29860]
"Ideas at Work: The Reality of Costs" in Business Strategy Review (Vol. 21, Summer 2010, No. 2, pp. 40) [18160], [18997], [19364], [23950]
Ident-A-Kid [33321]
"Identifying and Managing Business Risks" in Investopedia (August 2, 2019) [32388]
"Identity Theft Can Have Long-Lasting Impact" in Providence Business News (Vol. 28, February 10, 2014, No. 45, pp. 7) [4748], [4791], [11047], [13219], [20301], [28143]
IDG Capital [42760]
IDG Ventures [37370]
"IDI Plans Spec Industrial Space" in Memphis Business Journal (Vol. 33, February 10, 2012, No. 44, pp. 1) [4359], [13480]

iDigress: 90 Percent of Business Ideas Fail. Here's How to Be Part of the 10 Percent that Will Succeed. [24815]
Idyllwild Chamber of Commerce [36945]
I.E. Canada [20698]
ie: The Business of International Events [27787]
IECA Annual Conference and Expo [25615]
IEEE Computational Science and Engineering [32866]
IEEE Information Center [5405]
"If My Business Name Is Registered with the State, Do I Still Need a Trademark?" in Legal Zoom (March 21, 2023) [27187], [27890]
"If the Opportunity is There, Move Boldly" in Indoor Comfort Marketing (Vol. 70, March 2011, No. 3) [493], [29861], [32552]
"If Palmer's Is Your Go-To Place to Cut a Christmas Tree, You're Out of Luck This Year" in Statesman Journal (October 13, 2019) [2923], [32954]
"If Pennsylvania Is Going to Legalize Adult-Use Marijuana, This is How it Should be Done" in Queen Muse (September 15, 2020) [5011]
"If They Build It, Will Customers Come?" in Business Journal Portland (Vol. 30, February 7, 2014, No. 49, pp. 7) [895], [4142], [13952], [15163], [31355]
"If We Build Them, Will They Rent Them?" in Birmingham Business Journal (Vol. 31, August 1, 2014, No. 31, pp. 4) [4143], [13481], [13798]
If You Have to Cry, Go Outside: And Other Things Your Mother Never Told You [3032], [8661], [12939], [17693], [19867], [31773], [31876], [35807]
IFA Annual Convention [24469]
IFAI Expo [14660]
IFCA Convention [17170]
IFCA Life Communicators Association Convention [27368]
IFMA World Workplace [24778]
IFMA's World Workplace Conference & Expo [24778]
IFPA Film and Video Communicators [6165]
The iFranchise Group Inc. [2355], [18755], [24503]
IFT Annual Event and Food Expo [11589]
IFT FIRST Annual Event & Expo [11589]
IFT Food Expo [11589]
iGaming Business Directory [15812]
iGan Partners [46791]
Ignite Fredericton [46738]
Ignite Northwest [46216]
Ignition Communications [46847]
Ignition Point Capital Group [38537]
Ignore the Hype - Startup Different with David Sinkinson [34628]
"IGT Expands Partnership with Olympic Entertainment Group" in Travel & Leisure Close-Up (October 8, 2012) [7294], [31356]
IHG Owners Association (IHGOA) [8349]
"Ihilani's New Day" in Pacific Business News (Vol. 26, August 22, 2014, No. 26, pp. 14) [896], [8417], [19365], [31357]
IIA International Conference [119], [15441]
iiM, LLC [39965]
IIT Research Institute (IITRI) [30858]
"IJ Challenges Atlanta's Vending Monopoly" in Benzinga.com (July 28, 2011) [10027], [16257], [18603]
Ilium Associates Inc. [10695], [30202]
"I'll Have What She's Having" in Canadian Business (Vol. 85, September 17, 2012, No. 14, pp. 17) [6466], [9599], [23951]
"Ill Winds; Cuba's Economy" in The Economist (Vol. 390, January 3, 2009, No. 8612, pp. 20) [8726], [9600], [15748], [15999], [17062], [18998], [20959], [27607]
Illinois Association of Chamber of Commerce Executives (IACCE) [39206]
Illinois Association of Mortgage Professionals [28077]
Illinois Black Chamber of Commerce (ILBCC) [39207]
Illinois Business Law Journal (IBLJ) [18772]
Illinois Chamber of Commerce [39208]
Illinois Department of Commerce and Economic Opportunity - Energy and Recycling [39004]
Illinois Department of Commerce & Economic Opportunity - Illinois Small Business Development Center [33462]
Illinois Department of Natural Resources [5772], [7982]
Illinois Early Childhood Intervention Clearinghouse Library [2914]
Illinois Farm Bureau Information Research Center (IFB) [17212]
"Illinois Farmland Tops $11,000 Per Acre" in Farm Industry News (June 27, 2011) [13220], [13482], [17063], [18161]
Illinois Fertilizer and Chemical Association Annual Convention [17170]
Illinois Institute of Technology - IIT Research Institute [30858]
Illinois Institute of Technology Research Institute [30858]
Illinois Issues [31705]

Illinois Procurement Technical Assistance Center - College of DuPage [39389]
Illinois Procurement Technical Assistance Center-Illinois Hispanic Chamber of Commerce (IHCC) [39390]
Illinois Procurement Technical Assistance Center - North Business & Industrial Council (PTAC) [39391]
Illinois Procurement Technical Assistance Center-South Suburban College (SSC) [39392]
Illinois Procurement Technical Assistance Center - U.S. General Services Administration - Great Lakes [39393]
Illinois Procurement Technical Assistance Center - Women's Business Development Center (WBDC) [39394]
"Illinois Regulators Revoke Collection Agency's License" in Collections & Credit Risk (Vol. 15, August 1, 2010, No. 7, pp. 13) [4792], [18604], [20302], [25386], [27891]
Illinois SBDC at Harper College [38979]
Illinois Small Business Development Center at Chicago State University (SBDC) [38980]
Illinois Small Business Development Center at College of DuPage (SBDC) [38981]
Illinois Small Business Development Center at College of Lake County [38982]
Illinois Small Business Development Center at Danville Area Community College (ILSBDC-DACC) [38983]
Illinois Small Business Development Center at Elgin Community College (ECC) [38984]
Illinois Small Business Development Center at Highland Community College [38985]
Illinois Small Business Development Center at Illinois Eastern Community College [38986]
Illinois Small Business Development Center at Illinois Valley Community College [38987]
Illinois Small Business Development Center at Industrial Council of Nearwest Chicago [38988]
Illinois Small Business Development Center Joliet Junior College (ISBDCJJC) [38989]
Illinois Small Business Development Center at the Joseph Center [38990]
Illinois Small Business Development Center at Kankakee Community College [38991]
Illinois Small Business Development Center at Kaskaskia College [38992]
Illinois Small Business Development Center at Lincoln Land Community College (ISBDC LLCC) [38993]
Illinois Small Business Development Center at McHenry County College (ISBDC) [38994]
Illinois Small Business Development Center at Rend Lake College [38995]
Illinois Small Business Development Center at Rock Valley College [38996]
Illinois Small Business Development Center at Shawnee Community College (SBDC) [38997]
Illinois Small Business Development Center at SIU-E/East St. Louis [38998]
Illinois Small Business Development Center at Southeastern Illinois College [38999]
Illinois Small Business Development Center at Southern Illinois University [39000]
Illinois Small Business Development Center at Waubonsee Community College [39001]
Illinois Small Business Development Center at Western Illinois University [39002]
Illinois State Beekeepers Association [1439]
Illinois State University College of Arts and Sciences - Applied Social Research Unit (ASRU) [46931]
Illinois Sustainable Technology Center (ISTC) [5772], [7982]
Illinois Valley Area Chamber of Commerce and Economic Development (IVACED) [39209]
Illinois Venture Capital Association (IVCA) [38972]
Illinois Ventures [39360]
Illumina Accelerator [37392]
Illumina Ventures [37393]
Illuminate Ventures [37394]
Illuminated Concepts Inc. [31078]
Illumination Consulting [44077]
"'I'm Kind of a Vanilla Guy': Steve Herrell Shares Confessions and Memories in His New Book, 'Ice Cream and Me'" in Masslive.com(January 3, 2022) [8573], [23628]
I'm on LinkedIn - Now What? [9159], [16431], [17694], [21891], [31358]
"Image Consultants" in Entrepreneur (June 2014) [3033], [3124], [3510], [8662], [10835], [15261], [26306], [31359]
"The Image Management Function of Sponsorship: A General Theoretical Framework" in International Journal of Advertising (Vol. 31, February 2012, No. 1, pp. 85) [8663], [10659]
Image Sun Tanning Centers [15268]
ImageFirst Healthcare Laundry Specialists [5256]

ImageOne Janitorial Service Inc. [2034]
ImageOps [33930]
Imagine Canada [7188]
Imagine H2O [8800]
Imagine K12 [37583]
Imagine Kitchen [44607]
The Imaging Alliance [2491]
Imaging World [4945]
IMC [31005], [31079]
IMDA Convention & Tradeshow [1125]
IME Annual Conference & Expo [1779]
IMLS Annual Report [971]
Immigration Digest [7378]
"Immigration: Give Us Your Skilled" in Canadian Business (Vol. 80, October 8, 2007, No. 20, pp. 78) [25387], [26587], [26972], [30575]
Immokalee Chamber of Commerce [38432]
IMPACT 307 (WTBC) [46627]
"The Impact of Acquisitions On the Productivity of Inventors at Semiconductor Firms: A Synthesis of Knowledge-Based and Incentive-Based Perspective" in Academy of Management Journal (Vol. 50, No. 5, October 1, 2007, pp. 1133) [9601], [26307], [27892], [28034], [31360]
Impact Business Network Ltd. [2275], [28999]
Impact of Community [29546]
Impact Engine [39460]
"IMPACT Fitness Boot Camp Training Now Approved for NESTA Credits for Personal Trainer Certification" in Marketing Weekly News (January 28, 2012) [12423], [21548]
Impact Hub Baltimore [40459]
Impact Hub Salt Lake [45680]
"The Impact of Incomplete Typeface Logos on Perceptions of the Firms" in Journal of Marketing (Vol. 75, July 2011, No. 4, pp. 86) [29862], [31877]
"The Impact of Organizational Context on the Failure of Key and Strategic Account Management Programs" in Journal of Business & Industrial Marketing (Vol. 29, June 2014, No. 5) [16809], [33862]
Impact of Private Label in the Online Food and Drink Market - US - February 2019 [7793], [8060]
Impact Venture Capital [37741]
Impact Washington [46234]
IMPAQ Accountability Business & Human Resources Development Inc. [29000]
Imperial Beach Chamber of Commerce (IBCOC) [36946]
Imperial Chamber of Commerce [36947], [41863]
Imperial Tobacco Ltd. - Corporate Information Center [15714]
Imperial Valley Small Business Development Center at Imperial Valley College [36574]
"Implementing a Small Business Compensation Structure" in Salary.com Blog (May 1, 2018) [19741]
"Implementing Statically Typed Object-Oriented Programming Languages" in ACM Computing Surveys (Vol. 43, Fall 2011, No. 3, pp. 18) [3430], [3626]
Import/Export Kit For Dummies [8727], [18162], [27608], [34063]
Import/Export Procedures and Documentation (Onsite) [8684]
Import Vehicle Community [1091]
"Importance of Compensation in the Workplace" in Chron (March 1, 2019) [19742]
"The Importance of Healthy Business Relationships" in Business News Daily (February 21, 2023) [34531]
"The Importance of Mixing Equity, Diversity, and Inclusion into Your Company's DNA" in U.S. Chamber of Commerce (Oct. 26, 2021) [30576]
"Importance of Pricing in Business" in Chron (Jan. 28, 2019) [20035]
The Importance of Pricing for the Profitability of Your Business [20036]
The Importance of Small Business to the U.S. Economy [20960]
ImportCar [1119], [1135], [8783]
"Imports Frothing Up Beer Market" in Globe & Mail (February 16, 2006, pp. B4) [1337], [6467], [9602], [10324], [29254]
Impressionism and Its Sources [3360]
"Improve Passwords and More during Cybersecurity Awareness Month" in Small Business Trends (September 29, 2022) [16572]
Improve Small Business Marketing Strategy with Social Media [29527]
Improving Editing Skills (Onsite) [21391]
Improving Your Communication Skills for Success (Onsite) [17590]
Improving Your Managerial Effectiveness [28353]
Improving Your Project Management Skills: The Basics for Success [28354]
IM=X Pilates Studio [12456]
"In 2011, Wichita-Area Banks Cleaned Up Books, Grew Earnings" in Wichita Business Journal (Vol. 27, February 17, 2012, No. 7, pp. 1) [18163], [23952], [28144]

"In the 2019 Dating World, Nobody Meets in Person Anymore" in The Philadelphia Inquirer (February 13, 2019) [3815], [11764]
"In the Afternoon, the Moral Slope Gets Slipperier" in Harvard Business Review (Vol. 92, May 2014, No. 5, pp. 34) [23506]
"In Ambassador Hotel Debate, Some Dispute Need for Rooms" in Wichita Business Journal (Vol. 27, January 20, 2012, No. 3, pp. 1) [8418]
"In Atlanta, Concessions Prices Go Down and Revenue Goes Up" in The New York Times (January 25, 2018) [3847]
"In Chesterfield: Paletta's Operations Raise Competitors' Blood Pressure" in St. Louis Business Journal (Vol. 33, August 17, 2012, No. 52, pp. 1.) [19179], [25833], [27893]
"In China, Railways to Riches" in Barron's (Vol. 88, July 7, 2008, No. 27, pp. M9) [6468], [8728], [9603], [19366], [23953], [27609], [35352]
"In Control: Tips For Navigating a Buyer's Market" in Black Enterprise (Vol. 38, December 2007, No. 5, pp. 64) [11048], [13221], [13483]
"In the Era of Endless Robocalls, Why Telemarketers Persist" in NBC News (December 9, 2018) [15550]
In Home Pet Services [12271]
In Home Pet Services Inc. (IHPS) [12271]
"In the Hot Finance Jobs, Women Are Still Shut Out" in Harvard Business Review (Vol. 90, July-August 2012, No. 7-8, pp. 30) [6469], [9604], [23954], [28657], [34064], [35808]
"In-House Agencies Grew During COVID-19" in AdAge (November 23, 2021) [290], [16904]
"In India, A Gold-Price Threat?" in Barron's (Vol. 88, June 30, 2008, No. 26, pp. M12) [6470], [8729], [9605], [23955], [27610]
"In My Shoes: A Memoir" [14677], [22651], [31361], [31774], [35809]
In-N-Out Burger: A Behind-the-Counter Look at the Fast-Food Chain That Breaks All the Rules [13953], [23629]
"In the News: Grants of Up To $20,000 for Small Business Improvements and More" in Small Business Trends(February 24, 2023) [33577], [47973]
"In the News: Hundreds of Millions of Dollars Available to Small Businesses from SSBCI" in Small Business Trends(March 3, 2023) [25006], [28145], [33578], [47974]
"In the News: New Pandemic Relief Grant Programs of $500 to $35K for Small Businesses" in Small Business Trends(January 27, 2023) [47975]
"In the Options Market, Financial-Sector Trading Is Moody and Paranoid" in Barron's (Vol. 88, March 10, 2008, No. 10, pp. M14) [6471], [9606], [20961], [23956]
"In-Person vs Online Estate Sales" in EstateSales.org Blog [6072]
In Plain English [2276], [17403], [17809], [20197], [27146], [29001], [30203]
In-Plant Printing and Mailing Association (IPMA) [12719]
"In Praise of How Not to Invest" in Barron's (Vol. 89, July 13, 2009, No. 28, pp. 11) [6472], [9607], [23957]
In-Q-Tel, Inc. (IQT) [45989]
"In the Raw: Karyn Calabrese Brings Healthy Dining to a New Sophisticated Level" in Black Enterprise (Vol. 41, September 2010) [1389], [1584], [8027], [8100], [11578], [13954], [25834], [35810]
"In the SBA's Face" in American Small Business League (December 2010) [25007], [25388], [28146]
In Search of Your German Roots: A Complete Guide to Tracing Your Ancestors in the Germanic Areas of Europe [7365]
"In Somerville, a Powerhouse of Custom Costumemaking for Boston and Beyond" in Boston Globe (July 4, 2019) [4554]
"In Surging Oil Industry, Good Fortune Comes In Stages" in Barron's (Vol. 88, July 7, 2008, No. 27, pp. 12) [6473], [9608], [20962], [23958], [33183]
In Touch [40285]
"In a Twist, Pretzel Vendors Will Be Selling Pizza: Wetzels to Launch Blaze Fast-Fire'd Concept with Two So-Cal Locations" in Los Angeles Business Journal (Vol. 34, June 4, 2012, No. 23, pp. 12) [12526], [13867], [23630], [30743]
"In 'Unprecedented' Case, Maine Suspends Mail-Order Pharmacy Whose Drugs Killed Two Racehorses" in Bangor Daily News (October 7, 2019) [10464]
"In the Wake of Pet-Food Crisis, Iams Sales Plummet Nearly 17 Percent" in Advertising Age (Vol. 78, May 14, 2007, No. 18, pp. 3) [6474], [7744], [9609], [12202], [27611], [29863], [31775]
INC Education [16149]
"Incapital Set to Add Jobs, Expand Space" in South Florida Business Journal (Vol. 33, August 3, 2012, No. 1, pp. 1) [4144], [6475], [18164], [26588]

Master Index Industrial

"*The Incentive Bubble: Outsourcing Pay Decisions To Financial Markets Has Skewed Compensation and, With It, American Capitalism" in Harvard Business Review (Vol. 90, March 2012, No. 3, pp. 124)* **[6476]**, **[9610]**, **[17315]**, **[26973]**, **[28658]**, **[31123]**
Incentive Solutions Inc. (ISI) **[27147]**
"*Incentives In Play for Astronautics" in Business Journal-Milwaukee (Vol. 28, November 5, 2010, No. 5, pp. A1)* **[25008]**, **[26308]**, **[33375]**
Incline Village Chamber of Commerce **[41940]**
Inclusive Sustainability **[23272]**, **[30577]**
"*Inco Takeover Faces Foreign Hurdles" in Globe & Mail (February 13, 2006, pp. B1)* **[25389]**, **[31362]**
"*Income Tax Credit for Business Pushes the Job Creation Button" in Idaho Business Review (August 27, 2014)* **[25009]**, **[26589]**, **[34816]**
Incorporate Your Business: A Legal Guide to Forming a Corporation in Your State **[18605]**, **[25390]**, **[32407]**
Inc. 5000 **[22935]**, **[33635]**
Inc. Magazine: The Magazine for Growing Companies **[24779]**
Inc.--The Inc. 500 Issue **[24689]**
"*Incorporated Versus Unincorporated Self Employment" in Small Business Trends (January 14, 2014)* **[27188]**, **[34532]**
Incorporation Forms For Washington **[46238]**
"*Inco's Takeover Offer Extended Four Months" in Globe & Mail (February 22, 2006, pp. B1)* **[19868]**, **[25391]**, **[31363]**
"*Increasing Business-to-Business Buyer Word-of-Mouth and Share-of-Purchase" in Journal of Business & Industrial Marketing (Vol. 29, June 2014, No. 5)* **[17695]**, **[20451]**, **[32553]**
"*Increasing HR's Strategic Participation: the Effect of HR Service Quality and Contribution Expectations" in Human Resource Management (Vol. 51, January-February 2012, No. 1, pp. 3-23)* **[22186]**, **[26974]**
INC.spire Education Foundation **[45957]**
The Incubaker LLC **[45530]**
INCubator **[44847]**
The Incubator **[39406]**
Incubator 39 **[42888]**
"*Incubator, Apartment Mix Eyed" in Providence Business News (Vol. 29, April 14, 2014, No. 2, pp. 1)* **[8792]**, **[13484]**, **[13868]**
The Incubator/Business One Stop Service (BOSS) **[42235]**
The Incubator at MAGNET [43672]
"*Incubators Experiencing a Baby Boom" in Philadelphia Business Journal (Vol. 31, March 23, 2012, No. 6, pp. 1)* **[7123]**, **[27211]**
"*Incubators Heat Up Chances of Small Business Survival" in Business News Daily (Aug. 5, 2022)* **[8793]**, **[8812]**
InCube Labs L.L.C. **[45531]**
InCube Ventures, LLC **[37584]**
IncWell **[41093]**
Independence Area Chamber of Commerce **[39755]**
"*Independence Blue Cross Reverses Membership Slide" in Philadelphia Business Journal (Vol. 30, September 23, 2011, No. 32, pp. 1)* **[8926]**, **[25835]**, **[27288]**
Independence Chamber of Commerce **[41577]**
Independence Chamber of Commerce (ICC) **[39906]**
Independence Commercial Association [39906]
"*Independence Station Utilizes Sustainable Technologies" in Contractor (Vol. 56, September 2009, No. 9, pp. 3)* **[494]**, **[4145]**, **[5653]**, **[23273]**
Independent Automotive Service Association [402], [1089], [14531], [14604]
Independent Bakers Association (IBA) **[1244]**
Independent Book Publishers Association (IBPA) **[1623]**
Independent Business Alliance [26754]
Independent College Bookstore Association (ICBA) **[1805]**
Independent Community Bankers of America (ICBA) **[6728]**
"*Independent Contractor, Sole Proprietor, and LLC Taxes Explained in 100 Pages or Less"* **[15392]**, **[18999]**, **[26795]**, **[34817]**
Independent Educational Consultants Association (IECA) **[16123]**
Independent Educational Counselors Association [16123]
Independent Electrical Contractors (IEC) **[5351]**
Independent Film & Television Alliance (IFTA) **[11118]**
Independent Film and Video Alliance [6164]
Independent Financial Brokers of Canada (IFB) **[8866]**
Independent Glass Association (IGA) **[7488]**
Independent Insurance Agents and Brokers of America, Inc. (IIABA) **[8867]**
Independent Literary Agents of America [10344]
Independent Literary Agents Association [10344]
Independent Media Arts Alliance (IMAA) **[6164]**
Independent Medical Distributors Association [10822]
Independent Medical Specialty Dealers Association (IMDA) **[10822]**
Independent Meeting Planners Association of Canada [14505]
Independent Natural Food Retailers Association (INFRA) **[7998]**
Independent Publishing Now eNewsletter **[1690]**
Independent Retailers Buying Group Spring Trade Show **[3164]**, **[14693]**, **[15119]**, **[32351]**
Independent Turf and Ornamental Distributors Association (ITODA) **[10048]**, **[10076]**
Independent Visually Impaired Enterprisers [25675]
Independent Visually Impaired Entrepreneurs (IVIE) **[25675]**
Indexing and Abstracting Society of Canada [2]
Indexing I (Onsite) **[17591]**
Indexing II (Onsite) **[17592]**
Indexing Society of Canada (ISC) **[2]**
Indexing Society of Canada Annual Conference **[7]**, **[35123]**
Indian American Women Entrepreneurs Association (IAWEA) **[35624]**
"*Indian Buyer Gives Life to Algoma Expansion" in Globe & Mail (April 17, 2007, pp. B1)* **[18165]**, **[31364]**
Indian Diamond and Colorstone Association (IDCA) **[9963]**
Indian Hills Small Business Development Center **[39676]**
Indian Lake Area Chamber of Commerce (ILACOC) **[43498]**
Indian River Area Library (IRAL) **[2623]**, **[33717]**, **[34231]**
Indian River County Chamber of Commerce **[38433]**
Indian River Regional Chamber of Commerce **[40944]**
Indian Rocks Beach Chamber of Commerce [38507]
Indian Valley Chamber of Commerce (IVCC) **[36948]**, **[44246]**
Indiana Agricultural Leadership Institute [17227]
Indiana APEX Accelerator (PTAC) **[39635]**
Indiana Association of Realtors (IAR) **[13093]**
Indiana Builders Construction Showcase [4296]
Indiana Business Bulletin **[39665]**
Indiana Business Diversity Council [39626]
Indiana Business and Professional Women's Club **[35625]**
Indiana Chamber of Commerce (ICC) **[39559]**
"*Indiana Collection Agency Announces Expansion Plans" in PaymentsSource (March 23, 2012)* **[4793]**, **[18166]**, **[20303]**, **[26590]**, **[33376]**, **[34818]**
Indiana County Chamber of Commerce **[44247]**
Indiana Department of Administration (IDOA) - Minority & Women's Business Enterprises Div. **[39623]**
Indiana Department of Commerce (IEDC) - International Development **[39481]**
Indiana Department of Transportation - Economic Opportunity Division - Disadvantaged Business Enterprise Program **[39624]**
Indiana Design Consortium Inc. (IDC) **[17196]**
Indiana Economic Development Corp. (IEDC) **[39482]**, **[47417]**
Indiana Education Policy Center [21743]
Indiana Grocery & Convenience Store Association (IGCSA) **[39469]**
Indiana Institute of Agriculture, Food, and Nutrition [17227]
Indiana Institute of Technology - McMillen Productivity and Design Center **[39483]**
Indiana Limestone Institute of America, Inc. (ILIA) **[10727]**
Indiana Minority Supplier Development Council [39626]
Indiana Procurement Technical Assistance Center [39635]
Indiana Regional Minority Supplier Development Council [39626]
Indiana Senate Committee on Agriculture and Natural Resources **[39660]**
Indiana Senate Committee on Agriculture and Small Business [39660]
Indiana Small Business Development Center (ISBDC) **[32980]**, **[39473]**, **[39625]**
Indiana State Library State Data Center (SDC) **[47418]**
Indiana State University - Office of Sponsored Programs (OSP) **[27984]**
Indiana State University Small Business Development Center **[39484]**
"*Indiana Town Reports Success With Collection Agency" in PaymentsSource (August 20, 2012)* **[4794]**, **[20304]**, **[25141]**, **[25392]**
Indiana University Bloomington - Center for Evaluation and Education Policy (CEEP) **[21743]**
Indiana University Bloomington - Center for Postsecondary Research (CPR) **[21744]**
Indiana University Bloomington - Center for Studies of Law in Action **[34699]**
Indiana University Bloomington - Center for the Study of Institutions, Population, and Environmental Change (CIPEC) **[21745]**
Indiana University Bloomington - Kelley School of Business - Benecki Center for Real Estate Studies (BCRES) **[13633]**
Indiana University - Indiana Molecular Biology Institute **[39485]**
Indiana University - Kelley School of Business - Indiana Business Research Center (IBRC) **[21277]**, **[39486]**, **[46932]**
Indiana University of Pennsylvania Government Contracting Assistance Program (GCAP) **[44358]**
Indiana University of Pennsylvania Small Business Development Center (SBDC) **[44096]**
Indiana University-Purdue University at Indianapolis - Center for the Study of Religion and American Culture (CSRAC) **[21746]**
Indiana University-Purdue University at Indianapolis (IUPUI) - CyberLab **[21747]**
Indiana University-Purdue University Indianapolis - Indiana Alzheimer Disease Center (IADC) **[10941]**
Indiana University-Purdue University at Indianapolis - Lilly Family School of Philanthropy **[7190]**
Indiana University-Purdue University at Indianapolis - Peirce Edition Project (PEP) **[21748]**
Indiana University-Purdue University Indianapolis Physics Department - Nuclear Magnetic Resonance Center (NMR) **[21749]**
Indiana University-Purdue University at Indianapolis - William S. and Christine S. Hall Center for Law and Health **[26121]**
Indiana University School of Public Health (IUSPH) - Department of Applied Health Science **[5122]**
Indianapolis Monthly City Guide **[39560]**
Indianapolis SCORE **[39489]**
Indiana's Midwest Builders Convention **[4296]**
Indianola Chamber of Commerce (ICC) **[39756]**
Indiantown Western Martin County Chamber of Commerce **[38434]**
Indicator Ventures **[40699]**
Indie Bio **[37585]**
"*Indie Bookstores Flourish in an Amazon World" in Axios (January 12, 2019)* **[1828]**
"*IndieCompanyDk Offers Eco-Friendly Furniture That Stands Out" in Ecology, Environment & Conservation Business (September 6, 2014, pp. 39)* **[5654]**, **[5921]**, **[8210]**, **[23274]**, **[30744]**
"*Indigenous Tourism Operators: The Vanguard of Economic Recovery in the Chatham Islands" in International Journal of Entrepreneurship and Small Business (Vol. 10, July 6, 2010, No. 4)* **[15749]**, **[16000]**, **[20963]**, **[27612]**, **[34065]**
Indio Chamber of Commerce **[36949]**
The Indispensable Assistant (Onsite) **[34971]**
"*Individual and Organizational Reintegration After Ethical or Legal Transgressions: Challenges and Opportunities" in Business Ethics Quarterly (Vol. 24, July 2014, No. 3, pp. 315)* **[18606]**, **[23507]**
Indo Expo Winter Show **[5054]**
Indoor Air Quality Association (IAQA) **[552]**
"*Indoor Tanning Business Is Drying Up, Says National Group" in Idaho Business Review (August 20, 2014)* **[15262]**, **[34066]**
"*Indoor Tanning and the Myth of a Healthy Tan" in U.S. News and World Report (September 1, 2015)* **[15263]**
Indoor Tennis Association [12378], [15666]
"*Indulgent Parsimony: an Enduring Marketing Approach" in Strategy and Leadership (Vol. 39, March-April 2011, No. 2, pp. 36)* **[20964]**, **[29864]**, **[32554]**
The Indus Entrepreneurs (TIE) **[22461]**
The Indus Entrepreneurs Austin **[44895]**
The Indus Entrepreneurs Boston **[40488]**
The Indus Entrepreneurs Houston **[44896]**
The Indus Entrepreneurs Midwest **[38973]**
The Indus Entrepreneurs New York (TiE NY) **[42382]**
The Indus Entrepreneurs Pittsburgh **[44087]**
The Indus Entrepreneurs South Coast (TIE) **[36539]**
Industrial and Business Directory **[39561]**
"*Industrial Buyers' Use of References, Word-of-Mouth and Reputation in Complex Buying Situation" in Journal of Business & Industrial Marketing (Vol. 29, May 2014, No. 4, pp. 344-352)* **[20452]**, **[31776]**
Industrial Consultants Company [24486]
Industrial Council of Nearwest Chicago (ICNC) **[39407]**
Industrial Development Bank [11105]
Industrial Guide **[44565]**
Industrial Health Foundation (IHF) **[35975]**
Industrial Laser Solutions **[29452]**
Industrial Methods Society [28268], [34965]
Industrial Patent Activity in the United States Parts 1 and 2, 1971-1995 [18789], [27978]
Industrial Patent Activity in the United States Parts 1 and 2, 1974-1998 **[18789]**, **[27978]**
Industrial Relations Research Association [35220]
"*Industrial Vacancies Hit High" in Crain's Chicago Business (Apr. 21, 2008)* **[12889]**, **[13222]**, **[13485]**, **[20965]**, **[29255]**

Small Business Sourcebook • 42nd Edition 3263

Master Index

Industry Master Index

"Industry Associations Seek Clarity of CFPB's Large Collection Agency Definition" in PaymentsSource (May 24, 2012) **[4795], [20305], [25393]**
Industry Business Council (IMC) **[36950]**
Industry Council for Tangible Assets [3229]
"Industry Escalates Lobbying Efforts For Loan Program" in Crain's Detroit Business (Vol. 24, September 22, 2008, No. 38, pp. 22) **[5655], [5922], [20629], [23275], [25394], [28147], [34067]**
Industry Film Producers Association [6165]
Industry Manufacturers Council [36950]
Industry Ventures **[37395]**
Indy Chamber **[39562]**
"Inesoft Cash Organizer Desktop: A New Approach to Personal Accounts Bookkeeping" in America's Intelligence Wire (August 7, 2012) **[70], [1761], [12834], [23959], [33863]**
iNetworks Advisors **[44442], [44444]**
Infant Massage WINC - World Institute for Nurturing Communication [10757]
Infection Prevention and Control Canada (IPAC) **[25676]**
Infirmieres et Infirmiers en Santé Communautaire du Canada (IISCC) **[25677]**
Inflatable Advertising Dealers Association (IADA) **[31830]**
Influence Skills: Getting Results Without Direct Authority (Onsite) **[17593]**
Influence Strategies **[17594]**
Influencer Marketing: A Research Guide **[29511]**
"Info Junkie: Karen Eng" in Crain's Chicago Business (Vol. 34, October 24, 2011, No. 42, pp. 35) **[5656], [5923], [6830], [22652], [23276], [29865], [32555]**
InfoComm International [6159]
"Infographic: Social Spending by Country: How Bloated is European Social Spending?" in Canadian Business (Vol. 85, August 13, 2012, No. 13, pp. 66) **[25010], [25836]**
"Infomercial King on TeleBrands, Going Broke, Making Millions" in Philadelphia Business Journal (Vol. 33, July 11, 2014, No. 22, pp. 3) **[291], [22653], [23960], [29866]**
InfoQuick **[17418]**
The Information Advisor's Guide to Internet Research **[8838]**
Information Film Producers of America [6165]
Information International **[45984]**
Information Standards Quarterly (ISQ) **[8839]**
Information Storage Industry Consortium (INSIC) **[3474]**
Information Technology Association of Canada [8833]
"Information Technology Changes Roles, Highlights Hiring Needs" in South Florida Business Journal (Vol. 34, February 14, 2014, No. 30, pp. 3) **[21892], [23006], [26309], [26591], [28659]**
Information Technology Industry Council (ITI) **[3689], [11660]**
Information Technology Project Management **[28355]**
Information Technology for the Small Business: How to Make IT Work For Your Company **[3511], [3715], [9160], [17696], [17862], [21893], [26310]**
Information Today (IT) **[8840], [9275]**
"Infrastructure Investment and Jobs Act Includes New Vehicle Safety Provisions" in Autobody News (November 19, 2021) **[1103], [1187]**
"Infrastructure: Things Fall Apart" in Canadian Business (Vol. 80, October 8, 2007, No. 20, pp. 187) **[4146], [20966], [25395]**
"Infusion Device Gets $1.47 Million Army Grant" in Memphis Business Journal (Vol. 33, January 20, 2012, No. 41, pp. 1) **[10836], [25142], [25837]**
Infusionsoft Inc. [36398]
Ingk Labs L.L.C. **[42889]**
Ingleside Chamber of Commerce **[45220]**
Ingleside Chamber of Commerce Newsletter **[45221]**
Inglewood Airport Area Chamber of Commerce (IAACC) **[36951]**
Inglewood/Airport Area Chamber of Commerce [36951]
Ingram Micro ITAD **[3664]**
Ingram's: Kansas City's Business Magazine **[41701]**
Ingram's Magazine **[41702]**
"The Ingredients of a Marketing Plan" in Entrepreneur **[29528]**
"Ingrian and Channel Management International Sign Distribution Agreement" in Canadian Corporate News (May 16, 2007) **[9161], [14789], [20630], [26311], [31365], [33184]**
"Initial Crowd Offering, Inc. Announces Launch of Equity Crowdfunding Intermediary Site" in GlobeNewswire (June 21, 2012) **[23007], [30921], [31366]**
Initialized Capital Management **[37396]**
Initiatives Review **[36129]**
Ink People Center for the Arts **[37586]**
"Inking the Deal" in Slate (October 1, 2014) **[15304], [25396], [33579]**
"Inking the Deal - Why Tattoo Parlors Are a Great Small-Business Bet" in Slate (October 1, 2014) **[15305]**
Inkster Chamber of Commerce **[40945]**
Inland Empire North Small Business Development Center **[36575]**
Inland Empire Small Business Development Center (IESBDC) **[36576]**
Inland Seas Education Association (ISEA) **[10588]**
"Inland Snaps Up Rival REITs" in Crain's Chicago Business (Vol. 31, November 17, 2008, No. 46, pp. 3) **[6477], [8419], [9611], [19000], [19534], [19869], [20967], [23961], [31367], [32184]**
Inlet Chamber of Commerce [42619]
Inlet Information Office **[42619]**
"Inmet Selling Nunavut Mining Properties" in Globe & Mail (February 15, 2006, pp. B6) **[6478], [9612], [31368], [33019]**
"InnoCentive Announces Next Generation Crowdsourcing Platform" in Marketwired (June 15, 2010) **[21894], [29867], [30745]**
Innosphere **[37945]**
InnoSpring **[37587]**
InnoTech Alberta **[46673]**
Innova Memphis **[44871]**
Innovacorp **[46747]**
Innovate Angel Funds, LLC **[45455]**
Innovate Calgary **[46674]**
Innovate Coalition **[22465]**
Innovate to Great: Re-Igniting Sustainable Innovation to Win in the Global Economy **[20968], [27613], [27894]**
Innovate Mississippi **[41447]**
Innovate New Albany **[43668]**
Innovate Niagara (IN) **[46825]**
"Innovate or Stagnate: How Doing Things Differently Helps Business" in South Florida Business Journal (Vol. 34, January 10, 2014, No. 25, pp. 10) **[2190], [19535], [20111], [27895], [29868]**
Innovate Washington Foundation (IWF) **[46217]**
"Innovating Globally" in Business Strategy Review (Vol. 21, Spring 2010, No. 1, pp. 24) **[18167], [19001], [19367], [27614], [27896], [34333]**
Innovating with the Grain World's First Bulk Solids Locomotion Devices **[17158]**
"Innovating Low-Cost Business Models" in Strategy and Leadership (Vol. 39, March-April 2011, No. 2, pp. 43) **[20037], [27615], [27897], [30746]**
"Innovation in 3D: NextFab" in Philadelphia Business Journal (Vol. 28, January 22, 2010, No. 49, pp. 1) **[26312], [30747]**
"Innovation: A Blood Test on a Chip" in Inc. (Vol. 33, November 2011, No. 9, pp. 42) **[10921], [25838], [32778], [33185]**
"Innovation Adoption and Diffusion in Business-to-Business Marketing" in Journal of Business & Industrial Marketing (Vol. 29, May 2014, No. 4, pp. 324-331) **[29256], [29869], [31369]**
"Innovation Can Be Imperative for Those in Hands-On Trades" in Crain's Cleveland Business (Vol. 28, November 12, 2007, No. 45) **[897], [4595], [29870], [34068]**
The Innovation Center **[41448]**
"Innovation Central: Tech, Tweets, and Trolls" in Inc. (Vol. 36, September 2014, No. 7, pp. 102) **[14790], [21895], [25397], [27898], [33864], [34069]**
Innovation Connector (IC) **[39641]**
Innovation Depot **[36183]**
"Innovation Despite Reorganization" in Journal of Business Strategy (Vol. 35, May-June 2014, No. 3, pp. 18-25) **[19536], [20969], [22187]**
Innovation Endeavors **[37397]**
Innovation Enterprise **[40123]**
Innovation and Export: The Joint Challenge of the Small Company **[16573]**
The Innovation Factory (TIF) **[38835]**
The Innovation Group (TIG) **[7324]**
Innovation Hub at Broward College **[38572]**
Innovation Hub at the University of Florida (UF Innovate) **[38573]**
Innovation Incubator **[42890]**
"Innovation Incubators Attract Printers, Designers" in PrintingImpressions October 16, 2019) **[8813], [12706]**
Innovation Maritime (IMAR) **[46896]**
Innovation in Motion [39965]
Innovation Norway - United States **[27416]**
Innovation Partnerships **[41094]**
Innovation Pavilion **[37946]**
Innovation PEI **[46878]**
Innovation Policyworks **[40329]**
"Innovation Station" in Canadian Business (Vol. 80, October 8, 2007, No. 20, pp. 42) **[20970], [21549], [22654], [26313], [27899], [31992]**
Innovation Stockyard **[41677]**
Innovation Underground (IU) **[45532]**
Innovation Works, Inc. **[44341]**
"Innovation's Holy Grail" in Harvard Business Review (Vol. 88, July-August 2010, No. 7-8, pp. 132) **[19368], [27900]**
"Innovative Ability and Entrepreneurial Activity: Two Factors to Enhance 'Quality of Life" in Journal of Business & Industrial Marketing (Vol. 29, July 2014, No. 6) **[22393], [27901], [28035]**
Innovative Business Systems Inc. (IBS) **[3665]**
Innovative Lease Services Inc. (ILS) **[35462]**
Innovative Partners Incubation (IPI) **[40460]**
"Innovative Trauma Care Sets Up U.S. HQ in San Antonio" in San Antonio Business Journal (Vol. 26, August 31, 2012, No. 31, pp. 1) **[25839], [26314], [33377]**
"Innovators Critical in Technical Economy" in Crain's Cleveland Business (Vol. 28, November 5, 2007, No. 44, pp. 10) **[20971], [21550], [26315], [27616]**
The Innovators: How a Group of Hackers, Geniuses, and Geeks Created the Digital Revolution **[3716], [22655], [27902]**
"The Innovator's Method: Bringing the Lean Start-up into Your Organization" **[24544], [27821]**
"The Innovator's Solution: Creating and Sustaining Successful Growth" **[18168], [19002], [22656], [27903], [28660]**
InnoVentures Capital Partners **[45662]**
INNside Scoop: Everything You Ever Wanted to Know About Bed & Breakfast Inns **[1418], [8420]**
Inovia Capital **[46886]**
"The Ins and Outs of Wi-Fi-Enabled Air Conditioning" in AC Heating and Air Conditioning Services (August 28, 2018) **[495]**
"Inside the High-Drama World of Youth Competition Dance" in The New York Times (December 21, 2017) **[4853]**
"Inside Indie Movie Theaters' Battle to Survive" in Variety **[11124]**
"Inside Intel's Effectiveness System for Web Marketing" in Advertising Age (Vol. 81, January 25, 2010, No. 4, pp. 4) **[9162], [14791], [16432], [29871], [33865]**
Inside MBS & ABS **[11094]**
"Inside the Mind of an Investor: Lessons from Bill Draper" in Inc. (Volume 32, December 2010, No. 10, pp. 140) **[28148], [35353]**
Inside Missile Defense **[25170]**
"Inside the New Amazon 4-Star Store, a Novelty Gift Shop" in The Wall Street Journal (September 27, 2018) **[7479]**
"Inside Out" in Playthings (Vol. 107, January 1, 2009, No. 1, pp. 3) **[15791], [27904], [32185]**
Inside Supply Management: Resources to Create Your Future **[31911]**
"Inside True Value's $150M Supply Chain Investment" in Hardware Retailing (November 11, 2019) **[7921]**
Inside Tucson Business **[19246]**
"Inside Waterloo's Quiet Tech Titan" in Canadian Business (Vol. 87, July 2014, No. 7, pp. 39) **[3512], [14792], [18169], [26316], [33866]**
"Inside the World of Check-Cashing Outlets" in Dollars&Sense (January/February 2015) **[2837]**
Insight **[40946]**
Insight Center for Community Economic Development **[20699]**
Insight into Diversity: The EEO Recruitment Publication **[14981], [14990], [26711], [30627]**
Insight Park **[41449]**
Insight Venture Partners / Insight Capital Partners **[42761]**
Insights **[5472], [36952]**
InSite **[2527]**
InSite Business Solutions Inc. **[3459]**
"Insitu May Move to Oregon" in Business Journal Portland (Vol. 27, October 29, 2010, No. 35, pp. 1) **[20972], [33378]**
Insomnia Cookies Franchising, LLC - 14th Street New York City **[1296], [6938]**
Inspect-It 1st L.L.C. **[2035]**
InspectAmerica Engineering P.C. **[2024]**
Inspiration Venture Partners LLC **[37398]**
Inspire Brands, Inc. **[14186]**
Inspiring Capital (IC's) **[43022]**
"Install a Tasting System to Improve Food Truck Consistency" in Mobile-Cuisine.com **[6994], [19003]**
Installing, Configuring, and Troubleshooting Microsoft SQL Server **[21392]**
Instant Imprints **[12034]**
Instant Income: Strategies That Bring in the Cash **[292], [22657], [29872], [31370], [32556]**
Instinct: Tapping Your Entrepreneurial DNA to Achieve Your Business Goals **[19004], [22658]**
Institut canadien de la construction en acier [3928]
Institut agree de la logistique et des transports Amerique du Nord [15506]
Institut Canadien des Economistes en Construction [19], [1737]
Institut Canadien de Gestion [28256]

3264 Small Business Sourcebook • 42nd Edition

Master Index International

Institut Canadien de la Recherche sur la Condition Physique et le Mode de Vie (ICRCP) **[12375]**, **[12478]**
Institut Canadien de Relations avec les Investisseurs [6230]
Institut Canadien des Valeurs Mobilieres [9292]
Institut d'arbitrage et de Médiation du Canada Inc. [10784]
Institut International de l'Ombusdman [10788]
Institut de Radioprotection du Canada (RSI) **[13072]**
Institut Royal d'Architecture du Canada (IRAC) **[862]**
Institute for the Advancement of Criminal Justice [34672]
Institute for Aerobics Research [12477]
Institute for Agriculture and Trade Policy (IATP) **[17232]**
Institute of Business Designers [9025], [11630]
Institute of Business Forecasting and Planning (IBF) **[30204]**
Institute for Business and Home Safety Library [35976]
Institute for Business Technology (IBT) **[29002]**
Institute of Certified Financial Planners [6232]
Institute for Certified Investment Management Consultants [9294], [13360]
Institute of Certified Travel Agents [15979]
Institute of Chartered Financial Analysts [9290]
Institute of Communication Agencies (ICA) **[1806]**
Institute of Communications and Advertising [1806]
Institute for the Cooperative Study of International Seafood Markets [6740], [6765]
Institute for Distribution Excellence **[20603]**, **[20675]**, **[35483]**
Institute for Diversity Certification (IDC) **[34261]**
Institute of Energy: Sustainability, Environment and Equity (IESEE) **[42891]**
Institute for Entrepreneurial Leadership (IFEL) **[42236]**
Institute for Environmental Policy and Planning [5789]
Institute of Environmental Program Affairs [5789]
Institute de la Fondation D'Acupuncture du Canada [11334], [12480]
Institute for the Future (IFTF) **[30859]**
Institute for Health Services Research [26156]
Institute for Industrial and Applied Life Sciences (IALS) **[40752]**
Institute of Internal Auditors - International Conference **[119]**, **[15441]**
Institute for International Economics [15498]
Institute of Law and Government [31733]
Institute for Life Science Entrepreneurship (ILSE) **[42237]**
Institute for Local Self-Reliance (ILSR) **[13750]**
Institute of Management Accountants (IMA) **[31]**, **[167]**
Institute of Management Consultants USA (IMC USA) **[10475]**
Institute for Management Excellence **[2277]**, **[2389]**, **[10537]**, **[20198]**, **[29003]**, **[29469]**, **[33673]**
Institute for Mediation and Conflict Resolution (IMCR) **[10787]**
Institute of Museum & Library Services--Annual Report **[971]**
Institute of Museum Services--Annual Report [971]
Institute of Nutrition Sciences [11625]
Institute for Operations Research and the Management Sciences (INFORMS) **[34961]**
Institute for Performance and Learning (I4PL) **[26839]**
Institute of Programming and Logics [3686]
Institute for Public Relations (IPR) **[31816]**
Institute for Public Service (IPS) **[44829]**
Institute of Real Estate Management (IREM) **[12863]**, **[13094]**, **[39451]**
Institute of Religion and Health [26106]
Institute of Scrap Iron and Steel [13688]
Institute of Scrap Recycling Industries (ISRI) **[13688]**
Institute of Scrap Recycling Industries--Membership Directory **[13719]**
Institute of Signage Research [14700]
Institute for Supply Management (ISM) **[31905]**
Institute for Technology & Business Development (ITBD) **[38110]**
Institute for Traditional Medicine and Preventive Health Care (ITM) **[12487]**
Institute of Waste Equipment Distributors [7941]
Institute for Women's Policy Research (IWPR) **[26122]**
Institutional Food Manufacturers of America [6889], [13881]
Institutional Food Manufacturers Association [6889], [13881]
Institutional Food-Service Manufacturers Association [6889], [13881]
Institutional Locksmiths' Association (ILA) **[10351]**
The Institutional Real Estate Letter **[13315]**, **[13602]**
Institutional Venture Partners (IVP) **[37399]**
Instituto Internacional del Ombudsman [10788]
Instructional Design for Participant-Centered Training (Onsite) **[26865]**
Instructional Design for Trainers (Onsite) **[26866]**
Instrumentation, Process Measurement & Control (Onsite) **[19444]**, **[21393]**
Insulation Contractors Association of America (ICAA) **[8846]**
Insulation Distributor Contractors National Association [3960], [8847]
Insurance Advertising Conference [8872]
Insurance Brokers Association of Canada (IBAC) **[8868]**
Insurance Bureau of Canada (IBC) **[8869]**
Insurance Consumer Affairs Exchange (ICAE) **[8870]**
"Insurance Firm Consolidates Offices: Integro Finds the Right Price Downtown" in Crain's New York Business (January 13, 2008) **[8927]**, **[19180]**, **[27289]**
Insurance Information Institute (III) **[8871]**, **[9006]**
Insurance Institute for Business And Home Safety (IBHS) **[35976]**
Insurance Institute for Highway Safety (IIHS) **[409]**
Insurance Institute of Ontario Library (IIO) **[9007]**
Insurance Institute for Property Loss Reduction [35976]
The Insurance Journal of the West **[8988]**
Insurance Marketing & Communications Association (IMCA) **[8872]**
Insurance Research Council (IRC) **[9013]**
Insurance Risk Management Forum [14491]
"Insurance Roars Back Into Style" in Barron's (Vol. 92, September 17, 2012, No. 38, pp. 11) **[9613]**, **[25398]**
"An Insurer Stretches Out" in Business Journal Portland (Vol. 30, February 21, 2014, No. 51, pp. 4) **[8853]**, **[25632]**, **[27214]**
"Insurers Enter Ridesharing Dispute" in Sacramento Business Journal (Vol. 31, June 6, 2014, No. 15, pp. 8) **[15516]**, **[25399]**, **[27290]**
"Insurers No Longer Paying Premium for Advertising" in Brandweek (Vol. 49, April 21, 2008, No. 16, pp. SR3) **[293]**, **[8928]**, **[17504]**, **[18170]**, **[19005]**, **[19870]**, **[20038]**, **[20973]**, **[27291]**, **[29873]**
Integrated Business Resources Inc. **[26840]**
Integrated Conservation Resources Inc. (ICR) **[940]**
Integrated Development Consulting **[35452]**
Integrated Security Technologies (IST) **[31006]**, **[31080]**
Integrating Forms and Databases on the Web (Onsite) **[21394]**
"Integrating Your Compliance Program" in Franchising World (Vol. 42, November 2010, No. 11, pp. 49) **[19006]**, **[24377]**
Intel Corporation Library **[3471]**
"Intel Joins Movement to Turn Cube Farms Into Wide-Open Spaces" in Sacramento Business Journal (Vol. 28, May 27, 2011, No. 13, pp. 1) **[9043]**, **[11639]**, **[31048]**, **[34070]**
"The Intel Trinity: How Robert Noyce, Gordon Moore, and Andy Grove Built the World's Most Important Company" **[2750]**, **[3717]**, **[4396]**, **[9163]**, **[22659]**, **[26317]**, **[27905]**
Intellectual Property Owners [12864]
Intellectual Property Owners Association (IPO) **[12864]**
Intelligent Systems Corporation [38830]
IntelliShift (VTS) **[3791]**
IntelliTurf [10137]
"Intentional Networking: Your Guide to Word of Mouth Marketing Greatness" **[21896]**, **[29874]**, **[32557]**
INTENZE Advanced Tattoo Ink [15326]
Intenze Products Inc. **[15326]**
"Inter-firm Marketing Collaboration in Family Business: The Role of Risk Aversion" in Journal of Small Business Strategy (April 13, 2021) **[33700]**
Inter-Industry Conference on Auto Collision Repair (I-CAR) **[14534]**
Interactive Business Systems Inc. **[3460]**, **[3461]**
"Interactive Stores a Big Part of Borders' Turnaround Plan" in Crain's Detroit Business (Vol. 24, February 18, 2008, No. 7, pp. 4) **[1829]**, **[4938]**, **[7366]**, **[12282]**, **[26318]**
Interactive Training Techniques for the Classroom (Onsite) **[17595]**
Interamerican Accounting Association (AIC) **[32]**
Intercept Ventures LLC **[37400]**
"Interchangeable or Irreplaceable?" in American Printer (Vol. 128, August 1, 2011, No. 8) **[3318]**, **[12741]**, **[16194]**, **[20453]**
Intercoiffure America [7853]
Intercoiffure America/Canada (ICA) **[7853]**
Intercollegiate Broadcasting System Inc. (IBS) **[4948]**
Intercollegiate Horse Shows Association (IHSA) **[8308]**
Intercultural Communication Institute (ICI) **[30657]**
"Interesting Stats on Too Many Virtual Meetings" in Small Business Trends (October 17, 2022) **[16574]**
The Interface Financial Group (IFG) **[6715]**
Intergovernmental Health Policy Project [26114]
Interim HealthCare Inc. **[26094]**
Interim HomeStyle Services **[5456]**
Interior Design **[9061]**, **[11648]**, **[14714]**
The Interior Design Business Handbook: A Complete Guide to Profitability **[9044]**
Interior Design Society (IDS) **[9022]**
Interior Designers Industry in the US - Market Research Report **[9054]**
Interior Magic International L.L.C. **[16239]**
Interlochen Area Chamber of Commerce (IACC) **[40947]**
Interlochen Center for the Arts (ICA) **[11223]**
Intermarket Agency Network (IAN) **[220]**, **[31831]**
Intermarket Association of Advertising Agencies [220], [31831]
Interminds & Federer Resources Inc. **[2278]**, **[10538]**, **[20199]**, **[22318]**, **[24249]**, **[29004]**, **[30851]**, **[33674]**
"Intermodal Makes Suppliers Look to Rack Up Big Sales to Distributors" in The Business Journal-Serving Metropolitan Kansas City (August 15, 2008) **[18171]**, **[19007]**, **[19181]**, **[19537]**, **[20631]**, **[29257]**, **[32558]**
"Internal Auditor Wants Ethics Review of City's Billy Casper Golf Contract" in Business Courier (Vol. 27, September 10, 2010, No. 19, pp. 1) **[71]**, **[7522]**, **[15393]**, **[16810]**, **[23508]**
Internal Revenue Service - Martinsburg Computing Center [47794]
Internamerican Accounting Conference [32]
International Academy of Compounding Pharmacists [5124]
International Academy of Nutritional Consultants [11558]
International Academy of Opticianry [16290]
International Accelerator (IA) **[45533]**
International Advertising Association (IAA) **[221]**, **[399]**, **[31832]**
International Aloe Science Council (IASC) **[1381]**
International Appraisal Conference [822]
International Appraisers Conference **[822]**
International Artisan Bakery Expo **[1284]**
International Assembly of Grocery Manufacturers Associations [7708]
International Association of Administrative Professionals Summit **[24840]**
International Association of Amusement Parks [595]
International Association of Amusement Parks and Attractions (IAAPA) **[595]**
International Association of Assessing Officers - Research and Technical Services Department **[15493]**
International Association of Astacology (IAA) **[6764]**
International Association of Audio Visual Communicators (IAA-VC) **[6165]**
International Association of Better Business Bureaus **[45825]**
International Association of Blue Print and Allied Industries [4486]
International Association of Boards of Examiners in Optometry [16281]
International Association of Business Communicators (IABC) **[17526]**, **[17821]**
International Association of Business Communicators Atlanta **[38623]**
International Association of Business Communicators Austin **[44897]**
International Association of Business Communicators British Colombia (IABC BC) **[46689]**
International Association of Business Communicators Calgary (IABC) **[46654]**
International Association of Business Communicators Columbus **[43340]**
International Association of Business Communicators Connecticut (CT-IABC) **[37976]**
International Association of Business Communicators - DC Metro (IABC) **[45762]**
International Association of Business Communicators Harrisburg (IABC) **[44088]**
International Association of Business Communicators Houston **[44898]**
International Association of Business Communicators Kansas City (KC IABC) **[41463]**
International Association of Business Communicators Minnesota (IABC MN) **[41150]**
International Association of Business Communicators New Jersey (IABC NJ) **[42031]**
International Association of Business Communicators New York (NY IABC) **[42383]**
International Association of Business Communicators Newfoundland and Labrador (IABC-NL) **[46739]**
International Association of Business Communicators Omaha (IABC) **[41815]**
International Association of Business Communicators Ottawa **[46752]**
International Association of Business Communicators Regina (IABC) **[46913]**
International Association of Business Communicators St. Louis (IABC-St. Louis) **[41464]**
International Association of Business Communicators - San Francisco Bay Area (SF IABC) **[36540]**
International Association for Cold Storage Construction [12968]

Master Index

Small Business Sourcebook • 42nd Edition 3265

International Association of Commercial Collectors (IACC) **[4759]**
International Association for Computer Information Systems (IACIS) **[3422]**, **[3546]**
International Association of Conference Center Administrators (IACCA) **[15822]**
International Association of Conference Centres (IACC) **[15823]**
International Association of Cooking Professionals [4458]
International Association of Cooking Schools [4458]
International Association of Counseling Services (IACS) **[2593]**
International Association for Creative Dance (IACD) **[4842]**
International Association of Credit Cards [4760]
International Association of Culinary Professionals (IACP) **[4458]**
International Association for Exhibition Management [15824]
International Association of Exhibitions and Events (IAEE) **[15824]**
International Association of Financial Crimes Investigators (IAFCI) **[4760]**
International Association for Financial Planning [6232]
International Association of Health Underwriters [8875]
International Association of Holiday Inns [8349]
International Association of Hospitality Accountants [8345]
International Association of Ice Cream Manufacturers [16938]
International Association of Independent Information Brokers [3763]
International Association of Infant Massage (IAIM) **[10757]**
International Association of Infant Massage Instructors [10757]
International Association of Insurance Professionals (IAIP) **[8873]**
International Association of Insurance Receivers (IAIR) **[27221]**
International Association of Lighting Designers (IALD) **[5409]**, **[9023]**, **[31023]**
International Association of Lighting Management Companies Conference **[5419]**
International Association of Master Penmen, Engrossers, and Teachers of Handwriting (IAMPETH) **[2476]**
International Association of Outsourcing Professionals (IAOP) **[31109]**
International Association for Personnel Women [26842]
International Association of Pet Cemeteries Annual Convention **[12133]**
International Association of Pet Cemeteries and Crematories (IAOPCC) **[12131]**
International Association of Piano Builders and Technicians (IAPBT) **[11310]**
International Association of Plumbing and Mechanical Officials (IAPMO) **[455]**, **[15237]**
International Association Private Investigators [12789]
International Association of Professional Business Consultants (IAPO) **[2173]**
International Association of Professional Security Consultants (IAPSC) **[14373]**, **[22338]**
International Association of Refrigerated Warehouses [12968]
International Association of Registered Financial Consultants (IARFC) **[20078]**
International Association of Speakers Bureaus (IASB) **[14503]**
The International Association for Strategy Professionals (ASP) **[18871]**
International Association for Time Use Research (IATUR) **[2174]**, **[10476]**
International Association of Trade Exchanges [17238]
International Association of Wiping Cloth Manufacturers [13694]
International Association of Women (IAW) **[33463]**
International Association of Women Albuquerque Chapter (ABQ NOW) **[42271]**
International Association of Women Anchorage Chapter **[36203]**
International Association of Women Annapolis Chapter **[40333]**
International Association of Women Atlanta Chapter **[38624]**
International Association of Women Austin Chapter **[44899]**
International Association of Women Bakersfield Chapter **[36541]**
International Association of Women Bellevue Chapter **[45994]**
International Association of Women Boston Chapter **[40489]**
International Association of Women Central Houston Chapter **[44900]**

International Association of Women Chefs and Restaurateurs [13892]
International Association of Women Chesapeake Chapter **[45763]**
International Association of Women Chicago Chapter (IAW) **[38974]**
International Association of Women Cincinnati Chapter **[43341]**
International Association of Women Cleveland Chapter **[43342]**
International Association of Women Coral Gables Chapter **[38209]**
International Association of Women Dallas Chapter **[44901]**
International Association of Women DeKalb-Gwinnett Chapter **[38625]**
International Association of Women Detroit Chapter **[40799]**
International Association of Women Fairfield County Chapter **[37977]**
International Association of Women Greensboro Chapter **[43035]**
International Association of Women Hartford County Chapter **[37978]**
International Association of Women Honolulu Chapter **[38861]**
International Association of Women Kansas City Metro Chapter **[41465]**
International Association of Women Long Beach Chapter **[36542]**
International Association of Women Los Angeles Chapter **[36543]**
International Association of Women Manchester Chapter **[41968]**
International Association of Women Memphis Chapter **[44681]**
International Association of Women Miami Chapter **[38210]**
International Association of Women Milwaukee Chapter **[46314]**
International Association of Women Minneapolis-St. Paul Chapter **[41151]**
International Association of Women Nashville Chapter **[44682]**
International Association of Women New Orleans Chapter **[40122]**
International Association of Women New York City Chapter **[42384]**
International Association of Women Oakland Chapter **[36544]**
International Association of Women Ocala Chapter **[38211]**
International Association of Women Oklahoma City Chapter **[43704]**
International Association of Women Orlando Chapter **[38212]**
International Association of Women Pasadena Chapter **[36545]**
International Association of Women Pembroke Pines Chapter **[38213]**
International Association of Women Philadelphia Chapter **[44089]**
International Association of Women Phoenix Chapter **[36263]**
International Association of Women Pittsburgh Chapter **[44090]**
International Association of Women Portland Chapter **[43903]**
International Association of Women Providence Chapter **[44450]**
International Association of Women Raleigh Durham Chapter **[43036]**
International Association of Women San Diego Chapter **[36546]**
International Association of Women San Fernando Valley Chapter **[36547]**
International Association of Women San Francisco Chapter **[36548]**
International Association of Women Santa Monica Chapter **[36549]**
International Association of Women Schaumburg Chapter **[38975]**
International Association of Women Seattle Chapter **[45995]**
International Association of Women South Denver Chapter **[37775]**
International Association of Women Tulsa Chapter **[43705]**
International Association of Women West Denver Chapter **[37776]**
International Association of Workforce Professionals (IAWP) **[5434]**
International Atlantic Salmon Foundation [6762]

International Auto Sound Challenge Association (IASCA) **[2562]**
International Avenue Technology Centre (IATC) **[46675]**
International Beauty Exposition **[1401]**
"International Benefits Roundup" in Employee Benefit News (Vol. 25, December 1, 2011, No. 15) **[17316]**, **[26975]**, **[27617]**, **[34819]**
The International Boatbuilders Exhibition & Conference (IBEX) **[10621]**
International Bottled Water Association (IBWA) **[1854]**
International Bowl Expo **[1884]**
International Bowling Media Association (IBMA) **[5284]**
International Budget Partnership (IBP) **[33]**, **[16737]**, **[17486]**
International Budget Project of the Center on Budget and Policy Priorities [33], [16737], [17486]
International Business **[27618]**
International Business Associates **[8784]**
International Business Aviation Council (IBAC) **[420]**, **[19302]**
International Business Brokers Association (IBBA) **[2134]**
International Business - Government Counsellors Inc. (IBC) **[25625]**
International Business Innovation Association (InBIA) **[8801]**, **[33464]**
"International Business Law: Interpreting the Term 'Like Products" in Business Recorder (June 7, 2012) **[8730]**, **[15941]**, **[18607]**, **[19871]**, **[20039]**, **[27619]**
International Business Planning: Law and Taxation (United States) **[18773]**
International Business Resource Center **[27784]**
International Business Strategies Inc. (IBS) **[2279]**
International Business & Technical Consultants Inc. (IBTCI) **[2280]**
International Car Rental Show **[1165]**
International Carwash Association (ICA) **[2580]**
International Casual Furnishings Association (ICFA) **[8195]**
International Caterers Association (ICA) **[2664]**
International Cement Seminar **[10742]**
International Cemetery, Cremation and Funeral Association (ICCFA) **[7198]**
International Cemetery and Funeral Association [7198]
International Center of Photography (ICP) **[12285]**, **[12362]**
International Centre for Comparative Criminology [22357]
International Cheese and Deli Seminar [4877], [15001]
International Civil Aviation Organization (ICAO) **[421]**
International Claim Association (ICA) **[10888]**
International Claim Association Annual Education Conference **[27369]**
International Clown Hall of Fame and Research Center (ICHOF) **[11899]**
International Commission for the Northwest Atlantic Fisheries [6770]
International Communications Agency Network (ICOM) **[222]**, **[31833]**
International Communications Industries Association [6159]
International Computer Music Association (ICMA) **[11167]**, **[14751]**
International Conference [5109]
International Council on Hotel, Restaurant, and Institutional Education (ICHRIE) **[4459]**, **[8350]**
International Council of Shopping Centers (ICSC) **[32080]**
International Council for Small Business (ICSB) **[24589]**, **[28259]**, **[38187]**
International Counseling Center [30508], [30658]
International Cut Stone Quarrymen's Association [10732]
International Dairy-Deli-Bakery Association (IDDBA) **[4877]**, **[15001]**
International Dairy Foods Association (IDFA) **[16938]**
International Dance Entrepreneurs Association (IDEA) **[4843]**
International Data Corporation [2125], [3678], [3809], [9283]
International Data Group, Inc. (IDC) **[2125]**, **[3678]**, **[3809]**, **[9283]**
International Development Research Centre [26111]
International Digital Enterprise Alliance [12718], [16368]
The International Directory of Little Magazines & Small Presses **[1660]**, **[11983]**
International District Energy Association (IDEA) **[456]**
International District Heating Association [456]
International District Heating and Cooling Association [456]
International Documentary Association (IDA) **[6166]**
International Documentary Foundation [6166]
International Economic Development Council (IEDC) **[20700]**
International Economic Development Council-- Membership Directory **[20974]**

International Employment Hotline **[14988]**
International Entertainment Buyers Association (IEBA) **[15256]**
International Entrepreneurship: Starting, Developing, and Managing a Global Venture **[22394]**, **[27389]**
International Erosion Control Association [25615]
"*International ETFs: Your Passport to the World*" in *Barron's (Vol. 89, July 13, 2009, No. 28, pp. L10)* **[6479]**, **[9614]**, **[20975]**, **[23962]**, **[27620]**
International Exer-Safety Association [12372]
International Fabricare Institute [5226], [5264], [5265]
International Facilities Management Association's Facility Fusion Conference and Expo **[12912]**
International Facility Management Association (IFMA) **[12865]**
International Facility Management Association - Toronto Chapter (IFMA) **[2049]**
International Falls Area Chamber of Commerce **[41247]**
International Federation of Advertising Agencies [222], [31833]
International Federation of Bodybuilding and Fitness (IFBB) **[12376]**
International Federation of Pharmaceutical Wholesalers, Inc. (IFPWI) **[5139]**, **[35484]**
International Fence Industry Association [3915]
International Fertilizer Development Center (IFDC) **[17213]**
International Finance Corp. (IFC) **[20701]**
International Fitness Professionals Association (IFPA) **[12377]**
International Food and Agribusiness Management Association (IFAMA) **[16939]**
International Food Policy Research Institute (IFPRI) **[17214]**
International Food Wine and Travel Writers Association (IFWTWA) **[5285]**
International Foodservice Editorial Council (IFEC) **[5286]**
International Foodservice Manufacturers Association (IFMA) **[6889]**, **[13881]**
International Footwear Association [14667]
International Formalwear Association (IFA) **[3087]**
International Foundation of Employee Benefit Plans (IFEBP) **[17264]**, **[19730]**
International Foundation for Protection Officers (IFPO) **[12787]**
International Franchise Association (IFA) **[24310]**, **[38188]**
International Franchise Association--Franchise Opportunities Guide **[24378]**
International Franchise Association--Membership Directory: What You Need to Know When You Buy a Franchise [24378]
International Franchise Expo (IFE) **[24470]**
International Fund for Concerned Photography [12285], [12362]
International Furnishings and Design Association (IFDA) **[1570]**, **[9024]**
International Furniture Rental Association (IFRA) **[8196]**, **[13763]**
International Furniture Transportation and Logistics Council (IFTLC) **[8197]**
International Galapagos Tour Operators Association (IGTOA) **[15723]**, **[15972]**
International Game Fish Association (IGFA) **[1229]**, **[1235]**
International Gay and Lesbian Travel Association [15973]
International Gay Rodeo Association (IGRA) **[8309]**, **[15127]**
International Genealogical Index® **[7390]**
International Golf Federation (IGF) **[7510]**
International Graphoanalysis Society (IGAS) **[7904]**
International Ground Source Heat Pump Association (IGSHPA) **[457]**
International Group of Agencies and Bureaus [14503]
International Growth of Small and Medium Enterprises **[18172]**, **[27621]**, **[27906]**
International Handbook of Entrepreneurship and HRM **[22660]**, **[26976]**
International Hardwood Products Association [10379]
International Hardwood Products Association--Directory [10395]
International Harvester Collectors (IHC) **[3227]**
International Health, Racquet and Sportsclub Association (IHRSA) **[12378]**, **[15666]**
International Hearing Aid Society [8133]
International Hearing Society (IHS) **[8133]**
International Herb Association (IHA) **[8153]**
International Herb Growers and Marketers Association [8153]
International Home Furnishings Marketing Association [8193]
International Home Furnishings Representatives Association (IHFRA) **[8198]**

The International Hotel, Motel and Restaurant Show [8488], [14091]
International Housewares Association (IHA) **[786]**, **[8174]**
International Ice Cream Association [16938]
International Immigration and Business Consulting (IIBC) **[2281]**
International Institute of Conference Management [14502]
International Institute of Convention Management [14502]
International Institute of Fisheries Economics and Trade (IIFET) **[6740]**, **[6765]**
International Institute of Trading Mastery Inc. (IITM) **[9930]**
International Interior Design Association (IIDA) **[9025]**, **[11630]**
International Journal of Adaptive Control and Signal Processing **[32876]**
International Journal of Andrology: The Official Journal of the European Academy of Andrology [32854]
International Journal on Artificial Intelligence Tools **[32877]**
International Journal of Business Analytics (IJBAN) [24866]
International Journal of Business Communication (IJBC) **[17818]**
International Journal of Business and Industrial Marketing **[24867]**
International Journal of Business Intelligence Research (IJBIR) **[24868]**
International Journal of Business Management and Information Technology **[24869]**
International Journal of Business Strategy (IJBS) **[24870]**
International Journal of Computer Integrated Manufacturing **[32878]**
International Journal of Digital Strategy, Governance, and Business Transformation (IJDSGBT) **[3672]**
International Journal of Disability, Community & Rehabilitation **[12488]**
International Journal of Energy Research (IJER) **[32879]**
International Journal of Engineering Business Management (IJEBM) **[32934]**
International Journal of Entrepreneurship and Small Business (IJESB) **[27622]**
International Journal of Globalisation and Small Business (IJGSB) **[33627]**
International Journal of Health Planning and Management **[26015]**
International Journal of Hyperthermia **[32880]**
International Journal of Intelligent Systems **[3654]**, **[3775]**, **[32881]**
International Journal of IT/Business Alignment and Governance [3672]
International Journal of Purchasing & Materials Management [31912]
International Journal of Technology Assessment in Health Care **[26016]**
International Journal of Tourism Research [16026]
International Juvenile Product Show **[1201]**
International Kindergarten Union [2867]
International Labor Rights Education and Research Fund [35219]
International Labor Rights Forum (ILRF) [35219]
International Labor Rights Fund [35219]
International League of Antiquarian Booksellers (ILAB) **[736]**, **[1807]**
International League of Antiquarian Booksellers [1800]
The International LGBTQ+ Travel Association [15973]
International Licensing Industry Merchandisers' Association (LIMA) **[27828]**
International Literary Market Place: The Directory of the International Book Publishing Industry **[5319]**, **[8835]**, **[10348]**
International Live Events Association (ILEA) **[6081]**
International Manufacturing Technology Show (IMTS) **[29460]**
International Marketplace Newsletter **[39210]**
International Masonry Institute (IMI) **[3940]**, **[10728]**
International Midas Dealers Association (IMDA) **[14535]**
International Midas Dealers Association Annual Convention **[1125]**
International Money Management Group Inc. **[29005]**, **[33675]**
International MultiCultural Institute (IMCI) **[30508]**, **[30658]**
International Nanny Association (INA) **[11325]**
International News Media Association (INMA) **[11965]**
The International Newspaper Marketing Association [11965]
International Newspaper Promotion Association [11965]
International Ombudsman Institute (IOI) **[10788]**
International Pacific Salmon Fisheries Commission [6774]
International Paddle Association [12389], [15675]

International Paddle Rackets Association [12389], [15675]
"*International Paper Weighs Expansion Options*" in *Memphis Business Journal (Vol. 34, September 14, 2012, No. 22, pp. 1)* **[18173]**, **[19182]**
International Paperweight Society [735], [3226]
International Personnel Management Association - Canada (IPMA) **[26841]**
International Perspectives in Public Health **[25678]**
International Pharmaceutical Abstracts (IPA) **[5210]**
International Photographer [6212], [12312]
International Physical Fitness Association, Inc. (IPFA) **[12379]**
International Popcorn Association [3831]
International Pow Wow [16032]
International Premium Cigar & Pipe Retailers Association [15693]
International Prepress Association [12718], [16368]
International Public Management Association for Human Resources (IPMA-HR) **[11949]**
International Puzzle Features **[43265]**
International Racquet Sports Association [12378], [15666]
International Racquetball Association [12389], [15675]
International Radio and Television Society Foundation (IRTS) **[13019]**, **[15573]**
International Real Estate Institute (IREI) **[13359]**
International Real Estate, U.S. Chapter [13089]
International Reciprocal Trade Association (IRTA) **[17238]**
International Repertory of the Literature of Art [986]
International Reprographic Association [4486]
International Reprographic Association Trade Show **[4492]**
International Reprographic Blueprint Association [4486]
International Research Centers Directory (IRCD) **[32779]**
International Roofing Expo **[14335]**
International Sanitary Supply Association (ISSA) **[2050]**
International Sanitary Supply Association--Membership Directory **[5077]**
International Security Management Association (ISMA) **[14374]**
International Shade Tree Conference [10077]
International Shipmasters Association (ISMA) **[10589]**
International Sign Association (ISA) **[14700]**
International Slurry Seal Association [1547]
International Slurry Surfacing Association (ISSA) **[1547]**
International Society of Appraisers (ISA) **[807]**
International Society of Arboriculture (ISA) **[10077]**
International Society of Certified Electronics Technicians (ISCET) **[3572]**, **[15560]**
International Society of Certified Employee Benefit Specialists (ISCEBS) **[17265]**
International Society of Cleaning Technicians [16227]
The International Society for the Study of Ghosts and Apparitions (ISSGA) **[11340]**
International Society for the Study of Time (ISST) **[34962]**
International Society of Wood Science and Technology (SWST) **[10412]**
International Spa Association (ISPA) **[1578]**, **[4504]**
International Special Events Society [6081]
International Spin Fishing Association [1229], [1235]
International Sporthorse Registry, Inc. (ISR) **[636]**
International Spotted Horse Registry Association (ISHR) **[637]**
International Swimming Hall of Fame (ISHOF) **[15249]**
International Symposium on Forms and Business Processes **[33928]**
International Tap Association (ITA) **[4844]**
International Tax and Public Finance **[6697]**, **[15433]**
International Taxicab and Livery Association [15508]
International Tennis Hall of Fame (ITHOF) **[15667]**
International Tennis Hall of Fame and Museum Library **[15679]**
International Textile & Apparel Association--Membership Directory **[3034]**
International Tire and Rubber Association [15680]
International Tire & Rubber Association Foundation Inc. [15680]
International Trade Administration - Office of Public Affairs **[47116]**
International Trade Administration - U.S. Commercial Service - Export Assistance Center **[47117]**
International Trade Administration - U.S. and Foreign Commercial Service - Export Assistance Center **[47118]**
International Trade Administration - U.S. and Foreign Commercial Service - Export Assistance Center **[47119]**
International Trade Administration (EAC) - U.S. and Foreign Commercial Service - Export Assistance Center **[47120]**

International   Master Index

International Trade Administration (ITA) - U.S. and Foreign Commercial Service - Export Assistance Center **[47121]**
International Trade Administration (EAC) - U.S. and Foreign Commercial Service - Export Assistance Center **[47122]**
International Trade Administration - U.S. and Foreign Commercial Service - Export Assistance Center **[47123]**
International Trade Administration - U.S. and Foreign Commercial Service - Export Assistance Center **[47124]**
International Trade Administration - U.S. and Foreign Commercial Service - Export Assistance Center **[47125]**
International Trade Administration - U.S. and Foreign Commercial Service - Export Assistance Center **[47126]**
International Trade Administration - U.S. and Foreign Commercial Service - Export Assistance Center **[47127]**
International Trade Administration - U.S. and Foreign Commercial Service - Export Assistance Center **[47128]**
International Trade Administration (EAC) - U.S. and Foreign Commercial Service - Export Assistance Center **[47129]**
International Trade Administration - U.S. and Foreign Commercial Service - Export Assistance Center **[47130]**
International Trade Administration - U.S. and Foreign Commercial Service - Export Assistance Center [47219]
International Trade Administration - U.S. and Foreign Commercial Service - North Texas U.S. Export Assistance Center (USEAC) **[47131]**
International Trade Administration - U.S. and Foreign Commercial Service - Trenton Export Assistance Center [47132]
International Trade Commission - Office of Operations **[47272]**
International Trade Commission - Office of Tariff Affairs and Trade Agreements (TATA) **[47273]**
The International Trade Journal: Western Hemispheric Studies [27780]
International Trade Reporter **[8786]**, **[27793]**
International Trade Reporter: Current Reports [8786], [27793]
International Trademark Association (INTA) **[27829]**, **[42999]**
International Traditional Karate Federation (ITKF) **[10714]**
International Truck Parts Association (ITPA) **[16054]**
International Union of Gospel Missions [26100]
International Union of Nutritional Sciences (IUNS) **[11567]**
International Union of Operating Engineers (IUOE) **[35977]**
International Union, United Welders [35977]
International Valuation Conference [821]
International Vital Records Handbook **[7367]**
International Warehouse Logistics Association (IWLA) **[12969]**
"International Waters: Hawaii Aquarium Legislation Dead...Or Is It?" in Pet Product News (Vol. 66, September 2012, No. 9, pp. 76) **[840]**, **[12203]**, **[25400]**
International Wealth Success Inc. (IWS) **[43000]**
International Window Film Association (IWFA) **[7489]**
International Women's Media Foundation (IWMF) **[31834]**
International Women's Writing Guild--Network **[5338]**
International Wood Products Association (IWPA) **[10379]**
International Wood Products Association--Membership Directory **[10395]**
Internationale des Coiffures de Dames [7853]
"Internet Cafe Logging in to Chardon Plaza?" in News-Herald (July 16, 2011) **[7295]**, **[7559]**, **[13955]**, **[25401]**
"Internet Marketing 2.0: Closing the Online Chat Gap" in Agent's Sales Journal (November 2009, pp. 14) **[8929]**, **[9164]**, **[16433]**, **[17697]**, **[27292]**, **[29875]**, **[32559]**
"Internet Marketing 101 for Small Businesses" in The Balance Small Business (June 25, 2019) **[27809]**
Internet Marketing Association (IMA) **[27802]**, **[29574]**
"The Internet Of You" in Canadian Business (Vol. 87, July 2014, No. 7, pp. 43) **[3718]**, **[26319]**, **[30748]**
Internet Pinball Database **[583]**
"Internet Providers Look to Cash In on Your Web Habits" in The Wall Street Journal (June 27, 2019) **[9165]**
Internet Resources and Services for International Real Estate Information **[13223]**
"Internet Sales of Pet Products Increasingly 'Big Box'" in Pet Product News (Vol. 66, September 2012, No. 9, pp. 4) **[11765]**, **[12204]**, **[18174]**, **[32186]**

Internet Society **[9087]**, **[11691]**
Internet Telephone - Green Data Centers [2817], [9274]
"Interning Your Way to the Right Career" in Business Review Albany (Vol. 41, June 20, 2014, No. 12, pp. 9) **[21551]**, **[26977]**
Interpersonal Communication Programs Inc. (ICP) **[22319]**
Interpersonal Skills for Managers **[17596]**
Interpersonal Skills for Managers (Onsite) **[28356]**
Interplay Ventures **[42892]**
The Intersection Between Community Food and Justice with Erika Allen **[34434]**
Intersections **[11168]**
Intersouth Partners **[43223]**
Interstate Carriers Conference [16069]
Interstate Truckload Carriers Conference [16069]
Intertax **[15434]**, **[34933]**
InterTech Science Park **[40218]**
InterWest Partners L.L.C. (IW) **[35469]**
INTEX Expo **[4297]**
"Into the Groove: Fine-Tune Your Biz By Getting Into the Good Habit Groove" in Small Business Opportunities (Spring 2008) **[2191]**, **[2751]**, **[9166]**, **[20112]**, **[22661]**, **[26320]**
"Into the Light: Making Our Way Through the Economic Tunnel" in Agency Sales Magazine (Vol. 39, August 2009, No. 8, pp. 26) **[9167]**, **[19872]**, **[20976]**, **[29876]**
"Intrawest Puts Itself on Market" in Globe & Mail (March 1, 2006, pp. B1) **[19008]**, **[19538]**, **[31371]**, **[33020]**
"Intrepid Souls: Meet a Few Who've Made the Big Leap" in Crain's Chicago Business (Vol. 31, November 10, 2008, No. 45, pp. 26) **[2851]**, **[2884]**, **[4466]**, **[9168]**, **[20977]**, **[22662]**, **[33580]**
Intro to Launching (What, Why + How) **[24816]**
Introduction to ASP.NET 2.0 Applications **[33798]**
Introduction to .Net and ASP.NET **[33799]**
Introduction to PHP and MySQL **[33800]**
Introduction to System and Network Security (Onsite) **[21395]**
"The Introvert's Guide to Entrepreneurship: How to Become a Successful Entrepreneur as an Introvert" **[22395]**, **[28247]**, **[31140]**
"An Introvert's Guide to Schmoozing" in Canadian Business (Vol. 83, July 20, 2010, No. 11-12, pp. 73) **[17698]**, **[17863]**
Intuition Design Inc. **[30852]**
Inuit Art Foundation (IAF) **[963]**
Inuit Art Quarterly (IAQ) **[964]**
Invanti **[22937]**, **[33676]**
"Invention Submission Companies: Scams or Valuable Services?" in Legal Zoom (March 27, 2023) **[19268]**, **[27907]**
"Inventive Doctor New Venture Partner" in Houston Business Journal (Vol. 40, January 29, 2010, No. 38, pp. A2) **[10837]**, **[25840]**, **[27908]**, **[29877]**, **[30749]**, **[31372]**, **[31993]**, **[32780]**, **[35354]**
Inventory Control for Maintenance (Onsite) **[19445]**, **[21396]**
Inventory Management Techniques (Onsite) **[27990]**
Inventrek Technology Park **[39642]**
Inventus Capital Partners (ICP) **[37401]**
Invest Buffalo Niagara **[42418]**
"Invest in Energy-Efficient Equipment for Your Pet Store" in Pet Product News (Vol. 66, September 2012, No. 9, pp. 72) **[841]**, **[5657]**, **[5924]**, **[12205]**, **[18175]**, **[20454]**, **[21552]**, **[23277]**, **[32187]**
Invest Georgia (IG) **[38809]**
"Invest Like Harvard" in Barron's (Vol. 92, September 15, 2012, No. 38, pp. 32) **[6480]**, **[7124]**, **[9615]**, **[23963]**
Invest Michigan **[41049]**
Invest Ottawa (IO) **[46826]**
Investigation Tools and Techniques: Developing Facts and Evidence (Onsite) **[35163]**
Investigative Open Network [12788]
Investigative Reporters and Editors (IRE) **[5287]**
Investigators Anywhere [12788]
Investigators Anywhere Resource Line [12788]
Investing in Cryptocurrency for Dummies **[9616]**
"Investing in an HR Team Can Ease the Burden of Mass Hiring" in Crain's Detroit Business (Vol. 36, September 8, 2014, No. 36, pp. 15) **[3513]**, **[3627]**, **[18608]**
"Investing In Employee Health, Wellness" in South Florida Business Journal (Vol. 34, June 6, 2014, No. 46, pp. 28) **[17317]**, **[25841]**
Investing in Radio Market Report **[13034]**
Investissement Desjardins **[46887]**
Investment Adviser Association (IAA) **[9293]**
Investment Adviser Association-Directory of Member Firms **[9617]**
Investment Advisor Magazine **[2152]**
"Investment Bank Dinan & Company Launches ConfidentCrowd Exclusive Crowdfunding Portal for FINRA Broker-Dealers" in Investment Weekly (June 9, 2012, pp. 458) **[9618]**, **[19269]**, **[30922]**

"Investment Bank Predicts Shakeup in Farm Equipment Industry" in Farm Industry News (November 16, 2011) **[9619]**, **[17064]**, **[28149]**, **[31373]**
Investment Banker's Association **[14379]**
"Investment Banks" in Black Enterprise (Vol. 44, June 2014, No. 10, pp. 88) **[6481]**, **[9620]**
Investment Company Institute (ICI) **[9950]**, **[30272]**, **[35285]**
Investment Counsel Association of America [9293]
Investment Counsel Association of America--Directory of Member Firms [9617]
"Investment Firms Unite: Coalition Fights New Tax Law" in Black Enterprise (Vol. 38, December 2007, No. 5, pp. 52) **[9621]**, **[18609]**, **[30359]**, **[30578]**, **[31374]**, **[34820]**
"Investment Funds: Friends with Money" in Canadian Business (Vol. 81, May 22, 2008, No. 9, pp. 22) **[6482]**, **[9622]**, **[23964]**, **[28661]**, **[31375]**, **[35355]**
"Investment In Israel Is Investment in the Future of Georgia" in Atlanta Business Chronicle (May 30, 2014, pp. 22A) **[14428]**, **[17065]**, **[25402]**, **[25842]**, **[26321]**, **[27623]**, **[31376]**
Investment Management Consultants Association **[9294]**, **[13360]**
"Investment Market Heats Up on the Eastside" in Puget Sound Business Journal (Vol. 35, August 1, 2014, No. 15, pp. 4) **[13486]**, **[13799]**, **[18176]**, **[32560]**
"Investment Needs to Come From Our Community" in Crain's Chicago Business (November 12, 2021) **[30360]**
Investments & Wealth Institute **[9294]**, **[13360]**
Investopedia (Jan. 6, 2020); "6 Steps to a Better Business Budget" in [17488]
Investopedia (June 29, 2021); "The 3 Pillars of Corporate Sustainability" in [34263]
Investor Inside **[41578]**
Investor's Business Daily **[9937]**
Investors Collaborative (IC) **[42213]**
Investor's Daily [9937]
"Investors Eager to Buy Properties Regionwide" in Philadelphia Business Journal (Vol. 33, August 1, 2014, No. 25, pp. 10) **[13487]**, **[33379]**
"Investors Eye Old Buildings" in Business Journal-Portland (Vol. 24, October 19, 2007, No. 34, pp. 1) **[898]**, **[13488]**, **[13800]**
Investors' Property Services **[12917]**
IOA World Congress and Exhibition **[23441]**
"Iogen in Talks to Build Ethanol Plant in Canada" in Globe & Mail (March 21, 2007, pp. B7) **[4147]**, **[23278]**, **[29258]**
Iola Area Chamber of Commerce **[39907]**
Iola - Scandinavia Area Chamber of Commerce **[46433]**
Ionia Area Chamber of Commerce (IACC) **[40948]**
IOTA **[42347]**
Iowa Business & Technology Resource Guide **[39836]**
Iowa City Area Business Partnership **[39757]**
Iowa City Area Chamber of Commerce [39757]
Iowa Department of Economic Development (IDED) - Business Development **[39689]**
Iowa Department of Economic Development - Targeted Small Business Program (TSB) **[39690]**
Iowa Department of Education - Census Data Center **[46933]**
Iowa Falls Chamber of Commerce - Main Street **[39758]**
Iowa Great Lakes Area Chamber of Commerce (IGLACC) **[39759]**
Iowa Grocer **[2434]**, **[7802]**
Iowa Lakes Community College **[39831]**
Iowa Lumber Association **[10385]**
Iowa Lumber Convention **[10404]**
Iowa Procurement Technical Assistance Center - Iowa State University Extension Office - Center for Industrial Research and Service (CIRAS) **[39815]**
Iowa Senate Committee on Small Business, Economic Development and Tourism **[39833]**
Iowa Small Business Development Center Lead Office (SBDC) **[39677]**
Iowa Small Business Resource Guide [39836]
Iowa Startup Accelerator (ISA) **[39819]**
Iowa State University - Iowa Community Indicators Program (ICIP) **[47419]**
Iowa State University - North Central Regional Aquaculture Center (NCRAC) **[6755]**
Iowa State University Pappajohn Center for Entrepreneurship **[39820]**
Iowa State University Research Park (ISURP) **[39821]**
Iowa State University of Science & Technology - Center For Industrial Research & Service (CIRAS) - Iowa Procurement Technical Assistance Center **[39816]**
Iowa State University of Science and Technology College of Engineering - Center for Industrial Research and Service (CIRAS) **[30860]**
Iowa State University of Science and Technology - Institute for International Cooperation in Animal Biologics (IICAB) **[721]**

3268   Small Business Sourcebook • 42nd Edition

Master Index Ivy

Iowa State University of Science and Technology - Veterinary Diagnostic Laboratory (VDL) [722]
Iowa State University (SBDC) - Small Business Development Center [39678]
Iowa State University Small Business Development Center Ames [39679]
"IP Transition Is Unlikely To Make Waves In R.I." in Providence Business News (Vol. 28, January 13, 2014, No. 41, pp. 1) [2752], [9169], [25403]
The IPM Practitioner [12052]
"IPOs: Can You Keep a Secret?" in Silicon Valley/San Jose Business Journal (Vol. 30, August 31, 2012, No. 23, pp. 1) [25404], [31377]
IPW [16032]
IRE [14335]
Irell & Manella Library [6060]
IrishAngels Inc. [39361]
"iRobot Appoints Former BAE Systems Vice President, Frank Wilson to Lead Defense & Security Business Unit" in News Bites US (August 9, 2012) [14429], [25143], [28662]
Iron Gate Capital [37969]
Ironwood Area Chamber of Commerce (IACC) [40949]
"IRS Announces New Standards for Tax Preparers" in Bellingham Business Journal (Vol. February 2010, pp. 9) [1762], [15394], [16811], [25405]
"IRS Imposes More Electronic Filing Mandates on Small Businesses" in Small Business Trends(March 3, 2023) [34821]
IRS Practice and Procedure [15458], [34953]
"IRS Proposing New Tip Reporting Program for Service Business Owners" in Small Business Trends(February 7, 2023) [33186], [34822]
"IRS Sends Reminder about New 1099 Rules" in Small Business Trends(November 9, 2022) [34823]
"IRS Updates Dirty Dozen Tax Scams List" in Small Business Trends (March 23, 2023) [34824]
IRSA, The Association of Quality Clubs [12378], [15666]
Irvine Chamber of Commerce (ICC) [36953]
Irvine Team [4323]
Irving Chamber of Commerce [45181]
Irvington Chamber of Commerce (ICC) [42146]
Irwin Broh & Associates Inc. [10696]
Irwindale Chamber of Commerce [36954]
IRZ Consulting L.L.C. [4324]
"Is Amazon Training Its Workers or Creating a College Alternative?" in Inside Higher Ed (July 17, 2019) [9996], [21553]
"Is B2B a New Growth Area for Car Rental?" in AutoRental News (November 6, 2019) [1159], [13801]
"Is Bowling in Its Final Frames or Will It Roll On?" in USA Today (March 10, 2015) [1878]
"Is Business Ethics Getting Better? A Historical Perspective" in Business Ethics Quarterly (Vol. 21, April 2011, No. 2, pp. 335) [21554], [23509], [28663], [34071]
Is Buying an Existing Business Right for You? [19675]
"Is Culinary School Still Worth It? Four Chefs Weigh In" in Food&Wine (November 14, 2017) [4467], [21555]
"Is the Death Knell Upon Bookkeepers in 2019?" in AccountantsDaily (February 13, 2019) [1763]
"Is Dog Breeding Profitable?" in BreedingBusiness.com (October 21, 2016) [654]
Is Entrepreneurship Right for You? [22466], [33524], [35710]
"Is Fannie Mae the Next Government Bailout?" in Barron's (Vol. 88, March 10, 2008, No. 10, pp. 21) [4148], [6483], [9623], [11049], [13224], [13489], [20306], [20978], [23965], [25011], [28150]
"Is Formal Ethics Training Merely Cosmetic? A Study of Ethics Training and Ethical Organizational Culture" in Business Ethics Quarterly (Vol. 24, January 2014, No. 1, pp. 85) [21556], [23510]
"Is an Incubator Right for Your Start-up?" in Inc. [8794], [8814]
"Is It Cruel to Use a Choke Collar on Your Dog?" in Dog Training Central [12145]
"Is It Ever OK to Break a Promise? A Student Must Decide Whether to Leave the Company that Sponsored His MBA for a Dream Job" in Harvard Business Review (Vol. 92, September 2014, No. 9, pp. 119) [19743], [21557], [23511]
"Is It OK To Expense a Parking Ticket? Straight Answers To Some Common Expense Report Conundrums" in Canadian Business (Vol. 85, June 11, 2012, No. 10, pp. 70) [19369], [23966]
"Is It Time to Ban Swearing in the Workplace?" in HR Specialist (Vol. 8, September 2010, No. 9, pp. 2) [17699], [17864], [26978]
"Is It Time to Convert Your Sole Proprietorship to a Corporation or LLC?" in Legal Zoom (March 27, 2023) [32408], [34459], [34533]
"Is Maid Service Right For Your Home?" in Internet Wire (April 18, 2012) [2067], [2379], [32975]
"Is Medically Supervised Weight Loss Right for You?" in U.S. News and World Report (March 11, 2016) [16507]
"Is Mulcair Good for Business?" in Canadian Business (Vol. 85, June 11, 2012, No. 10, pp. 20) [23279], [25012], [34825]
"Is Owning a Campground Profitable?" in Outdoor Command (March 16, 2020) [2516]
Is Owning a Hair Salon Profitable? [7870]
"Is Peer-to-Peer Insurance Right for Your Business?" in Business News Daily (February 21, 2023) [27293]
"Is Raising CPP Premiums a Good Idea?" in Canadian Business (Vol. 83, July 20, 2010, No. 11-12, pp. 37) [17318], [19744], [23967], [35193]
"Is Remote Working Really Impeding Collaboration and Communication?" in Reworked(September 21, 2021) [22188]
"Is Fierce Competition Loosening Standards?" in Birmingham Business Journal (Vol. 31, February 14, 2014, No. 7, pp. 6) [23968], [28151], [34072]
Is Starting an LLC for a Tattoo Parlor Good Idea? [15306]
Is Starting a Tutoring Business a Good Idea? [16121]
"Is the Sun Setting on Oil Sector's Heydey?" in Globe & Mail (January 25, 2007, pp. B3) [8731], [24690], [27624]
"Is That the Best You Can Do?" in Entrepreneur (Vol. 37, October 2009, No. 10, pp. 85) [20040], [20455], [24691]
"Is There a Doctor In the House?" in Black Enterprise (Vol. 41, December 2010, No. 5, pp. 42) [8930], [17319], [23969], [27294]
"Is There a Future for Traditional Sign Shops in the Face of Digital Signage?" in Digital Signage Today (April 8. 2016) [14703]
"Is This the Suitcase of the Summer?" in The New York Times (August 28, 2018) [10366]
"Is the VIX in Denial?" in Barron's (Vol. 88, July 7, 2008, No. 27, pp. M12) [6484], [9624], [20979], [23970]
"Is Wall Street the Best Start-Up Incubator?" in Inc. [8795], [8815]
"Is Your Anxiety Affecting Your Leadership?" in Small Business Trends (December 8, 2022) [28664]
"Is Your Business Disaster Proof? How To Keep Your Company Up and Running Even After an Emergency" in Black Enterprise (Vol. 44, March 2014, No. 7, pp. 15) [27295]
"Is Your Business Protecting Its Classified Documents?" in Small Business Trends(February 12, 2023) [16575]
"Is Your Company Ready to Succeed?" in Business Strategy Review (Vol. 21, Spring 2010, No. 1, pp. 68) [18177], [24692]
"Is Your Employees' BMI Your Business?" in Canadian Business (Vol. 83, September 14, 2010, No. 15, pp. 98) [25843], [26979], [32781]
"Is Your Lawn Care Business Legal?" in Service Autopilot Blog (May 28, 2019) [10104]
"Is Your Smartphone Disaster Proof? If Not, These Rugged Cases Could Help: After Shelling Out a Couple of Hundred Dollars for a New Smartphone, You Don't Want to Worry About Breaking It" in Inc. (Vol. 34, September 2012, No. 7, pp. 48) [2753]
"Is Your Supply Chain Sustainable?" in Harvard Business Review (Vol. 88, October 2010, No. 10, pp. 74) [24693], [28003]
"Is Your Tax Pro Worth the Money?" in U.S. News & World Report (February 15, 2018) [15395], [16812], [34826]
ISA Annual Conference [823]
ISA Annual International Conference [10131]
ISA Annual International Conference & Trade Show [10131]
Isanti Area Chamber of Commerce [41280]
ISC Conference [7], [35123]
ISC/SCI Bulletin [3]
ISGS Newsletter [7379]
ISI EDGE [14723]
Islamorada Chamber of Commerce [38435]
Island Guide [43499]
Island Ink-Jet Systems Inc. [11676]
Island Pond Chamber of Commerce [45727]
Islands of Profit in a Sea of Red Ink: Why 40 Percent of Your Business Is Unprofitable and How to Fix It [18178], [32561]
Isle of Wight - Smithfield - Windsor Chamber of Commerce (IOW) [45875]
Isleton Chamber of Commerce (ICC) [36955]
Islip Chamber of Commerce [42620]
ISM Annual International Supply Management Conference [31914]
ISM World [31914]
ISM World Annual Conference [31914]
"Israeli Spam Law May Have Global Impact" in Information Today (Vol. 26, February 2009, No. 2, pp. 28) [294], [2754], [9170], [17700], [17865], [18610], [21897], [29878]
Issaquah Chamber of Commerce [46094]
Issue [39908]
Issues in Health Care of Women [26005]
iStart Valley [45534]
IT Auditing and Controls (Onsite) [26198]
IT Business Management Solutions Inc. (ITBMS) [3462]
"It Could Be Worse" in Barron's (Vol. 89, July 27, 2009, No. 30, pp. 5) [6485], [9625], [11050], [13035], [13225], [15596], [20980], [23971]
I.T. Financial Management Association (ITFMA) [3605]
It Is Innovation [1120], [2566]
"It May Be Cheaper to Manufacture At Home" in Harvard Business Review (Vol. 88, October 2010, No. 10, pp. 84) [23972], [27625], [28004], [29259]
IT Relationship Management: Aligning IT with the Business (Onsite) [28357]
"It Was a Very Good Year..To Be Ted Rogers" in Canadian Business (Vol. 80, Winter 2007, No. 24, pp. 121) [2755], [3719], [9171], [22663]
"It's Never Too Late: Entrepreneurial Spirit Drives Older Women" in USA Today (Jan. 6, 2021) [35811]
Italian-American Chamber of Commerce (IACC) [27417]
Italian Genealogical Group (IGG) [7346]
Italo's Pizza Shop Inc. [12558]
Italy-America Chamber of Commerce (IACC) [27418]
Itawamba County Development Council (ICDC) [41406]
ITEC Inc. [30644]
ITG Journal [11276]
Ithaca Chamber [40919]
"It's 4:30 p.m. Do You Know Where Your Staff Is?" in Canadian Business (Vol. 85, August 13, 2012, No. 13, pp. 62) [1338], [13956]
"It's 2019 and Faxing Is Still a Thing" in Quartz (February 6, 2019) [21898]
It's A Grind Coffee House [7587]
"It's Good To Be a CEO: Top Execs Pull Millions In Raises for 2013" in Atlanta Business Chronicle (June 20, 2014, pp. 22A) [19745], [20981], [23973], [28665]
"It's Good To Be King" in South Florida Business Journal (Vol. 35, August 29, 2014, No. 5, pp. 12) [1257], [13957], [24379], [27626], [31378], [34827]
"It's Here: the New World of $3+ Corn" in Farm Journal (Vol. 138, September 2014, No. 8, pp. 6) [17066]
"It's New or Improved, But Does It Work?" in Contractor (Vol. 57, January 2010, No. 1, pp. 22) [496], [12641], [30750]
"It's Not the How or the What but the Who: Succeed by Surrounding Yourself with the Best" [6106], [22189], [28666], [30579], [31379]
It's Not Just Who You Know: Transform Your Life (and Your Organization) by Turning Colleagues and Contacts into Lasting Relationships [17701], [24694], [28667]
It's Not Who You Know - It's Who Knows You!: The Small Business Guide to Raising Your Profits by Raising Your Profile [295], [17702], [18179], [22664], [29879], [31777], [31878], [32976]
"It's So You! Consignment Shop Owner Thrilled to See Vision Come to Fruition" in News-Herald (August 27, 2010) [3035], [3125], [3895], [6134]
"It's Time for Insurance Carriers To Win More Customers; About One-Third of Insurance Customers are Engaged. This Means the Industry Has a Massive Opportunity to Gain More Business" in Gallup Business Journal (May 28, 2014) [8931], [27296], [32562]
"It's Time to Strengthen Your Small Business Brand Identity" in Keap (November 7, 2019) [17448]
"It's Time To Swim" in Canadian Business (Vol. 81, March 3, 2008, No. 3, pp. 37) [8732], [20982], [25013], [27627], [29260], [31124]
"It's What You Know. It's Who You Know. It's China" in Inc. (Vol. 33, October 2011, No. 8, pp. 80) [4149], [18180], [27628]
"ITT Places Its Bet With Defense Buy: Selling Equipment to Army Pays Off" in Crain's New York Business (Vol. 24, January 6, 2008) [18181], [29261], [31380]
The Itty Bitty Guide to Business Travel [16001], [19370]
IU Angel Network [39632]
"IU Health Bloomington's Contract with Local Cleaning Service Set to Expire" in Herald-Times (March 16, 2012) [2068], [19873]
"I've Always Been an Entrepreneur" in South Florida Business Journal (Vol. 34, June 13, 2014, No. 47, pp. 11) [2192], [22665], [25844]
"Ivernia Mine Closing Could Boost Lead" in Globe & Mail (April 4, 2007, pp. B5) [6486], [9626], [25406]
Ivey Publishing [46859]
Ivins, Phillips, Barker Library (IPB) [17419]
IVP [37402]
Ivy Software Inc. [45985]
Ivy Tech Community College of Indiana - Columbus [39657]
Ivy Tech Community College of Indiana-Fort Wayne [39658]

Master Index

Small Business Sourcebook • 42nd Edition 3269

Ivy Tech Community College of Indiana-Gary **[39659]**
Ivy Tech State College of Indiana - Columbus [39657]
IWPA's World of Wood Convention [10410]
"*Izod, Loft Outlets Coming To Tanger*" in *New Hampshire Business Review* (Vol. 33, March 25, 2011, No. 6, pp. 30) **[3126]**, **[6135]**, **[32188]**
Izzo's Illegal Burrito **[14187]**

J

J. S. Eliezer Associates Inc. (JSEA) **[1700]**, **[12008]**, **[12772]**
J-U-B Engineers Inc. **[10626]**
"*Jab, Jab, Jab, Right Hook: How to Tell Your Story in a Noisy Social World*" **[2756]**, **[9172]**, **[11766]**, **[17703]**, **[20456]**, **[21899]**, **[28668]**, **[29880]**
Jacalyn E. S. Bennett & Co. **[31613]**
Jack McGarry Founder & Managing Partner at The Dead Rabbit **[14065]**
Jacksboro Chamber of Commerce **[45222]**
Jackson Area Chamber of Commerce **[44764]**
Jackson Area Chamber of Commerce (JACC) **[41248]**, **[43500]**
Jackson Business and Professional Women **[35626]**
Jackson County Area Chamber of Commerce **[38755]**
Jackson County Business Development Corporation [33465]
Jackson County Chamber of Commerce **[38436]**, **[43153]**
Jackson County Public Library - Indiana & Jackson County History and Genealogy Collection **[7422]**
Jackson Growth Alliance (JGA) **[33465]**
Jackson Hewitt Inc. (JH) **[15448]**
Jackson Hole Chamber of Commerce **[46609]**
Jackson State University (BBER) - Bureau of Business and Economic Research **[32421]**
Jackson State University (JSU) - Mississippi e-Center **[41450]**
Jackson State University Small Business Development Center (JSU) **[41371]**
Jacksonville Area Chamber of Commerce **[39211]**
"*Jacksonville-based Interline Expanding in Janitorial-Sanitation Market*" in *Florida Times-Union* (May 10, 2011) **[2069]**, **[18182]**, **[20632]**, **[29881]**, **[33187]**
Jacksonville Business Journal **[38606]**
Jacksonville Chamber of Commerce **[45223]**
Jacksonville Chamber of Commerce and Visitor Center **[43983]**
"*Jacksonville Doing Well In Growing Economy*" in *Orlando Business Journal* (Vol. 30, June 27, 2014, No. 53, pp. 8) **[6487]**, **[19183]**, **[26322]**, **[29262]**, **[31994]**, **[32782]**, **[33380]**
Jacksonville - Onslow Chamber of Commerce **[43154]**
Jacksonville Regional Chamber of Commerce [38437]
Jacksonville State University - Center for Economic Development and Business Research (CEDBR) **[21278]**
Jacobs Schneider Interior Design **[31081]**
Jaffrey Chamber of Commerce (JCC) **[42002]**
James Bonanno CEO of Upstream Hospitality Group **[14066]**
"*James Clift on How to Use AI to Create a Small Website*" in *Small Business Trends* (November 8, 2022) **[16434]**
"*James Donnelly on Keeping His Company's Edge: 'We Have Documented Best Practice for Everything'*" in *South Florida Business Journal* (Vol. 34, May 23, 2014, No. 44, pp. 15) **[12890]**, **[20457]**, **[30962]**
James E. Rogers Community Law Group **[36396]**
James and Johanna Windon Founders of Buena Papa Fry Bar **[14067]**
James Madison University - Carrier Library Special Collections **[5406]**
James Madison University Small Business Development Center [45788]
Jamestown Area Chamber of Commerce **[43301]**
Jamestown Small Business Development Center **[42401]**
Jamie Schrotberger CEO of Spread Bagelry **[1216]**
"*Jamieson Eyes $175 Million Trust IPO*" in *Globe & Mail* (March 7, 2006, pp. B1) **[6488]**, **[9627]**, **[19009]**, **[31381]**
Jan Rubin Associates Inc. **[941]**
Janco Associates Inc. **[45689]**
Jane Capital Partners (JCP) **[37403]**
Jane's Aero Engines **[442]**
Jane's All the World's Aircraft: In Service **[443]**
Jane's All the World's Aircraft: Unmanned **[444]**
Jane's Unmanned Aerial Vehicles and Targets [444]
Jani-King Canada **[5085]**
Jani-King International Inc. **[2105]**
"*Janitorial Equipment and Supplies US Market*" in *PR Newswire* (October 24, 2011) **[2070]**, **[18183]**, **[30751]**, **[33188]**

Janitorial Services Industry in the US - Market Research Report **[2988]**
Jantize America **[2106]**
Japan Aikido Association U.S.A. [10715]
"*Japan-Brand Shortages Will Linger Into '12*" in *Automotive News* (Vol. 86, October 31, 2011, No. 6488, pp. 1) **[1104]**, **[11415]**, **[29263]**
Japan Business Consultants Ltd. **[29470]**
Japanese Chamber of Commerce and Industry of New York, Inc. (JCCINY) **[27419]**
Japanese Chamber of Commerce of New York [27419]
Japanese Chamber of Commerce of Southern California (JCCSC) **[36956]**
Jasper Chamber of Commerce (JCC) **[39563]**
Jasper Chamber of Commerce [45224]
Jasper County Chamber of Commerce (JCCC) **[44566]**
Jasper County Improvement Association [44566]
Jasper-Lake Sam Rayburn Area Chamber of Commerce **[45224]**
Jasper, TX **[45225]**
JatoTech Ventures L.P. **[45456]**
Java for Non-Programmers (Onsite) **[21397]**
Javelin Venture Partners **[37404]**
"*Javo Beverage to Feature On-Demand Coffee System and Introduce New Specialty Dispensed Beverages at the National Convenience Store Show*" in *GlobeNewswire* (October 20, 2009) **[4439]**, **[15868]**, **[35064]**
JAX Chamber **[38437]**
JAX Chamber Small Business Center **[38547]**
JB Associates **[30205]**
JBSB [24874]
"*J.C. Evans Files for Ch. 11 Protection*" in *Austin Business Journal* (Vol. 31, August 12, 2011, No. 23, pp. A1) **[4150]**, **[20983]**, **[23974]**
"*J.C. Penney Head Shops for Shares*" in *Barron's* (Vol. 88, July 7, 2008, No. 27, pp. 29) **[6489]**, **[9628]**, **[17320]**, **[22666]**, **[23975]**, **[28669]**, **[32189]**
JCF Capital Markets, LLC **[37677]**
J.D. Byrider **[11466]**
JDC Consultancy **[38848]**
JDE Construction Management Ltd. **[4325]**
JDI Cleaning Systems Inc. **[2107]**
JEDCO Enterprise Center (JEDCO) **[40219]**
Jefferson Area Chamber of Commerce **[43501]**
Jefferson Chamber of Commerce **[40176]**, **[46434]**
Jefferson College-Extended Learning **[41697]**
Jefferson County Chamber of Commerce **[43502]**, **[44765]**, **[46110]**, **[46274]**
Jefferson County Chamber of Commerce (JCCC) **[39212]**
Jefferson County Chamber of Commerce [43990]
Jefferson County Economic Development (JCED) **[42893]**
Jefferson County Small Business and Technology Development Center **[41470]**
Jefferson Parish Economic Development Commission (JEDCO) - Business Innovation Center **[40220]**
Jefferson Park Chamber of Commerce **[39213]**
Jefferson Partners **[46792]**
Jeffersontown Chamber of Commerce **[40055]**
Jeffrey Lant Associates, Inc. (JLA) **[7179]**, **[10472]**, **[30206]**, **[31811]**, **[40779]**
"*Jeffrey Watanabe: 'Promise Less and Deliver More'*" in *Canadian Business* (Vol. 85, August 13, 2012, No. 13, pp. 16) **[19874]**, **[20041]**, **[20458]**
Jegi Capital L.L.C. **[42762]**
JEI Learning Centers, LLC **[16165]**
Jenkins Group Inc. (JGI) **[41138]**
Jenks Chamber of Commerce (JCC) **[43774]**
"*Jenna Bush Hager: Forging Her Own Career and Identity*" in *Women in Business* (Vol. 66, Summer 2014, No. 1, pp. 10) **[22190]**
Jennifer Cramer Lewis **[22938]**, **[33677]**
Jenny Craig Weight Loss & Management Centers **[16514]**
Jensen Beach Chamber of Commerce **[38438]**
Jerome Chamber of Commerce **[38925]**
Jerome Chamber of Commerce (JCC) **[36342]**
Jerry's Subs and Pizza **[12559]**, **[14188]**
Jersey Cape Vacation Guide **[42147]**
Jersey Caper **[42148]**
Jersey County Business Association (JCBA) **[39214]**
Jersey Mike's Franchise Systems Inc. **[4903]**, **[14189]**
Jersey Mike's Subs [4903], [14189]
"*Jersey Pet Store Regs Poised for Change*" in *Pet Product News* (Vol. 66, March 2012, No. 3, pp. 18) **[12092]**, **[12206]**
Jersey Shore Chamber of Commerce (JSCC) **[42149]**
Jerusalem Venture Partners (JVP) **[42763]**
Jess Barker, Document Research/Retrieval L.L.C. **[11288]**, **[13663]**
Jessamine County Chamber of Commerce **[40056]**
Jessamine Journal **[40057]**

Jesup Chamber of Commerce **[39760]**
Jet City Pizza Co. **[12560]**
"*Jet Sales Put Bombardier Back in Black*" in *Globe & Mail* (March 30, 2006, pp. B1) **[9629]**, **[18184]**, **[29264]**
JETRO New York (JETRO) **[27420]**
Jet's America Inc. **[12561]**
Jet's Pizza [12561]
Jewelers of America (JA) **[9964]**
Jewelers' Security Alliance (JSA) **[808]**, **[9965]**, **[14375]**
Jewelers Security Alliance of the U.S. [808], [9965], [14375]
Jewelers Vigilance Committee (JVC) **[9966]**
Jewellers Vigilance Canada (JVC) **[9967]**
"*Jewelry and Luxury Goods Sales on Rebound*" in *Jewelry Industry* (November 17, 2021) **[9977]**
Jewelry Stores Industry in the US - Market Research Report **[9986]**
Jewels by Stacy Appraisals **[35453]**
Jewish Board of Family and Children's Services Child Development Center **[2917]**
The Jewish Funeral Directors of America, Inc. (JFDA) **[7199]**
Jewish Lights Publishing **[29006]**
J.H. Hare & Associates Ltd. **[17197]**
Jhn Inc. **[2108]**
Jiffy Lube Canada **[13006]**
Jiffy Lube International Inc. **[13007]**
"*Jim Cramer's Get Rich Carefully*" **[6490]**, **[9630]**, **[20984]**
"*Jim Kukral Answers the Question: What is Marketing?*" in *Small Business Trends* (December 6, 2022) **[29496]**, **[29529]**, **[29882]**
Jim Thorpe Chamber of Commerce **[44248]**
Jimmy John's [4904]
Jimmy John's Franchisor SPV, LLC (JJ) **[4904]**
Jimmy John's Inc. [4904]
Jim's Mowing Canada Inc. **[10266]**
Jindal Journal of Business Research (JJBR) **[24871]**
J.J. Keller & Associates Inc. - Editorial Resource Center - Research & Technical Library **[35978]**
J.K. Lasser's 1001 Deductions and Tax Breaks 2023: Your Complete Guide to Everything Deductible **[15396]**, **[34828]**
"*JK Lasser's New Rules for Estate, Retirement, and Tax Planning*" **[19010]**, **[23631]**, **[23976]**, **[27297]**, **[31382]**, **[34829]**
JKandB Capital **[39362]**
J.L. Meaher and Associates Inc. **[5752]**
JLL Global Hotels Investment Outlook Report 2021 **[8522]**
J.L.T. Management Company, L.L.C. **[41095]**
JMCE [32894]
"*Jo-Ann Fabric and Craft Stores Joins ArtFire.com to Offer Free Online Craft Marketplace*" in *Marketwired* (January 26, 2010) **[4596]**, **[4660]**, **[11767]**, **[14654]**, **[21900]**, **[11383]**
"*Jo-Ann Launches Quilt Your Colors Contest to Celebrate National Sewing Month*" in *Marketwired* (September 10, 2010) **[4661]**, **[14655]**, **[29883]**
"*Joanna Crangle Named MBJ Publisher*" in *Sacramento Business Journal* (Vol. 31, March 28, 2014, No. 5) **[296]**, **[11984]**, **[28670]**
Joanna Kelley Founder of Cup of Joe **[14068]**
"*Job Corps Center Remains Vacant After Operator is Booted*" in *Tampa Bay Business Journal* (Vol. 30, January 15, 2010, No. 4, pp. 1) **[25144]**, **[26980]**
Job Creators Network (JCN) **[33466]**
Job Finders Employment Service (JF) **[137]**
"*Job Program is 'Giving People Dignity'*" in *Forest Park Review* (September 17, 2019) **[2639]**
"*Jobs Gain Cast Shadow On Recovery*" in *Providence Business News* (Vol. 29, April 7, 2014, No. 1, pp. 1) **[20985]**, **[26592]**
"*Job Reviews: Annual Assessments Still the Norm*" in *HR Specialist* (Vol. 8, September 2010, No. 9, pp. 1) **[26981]**, **[28671]**
"*Job Seeker's Readiness Guide: Unemployment's High and Competition is Tough*" in *Black Enterprise* (Vol. 40, July 2010, No. 12, pp. 83) **[19875]**, **[26593]**, **[26982]**
"*The Job Survival Equation*" in *Women in Business* (Vol. 65, Winter 2013, No. 3, pp. 36) **[22191]**
Job Training and Career Counseling - 2022 U.S. Market Research Report with Updated Forecasts **[2608]**, **[10003]**
Job Training & Career Counseling in the US - Industry Market Research Report **[2609]**, **[10004]**
"*JOBS Act Spurring Bio IPOs*" in *Philadelphia Business Journal* (Vol. 33, May 2, 2014, No. 12, pp. 4) **[25176]**, **[26170]**, **[31141]**
"*A Jobs Compact for America's Future: Badly Needed Investments In Human Capital Are Not Being Made. What We Can Do - Together - To Jump-Start the Process?*" in *Harvard Business Review* (Vol. 90, March 2012, No. 3, pp. 64) **[21558]**, **[26594]**, **[26983]**, **[31384]**

"Jobs Data Show A Slow Leak" in Barron's (Vol. 88, July 7, 2008, No. 27, pp. 34) [18185], [20986], [26595], [28672], [29265]
"Jobs Data Show Wild Card" in Barron's (Vol. 90, September 6, 2010, No. 36, pp. M12) [26596], [26984], [34073]
Jobs for the Future (JFF) [3547]
"Jobs for the Future Asks Congress to Help Promote Youth Apprenticeship and Workforce Development" in Small Business Trends (September 22, 2022) [16576]
Jobs In Horticulture Inc. [2614], [7652], [10133]
Jockey Club Research Foundation [8337]
Joe To Go Coffee [1297], [3208]
Joe Turner [4326], [20547]
"Joe Wikert, General Manager, O'Reilly Technology Exchange" in Information Today (Vol. 26, February 2009, No. 2, pp. 21) [11985], [19876], [21901], [28673]
"Joel Libava on Looking for the Perfect Franchise Opportunity" in Small Business Trends(October 31, 2022) [24380]
Joey's Only Seafood Restaurant [14190]
John Alan Cohan [15444], [19139], [24250]
John Bollinger's Capital Growth Letter [9917]
John Brown University - Music Library [11224], [11299]
John C. Randall & Associates Inc. [10539]
John Chute & Associates [17404]
John E. Allen Inc. - Motion Picture Archives [11136]
John Kunkel CEO at 50 Eggs Hospitality [14069]
John Leeke [942]
The John Liner Letter [8989], [27361]
John Michael Kohler Arts Center Resource Center [4695]
John N. Zaremba [138]
John Papajohn Entrepreneurial Center (JPEC) [39822]
John Papajohn Entrepreneurial Center (JPEC) [39823]
John Tyler Community College [45975]
John Wiley & Sons, Inc. [1710]
Johnny Rockets Licensing Corp. [14191]
Johns Hopkins University Bloomberg School of Public Health - Center for Health Services and Outcomes Research (CHSOR) [26123]
Johns Hopkins University - Bloomberg School of Public Health Department of Health Policy and Management - Center for Hospital Finance and Management [26124]
Johnson City Chamber of Commerce [45226]
Johnson County Chamber of Commerce [44766]
Johnson County Chamber of Commerce [36446]
Johnson Creek Area Chamber of Commerce [46435]
Johnson & Wales University (JWU) [44489]
Johnson & Wales University-Harborside Culinary Library (JWU) [2698], [4478], [8530]
Johnston Associates Inc. (JAI) [42214]
Johnston Co. [2282], [10540], [20200], [24251], [29007], [33678]
Johnstown Area Regional Industries (JARI) [44359]
JOI [9920]
"Joining Business Organizing and Networking Groups" in The Balance Small Business (July 28, 2019) [18849]
"Joining the Fiber" in San Antonio Business Journal (Vol. 28, April 4, 2014, No. 8, pp. 4) [9173], [33381]
The Joint Commission Journal on Quality Improvement [26017]
The Joint Commission Journal on Quality and Patient Safety [26017]
Joint Committee on Mortuary Education [7192]
Joint Directory: Financial Analysts Federation and Institute of Chartered Financial Analysts [9407]
Joker Tattoo [15327]
Joliet City Center Partnership (CCP) [39408]
Joliet Region Chamber of Commerce & Industry [39215]
JOLT [46866]
Jon Brumley Texas Venture Labs [45535]
Jon Seelbinder Founder of Local Icon Hospitality [14070]
Jones & Co. [20233], [24504]
Jones County Chamber of Commerce [41407]
Jones County Junior College Small Business Development Center [41372]
Jones NCTI [2443], [15574]
Jonesboro Regional Chamber of Commerce [36473]
Jonesboro - Washington County Chamber of Commerce [44767]
Joplin Area Chamber of Commerce (JACC) [41579]
The Jordan Edmiston Group Inc. (JEGI) [42764]
"Jordan Still Soaring" in Business Journal Portland (Vol. 30, January 17, 2014, No. 46, pp. 7) [3036], [3127], [14678], [15096], [18186], [32190]
Joseph Business Center [39409]
Joseph J. Walczak P.C. [18756]
Joseph & Lucille Cacciatore Owners of Joe's Depot Diner [14071]
Joseph Newman Innovation Center [41678]
Josephson Institute of Ethics [23574]
Joshua Area Chamber of Commerce (JACC) [45227]

Journal Academy of Business and Economics (JABE) [24872]
Journal of Accountancy [109]
Journal of Accounting Research (JAR) [110]
Journal of Advertising Research (JAR) [385]
Journal of African Research in Business & Technology (JARBT) [32070]
Journal of Agromedicine [26018]
Journal of Air Medical Transport [435], [25985]
Journal of the American Animal Hospital Association (JAAHA) [704]
Journal of the American Board of Family Medicine (JABFM) [26019]
Journal of American College Health [26020]
Journal of the American Oil Chemists' Society (JAOCS) [32882]
Journal of the American Pharmaceutical Association [5199]
Journal of the American Pharmacists Association (JAPhA) [5199]
Journal of the American Society for Information Science and Technology [8841]
Journal of the American Taxation Association (JATA) [111], [15435]
Journal of Analytic Social Work [26046]
Journal of Andrology [32854]
Journal of Applied Business Research (JABR) [24873]
Journal of the Association for Information Science and Technology (JASIST) [8841]
Journal of the Association of Nurses in AIDS Care (JANAC) [26021]
Journal of Asynchronous Learning Networks [21318]
Journal of the Audio Engineering Society: Audio/Acoustics/Applications [13657]
Journal of Behavioral Health Services & Research [26022]
Journal of Behavioral Studies in Business (JBSB) [24874]
Journal of Biochemical and Molecular Toxicology (JBMT) [32883]
Journal of Biochemical Toxicology [32883]
Journal of bioenergetics [32884]
Journal of Bioenergetics and Biomembranes [32884]
Journal of Biological Rhythms (JBR) [32885]
Journal of Business Case Studies (JBCS) [24875]
Journal of Business Communication [17818]
Journal of Business & Economic Research (JBER) [24876]
Journal of Business and Economics [24877]
Journal of Business Law (JBL) [18774]
Journal of Business Logistics (JBL) [24878]
Journal of Business & Management (JBM) [24879]
Journal of Business and Psychology (JBP) [24880]
Journal of Business Research (JBR) [24881]
Journal of Business Strategies [24882]
Journal of Business and Technical Communication (JBTC) [17819]
Journal of Business-to-Business Marketing: Innovations in Basic and Applied Research for Industrial Marketing [19248]
Journal of Business Venturing: A Journal Dedicated to Entrepreneurship [24883]
Journal of Cellular Biochemistry [32886]
Journal of Chemical Ecology [32887]
Journal of Chemical Technology and Biotechnology (JCTB) [32888]
Journal of Clinical Microbiology (JCM) [32889]
The Journal of the Coin Laundry Industry [5263], [10211]
Journal of Communications Technology and Electronics [32890]
Journal of Compensation and Benefits [17384]
Journal of Culinary Science & Technology [11583]
Journal of Customer Service in Marketing & Management [20536], [30141]
Journal of Cutaneous Medicine and Surgery (JCMS) [25679]
Journal of Database Management (JDM) [3534], [3655]
Journal of Database Marketing & Customer Strategy Management [10706]
Journal of East-West Business [27781]
Journal of Economics and Business [24884]
Journal of Economics and Management Strategy (JEMS) [21248], [28917]
Journal of Employment Counseling (JEC) [2612], [5451]
Journal of Environmental Engineering [32891]
Journal of Ethnic & Cultural Diversity in Social Work: Innovations in Theory, Research & Practice [26023]
Journal of Farm Economics [17141]
Journal of Film and Video (JFV) [6213]
Journal of Foodservice Business Research [14046]
Journal of Gambling Behavior [7334]
Journal of Gambling Studies [7334]
Journal of Global Academic Institute Business & Economics (JGAIBE) [24885]

Journal of Global Marketing [30139]
Journal of Health Care Chaplaincy [26024]
Journal of Health Care for the Poor and Underserved (JHCPU) [26025]
Journal of Health and Human Behavior [26026]
Journal of Health and Social Behavior (JHSB) [26026]
Journal of Health & Social Policy [26054]
Journal for Healthcare Quality [26027]
Journal of Hospitality & Leisure Marketing [8481]
Journal of Hospitality Marketing & Management [8481]
Journal of Hotel and Business Management [8523]
Journal of Independent Social Work [26046]
"Journal Indexing 101: Understanding the Basics" in Editage Insights (May 20, 2015) [5]
Journal of Innovation and Business Best Practices (JIBBP) [24886]
Journal of Insurance Regulation (JIR) [8990]
Journal of Intensive Care Medicine (JIC) [26028]
Journal of International Business and Cultural Studies (JIBCS) [27788]
Journal of International Business Studies (JIBS) [27789]
Journal of International Consumer Marketing [30140]
Journal of International Food & Agribusiness Marketing [17155]
Journal of International Law and Business [18775]
Journal of Internet and e-business Studies (JIEBS) [22031]
Journal of Investigative Surgery [32892]
The Journal of Investing [9920]
Journal of IT Financial Management [6698]
Journal of Labelled Compounds and Radiopharmaceuticals (JLCR) [32893]
The Journal of Laboratory and Clinical Medicine [10933]
Journal of Law and Business (JLB) [18776]
Journal of Management Accounting Research (JMAR) [112]
Journal of Marketing Analytics [10706]
Journal of Marketing Research (JMR) [10682]
Journal of Materials in Civil Engineering [32894]
Journal of Morphology [32895]
Journal of Multicultural Social Work [26023]
Journal of Music Teacher Education (JMTE) [11192]
Journal of Natural History [32896]
Journal of Northwest Atlantic Fishery Science (JNAFS) [6766]
Journal of Nutrition (JN) [11584]
Journal of Nutrition in Recipe and Menu Development [11583]
Journal of Pharmaceutical Sciences (JPharmSci) [5200], [32897]
Journal of Policy Analysis and Management (JPAM) [31706]
Journal of Polymer Science [32898]
Journal of Pressure Vessel Technology [32899]
Journal of Property Management [12905], [13316]
Journal of Purchasing [31912]
Journal of Relationship Marketing [20536], [30141]
Journal of Research in Music Education [11193]
Journal of Restaurant & Foodservice Marketing [14046]
Journal of Scholarly Publishing [1691]
Journal of School Health (JOSH) [26029]
Journal of Small Business and Enterprise Development [33701]
Journal of Small Business & Entrepreneurship [16717]
Journal of Small Business and Entrepreneurship Development (JSBED) [16718]
Journal of Small Business Management (JSBM) [16719]
Journal of Small Business Strategy (JSBS) [33702]
Journal of Social Service Research [26030]
Journal of the Society of Architectural Historians (JSAH) [922]
Journal of Software: Evolution and Process [14855], [32900]
Journal of Software Maintenance and Evolution [14855], [32900]
Journal of Supply Chain Management: A Global Review of Purchasing and Supply [31912]
Journal of Targeting, Measurement and Analysis for Marketing [10706]
The Journal of Taxation [15436]
Journal of Technical Writing and Communication (JTWC) [5339]
Journal of The Canadian Dietetic Association [11562], [25993]
The Journal of Time Use Research (eIJTUR) [2175], [10477]
Journal of Turbomachinery [32901]
Journal of World Energy Law & Business [18777]
The Journey Forward: DE&I in the Workplace [30580]
"Joystick Operated Zero-Turn Mower Marks 30 Years" in Turf Magazine (November 11, 2019) [10052], [10105], [10238]
JS Consulting Inc. [12788]

Jsb Enterprises [5428]
Judah L. Magnes Memorial Museum - Western Jewish History Center [7455]
"Judge Gives RIM One Last Chance" in Globe & Mail (February 24, 2006, pp. B5) [6491], [9631], [18611], [27909]
"Judgment Day" in Canadian Business (Vol. 79, September 11, 2006, No. 18, pp. 27) [18612]
Jugo Juice [14192]
Juiceblendz International [8623]
"Juiced on Energy" in Barron's (Vol. 88, July 14, 2008, No. 28, pp. 33) [6492], [9632], [23977], [33189]
JuiceTank [42238]
"Juicy Couture (1997-2014) Couldn't Evolve When Its Cachet Dried Up" in Canadian Business (Vol. 87, July 2014, No. 7, pp. 16) [3037], [3128], [31385], [35812]
The Juilliard School [1000]
Julian Chamber of Commerce [36957]
Julian Guide [36958]
Jump Consulting [12267]
Jump Start [16106]
Jump Start Incubator (JSI) [44405]
The JumpFund [44824]
Jumpstart Foundry (JSF) [44825]
Jumpstart Inc. [43669]
Jumpstart New Jersey Angel Network [35286], [42215]
JumpStartbiz [36397]
"Jumpstarting Your Business Through Non-Traditional Funding" in SBA.gov [30923]
Junction City Area Chamber of Commerce (JCACC) [39909]
Junction City-Harrisburg Chamber of Commerce [43984]
June Lake Loop Chamber of Commerce [36959]
Juneau Chamber of Commerce [36236], [46436]
Juneau County Inventors & Entrepreneurs Club [27830]
Juniata River Valley Chamber of Commerce and Visitors Bureau (JVACC) [44249]
Junior Billboard Association (JBA) [31835]
Junior Panel Outdoor Advertising Association [31835]
Juroviesky & Ricci L.L.P. [18745]
"Just 10% of Retail Businesses Use AI" in Small Business Trends (December 17, 2019) [29884]
Just-A-Buck (JAB) [4453]
"Just Be Nice: Providing Good Customer Service" in Canadian Business (Vol. 79, October 9, 2006, No. 20, pp. 141) [19539], [20459], [28674], [33190]
Just the Fax [3941]
"Just Hang Up" in Barron's (Vol. 88, March 10, 2008, No. 10, pp. 45) [6493], [9633], [19011], [19877], [20042], [23978], [33191]
"Just a Slight Rate Bump for Local Law Firms" in Philadelphia Business Journal (Vol. 30, January 20, 2012, No. 49, pp. 1) [18613], [20043]
Justice Entrepreneurs Project (JEP) [39410]
"Justice In Self-Managing Teams: the Role of Social Networks In the Emergence of Procedural Justice Climates" in Academy of Management Journal (Vol. 55, June 1, 2012, No. 3, pp. 685) [22192], [28675]

K

K and N Mobile Distribution Systems [4417]
K5 Ventures [37405]
K9 Resorts [12120]
K9 Ventures LLC [37406]
Kabbage Inc. [11007]
"Kaboom!" in Canadian Business (Vol. 81, November 10, 2008, No. 19, pp. 18) [72], [1764], [15397], [16813], [25407]
Kailua Chamber of Commerce (KCOC) [38877]
Kaiser Permanente Center for Health Research (CHR) [26125]
Kaiser Permanente - Division of Research [26126]
Kaiser-Permanente Medical Center Health Sciences Library [1042]
Kaiser Permanente Ventures (KPV) [37407]
"Kaiser Permanente's Innovation on the Front Lines" in Harvard Business Review (Vol. 88, September 2010, No. 9, pp. 92) [25845], [27910], [30752]
"Kaiser Says Hospital Room Service Saves Money" in Pacific Business News (Vol. 26, August 22, 2014, No. 26, pp. 10) [6913], [25846]
Kalama Chamber of Commerce [46111]
The Kaleel Jamison Consulting Group Inc. (KJCG) [20595]
Kalin Associates Inc. (KA) [4327]
Kalispell Chamber of Commerce [41774], [41803]
Kalispell Small Business Development Center [41723]
Kalona Area Chamber of Commerce (KACC) [39761]
Kamiah Chamber of Commerce [38926]
Kamloops Innovation (KIC) [46706]
KampGround Owners Association (KOA) [2505]
Kampgrounds of America Inc. (KOA) [2531]

Kanab Chamber of Commerce (KCOC) [45638]
Kankakee Area Chamber of Commerce [39216]
Kankakee County Chamber of Commerce [39216]
Kanouse and Walker P.A. [18757], [24505]
Kansas Agri Business Expo [17171]
Kansas Agribusiness Retailers Association (KARA) [39838]
Kansas Chamber of Commerce [39910]
Kansas Chamber of Commerce and Industry [39910]
Kansas City Boat Sportshow [15120]
Kansas City Business Journal (KCBJ) [41704]
Kansas City Business Journal [41703]
Kansas City Business Travel Association (KCBTA) [19303]
Kansas City Kansas Area Chamber of Commerce [39911]
Kansas City Sportshow [15120]
Kansas Department of Commerce - Agriculture Marketing Division [39842]
Kansas Department of Commerce - Business and Community Development Div. [39843]
Kansas Department of Commerce - Business Development Division [39843]
Kansas Department of Commerce - Office of Minority and Women Business Development [39964]
Kansas Department of Commerce - Rural Development Division [39843]
Kansas Department of Commerce - Trade Development Div. [39844]
Kansas Department of Transportation (KDOT) [1177], [5114], [10294], [15530]
Kansas Division of the Budget [47420]
Kansas House Standing Committee on Economic Development and Tourism (LAS) [39982]
Kansas Small Business Development Center at Fort Hays State University (KSBDC) [39839]
Kansas Small Business Development Center - Lead Center (KSBDC) [39840]
Kansas State Library (KSL) [47421]
Kansas State University - Hale Library - Research, Education, and Engagement Division - Richard L.D. and Marjorie J. Morse Department of Special Collections [4563]
Kansas State University - John C. Pair Center [10273]
Kansas State University - John C. Pair Horticultural Center [10273]
Kansas State University, Salina - Libraries [3679]
Kansas Venture Capital Inc. (KVCI) [39966]
Kaplan EdTech Accelerator [42894]
Kaplan Financial Education (KFE) [21738]
Kapor Capital (KC) [37408]
Kapor Center [21314], [30509]
Karaoke Bars Industry in the US - Market Research Report [1358]
Karl Kardel Consultancy [943]
"Karl Lagerfeld, Pioneering Fashion Designer, Has Died" in CNN (February 20, 2019) [3038]
Karlani Capital [42765]
Karn Charuhas Chapman & Twohey (KCCT) [944]
Karpeles Manuscript Library [752]
Karpeles Manuscript Library - Buffalo Museum [753]
Karpeles Manuscript Library - Charleston Museum [754]
Karpeles Manuscript Library - Duluth Museum [5773]
Karpeles Manuscript Library - Santa Barbara Museum [755]
Karpeles Manuscript Library - Tacoma Museum [756]
Katahdin Area Chamber of Commerce [40286]
"Katharine Grayson: Three Questions with John Brownlee, CEO of Vidscrip.com" in Business Journal (Vol. 32, June 27, 2014, No. 5, pp. 6) [6154], [21298], [25633], [31142]
Katie Dixon Head Chef/Owner Birdhouse Cafe [14072]
"Katie's Cupcakes to Celebrate One-Year Anniversary" in Bellingham Business Journal (Vol. March 2010, pp. 3) [1258], [7125], [35813]
Katy Area Chamber of Commerce (KACC) [45228]
Katy Business Association--Directory (Member listings) [45586]
Kauai Chamber of Commerce (KCC) [38878]
Kaua'i Small Business Development Center [38864]
Kauffman and Drebing Registered Investment Advisors [9931]
Kauffman Entrepreneurs [41711]
Kaufman & Canoles, P.C. [20234], [24506]
Kaufman Global [2283]
Kavanagh Christmas Trees [2956]
Kaysville Chamber of Commerce [45632]
Kaysville Small Business Development Center (SBDC) [45607]
KAYWEB Angels [42980]
K.B. Ackerman Co. (KBA) [12993]
KB Partners [39363]
"KBA, Graphic Art System Partner on Cold Foil" in American Printer (Vol. 128, June 1, 2011, No. 6) [3319], [12742], [16195], [31386]

KBL Healthcare Ventures (KBL) [42766]
"KC Incentives Debate Rages on Unabated" in The Business Journal-Serving Metropolitan Kansas City (Vol. 26, September 5, 2008, No. 52) [4151], [13226], [13490], [20987], [25014], [25408], [34074], [34830]
"KCET Takes On Elder-Care With Robust Your Turn To Care Website" in PR Newswire (July 31, 2012) [9174], [15597], [25847], [34334]
KCS Computer Technology Inc. (KCS) [31007], [31082]
Keap Inc. [36398]
Kearney Area Chamber of Commerce (KACC) [41864]
Kearney Business Agenda [41865]
Kearney Inc. [2421]
Kearny Chamber of Commerce [36326]
Kearny Venture Partners (KVP) [37409]
KEC Ventures [42767]
Keecha Harris and Associates [10541], [33679]
Keene and Cheshire County Profile [42003]
"Keene: Nominations are Being Sought by the Keene Cities for Climate Protection Committee for the Monadnock Green Business of the Year Award" in New Hampshire Business Review (Vol. 34, February 24, 2012, No. 4, pp. 7) [5658], [5925], [20988], [23280], [34335]
Keeneland Library [8333]
"Keep Customers Out of the Yellow Pages" in Contractor (Vol. 56, November 2009, No. 11, pp. 47) [14623], [19878], [29885]
"Keep Steel Wool Away from Your Antique Furniture; You'll Do More Harm Than Good" in Antique Trader (March 8, 2012) [7242]
"Keep The (Cage) Customer Satisfied" in Pet Product News (Vol. 64, December 2010, No. 12, pp. 10) [12075], [12207], [20460], [32191]
Keep on Truckin News [16098]
Keep Up to Date on Accounts Payable [16853]
Keep Up to Date on Payroll [11940]
Keep Your Small Business Safe from Scams: Here's How to Handle Fraud Prevention [19270]
"The Keeper of Records" in Black Enterprise (Vol. 41, December 2010, No. 5, pp. 54) [3805], [8932], [25848], [27298], [34075]
"Keeping Data Secure When Your Laptop Is in the Shop" in The New York Times (December 6, 2017) [3577]
"Keeping the Faith in Fuel-Tech" in Barron's (Vol. 88, March 24, 2008, No. 12, pp. 20) [6494], [9634], [19879], [23281], [23979]
"Keeping Pace With Creative Compliance in the Fast-Moving Cannabis Space" in Cannabis Business Executive (March 24, 2020) [5012]
"Keeping Railcars 'Busy At All Times' At TTX" in Crain's Chicago Business (Vol. 31, April 28, 2008, No. 17, pp. 6) [8733], [19012], [19371], [27629], [28676], [31387], [33192]
Keeping the Team on Track (Onsite) [17597]
Keeping in Touch [11568]
"Keeping the Vehicle On the Road--A Survey On On-Road Lane Detection Systems" in ACM Computing Surveys (Vol. 46, Spring 2014, No. 1, pp. 2) [11416], [26323], [29266]
Keg Restaurants Ltd. [14193]
Keg Steakhouse & Bar [14193]
"KEH Is Opening a Brick-and-Mortar Location in Atlanta" in PetaPixel (November 4, 2021) [2494]
Keiretsu Forum [35287], [37410]
"Keith Crain: Business Must Stand Up And Be Counted" in Crain's Detroit Business (Vol. 24, October 6, 2008, No. 40, pp. 6) [17505], [20989], [24695], [25409], [28677], [34076], [34831]
Keizer Chamber of Commerce [43985]
Keizer Merchant Association [43985]
Kellanova [11613]
Keller and Heckman L.L.P. (KH) [5216], [5774]
Kelley Chunn & Associates (KCA) [30207], [31812]
Kelleys Island Chamber of Commerce (KICC) [43503]
Kellogg Company [11613]
Kelly Business Advisors L.L.C. [10542]
Kelly's Cajun Grill Franchise Corp. [14194]
Kelly's Coffee and Fudge Factory [7588]
Kelso Longview Chamber of Commerce [46112]
"Keltic Gets Nod to Build N.S. Petrochemical Plant" in Globe & Mail (March 15, 2007, pp. B9) [25410], [29267]
The Ken Blanchard Cos. [22320]
Kenai Chamber of Commerce [36237]
Kenai Peninsula Economic Development District (KPEDD) [36252]
Kendall College of Art & Design Library (KCAD Library) [7256]
Kendallville Area Chamber of Commerce [39564]
Kenmare Association of Commerce [43302]
Kenmore Business Incubator (KBI) [46218]
Kenmore-Town of Tonawanda Chamber of Commerce (KTCC) [42621]

Kennebec Valley Chamber of Commerce (KVCC) **[40287]**
Kennebunk-Kennebunkport-Arundel Chamber of Commerce **[40288]**
Kennebunk-Kennebunkport Chamber of Commerce [40288]
Kennedy Franchise Consultants **[24484]**
Kennelwood Pet Resorts **[12121]**
Kennelwood Village Inc. **[12121]**
Kennesaw State University - Coles College of Business - Cox Family Enterprise Center **[23588]**
Kennesaw State University - Michael J. Coles College of Business - Small Business Development Center [38641]
Kennett Chamber of Commerce (KCC) **[41580]**
Kennett Library **[757]**
Kennewick Chamber of Commerce [46167]
Kenosha Area Chamber of Commerce (KACC) **[46437]**
Kenpo Karate International [10712]
Kent Area Chamber of Commerce (KACC) **[43504]**
Kent Area Chamber of Commerce and Information Center [43504]
Kent Chamber of Commerce **[38057], [46113]**
Kent County Chamber of Commerce (KCCC) **[40396]**
Kent/Portage Small Business Development Center **[43349]**
Kentucky Cabinet for Economic Development - International Trade Div. **[40005]**
Kentucky Cabinet for Economic Development (SBSD) - Small Business Services Div. **[40006]**
Kentucky Cabinet for Economic Development - Small & Minority Business Div. **[40091], [40117]**
Kentucky Chamber of Commerce (KCC) **[40058]**
Kentucky Chamber News **[40059]**
"Kentucky Counties Rely on 911 Translation Services as Diversity Increases" in *EMS1.com* (November 25, 2019) **[15942]**
Kentucky Fried Chicken Canada Company (KFC) **[14195]**
Kentucky Governor's Office for Policy and Management **[47422]**
Kentucky Highlands Investment Corp. (KHIC) **[40098]**
Kentucky Innovation Network (KIN) **[40107]**
Kentucky Science & Technology Corporation (KSTC) **[40108]**
Kentucky Small Business Development Center (kSBDC) **[39993]**
Kentucky Small Business Development Center at Eastern Kentucky University Richmond **[39994]**
Kentucky Small Business Development Center Lead Office (KSBDC) **[39995]**
Kentucky & Tennessee Procurement Center **[40099]**
Kentwood Area Chamber of Commerce **[40177]**
KEOGH Consulting Inc. **[12994]**
Keokuk Area Chamber of Commerce **[39762]**
Kepha Partners **[40700]**
Kerens Chamber of Commerce (KCC) **[45229]**
"Kerkorian Shakes Up Chrysler Race" in *Globe & Mail* (April 6, 2007, pp. B1) **[19880], [29268], [31388]**
Kerman Chamber of Commerce **[36960]**
Kern River Valley Chamber of Commerce (KRVCC) **[36961]**
Kern Venture Group (KVG) **[37411]**
Kernersville Chamber of Commerce (KCC) **[43155]**
Kernville Chamber of Commerce **[36962]**
Kerr Center for Sustainable Agriculture (KCSA) **[12071]**
Kerrville **[45230]**
Kerrville Area Chamber of Commerce **[45231]**
Kershaw County Applied Technology Education Campus - Vocational-Technical Library **[2624]**
Kershaw County Chamber of Commerce **[44567]**
Keshet Ideas and Innovation Center (KIIC) **[42348]**
Ketchum Advertising - Library Services **[31901]**
"Ketchup King Heinz Seeks to Boost Soy-Sauce Empire in China" in *Advertising Age* (Vol. 83, October 8, 2012, No. 36, pp. 3) **[18187], [19676], [27630]**
Kettering Chamber of Commerce **[43505]**
Kettering-Moraine-Oakwood Chamber of Commerce (KMOCC) **[43505]**
Kettering University Small Business Development Center (KU SBDC) **[41096]**
Kevin Herring - Redefining Roles in a Challenging Business Landscape **[27106]**
Kewanee Chamber of Commerce **[39217]**
Kewaunee Area Chamber of Commerce **[46438]**
Keweenaw Chamber of Commerce (KCC) **[40950]**
Keweenaw Street Map & Business Guide **[40951]**
"The Key to Cheap Internet Service: A Local SIM Card" in *The New York Times* (April 9, 2019) **[12700]**
Key Largo Chamber of Commerce **[38439]**
Key Largo Chamber of Commerce and Florida Keys Visitor Center [38439]
Key Newsletter **[38440]**

"Key Points You Must Know Before Buying an Existing Antiques Business" in *Antique Trader* (December 6, 2012) **[741]**
The Key to Real Business Sucess May Surprise You with Penny Sansevieri **[16667]**
"Key Tips to Keeping Corporate Minutes" in *Legal Zoom* (March 27, 2023) **[17866]**
Key West Chamber of Commerce (KWCC) **[38441]**
Keybridge Venture Partners LLC **[37412]**
KEYGroup **[27148]**
Keynotes **[10358]**
Keys to Effectively Supervising People (Onsite) **[28358]**
"Keys to Overcome Fear of Follow-Up" in *Agency Sales Magazine* (Vol. 39, December 2009, No. 11, pp. 26) **[17704], [32563]**
Keystone Wildflowers **[1503]**
KFC Canada **[14195]**
"KFC Franchises Getting Rid of Popcorn Chicken" in *Small Business Trends* (February 17, 2023) **[24381]**
KGI Advisors Inc. **[31614]**
Khosla Ventures **[37413], [37742]**
Kiamichi Area Vo-Tech - Atoka **[43886]**
Kiamichi Technology Center (KTC) **[43887]**
Kiamichi Technology Center - Stigler (KTC) **[43888]**
Kiamichi Technology Centers **[43861], [43862]**
Kiamichi Technology Centers - Atoka [43886]
Kibel Green Inc. [31614]
KiBiz Inc. **[3349]**
Kick Start Your Dream Business: Getting it Started and Keeping You Going **[24545]**
Kickapoo Culinary Center (KCC) **[46565]**
Kickstart Seed Fund **[45663]**
Kickstart Your Social Media Blueprint with TikTok and IG Reels, Part I **[29514], [33525], [35711]**
"Kickstarter Funds the Future; Crowdfunding Services Such as Kickstarter Have Been Hailed as a New Way To Get Started In Business and Cut Out the Traditional Money Men" in *Telegraph Online* (August 24, 2012) **[22963], [28065], [30894], [31143], [33933], [35238]**
Kickstarter Inc. **[42768]**
Kickstarter, PBC **[42768]**
Kid to Kid **[2899]**
Kiddie Academy Child Care Learning Centers **[2900]**
Kiddie Kobbler Ltd. **[14695]**
Kidokinetics **[2901], [30496]**
Kids At Heart Photography **[12321]**
"Kids in Crisis" in *Employee Benefit News* (Vol. 25, November 1, 2011, No. 14, pp. 26) **[17321], [25849]**
Kidspark Inc. **[2902]**
Kidstage Wisconsin **[11134]**
KidzArt **[21722]**
Kii Capital [37495]
Kilgore Chamber of Commerce **[45232]**
Kilgore College **[45577]**
Kilgore College Small Business Development Center **[44918]**
Kilgore Small Business Development Center [44918]
Killington Pico Area Association (KPAA) **[45728]**
Killington - Pico Area Chamber of Commerce [45728]
Kilmer Capital Partners **[46793]**
Kilwin's Chocolates and Ice Cream **[2556]**
Kimball Banner County Chamber of Commerce (KBCCC) **[41866]**
Kimble County Chamber of Commerce (KCCC) **[45233]**
Kimmel & Associates, Inc. **[7975]**
Kimoyo: Is This African Startup Venture Backable? **[34629]**
Kinderdance International Inc. **[2903]**
"Kinderhook Acquires Chemtron Corp." in *Waste Today* (August 23, 2019) **[7957], [31389]**
Kindle Self-Publishing for Beginners: Step by Step Author's Guide to Writing, Publishing and Marketing Your Books on Amazon **[5426]**
Kindred Kitchen **[46219]**
"Kinek Offers Secure Prescription Drop-Off For Online Shoppers" in *Pittsburgh Post-Gazette* (June 14, 2012) **[5167], [7039], [11768], [33193]**
"Kineta Helps Grow Start Group of 5 Biotech Partners" in *Puget Sound Business Journal* (Vol. 35, June 13, 2014, No. 8, pp. 6) **[5168], [7126], [9635], [26324], [31995]**
Kinetic Ventures L.L.C. **[40429]**
"Kinetico Exec Going Global to Increase Growth Flow" in *Crain's Cleveland Business* (Vol. 28, October 1, 2007, No. 39, pp. 5) **[18188], [19013], [27631], [28678], [29269]**
King Chamber of Commerce (KCC) **[43156]**
King City Chamber of Commerce and Agriculture [36963]
King City and Southern Monterey Chamber of Commerce and Agriculture **[36963]**
"King of the Crib: How Good Samaritan Became Ohio's Baby HQ" in *Business Courier* (Vol. 27, June 18, 2010, No. 7, pp. 1) **[1195], [14982], [18189], [19881], [25850]**

"King Ink" in *Inc.* (November 2007, pp. 98-102, 104, 106, 108) **[15307]**
The King of Madison Avenue: David Ogilvy and the Making of Modern Advertising **[297], [29886]**
The King of Vodka: The Story of Pyotr Smirnov and the Upheaval of an Empire **[1923], [22667], [29270], [29887]**
The Kingdom Builders' Center (KBC) **[45536]**
Kingdom of Callaway Chamber of Commerce [41532]
Kingfisher Chamber of Commerce **[43775]**
Kingman Area Chamber of Commerce **[36343]**
Kingman Area Chamber of Commerce (KACC) **[39912]**
Kingman Chamber of Commerce [39912]
Kingpin Tattoo Supply **[15328]**
Kings County Museum Library **[7423]**
Kings Mountain Chamber of Commerce [43120]
Kings Park Chamber of Commerce **[42622]**
Kingsburg District Chamber of Commerce **[36964]**
Kingsland/Lake LBJ Chamber of Commerce **[45234]**
Kingsport Area Chamber of Commerce **[44768]**
Kingston Economic Development Corporation **[46763]**
Kingstree Chamber of Commerce [44587]
Kingsville Chamber of Commerce (KCOC) **[45235]**
Kingwood Center Library **[8164]**
"Kinnser: Sales In Overdrive" in *Austin Business Journal* (Vol. 32, March 30, 2012, No. 4, pp. 1) **[14793], [18190], [19540], [26597], [31390], [33867]**
"Kinross Holds Firm on Offer for Bema" in *Globe & Mail* (January 20, 2007, pp. B5) **[24696], [31391]**
Kinsley Area Chamber of Commerce [45133]
Kinston-Lenoir County Chamber of Commerce (KLCCC) **[43157]**
"Kiosk Outfit ecoATM Now Recycling Video Games" in *San Diego Union-Tribune* (October 7, 2010) **[584], [10028], [13720]**
Kiplinger Washington Editors Inc. **[38189]**
Kirksville Area Chamber of Commerce **[41581]**
Kirkus Reviews **[1692]**
Kirkwood Business Owners' Association (KBOA) **[38626]**
Kirkwood Community College Small Business Development Center **[39680]**
Kirkwood-Des Peres Area Chamber of Commerce **[41582]**
Kirlan Venture Capital Inc. **[46193]**
Kissimmee - Osceola County Chamber of Commerce **[38442]**
The Kitch Enterprises Inc. **[43243]**
"Kitchen Aid: D.C. Food Incubator Turns Growth Tactics Inward" in *Washington Business Journal* (Vol. 32, February 28, 2014, No. 46, pp. 6) **[1307], [8796], [13869], [17890]**
Kitchen Cabinet Manufacturers Association (KCMA) **[8199]**
Kitchen Chicago **[39411]**
Kitchen CoOp (TKC) **[37947]**
Kitchen Incubator **[45537]**
Kitchen Incubator @ CTTC **[44406]**
Kitchen Network **[37948]**
Kitchen Sisters **[46220]**
Kitchen Solvers **[2654]**
Kitchen Tune-Up **[2655]**
Kitten Sittin' **[12272]**
Kittitas County Chamber of Commerce **[46114]**
Kittochtinny Historical Society Library **[7424]**
Kiva **[37743]**
Klamath County Chamber of Commerce (KCCC) **[43986]**
Kleiner Perkins (KPCB) **[37414], [37744]**
Kleiner Perkins Caufield and Byers [37414], [37744]
KLM Capital Group **[37415]**
Kluger and Associates Inc. **[3808]**
KMWorld: Creating and Managing the Knowledge-Based Enterprise **[4945]**
"Knife Sharpening Tools – Your List for Starting a Business" in *Small Business Trends* (March 2, 2023) **[7922], [26796]**
Knifemakers' Guild (KG) **[4582]**
Knightdale Chamber of Commerce **[43158]**
Knightstown Indiana Chamber of Commerce **[39565]**
The Knitting Guild of America **[4583]**
The Knitting Guild Association (TKGA) **[4583]**
"Knocking On the World's Door" in *Business Journal Portland* (Vol. 31, March 28, 2014, No. 4, pp. 4) **[20990], [21559], [33382]**
Knopf Doubleday Publishing Group **[43001]**
"Know the Difference Between a Franchise Advisor, Consultant & Broker?" in *The Franchise Maker website* **[2356], [24485]**
Knowledge Ecology in Global Business: Managing Intellectual Capital **[27790]**
Knowledge Management Strategies for Business Development **[24887]**
Knowledge Park **[46735]**
The Knowledge Project: Alan Mulally: The Power of Working Together **[19634]**

The Knowledge Project: Award Winning Chef Dan Kluger: Taking Time to Get It Right **[14073]**
The Knowledge Project: Bethany McLean: Crafting a Narrative **[19635]**
The Knowledge Project: Brian Halligan: Scaling Culture from Startup to IPO **[34630]**
The Knowledge Project: Danny Meyer: Hospitality and Humanity **[14074]**
The Knowledge Project: Jim Collins: Relationships vs. Transactions **[28927]**
The Knowledge Project: Ravi Gupta: The Realities of Success **[28928]**
The Knowledge Project: Reid Hoffman: Better Decision, Fewer Mistakes **[28929]**
The Knowledge Project: Roger Martin: Forward Thinking **[28930]**
The Knowledge Project: Shreyas Doshi: Better Teams, Better Products **[30844]**
The Knowledge Project: The Marketing Expert: A Masterclass in Strategic Positioning **[29547]**
The Knowledge Project: The Storytelling Expert: The Architecture of Influence **[17792]**
Knox County Chamber of Commerce **[43506]**
Knox County Chamber of Commerce (KCCC) **[39566]**
"Knox County Schools Debate Outsourcing Janitorial Services" in (March 29, 2011) **[2071]**, **[21560]**, **[31125]**, **[33194]**
Knoxville Area Chamber Partnership (KACP) **[44769]**
Knoxville Chamber of Commerce **[39763]**
Kochman Mavrelis Associates Inc. (KMA) **[30645]**
"Kodak Offers Cloud-Based Operating Option" in American Printer (Vol. 128, June 1, 2011, No. 6) **[3320]**, **[12743]**, **[16196]**, **[21902]**, **[31392]**
Kodaly Envoy **[11194]**
Kodiak Chamber of Commerce (KCC) **[36238]**
"Kohler Building Earns LEED Silver Certification" in Contractor (Vol. 56, September 2009, No. 9, pp. 12) **[5659]**, **[12642]**, **[23282]**, **[29271]**
Kohn Engineering **[2025]**, **[4328]**
Kohr Bros. Frozen Custard and Smoothie Station **[8624]**
"Kokanee Films World's Longest Beer Commercial: Ready for a 90-Minute Feature Starring the Cast of Kokanee?" in Canadian Business (Vol. 85, July 16, 2012, No. 11-12, pp. 11) **[298]**, **[1924]**, **[6187]**, **[29888]**, **[33383]**
Kolache Factory Inc. (KF) **[1298]**
Kona Kohala Chamber of Commerce (KKCC) **[38879]**
"Koneco Building Services Inc. to Add Theme Park Division" in Orlando Business Journal (Vol. 30, April 25, 2014, No. 44, pp. 3) **[605]**, **[2072]**, **[22668]**
The KonLin Letter **[9921]**
Kora Management Ltd. **[4329]**
Kosciusko-Attala Chamber of Commerce (KACC) **[41408]**
Kosciusko Chamber of Commerce **[39567]**
"Kosher Ice Cream Features Traditional Jewish Ingredients" in Ice Cream Reporter (Vol. 23, August 20, 2010, No. 9, pp. 5) **[8574]**, **[30753]**
Kott Koatings Inc. **[12691]**
Kountze Chamber of Commerce (KCC) **[45236]**
KPMG L.L.P., Library **[1790]**
KPMG - Research Centre **[168]**, **[1791]**, **[15473]**
"Kraft Taps Cheese Head; Jordan Charged With Fixing Foodmaker's Signature Product" in Crain's Chicago Business (April 14, 2008) **[17067]**, **[19882]**, **[28679]**, **[29272]**
Krantz Marketing Services L.L.C. **[30208]**
"Kratos Announces Buy of Critical Infrastructure Security Business" in M & A Navigator (January 3, 2012) **[14430]**, **[19677]**, **[31393]**
Kremer Kehe Inc. **[39834]**
Kremmling Area Chamber of Commerce and Visitor Center **[37871]**
Kresge Hearing Research Laboratory [8140]
"Kroger Family of Pharmacies to Offer Health Assessment Kiosks at Locations Nationwide" in Entertainment Close-Up (August 22, 2012) **[5169]**, **[7745]**, **[10029]**, **[32192]**
"Kroger Launches Car-Buying Program" in Supermarket News (November 7, 2019) **[7746]**, **[11417]**
"Kroger Recasts Its Brand" in Supermarket News (November 6, 2019) **[299]**, **[7747]**, **[10660]**
"Kroger Releases Annual Sustainability Report" in Ecology, Environment & Conservation Business (July 26, 2014, pp. 46) **[5660]**, **[5926]**, **[7748]**, **[23283]**
Krumkill Stables **[11596]**
The Krystal Co. [14196]
Krystal Restaurants LLC **[14196]**
"KSE Imprints Hits Mother Lode With Logos" in Denver Business Journal (Vol. 65, January 31, 2014, No. 38, pp. A9) **[14354]**, **[15164]**
KTB Ventures / KTB Venture Capital **[37416]**
KU Innovation Park (BTBC) **[39975]**

"Kubient Audience Cloud Launched" in ResearchLive (November 18, 2019) **[10661]**
Kugarand Capital Holdings **[38855]**
Kumon Math & Reading Centers [21723]
Kumon Math and Reading Centres (KUMON) **[16166]**
Kumon North America Inc. **[21723]**
Kuna Chamber of Commerce **[38927]**
"Kuno Creative to Present the Three Steps of a Successful B2B Social Media Campaign" in Business Tech & Wireless (August 25, 2011) **[9175]**, **[15869]**, **[16435]**, **[21903]**, **[29889]**, **[31778]**, **[31879]**, **[35065]**
Kurz Purdue Technology Center **[39643]**
Kutler Consultants **[20548]**
Kutztown University Procurement Technical Assistance Center (PTAC) **[44360]**
Kutztown University Small Business Development Center (KUSBDC) **[44097]**
KV Marketing Inc. **[8190]**, **[8222]**
Kwik Kopy Business Centers, Inc. **[392]**, **[3356]**, **[4494]**, **[12777]**
"Kwik Shop Finishing New South Seneca Store" in Wichita Business Journal (Vol. 27, January 13, 2012, No. 2, pp. 1) **[4440]**
"KXAN Seeks Larger Studio, Office Space in Austin" in Austin Business Journal (Vol. 31, May 27, 2011, No. 12, pp. A1) **[2458]**, **[4152]**, **[11149]**, **[13491]**, **[15598]**, **[19184]**, **[33384]**
KYDA The Kentucky Meeting **[10877]**
Kyle Area Chamber of Commerce Business Directory **[45237]**
Kyle Area Chamber of Commerce and Visitor's Bureau **[45238]**
Kyle Chamber of Commerce [45238]
Kyle and Maggie Gordon CEO and President of Dillas Quesadillas **[14075]**
Kyocera International Inc. **[37417]**
KZF Design Inc. **[619]**

L

L. Michael Schwartz, P.A. (LMSPA) **[20235]**, **[24507]**
LA Area Chamber Voice **[36965]**
LA Art Show **[983]**
La societe des comptables professionnels du Canada [45], [1741], [15362]
La Canada Flintridge Chamber of Commerce and Community Association (LCF) **[36966]**
"La Cantera Resort Expects to Benefit from Big Transformation" in San Antonio Business Journal (Vol. 28, July 18, 2014, No. 23, pp. 8) **[899]**, **[4153]**, **[8421]**, **[13958]**
La Chambre Canadienne Allemande de l'Industrie et du Commerce Inc. (CGCIC) **[20702]**
La Chambre de Commerce du Canada [20687]
La Cocina **[37588]**
La Conner Chamber of Commerce **[46115]**
La Crescent Chamber of Commerce **[41249]**
La Crosse Area Chamber of Commerce **[46439]**
La Fondation des Écrivains Canadiens (FEC) **[5288]**
La Grange Area Chamber of Commerce **[45239]**
La Guilde Canadienne des Realisateurs (GCR) **[6167]**
la Guilde canadienne des relieurs et des artistes du livre [1729]
La Habra Area Chamber of Commerce **[36967]**
La Jolla Village News **[12004]**
La Junta Chamber of Commerce (LJCC) **[37872]**
La Junta Small Business Development Center **[37786]**
La Mirada Chamber of Commerce **[36968]**
La Paletera Franchise Systems Inc. **[8625]**
La Paloma Gelateria & Cafe **[8626]**
"LA Passes HET Ordinance, California Greens Code" in Contractor (Vol. 56, September 2009, No. 9, pp. 1) **[4154]**, **[12643]**, **[14624]**, **[25411]**, **[34077]**
La Pine Chamber of Commerce **[43987]**
La Porte-Bayshore Chamber of Commerce **[45240]**
La Porte Economic Advancement Partnership (GLCC) **[39568]**
La Quinta Chamber of Commerce (LQCC) **[36969]**
La Salle Center for Entrepreneurship (LCE) **[44407]**
La Salsa **[14197]**
La Societe Opimian [15002]
La Societe Royale de Philatelie du Canada (RPSC) **[3228]**
La Verne Chamber of Commerce **[36970]**
La Veta/Cuchara Chamber of Commerce **[37873]**
La Vista Area Chamber of Commerce **[41867]**
L.A. Weight Loss Centers **[16515]**
Laban/Bartenieff Institute of Movement Studies (LIMS) **[4872]**
"Labatt to Swallow Lakeport" in Globe & Mail (February 2, 2007, pp. B1) **[1339]**, **[10325]**, **[19541]**, **[31394]**
Labette Community College - Advanced Respiratory Therapist Program **[39980]**

LabIX **[37589]**
The Labor Center - Institute for Research on Labor and Employment [26150]
Labor and Employment Relations Association (LERA) **[35220]**
Labor Finders International Inc. (LFI) **[5457]**
"Labor of Love" in Green Industry Pro (Vol. 23, March 2011, No. 3, pp. 14) **[7628]**, **[10106]**, **[10239]**, **[18191]**, **[22669]**, **[33195]**, **[36025]**
"Labor and Management: Working Together for a Stable Future" in Alaska Business Monthly (Vol. 27, October 2011, No. 10, pp. 130) **[22193]**, **[28680]**, **[35194]**
Labor Market Information Services [47425]
"Labor Pains" in Canadian Business (Vol. 79, August 14, 2006, No. 16-17, pp. 80) **[8933]**, **[17322]**, **[20991]**, **[26598]**, **[27299]**
The Labor Party **[39976]**
Labor Research Association (LRA) **[35221]**
"Labor Shortage Creates Growing Pains" in Orlando Business Journal (Vol. 30, January 31, 2014, NO. 32, pp. 5) **[4155]**, **[13227]**, **[13492]**, **[19883]**
Laboratory Medicine **[10931]**
Laboratory Medicine: An Official Publication of the American Society for Clinical Pathology [10931]
Laboratory Safety Guidelines **[10910]**
Labrador Ventures **[37418]**
"Laced Up and Ready to Run" in Barron's (Vol. 89, July 6, 2009, No. 27, pp. 12) **[14679]**, **[20992]**, **[28681]**
Lacey Chamber of Commerce **[46116]**
Lacey Thurston County Chamber of Commerce (LTCCC) **[46116]**
Lackawanna Area Chamber of Commerce **[42623]**
LaCloche Manitoulin Business Assistance Corp. (LAMBAC) **[24252]**
Ladies Professional Golf Association (LPGA) **[7511]**
Ladies Who Launch (LWL) **[33467]**
Lady Lake Area Chamber of Commerce **[38443]**
Lafayette Chamber of Commerce **[36971]**
Lafayette Chamber of Commerce (LCC) **[37874]**
Lafayette SCORE **[40135]**
Lago Vista and Jonestown Area Chamber of Commerce **[45241]**
LaGrange County Chamber of Commerce **[39569]**
LaGrange - Troup County Chamber of Commerce **[38756]**
Laguna Beach Chamber of Commerce (LBCC) **[36972]**
Laguna Niguel Chamber of Commerce (LNCC) **[36973]**
Lair East Labs L.L.C. (LEL) **[42895]**
Lake Agassiz Development Group Regional Small Business Center **[43316]**
Lake Alfred Chamber of Commerce (LACC) **[38444]**
Lake Almanor Area Chamber of Commerce **[36974]**
Lake Arrowhead Communities Chamber of Commerce (LACCC) **[36975]**
Lake Benton Area Chamber of Commerce and Convention and Visitors Bureau **[41250]**
Lake Buchanan Inks Lake Chamber of Commerce **[45242]**
Lake Capital Partners Inc. **[39364]**
Lake Champlain Islands Chamber of Commerce [45729]
Lake Champlain Islands Economic Development Corporation (LCIEDC) **[45729]**
Lake Champlain Regional Chamber of Commerce (LCRCC) **[45730]**
Lake Champlain Regional Chamber of Commerce Visitor and Convention Bureau [45730]
Lake Chelan Chamber of Commerce **[46117]**
Lake Cities Chamber of Commerce (LCCC) **[45243]**
Lake City Area Chamber of Commerce **[41251]**
Lake City Betterment Association (LCBA) **[39764]**
Lake City Chamber of Commerce **[38445]**, **[41252]**
Lake City Chamber of Commerce [37875], [39764]
Lake City/Hinsdale Chamber of Commerce [37875]
Lake City/Hinsdale County Chamber of Commerce (LCCCC) [37875]
Lake County Chamber of Commerce **[41253]**, **[43988]**
Lake County Chamber of Commerce (LCCC) **[36976]**, **[39218]**
Lake County Community Development Corp. (LCCDC) **[41807]**
Lake County Tech Hub Business and Technology Incubator **[39412]**
Lake Crystal Area Chamber of Commerce **[41254]**
Lake Elsinore Valley Chamber of Commerce **[36977]**
Lake Erie Islands Historical Society Library (LEIHS) **[7425]**
Lake Eustis Area Chamber of Commerce **[38446]**
Lake Forest - Lake Bluff Chamber of Commerce **[39219]**
Lake Gaston Regional Chamber of Commerce **[43159]**
Lake George Chamber of Commerce **[42624]**
Lake George Regional Chamber of Commerce & CVB **[42624]**
Lake Gogebic Area Chamber of Commerce **[40952]**

Lake Granbury Area Chamber of Commerce [45244]
Lake Guntersville Chamber of Commerce (LGCC) [36130]
Lake Havasu Area Chamber of Commerce (LHACC) [36344]
Lake Houston Area Chamber of Commerce [45245]
Lake Isabella Chamber of Commerce [36961]
Lake Mills Area Chamber of Commerce (LMCC) [46440]
Lake Norman Chamber and Convention and Visitors Bureau [43160]
Lake of the Ozarks West Chamber of Commerce [41583]
Lake Placid Map [38447]
Lake Region State College (LRSC) [43323]
Lake Sunapee Region Chamber of Commerce (LSRCC) [42004]
Lake Tahoe Community College (LTCC) [37658]
Lake Township Chamber of Commerce (LTCC) [43507]
Lake Vermilion Area Chamber of Commerce (LVACC) [41255]
Lake Village Chamber of Commerce [36474]
Lake Wales Area Chamber of Commerce and EDC (LWACC) [38448]
Lake Whitney Chamber of Commerce [45246]
Lake Wisconsin Chamber of Commerce [46443]
Lake Wylie Chamber of Commerce [44568]
Lake Zurich Area Chamber of Commerce (LZACC) [39220]
Lake Zurich Commercial Club [39220]
Lakehead University Resource Centre for Occupational Health and Safety [35979]
Lakeland Area Chamber of Commerce [38449]
Lakes Area Chamber of Commerce (LACC) [40953]
Lakes Country Chamber of Commerce [46441]
Lakes Region Chamber of Commerce [42005]
Lakeshore Advantage [41097]
Lakeshore Chamber of Commerce (LCC) [39221], [39570]
Lakeside Chamber of Commerce (LCC) [36978]
Lakeside-Somers Chamber of Commerce [41775]
Lakeview Chamber of Commerce [39222]
Lakeview East Chamber of Commerce (LVECC) [39222]
Lakewood Area Chamber of Commerce [46441]
Lakewood Chamber of Commerce [42150], [46118]
Lakewood Chamber of Commerce (LCC) [43508]
Lam Partners Inc. [31083]
Lamar Chamber of Commerce (LCC) [37876]
Lamar Chamber of Commerce [41517]
Lamar Community College (LCC) [37960]
Lamar County Chamber of Commerce [45247]
Lamar State College Small Business Development Center [44919]
Lamar University - Mary and John Gray Library - Justice Cookery Collection [4479]
Lamar University Small Business Development Center [44920]
Lamar's Donuts [1299]
The Lambda Funds [42769]
Lambertville Area Chamber of Commerce [42117]
Lampasas County Chamber of Commerce (LCCC) [45248]
"Lampton Welding Launches Work on New Compressed-Gas Facility" in Wichita Business Journal (Vol. 27, February 3, 2012, No. 5, pp. 1) [10434], [10953]
LAN Solutions [31008], [31084]
Lancaster Area Chamber of Commerce [46442]
Lancaster Area Chamber of Commerce (LACC) [42625]
Lancaster Chamber of Commerce (LCC) [44250]
Lancaster County Chamber of Commerce [44569]
Lancaster Fairfield County Chamber of Commerce [43509]
"Lancaster Firm Helps Tidy Navy Aircraft Carriers" in Business First of Buffalo (Vol. 30, February 7, 2014, No. 21, pp. 4) [25145], [29273]
Lancaster Mennonite Historical Society (LMHS) [7347]
"Lancaster Offers Kiosks to Downtown Businesses: In-Site Development is Planning to Lease Up to 20 Retail Units Along Lancaster Boulevard" in San Fernando Valley Business Journal (Vol. 17, June 25, 2012, No. 13, pp. 4) [10030], [32193]
LAND [10121]
Land Line [16099]
"Land Squeeze Stalls Portland Homebuilders" in Business Journal Portland (Vol. 31, March 21, 2014, No. 3, pp. 4) [4156], [13228], [13493], [20993]
Land Survey Calculator [15232]
"Land Swap Key to Ending Royal Oak Project Impasse" in Crain's Detroit Business (Vol. 25, June 8, 2009, No. 23, pp. 20) [4157], [12365], [25412]
LandaJob Advertising Staffing Specialists [3350]
Landauer Realty Group Information Center [13353], [13631]
LandCare [10260]

Lander Chamber of Commerce [46610]
Landlord's Legal Kit for Dummies [12891]
Landmark Angels [35288], [38097]
Landmark Partners Inc. [38098]
Landor Associates [3351]
L&R Publishing, LLC [44081]
Landscape Architect and Specifier News [10122]
Landscape Architecture Foundation (LAF) [10078], [10153]
Landscape Architecture Magazine: The Magazine of the American Society of Landscape Architects (LAM) [10123]
Landscape Journal (LJ) [10124]
"The Landscape of Landscaping Is Changing" in Lawn & Landscape (July 19, 2018) [10053], [10107], [10240]
Landscape Management [10125], [10253]
Landscape New Jersey Trade Show and Conference [10061]
Landscape Trades: Canada's Premier Horticultural Trade Publication [7646], [10060], [10126]
Landscapes [10256]
"Landscaping Insurance: Definition, Cost & Providers" in Fit Small Business (August 26, 2020) [10108]
Landscaping Services Industry in the US - Market Research Report [7637], [10059]
Langenwalter Carpet Dyeing [16240]
Langley Chamber of Commerce [46119]
Langley South Whidbey Chamber of Commerce [46119]
Langston University Small Business Development Center [43709]
Langstroth's Hive and the Honey-Bee: The Classic Beekeeper's Manual [1481]
"The Language of DEI and the Terms Every Business Owner Should Know" in U.S. Chamber of Commerce (April 6, 2021) [30581]
The Language That Will Get You The Most Profitable Translation Jobs [15943]
Lansing Regional Chamber of Commerce (LRCC) [40954]
Lansing Regional SmartZone (LRSZ) [41098]
Lantis Fireworks & Lasers [15777]
Lapeer Area Chamber of Commerce (LACC) [40955]
Lapels Dry Cleaning [5257]
Lappeenranta University of Technology (LUT) [29052]
Laredo Chamber of Commerce [45249]
Laredo - Webb County Chamber of Commerce [45249]
"Large Company: With Thomas Dugan, Chief Financial Officer, Westgate Resorts" in Orlando Business Journal (Vol. 31, July 18, 2014, No. 3, pp. 8) [8422]
"Large Homes can be Energy Efficient Too" in Contractor (Vol. 56, October 2009, No. 10, pp. 5) [497], [4158], [5661], [5927], [13229], [23284]
Large Structures and Materials Testing Facility [10752]
"Largest Commercial Real Estate Brokerages" in Dallas Business Journal (Vol. 37, March 14, 2014, No. 27, pp. 8) [13230], [13494]
"Largest Indianapolis-Area Minority-Owned Businesses" in Indianapolis Business Journal (Vol. 33, July 2, 2012, No. 18, pp. 14A) [30361]
"Largest North Texas Fundraising Events" in Dallas Business Journal (Vol. 37, March 7, 2014, No. 26, pp. 6) [7127]
"Largest North Texas Software Developers" in Dallas Business Journal (Vol. 37, January 31, 2014, No. 21, pp. 8) [14794], [33868]
"Largest North Texas Tenant Rep Firms" in Dallas Business Journal (Vol. 37, March 14, 2014, No. 27, pp. 6) [13495], [13802]
Larimer County Small Business Development Center (SBDC) [37787]
Larkspur Chamber of Commerce [36979]
Larned Area Chamber of Commerce [39913]
Larry's Giant Subs [4905]
LaRue County Chamber of Commerce [40060]
Las Cruces Hispanic Chamber of Commerce (LCHCC) [42324]
Las Cruces Small Business Development Center [42278]
"Las Vegas Casino Sues NHL's Evander Kane over $500K in Gambling Markers" in Las Vegas Review-Journal (November 11, 2019) [7296]
Las Vegas Chamber of Commerce [41941]
"Las Vegas Convention and Visitors Authority Kicks Off Halloween Promotion" in Travel & Leisure Close-Up (October 8, 2012) [15750], [16002], [19372], [32955]
Las Vegas Metro Chamber of Commerce [41941]
Las Vegas Nevada Small Business Development Center [41913]
Las Vegas Nevada Small Business Development Center Henderson [41914]
Las Vegas-San Miguel Chamber of Commerce (LVSMCC) [42325]
Las Vegas Small Business Development Center [41915]
LaSalle Capital [39365]

"LaSalle St. Firms Cherry-Pick Talent As Wall St. Tanks" in Crain's Chicago Business (Vol. 31, November 17, 2008, No. 46) [18192], [20994], [26599], [28682], [35195]
"Laser Hair Removal vs. Electrolysis: Which Is Better?" in Healthline (May 17, 2017) [7848]
Lassen County Chamber of Commerce (LCCC) [36980]
"Last Call?" in Puget Sound Business Journal (Vol. .35, August 8, 2014, No. 16, pp. 12) [2757], [20995], [31395]
"The Last Word Dirty Work Required" in Workforce Management (Vol. 88, November 16, 2009, No. 12, pp. 34) [20996], [22194], [24697], [28683], [35196]
LAT Annual Convention & Expo [10405]
LAT Convention & Buying Show [10405]
"The Latest on E-Verify" in Contractor (Vol. 56, September 2009, No. 9, pp. 58) [498], [4159], [5379], [14625], [25413]
"The Latest Grant Opportunities for Women- and Minority-Owned Small Businesses" in Small Business Trends(February 28, 2023) [30362], [33581], [35814]
"The Latest: Handwriting Expert to Examine Franklin Will" in U.S. News & World Report (August 6, 2019) [7907]
Latham Area Chamber of Commerce [42557]
Latham Business and Professional Association [42557]
Latin American Business Review [24888]
"The Latin Beat Goes On" in Barron's (Vol. 88, July 7, 2008, No. 27, pp. L5) [6495], [9636], [17068], [20997], [23980], [27632]
Latin Business Association (LBA) [30273]
Latin Chamber of Commerce [27421]
Latin Chamber of Commerce of Nevada, Inc. [41942]
The Latin Chamber of Commerce of the United States [27421]
"Latino Real Estate Investments Are Increasing at High Rate" in Atlanta Agent Magazine (October 7, 2021) [13231]
"LatinWorks Cozies Up to Chevy in Detroit" in Austin Business Journal (Vol. 31, August 12, 2011, No. 23, pp. A1) [300], [11418], [19185], [29890], [30582]
Latterell Venture Partners (LVP) [37419]
Lauderdale-By-The-Sea Chamber of Commerce (LSCC) [38450]
Lauderdale Chamber/Economic & Community Development [44770]
Laughlin Chamber of Commerce [41943]
Laughlin Nevada Small Business Development Center [41916]
Launch [46707]
Launch Chapel Hill [43244]
LAUNCH Innovative Business Accelerator [45538]
Launch Pad FT [43863]
The Launch Place (TLP) [45958]
Launch Tennessee [44865]
LaunchCapital [38099]
LaunchCyte L.L.C. [44342]
LaunchHouse [43670]
Launching & Building a Brand for Dummies [17449]
Launching and Growing a Consulting Business with Paul Beers [20142]
"Launching Your Massage Therapy Business" in American Massage Therapy Association (November 14, 2017) [10767]
LaunchIt Minto [46827]
Launchpad LA (LPLA) [37590]
Launchpad Republic: America's Entrepreneurial Edge and Why It Matters [22670]
Launchpad Venture Group LLC [40701]
Launchpad Ventures [45457]
LaunchPoint [36271]
LaundroLab LLC [10201]
Laundromat Business Startup for Beginners 2022 [10209]
Laundromat Consulting and Coaching [10193]
"Laundromat Franchise: 10 Steps to Buying Into a Franchise" in Mulberrys Berry Blog (Aug. 31, 2022) [10172]
Laundromat Franchises Industry in the US - Market Research Report [10184], [24444]
Laundromat Marketing Strategies to Promote Your Business [10173]
Laundromat Marketing Tips to Promote Your Business Online [10174]
Laundromat Ownership Step-by-Step: A Realistic Guide to Operating and Growing Laundromats [10210]
Laundromat Resource LLC [10193]
Laundromats - 2022 U.S. Market Research Report with Updated COVID-19 Forecasts [10185]
Laundromats in the US [10186]
Laundry One [10194]
Laundry Solutions Group [10195]
Laundrylux [10196]

Laurel Chamber of Commerce [41776]
"Laurent Beaudoin Interview: Deja Vu" in Canadian Business (Vol. 81, July 22, 2008, No. 12-13, pp. 38) [19542], [22671], [28684], [29274]
Laurentian Chamber of Commerce [41256]
Laurier Institute [46860]
Laurinburg/Scotland County Area Chamber of Commerce (LSCC) [43161]
Lava Hot Springs Chamber of Commerce (LHSCC) [38928]
"Lavante, Inc. Joins Intersynthesis, Holistic Internet Marketing Company" in Marketwired (November 5, 2009) [9176], [16436], [18193], [21904], [29891]
The Law of Equal Employment Opportunity (Onsite) [35164]
"Law Firms Cash In On Alcohol" in Business Journal Portland (Vol. 27, November 19, 2010, No. 38, pp. 1) [1340], [1925], [10326], [15015], [18614], [25414]
Law Firms Industry in the US - Market Research Report [10220]
"Law Firms See Improvement in Financing Climate" in Sacramento Business Journal (Vol. 28, October 14, 2011, No. 33, pp. 1) [11051], [18615], [20998], [28152]
Law Offices of Robert J. Keller P.C. [2123], [9279]
Law Offices of Suzanne C. Cummings and Associates P.C. [18758]
"Law School Not Such a Great Idea?" in Philadelphia Business Journal (Vol. 33, February 28, 2014, No. 3, pp. 8) [18616], [21561]
"Lawmakers, Execs Launch Effort to Save Rural Hospitals" in Atlanta Business Chronicle (June 13, 2014, pp. 7A) [20999], [25015], [25415], [25851]
Lawn Doctor [10267]
Lawn Doctor Inc. [10267]
Lawn & Landscape [10127], [10254]
Lawn Mower Institute [10082], [10224]
Lawrence Chamber of Commerce [39914]
Lawrence County Chamber of Commerce [36131], [44251], [44771]
Lawrence County Chamber of Commerce (LCCC) [36475]
Lawrence G. Spielvogel Inc. [545]
Lawrence Regional Technology Center [39975]
Lawrence Siegel-Consultant (LSC) [4330]
Lawrence University - Seeley G. Mudd Library Music Collections [11225], [11300]
"Laws for Selling Handmade Soap & Cosmetics" in Made Urban (July 6, 2015) [4597], [4662]
"Lawsuit Seeks To Shut Down Illinois Collection Agency" in PaymentsSource (January 12, 2012) [4796], [18617], [20307], [25416]
"Lawsuits Claim Coke Sent Illegal Ad Texts" in Atlanta Business Chronicle (June 13, 2014, pp. 4A) [301], [2758], [18618], [25417]
Lawton - Fort Sill Chamber of Commerce and Industry [43776]
Lawyer Entrepreneur Assistance Program [37561]
Lawyers for Equal Justice (L4EJ) [38836]
Lawyers for Family Justice [37591]
"Lawyers Lock Up Cops as Clients" in Sacramento Business Journal (Vol. 28, April 8, 2011, No. 6, pp. 1) [18619], [31690], [34078], [35197]
"Lawyers Object to New Online Court Fees" in Sacramento Business Journal (Vol. 31, August 8, 2014, No. 24, pp. 3) [3514], [18620], [20308], [21905]
"Lawyers Sued Over Lapsed Lacrosse Patent" in Crain's Detroit Business (Vol. 25, June 8, 2009, No. 23, pp. 5) [15097], [18621], [27911], [28036], [29275]
"Layoffs Continue to Be a Drag on Region's Recovery" in Philadelphia Business Journal (Vol. 28, January 22, 2010, No. 49, pp. 1) [21000], [26985], [34079]
Layout Software Basics (Onsite) [33801]
Lazard Technology Partners [42770]
Lazy Dog Restaurants, LLC (LDR) [14198]
LBM Expo [10406]
LBMAO Reporter [7912]
"LCB Puts a Cork in Kiosk Wine Sales" in Times Leader (December 22, 2010) [7749], [10031], [15016], [25418]
LCICon [23442]
LD+A [5417]
LDB Interior Textiles [8187], [9062]
LDG Associates [22321]
Le Bureau Canadien de Soudage [10418]
Le Camp [46897]
Le Centre d'entreprises et d'innovation de Montreal (CEIM) [46898]
Le Cordon Bleu College of Culinary Arts Library [4480], [8126], [8531], [11614], [14305]
Le Gourmet Factory (LGF) [42239]
Le Muffin Plus [14199]
Le Musee Canadien du Ski [14743]
Le Sueur Area Chamber of Commerce (LSACC) [41257]

Lead Area Chamber of Commerce (LACC) [44651]
"Lead-Free Products must Meet Requirements" in Contractor (Vol. 56, September 2009, No. 9, pp. 30) [12644], [25419], [29276], [34080]
"Lead Like It Matters...Because It Does: Practical Leadership Tools to Inspire and Engage Your People and Create Great Results" [22195], [22672], [28685]
Lead Upwards: How Startup Joiners Can Impact New Ventures, Build Amazing Careers, and Inspire Great Teams [22673]
Lead to Win (LTW) [46757]
"Leaders: 11 Tips to Consider When a Key Employee Quits" in Small Business Trends (March 21, 2022) [26600], [26986], [28686]
Leaders Eat Last Deluxe: Why Some Teams Pull Together and Others Don't" [22196]
"Leaders and Lagards" in Barron's (Vol. 89, July 13, 2009, No. 28, pp. 14) [6496], [9637], [21001], [23981]
"The Leaders Who Make M&A Work" in Harvard Business Review (Vol. 92, September 2014, No. 9, pp. 28) [28687], [31396]
"Leadership in Architecture: My Passion in Life" [900]
The Leadership Challenge: How to Make Extraordinary Things Happen in Organizations [21562], [22674], [28688], [29277], [32194], [34336]
"Leadership Development In the Age of the Algorithm" in (Vol. 90, June 2012, No. 6, pp. 86) [21563], [22675], [28689]
Leadership Development for Women [28359]
"The Leadership Equation: 10 Practices That Build Trust, Spark Innovation, and Create High-Performing Organizations" [2193], [5468], [22197], [26987], [28690]
Leadership Excellence L.L.C. [45690]
"Leadership: Growing Pains" in Canadian Business (Vol. 80, November 19, 2007, No. 23, pp. 41) [22198], [28691]
"Leadership Is a Conversation: How To Improve Employee Engagement and Alignment In Today's Flatter, More Networked Organizations" in Harvard Business Review (Vol. 90, June 2012, No. 6, pp. 76) [17705], [22199], [28692]
Leadership Lackawanna News [44252]
Leadership Management International Inc. (LMI) [17521]
Leadership Skills: Building Success Through Teamwork (Onsite) [22057], [28360], [28361]
Leadership Skills for Supervisors [28362]
Leadership Skills and Team Development for IT and Technical Professionals (Onsite) [28363]
Leadership and Supervisory Skills for Women (Onsite) [28364]
Leadership and Team Development for Managerial Success (Onsite) [28365]
"Leading Digital: Turning Technology into Business Transformation" [19424], [21767], [22964], [26171], [30952]
Leading Effective Teams II - Communicating with Your Teammates (Onsite) [22058], [28366]
Leading High-Performance Project Teams [28367]
Leading High Performance Teams [22059], [28368]
"Leading Ohio Internet Marketing Firm Announces Growth in September" in Marketing Weekly News (September 26, 2009, pp. 24) [302], [9177], [18194], [21002], [26601], [29892]
Leading Project Managers: A Guide to Success (Onsite) [28369]
"Leading the Way" in Business Strategy Review (Vol. 23, Spring 2012, No. 1, pp. 10) [28693], [30963]
"Leading With Meaning: Beneficiary Contact, Prosocial Impact, and the Performance Effects of Transformational Leadership" in Academy of Management Journal (Vol. 55, April 1, 2012, No. 2, pp. 458) [28694], [32564]
LeadingAge [11501]
LeadingAge Annual Meeting [11532]
LeadingAge Annual Meeting and Expo [11532]
LeadingAge Minnesota [27119]
LeadsCon [10687], [29507], [30173], [32689], [33636]
Leadville/Lake County Chamber of Commerce [37877]
League of American Bicyclists [1512]
League of American Wheelmen, Inc. [1512]
League of California Cities (LCC) [15494]
League of Rural Voters Education Project [17232]
"A League of Their Own" in St. Louis Business Journal (Vol. 32, May 4, 2012, No. 37, pp. 1) [26325], [31397], [35356]
Leake County Chamber of Commerce (LCCC) [41409]
"Lean Branding" [22396], [24546]
"Lean In: Women, Work, and the Will to Lead" [35815]
Lean In: Women, Work, and the Will to Lead [19425], [22397], [35506]
"Lean Machine: Health Care Follows Auto's Lead, Gears Up for Efficiency" in Crain's Detroit Business (Vol. 26, Jan. 11, 2010) [25852], [29278]

Lean Trimmings [2435]
"Leaning Tower" in Business Courier (Vol. 27, June 4, 2010, No. 5, pp. 1) [11052], [13496], [13803], [18622], [28153], [32195]
"Learn How To Start a Campground From Someone Who Did It" in Small Business Trends (June 18, 2015) [2517]
"Learn New Ideas from Experienced Menu Makers" in Nation's Restaurant News (Vol. 45, June 27, 2011, No. 13, pp. 82) [6914], [6995], [13959], [24382], [29279]
Learn to Organize: A Professional Organizer's Tell-All Guide to Home Organizing [12835]
"Learning Before Earning" in Pittsburgh Business Times (Vol. 34, August 15, 2014, No. 4, pp. 12) [21564]
"Learning Charisma: Transform Yourself Into the Person Others Want to Follow" in Harvard Business Review (Vol. 90, June 2012, No. 6, pp. 127) [14515], [17706], [22676]
The Learning Experience Academy of Early Education (TLE) [16167]
Learning Forward [14975]
Learning Resources Network (LERN) [3548]
Learning While Working: Structuring Your On-the-Job Training [9997], [21565]
LearningRx Inc. [21724]
LearnLaunch (LL) [40753]
The Lease Coach [2357]
Leather Medic [7251], [10372]
"Leave It Behind" in Crain's Chicago Business (Vol. 31, April 21, 2008, No. 16, pp. 32) [8423], [19373], [24698], [34989]
Leavenworth Chamber of Commerce [46120]
Leavenworth County Historical Society and Museum Library [7426]
Leavenworth-Lansing Area Chamber of Commerce (LLACC) [39915]
Leawood Chamber of Commerce (LCC) [39916]
Lebanon Area Chamber of Commerce [41584]
Lebanon Area Chamber of Commerce (LACC) [43510]
Lebanon Area Chamber of Commerce Directory [43511]
Lebanon Chamber of Commerce [39223]
Lebanon Chamber of Commerce [42015]
Lebanon Valley Chamber of Commerce [44253]
Lebanon/Wilson County Chamber of Commerce [44772]
LedgerPlus [153], [15449]
Ledgers Professional Services [1786], [15450]
Ledo Pizza Systems Inc. [12562]
Lee College Small Business Development Center (SBDC) [44921]
Lee County Chamber of Commerce [38757]
Lee Grossman Associates [30646]
Lee Hecht Harrison L.L.C. [2625]
Lee Resources International Inc. [10411]
Lee Vining Chamber of Commerce [36981]
Leech Lake Area Chamber of Commerce (LLACC) [41258]
Leeds Area Chamber of Commerce [36132]
Leeds Clark Inc. [945]
Leeds/Moody Chamber of Commerce [36132]
Leelanau County Chamber of Commerce [40956]
Leelanau Peninsula Chamber of Commerce [40956]
"Lee's Launches With Focus on Liqueur-based Ice Creams" in Ice Cream Reporter (Vol. 23, August 20, 2010, No. 9, pp. 6) [1341], [8535], [30754]
Leesburg Area Chamber of Commerce [38451]
Leesville-Vernon Chamber of Commerce [40173]
"Legal Assistance for Startups: Everything You Need to Know" in UpCounsel (June 26, 2020) [18623]
"Legal Barriers Keep 16-Story Horizon at Ground Level" in Memphis Business Journal (Vol. 34, August 24, 2012, No. 19, pp. 1) [4160], [18624], [28154]
Legal Basics for Small Businesses with Larissa Bodniowycz [16668]
Legal Considerations for Business Owners [33526], [35712]
Legal Documents Needed to Sell a Business [19227]
Legal Environments of Business [18778]
Legal Guide for Starting & Running a Small Business [18472], [22398], [24547]
A Legal Guide for Startups [18625], [19014]
Legal Innovators for Tomorrow (LIFT) [40221]
Legal Issues for Managers (Onsite) [28370], [35165]
Legal Issues in Real Estate Foreclosure (Onsite) [18491]
"Legal Matters: 'Crowdfunding' a Boon for Entrepreneurs, If They Clear Regulatory Hurdles" in Finance and Commerce (July 17, 2012) [1603], [6155], [18473], [22965], [28066], [30895], [35239]
Legal Protection for Entrepreneurs and How to Leverage It for Business Growth with Attorney Nuzayra Haque [28931]
"The Legal Side of Owning a Food Truck" in Entrepreneur (2020) [6996], [18626]
"Legal Structure: The Difference Between LLCs And LLPs" in Small Business Trends (May 21, 2013) [27189], [34534]

Master Index Lil'

The Legend **[38452]**
"Legg Mason Compensation Committee Chair Defends CEO Fetting's Pay" in Baltimore Business Journal (Vol. 29, July 22, 2011, No. 11, pp. 1) **[6497]**, **[9638]**, **[17323]**, **[23982]**, **[28695]**
"Legislating the Cloud" in Information Today (Vol. 28, October 2011, No. 9, pp. 1) **[9178]**, **[16437]**, **[18627]**, **[21906]**, **[25420]**, **[28037]**
"Legislative Changes Providing Boost to San Antonio Distillers" in San Antonio Business Journal (Vol. 28, March 7, 2014, No. 4, pp. 4) **[1926]**, **[25421]**
Legislative Guide to Elected & Appointed Officials **[39224]**
Legislative Report **[40397]**
Legislative Roster **[38135]**
"Legislators Must Cut Cost of Government" in Crain's Detroit Business (Vol. 24, October 6, 2008, No. 40, pp. 6) **[17324]**, **[21003]**, **[25422]**, **[26326]**, **[33582]**, **[34081]**, **[34832]**, **[35198]**
Legislature of the Virgin Islands - Virgin Islands Senate Standing Committee on Economic Development, Agriculture & Planning **[46651]**
Legislature of the Virgin Islands - Virgin Islands Senate Standing Committee on Economic Development Center [46651]
"Legoland Florida Plans $3M-$6M Expansion" in Orlando Business Journal (Vol. 29, August 24, 2012, No. 10, pp. 1) **[606]**, **[18195]**
"Legoland Florida Theme Park Construction to Start in May" in Orlando Business Journal (Vol. 26, January 29, 2010, No. 35, pp. 1) **[607]**, **[4161]**
Lehigh Acres Chamber of Commerce [38372]
Lehigh University Baker Institute for Entrepreneurship **[44408]**
Lehigh University Procurement Technical Assistance Center **[44361]**
Lehigh University Small Business Development Center (LUSBDC) **[22953]**, **[44098]**
Lehigh Valley Business (LVB) **[44437]**
Lehrer Financial and Economic Advisory Services **[13329]**
"Leica Beefs Up Steering Options, Steering Display Features" in Farm Industry News (January 10, 2011) **[17069]**, **[30755]**
"Leinenkugel's Looks Beyond Honey Weiss To Stay Relevant" in Business Journal (Vol. 31, January 3, 2014, No. 32, pp. 4) **[1927]**
Leipsic Area Chamber of Commerce **[43512]**
L.E.K. Consulting LLC **[7325]**
Leland Chamber of Commerce **[41410]**
Lemhi Ventures **[41334]**
Lemmen-Holton Cancer Pavilion Library **[8082]**, **[8127]**, **[11615]**, **[12471]**
Lemmon Chamber of Commerce **[44652]**
Lemnos Labs **[37592]**
Lemon Tree Family Hair Salon **[7893]**
Lemont Area Chamber of Commerce [39196]
"Lenders Get Boost from Low Rates" in Saint Louis Business Journal (Vol. 32, September 9, 2011, No. 2, pp. 1) **[11053]**, **[28155]**
"Lending Door Slams" in Puget Sound Business Journal (Vol. 29, October 24, 2008, No. 27, pp. 1) **[4162]**, **[6498]**, **[20309]**, **[28156]**
"Lending Grows as Banks Make Moves" in Pittsburgh Business Times (Vol. 33, May 9, 2014, No. 43, pp. 4) **[18196]**, **[19543]**, **[28157]**
Lenexa Chamber of Commerce (LCC) **[39917]**
Lenhardt Library of the Chicago Botanic Garden **[7671]**
Lennox Tech Enterprise Center **[42896]**
Lenox Chamber of Commerce (LCC) **[40592]**
Lenox Library Association - Music Department **[11226]**
Leo A Daly Company **[9078]**
Leo Burnett Detroit - Information Resource Center **[400]**
Leonard R. Friedman Risk Management Inc. **[27374]**, **[35968]**
Leonard's Guide Freight Transportation & Warehouse Directory (FTWD) **[12978]**
Leonard's Guide--International Air Cargo Directory **[8734]**
Leonard's Guide--International Postal, Parcel & Cargo Directory [8734]
Leonard's Guide National Warehouse and Distribution Directory [12978]
Lepercq, de Neuflize & Co **[42771]**
Lerer Hippeau (LH) **[43023]**
Les Franchises Panda Ltee./Panda Franchises Ltd. **[14696]**
Les Naturalistes **[5490]**
"Less Malaise in Malaysia" in Barron's (Vol. 88, March 17, 2008, No. 11, pp. M12) **[6499]**, **[9639]**, **[23983]**, **[25423]**
"Lessons From My Father" in Crain's Chicago Business (Vol. 31, November 10, 2008, No. 45, pp. 28) **[11986]**, **[21004]**
"The Lessons I Learned As a Teen Entrepreneur" in Entrepreneur (July 1, 2021) **[36026]**
"Lessons Learned From Animals, Part II" in South Florida Business Journal (Vol. 35, September 19, 2014, No. 8, pp. 11) **[18197]**, **[22677]**
"Lessons from SeaWorld's 'Blackfish' Nightmare" in Orlando Business Journal (Vol. 30, January 3, 2014, No. 28, pp. 7) **[608]**, **[6188]**, **[12940]**, **[31779]**
"Lessons from Turnaround Leaders" in Strategy and Leadership (Vol. 39, May-June 2011, No. 3, pp. 36-43) **[19884]**, **[22200]**, **[22678]**, **[28696]**
"Let the Light Shine" in Retail Merchandiser (Vol. 51, July-August 2011, No. 4, pp. 74) **[972]**, **[4598]**
"Let Markets Decide?" in Canadian Business (Vol. 80, October 8, 2007, No. 20, pp. 67) **[21005]**, **[25424]**
Lethal Logic: Exploding the Myths that Paralyze American Gun Policy **[7836]**, **[29280]**, **[29893]**
Let's Buy a Company: How to Accelerate Growth Through Acquisitions **[9640]**, **[18198]**, **[19678]**, **[31398]**
Let's Eat Fresh Commissary Kitchen & Catering **[38574]**
"Let's Go Team: When a Retail Professional Leads by Example, Everyone Benefits" in Black Enterprise (Vol. 41, November 2010, No. 4) **[22201]**, **[32196]**, **[32565]**
"Let's Make a Deal" in Pittsburgh Business Times (Vol. 33, July 18, 2014, No. 53, pp. 10) **[21006]**, **[23984]**, **[25425]**
"Let's Put On a Show" in Inc. (November 2007, pp. 127) **[15870]**, **[23285]**, **[35066]**
"A Level of Excitement That is Second to None" in South Florida Business Journal (Vol. 35, August 8, 2014, No. 2, pp. 9) **[609]**
Levelland Area Chamber of Commerce (LACC) **[45250]**
Levensohn Venture Partners (LVP) **[37420]**
Leveraging Fractional Talent **[27107]**
The Levison Letter **[31802]**
Lewes Chamber of Commerce and Visitors Bureau, Inc. **[38136]**
Lewis-Clark State College School of Technology (LCSC) **[38958]**
Lewis Clark Valley Chamber of Commerce **[46121]**
Lewis County Chamber of Commerce **[42626]**
Lewis County Chamber of Commerce Eco. Dev. Zone [42626]
Lewis County Small Business Development Center **[42402]**
Lewiston Area Chamber of Commerce (LACC) **[40957]**
Lewiston Auburn Metropolitan Chamber of Commerce **[40289]**
Lewiston Chamber of Commerce [46121]
Lewistown Area Chamber of Commerce **[41777]**
Lewisville Area Chamber of Commerce (LACC) **[45251]**
Lexington Area Chamber of Commerce **[43162]**
Lexington Area Chamber of Commerce (LCC) **[41585]**
Lexington Chamber of Commerce (LCC) **[40593]**
Lexington Medical Center - LMC Health Library **[5217]**, **[11543]**
Lexington-Rockbridge County Chamber of Commerce [45843]
Lexington SCORE **[40008]**
LexisNexis Technical Library **[9284]**
LF Leadership [29013]
LF USA Investment Inc. **[37421]**
LGBT Chamber of Commerce of Illinois **[39225]**
LGBTQ+ Resources in Business and the Workplace **[21259]**
LHA **[19640]**
Libby Area Chamber of Commerce (LACC) **[41778]**
Liberal Chamber of Commerce **[39918]**
Liberty Area Chamber of Commerce **[41586]**
Liberty Business Strategies Ltd. **[2284]**, **[20201]**, **[29008]**, **[30209]**
Liberty-Casey County Chamber of Commerce **[40061]**
Liberty County Chamber of Commerce **[38758]**
Liberty-Dayton Area Chamber of Commerce (LDACC) **[45252]**
Liberty Legal Institute [15489]
"Liberty Media Pushes to Close on Sirius XM While Cable Deals Wait" in Denver Business Journal (Vol. 65, February 28, 2014, No. 42) **[2459]**, **[9641]**, **[13036]**, **[31399]**
Liberty Mutual Innovation (LMI) **[40787]**
Liberty Tax, Inc. **[15451]**
Liberty Tax Service, Inc. **[2403]**, **[15452]**
"Liberty Tax Service is Registering Students for Fall Tax Preparation Courses" in Economics Week (August 3, 2012) **[15398]**, **[21566]**
Liberty Venture Partners Inc. **[44343]**
"LIBOR's Hidden Lesson: Instant Messages Are Deadly" in Canadian Business (Vol. 85, August 12, 2012, No. 14, pp. 75) **[6500]**, **[17707]**, **[17867]**, **[28038]**
Libraries Canada **[8836]**
The Library and Book Trade Almanac **[1661]**, **[1830]**, **[11987]**
Library of Congress (LOC) **[47277]**
Library of Congress Local History & Genealogy Reading Room **[7427]**
Library of Congress - Moving Image Resource Center **[13062]**
Library and Information Technology Association [8831]
Library Literature & Information Science Full Text™ **[8844]**, **[14996]**
The Library at the Mariners' Museum **[10630]**
Library of Michigan Government Documents Service **[47423]**
Library of Virginia - Records Management Div. **[47424]**
Licensed Merchandisers' Association [27828]
Licensing Industry Association [27828]
Lieber & Associates **[20549]**
Liespotting: Proven Techniques to Detect Deception **[17708]**, **[22679]**, **[23512]**, **[28697]**
"Life After Cod" in Globe & Mail (March 18, 2006, pp. B1) **[6749]**, **[6784]**, **[19885]**, **[30873]**, **[32197]**
"The Life of a Bridal Consultant" in Levittown Tribune (July 25, 2016) **[1977]**
"The Life Changers" in Canadian Business (Vol. 81, October 27, 2008, No. 18, pp. 86) **[6189]**, **[21567]**, **[31996]**, **[32783]**
"The Life and Death of the American Pool Hall" in Punch (January 23, 2015) **[1538]**
Life Insurance Marketing and Research Association [6236], [8997], [9008]
Life Science Angels, Inc. **[37422]**
Life Science Business Incubator at Monsanto Place **[41679]**
"Life Science Companies in I-35 Corridor Get New Booster" in Dallas Business Journal (Vol. 35, March 16, 2012, No. 2, pp. 1) **[21007]**, **[27212]**
"Life Sciences Become State's Growth Powerhouse" in Crain's Detroit Business (Vol. 25, June 1, 2009, No. 22, pp. M008) **[18199]**, **[31997]**, **[32784]**
Life Sciences Greenhouse of Central Pennsylvania (LSGPA) **[44447]**
"Life's Work: Interview with Alain Ducasse" in Harvard Business Review (Vol. 92, May 2014, No. 5, pp. 136) **[17709]**, **[19746]**, **[22202]**
"Life's Work: Ben Bradlee" in Harvard Business Review (Vol. 88, September 2010, No. 9, pp. 128) **[11988]**, **[18200]**, **[22203]**, **[22680]**, **[23513]**, **[28698]**
"Life's Work: James Dyson" in Harvard Business Review (Vol. 88, July-August 2010, No. 7-8, pp. 172) **[791]**, **[22681]**, **[27912]**, **[30756]**
"Life's Work: Interview With Kareem Abdul-Jabbar" in Harvard Business Review (Vol. 90, January-February 2012, No.1-2, pp. 156) **[15165]**, **[23514]**
"Life's Work: Manolo Blahnik" in Harvard Business Review (Vol. 88, December 2010, No. 12, pp. 144) **[3039]**, **[6136]**, **[14680]**, **[22682]**, **[23632]**
"Life's Work: Oliver Sacks" in Harvard Business Review (Vol. 88, November 2010, No. 11, pp. 152) **[17506]**, **[17868]**, **[22683]**, **[25853]**, **[28699]**
"Lifesavers" in Black Enterprise (Vol. 41, December 2010, No. 5, pp. 38) **[73]**, **[15399]**, **[16814]**, **[23985]**, **[25854]**
"Lifestyle Entrepreneurship and Innovation in Rural Areas: The Case of Tourism Entrepreneurs" in Journal of Small Business Strategy (Vol. 31, December 1, 2021, No. 4, 40-49) **[22684]**
Lifetime Benefit Solutions (LBS) **[33468]**
"A Lifetime of Giving: Food Bank CEO Fights Hunger One Mouth At a Time" in Black Enterprise (Vol. 41, November 2010, No. 4, pp. 86) **[7128]**, **[22685]**, **[34337]**, **[35816]**
LifeWorks **[34685]**
LiftFund **[28081]**
"A Light Bulb Came On, and It Was Energy Efficient" in Globe & Mail (January 27, 2007, pp. B3) **[22686]**, **[23286]**
Light Lines **[11346]**
"Lighter Than Air" in Game Developer (Vol. 18, November 1, 2011, No. 10, pp. 38) **[585]**, **[3431]**, **[3628]**
LIGHTFAIR International (LFI) **[5420]**
Lighthouse Capital Partners **[37423]**
Lighthouse Communities Inc. [41099]
Lighthouse Inspections Canada **[2036]**
Lighthouse Labs **[45959]**
Lighting Design & Application [5417]
Lighting Design Collaborative (LDC) **[31085]**
"Lights, Camera, Action: Tools for Creating Video Blogs" in Inc. (Volume 32, December 2010, No. 10, pp. 57) **[6190]**, **[14795]**, **[16438]**, **[19886]**, **[21907]**, **[29894]**, **[30964]**, **[33869]**
Lightship Capital **[43671]**
Lightspeed Venture Partners **[37424]**
Ligonier Chamber of Commerce (LCC) **[39571]**
Lil' Angels Photography **[12356]**

Small Business Sourcebook • 42nd Edition 3277

Lillington Master Index

Lillington Area Chamber of Commerce (LACC) **[43163]**
Lil'Pals Pet Photography **[12357]**
Lima/Allen County Chamber of Commerce **[43513]**
Limestone Chamber of Commerce **[40290]**
Limestone County Chamber of Commerce **[36133]**
Limited Liability Companies for Dummies **[19544]**, **[34535]**, **[34833]**
Limited Liability Companies: Tax & Business Law **[34954]**
"Limo University Launches First North American Tour" in Chauffeur Driven (November 12, 2019) **[10282]**
Limon Chamber of Commerce **[37878]**
LIMRA International **[6236]**, **[8997]**, **[9008]**
LINC Community Revitalization Inc. **[41099]**
Linchpin: Are You Indispensable? **[22687]**, **[28700]**
Lincoln Area Chamber of Commerce (LACC) **[36982]**
Lincoln Chamber of Commerce (LCOC) **[41868]**
Lincoln City Chamber of Commerce **[43989]**
Lincoln County Chamber of Commerce **[40062]**
Lincoln County-Stanford Chamber of Commerce [40062]
"Lincoln Firm Shows Finishing Kick" in Providence Business News (Vol. 29, June 30, 2014, No. 13, pp. 10) **[9978]**, **[16301]**
Lincoln Park Chamber of Commerce (LPCC) **[39226]**
"Lincoln Park to Lose Longtime Bike Shop after 73 Years as it Consolidates to Woodhaven Location" in News-Herald (July 15, 2019) **[1523]**
Lincoln Valley Chamber of Commerce (LVCC) **[41779]**
Lincoln-Woodstock Chamber of Commerce [42017]
Lincoln-Woodstock Chamber Newsletter **[42006]**
Lincolnton - Lincoln County Chamber of Commerce **[38759]**
Lincolnton-Lincoln County Chamber of Commerce **[43164]**
Lincolnwood Chamber of Commerce [39227]
Lincolnwood Chamber of Commerce & Industry (LCCI) **[39227]**
Linda Berkowitz **[8277]**
Linda Lipsky Restaurant Consultants Inc. **[2285]**, **[8118]**, **[20202]**
Lindale Area Chamber of Commerce (LACC) **[45253]**
"Lindbergh Receives Kiosks to Expedite Travel Through Customs: Vetting Process 'Pre-Screens' Low-Risk Travelers" in San Diego Business Journal (Vol. 33, August 20, 2012, No. 34, pp. 8) **[10032]**, **[19374]**, **[25426]**
Linden-Peters Chamber of Commerce (LPCC) **[36983]**
Lindenhurst - Lake Villa Chamber of Commerce **[39228]**
Lindsay Chamber of Commerce **[36984]**
Line-X Protective Coatings **[1143]**
"The Lines of Code That Changed Everything" in Slate (October 14, 2019) **[3629]**
Lingerie, Swimwear & Bridal Stores Industry in the US - Market Research Report **[2003]**, **[10308]**
"Linguists Wanted! 10 Language Jobs Big Tech is Hiring For Right Now" in Slator (November 24, 2021) **[15944]**
"Lining Up at the Ethanol Trough (Ethanol Production in Canada)" in Globe & Mail (January 25, 2007, pp. B2) **[23287]**, **[29281]**
LINK **[39765]**
LINK 2022 Retail Supply Chain Conference **[32352]**
Link Staffing Services **[15658]**
Linking Customer, Employee and Process Data to Drive Profitability (Onsite) **[29593]**
"Linking HRM and Knowledge Transfer Via Individual-Level Mechanisms" in Human Resource Management (Vol. 51,May- June 2012, No. 3, pp. 387-405) **[22204]**, **[26988]**, **[28039]**
"Linking Human Capital to Competitive Advantages: Flexibility in a Manufacturing Firm's Supply Chain" in Human Resource Management (Vol. 49, September-October 2010, No. 5) **[19887]**, **[26989]**, **[29282]**
Linn's Stamp News: World's Largest Weekly Stamp Newspaper **[3245]**
Linton Chamber of Commerce [39572], [43303]
Linton Industrial Development Corp. (LIDC) **[43303]**
Linton-Stockton Chamber of Commerce (LSCC) **[39572]**
Lions Clubs International Convention **[23442]**
Liquid Capital Canada Corp. **[154]**, **[26829]**
"Liquor-Sales Issue in Kansas Creates Strange Bedfellows" in Wichita Business Journal (Vol. 27, February 10, 2012, No. 6, pp. 1) **[4441]**, **[7750]**, **[10327]**, **[25427]**
"Liquor Stores Feeling Financial Impact Six Months after Grocery Stores Allowed to Sell Wine on Sundays" in wsmv.com (June 26, 2019) **[7751]**, **[10328]**, **[25428]**
"Liquor Stores Sips on Growth Cocktail" in Globe & Mail (February 6, 2006, pp. B5) **[10329]**, **[18201]**
Lisbon Area Chamber of Commerce (LACC) **[43514]**
"LISC and Uber Eats Announce Black Restaurant Fund" in Minority Business Entrepreneur (February 2, 2022) **[30363]**, **[35357]**
Lisle Area Chamber of Commerce (LCC) **[39229]**
"List of Credit Card Companies, Card Networks & Major Cards" in WalletHub (August 11, 2019) **[4721]**
List of Professional Genealogists and Related Services [7353]
"The List: Public Relations Agencies" in South Florida Business Journal (Vol. 35, August 8, 2014, No. 2, pp. 12) **[12941]**, **[31780]**
"The List: Top Insurance Agencies" in South Florida Business Journal (Vol. 34, May 2, 2014, No. 41, pp. 10) **[8934]**, **[27300]**
"The List: Top South Florida Diagnostic Centers" in South Florida Business Journal (Vol. 34, April 18, 2014, No. 39, pp. 12) **[10922]**, **[25855]**
"Listen Up: There's a Revolution in the Cubicle" in Barron's (Vol. 89, July 27, 2009, No. 30, pp. 18) **[6501]**, **[9642]**, **[17710]**, **[23986]**
Listing Business Directory **[37879]**
Litchfield Area Chamber of Commerce **[41259]**
Litchfield Chamber of Commerce **[39230]**, **[41260]**
Lite For Life **[16516]**, **[20236]**
LITE Memphis **[44848]**
LiteKey LLC **[37593]**
Literary Market Place: The Directory of the American Book Publishing Industry **[1662]**, **[4939]**, **[16197]**
Literary Press Group of Canada (LPG) **[1624]**
Literary Translators' Association of Canada [15925]
"Literati Bookstore Marks a New Chapter for Ann Arbor" in Forbes (February 6, 2018) **[1831]**
Litigation Management and Training Services Inc. **[20596]**
"The Little Biotech that Could" in Barron's (Vol. 89, July 27, 2009, No. 30, pp. 19) **[6502]**, **[9643]**, **[18202]**, **[23987]**, **[25856]**
The Little Black Book For Every Busy Woman **[1704]**
Little Brothers Friends of the Elderly Chicago Chapter (LBFE) **[176]**
Little Brothers of the Poor [176]
Little Caesars Pizza **[12563]**
"Little Cheer in Holiday Forecast for Champagne" in Advertising Age (Vol. 88, November 17, 2008, No. 43, pp. 6) **[1342]**, **[10330]**, **[15017]**, **[21008]**, **[29895]**
Little Falls Area Chamber of Commerce (LFACC) **[41261]**
"Little Guy is Taking On Potent Competition" in Philadelphia Business Journal (Vol 32, January 10, 2014, No. 48, pp. 4) **[5170]**, **[19888]**, **[30757]**, **[31998]**
The Little Gym **[2904]**
"Little Gyms Are Getting Bigger" in Sacramento Business Journal (Vol. 31, April 25, 2014, No. 9) **[12424]**, **[18203]**
Little King Inc. **[4906]**
The Little Miami River Chamber Alliance **[43515]**
Little River Chamber of Commerce (LRCC) **[44570]**
Little Rock Regional Chamber **[36476]**
Little Scientists **[2905]**
Littleton Area Chamber of Commerce (LACC) **[42007]**
"Littleton Firm Chips In On Security Solution" in Denver Business Journal (Vol. 65, May 9, 2014, No. 52, pp. A6) **[4722]**, **[4797]**, **[14431]**, **[20310]**, **[23988]**, **[32198]**
"Live and Learn" in Canadian Business (Vol. 80, April 23, 2007, No. 9, pp. 76) **[22688]**, **[33583]**
"Donald Tarlton" in Canadian Business (Vol. 80, March 26, 2007, No. 7, pp. 70) **[22689]**, **[24699]**
"Live & Learn: François Joly" in Canadian Business (Vol. 79, September 11, 2006, No. 18, pp. 146) **[9644]**, **[22690]**
"Live & Learn: Gordon Stollery" in Canadian Business (Vol. 81, December 19, 2007, No. 1, pp. 76) **[22399]**, **[24548]**
"Live & Learn: Ian Delaney" in Canadian Business (Vol. 81, Summer 2008, No. 9, pp. 168) **[22691]**, **[24700]**, **[28701]**, **[29283]**, **[32785]**, **[34990]**
"Laurent Beaudoin" in Canadian Business (Vol. 80, April 9, 2007, No. 8, pp. 68) **[22692]**, **[24701]**
"Live and Learn: Penny Chapman" in Canadian Business (Vol. 79, July 17, 2006, No. 14-15, pp. 75) **[8575]**, **[22693]**, **[28702]**
"Live & Learn: Philip Kives, Founder and CEO of K-Tel" in Canadian Business (Vol. 79, October 23, 2006, No. 21, pp. 160) **[22694]**, **[24702]**
"Live & Learn: Thomas D'Aquino" in Canadian Business (Vol. 80, November 19, 2007, No. 23, pp. 92) **[21009]**, **[22695]**, **[25429]**, **[28703]**
Live Oak District Chamber of Commerce **[36985]**
The Live Oak Press L.L.C. **[1701]**, **[4949]**
LiveOak Venture Partners **[45458]**
Livermore Chamber of Commerce Business Directory **[36986]**
Livermore Valley Chamber of Commerce (LVCC) **[36987]**
Livestock Marketing Association (LMA) **[1064]**
"Living in a 'Goldfish Bowl'" in WorkingUSA (Vol. 11, June 2008, No. 2, pp. 277) **[74]**, **[1765]**, **[15400]**, **[16815]**, **[25430]**, **[35199]**
Living Lighting **[5421]**
Living Magazine **[45254]**
Living Magazine Mckinney/Allen Edition [45254]
"LivingSocial's New 'Glue" in Washington Business Journal (Vol. 33, May 2, 2014, No. 2, pp. 10) **[11769]**, **[20461]**, **[21908]**, **[29896]**
Livingston Area Chamber of Commerce (LACC) **[41780]**
Livingston Chamber of Commerce (LCC) **[42151]**
Livingston Chamber of Commerce [45255]
Livingston County Chamber of Commerce **[42627]**
Livingston - Overton County Chamber of Commerce **[44773]**
Livingston Parish Chamber of Commerce (LPC) **[40178]**
Livingston-Polk County Chamber of Commerce **[45255]**
Livonia Business Directory **[40958]**
Livonia Chamber of Commerce (LCC) **[40959]**
Livres Canada Books **[1625]**
Livres Canada Books News **[1626]**
Llano County Chamber of Commerce (LCCC) **[45256]**
LLC Beginner's Guide: The Most Complete and Easy-to-Follow Handbook on How to Form, Manage and Maintain Your Limited Liability Company **[19015]**, **[19545]**, **[34536]**
"LLC Taxes: Everything You Need to Know" in Small Business Trends (February 14, 2023) **[34834]**
LLGMA Show [10371]
Lloyd Staffing **[14994]**
LM [10125], [10253]
LMI Canada Inc. (LMI) **[29042]**
"The Loan Arranger" in Canadian Business (Vol. 80, October 22, 2007, No. 21, pp. 15) **[28158]**, **[34338]**
"Loans Aplenty From Local Banks in Q4" in South Florida Business Journal (Vol. 34, February 7, 2014, No. 29, pp. 4) **[28159]**
"Loans Are Plentiful for Small Businesses" in South Florida Business Journal (Vol. 35, September 12, 2014, No. 7, pp. 16) **[18204]**, **[28160]**, **[31400]**
"Loblaw's Apparel Guru No Average Joe" in Globe & Mail (March 13, 2006, pp. B1) **[29897]**, **[32199]**
"Lobster Mania Hits China: They Just Had to Get Used to the Claws" in Canadian Business (Vol. 85, July 16, 2012, No. 11-12, pp. 10) **[6750]**, **[6785]**, **[8735]**, **[21568]**, **[27633]**, **[29898]**
"Local Artists and Curators Offer Some Gallery Dos and Dont's" in Phoenix New Times (October 1, 2019) **[973]**
"Local Brewers Hop Onboard Craft-Beer Train" in Providence Business News (Vol. 29, April 14, 2014, No. 2, pp. 1) **[1928]**, **[18205]**
Local Business Directory **[36988]**
"Local Community Revitalization Business Grants Available Across the US" in Small Business Trends(January 25, 2023) **[16577]**
"Local Companies Land Federal Securities Pacts" in Sacramento Business Journal (Vol. 31, March 7, 2014, No. 2, pp. 6) **[14432]**, **[25146]**
"Local Company Seeks Patent For Armored Trucks" in Crain's Detroit Business (Vol. 24, February 4, 2008, No. 5, pp. 10) **[14433]**, **[25147]**, **[27913]**, **[30758]**
"Local Couple Pushes for Change to Waco Beekeeping Ordinance" in Waco Tribune-Herald (May 31, 2019) **[1482]**, **[25431]**
Local Development Corporation of East New York (LDCENY) **[42897]**
Local Development Corporation of East New York - East Brooklyn Enterprise Center [42897]
"Local Film Industry Stands To Lose Jobs, Millions of Dollars Unless Florida Expands" in Orlando Business Journal (Vol. 30, March 14, 2014, No. 38, pp. 4) **[2460]**, **[6191]**, **[15599]**, **[25016]**
"Local Firm Snaps up 91 Area Pizza Huts" in Orlando Business Journal (Vol. 26, January 8, 2010, No. 32, pp. 1) **[303]**, **[12530]**, **[19679]**, **[24383]**, **[29899]**
Local Freight Trucking Industry in the US - Market Research Report **[16087]**
"Local Hotels Brace for Downturn" in Crain's Chicago Business (Vol. 31, March 31, 2008, No. 13, pp. 3) **[8424]**, **[17507]**, **[19375]**, **[21010]**, **[33196]**
"Local Independent Bookstore Owners Find Success With Author Events, Personal Touch" in Crain's Detroit Business (January 22, 2017) **[1832]**
"Local Industrial Vacancies Climb" in Crain's Chicago Business (Vol. 31, November 17, 2008, No. 46, pp. 18) **[12892]**, **[13232]**, **[13497]**, **[21011]**, **[29284]**
"Local Law Firms Quietly Boost Poaching" in Boston Business Journal (Vol. 31, July 29, 2011, No. 27, pp. 3) **[18628]**, **[19889]**
"Local Marketing Strategies for Success" in Business News Daily (August 17, 2020) **[29530]**
Local Media Association (SNA) **[11472]**
Local Networking + LinkedIn = Ideal Clients **[24817]**
"Local Outlook: Stronger Growth Ahead" in Montana Business Quarterly (Vol. 49, Spring 2011, No. 1, pp. 10) **[18206]**, **[21012]**

3278 Small Business Sourcebook • 42nd Edition

"Local Resale Shops Give Tips for Buying, Selling Used Items" in News Tribune (July 21, 2019) **[3896]**
Local Specialized Freight Trucking Industry in the US - Market Research Report **[16088]**
"Local Startup Hits Big Leagues" in Austin Business JournalInc. (Vol. 28, December 19, 2008, No. 40, pp. 1) **[14744]**, **[15166]**, **[20044]**, **[30759]**, **[33734]**
"Local TV Hits Media Radar Screen" in Business Courier (Vol. 27, July 2, 2010, No. 9, pp. 1) **[2461]**, **[9645]**, **[15600]**, **[31401]**
"Locals Eager for $785M Medical Marijuana Business" in Orlando Business Journal (Vol. 30, March 21, 2014, No. 39, pp. 4) **[5013]**, **[10923]**, **[18629]**, **[25432]**, **[25857]**
"Location-Based Advertising: Convenience and Personalization vs. Data Privacy" in Business News Daily (March 20, 2023) **[304]**, **[16905]**
Lochmueller Group Inc. **[5289]**, **[17527]**
Lock Haven University Small Business Development Center (SBDC) **[44099]**
Lock Museum of America (LMA) **[10352]**, **[10362]**
Lockhart Chamber of Commerce (LCC) **[45257]**
Lockheed Martin Manassas Library **[3680]**
Lockport **[39231]**
Lockport Chamber of Commerce (LCC) **[39232]**
Locus (VCC) **[45990]**
LODGING **[8425]**, **[8482]**
Lodging Professionals Conference and Marketplace **[8489]**
Lodi Chamber of Commerce **[36989]**
Lodi and Lake Wisconsin Chamber of Commerce **[46443]**
Loeb & Loeb L.L.P., Law Library **[6061]**
Loeb Partners Corp. **[42772]**
Logan County Area Chamber of Commerce **[43516]**
Logan County Chamber of Commerce **[37880]**, **[46275]**
Logan County Chamber of Commerce (LCCC) **[40063]**
Logan Farms Honey Glazed Hams **[2438]**
Logan - Hocking Chamber of Commerce **[43517]**
Logan Small Business Development Center **[45608]**
Logansport - Cass County Chamber of Commerce **[39573]**
Logistics and Distribution Planning for Small Businesses **[20633]**
"The Logo Redesign That's Cheesier Than Most: JKR Introduces Velveeta's New Look" in PRINT (November 4, 2021) **[7594]**
Loma Linda Chamber of Commerce (LLCC) **[36990]**
Loma Linda University - Del E. Webb Memorial Library **[1043]**
Lombard Area Chamber of Commerce and Industry **[39233]**
Lombard Investments **[37710]**
Lomira Area Chamber of Commerce **[46444]**
Lomita Chamber of Commerce **[36991]**
Lompoc Valley Chamber of Commerce [36992]
Lompoc Valley Chamber of Commerce and Visitors' Bureau (LVCC&VB) **[36992]**
London Area Chamber of Commerce [41412]
London-Laurel County Chamber of Commerce **[40064]**
"London's Gold-Medal Hotels" in Canadian Business (Vol. 85, August 13, 2012, No. 13, pp. 65) **[8426]**, **[15751]**, **[16003]**, **[19376]**
Lone Pine Chamber of Commerce (LPCC) **[36993]**
Lone Star College System Small Business Development Center **[44922]**
Long Beach Area Chamber of Commerce **[36994]**
Long Beach Business **[36995]**
Long Beach Chamber of Commerce (LBCC) **[42628]**
Long Beach City College Small Business Development Center **[36577]**
Long Beach Public Library - Performing Arts Department **[2486]**
"Long Days, Heady Loads: What the Best Boy Does on a Film Set" in The Conversation (October 27, 2019) **[6192]**
Long-Distance Freight Trucking Industry in the US - Market Research Report **[16089]**
"The Long Game" in Business Strategy Review (Vol. 21, Summer 2010, No. 2, pp. 36) **[19377]**, **[22696]**
Long Island Association (LIA) **[42629]**
Long Island Business News (LIBN) **[42994]**
Long Island City Partnership (LICP) **[33469]**
Long Island Commercial Review [42994]
Long Island High Technology Incubator (LIHTI) **[42898]**
Long Island Lighting Company Resource Center **[7983]**, **[13751]**
Long Island University - Center for Business Research (CBR) **[33729]**
Long Island University - C.W. Post Campus - Center for Business Research [33729]
Long Island University - Post **[42970]**
Long John Silver's LLC **[14200]**
Long & Levit Library **[18795]**, **[27383]**
"Long Live Rock" in Inc. (November 2007, pp. 130) **[4163]**, **[23288]**, **[23633]**
Long Prairie Area Chamber of Commerce (LPACC) **[41262]**
Long River Ventures [40702]
"A Long Road to Recovery" in Barron's (Vol. 89, July 27, 2009, No. 30, pp. 37) **[21013]**, **[25433]**
Long & Silverman Publishing Inc. (L&S) **[41963]**
"Long-Term Bull, Short-Term Bear" in Barron's (Vol. 92, September 17, 2012, No. 38, pp. 24) **[6503]**, **[9646]**, **[21014]**
"The Long View: Roberta Bondar's Unique Vision of Science, The Need for Education, and More" in Canadian Business (Vol. 81, October 27, 2008, No. 18) **[5662]**, **[5928]**, **[21569]**, **[23289]**
Longboat Key Chamber of Commerce (LKCC) **[38453]**
Longitude Capital **[37745]**
Longmont Area Chamber of Commerce **[37881]**
"Longmont's Comida Food Truck Now a Brick-and-Mortar Restaurant, Too" in Las Cruces Sun-News (February 17, 2012) **[3848]**, **[6997]**, **[13870]**, **[18207]**, **[35817]**
"Longtime Advocacy for Green Skin Care Is Paying Off" in Providence Business News (Vol. 29, June 2, 2014, No. 9, pp. 24) **[1585]**, **[4515]**, **[5929]**, **[35818]**
"Longtime Peoria Heights Second-Hand Clothing Shop Closing" in Journal Star (December 18, 2010) **[3129]**, **[3897]**
"Longtime Seattle Company Wards Cove Selling Last Seattle Properties" in Puget Sound Business Journal (Vol. 34, February 21, 2014, No. 45, pp. 4) **[10604]**, **[13498]**
Longview Chamber of Commerce **[45258]**, **[45539]**
Longview Partnership [45258], [45539]
Longwood Gardens **[7672]**
Longwood University Small Business Development Center Danville **[45777]**
Longwood University Small Business Development Center Farmville **[45778]**
Longwood University Small Business Development Center Martinsville (LSBDC) **[45779]**
Longwood University Small Business Development Center South Boston **[45780]**
"Longwood's FamilLab More Than Just a Hackerspace: It's a Free Form Research and Development Lab" in Orlando Business Journal (Vol. 30, January 17, 2014, No. 30, pp. 4) **[3630]**, **[14796]**, **[31999]**, **[32786]**, **[33870]**
Longy School of Music - Bakalar Music Library **[11227]**
"A Look at 2020 Food Trends" in FoodTruckOperator.com (February 20, 2020). **[6998]**, **[19016]**, **[29900]**
"A Look Ahead at How Rail Could Change Ala Moana" in Pacific Business News (Vol. 52, August 22, 2014, No. 26, pp. 7) **[901]**, **[4164]**
"Look Before You Lease" in Women Entrepreneur (February 3, 2009) **[12893]**, **[18630]**, **[19186]**, **[24703]**, **[33584]**
"Look, No Hands!" in Inc. (Vol. 33, September 2011, No. 7, pp. 52) **[2759]**, **[30965]**
"Look Out, Barbie, Bratz are Back" in Canadian Business (Vol. 83, August 17, 2010, No. 13-14, pp. 18) **[15792]**, **[18631]**, **[27914]**
"Looking for the Best Camera Stores in the World?" in Format (June 21, 2019) **[2495]**
"Looking for Diversity? How to Build a More Inclusive Small Business" in U.S. Chamber of Commerce (July 20, 2020) **[30583]**
"Looking To Hire Young? Be Careful" in Boston Business Journal (Vol. 30, November 19, 2010, No. 43, pp. 1) **[8576]**, **[13960]**, **[20571]**, **[25434]**, **[26602]**, **[26990]**
"Looking To Leap?" in Black Enterprise (Vol. 38, January 2008, No. 6, pp. 64) **[21909]**, **[22400]**, **[24549]**
"Looks Like We Made It (In Philadelphia)" in Philadelphia Business Journal (Vol. 32, January 24, 2014, No. 50, pp. 4) **[26327]**, **[32787]**
"Looming Labor Crunch Already Pushing Up Construction Prices" in Business Journal (Vol. 32, August 8, 2014, No. 11, pp. 10) **[4165]**, **[26603]**
Loomis Basin Chamber of Commerce **[36996]**
Loomsong **[4617]**
"Loonie Tunes: When Will the Dollar Rise Again?" in Canadian Business (Vol. 81, November 10, 2008, No. 19, pp. 62) **[9647]**, **[21015]**, **[23989]**, **[27634]**
"Loonies Buy U.S. Cable" in Canadian Business (Vol. 85, September 17, 2012, No. 14, pp. 8) **[2462]**, **[6504]**, **[9179]**, **[9648]**, **[27635]**
"Loop Hotel Plan Locks Up Funding" in Crain's Chicago Business (Vol. 31, March 24, 2008, No. 12, pp. 2) **[8427]**, **[18208]**
Loopholes of Real Estate: Secrets of Successful Real Estate Investing **[13233]**, **[13499]**
Lopez Island Chamber of Commerce **[46122]**
Lorain County Chamber of Commerce **[43518]**
Lord Fairfax Small Business Development Center **[45781]**
Lord Fairfax Small Business Development Center at Culpeper (LFSBDC) **[45782]**
Lord Fairfax Small Business Development Center at Fauquier **[45783]**
Lord and Partners Ltd. **[2404]**, **[5754]**
"The Lords of Ideas" in Business Strategy Review (Vol. 21, Autumn 2010, No. 3, pp. 57) **[19378]**, **[19546]**, **[22697]**, **[28704]**
Loris Chamber of Commerce **[44571]**
Los Alamitos Area Chamber of Commerce **[36997]**
Los Alamos Chamber of Commerce **[42326]**
Los Alamos Commerce & Development Corp. (LACDC) **[42327]**
Los Alamos National Laboratory - Advanced Computing Laboratory [3570]
Los Alamos Research Park (LARP) **[42349]**
Los Alamos Small Business Development Center **[42279]**
Los Alomitos Chamber of Commerce [36997]
Los Alomitos/Rossmoor Chamber of Commerce [36997]
Los Altos Chamber of Commerce **[36998]**
Los Altos Chamber of Commerce Business Directory **[36999]**
Los Angeles Advertising Agencies Association [31846]
Los Angeles Area Chamber of Commerce **[37000]**
Los Angeles Business Journal **[37001]**, **[37693]**
Los Angeles Business Travel Association (LABTA) **[19304]**
Los Angeles Cleantech Incubator (LACI) **[37594]**
Los Angeles County Arboretum & Botanic Garden **[7673]**
Los Angeles County/Harbor-UCLA Medical Center - A.F. Parlow Library of the Health Sciences **[1044]**
Los Angeles County Museum of Art (LACMA) **[4564]**
Los Angeles Gateway Chamber of Commerce **[37002]**
Los Angeles Incubator Consortium (LAIC) **[37595]**
"Los Angeles Jewish Home to Expand to Westside With New Senior Care Community and In-Home Services" in PR Newswire (September 12, 2012) **[8258]**, **[11513]**, **[25858]**
Los Angeles Minority Business Enterprise Center **[37264]**
Los Angeles Minority Business Opportunity Center **[37265]**
Los Angeles Public Library Arts, Music and Recreation Department **[4865]**
Los Angeles Small Business Development Center Network (LA SBDC) **[36578]**
Los Angeles Venture Association (LAVA) **[36550]**
Los Banos Chamber Directory **[37003]**
Los Fresnos Chamber of Commerce **[45259]**
Los Gatos Chamber of Commerce (TLGCC) **[37004]**
Los Lunas Small Business Development Center **[42280]**
Los Osos/Baywood Park Chamber of Commerce **[37005]**
"Loss of Rutgers Name Causing a Stir for Law School" in Philadelphia Business Journal (Vol. 28, April 20, 2012, No. 10, pp. 1) **[18632]**, **[21570]**, **[31402]**
"Loss of Tobacco Revenue Is Unlikely To Cost CVS" in Providence Business News (Vol. 28, February 17, 2014, No. 46, pp. 1) **[5171]**, **[15699]**, **[19017]**
"The Lost Art of Duckpin Bowling" in The New York Times (May 26, 2016) **[1879]**
"The Lost Civilization of Dial-Up Bulletin Board Systems" in The Atlantic (November 4, 2016) **[2121]**
"The Lost Opportunity for a Canadian Steel Giant" in Globe & Mail (April 23, 2007, pp. B1) **[29285]**, **[31403]**, **[34082]**
Lost Sierra Chamber of Commerce **[37006]**
Loto-Quebec Centre de Documentation **[7338]**
"Lots More Mr. Nice Guy" in Canadian Business (Vol. 80, October 22, 2007, No. 21, pp. 58) **[18209]**, **[22698]**, **[23634]**, **[28705]**
"Lotteries Scratch Their Way to Billions" in Saint Louis Business Journal (Vol. 31, August 19, 2011, No. 52, pp. 1) **[305]**, **[7297]**, **[31691]**
Lotus: Hardware Hail Mary **[34631]**
"Lotus Starts Slowly, Dodges Subprime Woes" in Crain's Detroit Business (Vol. 24, April 14, 2008, No. 15, pp. 3) **[6505]**, **[9649]**, **[11054]**, **[19018]**, **[19890]**, **[23990]**, **[28161]**
LoudBird LLC **[30210]**, **[35921]**
LoudBird Marketing [30210], [35921]
Loudon County Chamber of Commerce (LCCC) **[44774]**
Loudonville-Greater Mohican Area Chamber of Commerce [43530]
Loudoun County Chamber of Commerce (LCCC) **[45876]**
Lougheed Resource Group Inc. (LRG) **[620]**, **[13664]**, **[32359]**
Louisa County Chamber of Commerce (LCCC) **[45877]**
Louisburg Area Chamber of Commerce [39919]
Louisburg Chamber of Commerce (LCC) **[39919]**
Louise-Hillje Chamber of Commerce **[45260]**
Louisiana Business Incubation Association (LBIA) **[40222]**

Small Business Sourcebook • 42nd Edition 3279

Louisiana Business & Technology Center (LBTC) **[40223]**
Louisiana Minority Supplier Development Council [40202]
Louisiana Procurement Technical Assistance Center (LA PTAC) **[40208]**
Louisiana Procurement Technical Assistance Center at Lafayette Economic Development Authority (LEDA) **[40209]**
Louisiana Procurement Technical Assistance Center - University of Louisiana - LAPTAC State Administrative Office **[40210]**
Louisiana Public Health Association (LPHA) **[25680]**
Louisiana Small Business Development Center Greater New Orleans Region **[40124]**
Louisiana Small Business Development Center - Lead Center (LSBDC) **[40125]**
Louisiana Small Business Development Center at Louisiana State University in Shreveport **[40126]**
Louisiana Small Business Development Center at McNeese State University (LSBDC MSU) **[40127]**
Louisiana Small Business Development Center at Northwestern State University (LSBDC) **[40128]**
Louisiana Small Business Development Center at Southeastern Louisiana University **[40129]**
Louisiana Small Business Development Center at Southern University **[40130]**
Louisiana Small Business Development Center at University of Louisiana at Lafayette **[40131]**
Louisiana State University AgCenter Food Incubator **[40224]**
Louisiana State University (LSU) - LSU Research and Technology Foundation (RTF) - Louisiana Emerging Technology Center (LETC) **[40225]**
Louisiana State University in Shreveport College of Business Administration - Center for Business and Economic Research (CBER) **[40240]**
Louisiana State University Stephenson Entrepreneurship Institute (LSUSEI) **[40237]**
Louisiana Tech University - Center for Rural Development **[33730]**
Louisiana Tech University Innovation Enterprise **[40238]**
Louisiana Technology Park [40229]
Louisiana Workforce Commission - Media Relations **[47751]**
Louisiana Workforce Commission - Office of Management & Finance - Tax Accounting/Adjustments Unit **[47752]**
Louisiana Workforce Commission (LMI) - Research and Statistics Division - Labor Market Information **[47753]**
Louisville Area Chamber of Commerce **[43519]**
The Louisville Avenue Bridge or Lee Joyner Bridge [40199]
Louisville Business First: The Weekly Business Newspaper of Greater Louisville **[40116]**
Louisville Chamber of Commerce **[37882]**
Louisville Chamber of Commerce [40049]
Louisville SCORE **[40009]**
Louisville Small Business Development Center **[39996]**
Louisville-Winston County Chamber of Commerce **[41411]**
Loup City Chamber of Commerce **[41869]**
Love County Chamber of Commerce **[43777]**
"A Love of Likes: What's a Facebook Nod Worth to a Business? Serious Sales Growth, Say Some" in *Boston Business Journal* (Vol. 31, July 8, 2011, No. 24, pp. 1) **[21910]**, **[29901]**, **[32566]**, **[34083]**
Lovelady Consulting **[4950]**
Loveland Area Chamber [43515]
Loveland Center for Business Development (LCBD) **[37788]**
Loveland Chamber of Commerce **[37883]**
Loveland Small Business Development Center [37788]
Lovelock/Pershing County Chamber of Commerce [41949]
Loves Park - Machesney Park Chamber of Commerce **[39234]**
Lovett Miller & Co., Inc. **[38538]**
Lovington Chamber of Commerce **[42328]**
Low-Budget Online Marketing for Small Business **[21911]**, **[29902]**, **[33197]**
"Low Cost Methods for Marketing Your Tutoring Business" in *Teachworks Blog* (Dec. 28, 2021) **[16137]**
Low-Slope Roofing Materials Guide **[14329]**
Lowell Area Chamber of Commerce (LACC) **[40960]**
Lower Bucks County Chamber of Commerce (LBCCC) **[44254]**
Lower Keys Chamber of Commerce (LKCC) **[38454]**
"Lower Prices No Shoo-In as Telcos Near Deregulation" in *Globe & Mail* (March 28, 2007, pp. B1) **[6506]**, **[9650]**, **[25435]**, **[33198]**
"Lower Unemployment Hasn't Offset Total Losses" in *Sacramento Business Journal* (Vol. 31, May 23, 2014, No. 13, pp. 6) **[21016]**, **[21571]**, **[25859]**
"Lowering Retirement System Barriers for Women" in *Employee Benefit News* (Vol. 25, December 1, 2011, No. 15) **[17325]**, **[26991]**, **[30584]**

Loyalist Gazette **[7380]**
Loyola University Chicago School of Continuing and Professional Studies (SCPS) **[39443]**
LPD Enterprises **[4951]**
LRA Consulting [35221]
LRP Media Group **[27149]**
LRVHealth **[40702]**
LSA Associates Inc. **[33429]**
LSU Innovation Park **[40226]**
LSU Student Incubator **[40227]**
Lubar and Co. **[46549]**
Lubbock Angel Network (LAN) **[44874]**
Lubbock Chamber of Commerce (LCC) **[45261]**
Lubbock Small Business Development Center **[44923]**
Luby's Fuddruckers Restaurants, LLC [1293], [14169]
Lucas Area Chamber of Commerce (LACC) **[39920]**
Lucas Chamber of Commerce [39920]
Lucas Venture Group (LVG) **[37425]**
Lucchesi Business Consulting, L.L.C. (LBC) **[30211]**
Lucerne Valley Chamber of Commerce **[37007]**
Lucey Fund **[37746]**
Lucille Roberts Fitness Express (LR) **[12457]**, **[16517]**
Lucky Leaf Expo **[5055]**
"Lucky Strikes: Labor-Market Muscle" in *Barron's* (Vol. 92, August 25, 2012, No. 38, pp. 15) **[35200]**
Ludington & Scottville Area Chamber of Commerce **[40961]**
Lufkin/Angelina County Chamber of Commerce (LACCC) **[45262]**
Lum, Drasco and Positan L.L.C., Law Library **[6062]**
The Lumber and Building Materials Association of Ontario, Inc (LBMAO) **[7913]**
Lumberton Area Chamber of Commerce and Visitors Bureau [43165]
Lumberton NC Area Chamber of Commerce **[43165]**
Lumina Consulting Group **[41363]**
The Luminary **[37008]**
The Luminations Group L.L.C. **[31086]**
Lumira Ventures **[46873]**
Lumpkin County Chamber of Commerce [38720]
The Lunch Lady Group Inc. **[6939]**
"Lundin Deal Leaves Nickel Market Thin" in *Globe & Mail* (April 5, 2007, pp. B4) **[6507]**, **[9651]**, **[30874]**, **[31404]**
Lupke & Associates Inc. (L&A) **[46583]**
Luray-Page County Chamber of Commerce **[45878]**
Luttrell Staffing Group **[14995]**
Luverne Area Chamber of Commerce (LCC) **[41263]**
"Lux Coffees, Breads Push Chains to React" in *Advertising Age* (Vol. 77, June 26, 2006, No. 26, pp. S14) **[1259]**, **[7560]**, **[9652]**, **[13961]**, **[29903]**
Luxemburg Chamber of Commerce **[46445]**
Luxury Bath Systems **[2405]**
"Luxury Still Sells Well" in *Puget Sound Business Journal* (Vol. 29, September 5, 2008, No. 20, pp. 1) **[3130]**, **[32200]**, **[33385]**
Lynch Financial Advisors, Inc. (LFA) **[37678]**
Lynchburg Business Development Center (LBDC) **[45784]**
Lynchburg - Moore County Chamber of Commerce **[44775]**
Lynchburg Regional Business Alliance (LRBA) **[45879]**
Lynchburg Regional Chamber of Commerce [45879]
Lynden Chamber of Commerce (LCC) **[46123]**
Lyndon Area Chamber of Commerce **[45731]**
Lyndon State College Continuing Education Department **[45752]**
Lynn Area Chamber of Commerce [40586]
"Lynn Johnson, President: Dowland-Bach" in *Alaska Business Monthly* (Vol. 27, October 2011, No. 10, pp. 11) **[20634]**, **[22699]**, **[29286]**
Lynwood Chamber of Commerce **[37009]**
Lyons Chamber of Commerce (LCC) **[37884]**
LZ Area Chamber of Commerce [39220]

M

M. C. O'Brien Inc. **[13618]**
M/C Partners **[40703]**
M & M Meat Shops Ltd. **[2439]**
M13 **[37426]**
MAA Consulting Inc. **[22322]**
MAA WORLDWIDE [32429]
Maaco Franchising Inc. **[1144]**, **[1145]**, **[14585]**
MABA Outlook Conference [17172]
MAC 6 Leadership Academy **[36399]**
MaC Venture Capital **[30274]**, **[35289]**, **[37747]**
MACH37 **[45960]**
Machine Tool Reference Guide **[10435]**
Machine Tool Reference Guide for Metalworking Machinery [10435]
"Machine Transliteration Survey" in *ACM Computing Surveys* (Vol. 43, Fall 2011, No. 3, pp. 17) **[3432]**, **[3631]**, **[15945]**

Machinery Information Management Open Systems Alliance (MIMOSA) **[28260]**
Machining Science and Technology **[10453]**
Machinist's Workshop **[4618]**
"Macho Men" in *Canadian Business* (Vol. 81, November 10, 2008, No. 19, pp. 23) **[14434]**, **[28706]**
Mackinac Island Chamber of Commerce [40962]
Mackinac Island Tourism Bureau **[40962]**
Mackinaw City Chamber of Commerce **[40963]**
Macomb Area Economic Development Corp. (MAEDCO) **[39413]**
"Macomb County Man Accused of Illegally Operating Charter Boat" in *Macomb Daily* (July 7, 2019) **[2832]**
"Macomb County, OU Eye Business Incubator" in *Crain's Detroit Business* (Vol. 24, February 11, 2008, No. 6, pp. 1) **[14365]**, **[21572]**, **[35240]**
Macomb-Oakland University INCubator **[41100]**
Macomb Regional Procurement Technical Assistance Center (PTAC) **[41061]**
Macon Area Chamber of Commerce **[41587]**
Macon County Chamber of Commerce **[44776]**
"Macroeconomic Policy and U.S. Competitiveness: A Reformed Fiscal Policy Is Vital To Renewing America's Productivity" in *Harvard Business Review* (Vol. 90, March 2012, No. 3, pp. 112) **[11665]**, **[21017]**, **[25860]**, **[26992]**, **[30966]**, **[34835]**
Macrowikinomics: Rebooting Business and the World **[18210]**, **[19891]**, **[21018]**, **[27636]**
MACS Service Reports **[531]**
MACUL Conference **[3560]**, **[21689]**, **[35126]**
"Macy's, Home to $8,000 Mink Jackets, Will Stop Selling Fur Products by 2021" in *The New York Times* (October 21, 2019) **[7237]**, **[23515]**
"Macy's Seeks Balance in All Things Ad-Related" in *Crain's Chicago Business* (Vol. 31, March 31, 2008, No. 13, pp. 19) **[306]**, **[29904]**, **[32201]**
The Mad Matter **[6840]**
Mad River Valley Chamber of Commerce **[45732]**
The Mad Science Group (MSG) **[21725]**
Made in New York Media Center **[42899]**
Made in NY Media Center by IFP **[42900]**
"Made in San Francisco: Manufacturing a Comeback" in *San Francisco Business Times* (Vol. 28, February 14, 2014, No. 30, pp. 4) **[18211]**, **[29287]**
Madeira Beach Chamber of Commerce [38507]
Madelia Area Chamber of Commerce **[41264]**
Madeline Island Chamber of Commerce (MICC) **[46446]**
Madella Area Chamber Newsletter **[41265]**
"Made@Mayo: Mayo Professor Doubles As Founder of Text Tech Company" in *Business Journal* (Vol. 32, June 6, 2014, No. 2, pp. 10) **[7067]**, **[25634]**, **[26172]**, **[27822]**, **[31928]**, **[35241]**
Madera Business Beat **[37010]**
Madera Business Extravaganza & Home Expo [21682]
Madera Business Extravaganza and Trade Show [21682]
Madera Chamber of Commerce **[37011]**
Madera District Chamber of Commerce [37011]
Madison Area Chamber of Commerce (MACC) **[39574]**
Madison Chamber of Commerce **[42152]**
Madison Chamber of Commerce (MCC) **[38058]**
Madison Chamber of Commerce [46420]
Madison County Chamber (MCC) **[39575]**
Madison County Chamber of Commerce **[38455]**, **[39766]**, **[41412]**, **[41588]**, **[45263]**
Madison County Chamber of Commerce (MCCC) **[38760]**
Madison County Chamber of Commerce **[45880]**
Madison County Chamber of Commerce and Industrial Authority [38760]
Madison County Historical Society Library **[7428]**
Madison Dearborn Partners L.L.C. (MDP) **[39366]**
Madison Enterprise Center (MEC) **[46566]**
Madison Entrepreneur Resource, Learning and Innovation Network (MERLIN) **[46584]**
Madison Heights Chamber of Commerce [40964]
Madison Heights - Hazel Park Chamber of Commerce (MHHPCC) **[40964]**
Madison-Morgan County Chamber of Commerce **[38761]**
"Madison Partner Eyes Overton: French Quarter Suites May Become Luxury Hotel" in *Memphis Business Journal* (Vol. 34, April 27, 2012, No. 2, pp. 1) **[8428]**, **[13500]**, **[31405]**
Madison SCORE **[46341]**
Madras-Jefferson County Chamber of Commerce and Visitors Center **[43990]**
Madrona Venture Group **[46194]**
"Maersk Targets Forwarders As Digital-First Revolution Spreads in Latin America" in *The Load Star* (April 11, 2019) **[7040]**
Magazine Publishers of America **[11967]**, **[12016]**
Magazine Publishers Association **[11967]**, **[12016]**
Magazines Canada **[11966]**
Magdalena Chamber of Commerce **[42329]**

"Magellan Companies Establishes Century 21 Beachhead in Boise" in Idaho Business Review (September 15, 2014) [902], [4166], [12894], [13234], [13501], [24384]
Maggie Musings [43166]
Maggie Valley Area Chamber of Commerce and Visitors' Bureau (MVCC/VB) [43167]
Magicuts, Ltd. [7894]
"Magna Banks on Big Cash Hoard" in Globe & Mail (March 1, 2006, pp. B3) [6508], [9653], [24704]
MAGNET Incubation Center (MIC) [43672]
Magnetics Business & Technology (MB&T) [32935]
Magnolia Chamber of Commerce [46124]
Magnolia-Columbia County Chamber of Commerce [36477]
Magnolia Ventures [42773]
"Magpower May Build Solar Panels in Pflugerville" in Austin Business Journal (Vol. 31, May 13, 2011, No. 10, pp. A1) [5663], [5930], [14932], [23290], [27637], [31406], [33386]
Mahomet Area Chamber of Commerce (MACC) [39235]
Mahwah Regional Chamber of Commerce (MRCC) [42153]
Maid: Hard Work, Low Pay, and a Mother's Will to Survive [5078]
Maid to Perfection [5086]
Maid-Rite Sandwich Shoppe [4907]
Maid to Sparkle Inc. [5087]
Maid2Clean [5088]
MaidPro [5089]
Maids, Nannies & Gardeners Industry in the US - Market Research Report [2989], [10251], [11330]
Mail Boxes Etc. - MBEC Communications, Inc. [2406], [3396]
Mail Order Industry in the US - Market Research Report [10468]
Mailing & Shipping Technology [3392], [7056]
Mailing Systems Technology (MAST) [3392], [7056]
"The Main Ingredient of Change" in Harvard Business Review (Vol. 92, September 2014, No. 9, pp. 36) [18212], [28707]
Main Line Chamber of Commerce (MLCC) [44255]
Main Line Chamber of Commerce Membership Directory [44256]
Main Street America [20703]
Main Street Business Insights: Amber Lambke, Maine Grains [21249]
Main Street Business Insights: Danny Reynolds, Stephenson's Clothing [3162]
Main Street Business Insights: Ebenezer Akakpo, Akakpo Design Group & Maine Culture [6145]
Main Street Business Insights: Jamie & Jerry Baker, Trendy Teachers [15546]
Main Street Business Insights: Janet Hurn, Future Ready Consulting [16669]
Main Street Business Insights: Jennifer Jones, Owner of Good Times Coal Fired Pizza & Pub [12537]
Main Street Business Insights: Katie Pinard and Michael Macomber, Elements: Coffee Books Beer [1845]
Main Street Business Insights: Kaycee McCoy, Pawsnickety Pets [31594]
Main Street Business Insights: Kristin Smith, The Wrigley Appalachian Eatery [14076]
Main Street Business Insights: Lindsay Goodson McDonald, Keith McDonald Plumbing [35902]
Main Street Business Insights: Martha Moore and Ashley Owens, Martha & Ash Custom Drapery [8188]
Main Street Business Insights: Mileyka Burgos-Flores, Allapattah Collaborative CDC [21250]
Main Street Business Insights: Mindy Bergstrom, Cooks Emporium [32347]
Main Street Business Insights: Nicole Fleetwood and McKinzie Hodges, Scratch Made Bakery [1281]
Main Street Business Insights: Tee Rowe, America's SBDC [33632]
Maine Angels (MA) [35290], [40315]
Maine Aquaculture Innovation Center (MAIC) [6801]
Maine Association of Realtors (MAR) [13095]
Maine Cannabis Convention [5056]
Maine Center for Enterprise Development [40322]
Maine Center for Entrepreneurs (MCED) [40322]
Maine Chamber of Commerce [40291]
Maine Chamber of Commerce and Business Alliance [40291]
Maine Chamber of Commerce and Industry [40291]
Maine Department of Economic and Community Development [40244]
Maine Department of Economic and Community Development - Office of Business Development [40245]
Maine Department of Health and Human Services (OSAMHS) - Office of Substance Abuse and Mental Health Services [34690]

Maine Department of Labor - Center for Workforce Research and Information (CWRI) [47425]
Maine Department of Manpower Affairs [47425]
Maine Development Foundation (MDF) [40246]
Maine International Trade Center (MITC) [40247]
Maine Lobstermen's Association (MLA) [6741]
Maine Maritime Academy - Nutting Memorial Library [10631]
Maine Procurement Technical Assistance Center Bangor (PTAC) [40318]
Maine Procurement Technical Assistance Center (Maine PTAC) - Outreach Center [40319]
Maine Small Business Development Centers - Lead Center [40243]
Maine State Beekeepers Association (MSBA) [1440]
Maine State Chamber of Commerce (MSCC) [40291]
Maine State Library (MSL) [47426]
Maine State Planning Office - Census Information Office [46934]
Maine State Planning Office - Census State Data Center [46935]
Maingate Business Development Corp. [21254]
Mainstay Suites [8506]
Mainstreet News [41589]
Maintenance Council of the American Trucking Associations [16051]
Maintenance Made Simple [4351]
Maintenance Planning & Scheduling (Onsite) [18875], [19446]
Maintenance Welding (Onsite) [2057], [19447], [21398]
Maitland Area Chamber of Commerce [38456]
"Major Advances in Heat Pump Technology" in Contractor (Vol. 57, January 2010, No. 1, pp. 42) [4167], [5380], [12645], [14626], [34836]
"Major Advances in Heat Pump Technology - Part Two" in Contractor (Vol. 57, February 2010, No. 2, pp. 22) [5381], [8736], [12646], [20045], [27638]
Major County Economic Development Incubator (MCEDC) [43864]
Major Employers of Adams County [44257]
Major Employers Directory [40065]
"Major Golf Retail Show in the Rough for 2010" in Orlando Business Journal (Vol. 26, January 15, 2010, No. 33, pp. 1) [7523], [15871], [32202], [35067]
"Major Publishers Are Selling a Ton of Ebooks in 2021" in Good E-Reader (May 7, 2021) [1663], [11770]
Makarios Consulting [40115]
"Make Business Tax Deductions Work for You" in Legal Zoom (February 17, 2023) [34837]
Make It in America: How International Companies and Entrepreneurs Can Successfully Enter and Scale in U.S. Markets [22700], [27639]
"Make It Easier On Yourself" in Women In Business (Vol. 63, Fall 2011, No. 3, pp. 28) [12836], [34991]
"Make It Yourself: Home Sewing, Gender, and Culture, 1890-1930" in Business History Review (Vol. 84, Autumn 2010, No. 3, pp. 602) [14656], [34084]
Make in LA [37598]
Make Marketing Simple with These 7 Marketing Priniples [30157]
"Make Money in 2011: What to Invest In" in Small Business Opportunities (January 2011) [23991], [24550]
Make Money As a Freelance Writer: 7 Simple Steps to Start Your Freelance Writing Business and Earn Your First $1,000 [5320], [26797], [30478]
Make Sure It's Deductible [15401], [34838]
"Make Sustainability Part of Your Business Model" in Business News Daily (February 21, 2023) [23291]
"Making Automated Royalty Payments Work for Your Franchise" in Franchising World (Vol. 42, October 2010, No. 10, pp. 30) [4798], [20462], [23992], [24385]
"The Making of a Building Boom" in Philadelphia Business Journal (Vol. 32, January 31, 2014, No. 51, pp. 4) [4168], [18213]
Making Difficult Decisions: How to Be Decisive and Get the Business Done [22701], [28708]
"Making 'Freemium' Work: Many Start-Ups Fail to Recognize the Challenges of This Popular Business Model" in Harvard Business Review (Vol. 92, May 2014, No. 5, pp. 27) [18866], [19981], [27823]
"Making Healthy Food Affordable for All" in U.S. News & World Report (October 16, 2019) [8101]
"Making It Click: Annual Ranking Of the Best Online Brokers" in Barron's (Vol. 88, March 17, 2008, No. 11, pp. 31) [6509], [9180], [9654], [20463], [21912], [23993]
"Making It Work" in Pet Product News (Vol. 64, December 2010, No. 12, pp. S8) [11579], [12166], [12256], [20464]
"Making It Work" in Retail Merchandiser (Vol. 51, July-August 2011, No. 4, pp. 43) [3040], [3131], [6137], [20465]

Making Key Hires [26719]
"Making a Living from Genealogy" in ThoughtCo. (March 17, 2017) [7368]
"Making Money on Foreclosures" in Memphis Business Journal (Vol. 33, March 9, 2012, No. 48, pp. 1) [11055], [13502], [13804]
"Making Money Is Child's Play With This Retailer" in Small Business Opportunities (March 1, 2008) [2863], [24295]
"Making Sense of Marijuana Use: How Do State Laws Affect Your Business?" in America's SBDC (Aug. 6, 2019) [34681]
"Making Social Ventures Work" in Harvard Business Review (Vol. 88, September 2010, No. 9, pp. 66) [24551], [34252]
"Making Solar Energy Even More Sustainable with Light-Powered Technology" in Science Daily (November 16, 2021) [14933]
Making Successful Business Decisions: Getting it Right the First Time (Onsite) [22060], [28371]
Making the Transition to Supervising and Managing Others [28372]
Making Waves [44572]
Mako Design + Invent [30853]
"Malarkey Using Upcycled Plastics in Shingles" in Roofing Contractor (December 28, 2018) [13721], [14330], [23292]
Malden Chamber of Commerce (MCC) [40594], [41590]
Malibu Chamber of Commerce [37012]
"Mall On a Mission: KOP to Get $150 Million Makeover" in Philadelphia Business Journal (Vol. 33, March 14, 2014, No. 5, pp. 6) [903], [4169], [12895], [13503], [32203]
Malone Chamber of Commerce (MCC) [42630]
Mama Fu's Asian House [14201]
"A Man of Courage: Leon Sullivan, First Black Corporate Director Who Fought against Inequality and Apartheid" in Black Enterprise(February 25, 2023) [9998], [21019]
Managed Funds Association (MFA) [23699]
Managed Healthcare Executive: The News Magazine for Health Care Costs and Quality [26031]
Management Action Programs, Inc. (MAP) [24486]
Management Concepts Inc. (MC) [45986]
Management Consulting Services (MCS) [44858]
Management Growth Institute (MGI) [23683], [29009]
Management House L.L.C. [29010]
Management and Leadership Skills for First-Time Supervisors and Managers (Onsite) [28373]
"Management Matters with Mike Myatt: Are You Creating Growth in a Down Economy?" in Commercial Property News (March 17, 2008) [18214], [21020], [28709]
Management Methods Inc. [29011]
Management Recruiters International Inc. (MRI) [5458], [6118]
Management Services & Development Ltd. [33054]
Management Skills: Building Performance and Productivity [28374]
Management Skills: Building Performance and Productivity (Onsite) [28375]
Management Skills for First-Time Supervisors (Onsite) [28376]
Management Skills for an IT Environment (Onsite) [22061], [28377]
Management Skills for New Supervisors and Managers [28378]
Management Skills for Secretaries, Administrative Assistants, and Support Staff [28379]
The Management of Small and Medium Enterprises [22702], [28710]
"Managerial Rudeness: Bad Attitudes Can Demoralize Your Staff" in Black Enterprise (Vol. 37, January 2007, No. 6, pp. 58) [22205], [28711]
Managerial Skills of the New Supervisors [28380]
Managerial and Team-building Skills for Project Managers [28381]
"Managerial Ties with Local Firms and Governments: an Analysis of Japanese Firms In China" in International Journal of Business and Emerging Markets (Vol. 4, July 11, 2012, No. 3, pp. 181) [25436], [27640], [28712]
The Manager's Guide to Rewards: What You Need to Know to Get the Best of-and-from-Your Employees [22206], [28713]
"Managers as Visionaries: a Skill That Can Be Learned" in Strategy and Leadership (Vol. 39, September-October 2011, No. 5, pp. 56-58) [19019], [28714], [34085]
Managing Business Risk: A Practical Guide to Protecting Your Business [32402]
Managing the Busy Summer Season in a Seasonal Small Business [32956]
"Managing a Campground as a Business" in Financial Buzz (December 19, 2018) [2518]

Managing Change: People and Process (Onsite) [28382]
Managing Chaos: How to set Priorities and Make Decisions Under Pressure [28383]
Managing Chaos: Tools to Set Priorities and Make Decisions Under Pressure (Onsite) [28384]
Managing Client Expectations: A Guide for Organizing Professionals [12837]
Managing Economies, Trade and International Business [8737], [18215], [18633], [21021], [27641], [28715], [29905]
Managing Emotions under Pressure [17598]
Managing Emotions and Thriving Under Pressure (Onsite) [17599]
"Managing Estate Sales Becomes Big Business" in The New York Times (March 11, 2015) [6073]
"Managing the Facebookers; Business" in The Economist (Vol. 390, January 3, 2009, No. 8612, pp. 10) [2194], [9181], [17711], [19020], [20113], [21573], [26328], [26604], [28716], [35201]
"Managing the Federal HOME Program: Past and Future" in Real Estate Review (Vol. 41, Spring 2012, No. 1, pp. 29) [4170], [13504], [25437]
"Managing and Forming a Qualified Joint Venture" in Legal Zoom (March 14, 2023) [34460]
Managing Information Overload: Techniques for Working Smarter (Onsite) [28385], [34972]
Managing Inventories and Cycle Counts (Onsite) [27991]
Managing a Massage Business [10768]
"Managing Member Pushback to DEI Initiatives" in Associations Now (May 9, 2022) [30585]
Managing Multiple Priorities (Onsite) [34973]
Managing Multiple Project, Competing Priorites and Tight Deadlines (Onsite) [28386]
Managing Multiple Projects, Competing Priorities & Tight Deadlines (Onsite) [34974]
Managing Multiple Projects, Objectives and Deadlines (Onsite) [34975]
Managing Multiple Projects and Priorities (Onsite) [28387]
Managing the Older Worker: How to Prepare for the New Organizational Order [22207], [26605], [26993], [28040], [28717], [30586], [34086]
Managing Organizational Transition (Onsite) [28388]
Managing People in Projects (Onsite) [28389]
"Managing Risks: A New Framework: Smart Companies Match Their Approach to the Nature of the Threats They Face" in Harvard Business Review (Vol. 90, June 2012, No. 6, pp. 48) [19547], [26994], [28718]
"Managing a Sponsored Brand: The Importance of Sponsorship Portfolio Congruence" in International Journal of Advertising (Vol. 31, February 2012, No. 1, pp. 63) [10662]
Managing Stress Productively (Onsite) [21399]
Managing Subcontracts (Onsite) [28390]
Managing Successful Negotiations (Onsite) [17600]
Managing Today's IT and Technical Professionals (Onsite) [22062]
Managing in Tough Times (Onsite) [22063], [28391]
"Managing Your Innovation Portfolio: People Throughout Your Organization Are Energetically Pursuing the New. But Does All That Add Up To a Strategy?" in Harvard Business Review (Vol. 90, May 2012, No. 5, pp. 66) [23994], [28041], [28719]
"Managing Your Tattoo Shop" in Painful Pleasures Blog (March 1, 2015) [15308]
Managing Your Time and Resources Most Effectively [32957]
"Managing Yourself: How to Save Good Ideas" in Harvard Business Review (Vol. 88, October 2010, No. 10, pp. 129) [27915], [30760]
"Managing Yourself: Job-Hopping to the Top and Other Career Fallacies" in Harvard Business Review (Vol. 88, July-August 2010, No. 7-8, pp. 154) [26606], [26995]
"Managing Yourself: What Brain Science Tells Us About How to Excel" in Harvard Business Review (Vol. 88, December 2010, No. 12, pp. 123) [20466], [28720], [34992]
"Managing Yourself: What's Your Personal Social Media Strategy?" in Harvard Business Review (Vol. 88, November 2010, No. 11, pp. 127) [21913], [29906]
Manasota SCORE, Chapter 116 [38277]
Manatee Chamber of Commerce [38457]
Mancelona Area Chamber of Commerce [40965]
Mancelona Regional Chamber of Commerce [40965]
Manchester Area Chamber of Commerce [39767], [44777]
Manchester Area Chamber of Commerce (MACC) [40966]
Manchester Chamber of Commerce [38762]
Manchester College - Peace Studies Institute - Program in Conflict Resolution [31925]
Manchester Signature Show [3165]
Manchester University - Peace Studies Institute - Program in Conflict Resolution [31925]

Manchu Wok Inc. [14202]
Mancino's, Samuel Italian Eatery [6940], [14203]
Mancuso Business Development Group [42901]
"M&A Weakness Takes Toll on Phila. Law Firms" in Philadelphia Business Journal (Vol. 28, August 10, 2012, No. 26, pp. 1) [18634], [26607], [31407]
Mandarin Restaurant Franchise Corp. [14204]
M&M Meetings [32924]
"M&T On the March?" in Baltimore Business Journal (Vol. 28, November 12, 2010, No. 27, pp. 1) [6510], [9655], [18216], [23995], [31408], [33387]
Manhasset Chamber of Commerce (MCC) [42631]
Manhattan Area Chamber of Commerce [39921], [41781]
Manhattan Beach Chamber of Commerce (MBCC) [37013]
Manhattan Chamber of Commerce (MCC) [39236], [42632]
Manhattan Chamber of Commerce [39921]
Manhattan Innovation Lab, LLC [42981]
Manhattan School of Music - Peter Jay Sharp Library [11228]
Manhattan Small Business Development Center at Pace University [42403]
Manheim Area Chamber of Commerce [44258]
Manistee Area Chamber of Commerce [40967]
Manistee County Chamber of Commerce [40967]
Manitoba Business Gateway [46720]
Manitoba Crafts Museum & Library (MCML) - Gladys Chown Memorial Library [4642], [4696]
Manitoba Department of Labour & Immigration-Workplace Safety and Health Division-Client Resource Centre [35980]
Manitoba Department of Labour - Manitoba Labour Board Library [35217]
Manitoba Genealogical Society (MGS) [7429]
Manitoba Nursing Research Institute [26154]
Manitoba Tax Assistance Office [46722]
"Manitoba Tax Credits Create Film and TV Boom" in Canadian Business (Vol. 85, June 11, 2012, No. 10, pp. 11) [6193], [34839]
Manitoba Technology Accelerator (MTA) [46727]
Manitou Springs Chamber of Commerce [37885]
Manitou Springs Chamber of Commerce and Visitors Bureau [37885]
Manitowish Waters Chamber of Commerce (MWCC) [46447]
Mankato Chamber of Commerce (MCC) [39922]
Mankind Research Foundation [2286], [20203], [32931]
Mankind Research Unlimited (MRU) [2286], [20203], [32931]
Mannes College The New School for Music - Harry Scherman Music Library [11229]
Manning Chamber of Commerce (MCC) [39768]
Manoa Innovation Center (MIC) [38889]
Manon's Shared Kitchen [45540]
Mansfield Area Chamber of Commerce (MCC) [45264]
Mansfield Bio-Incubator (MBA) [40754]
Mansfield Chamber of Commerce (MCC) [44259]
Mansfield-Richland Area Chamber of Commerce [43561]
Manteca Chamber of Commerce [37014]
Mantella Venture Partners (MVP) [46874]
Manufacturers' Agents Association for the Foodservice Industry (MAFSI) [10572]
Manufacturers' Agents for Foodservice Industry [10572]
Manufacturers' Agents N.A. (MANA) [10573]
"Manufacturers Become Part of Coalition" in Contractor (Vol. 56, July 2009, No. 7, pp. 40) [499], [23293], [29288], [31409]
Manufacturers' Mart [29453]
Manufacturers Representatives of America (MRA) [10574]
Manufacturers' Representatives Educational Research Foundation (MRERF) [10575], [10584]
Manufacturing Advocacy & Growth Network (MAGNET) [3681], [43673]
"Manufacturing Behind the Great Wall: What Works, What Doesn't" in Canadian Electronics (Vol. 23, February 2008, No. 1, pp. 6) [4397], [27642], [29289]
"Manufacturing Boom Leads to Local Warehouse Leasing Fury" in Houston Business Journal (Vol. 44, April 11, 2014, No. 49, pp. 10A) [12979], [29290]
Manufacturing Confectioner--Directory of Equipment and Supplies [2544]
Manufacturing Control in the Small Plant [29457]
Manufacturing CPAs [34], [16738]
Manufacturing Jewelers and Suppliers of America (MJSA) [9968], [29078]
Manufacturing Perfumers' Association [1383], [1579], [4507]
Manufacturing Perfumers Association of the United States [1383], [1579], [4507]
"Manufacturing Skills Fading Away" in Memphis Business Journal (Vol. 34, July 20, 2012, No. 14, pp. 1) [29291]

Manufacturing Systems Engineering Center [30864]
Manufacturing & Technology Enterprise Center (MTEC) [42902]
Manufacturing and Technology News [29454]
"The Many Dimensions of DEI" in Associations Now (May 9, 2022) [30587]
"Many Roads Lead to Value Says David J. Williams, Manager of Excelsior Value & Restructuring Fund" in Barron's (Vol. 88, March 10, 2008, No. 10, pp. 46) [6511], [9656], [19021], [23996]
"Many Sectors Lost Jobs In Detroit Area, State" in Crain's Detroit Business (Vol. 24, February 11, 2008, No. 6, pp. 3) [21022], [24705]
"Many in Tech Look to Push More Community Involvement, But Not in Traditional Ways" in Boston Business Journal (Vol. 31, August 5, 2011, No. 28, pp. 1) [7129], [22703], [26329], [34339], [35358], [36027]
Map [42008]
Map of Hammonton, NJ [42154]
Maple Flooring Manufacturers Association, Inc. (MFMA) [6824]
Maple Leaf Angels (MLA) [46753]
The Maple Leaflet [73811]
Maplewood Chamber of Commerce [42155]
Mapping Business Communications (Onsite) [17850]
"Mapping the Gender Gap" in Business Journal Portland (Vol. 31, April 25, 2014, No. 8, pp. 4) [13505], [20572], [23997], [25861], [26330]
"Mapping Out a Career: An Analysis of Geographic Concentration of Occupations" in Occupational Outlook Quarterly (Vol. 54, Fall 2010, No. 3, pp. 12) [26996], [33388], [34087]
Maquoketa Area Chamber of Commerce [39769]
Mara Perez, Ph.D. Fund Development and Planning Services [35454]
Marana Chamber of Commerce [36345]
maranGraphics Inc. [46861]
Marble Falls Chamber of Commerce [45265]
Marble Falls - Lake LBJ Chamber of Commerce [45265]
Marble Institute of America [10732]
Marble Slab Creamery [8627]
Marble Slab Creamery Inc. [8628]
Marblehead Chamber of Commerce [40595]
Marblehead Peninsula Chamber of Commerce [43520]
Marblelife, Inc. [6841]
Marcello's Market & Deli Inc. [32368]
"Marcia Tiago Shares How to Start and Run a Successful Business in 2023" in Home Business (March 2, 2023) [26798], [34537]
Marco Island [38458]
Marco Island Area Chamber of Commerce [38459]
Marco's Inc. [12564]
Marco's Pizza [12564]
Marcus & Millichap Venture Partners [37751]
Marengo County Economic Development Authority [36184]
Marengo Union Chamber of Commerce [39237]
Marfa Chamber of Commerce [45266]
Margolis Advisory Group [42982]
Marianna Chamber of Commerce [38436]
Maricopa Community Colleges at Phoenix Small Business Development Center [36272]
Marietta Area Chamber of Commerce (MACC) [43521]
MARIJUANA BUSINESS CONFERENCE & EXPO [5057]
Marijuana Business Daily [5014], [5044]
Marijuana Business Magazine [5015], [5027]
Marijuana - MyGreenz Venture Locator [5071]
Marijuana Nation [5050]
MarijuanaStocks.com [5031]
"Marilyn Monroe-Themed Spas to Open in Orlando This Fall: Former Disney Exec Al Weiss Co-Heading Up Venture [11320]
Marin Self-Publishers Association - Marin Small-Publishers Association [1612], [5273]
Marin Small-Publishers Association [1612], [5273]
Marina Chamber of Commerce [37015]
Marine City Chamber of Commerce [40968]
Marine Fuels: Specifications, Testing, Purchase & Use [23068]
Marine Retailers Association of Americas (MRAA) [10590]
"Marine-Services Firm Eyes Expansion" in Providence Business News (Vol. 29, August 25, 2014, No. 21, pp. 8) [10283], [10605], [12980], [18217]
Marinette Area Chamber of Commerce [46448]
Marinette Menominee Area Chamber of Commerce [46448]
Marion Area Chamber of Commerce [43522]
Marion Area Genealogical Society Library [7430]
Marion Chamber of Commerce [36478], [39238]
Marion County Chamber of Commerce [40066], [44778]
Marion County Chamber of Commerce (MCCC) [45267], [46276]

Marion County Chamber of Commerce [41413]
Marion County Development Partnership (MCDP) [41413]
Marion-Grant County Chamber of Commerce [39576]
Mariposa County Chamber of Commerce [37016]
Marisa Moore Nutrition, LLC [8070], [11597], [34665]
Maritime College of Forest Technology Library (MCFT) [5775]
Maritime Register [46640]
Maritz Inc. [10697]
Maritz Travel Company Resource Center [19421]
Mark West Area Chamber of Commerce [37017]
"Markel American Insurance Company Announces Wedding and Special Event Insurance for Consumers" in Benzinga.com (February 16, 2011) [1978], [8935], [27301]
Market Focus, Inc. [19140], [29012], [30212]
The Market for Minimally Invasive Medical Devices [10857]
"Market Research Guide for Business Owners" in Business News Daily (August 31, 2020) [29497]
Market Research: How To Get The Right Data to Make the Right Decisions (Onsite) [29594]
Market Research Industry in the US - Market Research Report [29502]
Market Resource Guide (Furniture industry) [8211]
"Market Resource Set for Expansion: Supply Chain Firm to Add Up to 700 Employees" in Memphis Business Journal (Vol. 34, May 11, 2012, No. 4, pp. 1) [18218], [20635], [26608], [31410], [33199]
Market Segmentation and Positioning Research (Onsite) [29595]
"Market Takes Shape for Emissions Credits" in Globe & Mail (April 16, 2007, pp. B3) [23294], [25438], [29292]
"Market and Technology Orientations for Service Delivery Innovation: the Link of Innovative Competence" in Journal of Business & Industrial Marketing (Vol. 29, July 2014, No. 6) [19892], [26331], [27916], [29907]
Market, Traction, and Milestones - Back of the Napkin to Business Plan in 11 Slides with Brandon White [19114]
"Market Watch" in Barron's (Vol. 88, March 24, 2008, No. 12, pp. M18) [6512], [8738], [9657], [21023], [23998], [25017], [25439], [27643]
"Market Watch: A Sampling of Advisory Opinion" in Barron's (Vol. 88, March 17, 2008, No. 11, pp. M10) [6513], [9658], [21024], [23999], [27644], [28162]
"Market Watch: A Sampling of Advisory Opinion US Stock Price Trends, Economic Effects of Global Trade, Chinese Economic Trends" in Barron's (Vol. 92, July 23, 2012, No. 30, pp. M14) [6514], [8739], [9659], [21025], [24000], [27645], [34088]
Market Watch: Market Intelligence on the Wine, Spirits, and Beer Business [15067]
"Marketer Bets Big on U.S.'s Growing Canine Obsession" in Advertising Age (Vol. 79, April 14, 2008, No. 15, pp. 14) [7752], [12208], [17070], [18219], [29293], [29908], [30761]
"Marketers Push for Mobile Tuesday as the New Black Friday" in Advertising Age (Vol. 79, December 1, 2008, No. 44, pp. 21) [307], [2760], [17712], [24386], [26332], [29909], [32204]
Marketing 101 for Commercial Photographers [12308]
"Marketing 101: How to Advertise Tutoring Services" in Constant Contact Blog (Jan. 21, 2022) [16138]
Marketing and Advertising Global Network (MAGNET) [223], [31836]
Marketing Agencies Association Worldwide (MAA) [32429]
Marketing Agents for Food Service Industry [10572]
Marketing for Beginners (Let's Start from Scratch) [30158]
Marketing and Business Expo [30169]
"Marketing in the Digital World: Here's How to Craft a Smart Online Strategy" in Black Enterprise (Vol. 40, July 2010, No. 12, pp. 47) [308], [21914], [29910], [32567], [34089]
Marketing and Distribution Channels for Small Businesses [20636]
Marketing Do's and Don'ts for Managing a Tutoring Business [16139]
Marketing for Dummies [29498], [29911]
Marketing for Entrepreneurs [10663], [20637], [22704], [29912], [32000], [32568], [33200]
"Marketing is Everything, But Timing Helps" in Idaho Business Review (September 9, 2014) [5172], [18220], [23635], [28163], [29913]
Marketing Financial Services [46848]
"Marketing Guide to Promote Tattoo and Piercing Studios" in EDIT.org blog [15309]
Marketing Industry: A Resource Guide [16915], [30230], [31815]
"Marketing a Laundromat" in Chron [10175]
Marketing Management Council [11005]

"Marketing the Modern Estate-Planning Practice" in WealthManagement.com (May 9, 2017) [6042], [29914]
"Marketing at the Olympics is No Longer Worth It: An Exercise in Olympic Vanity" in Canadian Business (Vol. 85, August 13, 2012, No. 13, pp. 15) [309], [15167], [15601], [29915]
Marketing Outrageously Redux: How to Increase Your Revenue by Staggering Amounts [310], [15168], [29916]
The Marketing Plan Handbook [22401], [29481], [33433]
Marketing Resource Group Inc. [30213], [32694]
"Marketing Scholarship 2.0" in Journal of Marketing (Vol. 75, July 2011, No. 4, pp. 225) [17713], [21574], [21915], [29917], [34090]
"Marketing Strategies in Family Firms" in Journal of Small Business Strategy (April 13, 2021) [23689], [29556], [33703]
"Marketing Tips for Online Tutoring Business" in Smarty-Ads blog (Sept. 22, 2020) [16140]
Marketing Without Money for Small and Midsize Businesses: 300 FREE and Cheap Ways to Increase Your Sales [311], [21916], [29918], [32569]
Marketing that Works: How Entrepreneurial Marketing Can Add Sustainable Value to Any Sized Company [22705], [29919]
Marketing Works: Unlock Big Company Strategies for Small Business [312], [29920]
"Marketing: You Are On the Air: Radio and TV Producers Are Looking For Shows Starring Smart CEOs" in Inc. (December 2007, pp. 67-69) [13037], [15602], [22706], [29921]
Marketplace: A Yacht Broker Turned Her Love of Sailing into a Career Where There's "Only Room for Growth" [24818]
Marketplace: At This Detroit Frame Shop, It Might Be Time to Bring Another Employee into the Picture [26720]
Marketplace: For Indigenous Artists, Pricing Is a Tricky Proposition [31665]
Marketplace: For This Michigan Business Owner, Wage Hikes Are Tied to Price Hikes [16670]
Marketplace: Immigrant Woman Are Increasingly Running Their Own Businesses [35903]
Marketplace: In the Face of High Inflation, This Couple's Plant Keeps Growing [31666]
Marketplace: Mississippi Record Store Owner Hopes "Greatest Hits" Compilations Sound Good to Collectors [11280]
Marketplace: On Tulsa's Black Wall Street, Shop Owner Finds Inspiration in Local Sports History [14691]
Marketplace: Persistance Pays Off Agan for L.A. Gelato Maker [8604]
Marketplace: Small Businesses Are Still Struggling to Hire. But the Situation's Improving. [26721]
Marketplace: Summertime Is Stocking Season for This Toy Store Owner [15805]
Marketplace: The Second-Hand Clothing Reseller Who's Bundling Up Style [3163]
Marketplace: Time Again for Home-Based Utah Baker to "Fly the Coop" for a Commercial Space [1282]
Marketplace: With Higher Interest Rates, Small Businesses and Lenders Proceed with Caution [28238]
"Markets Defy the Doomsayers" in Barron's (Vol. 88, March 24, 2008, No. 12, pp. M5) [6515], [9660], [17071], [24001], [29294]
"Markets: The Great Deleveraging" in Canadian Business (Vol. 81, October 13, 2008, No. 17, pp. 45) [4799], [6516], [9661], [20311], [21026]
Marks and Klein L.L.P. (MK) [18759]
Marksville Chamber of Commerce (MCC) [40179]
Marlborough Regional Chamber of Commerce (MRCC) [40596]
Marlin Chamber of Commerce (MCC) [45268]
Marquette Area Chamber of Commerce - Lake Superior Community Partnership (LSCP) [40969]
"Marriott Readies for Uptick in Leisure Travel" in Dallas Business Journal (Vol. 35, April 13, 2012, No. 31, pp. 1) [8429], [16004], [18221]
"Mars Advertising's Orbit Grows as Other Ad Segments Fall" in Crain's Detroit Business (Vol. 25, June 1, 2009, No. 22, pp. 10) [313], [10664], [23636], [29922], [32205]
MaRS Discovery District [46828]
Marshall Area Chamber of Commerce [39239]
Marshall Area Chamber of Commerce (MACC) [41266]
Marshall Area Economic Development Alliance (MAEDA) [40970]
Marshall Chamber of Commerce (MCC) [41591]
Marshall County Chamber of Commerce [40067], [44779]
Marshall County Chamber of Commerce (MCCC) [46277]

Marshall Craft Associates Inc. (MCA) [31087]
Marshall Texas Chamber of Commerce [45269]
Marshall University Research Corp. (MURC) [26127]
Marshalltown Area Chamber of Commerce (MACC) [39770]
Marshalltown Community College (MCC) [39832]
Marshfield Area Chamber of Commerce and Industry (MACCI) [46449]
Martha's Vineyard Chamber of Commerce (MVCC) [40597]
Martha's Vineyard Information [40597]
Martin Cook Associates Ltd. [1702]
Martin County Chamber of Commerce [43168]
Martin County Chamber of Commerce (MCCC) [39577]
Martin County Development Board [38201]
Martin/Williams Advertising Library [31902]
Martinez Area Chamber of Commerce [37018]
Martinez Area Chamber of Commerce and Visitors and Information Center [37018]
Martinizing Dry Cleaning [5258]
Martinsburg-Berkeley County Chamber of Commerce [46278]
Martinsville - Henry County Chamber of Commerce (MHCCC) [45881]
Mary Browns Inc. (MB) [14205]
Mary Kay Inc. Information Resources [1406], [1601], [4548]
"Mary Kramer: Good Things Happen When We Buy Local" in Crain's Detroit Business (Vol. 24, October 6, 2008, No. 40, pp. 7) [6517], [7753], [9662], [17072], [21027], [24002], [24706], [32206], [33201]
Maryland APEX Accelerator (MD PTAC) [40438]
Maryland Association of Certified Public Accountants (MACPA) [16739]
Maryland Business Incubation Association (MBIA) [33470]
"Maryland Casinos Face Atlantic City's $150M Might" in Baltimore Business Journal (Vol. 30, June 1, 2012, No. 4, pp. 1) [7298], [29923], [32207], [33389]
Maryland Center for Entrepreneurship's Innovation Catalyst [40461]
Maryland Chamber of Commerce (MCC) [40398]
Maryland Daily Record [40479]
Maryland Department of Business and Economic Development - Business Development Div. [40346]
Maryland/District of Columbia Minority Supplier Development Council [30255], [40421]
Maryland Economic Development Corporation (MEDCO) [40347]
Maryland Heights Chamber of Commerce (MHCC) [41592]
"Maryland Hospitals Cope with Rare Drop in Patient Admissions" in Baltimore Business Journal (Vol. 29, September 23, 2011, No. 20, pp. 1) [8936], [25862], [27302], [34091]
Maryland International Incubator (MI2) [40462]
"Maryland May Avoid Congress on Medicare Waiver" in Baltimore Business Journal (Vol. 30, June 15, 2012, No. 6, pp. 1) [25018], [25863]
Maryland Municipal League Convention [31713], [35124]
"Maryland Nonprofits May Lose Minority Business Enterprise Status" in Baltimore Business Journal (Vol. 29, September 2, 2011, No. 17, pp. 1) [7130], [25148], [25440], [30364], [35819]
Maryland Pharmacists Association (MPhA) [5218]
Maryland Procurement Technical Assistance Center [40438]
"Maryland Ready to Defend Slots Minority Policy" in Boston Business Journal (Vol. 29, July 8, 2011, No. 9, pp. 3) [7299], [18635], [20573], [25149], [25441], [30365]
Maryland RV Show [13682]
Maryland Small Business Development Center - Capital Region [40338]
Maryland Small Business Development Center - Eastern Region [40339]
Maryland Small Business Development Center Northern Region [40340], [46936]
Maryland Small Business Development Center - Southern Region [40341]
Maryland State Beekeepers Association Inc. (MSBA) [1441]
Marysville Chamber of Commerce [39923]
Maryville Chamber of Commerce [41565]
Mason Area Chamber of Commerce (MACC) [40971]
Mason City Area Chamber of Commerce [39771]
Mason Contractors Association of America (MCAA) [10729]
Mason County Area Chamber of Commerce [46279]
Mason County Chamber of Commerce [45270]
Mason County Chamber of Commerce [46279]
Mason Enterprise Center - Leesburg/Loudoun (MEC) [45961]

"Mason Group Seeks $20M for 'Gray' Fund" in Business Courier Serving Cincinnati-Northern Kentucky (Vol. 29, June 15, 2012, No. 7, pp. 1) **[7131]**, **[8259]**
Mason Small Business Development Center (SBDC) **[45785]**
Mason Wells Private Equity / M&I Ventures **[46550]**
Masonry Heater Association of North America (MHA) **[458]**
Masonry Industry Committee [3940], [10728]
Masonry Research Foundation [3940], [10728]
The Masonry Society (TMS) **[10730]**
Mass Customization Information Systems in Business **[3793]**
"Mass. STEM Approach and R.I. Model?" in Providence Business News (Vol. 28, March 10, 2014, No. 49, pp. 1) **[21575]**, **[26333]**
Massachusetts APEX Accelerator **[40741]**
Massachusetts Association of Business Incubators (MABI) **[40755]**
Massachusetts Beekeepers Association (MBA) **[1442]**
Massachusetts Biomedical Initiatives (MBI) **[40756]**
Massachusetts Capital Resource Co. (MCRC) **[40704]**
Massachusetts Clean Energy Center (MassCEC) **[40757]**
Massachusetts Executive Office of Energy and Environmental Affairs - Massachusetts Department of Environmental Protection - Waste and Recycling **[46997]**
Massachusetts Executive Office of Housing and Economic Development (MA EOHED) **[40502]**
Massachusetts Export Center **[40503]**
"Massachusetts Gaming Commission Hiring Consultants for Sports Betting Launch" in PlayUSA (Oct. 14, 2022) **[7300]**
Massachusetts Gaming Regulators Contract Consultants to Expedite Sports Betting **[7301]**
Massachusetts Horticultural Society (MHS) **[7674]**
Massachusetts Institute of Technology - Center for Biomedical Innovation (CBI) **[21750]**
Massachusetts Institute of Technology - Center for Collective Intelligence (CCI) **[3567]**
Massachusetts Institute of Technology - Center for Real Estate (CRE) **[13634]**
Massachusetts Institute of Technology (MIT) - The Entrepreneur Forum **[22954]**
Massachusetts Institute of Technology - Entrepreneurship Center **[40781]**
Massachusetts Institute of Technology - Japan Program **[21751]**
Massachusetts Institute of Technology - Martin Trust Center for Entrepreneurship **[40781]**
Massachusetts Institute of Technology School of Architecture and Planning - Media Lab **[15633]**
Massachusetts Medical Device Development Center (M2D2) **[40758]**
"The Massachusetts Mess" in Barron's (Vol. 89, July 27, 2009, No. 30, pp. 39) **[8937]**, **[17326]**, **[21028]**, **[25864]**, **[27303]**
Massachusetts Office of Housing and Economic Development **[40504]**
Massachusetts Office of International Trade and Investment (MOITI) **[40505]**
Massachusetts Procurement Technical Assistance Center [40741]
Massachusetts Small Business Development Center Network **[40493]**, **[40494]**
Massachusetts Small Business Development Center Network Berkshire Regional Office **[40495]**
Massachusetts Small Business Development Center Network Boston Regional Office & Minority Business Center (MSBDC) **[40652]**
Massachusetts Small Business Development Center Network Central Office **[40496]**
Massachusetts Small Business Development Center Network Northeast Regional Office **[40497]**
Massachusetts Small Business Development Center Network Southeast Regional Office **[40498]**
Massachusetts Small Business Development Center Network Western Regional Office (WRO) **[40499]**
Massachusetts Society for the Prevention of Cruelty to Animals - Angell Memorial Animal Hospital Veterinary Library **[716]**
Massachusetts Water Resources Authority (MWRA) **[16350]**
Massage Envy Franchising L.L.C. **[10783]**
"Massage Heights Chasing Big Expansion Opportunities" in San Antonio Business Journal (Vol. 28, April 25, 2014, No. 11, pp. 6) **[9663]**, **[10769]**, **[18222]**, **[27646]**
Massage Services Industry in the US - Market Research Report **[10778]**
"Massage Therapy Field on the Rise, According to AMTA Survey" in Well Spa 360 **[10770]**
Massage Therapy Journal (MTJ) **[26032]**
"Massage Therapy Practice Marketing Tips" in Click4Time Blog **[10771]**

Massapequa Chamber of Commerce **[42633]**
MassBay Community College **[40770]**
MassChallenge (MC) **[40759]**
Massena Chamber of Commerce [42590]
Massillon Area Chamber of Commerce (MACC) **[43523]**
"Massive Loss of Thousands of Hives Afflicts Orchard Growers and Beekeepers" in NPR (February 18, 2019) **[1483]**
MassVentures (MV) **[40705]**
Master Brewers Association of America [1893]
Master Brewers Association of the Americas (MBAA) **[1893]**
Master Care **[2109]**
"A Master Chef's Recipe for Business Success" in Business Strategy Review (Vol. 23, Spring 2012, No. 1, pp. 65) **[4468]**, **[13962]**, **[19022]**, **[19893]**, **[21576]**, **[32001]**
"Master of His Domain" in Canadian Business (Vol. 81, December 8, 2008, No. 21, pp. S17) **[4516]**, **[22707]**
The Master Mechanic **[14586]**
Mastering Accountable Plans: Unlock Tax Savings and Streamline Business Expenses **[34936]**
Mastering the Art of Debt Collection for Small Businesses **[20312]**
Mastering the Art of Word of Mouth Marketing with Joe Blackburn **[30159]**
Mastering Business Negotiation: A Working Guide to Making Deals and Resolving Conflict **[17714]**, **[22708]**, **[28721]**
Mastering the Business of Organizing: A Guide to Plan, Launch, Manage, Grow, and Leverage a Profitable, Professional Organizing Business **[12838]**, **[18223]**
Mastering the Complex Sale: How to Compete and Win When the Stakes Are High! **[19894]**, **[32570]**
Mastering the Complex Sale (Onsite) **[32444]**
Mastering Microsoft Excel **[33802]**
Mastering Microsoft Project (Onsite) **[21400]**
Mastering QuickBooks Seminars and QuickBooks Classes (Onsite) **[21401]**
Mastering Software Sales **[32682]**
Mastering Specialization for Growth **[18446]**
Masthead Venture partner, LLC **[40706]**
Matawan - Aberdeen Chamber of Commerce (MACOC) **[42156]**
The Match King: Ivar Kreuger, the Financial Genius Behind a Century of Wall Street Scandals **[6518]**, **[9664]**
Matco Tools Corp. **[7931]**
Material Handling Industry of America - Order Fulfillment Solutions (MHI) **[3475]**, **[12970]**
Mathematical Association of America, Texas Section Conference **[21688]**
Mathnasium Learning Centers **[16168]**, **[21726]**
Matrix Partners **[37427]**
Matt Lombardo Chef/Owner Pink Door Catering + Market **[2688]**
Matt Takes the Exit, Matt Goes All In **[33048]**
Matter **[37596]**, **[39414]**
"A Matter of Interest: Payday Loans" in Canadian Business (Vol. 79, July 17, 2006, No. 14-15, pp. 21) **[18224]**, **[24003]**, **[28164]**
"A Matter of Perspective" in Business Journal-Portland (Vol. 24, November 2, 2007, No. 35, pp. 1) **[11056]**, **[13235]**, **[13506]**, **[25442]**
Matterhorn Business Solutions **[30214]**
Matthew Pritzker Company LLC **[39461]**
Matthews Chamber of Commerce (MCC) **[43169]**
Mattituck Chamber of Commerce **[42634]**
Mattoon Chamber of Commerce **[39240]**
Maui Chamber of Commerce **[38880]**
Maui Research and Technology Center (MRTC) **[38890]**
Maui Small Business Development Center **[38865]**
Maumee Chamber of Commerce **[43524]**
Maumelle Area Chamber of Commerce (MACC) **[36479]**
Maury Alliance [44780]
Maury County Chamber of Commerce [44780]
Maury County Chamber and Economic Alliance **[44780]**
Mauston Chamber of Commerce [46421]
Max Freund **[29013]**
Max Muscle Sports Nutrition **[32369]**
"Maximize Your Marketing Results In a Down Economy" in Franchising World (Vol. 42, November 2010, No. 11, pp. 45) **[21029]**, **[24387]**, **[29924]**
Maximizing Tax Savings with Depreciation and Capitalization Policies for Small Business Owners **[34937]**
"Maximizing Your Patent Application" in Legal Zoom (March 22, 2023) **[27917]**
Maximum Performance Leadership Canada **[28392]**
Maxwell School of Citizenship & Public Affairs - Program on the Analysis and Resolution of Conflicts [10812]
"Maybe We're Exploiting China" in Canadian Business (Vol. 85, September 17, 2012, No. 14, pp. 4) **[9665]**, **[27647]**, **[31411]**

Mayfield Fund, L.L.C. (MF) **[37428]**
Mayfield-Graves County Chamber of Commerce (MG) **[40068]**
Mayo Clinic - Richard A. Robb Biomedical Imaging Lab Library **[3682]**
Mayo Clinic Ventures **[41335]**
"Mayor Rawlings Pushes for South Dallas Development to Take Root" in Dallas Business Journal (Vol. 35, March 16, 2012, No. 27, pp. 1) **[4171]**, **[13507]**
Mayor's Office of Baltimore - Minority & Women-Owned Business Development **[40422]**
Maysville-Mason County Area Chamber of Commerce **[40069]**
Maysville-Mason County Chamber of Commerce [40069]
Maytag Commercial Laundry **[10202]**
Mayville Area Chamber of Commerce (MACC) **[46450]**
Mayville - Chautauqua Area Chamber of Commerce **[42635]**
Maywood Chamber of Commerce (MCC) **[39241]**
"Mazel Tov: L'Chaim Gets a Deal to Expand with Southern Wine" in South Florida Business Journal (Vol. 33, September 7, 2012, No. 6, pp. 1) **[10331]**, **[15018]**, **[20638]**, **[31412]**
Mazomanie Chamber of Commerce **[46451]**
Mazzio's Italian Eatery **[12565]**
MB Venture Partners L.L.C. (MBVP) **[44872]**
"MBAs for Hire, By the Hour" in Entrepreneur (August 2014) **[2195]**, **[15641]**, **[21577]**, **[26609]**
MBC BioLabs **[37597]**
MBDA Business Centers **[38148]**
MBE Magazine **[30439]**
MBG Marketing - The Blueberry People **[16940]**
"MBlox, Which Sends Coupons to Phones and Tables, Raises $43.5M" in Atlanta Business Chronicle (July 11, 2014, pp. 12A) **[2761]**, **[3720]**, **[26334]**, **[29925]**
"MBT Add-On: Gone by 2012?" in Crain's Detroit Business (Vol. 24, October 6, 2008, No. 40, pp. 1) **[19187]**, **[21030]**, **[24707]**, **[25443]**, **[34092]**
MCAA Convention **[10743]**
McAlester Area Chamber of Commerce and Agriculture (MACCA) **[43778]**
McAlester Chamber of Commerce and Agriculture [43778]
McAlister's Deli **[4908]**
McAllen Chamber of Commerce **[45271]**
McAllen Convention and Visitors Bureau [45271]
McAllen Creative Incubator (McA2) **[45541]**
McAllen Public Library (MPL) **[7431]**
MCBA Newsletter **[1727]**
McCallum & Kudravetz P.C. **[139]**
McCamey Chamber of Commerce **[45272]**
McCarthy Tetrault Library **[18796]**
McCleary Community Chamber of Commerce **[46125]**
McCloud Chamber of Commerce (MCC) **[37019]**
McCook Area Chamber of Commerce [41870]
McCook Chamber of Commerce **[41870]**
McCord Museum of Canadian History **[1001]**
McCormick County Business League [44573]
McCormick County Chamber of Commerce **[44573]**
"McCormick Focuses on Customer, Dealer Service" in Farm Industry News (September 17, 2010) **[17073]**, **[19023]**, **[20467]**
McCreary County Chamber of Commerce **[40070]**
McDaniel Consulting **[45580]**
McDargh Communications **[20550]**
McDonald's Corporation **[14206]**
"McDonald's Finds a Flaw in Ordering Kiosks: No Cash Accepted" in Bloomberg (November 13, 2019) **[10033]**, **[13963]**
"McDonald's Loses Its Sizzle" in Barron's (Vol. 88, March 17, 2008, No. 11, pp. 47) **[6519]**, **[9666]**, **[13964]**, **[21031]**, **[24004]**, **[24388]**
McDonald's Restaurants of Canada Ltd. **[14207]**
McDowell Chamber of Commerce **[43170]**
MCEE: Mecanex/Climatex/Expolectriq/Eclairage (MECANEX) **[12680]**
McFarland Chamber of Commerce **[46452]**
McGehee Area Chamber of Commerce [36480]
McGehee Chamber of Commerce **[36480]**
McGhin's Southern Pit Bar-B-Que **[14208]**
McGill Business Consulting Group (MBCG) **[24253]**
McGill University Department of Civil Engineering and Applied Mechanics - Environmental Engineering Laboratory **[16356]**
McGill University - Desautels Faculty of Management - Desmarais Global Finance Research Centre **[6736]**
McGill University - International Centre for Youth Gambling Problems and High-Risk Behaviors (YGI) **[7341]**
McGill University - McGill Finance Research Centre [6736]
McGraw Hill Education [43002]
McGraw Hill LLC **[43002]**

McGraw-Hill Ventures /McGraw-Hill Capital Corp. [42774]
McGraw Publishing Company [1712]
McGregor Chamber of Commerce and Agriculture [45273]
McGregor/Marquette Chamber of Commerce [39772]
McHenry Area Chamber of Commerce (MACC) [39242]
McKay/Moore Consultants L.L.C. (MM) [4331]
McKinleyville Chamber of Commerce [37020]
McKinney Chamber of Commerce (MCC) [45274]
McKinney Focus [45275]
McKinsey & Company Inc. - Resource Library [2422]
McLean County Chamber of Commerce (MCC) [39243]
McLean Watson Capital Inc. [46794]
McLennan Small Business Development Center (MCCSBDC) [44924]
"MCM Bulks Up by Merging With Maritime Insurer" in Puget Sound Business Journal (Vol. 33, June 1, 2012, No. 6, pp. 1) [8938], [17327], [27304]
McMann & Ransford [2287], [18459]
McMaster University Health Sciences Library (HSL) [1045]
McMinnville Area Chamber of Commerce (GMCC) [43991]
McMinnville - Warren County Chamber of Commerce [44781]
McMullen Valley Chamber of Commerce [36346]
MCNC Research and Development [43245]
MCNC Ventures L.L.C. [43224]
McPherson Chamber of Commerce [39924]
McQueen of Scots [3041]
MCR Capital Advisors Corp. [29014]
McShane Group L.L.C. [2288], [10543], [19141], [20204], [24254], [29015]
McTevia & Associates [31615]
"Md. Bankers Say 'Devil Is In the Details' of New $30B Loan Fund" in Baltimore Business Journal (Vol. 28, October 8, 2010, No. 22) [25019], [28165]
"Md. Banks Beef Up Deposits, But Lending Lags" in Baltimore Business Journal (Vol. 28, October 29, 2010, No. 25, pp. 1) [24005], [28166]
"Md. Faces Daunting Task of Educating Masses About Health Reform Law" in Baltimore Business Journal (Vol. 28, October 15, 2010, No. 23, pp. 1) [8939], [25444], [25865], [27305]
"Md. Housing Leaders Race to Stem Rising Tide of Foreclosures: Neighborhood Watch" in Baltimore Business Journal (Vol. 28, July 23, 2010, No. 11, pp. 1) [11057], [13236], [13508], [25020], [28167]
"Md. Pension System Tries to Recoup $73M from Actuary" in Baltimore Business Journal (Vol. 28, June 11, 2010, No. 5, pp. 1) [17328], [18636], [31692]
MD Tattoo Consulting [15341]
MDA Engineering Inc. [4332]
"Md.'s Boring Bonds Gain Pizzazz as Investors Flock to Debt Issues" in Baltimore Business Journal (Vol. 28, June 11, 2010, No. 5, pp. 1) [4800], [6520], [7132], [9667], [20313]
"Md.'s Film Industry Professionals have to Leave the State to Find Work: Exiting Stage Left" in Baltimore Business Journal (Vol. 28, June 18, 2010, No. 6, pp. 1) [2463], [6194], [15603], [25021], [33390], [34093]
Me-n-Ed's Pizzerias [12566]
Meade Chamber of Commerce (MCC) [39925]
"Meadowbrook To Acquire ProCentury in $272.6 Million Deal" in Crain's Detroit Business (Vol. 24, February 21, 2008, No. 8, pp. 4) [8940], [9668], [18225], [27306], [31413]
Meadowlands Regional Chamber of Commerce (MRCC) [42157]
Meadowlands/USA [42158]
Meadville Area Chamber of Commerce [44260]
Meadville - Western Crawford County Chamber of Commerce [44260]
Mealey's Emerging Insurance Disputes [20591]
"Meals on Wheels; Chicago Puts the Brakes on Upwardly Mobile Food Truck Operators" in Wall Street Journal (August 7, 2012, pp. A12) [3849], [6999], [25445], [30479]
"Meals on Wheels Filling 'Blizzard Bags'" in Tulsa World (November 5, 2011) [6915], [7133]
Means Labor Rates for the Construction Industry [4267]
Measuring Customer Satisfaction [20557]
Measuring and Maximizing Marketing ROI (Onsite) [29596]
Meat Markets Industry in the US - Market Research Report [2433], [7794]
Meat + Poultry: The Business Journal of the Meat & Poultry Industry [2436]
Meat and Poultry: The Business Journal of the Meat and Poultry Industry [17202]
"Mechanic Theatre's Brutalist Style at Battle's Center" in Baltimore Business Journal (Vol. 30, May 11, 2012, No. 1, pp. 1) [769], [904], [4172], [32308]

Mechanical Contractors Association of Akron (MCAA) [43343]
Mechanical Contractors Association of America (MCAA) [459]
Mechanical Contractors Association of Canada (MCAC) [3942]
Mecosta County Area Chamber of Commerce (MCACC) [40972]
"Med-Tech Vet's Trip From Heart to Sleeve" in Business Journal (Vol. 31, February 14, 2014, No. 38, pp. 8) [10838], [26335], [32002], [35359]
Meda Angels, LLC (MA) [45923]
Medema Consulting Associates L.L.C. [29016]
Medford Area Chamber of Commerce [46453]
Medford Chamber of Commerce [40598]
Media & Content Marketing Association (MCMA) [29482]
The Media Guys Inc. [12956]
"Media Measurement Uncertainty - Tracking TV, Social and Digital" in AdAge (March 23, 2023) [15604]
Media, Organizations and Identity [2464], [8664], [11989], [12942], [13038], [15605], [31781], [31880]
Media Technology Ventures [37429]
"Media Terminology" in MarketingMagazine (Vol. 115, September 27, 2010, No. 13, pp. 80) [21917], [29926]
"Mediation Can Help Small Businesses Solve Conflicts and Protect Relationships" in Bloomberg Businessweek (July 10, 2020) [10798]
Mediation for Small Businesses [10799]
"Mediation vs. Arbitration vs. Litigation: The Differences You Need to Know about in Business" in Mediate.com (November, 2019) [10800]
"Medicaid Insurers See Growth in Small Biz Market" in Boston Business Journal (Vol. 31, July 15, 2011, No. 25, pp. 1) [8941], [18226], [20046], [27307], [31414], [34094]
Medical Association of the State of Alabama Annual Meeting [10878]
Medical Business Associates Inc. (MBA) [26088]
Medical Business Consultants Inc. [26089]
Medical Claims Processing Services Industry in the US - Market Research Report [10892]
"Medical Collection Agency Refutes Allegations In AG's Report" in PaymentsSource (May 1, 2012) [4801], [18637], [20314], [25446], [25866]
Medical College of Wisconsin - Center for the Study of Bioethics [30659]
Medical Dental Business Consultants LLC [26090]
Medical Dental Hospital Business Associates Annual Convention [10879]
"Medical-Device Firm Targets a Heart-Valve Market in Flux" in Philadelphia Business Journal (Vol. 33, May 9, 2014, No. 13, pp. 9) [7134], [10839], [10954], [32003]
"Medical Device Makers Brace for Excise Tax" in Memphis Business Journal (Vol. 34, July 20, 2012, No. 14, pp. 1) [10840], [29295], [34840]
Medical Device Manufacturing Industry in the US - Market Research Report [10841]
A Medical Device-to-Market Journey [10866]
Medical Devices, Diagnostics & Instrumentation Reports - The Gray Sheet [10863]
Medical Fitness Association (MFA) [12380]
Medical Imaging Consultants Inc. (MIC) [2289], [10544], [20205], [29017], [30215], [30854], [32067]
Medical Imaging: News, Issues, and Trends in Health Technology Management [10864]
Medical Marijuana Dispensaries in the US in the US - Industry Market Research Report [5032]
Medical Outcomes Management Inc. (MOM) [2290], [10545], [20206], [29018]
"Medical Pot Backers Say Industry Will Survive" in Sacramento Business Journal (Vol. 28, October 14, 2011, No. 33, pp. 1) [5016], [25447], [25867]
Medical Professional Liability Association (MPL) [8874]
Medical Society of Virginia Annual Meeting [10880]
"Medical Supplies Market Size to Hit USD 186 Billion by 2030" in Globe Newswire (November 24, 2021) [10842], [10955]
Medical Supplies Wholesaling Industry in the US - Market Research Report [10957]
Medical-Surgical Manufacturers Association [10817], [10944]
"Medical Tech Jobs Take More Than a Month To Fill" in Austin Business Journal (Vol. 34, July 11, 2014, No. 21, pp. 10) [25868], [26610]
Medical Technology and Practice Patterns Institute (MTPPI) [26128]
"Medicare Fraudsters Turn to Pharmacies" in South Florida Business Journal (Vol. 32, June 15, 2012, No. 47, pp. 1) [5173], [23516], [25448]
"Medicare Plans Step Up Battle for Subscribers" in Sacramento Business Journal (Vol. 28, October 21, 2011, No. 34, pp. 1) [8942], [17329], [25869], [27308]
Medicare & You Handbook [25870]

Medicine Lodge Area Chamber of Commerce (MLACC) [39926]
Medicine Lodge Chamber of Commerce [39926]
"Medicine Men" in Canadian Business (Vol. 80, February 12, 2007, No. 4, pp. 19) [314], [8028], [29927]
Medicine on the Net [9276], [26033]
The Medicine Shoppe Pharmacy [5208]
Medina Area Chamber of Commerce [42645], [43483]
"Medtronic Heading to Foreign Markets" in Memphis Business Journal (Vol. 34, September 28, 2012, No. 24, pp. 1) [10843], [27648], [30762]
Meeker Chamber of Commerce [37886]
"Meet the Class of 2014, In their Own Words" in South Florida Business Journal (Vol. 34, June 27, 2014, No. 49, pp. 18) [22709], [34340], [36028]
"Meet the Dropouts: the Students Who Chose Start-Ups Over College" in Inc. (Vol. 33, September 2011, No. 7, pp. 32) [35360], [36029]
"Meet the Golden 100 List's Youngest Firm: Kavaliro" in Orlando Business Journal (Vol. 29, September 21, 2012, No. 14, pp. 1) [5440], [26336]
"Meet Houston's Top Legal Dealmakers" in Austin Business Journal (Vol. 34, June 27, 2014, No. 19, pp. A15) [9669], [18638], [31415]
"Meet the Maker: Sean Dempsey, Dempsey's Brewery Restaurant & Pub, SD" in Pizza Today (October 24, 2019) [1929], [12531]
"Meet the Money Whisperer to the Super-Rich N.B.A. Elite" in The New York Times (June 6, 2019) [6521], [24006]
"Meet the New Convenience Store" in Supermarket News (August 3, 2018) [4442], [8029], [18227]
"Meet the Next Big Name in Residential Construction" in Houston Business Journal (Vol. 44, February 21, 2014, No. 42, pp. 8) [4173], [13237], [13509], [21578]
"Meet Two of Universal CityWalk's New Restaurateurs" in Orlando Business Journal (Vol. 30, January 10, 2014, No. 29, pp. 3) [13965]
"Meet University of Texas' New Business Mind" in Austin Business Journal (Vol. 31, May 13, 2011, No. 10, pp. A1) [21579], [30924], [32004], [32788], [33391], [35361]
"Meet the White-Label Cash Kings" in Globe & Mail (April 23, 2007, pp. B1) [26337], [34095]
"Meeting and Banquet Venues" in Business Review Albany (Vol. 41, August 8, 2014, No. 20, pp. 6) [2675], [8430], [13966], [15872]
Meeting Planners International [6082]
Meeting Professionals International (MPI) [6082]
Meetings & Conventions [15917], [30142]
Mefford, Knutson & Associates Inc. (MKA) [2291], [10546], [19142], [20207], [24255], [30216], [30855], [33680]
"Megachurch Movie Mogul" in Dallas Business Journal (Vol. 37, June 6, 2014, No. 39, pp. 4) [6195], [22710]
Meigs County Chamber of Commerce (MCCC) [43525]
Meineke Car Care Centers, LLC (MCCC) [14587]
"Melamine Analytical Methods Released" in Feedstuffs (Vol. 80, October 6, 2008, No. 41, pp. 2) [8740], [12209], [14435], [17074], [27649]
Melbourne-Palm Bay Area Chamber of Commerce [38460]
Melbourne Regional Chamber of the East Central Florida [38460]
Mellen Area Chamber of Commerce [46454]
"Melnyk Loses Round in Battle for Hemosol" in Globe & Mail (January 24, 2007, pp. B3) [18639], [31416]
Melrose Area Chamber of Commerce [41267]
Melrose Chamber of Commerce [40599]
Melrose Park Chamber of Commerce and Community Development (MPCCCD) [39244]
The Melting Pot Restaurants [14209]
Melting Pot Restaurants Inc. [14209]
"The Melting Pot Targets Calgary, Canada For Franchise Expansion" in CNW Group (September 9, 2014) [13871], [19548], [24296]
Member Directory (Cosmetics industry) [4517]
Member Directory [36481], [39773], [40399], [40973], [45882]
Member Matters [46455]
Member Services Directory [46611]
Members Buyer's Guide [42636]
Membership and Business Directory [41944]
Membership Directory [37021], [41268], [45276], [45277]
Membership Directory & Buyers' Guide [39245]
Membership Directory and Buyers' Guide [37887]
Membership Directory and Community Guide [41414]
Membership Directory and Community Profile [40400]
Membership Directory and Information Guide [43779]
Membership List [39246]
Memorial University of Newfoundland - Canadian Centre for Fisheries Innovation (CCFI) [6802]

Memorial University of Newfoundland - Fisheries and Marine Institute School of Fisheries - Centre for Aquaculture and Seafood Development (CASD) **[6803]**
"Memphis Area Manufacturing Companies" in Memphis Business Journal (No. 35, March 14, 2014, No. 49, pp. 10) **[29296]**
"Memphis BBQ: It's Just About the Pork" in Women in Business (Vol. 64, Summer 2012, No. 2, pp. 14) **[13967]**, **[44857]**
Memphis Bioworks **[44849]**
Memphis Bioworks Foundation **[44683]**
Memphis Botanic Garden Foundation, Inc. - Goldsmith Civic Garden Center - Sybile Malloy Memorial Library **[7675]**
Memphis Business Journal **[44861]**
Memphis Garrett Founder & CEO Garett Hospitality Group **[14077]**
"Memphis Marriott Downtown Offers Wedding Reception Discounts to Soon-To-Be Newlyweds" in Benzinga.com (June 23, 2011) **[1979]**, **[8431]**
Memphis Minority Business Development Center (MMBC) **[44818]**
"Memphis Pays Healthy Price To Compete for Jobs, Investment" in Memphis Business Journal (Vol. 35, January 3, 2014, No. 39, pp. 4) **[21032]**, **[26611]**, **[34841]**
Memphis Procurement Technical Assistance Center (PTAC) - Center for Industrial Services (CIS) **[44830]**
Memphis Regional Chamber of Commerce [44753]
"Men May Wear the Pants in the Family, But Women Retain the Power of the Purse" in Marketing to Women (Vol. 22, August 2009, No. 8) **[29928]**, **[32209]**
"Men and Menu: A Switch in the Kitchen" in Barron's (Vol. 88, March 24, 2008, No. 12, pp. 17) **[792]**, **[7754]**, **[8030]**, **[29929]**, **[34096]**
The Menagerie LLC **[38145]**
MENC National Association for Music Education [11171]
MENC National In-Service Conference [11200], [11284]
"Menchie's Tops Restaurant Business' Future 50 List" in Ice Cream Reporter (Vol. 23, August 20, 2010, No. 9, pp. 4) **[8577]**, **[13968]**, **[18228]**, **[24389]**
Mendocino Coast Chamber of Commerce [36896]
Mendocino Map and Visitor Information Guide **[37022]**
Mendocino Small Business Development Center **[36579]**
Mendota Area Chamber of Commerce **[39247]**
Menifee Valley Chamber of Commerce **[37023]**
Menil Collection Library **[1002]**
Menlo Park Chamber of Commerce (MPCC) **[37024]**
Menlo Ventures **[37430]**
Mennonite Historians of Eastern Pennsylvania (MHEP) **[7432]**
Menomonie Area Chamber and Visitor Center **[46456]**
Men's Clothing Stores Industry in the US - Market Research Report **[3059]**, **[3157]**
Mentone Chamber of Commerce **[39578]**
Mentor Area Chamber of Commerce (MACC) **[43526]**
Mentor Capital Partners Ltd. **[44445]**
Mequon-Thiensville Area Chamber of Commerce [46457]
Mequon-Thiensville Chamber of Commerce (MTCC) **[46457]**
Mercato Partners **[45664]**
Mercedes Chamber of Commerce (MCC) **[45278]**
Mercer Area Chamber of Commerce **[46458]**
Mercer County Chamber of Commerce (MCCC) **[40071]**
Mercer Island Chamber of Commerce **[46126]**
Mercersburg Area Chamber of Commerce (MACC) **[44261]**
Merchants and Manufacturers Association [34960]
"Mercury (1939-2010)" in Canadian Business (Vol. 83, June 15, 2010, No. 10, pp. 27) **[11419]**, **[29297]**
Mercury Fund **[45459]**
"Mercy Parent Nets Almost $1B in 2011" in Sacramento Business Journal (Vol. 28, September 30, 2011, No. 31, pp. 1) **[7135]**, **[18229]**, **[25022]**, **[25871]**
"Mercyhurst Rolls Out Culinary Cab Food Truck" in Erie Times-News (June 19, 2012) **[3825]**, **[7000]**, **[13872]**, **[21580]**, **[30480]**
Meredith Area Chamber of Commerce **[42009]**
"Merger Expected to Bring New Player to TV Market" in Providence Business News (Vol. 28, March 31, 2014, No. 52, pp. 1) **[2465]**, **[15606]**, **[25449]**, **[31417]**
Mergers and Acquisitions from A to Z **[75]**, **[9670]**, **[16816]**, **[18640]**, **[19680]**, **[31418]**, **[33021]**, **[34842]**
Mergers & Acquisitions for Dummies **[19228]**
Mergers, Acquisitions, and Joint Ventures: A Resource Guide **[19235]**
Meridian Chamber of Commerce **[38929]**
Meridian Technology Center (MTC) **[43889]**
Meridian Technology Center for Business Development Center [43865]
Meridian Technology Center - Center for Business Development **[43865]**
Meritage Funds **[37923]**

Meriwether County Chamber of Commerce (MCCC) **[38762]**
Merkel Chamber of Commerce **[45279]**
"Merkle Lands $75M Private-Equity Investment" in Baltimore Business Journal (Vol. 28, October 15, 2010, No. 23, pp. 1) **[26338]**, **[35362]**
Merle Norman Cosmetics Inc. (MNC) **[4542]**
Merlin 200,000 Mile Shops **[14588]**
MERLIN Mentors [46584]
Merrill Area Chamber of Commerce (MACC) **[46459]**
"Merrill Lynch in Talks to Buy BlackRock Stake" in Globe & Mail (February 13, 2006, pp. B4) **[6522]**, **[24007]**, **[31419]**
Merrillville Chamber of Commerce [39530]
Merrimac Associates Inc. **[24256]**
Merrimack Valley Chamber of Commerce (MVCC) **[40600]**
Merritt & Harris Inc. (MH) **[13619]**
Merry Maids of Canada **[5090]**
Merry Maids L.P. **[5091]**
Mertz Associates Inc. **[31616]**, **[33055]**
Merus Capital **[37748]**
Mesa Chamber of Commerce **[36347]**
Mesa Komal **[44850]**
Mesa Minority/Micro Small Business Development Center (M3SBDC) **[36273]**
Mesa Verde Venture Partners **[37431]**
Mesalands Community College Small Business Development Center **[42281]**
Mesirow Financial Private Equity **[39367]**
Mesquite Chamber of Commerce **[41945]**
Mess Hall **[38180]**
"Message to the Masses" **[21918]**, **[29930]**
"Messaging Apps: What the New Face of Social Media Means for Brands" in New Generation Latino Consortium (December 2010) **[21919]**, **[29931]**, **[30588]**, **[34097]**
Messenger Courier Association of America [10976]
"Messing with Corporate Heads? Psychological Contracts and Leadership Integrity" in Journal of Business Strategy (Vol. 35, May-June 2014, No. 3, pp. 38-46) **[23517]**, **[28722]**
"A Messy Job" in Washington Business Journal (Vol. 33, May 30, 2014, No. 6, pp. 6) **[1238]**, **[1308]**, **[13873]**, **[27209]**
Metal Building Contractors and Erectors Association (MBCEA) **[3943]**
Metal Building Dealers Association [3943]
Metal Building Manufacturers Association (MBMA) **[3944]**
Metal Construction Association (MCA) **[3945]**
Metal Cookware Manufacturers Association [8172]
Metal Cutting Tool Institute [10424]
Metal Framing Manufacturers Association (MFMA) **[3946]**
Metalcon **[10457]**
METALfab **[10458]**
METALFORM Mexico **[10459]**
Metalmorphosis: Serving the Precision Metalforming Industry **[10454]**
Metallurgistes Unis d'Amerique [35162]
"Metamorphosis Makes Family Dollar a Destination" in MMR (Vol. 29, August 20, 2012, No. 13, pp. 8) **[18230]**, **[32210]**
MetaProp **[42903]**
"Methodist Plans Richardson Hospital" in Dallas Business Journal (Vol. 35, June 29, 2012, No. 42, pp. 1) **[4174]**, **[25872]**
Methodist Research Institute (MRI) **[26129]**
"Methodist Sees Dwindling Transplant Organs" in Memphis Business Journal (Vol. 34, June 29, 2012, No. 11, pp. 1) **[25873]**, **[31420]**
"Methods of Distributing a Product" in Chron (Jan. 28, 2019) **[20639]**
Methods Time Measurements Association for Standards and Research [11631]
MetLife, Inc. **[9009]**
Metric Business Associates Inc. **[29019]**
Metro Accounting Services Inc. **[24257]**
Metro Atlanta Chamber of Commerce (MAC) **[38763]**
Metro-East Regional Chamber of Commerce **[39248]**
Metro Guide **[40974]**
Metro Small Business Development Center **[37789]**
Metro South Chamber of Commerce **[40601]**
Metro Technology Centers (MTC) **[43890]**
Metro Tulsa Chamber of Commerce **[43816]**
Metro Vocational Technical School [43890]
Metro Work Space [41095]
Metrocrest Chamber of Commerce **[45280]**
Metroline **[42159]**
MetroNorth Chamber of Commerce (MNC) **[41269]**
Metropolis Area Chamber of Commerce, Tourism and Economic Development [39249]
Metropolis Chamber of Commerce **[39249]**
Metropolitan Business League (MBL) **[45916]**

Metropolitan Detroit Landscaping Association [10079]
Metropolitan Economic Development Association (MEDA) **[41326]**, **[41346]**
Metropolitan Evansville Chamber of Commerce [39638]
Metropolitan Life and Affiliated Companies [9009]
Metropolitan Milwaukee Association of Commerce (MMAC) **[46460]**, **[46555]**
Metropolitan Museum of Art - Irene Lewisohn Costume Reference Library **[3075]**, **[4565]**
Metropolitan Venture Partners L.L.C. (MetVP) **[42775]**
Metropolitan Washington Council of Governments (COG) **[47427]**
MetroWest Chamber of Commerce **[40602]**
Metter-Candler Chamber of Commerce **[38764]**
Metuchen Area Chamber of Commerce **[42160]**
Mexia Area Chamber of Commerce **[45281]**
Mexicali Rosa's **[14210]**
Mexico Area Chamber of Commerce (MACC) **[41593]**
"MFG Wind Launched at AWEA WindPower 2012 Conference and Exhibition" in Marketing Weekly News (June 23, 2012, pp. 169) **[5664]**, **[5931]**, **[23295]**, **[30763]**
MFM Annual conference **[2473]**, **[35125]**
MFM Conference [2473], [35125]
MFServices **[46848]**
MGCCI It's Your Business **[39250]**
MGIA Trade Show & Convention [23443]
"MGM Resorts Leads U.S. Travel Sector with Job Cuts So Far in 2019" in Skift (October 4 2019) **[8432]**
MHS Capital **[37432]**
mHUB **[39415]**
Mi Kitchen es su Kitchen **[42904]**
MIAAA Mid-Winter Conference [15211], [35127]
Miami Area Chamber of Commerce **[43780]**
Miami Beach Chamber Business Directory **[38461]**
Miami Beach Chamber of Commerce **[38462]**
Miami County Chamber of Commerce (MCCC) **[39579]**
Miami-Dade County Chamber of Commerce (MDCC) **[38463]**
Miami Hospitality Suppliers Expo **[8490]**
Miami International Boat Show **[10622]**, [10623]
Miami Subs Grill **[4909]**
Miami University - Southwest Ohio Regional Depository (SWORD) **[758]**
Miami University - Walter Havighurst Special Collections Library **[8165]**
Miami Valley Venture Association (MVVA) **[36551]**
Miami Yacht Show **[10623]**
"Michael Daszkal On Going Beyond the Role of CPA" in South Florida Business Journal (Vol. 34, April 25, 2014, No. 40) **[76]**, **[16817]**, **[18231]**
Michael Edmond Gray **[41709]**
Michael S. Kenny & Company LLC **[37433]**, **[37679]**
"Michaud Touts Small-Business Credentials" in Bangor Daily News (September 10, 2010) **[25023]**, **[34098]**, **[34843]**
MichBusiness **[33471]**
Michelle Politano Chef/Owner of Pianta **[14078]**
Michel's Bakery Cafe **[1300]**
Michiana Business **[39666]**
Michigan Accelerator Fund 1 (MAF-1) **[41050]**
Michigan Agri Business Association (MABA) **[40800]**
Michigan Agri-Business Association Outlook Conference **[17172]**
Michigan Agri-Dealers Association [40800]
Michigan Alternative & Renewable Energy Center (MAREC) **[41101]**
Michigan Angel Fund (MAF) **[41051]**
Michigan Association of Calligraphers (MAC) **[2477]**
Michigan Association of Certified Public Accountants (MICPA) **[16740]**
Michigan Association for Computer Users in Learning Conference **[3560]**, **[21689]**, **[35126]**
Michigan Association of Convenience Stores (MACS) **[40801]**
Michigan Association for Female Entrepreneurs (MAFE) **[35627]**
Michigan Association of Insurance Agents [27220]
Michigan Association of Private Campground Owners [2506]
Michigan Bean Commission (MBC) **[16941]**
Michigan Beef Industry Commission (MBIC) **[16942]**
Michigan Beekeepers Association (MBA) **[1443]**
Michigan Biotechnology Institute (MBI) **[41102]**
Michigan Blueberry Growers Association [16940]
Michigan Business Brokers Association (MBBA) **[2135]**
Michigan Business Incubator Association (MBIA) **[33514]**
Michigan Business Innovation Asssociation (MBIA) **[40802]**
Michigan Business and Professional Association [33471]
Michigan Business Travel Association (MBTA) **[40803]**
Michigan CFO Associates Inc. **[27150]**
Michigan Chamber of Commerce (MCC) **[40975]**

Michigan Charter Boat Association (MCBA) **[2827]**
Michigan City Area Chamber of Commerce **[39580]**
Michigan Construction Design Tradeshow **[4298]**
Michigan Corn Growers Association (MCGA) **[16943]**
Michigan Department of Environmental Quality - Office of Waste Management and Radiological Protection (OWMRP) **[46998]**
Michigan Distributors and Vendors Association (MDVA) **[7713]**
Michigan Economic Development Corp. (MEDC) **[40820]**, **[41034]**
Michigan Economic Development Corp. - Office of Women Business Owners Services **[41035]**
Michigan Emu Growers Association (MEGA) **[638]**, **[16944]**, **[40804]**
Michigan Family Forum (MFF) **[26130]**
Michigan Federation of Business and Professional Women's Clubs (BPW/MI) **[35628]**
"Michigan Governor: Drivers to See More Savings Under Auto Insurance Reform Law" in Insurance Journal (November 16, 2021) **[8943]**, **[27309]**, **[41133]**
Michigan Grain and Agri-Dealers Association [40800]
Michigan Grain Dealers Association [40800]
Michigan & Great Lakes Food Service Show [8114], [14092], [35128]
Michigan Green Industry Association (MGIA) **[10079]**
Michigan Green Industry Association Trade Show **[23443]**
Michigan Grocers Association Annual Convention and Trade Show **[7813]**
Michigan International Trade Authority, Michigan Department of Commerce [40820], [41034]
Michigan Interscholastic Athletic Administrators Mid-Winter Conference **[15211]**, **[35127]**
Michigan Jobs Commission [40820], [41034]
Michigan Life Science and Innovation Center (MLSIC) **[41103]**
Michigan Mason Contractors Association (MMCA) **[3947]**
"Michigan Means Growth: Sustaining Growth Through Thick and Thin: Michigan Companies Sustain Growth with Well-Timed Access to Capital" in Inc. (Vol. 36, September 2014, No. 7, pp. 164) **[21033]**, **[22711]**, **[25024]**, **[26612]**, **[28168]**, **[35363]**
Michigan Milk Producers Association (MMPA) **[16945]**
Michigan Minority Supplier Development Council (MMSDC) **[41036]**
Michigan Molecular Institute and Impact Analytical **[41104]**
Michigan Plumbing and Mechanical Contractors Association (MPMCA) **[40805]**
Michigan Procurement Technical Assistance Center (PTAC) **[41062]**
Michigan Procurement Technical Assistance Center (BDC) - Business Development Center **[41063]**
Michigan Procurement Technical Assistance Center (DCC) - Downriver Community Conference **[41064]**
Michigan Procurement Technical Assistance Center (NMC) - Northeast Michigan Consortium **[41065]**
Michigan Procurement Technical Assistance Center of Saginaw Future Satellite Office **[41066]**
Michigan Procurement Technical Assistance Center - West Central Michigan Employment & Training Consortium **[41067]**
Michigan Produce Haulers Inc. (MPH) **[16055]**
Michigan Realtors (MR) **[13096]**
Michigan Restaurant Association [8351], [13882]
Michigan Restaurant & Lodging Association (MRLA) **[8351]**, **[13882]**
Michigan Restaurant Show **[8114]**, **[14092]**, **[35128]**
Michigan Retailers Association (MRA) **[32081]**
Michigan Sheep Breeders Association [16946]
Michigan Sheep Producers Association (MSBA) **[16946]**
Michigan Shoe Market **[14694]**, **[32353]**
Michigan Small Business Development Center [29475], [41033]
Michigan Small Business Development Center Capital Region **[40809]**
Michigan Small Business Development Center Great Lakes Bay Region **[40810]**
Michigan Small Business Development Center Greater Washtenaw Region (SBDC) **[40811]**
Michigan Small Business Development Center I-69 Trade Corridor **[40812]**
Michigan Small Business Development Center Mid Michigan Region **[40813]**
Michigan Small Business Development Center Northwest Michigan Region **[40814]**
Michigan Small Business Development Center Southeast Michigan Region **[40815]**
Michigan Small Business Development Center Southwest Michigan Region **[40816]**
Michigan Small Business Development Center West Michigan Region **[40817]**
Michigan Small Business and Technology Development Center - Lead Center **[40818]**
Michigan Small Business and Technology Development Center - Region [40817]
Michigan Small Business and Technology Development Center - Region 2 [40814]
Michigan Small Business and Technology Development Center - Region 4 [40813]
Michigan Small Business and Technology Development Center - Region 5 [40810]
Michigan Small Business and Technology Development Center - Region 6 [40812]
Michigan Small Business and Technology Development Center - Region 8 [40809]
Michigan Small Business and Technology Development Center - Region 9 [40815]
Michigan Small Business and Technology Development Center - Region 11 [40816]
Michigan Small Business and Technology Development Center - Region 12 [40811]
Michigan Society of Professional Surveyors Annual Meeting **[15231]**
Michigan Soybean Association (MSA) **[16947]**
Michigan State University (MSU) - Horse Teaching and Research Center **[8338]**
Michigan State University Institute for Food Laws and Regulations (MSU IFLR) **[41105]**
Michigan State University - Institute for Public Policy and Social Research (IPPSR) **[34236]**
Michigan State University Product Center **[41106]**
Michigan State University - Software Engineering and Network Systems Laboratory (SENS) **[3568]**
Michigan State University - Special Collections Division - Russel B. Nye Popular Culture Collection **[3276]**
Michigan State University - Special Collections Library **[1505]**
Michigan Tech Enterprise SmartZone (MTEC) **[41107]**
Michigan Tooling Association [10423]
Michigan Trucking Association (MTA) **[16056]**
Michigan Vegetable Council **[16948]**
Michigan Venture Capital Association (MVCA) **[40806]**
Michigan Venture Fund (VMF) **[41052]**
Michigan West Coast Chamber of Commerce **[40976]**
Michigan Works Association (MWA) **[5435]**
Micro Businesses Board of Trade [30312]
Micro Enterprise Services of Oregon (MESO) **[43921]**
"Micro-Finance Agencies and SMEs: Model of Explication of Tacit Knowledge" in International Journal of Entrepreneurship and Small Business (Vol. 11, August 3, 2010) **[21034]**, **[24008]**, **[27650]**, **[28169]**, **[31421]**
Micro-Macro International Inc. (MMI) **[17198]**
"Microbrewery Aims Big with New Facility" in Business Journal (Vol. 31, May 9, 2014, No. 50, pp. 6) **[1930]**, **[19549]**
MicroBusiness Enterprise Center **[38837]**
"Microeconomic Methods: A Simple Introduction" **[21035]**
Microfranchising: Creating Wealth at the Bottom of the Pyramid **[22712]**, **[24297]**, **[34341]**
"Microlending Seen as Having a Major Impact" in Business Journal Serving Greater Tampa Bay (Vol. 30, November 26, 2010, No. 49, pp. 1) **[25025]**, **[28170]**, **[30925]**
Microprocessor Report **[3440]**, **[3581]**, **[3750]**, **[3776]**
Microscopy Research and Technique (MRT) **[32902]**
Microscopy Society of America Microscopy & Microanalysis Meeting **[32924]**
Microsoft Access 2003: A Comprehensive Hands-On Introduction - Building a Foundation for Client/Server Database Applications (Onsite) **[21402]**
Microsoft Access 2007: A Comprehensive Hands-On Introduction (Onsite) **[21403]**
Microsoft Access: A 2-Day Hands-On Workshop **[33803]**
Microsoft® Access® - Database Design, Queries and Reports [33803]
Microsoft Excel **[33804]**
Microsoft Excel 2007 - I (Onsite) **[21404]**
Microsoft Excel 2007 - II (Onsite) **[33805]**
Microsoft FrontPage (Onsite) **[21405]**
"Microsoft Goes Macrosoft" in Barron's (Vol. 89, July 27, 2009, No. 30, pp. 25) **[9671]**, **[14797]**, **[26339]**, **[33871]**, **[35364]**
Microsoft Office **[21406]**
"Microsoft Partners With Good Technology to Provide Enterprise-Class Security for Business Customers on Windows Phone Devices" in Benzinga.com (February 27, 2012) **[2762]**, **[14436]**, **[31422]**
Microsoft PowerPoint 2007/2010 **[33806]**
Microsoft Project 2007 - I (Onsite) **[21407]**
Microsoft Project 2007 - II (Onsite) **[33807]**
Microsoft Project: Managing Multiple and Complex Projects (Onsite) **[21408]**
"Microsoft Releases Office Security Updates" in Mac World (Vol. 27, November 2010, No. 11, pp. 66) **[3721]**, **[14437]**, **[14798]**, **[21920]**, **[33872]**
Microsoft SharePoint I - Using SharePoint (Onsite) **[33808]**
Microsoft SharePoint II - Building SharePoint Sites (Onsite) **[33809]**
Microsoft SharePoint III - Installing and Working With SharePoint Server (Onsite) **[33810]**
"Microsoft's Big Gamble" in Canadian Business (Vol. 81, March 3, 2008, No. 3, pp. 13) **[6523]**, **[9182]**, **[9672]**, **[19024]**, **[19550]**, **[24009]**, **[26340]**, **[31423]**
"Microsoft's Diversity Program Clicks into High Speed" in Hispanic Business (Vol. 30, July-August 2008, No. 7-8, pp. 54) **[14799]**, **[19551]**, **[26341]**, **[26613]**, **[28723]**, **[29932]**, **[30764]**, **[31782]**, **[33202]**, **[33873]**
Microspot Interiors **[9070]**
"MicroTech Is Fastest Growing Private Company in Washington Area on Deloitte Technology Fast 500" in Hispanic Business (July-August 2009, pp. 20, 22) **[18232]**, **[26342]**, **[30366]**
Microtel Inns and Suites Franchising, Inc. **[8507]**
MicroVentures **[45460]**
"MicroVentures: New Crowdfunding Game Makes Startups the Stars, Prepares Players for a New Kind of Investing" in Health & Beauty Close-Up (July 31, 2012) **[22966]**, **[28067]**, **[30896]**, **[35242]**
Mid-America Science Park (MASP) **[39644]**
Mid-America Technology Center **[43834]**, **[43891]**
Mid-Atlantic Bio Angels (MABA) **[35291]**, **[42776]**
Mid-Atlantic Business Brokers Association (MABBA) **[2136]**
Mid-Atlantic Venture Association (MAVA) **[38152]**
Mid-Columbia Tri-Cities SCORE **[46024]**
Mid-Florida SCORE **[38258]**
Mid-Hudson Small Business Development Center **[42404]**
Mid-Maine Chamber of Commerce **[40292]**
Mid Michigan Community College (MMCC) **[41128]**
Mid-Missouri SCORE **[41498]**
Mid-Ohio Valley Regional Council (MOVRC) **[46296]**
Mid-Shore SCORE **[40352]**
Mid South Area Business Travel Association (MSA-BTA) **[19305]**, **[44684]**
Mid-South Farm & Gin Show **[17173]**
The Mid-South Minority Business Council Continuum and/or The MMBC Continuum **[44851]**
Mid-South Region PTAC - Howell County Extension Center - University of Missouri [41668]
Mid-States Minority Supplier Development Council **[39626]**
Mid-West Truck & Trailer Show **[16107]**
Mid-West Truckers Association Inc. (MTA) **[16057]**
Midas Inc. **[14589]**
Midcoast Regional Redevelopment Authority (MRRA) **[40323]**
Middle Department Inspection Agency, Inc. (MDIA) **[2026]**
Middle Township Chamber of Commerce (MTCC) **[42161]**
Middlefield Capital Corp. **[46795]**
Middlefield Chamber of Commerce **[43527]**
Middleport Chamber of Commerce [43525]
Middlesex County Chamber of Commerce **[38059]**
Middlesex County Regional Chamber of Commerce (MCRCC) **[42162]**
Middlesex West Chamber of Commerce (MWCOC) **[40603]**
Middleton Chamber of Commerce (MCC) **[46461]**
Middletown Area Chamber of Commerce [42164]
Midland Area Chamber of Commerce (MACC) **[40977]**
Midland Business Alliance Foundation (MBA) **[40821]**
Midland Chamber of Commerce **[45282]**
Midland Hispanic Chamber of Commerce (MHCC) **[45283]**
Midland Tomorrow [40821]
Midland Tomorrow Innovation Center (MMIC) **[41108]**
Midlands Technical College Business Accelerator **[44608]**
Midlothian Chamber of Commerce (MCC) **[45284]**
MidMichigan Innovation Center [41108]
Midsouth Indemnity Association and Asian American Hotel Owners Association [8342]
Midstate Chamber of Commerce (MCC) **[38060]**
Midtown Manhattan Small Business Development Center at Baruch College **[42405]**
Midvale Area Chamber of Commerce **[45639]**
Midwest Automatic Laundry and Cleaning Council [5225]
Midwest Business Brokers and Intermediaries (MBBI) **[2137]**, **[38976]**
Midwest Center for Law & Justice **[41680]**
Midwest City Chamber of Commerce **[43781]**
Midwest Cleaning and Restoration Association (MCRA) **[2968]**
Midwest Computer Group L.L.C. (MCG) **[140]**, **[2292]**, **[10547]**, **[12957]**, **[20208]**
Midwest Construction Showcase [4296]

Small Business Sourcebook • 42nd Edition 3287

Midwest **Master Index**

"Midwest Drought Hurts Agriculture in California" in Sacramento Business Journal (Vol. 29, August 24, 2012, No. 26, pp. 1) **[17075]**
Midwest Feed Manufacturers Association [16925]
Midwest Minority Supplier Development Council (MMSDC) **[30275]**, **[41327]**
Midwest Moxie: Autonomous Drones and Video Interviewing: Danny Ellis and Kurt Heikkinen **[34632]**
Midwest Moxie: Coffee Meetings and Phishing Attacks: Taralinda Willis and Norman Sadeh **[22907]**
Midwest Moxie: Computer Engineering and Biological Products: Nancy Benovich Gilby and Katie Thompson **[16671]**
Midwest Moxie: Curious Robots and Inventory Management: Sankalp Arora **[34633]**
Midwest Moxie: Grain Elevators and Specialty Meds: Jake Joraanstad and Julia Regan **[22908]**
Midwest Moxie: Helping Workplace Resources Find Their Next Use: Garry Cooper **[23434]**
Midwest Moxie: Nuclear Fusion and the Era of Abundant Energy: Greg Piefer **[22909]**
Midwest Moxie: Pea Protein and Novel Battery Materials: Nicole Atchison and Francis Wang **[23435]**
Midwest Moxie: Protecting the Wellbeing of Youth Athletes: Tyrre Burks **[22910]**
Midwest Moxie: Providing Virtual, Pediatric Mental Health Service: Monika Roots **[26059]**
Midwest Moxie: Redefining Flavor and Live Event Streaming: Matt Rubin and Gordon Daily **[22911]**
Midwest Musicians Hotline [11279], [11316]
Midwest Organic and Sustainable Education Service Organic Farming Conference **[17174]**
Midwest Organization Development Network [29060]
Midwest Research Institute (MRI) **[2293]**, **[20209]**, **[32072]**, **[32932]**
Midwest Ski Representatives Association [14729]
Midwest Venture Alliance (MVA) **[39984]**
Midwest Winter Ski Representative Association [14729]
Midwest Winter Sports Representatives Association **[15121]**
Midwest Winter Sports Reps Association (MWSRA) **[14729]**
Midwestern Advertising Agency Network [223], [31836]
Midwestern Representatives [32355]
Midwestern State University Small Business Development Center (MSU SBDC) **[44925]**
Mifflin County Industrial Development Corp. (MCIDC) **[33515]**, **[44409]**
Mighty Capital **[37749]**
Mighty Distributing System of America Inc. **[14590]**
Migrating to Structured Authoring in Adobe Framemaker (Onsite) **[33811]**
Mikes Restaurants Inc. **[4910]**
Mila Capital **[37598]**
Milaca Area Chamber of Commerce **[41270]**
Milan Area Chamber of Commerce **[40978]**
Milbank Area Chamber of Commerce **[44653]**
"Mileage Reimbursement: What You Need to Know" in Business News Daily (March 8, 2023) **[16078]**, **[16578]**
MileMaker **[7061]**
Miles City Area Chamber of Commerce **[41782]**
Milestone Venture Partners L.L.C. [42710]
Milex Complete Auto Care **[14591]**
Milford Area Chamber of Commerce (MACC) **[40604]**
Milford Area Historical Society (GMAHS) **[7433]**
Milford Miami Township Chamber of Commerce (MMTCC) **[43528]**
Milford Regional Chamber of Commerce **[38061]**
"Military Brides Can Get Free Wedding Gowns" in Virginian-Pilot (November 10, 2010) **[1980]**, **[3042]**, **[3132]**, **[34342]**
"Military Vet Uses SBA Program to Help Fund His Business" in Philadelphia Business Journal (Vol. 33, May 9, 2014, No. 13, pp. 6) **[11891]**, **[23579]**, **[24931]**, **[28068]**
The Mill **[43674]**
Mill Valley Business Directory **[37025]**
Mill Valley Chamber of Commerce (MVCC) **[37026]**
Millbrae Chamber of Commerce (MCC) **[37027]**
Millburn-Short Hills Chamber of Commerce **[42163]**
Millcreek Community Hospital/LECOM Medical Library **[11544]**
Milledgeville-Baldwin County Chamber of Commerce **[38765]**
Millenium Technology Value Partners (MTVLP) **[43013]**
"Millennial Money: How Young Investors Can Build a Fortune" **[6524]**, **[9673]**, **[24010]**
"Millennial Spending Influences County Budget" in Puget Sound Business Journal (Vol. 35, September 26, 2014, No. 23, pp. 6) **[21036]**, **[24011]**, **[34844]**
"Millennials Are Ready for Crafting, but Is the $36B Crafting Industry Ready for Them?" in Forbes **[4599]**
"Millennials Driving New Types of Space" in Philadelphia Business Journal (Vol. 33, April 25, 2014, No. 11, pp. 8) **[11640]**, **[34099]**
"Millennials: The Great White Hope for Wine Industry" in Advertising Age (Vol. 81, December 6, 2010, No. 43, pp. 2) **[15019]**, **[18233]**
Millennium Hanson **[37434]**
Miller Business Innovation Center (MBIC) **[45681]**
Miller Business Resource Center (MBRC) **[45682]**
Miller Campus Salt Lake Community College Procurement Technical Assistance Center **[45670]**
Miller Capital Corp. **[36384]**
Miller Center for Social Entrepreneurship **[37599]**
Miller/Cook & Associates Inc. **[24258]**, **[29020]**
Miller, Leiby & Associates P.C. **[2294]**, **[10548]**, **[17810]**, **[20210]**, **[22323]**, **[29021]**, **[32068]**, **[33681]**
Miller Thomson L.L.P. **[18797]**
"MillerCoors Needs the Quickie Mart" in Crain's Chicago Business (Vol. 32, November 16, 2009, No. 46, pp. 2) **[4443]**, **[10332]**, **[29933]**
"Miller's Crossroad" in Canadian Business (Vol. 83, September 14, 2010, No. 15, pp. 58) **[4398]**, **[10665]**, **[19895]**, **[26343]**, **[28005]**, **[28724]**
Millers' National Federation [16962]
Milling & Baking News **[1215]**, **[1277]**
Millington Area Chamber of Commerce [44782]
Millington Chamber of Commerce **[44782]**
Millinocket Chamber of Commerce [40286]
"Millions in Grant Funding Available to Help Businesses with Employee Training, Storefront Improvements" in Small Business Trends(January 5, 2023) **[47976]**
"Millions of Senior Citizens Swindled by Financial Fraud" in Black Enterprise (Vol. 41, September 2010, No. 2, pp. 24) **[18641]**, **[23518]**, **[24012]**
Mills College - F.W. Olin Library - Special Collections **[1732]**
Mills County Chamber of Commerce (MCCOC) **[45285]**
Millville Chamber of Commerce [42132]
Millwork Cost Bureau [2630]
Milpitas Chamber of Commerce **[37028]**
Milton S. Eisenhower Foundation **[30276]**
Milwaukee Area Technical College - Rasche Memorial Library **[3369]**
Milwaukee Art Museum - George Peckham Miller Art Research Library **[3370]**
Milwaukee County Research Park - Technology Innovation Center (TIC) **[46567]**
Milwaukee Institute of Art & Design Library (MIAD Library) **[3371]**
Minden Chamber of Commerce (MCC) **[41871]**
Minden-south Webster Chamber Of Commerce [40171]
Mindfully Creating Products that People Really Want with Varshil Patel **[34435]**
Minding Her Own Business, 4th Ed. **[77]**, **[16818]**, **[24013]**, **[34845]**, **[35820]**
Minding Your Dog Business: A Practical Guide to Business Success for Dog Professionals **[12132]**, **[12146]**, **[12210]**, **[12257]**
Mindset, Curiosity, and Coaching Yourself with Antonia Bowring **[20143]**
"Mine Woes Could Rouse Zinc" in Barron's (Vol. 88, July 7, 2008, No. 27, pp. M12) **[6525]**, **[9674]**, **[21037]**, **[24014]**, **[27651]**
Mineola Chamber of Commerce **[42637]**
Mineral County Chamber of Commerce **[41946]**, **[46280]**
Mineral County Chamber of Commerce (MCCC) **[41783]**
Mineral Insulation Manufacturers Association [8848]
Mineral Point Chamber of Commerce (MPCCMS) **[46462]**
Mineral Wells Area Chamber of Commerce **[45286]**
Minerva Area Chamber of Commerce (MACOC) **[43529]**
Mini-Cassia Chamber of Commerce **[38930]**
Mini Maid **[5092]**
Mini Melts Inc. **[8629]**
"Mini Melts Offers 'Win an Ice Cream Business' Contest" in Ice Cream Reporter (Vol. 23, October 20, 2010, No. 11, pp. 3) **[8578]**, **[29934]**
"Mining Goldman for Insight" in Barron's (Vol. 89, July 20, 2009, No. 29, pp. M8) **[6526]**, **[9675]**, **[24015]**
Minneapolis Area Chamber of Commerce **[39927]**
Minneapolis College of Art and Design Library (MCAD) **[3372]**, **[4566]**
Minneapolis Regional Chamber of Commerce **[41271]**
Minneapolis-Saint Paul Business Journal **[41364]**
"Minnesota ABC Event Looks at Government Contracting" in Finance and Commerce Daily Newspaper (November 23, 2010) **[4175]**, **[15873]**, **[25026]**, **[35068]**
Minnesota Airport Directory & Travel Guide **[429]**
Minnesota Association of Realtors (MNAR) **[13097]**
Minnesota Beer Wholesalers Association (MBWA) **[35485]**
Minnesota Business and Professional Women, Inc. (MFBPW) **[35629]**
Minnesota Business and Professional Women's Club [35629]
Minnesota Business Women [35629]
Minnesota Chamber of Commerce **[41272]**
Minnesota Department of Administration - Minnesota State Demographic Center **[47428]**
Minnesota Department of Education - Minnesota Resource Center for the Blind and Visually Impaired **[47429]**
Minnesota Department of Employment and Economic Development (MDEED) **[41162]**
Minnesota Department of Employment and Economic Development - Business and Community Development Div. (BCD) **[41163]**
Minnesota Department of Employment and Economic Development (DEED) - Minnesota Trade Office **[41164]**
Minnesota Department of Labor and Industry - Research and Statistics Unit **[18468]**
Minnesota Federation of Business and Professional Women's Clubs, Inc. [35629]
Minnesota Labor and Industry Department - Policy Development, Research and Statistics Unit [18468]
Minnesota Labor and Industry Department - Research and Statistics Office [18468]
Minnesota Minority Supplier Development Council [30275], [41327]
Minnesota Procurement Technical Assistance Center [41345]
Minnesota State Community and Technical College - Detroit Lakes **[41359]**
Minnesota State Community and Technical College - Fergus Falls **[41360]**
"Minnesota State Fair Vendors Accept Big Risks for Big Rewards" in Business Journal (Vol. 32, August 22, 2014, No. 13, pp. 10) **[1343]**, **[3850]**, **[10034]**, **[19896]**, **[23637]**
Minnesota West Community and Technical College (MWCTC) **[41361]**
Minocqua Area Chamber of Commerce (MACC) **[46463]**
"Minor-League Baseball's Sliders Plan Stock Offering" in Crain's Detroit Business (Vol. 25, June 15, 2009, No. 24, pp. 3) **[4176]**, **[9676]**, **[15169]**, **[31424]**
"Minority Auto Suppliers Get Help Diversifying" in Crain's Detroit Business (Vol. 26, January 11, 2010, No. 2, pp. 3) **[20640]**, **[25027]**, **[29298]**, **[30367]**, **[33585]**
Minority Business Entrepreneur **[8823]**, **[30414]**
Minority Cannabis Business Association (MCBA) **[4974]**, **[30277]**
Minority Chamber of Commerce **[30312]**
Minority Christian Women Entrepreneurs Network (MCWEN) **[30278]**
"Minority Entrepreneurs Must Make Growth a Priority" in Crain's Chicago Business (November 12, 2021) **[30368]**, **[33586]**
Minority & Multicultural Business News **[30440]**
Minority and Small Business Alliance of Southern Arizona (MSBASA) **[36264]**
Minority Supplier Development Council of PA-NJ-DE (MSDC PA-NJ-DE) **[44327]**
Minority Vendor Information Service [30298]
Minority Women Entrepreneurs: How Outsider Status Can Lead to Better Business Practices **[22713]**, **[30369]**, **[35821]**
Minuteman Press International Inc. **[12778]**
"MIR Growing With Help From Former Pfizer Workers" in Crain's Detroit Business (Vol. 24, January 28, 2008, No. 4, pp. 33) **[18234]**, **[30765]**, **[32005]**, **[32789]**
Miracle Ear **[8137]**
Miracle Method Surface Refinishing (MMSR) **[8191]**
Miramar Digital Ventures (MDV) **[37435]**
Miramar Pembroke Pines Regional Chamber of Commerce **[38464]**
The Mirror Test: Is Your Business Really Breathing? **[2196]**, **[10486]**, **[18235]**, **[20114]**, **[28725]**
Mishicot Area Growth and Improvement Committee (MAGIC) **[46464]**
Mishicot Newsletter **[46465]**
"Mismanaging Pay and Performance" in Business Strategy Review (Vol. 21, Summer 2010, No. 2, pp. 54) **[19747]**, **[26997]**, **[28726]**
"Miss Manners Minds Your Business" **[26998]**, **[28727]**
Missaukee Area Chamber of Commerce **[40979]**
"Missing Ingredients In Cause-Related Advertising: The Right Formula of Execution Style and Cause Framing" in International Journal of Advertising (Vol. 31, May 2012, No. 2, pp. 231) **[315]**, **[10666]**, **[29935]**
"The Missing Piece" in Washington Business Journal (Vol. 33, April 25, 2014, No. 1, pp. 6) **[8433]**, **[15874]**, **[35069]**
Mission Area Chamber of Commerce [39936]
"Mission to China" in Canadian Business (Vol. 81, December 8, 2008, No. 21, pp. 28) **[8741]**, **[27652]**
Mission Mountain Food Enterprise Center (LCCDC) **[41808]**
Mission Ventures **[37436]**

3288 **Small Business Sourcebook • 42nd Edition**

Mississippi Development Authority - Mississippi Procurement Technical Assistance Program (MPTAP) [41439]
Mississippi Action for Community Education, Inc. (MACE) [41451]
Mississippi Association of Realtors (MAR) [13098]
Mississippi Bar Business Law Section [18478]
Mississippi Business Incubation Association [33472]
Mississippi Business Journal [41458]
Mississippi Contract Procurement Technical Assistance Center - East Central Satellite [41440]
Mississippi Contract Procurement Technical Center, Inc. - Central Mississippi Procurement Center, Inc. (CMPC) [41441]
"Mississippi County Left Without Pharmacy after Chain Closes" in U.S. News & World Report (October 28, 2019) [5174]
Mississippi Department of Economic and Community Development [41378], [47513]
Mississippi Development Authority (MSD) - Minority and Small Business Development Div. [41436]
Mississippi Development Authority - Mississippi Contract Procurement Center Inc. [41442]
Mississippi Enterprise for Technology (MSET) - Mississippi Technology Transfer Office [41376], [41452]
Mississippi Gulf Coast Chamber of Commerce, Inc. [41415]
Mississippi Lumber Manufacturers Association Convention and Trade Show [10407]
Mississippi Market Wholesale Show [32354]
Mississippi Minority Business Enterprise Center [41437]
Mississippi Procurement Technical Assistance Program (MPTAP) - Delta Contract Procurement Center (DCPC) [41443]
Mississippi Procurement Technical Assistance Program - Mississippi Development Authority - Minority and Small Business Development Div. (MSBDD) (MSBDD) [41444]
Mississippi State University - Agricultural & Forestry Experiment Station - Delta Research and Extension Center (DREC) [17215]
Mississippi State University - Carl Small Town Center (CSTC) [958]
Mississippi State University - Center for Entrepreneurship [41453]
Mississippi State University Small Business Development Center (MSUSBDC) [41373]
Mississippi Technology Alliance [41447]
Mississippi University for Women Career Services [41377]
Missoula Area Chamber of Commerce [41784]
Missoula Area Chamber of Commerce and Convention and Visitors' Bureau [41784]
Missoula SCORE [41739]
Missoula Small Business Development Center [41724]
Missouri Agribusiness Association (MO-AG) [16949], [41466]
Missouri Botanical Garden Library [7676]
Missouri Business Development Program [41495]
Missouri Chamber of Commerce [41594]
Missouri Chamber of Commerce and Industry (MCCI) [41594]
Missouri Department of Economic Development (DED) [41699]
Missouri Department of Economic Development - Division of Business and Community Services [41496]
Missouri Department of Transportation-Division of Materials Library [1178], [5115], [10295], [15531]
Missouri Economic Development Council (MEDC) [41467]
Missouri Enterprise [41681]
Missouri Historical Society Archives - Architecture Collection. [4365]
Missouri History Museum Architecture Collection [4365]
Missouri Innovation Center (MIC) [41682]
Missouri Municipal Review [31707]
Missouri Procurement Technical Assistance Center (MO PTAC) [41664]
Missouri Procurement Technical Assistance Center Center for Entrepreneurship and Outreach [41665]
Missouri Rural Enterprise and Innovation Center (MREIC) [41683]
Missouri Small Business Development Center - Lead Office [41486]
Missouri Small Business Development Centers - Northwest Region [41489]
Missouri Small Business Development Centers - St. Joseph [41490]
Missouri Small Business and Technology Development Center Audrain County [41471]
Missouri Small Business and Technology Development Center Barton County [41472]
Missouri Small Business and Technology Development Center Camden County [41473]

Missouri Small Business and Technology Development Center Cape Girardeau County [41474]
Missouri Small Business and Technology Development Center Cole County [41475]
Missouri Small Business and Technology Development Center - Holt County [41476]
Missouri Small Business and Technology Development Center Howell County [41477]
Missouri Small Business and Technology Development Center Macon County [41478]
Missouri Small Business and Technology Development Center Madison County [41479]
Missouri Small Business and Technology Development Center Monroe County [41480]
Missouri Small Business and Technology Development Center MSU West Plains [41481]
Missouri Small Business and Technology Development Center Phelps County [41482]
Missouri Small Business and Technology Development Center St. Charles [41483]
Missouri Small Business and Technology Development Center Taney County [41484]
Missouri Small Business and Technology Development Center University of Missouri, Columbia [41485]
Missouri Small Business and Technology Development Centers (MO SBTDC) [47430]
Missouri Small Business Technology and Development Centers - Lead Center (MO SBDC) [41486]
Missouri Southern State University - Heartland Procurement Technical Assistance Center - Institute for Procurement Assistance [41666]
Missouri Southern State University Small Business and Technology Development Center [41487]
Missouri State Genealogical Association Journal [7382]
Missouri State Library [47431]
Missouri State Office of Administration [47432]
Missouri State Office of Social and Economic Data Analysis (OSEDA) [47433]
Missouri State University - Center for Business and Economic Development (CBED) [41712]
Missouri State University - The eFactory Business Incubator [41684]
Missouri State University Small Business and Technology Development Center (MSU SBDC) [41488]
Missouri Valley Chamber of Commerce [39774]
Missouri Veterinary Medical Association Annual Convention [709]
Mistake-Free Grammar & Proofreading [17851]
"Mistakes to Avoid While Deploying CRM" in Small Business Trends (September 7, 2022) [20468]
Mister Softee Inc. [8630]
Mister Transmission International Ltd. [14592]
MIT Alumni Angels of Boston (MITAAB) [35292], [40707]
MIT Alumni Angels of New York (MITAANY) [35293], [42777]
MIT Alumni Angels of Washington DC (MITAADC) [35294], [38172]
MIT Alumni Life Sceince Angels of Boston [35295], [40708]
MIT Enterprise Forum Cambridge [22954]
Mitchell Area Chamber of Commerce [44654]
Mitchell B. Kohn Lighting Design [31088]
Mitchell County Chamber of Commerce [43171]
Mitchell J. Kassoff, Esq., Attorney [18760]
Mitchell Technical Institute (MTI) [44673]
Mitchell and Titus L.L.P. [15445], [16883], [24259]
Mitsui Global Investment (MGI) [37750]
"A Mixed-Bag Quarter" in Barron's (Vol. 88, July 7, 2008, No. 27, pp. 19) [6527], [9677], [18236], [21038], [24016], [33203]
Mixing Bowl Kitchen [42350]
"Mixing Business and Pleasure On the Green" in Black Enterprise (Vol. 41, October 2010, No. 3, pp. 65) [5665], [5932], [7524], [23296], [35822]
Mixson Business Center (MBC) [36185]
MJBiz Magazine [5027]
MJBizCon [5057]
MJBizCon cannabis conference [5057]
MJBizDaily [5044]
MJS Lighting Consultants [31089]
MLM Consultants [45590]
MLMA Convention and Trade Show [10407]
MMA Cycles Report [9922]
MMA Global Inc. (MMA) [30452]
MMC Technology Ventures (MMCT) [37751]
"MMRGlobal Home Health and Senior Care Programs to Be Showcased at Visiting Nurse Associations of America's Annual Meeting" in Marketwired (April 12, 2012) [3515], [8260], [11514], [25874]
MOA Fall Seminar [16312]
Moab Area Chamber of Commerce (MACC) [45640]
Moapa Valley Chamber of Commerce [41947]
Mobile Air Climate Systems Association (MACS) [460]

Mobile Air Conditioning Society [460]
Mobile Area Chamber of Commerce (MACC) [36134]
Mobile Cuisine, LLC [4975]
"Mobile Discounts: A Matter of Distance and Time" in Harvard Business Review (Vol. 92, May 2014, No. 5, pp. 30) [20047], [29936], [30481], [32571]
Mobile Electronics Association (MEA) [2563]
Mobile Electronics Competition Association (MECA) [2564]
Mobile Marketing Association [30452]
"Mobile Marketing Grows With Size of Cell Phone Screens" in Crain's Detroit Business (Vol. 24, January 14, 2008, No. 2, pp. 13) [316], [2763], [18237], [26344], [29937]
Mobile Modular Office Association [3948]
Mobile Office: The Essential Small Business Guide to Office Technology [2764], [3722], [24552], [26345], [30967]
"Mobile Pet Grooming Business" in The Balance Careers (January 26, 2019) [12093]
Mobile Vending: How to Run a Traveling Food or Merchandise Concession [3826], [6954]
"The Mobility Imperative" in Business Strategy Review (Vol. 23, Spring 2012, No. 1, pp. 70) [2765], [17715]
Mobility: The total relocation magazine [14991]
Mobility Ventures [45596]
"Mobis to Set Up Lancaster Distribution Center" in Dallas Business Journal (Vol. 35, April 6, 2012, No. 30, pp. 1) [11420], [20641], [26614]
Mobridge Chamber of Commerce [44655]
MOD Pizza [12567], [14211]
MOD Super Fast Pizza Holdings L.L.C. [12567], [14211]
Model Agencies Industry in the US - Market Research Report [10995]
Model Airplane News: The World's Premier R/C Modeling Magazine [4676]
"A Model Development" in Crain's Cleveland Business (Vol. 28, October 1, 2007, No. 39, pp. 12) [4177], [13238], [13510], [26346], [26615]
"A Model Machine for Titanium" in Modern Machine Shop (Vol. 84, October 2011, No. 5, pp. 84) [10436], [29299], [30766]
Model Railroader [4677]
Modeling Association of America International (MAAI) [10991]
"Modeling How to Grow: an Inductive Examination of Humble Leader Behaviors, Contingencies, and Outcomes" in Academy of Management Journal (Vol. 55, August 1, 2012, No. 4, pp. 787) [28728]
"The Moderating Effects of Organizational Context On the Relationship Between Voluntary Turnover and Organizational Performance: Evidence from Korea" in Human Resource Management (Vol. 51, January-February 2012, No. 1, pp. 47-70) [22208], [26999], [27653]
Modern Art Museum of Fort Worth Library [3373]
Modern Brewery Age [1362], [1949], [10340]
"Modern Bride Unveiled Exclusively at JCPenney" in Benzinga.com (February 3, 2011) [1981], [9979], [32211]
"Modern Meal Offers Recipe Inspiration, Curation and Home Delivery" in Orlando Business Journal (Vol. 30, April 4, 2014, No. 41, pp. 3) [7755], [11771], [21768], [22967]
Modern Music Masters [11171]
Modernistic Cleaning LLC [16241]
Modesto Chamber of Commerce [37029]
Modesto Memo [37030]
Modicum Agency [42983]
Modoc County Chamber of Commerce [36725]
Modular Building Institute (MBI) [3948]
Moe's Franchisor SPV LLC [14212]
Moe's Southwest Grill [14212]
Mohave Community College Small Business Development Center (MCC SBDC) [36274]
Mohawk Valley Chamber of Commerce [42605]
Mohawk Valley Small Business Development Center [42406]
Mohican-Loudonville Convention & Visitors Bureau [43530]
Mokena Chamber of Commerce [39251]
Molalla Area Chamber of Commerce (MACC) [43992]
Molecular Physics: An International Journal in the Field of Chemical Physics [32903]
Molly Maid Inc. [5093]
Moloka'i Chamber of Commerce [38881]
The Mom & Pop Store: How the Unsung Heroes of the American Economy Are Surviving and Thriving [20469], [21039], [23638], [32212], [34343]
Momence Chamber of Commerce [39252]
"The Moment You Can't Ignore: When Big Trouble Leads to a Great Future" [19897], [27000], [28729]
Momentum [44262]

Momentum — Master Index

Momentum Business Consulting L.L.C. **[2295]**
Momentum Capital Partners **[45461]**
"Moms Mean Business: A Guide to Creating a Successful Company and Happy Life as a Mom Entrepreneur" **[22402]**, **[26747]**, **[35507]**
Mon Valley Regional Chamber of Commerce **[44263]**
Mon Yough Area Chamber of Commerce **[44264]**
Mon-Yough Chamber of Commerce [44264]
Mon-Yough Membership Directory **[44265]**
Monahans Chamber of Commerce **[45287]**
Monday Morning Report **[44783]**
"Monday Organizer: Clean and De-Clutter in 15 Minutes" in Tulsa World (June 13, 2011) **[9045]**, **[12839]**, **[34993]**
MONETS Business Accelerators **[46899]**
Monett Chamber of Commerce **[41595]**
Money **[2153]**
"Money Basics: How to Handle a Bank Error" in Black Enterprise (Vol. 41, December 2010, No. 5) **[6528]**, **[24017]**
"Money Isn't Enough: 6 Incentives to Motivate Your Employees" in Business News Daily (March 17, 2023) **[22209]**
"Key Challenges Dog International Banking in South Florida" in South Florida Business Journal (Vol. 35, August 1, 2014, No. 1, pp. 4) **[8742]**, **[24018]**, **[25450]**
Money Magazine **[40180]**
Money Matters: A Critical Look at Bank Architecture **[863]**
Money Source Financial Services Inc. **[17405]**
The Moneychanger **[9923]**
"MoneyGram Hopes Digital Push Will Click With Customers" in Dallas Business Journal (Vol. 37, July 4, 2014, No. 43, pp. 17) **[19898]**, **[20470]**, **[21921]**, **[24019]**, **[34100]**
MoneySoft Inc. **[19143]**, **[33931]**
"Monique Johnson on the Pros and Cons of Hybrid Events" in Small Business Trends (November 1, 2022) **[17716]**, **[33587]**
MonitorClosely **[14495]**
Monkey Joe's Party And Play **[592]**
Monmouth Area Chamber of Commerce **[39253]**
Monmouth Commercial Club [39253]
Monmouth-Independence Area Chamber of Commerce & Visitors Center (MICC) **[43993]**
Monmouth-Independence Chamber of Commerce [43993]
Monmouth/Ocean Small Business Development Center (MOSBDC) **[42036]**
Monmouth Regional Chamber of Commerce (MRCC) **[42164]**
Monmouth SCORE [42074]
Monmouth University Center for Entrepreneurship (MUCE) **[42254]**
"Monogram Foods Eyes Acquisition: Midwest Manufacturer Target of Latest Expansion" in Memphis Business Journal (Vol. 34, August 10, 2012, No. 17, pp. 1) **[26616]**, **[29300]**, **[31425]**
"Monogram Foods Lands Another Acquisition In Quest for Growth Goals" in Memphis Business Journal (Vol. 34, September 14, 2012, No. 22, pp. 1) **[29301]**, **[31426]**
"Monogram Shoppe Found a True Window-Shopping Alternative to Keep Business Going During COVID-19" in Greater Fort Worth Business Weekly (June 30, 2021) **[5469]**
Monona Chamber of Commerce [46466]
Monona East Side Business Alliance (MESBA) **[46466]**
Monroe Chamber of Commerce **[46127]**
Monroe Chamber of Commerce (MCC) **[38062]**, **[40181]**
Monroe Chamber of Commerce and Industry (MCCI) **[46467]**
Monroe Chamber of Commerce and Visitor Information Center [46127]
Monroe City Chamber of Commerce **[41596]**
Monroe County Chamber of Commerce **[41416]**, **[41417]**, **[44784]**
Monroe County Chamber of Commerce (SOCC) **[40980]**
Monroe County Chamber of Commerce [38732]
Monroe County Finger Lakes Procurement Technical Assistance Center (MCFL PTAC) **[42820]**
Monroeville Area Business Directory **[44266]**
Monroeville Area Chamber of Commerce (MACC) **[44267]**
Monroeville/Monroe County Chamber of Commerce **[36135]**
Monrovia Chamber of Commerce **[37031]**
Monrovia Insider **[37032]**
"Monsanto Acquires Targeted-Pest Control Technology Start-Up; Terms Not Disclosed" in Benzinga.com (September 2011) **[9678]**, **[12035]**, **[19681]**, **[32006]**, **[32790]**, **[33204]**
"Monsanto Wins Patent Case Against DuPont" in Farm Journal (Vol. 136, September 2012, No. 8, pp. 8) **[18642]**, **[27918]**

"Monsanto's Next Single-Bag Refuge Product Approved" in Farm Industry News (December 5, 2011) **[17076]**, **[25451]**, **[30767]**
Monster Mini Golf (MMG) **[10989]**
Mont Clare - Elmwood Park Chamber of Commerce [39179]
Montague County Small Business Development Center **[44926]**
Montana Agricultural Business Association (MABA) **[16950]**, **[41716]**
Montana Chamber of Commerce (MCC) **[41785]**
Montana Department of Administration - State Procurement Bureau (SPB) **[41804]**
Montana Department of Agriculture - Agricultural Development Div. (ADD) **[41729]**
Montana Department of Commerce - Business Resources Div. **[41730]**
Montana Department of Commerce - Census and Economic Information Center (CEIC) **[41731]**, **[46937]**
Montana Department of Commerce - Community Development Div. (CDD) **[41732]**
Montana Department of Commerce - Montana Office of Tourism and Business Development - Office of Trade and International Relations **[41733]**
Montana Department of Commerce - Office of Trade & International Relations - Business Resources Division - Made in Montana Program **[41734]**
Montana Department of Labor and Industry - Research and Analysis Bureau - Employment Relations Div. **[47434]**
Montana Department of Transportation (MDT) **[1179]**, **[5116]**, **[10296]**, **[15532]**
Montana Enterprise Center [41811]
Montana Governor's Office of Economic Development (GOED) **[41809]**
"Montana Outlook: Stronger Growth Ahead" in Montana Business Quarterly (Vol. 49, Spring 2011, No. 1, pp. 7) **[18238]**, **[21040]**
Montana Procurement Technical Assistance Center [41728], [41802]
Montana Procurement Technical Assistance Center - Great Falls Development Authority **[41805]**
Montana Small Business Development Center (MT) **[41725]**
Montana State Library-Digital Library Div. (MSL) **[47435]**
Montana State University, Bozeman - University Information Technology (UIT) **[14893]**
Montana Tech of the University of Montana **[35981]**
Montana Technology Enterprise Center (MonTEC) **[41810]**
"Montana's Manufacturing Industry" in Montana Business Quarterly (Vol. 49, Spring 2011, No. 1, pp. 29) **[10396]**, **[18239]**, **[29302]**
Montcalm Community College (MCC) **[41129]**
Montclair Chamber of Commerce **[37033]**
Monte Jade Science and Technology Association of Greater Washington **[38153]**
Monte Rio Chamber of Commerce (MRCC) **[37034]**
Monte Vista Chamber of Commerce (MVCC) **[37888]**
Montebello Chamber of Commerce **[37035]**
MonTEC **[41811]**
Montello Area Chamber of Commerce (MCC) **[46468]**
Monterey Peninsula Chamber of Commerce (MPCC) **[37036]**
Montevallo Chamber of Commerce (MCC) **[36136]**
Montevideo Area Chamber of Commerce (MACC) **[41273]**
Montgomery Area Chamber of Commerce (MACOC) **[36137]**, **[36186]**
Montgomery Area Chamber of Commerce Incubation Program **[36187]**
"Montgomery & Barnes: a Service-Disabled, Veteran-Owned Small Business" in Underground Construction (Vol. 65, October 2010, No. 10) **[2197]**, **[25150]**, **[33205]**
Montgomery City Area Chamber of Commerce **[41597]**
Montgomery County Chamber of Commerce (MCCC) **[40401]**, **[45883]**
Montgomery County Chamber of Commerce [39529]
Montgomery County Department of Economic Development - Business Innovation Network (BIN) **[40463]**
The Montgomery County Genealogy Society Library **[7434]**
Monthly Networking **[45288]**
Monthly Newsletter **[36138]**
Monticello Area Chamber of Commerce (MACC) **[39775]**
Monticello Area Chamber of Commerce and Industry (MCCI) **[41274]**
Monticello Chamber of Commerce **[39254]**
Monticello Chamber of Commerce [41274]
Monticello Drew County Chamber of Commerce **[36482]**
Monticello-Jasper County Chamber of Commerce **[38766]**

Monticello-Jefferson County Chamber of Commerce **[38465]**
Monticello/Wayne County Chamber of Commerce **[40072]**
Montpelier Area Chamber of Commerce (MACC) **[43531]**
Montreux Growth Partners (MGP) **[37437]**
Montrose-Verdugo City Chamber of Commerce (MVCC) **[37037]**
Montville Township Chamber of Commerce **[42165]**
Monument Builders of Canada [7200]
Monument Builders of North America (MBNA) [7200]
Monument Ventures **[45597]**
Moonshot **[36400]**
Moore Chamber of Commerce **[43782]**
Moore County Chamber of Commerce **[43172]**
Moore Norman Technology Center (MNTC) **[43892]**
Moore Norman Technology Center Business (MNTC) **[43866]**
Moore Norman Technology Center (MNTC) - Business Development Center **[43835]**
Moore Norman Technology Center's Business Development Center **[43867]**
Moore North America **[35]**
Moore Stephens North America [35]
Moore Venture Partners (MVP) **[37752]**
Mooresville-South Iredell Chamber of Commerce **[43173]**
Moose Lake Area Chamber of Commerce **[41275]**
Moosehead Lake Region Chamber of Commerce **[40274]**
"The Moral Legitimacy of NGOs as Partners of Corporations" in Business Ethics Quarterly (Vol. 21, October 2011, No. 4, pp. 579) **[23519]**, **[33206]**
"Morbark Launches New Equipment" in Lawn & Landscape (November 14, 2019) **[10054]**
Morbidity and Mortality Weekly Report (MMWR) **[26034]**
"More Brides, Grooms Say 'I Do' to Interracial Marriage" in Black Enterprise (Vol. 41, August 2010, No. 1, pp. 36)* **[1982]**, **[34101]**
"More Corporate Welfare?" in Canadian Business (Vol. 80, February 12, 2007, No. 4, pp. 96) **[25028]**, **[34846]**
"More Gains in the Pipeline" in Barron's (Vol. 89, August 3, 2009, No. 31, pp. M5) **[4178]**, **[6529]**, **[9679]**, **[24020]**
"The More Incredible Egg" in Entrepreneur (June 2014) **[8031]**, **[29303]**, **[30768]**
"More Leading Retailers Using Omniture Conversion Solutions to Boost Sales and Ecommerce Performance" in Marketwired (September 22, 2009) **[317]**, **[9183]**, **[14800]**, **[21922]**, **[29938]**, **[32213]**, **[32572]**, **[33874]**
"More Power to Your Presentation" in Business Strategy Review (Vol. 21, Spring 2010, No. 1, pp. 50) **[17717]**, **[22714]**
"More Small Businesses in Baltimore Willing to Fund Employees' Health Benefits" in Baltimore Business Journal (Vol. 28, June 18, 2010, No. 6, pp. 1) **[8944]**, **[17330]**, **[25875]**, **[27001]**, **[27310]**, **[34102]**
"More SouthPark Shopping for Charlotte" in Charlotte Business Journal (Vol. 25, July 16, 2010, No. 17, pp. 1) **[13969]**, **[18240]**, **[25452]**, **[32214]**
More Space Place, Inc. (MSP) **[8226]**
"More Than a Feeling" in Entrepreneur (Vol. 36, April 2008, No. 4, pp. 10) **[22715]**, **[24708]**
Morehead-Rowan County Chamber of Commerce **[40073]**
Morehead Small Business Development Center **[39997]**
Morehead State University (MSU) **[40113]**
Morehead State University Water Testing Laboratory (MSU WTL) **[16357]**
MoreSALES **[2358]**
"Morgan Hill Attracts Manufacturing to South County" in Silicon Valley/San Jose Business Journal (Vol. 30, September 21, 2012, No. 26, pp. 1) **[28171]**, **[29304]**
Morgan Hill Chamber of Commerce (MHCC) **[37038]**
Morgan Hill Partners [38539], [38605]
"Morgan Keegan Feeds Wunderlich" in Memphis Business Journal (Vol. 34, May 18, 2012, No. 5, pp. 1) **[9680]**, **[26617]**, **[32573]**
Morgantown Area Chamber of Commerce (MACOC) **[46281]**
Morgantown-Butler County Chamber of Commerce **[40074]**
Morgenthaler Ventures **[43622]**
Morin Center for Banking and Financial Law [6733]
Moroccan American Business Council, Ltd. (AMBC) **[27422]**
MORPACE International Inc. [10708]
Morrilton Area Chamber of Commerce (MACC) **[36483]**
Morrilton Chamber of Commerce [36483]
Morris Area Chamber of Commerce **[41276]**
Morris County Chamber of Commerce **[42166]**
Morrison Chamber of Commerce **[39255]**
Morristimes **[44785]**
Morristown Area Chamber of Commerce **[44786]**

Morrisville Chamber of Commerce [43174]
Morro Bay Chamber of Commerce [37039]
Morrow County Chamber of Commerce [43532]
Morrow County Chamber of Commerce and Visitors' Bureau [43532]
Mortgage Bankers Association (MBA) [10998], [13099]
Mortgage Banking Magazine: The Magazine of Real Estate Finance [11095]
"Mortgage Companies are Adding Staff" in Sacramento Business Journal (Vol. 29, September 14, 2012, No. 29, pp. 1) [11058], [26618], [27919]
"The Mortgage Red Flags that Bankers See" in Providence Business News (Vol. 29, August 4, 2014, No. 18, pp. 9) [4802], [11059], [20315]
"Mortgage Servicer Wingspan Portfolio Advisors Makes Mark in Frisco" in Dallas Business Journal (Vol. 35, September 7, 2012, No. 52, pp. 1) [11060], [18241], [26619], [33392]
Mortgage Technology [11096], [28235]
Morton Arboretum [7677], [10147]
Morton Arboretum - Sterling Morton Library [7677], [10147]
Morton Chamber of Commerce [39256]
Morton Grove Chamber of Commerce and Industry (MGCCI) [39257]
Morton Matters [39258]
Mosaic Capital Partners [46796]
"Mosaid Grants First Wireless Patent License To Matsushita" in Canadian Electronics (Vol. 23, June-July 2008, No. 5, pp. 1) [4399], [17718], [17869], [18643], [26347], [27920], [29305], [32791]
Mosaix Ventures [39368]
Mosby's Pathology for Massage Therapists [10772]
Moscow Chamber of Commerce (MCC) [38931]
Moses Lake Area Chamber of Commerce [46128]
MOSES Organic Farming Conference [17174]
Mosinee Area Chamber of Commerce [46469]
Mosquito Squad [12059]
MosquitoNix [12060]
Moss Landing Chamber of Commerce (MLCC) [37040]
"Most Americans Expect to Keep Working in Retirement" in Business News Daily (March 20, 2023) [16579], [21041]
"Most Charitable Zip Codes" in Dallas Business Journal (Vol. 37, March 7, 2014, No. 26, pp. 8) [7136]
"The Most Common Frauds in Small Business" in Go-Cardless website (August 2021) [19271]
"Most Popular Tools? The Survey Says" in Contractor (Vol. 57, February 2010, No. 2, pp. 1) [5382], [7923], [14627], [33207]
"Most See Gloomy Year For Michigan Business" in Crain's Detroit Business (Vol. 24, October 6, 2008, No. 40, pp. 4) [21042], [24709]
Motel 6 [8508]
Motel 6 Operating L.P. [8508]
"Mother and Daughter Create Tool to Unbraid 8 Braids at One Time" in Black Enterprise(February 25, 2023) [1390], [4518], [7871]
Motion Picture Association of America, Inc. (MPAA) [11119]
Motion Picture Association-Canada (MPA) [6168]
Motion Picture Producers and Distributors of America [11119]
Motion Picture TV and Theatre Directory [11125]
"Motivating Salespeople: What Really Works. Companies Fiddle Constantly With Their Incentive Plans - But Most of Their Changes Have Little Effect" in Harvard Business Review (Vol. 90, July-August 2012, pp. 7-8, pp. 70) [32574]
Motivation and Trust Building for Group Leaders (Onsite) [28393]
Motor and Equipment Manufacturers Association (MEMA) [1092]
Motor Freight Carriers Association [16068]
Motor Magazine [14566]
Motor Selection, Maintenance, Testing & Replacement [19448], [21409]
Motorcycle and Allied Trades Association [11107]
Motorcycle Dealership and Repair Industry in the US - Market Research Report [11111]
Motorcycle Industry Council (MIC) [11107]
Motorcycle, Scooter and Allied Trades Association [11107]
"Motors and Motion Control" in Canadian Electronics (Vol. 23, February 2008, No. 1, pp. 23) [3723], [4400], [26348], [29306], [30769]
Moulding and Millwork Producers Association (MMPA) [2631]
Moulton Chamber of Commerce [45289]
Moulton Chamber of Commerce and Agriculture [45289]
Moultrie-Colquitt County Chamber of Commerce [38767]
Mound City Area Chamber of Commerce [39928]
Mound City Chamber of Commerce [39929]

Moundridge Community Chamber of Commerce [39930]
Mount Adams Chamber of Commerce [46129]
Mount Angel Chamber of Commerce [43994]
Mount Carroll Chamber of Commerce [39259]
Mount Desert Chamber of Commerce [40293]
Mount Dora Area Chamber of Commerce (MDACC) [38466]
Mount Gilead Area Chamber of Commerce [43532]
Mount Greenwood Chamber of Commerce [39260]
Mount Holyoke College Music and Dance Library [11230]
Mt. Hood Community College (MHCC) [44072]
Mt. Hood Community College Small Business Development Center (MHCC SBDC) [43912]
Mount Horeb Area Chamber of Commerce (MHACC) [46470]
Mount Ida Area Chamber of Commerce [36484]
Mount Ida Area Visitor Guide [36485]
Mt. Ida College-Division of Continuing Education [40771]
Mt. Juliet Chamber of Commerce [44787]
Mount Juliet - West Wilson County Chamber of Commerce [44787]
Mount Kisco Chamber of Commerce (MKCC) [42638]
"Mount Laurel Woman Launches Venture Into Children's Used Clothing" in Philadelphia Inquirer (September 17, 2010) [2842], [3084], [3881], [22403], [24390], [35508]
Mount Olive Area Chamber of Commerce [43175]
Mount Olive Area Chamber of Commerce (MOACC) [42167]
Mount Pleasant Area Chamber Alliance [39776]
Mount Pleasant Area Chamber of Commerce (MPACC) [40981]
Mount Pleasant Area Chamber of Commerce [39776]
Mount Pleasant Sugarworks [2955]
Mount Pleasant/Titus County Chamber of Commerce [45290]
Mount Prospect Chamber of Commerce [39261]
Mount Royal Ventures (MRV) [43024]
Mount Shasta Chamber of Commerce [37041]
Mount Snow Valley Chamber of Commerce [45733]
Mount Sterling-Montgomery County Chamber of Commerce [40075]
Mount Vernon Chamber Chat [46130]
Mount Vernon Chamber of Commerce [46131]
Mount Vernon - Knox County Chamber of Commerce [43533]
Mount Vernon-Lee Chamber of Commerce (MVLCC) [45884]
Mt. Vernon, MO Chamber of Commerce [41598]
Mount Zion Chamber of Commerce (ZCC) [39262]
Mountain City Chamber of Commerce [44766]
Mountain Empire Community College (MECC) [45976]
Mountain Empire Community College Small Business Development Center (SBDC) [45786]
Mountain Grove Chamber of Commerce [41599]
Mountain Home Area Chamber of Commerce [36486]
Mountain Home Chamber of Commerce [38932]
Mountain Lakes Chamber of Commerce [36139]
Mountain Mudd Espresso [7589]
Mountain Mudd L.L.C. [7589]
Mountain Plains Minority Supplier Development Council (MPMSDC) [37914]
Mountain Realty Inc. [31009]
Mountain View Chamber of Commerce [36815]
"Move Marks KKR's Latest Push into Retail" in Globe & Mail (March 13, 2007, pp. B17) [9681], [31427], [32215]
"Mover and Sheika" in Conde Nast Portfolio (Vol. 2, June 2008, No. 6, pp. 104) [6530], [8743], [9682], [21043], [22716], [24021], [27654], [29307]
Moving Ahead: Breaking Behavior Patterns That Hold You Back (Onsite) [21410]
Moving Ahead: Breaking Behaviour Patterns That Hold You Back [28394]
"Moving Company Accused of Holding Customers' Belongings Hostage" in CBSnews (January 28, 2019) [11150]
Moving Services Industry in the US - Market Research Report [11154]
Moving Solutions Franchise L.L.C. [11159]
MP Healthcare Venture Management, Inc. (MPH) [40709]
MPA-Canada [6168]
MPA - The Association of Magazine Media (MPA) [11967], [12016]
"MPI Expansion Goes Back to Family Roots" in Crain's Detroit Business (Vol. 25, June 1, 2009, No. 22, pp. M007) [5175], [18242], [23639], [32007], [32792]
MPM BioImpact, Inc. [40710]
MPM Capital / MPM Asset Management L.L.C. [40710]
Mr. Appliance Corp. [33322]
"Mr. Cranky: Glen Hellman Calls It Like He Sees It, Whether D.C. Tech Likes It or Not" in Washington Business Journal (Vol. 31, August 17, 2012, No. 17, pp. 1) [35365]

Mr. C's Kitchen Rentals [37600]
Mr. Electric [5403]
Mr. Electric-Canada [5404]
Mr. Goodcents Franchise Systems Inc. [4911]
Mr. Goodcents Subs & Pastas [4912], [14213]
Mr. Greek Mediterranean Grill [14214]
Mr. Greek Rxpress [14215]
Mr. Handyman International [5094]
Mr. Hero Restaurants [14216]
Mr. Lube [14593]
Mr. Pickle's Sandwich Shop [4913], [10041]
Mr. Pita [4914]
Mr. Rooter Plumbing [12686]
Mr. Sandless [6842]
Mr. SUB [14217]
Mr. Transmission [14594]
MRA Blue Book Research Services Directory [29677]
MRA January Lansing Market [32355]
MRIGlobal [2293], [20209], [32072], [32932]
MRPR Group, P.C. [41134]
Mrs. Fields' Original Cookies, Inc. [1301]
MRVDA RV Shows [13682]
Ms.Tech Co. [35922]
MTEC SmartZone (MTECSZ) [41109]
Mtech Technology Advancement Program [40464]
MTM Association for Standards and Research [11631]
MTS Allstream Inc. [3444]
MU Extension in Madison County [41479]
"Much Work Still To Be Done on Meadows Deal" in Pittsburgh Business Times (Vol. 33, May 16, 2014, No. 44, pp. 3) [7302], [27921], [31428]
Mucho Burrito [14218]
Mucker Capital (MC) [37601]
MuckerLab [37602]
"A Muddle at Marks & Spencer" in Barron's (Vol. 88, July 7, 2008, No. 27, pp. M7) [27655], [32216]
Mueser Rutledge Consulting Engineers (MRCE) [4333]
"Muirhead Farmhouse B&B Owners Get Hospitality Wright" in Chicago Tribune (July 31, 2008) [905], [1419], [19379], [20471], [23640]
Mukwonago Area Chamber of Commerce [46471]
Mukwonago Area Chamber of Commerce & Tourism Center [46471]
Mukwonago Chamber of Commerce [46471]
Muleshoe Chamber of Commerce and Agriculture [45291]
Muleshoe Journal [45292]
Mullaney Publishing Group LLP [45591]
Multi-Housing Laundry Association (MLA) [5227]
Multi-Lingual Directory of Machine Tools & Related Products [10425]
Multi-Menu [12238]
Multi-Unit Foodservice Operators Conference (MUFSO) [14093]
Multi-Unit Restaurant Technology Conference [14094]
"A Multicategory Model of Consumers' Purchase Incidence, Quantity, and Brand Choice Decisions: Methodological Issues and Implications On Promotional Decisions" in Journal of Marketing Research (Vol. 49, August 2012, No. 4, pp. 435) [10667], [32217]
Multicultural Institute of the International Counseling Center [30508], [30658]
Multicultural Marketing News (MMN) [30415], [35895]
Multidisciplinary Research Center on Drug and Alcohol Abuse [34705]
"Multifamily Banks on Fannie, Freddie" in Memphis Business Journal (Vol. 33, February 24, 2012, No. 46, pp. 1) [13805], [25029], [28172]
The Multinational Enterprise Revisited: The Essential Buckley and Casson [18243], [27656]
Mulvane Chamber of Commerce [39931]
MunaLuchi Bride [2006]
Muncie Chamber of Commerce [39581]
Muncie-Delaware County Chamber of Commerce [39581]
Municipal Art Society Newsletter [923]
Municipal Market Data-Line® [6720], [9940]
Municipal Waste Association (MWA) [5491], [13689], [23039]
Municipal World [31708]
Munising Visitors Bureau [40849]
Munster Chamber of Commerce [39582]
Murphree Venture Partners (MVP) [45462]
Murphy Business and Financial Corp. [2162]
Murphysboro Chamber of Commerce [39263]
Murray Area Chamber of Commerce (MACC) [45641]
Murray-Calloway County Chamber of Commerce [40076]
Murray Dropkin & Associates [2296], [10549], [20211], [22324], [29022], [33682]
Murray State SBDC [39998]
Murray State University - Bureau of Business and Economic Research (BBER) [31727]
Muscatine Chamber of Commerce and Convention and Visitor Bureau [39746]

Muscatine SCORE **[39694]**
Muscular Development **[12445]**
Musee McCord d'Histoire Canadienne [1001]
Museum of the City of New York - Department of Collections Access **[4567]**
Museum of Contemporary Craft Library **[4643]**, **[4697]**, **[11488]**
Museum of International Folk Art (MOIFA) - The Bartlett Library **[4702]**
Museum of Western Colorado - Loyd Files Research Library **[3277]**
Music Business Association (MBA) **[3410]**, **[13648]**
Music Business Solutions (MBS) **[11203]**
Music Canada **[13649]**
Music Educators Journal (MEJ) **[11195]**
Music Go Round (MGR) **[11289]**
Music Inc. **[3414]**, **[11277]**
"Music and Its Effect on Productivity" in Business News Daily (March 7, 2023) **[22210]**
Music Operators of America [576]
Music Power [11200], [11284]
Music Publishers' Association of the United States (MPA) **[11169]**
"Music Students Do Better in School Than Non-Musical Peers" in ScienceDaily (June 24, 2019) **[11179]**
Music Supervisors National Conference [11171]
Music Teachers National Association (MTNA) **[11170]**
Music Trades **[11196]**, **[11278]**
Music Trades--The Purchaser's Guide to the Music Industries **[11185]**, **[11266]**
Musicals Tonight Inc. **[10698]**
Musicians Hotline [11279], [11316]
Muskego Area Chamber of Commerce **[46472]**
Muskegon Area Chamber of Commerce [40982]
Muskegon Area First **[41110]**
Muskegon Area First Procurement Technical Assistance Center [41070]
Muskegon Community College (MCC) - Hendrik Meijer Library Special Collections **[5465]**
Muskegon Lakeshore Chamber of Commerce (MLCC) **[40982]**
Muslim Entrepreneur Association (MEA) **[30510]**
Muslim Entrepreneurs Association [30510]
Must Be Heaven Franchise Corp. **[4915]**
Mustang Chamber of Commerce **[43783]**
Mustard Cafe & Grill **[4916]**
Mutual Advertising Agency Network [223], [31836]
MVMA Annual Convention [709]
MVP Capital Partners **[44344]**
MVTL Laboratories Inc. **[7976]**
MWACA Midwest Auto Care Alliance [14532]
MWSRA Show [15121]
My Big Idea: 30 Successful Entrepreneurs Reveal How They Found Inspiration **[22717]**
"My Day" in Business Strategy Review (Vol. 21, Autumn 2010, No. 3, pp. 77) **[22718]**, **[33022]**, **[35823]**
"My Favorite Tool for Managing Expenses" in Inc. (Volume 32, December 2010, No. 10, pp. 60) **[78]**, **[1766]**, **[2766]**, **[15402]**, **[16819]**, **[21923]**, **[24022]**, **[33208]**
"My Favorite Tool for Organizing Data" in Inc. (Vol. 33, November 2011, No. 9, pp. 46) **[2767]**, **[3724]**, **[14801]**, **[33875]**
My Gym Enterprises **[12458]**
"My Home-Based Business Is Being Audited: Now What?" in Legal Zoom (March 8, 2023) **[34847]**
"My Inglorious Road to Success" in Harvard Business Review (Vol. 88, July-August 2010, No. 7-8, pp. 38) **[22719]**, **[28730]**
My Life From Scratch: A Sweet Journey of Starting Over, One Cake at a Time **[1239]**, **[6196]**, **[13970]**, **[35824]**
MyKitchens L.L.C. **[39416]**
"MyReviewsNow.net Announces New Affiliate Partner Gift Baskets Overseas" in M2 EquityBites (EQB) (June 22, 2012) **[6859]**, **[7469]**, **[11772]**, **[27657]**, **[31429]**
Myron I. Blumenfeld & Associates (MIBA) **[20672]**
Myrtle Beach Area Chamber of Commerce **[44574]**
Myrtle Beach Area Small Business Development Center **[44508]**
Mystic Seaport **[10632]**
Mystic Seaport Museum [10632]
"The Myth of the Overqualified Worker" in Harvard Business Review (Vol. 88, December 2010, No. 12, pp. 30) **[26620]**, **[27002]**, **[28731]**
"Myths of Deleveraging" in Barron's (Vol. 90, August 23, 2010, No. 34, pp. M14) **[9683]**, **[11061]**, **[13239]**, **[18244]**, **[21044]**, **[29308]**, **[34103]**
"MyWireless.org Commends Arizona Congressman Trent Franks for Committing to Wireless Tax Relief for American Consumers and Businesses" in PR Newswire (September 21, 2012) **[2768]**, **[3725]**, **[3770]**, **[9184]**, **[25453]**, **[30968]**, **[34848]**

N

N-Hance Wood Refinishing **[6843]**
N29 Capital Partners, LLC (N) **[46551]**

NAA Conference and Show **[1086]**
NAA International Auctioneers Conference & Show [1086]
NAACLS News **[10932]**
NAADAC: The Association for Addiction Professionals **[34669]**
NAAPA [1066], [11362]
NAB Show **[15618]**
NABA National Convention & Expo **[16863]**, **[30425]**
NABE Annual Meeting [21251]
NABIP Capitol Conference [27365]
NACAA Annual Meeting and Professional Improvement Conference (NACAA AM/PIC) **[17175]**
"NACE Becomes the National Association for Catering and Events" in Entertainment Close-Up (July 29, 2012) **[2676]**, **[11894]**, **[11908]**
NACM Credit Congress and Exposition **[20364]**
Nacogdoches County Chamber of Commerce (NCCC) **[45293]**
NACS: The Association for Convenience and Fuel Retailing **[4423]**, **[4455]**
NACUBO Annual Meeting **[21690]**
NADA Show [16103]
Nádasdy Ferenc Múzeum Könyvtár **[16046]**, **[19422]**
NAFA Annual Convention [557]
NAFA Fleet Management Association **[1151]**, **[11471]**
NAFCU's Annual Conference [24226]
NAfME National In-Service Conference **[11200]**, **[11284]**
NAFO Meeting Proceedings of the Commission **[6767]**
NAGMR Consumer Products Broker [1382], [2138], [10576]
NAGMR Consumer Products Sales Agencies [1382], [2138], [10576]
NAHB Leading Suppliers Council (NAHB) **[3949]**
NAHC's Annual Meeting and Home Care and Hospice Expo **[8276]**
"Nailing the Next Five Years: Three Deceptively Simple Questions Will Change the Way You Think About Your Company's Future" in Inc. (Vol. 36, September 2014, No. 7, pp. 145) **[19552]**
NAIOP **[13361]**
NALS The Association for Legal Professionals (NALS) **[16221]**
Nalukai Foundation **[38891]**
The NAMA Show **[16268]**
"The Name Game: How Monograms and Personalization Have Become Key Retail Trends" in Shopify (February 1, 2018) **[5470]**
NAMM International Music Market [11285], [13660]
NAMM NeXT [13661]
The NAMM Show **[11285]**, **[13660]**
Nampa Chamber of Commerce **[38933]**
NAMTA - The International Art Materials Association (NAMTA) **[1014]**
Nana Clare's Kitchen **[39645]**
Nando's **[14219]**
Nanny Poppinz Corporate, Inc. **[11332]**
"Nanny Shortage Could Create a Crisis as Families Return to Work" in Crains New York (July 22, 2021) **[11326]**
Nantucket Island Chamber of Commerce **[40605]**
Napa Chamber of Commerce (NCC) **[37042]**
Napa-Sonoma SBDC **[36580]**
Napa Valley Genealogical Society Library **[7435]**
Napa Valley Wine Library Association Library (NVWLA) **[15070]**
Naperville Area Chamber of Commerce (NACC) **[39264]**
Naples Area Chamber of Commerce [38405]
Naples on the Gulf **[38467]**
NAPM Insights [31911]
Napoleon Area Chamber of Commerce [43489]
Nappanee Area Chamber of Commerce **[39583]**
Narcotics Anonymous (NA) **[34670]**
"Naresh Kumar on Using Heat Maps to Grow Your Business" in Small Business Trends (August 25, 2022) **[20472]**, **[33588]**, **[33876]**
Narragansett Chamber of Commerce (NCC) **[44476]**
NARSA - The International Heat Exchange Association **[14536]**
NARTS - The Association of Resale Professionals **[3883]**
Nashoba Valley Chamber of Commerce (NVCOC) **[40606]**
Nashville Area Chamber of Commerce (NACC) **[44788]**
Nashville Business Incubation Center (NBIC) **[44852]**
Nashville Business Journal **[44863]**
Nashville Business Journal **[44862]**
Nashville Capital Network (NCN) **[44873]**
NASJA Directory **[5290]**, **[11968]**
NASPL Annual Conference **[7320]**, **[35129]**
NASSCO **[14606]**
NATA AT Expo [12448]
NATA Clinical Symposia & AT Expo **[12448]**
Natchez-Adams County Chamber of Commerce (NACCC) **[41418]**

Natchitoches Area Chamber of Commerce **[40182]**
Nathan Associates Inc. **[10550]**
Nathan's **[14220]**
National 8(a) Association **[30279]**
National 8(a) Association Small Business Conference **[33637]**
National AAU Taekwondo Union of the United States of America [10717]
National Academy of Arbitrators (NAA) **[10789]**
National Academy of Opticianry (NAO) **[16290]**
National Academy of Public Administration (NAPA) **[31674]**
National Academy of Recording Arts and Sciences (NARAS) **[13650]**
National Account Management Association [10570], [24283]
National Accrediting Agency for Clinical Laboratory Sciences (NAACLS) **[10911]**
National Accrediting Commission of Career Arts and Sciences (NACCAS) **[7854]**
National Accrediting Commission of Cosmetology Arts and Sciences [7854]
National Acoustical Contractors Association [3929], [10726]
National Action Council for Minorities in Engineering (NACME) **[30511]**
National Adult Day Services Association (NADSA) **[177]**
National Advertising Review Board (NARB) **[224]**, **[31837]**
National Advisory Council, Small Business Administration (NAC) **[38154]**
National Aeronautics and Space Administration - Ames Research Center - Small Business Specialist **[47282]**
National Aeronautics and Space Administration (NASA) - Goddard Space Flight Center - Small Business Specialist **[47283]**
National Aeronautics and Space Administration (NASA) - John C. Stennis Space Center - Small Business Specialist - Procurement Office **[47284]**
National Aeronautics and Space Administration (NASA) - John H. Glenn Research Center at Lewis Field - Small Business Specialist **[47285]**
National Aeronautics and Space Administration - Johnson Space Center - Small Business Specialist **[47286]**
National Aeronautics and Space Administration - Langley Research Center - Small Business Specialist **[47287]**
National Aeronautics and Space Administration (NASA) - Marshall Space Flight Center - Small Business Specialist **[47288]**
National Aeronautics and Space Administration (NASA) - Office of Small Business Programs (OSBP) **[47289]**
National Aeronautics and Space Administration - Resident Office--Jet Propulsion Laboratory - Small Business Specialist **[47290]**
National Aeronautics and Space Administration (NASA) - Resident Office--JPL - Small Business Specialist **[47291]**
National Aeronautics and Space Administration (NASA) - Small Business Innovation Research Office **[47292]**
National Aeronautics and Space Administration (STAC) - Southern Technology Applications Center **[47293]**
National Agri-Marketing Association--Membership Directory **[17077]**
National Agricultural Aviation Association--Membership Directory **[30875]**
National Agricultural Bankers Conference **[6705]**, **[24229]**, **[35130]**
National Air Carrier Association (NACA) **[422]**
National Air Filtration Association (NAFA) **[553]**
National Air Filtration Association National Convention **[557]**
National Air Transportation Association (NATA) **[423]**
National Air Transportation Association - Aviation Resource and Membership Directory **[430]**
National Air Transportation Conferences [423]
National Alcohol Research Center [34693]
National Alliance of Community Economic Development Associations (NACEDA) **[20704]**
National Alliance of Independent Crop Consultants - AG PRO EXPO **[17176]**
National Aloe Science Council [1381]
National-American Wholesale Lumber Association [10382]
National Amusement Park Historical Association (NAPHA) **[596]**
National Angel Capital Organization (NACO) **[46754]**
National Antique & Art Dealers Association of America (NAADAA) **[737]**
National Antique & Art Dealers Association of America-- Membership Directory (Internet only) **[742]**
National Antique Vintage Decoy & Sporting Collectibles Show **[747]**

National Apartment Association (NAA) [13362]
National Apartment Owners Association [13362]
National Art Materials Trade Association [1014]
National Asian American Telecommunications Association [6161]
National Asphalt Pavement Association (NAPA) **[1548]**, **[1561]**
National Association of Accident and Health Underwriters [8875]
National Association of Addiction Treatment Providers (NAATP) **[34671]**
National Association of Administrators for Disordered Gambling Services **[7263]**
National Association of Alcoholic Beverage Importers [10311]
National Association of Alcoholism and Drug Abuse Counselors [34669]
National Association of Alcoholism Treatment Programs [34671]
National Association of Amusement Parks [595]
National Association of Amusement Parks, Pools and Beaches [595]
National Association of Appraisers (NAA) **[809]**
National Association of Barber Boards [7855]
National Association of Barber Boards of America (NABBA) **[7855]**
National Association of Beverage Importers Inc. (NABI) **[10311]**
National Association of Beverage Retailers [10310]
National Association of Black Accountants, Inc. (NABA) **[36]**, **[30280]**
National Association of Black Journalists (NABJ) **[5291]**, **[30281]**
National Association of Black Owned Broadcasters (NABOB) **[13020]**, **[30282]**
National Association of Black Professional Organizers (NABPO) **[12817]**, **[30512]**
National Association for Black Veterinarians (NABV) **[686]**
National Association of Black Women in Construction, Inc. (NABWIC) **[3950]**, **[30283]**, **[35630]**
National Association of Boards of Barbers Examiners of America [7855]
National Association of Boards of Examiners of Nursing Home Administrators [11503]
National Association of Boards of Pharmacy (NABP) **[5219]**
National Association of Broadcasters (NAB) **[13021]**, **[13063]**, **[15575]**
National Association of Building Owners and Managers [13629]
National Association of Building Service Contractors [2046]
National Association for Business Economics (NABE) **[38190]**
National Association Business Economics Annual Meeting **[21251]**
National Association of Business and Educational Radio [1509], [2704]
National Association of Business and Educational Radio and Association of Communications Technicians [1509], [2704]
National Association of Business Owners & Entrepreneurs (NABOE) **[33473]**
National Association of Cannabis Businesses (NACB) **[4976]**
National Association of Casino Party Operators (NACPO) **[7264]**, **[11901]**
National Association of Casino and Theme Party Operators [7264], [11901]
National Association of Catastrophe Adjusters Annual Convention **[27370]**
National Association for Catering and Events (NACE) **[2665]**, **[6083]**
National Association of Catering Executives [2665], [6083]
National Association of Cemeteries [7198]
National Association of Certified Mediators (NACM) **[10790]**
National Association of Certified Professional Midwives (NACPM) **[8239]**
National Association of Certified Public Bookkeepers, LLC (NACPB) **[1740]**
National Association of Chain Drug Stores (NACDS) **[5140]**
National Association of Chain Drug Stores Resource Center (NACDS) **[5220]**
National Association of Charitable Gift Planners (NACGP) **[7078]**
National Association of Chemical Distributors (NACD) **[20604]**
National Association of Child Care Professionals [2865]
National Association of Christian Women Entrepreneurs (NACWE) **[35631]**

National Association of Clean Air Agencies (NACAA) **[23040]**
National Association of Clean Water Agencies (NACWA) **[23041]**
National Association of Coin Laundry Equipment Operators [5227]
National Association of College Stores (NACS) **[1808]**
National Association of Colleges and Employers (NACE) **[2626]**, **[5436]**
National Association of Competitive Mounted Orienteering (NACMO) **[8310]**
National Association of Computer Consultant Brokers [3423], [3606]
National Association of Computer Consultant Businesses [3423], [3606]
National Association of Computer Database Consultant Businesses [3423], [3606]
National Association of Concessionaires (NAC) **[3831]**
National Association of Concessionaires--Membership Directory [3839]
National Association of Convenience Stores [4423], [4455]
National Association of Corporation Schools [10474], [28251]
National Association of County Agricultural Agents Annual Meeting and Professional Improvement Conference [17175]
National Association of Credit Management (NACM) **[4735]**, **[4761]**, **[20241]**
National Association of Demolition Contractors [3957]
National Association of Development Companies (NADCO) **[28078]**, **[35296]**
National Association of Development Organizations Research Foundation (NADO) **[20705]**
National Association of Direct Sellers [7072]
National Association of Directors of Nursing Administration in Long Term Care (NADONA/LTC) **[11502]**
National Association of Dog Obedience Instructors (NADOI) **[12134]**
National Association for Drama Therapy--Membership List [30877]
National Association on Drug Abuse Problems (NADAP) **[34672]**
National Association for the Education of Young Children (NAEYC) **[2869]**
National Association for the Education of Young Children Annual Conference **[2892]**
National Association of Electrical Distributors (NAED) **[5352]**
National Association of Employment Agencies [5437], [15637]
National Association of Employment Managers [10474], [28251]
National Association of Entrepreneurship (NAE) **[22976]**, **[33474]**
National Association of Environmental Professionals (NAEP) **[31916]**
National Association for Equity, Diversity & Inclusion (NAEDI) **[30513]**
National Association of Export Companies (NEXCO) **[8678]**, **[27423]**
National Association of Exposition Managers [15824]
National Association for Female Executives (NAFE) **[35632]**
National Association of Fine Art Dealers [961]
National Association of Fisheries Commissioners [6768]
National Association of Fleet Administrators [1151], [11471]
National Association of Flood and Stormwater Management Agencies (NAFSMA) **[4825]**
National Association of Floor Covering Distributors [6825]
National Association of Food Equipment Manufacturers [13889]
National Association of Foreign-Trade Zones (NAFTZ) **[27424]**
National Association of Forensic Accountants (NAFA) **[16741]**
National Association of Gambling Regulatory Agencies [7269]
National Association of General Merchandise Representatives (NAGMR) **[1382]**, **[2138]**, **[10576]**
National Association of General Merchandise Representatives Annual Convention **[10583]**
National Association of Government Guaranteed Lenders (NAGGL) **[24935]**
National Association of Governor's Councils on Physical Fitness and Sport [12381]
National Association of Governors' Highway Safety Representatives [5099]
National Association of Greeting Card Publishers [7697]
National Association for Health and Fitness (NAHF) **[12381]**
National Association of Health Stores (NAHS) **[7999]**

National Association of Health Underwriters (NAHU) **[8875]**
National Association of Hispanic Journalists (NAHJ) **[5292]**
National Association of Hispanic Publications, Inc. (NAHP) **[11969]**, **[30284]**
National Association of Holiday Inns of America [8349]
National Association of Home Based Businesses Convention **[26822]**
National Association of Home Builders (NAHB) **[3951]**
National Association of Home Builders Library and Archive Services [3951]
National Association of Home Builders of the U.S. **[3952]**
National Association for Home Care and Hospice (NAHC) **[8240]**
National Association of Hotel Accountants [8345]
National Association of Hotel and Motel Accountants [8345]
National Association of Housing Cooperatives Annual Conference **[24841]**
National Association of Independent Insurers [8857], [9003]
National Association of Independent Lighting Distributors [5410]
National Association of Independent Lubes [12997]
National Association of Independent Publishers Representatives (NAIPR) **[10346]**
National Association of Independent Tire Dealers [15680]
National Association for Indiana Limestone [10727]
National Association of Industrial and Office Properties [13361]
National Association of Innovative Lighting Distributors (NAILD) **[5410]**
National Association of Institutional Agribusiness (NAIA) **[16951]**
National Association of Insurance Commissioners (NAIC) **[9010]**
National Association of Insurance and Financial Advisors - Virginia (NAIFA) **[8876]**
National Association of Insurance and Financial Advisors - Wisconsin **[27222]**
National Association of Investigative Specialists (NAIS) **[12789]**
National Association of Investment Companies [9950], [30272], [35285]
National Association of Jewelry Appraisers (NAJP) **[810]**, **[9969]**
National Association of Landscape Professionals (NALP) **[10080]**
National Association of Legal Investigators (NALI) **[12790]**
National Association of Legal Secretaries [16221]
National Association of Long Term Care Administrator Boards (NAB) **[11503]**
National Association of Magazine Publishers [11967], [12016]
National Association of Mail Service Pharmacies [5142]
National Association of Manufacturers (NAM) **[29079]**
National Association of Master Steam and Hot Water Fitters [459]
National Association of Minority Automobile Dealers (NAMAD) **[11361]**, **[30285]**
National Association of Minority Companies Inc. (NAMCO) **[30286]**
National Association of Minority Contractors (NAMC) **[30287]**
National Association of Mold Inspectors [31917]
National Association of Mold Remediators and Inspectors (NAMRI) **[31917]**
The National Association of Mortgage Brokers (NAMB) **[10999]**
National Association for Music Education (NAFME) **[11171]**
National Association of Music Merchants (NAMM) **[11172]**
National Association of Mutual Insurance Cos (NAMIC) **[27223]**
National Association of Negro Business and Professional Women's Clubs, Inc. (NANBPWC) **[30288]**, **[35633]**
National Association of Part-Time and Temporary Employees (NAPTE) **[31133]**
National Association of Pension Consultants and Administrators [25181]
National Association of Periodical Publishers [11967], [12016]
National Association of Personal Financial Advisors (NAPFA) **[6237]**
National Association of Personnel Consultants [5437], [15637]
National Association of Personnel Services (NAPS) **[5437]**, **[15637]**
National Association of Pet Cemeteries [12131]
National Association of Pet Sitters [12078], [12248]

National Association of Piano Tuners [11313]
National Association of Pizzeria Operators (NAPO) **[13883]**
National Association of Popcorn Manufacturers [3831]
National Association of Postmasters of the United States Convention **[3394]**
National Association Practical Refrigerating Engineers [462]
National Association for the Prevention of Addiction to Narcotics [34672]
National Association of Printing Ink Makers [12720]
National Association of Printing Ink Manufacturers (NAPIM) **[12720]**
National Association of Private Geriatric Care Managers [11491]
National Association of Product Fund Raisers [7072]
National Association of Productivity & Organizing Professionals [12818]
National Association of Professional Accountants (NAPA) **[16742]**
National Association of Professional Background Screeners (NAPBS) **[12791]**
National Association of Professional Band Instrument Repair Technicians Inc. (NAPBIRT) **[11311]**
National Association of Professional Employer Organizations (NAPEO) **[15638]**
National Association of Professional Geriatric Care Managers [11491]
National Association of Professional Insurance Agents (PIA) **[8877], [27384]**
National Association of Professional Mortgage Women (NAPMW) **[11000]**
National Association of Professional Organizers (NAPO) **[12818]**
National Association of Professional Pet Sitters (NAPPS) **[12078], [12248]**
National Association of Professional Process Servers (NAPPS) **[10977]**
National Association of Professional Women [33463]
National Association of Professional Women Albuquerque Chapter [42271]
National Association of Professional Women Anchorage Chapter [36203]
National Association of Professional Women Annapolis Chapter [40333]
National Association of Professional Women Atlanta Chapter [38624]
National Association of Professional Women Bakersfield Chapter [36541]
National Association of Professional Women Bellevue Chapter [45994]
National Association of Professional Women Boston Chapter [40489]
National Association of Professional Women Central Houston Chapter [44900]
National Association of Professional Women Chesapeake Chapter [45763]
National Association of Professional Women Chicago Chapter [38974]
National Association of Professional Women Cincinnati Chapter [43341]
National Association of Professional Women Cleveland Chapter [43342]
National Association of Professional Women in Construction (PWC) **[3953]**
National Association of Professional Women Coral Gables Chapter [38209]
National Association of Professional Women Dallas Chapter [44901]
National Association of Professional Women DeKalb-Gwinnett Chapter [38625]
National Association of Professional Women Detroit Chapter [40799]
National Association of Professional Women Fairfield County Chapter [37977]
National Association of Professional Women Greensboro Chapter [43035]
National Association of Professional Women Hartford County Chapter [37978]
National Association of Professional Women Long Beach Chapter [36542]
National Association of Professional Women Los Angeles Chapter [36543]
National Association of Professional Women Manchester Chapter [41968]
National Association of Professional Women Memphis Chapter [44681]
National Association of Professional Women Milwaukee Chapter [46314]
National Association of Professional Women Minneapolis-St. Paul Chapter [41151]
National Association of Professional Women Nashville Chapter [44682]

National Association of Professional Women Oakland Chapter [36544]
National Association of Professional Women Ocala Chapter [38211]
National Association of Professional Women Oklahoma City Chapter [43704]
National Association of Professional Women Orlando Chapter [38212]
National Association of Professional Women Pasadena Chapter [36545]
National Association of Professional Women Pembroke Pines Chapter [38213]
National Association of Professional Women Philadelphia Chapter [44089]
National Association of Professional Women Phoenix Chapter [36263]
National Association of Professional Women Pittsburgh Chapter [44090]
National Association of Professional Women Providence Chapter [44450]
National Association of Professional Women Raleigh Durham Chapter [43036]
National Association of Professional Women San Diego Chapter [36546]
National Association of Professional Women San Francisco Chapter [36548]
National Association of Professional Women Santa Monica Chapter [36549]
National Association of Professional Women Schaumburg Chapter [38975]
National Association of Professional Women Seattle Chapter [45995]
National Association of Professional Women South Denver Chapter [37775]
National Association of Professional Women Tulsa Chapter [43705]
National Association of Professional Women West Denver Chapter [37776]
National Association of Professionals in Energy Conservation [32713]
National Association of Public Insurance Adjusters (NAPIA) **[27224]**
National Association of Public Relations Counsel [12924], [31744]
National Association of Public Television Stations [15567]
National Association of Publishers' Representatives, Inc. (NAPR) **[31838]**
National Association of Purchasing Agents [31905]
National Association of Purchasing Management [31905]
National Association of Radio Telephone Systems [1509], [2704]
National Association of Radio and Television Broadcasters [13021], [13063], [15575]
The National Association of Railway Business Women (NARBW) **[35634]**
National Association of Real Estate Appraisers (NAREA) **[811]**
National Association of Real Estate Brokers (NAREB) **[11001], [13100]**
National Association of Real Estate Companies (NAREC) **[13363]**
National Association of Real Estate Exchanges [13101], [13354], [13365]
National Association of Real Estate Investment Funds [13364]
National Association of Real Estate Investment Trusts (NAREIT) **[13364]**
National Association of Realtors (NAR) **[13101], [13354], [13365]**
National Association of Record Merchandisers [3410], [13648]
National Association Recycling Industries [13688]
National Association of Recycling Industries [13688]
National Association of Registered Nursing Homes [1021], [11494], [25641]
National Association of Reinforcing Steel Contractors (NARSC) **[3954]**
National Association of the Remodeling Industry (NARI) **[3955]**
National Association of Residential Property Managers (NARPM) **[12866]**
National Association of Retail Grocers of the United States [4424], [7715]
National Association of Retail Ice Cream Manufacturers [8540]
National Association of Review Appraisers and Mortgage Underwriters (NARA/MU) **[11002], [13102]**
National Association of Review Appraisers and Mortgage Underwriters Convention - National Conference & Expo **[11097]**
National Association of RV Parks & Campgrounds (ARVC) **[2506]**
National Association of Sales Managers [10474], [28251]

National Association of Sales Professionals (NASP) **[32430]**
National Association of School Music Dealers, Inc. (NASMD) **[11173], [11258]**
National Association of Schools of Dance (NASD) **[4845]**
National Association of Schools of Music (NASM) **[11174]**
National Association of Schools of Music--Directory Lists **[11180]**
National Association of Schools of Public Affairs and Administration [31677]
National Association of Securities Commissioners [9298]
National Association of Security Companies (NASCO) **[14376]**
National Association for the Self-Employed (NASE) **[33475], [34456]**
National Association of Shellfish Commissioners [6768]
National Association of Shoe Chain Stores [14667]
National Association of Small Business Contractors (NASBC) **[38167]**
National Association of Small Business Investment Companies [24592], [35309]
National Association of Social Workers (NASW) **[25681]**
National Association for the Specialty Food Trade [8002], [15003]
National Association of Sporting Goods Wholesalers (NASGW) **[15078]**
National Association of State Beer Association Secretaries [35485]
National Association of State Boards of Accountancy (NASBA) **[37]**
National Association of State Civil Defense Directors [28261]
National Association of State Directors for Disaster Preparedness [28261]
National Association of State Farm Agents (NASFA) **[8878]**
National Association of State Units on Aging [11504]
National Association of States United for Aging and Disabilities (NASUAD) **[11504]**
National Association for the Study and Performance of African-American Music (NASPAAM) **[11175]**
National Association of Tax Practitioners [38], [15354]
National Association of Tax Professionals (NATP) **[38], [15354]**
National Association of Tax Professionals Convention **[16864]**
National Association of Taxicab Owners [15508]
National Association of Teachers of Singing (NATS) **[11176]**
National Association of Television and Electronic Servicers of America [3573], [4381]
National Association of Television Program Executives (NATPE) **[15576]**
National Association of Theatre Owners (NATO) **[11120]**
National Association of Truck Stop Operators Connect [14572], [32356]
National Association of Tutoring [16124]
National Association of Urban Flood Management Agencies [4825]
National Association of Vision Professionals (NAVP) **[16291]**
National Association of Vision Program Consultants [16291]
National Association of Visual Education Dealers [6159]
National Association of Webmasters [9088]
National Association of Wheat Growers (NAWG) **[16952]**
National Association of Wholesaler-Distributors (NAW) **[20605], [35486]**
National Association of Wholesalers [20605], [35486]
National Association of Women Artists, Inc. News **[980]**
National Association of Women Business Owners (NAWBO) **[35635]**
National Association of Women Business Owners Atlanta (NAWBO) **[35636]**
National Association of Women Business Owners Baltimore Regional Chapter (NAWBO) **[35637]**
National Association of Women Business Owners Buffalo Niagara (NAWBO) **[35638]**
National Association of Women Business Owners Central Illinois **[35639]**
National Association of Women Business Owners Central Jersey **[35640]**
National Association of Women Business Owners Central Oklahoma **[43706]**
National Association of Women Business Owners Charlotte **[43037]**
National Association of Women Business Owners Chicago **[35641]**
National Association of Women Business Owners Cleveland **[35642]**
National Association of Women Business Owners Columbus Ohio **[35643], [43344]**

National Association of Women Business Owners Dallas/Ft. Worth (NAWBO) **[35644]**
National Association of Women Business Owners Delaware **[35645]**
National Association of Women Business Owners - Greater Detroit Chapter (NAWBO-GDC) **[35646]**, **[40807]**
National Association of Women Business Owners - Greater Philadelphia Chapter (NAWBO) **[35647]**
National Association of Women Business Owners Greater Raleigh (NAWBOGR) **[43038]**
National Association of Women Business Owners Houston **[35648]**
National Association of Women Business Owners - Indianapolis (NAWBO) **[35649]**
National Association of Women Business Owners Kansas City (NAWBO-KC) **[41468]**
National Association of Women Business Owners Lakeland Metro **[38214]**
National Association of Women Business Owners - Lexington **[35650]**
National Association of Women Business Owners Long Island Chapter (NAWBO/LI) **[42385]**
National Association of Women Business Owners Los Angeles (NAWBO-LA) **[35651]**, **[36552]**
National Association of Women Business Owners Louisville **[39989]**
National Association of Women Business Owners Miami **[35652]**
National Association of Women Business Owners Minnesota (NAWBO-MN) **[35653]**
National Association of Women Business Owners Nashville (NAWBO) **[35654]**
National Association of Women Business Owners New York City (NAWBO-NYC) **[35655]**
National Association of Women Business Owners - Northern New Mexico **[35656]**
National Association of Women Business Owners Orange County (NAWBO-OC) **[35657]**
National Association of Women Business Owners Phoenix Metro Chapter **[35658]**
National Association of Women Business Owners Richmond **[35659]**
National Association of Women Business Owners Sacramento Valley **[35660]**
National Association of Women Business Owners Salt Lake City (NAWBO/SLC) **[45603]**
National Association of Women Business Owners San Diego **[35661]**
National Association of Women Business Owners San Francisco Bay Area (NAWBO-SFBA) **[36553]**
National Association of Women Business Owners Sedona-Verde Valley **[35662]**
National Association of Women Business Owners Silicon Valley (NAWBOSV) **[35663]**
National Association of Women Business Owners South Florida **[38215]**
National Association of Women Business Owners South Jersey (NAWBO SJ) **[35664]**
National Association of Women Business Owners Southern Nevada (NAWBO SNV) **[41908]**
National Association of Women Business Owners Ventura County (NAWBO-VC) **[35665]**
National Association of Women in Construction (NAWIC) **[3956]**
National Association of Women MBAs (NAWMBA) **[35666]**
National Association of Women Sales Professionals (NAWSP) **[32431]**, **[35667]**
National Association of Women's Yellow Pages [29576], [35696]
National Auctioneers Association (NAA) **[1065]**, **[6065]**
National Audio-Visual Association [6159]
National Audubon Aullwood Center [6006]
National Auto Auction Association (NAAA) **[1066]**, **[11362]**
National Auto Auction Association--Membership Directory **[1075]**
National Auto Body Council (NABC) **[14537]**
National Automatic Laundry and Cleaning Council [5225]
National Automatic Merchandising Association (NAMA) **[16247]**
National Automobile Dealers Association (NADA) **[11363]**
National Automotive Radiator Service Association [14536]
National Automotive Radiator Service Association National Convention **[14571]**
National Autosound Challenge Association [2562]
National Aviation Trades Association [423]
"National Award Goes to eSmartTax.com for Having 'Best Tax Preparation Software' Available to Online Tax Filers" in Investment Weekly News (February 18, 2012, pp. 706) **[15403]**, **[33877]**

National Ayurvedic Medical Association (NAMA) **[12489]**
National Bagel Association (NBA) **[1207]**
National Ballroom & Entertainment Association (NBEA) **[4846]**
National Ballroom Operators Association [4846]
National Barbecue Association (2666], [13884]
National Barbecue & Grilling Association (NBBQA) **[2666]**, **[13884]**
National Beauty Culturists' League, Inc. (NBCL) **[4505]**, **[7856]**
National Beef Council [2427], [2440]
National Beer Wholesalers Association (NBWA) **[10312]**
National Beer Wholesalers' Association of America [10312]
National Bicycle Dealers Association (NBDA) **[1513]**
National Bituminous Concrete Association [1548], [1561]
National Black Chamber of Commerce (NBCC) **[30289]**, **[38168]**
National Black Child Development Institute (NBCDI) **[2870]**
National Black MBA Association, Inc. (NBMBAA) **[30290]**
National Black MBA Association Inc. - Chicago Chapter **[21315]**, **[30291]**
National Black McDonald's Operators Association (NBMOA) **[13885]**
National Black Music Caucus of the Music Educators National Conference [11175]
National Black Owned Broadcasters Association [13020], [30282]
National Black Public Relations Society (NBPRS) **[31743]**
National Board for Certified Counselors [2594]
National Board for Certified Counselors, Inc. and Affiliates (NBCC) **[2594]**
National Board of Examiners in Optometry (NBEO) **[16292]**
National Bottlers Association [3865], [14300]
National Bottlers Protective Association [3865], [14300]
National Bowlers Journal [1882]
The National Bowling Association Inc. (TNBA) **[1873]**
National Bowling Writer's Association [5284]
National Brotherhood of Skiers (NBS) **[14730]**
National Building Material Distribution Association--Membership & Product Directory [10397]
National Building Material Distributors Association [3962]
National Building Material Distributors Association--Membership & Product Directory [10397]
National Bulk Vendors Association (NBVA) **[16248]**
National Bureau of Economic Research (NBER) **[15495]**
National Burglar and Fire Alarm Association [14372]
National Bus Trader **[15769]**
National Bus Traffic Association (NBTA) **[15507]**
National Business Association (NBA) **[33476]**
National Business Aviation Association (NBAA) **[424]**
National Business Coalition on Health Conference **[24842]**
National Business Development Association (NBDA) **[19427]**
National Business and Disability Council (NBDC) **[5438]**
National Business Education Association (NBEA) **[21316]**
National Business Education Association Convention **[21691]**
National Business Forms Association [11661]
National Business Incubation Association [8801], [33464]
National Business Research Institute Inc. (NBRI) **[29508]**
National Business Teachers Association [21316]
National Cable and Telecommunications Association (NCTA) **[2444]**, **[15577]**
National Cable Television Association [2444], [15577]
National Campers and Hikers Association [2504]
National Campground Owners Association [2506]
National Candy Wholesalers Association [2535], [15692]
National Cannabis Chamber of Commerce (NCCC) **[4977]**
National Cannabis Industry Association (NCIA) **[4978]**
National Career Development Association (NCDA) **[2595]**
National Cattlemen's Beef Association (NCBA) **[2427]**, **[2440]**
"National Cattlemen's Beef Association" in Retail Merchandiser (Vol. 51, September-October 2011, No. 5, pp. 77) **[17078]**, **[32218]**
The National Center American Indian Procurement Technical Assistance Center - Virginia **[45931]**
National Center for Assisted Living [1021], [11494], [25641]
National Center for Bicycling and Walking (NCBW) **[1514]**
National Center for Manufacturing Sciences (NCMS) **[29476]**
National Center for Montessori Education and American Montessori Society [2864]
National Center for Public Policy Research (NCPPR) **[2297]**, **[20212]**, **[31715]**

National Center for Research in Vocational Education [9993]
National Center for Social Policy and Practice [25681]
National Center for Technology Planning (NCTP) **[26476]**
National Chimney Sweep Guild (NCSG) **[2919]**
National Chimney Sweep Guild Conference and Expo **[2921]**
National Chincoteague Pony Association (NCPA) **[639]**
National Christmas Tree Association (NCTA) **[2928]**
National Citizens' Coalition for Nursing Home Reform [11505]
National City Chamber of Commerce (NCCC) **[37043]**
National Cleaners Association (NCA) **[5228]**
National Clearinghouse for Alcohol and Drug Information Library **[34691]**
National Clearinghouse for Smoking and Health Database [10938], [12469]
National Clothesline **[5249]**
National Club Council [1310]
National Club Industry Association of America [1310]
National Coalition for Advanced Manufacturing [29080]
National Coalition for Campus Child Care [2871]
National Coalition for Campus Children's Centers (NCCCC) **[2871]**
National Coalition for Children's Centers [2871]
National Coalition to Preserve Scenic Beauty [31843]
National Coffee Association of U.S.A. Annual Convention **[3204]**
National Coffee Association of U.S.A. Inc. (NCA) **[3173]**, **[7541]**
National Coffee Service Association [16247]
National Coin & Bullion Association (NCBA) **[3229]**
National Commercial Finance Association [28080], [35307]
National Commercial Finance Conference [28080], [35307]
National Committee on Aging of National Social Welfare Assembly [178]
National Committee for Clinical Laboratory Standards [10909]
National Committee for the Improvement of Nursing Services [8242]
National Committee on Property Insurance [35976]
National Committee for Women in Public Administration [31678]
National Communication Council for Human Services [12924], [31744]
National Community Pharmacists Association (NCPA) **[5141]**, **[15496]**
National Community Pharmacists Association's Annual Convention [5205]
National Community Television Association [2444], [15577]
National Concierge Association (NCA) **[3868]**
National Concrete Burial Vault Association (NCBVA) **[7201]**
National Concrete Masonry Association (NCMA) **[10731]**, **[10750]**, **[10751]**
National Confectioners Association (NCA) **[2536]**
National Confectioners Sales Association (NCSA) **[2537]**
National Confectionery Sales Association of America [2537]
National Conference [21695]
National Conference of Commercial Receivable Companies [28080], [35307]
National Conference on Correctional Health Care **[26070]**
National Conference of CPA Practitioners (NCCPAP) **[39]**
National Conference on Education **[21692]**
National Conference & Expo [10256]
National Conference of State Liquor Administrators--Official Directory **[1344]**
National Consortium for Computer-Based Music Instruction [11163]
National Consumer Voice for Quality Long-Term Care [11505]
National Contact Lens Examiners (NCLE) **[16293]**
National Contract Management Association (NCMA) **[25102]**
National Convenience Store Distributors Association [20599]
National Cooperative Bank, Corporate Banking Div. (NCB) **[24487]**
National Coordinating Committee for Multiemployer Plans (NCCMP) **[17266]**
National Corporate Cash Management Association [23695]
National Costumers Association (NCA) **[4552]**
National Council of Acoustical Consultants--Directory **[30876]**
National Council for Advanced Manufacturing (NACFAM) **[29080]**
National Council on Aging (NCOA) **[178]**

National Council on the Aging [178]
National Council of Agricultural Employers (NCAE) **[16953]**
National Council of American Importers [8677], [27391]
National Council on Bioethics in Human Research [23461]
National Council for Business Education [21316]
National Council of Chain Restaurants (NCCR) **[6890]**, **[13886]**
National Council on Compulsive Gambling [7265]
National Council to Control Handguns [7840]
National Council of Entrepreneurial Tech Transfer (NCET2) **[34667]**
National Council on Ethics in Human Research [23461]
National Council of Exchangors (NCE) **[13103]**
National Council on Family Relations Annual Conference [21696]
National Council of Health Centers [1021], [11494], [25641]
National Council on Hotel and Restaurant Education [4459], [8350]
National Council of the Housing Industry - National Housing Center Council [3949]
National Council for Interior Design Qualification (NCIDQ) **[9026]**
National Council of Investigation and Security Services Inc. (NCISS) **[12792]**, **[14377]**
National Council of Primary Education [2867]
National Council on Problem Gambling (NCPG) **[7265]**
National Council of Self-Insurers (NCSI) **[27225]**
National Council of Teachers of Mathematics Annual Convention **[21693]**
National Court Clubs Association [12378], [15666]
National Court Reporters Association (NCRA) **[16222]**
National CPA Group [17]
National Credit Union Administration - Office of Small and Disadvantaged Business Utilization **[47299]**
National Credit Union Administration, Region 2 - Alexandria Regional Office [47301]
National Credit Union Administration Region I - Albany **[47300]**
National Credit Union Administration Region II - Capital **[47301]**
National Credit Union Administration Region III - Atlanta **[47302]**
National Credit Union Administration Region IV - Austin **[47303]**
National Credit Union Administration Region V - Tempe **[47304]**
The National Culinary Review (NCR) **[2687]**, **[14047]**, **[15042]**
National Customs Brokers and Forwarders Association of America, Inc. (NCBFAA) **[2139]**, **[7024]**
National Cybersecurity Society (NCSS) **[3463]**
National Dairy Council [8538]
National Dance Guild [4834]
National Dance Teachers Guild [4834]
National Decorating Products Association [9029], [11873]
National Delinquency Survey (NDS) **[13317]**
National Demolition Association (NDA) **[3957]**
National Development Council (NDC) **[20706]**
National Dietary Foods Association [8000]
National Directory of Woman-Owned Business Firms **[35825]**, **[35927]**
National District Heating Association [456]
National Diversity Council (NDC) **[30514]**
National Dog Groomers Association of America, Inc. (NDGAA) **[12079]**
National Door Manufacturers Association [2632]
National Drug Code Directory **[5176]**
National Eating Disorder Information Centre (NEDIC) **[11569]**, **[11616]**, **[16519]**
National Economic Association (NEA) **[20707]**, **[30515]**
National Economic Development and Law Center [20699]
National Education Association Annual Meeting **[27371]**
National Electric Sign Association [14700]
National Electrical Contractors Association (NECA) **[5353]**
National Electrical Contractors Association - West Virginia-Ohio Valley Chapter [46249]
National Electrical Manufacturers Association (NEMA) **[5354]**
National Electrical Manufacturers Representatives Association (NEMRA) **[5355]**
National Electrical Wholesalers Association [5352]
National Electrolysis Organization [7847]
National Electronic Service Dealers Association [3573], [4381]
National Electronics Sales and Service Dealers Association [3573], [4381]
National Electronics Service Dealers Association (NESDA) **[3573]**, **[4381]**

National Emergency Management Association (NEMA) **[28261]**
National Employment Association [5437], [15637]
National Employment Association and National Association of Personnel [5437], [15637]
National Employment Board [5437], [15637]
National Employment Counseling Association (NECA) **[2596]**
National Entrepreneur Center (NEC) **[38575]**
National Entrepreneurs Association **[22462]**
National Entrepreneurs Association (NEA) **[22977]**, **[34478]**
National Environmental Balancing Bureau (NEBB) **[461]**
National Environmental Health Association (NEHA) **[6010]**
National Environmental, Safety and Health Training Association (NESHTA) **[23042]**
National Environmental Training Association [23042]
National Erectors Association [3925]
National Ethics Association (NEA) **[23462]**
National Ethics Bureau [23462]
National Facilities Management and Technology Conference and Expo **[2083]**
National Facility Management Association [12865]
National Fall Conference **[926]**
National Families in Action (NFIA) **[26101]**
National Farm Medicine Center (NFMC) **[35995]**
National Farm and Ranch Business Management Education Association (NFRBMEA) **[16954]**
National Federation of Community Broadcasters (NFCB) **[13022]**
National Federation of Filipino American Associations (NaFFAA) **[22463]**
National Federation of Independent Business (NFIB) **[33477]**
National Federation of Independent Business Alabama **[36046]**
National Federation of Independent Business Alaska **[36204]**
National Federation of Independent Business Connecticut **[37979]**
National Federation of Independent Business Delaware (NFIB) **[38123]**
National Federation of Independent Business Georgia **[38627]**
National Federation of Independent Business Maine **[40242]**
National Federation of Independent Business Maryland **[40334]**
National Federation of Independent Business Mississippi **[41369]**
National Federation of Independent Business Missouri **[41469]**
National Federation of Independent Business Montana **[41717]**
National Federation of Independent Business Nebraska **[41816]**
National Federation of Independent Business New Jersey **[33478]**, **[42032]**
National Federation of Independent Business Oregon (NFIB-OR) **[43904]**
National Federation of Independent Business Rhode Island **[44451]**
National Federation of Independent Business South Carolina **[44497]**
National Federation of Independent Business Tennessee **[44685]**
National Federation of Independent Business Virginia **[45764]**
National Federation of Nonprofits [1048]
National Federation of Professional Trainers (NFPT) **[12382]**
National Federation of Tourist Guide Associations USA (NFTGA-USA) **[15724]**
National Feed Ingredients Association [16925]
National Fertilizer Development Center [17213]
National Fertilizer and Environmental Research Center [17213]
National Field Archery Association (NFAA) **[845]**
National Fiery Foods and Barbeque Show **[7814]**, **[14095]**
National Fisherman **[6789]**
National Floor Trends Magazine [6836], [16231]
The National Food Lab (NFL) **[3867]**
National Food Service Management Institute [11571]
National Food Truck Association (NFTA) **[6960]**, **[13887]**
National Foodworks Services (NFS) **[39417]**
National Foreign Trade Council (NFTC) **[8679]**
National Forest Recreation Association (NFRA) **[2507]**
National Forum for Black Public Administrators (NFBPA) **[31675]**
National Foundation on the Arts and the Humanities-- Institute of Museum Services Grant Awards [971]

National Foundation for Credit Counseling (NFCC) **[4736]**, **[4754]**
National Foundation of Health, Welfare and Pension Plans [17264], [19730]
National Foundation for Teaching Entrepreneurship [22464], [36004]
National Frame Building Association (NFBA) **[3958]**
National Franchise Associates, Inc. (NFA) **[2359]**, **[24488]**, **[24508]**
National Franchise Association [24311]
National Franchise Sales (NFS) **[24489]**
National Franchisee Association (NFA) **[24311]**
National Frozen Food Association--Membership Directory [7756]
National Frozen Food Locker Association [2425]
National Frozen Food Locker Institute [2425]
National Frozen and Refrigerated Foods Association (NFRA) **[7714]**
National Frozen and Refrigerated Foods Association-- Membership Directory [7756]
National Funeral Directors Association (NFDA) **[7202]**, **[7224]**
National Funeral Directors and Morticians Association (NFDMA) **[7203]**
National Furniture Traffic Conference [8197]
National Gardening Association (NGA) **[7609]**, **[7678]**
National Glass Association (NGA) **[7490]**
National Glass Clubs Affiliate [734], [3225]
National Glaucoma Research Report **[16308]**
National Golf Foundation (NGF) **[7512]**, **[10983]**
National Grocers Association (NGA) **[4424]**, **[7715]**
National Grocers Association Convention and Buying/Merchandising Expo [7807]
National Guild for Community Arts Education-- Membership Directory [4854]
National Guild of Community Schools of the Arts-- Membership Directory [4854]
National Guild of Professional Paperhangers [11875]
National Hair System Culture League [4505], [7856]
National Hardwood Lumber Association (NHLA) **[10380]**, **[10413]**
National Hay Association (NHA) **[16955]**
National Head Start Association (NHSA) **[2872]**
National Head Start Association Conference **[21694]**
National Health Council (NHC) **[8241]**
National Hearing Aid Society [8133]
National Hemp Association (NHA) **[4979]**
National Hispanic Business Group (NHBG) **[30292]**
National Hispanic Business Women Association (NHBWA) **[30293]**
National Hispanic Corporate Council (NHCC) **[30294]**
National Hispanic Media Coalition (NHMC) **[30295]**, **[31839]**
National Home Furnishings Association [8194]
National Home Furnishings Representatives Association [8198]
National Home Improvement Council [3955]
National Honey Packers and Dealers Association (NHPDA) **[1444]**
National Housing Endowment (NHE) **[3959]**
National Housing Law Project (NHLP) **[780]**
National Human Resources Association (NHRA) **[26842]**
National Ice Cream Retailers Association [8540]
National Ice Cream and Yogurt Retailers Association [8540]
National Independent Automobile Dealers Association (NIADA) **[11364]**
National Indian Gaming Association (NIGA) **[7266]**
National Indian Gaming Commission (NIGC) **[7267]**
National Indoor Tennis Association [12378], [15666]
National Industrial Conference Board [29059]
National Industrial Property Management Association [12867]
National Industrial Traffic League [7025]
The National Industrial Transportation League (NITL) **[7025]**
National Information Standards Organization (NISO) **[1627]**
National Institute for Automotive Service Excellence (ASE) **[14538]**
National Institute of Building Sciences (NIBS) **[4376]**
National Institute of Credit [4735], [4761], [20241]
National Institute for Dispute Resolution [10786]
National Institute of Drycleaning [5226], [5264], [5265]
National Institute for Fitness and Sport (NIFS) **[12515]**
National Institute for the Foodservice Industry - Educational Foundation of the National Restaurant Association [4460], [6891], [13888]
National Institute of Governmental Purchasing [25174]
National Institute of Locker and Freezer Provisioners [2425]
National Institute of Mental Health - Division of Adult Translational Research and Treatment Development - Small Business Innovation Research Program [40349]

National Institute of Mental Health - Division of Adult Translational Research and Treatment Development - Small Business Technology Transfer Program [40350]
National Institute for Occupational Safety and Health Education and Research Center [35997]
National Institute for Occupational Safety and Health - Small Business Assistance and Outreach Cross-Sector Program [30951], [43370]
National Institute of Pension Administrators (NIPA) [17267]
National Institute of Wood Kitchen Cabinets [8199]
National Institutes of Health - Division of Contracts and Grants - Small and Disadvantaged Business Utilization Specialist [47635]
National Insulation and Abatement Contractors Association [3960], [8847]
National Insulation and Abatement Contractors Association--Membership [8850]
National Insulation Association (NIA) [3960], [8847]
National Insulation Association Annual Convention [8852]
National Insulation Association--Membership Directory and Resource Guide [8850]
National Insulation Contractors Association [3960], [8847]
National Insurance Buyers Association [8879]
National-Interstate Council of State Boards of Cosmetology (NIC) [4506], [7857]
National Investment Company Service Association (NICSA) [9295]
National Investor Relations Institute (NIRI) [9296]
National Junior Hereford Association (NJHA) [16956]
National Kitchen and Bath Association (NKBA) [8200], [9027]
National Kitchen Cabinet Association [8199]
National Labor Relations Board (NLRB) [47305]
National Labor Relations Board - Region 1 - Boston Regional Office [47306]
National Labor Relations Board - Region 2 - New York Regional Office [47307]
National Labor Relations Board - Region 3 - Buffalo Regional Office [47308]
National Labor Relations Board - Region 4 - Philadelphia Regional Office [47309]
National Labor Relations Board Region 5 [47310]
National Labor Relations Board - Region 5 - Baltimore Regional Office [47311]
National Labor Relations Board - Region 6 - Pittsburgh Regional Office [47312]
National Labor Relations Board - Region 7 - Detroit Regional Office [47313]
National Labor Relations Board - Region 8 - Cleveland Regional Office [47314]
National Labor Relations Board - Region 9 - Cincinnati Regional Office [47315]
National Labor Relations Board - Region 10 - Atlanta Regional Office [47316]
National Labor Relations Board - Region 11 - Winston-Salem Regional Office [47317]
National Labor Relations Board - Region 12 - Tampa Regional Office [47318]
National Labor Relations Board - Region 13 - Chicago Regional Office [47319]
National Labor Relations Board - Region 14 - St. Louis Regional Office [47320]
National Labor Relations Board - Region 16 - Ft. Worth Regional Office [47321]
National Labor Relations Board - Region 17 - Overland Park Regional Office [47322]
National Labor Relations Board - Region 18 - Minneapolis Regional Office [47323]
National Labor Relations Board - Region 19 - Seattle Regional Office [47324]
National Labor Relations Board - Region 20 - San Francisco Regional Office [47325]
National Labor Relations Board - Region 21 - Los Angeles Regional Office [47326]
National Labor Relations Board - Region 22 - Newark Regional Office [47327]
National Labor Relations Board - Region 25 - Indianapolis Regional Office [47328]
National Labor Relations Board - Region 26 - Memphis Regional Office [47329]
National Labor Relations Board - Region 27 - Denver Regional Office [47330]
National Labor Relations Board - Region 28 - Phoenix Regional Office [47331]
National Labor Relations Board - Region 29 - Brooklyn Regional Office [47332]
National Labor Relations Board - Region 31 - Los Angeles Regional Office [47333]
National Labor Relations Board - Region 32 - Oakland Regional Office [47334]
National Labor Relations Board - Region 34 - Hartford Regional Office [47335]

National Latina Business Women Association (NLBWA) [30296], [35668]
National Laundry Equipment [10197]
The National Law Journal [18790]
National League for Nursing (NLN) [8242]
National League for Nursing Education [8242]
National Leather and Shoe Finders Association [14662]
National LICA Winter Convention [10062]
National Licensed Beverage Association [10310]
National Lighting Bureau (NLB) [5411]
National Limousine Association (NLA) [10277]
National Live Stock and Meat Board [2427], [2440]
The National Locksmith [10359]
National Locksmith Suppliers Association [10353]
National Luggage Dealers Association (NLDA) [10363]
National Lumber and Building Material Dealers Association (NLBMDA) [7914], [10381]
National Machine Accountants Association [3766]
National Machine Tool Builders' Association [29072]
National Management Association [28262]
National Marine Bankers Association [10593]
National Marine Distributors Association (NMDA) [10591]
National Marine Electronics Association (NMEA) [10592]
National Marine Lenders Association (NMLA) [10593]
National Marine Manufacturers Association (NMMA) [1230], [10594]
National Marine Representatives Association-- Membership Directory (Internet only) [10606]
National Midas Dealers Association [14535]
National Mineral Feed Association [16925]
National Minority Business Campaign [30263]
National Minority Business Council (NMBC) [30297]
National Minority Business Directories [30263]
National Minority Purchasing Council [30298]
National Minority Supplier Development Council (NMSDC) [30298]
National Minority and Women-Owned Business Directory [30370]
National Mobile Radio System [1509], [2704]
National Mortgage News [11096], [28235]
National MultiCultural Institute [30508], [30658]
National Museum of Roller Skating Archives [14726]
National Music Camp [11223]
National Needlework Association Trade Show [4631]
National Negro Funeral Directors and Morticians Association [7203]
National Newspaper Promotion Association [11965]
National Notary Association (NNA) [31676]
National Nursing Accrediting Service [8242]
National Nutritional Foods Association [8000]
National Oak Flooring Manufacturers Association [3961]
National Office Machine Dealers Association [11658], [16528]
National Oil and Acrylic Painters' Society (NOAPS) [3289]
National Onion Association (NOA) [16957]
National Opera Association--Membership Directory [11181]
National Optometric Association (NOA) [16294]
National Organization for Public Health Nursing [8242]
National Organization for the Reform of Marijuana Laws (NORML) [4980]
National Organization of Tutoring and Mentoring Centers [16124]
National Outdoor Showmen's Association [595]
National Paint and Coatings Association [11854], [11871]
National Paint, Oil and Varnish Association [11854], [11871]
National Park Service - Business Utilization and Development Specialist - Outdoor Recreation Information Center [47681]
National Park Service - Business Utilization and Development Specialist - Pacific Northwest Region [47682]
National Pawnbrokers Association (NPA) [11914]
National Payment Integrity and Resolution Center [47808]
National Payroll Institute [11925], [16743]
National Pediculosis Association (NPA) [21711]
National Personnel Association [10474], [28251]
National Pest Management Association (NPMA) [12038], [12065]
National Pesticide Information Retrieval System (NPIRS) [12063]
National Pharmaceutical Alliance [5133]
National Piano Foundation (NPF) [11312]
National Piano Manufacturers Association of America [11312]
National Pool League [1542], [12684]
The National Press Club (NPC) [5349], [15629]
National Printing Equipment Association [12716]
National Private Truck Council (NPTC) [16058]
National Procurement Institute (NPI) [31906]

National Professional Service Convention (NPSC) [4415]
National Property Inspections (NPI) [2037]
National Property Management Association (NPMA) [12867]
National and Provincial Parks Association of Canada [5503]
National Public Records Research Association (NPRRA) [7348]
National Publishers Association [11967], [12016]
National Purchasing Institute [31906]
National Radio Broadcasters Association [13021], [13063], [15575]
National Ready Mixed Concrete Association Annual Convention [4299]
National Real Estate Investor [13325], [13607]
National Remodelers Association [3955]
National Renewable Energy Laboratory - Office of Education Programs [14972]
National Research Council of Canada (NRC) [46829]
National Resource Center for Health and Safety in Child Care [2873]
National Resource Center for Health and Safety in Child Care and Early Education (NRC) [2873]
National Restaurant Association (NRA) [3832], [4878], [8090], [14306]
National Restaurant Association Educational Foundation (NRAEF) [4460], [6891], [13888]
National Restaurant Association-Quality Assurance Executive Study Group [6948]
National Restaurant Association Restaurant and Hotel-Motel Show [8491]
National Restaurant Association Show [8491]
National Restaurant Show [8491]
National Resume Writers' Association (NRWA) [14310]
National Retail Federation (NRF) [3088], [32082]
National Retail Furniture Association [8194]
National Retail Grocers Secretaries Association [7710]
National Retail Liquor Package Stores Association [10310]
National Retail Lumber Dealers Association [7914], [10381]
National Retail Merchants Association [3088], [32082]
National Roofing Contractors Association (NRCA) [14321]
National Roofing Contractors Association--Membership Directory [14331]
National Rural Health Association Annual Rural Health Conference [26071]
The National RV Trade Show [13683]
National Safety Council (NSC) [35933], [35982]
National Sales Network (NSN) [30299], [32432]
National Sash and Door Jobbers Association [2633]
National School Orchestra Association [11162]
National Science Foundation (OSDBU) - Office of Small and Disadvantaged Business Utilization [47336]
National Science Foundation (NSF) - Small Business Innovation Research Programs [47337]
National Science Foundation - Small Business Technology Transfer Program [47338]
National Science Teachers Association Conference [21695]
National Scientific Services [34686]
National Security Traders Association [9300]
National Selected Morticians [7204]
National Shade Tree Evaluation [10077]
National Shellfisheries Association (NSA) [6768]
National Shoe Retailers Association (NSRA) [14668], [14699]
National Ski Equipment and Apparel Association [14735]
National Ski Patrol (NSP) [14731]
National Ski Retailers Association [14732], [15079]
National Ski and Snowboard Retailers Association (NSSRA) [14732], [15079]
National Small Business Association (NSBA) [24590], [33479], [38191]
National Small Business Development Center Advisory Board [38157]
National Small Business Federal Contracting Summit [33638]
National Small Business United [24590], [33479], [38191]
National Small Business United-Arizona Chapter [36259]
National Social Work Library [25681]
National Society of Accountants (NSA) [40], [15355]
National Society of Accountants for Cooperatives (NSAC) [41]
National Society of Compliance Professionals (NSCP) [9297]
National Society of Controllers and Financial Officers of Savings Institutions - Financial Managers Society for Savings Institutions - Society of Savings and Loan Controllers [6231]
National Society of Fund Raisers [7073]
National Society of Fund Raising Executives [7073]

National Society of Fund Raising Executives - Greater Detroit Chapter [40791]
National Society of Professional Surveyors (NSPS) [15216]
National Society of the Sons of Utah Pioneers (NSSUP) [7436]
National Soft Drink Association [3865], [14300]
National Soft Wheat Association [16962]
National Solid Wastes Management Association [7941]
National Speakers Association (NSA) [14504], [14528]
National Sporting Clays Association (NSCA) [846]
National Sporting Goods Association (NSGA) [14733], [15080]
National Staff Leasing Association [15638]
National Stationery Show (NSS) [7706]
National Statistical Onion Association [16957]
National Storage Industry Consortium [3474]
National Sunflower Association (NSA) [16958]
National Tank Truck Carrier Membership Directory [16079]
National Tank Truck Carriers (NTTC) [16059]
National Tattoo Association, Inc. (NTA) [15282]
National Tattoo Club of the World [15282]
National Tattoo Supply Inc. [15329]
National Tavern Association [10310]
National Tax Association (NTA) [42], [15356]
National Teaching Institute & Critical Care Exposition (NTI) [26072]
National Technical Honor Society Gordon Cooper Technology Center (GCTC) [43893]
National Tenant Network Inc. (NTN) [4821]
National Tennis Association [12378], [15666]
National Tennis Educational Foundation [15667]
National Tennis Foundation and Hall of Fame [15667]
National Tile Roofing Manufacturers Association [14324]
National Tire Dealers and Retreaders Association [15680]
National Tooling and Machining Association (NTMA) [29081]
National Topical Stamp Show (NTSS) [3252]
National Tour Association (NTA) [15725], [15974]
National Tour Brokers Association [15725], [15974]
National Training and Simulation Association (NTSA) [9992]
National Translator Association (NTA) [15928]
National Translator LPTV Association [15928]
National Tribal Gaming Commissioners & Regulators (NTGCR) [7268]
National Truck Equipment Association (NTEA) [1093], [16060]
National Truck Leasing System [1153]
National Truck Rate Report [16096]
National Truckers Association (NTA) [16061]
National Tutoring Association (NTA) [16124]
National Typewriter and Office Machine Dealers Association [11658], [16528]
National Underwriter Life & Health [9000]
National Underwriter Property & Casualty [9001]
National Urban League (NUL) [30516]
National Used Car Dealers Association [11364]
National Vehicle Leasing Association (NVLA) [1152]
National Vendors Association [16248]
National Venture Capital Association (NVCA) [35297]
National Verification Agency [23462]
National Veteran-Owned Business Association (NaVOBA) [33480]
National Vocational Guidance Association [2595]
National Warm Air Heating and Air Conditioning Association [450]
National Waste and Recycling Association (NWRA) [7941]
National Watermelon Association (NWA) [16959]
National Weather Association (NWA) [32716]
National Wellness Institute--Membership Directory (Online only) [25876]
National Wholesale Druggists' Association [5138]
National Wholesale Furniture Salesmen's Association [8198]
National Wholesale Lumber Distributing Yard Association [10377]
National Wholesale Representatives Association [8198]
National Winter Convention [10062]
National Women's Business Council (NWBC) [35931]
National Women's Sailing Association (NWSA) [2828]
National Wood Flooring Association (NWFA) [3961]
National Wood Window & Door Association [2632]
National Woodwork Manufacturers Association [2632]
National Writers Association (NWA) [5293]
National Writers Club [5293]
NationaLease [1153]
NationaLease Inc. [1153]
"The Nation's #1 Children's Shoe Retailer, Payless ShoeSource(R), Launches Hassle-Free Back-to-School Shoe Shopping" in Benzinga.com (July 25, 2012) [2852], [14681], [20473]

The Nation's Health [26035]
Nations of the World: A Political, Economic and Business Handbook [27791]
Native American Economic Development Project - Yankton Sioux Tribe (YST) [44666]
Native American Journalists Association (NAJA) [5294]
Native American Press Association [5294]
Native American Research and Training Center [26149]
Native Hawaiian Chamber of Commerce (NHCC) [38882]
Native Hawaiian Organizations Association (NHOA) [30517]
Natrion: The Holy Grail of Battery Tech [35423]
NATSO Connect [14572], [32356]
Natural Beekeeping: Organic Approaches to Modern Apiculture [1484]
Natural Gas Partners (NGP) [45463]
Natural Grocer Association [7716]
Natural Hazards Image Database [5760]
"Natural Pet Product Merchandiser Roundtable: Functional Foods and Treats" in Pet Product News (Vol. 64, December 2010, No. 12, pp. S1) [12167], [29939], [32219]
Natural Products Association (NPA) [8000]
Natural Products Consulting LLC [8071]
Natural Products Marketing Council (NPMC) [5492], [5795]
Natural Stone Institute [10732]
NaturaLawn of America [10268]
NaturaLawn of America, Inc. [10268]
Nature Conservancy in Maine [10154]
Nature Conservancy - New Jersey [24511]
The Nature Conservancy - Ohio Chapter [7986]
Nature Stone Flooring Inc. [5095]
Nauvoo Chamber of Commerce [39265]
Navajo-Churro Sheep Association (NCSA) [640]
Naval School of Music Reference Library [11231]
Navarre Beach Area Chamber of Commerce [38468]
Navarro Small Business Development Center [44927]
Navasota Grimes County Chamber of Commerce [45294]
Navia Benefit Solutions Inc. [17406]
Navigating the Crowded Market Space [29548]
"Navigating Dog Trainer Partnerships" in Pet Product News (Vol. 66, September 2012, No. 9, pp. 47) [12147], [12211], [31430], [32220]
Navigating Entrepreneurship with Ashley Menzies Babatunde [16672]
Navigating Entrepreneurship's Unexpected Challenges with Caitlin Saenz [22912]
Navigating Your Way to Business Success: An Entrepreneur's Journey [19553], [22720], [25030]
Navigator Technology Ventures (NTV) [40711]
Navis Pack & Ship Centers [3397]
Navis Pack and Ship Centers [3398]
"Navistar, Cat Talk Truck Deal" in Crain's Chicago Business (Vol. 31, March 24, 2008, No. 12, pp. 1) [29309], [31431]
NAWBO Charlotte [43037]
NAWBO Chicago [35641]
Nazareth Area Chamber of Commerce [44268]
Nazareth-Bath Area Chamber of Commerce [44268]
Nazem and Co. [42778]
NBEA Annual Convention [21691]
NBMBAA Annual Conference and Exposition [30629]
NBWA Annual Convention [1951]
NBWA Annual Convention & Trade show [1951]
"N.C. Data-Center Plan Bearing Fruit From Apple, Spec Center" in Charlotte Business Journal (Vol. 25, October 15, 2010, No. 30, pp. 1) [3516], [3632], [4179], [18245]
N.C. Rural Center [43044]
NCA Convention [3204]
NCA Sweets & Snacks Expo [1285], [7818]
NCCLS: The Clinical Laboratory Standards Organization [10909]
NCFR Annual Conference [21696]
NCFR annual conference [23678]
"nCircle Launches PCI DSS Compliance Package for Small Businesses" in Health & Beauty Close-Up (May 14, 2012) [9185], [14438]
NCPA Annual Convention [5205]
NCPA Annual Convention and Expo [5205]
NCRA Annual Educational Conference [26073]
NCSA Annual Meeting [26074]
NCSG National Convention [12448]
NCSG National Convention & Tradeshow [2922]
NCT Ventures [43623]
NCTE Annual Convention [21697]
NDA Annual Convention & Expo [4300]
NDGA Annual Convention with Glass Show and Sale [7499]
NDSU Research & Technology Park [43317]

"Nearly 40% Decline in Honey Bee Popularion Last Winter 'Unsustainable,' Experts Say" in ABC News (July 9, 2019) [1485]
"A Neat SocialTrade" in Barron's (Vol. 92, July 23, 2012, No. 30, pp. 23) [6531], [9684], [11773], [23008], [24023]
Nebraska Agri-Business Association, Inc. [16960], [41817]
Nebraska Angels [41903]
Nebraska Business and Professional Women (NEBPW) [35669]
Nebraska Chamber of Commerce and Industry (NCCI) [41872]
Nebraska City Chamber of Commerce [41873]
Nebraska City Tourism and Commerce (NCTC) [41873]
Nebraska Department of Economic Development-Industrial Training Programs (DED) [41899]
Nebraska Department of Natural Resources (NeDNR) [47436]
Nebraska Fertilizer and Ag-Chemical Institute [16960], [41817]
Nebraska Library Commission (NLC) [47437]
Nebraska Natural Resources Commission [47436]
Nebraska Ombudsman's Office [41825]
Nebraska Procurement Technical Assistance Center (PTAC) - Nebraska Business Development Center - University of Nebraska at Kearney [41892]
Nebraska Small Business Development Center Chadron State College (NBDC) [41818]
Nebraska Small Business Development Center Kearney [41819]
Nebraska Small Business Development Center - Lead Office [41822]
Nebraska Small Business Development Center Lincoln [41820]
Nebraska Small Business Development Center North Platte [41821]
Nebraska Small Business Development Center Omaha (NBDC) [41822]
Nebraska Small Business Development Center Scottsbluff [41823]
Nebraska Small Business Development Center Wayne [41824]
NECA Convention & Trade Show [5399]
The NECA Show [5399]
"A Necessary Balancing Act: Bookkeeping" in Contractor (Vol. 56, November 2009, No. 11, pp. 22) [79], [500], [1767], [4180], [5383], [12647], [14628]
The Necessary Revolution: Working Together to Create a Sustainable World [5666], [5933], [23297]
"Necessity Mother of This Startup" in Providence Business News (Vol. 28, January 6, 2014, No. 40, pp. 1) [1196], [27922], [30770]
"Need Fiber in Your Diet? Pour Some Milk" in Globe & Mail (April 10, 2007, pp. B7) [7757], [8032], [34104]
"Needed: A Strategy; Banking In China" in The Economist (Vol. 390, January 3, 2009, No. 8612, pp. 54) [6532], [9685], [19025], [19554], [19899], [20316], [24024], [27658]
Needham Asset Management [42779]
Needlejig Tattoo Supply [15330]
Needles Chamber of Commerce [37044]
Needlework Retailer [1019], [4678]
Neeley Entrepreneurship Center [45542]
Neenah-Menasha Chamber of Commerce [46411]
Negative Effects of E-Commerce [21924]
Negotiating Effectively (Onsite) [17573]
"Negotiating for Success: Essential Strategies and Skills" [17719]
"Negotiating Tips" in Black Enterprise (Vol. 37, December 2006, No. 5, pp. 70) [1664], [1833], [21581], [22211], [28732]
Negotiating to Win [17601], [17602]
Negotiation Skills: Achieving Successful Outcomes (Onsite) [17603]
Negro Chamber of Commerce [45024]
"Neighborhood Awaits Its 'Very Sexy Building'" in Dallas Business Journal (Vol. 37, June 27, 2014, No. 42, pp. 12) [13511], [29940], [32221], [33393]
Neighborhood Cleaners Association [5228]
"The Neighborhood Watch" in Hawaii Business (Vol. 53, March 2008, No. 9, pp. 36) [2147], [9186], [13240], [13512], [16439]
NeighborhoodInfo DC [47568]
"Neighboring Auto Body Shops Merge as Parks Royal Body Works" in Idaho Business Review (August 26, 2014) [1133], [14555], [18246], [19682], [19900], [33023]
"Neighbors Rally for Dollar Store" in Chattanooga Times/Free Press (August 4, 2010) [7758], [32222]
Neillsville Area Chamber of Commerce (NACC) [46473]
Nelson & Pickens [141]
Nelson Worldwide [31090]

Neponset River Regional Chamber (NRRC) [40607]
Neponset Valley Business Connection [40608]
Nerac Inc. [47294]
NERCA Convention and Trade Show [14336]
"Nerd Alert on 3rd" in Philadelphia Business Journal (Vol. 28, August 17, 2012, No. 27, pp. 1) [16440], [18247], [26349]
Nerd Force [3590]
NerdWallet (Oct. 22, 2020); "20 Best Seasonal Business Ideas for Warm Weather" in [32945]
Neshoba Business Enterprise Center [41454]
"Nespresso Professional Introduces Momento Line for Office Service" in Vending Times (October 8, 2019) [3187]
Ness City Chamber of Commerce (NCCC) [39932]
"Nestle Acquires Waggin' Train Dog Treat Company" in Pet Product News (Vol. 64, November 2010, No. 11, pp. 7) [9686], [12168], [27659], [31432]
"Nestlé Makes Billions Bottling Water It Pays Nearly Nothing For" in Bloomberg (September 27, 2017) [1859]
"Net Savings Link Announces SpyderShare Inc. Contract for Development of Search Engine Optimization (S.E. O.) Program" in Internet Wire (February 21, 2012) [9187], [16441], [29941], [31433], [32575]
"NETGEAR Upgrades Small Business Security Line With Multiple Industry Firsts" in Benzinga.com (March 1, 2012) [14439], [26350]
Netherlands Chamber of Commerce in the United States (NLCOC) [27425]
"NetSpend and Family Dollar Announce New Prepaid Card Agreement" in GlobeNewswire (May 10, 2012) [4723], [20317], [31434], [32223], [32576]
NETwork [45295]
Network Consulting & Associates Inc. (NCA) [16328]
"Network Detection and Response Explained" in Small Business Trends (March 23, 2023) [3633], [16580]
The Network Hub [46708]
The Network Journal (TNJ) [30441]
NetWork Kansas [39845]
Network of Schools of Public Policy, Affairs, and Administration (NASPAA) [31677]
Network for Teaching Entrepreneurship (NFTE) [22464], [36004]
Networked Solutions Inc. [31000], [31074]
The Networker [39266]
"Networking Groups You Should Join to Grow Your Business" in InvoiceBerry Blog (July 3, 2018) [18850]
Networking Strategies for Introverts with Matthew Pollard: An EOFire Classic from 2021 [16673]
Networking: The Cheapest Way to Grow Your Small Business [18851]
"Networking Web Sites: a Two-Edge Sword" in Contractor (Vol. 56, October 2009, No. 10, pp. 52) [9188], [16442], [17720], [26621], [29942]
NeueHouse L.L.C. [42905]
Neumeier Consulting Inc. [14109]
Neurobiology of Learning and Memory: An Interdisciplinary Journal [32904]
The Neurodiagnostic Journal [26036]
Neurodiversity in the Workplace: An Untapped Superpower [30589]
"Neuromed Strikes Major Merck Deal" in Globe & Mail (March 21, 2006, pp. B1) [31435], [32793]
NeuroVentures Capital L.L.C. [45924]
Nevada Association of Realtors [13104]
Nevada Business Brokers Association (NBBA) [2140]
Nevada City Chamber of Commerce (NCCC) [37045]
Nevada Commission on Economic Development [41958]
Nevada Department of Business and Industry [41920]
Nevada Department of Tourism and Cultural Affairs [47438]
Nevada Governor's Office of Economic Development (GOED) [41958]
Nevada Governor's Office of Economic Development (GOED) [41921]
Nevada Governor's Office of Economic Development - Procurement Outreach Program Southern Nevada Regional Office [41959]
Nevada Minority Supplier Development Council [41953]
Nevada Realtors (NVAR) [13104]
Nevada Small Business Development Center - Lead Office (NSBDC) [41917]
Nevada-Vernon County Chamber of Commerce (NVCCC) [41600]
"Never Buy a Franchise Without Researching These 5 Sources" in Entrepreneur (Jan. 16, 2019) [24391]
Never Eat Alone: And Other Secrets to Success, One Relationship at a Time [22721], [28733]
"Never Eat Alone, Expanded and Updated: And Other Secrets to Success, One Relationship at a Time" [17721], [28734]
"Never Run Out of Leads" in Senior Market Advisor (Vol. 13, October 2012, No. 10, pp. 34) [32577]

"Never Stop Learning: Education Opportunities for Small Business Owners" in The Bottom Line Blog (Sept. 10, 2019) [21582]
"Never Worry About Cash Flow Again Using These 5 Strategies" in Entrepreneur (August 15, 2018) [19721]
"The New Alchemists" in Canadian Business (Vol. 81, October 27, 2008, No. 18, pp. 22) [5667], [5934], [17079], [23298], [30771]
"A New Alliance For Global Change" in Harvard Business Review (Vol. 88, September 2010, No. 9, pp. 56) [5668], [5935], [7137], [23299], [27660], [31436]
"New Angel Group Aims To Keep Cash Local" in Puget Sound Business Journal (Vol. 35, September 26, 2014, No. 23, pp. 5) [7068], [30897]
"New Apartments To Rise Downtown" in Memphis Business Journal (Vol. 33, January 27, 2012, No. 42, pp. 1) [4181], [25031]
"A New Approach to Funding Social Enterprises: Unbundling Societal Benefits and Financial Returns Can Dramatically Increase Investment" in Harvard Business Review (Vol. 90, January-February 2012, No. 1-2, pp. 118) [7138], [24025], [34344]
"A New Approach to Learning Centers" in Scholastic [3550], [21583]
"New Approach to Mechanical Binding" in American Printer (Vol. 128, July 1, 2011, No. 7) [1665], [3321], [12744], [16198]
"New APS AZ Sun Launches" in Manufacturing Close-Up (September 19, 2012) [4182], [14934], [31693]
"New Argentine Investment Taps Real Estate" in South Florida Business Journal (Vol. 32, June 22, 2012, No. 48, pp. 1) [4183], [13241], [13513], [27661]
New Atlantic Ventures (NAV.VC) [40712]
"New Backers, New Products at Halo" in Business Journal (Vol. 32, July 18, 2014, No. 8, pp. 5) [1197], [9687], [30772]
"New Beat for Marley's Daughter: Offspring of Reggae Royalty Opens Vintage Clothing Shop with Pal" in Los Angeles Business Journal (Vol. 34, March 12, 2012, No. 11, pp. 3) [743], [3043], [3133], [3898], [31437], [35826]
New Bedford Area Chamber of Commerce [40629]
New Berlin Chamber of Commerce and Visitors Bureau (NBCC/VB) [46474]
New Bern Area Chamber of Commerce [43176]
New Bern Area Guide and Business [43177]
"New Biz Mixes Paint, Wine; Will It Yield Green?" in Crain's Detroit Business (Vol. 30, September 8, 2014, No. 36, pp. 6) [1017], [15020], [21584], [35827]
New Bohemian Innovation Collaborative (NEW) [39824]
"New Book Takes Alternate View on Ontario's Wind Industry" in CNW Group (September 19, 2011) [1666], [1834], [5669], [5936], [23300], [25877]
New Boston Chamber of Commerce [45296]
"A New Breed of Innkeepers for the Airbnb Era" in The Wall Street Journal (November 8, 2018) [1420]
"New Brewpub Includes a Manapua Shop" in Pacific Business News (Vol. 52, March 14, 2014, No. 3, pp. 6) [1931], [13971], [31438]
New Bridgeport Chamber of Commerce [38032]
New Britain Chamber of Commerce [38048]
New Brunswick Department of Economic Development [46732]
New Brunswick Innovation Foundation (NBIF) [46734]
New Brunswick Translation Bureau Library [15960]
"New 'Build California' Program Hopes to Grow Workforce" in Electrical Contractor (October, 2019) [4184], [5384]
The New Business of Consulting: The Basics and Beyond [2198], [20115]
"New Business Idea? How to Test It Before Launching" in Business News Daily (August 25, 2020) [34538]
New Canaan Chamber of Commerce (NCCC) [38063]
New Canaan Historical Society (NCHS) [7349]
New Castle Chamber of Commerce [37889]
New Castle County Chamber of Commerce (NCCCC) [38137]
New Castle-Henry County Chamber of Commerce [39584]
"The New CEO: 185 Easy-To-Set-Up Businesses for Youth and Adult Entrepreneurs" [22404], [36000]
"New to the Class" in Lawn & Landscape (November 14, 2019) [10055], [10109], [10241]
"A New Cloud-Based Phone System Is Installed Remotely for North Carolina Senior Care Council" in Information Technology Business (June 19, 2012) [2769], [8261], [9189], [25878], [31439]
"New Crop Protection Products from Monsanto, Valent, DuPont, FMC, BASF" in Farm Industry News (December 17, 2010) [17080], [30773]
"New Data Reveals the Best Dog Breeds for Remote Workers" in Small Business Trends (June 2, 2021) [16581]

"New Data Shows Small Businesses Are Embracing Diversity, Equity & Inclusion in the Workplace" in Business Wire (July 20, 2022) [30590]
"A New Day is Dawning" in Indoor Comfort Marketing (Vol. 70, August 2011, No. 8, pp. 18) [501], [5670], [5937], [23301], [29943], [30771]
"New Developments in Cat's Play" in Pet Product News (Vol. 66, September 2012, No. 9, pp. 1) [12212], [29310]
New Dominion Angels LLC (NDA) [45925]
New Dynamics Associates [30647]
"New Earth Poised to Expand as Organic Recycling Grows" in San Antonio Business Journal (Vol. 28, May 23, 2014, No. 15, pp. 12) [10056], [13722]
New Economics For Women (NEW) [37603]
"New Economy Initiative Gains Partners" in Crain's Detroit Business (Vol. 25, June 1, 2009, No. 22, pp. M014) [21045], [30926], [31440], [34345]
New England Apparel Club [3165]
New England Association of Amusement Parks and Attractions (NEAAPA) [597]
New England Business Association (SBANE) [33481]
New England Business Brokers Association (NEBBA) [2141], [40490]
New England Business Travel Association (NEBTA) [19306], [40491]
New England Camping Association [2508]
New England Cannabis Convention [5058]
New England Conservatory of Music (NEC) - Harriet M. Spaulding Library [11232]
New England Family Campers Association [2508]
New England Historical and Genealogical Register (NEHGS) [7383]
New England Minority Purchasing Council [40651]
New England Minority Supplier Development Council [40651]
New England Real Estate Journal [13603]
New England Sound Healers [12491]
New England Venture Capital Association (NEVCA) [40492]
New Enterprise Associates (NEA) [37438]
New Enterprise Associates, Inc. (NEA) [40430], [40484]
The New Era of Entrepreneurs - Doing Good While Still Making Money with Kurt Long [34436]
"A New Era for Raiders" in Harvard Business Review (Vol. 88, November 2010, No. 11, pp. 34) [24710], [25454]
"New Ethanol Plant, Planned for Nevada, IA, Will Use Corn Stover" in Farm Industry News (June 27, 2011) [17081], [29311], [30774]
"The New Face of Aging: Chasing the Secret to Stopping the Clock" in San Francisco Business Times (Vol. 28, January 31, 2014, No. 28, pp. 4) [7139], [32008], [32794]
"New Family Dollar Store Now Open in Hermon" in Bangor Daily News (August 12, 2010) [32224]
"New Federal Law Will Promote Target Range Development on Public Lands" in NRA-ILA (May 24, 2019) [852]
"A New Flavor for Second Street: Lamberts Chef Backs New Restaurant" in Austin Business JournalInc. (Vol. 28, January 2, 2009) [1345], [13972], [31441]
"New Food Concepts Flood Market" in Business Journal (Vol. 30, June 8, 2012, No. 2, pp. 1) [4882], [8579], [13242], [13514], [18248], [34106]
"The New Free Apple Business Connect Tool – What Is It?" in Small Business Trends(January 18, 2023) [16582]
"The New Frontier" in Crain's Detroit Business (Vol. 26, January 18, 2010, No. 3, pp. S025) [11421], [29312]
"New Game Plan to Grow Trade?" in Providence Business News (Vol. 29, May 19, 2014, No. 7, pp. 1) [27662]
"New Generation Deans Lead Atlanta Area Business Schools Into the Future" in Atlanta Business Chronicle (July 25, 2014, pp. 3A) [21585], [27663], [30591], [35828]
"New Giants CEO Goes to Bat for Sponsorships" in Silicon Valley/San Jose Business Journal (Vol. 29, February 3, 2012, No. 45, pp. 1) [318], [15170], [26351]
New Glarus Chamber of Commerce [46475]
"A New Globe - In Print and Online" in Marketing to Women (Vol. 22, August 2009, No. 8, pp. 3) [9190], [11990], [16443], [29944]
"New Gmail Design Integrates Workspace and Chat Features" in Small Business Trends (August 10, 2022) [16583]
"New Government Tool Opens Window into Nursing-Home Abuse" in The Wall Street Journal (November 19, 2019) [11515], [25455]
New Hampshire Association of Realtors (NHAR) [13105]
New Hampshire Beekeepers Association (NHBA) [1445]

New Hampshire Master Index

New Hampshire Department of Environmental Services (NHDES) - Office of the Commissioner **[46999]**
New Hampshire Department of Resources and Economic Development - Division of Economic Development - Business Resource Center **[41972]**
New Hampshire Procurement Technical Assistance Center - New Hampshire Economic Development **[42021]**
New Hampshire State Library (NHSL) **[47439]**
New Hampshire Technical Institute [24913]
New Hartford Chamber of Commerce **[42639]**
"New Health Care Payment Model Coming to Boise" in Idaho Business Review (August 20, 2014) **[25879]**, **[34107]**
"New Holiday Inns Set for Airport Area, Graceland" in Memphis Business Journal (Vol. 34, August 17, 2012, No. 18, pp. 1) **[4185]**, **[8434]**, **[18249]**
New Horizons Computer Learning Centers Inc. **[3563]**
"New Hydronic Heating Technologies Work" in Contractor (Vol. 57, January 2010, No. 1, pp. 58) **[502]**, **[4186]**, **[5385]**, **[23302]**
"New Ideas Urged for 'Superman' Reuse" in Providence Business News (Vol. 28, March 10, 2014, No. 49, pp. 1) **[906]**, **[13515]**, **[29945]**
"The New and Improved Ski Shop" in Powder (January 11, 2017) **[11774]**, **[14738]**, **[19555]**
NEW Inc. **[42906]**
"New Institutional Accounting and IFRS" in Accounting and Business Research (Vol. 41, Summer 2011, No. 3, pp. 309) **[80]**, **[1768]**, **[15404]**, **[16820]**, **[27664]**, **[32009]**, **[32795]**
"New IPhone Also Brings New Way of Mobile Marketing" in Advertising Age (Vol. 79, June 16, 2008, No. 24, pp. 23) **[2770]**, **[9191]**, **[14802]**, **[26352]**, **[29946]**
"The New Janus CEO of Battle-Hardened Money Manager Plots Comeback" in Denver Business Journal (Vol. 64, August 31, 2012, No. 15, pp. 1) **[6533]**, **[8945]**, **[9688]**, **[27311]**, **[31442]**
New Jersey Accounting, Business & Technology Show & Conference **[120]**, **[1780]**, **[15442]**
New Jersey Air Services Development Office (NJASDO) **[42227]**
New Jersey Association of Realtors [13106]
New Jersey Association of Women Business Owners (NJAWBO) **[35670]**
New Jersey Beekeepers Association (NJBA) **[1446]**
"New Jersey Bio Grows Despite Turbulent Times" in Philadelphia Business Journal (Vol. 28, August 17, 2012, No. 27, pp. 1) **[18250]**, **[26353]**
New Jersey Business **[42262]**
New Jersey Business Action Center (NJBAC) **[42047]**
New Jersey Business Incubation Network (NJBIN) **[33482]**
New Jersey Business & Industry Association (NJBIA) **[42033]**
New Jersey Business Magazine **[42263]**
New Jersey Business Travel Association (NJBTA) **[19307]**
New Jersey Cannabis Convention **[5059]**
New Jersey Chamber of Commerce (NJCC) **[42168]**
New Jersey City University Business Development Incubator **[42240]**
New Jersey City University Small Business Development Center (NJCUSBDC) **[42037]**
New Jersey Commerce Economic Growth and Tourism Commission - International Trade and Protocol [42049]
New Jersey Department of Business and Economic Development **[42048]**
New Jersey Department of Labor and Workforce Development - Labor Market Information **[47440]**
New Jersey Department of Transportation Research Library (NJDOT) **[1180]**, **[5117]**, **[10297]**, **[15533]**
New Jersey Division of Revenue & Enterprise Services - Small Business Set-Aside Program **[42202]**
New Jersey Economic Development Authority - International Trade and Protocol **[42049]**
New Jersey Economic Development Authority - Office of the Business Advocate **[42050]**
"New Jersey Enacts Strict Opioid Prescribing Law" in Pharmacy Times (February 21, 2017) **[5177]**, **[25456]**, **[25880]**
New Jersey Institute of Technology - Center for Architecture and Building Science Research [31107]
New Jersey Institute of Technology (NJIT) - Center for Building Knowledge (CBK) **[31107]**
New Jersey Institute of Technology - Enterprise Development Center (NJIT) **[42241]**
New Jersey Institute of Technology - Procurement Technical Assistance Center (PTAC) **[42228]**
New Jersey Institute of Technology;Procurement Technical Assistance Center [42228]
New Jersey League of Municipalities Annual Conference **[31714]**, **[35131]**
New Jersey Monthly **[42264]**
"New Jersey Passes Nevada in Sports Gambling — Should Las Vegas Be Worried?" in MarketWatch (November 5, 2019) **[7303]**
New Jersey Realtors (NJR) **[13106]**
New Jersey Small Business Development Center - Lead Office (NJSBDC) **[42038]**
New Jersey Small Business Development Center at Raritan Valley Community College **[42039]**
New Jersey Small Business Development Center at Rutgers University-Camden (NJ SBDC) **[42040]**
New Jersey State Library U.S. Documents Collection **[47441]**
New Jersey Technology Council/NJTC Venture Fund **[42216]**
The New Job Security: The 5 Best Strategies for Taking Control of Your Career **[26622]**, **[27003]**
"New Jobs Coming From New Breed" in Memphis Business Journal (Vol. 34, September 21, 2012, No. 23, pp. 1) **[18251]**, **[20642]**, **[26623]**
New Kent Chamber of Commerce **[45885]**
"A New Kid on the Block" in Barron's (Vol. 88, March 17, 2008, No. 11, pp. 58) **[6534]**, **[9689]**, **[20318]**, **[24026]**, **[25032]**, **[28173]**
"New Law Regarding Notre Dame Says Restoration Must Preserve it's 'historic, artistic and architectural interest'" in The Art Newspaper (August 2, 2019) **[907]**
New Leaf Venture Partners (NLVP) **[42780]**
New Lenox Chamber of Commerce (NLCC) **[39267]**
The New Library at New Hampshire Technical Institute, Concord [24913]
"New Life for Porsche's VW Dreams" in Barron's (Vol. 89, July 6, 2009, No. 27, pp. 9) **[11422]**, **[29313]**, **[31443]**
The New Lighting for Product Photography: The Digital Photographer's Step-by-Step Guide to Sculpting with Light **[12309]**
New Lisbon Area Chamber of Commerce (NLCC) **[46476]**
New Lodging Professionals Conference **[8492]**
New London Area Chamber of Commerce **[46477]**
New London Area Chamber of Commerce and the Lake Sunapee Business Association [42004]
New London - Lake Sunapee Region Chamber of Commerce [42004]
New Madrid Chamber of Commerce **[41601]**
New Market Venture Partners (NMVP) **[40431]**
"New Meridian Candy Shop Hires People with Special Needs" in KTVB.com (February 1, 2019) **[2545]**
New Mexico Angels **[42364]**
New Mexico Clinical Research and Osteoporosis Center **[26131]**
New Mexico Community Capital (NMCC) **[42366]**
New Mexico Department of Agriculture - Marketing and Development Div. **[42290]**
New Mexico Department of Agriculture, Marketing and Economic Development Division [42290]
New Mexico Department of Environment - NMED Library **[35983]**
New Mexico Economic Development Department (EDD) **[42291]**
New Mexico General Services Department **[42292]**
New Mexico Junior College - Business Assistance Center [42360]
New Mexico Junior College Small Business Development Center (NMJCSBDC) **[42360]**
New Mexico Procurement Assistance Program - General Services Department [42292]
New Mexico Small Business Assistance (NMSBA) **[42293]**
New Mexico Small Business Development Center - Lead Office **[42282]**
New Mexico State Library (NMSL) **[47442]**
New Mexico State University - Arrowhead Center **[42294]**
New Mexico State University Arts and Sciences Research Center **[32938]**
New Mexico State University - College of Agricultural, Consumer and Environmental Sciences - Agricultural Experiment Station (AES) **[17233]**
New Mexico State University - College of Business - Economics, Applied Statistics and International Business Department (EASIB) **[47443]**
New Mexico State University-Grants Small Business Development Center **[42283]**
New Milford Chamber of Commerce [38050]
New Milford Living Magazine **[38064]**
"A New Mix of Tenants Settles In Downtown" in Crain's New York Business (Vol. 24, January 13, 2008, No. 2, pp. 26) **[12896]**, **[13243]**, **[13516]**, **[13973]**, **[19188]**, **[32225]**, **[34108]**
"New Money for New Ideas" in St. Louis Business Journal (Vol. 33, September 7, 2012, No. 2, pp. 1) **[35243]**
"The New Nimble" in Barron's (Vol. 90, August 30, 2010, No. 35, pp. S12) **[6535]**, **[9690]**, **[34109]**
"New No. 1 at Element 8: Angel Group Brings on New Executive Director" in Puget Sound Business Journal (Vol. 35, September 19, 2014, No. 22, pp. 6) **[5671]**, **[5938]**, **[9691]**, **[17082]**, **[23303]**
New Orleans BioInnovation Center **[40228]**
New Orleans City Business **[40239]**
New Orleans Pizza (NOP) **[12568]**
"New Owner Eyes Big Changes at Brookwood Village" in Birmingham Business Journal (Vol. 31, April 4, 2014, No. 14, pp. 10) **[32226]**
"New Owners Take Over at Leather District Restaurants" in Boston Business Journal (Vol. 33, January 31, 2014, No. 53, pp. 4) **[13974]**, **[31444]**
New Palestine Area Chamber of Commerce (NPACC) **[39585]**
"New Pet Product Launches IndieGoGo Crowdfunding to Remain American Made" in Benzinga.com (June 11, 2012) **[12213]**, **[30775]**, **[30927]**, **[34346]**
"New PHH Building Still Going Up In Amherst Despite Job Cuts" in Business First of Buffalo (Vol. 30, February 28, 2014, No. 24, pp. 5) **[4187]**, **[11062]**
New Prague Chamber of Commerce (NPCC) **[41277]**
New Product Research: Laying the Foundation for New Product Success (Onsite) **[29597]**, **[30669]**
"New Project? Don't Analyze - Act: Entrepreneurs Take Small, Quick Steps To Get Initiatives Off the Ground. You Can Do the Same In Your Organization" in Harvard Business Review (Vol. 90, March 2012, No. 3, pp. 154) **[22722]**
"New Push for Mainers to Test for Radon in Homes" in News Center Maine (January 28, 2019) **[13070]**, **[25457]**
"New Recession-Proof Internet Marketing Package Allows Businesses to Ramp Up Web Traffic and Profits" in PR Newswire (January 25, 2010) **[6197]**, **[9192]**, **[16444]**, **[29947]**, **[34110]**
"New Recipes Added to IAMS Naturals Pet Food Line" in MMR (Vol. 28, August 1, 2011, No. 11, pp. 17) **[8033]**, **[12214]**, **[15021]**, **[30776]**
"New Research and Infographic: Vacation Much More Important than 'Nice to Have'" in PR Newswire (August 26, 2014) **[9193]**, **[16445]**
New Richmond Area Chamber of Commerce [46478]
New Richmond Area Chamber of Commerce & Visitors Bureau **[46478]**
New Rochelle Chamber of Commerce (NRCC) **[42640]**
The New Role of Regional Management **[18252]**, **[27665]**, **[28735]**, **[34111]**
"New Rule Rankles In Jersey" in Philadelphia Business Journal (Vol. 30, September 16, 2011, No. 31, pp. 1) **[4724]**, **[11063]**, **[18644]**, **[24027]**, **[25458]**, **[34849]**
A New Sales Paradigm with Jen Szpigel **[32683]**
"New Sales. Simplified: The Essential Handbook for Prospecting and New Business Development" **[17722]**, **[19026]**, **[21925]**, **[32578]**, **[34994]**
The New School - Center for New York City Affairs **[26132]**
New School University - Center for New York City Affairs [26132]
"The New Science of Building Great Teams: The Chemistry of High-Performing Groups Is No Longer a Mystery" in Harvard Business Review (Vol. 90, April 2012, No. 4, pp. 60) **[17723]**, **[22212]**
"The New Science of Viral Ads: Five Techniques Can Help Companies Make Commercials That People Will Watch and Share" in Harvard Business Review (Vol. 90, April 2012, No. 4, pp. 25) **[319]**
New Smyrna Beach-Edgewater-Oak Hill Chamber of Commerce [38504]
"New Sony HD Ads Tout Digital" in Brandweek (Vol. 49, April 21, 2008, No. 16, pp. 5) **[320]**, **[9194]**, **[11991]**, **[15607]**, **[26354]**, **[29948]**, **[30777]**, **[31881]**
"New Sprint Phone Whets Appetite for Applications, Brings Revenue for Handmark" in The Business Journal-Serving Metropolitan Kansas City (Vol. 26, July 25, 2008) **[2771]**, **[17724]**, **[30778]**, **[33878]**
"New State Rules Require Cranes and Operators to be Certified" in Bellingham Business Journal (Vol. February 2010, pp. 11) **[4188]**, **[25459]**
"New Stem Cell Research Awareness Org Launched in Austin" in Austin Business Journal (Vol. 31, June 3, 2011, No. 13, pp. 1) **[7140]**, **[21586]**, **[25881]**, **[31445]**, **[32010]**, **[32796]**, **[35366]**
"New Tailor Shop in Uptown Dallas Is a Great Fit for the Neighborhood's Renewed Energy" in Dallas News (July 26, 2019) **[15252]**, **[19901]**
"New Tax Sends Biz Scrambling: Service Levy Will Affect 16,000 Businesses" in Crain's Detroit Business (October 8, 2007) **[33209]**, **[34850]**
New Technology Ventures (NTV) **[40713]**
"New Texas South-International Alliance Seeking to Net Foreign Firms for South Texas" in San Antonio Business Journal (Vol. 26, June 22, 2012, No. 21, pp. 1) **[21046]**, **[27666]**, **[31446]**

3300 Small Business Sourcebook • 42nd Edition

"New Typesetting Technology from Scholastica Propels Freer Future for Academic Journals" in EurekAlert! (February 8, 2018) **[16199]**
New Ulm Area Chamber of Commerce **[41278]**
"New Under-18 Model Bans Are Changing How Agencies Recruit and Sign Talent" in Fashionista (June 13, 2019) **[10994]**
New Venture Challenge (NVC) **[39418]**
New Venture Creation: Entrepreneurship for the 21st Century with Online Learning Center Access Card **[22405]**, **[24553]**
New Venture Partners L.L.C. (NVP) **[42217]**
"New Wave of Business Security Products Ushers in the Kaspersky Anti-Malware Protection System" in Internet Wire (October 26, 2010) **[3517]**, **[14440]**, **[14803]**, **[21926]**, **[33879]**
"A New Way to Tell When to Fold 'Em" in Barron's (Vol. 88, July 7, 2008, No. 27, pp. 27) **[6536]**, **[9195]**, **[9692]**, **[16446]**, **[21927]**, **[24028]**, **[26355]**, **[33210]**
New Ways **[17407]**, **[31137]**
"New Ways to Finance Solar Power Projects Expected to Lower Cost of Capital, Cut Electricity Rates, Boost Profits, and Expand Investor Pool" in PR Newswire (September 28, 2012) **[14935]**, **[25033]**, **[35367]**
New Ways to Work **[17407]**, **[31137]**
"A New World" in Canadian Business (Vol. 80, October 8, 2007, No. 20, pp. 136) **[21047]**, **[23304]**
New World Angels **[38613]**
"New Year's Resolutions: How Three Companies Came Up With Their 2008 Growth Strategies" in Inc. (January 2008, pp. 47-49) **[1586]**, **[2772]**, **[8179]**, **[8435]**, **[18253]**
"New Yetter Stubble Solution Prevents Tire, Track Damage" in Farm Industry News (November 21, 2011) **[17083]**, **[30779]**
New York Angels (NYA) **[43011]**
New York Association of Business Brokers (NYABB) **[2142]**
New York Association of Mortgage Brokers (NYAMB) **[11003]**
New York Botanical Garden (NYBG) **[7679]**
New York Business Development Corp. [33507]
New York Cannabis Conference **[5060]**
New York Chamber of Commerce and Industry [42647]
"New York City-Based New Street Realty Advisors has Secured a New Flagship for David's Bridal" in Chain Store Age (August 2008) **[1983]**, **[13244]**, **[13517]**
New York City Business Travel Association (NYCBTA) **[19308]**
New York City Department of Business Services - New York City Procurement Outreach Program **[42821]**
New York City Partnership [42647]
New York Customs Brokers Association [2139], [7024]
New York Department of Economic Development (DED) - Division of Minority and Women's Business Development **[42419]**
New York Department of Labor **[14998]**
"New York Developer Revives Adams Morgan Hotel Project" in Washington Business Journal (Vol. 31, July 6, 2012, No. 11, pp. 1) **[8436]**, **[13518]**, **[31447]**
New York Digital Health Accelerator [42907]
New York Digital Health Innovation Lab **[42907]**
New York Farm Show (NYFS) **[17177]**
New York Fashion Tech Lab (NYFTL) **[43025]**
New York Genealogical and Biographical Society (NYG&B) **[7437]**
New York Grant Co. (NYGC) **[35455]**
"New York Identifies Hospitals and Nursing Homes with Deadly Fungus" in The New York Times (November 13, 2019) **[11516]**
New York Medical College - BioInc **[42908]**
New York/New England & Eastern Canada Campground Guide **[2519]**
New York and New Jersey Minority Supplier Development Council (NY & NJ MSDC) **[42706]**
New York Procurement Center **[42822]**
New York Procurement Technical Assistance Center - Cattaraugus County **[42823]**
New York Procurement Technical Assistance Center - LaGuardia Community College PTAC **[42824]**
New York Procurement Technical Assistance Center - Long Island Development Corp. (LIDC) **[42825]**
New York Procurement Technical Assistance Center;LaGuardia Community College PTAC [42824]
New York Public Interest Research Group - Albany (NYPIRG) **[15497]**
New York Public Library - Jerome Robbins Dance Division **[4866]**
New York Public Library Rare Books Division - Arents Tobacco Collection **[8166]**, **[15715]**
New York Public Library - The Research Libraries - Humanities and Social Sciences Library Arents Tobacco Collection [8166], [15715]

New York School of Interior Design: Home: The Foundations of Enduring Spaces **[9046]**
New York Senate Standing Committee **[42973]**
New York State Agribusiness Association (NYSABA) **[16961]**, **[42386]**
New York State Assembly Committee on Small Business **[42974]**
New York State Association of Service Stations [14539]
New York State Association of Service Stations and Repair Shops (NYSASSRS) **[14539]**
New York State Business Travel Association [19299], [42381]
New York State Department of Environmental Conservation (NYSDEC) - Division of Environmental Remediation - Hazardous Waste Management **[47000]**
New York State Education Department - Office of Cultural Education (OCE) **[47444]**
New York State Foundation for Science, Technology and Innovation [42420]
New York State Office of Fire Prevention and Control - Academy of Fire Science (AFS) **[35984]**
New York State Office of General Services - Minority and Women-Owned Business and Community Relations **[42707]**
New York State School Music Association Winter Conference **[11201]**, **[11286]**
New York State Small Business Development Center (NYS SBDC) **[33718]**, **[42407]**
New York State Turf and Landscape Association (NYSTLA) **[10049]**, **[10081]**
New York State's Empire State Development - Division of Science, Technology and Innovation **[42420]**
New York State's Empire State Development - Division for Small Business - Small Business Ombudsman **[42421]**
New York University Graduate School of Arts and Science - Institute of Fine Arts - Conservation Center **[1012]**
New York University - Leonard N. Stern School of Business - Berkley Center for Entrepreneurial Studies (BCES) **[22955]**
New York University - Leonard N. Stern School of Business - Glucksman Institute **[9953]**
New York University - Leonard N. Stern School of Business - Salomon Center for the Study of Financial Institutions **[1795]**
New York University School of Law - National Center on Philanthropy and the Law (NCPL) **[7191]**
New York Women's League for Animals [714]
"New York's Duane Reade Adds In-Store Yogurt Kiosks" in ADWEEK (Vol. 53, February 6, 2012, No. 5, pp. 16) **[8034]**, **[8580]**, **[10035]**
"New Zealand Natural Co-Branding with Mrs. Fields" in Ice Cream Reporter (Vol. 23, November 20, 2010, No. 12, pp. 2) **[1260]**, **[8581]**, **[27667]**, **[31448]**
Newark Chamber of Commerce **[37046]**
"Newark Phasing Out Bottled Water in Wake of Filter Tests" in The New York Times (October 4, 2019) **[1860]**
Newark Public Library Reference Center **[4568]**
Newark Public Library - Special Collections Division **[1733]**
Newark SBDC [38124]
Newark Venture Partners (NVP) **[42218]**
Newaygo Area Chamber of Commerce **[40999]**
Newberry Area Chamber of Commerce **[40983]**
Newbridge Partners LLC **[45991]**
Newcastle Area Chamber of Commerce **[46612]**
Newcomb Chamber of Commerce **[42641]**
Newfoundland & Labrador Organziation of Women Entrepreneurs (NLOWE) **[46740]**
NewGate Capital **[38618]**
Newington Chamber of Commerce (NCC) **[38065]**
NewMe Accelerator [43671]
Newport Area Chamber of Commerce **[42010]**
Newport Beach Chamber of Commerce (NBCC) **[37047]**
Newport Chamber of Commerce [42010]
Newport/Cocke County Chamber of Commerce [44729]
Newport County Chamber of Commerce [44474]
Newport - Oldtown Chamber of Commerce **[46132]**
News **[39933]**
News & Analyisis [5758]
News Break! **[46479]**
News Capsule **[40984]**
News Media Canada **[11970]**
News & Views **[39934]**
News and Views **[36140]**, **[42169]**
NewsAccount **[113]**
NewsBreak **[38469]**
Newsbriefs **[16062]**, [44262]
Newsline [14490]
Newspaper Promotion Association [11965]
NewSpring Capital [44345]

NewSpring Ventures **[44345]**
Newtek Business Services Corp. [35470]
Newtek Business Services Inc. [35470]
NewtekOne, Inc. **[35470]**
Newton Area Chamber of Commerce (NACC) **[39935]**
Newton Area Chamber of Commerce and Visitors Bureau [39935]
Newton Chamber of Commerce (NCC) **[41419]**
Newton - Needham Chamber of Commerce **[40609]**
"Newton Robotics Company Bets on Rehab Robots for Growth" in Boston Business Journal (Vol. 34, April 4, 2014, No. 9, pp. 6) **[10844]**, **[10956]**, **[25882]**, **[26356]**
Newtown Area Chamber of Commerce [38034]
"NexCen Brands Sells Chains and Will Liquidate" in Ice Cream Reporter (Vol. 23, August 20, 2010, No. 9, pp. 1) **[8582]**, **[24392]**, **[33024]**
"Nexen, OPTI Boost Oil Sands Spending" in Globe & Mail (February 18, 2006, pp. B5) **[19027]**, **[19556]**, **[29314]**
Nexit Ventures **[37439]**
"Nexstar Super Meeting Breaks Business Barriers" in Contractor (Vol. 56, November 2009, No. 11, pp. 3) **[503]**, **[21048]**, **[28736]**, **[34112]**
NEXT **[12502]**
Next Act Fund (NAF) **[44346]**
Next Canada [33683]
"The Next Economic Disaster: Why It's Coming and How to Avoid It" **[21049]**, **[24029]**
"The Next Frontier" in San Francisco Business Times (Vol. 28, February 28, 2014, No. 32, pp. 4) **[2773]**, **[21928]**, **[22723]**, **[35368]**
Next Generation Qualitative Tools: Social Media, Online Communities & Virtual Research Platforms (Onsite) **[29598]**
"Next Generation Security Awareness" in Security Management (Vol. 56, September 2012, No. 9, pp. 32) **[14441]**, **[14804]**, **[21587]**, **[33880]**
"The Next Great Canadian Idea: Peripiteia Generator" in Canadian Business (Vol. 81, July 21, 2008, No. 11, pp. 45) **[5939]**, **[19902]**, **[23305]**, **[27923]**, **[29949]**
"Next-Level E-Commerce" in Entrepreneur (June 2014) **[14805]**, **[16447]**, **[20474]**, **[21929]**, **[33211]**, **[33881]**
"Next-Level Networking: You Know Who, But Does Who Know You?" in South Florida Business Journal (Vol. 34, February 7, 2014, No. 29, pp. 10) **[17725]**
"The Next Real Estate Boom" in Canadian Business (Vol. 80, March 26, 2007, No. 7, pp. 25) **[13245]**, **[13519]**
"Next Stage of Green Building will be Water Efficiency" in Contractor (Vol. 56, July 2009, No. 7, pp. 41) **[4189]**, **[5672]**, **[16334]**, **[23306]**
Next Step Business Education Ltd. **[21712]**
"The Next Step in Patent Reform" in Information Today (Vol. 28, November 2011, No. 10, pp. 1) **[18645]**, **[25460]**, **[27924]**
"The Next Wave" in Hawaii Business (Vol. 53, January 2008, No. 7, pp. 27) **[15752]**, **[16005]**, **[21050]**, **[25461]**, **[27668]**
Next Wave Impact (NWI) **[37924]**
Next47 Inc. **[37440]**
NextCorps **[42909]**
NextEnergy **[23057]**
NextFab **[44410]**
NextGen The Future of the WBENC Network **[33527]**, **[35713]**
NextMove Dance (NMD) **[4847]**
NextView Ventures **[40714]**
Nexus Business Solutions **[2298]**
Nexus Louisiana **[40229]**
Nexus Venture Partners **[37441]**
NexusLab **[37604]**
NFDA Bulletin **[7219]**
NFRA Convention **[7815]**
NGEN Partners LLC **[42781]**
NGN Capital (NGN) **[42782]**
NGP Capital (NGP) **[37753]**
NGP Energy Capital (NGP) **[45464]**
NHAR Fall Business and Education Conference **[24843]**
NHLA Annual Convention & Exhibit Showcase **[10408]**
NHSA's annual National Conference & Expo [21694]
NHTI, Concord's Community College **[24913]**
NIA's Annual Convention [8852]
Niagara Small Business Development Center (SBDC) **[42408]**
Niagara University Library's Rare Book Collection **[759]**
Niagara USA Chamber **[42642]**
"Nice Toes, Bro. Young Men Invade Nail Salons" in The Wall Street Journal (July 28, 2019) **[11321]**
Niceville Valparaiso Bay Area Chamber of Commerce [38470]
Niceville Valparaiso Chamber of Commerce **[38470]**
"Niche Areas Seeing the Bulk of Retail Activity" in San Antonio Business Journal (Vol. 28, August 29, 2014, No. 29, pp. 8) **[13246]**, **[13520]**, **[32227]**

Niche Master Index

Niche and Grow Rich **[19903]**, **[20116]**, **[20475]**, **[22406]**, **[24554]**, **[29950]**, **[33212]**
"Nicholas Markets Joins Wakefern, Rebrands as The Fresh Grocer" in Grocery Dive (November 1, 2019) **[7759]**
Nicholby's Franchise Systems Inc. **[32370]**
Nichols College - Conant Library **[16899]**, **[24282]**, **[29053]**
Nick Mathews CEO and Founder of Mainvest **[35424]**
Nidus Partners L.P. **[41685]**
Nightingale Associates **[2299]**, **[10551]**, **[19144]**, **[20213]**, **[27151]**, **[27785]**, **[29023]**
"Nightmare on Wall Street" in Canadian Business (Vol. 80, November 19, 2007, No. 23, pp. 33) **[9693]**, **[11064]**
"Nightmare on Wall Street" in Canadian Business (Vol. 81, October 13, 2008, No. 17, pp. 9) **[6537]**, **[9694]**, **[21051]**, **[24030]**
"Nighttime Shuttle to Connect Detroit, Ferndale, Royal Oak" in Crain's Detroit Business (Vol. 24, October 6, 2008, No. 40, pp. 24) **[1346]**, **[13975]**, **[19380]**, **[33213]**
NIGP: The Institute for Public Procurement **[25174]**
"Nike's FlyEase Continues Smart Innovations in Growing Adaptive Fashion Market" in Footwear News (November 22, 2019) **[14682]**
Niles Chamber of Commerce and Industry **[39268]**
Niles Entrepreneur and Culinary Incubator **[41111]**
Niles Society [40927]
Nimbus Synergies **[46714]**
"Nine Austin-Area Realtors on National Latino List" in Austin Business Journal (Vol. 34, July 11, 2014, No. 21, pp. 8) **[13247]**
Nine Collection Tips for Small Business **[20319]**
Nine Lives Associates (NLA) **[12793]**, **[14378]**
"Nine Paradoxes of Problem Solving" in Strategy and Leadership (Vol. 39, May-June 2011, No. 3, pp. 25-31) **[22213]**, **[28737]**
"Nine Things You're Doing Wrong in a Cocktail Bar" in Bloomburg (March 9, 2017) **[1347]**
"Nine-Year-Old Turning Heads at Englewood Pool Hall" in 9News.com (June 9, 2019) **[1539]**
Nineteen90 Business Consulting **[33684]**
Niobrara Chamber of Commerce **[46613]**
"NIOSH Teams with Staffing Association to Promote Temp Worker Safety and Health" in Safety+Health (August 30, 2021) **[15642]**, **[35949]**
Nisku Business Directory **[46680]**
Nisswa Chamber of Commerce **[41279]**
NiteLites Outdoor Lighting Franchise **[10269]**
Nitem Foundation **[21317]**, **[23043]**, **[34257]**
Nixa Area Chamber of Commerce **[41602]**
"Nixon Assails Insurance Rules" in Globe & Mail (March 4, 2006, pp. B5) **[25462]**, **[27312]**
Nixon Peabody L.L.P. **[18746]**
Nixon Peabody L.L.P., Law Library **[6063]**
NJ League of Municipalities Annual Conference [31714], [35131]
"N.J. Venture Investing Hits $39M" in Philadelphia Business Journal (Vol. 28, April 13, 2012, No. 9, pp. 1) **[21052]**, **[35369]**
NJIT Enterprise Development Center **[42242]**
NJLM Annual Conference [31714], [35131]
"NKC Keeps Pace with Auto Industry" in Memphis Business Journal (Vol. 34, September 14, 2012, No. 22, pp. 1) **[1105]**, **[18254]**, **[29315]**, **[32579]**
NLDA Associates Inc. [10363]
NMA - The Leadership Development Organization (NMA) **[28262]**
NMMA Currents **[2833]**
NMotion **[41894]**
"No Assets for Retirement? Eh, Who Cares?" in Financial Advisor (November, 2019) **[6538]**, **[24031]**
"No Charlotte Tax Hike, But Plenty of Challenges" in Charlotte Business Journal (Vol. 27, June 29, 2012, No. 15, pp. 1) **[16584]**, **[34851]**
"No Frills - And No Dodge" in Crain's Detroit Business (Vol. 24, September 22, 2008, No. 38, pp. 3) **[11423]**, **[18255]**, **[19028]**, **[19557]**, **[29316]**, **[32228]**
"No End to the Nightmare; America's Car Industry" in The Economist (Vol. 390, January 3, 2009, No. 8612, pp. 46) **[11424]**, **[21053]**, **[25034]**, **[25463]**, **[28174]**, **[29317]**, **[35202]**
No Man's Land: What to Do When Your Company Is Too Big to Be Small but Too Small to Be Big **[18256]**, **[24711]**
"No More Ivory Towers: Local Colleges and Universities are Here to Help Your Business" in Orlando Business Journal (Vol. 30, February 28, 2014, No. 36, pp. 4) **[21588]**, **[26357]**, **[31449]**, **[32797]**
The No-Nonsense Home Organization Plan: 7 Weeks to Declutter in Any Space **[12840]**
"No Place Like Home? An Identity Strain Perspective On Repatriate Turnover" in Academy of Management Journal (Vol. 55, April 1, 2012, No. 2, pp. 399) **[22214]**, **[30592]**
"No Shortage of Challenges for Cross-Border Trade" in Canadian Sailings (June 30, 2008) **[8744]**, **[21054]**, **[25464]**, **[27669]**, **[34113]**
"'No Snitch' Culture in American Business" in Business Owner (Vol. 35, September-October 2011, No. 5, pp. 7) **[17726]**, **[23520]**
"No, Those Casino Rama Ads Aren't Running in NYC" in Globe & Mail (March 15, 2006, pp. B1) **[321]**, **[29951]**
"No Time to Grieve" in Women In Business (Vol. 63, Fall 2011, No. 3, pp. 22) **[26624]**, **[27004]**
"No Trader Joe's for Mid-South" in Memphis Business Journal (Vol. 34, July 13, 2012, No. 13, pp. 1) **[7760]**, **[33394]**
Noah Glass Founder and CEO of Olo **[14866]**
"Nobel Prize Winners Provide Insight on Outsourcing, Contract Work" in Workforce Management (Vol. 88, November 16, 2009, No. 12, pp. 11) **[17331]**, **[18646]**, **[28738]**, **[31126]**
Noblesville Chamber of Commerce (NCC) **[39586]**
"'Nobody Knows What To Do' To Make Money on the Web" in Barron's (Vol. 88, March 17, 2008, No. 11, pp. 40) **[9196]**, **[15875]**, **[19029]**, **[21930]**, **[28739]**, **[29952]**, **[35070]**, **[35370]**
Nocona Area Chamber of Commerce (NCC) **[45297]**
Nogales-Santa Cruz County Chamber of Commerce (NSCCC) **[36348]**
Noise and Vibration Conference and Exhibition **[1126]**
The Noisy Water Gazette **[42330]**
Nokia Growth Partners [37753]
The Nokia Revolution: The Story of an Extraordinary Company That Transformed an Industry **[2774]**, **[26358]**, **[31450]**
Nomad Nation: Thriving as a Location-Independent Entrepreneur with Bobby Casey **[34938]**
Non-profit Management Association and Support Centers of America [31670]
Non-Standard Employment under Globalization: Flexible Work and Social Security in the Newly Industrializing Countries **[22724]**, **[25465]**, **[27005]**, **[27670]**, **[28740]**, **[30593]**, **[34114]**
Non-Traditional Financing for Your Small Business **[30928]**
"Non-Users Still Inhale Nicotine From E-Cigarettes" in Business First of Buffalo (Vol. 30, February 7, 2014, No. 21, pp. 6) **[15700]**, **[25883]**, **[32011]**
The Nonfinancial Manager's Guide to Understanding Financial Statements (Onsite) **[23715]**
Nonprescription Drug Manufacturers Association [25668]
Nonprofit Mailers Federation [1048]
Nonprofit Management All-in-One for Dummies **[16821]**, **[19558]**
"Nonprofit NAIC Acquires Software Developer as For-Profit Arm" in Crain's Detroit Business (Vol. 25, June 22, 2009, No. 25, pp. 10) **[9695]**, **[14806]**, **[31451]**, **[33882]**, **[34347]**
The Nonprofit Times **[7174]**
"Nonprofits Pressured to Rein in Fundraising Events" in Crain's Detroit Business (Vol. 25, June 15, 2009, No. 24, pp. 1) **[21055]**, **[24032]**, **[34348]**
"Nonstop Round Baler Earns Top International Award for Krone" in Farm Industry News (November 18, 2011) **[17084]**, **[29318]**, **[30780]**
Noodle Time Inc. **[14221]**
"Noodles Founder Becomes Colorado's Chief Marketing Officer" in Denver Business Journal (Vol. 64, August 24, 2012, No. 14, pp. 1) **[13976]**, **[22725]**, **[29953]**
NORCAL BMA [36535]
Norcal Landscape and Nursery Show **[10063]**
Norco Area Chamber of Commerce (NACC) **[37048]**
Nordic Innovation House **[37605]**
Nordonia Hills Chamber of Commerce (NHCC) **[43534]**
"Nordstrom Points for Richmond Heights" in Saint Louis Business Journal (Vol. 31, August 5, 2011, No. 50, pp. 1) **[32229]**, **[33395]**
Norfolk Area Chamber of Commerce (NACC) **[41874]**
Norfolk Botanical Garden Society - Frederic Heutte Memorial Library **[7680]**
Norfolk Chamber of Commerce [41874]
Norfolk Historical Society (NHS) **[7438]**
Norman Chamber of Commerce **[43784]**
Norman Peterson and Associates (NPA) **[27152]**
Normandale Community College (NCC) **[41362]**
Normes Canadiennes de la Publicité [209]
Noro-Moseley Partners (NMP) **[38810]**
Norris Bernstein, CMC **[33685]**
"Nortel Makes Customers Stars in New Campaign" in Brandweek (Vol. 49, April 21, 2008, No. 16, pp. 8) **[322]**, **[15608]**, **[17727]**, **[26359]**, **[28741]**, **[29954]**, **[33214]**, **[34115]**
"Nortel Outlook Shows Recovery Won't Come Quickly" in Globe & Mail (March 20, 2007, pp. B4) **[9696]**, **[33215]**
"Nortel Plays Big to Settle Lawsuits" in Globe & Mail (February 9, 2006, pp. B1) **[6539]**, **[9697]**, **[18647]**
"Nortel Romances Chinese Rival Huawei" in Globe & Mail (February 2, 2006, pp. B1) **[26360]**, **[31452]**
"Nortel Starting From Scratch, New CEO Says" in Globe & Mail (February 24, 2006, pp. B3) **[19030]**, **[19559]**
Nortext Multimedia Inc. **[46750]**
North 65 Chamber of Commerce **[41280]**
North America Christmas Tree Market - Growth, Trends, COVID-19 Impact, and Forecasts (2022 - 2027) **[2949]**
North American Association of Floor Covering Distributors (NAFCD) **[6825]**
North American Association of Floor Covering Distributors--Membership Directory **[6831]**
North American Association of Food Equipment Manufacturers (NAFEM) **[13889]**
North American Benefit Association [17268]
North American Broadcasters Association (NABA) **[13023]**, **[15578]**
North American Building Material Distribution Association (NBMDA) **[3962]**
North American Building Material Distribution Association--Membership Directory (Internet only) **[10397]**
North American Business Development Company L.L.C. [39369]
North American Drama Therapy Association--Membership List **[30877]**
North American Family Campers Association (NAFCA) **[2508]**
North American Farm and Power Show **[17178]**
North American Funds L.L.C. **[39369]**
North American Gaming Regulators Association (NAGRA) **[7269]**
North American Horsemen's Association (NAHA) **[8311]**
North American Ice Cream Association (NICRA) **[8540]**
North American Insulation Manufacturers Association (NAIMA) **[8848]**
North American International Auto Show (NAIAS) **[11463]**
North American Journal of Aquaculture **[6790]**
North American Manufacturing Research Conference **[29461]**
North American Manufacturing Research Institution of SME (NAMRI-SME) **[29477]**
North American Meat Institute (NAMI) **[2428]**
North American Millers' Association (NAMA) **[16962]**
North American National Broadcasters Association [13023], [15578]
North American Olive Oil Association (NAOOA) **[16963]**
"North American Pet Health Insurance Market Poised for Growth" in Pet Product News (Vol. 64, December 2010, No. 12, pp. 4) **[8946]**, **[12169]**, **[27313]**, **[32580]**, **[34116]**
North American Retail Hardware Association (NRHA) **[7915]**
North American Securities Administrators Association (NASAA) **[9298]**
North American Ski Journalists Association [5295], [11971]
North American Snowsports Journalists Association (NASJA) **[5295]**, **[11971]**
North American Wholesale Lumber Association (NAWLA) **[10382]**
North Atlantic Capital Corp. **[40316]**
North Attleboro and Plainville Chamber of Commerce [40637]
North Augusta Chamber of Commerce **[44575]**
North Baldwin Chamber of Commerce (NBCC) **[36141]**
North Bay Angels (NBA) **[37711]**
North Branch Area Chamber of Commerce **[41281]**
North Bridge Venture Partners (NBVP) **[40715]**
North Canton Area Chamber of Commerce **[43535]**
North Carolina Agribusiness Council (NCAg) **[16964]**, **[43039]**
North Carolina Association of Certified Public Accountants (NCACPA) **[16744]**
North Carolina Association of Health Care Recruitment (NCAHCR) **[25682]**
North Carolina Association of Realtors (NCAR) **[13107]**
North Carolina Business Incubators Association (NCBIA) **[33483]**
North Carolina Business Travel Association (NCBTA) **[19309]**
North Carolina Community College System Small Business Center Network (SBCN) **[43045]**
North Carolina Department of Agriculture and Consumer Services - Research Stations Div. **[17234]**
North Carolina Department of Agriculture and Consumer Services - Sandhills Research Station (SRS) **[10274]**
North Carolina Department of Agriculture and Consumers Services (NCDA&CS) - Marketing Div. **[43046]**
North Carolina Department of Commerce - Business/Industry Development Div. **[43047]**
North Carolina Department of Labor (NCDOL) - Occupational Safety and Health Div. - Education, Training and Technical Assistance Bureau - Charles H. Livengood, Jr. Memorial Library **[35985]**

3302 Small Business Sourcebook • 42nd Edition

North Carolina Fair Share CDC [2300], [20214], [31716]
North Carolina Institute of Minority Economic Development - NC Minority Business Enterprise Center [43215]
North Carolina Medical Society Annual Meeting [10960]
North Carolina Retail Merchants Association (NCRMA) [43040]
North Carolina Rural Economic Development Center [43044]
North Carolina Small Business and Technology Development Center (NCSBTDC) [43048], [43236]
North Carolina Small Business and Technology Development Center - Lead Office (SBTDC) [43042]
North Carolina Small Business and Technology Development Center (SBTDC) - SBTDC Regional Office [43237]
North Carolina Society of Anesthesiologists Annual Meeting [26074]
North Carolina State Beekeepers Association (NCSBA) [1447]
North Carolina State University - Industrial Extension Service [43049]
North Carolina State University Industrial Extension Solutions (NCSU IES) [43049]
North Carolina State University Libraries - D.H. Hill Library Special Collections Research Center (SCRC) [4366]
"North Carolina Town Hires Collection Agency" in PaymentsSource (April 24, 2012) [4803], [20320], [25151]
North Central Connecticut Chamber of Commerce (NCCCC) [38066]
North Central Global Business Travel Association (NCBTA) [19310]
North Central Iowa Small Business Development Center [39681]
North Central ISBDC [39474]
North Central Massachusetts Chamber of Commerce (NCMCC) [40610]
North Central Michigan College (NCMC) [41130]
North Central Ohio SCORE [43376]
North Central Pennsylvania Regional Planning and Development Commission (NCPRPDC) [44362]
North Central Pennsylvania Regional Planning and Development Commission Enterprise Development [44411]
North Central Texas College - Corinth Small Business Development Center (SBDC) [44928]
North Central Texas Small Business Development Center (NCTSBDC) [44929]
North Channel Area Chamber of Commerce (NCACC) [45298]
North Charles Mental Health Research and Training Foundation Inc. [34700]
North Clackamas County Chamber of Commerce [43995]
North Coast Angel Fund [43624]
North Coast Chamber of Commerce [43536]
North Coast Technology Investors [41053]
North Coast Ventures (NCV) [43624]
North Conway Institute - Resource Center - Alcohol and Drugs [34692]
North Country Angels (NCA) [35298], [45745]
North Country Chamber of Commerce [42011]
North Country Small Business Development Center (SBDC) [42409]
North Dade Regional Chamber of Commerce [38471]
North Dakota Chamber of Commerce [43298]
North Dakota Department of Commerce - Economic Development & Finance Div. (EDF) [43277]
North Dakota Department of Commerce - North Dakota Division of Community Services - Governmental/Technical Assistance [47445]
North Dakota Department of Health - Division of Waste Management [47001]
North Dakota Department of Transportation - Materials and Research Division [1181], [5118], [10298], [15534]
North Dakota Development Fund (NDDF) [43312]
North Dakota Office of Management and Budget - State Procurement Office (SPO) [43314]
North Dakota Small Business Development Center (NDSBDC) [43270]
North Dakota Small Business Development Center Bismarck (ND SBDC) [43271]
North Dakota Small Business Development Center Devils Lake (NDSBDC) [43272]
North Dakota Small Business Development Center Dickinson (ND SBDC) [43273]
North Dakota Small Business Development Center Fargo [43274]
North Dakota Small Business Development Center Grand Forks (ND SBDC) [43275]
North Dakota Small Business Development Center Minot (NDSBDC) [43276]
North Dakota State Library (NDSL) [47446]

North Dakota State University - Institute for Business and Industry Development (IBID) [21279]
North Dakota State University - Upper Great Plains Transportation Institute - North Dakota Local Technical Assistance Program (NDLTAP) [43318]
North Dallas Chamber of Commerce (NDCC) [45299]
North East Area Chamber of Commerce (NEACC) [44269]
North East Chamber of Commerce [40402]
North/East Roofing Contractors Association Convention and Trade Show [14336]
North Essex Chamber of Commerce (NECC) [42170]
North Florida Regional Chamber of Commerce [38472]
North Forge Technology Exchange [46728]
North Fort Myers Chamber of Commerce [38473]
North Fulton Chamber of Commerce [38743]
North Galveston County Chamber of Commerce [45300]
North Harris Montgomery Community College Small Business Development Center [44922]
North Haven Gardens Inc. (NHG) [10261]
"North Haven Gardens to Rebuild after Devastating Tornado" in GardenCenter (October 22, 2019) [7629]
North Hill Ventures [40716]
North Houston-Greenspoint Chamber of Commerce [45213]
North Idaho Business Journal [38962]
North Idaho College Professional-Technical Education [38959]
North Jersey Chamber of Commerce (NJCC) [42171]
North Judson Chamber of Commerce [39608]
North Kingstown Chamber of Commerce (NKCC) [44477]
North Little Rock Chamber of Commerce (NLRCC) [36487]
North Logan Chamber of Commerce [36490]
North Manchester Chamber of Commerce (NMCC) [39587]
North Mason Chamber of Commerce (NMCC) [46133]
North Metro Small Business Development Center [37790]
North Miami Chamber of Commerce [38407]
North Mississippi Enterprise Initiative (NMEI) [41455]
North Mobile Business [36142]
North Monterey County Chamber [37049]
North Monterey County Chamber of Commerce [37050]
North Myrtle Beach Chamber of Commerce [44576]
North Myrtle Beach Chamber of Commerce Convention and Visitors Bureau (NMBCOC) [44576]
North Olmsted Businessmen's Association [43537]
North Olmsted Chamber of Commerce (NOCC) [43537]
North Orange County Chamber of Commerce [37051]
North Pacific Anadromous Fish Commission (NPAFC) [6769]
North Penn Chamber of Commerce [44277]
North Phoenix Chamber of Commerce (NPCC) [36349]
North Platte Area Chamber of Commerce & Development Corporation (NPAREA) [41875]
North Platte Area Chamber of Commerce and Development Corporation of North Platte [41875]
North Platte Chamber of Commerce [41875]
North Port Area Chamber of Commerce (NPACC) [38474]
North Quabbin Chamber of Commerce (NQ) [40611]
North Sacramento Chamber of Commerce (NSCC) [37052]
North San Antonio Chamber of Commerce (NSACC) [45301]
North San Diego Business Chamber [37053]
North San Diego Small Business Development Center [36581]
North Santiam Chamber of Commerce (NSCC) [43996]
North Shelby Chamber of Commerce [36116]
North Shore Chamber of Commerce [40612]
North Shore InnoVentures (NSIV) [40760]
"North Side Story: 1 Step Forward, 1 Step Back" in Puget Sound Business Journal (Vol. 35, June 6, 2014, No. 7, pp. 4) [13521]
North Silicon Valley Chamber of Commerce [37046]
North Star Innovation Partners [40465]
North Suburban Chamber of Commerce [40613]
North Texas Angel Network (NTAN) [44902]
North Texas Enterprise Center for Technology (NTEC) [45543]
North Texas Regional Center for Innovation & Commercialization [45561]
North Texas Small Business Development Center (NTSBDC) [44930]
North Valley Regional Chamber of Commerce (NVRCC) [37054]
North Webster Tippecanoe Township Chamber of Commerce (NWTT) [39588]
Northampton Community College (NCC) [44431]
Northampton Community College - Paul and Harriett Mack Library [7225]

Northampton County Chamber of Commerce [43178]
Northbrook Chamber of Commerce [39269]
Northbrook Chamber of Commerce and Industry (NCCI) [39269]
NorthCentralMass.com [40614]
Northcoast Small Business Development Center Del Norte [36582]
Northcoast Small Business Development Center Humboldt [36583]
Northeast Alabama Entrepreneurial Center (NEAES) [36188]
Northeast Alabama Entrepreneurial System (NEAES) [36189]
Northeast-East Central Colorado Small Business Development Center [37791]
Northeast Floral Expo [6871]
Northeast Georgia SCORE [38649]
Northeast Homeland Security Regional Advisory Council (NERAC) [47295]
Northeast Indiana Innovation Center (NIIC) [39646]
Northeast Iowa Small Business Development Center [39682]
Northeast ISBDC [39475]
Northeast Johnson County Chamber of Commerce (NEJC) [39936]
Northeast Johnson County Chamber of Commerce and Visitors Bureau [39936]
Northeast Kingdom Chamber of Commerce (NEKCC) [45734]
Northeast Louisiana Business and Community Development Center (NLBCDC) [40230]
Northeast Louisiana SCORE [40140]
Northeast Massachusetts SCORE [40508]
Northeast Minnesota's Small Business Development Center [41154]
Northeast Mississippi Contract Procurement Center, Inc. [41445]
Northeast Mississippi Procurement Technical Assistance Program [41445]
Northeast Ohio Medical University - Research, Entrepreneurship, Discovery and Innovation Zone (REDIzone) [43675]
Northeast Ohio Procurement Technical Assistance Center - Lake Erie College Campus [43632]
Northeast Oregon Economic Development District (NEO EDD) [43905]
Northeast Polk Chamber of Commerce [38475]
Northeast SCORE [42425]
Northeast Sustainable Energy Association (NESEA) [14968]
Northeast Tarrant Chamber of Commerce [45302]
Northeast Technology Center - Pryor, Oklahoma [43894]
Northeast Texas Nursery Growers Association Trade Show [6872], [10064]
Northeast Texas Small Business Development Center [44931]
Northeastern Connecticut Chamber of Commerce (NCCC) [38067]
Northeastern Illinois Planning Commission [47398]
Northeastern Lumber Manufacturers Association (NELMA) [10383]
Northeastern Retail Lumber Association (NRLA) [10384]
Northeastern Retail Lumberman's Association [10384]
Northeastern State University Small Business Development Center (NSUSBDC) [43710]
Northeastern State University Small Business Development Center [43711]
Northeastern University Center for Entrepreneurship Education (NUCEE) [40761]
Northeastern University - Center for Nano and Microcontamination Control (CMC) [564]
Northern Alberta Business Incubator (NABi) [46676]
Northern Anne Arundel County Chamber of Commerce (NAACCC) [40403]
Northern Arizona Center for Entrepreneurship and Technology [36400]
Northern Arizona Genealogical Society Bulletin [7384]
Northern Arizona University - W.A. Franke College of Business [47447]
Northern Burlington Regional Chamber of Commerce [42105]
Northern California Minority Business Enterprise Center [37266]
Northern Cincinnati Chamber of Commerce (SCC) [43538]
Northern Dakota County Chamber of Commerce [41220]
Northern Gateway Regional Chamber of Commerce [42012]
Northern Hamilton County Chamber of Commerce [39589]
Northern Illinois University - Outreach, Engagement, and Regional Development Division - Center for Governmental Studies (CGS) [47448]

Northern Illinois University - The Regional Development Institute - Center for Governmental Studies (CGS) [47449]
The Northern Kentucky Business Journal [40077]
Northern Kentucky Chamber of Commerce [40078]
Northern Kentucky Tri-Ed [40103]
Northern Kentucky University Small Business Development Center (NKU SBDC) [39999]
The Northern Lancaster County Chamber of Commerce (EACC) [44270]
Northern Light Venture Capital (NLVC) [37442]
Northern Michigan Angels (NMA) [35299], [41054]
Northern Monmouth Chamber of Commerce [42164]
Northern Ontario Angels [46797]
Northern Ontario Heritage Fund Corporation (NOHFC) [46764]
Northern Palm Beach County Chamber of Commerce [38476]
Northern Region Small Business and Technology Development Center at Harford Community College [40342]
Northern Rhode Island Chamber of Commerce (NRICC) [44478]
Northern Virginia Business Travel Association [19300], [45761]
Northern Virginia Chamber of Commerce (NVCC) [45886]
Northern Virginia Community College - Annandale Campus [45977]
Northfield Area Chamber of Commerce [41282]
Northland Center for Advanced Professional Studies [41686]
Northland Pioneer College's Small Business Development Center (NPC:SBDC) [36275]
Northland Regional Chamber of Commerce (NRCC) [41603]
Northmont Area Chamber of Commerce (NACC) [43539]
Northridge Chamber of Commerce [37054]
Northshore SCORE [40136]
Northville Chamber of Commerce (NCC) [40985]
Northwest Alabama Junior Chamber of Commerce [36143]
Northwest Atlantic Fisheries Organization (NAFO) [6770]
Northwest Cartoonists Association [3264]
Northwest Chamber of Commerce [43785]
Northwest Chamber of Commerce (ROMG) [40404]
Northwest Christmas Tree Association [2929]
Northwest Communities Chamber of Commerce [40404]
Northwest Connecticut SCORE [37983]
Northwest Development Officers Association [45993]
Northwest Enterprise Center Network (NWECN) [46568]
Northwest Environmental Business Council (NEBC) [44050]
Northwest Fisheries Association (NWFA) [6742]
Northwest Food Processors Association [7810], [14090]
Northwest Indiana SCORE [39490]
Northwest Indiana Small Business Development Center (NISBDC) [39476]
Northwest Iowa Small Business Development Center [39683]
Northwest Louisiana Government Procurement Center [40211]
Northwest Louisiana SCORE [40137]
Northwest Lumbermen's Association [10385]
Northwest Marine Trade Association (NMTA) [10595]
Northwest Metro Chamber of Commerce [37814]
Northwest Minority Business Council [45996]
Northwest Missouri State University Small Business and Technology Development Center (SBDC) [41489]
Northwest Missouri State University Small Business and Technology Development Center St. Joseph Center (SBDC) [41490]
Northwest Mountain Minority Supplier Development Council [45996]
Northwest Ohio SCORE (SCORE) [43377]
Northwest Small Business Development Center (NWSBDC) [41155]
Northwest Sportshow [15122]
Northwest Technology Center Small Business Incubator [43868]
Northwest Texas Small Business Administration Development Center (NWTSBDC) [44932]
Northwest Texas Small Business Development Center (NWTSBDC) [44933]
Northwest Trade Adjustment Assistance Center (NWTAAC) [29471]
"Northwest Washington Fair Building New Horse Arena" in *Bellingham Business Journal* (Vol. March 2010, pp. 6) [4190], [8321]
Northwestern Building Products Expo [7930], [10409]
Northwestern Journal of International Law & Business (JILB) [18779]
Northwestern Lumber Association (NLA) [10385]

Northwestern Lumbermen's Association [10385]
"Northwestern Mutual Promotes Exec to Chief Insurance Officer" in *Bizwomen* (March 24, 2023) [27314]
Northwestern Oklahoma State University Small Business Development Center [43712]
Northwestern Oklahoma State University Small Business Development Center [43713]
Northwestern Ontario Innovation Centre (NOIC) [46830]
Northwestern University - Center for Business, Government and Society [34447]
Northwestern University - Dispute Resolution Research Center (DRRC) [10810]
Northwestern University - Kellogg School of Management - Ford Motor Co. Center for Global Citizenship [34447]
Northwestern University - Kellogg School of Management - Guthrie Center for Real Estate Research [13635]
Northwood Area Chamber of Commerce (NACC) [39777]
Norton Area Chamber of Commerce [39937]
"Norvax University Health Insurance Sales Training and Online Marketing Conference" in *Marketwired* (January 27, 2010) [8947], [9197], [15876], [16448], [27315], [29955], [32581], [35071]
Norwalk Area Chamber of Commerce (NACC) [39778]
Norwalk Chamber of Commerce [37055]
"Norway to Ban Fur Farms as Fox and Mink Go Out of Fashion" in *Business of Fashion* (January 15, 2018) [7230], [25466]
Norwegian American Chamber of Commerce, Inc. (NACC) [27426]
Norwegian American Genealogical Center and Naeseth Library (NAGC & NL) [7439]
Norwegian-American Historical Association Archives (NAHA) [7440]
"Norwegian Cruise Line Adds to Fleet with $3B Prestige Deal" in *South Florida Business Journal* (Vol. 35, September 5, 2014, No. 6, pp. 6) [15753], [31453]
Norwegian Trade Council [27416]
Norwegian Trade Council - United States [27416]
Norwest Equity Partners (NEP) [41336]
Norwest Venture Partners XII, LP (NVP) [37443]
Norwich Ventures [40717]
Norwin Chamber of Commerce [44271]
Norwood Park Chamber of Commerce and Industry [39270]
Nostradamus Advertising [4952]
"Not In Our Backyard" in *Canadian Business* (Vol. 80, October 22, 2007, No. 21, pp. 76) [14442], [18648], [25467]
"Not Normal: Inflation Taking Its Toll on Small Business" in *Small Business Trends* (February 19, 2023) [16585]
"Not Sales, But a Secret Sauce" in *Memphis Business Journal* (Vol. 35, March 14, 2014, No. 49, pp. 15) [17728], [29956], [32582]
"Not in Your Backyard?" in *Canadian Business* (Vol. 80, March 12, 2007, No. 6, pp. 44) [25152], [30878]
"Not Your Father's Whiteboard" in *Inc.* (Vol. 33, November 2011, No. 9, pp. 50) [3726], [14516], [14807], [26361], [30969], [33883]
"Notes on Current Labor Statistics" in *Montly Labor Review* (Vol. 133, September 2010, No. 9, pp. 75) [19748], [20048], [25884], [27006]
"Nothing But Green Skies" in *Inc.* (November 2007, pp. 115-120) [13806], [23307], [23641]
Nothing But Noodles [14222]
"Nothing Says Celebration Like Cake" in BakingBusiness.com (November 18, 2021) [1261]
Notre Dame Center for Business Communication [17888]
Nouvelles CSQ [35155]
The Nova Collective [30428], [30648], [35923]
Novak Biddle Venture Partners L.P. (NBVP) [40432]
Novartis Venture Fund (NVF) [40718]
Novelists Inc. (NINC) [5296]
Novi Chamber of Commerce (NCC) [40986]
Novi Chamber of Commerce Newsletter [40987]
Novus Business Services Inc. [24260]
Novus Glass [7504]
"Now in Play, Score Keeps Head Up and Stick on Ice" in *Globe & Mail* (January 20, 2007, pp. B5) [6540], [9698]
"Now That's Rich" in *Canadian Business* (Vol. 80, February 12, 2007, No. 4, pp. 92) [6541], [9699], [23521]
"Now You Can Sign Docs in Real Time on Microsoft Teams Meetings" in *Small Business Trends* (September 25, 2022) [16586]
"Nowspeed and OneSource to Conduct Webinar: How to Develop Social Media Content That Gets Results" in *Marketwired* (December 14, 2009) [323], [9198], [15877], [21931], [29957], [32583], [34117], [35072]
NPAFC Annual Report [6771]
NPAFC Technical Report [6772]
NPES: Association for Suppliers of Printing, Publishing and Converting Technologies [12716]
N.R. Goldstein and Associates [2027]

NRA-ILA Library [7842]
NRA Technical Library [859]
NRCA Annual Convention and International Roofing Expo [14337]
NRI Relocation Inc. [19215]
NRMCA [4299]
NSBA Annual Conference and Exhibition [21698]
NSSRA Newsletter [15114], [32344]
"NStar Feels the Heat" in *Cape Cod Times* (September 30, 2011) [5673], [5940], [9700], [23308], [31454]
"NSU Seeks Private Partners For New $80M Research Building" in *South Florida Business Journal* (Vol. 34, February 21, 2014, No. 31, pp. 4) [8816], [10924], [21589], [31455], [32012], [32798]
NTA Convention [15340]
NTC Group Inc. [38100]
NTCA Rural Telecom Industry Meeting & EXPO (RTIME) [12701]
Nu-Look 1-Hour Cleaners [5259]
"Nuclear Plans May Stall on Uranium Shortage" in *Globe & Mail* (March 22, 2007, pp. B4) [9701], [29319], [33216]
"Nuclear Renaissance" in *Canadian Business* (Vol. 83, August 17, 2010, No. 13-14, pp. 46) [5674], [5941], [23309]
NuCoPro [44435]
"Nude Maid Service Could Face Fines" in *UPI NewsTrack* (April 10, 2012) [2045], [25468]
Nueces Canyon Chamber of Commerce [45303]
NUMA New York [42960]
"No. 64: Scaling the Business Meant Rebuilding a Bridge" in *Inc.* (Vol. 36, September 2014, No. 7, pp. 48) [10996], [22407], [28069], [35509]
"No. 82: a Few Good Apps" in *Inc.* (Vol. 36, September 2014, No. 7, pp. 103) [2466], [15609], [26362], [30482]
"No. 123: Protecting People, From the Bronx to the Beltway" in *Inc.* (Vol. 36, September 2014, No. 7, pp. 106) [14443], [22726]
"No. 156: Divorced, But Still Running the Company Together" in *Inc.* (Vol. 36, September 2014, No. 7, pp. 78) [7041], [23642]
"No. 252: H. Bloom: Floral Subscriptions" in *Inc.* (Vol. 36, September 2014, No. 7, pp. 132) [6860], [28006]
"No. 300: My Job Is To Solve Every Kind of Crisis" in *Inc.* (Vol. 36, September 2014, No. 7, pp. 72) [20072], [29320], [32230]
"No. 359: FlexGround: Recreational Surfaces" in *Inc.* (Vol. 36, September 2014, No. 7, pp. 130) [6820], [23580]
"No. 373: Back To the Roots" in *Inc.* (Vol. 36, September 2014, No. 7, pp. 82) [6758], [8146], [16917]
"No. 381: Metallica and Other Forms of Hardware" in *Inc.* (Vol. 36, September 2014, No. 7, pp. 107) [7826], [11689], [22968], [27671]
"No. 407: What I Learned in the Military, and What I Had to Unlearn" in *Inc.* (Vol. 36, September 2014, No. 7, pp. 80) [7023], [22408], [25099], [25635], [26173], [34253]
"No. 423: How a Date Led To al Bowling Juggernaut" in *Inc.* (Vol. 36, September 2014, No. 7, pp. 42) [1880], [22727]
"No. 479: SeaSnax Seaweed Snacks" in *Inc.* (Vol. 36, September 2014, No. 7, pp. 44) [7991], [22409]
"Number-Cruncher Gets 'Pushback" in *Philadelphia Business Journal* (Vol. 33, August 22, 2014, No. 28, pp. 10) [3518], [3634], [25885], [27316]
"The Numbers Speak For Themselves" in *Barron's* (Vol. 88, July 14, 2008, No. 28, pp. 16) [6542], [9702], [18257], [24033]
Numerical Heat Transfer, Part A: Applications: An International Journal of Computation and Methodology [32905]
"Numerous Changes Made to Crop Production and Consumption Forecasts" in *Farm Industry News* (November 9, 2011) [17085], [19560]
Numismatic News [3246]
Numismatics International (NI) [3230], [3259]
The Numismatist [3247]
Nunacor Development Corporation (NDC) [46741]
"NuPathe: From Tight On Cash to a Big Payday" in *Philadelphia Business Journal* (Vol. 33, May 16, 2014, No. 14, pp. 6) [5178], [33025]
Nurse Next Door Home Care Services [8287]
Nursery Association Secretaries [7610]
Nursery & Garden Stores Industry in the US - Market Research Report [7638]
Nursery and Landscape Association Executives of North America (NLAE) [7610]
Nursery/Landscape Expo [6873], [7650], [12601]
Nurses Associated Alumnae of United States and Canada [1040]
Nursing Education Perspectives (NEP) [26037]

"A Nursing Home Chain Grows Too Fast and Collapses, and Elderly and Disabled Residents Pay the Price" in NBCnews (July 19, 2019) **[11517]**
"Nursing Home Group Put on the Block" in Globe & Mail (February 23, 2006, pp. B1) **[11518]**, **[19031]**, **[33026]**
Nurture Small Business: A CEO's Guide to Triumph **[24819]**
Nurture Small Business: A Guide to Buying and Maintaining a Franchise **[24458]**
Nurture Small Business: A Small Business Guide to the Corporate Transparency Act **[18737]**
Nurture Small Business: Denise's Opinions: Employee Values in a New Era **[34226]**
Nurture Small Business: Denise's Opinions: Mastering Your Business Financial Plan with Budgets, Forecasts, and a Vision **[17518]**
Nurture Small Business: Fostering Pay Equity at Work **[19763]**
Nurture Small Business: Harnessing the Power of People **[27108]**
Nurture Small Business: How Organizational Psychology Transforms Leadership **[27109]**
Nurture Small Business: Leveraging Skills-Based Hiring for a Stronger Workforce **[26722]**
Nurture Small Business: Mastering the Unspoken: A Guide to Authentic Business Communication **[17793]**
Nurture Small Business: Navigating Onboarding: Discover How to Create Smooth Employee Starts **[26723]**
Nurture Small Business: Nesha Pai: Kicking Your Obstacles to the Curb **[35904]**
Nurture Small Business: Outsmarting Burnout: Strategies for Sustainable Success **[22913]**
Nurture Small Business: Overcoming Entrepreneur Isolation by Building Authentic Connections **[34468]**
Nurture Small Business: Partner Up by Conquering Your Money Anxiety **[35425]**
Nurture Small Business: Profits with Purpose: Building a Sustainable Social Enterprise **[34437]**
Nurture Small Business: Purpose-Driven Entrepreneurship: A Path for Business Success **[19636]**
Nurture Small Business: Sales Success Secrets: Focusing on the Right Activities **[32684]**
Nurture Small Business: Scaling Impact: Shortcuts for Entrepreneurial Growth **[18447]**
Nurture Small Business: TeamCatapult Talks: Unveiling the Secrets of Effective Communication **[17794]**
Nurture Small Business: The Perfectionism Trap: A Guide to Entrepreneurial Success **[35905]**
Nurture Small Business: Unleashing Entrepreneurial Magic: Stories of Triumph and Transformation **[34634]**
Nurture Small Business: Unlocking Employee Passion: Strategies for a Resilient Workplace **[22302]**
Nurture Small Business: Unlocking Leadership Excellence with Emotional Intelligence **[22303]**
"Nurturing Talent for Tomorrow" in Restaurants and Institutions (Vol. 118, September 15, 2008, No. 14, pp. 90) **[4469]**, **[13977]**, **[21590]**
Nussbaum Center for Entrepreneurship (NCFE) **[43246]**
Nutley Chamber of Commerce **[42172]**
Nutri-Lawn **[10270]**
Nutri-lawn Corp. [10270]
Nutrition Action Healthletter **[8064]**
Nutrition & Foodservice Edge Magazine **[26038]**
Nutrition House Canada Inc. **[32371]**
Nutrition for Optimal Health Association [11559]
Nutrition Today **[11585]**, **[26039]**
Nuu-Chah-Nulth Eonomic Developement Corporation (NEDC) **[46698]**
"Nvidia Shares Clobbered After Gloomy Warning" in Barron's (Vol. 88, July 7, 2008, No. 27, pp. 25) **[4401]**, **[6543]**, **[9703]**, **[24034]**, **[26363]**, **[29321]**
"Nvidia's Picture Brighter Than Stock Price Indicates" in Barron's (Vol. 88, March 24, 2008, No. 12, pp. 46) **[6544]**, **[9704]**, **[21056]**, **[24035]**, **[26364]**, **[29322]**
"NY: T-Mobile's Metro Stores Sold Used Phones as New to Consumers" in PCMag (September 6, 2019) **[2775]**
NYC ACRE **[42910]**
NYC Advisors LLC **[42984]**
NYC Commercial Kitchen **[42911]**, **[42912]**
NYC Media Lab (NYCML) **[42913]**
NYC Seed **[43026]**
"NYC Tops Hub in Tech VC Dollars" in Boston Business Journal (Vol. 31, August 5, 2011, No. 28, pp. 1) **[26365]**, **[26625]**, **[35371]**
NYDesigns **[42914]**
Nyhart **[17408]**, **[19764]**
Nyikos Associates Inc. [621]
Nyikos-Garcia Foodservice Design, Inc. **[621]**
"Nymex Dissidents Rattle Sabers" in Crain's Chicago Business (Vol. 31, April 21, 2008, No. 16, pp. 2) **[6545]**, **[9705]**, **[24036]**, **[31456]**
"NYPA Grants Aid Area Companies" in Business First of Buffalo (Vol. 30, January 10, 2014, No. 17, pp. 6) **[25035]**, **[29323]**, **[34852]**

NYPD Pizza **[12569]**
Nyssa Chamber of Commerce [43997]
Nyssa Chamber of Commerce & Agriculture **[43997]**
NYSSMA Winter Conference [11201], [11286]
NYU Innovation Fund **[42783]**
NYU Poly Incubators **[42915]**

O

"Oahu Contractors Worry About Worker Shortage" in Pacific Business News (Vol. 52, March 14, 2014, No. 3, pp. 3) **[4191]**
Oak Cliff Chamber of Commerce (OCCC) **[45304]**
Oak Flooring Manufacturers of United States [3961]
Oak Forest - Crestwood Area Chamber of Commerce **[39271]**
Oak Grove Chamber of Commerce **[41604]**
Oak Harbor Area Chamber of Commerce (OHACC) **[43540]**
Oak Investment Partners **[37444]**
Oak Lawn Chamber of Commerce **[39272]**
Oak Park-River Forest Chamber of Commerce (OPRF) **[39273]**
Oak Ridge Chamber of Commerce **[44789]**
Oakdale Chamber of Commerce **[37056]**
Oakes Area Chamber of Commerce **[43304]**
Oakhurst Area Chamber of Commerce (OACC) **[37057]**
Oakland African-American Chamber of Commerce (OAACC) **[37058]**
Oakland Chamber of Commerce [37060]
Oakland Chinatown Chamber of Commerce (OCCC) **[37059]**
"Oakland County to Survey Employers on Needed Skills" in Crain's Detroit Business (Vol. 24, April 14, 2008, No. 15, pp. 30) **[21591]**, **[26626]**
Oakland Five East Bay Counties Black Chamber of Commerce [37058]
Oakland Metropolitan Chamber of Commerce (OMCC) **[37060]**
Oakland University-School of Education and Human Services-Educational Resources Laboratory **[16178]**
Oakley Area Chamber of Commerce **[39938]**
Oakley Chamber of Commerce **[37061]**
Oakridge - Westfir Chamber of Commerce **[43998]**
OAS Staff Association (OASSA) **[14976]**
Oatman-Gold Road Chamber of Commerce **[36350]**
"Obama Orders Contractors To Raise Minimum Wage" in Atlanta Business Chronicle (June 20, 2014, pp. 9A) **[6546]**, **[20574]**, **[25469]**
"Oberg Industries' Initiative Offers Many Paths Down Wellness Road" in Pittsburgh Business Times (Vol. 33, June 6, 2014, No. 47, pp. 12) **[17332]**, **[25886]**
"Oberweis Tests Home Ice Cream Delivery" in Ice Cream Reporter (Vol. 21, November 20, 2008, No. 12, pp. 1) **[6916]**, **[8583]**, **[23643]**
Obesity Medicine Association (OMA) **[16502]**
Obion County Chamber of Commerce **[44790]**
Object-Oriented Programming (OOP) Boot Camp **[33812]**
"Observers See Different Messages if Voters Reject Ambassador Tax Rebate" in Wichita Business Journal (Vol. 27, February 17, 2012, No. 7, pp. 1) **[8437]**, **[13522]**, **[25470]**, **[34853]**
Obsessive Branding Disorder: The Illusion of Business and the Business of Illusion **[324]**, **[29958]**
Obsidian Tattoo Supply **[15331]**
"The Obstacle Is the Way: The Timeless Art of Turning Trials into Triumph" **[22728]**, **[28742]**
OCA Ventures **[39370]**
Ocala/Marion County Chamber & Economic Partnership **[38477]**
Ocala/Marion County Economic Development Corp. [38477]
OC&C Strategy Consultants **[7326]**
Occupational & Environmental Health Consulting Services Inc. (OEHCS) **[2301]**, **[20215]**, **[26091]**
Occupational and Environmental Medical Association of Canada [25647]
Occupational Health & Safety **[35955]**
Occupational Medicine **[25683]**
Occupational Outlook Handbook **[5441]**
Occupational Therapy in Health Care: A Journal of Contemporary Practice **[26040]**
Ocean City Chamber of Commerce **[40405]**
Ocean City Regional Chamber of Commerce (OCRCC) **[42173]**
Ocean City Trade Expo **[8493]**, **[14096]**
Ocean City Visitors Guide **[42174]**
Ocean Community Chamber of Commerce **[44479]**
Ocean Grove Chamber of Commerce **[42175]**
Ocean Park Area Chamber of Commerce **[46134]**
Ocean Pines Area Chamber of Commerce **[40406]**
Ocean Pines Chamber of Commerce [40406]

Ocean Springs Chamber of Commerce (OSCC) **[41420]**
Oceanic Institute (OI) **[6804]**
Oceanside Chamber of Commerce **[42643]**
Oceanside Chamber of Commerce (OCC) **[37062]**
O'Charley's Restaurants **[14223]**
Ocilla - Irwin Chamber of Commerce **[38768]**
Oconee County Chamber of Commerce **[38769]**
Oconee County Chamber of Commerce (OCCC) **[44577]**
Oconomowoc Area Chamber of Commerce (OACC) **[46480]**
Oconto Falls Area Chamber of Commerce (OFACC) **[46481]**
"October 2009: Recovery Plods Along" in Hispanic Business (October 2009, pp. 10-11) **[6547]**, **[9706]**, **[11065]**, **[13248]**, **[13523]**, **[21057]**, **[24037]**
Octoclean **[2110]**
"The Ode: CoolBrands (1986 - 2010)" in Canadian Business (Vol. 83, September 14, 2010, No. 15, pp. 25) **[8584]**, **[9707]**, **[28743]**, **[31457]**, **[33217]**
"The Ode: S. M. Whitney Co. (1868 – 2010)" in Canadian Business (Vol. 83, October 12, 2010, No. 17, pp. 27) **[3134]**, **[14657]**, **[29324]**, **[33027]**
Odessa Black Chamber of Commerce **[45305]**
Odessa Chamber of Commerce **[45306]**, **[46135]**
O'Dwyer's Directory of Public Relations Firms **[12943]**, **[31783]**
Odyssey Venture Partners **[37445]**
Oelwein Area Chamber of Commerce and Area Development [39779]
Oelwein Chamber and Area Development (OCAD) **[39779]**
OF+ Consulting **[8072]**, **[30217]**
"Of Marks and Men" in Canadian Business (Vol. 80, March 12, 2007, No. 6, pp. 59) **[18649]**, **[27925]**
"Of Paper Towels and Health Insurance" in Philadelphia Business Journal (Vol. 28, May 11, 2012, No. 13, pp. 1) **[8948]**, **[25887]**, **[27317]**, **[31458]**, **[32231]**
O'Fallon Chamber of Commerce & Industries **[41605]**
OFDA Convention and Exhibition [7221]
Off the Beaten Path, L.L.C. **[19419]**
"Off the Wall: Keith Collins' Larger-Than-Life Designs" in Black Enterprise (Vol. 37, February 2007, No. 7, pp. 138) **[4600]**, **[22729]**
"Offer for Sears Canada 'Inadequate'" in Globe & Mail (February 10, 2006, pp. B4) **[31459]**, **[32232]**
"Offer Your Own Authentic Truth" in South Florida Business Journal (Vol. 34, July 25, 2014, No. 53, pp. 13) **[325]**, **[8665]**, **[12944]**, **[29959]**, **[31784]**
"Offering Service With a :)" in Puget Sound Business Journal (Vol. 35, July 11, 2014, No. 12, pp. 12) **[3874]**, **[8438]**, **[33218]**
Office of Adult Mental Health Services [34690]
Office of Aircraft Services - Business Utilization and Development Specialist - Division of Contracting **[47683]**
Office Business Center Association International Annual Convention **[24844]**
"The Office Christmas Party and Legal Liability" in Legal Zoom (March 23, 2023) **[22215]**, **[27007]**
"Office Depot Closing 400 Stores" in San Antonio Business Journal (Vol. 28, May 9, 2014, No. 13, pp. 3) **[11666]**, **[19032]**
"Office Depot Enhances Customer Experience with New Business Services" in Stores.org (June 25, 2018) **[11667]**
"Office Design: The Latest Trends in Workspace Architecture" in Wallpaper.com (October 25, 2019) **[11641]**
"The Office: Do Not Disturb" in Inc. (November 2007, pp. 144) **[22730]**, **[28744]**
Office of Equal Opportunity and Civil Rights [47637]
Office Equipment Manufacturers Institute [3689], [11660]
Office Evolution (OE) **[24286]**
"Office For One: The Sole Proprietor's Survival Guide" **[18474]**, **[22410]**, **[23693]**
Office of the Governor - Economic Development and Tourism Division - Economic Information Clearinghouse **[10635]**
Office of the Governor - Texas Economic Development **[44958]**
Office of Labor Relations & Workforce Performance [47344]
Office of Personnel Management Division for Human Capital Leadership and Merit System Accountability **[47342]**
Office of Personnel Management - Office of Small and Disadvantaged Business Utilization - Contracting Div. **[47343]**
Office Pride Commercial Cleaning Services **[2111]**
Office of Procurement [47028]
Office of Research [27984]
"Office Space" in Business Strategy Review (Vol. 25, Summer 2014, No. 2, pp. 18) **[610]**, **[11642]**

Office Master Index

Office Staffing & Temp Agencies Industry in the US - Market Research Report **[15649]**
Office of Substance Abuse [34690]
Office Supply Stores Industry in the US - Market Research Report **[11673]**
Office of Surface Mining Reclamation and Enforcement (OSMRE) - Appalachian Regional Office **[47684]**
"The Office: The Bad and the Ugly" in Inc. (January 2008, pp. 120) **[28745]**
Official Buyers Guide to the Southern Market [8211]
Official Guide to Lakeview East **[39274]**
Official Guide to Wellington **[38478]**
Official Summary of Security Transactions and Holdings **[2154]**
Ogallala - Keith County Chamber of Commerce (OKCCC) **[41876]**
Ogden Roemer Wilkerson Architecture (ORW) **[9066]**
Ogden SCORE **[45616]**
Ogden Small Business Development Center **[45609]**
Ogden/Weber Chamber of Commerce (OWCC) **[45642]**
OGS Quarterly **[7385]**
Ogunquit Chamber of Commerce (OCC) **[40294]**
OHCA Convention & Expo **[26075]**
Ohio Association of Realtors (OAR) **[13108]**
Ohio Bureau of Workers' Compensation - BWC Library **[35986]**
Ohio Capital Fund (OCF) **[43625]**
Ohio Chamber of Commerce (OCC) **[43541]**
"Ohio Commerce Draws Closer to Profitability" in Crain's Cleveland Business (Vol. 28, October 29, 2007, No. 43, pp. 14) **[6548], [18258], [19033], [24038], [28175]**
Ohio Department of Development [43372]
Ohio Department of Development - Office of Small Business and Entrepreneurship **[43371]**
Ohio Department of Job and Family Services - Ohio Labor Market Information **[47450]**
Ohio Development Services Agency - Office of Research **[46938], [47451]**
Ohio Development Services Agency (TID) - Technology and Innovation Div. **[43372]**
Ohio Environmental Protection Agency - Division of Environmental Response and Revitalization (DERR) **[47002]**
"Ohio Franchisee Buys 21 Jacksonville-Area Papa John's" in Florida Times-Union (December 20, 2010) **[12532], [13978], [18259], [24393]**
Ohio Funeral Directors Convention **[7221]**
Ohio Genealogical Society - Coshocton County Chapter Library **[7441]**
Ohio Genealogical Society Perry County, Ohio Chapter Library **[7442]**
Ohio Health Care Association Convention & Expo [26075]
Ohio Innovation Fund (OIF) **[43626]**
Ohio Insurance Agents Association Inc. (OIA) **[27226]**
Ohio-Israel Chamber of Commerce (OICC) **[43542]**
Ohio Matters **[43543]**
Ohio Minority Supplier Development Council (OMSDC) **[43617]**
"Ohio National to Pay $213,000 to Insurance Agent for Breaching Contract" in Investment News (November 12, 2019) **[8949]**
Ohio Organization Development Network [29060]
Ohio Procurement Technical Assistance Center **[43633]**
Ohio Procurement Technical Assistance Center - Cincinnati Procurement Outreach Center **[43634]**
Ohio Procurement Technical Assistance Center - Lawrence Economic Development Corporation - Southern Ohio Procurement Outreach Center (SOPTAC) **[43635]**
Ohio Procurement Technical Assistance Center - Mahoning Valley Technical Procurement Center - Mahoning Valley Economic Development Corporation (MVEDC) **[43636]**
Ohio Procurement Technical Assistance Center - Procurement Technical Assistance Program **[43638]**
Ohio Procurement Technical Assistance Center - Procurement Technical Assistance Program (PTAC) **[43637]**
Ohio Procurement Technical Assistance Center;Mahoning Valley Technical Procurement Center;Mahoning Valley Economic Development Corporation [43636]
"Ohio Regulator Sues Collection Agency" in Payments-Source (September 21, 2012) **[4804], [18650], [20321], [25471]**
Ohio Small Business Development Center **[43350]**
Ohio Small Business Development Center for Butler County **[43351]**
Ohio Small Business Development Center at the Clermont Chamber of Commerce **[43352], [43544]**
Ohio Small Business Development Center at Columbus State Community College **[43353]**
Ohio Small Business Development Center at James A. Rhodes State College **[43354]**
Ohio Small Business Development Center at Kent State University Stark Campus **[43355]**
Ohio Small Business Development Center at Kent State University Tuscarawas Campus **[43356]**
Ohio Small Business Development Center at Lorain County Community College **[43357], [43545]**
Ohio Small Business Development Center at Marietta (SBDC) **[43358]**
Ohio Small Business Development Center at Ohio University **[43359]**
Ohio Small Business Development Center at Terra Community College **[43360]**
Ohio Small Business Development Center at The OSU South Centers (SBDC) **[43361]**
Ohio Small Business Development Center at The Urban League of Greater Cleveland **[43362]**
Ohio Small Business Development Center at Toledo Regional Chamber of Commerce **[43363], [43546]**
Ohio Small Business Development Center at Youngstown State University **[43364]**
Ohio Small Business Development Center at Zane State College (ZSC) **[43365]**
Ohio State Beekeepers Association (OSBA) **[1448]**
Ohio State Journal on Dispute Resolution **[10804]**
Ohio State University - Advanced Computing Center for the Arts and Design (ACCAD) **[3685]**
Ohio State University - Agricultural Technical Institute (ATI) **[7696]**
Ohio State University - Billy Ireland Cartoon Library and Museum **[3278]**
Ohio State University - Career Connection **[2627]**
Ohio State University - Cartoon Research Library [3278]
Ohio State University College of Education and Human Ecology - Center on Education and Training for Employment (CETE) **[9993]**
Ohio State University College of Engineering - Ohio Water Resources Center (WRC) **[16358]**
Ohio State University College of Food, Agricultural, and Environmental Sciences - C. Wayne Ellett Plant and Pest Diagnostic Clinic (PPDC) **[12604]**
The Ohio State University Endeavor Center **[43676]**
Ohio State University - Engineering Research Center for Net Shape Manufacturing (ERC/NSM) **[29478]**
Ohio State University - Fisher College of Business - Ohio State Center for Real Estate **[13357]**
Ohio State University Library - Census Data Center **[46939]**
Ohio State University - Wilbur A. Gould Food Industries Center **[11626]**
Ohio TechAngels **[43627]**
Ohio Tri-State Hispanic Chamber of Commerce [43492]
Ohio University Innovation Center (OUIC) **[43677]**
Ohio University Procurement Technical Assistance Center at Athens (PTAC) **[43639]**
Ohio University - Voinovich School of Leadership & Public Affairs - Institute for Local Government Administration and Rural Development (ILGARD) **[31728]**
Ohio Valley Business Travel Association (OVBTA) **[19311], [43345]**
Ohio Veterinary Medical Association/Midwest Veterinary Conference **[710]**
Ohio Wesleyan University - Kinnison Music Library **[11233], [11301]**
Ohio Wesleyan University - L.A. Beeghly Library Archives/Special Collections **[760]**
Ohlone College **[37659]**
OHSU Health Hillsboro Medical Center [12474]
Oil and Automotive Service Marketing News **[13000]**
Oil Butler International Corp. **[13008]**
Oil Change Services Industry in the US - Market Research Report **[12999]**
"Oil Markets: A Nasty Russian Tale" in Canadian Business (Vol. 81, March 3, 2008, No. 3, pp. 85) **[18651], [19272], [22731], [31460], [33219]**
"Oil's Going Down, Down, Down" in Canadian Business (Vol. 79, October 9, 2006, No. 20, pp. 148) **[6549], [9708]**
Oilton Chamber of Commerce [43744]
Ojai Valley Chamber of Commerce (OVCofC) **[37063]**
"OK, Bring in the Lawyers" in Crain's Chicago Business (Vol. 31, November 17, 2008, No. 46, pp. 26) **[11066], [13249], [18260], [18652], [20322], [21058], [28176], [33220]**
Okapi Venture Capital LLC **[37446]**
Okawville Chamber of Commerce **[39275]**
Okeechobee County Chamber of Commerce [38343]
Okefenokee Chamber of Commerce and Development Authority of the City of Folkston and Charlton County, Georgia [38770]
Okefenokee Chamber of Commerce and Folkston - Charlton County Development Authority [38770]
Okefenokee Chamber and Development Authority **[38770]**
Okemah Chamber of Commerce **[43786]**
Oklahoma APEX Accelerator (OkAPEX) **[43836]**
Oklahoma Association of Realtors (OAR) **[13109]**
Oklahoma Business Incubator Association (OkBIA) **[43869]**
Oklahoma Cannabis Convention **[5061]**
Oklahoma Census Data Center - Oklahoma Department of Commerce **[46940]**
Oklahoma Center for the Advancement of Science Technology Inventor's Assistance Service (IAS) **[43718]**
Oklahoma City Black Chamber of Commerce (OKCBCC) **[43787]**
Oklahoma City, National Association of Women Business Owners [43706]
Oklahoma City SCORE **[43725]**
Oklahoma Department of Agriculture, Food and Forestry - Market Development Div. **[43719]**
Oklahoma Department of Career and Technology Education **[43720], [43837]**
Oklahoma Department of Commerce-Administration and Central Services **[43721]**
Oklahoma Department of Commerce - Business Services & Start-up Guide - Women & Minority Business Certifications - Minority-Owned Businesses **[43826]**
Oklahoma Department of Commerce Export Assistance Program **[43722]**
Oklahoma Department of Commerce - New and Existing Businesses - Minority-Owned Businesses [43826]
Oklahoma Department of Libraries (ODL) - Office of Government Information - U.S. Government Information Div. **[47452]**
Oklahoma Native American Business Enterprise Center **[43827]**
Oklahoma Procurement Technical Assistance Center [43836]
Oklahoma Procurement Technical Assistance Center - Eastern Oklahoma County Technology Center **[43838]**
Oklahoma Procurement Technical Assistance Center-Gordon Cooper Technology Center (GCTC) **[43839]**
Oklahoma Procurement Technical Assistance Center - Kiamichi Technology Center **[43840]**
Oklahoma Procurement Technical Assistance Center (OkPTAC) - Oklahoma Bid Assistance Network (OBA) - Southwest Technology Center (SWTC) **[43841]**
Oklahoma Procurement Technical Assistance Center - Oklahoma Bid Assistance Network (OBA) - Tri-County Technology Center **[43842]**
Oklahoma Public Human Resources Association [11949]
Oklahoma Small Business Development Center (OKSBDC) **[43714]**
Oklahoma State Chamber **[43788]**
Oklahoma State University - Center for Local Government Technology (CLGT) **[31729]**
Oklahoma State University Department of Integrative Biology - Ecotoxicology and Water Quality Research Laboratory (EWQRL) **[16359]**
Oklahoma State University - Ecotoxicology and Water Quality Research Laboratory Library **[16351]**
Oklahoma Super Trade Show **[7816], [35499]**
Okolona Area Chamber of Commerce **[41421]**
Okolona Chamber of Commerce [41421]
Olathe Chamber of Commerce (OCC) **[39939]**
Old Bridge, Sayreville & South Amboy Chamber of Commerce [42111]
Old Chicago Pizza & Taproom **[1369], [12570]**
Old Dogs New Tricks Version 2.0 - Awakening and Cultivating Leadership at Any Age **[28746]**
"Old Ford Plant to Sign New Tenants" in Business Courier (Vol. 27, August 13, 2010, No. 15, pp. 1) **[13250], [13524], [13807], [20643], [26627], [29325], [33396]**
"Old Friends Make Old Buildings Successful Restaurants" in Crain's Detroit Business (Vol. 24, February 4, 2008, No. 5, pp. 14) **[13979], [31461]**
Old Hippy Wood Products Inc. **[29473]**
Old-House Interiors **[9063]**
Old Orchard Beach Chamber of Commerce (OOBCC) **[40295]**
"The Old Railway is on a Roll" in Globe & Mail (January 26, 2006, pp. B1) **[6550], [9709], [33221]**
Old Saybrook Chamber of Commerce **[38068]**
"Old Spice Guy (Feb.-July 2010)" in Canadian Business (Vol. 83, August 17, 2010, No. 13-14, pp. 23) **[326], [1587], [21932], [29960]**
"Old Town Just the First Stop for Carluccio's" in Washington Business Journal (Vol. 33, May 30, 2014, No. 6, pp. 7) **[13874], [19426], [33333]**
Oldenburg Registry North America (OLD NA) **[641]**
"Older, But Not Wiser" in Canadian Business (Vol. 85, July 16, 2012, No. 11-12, pp. 54) **[11067], [11425], [13251], [20323], [24039], [34118]**
"Oldest Hat Retailer in the United States Contemplates Future in Changing Detroit" in Crain's Detroit (June 25, 2017) **[7935]**

3306 Small Business Sourcebook • 42nd Edition

Master Index Open

Master Index

Oldham Chamber & Economic Development (OCED) **[40079]**
Olive Branch Chamber of Commerce (OBCC) **[41422]**
Olive Oil Association [16963]
Olive Oil Association of America [13878]
Olive Oil Group [16963]
"Olive Oil Store and Tap Room To Open In Downtown Boise" in Idaho Business Review (May 15, 2014) **[15022]**, **[32078]**
"Oliver Russell Acquiring Social Good Network" in Idaho Business Review (August 29, 2014) **[327]**, **[7069]**, **[19561]**, **[21933]**, **[31462]**
Olivia Area Chamber of Commerce **[41283]**
Olmstead & Associates (OA) **[30218]**
Olney Chamber of Commerce **[45307]**
Olney Chamber of Commerce (OCC) **[40407]**
"O'Loughlin Cuts $6 Million Deal for Chesterfield Doubletree" in Saint Louis Business Journal (Vol. 32, September 2, 2011, No. 1, pp. 1) **[8439]**, **[15878]**, **[35073]**
Olson Research Associates, Inc. (ORA) **[6710]**
"Olympic Challenge: The Skinny on Sponsors" in Barron's (Vol. 92, July 23, 2012, No. 30, pp. 13) **[328]**, **[15171]**, **[29961]**
Olympic College (OC) **[46230]**
"Olympus is Urged to Revise Board" in Wall Street Journal Eastern Edition (November 28, 2011, pp. B3) **[81]**, **[2496]**, **[9710]**, **[15405]**, **[16822]**, **[19034]**, **[27008]**, **[27672]**, **[28747]**, **[31463]**
The Omaha Business Journal **[41902]**
O'Maine Studios **[40324]**
Omak Chamber of Commerce (OCC) **[46136]**
"O'Malley, Ehrlich Court Business Vote" in Baltimore Business Journal (Vol. 28, October 1, 2010, No. 21, pp. 1) **[24712]**, **[25472]**
O'Melveny & Myers LLP **[27982]**
"OMERS Joins Bid for U.K. Port Giant" in Globe & Mail (March 28, 2006, pp. B1) **[19035]**, **[27673]**, **[31464]**
OMERS Ventures **[37754]**
Omex Office Maintenance Experts **[2112]**
Omidyar Network (ON) **[37447]**
Omninet Capital L.L.C. **[37448]**
"OmniSYS Plans Big Richardson Expansion" in Dallas Business Journal (Vol. 35, June 8, 2012, No. 39, pp. 1) **[10893]**, **[18261]**, **[26628]**
Omohundro Institute of Early American History and Culture (OIEAHC) **[1711]**
Omphalos Ventures **[41368]**
Omro Area Chamber of Commerce **[46482]**
"On Comcast, Sarge, Wheels and the Big Price" in Philadelphia Business Journal (Vol. 32, February 7, 2014, No. 52, pp. 4) **[2467]**, **[15172]**, **[15610]**, **[29962]**
"On the Edge: The Art of High-Impact Leadership" **[22216]**, **[28748]**
"On the Go: a Busy Executive Is Always Well-Equipped for Travel" in Black Enterprise (Vol. 40, July 2010, No. 12, pp. 106) **[19381]**, **[32584]**
"On the Green: Sheila Johnson Adds $35 Million Golf Resort To Her Expanding Portfolio" in Black Enterprise (January 2008) **[7525]**, **[8440]**, **[13980]**, **[30371]**, **[35829]**
"On the Horizon" in Advertising Age (Vol. 83, October 1, 2012, No. 35, pp. 5) **[9199]**, **[25473]**
"On the House: Housing Developers Try to Read Generation Y" in Philadelphia Inquirer (December 2, 2010) **[4192]**, **[13252]**, **[13525]**, **[34119]**
On the Make: Clerks and the Quest for Capital in Nineteenth-Century America **[28749]**, **[32233]**, **[34120]**
"On Managerial Relevance" in Journal of Marketing (Vol. 75, July 2011, No. 4, pp. 211) **[28750]**, **[29963]**
"On the Money" in San Antonio Business Journal (Vol. 28, June 27, 2014, No. 20, pp. 4) **[19749]**, **[28751]**, **[34121]**
On Nature **[5493]**
On-Q Software Inc. **[142]**, **[1783]**, **[2390]**, **[14881]**, **[33932]**
"On-Site Used-Car Inspections Better the Odds in Buying Used" in Autotrader (September, 2012) **[2570]**
"On Technology: The Web Gets Real" in Canadian Business (Vol. 79, July 17, 2006, No. 14-15, pp. 19) **[3771]**, **[9200]**, **[17729]**, **[26366]**
On The Button **[3002]**
"On Their Own: Bronx High School Students Open a Bank Branch" in Black Enterprise (Vol. 38, February 2008, No. 7, pp. 42) **[6225]**, **[21592]**, **[36001]**
"On the U.S. Election: Shaky on Free Trade" in Canadian Business (Vol. 81, December 19, 2007, No. 1, pp. 29) **[8745]**, **[18653]**, **[25474]**, **[27674]**
"On the Use of Neurophysiological Tools In IS Research: Developing a Research Agenda for NeuroIS" in MIS Quarterly (Vol. 36, September 2012, No. 3, pp. 679) **[10845]**, **[25888]**, **[32013]**
"On With the Show: A.T. Jones & Sons, the Oldest Costume Shop in America, Turns 150" in Baltimore Magazine **[4555]**
"On Your Marks, American Airlines, Now Vote! Contest Creating Possibilities and Opportunities for Delray Beach Wedding Planner" in Benzinga.com (2011) **[1984]**, **[11909]**, **[29964]**, **[35830]**
Onawa Chamber of Commerce (OCC) **[39780]**
"Once Derided As Rabbit Food, Humble Salad Now Fuels Business Plans" in Dallas Business Journal (Vol. 35, August 17, 2012, No. 49, pp. 1) **[8102]**, **[13981]**, **[18262]**, **[19036]**
"Once Is Not Enough for These Restaurateurs" in Baltimore Business Journal (Vol. 31, April 25, 2014, No. 52, pp. 16) **[13982]**, **[18263]**, **[19562]**
Once Upon a Child **[3909]**, **[15811]**
One 2 One Bodyscapes **[12459]**
One Acadiana **[40183]**
"One of the Best Ways to Build Wealth...Is to Take Equity In a Company" in Business Journal (Vol. 31, May 2, 2014, No. 49, pp. 9) **[22411]**, **[25636]**, **[27215]**
"One of Dallas' Best Bread Geniuses Announces Plans for a New Storefront Bakery" in The Dallas Morning News (July 5, 2019) **[1262]**
"One of the First Food Trucks in Montreal" in America's Intelligence Wire (May 31, 2012) **[3851]**, **[7001]**, **[30483]**
One Hour Heating and Air Conditioning **[547]**
"One Hundred Years of Excellence in Business Education: What Have We Learned?" in Business Horizons (January-February 2008) **[21593]**, **[24713]**, **[28752]**, **[34122]**
"One Laptop Per Child Weighs Going For-Profit" in Boston Business Journal (Vol. 31, May 20, 2011, No. 17, pp. 1) **[3727]**, **[7141]**, **[21594]**, **[34349]**
"One of the Last Music Stores in San Francisco Is Closing" in San Francisco Chronicle (September 14, 2019) **[11182]**
One Liberty Ventures **[40719]**
One Million by One Million (1M/1M) **[37606]**
"One-on-One with Enterprise Florida's Gray Swoope" in Orlando Business Journal (Vol. 31, August 15, 2014, No. 7, pp. 4) **[19189]**, **[33397]**
The One Page Business Plan Co. **[19145]**
"One Personal Trainer's Fitness Goal: Help Cancer Patients Feel Better During and After Treatment" in America's Intelligence Wire (February 1, 2012) **[12425]**, **[25889]**
One Southern Indiana Chamber and Economic Development **[39590]**
"The One Thing That's Holding Back Your Wellness Program" in Employee Benefit News (Vol. 25, December 1, 2011, No. 15, pp. 8) **[25890]**, **[30594]**, **[32014]**, **[32799]**, **[35831]**, **[35950]**
"One Thing You Can Do: Brew a Greener Cup of Coffee" in The New York Times (March 27, 2019) **[3188]**, **[23310]**
"The One Thing You Must Get Right When Building a Brand" in Harvard Business Review (Vol. 88, December 2010, No. 12, pp. 80) **[329]**, **[11775]**, **[17730]**, **[20476]**, **[21934]**, **[29965]**, **[32585]**
"One-Time Area Trust Executive Finds Trouble in N.H." in The Business Journal-Serving Metropolitan Kansas City (September 12, 2008) **[6551]**, **[9711]**, **[19273]**, **[23522]**, **[24040]**, **[28753]**
One Valley (OV) **[37607]**
"One World" in American Printer (Vol. 128, August 1, 2011, No. 8) **[3322]**, **[12745]**, **[15879]**, **[16200]**, **[35074]**
One World KitchenShare **[39647]**
Oneida Chamber of Commerce [42596]
O'Neill Area Chamber of Commerce **[41877]**
OneRedmond **[46137]**
OneSource Business Browser North America **[27794]**
OneTraction **[37449]**
Onex Capital Corporation [46798]
Onex Corporation **[46798]**
OneZone **[39591]**
"Online Alcohol Purchasing Comes of Age" in Supermarket News (September 16, 2021) **[10333]**, **[11776]**
Online Beauty Retailing - US - 2021 **[1376]**, **[1394]**, **[4525]**, **[11833]**
Online Beer, Wine & Liquor Sales Industry in the US - Market Research Report **[1945]**, **[10337]**, **[11834]**
"Online Book Sales Surpass Bookstores" in Information Today (Vol. 28, September 2011, No. 8, pp. 11) **[1667]**, **[1835]**, **[21935]**, **[32586]**, **[34123]**
"Online Business Laws Your Small Business Needs to Know" in Business News Daily (Nov. 9, 2020) **[18654]**
"Online Consignment Is Big Business and a Bargain Hunter's Heaven" in CBS News (April 13, 2017) **[3899]**, **[11777]**
"Online Directories: Your Silent Sales Staff" in South Florida Business Journal (Vol. 34, June 20, 2014, No. 48, pp. 14) **[21936]**, **[23009]**, **[32587]**
Online Food Delivery Services Global Market Opportunities And Strategies To 2030 **[6929]**
"Online Forex Broker Tadawul FX Intros Arabic Website" in Services Close-Up (June 23, 2011) **[9712]**, **[16449]**, **[21937]**
"Online Gambling Businesses You Can Start from Home" in Home Business (Nov. 3, 2020) **[7304]**
Online Gambling Market in US 2022-2026 **[7316]**
Online Gambling Services in the US - Industry Market Research Report **[7317]**
Online Greeting Card Sales Industry in the US - Market Research Report **[7705]**, **[11835]**
Online Insurance Brokers Industry in the US - Market Research Report **[8983]**, **[11836]**, **[27360]**
Online Learning **[21318]**
"Online Marketing and Promotion of Canadian Films via Social Media Tools: Telefilm Launches New Initiative to Foster Innovative Distribution Strategies" in CNW Group (January 27, 2010) **[6198]**, **[9201]**, **[16450]**, **[20644]**, **[29966]**
Online Marketing and Search Engine Optimization **[21411]**, **[29599]**
"Online Marketing for Small Businesses in 2020: The Essentials" in International Business Times (June 16, 2020) **[27810]**
Online Media News **[30143]**
Online Member Directory **[45308]**
Online Research Best Practices and Innovations (Onsite) **[29600]**, **[29601]**
Online Searcher **[3441]**, **[3535]**, **[3557]**, **[3656]**, **[3751]**, **[3777]**, **[9277]**, **[11842]**, **[16494]**
"Online Security Crackdown" in Chain Store Age (Vol. 84, July 2008, No. 7, pp. 46) **[1985]**, **[11778]**, **[14444]**, **[21938]**, **[32234]**
"Online Shopping Overtakes a Major Part of Retail for the First Time Ever" in CNBC.com (April 2. 2019) **[11779]**
"Online Small Business Training Courses" in The Balance Small Business (Nov. 20, 2019) **[21595]**
Online: The Leading Magazine for Information Professionals [3441], [3535], [3557], [3656], [3751], [3777], [9277], [11842], [16494]
Online Trading Academy **[21727]**
"Online Training Requires Tools, Accessories" in Contractor (Vol. 56, September 2009, No. 9, pp. 67) **[12648]**, **[21596]**, **[26367]**
"Online Translation Service Aids Battlefield Troops" in Product News Network (August 30, 2011) **[2776]**, **[15946]**, **[21939]**
Onondaga Small Business Development Center **[42410]**
Onondaga Venture Capital Fund, LLC (OVCF) **[42784]**
Onset Ventures **[37450]**
Ontario Area Chamber of Commerce **[43999]**
Ontario Association of Landscape Architects Library (OALA) **[10148]**
Ontario Centers of Excellence Inc. [46831]
Ontario Centre of Innovation (OCI) **[46831]**
Ontario Centres of Excellence [46831]
Ontario Chamber of Commerce [36922]
"Ontario Keeps Bleeding Jobs as Michelin Closes Tire Plant" in Globe & Mail (February 3, 2006, pp. B1) **[19563]**, **[29326]**
Ontario Ministry of Community Safety and Correctional Services - Centre of Forensic Sciences (CFS) **[7843]**
Ontario Ministry of Community Safety and Correctional Services;Centre of Forensic Sciences [7843]
Ontario Nature **[5494]**
The Ontario Professional Surveyor (OPS) **[15229]**
Ontario Teachers' Pension Plan Board (OTPP) **[6729]**, **[9951]**
Ontonagon County Chamber of Commerce **[40988]**
Ontonagon County Chamber of Commerce and Tourism Association [40988]
Onward Orangeburg **[44578]**
OOC Inc. **[12571]**
Oogles N Googles **[12460]**
Oologah Area Chamber of Commerce **[43789]**
Ooo La La! **[38576]**
Opelika Chamber of Commerce **[36144]**
Opelousas-St. Landry Chamber of Commerce (OSLCC) **[40184]**
"Open English Touted as Startup Worth Emulating" in South Florida Business Journal (Vol. 34, January 24, 2014, No. 27, pp. 30) **[15921]**, **[21299]**, **[21769]**, **[22969]**
"Open Enrollment: Staying Healthy During Enrollment Season" in Employee Benefit News (Vol. 25, November 1, 2011, No. 14, pp. 41) **[8950]**, **[17333]**, **[25891]**, **[27009]**, **[27318]**
"Open Enrollment: What Small Businesses Need to Know About the Affordable Care Act" in Business News Daily (February 21, 2023) **[25892]**, **[27010]**, **[27319]**
"Open For Business" in Baltimore Business Journal (Vol. 30, June 22, 2012, No. 7, pp. 1) **[11643]**, **[22217]**, **[23311]**

Small Business Sourcebook • 42nd Edition 3307

Open Master Index

Open Legal Services (OLS) **[45683]**
"The Open Mobile Summit Opens in San Francisco Today: John Donahoe CEO eBay to Keynote" in Benzinga.com (November 2, 2011) **[1076]**, **[15880]**, **[21940]**, **[35075]**
"Open Office Design of Today Focuses on Choice and Collaboration" in Buildings (September 24, 2019) **[11644]**, **[31049]**
Open Prairie Ventures **[39371]**
"Open Price Agreements: Good Faith Pricing in the Franchise Relationship" in Franchise Law Journal (Vol. 27, Summer 2007, No. 1, pp. 45) **[18655]**, **[24394]**
Open Season Sportsman's Expo **[15207]**
"Open Source Intelligence for Private Investigators" in PInow.com (October 14, 2019) **[11780]**, **[12797]**
Open Technology Business Center [44061]
Open Works (OW) **[40466]**
Openair Equity Partners **[39967]**
"Opening an Auto Repair Shop: 6 Things You Should Know" in Advanced Technology Institute (April 21, 2016) **[14556]**
"Opening a Bike Shop: Advice, Common Pitfalls and Money Saving Tips from Those Who Have Done It" in Cycling Industry News (July 5, 2016) **[1524]**
Opening Door **[15975]**
"Opening and Operating a Franchise" in Legal Zoom (March 27, 2023) **[24395]**
"Opening a Restaurant? Here's Your Equipment Checklist" in Business News Daily (February 21, 2023) **[13983]**
Opening a Tattoo Shop: Everything You Need To Know **[15279]**
Openworks **[2113]**
Operation Eyesight Universal (OEU) **[25684]**
Operation Oswego County (OOC) **[42916]**
OPEX Business Transformation World Summit **[19125]**
Opimian Society **[15002]**
"Opinion: Prison Farms are Closing, but the Manure Remains" in Canadian Business (Vol. 83, August 17, 2010, No. 13-14, pp. 9) **[17086]**, **[21597]**, **[25475]**
Opp and Covington County Area Chamber of Commerce **[36145]**
Opportunities for Study in Hand Bookbinding and Calligraphy [1724]
OpportunitiesNB (ONB) **[46737]**
"Opportunity Knocks" in Small Business Opportunities (September 2008) **[3875]**, **[19190]**, **[24396]**, **[26799]**, **[34124]**
"Opportunity Now Lies at Short End of the Market" in Barron's (Vol. 88, June 30, 2008, No. 26, pp. M9) **[6552]**, **[9713]**, **[20324]**, **[24041]**
Opportunity Through Entrepreneurship Foundation (OTEF) **[36277]**
Optial UK Ltd. **[2302]**
Opticality Ventures **[42785]**
Opticians Association of Canada [16280]
"Optima Public Relations Gains Partners" in Alaska Business Monthly (Vol. 27, October 2011, No. 10, pp. 10) **[8666]**, **[12945]**, **[33222]**
"Optimal Awarded US $256 Thousand Contract to Conduct LiDAR Survey for a Major Electric Utility in the Southwest" in Canadian Corporate News **[26368]**, **[32800]**, **[33223]**
"Optimizing the Power of Your Employees through Diversity and Inclusion" in Minority Business Entrepreneur (Vol. 39, Fall, 2022, No. 4, pp. 10-11) **[22218]**
Optimizing Product Launches for Growth **[29549]**
"Optimum Nutrition, Maximum Profit" in Pet Product News (Vol. 66, September 2012, No. 9, pp. S1) **[8035]**, **[12215]**, **[29327]**
Optimus I SBR **[2303]**, **[14993]**, **[20216]**
The Option Strategist Newsletter **[9924]**
"Options Abound in Winter Wares" in Pet Product News (Vol. 64, November 2010, No. 11, pp. 1) **[3044]**, **[12216]**, **[29328]**, **[29967]**, **[32235]**, **[32588]**, **[32942]**
Optometric Education **[16309]**
Opus Capital **[37451]**
"Oracle: No Profit of Doom" in Barron's (Vol. 88, March 31, 2008, No. 13, pp. 40) **[6553]**, **[9714]**, **[18264]**, **[24042]**, **[26369]**, **[27675]**
Oracle Venture Fund **[37452]**
Orange Business News **[37064]**
Orange Chamber of Commerce **[37065]**, **[38069]**
Orange City Chamber of Commerce **[39781]**
Orange County Business Accelerator **[42917]**
Orange County Business Council (OCBC) **[37066]**
Orange County Business Journal (OCBJ) **[37694]**
Orange County Chamber of Commerce (OCCC) **[45887]**
Orange County Chamber of Commerce [37066]
Orange County Chamber of Commerce & Industry [37066]
Orange County Hispanic Chamber of Commerce (OCHCC) **[37067]**
Orange County SCORE **[36607]**
Orange County Small Business Development Center (SBDC) **[36584]**
"Orange County's Paid Sick Leave Initiative Draws Ire of Businesses" in Orlando Business Journal (Vol. 29, August 24, 2012, No. 10, pp. 1) **[17334]**, **[25476]**
Orange Fab **[37608]**
The Orange Revolution: How One Great Team Can Transform an Entire Organization **[17731]**, **[22219]**, **[28754]**
Orangeburg County Chamber of Commerce (OCCC) **[44579]**
Orangevale Chamber of Commerce (OCC) **[37068]**
Orangevale Chamber of Commerce Member Directory **[37069]**
The Orbiter **[14346]**
Orchard Park Chamber of Commerce **[42644]**
Orchestras Canada (OC) **[11234]**
Orchestres Canada [11234]
Orchid Black **[38539]**, **[38605]**
Ord Area Business **[41878]**
Ord Area Chamber of Commerce (OCC) **[41879]**
Order Selection, Staging and Storage Council of the Material Handling Industry of America [3475], [12970]
Oregon Association of Minority Entrepreneurs (OAME) **[44040]**
Oregon Best [44071]
Oregon Business **[44078]**
Oregon Business Council (OBC) **[33484]**
Oregon Business Magazine **[44079]**
Oregon Business Travel Association (OBTA) **[19312]**
Oregon Career Information System **[2619]**, **[5464]**
Oregon Chamber of Commerce **[39276]**
Oregon City Chamber of Commerce **[44000]**
Oregon Coast Community College Small Business Development Center **[43913]**
Oregon College of Art and Craft Library (OCAC) **[4698]**
Oregon-Columbia Chapter of the International Association of Business Communicators (OCIABC) **[43906]**
Oregon Department of Agriculture (ODA) - Agricultural Development and Marketing Div. **[43922]**
Oregon Department of Business Development - Business Development Div. **[43923]**
Oregon Department of Business Development - Business Development Division - Eastern Regional Business Development Office **[43924]**
Oregon Department of Environmental Quality - Land Quality Division - Environmental Cleanup Program **[47003]**
Oregon Economic and Community Development Department **[43925]**
Oregon Entrepreneurs Network (OEN) **[35300]**, **[44046]**
Oregon Geographic Information Systems - Oregon Geospatial Enterprise Office (GEO) **[47453]**
Oregon Health and Science University - Oregon Hearing Research Center (OHRC) **[8140]**
Oregon Hotel and Motel Association [8532]
Oregon Housing and Community Services Department (OHCS) **[47454]**
Oregon Innovation Center (OIC) **[44060]**
Oregon Lodging Association [8532]
Oregon Lodging Association - Materials Library. [8532]
Oregon Motor Hotel Association [8532]
Oregon NORML News **[5045]**
Oregon Office of Minority, Women, & Emerging Small Businesses New Certifications **[44041]**
Oregon Procurement Technical Assistance Center (OR-PTAC) **[44051]**
Oregon Procurement Technical Assistance Center - Government Contract Assistance Program (GCAP) **[44052]**
Oregon Procurement Technical Assistance Center - Government Contract Assistance Program - Pacific Northwest Defense Coalition (PNDC) **[44053]**
Oregon Procurement Technical Assistance Center (OEI) - Organization for Economic Initiatives, Inc. **[44054]**
Oregon Publisher **[4946]**, **[11477]**
Oregon REALTORS **[13110]**
Oregon Research Institute (ORI) **[34701]**
Oregon Restaurant & Lodging Association (ORLA) **[8532]**
Oregon Small Business Development Center - Lead Office (OSBDC) **[43914]**
Oregon Sports Angels (OSA) **[44047]**
Oregon State Library **[47455]**
Oregon State Office [47698]
Oregon State University - College of Engineering - Department of Civil and Construction Engineering - Kiewit Center for Infrastructure and Transportation **[1565]**
Oregon State University (OSU) - Seafoods Research Laboratory Library **[6754]**
Oregon Technology Business Center (OTBC) **[44061]**
Oregon Thoroughbred Breeders Association Library. [669]
Oregon Thoroughbred Breeding Association [669]
Oregon Thoroughbred Owners & Breeders Association (OTOBA) **[669]**
Oregon's Procurement Technical Assistance Center - Disadvantaged Business Enterprise (GCAP) **[44055]**
O'Reilly Alpha Tech Ventures (OATV) **[37755]**
Orem/Provo Small Business Development Center **[45610]**
"Oreos, Mercedes Join Super Bowl Ad Lineup; 90 Percent of Inventory Sold" in Advertising Age (Vol. 83, October 8, 2012, No. 36, pp. 3) **[330]**, **[28007]**, **[29968]**
Organic Certifiers Caucus [5796]
"Organic Chain Scouting Cincinatti Sites, Including Kenwood" in Business Courier (Vol. 27, December 3, 2010, No. 31, pp. 1) **[7992]**, **[8086]**, **[33398]**, **[34125]**
"Organic Dog Food Options" in Pet Product News (Vol. 66, September 2012, No. 9, pp. 54) **[8036]**, **[12217]**, **[29969]**
"Organic Dog Treats" in Veterinary Economics (Vol. 49, November 2008, No. 11, pp. 52) **[8037]**, **[12218]**
Organic Food Alliance [5796]
"Organic Food Company's a Hit With the Sippy-Cup Crowd" in Investor's Business Daily (March 27, 2012, pp. A5) **[8038]**, **[35832]**
Organic Food Incubator (OFI) **[42243]**
"Organic Food Industry Goes to College" in USA Today (April 9, 2012) **[8039]**, **[17087]**, **[18265]**, **[21598]**, **[25036]**, **[32015]**, **[32801]**
Organic Foods Production Association of North America [5796]
Organic Inc. **[22029]**
Organic & Natural Health Association **[8001]**, **[11570]**
Organic Produce Summit **[17179]**
Organic Trade Association (OTA) **[5796]**
Organisation Mondiale pour l'Education Prescolaire - Canada [2876]
Organisation des Peches de l'Atlantique Nord-Ouest [6770]
Organization of American Kodaly Educators (OAKE) **[11177]**
Organization of Black Designers (OBD) **[3003]**, **[3290]**, **[9028]**
Organization for Competitive Markets (OCM) **[16965]**
Organization of Country Radio Broadcasters [13018]
Organization Design Forum (ODF) **[28263]**
Organization Development Institute **[29060]**
Organization & Environment: The Journal of Business Sustainability (O&E) **[23451]**
"Organization Redesign and Innovative HRM" in Human Resource Management (Vol. 49, July-August 2010, No. 4, pp. 809-811) **[19037]**, **[27011]**, **[27926]**
Organization of Women in International Trade (OWIT) **[27427]**, **[35671]**
"Organizational Virtue Orientation and Family Firms" in Business Ethics Quarterly (Vol. 21, April 2011, No. 2, pp. 257) **[23523]**, **[23644]**
Organizations Alive!: Six Things That Challenge - Seven That Bring Success **[18266]**, **[20477]**, **[24714]**, **[27012]**, **[28042]**
Organize Your Genealogy: Strategies and Solutions for Every Researcher **[7369]**
Organize Your Space **[26823]**, **[31091]**
Organized Business Techniques, Inc. **[21713]**
"The Organized Mind: Thinking Straight in the Age of Information Overload" **[28755]**
"Organizing the Family-Run Business" in Small Business Opportunities (Get Rich At Home 2010) **[19038]**, **[23645]**
Organizing and Managing Accounts Payable (Onsite) **[16770]**
Origin Partners **[42219]**
Origin Ventures (OV) **[39462]**
Originate, Motivate, Innovate: 7 Steps for Building a Billion Dollar Network **[30372]**, **[34539]**, **[35372]**
Originate Ventures **[44347]**
Orinda Chamber of Commerce (OCC) **[37070]**
Orion Area Chamber of Commerce (OACC) **[40989]**
Orland Park Area Chamber of Commerce (OPACC) **[39277]**
Orlando Business Journal (OBJ) **[38607]**
"Orlando City Lions May Score MLS Dream With Stadium" in Orlando Business Journal (Vol. 29, August 31, 2012, No. 11, pp. 1) **[4193]**, **[15173]**
"Orlando Health to Build $24M Proton Therapy Facility" in Orlando Business Journal (Vol. 26, January 22, 2010, No. 34, pp. 1) **[4194]**, **[25893]**
"Orlando Patents Forecast Biz Diversity and Growth" in Orlando Business Journal (Vol. 30, April 18, 2014, No. 43, pp. 4) **[26370]**, **[27927]**, **[34126]**
Orleans Chamber of Commerce (OCC) **[39592]**
Orleans County Chamber of Commerce (OCCC) **[42645]**

3308 Small Business Sourcebook • 42nd Edition

Master Index Packing

Master Index

Orleans Economic Development (OEDA) **[42411]**
Ormond Beach Chamber of Commerce **[38479]**
Ornamental Concrete Producers Association (OCPA) **[7611]**
Oroville Area Chamber of Commerce (OACC) **[37071]**
Oroville Chamber of Commerce **[37072]**
Oroville, WA Chamber of Commerce **[46138]**
OrthoKinetic Review **[10958]**
"OrthoPediatrics Launches PediFood System" in Mass Device (November 18, 2019) **[10846]**
Osage Chamber of Commerce **[39782]**
Osage City Chamber of Commerce **[39940]**
Osage Venture Partners (OVP) **[44348]**
Osawatomie Chamber of Commerce **[39941]**
Osborne Area Chamber of Commerce (OACC) **[39942]**
"OSC Eyes New Tack on Litigation" in Globe & Mail (April 9, 2007, pp. B1) **[9715]**, **[18656]**, **[25477]**
Osceola Area Chamber of Commerce **[46483]**
Osceola Chamber-Main Street **[39783]**
Osceola/South Mississippi County Chamber of Commerce **[36488]**
OSHA 30-Hour Compliance Course (Onsite) **[35936]**
"OSHA Begins Process of Creating Standard to Protect Workers From Hazardous Heat" in GardenCenter (October 26, 2021) **[7630]**, **[17088]**
OSHA Compliance and Training for Medical and Dental (Onsite) **[35937]**
OSHA Compliance and Workplace Safety **[29087]**
OSHA Compliance & Workplace Safety (Onsite) **[35938]**
Oshkosh Association of Manufacturers and Commence [46484]
Oshkosh Chamber of Commerce **[46484]**
Osler, Hoskin & Harcourt L.L.P. **[2360]**
Osteoporosis Canada **[25685]**
Osteoporosis International: with other metabolic bone diseases **[26041]**
Oswego Chamber of Commerce **[39278]**
Oswego County Business Expansion Center (BEC) **[42918]**
"OTA Broadcaster Adding Telemundo, Other Channels" in Idaho Business Review (September 12, 2014) **[15611]**
Otay Mesa Chamber of Commerce **[37073]**
OTC Markets Newsletter **[6721]**, **[9941]**
OTHELLO Chamber of Commerce [46101]
"Other Players Want In On Ellis-St. Peter's Deal" in Business Review Albany (Vol. 41, July 4, 2014, No. 15, pp. 9) **[25894]**, **[31465]**
Otis College of Art and Design - Millard Sheets Library **[3076]**
OTRADI Bioscience Incubator (OBI) **[44062]**
Otsego County Chamber of Commerce **[42646]**
Ottawa Area Chamber of Commerce **[39943]**, **[43547]**
Ottawa Area Chamber of Commerce and Industry **[39279]**
Ottawa Centre for Research and Innovation [46826]
"Ottawa to Push for Gas Deal Between Petrocan, Gazprom" in Globe & Mail (February 13, 2006, pp. B1) **[21059]**, **[27676]**, **[31466]**
OU Inc. **[41112]**
Our Choice [1613]
"Our Gadget of the Week: Eye Candy From Dell" in Barron's (Vol. 89, July 27, 2009, No. 30, pp. 26) **[26371]**, **[30781]**, **[34995]**
Our Town America, A Franchising Corp. **[393]**
Ouray Chamber Resort Association (OCRA) **[37890]**
Out and About **[41606]**
Out of the Box Advisors **[43259]**
Out in Front **[36351]**
Out of Home Advertising Association of America, Inc. (OAAA) **[31840]**
"Out of Juice?" in Canadian Business (Vol. 81, October 27, 2008, No. 18, pp. 32) **[5675]**, **[5942]**, **[23312]**
Out-of-Home Measurement Bureau [219], [31829]
"Out of This World" in Black Enterprise (November 2007) **[13039]**, **[22732]**, **[31467]**
Out-U-Go! Pet Care Services Inc. **[12273]**
Out Your Backdoor (OYB) **[4679]**, **[15115]**
Out of Your Mind..and Into the Marketplace **[37703]**
"The Outcome of an Organization Overhaul" in Black Enterprise (Vol. 41, December 2010, No. 5) **[18267]**, **[19039]**, **[21599]**, **[22220]**, **[28756]**
Outdoor Amusement Business Association (OABA) **[598]**, **[3833]**
Outdoor Life Field & Stream Expo [15207]
Outdoor Lighting Perspectives Franchise Inc. (OLP) **[5422]**, **[10066]**
Outdoor Power Equipment Institute (OPEI) **[10082]**, **[10224]**
Outdoor Retailer Snow Show **[14742]**
Outdoor Writers Association of America (OWAA) **[5297]**
Outer Banks Chamber of Commerce (OBCC) **[43179]**
Outer Banks SCORE **[43053]**
"Outfitting your Office to Support the Return to Office" in Owl Labs (Apr 27, 2021) **[31050]**
OutLEADERSHIP (OL) **[30518]**
Outlet Coworking **[37609]**
Outliers: The Story of Success **[22733]**, **[24715]**
Outlook [39944]
"Outlook 2008 (9 Sectors to Watch): Construction" in Canadian Business (Vol. 81, December 19, 2007, No. 1, pp. 48) **[4195]**, **[18268]**
"Outlook 2008 (9 Sectors to Watch): Gold" in Canadian Business (Vol. 81, December 19, 2007, No. 1, pp. 53) **[9716]**, **[11068]**, **[18269]**
"Outlook 2008 (9 Sectors to Watch): Metals" in Canadian Business (Vol. 81, December 19, 2007, No. 1, pp. 46) **[18270]**, **[21060]**, **[29329]**
Outlook for the American Beer Market **[1946]**
Outlook Business Journal **[39944]**
"Outlook In Other Industries" in Crain's Detroit Business (Vol. 30, January 6, 2014, No. 1, pp. 3) **[1106]**, **[7142]**, **[13984]**, **[24043]**, **[25153]**, **[25895]**, **[34127]**
"Outlook for Montana Agriculture" in Montana Business Quarterly (Vol. 49, Spring 2011, No. 1, pp. 26) **[17089]**, **[18271]**, **[21061]**
"Outside Cash Fuels 'Growth' Tech Deals" in Washington Business Journal (Vol. 31, September 7, 2012, No. 20, pp. 1) **[14445]**, **[35373]**
"Outside In: The Power of Putting Customers at the Center of Your Business" **[19904]**, **[20478]**, **[32589]**
"Outside Investors Help Fill Need for North Texas Businesses" in Dallas Business Journal (Vol. 35, March 16, 2012, No. 27, pp. 1) **[13526]**, **[35374]**
"Outside Investors Hot On Detroit Commercial Real Estate" in Crain's Detroit Business (Vol. 24, January 28, 2008, No. 4, pp. 25) **[13253]**, **[13527]**
Outsourcing Institute (OI) **[31110]**
The Outstanding Receptionist **[17604]**
"Over-50 Singles Might Have the Best Luck Online" in USA Today (August 31, 2019) **[3816]**, **[11781]**
"Over A Barrel" in Canadian Business (Vol. 81, July 21, 2008, No. 11, pp. 13) **[6554]**, **[9717]**, **[21062]**, **[24044]**
Over-The-Rhine Chamber of Commerce (OTRCC) **[43548]**
OverAdMedia **[46235]**, **[46243]**
Overcoming Doubt and Imposter Syndrome **[35906]**
Overdressed: The Shockingly High Cost of Cheap Fashion **[3045]**, **[23313]**
Overeaters Anonymous, Inc. [16503]
Overeaters Anonymous World Service Office (OA WSO) **[16503]**
"Overheating Taking Place? Pay Attention to Details.." in Indoor Comfort Marketing (Vol. 70, March 2011, No. 3) **[504]**, **[5676]**, **[5943]**, **[23314]**, **[29970]**, **[34128]**
Overland, Pacific & Cutler Inc. (OPC) **[19216]**
Overland Park Chamber of Commerce (OPCC) **[39945]**
"The Overlicensed Society" in Harvard Business Review (Vol. 90, April 2012, No. 4, pp. 38) **[18657]**, **[25478]**, **[25896]**, **[27928]**, **[31468]**
Overnight Success. Don't Kid Yourself with Todd Sawyer **[22914]**
"Overqualified. Underemployed" in Philadelphia Business Journal (Vol. 33, August 1, 2104, No. 25, pp. 14) **[21063]**, **[21600]**, **[26629]**, **[27013]**
Overseas Automotive Club [7026]
Overseas Automotive Council (OAC) **[7026]**
"Overseas Marketing Key to Success of Chicago Spire" in Commercial Property News (March 17, 2008) **[4196]**, **[27677]**, **[29971]**
"Overseas Overtures" in Business Journal-Portland (Vol. 24, October 26, 2007, No. 35, pp. 1) **[5442]**, **[6107]**, **[15643]**, **[26630]**, **[27678]**, **[30595]**, **[31127]**
Oversubscribed: How to Get People Lining up to Do Business with You **[17450]**, **[29972]**
"Oversubscribed: Startup Funds Pour In" in Boston Business Journal (Vol. 31, July 22, 2011, No. 26, pp. 1) **[35244]**
"An Overview of Energy Consumption of the Globalized World Economy" in Energy Policy (Vol. 39, October 2011, No. 10, pp. 5920-2928) **[5677]**, **[5944]**, **[21064]**, **[23315]**, **[25479]**, **[27679]**
"An Overview of Rural Entrepreneurship and Future Directions " in Journal of Small Business Strategy (Vol. 31, December 1, 2021, No. 4, pp. 1-4) **[22734]**
Oviedo-Winter Springs Regional Chamber of Commerce (OWSRCC) **[38480]**
Owasso Chamber of Commerce **[43790]**
Owatonna Area Business Development Center [41353]
Owatonna Area Chamber of Commerce and Tourism (OACCT) **[41284]**
Owatonna Incubator [41353]
Owatonna Partners For Economic Development (OPED) **[41353]**
Owen County Chamber of Commerce and Economic Development Corp. **[39593]**
Owensboro Small Business Development Center **[40000]**
Owensville Chamber of Commerce (OCC) **[41607]**
Owner-Operator Independent Drivers Association (OOIDA) **[16063]**
"Owner of Skin Care Business Offers Westfield State Scholarships If Ex-President Drops Lawsuit" in Boston Business Journal (Vol. 34, April 25, 2014, No. 12, pp. 5) **[1588]**, **[4519]**, **[18658]**, **[21601]**
"Owners Consider Remodeling Westlake Center" in Puget Sound Business Journal (Vol. 33, September 28, 2012, No. 23, pp. 1) **[3135]**, **[12897]**, **[13808]**, **[32236]**
"Owner's Guide to Selling a Business" in ExitAdviser (November 16, 2018) **[19229]**
Owosso-Corunna Area Chamber of Commerce [41009]
"The Owyhee Is Filling Up Faster Than Expected" in Idaho Business Review (September 5, 2014) **[908]**, **[1986]**, **[8441]**, **[32237]**
Oxantium Ventures **[38173]**
Oxford Area Chamber of Commerce (OACC) **[40990]**, **[44272]**
Oxford Brookes University - Wheatley Library **[24914]**
Oxford Chamber of Commerce (OCC) **[43549]**
Oxford Chamber of Commerce [44272]
Oxford Hills Chamber of Commerce (OHCC) **[40296]**
Oxford Hills SCORE **[40250]**
Oxford-Lafayette County Chamber of Commerce (OLCCC) **[41423]**
Oxford Learning Centers Inc. **[2906]**, **[21728]**
Oxford Merchant Association [40990]
Oxfordian **[44273]**
Oxxo Care Cleaners **[5260]**
The Oz Principle **[18272]**, **[22735]**
Ozark Area Chamber of Commerce **[36146]**
Ozark Chamber of Commerce (OCC) **[41608]**
Ozark Foothills Business Incubator **[41687]**
Ozark Technology Center (OTC) **[36190]**
Ozona Chamber of Commerce **[45309]**

P

PA Consulting Group (PA) **[5776]**
"Pa. Pushes for Collection of Online Sales Tax" in Philadelphia Business Journal (Vol. 31, March 2, 2012, No. 3, pp. 1) **[11782]**, **[25480]**, **[34854]**
PA Times **[31709]**
PACE Business Development Center [37680]
PACE Finance Corporation (PFC) **[37680]**
Pacific Area Chamber of Commerce **[41609]**
Pacific Area Travel Association [15976]
Pacific Asia Travel Association (PATA) **[15976]**
Pacific Boating Almanac **[10607]**
Pacific Business News **[43264]**
Pacific Coast Builders Conference [4301]
Pacific Coast Oyster Growers Association [6773]
Pacific Coast Regional Small Business Development Corp. **[36585]**
Pacific Coast Shellfish Growers Association (PCSGA) **[6773]**
Pacific Community Ventures Inc. **[20708]**
Pacific Grove Chamber of Commerce (PGCC) **[37074]**
Pacific Health Research and Education Institute (PHREI) **[26133]**
Pacific Horizon Ventures (PHV) **[46195]**
Pacific Institute of Gemmology [9960]
Pacific Islands Small Business Development Center Network (PISBDCN) **[46629]**
Pacific Northwest Christmas Tree Association (PNWCTA) **[2929]**
Pacific Northwest Christmas Tree Association Buy-Sell Directory **[2947]**
Pacific Northwest Grain and Feed Association (PNWGFA) **[16966]**
Pacific Palisades Chamber of Commerce **[37075]**
Pacific Research Institute for Public Policy (PRI) **[26134]**
Pacific Salmon Commission (PSC) **[6774]**
Pacific Salmon Commission Annual Report (PSC) **[6775]**
Pacific Southwest Minority Supplier Development Council (PSWMSDC) **[36380]**
Pacific Ventures Group (PACV) **[37453]**
Pacifica Chamber of Commerce (PCC) **[37076]**
Paciugo Gelato Caffe **[8631]**
"Pack Mentality: Why Black Can Be Slimming" in Crain's Chicago Business (Vol. 31, April 21, 2008, No. 16, pp. 31) **[19382]**, **[27014]**, **[27680]**, **[28757]**, **[34996]**
"Packaging Firm Wraps Up Remake: Overseas Plants Help Firm Fatten Margins" in Crain's New York Business (January 6, 2008) **[6555]**, **[9718]**, **[24045]**, **[29330]**
Packaging and Label Gravure Association Global [12785]
Packaging and Shipping Specialists (PASS) **[3399]**
The Packer: The Business Newspaper of the Produce Industry **[7803]**
"Packing Chic" in Black Enterprise (Vol. 38, February 2008, No. 7, pp. 154) **[10367]**, **[19383]**, **[35833]**

Small Business Sourcebook • 42nd Edition 3309

PacRim Venture Partners [37454]
Padgett Business Services [2408], [26830]
Padgett Business Services (PBS) [155], [2407], [15453]
Padows's Hams & Deli, Inc. [6941]
Paducah Area Chamber of Commerce [40080]
Paediatrics & Child Health [25686]
Page County Chamber of Commerce [45878]
Page-Lake Powell Chamber of Commerce (PLPCC) [36352]
"Paging Dr. Phil" in Canadian Business (Vol. 79, September 25, 2006, No. 19, pp. 21) [14808], [18659], [23524], [26372]
Pagosa Springs Area Chamber of Commerce (PSACC) [37891]
Pahokee Chamber of Commerce [38481]
Pahrump Valley Chamber of Commerce (PVCC) [41918], [41948]
"Paid to Persuade: Careers in Sales" in Occupational Outlook Quarterly (Vol. 55, Summer 2011, No. 2, pp. 24) [2603], [27015], [32590]
"Paid Petsitting in Homes Is Illegal in New York. That's News to Some Sitters" in The New York Times (July 21, 2017) [12094], [12258], [25481]
Paier College of Art Inc. Library [3374]
"The Pain of Losing a Local Record Store" in The New York Times (August 17 2019) [3411]
Painesville Area Chamber of Commerce [43462]
Painful Pleasures, Inc. [15332]
Paint & Decorating Retailer [11867], [14715]
Paint and Decorating Retailers Association (PDRA) [9029], [11873]
"Paint Price Hikes Continue" in American Painting Contractor (October 11, 2021) [11860], [11880]
Paint Stores Industry in the US - Market Research Report [11865]
Paint and Wallpaper Association of America [9029], [11873]
"PaintCare Celebrates 10 Years with 10 Paint Recycling Programs" in Waste Today (October 29, 2019) [7958]
The Painted Penguin L.L.C. [4633]
Painters Industry in the US - Market Research Report [11884]
Painting [4619]
Painting Contractors Association (PCA) [9030], [11874]
Painting and Decorating Contractors of America [9030], [11874]
Paintsville Small Business Development Center [40001]
Pajaro Valley Chamber of Commerce [37077]
Pak Mail [3400], [9280]
Pak Mail Centres Ltd. [3401]
Palacios Chamber of Commerce [45310]
Paladin Consultants L.L.C. [31010]
Paladin Partners [46196]
Palatine Area Chamber of Commerce (PACC) [39280]
Palestine Area Chamber of Commerce (PCC) [45311]
The Paley Center for Media - Research Services [13064]
Palisade Chamber of Commerce (PCC) [37892]
Palm Bay Chamber [38460]
Palm Beach Chamber of Commerce (PBCC) [38482]
Palm Beach County Resource Center Inc. (PBCRC) [38531]
Palm Beach Guide [38483]
Palm Beach Mega Tan [15269]
Palm City Chamber of Commerce (PCCC) [38484]
Palm Desert Area Chamber of Commerce [37078]
Palm Springs Chamber of Commerce (PSCC) [37079]
Palm Tree Tech Center [3755]
Palm Ventures LLC [38120], [38121]
Palmerton Area Chamber of Commerce [44274]
Palms West Chamber of Commerce [38342]
Palo Alto Chamber of Commerce [37080]
Palo Alto Venture Partners [37455]
Palomar Ventures [37456]
Palomino Horse Breeders of America (PHBA) [8334]
Palos Hills Chamber of Commerce [39201]
Palos Verdes Peninsula Chamber of Commerce [37081]
Palouse Chamber of Commerce [46139]
Pamela K. Henry & Associates [27153]
Pampa Chamber of Commerce [45186]
Pan American Journal of Public Health [26048]
Pana Chamber of Commerce [39281]
Panago Pizza Inc. [12572]
Panama City/Bay County Chamber of Commerce [38329]
Panama City Beach Chamber of Commerce [38485]
Panaram International Trading Co. [33686]
"Pandemic Leads to a Bicycle Boom, and Shortage, around World" in AP NEws (June 14, 2020) [1525]
"Pandemic Recovery Grant Programs Launch Additional Funding Rounds" in Small Business Trends (March 11, 2023) [33589], [47977]
"The Pandemic Scramble to Legalize Home-Based Businesses" in Bloomberg CityLab (Jan. 31, 2022) [26800]

"Pandemic Woes and a 'YOLO Mentality' Have Ignited a Boom Time for Tattoo Artists" in Time (Aug. 25, 2021) [15310]
"Panel to Call for Reduced Restraints on Telecom Sector" in Globe & Mail (March 17, 2006, pp. B1) [25482], [26373], [33224]
"Panel Calls for 'Fundamental' Change to Telecom Regulation" in Globe & Mail (March 23, 2006, pp. B1) [25483], [26374], [33225]
Panel World [4285], [10402]
"Panera Breadwinner Tries on Tattu Designer Jeans" in Houston Business Journal (Vol. 40, December 18, 2009, No. 32, pp. 1) [1263], [3046], [3136], [21065], [22736], [24397], [31469]
"Panera Opens First Next-Generation Bakery-Cafe" in BakingBusiness.com (November 18.2021) [1264]
Pangaea Ventures Ltd. [36424]
Panhandle Area Development District (PADD) [41895]
Panola County Chamber of Commerce (PCCC) [45312]
Panoptic Enterprises [24889]
The Pantry Restaurants [14224]
Paola Chamber of Commerce [39946]
Paoli Chamber of Commerce [39594]
Papa Gino's, Inc. [12573]
Papa John's International, Inc. [12574]
Papa Murphy's Holdings, Inc. [12575]
Papa's Pizza To-Go Inc. [12576]
Paper Fortunes: Modern Wall Street: Where It's Been and Where It's Going [6556], [9719], [21066], [24046]
"Paper Replaces PVC for Gift Cards" in American Printer (Vol. 128, June 1, 2011, No. 6) [3323], [12746], [16201], [34129]
"Paper Tigers" in Conde Nast Portfolio (Vol. 2, June 2008, No. 6, pp. 84) [331], [11992], [21067], [29973]
Papillion Area Chamber of Commerce [41883]
Pappas Ventures [43225]
Par-T-Perfect Party Planners [26831]
Parachute [25687]
"Paradise Banquet Hall of Toronto: Breaking Traditions Can Keep a Wedding Budget Intact" in Internet Wire (June 12, 2012) [1987], [24047]
Paradise Ridge Chamber of Commerce (PRCoC) [37082]
Paragon Micro [3666]
Paragould Regional Chamber of Commerce [36489]
Parakletos Ventures [37756]
Parallel 18 [46644]
Paramount Chamber of Commerce (PCC) [37083]
"Paramount Said to be Working on Sale of Oil Sands Assets" in Globe & Mail (April 24, 2007, pp. B1) [19040], [19564]
Paramus Regional Chamber of Commerce [42176]
Parc Scientifique Bromont [46890]
Parcel Plus [10982]
"Parent Firm's Global Reach, Stricter Air Quality Rules Have Stock Smiling" in Crain's Cleveland Business (October 15, 2007) [8746], [18273], [27681], [29331], [31470]
Paris Area Chamber of Commerce (PACC) [36490], [41610]
Paris Area Chamber of Commerce [39282]
Paris Area Chamber of Commerce & Tourism (PACCT) [39282]
Paris-Bourbon County Chamber of Commerce [40081]
Paris/Henry County Chamber of Commerce [44791]
Paris Small Business Development Center (SBDC) [44934]
Parisi Speed School [21729]
"A Parisian Vending Machine for Baguettes 24/7" in Benzinga.com [16258]
Parisoma [37610]
Park City Chamber of Commerce (PCCC) [45643]
Park Falls Area Chamber of Commerce (PFACC) [46485]
Park Hills-Leadington Chamber of Commerce (PHLCOC) [41611]
Park Rapids Lakes Area Chamber of Commerce (PRLACC) [41285]
Parke County Chamber of Commerce [39595]
Parker Area Chamber of Commerce (PACC) [36353], [37893]
Parker Finch & Associates, LLC [12918]
Parker, Smith and Feek Inc. (PSF) [9011]
"Parkland Approves First "Luxury" Consignment Shop" in Sun Sentinel (May 7, 2012) [3900], [32238], [34130]
Parma Area Chamber of Commerce (PACC) [43550]
Parmasters Golf Training Centers [21730]
Parsippany Area Chamber of Commerce (PACC) [42177]
Parsons Chamber of Commerce [39947]
Parsons School of Design - Adam & Sophie Gimbel Design Library [3375], [4644]
Partech Ventures [37457]
Particulate Science and Technology: An International Journal [32906]

Parties By Terrye [12862]
Partis Solutions Ltd. [7327]
Partisan Management Group [37925]
"Partisan Vote in House for Export-Import Bank Measure" in U.S. News & World Report (November 15, 2019) [8747], [25484]
"Partner" On-Call Network L.L.C. (POCN) [2361]
"Partnering for Success" in Art Business News (Vol. 36, October 2009, No. 10, pp. 4) [3324], [4601], [9202], [17870], [29974], [31471]
Partners [44792]
Partners in Business [33485]
Partnership for New York City (PFNYC) [42647]
Partnership for Philanthropic Planning [7078]
Partnership: Small Business Start-Up Kit [9720], [18475], [24555], [31144]
Partnership for Tomorrow (PFT) [44580]
Partnerwerks Inc. [22325]
"A Parts Maker Primed for Takeoff" in Barron's (Vol. 92, August 25, 2012, No. 35, pp. 39) [9721], [10437], [29332]
"Parts, Tooling Manufacturer Machinists Inc. Opts to Expand in South Park" in Puget Sound Business Journal (Vol. 34, February 21, 2014, No. 45, pp. 6) [10438], [19191], [29333], [33399]
Party Land [7486], [11898]
Pasadena Angels [37458]
Pasadena Chamber of Commerce [45313]
Pasadena Chamber of Commerce and Civic Association [37084]
Pasadena Chamber of Commerce Membership Directory [45314]
Pasadena Commerce [37085]
Pasco Area Chamber of Commerce [46102]
Pasco-Hernando County SCORE - Chapter 439 [38294]
Paso Robles Chamber of Commerce (PRCC) [37086]
Passaic Chamber of Commerce [42171]
Passaic County, New Jersey - Department of Economic Development [42265]
Passaic County, New Jersey - Planning and Economic Development Department [42265]
Passenger Vessel Association (PVA) [2829]
"'Passion Is the Key to Accomplishment" in South Florida Business Journal (Vol. 35, August 15, 2014, No. 3, pp. 11) [13074], [20678], [22412]
A Passion for Planning: Financials, Operations, Marketing, Management, and Ethics [28758]
Passion Profit Co. [43003]
"Passionate About Empowering Women" in Women In Business (Vol. 63, Spring 2011, No. 1, pp. 24) [28759], [35834]
Passport Health Inc. (PH) [192]
"Past Due: $289 Million in Loans - University Club Tower, Sheraton St. Louis City Center in Default" in Saint Louis Business Journal (Vol. 32, September 23, 2011, No. 4, pp. 1) [11069], [28177]
PATCA Directory of Consultants [10487]
"Patent Squatters: Is It Possible to Patent an Invention That Everyone's Been Using for Years?" in Legal Zoom (March 27, 2023) [27929]
Patent and Trademark Office - Board of Patent Appeals and Inferences [47357]
Patent and Trademark Office - Office of Policy and External Affairs [47354]
"Patently Absurd" in Globe & Mail (January 28, 2006, pp. B4) [18660], [27930], [32016]
"Patently (Un)Clear" in Business Strategy Review (Vol. 21, Spring 2010, No. 1, pp. 28) [27931], [30782], [31128]
Patent's Handbook: A Guide for Inventors and Researchers to Searching Patent Documents and Preparing and Making an Application [27932]
"Paterson Plots Comeback With Internet IPO" in Globe & Mail (February 20, 2006, pp. B1) [6557], [9203], [9722], [16451], [26375], [31472]
Pathlight Kitchens [38577]
Pathogen Control Associates Inc. [558]
"Pathology Firm Building New HQ: Poplar Healthcare Facility Will Be Near FedEx Corp." in Memphis Business Journal (Vol. 34, June 29, 2012, No. 11, pp. 1) [4197], [10925]
Pathways Unlimited, Inc. [3786]
"Patience May Pay Off" in Barron's (Vol. 89, July 13, 2009, No. 28, pp. 30) [7761], [9723], [28760]
"Patience Will Pay Off in Africa" in Barron's (Vol. 92, September 17, 2012, No. 38, pp. M8) [9724], [18274], [21068], [27682]
"Patient Monitoring Tool Nears Testing Phase" in Pittsburgh Business Times (Vol. 33, February 7, 2014, No. 30, pp. 5) [10847], [30783], [31473]
"Patients to Elect to Cut Care" in The Business Journal-Serving Metropolitan Kansas City (Vol. 27, November 21, 2008, No. 11, pp. 1) [8951], [21069], [25897], [27320], [33226]

Master Index Pentagon

Patrick County Chamber of Commerce **[45888]**
Patrick County Chamber of Commerce and Visitors Center [45888]
Patterson-Westley Chamber of Commerce **[37087]**
Paul A. Warner Associates Inc. **[10699]**
Paul Davis Restoration Inc. (PDR) **[27378]**
Paul Davis Systems Canada Ltd. **[8999]**
"Paul Hawken and Other Top Lumnaries to Participate in Green Business BASE CAMP in Los Angeles" in Benzinga.com (April 19, 2012) **[5678]**, **[5945]**, **[22413]**, **[23316]**, **[26376]**
Paul Hornsby & Co. **[13620]**
Paul Revere's Pizza **[12577]**
Paul Smith's College of Arts & Sciences **[4481]**, **[8533]**
Paulding Chamber Business Directory **[38771]**
Paulding Chamber of Commerce **[38772]**
Paulding County Chamber of Commerce [38772]
"Paulino Gardens' Closure This Summer Was a Sign of the Times in Denver's Shifting Garden Center Industry" in The Denver Post (September 6, 2019) **[7631]**
Pauls Valley Chamber of Commerce **[43791]**
Pavement: The International Journal of the Asphalt Aftermarket **[4286]**
Paw Paw Area Chamber of Commerce **[40991]**
Paw Paw Chamber of Commerce [40991]
Pawhuska Chamber of Commerce **[43792]**
Pawling Chamber of Commerce (PCC) **[42648]**
"Pawn Shop Plan Snubbed by Citizen Group" in North County Times (October 14, 2010) **[11920]**
Pawn Shops Industry in the US - Market Research Report **[11922]**
Pawnee Community Chamber of Commerce **[43793]**
Pawsitively Spoiled **[12274]**
"Pay Fell for Many Baltimore Execs in '09" in Baltimore Business Journal (Vol. 28, July 2, 2010, No. 8, pp. 1) **[19750]**, **[27016]**, **[28761]**
"Pay Heed to 'Smack Stack" in Puget Sound Business Journal (Vol. 35, May 16, 2014, No. 4, pp. 6) **[2199]**, **[20117]**, **[25485]**, **[26377]**, **[34131]**, **[35076]**
"Pay or Play: Do Nice (Sales) Guys Finish Last?" in Agency Sales Magazine (Vol. 39, August 2009, No. 8, pp. 8) **[20479]**, **[22221]**, **[32591]**
"Paychecks of Some Bank CEOs Have a Pre-Recession Look" in Boston Business Journal (Vol. 29, May 13, 2011, No. 1, pp. 1) **[17335]**, **[27017]**, **[28762]**
"PayDragon Brings Mobile Payment App to Food-Truck Vendors" in PaymentsSource (April 16, 2012) **[3852]**, **[7002]**, **[20325]**, **[30484]**, **[33884]**
"Paying for the Recession: Rebalancing Economic Growth" in Montana Business Quarterly (Vol. 49, Spring 2011, No. 1, pp. 2) **[8748]**, **[11070]**, **[13254]**, **[13528]**, **[21070]**, **[24048]**, **[25486]**, **[27683]**
Payless Car Rental System, Inc. **[1172]**
Payments Conference **[24845]**
Paynesville Area Chamber of Commerce (PACC) **[41286]**
"PayPal and Venmo Launch New Small Business Grant Program for Emerging Businesses" in Small Business Trends (August 20, 2022) **[33590]**
The Payroll Book: A Guide for Small Businesses and Startups **[11935]**
Payroll & Bookkeeping Services Industry in the US - Market Research Report **[1776]**, **[11939]**
"Payroll Deductions: The Ultimate Guide for Business Owners" in NerdWallet (Feb. 4, 2021) **[31633]**
Payroll Law **[18492]**
Payroll Law (Onsite) **[18493]**, **[18494]**
Payroll Processors **[14882]**
Payroll Solution Inc. **[14883]**
Payroll Tax Basics for Small Business Owners **[31634]**
Payroll Tax Penalties Small Businesses Should Know About **[31635]**
"Payroll Tax for Small Business" in Mile IQ Blog (May 8, 2021) **[31636]**
Payroll Tax: What It Is, How to Calculate It **[31637]**
Payroll Taxes: A Small Business Employer's Guide **[31638]**
"Payroll Taxes for Small Businesses: The Basics" in Human Interest Blog (March 26, 2017) **[31639]**, **[34246]**
"Payroll Taxes Take up to 5 Hours Per Pay Period for Small Business Owners" in Small Business Trends (Jan. 12, 2020) **[31640]**
Payson Area Chamber of Commerce [45644]
Payson & Santaquin Area Chamber of Commerce **[45644]**
PBC Advisors L.L.C. **[2304]**, **[24261]**
PBExpo Aviation Technology Innovation **[440]**
PBI Laundry Consulting **[10198]**
"PBSJ Launches Internal Probe" in Tampa Bay Business Journal (Vol. 30, January 8, 2010, No. 3, pp. 1) **[18661]**, **[27684]**
"PC Connection Acquires Cloud Software Provider" in New Hampshire Business Review (Vol. 33, March 25, 2011, No. 6, pp. 8) **[3728]**, **[9725]**, **[14446]**, **[14809]**, **[21941]**, **[26378]**, **[31474]**, **[33885]**
"PC Running Slowly? How to Rev Up Your Machine" in Inc. (Vol. 33, November 2011, No. 9, pp. 46) **[3729]**, **[14810]**, **[33886]**
PCBC **[4301]**
"PCH Solutions Named New Sales Representative for Nor-Lake" in ACHR News (July 19, 2019) **[10580]**
PDA Annual Meeting **[5206]**
PDA Week [5206]
PDRA Decorating Registry **[11861]**, **[11883]**
Peabody Chamber of Commerce **[40615]**
"Peabody Launching 464-Room Renovation" in Memphis Business Journal (Vol. 34, July 13, 2012, No. 13, pp. 1) **[909]**, **[8442]**, **[12898]**
Peace Center **[10806]**
Peace Education Foundation **[10791]**
Peak Ventures [45657]
Pearl Chamber of Commerce (PCC) **[41424]**
Pearland Chamber of Commerce **[45315]**
Pearle Vision Inc. **[16313]**
"Pearson Bitman Strives to be the 'Google' of Law Firms" in Orlando Business Journal (Vol. 30, June 6, 2014, No. 50, pp. 3) **[18662]**, **[19565]**
Pearson Canada Inc. **[46862]**
Peckham Guyton Albers and Viets Inc. (PGAV) **[31092]**
Pecos Area Chamber of Commerce **[45316]**
"Pedal to the Medal" in Small Business Opportunities (Summer 2010) **[10439]**, **[35835]**
Pediatric Physical Therapy **[12497]**
Pedorthic Footcare Association (PFA) **[14669]**
Pedorthic Footwear Association [14669]
Peekskill - Cortlandt Chamber of Commerce [42616]
"Pegasus Logistics Expanding in Coppell" in Dallas Business Journal (Vol. 35, July 6, 2012, No. 43, pp. 1) **[7042]**, **[13809]**, **[20645]**
Peggy's Corner: The Art of Staging **[9047]**, **[13255]**, **[13529]**
PEI BioAlliance **[46882]**
Pekin Area Chamber of Commerce (PACC) **[39283]**
Pelham Area Chamber of Commerce [36116]
Pelican Lake Area Chamber of Commerce **[46486]**
Pelican Rapids Area Chamber of Commerce (PRACC) **[41287]**
Pelion Venture Partners **[45665]**
Pella Chamber of Commerce (PCC) **[39784]**
Pellet Fuels Institute (PFI) **[23044]**
Pembina Institute **[5495]**, **[23045]**
Pembina Institute for Appropriate Development [5495], [23045]
"Pending Shutdown of Coldwater Creek Will Affect Eight Stores In Massachusetts" in Boston Business Journal (Vol. 34, April 11, 2014, No. 10) **[3137]**, **[32239]**
Pendleton Business **[44001]**
Pendleton Chamber of Commerce **[44002]**
Pendleton Chamber of Commerce Directory **[44003]**
Pendleton County Chamber of Commerce **[46282]**
Penfund Partners Inc. **[46799]**
Peninsula Chamber of Commerce [43520]
Peninsula Ventures **[37459]**
Penn Foster Career School **[3574]**, **[44432]**
Penn Hills Chamber of Commerce (PHCC) **[44275]**
Penn State Small Business Development Center **[44100]**
Penn State University at Harrisburg (PSDC) - Institute of State and Regional Affairs - Pennsylvania State Data Center **[47456]**
Penn Station East Coast Subs [4917]
Penn Station Inc. **[4917]**
Pennell Venture Partners II L.L.C. **[37926]**
"Penney's Buys Wal-Mart Site" in Crain's Chicago Business (Vol. 31, March 31, 2008, No. 13, pp. 13) **[18275]**, **[19192]**, **[32240]**
Pennridge Chamber of Commerce (PCC) **[44276]**
PennSuburban Chamber of Commerce **[44277]**
Pennsylvania Association of Mortgage Brokers (PAMB) **[11004]**
Pennsylvania Association of Realtors (PAR) **[13111]**
Pennsylvania Biotechnology Center of Bucks County (PB) **[44412]**
Pennsylvania Business Brokers Association (PBBA) **[2143]**
Pennsylvania Business and Industry Chamber of Commerce [44278]
Pennsylvania Chamber of Business and Industry **[44278]**
Pennsylvania and Delaware Cleaners Association (PDCA) **[5229]**
"Pennsylvania DEP To Conduct Natural Gas Vehicle Seminar" in Travel & Leisure Close-Up (October 8, 2012) **[5679]**, **[5946]**, **[11426]**, **[14517]**, **[23317]**, **[25037]**
Pennsylvania Department of Community and Economic Development (OIBD) - Office of International Business Development **[44110]**
Pennsylvania Department of Community and Economic Development - Pennsylvania Industrial Development Authority (PIDA) **[44111]**
Pennsylvania Department of Community & Economic Development - Site Development Div. **[44112]**
Pennsylvania Department of Community and Economic Development, Technology Innovation - Ben Franklin Technology Partners **[44113]**, **[44413]**
Pennsylvania Department of Environmental Protection - Bureau of Waste Management **[47004]**
Pennsylvania Department of General Services - Bureau of Minority and Women's Business Opportunities [44328]
Pennsylvania Department of General Services - Bureau of Small Business Opportunities (BSBO) **[44328]**
Pennsylvania Drycleaners and Launderers Association [5229]
Pennsylvania Environmental Council (PEC) **[7984]**, **[13752]**
Pennsylvania Family Institute (PFI) **[7342]**
Pennsylvania Horticultural Society (PHS) **[7681]**, **[8167]**
Pennsylvania Minority Business Development Authority (PMBDA) **[44329]**
Pennsylvania Minority Business Enterprise Center **[44330]**
Pennsylvania Procurement Technical Assistance Center (GACO) - California University of Pennsylvania - Government Agency Coordination Office **[44364]**
Pennsylvania Procurement Technical Assistance Center - California University of Pennsylvania - Government Agency Coordination Office (GACO) **[44363]**
Pennsylvania Procurement Technical Assistance Center (EDD) - Economic Development Council of Northeast Pennsylvania - The Northeastern Pennsylvania Alliance - Enterprise Development District **[44365]**
Pennsylvania Procurement Technical Assistance Center (NEPA) - Northeastern Pennsylvania Alliance **[44366]**
Pennsylvania Procurement Technical Assistance Center (NTRPDC) - Northern Tier Regional Planning and Development Commission **[44367]**
Pennsylvania Procurement Technical Assistance Center - Northwest Pennsylvania Regional Planning and Development Commission **[44368]**
Pennsylvania Procurement Technical Assistance Center (SEDA-COG) - SEDA Council of Governments **[44369]**
Pennsylvania Procurement Technical Assistance Center (SPC) - Southwestern Pennsylvania Commission **[44370]**
Pennsylvania Small Business Development Centers (SBDC) **[34237]**, **[44101]**, **[44371]**
Pennsylvania Society of Tax and Accounting Professionals - Buxmont Chapter **[15357]**, **[16745]**
Pennsylvania Society of Tax and Accounting Professionals - Lehigh Valley Chapter **[15358]**, **[16746]**
Pennsylvania Society of Tax and Accounting Professionals - Northeast Chapter **[15359]**, **[16747]**
Pennsylvania Society of Tax and Accounting Professionals - Philadelphia Tri-County Chapter **[15360]**, **[16748]**
Pennsylvania Society of Tax and Accounting Professionals - South Central Chapter **[15361]**, **[16749]**
Pennsylvania Society of Tax and Accounting Professionals - Southeast Chapter **[16750]**
Pennsylvania Society of Tax and Accounting Professionals - West Central Chapter **[16751]**
Pennsylvania Society of Tax and Accounting Professionals - Western Pennsylvania Chapter **[16752]**
Pennsylvania State Beekeepers Association (PSBA) **[1449]**
Pennsylvania State Data Center (SCO) - State Capital Office **[47457]**
Pennsylvania State University Harrisburg - Institute of State and Regional Affairs - Pennsylvania State Data Center (PASDC) **[9286]**, **[47458]**
Pennsylvania State University at Harrisburg - Pennsylvania State Data Center [9286], [47458]
Pennsylvania State University - Institute for the Study of Business Markets (ISBM) **[30861]**
Pennsylvania State University - Risk Management Research Center (RMRC) **[17420]**
Pennsylvania State University - Smeal College of Business - Center for Research in Conflict and Negotiation (CRCN) **[10811]**
Pennsylvania State University Technical Assistance Program (TAP) **[44114]**
Penny & Associates Inc. (PA) **[143]**, **[16884]**, **[24262]**
Penobscot Bay Regional Chamber of Commerce (PBRCC) **[40297]**
Pensacola Area Chamber of Commerce [38409]
Pension Research Council (PRC) **[17421]**
Pension and Welfare Research Center [17420]
"Penske Opens Its First Smart Car Dealership In Bloomfield Hills" in Crain's Detroit Business (Vol. 24, January 21, 2008, No. 3) **[11427]**, **[18276]**
"Pentagon Awards $17.6B Contract for EB-Built Subs Through 2018" in Providence Business News (Vol. 29, April 28, 2014, No. 4) **[4198]**, **[10608]**, **[25154]**, **[26631]**

Small Business Sourcebook • 42nd Edition 3311

Pentwater Master Index

Pentwater Area Chamber of Commerce [40992]
Pentwater Chamber of Commerce **[40992]**
"People; E-Commerce, Online Games, Mobile Apps" in Advertising Age (Vol. 80, October 19, 2009, No. 35, pp. 14) **[6199]**, **[9204]**, **[11993]**, **[15517]**, **[19041]**, **[19566]**, **[21942]**, **[29975]**, **[32241]**
People Engineering **[34635]**
People Operations: Automate HR, Design a Great Employee Experience, and Unleash Your Workforce **[27018]**
The People Playbook: How to Build Your Dream Team **[27110]**
"The People Puzzle; Re-Training America's Workers" in The Economist (Vol. 390, January 3, 2009, No. 8612, pp. 32) **[8952]**, **[14983]**, **[17336]**, **[21071]**, **[21602]**, **[25038]**, **[26632]**, **[27321]**
"People and Their Pets: Life Inside an Animal Clinic" in Midland Daily News (April 13, 2019) **[693]**
"People Tools for Business: 50 Strategies for Building Success, Creating Wealth, and Finding Happiness" **[27019]**, **[28763]**
"People Want Organic Food Because of What Isn't On It, Local Producers Say" in Republican & Herald (September 24, 2012) **[8040]**, **[17090]**
"PeoplesVC Becomes the 1st Stock-Based Crowdfunding Site to Open Its Doors to Investors" in Investment Weekly (June 23, 2012) **[22970]**, **[30898]**, **[34132]**, **[35375]**
Peoria Area Chamber of Commerce (PACC) **[39284]**
Peoria Chamber of Commerce (PCC) **[36354]**
Peoria NEXT Innovation Center **[39419]**
Peoria SCORE **[39008]**
"Pep Boys to Pay $3.7M for Illegally Disposing of Hazardous Waste" in Waste Today (October 1, 2019) **[1107]**, **[7959]**, **[25487]**
"Pep Talk: Marketing An Independent Film" in Black Enterprise (Vol. 40, July 2010, No. 12, pp. 104) **[22222]**, **[28764]**
Pepe's Mexican Restaurants **[14225]**
"Pepperidge Farm Getting New Life" in Orlando Business Journal (Vol. 28, August 24, 2012, No. 28, pp. 1) **[18277]**, **[34133]**, **[35836]**
Perceptive Technology Corp. **[31011]**, **[31093]**
Percussive Arts Society (PAS) **[11235]**
The Perfect Pita L.L.C. **[14226]**
The Perfect Profit and Loss Statement with Adam Rundle **[16855]**
"Perfecting Customer Services" in Pet Product News (Vol. 64, November 2010, No. 11, pp. 18) **[12170]**, **[20480]**, **[21603]**, **[28008]**, **[28043]**, **[32242]**, **[32592]**
"Perfecting the Process: Creating a More Efficient Organization on Your Terms" in Black Enterprise (Vol. 41, October 2010, No. 3) **[18278]**, **[19042]**, **[19567]**, **[20481]**, **[22737]**, **[28765]**
Perfecto's Caffe **[1226]**, **[4918]**
Performance Consultants Group, Inc. (PCG) **[2305]**, **[10552]**, **[19146]**, **[20217]**, **[29024]**, **[33687]**
Performance Consulting Associates, Inc. (PCA) **[2306]**, **[10553]**, **[19147]**, **[20218]**, **[22326]**, **[29025]**
Performance Dynamics Group L.L.C. **[2307]**, **[20219]**, **[31923]**
Performance Group Ltd. (TPG) **[2362]**
Performance Improvement Institute (PII) **[39420]**
Performance Management, Leading Change, and Putting It All Together (Onsite) **[28395]**
Performance Measurement Analysis (Onsite) **[17605]**
Performance Technologies Inc. (PTC) **[22327]**
"The Performer: Soulpepper Theatre Company's Albert Shultz" in Canadian Business (Vol. 83, August 17, 2010, No. 13-14, pp. 71) **[22223]**, **[22738]**, **[28766]**, **[29976]**
"Performing Leadership" in Business Strategy Review (Vol. 23, Spring 2012, No. 1, pp. 56) **[11183]**, **[28767]**
Perham Area Chamber of Commerce **[41288]**
"The Perils of Partnering in Developing Markets: How a Health Care Provider Addresses the Risks That Come With Globalization" in Harvard Business Review (Vol. 90, June 2012, No. 6, pp23) **[18279]**, **[19568]**, **[27685]**, **[31475]**
"The Perils and Pitfalls of S Corporations" in allBusiness **[31641]**, **[32409]**
"The Perils of Popularity" in Business Strategy Review (Vol. 23, Spring 2012, No. 1, pp. 51) **[2777]**, **[19905]**, **[32593]**
Peritoneal Dialysis International (PDI) **[26042]**
Perkins Community Chamber of Commerce **[43794]**
Perkiomen Valley Chamber of Commerce (PVCC) **[44279]**
"The Perks of Going Public" in Austin Business Journal (Vol. 31, July 15, 2011, No. 19, pp. A17) **[9726]**, **[13810]**, **[35376]**
"Perks Still Popular: Jets May be Out, but CEO Benefits Abound" in Crain's Detroit Business (Vol. 25, June 22, 2009) **[17337]**, **[27020]**, **[28768]**
Perma-Glaze Inc., Multi-Surface Restoration **[12692]**
Perma-Jack Co. **[4352]**
Permal Capital Management [40691]
Perquimans County Chamber of Commerce (PECO) **[43180]**
Perris Valley Chamber of Commerce **[37088]**
Perry Chamber of Commerce **[43795]**
Perry County Chamber of Commerce (PCCC) **[44280]**
Perry County Development Corp. (PCDC) **[39648]**
"Perry Ellis and G-III Apparel--Out of Fashion, but Still in Style" in Barron's (Vol. 88, March 17, 2008, No. 11, pp. 48) **[6558]**, **[9727]**, **[18280]**, **[24049]**, **[29334]**
Perry Historians Library **[7443]**
"Perry's Goes Organic" in Ice Cream Reporter (Vol. 22, December 20, 2008, No. 1, pp. 1) **[8041]**, **[8585]**, **[17091]**, **[23646]**, **[30784]**
Perrysburg Area Chamber of Commerce **[43551]**
Perryton-Ochiltree Chamber of Commerce **[45317]**
Perryville Chamber of Commerce **[41612]**
Persepolis Ventures **[37460]**
Pershing County Chamber of Commerce [41949]
Pershing County Chamber of Commerce and Visitors Center **[41949]**
"Person To Watch: Wedding Planner Brings Energy to Her Job" in Chattanooga Times/Free Press (April 24, 2012) **[1988]**, **[11910]**, **[35837]**
Personal Care Product Council **[1383]**, **[1579]**, **[4507]**
Personal Communications Industry Association [1509], [2704]
Personal Edge **[32372]**
Personal Skills for Professional Excellence (Onsite) **[28396]**
Personal Success and the Bottom Line **[22739]**, **[24050]**
Personal Success Strategies (Onsite) **[21412]**
"Personal Trainer to Attempt to Break World Record" in Pantagraph (August 23, 2012) **[12426]**
Personal Watercraft Industry Association (PWIA) **[10596]**
"Personality Traits You Need to Start a Business" in Business News Daily (Oct. 12, 2021) **[22740]**
Perspectives **[16967]**, **[46487]**
Persuasive Business Proposals **[17732]**, **[17871]**
Persuasive Communications **[17606]**, **[28397]**
Persuasive Communications in Marketing and Public Relations [17606], [28397]
Persuasive Leadership: Storytelling that Inspires (Onsite) **[17607]**, **[28398]**
Perth Amboy Chamber of Commerce (PACC) **[42178]**
Pest Control Industry in the US - Market Research Report **[12048]**
Pest Control Operators of California Convention **[12057]**
Pest Control Technology (PCT) **[12053]**
Pesticide Biochemistry and Physiology (PBP) **[12054]**
The Pet Advocacy Network (PIJAC) **[12080]**, **[12180]**
Pet Assist **[12275]**
Pet Business 101: From Puppy School to Running With the Big Dogs **[12095]**, **[12148]**, **[12259]**
"Pet Care Services in Rhode Island to be Taxed' in Pet Product News (Vol. 66, September 2012, No. 9, pp. 1) **[12096]**, **[12149]**, **[12219]**, **[12260]**, **[34855]**
Pet Care Trust (PCT) **[12249]**
"Pet Food Bank 'Shares the Love" in Pet Product News (Vol. 64, December 2010, No. 12, pp. 6) **[7143]**, **[12171]**, **[29335]**, **[34350]**
Pet Food Institute (PFI) **[12181]**
Pet Groomers Business Insurance **[12097]**
Pet Grooming & Boarding Industry in the US - Market Research Report **[12100]**
Pet Industry Distributors Association (PIDA) **[12182]**
Pet Industry Joint Advisory Council [12080], [12180]
"Pet Project Pays Off" in Small Business Opportunities (March 2011) **[12246]**
Pet Sit Pros Inc. (PSP) **[12276]**
Pet Sitters Associates LLC **[12250]**
Pet Sitters International (PSI) **[12251]**
Pet Sitting Market Research Report by Pet Type, Application, Region - Global Forecast to 2027 - Cumulative Impact of COVID-19 **[12265]**
"Pet Store Fish Provide Clue to How Alzheimer's Disease May Start" in Marketwired (July 9, 2012) **[21604]**, **[25898]**, **[32017]**, **[32802]**
"Pet Store Pro Adds New Curriculum" in Pet Product News (Vol. 66, February 2012, No. 2, pp. 2012) **[12220]**, **[21605]**, **[22224]**, **[28769]**
Pet Supplies Plus [12123], [12241]
Pet-Tenders **[12277]**
Petaluma Area Chamber of Commerce (PACC) **[37089]**
Petaluma Business **[37090]**
"Pete Carroll's Winning Rule: Protect Your Team" in Puget Sound Business Journal (Vol. 35, July 25, 2014, No. 14, pp. 12) **[14447]**, **[22225]**, **[28770]**
"Peter Bynoe Trades Up" in Black Enterprise (Vol. 38, July 2008, No. 12, pp. 30) **[6559]**, **[9728]**, **[13530]**, **[15174]**, **[22741]**, **[24051]**, **[28771]**
Peter C. Lagarias, Esq. **[18761]**
"Peter French Tapped to Lead Cafe Commerce" in San Antonio Business Journal (Vol. 28, May 30, 2014, No. 16, pp. 6) **[22742]**
Peter G. Peterson Institute for International Economics (PIIE) **[15498]**
Peterborough & the Kawartha Economic Development (PKED) **[46765]**
Peterborough Region Angel Network (PRAN) **[46800]**
Peters Township Chamber of Commerce **[44281]**
Petersburg Chamber of Commerce **[36239]**, **[45889]**
Petersburg Chamber of Commerce (PCC) **[39285]**
Petersburg Chamber of Commerce [46267]
Peterson Ventures **[45666]**
Petland Inc. **[12239]**
Petoskey Regional Chamber of Commerce (PRCC) **[40993]**
Pets Are Inn Inc. **[12240]**
"PetSmart: A Barking Buy" in Barron's (Vol. 89, July 6, 2009, No. 27, pp. 15) **[9729]**, **[12221]**, **[18281]**
Pfizer Ventures (PV) **[43027]**
PFM Capital Inc. **[46919]**
PGA Merchandise Show **[7537]**
PGA Show [7537]
PG&E Corporation (PG&E) **[4367]**
PH Canada Company **[14227]**
Pharmaceutical Care Management Association (PCMA) **[5142]**
Pharmaceutical Manufacturers Association [5143]
Pharmaceutical News Index® **[1599]**
Pharmaceutical Research and Manufacturers of America (PhRMA) **[5143]**
"Faster To Dissolve, Faster To Work" in Philadelphia Business Journal (Vol. 33, March 14, 2014, No. 5, pp. 8) **[25899]**, **[30785]**, **[32018]**, **[32803]**
"Pharmacies Vie for Sites, Customers" in Philadelphia Business Journal (Vol. 30, January 6, 2012, No. 47, pp. 1) **[5179]**, **[19906]**
Pharmacy Times: Practical Information for Today's Pharmacist **[5201]**
Pharmacy Today **[5202]**
"PHCC Convention, Show Get High Marks" in Contractor (Vol. 56, December 2009, No. 12, pp. 1) **[505]**, **[12649]**, **[15881]**, **[35077]**
PHE Journal [12384]
Phelan Chamber of Commerce **[37091]**
Phelps Chamber of Commerce **[46488]**
Phenix City-Russell County Chamber of Commerce [36105]
"Phila.-Area Foreclosures Rising" in Philadelphia Business Journal (Vol. 28, May 18, 2012, No. 14, pp. 1) **[11071]**, **[13256]**, **[21072]**
"Phila. Tax Break Aimed at Luring Investment Funds" in Philadelphia Business Journal (Vol. 28, April 13, 2012, No. 9, pp. 1) **[9730]**, **[34856]**
Philadelphia Area Council for Excellence [44230]
Philadelphia Business Journal **[12013]**
Philadelphia Business Journal **[44438]**
Philadelphia Business Travel Association **[19313]**
Philadelphia Community Development Partnership [41395]
Philadelphia Corporation for Aging Library (PCA) **[198]**
Philadelphia Fashion Incubator (PFI) **[44414]**
Philadelphia-Israel Chamber of Commerce (PICC) **[44282]**
"Philadelphia Tourism Push Rising in Fall" in Philadelphia Business Journal (Vol. 30, August 26, 2011, No. 28, pp. 1) **[8443]**, **[15754]**, **[16006]**, **[31694]**, **[34857]**
Philadelphia University|Paul J. Gutman Library [3080]
"Philadelphia's Largest Employers Will Fill 6,000 Jobs Within 6 Months" in Philadelphia Business Journal (Vol. 28, February 5, 2010, No. 51, pp. 1) **[18282]**, **[25488]**, **[26633]**
"Philanthropy Good For Business" in Crain's Detroit Business (Vol. 24, February 18, 2008, No. 7, pp. 14) **[9205]**, **[22743]**, **[26379]**, **[34351]**
Philatelic Foundation Archives and Library (PF) **[3260]**
Philatelic Literature Review **[3248]**
Philip Morris USA Inc. (PM USA) **[15716]**
Philipsburg Chamber of Commerce **[41786]**
"Phillip Frost: 'Technology Is the Future" in South Florida Business Journal (Vol. 34, June 20, 2014, No. 48, pp. 16) **[9731]**, **[19683]**, **[22744]**, **[27933]**
Phillips & Associates L.L.C. **[3352]**, **[8998]**
"Phillips Edison Launches $1.8B Retail REIT" in Business Courier (Vol. 27, October 15, 2010, No. 24, pp. 1) **[7762]**, **[9732]**, **[13257]**, **[13531]**, **[32243]**
Phillipsburg Area Chamber of Commerce **[39948]**
Phillipsburg Area Chamber of Commerce (PACC) **[42179]**
The Philly Connection **[14228]**
Philomath Area Chamber of Commerce (PACC) **[44004]**
Phoenix Business Consulting, Inc. (PBC) **[39448]**

Phoenix Business Journal **[16720]**
"Phoenix History: How Miniature Golf Made Its Way from California to the Valley" in azcentral (July 11, 2019) **[10986]**
"Phoenix Hospitality Plans to Develop Hotel in Live Oak" in San Antonio Business Journal (Vol. 28, May 2, 2014, No. 12, pp. 8) **[8444]**, **[15882]**
Phoenix Metropolitan Chamber of Commerce [36339]
Phoenix Venture Partners (PVP) **[37461]**
Phoenixville Area Chamber of Commerce **[44283]**
"Phone Scam Preys on Small Business Owners Looking for a Loan" in Small Business Trends (Jan. 19, 2022) **[19274]**
"The Phone-Service Test: Call Centres" in Canadian Business (Vol. 79, October 9, 2006, No. 20, pp. 137) **[20482]**, **[33227]**
Photo Marketing Association International Annual Convention and Trade Show (PMA) **[2500]**
The Photo Review **[12313]**
Photofinishing Industry in the US - Market Research Report **[12283]**
The Photograph Collector **[981]**
Photographic Merchandising and Distributing Association [2491]
Photographic Society of America (PSA) **[2492]**, **[12291]**, **[12334]**
Photography Collections Online **[12325]**
Photoimaging Manufacturers and Distributors Association [2491]
"PhotoMedex Bouncing Back from Brink of Bankruptcy" in Philadelphia Business Journal (Vol. 30, January 6, 2012, No. 47, pp. 1) **[19043]**, **[24052]**, **[28772]**
Photovoltaic Module Retail Businesses in the World **[23452]**
PHSC Journal **[3231]**
Physical and Health Education Canada (PHE Canada) **[12383]**
Physical & Health Education Journal **[12384]**
Physical Medicine and Rehabilitation Clinics of North America **[11529]**, **[12498]**
Physical & Occupational Therapy In Pediatrics: A Quarterly Journal of Developmental Therapy (POTP) **[12499]**, **[26043]**
Physical Therapy [12500]
Physical Therapy & Rehabilitation Journal (PTJ) **[12500]**
Physician Executive **[26044]**
Physician Insurers Association of America [8874]
Physicians Committee for Responsible Medicine (PCRM) **[25688]**
"Physicians Development Groupn Kicks Off $13M Skilled Nursing Facility in NE Wichita" in Wichita Business Journal (Vol. 27, January 20, 2012, No. 3, pp. 1) **[4199]**, **[11519]**, **[25900]**
"Physicians Hail New York's Surprise Billing Law as a Success" in RevCycle Intelligence (September 30, 2019) **[10894]**, **[25489]**
"Physics for Females" in Occupational Outlook Quarterly (Vol. 55, Summer 2011, No. 2, pp. 22) **[2604]**, **[21606]**, **[25901]**, **[32019]**, **[32804]**, **[35838]**
Piano Manufacturers Association International [11312]
Piano Technicians Guild (PTG) **[11313]**
"Pick A Name, Not Just Any Name" in Women Entrepreneur (December 17, 2008) **[4602]**, **[29977]**, **[33591]**
Pickaway County Chamber of Commerce - Circleville **[43552]**
Pickerington Area Chamber of Commerce (PACC) **[43553]**
Picket Fence Preview Inc. **[13339]**
Pico Rivera Chamber of Commerce (PRCC) **[37092]**
Pictorial Photographers of America (PPA) **[12292]**
Picture Framing Magazine: Online **[12708]**
Picture Perfect Guide **[43181]**
"The Picture Perfect Guide on How to Make a Fitness Video Strategy" in Glofox blog (April 17, 2019) **[12427]**, **[29978]**
"Picture Perfect: Startup Ships Camera Products After Kickstarter Campaign" in Austin Business Journal (Vol. 34, June 6, 2014, No. 16, pp. A12) **[2490]**, **[29979]**
Piedmont Area Chamber of Commerce **[41613]**
Piedmont Chamber of Commerce **[43796]**
Piedmont Food Processing Center (PFPC) **[43247]**
Piedmont Technical College Continuing Ed **[44613]**
Piedmont Technical College Library **[33719]**
"Piercing the Corporate Veil: Understanding the Limits of LLC Protection" in Legal Zoom (February 15, 2023) **[27190]**
Pierpont Community and Technical College of Fairmont State University Small Business Development Center **[46251]**
Pierpont Community and Technical College Small Business Development Center - Fairmont **[46252]**
Pierre Area Chamber of Commerce **[44656]**

Pierre Small Business Development Center **[44623]**
Pigeon Chamber of Commerce **[40994]**
Pigeon Forge Chamber of Commerce **[44793]**
Pike County Chamber of Commerce **[39286]**, **[39596]**, **[41425]**, **[44284]**
Pike County Chamber of Commerce (PCCC) **[43554]**
Pike County Chamber of Commerce [40087]
Pike County Chamber of Commerce and Economic Development District [41425]
Pike County Economic Development Center **[39003]**
Pikes Peak Small Business Development Center [37783]
Pikesville Chamber of Commerce [40386]
Pikeville - Bledsoe County Chamber of Commerce **[44794]**
Pikeville Small Business Development Center **[40002]**
Pillar to Post Inc. **[2039]**
Pillar to Post Inc. (PTP) **[2038]**
Pilot Consulting Corporation **[22328]**
Pilot Point Chamber of Commerce (PPCC) **[45318]**
Pilot Project Brewing **[1894]**
Pima College's Small Business Development Center [36276]
Pima Community College Small Business Development Center **[36276]**
Pima Council on Aging (PCOA) **[199]**
Pinch a Penny Inc. **[4687]**
Pinckneyville Chamber of Commerce **[39287]**
Pine Bluff Regional Chamber of Commerce **[36491]**
Pine City Area Chamber of Commerce **[41289]**
Pinedale Area Chamber of Commerce [46622]
Pinellas Park/Gateway Chamber of Commerce **[38486]**
Pinellas Park/Mid-County Chamber of Commerce [38486]
"Pink Label: Victoria's Sales Secret" in Advertising Age (Vol. 79, July 7, 2008, No. 26, pp. 4) **[3138]**, **[10304]**, **[29980]**, **[30786]**, **[32244]**
Pinky Cole CEO and Founder of Slutty Vegan **[14079]**
Pinnacle Capital Inc. **[46875]**
Pinnacle Franchise Development **[2363]**, **[24490]**
Pinon Hills Chamber of Commerce **[37093]**
Pinpoint Tactics Business Consulting **[2308]**, **[22939]**, **[29026]**
Pioche Chamber of Commerce **[41950]**
Pioneer **[37094]**
Pioneer Hi-Bred International, Inc. [17210]
"A Pioneer of Paying With Plastic" in Crain's Chicago Business (Vol. 31, April 28, 2008, No. 17, pp. 39) **[18283]**, **[20326]**, **[23647]**, **[29336]**
Pioneer Technology Center (PTC) **[43843]**, **[43895]**
Pioneer Technology Center Business Incubator **[43870]**
"Pioneer Unveils Drought-Tolerant Hybrids" in Farm Industry News (January 6, 2011) **[17092]**, **[30787]**
"Pioneering Strategies for Entrepreneurial Success" in Business Horizons (Vol. 51, January-February 2008, No. 1, pp. 21) **[17733]**, **[22745]**, **[24053]**, **[27934]**, **[30788]**, **[33228]**
PIP, Inc. **[4495]**, **[12779]**
Pipeline Angels **[30300]**, **[35301]**, **[35672]**, **[45598]**
"Pipeline Dreams" in Canadian Business (Vol. 80, October 22, 2007, No. 21, pp. 19) **[4200]**, **[25490]**
Pipeline Pigging and Integrity Management Conference **[4302]**
Pipestone Area Chamber of Commerce **[41290]**
Piqua Area Chamber of Commerce (PACC) **[43555]**
Pirtek USA **[33323]**
Piscataquis Chamber of Commerce (PCCC) **[40298]**
Pismo Beach Chamber of Commerce **[37095]**
Pitch-In Canada (PIC) **[5496]**
"Pitch Perfect: How to Say It Right the First Time, Every Time" **[17734]**
Pitney Bowes Inc. **[16330]**
Pitt County Development Commission - Technology Enterprise Center **[43248]**
Pitts - Aldrich Associates (PAA) **[27154]**
Pittsburg Area Chamber of Commerce **[39949]**
Pittsburg Chamber of Commerce **[37096]**
Pittsburgh Airport Area Chamber of Commerce (PAACC) **[44285]**
Pittsburgh Equity Partners (PEP) **[44349]**
Pittsburgh Life Sciences Greenhouse (PLSG) **[44350]**
"Pittsburgh Paint Maker Aims to Shake the Sales Blues" in The Wall Street Journal (July 2, 2019) **[11862]**
Pittsburgh SCORE **[44115]**
Pittsburgh Top Startups **[34636]**
Pittsburgh Venture Capital Association (PVCA) **[44091]**
Pittsford Chamber of Commerce (PCC) **[42649]**
Pittsylvania County Chamber of Commerce [45853]
PivotPoint Press **[39452]**
"Pizza or Beer? Why Kalil Made Right Call" in Business Journal (Vol. 31, January 31, 2014, No. 36, pp. 6) **[12533]**, **[13985]**, **[19684]**, **[24398]**
"Pizza Chain Enters Boston" in Boston Business Journal (Vol. 34, April 25, 2014, No. 12, pp. 3) **[12534]**, **[13986]**, **[24399]**

Pizza Delight **[14229]**
Pizza Depot **[12578]**
Pizza Factory Inc. **[12579]**, **[14230]**
Pizza Hut Canada [14227]
Pizza Inn Holdings Inc. [12589]
Pizza Nova Take Out Ltd. **[12580]**
Pizza Patron Inc. **[12581]**
The Pizza Pipeline **[12582]**
Pizza Pit **[12583]**
Pizza Pizza **[12584]**
Pizza Ranch Inc. **[14231]**
Pizza Schimizza **[12585]**
Pizzaville Inc. **[12586]**
Pizzeria Valdiano (PV) **[12587]**
Pizzicato Gourmet Pizza **[12588]**
PJ Materials Consultants Ltd. **[4334]**
PJC **[40720]**
PJ's Coffee of New Orleans **[1302]**, **[7590]**
"Place Restrictions on Your Stock Shares" in Business Owner (Vol. 35, July-August 2011, No. 4, pp. 14) **[82]**, **[6560]**, **[9733]**, **[16823]**, **[24054]**
Place Rosemère **[32373]**
A Place for Rover [12253]
"Place Your Bets: Horse, Dog Racing Kiosks Bring the Track to Local Bars" in Dickinson Press (March 28, 2012) **[7305]**, **[10036]**
Placentia Business Link [37098]
Placentia Chamber of Commerce **[37097]**
Placentia Chamber of Commerce Newsletter **[37098]**
"Places for People Who Want to Make Things" in Philadelphia Business Journal (Vol. 28, May 4, 2012, No. 23, pp. 1) **[7070]**, **[22414]**
"Plagiarism: What Is It, Exactly?" in Legal Zoom (March 27, 2023) **[27189]**
Plainfield Area Chamber of Commerce (PACC) **[39288]**
Plainfield-Central Jersey Chamber of Commerce [39911]
Plainfield Chamber of Commerce **[39597]**
Plains Angels **[39814]**
Plainview Chamber of Commerce (PCC) **[45319]**
Plainview Convention and Visitors Bureau [45319]
"Plan B Saloon Opens New Year's Eve" in Bellingham Business Journal (Vol. February 2010, pp. 7) **[1348]**, **[13987]**
Plan Sponsor: Insight on Plan Design & Investment Strategy **[6699]**
"Plan Would Give Face-Lift to Section of Italian Market" in Philadelphia Business Journal (Vol. 28, June 29, 2012, No. 20, pp. 1) **[4201]**, **[32245]**
Plan Your Estate **[6043]**, **[34858]**
"Plan Your Future with My Next Move" in Occupational Outlook Quarterly (Vol. 55, Summer 2011, No. 2, pp. 22) **[2605]**, **[21943]**, **[26634]**, **[27021]**
"Plan Your Next Event at Newport News Marriott at City Center" in Benzinga.com (July 29, 2011) **[1989]**, **[2200]**, **[8445]**, **[15883]**, **[35078]**
"Plan Your Wedding with Cleveland Airport Marriott's Certified Event Planners" in Benzinga.com (February 2, 2011) **[1990]**, **[8446]**, **[11911]**
Plan2Profit (P2P) **[46849]**
Planet Beach Franchising Corporation **[15270]**
Planet Clean **[32374]**
"Planet Dog Foundation Awards $25,000 In Grants" in Pet Product News (Vol. 66, September 2012, No. 9, pp. 13) **[7144]**, **[12150]**
Planet Mogul **[33528]**, **[35714]**
Planet Money: Green Energy Gridlock **[23436]**
Planet Money Summer School: MBA 1: Planet Money Goes to Business School **[16674]**
Planet Money Summer School: MBA 2: Competition and the Cheaper Sneaker **[16675]**
Planet Money Summer School: MBA 3: Accounting and the Last Supper **[16856]**
Planet Money Summer School: MBA 4: Marketing and the Ultimate Hose Nozzle **[30160]**
Planet Money Summer School: MBA 5: Tech and the Innovator's Dilemma **[24820]**
Planet Money Summer School: MBA 6: Operations and 25,000 Roses **[24821]**
Planet Money Summer School: MBA 7: Negotiating and the Empathetic Nibble **[24822]**
Planet Money Summer School: MBA 8: Graduation and the Guppy Tank **[24823]**
Planet Money: The Economics of the Influencer Industry and Its Pitfalls **[23016]**
Planet Smoothie **[8632]**
Planetary Association for Clean Energy Inc. (PACE) **[23046]**
PlanetLaundry **[5263]**, **[10211]**
Plank Road Chamber of Commerce [42593]
"Planned CO2 Regulations Could Hit Region Hard" in Pittsburgh Business Times (Vol. 33, June 6, 2014, No. 47, pp. 9) **[5680]**, **[5947]**, **[23318]**, **[25491]**
"Planned Convention Center Expansion Already Boosting Business" in San Antonio Business Journal (Vol. 27, January 3, 2014, No. 48, pp. 6) **[15884]**, **[35079]**

Planned Master Index

"Planned Rice MLP Latest In Series of Spinoffs" in Pittsburgh Business Times (Vol. 34, August 15, 2014, No. 4, pp. 6) **[20646]**, **[31476]**, **[34859]**
Planning and Developing New Products (Onsite) **[29602]**
"Planning to Start a Landscaping Business? Here Are Some Services You Should Offer" in Home Business (April 21, 2020) **[10242]**
Planning and Visual Education Partnership (PAVE) **[31024]**, **[32083]**
"Planning a Wedding Fit for a Royal? Read This First, Urge Legal & General" in Marketwired (April 21, 2011) **[1991]**, **[8953]**, **[27322]**
"Planning Your (Successful!) Professional Organizing Business" in A Personal Organizer blog **[12813]**
Plano Chamber of Commerce **[45320]**
"Plans for $160M Condo Resort in Wisconsin Dells Moves Forward" in Commercial Property News (March 18, 2008) **[4202]**, **[8447]**, **[13811]**, **[13988]**, **[15755]**, **[16007]**, **[32246]**
The Plant Cell **[32907]**
"Plant These Marketing Seeds to Watch Your Cannabusiness Grow and Thrive" in Cannabis Business Executive (October 22, 2020) **[5017]**
Planting Fields Arboretum - The Garden Library **[7682]**
"Planting Success: Nature's Herb Farm President Shares How He Grew His Mother's Business" in San Antonio Express-News (July 8, 2019) **[8155]**
Plantkeeper Inc. **[31094]**
Plantscape Inc. **[10262]**
"Plastic Particles Found in Bottled Water" in BBC (March 15, 2018) **[1861]**
Plastics Recycling Conference **[13744]**, **[23444]**
Plastics Recycling Update **[13739]**
"Platforms and Publishers: The End of an Era" in Columbia Journalism Review (November 22, 2019) **[14811]**
The Platinum Rule for Small Business Success **[22746]**, **[24716]**
Platoon Fitness **[12461]**
Plato's Closet **[3910]**
Platte City Area Chamber of Commerce and Economic Development Council **[41614]**
Platte City Chamber of Commerce [41614]
Platte County Chamber of Commerce (PCCC) **[46614]**
Platteville Business Incubator Inc. (PBII) **[46569]**
Platteville Regional Chamber of Commerce **[46489]**
Plattsburg Chamber of Commerce (PCC) **[41615]**
Plattsburgh and Clinton County Chamber of Commerce [42650]
Plattsburgh - North Country Chamber of Commerce **[42650]**
Plattsmouth Chamber of Commerce (PCC) **[41880]**
Play it Again Sports (PIAS) **[3911]**, **[15126]**
"Play By Play: These Video Products Can Add New Life to a Stagnant Website" in Black Enterprise (Vol. 41, December 2010, No. 5) **[332]**, **[2497]**, **[2778]**, **[16452]**, **[19907]**, **[21944]**, **[29981]**, **[30970]**
"Play It Safe At Home, Or Take a Risk Abroad? A US Lease-To-Own Chain Considers Whether To Test Its Business In Mexico" in Harvard Business Review (Vol. 90, January-February 2012, No.1-2, pp. 145) **[13812]**, **[18284]**, **[27686]**, **[33400]**
"Playfair Receives Drill Permit for Risby, Yukon Tungsten Deposit" in Marketwired (May 16, 2007) **[25492]**, **[30879]**, **[32958]**
"The Play's the Thing" in Business Strategy Review (Vol. 21, Summer 2010, No. 2, pp. 58) **[19044]**, **[19384]**
PLC Programming & Applications (Onsite) **[19449]**, **[21413]**
PLCs for Non-Programmers (Onsite) **[19450]**, **[21414]**
Pleasant Hill Chamber of Commerce (PHCC) **[37099]**
"Please Pass the Mayo" in Crain's Chicago Business (Vol. 31, April 28, 2008, No. 17, pp. 32) **[12747]**, **[19908]**, **[23648]**, **[29982]**, **[31477]**
Pleasure Island, Carolina Beach, and Kure Beach Chamber of Commerce **[43182]**
Pledge 1% Colorado (EFCO) **[37777]**
"Plenty of Businesses Are Ready to 'Up Their Game" in Crain's Chicago Business (November 12, 2021) **[30373]**
"Plenty of Jobs, Will Workers Follow?" in Providence Business News (Vol. 28, January 27, 2014, No. 43, pp. 1) **[10609]**, **[21607]**, **[26635]**
Plentywood Chamber of Commerce [46620]
PLMA's Annual Private Label Trade Show **[12805]**
The Plotkin Group **[20551]**, **[27155]**
Plug and Play **[37611]**
Plug and Play - Energy **[21771]**
Plug and Play - Fintech **[14753]**
Plug and Play - Food and Beverage **[7718]**
Plug and Play - Health **[25699]**
Plug and Play - Insurtech **[27227]**
Plug and Play - Internet of Things (-IoT) **[3476]**
Plug and Play - Mobility **[30453]**
Plug and Play - Real Estate and Construction **[3967]**, **[13367]**
Plug and Play - Retail Innovation Platform **[32085]**
Plug and Play - Supply Chain **[16071]**
Plug and Play Tech Center **[37612]**
Plug and Play - Travel and Hospitality **[13893]**
Plumbing Brass Institute [12611]
Plumbing & Drainage Institute (PDI) **[12610]**
Plumbing and Drainage Manufacturers Association [12610]
Plumbing Engineer **[12678]**
"Plumbing, Heating Products Shine at Greenbuild Expo" in Contractor (Vol. 56, December 2009, No. 12, pp. 1) **[506]**, **[12650]**, **[15885]**, **[30789]**, **[35080]**
Plumbing Manufacturers Institute [12611]
Plumbing Manufacturers International (PMI) **[12611]**
Plumbing & Pipefitting for Plants & Buildings (Onsite) **[19451]**, **[21415]**
Plunkett's E-Commerce & Internet Business Almanac **[22032]**
Plunkett's E-Commerce & Internet Business Almanac: Your Reference Source to All Facets of the Internet Business **[11849]**
Plunkett's Engineering and Research Industry Almanac: The Only Complete Guide to the Business of Research, Development, and Engineering **[3673]**, **[32936]**
Plymouth Area Chamber of Commerce **[39598]**
Plymouth Area Chamber of Commerce (PACC) **[40616]**
Plymouth Chamber of Commerce **[46490]**
Plymouth Community Chamber of Commerce **[40995]**
Plymouth Growth Partners **[41055]**
PM Springfest **[12913]**
PMA Independent [1690]
PMA - Independent Book Publishers Association [1623]
PMP Exam Prep Workshop (Onsite) **[28399]**
"PNC Begins Search for New Baltimore-Area Headquarters" in Baltimore Business Journal (Vol. 28, June 4, 2010, No. 4, pp. 1) **[6561]**, **[9734]**, **[24055]**, **[33401]**
PNC Erieview Capital **[43628]**
"PNC Study Highlights Small Business Gloom" in Pittsburgh Business Times (Vol. 33, April 11, 2014, No. 39, pp. 5) **[16587]**, **[21073]**
PNP Staffing Group **[144]**
Pocahontas Chamber of Commerce **[39785]**
Pocatello-Chubbuck Chamber of Commerce **[38934]**
The Pocket MBA: A Woman's Playbook for Succeeding in Business **[35839]**
Pocomoke Area Chamber of Commerce **[40408]**
Pocono Mountains Chamber of Commerce [44233]
Podiatric Products [10958]
POETALK **[5340]**
PoGoPix Studios **[12358]**
Point Judith [40720]
Point Of View Magazine [6169]
Point Pleasant Beach Chamber of Commerce **[42180]**
Point Roberts Chamber of Commerce **[46140]**
"Points of Law: Unbundling Corporate Legal Services to Unlock Value" in (Vol. 90, July-August 2012, No. 7-8, pp. 126) **[18663]**, **[31478]**
"Points of Light Sells MissionFish to eBay" in Non-Profit Times (Vol. 25, May 15, 2011, No. 7, pp. May 15, 2011) **[1077]**, **[7145]**, **[19685]**, **[21945]**, **[33028]**
"Poisoning Relationships: Perceived Unfairness in Channels of Distribution" in Journal of Marketing (Vol. 75, May 2011, No. 3, pp. 99) **[20647]**, **[29983]**, **[33229]**
The Polar Bear ROARS **[11913]**, **[12350]**
Polaris International [43], [16753]
Polaris Venture Partners **[40721]**
Polestar Venture Capital **[39372]**
Polish Business Consultants Group Ltd. **[8785]**
"Polish Family-Owned Cosmetics Company Bases U.S. Flagship in W.VA." in West Virginia Public Broadcasting (October 21, 2019) **[4520]**
"Political Environments and Business Strategy: Implications for Managers" in Business Horizons (Vol. 51, January-February 2008) **[25039]**, **[25493]**, **[27687]**, **[28773]**
Political Risk Letter (PRL) **[27782]**
"Politicians Who Really Get Business: Meet Four of the Entrepreneurs Running for Congress" in Inc. (Vol. 34, September 2012, No. 7, pp. 21) **[22747]**, **[35840]**
"Politics & Pros: D.C. Considering Sports-Based Marketing Campaign" in Washington Business Journal (Vol. 31, July 13, 2012, No. 12, pp. 1) **[15175]**, **[29984]**
Polk County Chamber of Commerce [43103], [45255]
Pollution Probe (PP) **[5497]**, **[23047]**
Polo Chamber of Commerce **[39289]**
Polsinelli PC **[13355]**, **[13632]**, **[15474]**
Polsinelli Shalton Welte Suelthaus PC [13355], [13632], [15474]
Polsinelli Shughart PC [13355], [13632], [15474]
Polson Chamber of Commerce (PCC) **[41787]**
Pomeroy Area Chamber of Commerce [43525]
Pomeroy Chamber of Commerce [43525]
Pomona Capital [42786]
Pomona Chamber Business Monthly **[37100]**
Pomona Chamber of Commerce **[37101]**
Pomona Management LLC **[42786]**
Ponca City Area Chamber of Commerce (PCACC) **[43797]**
Ponchatoula Chamber of Commerce **[40185]**
Pontiac Area Chamber of Commerce (PACC) **[39290]**
Pontiac Regional Chamber (PRC) **[40996]**
Pontotoc County Chamber of Commerce **[41426]**
Pontotoc Technology Center Business Incubator (PTC) **[43871]**
Ponyride **[41113]**
Pool & Spa Marketing **[15244]**
Poolesville Area Chamber of Commerce (PACC) **[40409]**
"Poor Economy Inspires Rich Alternatives In a Modern, and Tax-Free, Twist on Bartering" in Houston Chronicle (June 7, 2010) **[17255]**, **[21074]**, **[31479]**, **[33230]**, **[34860]**
Pop-A-Lock Franchise System **[10361]**, **[30497]**
"Pop a Cork: Lofts' Sale Bodes Well for Urban Living" in Pittsburgh Business Times (Vol. 33, May 30, 2014, No. 46, pp. 3) **[13532]**, **[13813]**
Popcorn and Concessions Association [3831]
Pope Consulting **[30649]**
Popeyes Louisiana Kitchen, Inc. **[14232]**
Popular Photography **[12351]**
Popular Photography and Imaging [12351]
Popular Price Shoe Retailer Association [14667]
Porcelain Enamel Institute (PEI) **[12688]**
Port Aransas Chamber of Commerce **[45321]**
Port Aransas Chamber of Commerce and Tourism [45321]
Port Arthur Chamber of Commerce (PACC) **[45322]**
Port Business Incubator **[44415]**
"Port of Call" in Entrepreneur (Vol. 35, November 2007, No. 11, pp. 66) **[3730]**, **[30971]**
"Port Canaveral Plans to Make Big Waves of Business in C. Fla." in Orlando Business Journal (Vol. 30, June 6, 2014, No. 50, pp. 4) **[7043]**, **[8749]**, **[15756]**, **[18285]**, **[19569]**, **[21075]**
Port City Java **[32375]**
Port Gibson-Claiborne County Chamber of Commerce **[41427]**
Port Hueneme Chamber of Commerce (PHCC) **[37102]**
Port Isabel Chamber of Commerce **[45323]**
Port Mansfield Chamber of Commerce **[45324]**
Port Neches Chamber of Commerce (PNCC) **[45325]**
Port O Call **[37103]**
Port Orange/South Daytona Chamber of Commerce **[38487]**
Port Orchard Chamber of Commerce (POCOC) **[46141]**
Port St. Joe - Gulf County Chamber of Commerce [38426]
"Port in the Storm" in Canadian Business (Vol. 81, October 13, 2008, No. 17, pp. 101) **[6200]**, **[19909]**, **[27688]**
Port of Subs, Inc. **[4919]**, **[14233]**
Port Washington Chamber of Commerce **[46491]**
"Portability and Durability Are Key When It Comes to Pet Containment" in Pet Product News (Vol. 66, September 2012, No. 9, pp. 64) **[12222]**, **[29337]**
Portable Toilet Rental & Septic Tank Cleaning Industry in the US - Market Research Report **[7967]**, **[14639]**
Portage Area Chamber of Commerce (PACC) **[46492]**
Portage County Business Council (PCBC) **[46493]**
Portage Park Chamber of Commerce (PPCC) **[39291]**
Portage Visitor Guides **[46494]**
Porter Henry & Company Inc. **[32695]**
Porterville Chamber of Commerce **[37104]**
Portfolia **[37462]**
"Portfolio Recovery Associates Expands Its Hampton Call Center" in Marketwired (January 20, 2010) **[4749]**, **[4805]**, **[18286]**, **[19045]**, **[20327]**
"Portion of Silver Line Will Run By Year's End" in Crain's Cleveland Business (Vol. 28, November 5, 2007, No. 44, pp. 6) **[19385]**, **[21076]**
Portland Business Alliance (PBA) **[44005]**
Portland Business Journal (PBJ) **[44080]**
Portland Business Journal **[44075]**
Portland Cement Association (PCA) **[4368]**
Portland Chamber of Commerce **[44795]**, **[45326]**
"Portland Home Is First in U.S. to Use Variable Speed Inverter Technology" in Contractor (Vol. 56, December 2009, No. 12, pp. 5) **[507]**, **[12651]**, **[30790]**
Portland Incubator Experiment (PIE) **[44063]**
Portland Maine SCORE **[40251]**
Portland Metropolitan Chamber of Commerce [44005]
Portland Minority Business Development Center **[44042]**

3314 Small Business Sourcebook • 42nd Edition

Portland Public Library Art/Audiovisual Department (PPL) [11236]
Portland Regional Chamber of Commerce (PRCC) [40299]
Portland Seed Fund (PSF) [44064]
Portland State Business Accelerator (PSU) [44065]
Portland State University Business Accelerator (PSU) [44066]
Portland State University Business School Business Accelerator (PSBA) [44067]
Portland State University - College of Urban and Public Affairs - Population Research Center (PRC) [47459]
Portland Top Startups [44076]
Portland VA Research Foundation (PVARF) [26135]
"Portland Wooing Under Armour to West Coast Facility" in Baltimore Business Journal (Vol. 27, January 29, 2010, No. 39, pp. 1) [3047], [3139], [14683], [15098], [18287], [19193], [33402]
"Portland's Hilton For Sale" in Business Journal Portland (Vol. 27, October 22, 2010, No. 34, pp. 1) [8448], [13533], [19686], [33029]
PortTech Los Angeles (LACI) [37613]
Positive Assertive Management (Onsite) [28400]
Positive Impact Consulting [22329]
Positively Anadarko [43798]
The Post-American World [21077], [34134]
Post Card Distributors Association of North America [7473], [7698]
Post Card and Souvenir Distributors Association [7473], [7698]
Post Falls Chamber of Commerce (PFCC) [38935]
"Post-Pandemic Rise in the Adoption of DEI Initiatives But Hiring Is a Different Story" in Incfile blog (July 20, 2022) [30596]
Postal Annex+ [3395]
Postal Bulletin [3393]
Postal Connections of America (PCA) [3402], [4496], [12780]
Postal History Society of Canada (PHSC) [3232]
The Posthorn: Journal of the Scandinavian Collectors Club [3249]
PostNet [3403], [11677]
"Pot Watch: Magic Butter Delivers THC-infused Food Truck" in Puget Sound Business Journal (Vol. 35, May 30, 2014, No. 6, pp. 10) [3827], [5018], [7003], [8147], [25637]
Potato Association of America (PAA) [16968]
"Potato Prices Rising Affecting Restaurant Owners" in Small Business Trends (October 4, 2022) [13989]
Potawatomi Business Development Corporation (PBDC) [46315], [46585]
Potawatomi Business Development Corp. [46315], [46585]
"Potbelly Sandwich Shop Inks Multi-Unit Development Deal to Open Restaurants in Macy's Stores" in Franchising.com (October 9, 2019) [4883], [24400]
Poteau Chamber of Commerce [43799]
Potential Energy DC (PEDC) [38181]
"Potential for Water Pumping in Africa" in Canadian Business (Vol. 79, October 23, 2006, No. 21, pp. 162) [18288], [29985]
Potomac Chamber of Commerce (PCC) [40410]
Potomac Equity Partners [38194]
Potosi - Tennyson Area Chamber of Commerce [46495]
Potsdam Chamber of Commerce [42651]
Potty Doctor Plumbing Service [12687]
Poughkeepsie Area Chamber of Commerce [42564]
Poured Concrete Contractors Association [3930]
POV [6169]
Poway Chamber of Commerce [37105]
Powell Chamber of Commerce (PVCC) [46615]
Powell County Chamber of Commerce [41788]
Powell's Sweet Shoppe [2557]
"The Power of Alumni Networks" in Harvard Business Review (Vol. 88, October 2010, No. 10, pp. 34) [6562], [9735]
Power Ambition Glory: The Stunning Parallels between Great Leaders of the Ancient World and Today... and the Lessons You Can Learn [22748], [28774]
"The Power Brokers" in Crain's Chicago Business (Vol. 31, April 28, 2008, No. 17, pp. 41) [18289], [25494], [33231]
"Power Cues: The Subtle Science of Leading Groups, Persuading Others, and Maximizing Your Personal Impact" [17735], [22749], [28775]
Power Excel: Making Better Decisions (Onsite) [21416]
"The Power of Habit: Why We Do What We Do in Life and Business" [29986]
"The Power of Influencer Networks for Education and Small Business" in Small Business Trends(December 4, 2022) [33592]
The Power of Knowledge & Bootstrapping for 20 Years [28052]

The Power of Many: Values for Success in Business and in Life [22750], [23525]
Power and Motoryacht [10614]
"The Power of Negative Thinking" in Inc. (Volume 32, December 2010, No. 10, pp. 43) [14812], [16453], [21946], [33887]
"The Power of Noticing: What the Best Leaders See" [17736], [22751], [28776]
"The Power of Online" in Advertising Age (Vol. 85, October 13, 2014, No. 21, pp. 4) [11783], [16454], [20483], [21947], [32247]
"Power Partnerships" in Business Courier (Vol. 27, October 22, 2010, No. 25, pp. 1) [4203], [7306], [9736], [18290], [21078], [30374], [31480]
Power Plant Business Incubator [38578]
"Power Play" in Harvard Business Review (Vol. 88, July-August 2010, No. 7-8, pp. 84) [19386], [22226], [28777], [34997]
The Power of Pull: How Small Moves, Smartly Made, Can Set Big Things in Motion [19046], [22752], [28778]
"The Power of Purpose" in Journal of Business Strategy (Vol. 35, May-June 2014, No. 3, pp. 55-58) [19570], [20484]
"Power Ranger" in Inc. (November 2007, pp. 131) [14813], [23319], [30972], [33888]
"The Power of Self Leadership" in Minority Business Entrepreneur (Vol. 39, Fall, 2022, No. 4, pp. 46-47) [22227]
The Power of Social Innovation: How Civic Entrepreneurs Ignite Community Networks for Good [22753], [34135], [34352]
The Power of Wholesale with Sarah of Simply Curated [35497]
Powerful Communication Skills for Women (Onsite) [17608]
"Powering Intelligent Commerce: eCommera Rebrands as OrderDynamics, Helping Retailers Activate Commerce from First Interaction to Fulfillment" in Computer Business Week (August 28, 2014, pp. 20) [11784], [14814], [21948], [30791], [32248], [33889]
"Powerlessness Corrupts" in Harvard Business Review (Vol. 88, July-August 2010, No. 7-8, pp. 36) [22228], [28779]
Powers Research and Training Institute [21752]
Powhatan Chamber of Commerce [45890]
Poynette Chamber of Commerce [46496]
PPC's Guide to Choosing Retirement Plans for Small Businesses [9737], [17338]
PPC's Guide to Compensation Planning for Small Business [17339], [24717]
PPC's Guide to Small Business Consulting Engagements [2201], [17737], [20118]
PPC's Small Business Tax Guide [18664], [34861]
PPC's Small Business Tax Guide, Vol. 2 [18665], [34862]
PR Council [31741]
PR Hacks You Need to Get Your Business Noticed with Billion Dollar Founder Suneera Madhani [31808]
The Practical Applications of Impact Accounting with Angel Lance [16857]
Practical Debt Collecting for Small Companies and Traders [4806], [20328]
Practical Funding & Founder-Market Fit [35426]
A Practical Guide to Controls for IT Professionals (Onsite) [26199], [28401]
Practical Marketing Research (Onsite) [29603]
Practical Multivariate Analysis (Onsite) [29604]
The Practical Real Estate Lawyer [13318]
The Practical Tax Lawyer [15437]
"Practical Tips for Starting and Managing a Mobile Business" in PowerHomeBiz.com (Sept. 16, 2021) [30485]
Practical Welding Today [10456]
Practice Development Counsel [2309], [20220], [31717]
Practice Periodical on Structural Design and Construction [4287]
"Practices, Governance, and Politics: Applying MacIntyre's Ethics to Business" in Business Ethics Quarterly (Vol. 24, April 2014, No. 2, pp. 229) [23526], [28780]
The Practicing CPA [114]
Prague Chamber of Commerce [43800]
Prairie Agricultural Machinery Institute (PAMI) [17235]
Prairie Business Magazine (PB) [41365], [43325], [44674]
Prairie Du Chien Area Chamber of Commerce [46497]
Prairie Family Business Association (PFBA) [23587]
Prairie Grove Chamber of Commerce [36492]
Prairie View A&M Small Business Development Center [44935]
Prairie View A&M University Small Business Development Center [44935]
Pratt Area Chamber of Commerce [39950]

Prattville Area Chamber of Commerce [36147]
"Pre-Certified LEED Hotel Prototype Reduces Energy Use, Conserves Water" in Contractor (Vol. 57, January 2010, No. 1, pp. 3) [5681], [8449], [12652], [14629], [23320]
"Pre-Deal Trades More Common in Canada, Study Finds" in Globe & Mail (March 23, 2007, pp. B5) [9738], [31481]
Pre-Seed Funding [35427]
"The Pre-Tail Revolution" in Canadian Business (Vol. 87, October 2014, No. 10, pp. 10) [3731], [4402], [7146], [12045], [21949], [30973]
Precast/Prestressed Concrete Institute (PCI) [10733]
"Preceptis Gets Gopher Angels' Biggest-Ever Investment" in Business Journal (Vol. 31, January 31, 2014, No. 36, pp. 8) [7147], [10848], [30792], [32020]
"A Precious Resource: Investing In the Fate of Fresh Water" in Black Enterprise (Vol. 38, February 2008, No. 7, pp. 44) [1862], [9739], [34136]
Precision Concrete Cutting (PCC) [10747]
"Precision Crop Control with Valley Irrigation/CropMetrics Partnership" in Farm Industry News (January 6, 2011) [10057], [14815], [17093], [31482], [33890]
Precision Door Service [33324]
"Precision Fertilizer Spreading Shown at Agritechnica" in Farm Industry News (November 23, 2011) [17094], [29338], [30793]
Precision Metalforming Association (PMA) [10420]
Precision Tune Auto Care Inc. [13009], [14595]
Precursor Ventures [30301], [35302], [37757]
Predictable Futures Inc. (PFI) [35456]
Predictably Irrational: The Hidden Forces That Shape Our Decisions [21079], [29987], [34137]
"Predicting Success: Evidence-Based Strategies to Hire the Right People and Build the Best Team" [26636], [27022]
Predictive Maintenance and Condition Monitoring (Onsite) [19452], [21417]
"Preleasing Drives Wedgewood Start" in Memphis Business Journal (Vol. 33, February 17, 2012, No. 45, pp. 1) [742], [13534], [32249]
Premiere Guitar [11279], [11316]
PremierGarage Serving Scottsdale [12693]
Premium Cigar Association (PCA) [15693]
Prentice Hall Business Publishing (PHBP) [42266]
Prep [38838]
"Prepaid Phones Surge in Bad Economy" in Advertising Age (Vol. 79, November 17, 2008, No. 43, pp. 6) [2779], [19910], [20049], [20329], [26380]
"The Preparation Gap: Teacher Education for Middle School Mathematics in Six Countries" in Hawaii Business (Vol. 53, February 2008, No. 8, pp. 37) [21608], [24718]
"Prepare to Take on Life's Challenges" in Minority Business Entrepreneur (Vol. 39, Fall, 2022, No. 4, pp. 20-21) [22229]
"Prepare for Your Fourth of July Party With a Maid Service" in Internet Wire (July 3, 2012) [2073], [11912], [33232]
Preparing for Leadership: What It Takes to Take the Lead [28402]
Preparing for the Project Management Professional PMP Exam (Onsite) [21418]
Preppy Pet [12122], [12278]
Prescott Area Chamber of Commerce (PACC) [46498]
Prescott Chamber of Commerce [36355]
Prescott Valley Chamber of Commerce [36356]
Prescription Footwear Association [14669]
Prescriptive Entrepreneurship [22754], [24719]
Presence: Bringing Your Boldest Self to Your Biggest Challenges [16588]
PresenTense NYC [42919]
"Presenting the Bizwomen 100, leading in their business communities" in Bizwomen (March 27, 2023) [35841]
"Preserving a Nonprofit's Mission: YWCA to Absorb Key Programs as the Boston Center for Community and Justice Fades" in Boston Business Journal (Vol. 31, June 17, 2011, No. 21, pp. 3) [7148], [34353]
"Presidential Address: Innovation in Retrospect and Prospect" in Canadian Journal of Electronics (Vol. 43, November 2010, No. 4) [2780], [16080], [17095], [25902], [26381], [27936], [30794], [30974]
Presidents Forum [22974], [33457]
President's Resource Organization (PRO) [2364]
Presque Isle Chamber of Commerce [46499]
"Press Release: New Corn Hybrid from Seed Consultants" in Farm Industry News (January 6, 2011) [17096], [30795]
"Press Release: Trimble Introduces CFX-750 Display" in Farm Industry News (January 4, 2011) [3732], [14816], [17097], [30796], [33891]
Pressed 4 Time [5261]
Pressed Metal Institute [10420]

Prestige Master Index

Prestige Food Trucks **[7019]**
Preston Area Chamber of Commerce [38919]
Preston County Chamber of Commerce **[46283]**
Prestressed Concrete Institute [10733]
Pretzelmaker Inc. **[3863]**
Pretzels Plus, Inc. **[15060]**
"Prevent Identity Theft: Simple Steps To Protect Yourself Against Identity Theft" in Small Business Opportunities (January 2008) **[14448]**
"Preventing Theft and Embezzlement Within Small Businesses" in Greater Fayetteville Business Journal (Jan. 31, 2022) **[22347]**
Prévention et contrôle des Infections Canada [25676]
"The Price of Citizenship" in Canadian Business (Vol. 79, August 14, 2006, No. 16-17, pp. 13) **[8954]**, **[17340]**, **[25040]**, **[27323]**, **[35951]**
"The Price Is Right: Turning a Profit in the Event Planning Business" in Entrepreneur **[6095]**, **[19047]**, **[29988]**
Price-Pottenger Foundation [8083], [11617]
Price-Pottenger Nutrition Foundation (PPNF) **[8083]**, **[11617]**
Price SBDC [45611]
Price Small Business Development Center **[45611]**
Priceless Car Rental **[13855]**
PricewaterhouseCoopers - North Toronto Research Centre **[1792]**
PricewaterhouseCoopers - Research Centre [169], [15475]
"Pricey Oil, High Dollar Wipe Out Jobs" in Globe & Mail (February 11, 2006, pp. B6) **[21080]**, **[29339]**
"Prichard the Third" in Canadian Business (Vol. 83, October 12, 2010, No. 17, pp. 34) **[18666]**, **[26637]**, **[28781]**
Pricing Strategies: Capturing and Sustaining a Competitive Advantage (Onsite) **[29605]**
"Pricing Strategies for Small Business" in The Balance Small Business (February 12, 2020) **[31654]**
"Pricing Strategies for a Strong Bottom Line" in Small Business Trends (May 26, 2020) **[31655]**
"Pricing To Create Shared Value: Rethinking the Way Prices Are Set Can Expand the Pie for Everyone" in Harvard Business Review (Vol. 90, June 2012, No. 6, pp. 96) **[15176]**, **[20050]**
"Pride Lands Janitorial Work at New Terminal" in Sacramento Business Journal (Vol. 28, June 10, 2011, No. 15, pp. 1) **[2074]**, **[19387]**, **[33233]**, **[34354]**
PrideStaff **[5459]**, **[6119]**, **[15659]**
Priest Lake Chamber of Commerce (PLCC) **[38936]**
Priest River Chamber of Commerce **[38937]**
Primary Venture Partners **[42787]**
PrimeGlobal **[43]**, **[16753]**
Primrose School Franchising Company Inc. **[2907]**
Primus Venture Partners Inc. **[43629]**
Prince Edward Island Food Technology Centre - Information Services **[4482]**, **[14307]**
Prince Edward Island's largest retail firm, R. T. Holman Ltd., [46881]
Prince George's Chamber of Commerce (PGCOC) **[40411]**
Prince George's Community College - Center for Minority Business Development **[40423]**
Prince of Wales Chamber of Commerce **[36240]**
Prince William Chamber of Commerce **[45891]**
Princeton Area Chamber of Commerce **[39292]**
Princeton Area Chamber of Commerce (PACC) **[41291]**
Princeton Chamber of Commerce [46422]
Princeton Community Hospital Library **[11545]**
Princeton Health Systems Inc. (PHS) **[17409]**
Princeton - Lowery Crossing Chamber of Commerce **[45327]**
Princeton Regional Chamber of Commerce **[42181]**
Princeton University - Bendheim Center for Finance (BCF) **[6737]**
Princeton University - Financial Research Center [6737]
Princeton University - Firestone Library - Social Science Reference Center - Data and Statistical Services **[47460]**
Princeton University - Woodrow Wilson School of Public and International Affairs - Research Program in Development Studies (RPDS) **[21280]**
Principal Financial Group Inc. **[6730]**
Principal Financial Services, Inc. [6730]
"Principles for Creating Growth in Challenging Times" in Agency Sales Magazine (Vol. 39, September-October 2009, No. 9, pp. 35) **[18291]**, **[21081]**, **[22230]**
Principles of Pricing **[33593]**
Prineville-Crook County Chamber of Commerce (PCCCC) **[44006]**
Print Council of America (PCA) **[12703]**
The Print-on-Demand Revolution **[12770]**
Print Services and Distribution Association (PSDA) **[11661]**
Print Three Franchising Corp. (PTFC) **[12322]**, **[12781]**
"PrintCity Shares Guide for Carbon Footprinting" in American Printer (Vol. 128, June 1, 2011, No. 6) **[1668]**, **[3325]**, **[5682]**, **[5948]**, **[12748]**, **[16202]**, **[23321]**, **[30975]**
"Printers to the Trade" in American Printer (Vol. 128, July 1, 2011, No. 7) **[3326]**, **[12749]**, **[16203]**, **[35493]**
Printing Brokerage Association [2144], [3376], [12721], [16180]
Printing Brokerage/Buyers Association International (PB/BA) **[2144]**, **[3376]**, **[12721]**, **[16180]**
"Printing Company Edwards Brothers Grapples With a Shrinking Market" in Crain's Detroit Business (Vol. 26, Jan. 4, 2010) **[11994]**, **[23649]**
Printing Impressions--400 List **[12750]**
Printing Impressions: America's Most Influential and Widely Read Publication for Commercial Printers **[12768]**
Printing Impressions--Top 100 General Commercial Printers Issue [12750]
Printing Impressions--Top 400 Printers Issue [12750]
Printing Industries of America's Center for Technology and Research [3377], [4956], [11972], [12722]
Printing United Alliance Center for Technology and Research **[3377]**, **[4956]**, **[11972]**, **[12722]**
Printwear Xpress **[14362]**, **[32376]**
Printwell Management Inc. **[10042]**
Printworld Directory of Contemporary Prints and Prices **[12707]**
Prior Lake Chamber of Commerce **[41292]**
"Prioritizing the Planet: 11 Ways Small Businesses Can Become More Eco-Friendly" in GreenBiz (Nov. 10, 2020) **[23322]**
"Priority: In Memoriam" in Inc. (December 2007, pp. 25-26, 28, 30) **[22755]**, **[24720]**, **[29340]**, **[34355]**
Prism Capital **[39373]**
Pritzker Group Venture Capital (PGVC) **[39374]**
"Privacy Concern: Are 'Group' Time Sheets Legal?" in HR Specialist (Vol. 8, September 2010, No. 9, pp. 4) **[83]**, **[1769]**, **[11936]**, **[15406]**, **[18667]**, **[25495]**, **[27023]**
"Private Equity Firm Links First Arizona Deal" in Business Journal-Serving Phoenix and the Valley of the Sun (November 2, 2007) **[1589]**, **[9740]**, **[31483]**, **[35377]**
"Private Equity Firms" in Black Enterprise (Vol. 44, June 2014, No. 10, pp. 89) **[6563]**, **[9741]**
"Private-Equity Firms Can Elevate ESG, Diversity — and Their Returns" in Crain's Chicago Business (October 15, 2021) **[24056]**
"Private Equity Firms Focus on Failing Banks" in Baltimore Business Journal (Vol. 28, July 16, 2010, No. 10, pp. 1) **[6564]**, **[9742]**, **[13535]**, **[31484]**, **[34138]**
"Private Equity Struggles with Its Diversity Problem" in Crain's Chicago Business (October 15, 2021) **[24057]**, **[30375]**
"Private Health-Care Services Growing in Canada" in Canadian Business (Vol. 85, June 11, 2012, No. 10, pp. 10) **[8955]**, **[25155]**, **[25903]**, **[27324]**, **[31485]**
Private Industry Council of Westmoreland/Fayette, Inc. (PIC) **[44372]**
"Private Investigators and Cold Cases" in Plnow.com (September 16, 2019) **[12798]**
"Private Label Is More Influential Than Ever in Determining Store Choice, Report Says" in Grocery Dive (November 8, 2019) **[7763]**, **[10668]**
Private Label Manufacturers Association (PLMA) **[12802]**
"Private Label Manufacturers Association" in Ice Cream Reporter (Vol. 23, July 20, 2010, No. 8, pp. 7) **[8586]**, **[18292]**, **[32594]**
Private Label Manufacturers Association Trade Show [12805]
Private Motor Truck Council of Canada (PMTC) **[16064]**
"Private Pitfalls" in Canadian Business (Vol. 80, October 22, 2007, No. 21, pp. 34) **[9743]**, **[34863]**
Private Practice Section of the American Physical Therapy Association (PPS) **[12490]**
"Private-Sector Is Back, Roadblocks Be Damned" in Business Review Albany (Vol. 41, July 4, 2014, No. 15, pp. 4) **[18293]**, **[21082]**, **[26638]**
Private Tutoring **[16142]**
Private Tutoring Market in US 2022-2026 **[16143]**
"Private TV Industry's Profit Climbs 4 Per Cent" in Globe & Mail (March 29, 2006, pp. B6) **[6565]**, **[9744]**, **[15612]**
Priveq Capital Funds **[46801]**
Pro Bike [1514]
Pro Business Plans **[37681]**
Pro Fleet Care Franchising Inc. **[2409]**
"Pro Livestock Launches Most Comprehensive Virtual Sales Barn for Livestock and Breed Stock" in Benzinga.com (October 29, 2011) **[1078]**, **[16455]**, **[17098]**, **[21950]**, **[29989]**
The Proactive Leader I: Develop an Effective Agenda, Build Support, and Gain Traction **[19453]**, **[28403]**
"Probability Processing Chip: Lyric Semiconductor" in Inc. (Volume 32, December 2010, No. 10, pp. 52) **[3598]**, **[3759]**, **[27937]**, **[30797]**, **[33735]**
Probe International **[5498]**
"The Problem of Private Ambulances Services" in Current Affairs (August 30, 2018) **[572]**, **[25904]**
Problem Solving and Decision Making (Onsite) **[28404]**
"Problem Solving Requires Total Team Approach" in Green Industry Pro (Vol. 23, September 2011) **[7632]**, **[10110]**, **[10243]**, **[22231]**, **[28782]**, **[33234]**, **[34998]**
"The Problem With Passwords" in Canadian Business (Vol. 85, August 13, 2012, No. 13, pp. 61) **[9206]**, **[14449]**
Problems and Materials on Debtor and Creditor Law **[24058]**
Process Heating and Cooling Show **[537]**
"Procter & Gamble vs. IRS: Split Decision" in Business Courier (Vol. 27, July 16, 2010, No. 11, pp. 1) **[18668]**, **[32021]**, **[32805]**, **[34864]**
Procurement Center Representative (PCR) **[38174]**
Procurement Technical Assistance Center [36166]
Procurement Technical Assistance Center Indian Capital Technology Center (PTAC) **[43844]**
Procurement Technical Assistance Center at Lincoln - Nebraska Business Development Center (NBDC) **[41893]**
Procurement Technical Assistance Center of Northern Virginia - Mason Enterprise Center (PTAC) **[45932]**
Procurement Technical Assistance Center of Schoolcraft College (PTAC) **[41068]**
Procurement Technical Assistance Center of South Central Michigan - The Enterprise Group of Jackson **[41069]**
Product Development and Management Association (PDMA) **[30668]**
Product Distribution 101: Get Your Product in Stores **[20648]**
Productive Publications **[46863]**
Productivity Press **[43004]**
Productivity Press **[39453]**
Productivity Software **[3442]**, **[10490]**, **[14856]**
Professional Association of Custom Clothiers [2999]
Professional Association of Health Care Office Management (PAHCOM) **[28264]**
Professional Association of Health Care Office Managers [28264]
Professional Association of Resume Writers and Career Coaches (PARW/CC) **[14311]**
Professional Association of Small Business Accountants (PASBA) **[39846]**
Professional Beauty Association (PBA) **[1384]**, **[7858]**, **[11318]**
Professional Bowlers Association of America (PBA) **[1874]**
Professional Builder: The Magazine of the Housing and Light Construction Industry **[4288]**
Professional Business Management, Inc. **[10554]**
Professional Businesswomen of California (PBWC) **[35673]**
Professional Carpet Systems Inc. (PCS) **[16242]**
Professional Communication: What Message Are You Sending? **[17609]**
Professional Construction Estimators Association of America, Inc. (PCEA) **[3963]**
Professional Convention Management Association (PCMA) **[15825]**
Professional Currency Dealers Association (PCDA) **[3233]**
Professional Engineering Inspections Inc. **[2028]**
Professional on the Go: Can I Use Venmo for My Business? **[16676]**
Professional on the Go: Do You Have What It Takes to Become a Life Coach? **[33308]**
Professional on the Go: How Are Professional Photographers Getting in on the Real Estate Game? **[12316]**
Professional on the Go: In Dog Trainers We Trust **[33309]**
Professional on the Go: Top Trends in the Esthetics Industry **[7883]**
Professional on the Go: Using Excel for Small Business Accounting **[16858]**
Professional on the Go: What are the Best Tools for Health & Wellness Professinals? **[6815]**
Professional on the Go: Who Are the Top Paid Freelancers? **[16677]**
Professional Golfers' Association of America (PGA) **[7513]**
"Professional Grooming Marketplace: Cash In On Green Products and Services" in Pet Product News (Vol. 66, September 2012, No. 9, pp. 84) **[5683]**, **[5949]**, **[12098]**, **[23323]**, **[29990]**
Professional Handlers' Association (PHA) **[642]**

3316 Small Business Sourcebook • 42nd Edition

Master Index Protingent

Master Index

"Professional Help: Cross That Off Your To-Do List" in Inc. (November 2007, pp. 89-90, 92) **[2677]**, **[3876]**, **[10284]**, **[12025]**, **[12261]**, **[34999]**
Professional House Doctors Inc. **[13071]**
Professional Landcare Network [10080]
Professional Lawn Tennis Association of United States [15671]
Professional Managers Association (PMA) **[28265]**
Professional Manufacturing Confectioners Association (PMCA) **[2538]**, **[2561]**
Professional Numismatic Guild [3234]
Professional Numismatists Guild (PNG) **[3234]**
"Professional Organizer" in Entrepreneur **[12814]**
Professional Organizer: How to Organize a Business **[12841]**
Professional Organizers Specializing In Small Businesses **[12842]**
Professional Photographers of America (PPA) **[12293]**, **[12335]**
Professional Picture Framers Association (PPFA) **[12704]**
Professional Polish Inc. (PPE) **[10139]**
Professional Purchasing **[31913]**
Professional Putters Association (PPA) **[10984]**
Professional Report [13323], [13606]
Professional Roofing **[14334]**
Professional Services Directory of the American Translators Association [15932]
Professional Services Marketing: How the Best Firms Build Premier Brands, Thriving Lead Generation Engines, and Cultures of Business Development Success **[20119]**, **[29991]**, **[33235]**
Professional Skaters Association (PSA) **[14717]**
Professional Skaters Guild of America [14717]
Professional Ski Instructors of America [14734]
The Professional Ski Instructors of America and the American Association of Snowboard Instructors (PSIA-AASI) **[14734]**
Professional Surveyors Canada (PSC) **[15217]**
Professional and Technical Consultants Association (PATCA) **[10478]**
Professional and Technical Consultants Association--Member Directory (Internet only) **[10487]**
Professional Tennis Registry (PTR) **[15668]**
Professional Tennis Registry - U.S.A. [15668]
Professional Tool & Equipment News: The Independent Tool Authority **[14567]**
Professional Truck Driver Institute (PTDI) **[16065]**
Professional Truck Driver Institute of America [16065]
Professional Turf and Landscape Conference [10049], [10081]
Professional Tutors of America Inc. **[16150]**
Professional United Pet Sitters (PUPS) **[12252]**
Professional Women of Color Network (PWOCN) **[30302]**
Professional Women Photographers (PWP) **[12294]**
Professional Women of St. Tammany (PWST) **[35674]**
Professional Women's Network (PWN) **[35675]**
Professionals for NonProfits Inc. [144]
Professionels en Produits Promotionnels du Canada (PPPC) **[29575]**
Professonal on the Go: The Business of Yoga from Expert Teacher Trainer **[6816]**
"Professor: More Will Follow CVS Ban on Tobacco" in Philadelphia Business Journal (Vol. 33, February 14, 2014, No. 1, pp. 6) **[5180]**, **[15701]**, **[25905]**, **[34139]**
Profile **[41881]**
"Profile: Charles Handy" in Business Strategy Review (Vol. 21, Summer 2010, No. 2, pp. 86) **[22756]**, **[28783]**
Profit Associates Inc. **[14884]**, **[22330]**
Profit First for Minority Business Enterprises **[22757]**, **[30376]**
Profit First Nation: Boost Your Business's Value and Maximize Profit **[24213]**
Profit First Nation: Don't Be the Hub **[22915]**
Profit First Nation: Fixing the Errors of Mis-Hires **[26724]**
Profit First Nation: How and Why to Let Employees Go **[27111]**
Profit First Nation: Mastering Inventory for E-Commerce Success **[11844]**
Profit First Nation: Mastering Profit First: A Comprehensive Guide to Allocating Funds for Financial Success **[24214]**
Profit First Nation: Play for Monopoly Control **[33049]**
Profit First Nation: Relish Your Ownership **[16678]**
Profit First Nation: Scaling You **[34469]**
Profit First Nation: The Owner's Trap **[18448]**
Profit First Nation: The Sum of All Things **[24215]**
Profit First Nation: The Switzerland Structure **[16679]**
Profit First Nation: Total Revenue Minus Materials, Subs, and More **[16859]**
Profit First Nation: Transform Your Restaurant into a Profitable Venture **[14080]**
Profit First Nation: Unlocking Intentional Growth: 6 Steps for Increased Profitability and Deliberate Expansion **[24216]**
Profit First Nation: Your Price Controls Your Profit **[31667]**
Profit First Naton: Unlocking Employee Loyalty: The Five-Star Retention Strategy Revealed! **[27112]**
Profit Motivators International (PMI) **[24263]**
Profit Planning Consultants **[23684]**
"The Profit Recipe: Top Restaurant Trends and How to Use Them to Boost Your Profits" **[13990]**, **[22758]**
Profiting from Diversity: The Business Advantages and the Obstacles to Achieving Diversity **[30597]**, **[34140]**
"The Profits of Good Works" in Barron's (Vol. 92, September 17, 2012, No. 38, pp. 14) **[7149]**, **[22232]**, **[23324]**, **[34356]**
Profits for Non-Profits: Running a Successful Non-Profit Gift Shop **[7150]**, **[7480]**
"Profits Without Prosperity: Stock Buybacks Manipulate the Market and Leave Most Americans Worse Off" in Harvard Business Review (Vol. 92, September 2014, No. 9, pp. 46) **[6566]**, **[9745]**, **[24059]**
ProFood Tech **[6932]**
Proforma Inc. **[11678]**
Program of Action **[39599]**
"Program Boosts 'Breakout' Companies" in Silicon Valley/San Jose Business Journal (Vol. 30, April 20, 2012, No. 4, pp. 1) **[32706]**, **[35245]**
Program on the Pharmaceutical Industry [21750]
"Program for Women Entrepreneurs: Tips for Surviving this Economy" in Crain's Detroit Business (Vol. 25, June 22, 2009, No. 25) **[21083]**, **[22759]**, **[35842]**
Program of Work **[43183]**
Programming Boot Camp (Onsite) **[21419]**
Programming Microsoft Access 2003: Hands-On - Building Database Applications with Access and VBA (Onsite) **[21420]**
"Programs Provide Education and Training" in Contractor (Vol. 56, September 2009, No. 9, pp. 56) **[508]**, **[5684]**, **[14817]**, **[21609]**, **[33892]**
Progress **[37106]**, **[38773]**
The Progress **[37107]**, **[41789]**
Progress Corporate Park **[26477]**
Progress-Driven Entrepreneurs, Private Equity Finance and Regulatory Issues **[22760]**, **[24060]**
"Progress Means Business" in Pet Product News (Vol. 66, September 2012, No. 9, pp. 88) **[12223]**, **[29992]**, **[32250]**, **[32595]**
Progress in Photovoltaics: Research and Applications **[32908]**
Progress Report **[44581]**
Progress Times **[45328]**
Progress in Tourism and Hospitality Research [16026]
Progressing Together **[43556]**
The Progressive Fish-Culturist [6790]
Progressive Grocer/Supermarket Business Marketing Guidebook [2546], [4444], [7764]
Progressive Grocer: The Industry's Source for News Analysis and Marketing Tactics **[7804]**
Progressive Grocer's Marketing Guidebook [2546], [4444], [7764]
Progressive Grocer's Marketing Guidebook: The Comprehensive Source for Grocery, Drug and Mass Merchant Insights **[2546]**, **[4444]**, **[7764]**
Progressive Sales & Service **[14110]**
Project Change Management (Onsite) **[28405]**
Project Cost Management: Estimating, Budgeting and Earned Value Analysis (Onsite) **[16771]**
Project Initiation and Planning (Onsite) **[19454]**
Project Leadership: Building High-Performance Teams (Onsite) **[22064]**, **[28406]**
Project Management for Auditors (Onsite) **[28407]**
"Project Management Courses for You" in Small Business Trends (July 25, 2022) **[28784]**
Project Management Essentials: Part 1 - The Fundamentals [28354]
Project Management Institute (PMI) **[34963]**
Project Management Institute - Dallas Chapter **[28266]**
Project Management: Skills for Success (Onsite) **[18876]**, **[28408]**
Project Management for Software Development - Planning and Managing Successful Projects (Onsite) **[28409]**, **[33813]**
Project Management: The Human and Technical View (Onsite) **[28410]**
Project Management for Web Development (Onsite) **[28411]**
Project Management Workshop **[28412]**
"Project Managers' Creed: Learn It, Live It" in Contractor (Vol. 56, November 2009, No. 11, pp. 46) **[28785]**, **[35952]**
Project Quality Management for Project Managers - Delivering Consistent Quality (Onsite) **[18877]**, **[19455]**
Project Report **[16969]**
Project Scheduling and Budgeting - Achieving Cost-Effective and Timely Delivery (Onsite) **[17487]**, **[19456]**
Project Scope and Requirements Management (Onsite) **[28413]**
Prolog Ventures **[41661]**
"The Promise of the Promised Land" in San Francisco Business Times (Vol. 28, January 3, 2014, No. 24, pp. 4) **[6567]**, **[9746]**, **[13258]**, **[13814]**, **[26382]**, **[33403]**
"Promotional Marketing: How to Create, Implement & Integrate Campaigns That Really Work" **[333]**, **[10669]**, **[16456]**, **[21951]**, **[29993]**
Promotional Products Association of Canada [29575]
Promotional Products Association International (PPAI) **[31841]**
Promotional Products Professionals of Canada [29575]
"Promotions Create a Path to Better Profit" in Pet Product News (Vol. 64, December 2010, No. 12, pp. 1) **[334]**, **[12172]**, **[21952]**, **[29994]**, **[32251]**, **[32596]**
Prompt [35730]
Property Administration Association [12867]
Property Condition Assessments Featuring E2018 Standard Guide (Onsite) **[18495]**
Property Management Association (PMA) **[12868]**
Property Management Association of America [12868]
Property Management Association--Directory (Washington DC) **[12899]**
"A Property Rights Analysis of Newly Private Firms" Opportunities for Owners to Appropriate Rents and Partition Residual Risks" in Business Ethics Quarterly (Vol. 21, July 2011, No. 3, pp. 445) **[9747]**, **[23527]**
Property Taking Through Eminent Domain: What You Need to Know (Onsite) **[18496]**
PropertyGuys.com Inc. **[13340]**
"Proposed Accounting Changes Could Complicate Tenants' Leases" in Baltimore Business Journal (Vol. 28, July 2, 2010, No. 8, pp. 1) **[84]**, **[1770]**, **[13259]**, **[13815]**, **[15407]**, **[16824]**, **[28178]**
"Proposed Triangle Redo in Motion" in Crain's Cleveland Business (Vol. 28, October 15, 2007, No. 41, pp. 1) **[13260]**, **[13536]**, **[13991]**, **[31486]**, **[32252]**
The Proprietary Association [25668]
ProQuest Accounting & Tax™ [157], [15459]
ProQuest Accounting, Tax and Banking Collection™ **[157]**, **[15459]**
Pros and Cons of Dog Breeding Business: Guide for Beginners **[655]**
"Pros and Cons of Joining a Group Purchasing Organization" in FoodTruckOperator.com (June 8, 2020) **[7004]**
"Pros and Cons of Owning a Laundromat for a New Business Owner" in Laundrylux Blog **[10176]**
The Pros and Cons of Running a Seasonal Business **[32959]**
"The Pros and Cons of Starting a Barbershop or Salon from Scratch" in American Barber (October 14, 2018) **[7872]**
"Pros & Cons of Starting a Lawn Business" in The Balance Small Business (September 10, 2019) **[10111]**, **[10244]**
"The Pros and Cons of Starting a Professional Organizer Business" in The Balance Small Business (January 14, 2020) **[12843]**
"The Pros and Cons of Starting a Translation Services Business" in The Balance Small Business (January 2, 2020) **[15947]**
ProSource Wholesale **[6844]**, **[35500]**
Prospanica **[30303]**
Prospect Area Chamber of Commerce **[40082]**
Prospect Silicon Valley **[37614]**
Prospect Street Ventures / Prospect Capital Corp. (PCM) **[42788]**
Prospect Venture Partners **[37463]**
Prospecting Strategies to Build a Qualified Pipeline (Onsite) **[32445]**
ProspectSV [37614]
Prosper Area Chamber of Commerce **[45329]**
Prosper Business Development **[30219]**
Prosperity Now **[20709]**, **[23018]**
Prosser Chamber of Commerce **[46142]**
Protect Painters **[11890]**
"Protect Your Domain Name From Cybersquatters" in Idaho Business Review (September 1, 2014) **[14450]**, **[16457]**, **[18669]**, **[21953]**, **[27938]**
Protecting the Legacy of Family-Owned MSME Businesses – Advancing Economic Growth & Job Creation **[23650]**
"Protecting Your Food Truck Recipes: Trade Secrets & Patents" in FoodTruckOperator.com (June 29, 2020) **[7005]**
Protein Cereal Products International [16962]
Protein Grain Products International [16962]
Protingent Staffing **[15660]**

Small Business Sourcebook • 42nd Edition 3317

Protocol L.L.C. [16269]
Proton Enterprises (PE) [38579]
"Proud Out Loud" in Canadian Business (Vol. 80, April 23, 2007, No. 9, pp. 52) [22233], [34357]
"The Proven 3 Step Formula For Growing Retail Profits: Without Having to Resort to Coupons or Discount Sales" [335], [20051], [20485], [32253], [32597]
Provide Addict Care Today [34672]
Providence Business Loan Fund [33511]
Providence Business News [44491]
Providence Business News Inc. (PBN) [44492]
Providence Economic Development Partnership [33511]
Providence Equity Partners L.L.C. [44483]
"Providence Exec Explains Why the Deal with Boeing is the Way of the Future" in Puget Sound Business Journal (Vol. 35, June 27, 2014, No. 10, pp. 6) [17341], [20486], [25906], [33236]
Provider: For Long Term Care Professionals [26045]
"Providers Ride First Wave of eHealth Dollars" in Boston Business Journal (Vol. 31, June 10, 2011, No. 20, pp. 1) [10971], [14818], [21954], [25041], [25907], [33893]
"Provinces Tackle E-Waste Problem" in Canadian Electronics (Vol. 23, June-July 2008, No. 4, pp. 1) [4403], [5950], [20120], [23325], [25496], [34141]
Provincetown Chamber of Commerce [40617]
Provincetown Chamber of Commerce--Visitor's Guide [40618]
Provincetown Chamber of Commerce - Winter Visitor Guide [40619]
Provo-Orem Chamber of Commerce [45650]
ProZyme, Inc. [3797], [4419], [37277]
Prunedale Chamber of Commerce [37050]
Pryor Area Chamber of Commerce (PACC) [43801]
PSA Journal [12314], [12352]
"PSC Approves $130M TECO Solar Project" in Tampa Bay Business Journal (Vol. 30, December 18, 2009, No. 52, pp. 1) [5685], [5951], [14936], [23326], [25497]
"PSC Decision Could Help Bolster a Solar Market Supernova" in Tampa Bay Business Journal (Vol. 29, November 6, 2009, No. 46, pp. 1) [5686], [5952], [14937], [23327], [29341], [29995]
"PSCPets.com Gives Back to Support Military Working Dogs" in Pet Product News (Vol. 66, September 2012, No. 9, pp. 17) [694], [7151], [34358]
"PSEG Queen Creek Solar Farm in Arizona Begins Commercial Operation" in Benzinga.com (October 4, 2012) [5687], [5953], [14938], [23328]
"PSI Repair Services to Showcase at Windpower Conference and Exhibition" in Entertainment Close-Up (May 19, 2012) [5688], [5954], [14939], [23329], [35081]
PSP Group, LLC [12123], [12241]
PSP Metrics [27156]
Psychoanalytic Dialogues [778]
Psychoanalytic Social Work [26046]
"Psychological Ownership: A Social Marketing Advertising Message Appeal? Not for Women" in International Journal of Advertising (Vol. 31, May 2012, No. 2, pp. 291) [336], [9207], [10670], [29996]
The Psychology of Entrepreneurship [22761]
"Psychology Professor Puts Sweet Mini Golf Course on the Roof of her Vacation Home" in Golf Digest (January 18, 2018) [10987]
PT Magazine [12496], [25988]
PT in Motion [12496], [25988]
""PTO vs. Vacation Time: Which Is Right for Your Company?" in Legal Zoom (February 14, 2023) [27024]
PTV Healthcare Capital (PTVHC) [45465]
PubCom/i-Imagery Design [4953]
Pubcon Fullstack Marketing Conference [30174]
PubEasy [42267]
Public Administration Abstracts [31710]
Public Administration Review (PAR) [31711]
"Public Bathroom Pressure Woes Resolved" in Contractor (Vol. 56, September 2009, No. 9, pp. 44) [4205], [12653], [14630]
Public Broadcasting Management Association [15579]
Public Budgeting & Finance [17516]
Public Citizen Health Research Group (PCHRG) [26136]
"Public Health Care Funding and the Montana Economy" in Montana Business Quarterly (Vol. 49, Spring 2011, No. 1, pp. 23) [8956], [25042], [25908], [27325]
Public Health Institute (PHI) [10942]
Public Health Institute - Alcohol Research Group (ARG) [34692]
Public Library of Cincinnati and Hamilton County - Government Resources [27983]
Public Management (PM) [31712]
Public Media Business Association (PMBA) [15579]
Public Personnel Management (PPM) [14992]
Public Relations Campaigns: An Integrated Approach [12946], [31785], [31882]

Public Relations Firms Industry in the US - Market Research Report [31801]
Public Relations Review: A Global Journal of Research and Comment [12951]
Public Relations Society of America (PRSA) [12924], [31744]
Public Relations Student Society of America (PRSSA) [12925]
Public Risk Management Association (PRIMA) [26843]
Public Sector Consultants Inc. (PSC) [2310], [20221], [31718]
Public Sector Consulting (PSC) [33688]
Public Securities Association [9299]
Public Speaking Tips [14526]
Public Telecommunications Financial Management Association [15579]
"Publisher Steve Forbes: Small Business Can Flourish in Boise" in Idaho Business Review (August 19, 2014) [25498], [34865]
Publishers Directory [1669], [1836], [5321]
Publishers and Distributors of the United States [1670], [14819]
Publishers, Distributors, and Wholesalers of the United States [1670], [14819]
Publishers Marketing Association [1623]
Publishers of the United States [1670], [14819]
Publishers Weekly: The International voice for Book Publishing and Bookselling [1693], [1844], [10349]
"Publishing: Art or Science? Reflections from an Editorial Perspective" in Accounting and Finance (Vol. 52, June 2012, No. 2, pp. 359) [1671], [4940], [5322]
"Publix Could Be Downtown's Tipping Point" in Birmingham Business Journal (Vol. 31, May 23, 2014, No. 21, pp. 6) [5181], [7765], [13261], [13537]
Puckmasters International [15213]
Pueblo Business and Technology Center [37949]
Pueblo Chamber of Commerce [37861]
Pueblo Economic Development Corp. (PEDCO) [37950]
Pueblo Small Business Development Center [37792]
Puerto Rico Chamber of Commerce [46638]
Puerto Rico Federal Contracting Center [46643]
Puerto Rico Minority Supplier Development Council (PRMSDC) [46641]
Puerto Rico Procurement Technical Assistance Center (FeCC) [46641]
Puerto Rico Small Business and Technology Development Center (PR SBDTC) [46631]
Puerto Rico Small Business and Technology Development Centers Arecibo [46632]
Puerto Rico Small Business and Technology Development Centers Caguas [46633]
Puerto Rico Small Business and Technology Development Centers Fajardo [46634]
Puerto Rico Small Business and Technology Development Centers Ponce [46635]
Puerto Rico Small Business and Technology Development Centers San German [33505]
Puerto Rico Supplier Development Council [46641]
Puget Sound Business Travel Association (PSBTA) [19314], [45997]
Puget Sound Council of Governments [47522]
Pulaski Area Chamber of Commerce [46500]
Pulaski County Chamber of Commerce (PCCC) [45892]
Pulaski - Eastern Shore Chamber of Commerce [42652]
Pullman Chamber of Commerce (PCC) [46143]
Pulse [36313]
The Pulse [13690]
Pulse Beat [37108]
Pump It Up - The Inflatable Party Zone [2908]
Pump Repair & Maintenance (Onsite) [19457], [21421]
"Pump Up the Profits" in Small Business Opportunities (Summer 2010) [12366], [24298]
"The Pumpkin Plan: A Simple Strategy to Grow a Remarkable Business in Any Field" [17099], [18294], [22762]
"Pumpkin Spice is Coming Early to Dunkin' and Starbucks" in The New York Times (August 13, 2019) [3189], [32960]
Pumps & Pump Systems: Specification, Installation & Operation (Onsite) [19458], [21422]
Pundmann & Company Inc. [19704]
"Punta Gorda Interested in Wi-Fi Internet" in Charlotte Observer (February 1, 2007) [9208], [21955], [26383]
Puppy Training: A Step-by-Step Guide to Crate Training, Potty Training, and Obedience Training [12151]
Purcell Chamber of Commerce [43769]
Purchasing Management Association of Chicago [31905]
"Purdue Agronomist: Consider Costs Before Tilling" in Farm Industry News (November 8, 2011) [17100], [19048]
Purdue Research Park (PRP) [39649]
Purdue Technology Center [39650]
Purdue University - Center for Food and Agricultural Business (CFAB) [17236]

Purdue University - College of Agriculture - Southeast-Purdue Agricultural Center (SEPAC) [2959]
Purdue University Department of Entomology - Center for Urban and Industrial Pest Management [12072]
Purdue University Libraries - KRAN Management and Economics Library [17216]
Purdue University - Roland G. Parrish Library of Management and Economics [17216]
Purdue University Technical Assistance Program (TAP) [39487]
PureTech Health PLC [40722]
Puroclean-The Paramedics of Property Damage [27379]
Pursuit (NYBDC) [33507]
"Put the Good, the Bad and the Ugly on the Table" in South Florida Business Journal (Vol. 35, September 19, 2014, No. 8, pp. 13) [7152], [25909], [34359]
Put-in-Bay Chamber of Commerce [43557]
"Put Power in Your Direct Mail Campaigns" in Contractor (Vol. 56, September 2009, No. 9, pp. 64) [337], [12654], [29997], [33237]
"Put Your Heating Cap On" in Indoor Comfort Marketing (Vol. 70, September 2011, No. 9, pp. 26) [509], [33238]
Putnam County Chamber of Commerce [38488], [46284]
Putnam SCORE [42426]
"Putting Customers' Wants First — Without Serving Bad Coffee" in Perfect Daily Grind (August 2, 2017) [7561], [20487]
"Putting Down Roots" in Entrepreneur (August 2014) [5019], [10926], [23010], [25499], [25910], [31487]
"Putting 'Extra' in Extra-Silky Shampoo" in Crain's Chicago Business (Vol. 31, April 28, 2008, No. 17, pp. 37) [18295], [29342], [30798], [32022], [32806]
"Putting 'Great' Back Into A&P" in Crain's New York Business (Vol. 24, January 6, 2008, No. 1, pp. 3) [7766], [18296], [19911]
"Putting SogoTrade Through Its Paces" in Barron's (Vol. 89, July 27, 2009, No. 30, pp. 27) [6568], [9748], [21956], [24061]
"Putting Vets to Work" in Business Week (September 22, 2008, No. 4100, pp. 18) [20121], [26639]
"Putting the World at Your Fingertips" in Barron's (Vol. 88, July 7, 2008, No. 27, pp. L13) [6569], [9749], [21084], [24062], [27689]
"PwC to Add 400 Workers in North Texas" in Dallas Business Journal (Vol. 35, April 6, 2012, No. 30, pp. 1) [85], [15408], [20122], [26640]
PwC Research Centre [169], [15475]
PwC - Toronto - Metro North [1792]
PYA GatesMoore [145], [16885], [29027]
Python and Algorithmic Thinking for the Complete Beginner: Learn to Think Like a Programmer [3635], [21610]

Q

"Q&A: Chuck Hughes, Celebrity Chef" in Canadian Business (Vol. 85, July 16, 2012, No. 11-12, pp. 65) [1672], [2678], [6201], [13992], [22763]
"Q&A with Google's Patrick Pichette" in Canadian Business (Vol. 81, October 13, 2008, No. 17, pp. 6) [2781], [9209], [21957], [24063], [28786]
"Q&A Interview With Perrin Beatty" in Canadian Business (Vol. 80, October 8, 2007, No. 20, pp. 13) [8750], [21085], [29343]
"Q&A: PSU's Tom Gillpatrick on How Quirkiness Gives Portland Its Edge" in Business Journal Portland (Vol. 30, January 17, 2014, No. 46, pp. 6) [8042], [8667], [13993], [18297], [31786]
"Q&A: RBC's Gordon Nixon" in Canadian Business (Vol. 80, May 31, 2011, No. 22, pp. 9) [6570], [19912], [25500], [27690]
"Q&A: The CAPP's Greg Stringham" in Canadian Business (Vol. 81, February 12, 2008, No. 3, pp. 8) [6571], [9750], [19913], [21086], [24064], [25501], [29344], [33239]
"Q&A With Devin Ringling: Franchise's Services Go Beyond Elder Care" in Gazette (October 2, 2010) [5443], [8262], [12026], [12494], [14984], [15644], [24401], [25911]
QB3 [37615]
qb3@953 [37597]
Qdoba Mexican Grill Inc. [14234]
Qdoba Restaurant Corp. [14234]
QED Investors [45926]
"Qorvis Communications Gets Sabre Award for Search Engine Optimization" in Entertainment Close-Up (May 29, 2012) [9210], [16458], [27691]
Quaboag Hills Chamber of Commerce (QHCC) [40620]
Quad Cities Chamber of Commerce [39786]
Quad Cities SCORE [39009], [39695]
"QuaDPharma Tripling Sales" in Business First of Buffalo (Vol. 30, January 31, 2014, No. 20, pp. 3) [5182], [19571]

Quake Capital [42920]
Quaker Partners Management LP [44351]
Qualcomm Ventures [37712]
Qualified Financial Services Inc. (QFS) [24264]
Qualitative Health Research (QHR) [26047]
"Quality at Bargain Prices" in Black Enterprise (Vol. 41, December 2010, No. 5, pp. 30) [6572], [9751], [34142]
Quality Business Consulting Inc. (QBCI) [2311], [29028]
Quality Center for Business (QCB) [42351]
Quality Courts Motels, Inc. [8502]
Quality of Life [36148], [39600], [44286]
Quality Management Journal (QMJ) [28918]
"Quality Performance of SMEs in a Developing Economy: Direct and Indirect Effects of Service Innovation and Entrepreneurial Orientation" in Journal of Business & Industrial Marketing (Vol. 29, July 2014, No. 6) [21087], [22764], [27692], [27939], [28787]
Quality Review Bulletin [26017]
"Quantivo Empowers Online Media Companies to Immediately Expand Audiences and Grow Online Profits" in Marketwired (November 18, 2009) [338], [9211], [18298], [26384], [29998]
The Quants [6573], [9752], [24065]
Quantum Capital Group (QEP) [45599]
Quantum Energy Partners [45599]
The Quarter Racing Journal [15208]
The Quarterly Review of Biology (QRB) [32909]
Quartz Hill Chamber of Commerce (QHCoC) [37109]
"Quasar Energy Group Completes Project in Ohio Wastewater Treatment Plant" in Waste Today (November 8, 2019) [7960]
Quebec Writers' Federation (QWF) [5298]
Queen Anne's County Chamber of Commerce (QACCC) [40412]
Queen City Angels (QCA) [35303], [43346]
Queens Borough Public Library - Information Services Division [9285]
Queen's Business Consulting (QBC) [2312], [19980], [24265]
Queens Chamber of Commerce [42653]
Queen's University at Kingston School of Policy Studies - Institute of Intergovernmental Relations (IIGR) [31730]
Queens-York Small Business Development Center [42412]
QueenSpotting [1486]
"The Quest for Content: How User-Generated Links Can Facilitate Online Exploration" in International Journal of Marketing Research (Vol. 49, August 2012, No. 4, pp. 452) [9212], [10671]
"The Quest for a Smart Prosthetic" in Canadian Business (Vol. 83, October 12, 2010, No. 17, pp. 26) [25043], [25156], [25912], [27940], [29345], [30799], [32023], [32807]
Quest Venture Partners (QVP) [37464]
"A Questionable Chemical Romance" in Barron's (Vol. 88, July 14, 2008, No. 28, pp. 28) [6574], [9753], [21088], [24066], [29346], [31488], [32808]
"Questioning Authority" in Entrepreneur (June 2014) [3636], [26641], [27025]
"Questions Abound in Voluminous Health Care Reform Law" in Memphis Business Journal (Vol. 34, July 6, 2012, No. 12, pp. 1) [8957], [25502], [25913], [27326]
"Questions to Ask Your Customers Before They Rent a Generator" in Rental Product News (Vol. 33, October 2011) [13816]
Questmark Partners [40433]
"Quick Earnings Revival Unlikely" in Barron's (Vol. 88, June 30, 2008, No. 26, pp. 31) [6575], [9754], [21089], [24067], [26642]
"A Quick Guide to Creating an Effective Gym Referral Program" in Glofox blog (April 30, 2019) [12428]
"A Quick Guide to Digital Marketing for Newbies" in Forbes (June 14, 2020) [27811]
"A Quick Guide to Hiring Freelancers in a Time of Crisis" in Legal Zoom (February 21, 2023) [26643]
"A Quick Guide To Putting Employees In The Driver's Seat For Customer Success" in Small Business Trends (March 20, 2023) [32598]
"Quick Guide VI - How to Sell Coaching" [32599]
Quick Printing: The Information Source for Commercial Copyshops & Printshops [4991], [12769]
"Quick Service Restaurants Spring in a New Direction with Focus on Healthy, High Quality Menus" in Forbes (August 8, 2018) [8103]
QuickBooks 2014 on Demand [86], [14820], [16825], [33894]
QuickBooks for the New Bean Counter: Business Owner's Guide 2006 [87], [656], [14739], [16826], [33895]
QuickBooks Online for Dummies [16827]
"Quicken Starter Edition 2008" in Black Enterprise (Vol. 38, March 1, 2008, No. 8, pp. 54) [88], [15409], [16828], [24068], [34866]

Quincy Area Chamber of Commerce (QACC) [39293]
Quincy Business & Technology Center (QBTC) [39395], [39421]
Quincy Center for Innovation (QCI) [40762]
Quincy Chamber of Commerce (QCC) [37110]
Quincy Chamber of Commerce [40628]
Quincy Main Street Chamber of Commerce [37110]
Quincy Valley Chamber of Commerce (QVCC) [46144]
"Quincy Veterinarian Advises That Pets as 'Young' as Seven Years Need Senior Care" in Benzinga.com (September 9, 2012) [695], [25914]
James Quinn Agency Inc. [11099]
Quinnipiac Chamber of Commerce [38070]
"Quintessential Gentleman: Going Old-School on Calvert" in Baltimore Business Journal (Vol. 31, February 7, 2014, No. 41, pp. 6) [1590], [7873], [15253], [19572]
Quitman-Brooks County Chamber of Commerce [38774]
"Quitting with Purpose with Erica Courdae and Tasha L. Harrison [19234]
Quitting Your Day Job? The Basics on Benefits Coverage for Entrepreneurs [27327]
"Quitting Your Job Might Be Tougher Than You Think" in Canadian Business (Vol. 85, July 16, 2012, No. 11-12, pp. 71) [22234], [27026], [28044]
The Quizno's Master L.L.C. [4920], [14235]
Quizno's Subs [4920], [14235]
Quma Learning Systems Inc. [35016]
"Quonset Steering To Import Records" in Providence Business News (Vol. 29, May 19, 2014, No. 7, pp. 1) [8751], [11428], [20649]
Quovis Consulting Corp. [46850]

R

R/GA Accelerator [42921]
R. L. Townsend & Associates Inc. [4335]
R. Miller Hicks & Co. [2313]
R Moon Consulting [45581]
R & S Design Computer Services Inc. [31012], [31095]
R. Shane Chance CPA P.C. [146]
"The Rabbi Trust: How to Earn It Now, But Defer the Tax to the Future" in Barron's (Vol. 88, March 24, 2008, No. 12, pp. 55) [25503], [34143], [34867]
Rabun County Chamber of Commerce [38775]
RACC Business Perspectives [44007]
"Race Benefits: Changes Afoot for Ironman" in Business Journal Serving Greater Tampa Bay (Vol. 30, October 29, 2010, No. 45, pp. 1) [15177], [19194]
Race and Entrepreneurial Success: Black-, Asian-, and White-Owned Businesses in the United States [22765], [23651], [27027], [28179], [30377], [34144]
"The Race Is On For High-Stakes Casino Gambling in Florida" in South Florida Business Journal (Vol. 34, January 10, 2014, No. 25, pp. 12) [7307], [25504]
"Race, Not Income, Played Role in Subprime Loans" in Black Enterprise (Vol. 40, July 2010, No. 12, pp. 26) [11072], [28180]
Rachel Carson Council (RCC) [12066]
Rachel Carson Trust for the Living Environment [12066]
"The Racial Divide and the Class Struggle in the United States" in WorkingUSA (Vol. 11, September 2008, No. 3, pp. 311) [21090], [30378], [30598], [34145]
Racial Equity Institute LLC (REI) [30304], [30519]
Racine Area Manufacturers and Commerce (RAMAC) [46501]
Racine Chamber of Commerce [46501]
"Racing to Beam Electricity to Devices Wirelessly" in San Francisco Business Times (Vol. 28, April 11, 2014, No. 38, pp. 6) [2782], [26385], [27941]
RAD Expo [5062]
Radford Chamber of Commerce (RCC) [45893]
Radiation Safety Institute of Canada [13072]
Radical Business with David Gaines [34438]
"A Radical Prescription for Sales: The Reps of the Future Won't Work On Commission" in Harvard Business Review (Vol. 90, July-August 2012, No. 7-8, pp. 76) [32600], [34146]
"Radio" in MarketingMagazine (Vol. 115, September 27, 2010, No. 13, pp. 24) [13040], [29999]
Radio Advertising Bureau (RAB) [13024], [13065], [31842]
Radio Broadcasting Industry in the US - Market Research Report [13045]
"Radio Feels Heat from iPod Generation" in Globe & Mail (March 16, 2006, pp. B1) [13041], [26386]
"Radio Producer Launches Food Truck, New Show" in Dickinson Press (April 18, 2012) [3828], [7006], [13012], [30449]
Radio Television Digital News Association - Canada (RTDNA) [13025], [15580]
Radio-Television News Directors' Association [13025], [15580]
Radio World [13047]

Radiotechniques Engineering, LLC [13057]
"Radisson Hotel San Jose Airport Headed Into Foreclosure" in Silicon Valley/San Jose Business Journal (Vol. 29, February 3, 2012, No. 45, pp. 1) [8450], [28181]
Radius Ventures LLC [42789]
Radnor Venture Partners [44356]
Raeford - Hoke Chamber of Commerce (RHCC) [43184]
RAF Netventures/RAF Ventures [44352]
"The Rage Offstage at Marvel" in Barron's (Vol. 88, June 30, 2008, No. 26, pp. 19) [3327], [6202], [18670]
RAIC Bulletin [864]
Railroad Model Craftsman [4680]
Railway Business Women's Association [35634]
RAIN Source Capital [41337]
Rainbow Media Holdings L.L.C. [14348]
Rainsville Chamber of Commerce [36149]
"Raise vs. Bonus for Your Small Business Employees" in Investopedia (July 27, 2020) [19751]
Raising Cane's Chicken Fingers [14236]
Raising Cane's USA L.L.C. [14236]
Raising Capital [18299], [18476], [28070], [28182], [30899], [30929], [35246], [35378]
Raising Capital Lessons, Big Pharma & Patient Support [35428]
Raising Capital in Saturated Markets [16680]
"Raising the Game" in Birmingham Business Journal (Vol. 31, May 2, 2014, No. 18, pp. 4) [15178], [15886], [27693], [35082]
"Ralcorp Investigated for Rejecting ConAgra Bid" in Saint Louis Business Journal (Vol. 32, September 16, 2011, No. 3, pp. 1) [7767], [9755], [18671], [31489]
Raleigh Business & Technology Center (RBTC) [43249]
Ralls Chamber of Commerce [45330]
Rally Ventures [37465]
Ralph Moss Ltd. (RML) [17410]
Ralston Area Chamber of Commerce (RACC) [41882]
Ramada International, Inc. [8509]
Ramona Business and Community News [37111]
Ramona Chamber of Commerce (RCC) [37112]
Ranch 1 Grilled Chicken [14237]
"Ranch Ice Cream? Brand Collab Figures, Why Not?" in Small Business Trends (March 13, 2023) [8587]
Rancho Cordova Chamber of Commerce [37113]
Rancho Cucamonga Chamber of Commerce [37114]
Rancho Mirage Chamber of Commerce (RMCC) [37115]
Rancho Mirage City Guide [37116]
Rancho Santa Ana Botanic Garden [7661]
Rand Capital Corporation [42790]
Randleman Chamber of Commerce [43185]
Randolph Area Chamber of Commerce (RACC) [42182]
Randolph Chamber of Commerce [46502]
Randolph Chamber of Commerce [45741]
Randolph County Chamber of Commerce [36493]
Randolph County Convention & Visitors Bureau (RCCVB) [46285]
Randolph Metrocom Chamber of Commerce [45379]
Random Lengths Weekly Report [10403]
Random Structures & Algorithms [32910]
"R&R Launches Upscale Spoony's and Low Fat Dragon's Den" in Ice Cream Reporter (Vol. 23, August 20, 2010, No. 9, pp. 3) [8043], [8104], [8588], [9756], [18300], [19914], [27694], [29347], [31490]
Rangeley Lakes Region Chamber of Commerce [40300]
Rangely Area Chamber of Commerce (RACC) [37894]
Rank and File [3284]
Rankin County Chamber of Commerce [41428]
Rantoul Area Chamber of Commerce (RACC) [39294]
Rapid City Small Business Development Center (SBDC) [44624]
Rapid Communications in Mass Spectrometry [32911]
Rapid Refill Fargo and Total Imaging LLC [4418]
Rappahannock Region Small Business Development Center - Fredericksburg [45790]
Rappahannock Region Small Business Development Center - Warsaw [45791]
Raptor Group Holdings [40723]
"Raptor Opens Austin Office" in Austin Business Journal (Vol. 31, July 8, 2011, No. 18, pp. 1) [6576], [9757], [15179], [20123], [26387], [35379]
RAVE Restaurant Group, Inc. [12589]
"RavenBrick Ready to Manufacture Its High-Tech Windows" in Denver Business Journal (Vol. 64, September 7, 2012, No. 16, pp. 1) [7494], [26388], [29348], [35380]
Ravenna Area Chamber of Commerce [43558]
Ravenna Chamber of Commerce [43558]
"Rawlings-Blake Unveils Business Plan for Next Four Years" in Baltimore Business Journal (Vol. 29, September 16, 2011, No. 19, pp. 1) [21091], [25044], [26389], [27028], [33404], [34868]
Rawlins-Carbon County Chamber of Commerce [46616]
RAY International [8785]

Raylon Corporation [7884]
Raymond Chamber of Commerce [46178]
Raymore Chamber of Commerce [41616]
Rayne Chamber of Commerce [40186]
"Raytheon Stock Up, Will Pay New Quarterly Dividend" in Barron's (Vol. 88, March 31, 2008, No. 13) [6577], [9758], [19049], [24069], [26390]
Raytown Area Chamber of Commerce (RACC) [41617]
"The RBC Dynasty Continues" in Globe & Mail (January 30, 2006, pp. B1) [6578], [9759], [18301], [24070], [28788]
RC Bryan [14885]
RCA Connector [5499], [13691], [23048]
RCNA Annual Convention [3253]
Re/focus Sustainability & Recycling Summit [13745], [23445], [29462]
Re-Imagine! Business Excellence in a Disruptive Age [24721]
Re/Max International [13341]
RE/MAX, LLC [13341]
REach [39422]
"Reaching Out: the LIFE Foundation Provides Free Tools and Resources to Help Agents Boost Their Life Insurance Sales" in Best's Review (Vol. 113, September 2012, No. 5, pp. 26) [8958], [27328]
"ReachLocal Plans to Double DFW Space, is Hunting for 150K Square Feet" in Dallas Business Journal (Vol. 35, March 23, 2012, No. 28, pp. 1) [4206], [11785], [30000]
"Readers' Choice Awards 2019: Internet Service Providers (ISP)" in PC Magazine (May 28, 2019) [9213]
Reader's Digest Association, Inc. [12017]
"Readers Share How Sewing Shaped the Fabric of Their Lives" in Virginian-Pilot (September 14, 2010) [14658], [34360]
Reading Chamber of Commerce [43559]
Reading Financial Reports for Dummies [89], [1771], [15410], [16829], [17738], [24071], [25505], [26391], [27695], [30976], [34147]
Reading Friends Forth Worth [2909]
Reading-North Reading Chamber of Commerce (RNRCC) [40621]
"Reading the Public Mind" in Harvard Business Review (Vol. 88, October 2010, No. 10, pp. 27) [15224], [32024], [32809]
ReadWrite Labs [37616]
"Ready, Aim, (Cool) Fire" in Saint Louis Business Journal (Vol. 32, September 2, 2011, No. 1, pp. 1) [2468], [6203], [13994]
Ready Decks Franchise Systems Inc. [2656]
"Ready to Launch a New Business? Amplify Success with These 4 Tips" in Minority Business Entrepreneur (Vol. 39, Fall, 2022, No. 4, pp.14-15) [34540]
"Ready for Our Ships to Come In" in Philadelphia Business Journal (Vol. 33, April 11, 2014, No. 9, pp. 4) [7044], [10610], [19915], [25045]
"Ready for a Rally?" in The Economist (Vol. 390, January 3, 2009, No. 8612, pp. 54) [6579], [9760], [11073], [20330], [21092], [24072], [28183]
"Ready to Rent an Office? What You Should Know About Leasing" in Business News Daily (February 21, 2023) [34541]
"Reagan HQ In Limbo" in Austin Business Journal (Vol. 32, April 6, 2012, No. 5, pp. A1) [339], [4207], [10112], [23330], [25506]
"Real Deals for Vacant Big Boxes" in Memphis Business Journal (Vol. 33, January 6, 2012, No. 39, pp. 1) [7768], [19195]
Real Estate Brokerage Council [11005]
Real Estate Brokerage Managers Council [11005]
Real Estate Business [13322], [13605]
Real Estate Business Institute (REBI) [11005]
Real Estate Business Magazine (REB) [13348]
"Real Estate Dealmakers of the Year: Where Are They Now?" in San Francisco Business Times (Vol. 28, March 28, 2014, No. 36) [4208], [13262], [13538]
"Real Estate Firm Joins Trend Toward Functional Offices" in Pacific Business News (Vol. 52, April 25, 2014, No. 9, pp. 3) [11645], [13263], [34148]
Real Estate Forum: America's Premier Business Real Estate Magazine [13319]
"Real Estate Funds Raise More Than $350M" in Business Journal Portland (Vol. 27, December 31, 2010, No. 44, pp. 1) [13264], [13539], [34149]
Real Estate Industry: A Resource Guide [13350]
Real Estate Law: Advanced Issues and Answers (Onsite) [18497]
"Real Estate Market Still in a Slump" in Montana Business Quarterly (Vol. 49, Summer 2011, No. 2, pp. 15) [13265], [13540], [21093], [34150]
The Real Estate Recipe: Make Millions by Buying Small Apartment Properties in Your Spare Time [13266], [13541]

"Real Estate Reinventions: Black Lotus Brewing Co." in Crain's Detroit Business (Vol. 23, October 1, 2007, No. 40, pp. 13) [1932], [22766]
"Real Estate Reinventions: Blue Tractor Barbeque and Brewery, Cafe Havana" in Crain's Detroit Business (Vol. 23, October 1, 2007, No. 40, pp. 15) [7562], [13995]
Real Estate Research Center [13639]
Real Estate Research Institute (RERI) [13636]
"The Real Estate Success Formula: 19 Proven Strategies to Making Money in Real Estate" [13267], [13542], [23652], [30001]
Real Estate Weekly [13320]
"Real Estate's New Reality" in Entrepreneur (Vol. 37, July 2009, No. 7, pp. 32) [9761], [13268], [13543]
"The Real Job of Boards" in Business Strategy Review (Vol. 21, Autumn 2010, No. 3, pp. 36) [24722], [28789]
The Real Leadership Lessons of Steve Jobs [22767], [28790]
"Real-Life Coursework for Real-Life Business People" in Women In Business (Vol. 63, Summer 2011, No. 2, pp. 22) [15887], [21611], [28791], [30002], [35083], [35843]
"Real Luxury: How Luxury Brands Can Create Value for the Long Term" [30003]
Real Property Association of Canada (REALPAC) [13112], [13366]
Real Resources (RR) [13330]
"The Real Risk of Entrepreneurial Strengths Becoming Addictive Weaknesses" in Entrepreneur (Oct. 18, 2016) [7308]
Real Ventures [46911]
Reality-Based Leadership: Ditch the Drama, Restore Sanity to the Workplace, & Turn Excuses into Results [22235], [22768], [27029], [28792]
"Reality Check at the Bottom of the Pyramid: To Succeed in the World's Poorest Markets, Aim For Much Higher Margins and Prices Than You Thought Were Necessary-Or Possible" in Harvard Business Review (Vol. 90, June 2012, No. 6, pp. 120) [20052], [20488], [32601], [33240]
Reality Check: The Irreverent Guide to Outsmarting, Outmanaging, and Outmarketing Your Competition [19916], [24723], [28793], [30004]
"The Really Big List of Small Business Associations" in Small Business Trends (June 20, 2021) [34542]
Realstar Hospitality [8510]
Realstar Management [8511]
Realtor Magazine: The Business tool for Real Estate Professionals [13321], [13604]
"Realtors Irate Over Tax Plan" in Providence Business News (Vol. 26, March 26, 2012, No. 51, pp. 1) [1421], [13817], [34869]
Realtors Land Institute (RLI) [13113]
REALTORS Trade Expo [13328]
Realty Executives International Inc. [13342]
Realty World (RW) [2163]
"Reasons Why Small Businesses Are Important" in Chron (Jan. 28, 2019) [21094]
Rebok Memorial Library [34694]
"Rebrand, Rebuild, and Recharge Your Business: How This BE 100s CEO Got a New Lease On Life With a Frozen Yogurt Café" in Black Enterprise (Vol. 44, March 2014, No. 7, pp. 11) [2075], [8589], [30379], [33071], [35844]
Rebuilding Success [6238]
ReCeil It International, Inc. [33325]
"Receiver's Report Uncovers Trouble in Fashion Mall Redevelopment" in South Florida Business Journal (Vol. 34, July 4, 2014, No. 50, pp. 4) [8451], [13544], [18672]
"Recession Creating Surge in Business for Auto Recyclers" in Business Journal-Serving Phoenix & the Valley of the Sun (Vol. 31, November 12, 2010, No. 10, pp. 1) [1108], [5689], [5955], [13723], [21095], [23331]
"Recession and Recovery: Employment Change by Industry" in Occupational Outlook Quarterly (Vol. 58, Summer 2014, No. 2, pp. 45) [21096], [33241], [34151]
Recinto Universitario De Mayaguez - Universidad de Puerto Rico [47461]
"Recipe for Disaster?" in Sacramento Business Journal (Vol. 25, July 4, 2008, No. 18, pp. 1) [13996], [17101], [21097], [33242]
"A Recipe for Food-Industry Growth?" in Providence Business News (Vol. 29, April 21, 2014, No. 3, pp. 1) [6917], [13997], [21098]
Recipe For Success: HALO Incubator Kitchen [46570]
"Reclaim Your Office" in Greater Baton Rouge Business Report (Vol. 30, June 12, 2012, No. 22, pp. 12) [12844], [33896]
Recognition Express [5474]

Recognition Review [5472]
"Reconsidering Pay Dispersion's Effect On the Performance of Interdependent Work: Reconciling Sorting and Pay Inequality" in Academy of Management Journal (Vol. 55, June 1, 2012, No. 3, pp. 585) [11937], [22236]
"Record Pot Sales Continue with $61M in July; Total for 2020 Eclipses $300M" in Chicago Sun-Times (August 3, 2020) [5020]
"Record Share of U.S. Small Businesses Raised Wages in December" in Bloomberg.com (Jan. 6, 2022) [19752]
"Record Store Day Black Friday Promises 177 Titles, Including Paul McCartney, Cardi B, Lizzo" in Variety (October 8, 2019) [3412]
Record Stores Industry in the US - Market Research Report [11269]
The Recording Academy [13650]
Recording Industry Association of America (RIAA) [13667]
Recordkeeping for Business Barter Transactions [17256], [34870]
ReCourses Inc. [388], [12958], [19641]
"Recovering Economy Puts Real Estate on Solid Ground" in San Antonio Business Journal (Vol. 28, February 7, 2014, No. 53, pp. 13) [13269], [13545], [21099]
"Recovery Starts to Set Roots in R.I." in Providence Business News (Vol. 28, January 20, 2014, No. 42, pp. 1) [21100], [24073]
"Recovery on Tap for 2010?" in Orlando Business Journal (Vol. 26, January 1, 2010, No. 31, pp. 1) [2469], [4209], [6204], [8959], [9762], [13270], [13546], [13998], [15099], [15180], [15613], [16008], [18673], [21101], [21612], [25915], [27329], [29349], [32254]
Recreation Vehicle Dealers Association--Membership Directory [13676]
Recreation Vehicle Dealers Association of North America [13673]
Recreation Vehicle Industry Association (RVIA) [13671]
Recreation Vehicle Rental Association (RVRA) [1154], [13672]
Recreational Vehicle Aftermarket Association (RVAA) [12971]
Recreational Vehicle Dealers Industry in the US - Market Research Report [13668]
Recreational Vehicle Division of the Trailer Coach Association [13671]
Recreational Vehicle Institute Inc. [13671]
"Recruiting Diversifies" in Advertising Age (Vol. 83, October 8, 2012, No. 36, pp. 25) [6108], [27030], [30005]
Rector Chamber of Commerce [36494]
Recurring, Repeatable, Reliable Online Income with Dan R. Morris [11845]
"Recycling 202: How to Take Your Recycling Practices to the Next Level" in Black Enterprise (Vol. 41, September 2010, No. 2, pp. 38) [5690], [5956], [13724], [23332]
Recycling Council of Alberta (RCA) [5500], [13692], [23049]
Recycling Council - Canada [5500], [13692], [23049]
Recycling Facilities Industry in the US - Market Research Report [13735]
"Recycling Old Cellphones" in San Jose Mercury News (September 26, 2012) [2783], [11786], [13725]
Recycling Today [13740]
Red Bluff-Tehama County Chamber of Commerce [37117]
"Red Cross CEO Mark Beddingfield: This Work Is In His Blood" in Birmingham Business Journal (Vol. 31, March 7, 2014, No. 10, pp. 11) [7153], [34361]
Red Hook Area Chamber of Commerce [42654]
RED Labs [45544]
"Red Light's Green Light" in Washington Business Journal (Vol. 32, April 11, 2014, No. 52, pp. 6) [1265], [1349], [13999]
Red Lodge Area Chamber of Commerce (RLACC) [41790]
Red Lotus Consulting (RLC) [30650]
"Red Mango Set to Grow in Florida" in Ice Cream Reporter (Vol. 23, September 20, 2010, No. 10, pp. 2) [8044], [8105], [8590], [18302]
"Red McCombs, Partner Rolling Out New Venture Capital Fund" in San Antonio Business Journal (Vol. 26, April 20, 2012, No. 12, pp. 1) [22769], [26174], [29064], [35247]
Red Oak Chamber of Commerce [39787]
Red Oak Chamber and Industry Association (ROCIA) [39787]
Red River Chamber of Commerce [42331]
Red River County Chamber of Commerce [45331]
Red River Technology Center [43845], [43896]
Red Rocket Ventures [39463]

Master Index Rep

Red Roof Inn **[8512]**
Red Sea Ventures (RSV) **[42791]**
"Red Velvet Cupcake Bites" in Candyindustry (Vol. 176, September 2011, No. 9, pp. RC4) **[1266]**, **[30800]**
Red Wheel **[2365]**
Red Wing Area Chamber of Commerce (RWACC) **[41293]**
Redefining Independence: Changing the Game for Freelancers with Rachel Renock **[5342]**
Redevelopment Authority of the City of Meadville **[44416]**
Redfield Area Chamber of Commerce **[44657]**
Redford Township Chamber of Commerce (RTCC) **[40997]**
Redhills Ventures **[41966]**
RedHouse Associates LLC **[45582]**
Redlands Chamber of Commerce **[37118]**
Redlands Daily Facts **[12005]**
Redleaf Venture Management **[37466]**
Redmond Chamber of Commerce **[44008]**
Redmond Technology Press **[46241]**
Redondo Beach Chamber of Commerce and Visitors Bureau (RBCC) **[37119]**
"Reduce, Reuse, Recycle, Reupholster, Is Motto of Willmar, Minn., Upholstery Hobbyist Turned Pro" in West Central Tribune (August 14, 2012) **[7243]**, **[13726]**, **[13818]**, **[16229]**
"Reduce Self-Employment Taxes with a Corporation or LLC" in LegalZoom (September 4, 2020) **[32991]**
"Reducing the Book's Carbon Footprint" in American Printer (Vol. 128, July 1, 2011, No. 7) **[1673]**, **[3328]**, **[5691]**, **[5957]**, **[11995]**, **[12751]**, **[16204]**, **[23333]**
"Reducing Small Business Social Security and Medicare Taxes" in Brady Ware & Company (May 8, 2019) **[34247]**
RedWind Group Inc. **[45545]**
Redwood Area Chamber and Tourism (RACT) **[41294]**
Redwood Enterprise LLC **[30429]**, **[30651]**
Reed City Area Chamber of Commerce (RCACC) **[40998]**
Reedsport - Winchester Bay Chamber of Commerce **[44009]**
"Reengineering the Appraisal Process, Revisited" in Appraisal Buzz (Fall 2016, No. 03, Year 2, pp. 51 - 54) **[814]**
Reference Book for Metalworking Machinery [10435]
"Refinance: To Do Or Not To Do?" in Real Estate Review (Vol. 41, Spring 2012, No. 1, pp. 91) **[815]**, **[11074]**, **[28184]**
"Refiners, Producers are at Odds in Debate Over U.S. Oil Exports" in San Antonio Business Journal (Vol. 27, January 17, 2014, No. 50, pp. 4) **[8752]**, **[25507]**
Reflect New Goals [42917]
"Reflecting State Economy, Banks Less Profitable in 1Q" in Providence Business News (Vol. 29, July 14, 2014, No. 15, pp. 8) **[6580]**, **[21102]**, **[24074]**
Reflexology Association of America (RAA) **[11341]**
"Reforms Equal Smaller 401(k)s" in Employee Benefit News (Vol. 25, December 1, 2011, No. 15, pp. 19) **[17342]**, **[24075]**, **[25508]**, **[34871]**
"A Refresher Course: California Tortilla Unveils New Logo, Colors, Store Design" in Washington Business Journal (Vol. 31, June 8, 2012, No. 7, pp. 1) **[14000]**, **[30006]**
"Refreshing! A Clearly Canadian Comeback" in Canadian Business (Vol. 79, September 11, 2006, No. 18, pp. 22) **[19050]**, **[19573]**, **[32602]**
Refrigerated Foods Association Expo **[7817]**
Refrigerating Engineers and Technicians Association (RETA) **[462]**
Refrigeration Research and Education Foundation [12968]
Refrigeration Research Foundation [12968]
Refrigeration Service Engineers Society (RSES) **[463]**, **[548]**
Regal Nails, Salon and Spa L.L.C. **[7895]**
"Regal Venture Puts Imax Back in the Spotlight" in Globe & Mail (March 13, 2007, pp. B5) **[6205]**, **[31491]**
ReGENERATION Partners **[23685]**
Regenstrief Institute (RI) **[26137]**
Regent Journal of Business and Technology (RJBT) **[24890]**
Regent University Center for Entrepreneurship (RCE) **[45962]**
"Regent's Signal, Once Powerful, Fading From Local Scene" in Business Courier (Vol. 27, June 4, 2010, No. 5, pp. 1) **[9763]**, **[13042]**, **[31492]**
Region 2000 Business and Economic Alliance [45879]
"Region to Be Named Innovation Hub" in Business Courier (Vol. 27, July 2, 2010, No. 9, pp. 1) **[21613]**, **[25046]**, **[26392]**, **[27942]**, **[29350]**, **[30007]**, **[32025]**, **[32810]**
"Region and City Need Influx of Youth" in Crain's Detroit Business (Vol. 24, April 14, 2008, No. 15, pp. 8) **[21103]**, **[24724]**, **[33594]**
"Region Wins as GE Puts Plants Close to R&D" in Business Review Albany (Vol. 41, July 4, 2014, No. 15, pp. 8) **[5692]**, **[5958]**, **[18303]**, **[25916]**, **[26644]**, **[29351]**, **[32026]**
Regional Business Accelerator [46677]
Regional Business Directory **[42332]**
Regional Chamber Alliance [44264]
Regional Contracting Assistance Center Inc. (RCAC) **[46297]**
Regional Contracting Assisting Center, Inc. (RCAC) **[46298]**
Regional and Distribution Carriers Conference (RDCC) **[16066]**
Regional Economics and Community Analysis Program [47419]
Regional Entrepreneurship, Leadership, and Innovation Center (RELI) **[39825]**
Regional Incubator for Sustainability and Entrepreneurship (RISE) **[43678]**
Regional Reporter **[44287]**
"Region's Small Business Lending Rises by $440M" in South Florida Business Journal (Vol. 33, September 7, 2012, No. 6, pp. 1) **[21104]**, **[28185]**
"Reglazing Tile Is the Most Transformative Fix for a Dated Bathroom" in Architectural Digest (August 31, 2017) **[12689]**
Regroupement des consultants canadiens en developpement internationale [2171], [20077]
Regulation: Cato Review of Business & Government **[25627]**
Regulation Foundation [25630]
"Regulator Issues Warning On Reverse Mortgage Loans" in Retirement Advisor (Vol. 13, October 2012, No. 10, pp. 28) **[6581]**, **[9764]**, **[11075]**, **[23528]**, **[24076]**, **[25509]**
"Regulatory Focus and Attribute Framing: Evidence of Compatibility Effects In Advertising" in International Journal of Advertising (Vol. 31, February 2012, No. 1, pp. 169) **[340]**
"Rehab Center Slashes Energy Bills By Going Tankless" in Contractor (Vol. 56, December 2009, No. 12, pp. 3) **[510]**, **[12655]**
Rehabilitation Institute of Michigan (RIM) **[12516]**
Rehmann, Robson and Co. **[31617]**
Rehoboth Beach-Dewey Beach Chamber of Commerce (RBDBCC) **[38138]**
REI Oklahoma (REI) **[43872]**, **[47296]**
"Reimbursement Limitations on Home Healthcare Are Being Loosened" in Modern Healthcare (October 27, 2018) **[8263]**, **[27330]**
Rein Capital LLC **[42268]**
Reinsurance News **[8991]**
Reinvent Yourself **[15347]**
"Reinventing the Cheeseburger" in Inc. (November 2007, pp. 124-125) **[14001]**, **[22770]**, **[23334]**
"Reinventing Management" in Harvard Business Review (Vol. 88, July-August 2010, No. 7-8, pp. 167) **[22771]**, **[28794]**
"Reinventing Marketing to Manage the Environmental Imperative" in Journal of Marketing (Vol. 75, July 2011, No. 4, pp. 132) **[5693]**, **[5959]**, **[21958]**, **[23335]**, **[30008]**
"Reinventing the Rings" in Business Strategy Review (Vol. 23, Spring 2012, No. 1, pp. 75) **[15181]**, **[30009]**
"The Reinvention of Management" in Strategy and Leadership (Vol. 39, March-April 2011, No. 2, pp. 9) **[19574]**, **[22772]**, **[28795]**
The Reinvestment Fund (TRF) **[44353]**
Reisterstown - Owings Mills - Glyndon Chamber of Commerce [40404]
"The REIT Stuff" in Canadian Business (Vol. 80, March 26, 2007, No. 7, pp. 72) **[6582]**, **[9765]**, **[13271]**, **[13547]**
"REITs Decry Foreign Limits on Investment" in Globe & Mail (March 29, 2007, pp. B4) **[6583]**, **[9766]**, **[13272]**, **[13548]**, **[25510]**
"Relationship Marketing Strategy: an Operant Resource Perspective" in Journal of Business & Industrial Marketing (Vol. 29, May 2014, No. 4, pp. 275-283) **[30010]**
Relax **[38489]**
"Relax! 5 Marketing Ideas for Massage Therapists" in Outbound Engine (January 13, 2020) **[10773]**, **[30011]**
Relax The Back Corp. (RTB) **[10962]**
Relay Ventures **[46802]**
"Relief for Gyms on Track, Congress Passes Infrastructure Bill" in IHRSA (November 15, 2021) **[12429]**
Religion and Family Life Section of the National Council on Family Relations Conference **[23679]**
"Religious Revival" in Canadian Business (Vol. 81, December 8, 2008, No. 21, pp. 57) **[8753]**, **[27696]**, **[34362]**
reLink Ventures **[43630]**
Relocation Guide and Membership Directory **[38490]**
Relocation Packet **[36357]**
"Relocation, Relocation, Relocation" in Conde Nast Portfolio (Vol. 2, June 2008, No. 6, pp. 36) **[24725]**, **[28796]**
Remarkable Leadership: Unleashing Your Leadership Potential One Skill at a Time **[22773]**, **[28797]**
Rembrandt Venture Partners (RVP) **[37467]**
Remediation & Environmental Cleanup Services Industry in the US - Market Research Report **[7968]**, **[23414]**
Remedy Intelligent Staffing **[15661]**
"Remember Crazy Eddie? His Prices Were Insane!" in Small Business Trends (August 29, 2022) **[4404]**
"Remember Those Great Volkswagen Ads?" **[341]**, **[11343]**, **[14704]**
Remerica Real Estate **[13343]**
"Remington Developer Says Project May Not Include Second Big Box" in Baltimore Business Journal (Vol. 30, June 8, 2012, No. 5, pp. 1) **[4210]**, **[13549]**, **[32255]**
Remote Control Hobbies (RCH) **[4688]**
Remote Not Distant: Design a Company Culture That Will Help You Thrive in a Hybrid Workplace **[22237]**
"Remote: Office Not Required" **[26801]**, **[34152]**
"Remote Work in Construction: 3 Tips for Success" in Home Business Magazine (Jan. 27, 2022) **[4211]**, **[26802]**
Renaissance Entrepreneur Center **[37617]**
Renaissance Entrepreneurship Center **[37618]**
Renaissance Executive Forums Inc. (REF) **[2366]**
Renaissance Soma **[36604]**
Renaissance Venture Capital **[41144]**
"Renal Solutions Move Not a Sign of the Times" in Pittsburgh Business Times (Vol. 33, February 14, 2014, No. 31, pp. 5) **[10927]**, **[19196]**, **[25917]**
Renasant Center for IDEAs (RCFI) **[41456]**
Rend Lake College (RLC) **[39444]**
Renew America [14900]
Renew the Earth (RTE) **[14900]**
"Renewable Energy Adoption in an Ageing Population: Heterogeneity in Preferences for Micro-Generation Technology Adoption" in Energy Policy (Vol. 39, October 2011, No. 10, pp. 6021-6029) **[5694]**, **[5960]**, **[23336]**, **[25511]**
Renewable Energy Businesses in the World **[23453]**
"Renewable Energy Market Opportunities: Wind Testing" in PR Newswire (September 22, 2011) **[5695]**, **[5961]**, **[23337]**, **[32027]**, **[32811]**
"Renewable Plants are Still On Valero Energy's Radar" in San Antonio Business Journal (Vol. 28, March 28, 2014, No. 7, pp. 10) **[5696]**, **[5962]**
RenewableTech Ventures **[45694]**
"A Renewed Sisterhood" in Women in Business (Vol. 64, Summer 2012, No. 2, pp. 6) **[14518]**, **[15888]**, **[22774]**, **[28798]**, **[35084]**, **[35845]**
RENOCanada-Bathroom and Kitchen Makeover Specialists **[2657]**
"Renren Partners With Recruit to Launch Social Wedding Services" in Benzinga.com (June 7, 2011) **[1992]**, **[11996]**, **[15889]**, **[21959]**, **[27031]**, **[27697]**, **[33243]**, **[35085]**
Rensselaer County Regional Chamber of Commerce (RCRCC) **[42655]**
Rensselaer Incubation Program **[42922]**
Rensselaer Polytechnic Institute - Lighting Research Center (LRC) **[31108]**
Rent-A-Center Franchising International, Inc. (RACFI) **[13856]**
Rent A Wreck **[13857]**
"Rent Check: New Lease on Life for Tenants" in Boston Business Journal (Vol. 31, July 29, 2011, No. 27, pp. 1) **[13819]**, **[32256]**
"Rent Hikes in South Florida Apartments Among Highest In Nation" in South Florida Business Journal (Vol. 34, July 4, 2014, No. 50, pp. 8) **[13820]**
"Rent Laws' Impact: Tenant Paradise or Return of the 'Bronx is Burning'?" in The New York Times (June 17, 2019) **[12900]**, **[25512]**
Rent-n-Roll Custom Wheels and Tires [15690]
Rental Management: Official Magazine of the American Rental Association **[13847]**
Rental Management--Who's Who in the Rental Industry **[13821]**
Rental Relocation Inc. (RRI) **[776]**, **[2314]**, **[20222]**
"Renters' Review ? Secret Shoppers Strike Again" in Rental Product News (Vol. 33, June 2011) **[13822]**, **[20489]**
Renton Chamber of Commerce **[46145]**
Renton Small Business Development Center **[46003]**
"Rep Contracts: Simple, Clear, Fair" in Agency Sales Magazine (Vol. 39, September-October 2009, No. 9, pp. 3) **[21105]**, **[29352]**, **[32603]**

Small Business Sourcebook • 42nd Edition 3321

Rep Master Index

"Rep Vs. Direct: Always an Interesting Story" in Agency Sales Magazine (Vol. 39, July 2009, No. 7, pp. 3) **[29353]**, **[31129]**, **[32604]**
"Repairing - Not Recycling - Is the First Step to Tackling E-Waste From Smartphones. Here's Why." in World Economic Forum (July 19, 2021) **[2784]**, **[13727]**, **[23338]**
Repertoire des Associations du Canada [1056]
Repertoire des bibliotheques canadiennes [8836]
RePlay [589]
RePlay Magazine **[589]**
The Report **[46503]**
Report on Business Corporate Database **[18462]**
"Report Card Gives Employees Health Grade" in Pittsburgh Business Times (Vol. 33, June 6, 2014, No. 47, pp. 7) **[25918]**
"Report Challenges Internet Providers' Advertised Speeds" in U.S. News & World Report (August 31, 2019) **[9214]**, **[11787]**
"Report: Grocery Stores Upcoming from Amazon" in Supermarket News (October 1, 2019) **[7769]**
"Report: McD's Pepsi Score Best With Young Hispanics" in Brandweek (Vol. 49, April 21, 2008, No. 16, pp. 8) **[14002]**, **[17102]**, **[24402]**, **[29354]**, **[30012]**, **[31787]**, **[31883]**, **[32257]**
Reporter [7912]
The Reporter [38358]
"Reportlinker.com Adds Report: GeoWeb and Local Internet Markets: 2008 Edition" in Entertainment Close-Up (September 11, 2009) **[9215]**, **[16459]**, **[26393]**, **[30013]**
"Reports of Banks' Revival were Greatly Exaggerated" in Barron's (Vol. 88, July 7, 2008, No. 27, pp. L14) **[6584]**, **[9767]**, **[24077]**, **[29355]**, **[30880]**, **[33244]**
Representative Jeff Mursau **[46581]**
"Reps Have Needs Too!" in Agency Sales Magazine (Vol. 39, December 2009, No. 11, pp. 16) **[20490]**, **[26645]**, **[29356]**, **[32605]**
"Reps Vs. Factory Direct Sales Force..Which Way to Go?" in Agency Sales Magazine (Vol. 39, September-October 2009, No. 9, pp. 28) **[26646]**, **[29357]**, **[32606]**
Republic Area Chamber of Commerce (RACC) **[41618]**
"Reputation and Identity in Family Firms: Current State and Gaps for Future Research" in Journal of Small Business Strategy (April 13, 2021). **[33704]**
"Reputation Warfare" in Harvard Business Review (Vol. 88, December 2010, No. 12, pp. 70) **[8668]**, **[12947]**, **[31788]**
"RES Stakes Its Claim in Area" in Philadelphia Business Journal (Vol. 28, January 29, 2010, No. 50, pp. 1) **[14821]**, **[19197]**, **[27698]**, **[33897]**
Rescue, Restore, Redecorate: Amy Howard's Guide to Refinishing Furniture and Accessories **[7244]**
Rescuecom **[3466]**
Research Centers Directory (RCD) **[32812]**
Research Foundation of AIMR [6734]
Research Foundation of Association for CFA Institute [6734]
Research Foundation of the Association for Investment Management and Research [6734]
Research Foundation of the Institute of Chartered Financial Analysts [6734]
"Research Highlights Disengaged Workforce" in Workforce Management (Vol. 88, November 16, 2009, No. 12, pp. 22) **[21106]**, **[22238]**, **[28799]**
Research and Innovative Technology Administration [47771]
Research Like a Pro: A Genealogist's Guide **[7370]**
"Research and Market Adds Report: Endpoint Security for Business" in Wireless News (October 26, 2009) **[14451]**, **[26394]**
"Research and Markets Adds Report: Cyprus: Convergence, Broadband and Internet Market" in Wireless News (September 4, 2009) **[9216]**, **[21107]**, **[27699]**, **[30014]**
"Research and Markets Adds Report: The U.S. Mobile Web Market" in Entertainment Close-Up (December 10, 2009) **[342]**, **[2785]**, **[9217]**, **[17739]**, **[17872]**, **[26395]**, **[30015]**
"Research and Markets: Directory of Solar Power Facilities, United States" in Benzinga.com (October 1, 2012) **[14939]**
"Research and Markets Offers Report on US Business Traveler's Green, New Technology Views" in Airline Industry Information (July 30, 2012) **[5697]**, **[5963]**, **[8452]**, **[19388]**, **[23339]**, **[34363]**
"Research: Mind the Gap" in Business Strategy Review (Vol. 21, Summer 2010, No. 2, pp. 84) **[20575]**, **[31130]**
Research Park & Enterprise Works **[39423]**
"Research Reports" in Barron's (Vol. 88, March 24, 2008, No. 12, pp. M10) **[6585]**, **[9768]**, **[20331]**, **[24078]**, **[28186]**, **[32813]**
"Research Reports" in Barron's (Vol. 90, August 23, 2010, No. 34, pp. M13) **[6586]**, **[9769]**, **[13043]**, **[32028]**, **[32258]**, **[32814]**
"Research Reports: How Analysts Size Up Companies" in Barron's (Vol. 88, June 30, 2008, No. 26, pp. M11) **[6587]**, **[9770]**, **[24079]**
Research Stations Division [17234]
"Research, Treatment to Expand" in Philadelphia Business Journal (Vol. 28, June 22, 2012, No. 19, pp. 1) **[4212]**, **[7154]**, **[21614]**, **[25919]**, **[31493]**, **[32029]**
Research Triangle Institute [26138]
Research Triangle Regional Partnership (RTRP) **[43250]**
Research USA, Inc. **[10700]**
Research Valley Funds, LLC [45455]
Réseau Canadien des Centres de Toxicologie [5479]
Reseau canadien de l'environment [5478], [13685], [23027]
Reseau canadien pour l'innovation en education [21310]
Reservation Economic Summit (RES) **[24846]**
Reservoir Research Center [16359]
Residence Inn by Marriott **[8513]**
"The Residential Appraisal Process Needs a New Standard" in Forbes (June 20, 2018) **[816]**, **[13273]**
The Residential Specialist **[13322]**, **[13605]**
Resilient Floor Covering Institute (RFCI) **[6826]**
The Resilient Founder: Lessons in Endurance from Startup Entrepreneurs **[22775]**
Resilient Tile Institute [6826]
"Resolve to Make the Most of Your Space With Professional Organizer Julie Morgenstern and Lowe's" in Marketwired (January 24, 2012) **[12845]**
Resolving Conflict (Onsite) **[17610]**
Resolving Real Estate Title Defects (Onsite) **[18498]**
Resort Data Processing **[8524]**
Resort Hotel Association (RHA) **[8352]**
Resort Timesharing Council of Canada [8343]
Resource Directory **[3733]**
Resource Efficient Agricultural Production - Canada (REAPC) **[23050]**
Resource and Environmental Management in Canada **[23340]**, **[24726]**
Resource Recycling Conference **[13746]**
"Resources Roundup: Diversity, Equity, and Inclusion" in Associations Now (May 9, 2022) **[30599]**
Responding to Conflict: Creating Resolution and Cooperation (Onsite) **[22065]**
Responding to Conflict: Strategies for Improved Communication **[17611]**
Responsible Distribution® Canada (CACD) **[20606]**
"The Responsible Entrepreneur: Four Game-Changing Archetypes for Founders, Leaders, and Impact Investors" **[22415]**, **[28248]**
Responsible Franchising for Entrepreneurs with Aaron Harper **[24459]**
Responsible Industry for a Sound Environment (RISE) **[12039]**
"A Responsive Approach to Organizational Misconduct: Rehabilitation, Reintegration, and the Reduction of Reoffense" in Business Ethics Quarterly (Vol. 24, July 2014, No. 3, pp. 343) **[18674]**, **[19575]**, **[23529]**
"Restaurant Customers React to First Encounters with a Robot Server" in Small Business Trends(February 8, 2023) **[14003]**, **[33245]**
Restaurant Hospitality **[8110]**, **[14048]**
Restaurant Loss Prevention & Security Association **[14097]**, **[14492]**
Restaurant Strong: The First Principles of Restaurant Outperformance and How to Make Them Yours **[14004]**
Restaurant Takeout and Delivery - US - May 2021 **[14039]**
RestaurantPoint East **[14098]**
RestaurantPoint West **[14099]**
Restaurants Canada **[2667]**, **[3834]**, **[4483]**, **[4879]**, **[6892]**, **[8091]**, **[13890]**, **[14308]**
"Restaurants Dish Up Meal Deals To Attract Customers" in Crain's Detroit Business (Vol. 24, October 6, 2008, No. 40, pp. 1) **[14005]**, **[21108]**, **[30016]**, **[31789]**, **[31884]**, **[34153]**
"Restaurateurs Follow High-End Apartments Into Kendall Square" in Boston Business Journal (Vol. 31, July 22, 2011, No. 26, pp. 3) **[13823]**, **[14006]**, **[33405]**
Reston Consulting Group Inc. (RCG) **[16329]**
Restoration Industry Association (RIA) **[31918]**
Restoration Industry Association International Restoration Convention & Industry Expo **[4830]**
Resume and Job Interview Mastery **[14314]**
"'Resume Mining' Services Can Save Time, Money" in HR Specialist (Vol. 8, September 2010, No. 9, pp. 7) **[14315]**, **[26647]**, **[27032]**, **[33246]**
Resume Writing (Onsite) **[21423]**
Retail Asset Protection Conference **[32357]**
"Retail in Austin Strong, Will Continue to Be" in Austin Business Journalinc. (Vol. 29, January 22, 2010, No. 46, pp. 1) **[5183]**, **[18304]**, **[20124]**, **[32259]**
Retail Bakers of America (RBA) **[1245]**
Retail Confectioners International (RCI) **[2539]**
Retail Credit Institute of America [4736], [4754]
The Retail & Dispensary Expo [5062]
"Retail Doesn't Cross Borders: Here's Why and What To Do About It" in Harvard Business Review (Vol. 90, April 2012, No. 4, pp. 104) **[27700]**, **[30801]**, **[32260]**
"Retail Happenings: Valentino Reopens Its O.C. Store with Big Focus on Menswear" in Los Angeles Times (October 30, 2019) **[6138]**
Retail Industry Leaders Association (RILA) **[32084]**
Retail Jewelers of America [9964]
"Retail Loyalty in the Digital Age is Focus of Retail Insights Southeast (RISE) Event" in GlobeNewswire (August 21, 2012) **[7770]**, **[32261]**
Retail Management Consultants **[20552]**
The Retail Market for Coffee Industry in the US - Market Research Report **[3197]**, **[7568]**
The Retail Market for Smartphones Industry in the US - Market Research Report **[2814]**
Retail Merchant Bakers of America [1245]
Retail Paint and Wallpaper Distributors of America [9029], [11873]
"Retail Product Management: Buying and Merchandising" **[21960]**, **[23530]**, **[32262]**
"Retail Remains Hot as More Stores Browse Around Houston" in Houston Business Journal (Vol. 44, January 17, 2014, No. 37, pp. 9A) **[13274]**, **[13550]**, **[13824]**, **[32263]**, **[33406]**
"The Retail Revolution: How Mail Order Changed Middle-Class Life" in BBC (May 8, 2019) **[10465]**
The Retail Revolution: How Wal-Mart Created a Brave New World of Business **[21109]**, **[32264]**
"Retail Slump Deflates Greater Cincinnati Development" in Business Courier (Vol. 24, February 28, 2008, No. 47, pp. 1) **[13551]**, **[18305]**, **[21110]**, **[32265]**
"Retail Tech Trend: The Future of Dry Cleaning" in Retail Info Systems (September 8, 2021) **[5241]**
Retail Tobacco Dealers of America [15693]
"Retailers at the Ready to Adopt Mobile Pay Options" in Dallas Business Journal (Vol. 35, August 24, 2012, No. 50, pp. 1) **[2786]**, **[20332]**, **[32266]**
"Retailers Report 'Shrinkage' - Disappearance of Inventory - on the Rise" in Arkansas Business (Vol. 26, September 28, 2009, No. 39, pp. 17) **[14452]**, **[19275]**, **[22348]**, **[32267]**
"Retailers Tap into War-Room Creativity of Employees" in Globe & Mail (March 12, 2007, pp. B1) **[30802]**, **[32268]**
"Retailers, Your Will, and More" in Agency Sales Magazine (Vol. 39, July 2009, No. 7, pp. 46) **[6044]**, **[18675]**, **[25920]**, **[32269]**, **[34872]**
"Retailing on a Budget: 8 Brick-and-Mortar Alternatives" in Business News Daily (February 21, 2023) **[34543]**
Rethinking Agriculture as a Climate Solution with Carlos Parea **[23437]**
"Rethinking the Organization" in Strategy & Leadership (Vol. 38, September-October 2010, No. 5, pp. 13-19) **[17740]**, **[20491]**, **[27943]**, **[28800]**
"Rethinking School: For the U.S. To Remain Competitive, Its Students Need To Learn Vastly More, Much More Quickly" in Harvard Business Review (Vol. 90, March 2012, No. 3, pp. 76) **[19917]**, **[21111]**, **[21615]**
Retire-At-Home Services [8280]
"Retirement Business Ideas: 12 Ideas for Getting Started After 50" in NewRetirement (Feb. 18, 2021) **[33072]**
"Retirement Plan Disclosures: Prepare Now for Fiduciary Rules" in Employee Benefit News (Vol. 25, November 1, 2011, No. 14, pp. 24) **[17343]**, **[25513]**, **[27033]**
"Retirement Plans in a Quandary" in Employee Benefit News (Vol. 25, December 1, 2011, No. 15, pp. 18) **[17344]**, **[24080]**, **[25514]**, **[27034]**
"Retiring Baby Boomers and Dissatisfied Gen-Xers Cause..Brain Drain" in Agency Sales Magazine (Vol. 39, November 2009, No. 10) **[19051]**, **[22239]**, **[26648]**, **[28801]**
Retro Fitness L.L.C. **[12462]**
"The Return of the Infomercial" in Canadian Business (Vol. 83, September 14, 2010, No. 15, pp. 19) **[343]**, **[21961]**, **[30017]**, **[32270]**
"Return to Wealth; Bank Strategy" in The Economist (Vol. 390, January 3, 2009, No. 8612, pp. 56) **[6588]**, **[9771]**, **[19052]**, **[19576]**, **[20333]**, **[21112]**, **[24081]**, **[28187]**
"Return to Wild for R.I. Oysters?" in Providence Business News (Vol. 29, August 25, 2014, No. 21, pp. 1) **[14007]**, **[23341]**
Rev1 Ventures **[43679]**
Rev3 Innovation Center **[39424]**
Revay and Associates Ltd. **[4336]**
Revel Partners **[42792]**
Revelations of Awareness **[11347]**
"Revenge of the Scorned Protege" in Canadian Business (Vol. 85, September 17, 2012, No. 14, pp. 48) **[6206]**, **[15614]**, **[18306]**, **[19918]**, **[31494]**

3322 Small Business Sourcebook • 42nd Edition

"ReVenture Plan Appears Close to Landing Key N.C. Legislative Deal" in Charlotte Business Journal (Vol. 25, July 9, 2010, No. 16, pp. 1) [4213], [5698], [5964], [23342], [25515]
Revere Chamber of Commerce (RCC) [40622]
"Reversal of Fortune" in Canadian Business (Vol. 85, June 11, 2012, No. 10, pp. 32) [18676], [25516], [27701], [27944]
"A Reverse-Innovation Playbook: Insights From a Company That Developed Products For Emerging Markets and Then Brought Them Back Home" in Harvard Business Review (Vol. 90, April 2012, No. 4, pp. 120) [19919], [22240], [27702], [29358], [30803]
The Review [42183]
Review of Business [24891]
Review of Business Information Systems (RBIS) [24780]
Review of Business Research (RBR) [24892]
Reviews in Medical Virology [32912]
"Revisiting Rep Coping Strategies" in Agency Sales Magazine (Vol. 39, December 2009, No. 11, pp. 32) [21616], [29359], [32607]
Revista Panamericana de Salud Pública/Pan American Journal (RPSP/PAJPH) [26048]
"Revive To Sell Women's Apparel in Downtown Space" in Memphis Business Journal (Vol. 33, February 3, 2012, No. 43, pp. 1) [3140], [13825], [14684]
"Reviving Entrepreneurship: Policy Decisions in 12 Areas Could Nurture - Or Cripple - America's Greatest Asset" in Harvard Business Review (Vol. 90, March 2012, No. 3, pp. 116) [22776], [24082], [25517], [25921], [27035], [27945], [28045], [34873]
Revolution [38195]
Revue fiscale canadienne [22], [15352]
Revue des Pharmaciens du Canada [5135]
Revue canadienne de sante publique [25994]
RevUp Capital [44484]
Rewiring Organziations for a Successful Digital Transformation [10491]
Rework [19053], [19577], [20492], [22777]
Rex Health Ventures (RHV) [43226]
Rexburg Chamber of Commerce [38938]
Reynolds Communication [17811]
Reynoldsburg Area Chamber of Commerce (RACC) [43560]
"RF Technologies Celebrates 25th Anniversary of Keeping Patients and Senior Care Residents Safe and Secure" in PR Newswire (August 1, 2012) [8264], [14453], [25922]
RFE Investment Partners [38101]
RG Digital Marketing [30220]
Rhinebeck Chamber of Commerce [42656]
Rhinelander Area Chamber of Commerce (RACC) [46504]
Rhode Island Association of Realtors (RIAR) [13114]
Rhode Island Beekeepers Association (RIBA) [1450]
Rhode Island Black Business Association (RIBBA) [44481]
Rhode Island Commerce Corp. (RIC) [44457], [47462]
Rhode Island Department of Environmental Management - Division of Agriculture and Resource Marketing [44458]
Rhode Island Department of Environmental Management - Office of Waste Management [47005]
Rhode Island Department of Environmental Management;Office of Waste Management [47005]
Rhode Island Department of Health - Center for Health Data and Analysis [47463]
Rhode Island Economic Development Corporation (RIPTAC) - Rhode Island Procurement Technical Assistance Center [44486]
Rhode Island Minority Business Enterprise (RI MBE) [44482]
Rhode Island Small Business Development Center [44452]
Rhode Island Small Business Development Center (RISBDC) [44453]
Rhode Island Small Business Development Center - Northern Rhode Island/Central Falls (RISBDC) [44454]
Rhode Island Small Business Development Center - State Office (RISBDC) [44455]
Rhode Island State Department of Revenue - Division of Municipal Finance [47464]
"RhodeMap for State Won't Focus on Finding a 'Big Fix'" in Providence Business News (Vol. 29, June 23, 2014, No. 12, pp. 4) [21113], [21617]
The Rhythm of Success: How an Immigrant Produced His Own American Dream [3413], [13655], [22778], [30380]
"R.I. Lags in Solar Incentives" in Providence Business News (Vol. 29, May 26, 2014, No. 8, pp. 1) [5699], [14940], [23343], [25047]
RIA International Restoration Convention & Industry Expo [4830]

"RIAC: Green Air Link to Ireland No Flight of Fancy" in Providence Business News (Vol. 29, May 26, 2014, No. 8, pp. 1) [7045], [19389], [27703]
Rialto Chamber of Commerce [37120]
Ribbit Capital [37468]
The Ribble Group [33666]
RIC Centre [46813]
Rice Alliance for Technology and Entrepreneurship [45546]
Rice King [14238]
Rice Lake Area Chamber of Commerce (RLACC) [46505]
"Rice & Roll Onigiri Food Truck to Tour Los Angeles Area" in Entertainment Close-Up (July 30, 2012) [3853], [7007], [27704], [30486]
Rice University - Center for Education [21753]
Rice University - Center for Languages and Intercultural Communication (CLIC) [21754]
Rice University - Ken Kennedy Institute for Information Technology (K2I) [3569]
Rich Dad, Poor Dad: What the Rich Teach Their Kids About Money-That the Poor and Middle Class Do Not! [9772], [24083]
Rich Dad's Increase Your Financial IQ: Get Smarter with Your Money [9773], [24084]
"Rich or Poor, Hospitals Must Work Together" in Crain's Chicago Business (Vol. 31, April 28, 2008, No. 17, pp. 22) [8960], [19920], [25048], [25923], [27331]
"Rich in Surprises and Secretes, There's a State Park Waiting for You" in The New York Times (July 29, 2019) [2520]
"Richard Faulk Covers Climate in Copenhagen" in Houston Business Journal (Vol. 40, December 25, 2009, No. 33, pp. 1) [5700], [5965], [18677], [23344]
Richard I. Anderson [3464]
Richardson Chamber of Commerce (RCC) [45332]
"Riches In Recreation" in Small Business Opportunities (March 2011) [12367], [24299]
Richfield Small Business Development Center [45612]
Richi Childhood Cancer Foundation [8802], [22978]
Richi Foundation [8802], [22978]
Richland Area Chamber of Commerce [43561]
Richlands Business Incubator (RBI) [45963]
Richmond Area Chamber of Commerce (RACC) [41619]
Richmond Chamber of Commerce [37121], [40083], [41620]
Richmond Chamber News [37122]
Richmond County Chamber of Commerce (RCCC) [43186]
Richmond Global Ventures (RGV) [35471]
Richmond Journal of Global Law and Business [18780]
Richmond Magazine [37123]
Richmond Sterling Inc. [4337]
Richmond View Ventures (RVV) [37469]
Richwood Area Chamber of Commerce (RACC) [46286]
Ricky's All Day Grill [14239]
"Ride Apps Uber, Lyft, Sidecar Hit Speed Bumps" in San Francisco Business Times (Vol. 28, January 24, 2014, No. 27, pp. 4) [10285], [15518], [18678], [27332]
Ride iQ: Peloton for Horses [35429]
"Ride-Share Field Has New Player" in Providence Business News (Vol. 29, April 21, 2014, No. 3, pp. 1) [10286], [15519], [21962], [25518]
"Ride-Share Programs Seem to Fit San Antonio's Future" in San Antonio Business Journal (Vol. 28, May 9, 2014, No. 13, pp. 6) [10287], [15520], [25049]
"Ride Sharing Market Size Worth Around US$344.4 Bn by 2030" in GlobeNewswire (September 28, 2021) [10288], [15521]
Rider University Center for Entrepreneurial Studies [42255]
Ridgecrest Chamber of Commerce [37124]
Ridgefield Chamber of Commerce [38071]
Ridgewood Businessman's Association [42184]
Ridgewood Capital Management L.L.C. [42220]
Ridgewood Chamber of Commerce (RCC) [42184]
Ridgway Area Business Directory [44288]
Ridgway-Elk County Chamber of Commerce [44289]
"Riding the Export Wave: How To Find a Good Distributor Overseas" in Inc. (January 2008, pp. 49) [8754], [25519], [27705]
"Riding Herd on Health Care" in Business Journal Portland (Vol. 30, February 7, 2014, No. 49, pp. 8) [25520], [25924], [27333]
"Riding High" in Small Business Opportunities (November 2008) [1526], [18307], [22779], [32271]
"Riding School Teaches Students to Master Selves While Bonding with Horses" in The Goshen News (December 27, 2018) [8322]
"Riding the Wave: Past Trends and Future Directions for Health IT Research" in MIS Quarterly (Vol. 36, September 2012, No. 3, pp. III) [25925], [26396]
Riedel Marketing Group (RMG) [4889], [8223], [12538], [14111]

Riegel and Emory Human Resource Research Center [22335]
Rifle Area Chamber of Commerce [37831]
Rifle: The Sporting Firearms Journal [855], [7839]
Riggins Chamber of Commerce [38940]
Right At Home Inc. (RAH) [8288]
"The Right Equipment and Premises to Start an Auto Repair Workshop" in AxleAddict (April 25, 2016) [14557]
"Right at Home China Celebrates 1 Year Anniversary as U.S. In-Home Senior Care Master Franchise" in Professional Service Close-Up (June 24, 2012) [24403], [26803], [27706]
Right Management Inc. [10569], [15630]
"The Right Remedy: Entrepreneur's Success Is a Matter of Life and Death" in Black Enterprise (Vol. 38, February 2008, No. 7, pp. 46) [20125], [22780], [25926], [32030], [32815], [35846]
"The Right Time for REITs" in Barron's (Vol. 88, July 14, 2008, No. 28, pp. 32) [6589], [9218], [9774], [13275], [16460], [21114], [21618], [24085]
"The Right and Wrong Reasons to Incorporate or Form an LLC" in Small Business Trends (February 8, 2016) [27191], [34544]
Rights Canada [1628]
Rim Country Regional Chamber of Commerce [36358]
"RIM Opts to Be Less Open" in Canadian Business (Vol. 83, October 12, 2010, No. 17, pp. 13) [2787], [20493], [30977]
"RIM Reinforces Claim as Top Dog by Expanding BlackBerry Service" in Globe & Mail (March 11, 2006, pp. B3) [25050], [26397], [31495], [32031]
"RIM Rocks Out: Billionaire Bosses Sponsor a Free Concert for Deserving Staff" in Canadian Business (Vol. 80, Winter 2007, No. 24) [17345], [22241]
"Rimfire Minerals Corporation: Jake Gold Project-Drilling Planned for 2007" in Marketwired (May 16, 2007) [30881], [31496], [32816]
"RIM's Demise Stems from Arrogance: It Didn't Have To Come To This" in Canadian Business (Vol. 85, August 13, 2012, No. 13, pp. 4) [2788], [20494], [28802]
"RIM's Options Story Under Fire" in Globe & Mail (March 16, 2007, pp. B1) [9775], [18679]
"Ringgold Computer Repair Owner Accused of Swindling Customers" in Chattanooga Times/Free Press (February 15, 2012) [3578], [19276], [23531]
Ringling College of Art and Design - Kimbrough Memorial Library [3378], [12326]
Ringling School of Art and Design [3378], [12326]
"RingMaster Ushering in Its 50th Year with a Return to Winston-Salem's Historic Reynolda Village" in Mid-America Jewelry News (October 1, 2019) [9980]
Ringwood Chamber of Commerce [42185]
Rio Grande Valley Angel Network (RGVAN) [35304], [45466]
Rio Grande Valley Partnership - Chamber of Commerce [45333]
Rio Linda/Elverta Chamber of Commerce [37125]
Rio Linda-Elverta Chamber of Commerce and Civic League [37125]
Rio Rancho Regional Chamber of Commerce (RRRCC) [42333]
Rio Salado Community College (RSCC) [36414]
Rio Vista Chamber of Commerce [37126]
Riordan Lewis & Haden (RLH) [37470]
"RipCode Founder Starts Private Equity Firm Vspeed Capital" in Dallas Business Journal (Vol. 35, September 9, 2012, No. 51, pp. 1) [19687], [20650], [29360]
Ripley County Chamber of Commerce [39601]
Ripley County Chamber of Commerce (RCCC) [41621]
Ripon Area Chamber of Commerce (RACC) [46506]
Ripon Chamber of Commerce [37127]
Ripple Effect Sales Management [8073]
"The Rise of Digital Currencies and Atlanta's Key Role" in Atlanta Business Chronicle (July 4, 2014, pp. 25A) [10037], [11788], [14745], [20334], [33736]
"The Rise, Fall, and Comeback of Victoria's Secret, America's Biggest Lingerie Retailer" in Business Insider (June 17, 2021) [10305]
"The Rise and Fall of Payless ShoeSource" in Business Insider (June 25, 2019) [14685]
"The Rise and Fall and Rise of the Old New Jewish Deli" in Haaretz (January 16, 2018) [4884], [42975]
"The Rise of Franchise Consultants as a Result of the Pandemic" in Forbes (Aug. 25, 2021) [24404]
"Rise Interactive, Internet Marketing Agency, Now Offers Social Media Services" in Marketwired (November 4, 2009) [9219], [16461], [17741], [21963], [30018]
Rise New York [42923]
"The Rise of Pompei" in Retail Merchandiser (Vol. 51, September-October 2011, No. 5, pp. 13) [10672], [17742], [20126], [30019], [32272], [32608]

"The Rise and Premiumization of Private Label: Sales Surpass $143bn, Notes Nielsen" in Food Navigator-USA (August 30, 2019) **[12804]**
"A Rise in Rental Units" in Philadelphia Business Journal (Vol. 30, October 7, 2011, No. 34, pp. 1) **[4214]**, **[13276]**, **[13552]**, **[13826]**, **[34154]**
"The Rise of the Supertemp: The Best Executive and Professional Jobs May No Longer Be Full-Time Gigs" in Harvard Business Review (Vol. 90, May 2012, No. 5, pp. 50) **[5444]**, **[6109]**, **[15645]**, **[18308]**, **[27036]**
"The Rise in Virtual Cooking Classes" in Integris Health (April 9, 2021) **[4470]**
"The Rise of 'Zero-Waste' Grocery Stores" in Smithsonian.com (February 15, 2019) **[5966]**, **[23345]**
"Rising Above Flood-Insurance Costs" in Providence Business News (Vol. 28, February 3, 2014, No. 44, pp. 1) **[8961]**, **[25521]**, **[27334]**
"Rising in the East; Research and Development" in The Economist (Vol. 390, January 3, 2009, No. 8612, pp. 47) **[8755]**, **[18309]**, **[21115]**, **[26398]**, **[27707]**, **[32817]**
The Rising Phoenix **[44290]**
Rising Tide **[37471]**
Risk-Based Corrective Action RBCA Applied at Petroleum Release Sites (Onsite) **[23069]**
Risk and Insurance Management Society (RIMS) **[8879]**
Risk Management Association (RMA) **[28079]**
"Risk Management: How Can Small Businesses Handle Crisis" in Full Scale (March 27, 2020) **[32389]**
"Risk Management: How Can You Protect Your Small Business?" in Medium (April 14, 2020) **[32390]**
Risk Management (Onsite) **[28414]**
The Risk Report **[8992]**
"Risk and Reward" in Canadian Business (Vol. 81, October 13, 2008, No. 17, pp. 21) **[6590]**, **[15541]**, **[21116]**, **[24086]**, **[27708]**
"The Risks and Rewards of Speaking Up: Managerial Responses to Employee Voice" in Academy of Management Journal (Vol. 55, August 1, 2012, No. 4, pp. 851) **[22242]**, **[28803]**
RIT Venture Creations [42925]
Rita's Italian Ice **[8633]**
Rittenhouse Ventures, LLC (RV) **[44448]**
Rittman Area Chamber of Commerce **[43562]**
Rituals for Virtual Meetings: Creative Ways to Engage People and Strengthen Relationships **[22243]**
"Ritz Kapalua Sells 93 Suites for $176M to Fund Renovation" in Commercial Property News (March 17, 2008) **[4215]**, **[8453]**, **[12430]**, **[14008]**
Ritzville Area Chamber of Commerce **[46146]**
"Ritzy Retail" in Time (September 17, 2012) **[21117]**, **[32273]**
River Biz **[43563]**
River Capital Inc. **[38811]**
River Country Chamber of Commerce of Newaygo County **[40999]**
River Falls Area Chamber of Commerce [46507]
River Falls Area Chamber of Commerce and Tourism Bureau **[46507]**
River Forest Kitchen (RFK) **[39425]**
River Heights Chamber of Commerce (RHCC) **[41295]**
River North Business Association (RNBA) **[33486]**, **[38977]**
River Valley Chamber of Commerce **[40301]**
River Valley Technology Center **[45747]**
"Riverfront Revival in Pawtucket?" in Providence Business News (Vol. 28, March 17, 2014, No. 50, pp. 1) **[910]**, **[4216]**, **[21118]**
Riverhead Chamber of Commerce **[42657]**
Riverside Center for Innovation (RCI) **[44417]**
Riverside Chamber of Commerce **[39295]**
Riverstone Energy Center [45964]
Riverton Area Chamber of Commerce [46617]
Riverton Chamber of Commerce (RCC) **[46617]**
RiverVest Venture Partners **[41662]**
"Riverview Food Truck Event Draws Huge Crowds" in Tampa Tribune (January 25, 2012) **[3854]**, **[7008]**, **[30487]**
RK Fischer & Associates **[46851]**
RK Ventures **[42793]**
"RM Sotheby's Botched the $22 Million Sale of the 'First Porshe: Because Bidders Couldn't Understand the Auctioneer's Dutch Accent" in Artnet News (August 19, 2019) **[1079]**
RMA Annual Statement Studies **[104]**, **[379]**, **[433]**, **[528]**, **[613]**, **[799]**, **[1115]**, **[1162]**, **[1275]**, **[1359]**, **[1395]**, **[1530]**, **[1686]**, **[1842]**, **[1881]**, **[2078]**, **[2499]**, **[2582]**, **[2644]**, **[2815]**, **[2887]**, **[2926]**, **[3158]**, **[3340]**, **[3651]**, **[3747]**, **[4268]**, **[4413]**, **[4446]**, **[4490]**, **[4666]**, **[5194]**, **[5246]**, **[5394]**, **[5450]**, **[6211]**, **[6833]**, **[6866]**, **[7055]**, **[7216]**, **[7484]**, **[7639]**, **[7795]**, **[7881]**, **[7927]**, **[8061]**, **[8216]**, **[8270]**, **[8472]**, **[8984]**, **[9987]**, **[10119]**, **[10290]**, **[10338]**, **[10369]**, **[10399]**, **[10449]**, **[10469]**, **[10489]**, **[10611]**, **[10739]**, **[10858]**, **[10928]**, **[11112]**, **[11128]**, **[11155]**, **[11270]**, **[11455]**, **[11525]**, **[11674]**, **[11866]**, **[11885]**, **[12001]**, **[12049]**, **[12284]**, **[12349]**, **[12444]**, **[12676]**, **[12764]**, **[12799]**, **[12986]**, **[13311]**, **[13680]**, **[13845]**, **[14040]**, **[14333]**, **[14486]**, **[14560]**, **[14688]**, **[14706]**, **[14722]**, **[14850]**, **[15111]**, **[15242]**, **[15525]**, **[15650]**, **[15799]**, **[16020]**, **[16090]**, **[16213]**, **[16264]**, **[16304]**, **[29449]**, **[32336]**, **[35494]**
RMA Information Center (RMA) **[4824]**
RMA's Annual Annual Risk Management Conference **[20365]**
RMJM **[31096]**
RNR Tire Express **[15690]**
"Road Map to Riches" in Small Business Opportunities (September 2010) **[16050]**, **[26748]**
"The Road Map for Scotiabank's Asian Expansion" in Globe & Mail (April 7, 2007, pp. B3) **[18310]**, **[19054]**, **[19578]**
The Road from Ruin: How to Revive Capitalism and Put America Back on Top **[21119]**, **[24727]**
Road & Track **[11461]**
"The Road Warrior: Pamela Rodgers Kept Rodgers Chevrolet On Course Despite Numerous Obstacles" in Black Enterprise (Vol. 44, June 2014, No. 10, pp. 76) **[11429]**, **[30381]**, **[35847]**
"Road Warriors: How To Survive Business Travel" in Crain's Detroit Business (Vol. 24, February 4, 2008, No. 5, pp. 11) **[19390]**, **[22781]**
Roads and Transportation Association of Canada [15509]
Roaming Hunger **[6961]**
Roane County Chamber of Commerce **[44796]**
Roanoke Regional Chamber of Commerce (RRCC) **[45894]**
Roanoke Regional Small Business Development Center (RRSBDC) **[45787]**
Roanoke Valley Chamber of Commerce (RVCC) **[43187]**
Roanoke Valley Chamber of Commerce **[45894]**
"Robai Aims to Commercialize Robot Arm for Manufacturers; Eyes Series A Funding" in Boston Business Journal (Vol. 34, July 4, 2014, No. 22, pp. 5) **[7155]**, **[29361]**, **[30804]**
Robbinex Inc. **[31618]**
Robbinsdale Chamber of Commerce **[41296]**
RobeCurls: From TikTok to Target **[34637]**
Robert & Carolyn Turner Center for Entrepreneurship **[39426]**
Robert Cizik Eye Clinic **[16320]**
Robert Guarino Owner and Head Coach of 5 Napkin Burger **[14081]**
Robert Morris Associates/Association of Lending and Credit Risk [28079]
Robert Newell Lighting Design (RNLD) **[31097]**
"Robert S. McNamara and the Evolution of Modern Management" in Harvard Business Review (Vol. 88, December 2010, No. 12, pp. 86) **[22782]**, **[28804]**
Robert W. Neill Cos, Jr. **[13621]**
Roberta - Crawford County Chamber of Commerce **[38776]**
Robertson County Chamber of Commerce **[44797]**
Robin Hood Ventures **[44443]**
Robin's Donuts **[1303]**
Robins Regional Chamber **[38777]**
Robins Regional Chamber of Commerce [38777]
Rochelle Chamber of Commerce **[39296]**
Rochester Angel Network (RAN) **[42387]**
Rochester Area Chamber of Commerce (RACC) **[41297]**
Rochester Business Alliance, Women''s Council [42601]
Rochester Business Journal **[42995]**
Rochester Institute of Technology - Albert J. Simone Center for Innovation and Entrepreneurship **[42971]**
Rochester Institute of Technology - Center for Integrated Manufacturing Studies (CIMS) **[29479]**
Rochester Institute of Technology - Melbert B. Cary, Jr. Graphic Arts Collection **[1734]**, **[2487]**, **[3379]**, **[16219]**
Rochester Institute of Technology - Venture Creations **[42924]**
Rochester Institute of Technology Venture Creations (RIT) **[42925]**
"Rock of Ages" in Barron's (Vol. 92, September 17, 2012, No. 38, pp. 23) **[9776]**, **[18311]**, **[21120]**
Rock Falls Chamber of Commerce (RFCC) **[39297]**
Rock Health **[37619]**
Rock Hill Area Small Business Development Center **[44509]**
Rock Hill Ventures, Inc. **[44354]**
Rock Hill Ventures, Inc. / Hillman Medical Ventures, Inc. [44354]
Rock Island County Illinois Genealogical Society Library **[7444]**
Rock Rapids Chamber of Commerce **[39788]**
Rock Rapids Community Affairs Corp. [39788]
Rock Springs Chamber of Commerce (RSCC) **[46618]**
Rock Valley Chamber of Commerce (RVCC) **[39789]**
Rock Valley College (RVC) **[39445]**
Rockdale Chamber of Commerce **[45334]**
"Rocket Lawyer Launches Tax Prep Tool for Small Business Owners" in Small Business Trends(January 22, 2023) **[34874]**
Rocket Ventures **[37472]**
RocketSpace **[37620]**
Rockford Chamber of Commerce **[39298]**
Rockford Chamber of Commerce (RCC) **[41000]**
Rockford Regional Chamber of Commerce Business Women's Council **[39299]**
Rockies Venture Club (RVC) **[35305]**, **[37927]**
Rockin'Baja Lobster **[14240]**
Rockland Economic Development Corporation (REDC) **[42826]**
Rockland SCORE **[42427]**
Rockland Small Business Development Center **[42413]**
Rockland-Thomaston Area Chamber **[40297]**
Rockland-Thomaston Area Chamber of Commerce [40297]
Rocklin Area Chamber of Commerce **[37128]**
Rockport-Fulton Chamber of Commerce (RFCC) **[45335]**
Rockstar Ready Tattoo Supplies [15322]
Rockton Chamber of Commerce [39311]
Rockville Area Chamber of Commerce **[38077]**
Rockville Centre Chamber of Commerce (RVCCC) **[42658]**
Rockville Chamber of Commerce (RCC) **[40413]**
Rockville Commercial Club [39595]
Rockville Innovation Center **[40467]**
Rockwall Area Chamber of Commerce **[45336]**
Rockwell City Chamber of Commerce [39790]
Rockwell City Chamber & Development **[39790]**
Rockwell City Chamber and Development Association [39790]
Rockwell's Grill & Bar **[14241]**
Rocky Hill Chamber of Commerce **[38072]**
Rocky Mount Area Chamber of Commerce (RMACC) **[43188]**
Rocky Mountain Agribusiness Association (RMAA) **[16970]**, **[37778]**
Rocky Mountain Business Travel Association (RMBTA) **[19315]**, **[37779]**
Rocky Mountain Center for Innovation and Technology **[37951]**
Rocky Mountain Chocolate Factory, Inc. (RMCF) **[2558]**
Rocky Mountain Dental Convention **[10881]**
Rocky Mountain Innosphere [37945]
Rocky Mountain Minority Supplier Development Council [37914]
Rocky Mountain Venture Capital Association (RMVCA) **[37780]**
Rocky River Chamber of Commerce (RRCC) **[43564]**
Rocky Rococo Pizza and Pasta **[12590]**
Roda Group **[37758]**
Rodale Inc. **[7683]**
Rodale Institute **[8170]**
Rodeway Inn **[8514]**
"Roger Hickel Contracting: Smoothing the Road for Owners" in Alaska Business Monthly (Vol. 27, October 2011, No. 10, pp. 114) **[4217]**, **[20495]**, **[22783]**
"Roger Rechler Played Major Role in Long Island's Evolution" in Commercial Property News (March 17, 2008) **[13553]**, **[18312]**, **[22784]**
Roger S. Peterson Marketing & Communications **[17812]**
Roger du Toit Architects Ltd. [934]
Rogers Area Chamber of Commerce [36495], [41246]
Rogers Chamber of Commerce [36495]
Rogers City Area Chamber of Commerce **[41001]**
Rogers-Dayton Chamber of Commerce [41246]
Rogers-Lowell Area Chamber of Commerce (RLACC) **[36495]**
"Rogue Caller Infiltrates Cincinnati Firms' Analyst Calls: 'Mr. CEO, Please Do Elaborate On Your Firm's Metrics'" in Business Courier (Vol. 24, February 28, 2008, No. 47, pp. 1) **[6591]**, **[9777]**, **[17743]**, **[17873]**, **[19055]**, **[19277]**
Rogue Community College Small Business Development Center (RCCSBDC) **[43915]**
Rogue River Area Chamber of Commerce **[44010]**
Rogue River Chamber of Commerce [44010]
Rogue Venture Partners **[44048]**
Rohnert Park Chamber of Commerce **[37129]**
"ROI for a Profitable Small Business and Bike Shop" in Bike Shop Girl blog (October 9, 2020) **[1527]**
"ROIonline Announces Streaming Video Products" in Marketing Weekly News (December 5, 2009, pp. 155) **[344]**, **[6207]**, **[9220]**, **[16462]**, **[21964]**, **[30020]**
"The Role of Advertising in Consumer Emotion Management" in International Journal of Advertising (Vol. 31, May 2012, No. 2, pp. 339) **[345]**, **[10673]**, **[30021]**
"The Role of Brand Image on Customer Loyalty" in Radiant Marketing Blog (April 4, 2020) **[17451]**

"The Role of Leadership In Successful International Mergers and Acquisitions: Why Renault-Nissan Succeeded and DaimlerChrysler-Mitsubishi Failed" in Human Resource Management (Vol. 51, May- June 2012, No. 3, pp. 433-456) **[9778]**, **[11430]**, **[27037]**, **[28805]**, **[29362]**, **[30600]**, **[31497]**
"Roll Your Own" in Business North Carolina (Vol. 28, March 2008, No. 3, pp. 66) **[15702]**, **[17103]**, **[31498]**
Rolla Area Chamber of Commerce **[41622]**
Roller Skating Association Convention and Trade Show **[14725]**
Roller Skating Association International (RSA) **[14718]**
Roller Skating Operators Association of America [14718]
Roller Skating Rink Operators Association [14718]
Rollerz **[14242]**
Rolling Meadows Chamber of Commerce (RMCC) **[39300]**
Rolston & Associates **[10555]**
"The Romance of Good Deeds: A Business with a Cause Can Do Good in the World" in Inc. (Volume 32, December 2010, No. 10, pp. 47) **[22785]**, **[23653]**, **[34364]**
Romanian-U.S. Business Council (AMRO) **[27428]**
Rome Area Chamber of Commerce **[42659]**
Romeo-Washington Chamber of Commerce **[40928]**
Romeoville Area Chamber of Commerce **[39301]**
Romulus Capital (RC) **[40724]**
Ronnia Langston Foundation, Inc. (RLF) **[36005]**
Ronzio Pizza **[14243]**
Roof Coatings Manufacturers Association (RCMA) **[14322]**
Roof Consultants Institute International Convention and Trade Show **[14338]**
Roof Tile Institute [14324]
Roofing Canada **[14323]**
Roofing Contractor **[4289]**, **[8851]**
Roofing Contractors Association of Texas Expo **[14339]**
"The Roofing Industry Continues Its Upward Slope" in Forbes (June 3, 2018) **[14332]**
Roofing Materials Guide [14329]
Roofing Materials Science & Technology **[14341]**
Roosevelt County Chamber of Commerce **[42334]**
ROOSTER Magazine **[5046]**
Roosters Men's Grooming Center [7896]
Roosters MGC International LLC **[7896]**
Rooter-Man **[14641]**
The Roots of Success: Transforming Landscapes and Lives with Steve Griggs **[10129]**
Rootstown Area Chamber of Commerce **[43565]**
Rosamond Chamber of Commerce **[37130]**
Roscoe Chamber of Commerce **[42660]**
Roscoe Chamber of Commerce [39311]
Rose & Crangle Ltd. **[2315]**, **[2391]**, **[6711]**, **[10556]**, **[20223]**, **[29029]**, **[33689]**
Rose-Hulman Ventures **[39662]**
"Rose Pest Solutions Acquires Indiana Pest Control" in PCTonline (November 18, 2019) **[12046]**, **[31499]**
Rose State College - Oklahoma Small Business Development Center - Procurement Center **[43715]**
Rose State College Small Business Development Center (SBDC) **[43716]**
Rose Tech Ventures LLC (RTV) **[42794]**
Roseburg Area Chamber of Commerce and Visitors Center **[44011]**
Roselle Chamber Business News **[39302]**
Roselle Chamber of Commerce and Industry **[39303]**
Rosemead Chamber of Commerce (RCC) **[37131]**
Rosemead Reports **[37132]**
Roser Ventures LLC **[37928]**
Rosetta Stone Associates **[15957]**
Roseville Area Chamber of Commerce [37133]
Roseville Chamber of Commerce **[37133]**
Roseville Insight **[37134]**
"Roseville Investing Big in Downtown" in Sacramento Business Journal (Vol. 28, September 2, 2011, No. 27, pp. 1) **[17104]**, **[33407]**
Rosevine Winery, LLC **[15061]**
"Rosewood Site Faces Big Cleanup Before Stevenson Can Expand" in Baltimore Business Journal (Vol. 27, February 6, 2010, No. 40, pp. 1) **[5701]**, **[5967]**, **[19688]**, **[21619]**, **[23346]**, **[25051]**
The Rosie Network **[33487]**
Ross County Genealogical Society (RCGS) **[7445]**
Ross & McBride Library **[34957]**
"Ross: There's Still Money In the Auto Industry" in Crain's Detroit Business (Vol. 24, January 28, 2008, No. 4, pp. 12) **[11431]**, **[29363]**
Ross University School of Veterinary Medicine - Stanley Mark Dennis Veterinary Library **[717]**
Roswell Chamber of Commerce **[42335]**
Roswell Small Business Development Center **[42284]**
Rotary International Convention **[23567]**
Rotelli Pizza & Pasta **[12591]**

Rothman Consulting Group Inc. **[14886]**
The Rothschild Image **[8675]**, **[12959]**
"Rough Headwinds" in Boston Business Journal (Vol. 30, November 12, 2010, No. 42, pp. 1) **[5702]**, **[5968]**, **[23347]**
Rough and Ready Chamber of Commerce **[37135]**
"Rough Trade: the Canada-Chile Free Trade Agreement" in Canadian Business (Vol. 79, September 11, 2006, No. 18, pp. 31) **[8756]**, **[21121]**, **[27709]**
Round Lake Area Chamber of Commerce and Industry **[39304]**
Round Rock Chamber of Commerce (RRCC) **[45337]**
Round13 Capital **[46803]**
"Roundy's Pushing Chicago Expansion" in Milwaukee Business Journal (Vol. 27, February 12, 2010, No. 20, pp. A1) **[7771]**, **[18313]**, **[21122]**, **[33408]**
Route 422 Business Advisor **[44291]**
"Route Optimization Impacts the Bottom Line" in Contractor (Vol. 56, November 2009, No. 11, pp. 48) **[511]**, **[12656]**, **[14822]**, **[19391]**, **[33898]**
Rover.com **[12253]**
Rowan College at Burlington County (RCBC) **[42256]**
Rowan County Chamber of Commerce **[43189]**
Rowlett Chamber of Commerce **[45338]**
Roxboro Area Chamber of Commerce (RACC) **[43190]**
Roxbury Area Chamber of Commerce (RACC) **[42186]**
"Roy MacDowell Jr. Version 2.0" in Boston Business Journal (Vol. 31, June 10, 2011, No. 20, pp. 1) **[13554]**, **[33030]**
Roy-Riverdale Chamber of Commerce [45642]
Roy Rogers Restaurants (RR) **[14244]**
Royal Academy of Dance (RAD) **[4848]**
Royal Academy of Dancing, United States Branch [4848]
Royal Architectural Institute of Canada [862]
Royal Canadian Numismatic Association [3217]
Royal Canadian Numismatic Association Library [3261]
"Royal Dutch's Grip Firm on Shell" in Globe & Mail (March 19, 2007, pp. B1) **[29364]**, **[31500]**
Royal Gorge Chamber Alliance (RGCA) **[37895]**
Royal LePage Real Estate Services Ltd. **[13628]**
Royal Maid Service **[5096]**
Royal Oak Chamber of Commerce (ROCC) **[41002]**
Royal Oak Foundation (ROF) **[865]**
Royal Philatelic Society of Canada [3228]
Roynat Ventures / Roynat Capital Corp. **[46804]**
Royse City Chamber of Commerce **[45339]**
RPA Canada [45], [1741], [15362]
"RPA Preps for Building Radiant Conference, Show" in Contractor (Vol. 57, January 2010, No. 1, pp. 5) **[512]**, **[8962]**, **[15890]**, **[18680]**, **[27335]**, **[35086]**
RPM Ventures (RPM) **[41056]**
RSA Capital **[46552]**
RSA Convention and Trade Show [14725]
RSC Business Group Inc. **[10557]**
RS+K **[35140]**
RSVP Publications, Inc. (RSVP) **[394]**
"RT Seeking Ways to Finance Expansion" in Sacramento Business Journal (Vol. 28, July 29, 2011, No. 22, pp. 1) **[4218]**, **[19392]**, **[25052]**
RTI International **[26138]**
RTNDA International Conference & Exhibition/Radio-Television News Directors Association **[13050]**, **[15619]**
RTO World [13850]
RTO World The National Rent-to-Own Convention and Trade Show **[13850]**
RTP Capital Associates, Inc. **[43227]**
RTP Ventures (RTP) **[42795]**
"Rubicon Is the Latest Small Real Estate Firm to Break Out" in Dallas Business Journal (Vol. 35, June 29, 2012, No. 42, pp. 1) **[12901]**, **[13277]**
Rubicon Venture Capital **[37473]**
"Rudy's Tortillas Wraps Up Expansion Plan in Carrollton" in Dallas Business Journal (Vol. 35, August 31, 2012, No. 51, pp. 1) **[4219]**, **[18314]**, **[19198]**, **[23654]**, **[26649]**
Ruf & Associates, L.L.C. **[18747]**
Ruffin's Pet Centres **[12242]**
Rug News and Design **[6837]**
Ruidoso Valley Chamber of Commerce (RVCC) **[42336]**
"Rule of the Masses: Reinventing Fashion Via Crowdsourcing" in WWD (Vol. 200, July 26, 2010, No. 17, pp. 1) **[3048]**, **[3141]**, **[6139]**, **[18315]**, **[20496]**, **[30022]**, **[30805]**, **[32274]**
"Run Your Business Like Clockwork" in Small Business Trends(October 24, 2022) **[28806]**
Runa Capital **[37474]**
Running a Family-Owned Business: Challenges and Benefits **[23655]**
Running a Food Truck for Dummies **[7009]**
Running an RV Park: Tips, Benefits and Business Models **[2521]**
Running Springs Area Chamber of Commerce **[37136]**
"Running Your Business: What Do You Need to Do to Retain Good Corporate Standing?" in Legal Zoom (March 28, 2023) **[18681]**, **[34875]**

Runway Innovation Hub **[37621]**
Runway Startup Postdoc Program **[42926]**
Rural Alberta Business Centres (RABC) **[46656]**
The Rural Development Center **[40468]**
"Rural Employment Trends in Recession and Recovery" **[21123]**, **[34155]**
Rural Enterprises Inc. [43872], [47296]
Rural Enterprises Of Oklahoma, Inc [43872], [47296]
"Rural Entrepreneurship Success Factors: An Empirical Investigation in an Emerging Market" in Journal of Small Business Strategy (Vol. 31, December 1, 2021, No. 4, pp. 5-19) **[22786]**, **[33595]**
Rush County Chamber of Commerce **[39602]**
Rusk Chamber of Commerce **[45340]**
Rusk County Chamber of Commerce [45205]
Russell Area Chamber of Commerce (RACC) **[39951]**
Russell County Chamber of Commerce **[40084]**
Russell County Historical Society & Genealogy Society Library (RCHS) **[7446]**
Russell Reynolds Associates Inc., Library **[6731]**
Russellville Area Chamber of Commerce [36496]
Russellville Chamber of Commerce **[36496]**
"Russia: Uncle Volodya's Flagging Christmas Spirit" in The Economist (Vol. 390, January 3, 2009, No. 8612, pp. 22) **[8757]**, **[11432]**, **[21124]**, **[25522]**, **[27710]**, **[29365]**
Russian Partners **[42796]**
"Russian Renaissance" in Chicago Tribune (September 22, 2008) **[8758]**, **[15023]**, **[17105]**, **[27711]**, **[29366]**
Russian River Chamber of Commerce **[37137]**
"Rust Belt No More: The Demise of Manufacturing" in Crain's Chicago Business (Vol. 31, March 31, 2008, No. 13, pp. 52) **[21125]**, **[29367]**
Ruston - Lincoln Chamber of Commerce **[40187]**
Rutgers Business School - Center for Urban Entrepreneurship & Economic Development (CUEED) **[42257]**
Rutgers Camden Technology Campus (RCTC) **[42244]**
Rutgers EcoComplex **[42245]**
Rutgers Food Innovation Center (RFIC) **[42246]**
Rutgers-Newark Small Business Development Center (RNSBDC) **[42041]**
Rutgers, The State University of New Jersey - EcoComplex Business Incubator **[42247]**
Rutgers, The State University of New Jersey - Institute for Health, Health Care Policy and Aging Research **[26139]**
Rutgers, The State University of New Jersey - Rutgers School of Business - Camden - New Jersey Small Business Development Center (NJ SBDC) **[42042]**
Rutgers University - Center of Alcohol Studies [34702]
Rutgers University - Center of Alcohol & Substance Use Studies (CAS) **[34702]**
Rutgers University - Edward J. Bloustein School of Planning and Public Policy - Rutgers Regional Report/State Data Center **[47465]**
Rutgers University - Institute for Health, Health Care Policy, and Aging Research - Division on Aging - AIDS Policy Research Group (ARG) **[26140]**
Rutgers University - Institute of Jazz Studies (IJS) **[11255]**
Rutgers University - Office of Information Technology - Camden Computing Services **[47466]**
Rutherford Chamber of Commerce **[42187]**
Rutherford County Chamber of Commerce **[44798]**
RV Dealers Convention/Expo [15774]
RV Park Model - 20 Ways RV Park Owners Make Money **[2522]**
"RV Sales Have Slumped. Here's Why the Stocks Have Rallied" in Barron's (August 20, 2019) **[13675]**
RVDA Online Membership Directory & Resource Guide (Recreation vehicles) **[13676]**
RVDA, The National RV Dealers Association (RVDA) **[13673]**
RVX: The RV Experience [13683]
"Ryan Gilbert Wants SBA To Mean Speedy Business Administration" in Philadelphia Business Journal (Vol. 33, May 9, 2014, No. 13, pp. 8) **[21965]**, **[25053]**, **[28188]**
Ryan Thorman CEO and Co-Founder of Bango Bowls **[14082]**
Ryan's Pet Food Inc. **[12124]**, **[12158]**, **[12243]**
"Ryder's Shock Absorbers Are In Place" in Barron's (Vol. 88, March 24, 2008, No. 12, pp. 19) **[6592]**, **[9779]**, **[16081]**, **[24087]**
Rye Chamber of Commerce **[42661]**
Rye Merchants Association [42661]
Ryerson Angel Network (RAN) **[46805]**
Ryerson University - The DMZ **[46832]**

S

S-Corp Beginner's Guide 2023 **[32410]**
"S Corporation: Lower Taxes but Limited Growth Potential" in NerdWallet (Oct. 27, 2020) **[32411]**

S-FX.com Small Business Solutions [19148]
S & S Office Solutions Inc. (SSOS) [31013], [31098]
S3 Ventures [45467]
"S.A. Chasing Tesla, Other Auto-Industry Firms" in San Antonio Business Journal (Vol. 28, April 4, 2014, No. 8, pp. 7) [29368], [33409]
"S.A. Officials Hunting for Prospects in California" in San Antonio Business Journal (Vol. 26, August 17, 2012, No. 29, pp. 1) [19199], [21126], [25523], [34876]
Saba Investmetnts, LLC [45468]
"SABER Research Institute's Steve Nivin" in San Antonio Business Journal (Vol. 28, April 4, 2014, No. 8, pp. 6) [9221], [22416], [32032]
Sabetha Chamber of Commerce [39952]
SABEW Annual Conference [5344]
SABEWNYC Fall Conference [5344]
"Sabia Signals a Bold, New Course for BCE" in Globe & Mail (February 2, 2006, pp. B1) [18682], [19579]
Sabinal Chamber of Commerce [45341]
Sabine Parish Chamber of Commerce [40188]
The SABLE Accelerator [37622]
"Sabra Food Truck Gives Canadians a New Reason to Take a Dip This Summer" in America's Intelligence Wire (August 1, 2012) [3855], [7010], [30488]
Sac City Chamber of Commerce [39722]
SACCNY Membership Directory [27730]
Sacramento Area Council of Governments (SACOG) [47467]
Sacramento Black Chamber of Commerce (SBCC) [37138]
Sacramento Business Journal [37695]
"Sacramento Businesses Must Cut Water Use 20 Percent" in Sacramento Business Journal (Vol. 30, January 17, 2014, No. 47, pp. 5) [7526], [8454], [14009], [23348], [25524]
Sacramento Hispanic Chamber of Commerce (SHCC) [37139]
Sacramento Metropolitan Chamber of Commerce [37140]
Sacramento State Census Data Center - Department of Finance [46941]
Sacramento Valley Better Business Bureau [36713]
"Sacred Success: A Course in Financial Miracles" [9780], [24088], [35848]
Saddle & Bridle: Oldest Name In Show Horse Magazines [8324]
Saddleback College [37660]
SAE Brake Colloquium [1123]
SAE International (SAE) [14540]
SAE International WCX World Congress Experience [1127]
Sae Kitchen [37623]
SAE Noise and Vibration Conference and Exhibition [1126]
SAE Thermal Management Systems Symposium [539]
Safe Communities Canada [25687]
Safe Kids Canada [25687]
"Safelite Auto-Glass Replacement Practice Challenged by Glass-Repair Resin Maker" in The Columbus Dispatch (February 13, 2018) [2571], [7495]
"Safety in 2020: Here's What the Stats Show" in BeSafe Technologies (December 4, 2019) [30947]
Safety Compliance Alert [35956]
Safety Harbor Chamber of Commerce (SHCC) [38491]
Safety Management Services (SMS) [25626], [35969]
Safety Net [6593], [9781], [24089]
"A Safety Net in Need of Repair" in The Economist (Vol. 390, January 3, 2009, No. 8612, pp. 33) [8963], [17346], [21127], [25054], [26650], [27336]
"Safety Products Firm Expanding" in Memphis Business Journal (Vol. 33, March 16, 2012, No. 49, pp. 1) [8759], [12981], [18316], [19200], [26651]
Saffire Systems & Development Inc. [3787]
Safford/Graham County Chamber of Commerce [36336]
Sag Harbor Chamber of Commerce [42662]
"Sage Advice" in Canadian Business (Vol. 80, October 22, 2007, No. 21, pp. 70) [22787], [24728], [30023], [34365]
Sage Property & Casualty [9002]
Saginaw Area Chamber of Commerce (SACC) [45342]
Saginaw County Chamber of Commerce [41003]
Saginaw County Chamber of Commerce Business Advocate [41004]
"SAIC To Be Honored For Supporting Veteran-Owned Businesses" in News Bites US (June 13, 2012) [16589], [25157]
Sail Capital Partners [37475]
St. Albans Area Chamber of Commerce [46287]
St. Charles Area Chamber of Commerce [39305]
St. Charles Chamber of Commerce [39305]
St. Charles Chamber of Commerce [41568]
St. Charles County Business Record [41705]
St. Charles County Economic Development Center (EDC) [41688]

St. Clair Area Chamber of Commerce [41623]
St. Clair Shores Public Library - Local History Center [7447]
St. Cloud Area Chamber of Commerce (SCACC) [41298]
St. Cloud Area Chamber of Commerce [38492]
St. Cloud Greater Osceola Chamber of Commerce [38492]
St. Cloud State University - Learning Resources Services - University Archives and Special Collections [1003]
St. Croix Valley Business Incubator (SCVBI) [46571]
St. Croix Valley Chamber of Commerce [40302]
Saint Francis University Small Business Development Center (SBDC) [44102]
Ste. Genevieve Chamber of Commerce [41624]
St. George Area Chamber of Commerce (SGACC) [45645]
St. Helena Chamber of Commerce [37141]
St. Helens-Scappoose Chamber of Commerce [44018]
St. Ignace Chamber of Commerce [41005]
St. James Chamber of Commerce [41625], [42663]
St. John Chamber of Commerce (SJCOC) [39603]
St. John Valley Chamber of Commerce [40303]
St. Johns Area Chamber of Commerce [40894]
St. Johns River Community College [38600]
St. John's River State College (SJRSC) [38600]
St. Joseph Area Chamber of Commerce [41299]
St. Joseph Chamber of Commerce [41626]
St. Joseph County Chamber [39606]
St. Joseph's University - Academy of Food Marketing - Campbell Library [15071]
St. Joseph's University - Erivan K. Haub School of Business - Academy of Food Marketing [7825]
St. Lawrence County Chamber of Commerce [42664]
St. Louis Arch Angels [41663]
St. Louis Bar & Grill [14245]
"St. Louis Blues Asking Price Out of Their League" in Saint Louis Business Journal (Vol. 32, September 23, 2011, No. 4, pp. 1) [15182], [20053]
St. Louis Boat Sports Show [10624]
St. Louis Builders Home & Garden Show [7651], [10257]
Saint Louis Business Journal [41707]
St. Louis Business Journal [41706]
Saint Louis Business Travel Association (STLBTA) [19316]
St. Louis Chamber [40919]
St. Louis Community College Institute for Continuing Education (STLCC CE) [41698]
"St. Louis Convention Business 'Fully Recovered'" in St. Louis Business Journal (Vol. 32, July 13, 2012, No. 47, pp. 1) [8156], [15891], [35087]
St. Louis County Economic Council [41667]
"St. Louis Digital Marketing Agency Publishes Free SEO Audit Tool" in Internet Wire (February 16, 2012) [9222], [16463], [30024]
St. Louis Economic Development Partnership (STLP) [41667]
St. Louis Enterprise Centers - Midtown [41689]
St. Louis Genealogical Society (StLGS) [7448]
"St. Louis Lending Tumbles $10 Billion Since '08" in Saint Louis Business Journal (Vol. 31, August 26, 2011, No. 53, pp. 1) [21128], [28189], [34156]
"St. Louis Restaurants Rewrite Menu to Get Financing" in Saint Louis Business Journal (Vol. 31, August 19, 2011, No. 52, pp. 1) [14010], [28190]
St. Louis University - Jefferson Smurfit Center for Entrepreneurial Studies [35463]
St. Louis University - John Cook School of Business - Center for Entrepreneurship [35463]
St. Louis University - Richard A. Chaifetz School of Business - Chaifetz Center for Entrepreneurship [35463]
St. Lucie County [38591]
St. Lucie County Chamber of Commerce [38493]
"St. Luke's Gets Shot in the Arm From Outpatient Services" in Saint Louis Business Journal (Vol. 31, August 19, 2011, No. 52, pp. 1) [25927], [33247]
St. Maries Chamber of Commerce [38939]
St. Marys Area Chamber of Commerce (SMACC) [44292]
St. Mary's County Chamber of Commerce Inc. [40414]
St. Mary's University (SMUEC) - Entrepreneurship Centre [46748]
St. Norbert Arts Centre Archives (SNAC) [1004], [4867], [11237], [11302]
Saint Paul Area Chamber of Commerce (SPACC) [41300]
Saint Peter Area Chamber of Commerce [41301]
St. Peters Chamber of Commerce [41568]
St. Petersburg Area Chamber of Commerce [38494]
The St. Simons Corporation (ETF) [15454]
St. Simons Island Chamber of Commerce [38698]
St. Tammany Chamber of Commerce [40189]
St. Tammany West Chamber of Commerce [40189]
St. Thomas - St. John Chamber of Commerce (STSJCC) [46650]

Saint Vincent College Small Business Development Center (SVC) [44103]
Saints Ventures [37476]
SAIR Collective [30652]
"Salad Creations To Open 2nd Location" in Crain's Detroit Business (Vol. 24, March 3, 2008, No. 9, pp. 26) [14011], [18317], [24405]
Salado Chamber of Commerce [45343]
Saladworks L.L.C. [14265]
Salamanca Area Chamber of Commerce [42671]
"Sale of Owings Mills Solo Cup Plant Pending" in Boston Business Journal (Vol. 29, June 17, 2011, No. 6, pp. 1) [13555], [19689], [29369], [33031]
Salem Area Chamber of Commerce (SACC) [41627], [43566], [44012]
Salem Area Chamber of Commerce Directory [43567]
The Salem Chamber [43568]
Salem Chamber of Commerce [40623]
Salem Chamber of Commerce [42013]
Salem County Chamber of Commerce [42188]
Salem Update [43568]
"Sales and the Absolute Power of Information" in Agency Sales Magazine (Vol. 39, July 2009, No. 7, pp. 16) [19921], [32609]
The Sales And Use Tax Seminar (Onsite) [16772]
The Sales Association [32433]
The Sales Bible [32610]
Sales with Generative AI [32685]
Sales Management Association [32434]
The Sales Manager's Guide to Greatness: Ten Essential Strategies for Leading Your Team to the Top [9999], [32611]
Sales and Marketing Communications Associates Inc. [30221], [32696]
Sales and Marketing Executives International (SMEI) [32435]
Sales Schema, LLC [42985]
"Sales Training Programs to Help Your Team Close More Deals" in Business News Daily (March 6, 2023) [32612]
"Sales of Unregistered Securities Are a Growing Problem That's Harming Investors — and the Industry" in Investment News (April 13, 2019) [9782]
Sales and Use Tax 2012 Workshop (Onsite) [28415]
Sales and Use Tax Workshop (Onsite) [28415]
"Sales of What's Under Feet Add Up Fast" in Pet Product News (Vol. 66, September 2012, No. 9, pp. S8) [5703], [5969], [12224], [23349], [29370], [30025]
Salina Area Chamber of Commerce (SACC) [39953]
Salinas Area Chamber of Commerce [37143]
Salinas Valley Chamber Business Journal [37142]
Salinas Valley Chamber of Commerce [37143]
Saline Area Chamber of Commerce (SACC) [41006]
Salisbury Area Chamber of Commerce (SACC) [40415]
Salisbury Business Journal [40416]
Salisbury Chamber of Commerce [38078]
"Sallie Krawcheck: Women Are the Untapped Recipe for Business Success" in Idaho Business Review (August 20, 2014) [35849]
Sallisaw Chamber of Commerce [43802]
Sallisaw Improvement Corporation Business Incubator [43873]
"Sally Beauty: What the Company Must Do Now" in Forbes (October 21, 2018) [1391]
"Sally Beauty's Plans Highlight Hair Color" in BizWomen (February 7, 2019) [1392]
Salmon Area Chamber of Commerce [38941]
Salmon River Chamber of Commerce [38940]
Salmon Valley Business and Innovation Center (SVBIC) [38953]
Salmon Valley Chamber of Commerce [38941]
"Salmon's Gem Air Wants Grant For Year-round Boise Flight" in Idaho Business Review (September 3, 2014) [15757], [19393], [19922], [25055]
Salon MCEE Expo [12680]
Salsarita's Fresh Cantina [14246]
Salsarita's Fresh Mexican Grill [14246]
Salt Lake Chamber (SLACC) [45646]
Salt Lake Community College-Redwood Road Campus (SLCC) [45686]
Salt Water Fly Rodders of America [1229], [1235]
Saltwater Tattoo Supply [15333]
Salus University - Gerard Cottet Library [16317]
"Salvation Army Prepares to Break Ground on South Mountain Community Center" in The Business Journal - Serving Phoenix and the Valley of the Sun (Vol. 28, September 12, 2008, No. 53, pp. 1) [4220], [13556], [34366]
Sam Hart Chef and Owner of Counter [14083]
Sam Houston State University Small Business Development Center (SHSU SBDC) [44936]
S.A.M. Singapore Math [16169]
"Same-Day Delivery's Second Act" in Inc. (Vol. 36, March 2014, No. 2, pp. 87) [7046], [11789], [21966], [32275]

Sammy J's Grill & Bar [14247]
Sample Employee Handbook [44293]
Samsung Next LLC [42927]
Samsung Ventures America (SVA) [37759]
"*Samsung's Metamorphosis in Austin*" in *Austin Business Journal* (Vol. 31, May 20, 2011, No. 11, pp. 1) [2789], [3734], [18318], [19580], [26399], [26652], [30978]
San Angelo Chamber of Commerce (SACC) [45344]
San Anselmo Chamber of Commerce (SACC) [37144]
San Antonio Angel Network [45429]
San Antonio Hispanic Chamber of Commerce (SAHCC) [45345]
"*San Antonio Ice Rink to Open Earlier than Expected at Travis Park with Free Skating*" in *My San Antonio* (November 23, 2019) [14721]
"*San Antonio Luring Biotech Firms With Venture Capital*" in *San Antonio Business Journal* (Vol. 28, August 8, 2014, No. 26, pp. 6) [10849], [19201], [35381]
San Antonio Minority Business Development Enterprise [45422]
"*San Antonio Museum of Art in the Center of New Urban Revival*" in *San Antonio Business Journal* (Vol. 28, July 11, 2014, No. 22, pp. 8) [21129]
"*San Antonio Office Market: What a Difference a Year Makes*" in *San Antonio Business Journal* (Vol. 28, August 8, 2014, No. 26, pp. 8) [4221], [13557], [21130]
"*San Antonio Researchers Develop New Laser-Based Imaging System*" in *San Antonio Business Journal* (Vol. 26, August 24, 2012, No. 30, pp. 1) [10850], [21620], [25928], [32033], [32818]
San Antonio Small Business Development Center (SA SBDC) [44937]
San Antonio Women's Chamber of Commerce (SAWCC) [45346]
"*San Antonio's Alamo Iron Works Is On the Prowl for Acquisitions*" in *San Antonio Business Journal* (Vol. 26, August 3, 2012, No. 27, pp. 1) [10440], [19690], [31501]
"*San Antonio's Craft-Brewing Industry is Gearing Up to Make More Suds*" in *San Antonio Business Journal* (Vol. 26, August 3, 2012, No. 27, pp. 1) [1933], [18319]
San Augustine County Chamber of Commerce [45347]
San Benito Area Chamber of Commerce [45348]
San Benito Chamber of Commerce [45348]
San Benito County Chamber of Commerce [37145]
San Bernardino Area Chamber of Commerce (SBACC) [37146]
San Bernardino Employment & Training Agency [37624]
San Clemente Chamber of Commerce (SCCC) [37147]
San Diego Association of Governments (SANDAG) [47468]
San Diego Business Journal [37696]
San Diego Business Travel Association (SDBTA) [19317], [36554]
San Diego Coastal Chamber of Commerce (SDCC) [37148]
San Diego County Hispanic Chamber of Commerce (SDCHCC) [37149]
San Diego East County Chamber of Commerce (SDECCC) [37150]
San Diego Regional Chamber of Commerce (SD) [37151]
San Diego Regional Economic Development Corp. (SDREDC) [33506]
San Diego State University College of Business Administration - Lavin Entrepreneurship Center [37625]
San Diego State University - Mount Laguna Observatory (MLO) [32939]
San Diego Technology Incubator [37626]
San Diego Telecom Council [37568]
San Dimas Chamber of Commerce [37152]
"*San Francisco Ad Agency Picks Boston For Its East Coast Beachhead*" in *Boston Business Journal* (Vol. 34, March 21, 2014, No. 7, pp. 4) [346]
San Francisco Botanical Garden at Strybing Arboretum - Helen Crocker Russell Library of Horticulture [7684]
San Francisco Camerawork (SFC) [12295], [12336]
San Francisco Chamber of Commerce (SFCC) [37153]
San Francisco Conservatory of Music Library (SFCM) [11238]
San Francisco, National Association of Women Business Owners [36553]
San Francisco Oven [12592]
San Francisco Planning and Urban Research Association (SPUR) [781]
San Francisco Public Library - Bernard Osher Foundation Art, Music & Recreation Center [1005], [4699], [11239], [11303], [12327]
San Francisco Public Library - Wallace Stegner Environmental Center [5777]
San Francisco Small Business Development Center [36586]
San Gabriel Chamber of Commerce (SGCC) [37154]
San Jacinto College Small Business Development Center [44938]
San Joaquin Angels (SJA) [35306], [37477]
San Joaquin Delta College - Northeastern California Small Business Development Center [37627]
San Joaquin Delta College Small Business Development Center (SBDC) [36587]
San Jose BioCenter [37628]
San Jose BioCube [37629]
"*San Jose Hopes to Build on Uptick in Manufacturing*" in *Silicon Valley/San Jose Business Journal* (Vol. 30, July 13, 2012, No. 16, pp. 1) [18320], [26400], [29371]
San Jose Silicon Valley Chamber of Commerce [37192]
San Jose State University - Institute for Social Responsibility, Ethics, and Education (ISREE) [23575]
San Juan Capistrano Chamber of Commerce [37155]
San Juan College - Enterprise Center [42352]
San Juan Island Chamber of Commerce [46147]
San Leandro Chamber of Commerce (SLCC) [37156]
San Leandro Technology Center (SLTC) [37630]
San Luis Business Incubator (SLBI) [36401]
San Luis Obispo Chamber of Commerce [37157]
San Luis Obispo Chamber of Commerce Visitors Guide [37158]
San Luis Valley Small Business Development Center [37793]
San Marcos Area Chamber of Commerce [45349]
San Marcos Chamber of Commerce (SMC) [37159]
San Marcos Chamber of Commerce [45349]
"*San Marcos May Ban Smoking*" in *Austin Business Journal* (Vol. 31, June 17, 2011, No. 15, pp. 1) [15703], [25525]
San Mateo Area Chamber of Commerce (SMCC) [37160]
San Pablo Chamber of Commerce (SPCC) [37161]
San Pedro Chamber of Commerce (SPCC) [37162]
San Rafael Chamber of Commerce (SRCC) [37163]
San Ramon Chamber of Commerce (SRCC) [37164]
San Saba County Chamber of Commerce [45350]
San Simeon Chamber of Commerce [37165]
San Ysidro Chamber of Commerce and Visitor Information Center [37166]
Sand Hill Angels (SHA) [36555]
Sand Springs Area Chamber of Commerce [43803]
Sandalwood Ventures [37478]
Sanderling Ventures [37479]
The Sanderson Group Inc. [18460], [30222]
Sandhills Area Chamber of Commerce [43172]
Sandhills Community College (SCC) [43256]
Sandia Science & Technology Park (SS&TP) [42353]
Sandler Capital Management [42797]
Sandler Systems Inc. [10566], [32701]
Sandler Travis and Rosenberg P.A. (ST&R) [29030]
Sandlin Private Investigators [12788]
Sandoval County Small Business Development Center [42285]
S&P Global Inc. [1712]
Sandstone Area Chamber of Commerce (SACC) [41302]
Sandwich Area Chamber of Commerce [39306]
Sandwich Chamber of Commerce [40624]
Sandy Area Chamber of Commerce (SACC) [44013]
Sandy Korem Founder and CEO at Festive Kitchen [2689]
Sanex WTA Tour [15669]
Sanford Rose Associates International Inc. (SRA) [5460], [6120]
Sanger Area Chamber of Commerce (SACC) [45351]
Sanger District Chamber of Commerce [37167]
Sangster's Health Centres [8077]
Sanibel-Captiva Islands Chamber of Commerce [38495]
Sanitary Brass Institute [12611]
Sanitary Institute of America [13694]
Sanitary Supply Wholesaling Association (SSWA) [2051]
Sanofi-Aventis U.S. LLC [5221]
Santa Ana Chamber (SAC) [37168]
Santa Ana College [37661]
Santa Barbara Botanic Garden (SBBG) [7685]
Santa Barbara Medical Research Foundation [8083], [11617]
Santa Clara Chamber of Commerce [37193]
Santa Clara University - de Saisset Museum Library [1006]
Santa Clara University - Markkula Center for Applied Ethics [34448]
"*Santa Clara Wineries at Odds with County Over Regulations*" in *Silicon Valley/San Jose Business Journal* (Vol. 30, September 7, 2012, No. 24, pp. 1) [15024], [15892], [17106], [25526], [35088]
Santa Clarita Valley Chamber of Commerce (SCVCC) [37169]
Santa Clarita Valley Chamber of Commerce Business Directory [37170]
Santa Cruz Area Chamber of Commerce [37171]
Santa Cruz County Chamber of Commerce [37171]
Santa Cruz County SCORE [36608]
Santa Cruz Small Business Development Center [36588]
Santa Fe Business Incubator (SFBI) [42354]
Santa Fe Chamber of Commerce [42337], [45352]
Santa Fe College (SF) [38601]
Santa Fe Small Business Development Center [42286]
Santa Fe Springs Chamber of Commerce [37172]
Santa Fe Springs Chamber of Commerce and Industrial League [37172]
Santa Maria Valley Chamber of Commerce (SMVCC) [37173]
Santa Maria Valley Chamber of Commerce and Visitor and Convention Bureau [37173]
Santa Monica Chamber of Commerce (SMCC) [37174]
Santa Paula Chamber of Commerce [37175]
Santa Rosa Chamber of Commerce [37176]
Santa Rosa County Chamber of Commerce [38496]
Santa Rosan [38497]
"*Santander 'Redlining' Suit is a Crass and Opportunistic Shakedown*" in *Boston Business Journal* (Vol. 34, June 6, 2014, No. 18, pp. 7) [11076], [18683], [20335], [20576], [25527]
Santé Ventures [45469]
Santee Chamber of Commerce (SCC) [37177]
SAP Ventures [37480]
Sapient Capital Partners Corp. [46876]
Sapphire Ventures (SV) [37480]
"*Sappi Announces North American 'Printers of the Year' Gold Winners*" in *American Printer* (Vol. 128, July 1, 2011, No. 7) [3329], [12752], [16205]
Sapulpa Area Chamber of Commerce [43804]
SARA Title III Workshop (Onsite) [25192]
Saraland Area Chamber of Commerce [36150]
Saraland Business Association [36150]
Saranac Lake Area Chamber of Commerce [42665]
Sarasota Chamber of Commerce [38416]
Saratoga Chamber of Commerce [37178]
Saratoga County Chamber of Commerce [42666]
Saratoga/Platte Valley Chamber of Commerce (SPVCC) [46619]
Sareen & Associates [156]
Sargon Partners Inc. [41057]
Sarnia-Lambton Business Development Corp. (SLBDC) [46758]
Sarpy County Chamber of Commerce (SCCC) [41883]
Saskatchewan Environmental Society (SES) [5501], [13693], [23051]
Saskatchewan Research Council (SRC) [5778], [33720]
Saskatchewan Tourism Authority [46914]
SaskMetis Economic Development Corporation (SMEDCO) [46916]
Satellite Dealers Association Inc. [14343], [15559]
Saturn Partners (SP) [40725]
Saugatuck Capital Company L.P. [38102]
Sauk Centre Area Chamber of Commerce (SCCC) [41303]
Sauk Prairie Area Chamber of Commerce (SPACC) [46508]
Sauk Prairie Area Chamber of Commerce Business/Membership Directory [46509]
Sauk Valley Area Chamber of Commerce (SVACC) [39307]
Sauk Valley Community College (SVCC) [39446]
Saukville Chamber of Commerce [46510]
Sault Area Chamber of Commerce [41007]
Sault Ste. Marie Innovation Centre (SSMIC) [46833]
Sault Sainte Marie Chamber of Commerce [41007]
Saunders Construction, Inc. [4338]
Sausalito Chamber of Commerce [37179]
Savage Chamber of Commerce [41304]
Savanna Chamber of Commerce (SCC) [39308]
Savannah Area Chamber of Commerce (SACC) [41628]
Savannah Area Chamber of Commerce (SACC) [38778]
Savannah Business Journal [38851]
Savannah Chamber of Commerce [41628]
"*Savatree Acquires Pauley Tree and Lawn Care*" in *Landscape Business* (November 17, 2019) [10113], [10245]
"*Save-A-Lot Adds Amazon PayCode and Hub Locker to St. Louis Stores*" in *Grocery Dive* (November 5, 2019) [7772], [11790]
Save Your Small Business: 10 Crucial Strategies to Survive Hard Times or Close Down & Move On [19056], [20336], [21131], [24090], [24729]
Saving Lives with Medical Device Startups [10867], [34638]
"*Saving the Planet: A Tale of Two Strategies: Thomas Malthus Advised Restraint; Robert Solow Promotes Innovation. Let's Pursue Both To Solve the Environmental Crisis*" in *Harvard Business Review* (Vol. 90, April 2012, No. 4, pp. 48) [5704], [5970], [13728], [14941], [23350]

The Savory Center [5788]
Savory Mercato Partners [45664]
The Savvy Gal's Guide to Online Networking: Or What Would Jane Austen Do? [9223], [17744], [21967], [31502], [35850]
"Savvy Solutions" in Black Enterprise (Vol. 41, December 2010, No. 5, pp. 42) [3280], [8676], [27390], [28191], [30930]
"Savvy Solutions" in Black Enterprise (Vol. 41, November 2010, No. 4, pp. 42) [1674], [2679], [4941], [5323], [23656], [28192], [30931]
"Sawatdee Rethinks Express Eatery Model" in Business Journal (Vol. 31, January 10, 2014, No. 33, pp. 4) [14012], [19581], [23657]
Sawmill Prime Rib & Steak House [14248]
Saxbys Coffee Worldwide, LLC [32377]
"Say Goodbye to Voicemail, Hello To Ribbit Mobile" in Agency Sales Magazine (Vol. 39, November 2009, No. 10, pp. 3) [9224], [17745], [17874], [26401], [32613]
"Say Yes to the New Wedding Collection from Pinhole Press" in Benzinga.com (May 1, 2012) [1993], [11791], [12753]
Sayner-Star Lake Chamber of Commerce (SSLCC) [46511]
Sayre Enterprise Center [44418]
SBA [38192], [47823]
"SBA Can Improve Your Cash Flow" in Business Owner (Vol. 35, September-October 2011, No. 5, pp. 3) [24091], [25056], [28193]
SBA Computers Inc. [31014], [31099]
SBA Expands Loan Program to Include Small Gaming Companies [7309]
"SBA Lending Hits Record" in Saint Louis Business Journal (Vol. 32, September 30, 2011, No. 5, pp. 1) [25057], [28194]
SBA Loan Options and Best Borrowing Practices for Women [28085], [33529], [35715]
SBA Online [33708]
"SBA Opens Program to Get Women Owned Businesses Federal Contracts" in Small Business Trends (August 30, 2022) [35851]
"SBA Program Helped New Company Survive As It Built Company Base" in Philadelphia Business Journal (Vol. 33, May 9, 2014, No. 13, pp. 4) [3417], [20073], [24932], [26175], [28071]
Sbarro LLC. [14249]
Sbarro The Italian Eatery [14249]
SBDC at FGCU - Clewiston [38233]
SBDC at University of Wisconsin - Eau Claire [46326]
SBDC at University of Wisconsin - Green Bay [46327]
SBDC at University of Wisconsin - Oshkosh [46329]
SBDC at University of Wisconsin - Parkside [46330]
SBDC at University of Wisconsin - Superior [46331]
SBE [33639]
SBM's Annual Meeting & Scientific Sessions [32926]
SBTDC Regional Office [43048], [43236]
SC Green Conference and Trade Show [10065]
SC Johnson iMET [46572]
SC Launch, Inc. [44592]
SC & RA News [16100]
SCAI Scientific Sessions [10882]
"Scaife's Legacy to Live On in Black and White" in Pittsburgh Business Times (Vol. 33, July 11, 2014, No. 52, pp. 3) [11997]
Scale Capital [37481]
Scale Like a Pro [24824]
Scale Venture Partners [37482]
Scaling DE&I Through Supplier Diversity [30601]
Scams & Fraud [19278]
"Scams Targeting Small Business" in Incorp website (2022) [19279]
"Scams and Your Small Business: A Guide for Business" (May 2018) [19280]
Scan Management Inc. [9932]
Scannell and Kurz Inc. [24266]
"Scanning Dell's Shopping List" in Barron's (Vol. 89, July 13, 2009, No. 28, pp. 24) [3519], [19057], [31503]
Scarborough Historical Society - Scarborough Archives [7449]
"Scarsdale's Bronx River Books the Latest in Independent Bookstore Comeback" in Westchester Journal News (December 6, 2018) [1837]
"Scary (But True) Small Business Statistics You Can't Afford to Ignore" on Digital.com (Jan. 27, 2022) [18321]
SCBIO [44609]
SCCG Management [7328]
Scenic America (SA) [31843]
Scenthound [12125]
"Scepticism Towards DTC Advertising: A Comparative Study of Korean and Caucasian Americans" in International Journal of Advertising (Vol. 31, February 2012, No. 1, pp. 147) [347], [5184], [10674], [30602]

Schakolad Chocolate Factory [2559]
The Schallert Group Inc. [32360], [32697]
Schaum's Outline of Financial Management [90], [9783], [15411], [16830], [24092], [34877]
Schenectady County Chamber Foundation [42667]
Schenectady County Community Business Center [42928]
Schererville Chamber of Commerce [39604]
Schlotzsky's [4921]
Schneider Consulting Group Inc. [2316], [2392], [10558], [20224], [23686], [29031]
Schoharie County Chamber of Commerce (SCCC) [42668]
Scholars Education Centre [16170]
Schoodic Area Chamber of Commerce [40304]
School [43865]
School is Easy Tutoring [16171]
School Nutrition Industry Conference (SNIC) [11590]
"School Supply Store Has Had to Learn How to Roll with the COVID-19 Tide" in Pilot Online (September 18, 2020) [15542]
"School for Tech Skills" in San Antonio Business Journal (Vol. 28, September 5, 2014, No. 30, pp. 4) [21621], [31504]
"School Uses Book Vending Machine to Get Kids Reading" in U.S. News & World Report (November 23, 2019) [1838], [16259]
School of Visual Arts Library (SVA) [3380], [12328]
Schoolcraft County Chamber of Commerce (SCCC) [41008]
"Schools Start Early with Career Counseling" in U.S. News & World Report (September 6, 2018) [2606]
Schostak Brothers and Company Inc. [13622]
Schroon Lake Chamber of Commerce [42669]
Schulenburg Chamber of Commerce [45190]
Schuyler Area Chamber of Commerce (SACC) [41884]
Schuyler County Chamber of Commerce [42697]
Schuylkill Chamber of Commerce (SCC) [44294]
"Science Museum, Theater Seeking State Loans" in Sacramento Business Journal (Vol. 31, May 30, 2014, No. 14, pp. 4) [4222], [25058], [28195]
"The Science of Serendipity in the Workplace" in The Wall Street Journal (April 30, 2013) [31051]
"Scientific American Builds Novel Blog Network" in Information Today (Vol. 28, September 2011, No. 8, pp. 12) [1675], [17746], [21968], [26402], [32034], [32819]
Scituate Chamber of Commerce [40625]
"SCO Expanding to Meet Optometry Growth" in Memphis Business Journal (Vol. 33, March 2, 2012, No. 47, pp. 1) [4223], [16302], [21622]
SCORE [24591], [28267]
SCORE - Aberdeen [44630]
SCORE - Acadiana [40138]
SCORE - Akron [43378]
SCORE - Alabama Capitol [36069]
SCORE - Alameda [36609]
SCORE - Alaska [36213]
SCORE - Albion [42428]
SCORE - Albuquerque [42295]
SCORE - Alexandria, Minnesota [41166]
SCORE - Alexandria, Virginia [45798]
SCORE - Alhambra [36610]
SCORE - Allen [44960]
SCORE - Alpharetta [38650]
SCORE - Altoona [44116]
SCORE - Alvin [44961]
SCORE - Amelia Island [38259]
SCORE - Amherst [40509]
SCORE - Anchorage [36214]
SCORE - Anderson [39491]
SCORE - Androscoggin County [40252]
SCORE - Angola [39492]
SCORE - Ann Arbor Area [40823]
SCORE - Annadale [45799]
SCORE - Anniston [36070]
SCORE - Anoka [41167]
SCORE - Antioch [39010]
SCORE - Apex [43054]
SCORE - Arlington Heights Chamber of Commerce (AHCC) [39011]
SCORE - Arlington Heights Library [39012]
SCORE - Arlington, Texas [44962]
SCORE - Arlington, Virginia [45800]
SCORE - Armonk [42429]
SCORE - Ashburn [45801]
SCORE - Asheboro [43064]
SCORE - Asheville [43055]
SCORE - Ashtabula [43379]
Score Association [24591], [28267]
SCORE - ASU SkySong [36278]
SCORE - Atascadero [36611]
SCORE - Atlanta [38651]

SCORE - Auburn [42430], [46025]
SCORE - Augusta [40253]
SCORE - Aurora Santori Library [39013]
SCORE - Austin, Minnesota [41168]
SCORE - Austin, Texas [44963]
SCORE - Azusa [36612]
SCORE - Bangor [40254]
SCORE - Banning [36613]
SCORE - Barrington Bank and Trust [39014]
SCORE - Barrington Library [39015]
SCORE - Batavia [42431]
SCORE - Bay City [44964]
SCORE - Beaumont [36614]
SCORE - Bedford [44965]
SCORE - Bedminster [42052]
SCORE - Belair [40353]
SCORE - Belfast [40255]
SCORE - Bellevue [46026]
SCORE - Bellingham [46027]
SCORE - Belmont [42432]
SCORE - Benton Harbor [40824]
SCORE - Berkeley [36615]
SCORE - Berks and Schuylkill County [44117]
SCORE - Beverly [40510]
SCORE - Billings [41740]
SCORE - Birmingham [36071]
SCORE - Bismarck-Mandan [43280]
SCORE - Bloomingdale [39016]
SCORE - Bloomington [39507]
SCORE - Blue Bell [44118]
SCORE - Blue Ridge [38652]
SCORE - Blue Springs [41826]
SCORE - Boise Public Library [38901]
SCORE - Bolingbrook [39017]
SCORE - Boone [43056]
SCORE - Boston [40511]
SCORE - Bowling Green [40010]
SCORE - Boyertown [44119]
SCORE - Boynton Beach [38260]
SCORE - Bozeman [41741]
SCORE - Brainerd [41169]
SCORE - Branchburg [42053]
SCORE - Branford [37984]
SCORE - Brattleboro [45711]
SCORE - Bridgeport [37985]
SCORE - Bridgewater [42054]
SCORE - Brigham City [45617]
SCORE - Brightwaters [42433]
SCORE - Bristol [37986]
SCORE - Bronx [42434]
SCORE - Brooklyn Borough Hall Branch [42435]
SCORE - Brooklyn Center [42436]
SCORE - Brooklyn Central Library Branch [42437]
SCORE - Brooklyn Park [41170]
SCORE - Brooksville [38261]
SCORE - Broward [38262]
SCORE - Broward County Main Library [38263]
SCORE - Brunswick [38653]
SCORE - Bucks County [44120]
SCORE - Buffalo Grove [39018]
SCORE - Buffalo Niagara [42438]
SCORE - Burlington, Massachusetts [40512]
SCORE - Burlington, Vermont [45712]
SCORE - Burton [43380]
SCORE - Calabasas [36616]
SCORE - Callahan [38264]
SCORE - Camarillo [36617]
SCORE - Cameron Village Library [43057]
SCORE - Camp Hill [44162]
SCORE - Campbell [36618]
SCORE - Canoga Park [36619]
SCORE - Canton [43381]
SCORE - Cape Cod & the Islands [40513]
SCORE - Cape Fear Region [43058]
SCORE - Cape May Court House [42055]
SCORE - Capital Corridor [36620]
SCORE - Carefree/Cave Creek Chamber [36279]
SCORE - Carlisle [44121]
SCORE - Cary [43059]
SCORE - Castro Valley [36621]
SCORE - CCP Northeast [44122]
SCORE - CCP Northwest [44123]
SCORE - CCP West Philadelphia [44124]
SCORE - Cedar Rapids [39700]
SCORE - Centereach [42439]
SCORE - Central Coast [36622]
SCORE - Central Florida [38265]
SCORE - Central Jersey [42056]
SCORE - Central Minnesota [41171]
SCORE - Central Nebraska [41828]
SCORE - Central Oregon [43928]
SCORE - Central Pennsylvania [44125]
SCORE - Central Valley [36623]

SCORE - Central Virginia [45802]
SCORE - Central Wisconsin [46342]
SCORE - Chamber of Commerce Ventura [36624]
SCORE - Chandler Chamber of Commerce [36280]
SCORE - Chandler Public Library [36281]
SCORE - Chapel Hill Durham [43060]
SCORE - Chapin [44518]
SCORE - Chapter 0143 [39852]
SCORE - Charleston, South Carolina [44519]
SCORE - Charleston, West Virginia [46261]
SCORE - Charlotte [43061]
SCORE - Chattanooga [44701]
SCORE - Cherry Hill [42057]
SCORE - Cheshire [37987]
SCORE - Chester County Economic Development Council (CCEDC) [44126]
SCORE - Chester and Delaware Counties [44127]
SCORE - Cheyenne [46595]
SCORE - Chicago [39019]
SCORE - Chicago Beverly Area Planning Association [39020]
SCORE - Chicago City Hall [39021]
SCORE - Chicago Harold Washington Library Center [39022]
SCORE - Chicago Lakeview [39023]
SCORE - Chicago Logan Square [39024]
SCORE - Chicago Ravenswood [39025]
SCORE - Chino [36625]
SCORE - Chino Hills [36626]
SCORE - City of Philadelphia [44128]
SCORE - Claremont [36627]
SCORE - Clarence [42440]
SCORE - Clarksburg [46259]
SCORE - Clawson [40825]
SCORE - Clay County [38266]
SCORE - Clear Lake Library [44966]
SCORE - Clermont [38267]
SCORE - Cleveland [43382]
SCORE - Clifton [42058]
SCORE - Clinton [42059]
SCORE - Clinton, Franklin, Essex (SCORE-CFE) [42441]
SCORE - Coachella Valley [36628]
SCORE - Coastal Carolina [43062]
SCORE - Coatesville [44129]
SCORE - Cobb Chamber of Commerce [38654]
SCORE - Cobb Sewell Mill Library [38655]
SCORE - College Park [38656]
SCORE - Collegeville [44130]
SCORE - Colleyville [44967]
SCORE - Colorado Springs [37804]
SCORE - Columbia, South Carolina [44520]
SCORE - Columbus, Georgia [38657]
SCORE - Columbus & Norfolk [41827]
SCORE - Columbus, Ohio [43383]
SCORE - Concord [36629]
SCORE - Connecticut [37988]
SCORE - Conway [41974]
SCORE - Coppell [44968]
SCORE - Corona [36630]
SCORE - Corpus Christi [44969]
SCORE - Cortlandt Manor [42442]
SCORE - Countryside [39026]
SCORE - Covina [36631]
SCORE - Culpeper [45803]
SCORE - Culver City [36632]
SCORE - Cumming [38658]
SCORE - Dallas [44970]
SCORE - Dallas Bill J. Priest Center [44971]
SCORE - Danbury [37989]
SCORE - Danville [36633]
SCORE - Darien [39027]
SCORE - Davenport [39696]
SCORE - Dayton [43384]
SCORE - Decatur [39028]
SCORE - Decorah [39697]
SCORE - Deer Park [44972]
SCORE - Deerfield [39029]
SCORE - DeKalb [39030]
SCORE - DeLand [38268]
SCORE - Delaware [38127]
SCORE - Denton [44973]
SCORE - Denver [37805]
SCORE - Des Moines [39698]
SCORE - Des Plaines [39031]
SCORE - DeSoto [44974]
SCORE - Detroit [40826]
SCORE - Devon [44131]
SCORE - Diamond Bar [36634]
SCORE - Dickinson [43281]
SCORE - Dix Hills [42443]
SCORE - Dorchester [40514]
SCORE - Downeast Maine [40256]

SCORE - Downey Chamber of Commerce [36635]
SCORE - Doylestown [44132]
SCORE - Duarte [36636]
SCORE - Dublin [36637]
SCORE - Dubuque [39699]
SCORE - Duluth City Hall [38659]
SCORE - Dunwoody [38660]
SCORE - Dutchess [42444]
SCORE - Eagle [36215]
SCORE - East Aurora [42445]
SCORE - East Bay (EB Score) [36638]
SCORE - East Brunswick [42060]
SCORE - East Brunswick Investors Bank [42061]
SCORE - East Central Iowa [39700]
SCORE - East Central Ohio [43385]
SCORE - East Hartford [37990]
SCORE - East San Gabriel Valley [36639]
SCORE - East Texas [44975]
SCORE - Eastern Idaho [38902]
SCORE - Eastham [40515]
SCORE - Eastvale [36640]
SCORE - Eden [42446]
SCORE - Edina [41172]
SCORE - Edison [42062]
SCORE - El Paso [44976]
SCORE - Elgin Gail Borden Library [39032]
SCORE - Elgin State Bank [39033]
SCORE - Elk Grove Village [39034]
SCORE - Elkader [39701]
SCORE - Elmhurst [39035]
SCORE - Elmont [42447]
SCORE - Encino [36641]
Score eNews [39493]
SCORE - Euless [44977]
SCORE - Evans [38661]
SCORE - Evanston [39036]
SCORE - Evansville [39494]
SCORE - Everett [46028]
SCORE ExpertAnswers [39495]
SCORE - Fairbanks [36216]
SCORE - Fairfax [45804]
SCORE - Fairfield, California [36642]
SCORE - Fairfield County [37991]
SCORE - Fairfield, Iowa [39702]
SCORE - Fairless Hills [44133]
SCORE - Falmouth [40516]
SCORE - Fargo [43282]
SCORE - Farmers Branch [44978]
SCORE - Farmington [37992]
SCORE - Farmingville [42448]
SCORE - Fishers [39496]
SCORE - Fitchburg [40517]
SCORE - Fleming Island [38269]
SCORE - Flemington [42063]
SCORE - Flint [40827]
SCORE - Florham Park [42064]
SCORE - Florissant [41499]
SCORE - Flower Mound [44979]
SCORE - Flushing [42449]
SCORE - Fontana [36643]
SCORE - Fort Pierce [38270]
SCORE - Fort Wayne [39504]
SCORE - Fort Worth [44980]
SCORE - Fort Worth SBA District Office [44981]
SCORE - Foster City [36644]
SCORE - Fox Cities [46343]
SCORE - Fox Valley [39037]
SCORE - Framingham [40518]
SCORE - Framingham Public Library [40519]
SCORE - Frankfort [39038]
SCORE - Frederick [40357]
SCORE - Fremont [36645]
SCORE - Frisco [44982]
SCORE - Front Royal [45805]
SCORE - Gaithersburg [40354]
SCORE - Galloway Township [42065]
SCORE - Garden City [42450]
SCORE - Georgetown [38128]
SCORE - Gig Harbor [46029]
SCORE - Gilbert-EZ Spaces [36282]
SCORE - Glastonbury [37993]
SCORE - Glen Ellyn [39039]
SCORE - Glen Mills [44134]
SCORE - Glendale [36646]
SCORE - Glendora [36647]
SCORE - Glens Falls [42451]
SCORE - Glenview Park Center [39040]
SCORE - Glenview Public Library [39041]
SCORE - Glenview State Bank [39042]
SCORE - Goodyear Library [36283]
SCORE - Goodyear Valley Chamber of Commerce [36284]
SCORE - Gordonsville [45806]

SCORE - Granbury [44983]
SCORE - Grand Blanc [40828]
SCORE - Grand Forks [43283]
SCORE - Grand Island [41828]
SCORE - Grand Prairie [44984]
SCORE - Grand Rapids [40829]
SCORE - Grand Strand [44521]
SCORE - Grandmont Rosedale [40830]
SCORE - Grapevine [44985]
SCORE - Great Falls [41742]
SCORE - Greater Aiken [44522]
SCORE - Greater Baltimore [40355]
SCORE - Greater Binghamton [42452]
SCORE - Greater Cincinnati [43386]
SCORE - Greater Hartford [37994]
SCORE - Greater Knoxville [44702]
SCORE - Greater Lynchburg [45807]
SCORE - Greater Omaha [41829]
SCORE - Greater Phoenix [36285]
SCORE - Greater Phoenix Better Business Bureau [36286]
SCORE - Greater Rochester [42453]
SCORE - Greater Seattle [46030]
SCORE - Greater Wabash Valley [39497]
SCORE - Green Bay [46344]
SCORE - Greenfield [40520]
SCORE - Greensboro [43063]
SCORE - Greenwich [37995]
SCORE - Greenwood [39498]
SCORE - Guilford [37996]
SCORE - Gurnee [39043]
SCORE - Gwinnett Chamber of Commerce [38667]
SCORE - Hamburg [42454]
SCORE - Hamden [37997]
SCORE - Hammond [39499]
SCORE - Hampton Bays [42455]
SCORE - Hampton Roads [45808]
SCORE - Hamtramck [40831]
SCORE - Hancock [40832]
SCORE - Harlem Community Development Corporation [42456]
SCORE - Harrisburg [44135]
SCORE - Harrison [42457]
SCORE - Hartsville [44523]
SCORE - Haverhill [40521]
SCORE - Haverstraw [42458]
SCORE - Hawaii [38868]
SCORE - HCC Alief Hayes Campus [44986]
SCORE - Hemet [36648]
SCORE - Henderson [41922]
SCORE - Highland Park [39044]
SCORE - Hillsborough [42066]
SCORE - Hinesville [38662]
SCORE - Hobe Sound [38271]
SCORE - Hoffman Estates [39045]
SCORE - Hollywood [36649]
SCORE - Hollywood/Pembroke Pines [38272]
"Score a Home Run for Women-Owned Small Businesses" in AZ Big Media (July 24, 2018) [35852]
SCORE - Hood River [43929]
SCORE - Hopkinton [40522]
SCORE - Horsham [44136]
SCORE - Houston [44987]
SCORE - Houston Business Solutions [44988]
SCORE - Humble [44989]
SCORE - Huntington, Indiana [39500]
SCORE - Huntington Station [42459]
SCORE - Huntington, West Virginia [46260]
SCORE - Huntsville [36072]
SCORE - Hutchinson [39849]
SCORE - Incubizo Ferndale [40833]
SCORE - Indianapolis [39501]
SCORE - Inland Empire [36650]
SCORE - Iola [46345]
SCORE - Irving [44990]
SCORE - Jackson [42067]
SCORE - Jacksonville [38273]
SCORE - Jamaica [42460]
SCORE - Jamaica Plain [40523]
SCORE - Jamestown [43284]
SCORE - JAX Chamber Office [38274]
SCORE - Jefferson City [41500]
SCORE - Jenkintown [44137]
SCORE - Jensen Beach [38275]
SCORE - Jersey City [42068]
SCORE - Jupiter [38276]
SCORE - Kalamazoo [40834]
SCORE - Kalispell [41743]
SCORE - Kansas City [41501]
SCORE - Katy [44991]
SCORE - Kaysville [45618]
SCORE - Keller [44992]
SCORE - Kendallville [39502]

SCORE - Kenmore [42461]
SCORE - Kennett Square [44138]
SCORE - Kent [38129]
SCORE - King of Prussia [44142]
SCORE - Kirkwood [41502]
SCORE - Kirstein Business Library [40524]
SCORE - Kitsap [46031]
SCORE - La Camara de Empresarios Latinos de Houston [44993]
SCORE - Lacey [46032]
SCORE - Lady's Island [44524]
SCORE - Lafayette [36651]
SCORE - Lake Bluff [39046]
SCORE - Lake Elsinore [36652]
SCORE - Lake Forest [39047]
SCORE - Lake of the Ozarks [41503]
SCORE - Lake Zurich [39048]
SCORE - Lakes Region [41973]
SCORE - Lakewood [42069]
SCORE - Lancaster [44139]
SCORE - Lancaster-Lebanon [44139]
SCORE - Largo [40356]
SCORE - Las Cruces [42296]
SCORE - Las Vegas [41923]
SCORE - Lawrence [40525]
SCORE - Leadville [37806]
SCORE - Lebanon [41504]
SCORE - Lebanon [41974]
SCORE - Lehigh Valley (LV SCORE) [44140]
SCORE - Lewisville [44994]
SCORE - Lexington Chamber of Commerce [40511]
SCORE - Lexington, Kentucky [40011]
SCORE - Lexington, South Carolina [44525]
SCORE - Libertyville [39049]
SCORE - Lincoln, Nebraska [41830]
SCORE - Lincoln, Rhode Island [44459]
SCORE - Lincolnshire [39050]
SCORE - Little Egg Harbor [42070]
SCORE - Little Rock [36429]
SCORE - Livermore [36653]
SCORE - Locust Grove [45809]
SCORE - Long Beach [42462]
SCORE - Long Beach Chamber of Commerce [36654]
SCORE - Long Beach Ironfire Coworking [36655]
SCORE - Long Beach Public Library - Michelle Obama Branch [36656]
SCORE - Long Beach/South Bay [36657]
SCORE - Long Island [42463], [42464]
SCORE - Longview [46033]
SCORE - Lorain [43387]
SCORE - Los Altos [36658]
SCORE - Los Angeles [36659]
SCORE - Los Angeles Public Library [36660]
SCORE - Los Gatos [36661]
SCORE - Louisville [40012]
SCORE - Lubbock [44995]
SCORE - Lynn [40526]
SCORE - Macon [38664]
SCORE - Madison, Connecticut [37998]
SCORE - Madison, Wisconsin [46340]
SCORE - Mahwah [42071]
SCORE - Malta [42465]
SCORE - Manahawkin [42072]
SCORE - Manasota [38277]
SCORE - Manassas [45810]
SCORE - Manchester, Connecticut [37999]
SCORE - Manchester, Iowa [39703]
SCORE - Manitowoc [46347]
SCORE - Maple Grove [41173]
SCORE - Marietta [38663]
SCORE - Marinette [46348]
SCORE - Martinsville [45811]
SCORE - Massapequa [42466]
SCORE - Matteson [39051]
SCORE - Maui County [38869]
SCORE - Mayaguez [46636]
SCORE - McHenry [39052]
SCORE - McKinney [44996]
SCORE - Media [44141]
SCORE - Melbourne [38278]
SCORE - Memphis [44703]
SCORE - Menlo Park [36662]
SCORE Mentors Monmouth [42074]
SCORE Mentors Nebraska Route 81 [41827]
SCORE - Meriden [38000]
SCORE - Merrillan [46349]
SCORE - Merrillville [39503]
SCORE - Merrimack Valley [41974]
SCORE - Merritt Island [38279]
SCORE - Mesa Chamber of Commerce [36287]
SCORE - Mesquite [41924]
SCORE - Metro Jackson [41379]
SCORE - Metro New Jersey [42073]

SCORE - Miami-Dade [38280]
SCORE - Mid-Columbia Tri-Cities [46034]
SCORE - Mid Florida [38281]
SCORE - Mid-Hudson Valley [42467]
SCORE - Mid-Maryland [40357]
SCORE - Mid-Shore [40358]
SCORE - Middle Georgia [38664]
SCORE - Middletown, Rhode Island [44460]
SCORE - Midlands [44526]
SCORE - Milford, Connecticut [38001]
SCORE - Milford, Massachusetts [40527]
SCORE - Milpitas [39704]
SCORE - Mineral [45812]
SCORE - Minneapolis [41174]
SCORE - Minneapolis Central Library [41175]
SCORE - Minot [43285]
SCORE - Miramar [38282]
SCORE - Missoula [41744]
SCORE - Modesto-Merced [36664]
SCORE - Monadnock [41975]
SCORE - Monmouth [42074]
SCORE - Monmouth Junction [42075]
SCORE - Montclair [42076]
SCORE - Montebello [36665]
SCORE - Monterey Bay [36622]
SCORE - Montgomery County, PA [44142]
SCORE - Monticello [42468]
SCORE - Montpelier [45713]
SCORE - Monument [37807]
SCORE - Moreno Valley [36666]
SCORE - Morgan Hill [36667]
SCORE - Morristown [42077]
SCORE - Moultrie [38665]
SCORE - Mount Airy [44143]
SCORE - Mount Prospect [39053]
SCORE - Mount Vernon, New York [42469]
SCORE - Mount Vernon, Washington [46035]
SCORE - Mountain View [36668]
SCORE - Mundelein [39054]
SCORE - Muscatine [39704]
SCORE - Muskegon [40835]
SCORE - Mystic [38002]
SCORE - Nantucket [40528]
SCORE - Napa [36669]
SCORE - Naperville [39055]
SCORE - Naperville Public Library Nichols Library [39056]
SCORE - Naples [38283]
SCORE - Nashua [41976]
SCORE - Nashville [44704]
SCORE - Natick [40529]
SCORE - NC Piedmont Triad [43064]
SCORE - Nebraska Route 81 [41827]
SCORE - New Bern [43065]
SCORE - New Britain [38003]
SCORE - New City [42470]
SCORE - New Haven [38004]
SCORE - New London [38005]
SCORE - New Milford [38006]
SCORE - New Orleans [40139]
SCORE - New Rochelle [42471]
SCORE - New Smyrna Beach [38284]
SCORE - New York City [42472]
SCORE - New York Public Library [42473]
SCORE - Newburyport [40530]
SCORE - Newport News [45813]
SCORE - Newton, Massachusetts [40531]
SCORE - Newton, New Jersey [42078]
SCORE - Newtown [38007]
SCORE - Niles [39057]
SCORE - Norcross [38666]
SCORE - North Augusta [44527]
SCORE - North Central Florida [38285]
SCORE - North Central Ohio [43388]
SCORE - North Chicago [39058]
SCORE - North Coast [36670]
SCORE - North Cook and Lake Counties [39059]
SCORE - North Haven [38008]
SCORE - North Kingstown [44461]
SCORE - North Metro Atlanta [38667]
SCORE - North Phoenix Chamber of Commerce [36288]
SCORE - North Richland Hills [44997]
SCORE - North Tonawanda [42474]
SCORE - Northampton [40532]
SCORE - Northbrook [39060]
SCORE - Northbrook Bank and Trust [39061]
SCORE - Northbrook Chamber of Commerce [39062]
SCORE - Northeast Fort Lauderdale [38286]
SCORE - Northeast Georgia [38668]
SCORE - Northeast Indiana [39504]
SCORE - Northeast Louisiana [40140]
SCORE - Northeast Massachusetts [40510]
SCORE - Northeast Mississippi [41380]

SCORE - Northeast New York [42475]
SCORE - Northeast Pennsylvania [44144]
SCORE - Northern Arizona [36289]
SCORE - Northern Nevada [41925]
SCORE - Northfield [39063]
SCORE - Northwest Activities Center [40836]
SCORE - Northwest Arkansas [36430]
SCORE - Northwest Chamber of Commerce [44998]
SCORE - Northwest Connecticut (SCORE-NWCT) [38009]
SCORE - Northwest Indiana [39505]
SCORE - Northwest Louisiana [40141]
SCORE - Northwest New Jersey [42079]
SCORE - Northwest Ohio [43389]
SCORE - Northwest Pennsylvania [44145]
SCORE - Norwalk, California [36671]
SCORE - Norwalk, Ohio [43390]
SCORE - Norwich [38010]
SCORE - Novi [40837]
SCORE - Oak Forest [39064]
SCORE - Oak Park [39065]
SCORE - Oak Park Public Library (OPPL) [39066]
SCORE - Ocean County [42080]
SCORE - Ogden [45619]
SCORE - Oil City [44146]
SCORE - Okemos [40838]
SCORE - Oklahoma City [43726]
SCORE - Old Bridge [42081]
SCORE - Olean [42476]
"Score One for Barron's" in Barron's (Vol. 89, July 13, 2009, No. 28, pp. 14) [6594], [9784], [24093]
SCORE - Orange [45814]
SCORE - Orange Park [38266]
SCORE - Orangeburg [44528]
SCORE - Orlando [38287]
SCORE - Orleans [40533]
SCORE - Ormond Beach [38288]
SCORE - Oro Valley Library [36290]
SCORE - Oshkosh [46350]
SCORE - Outer Banks [43066]
SCORE - Oxford Hills [40257]
SCORE - Oxford Hills [40259]
SCORE - Oxnard [36672]
SCORE - Painesville [43391]
SCORE - Palatine Bank & Trust [39067]
SCORE - Palatine Public Library [39068]
SCORE - Palm Bay [38289]
SCORE - Palm Beach [38290]
SCORE - Palm Center [44999]
SCORE - Palm City [38291]
SCORE - Palm Coast [38292]
SCORE - Palm Desert [36673]
SCORE - Palms-Rancho Park Library [36674]
SCORE - Palo Alto [36675]
SCORE - Palos Hills [39069]
SCORE - Paradise Valley Community College (PVCC) [36291]
SCORE - Park Rapids [41176]
SCORE - Park Ridge [39070]
SCORE - Parkland [38293]
SCORE - Pasadena [36676]
SCORE - Pasco County [38294]
SCORE - Pasco-Hernando [38294]
SCORE - Peachtree City [38669]
SCORE - Peachtree Corners [38670]
SCORE - Pearl River [42477]
SCORE - Pearland [45000]
SCORE - Pensacola [38295]
SCORE - Peoria [39071]
SCORE - Perry [42478]
SCORE - Petoskey [40842]
SCORE - Philadelphia [44147]
SCORE - Philadelphia Free Library (Lovett Branch) [44148]
SCORE - Philadelphia Free Library (Parkway) [44149]
SCORE - Phillipsburg [39850]
SCORE - Phoenix Anthem Chamber of Commerce [36292]
SCORE - Phoenix Mesquite Public Library [36293]
SCORE - Phoenixville [44150]
SCORE - Pico Rivera [36677]
SCORE - Piedmont [44529]
SCORE - Pima County Library [36294]
SCORE - Pinellas County [38296]
SCORE - Pittsburg [44151]
SCORE - Pittsburgh [44151]
SCORE - Pittsfield [40534]
SCORE - Plainfield [39072]
SCORE - Plainsboro [42082]
SCORE - Plainview [42479]
SCORE - Plano [45001]
SCORE - Playa Vista Branch, Los Angeles Public Library [36678]

SCORE - Pleasanton [36679]
SCORE - Plymouth, Massachusetts [40535]
SCORE - Plymouth, Minnesota [41177]
SCORE - Plymouth, New Hampshire [41977]
SCORE - Pompano Beach [38297]
SCORE - Port Charlotte [38298]
SCORE - Port Saint Lucie [38299]
SCORE - Portland [43930]
SCORE - Portland, Maine [40258]
SCORE - Pottstown [44157]
SCORE - Poughkeepsie [42480]
SCORE - Princeton [42083]
SCORE - Princeton Public Library [42084]
SCORE - Providence [44462]
SCORE - Providence Secretary of State [44463]
SCORE - Putnam County [42481]
SCORE - Quad Cities [39705]
SCORE - Quakertown [44152]
SCORE - Queen Creek Chamber of Commerce [36295]
SCORE - Queens [42449]
SCORE - Quincy [40536]
SCORE - Raleigh [43067]
SCORE - Raleigh Chamber of Commerce [43068]
SCORE - Randolph [42085]
SCORE - Rapid City [44632]
SCORE - Redwood City [36680]
SCORE - Reidsville [43069]
SCORE - Reston [45815]
SCORE - Revere [40537]
SCORE - Rhode Island [44464]
SCORE - Richmond, California [36681]
SCORE - Richmond County Savings Bank [42482]
SCORE - Richmond, Virginia [45816]
SCORE - Ridgefield [38011]
SCORE - Ridgewood [42086]
SCORE - Rio Grande Valley [45002]
SCORE - Riverhead [42483]
SCORE - Roanoke [45817]
SCORE - Rochester [41978]
SCORE - Rockford [39073]
SCORE - Rockland [40538]
SCORE - Rockland County [42484]
SCORE - Rockport [40539]
SCORE - Rockville Centre [42485]
SCORE - Rockwall [45003]
SCORE - Rocky Hill [38012]
SCORE - Rocky Mount [43070]
SCORE - Rosemont [39074]
SCORE - Rumford [40259]
SCORE - Sacramento [36620]
SCORE - St. Augustine [38300]
SCORE - St. Charles [41505]
SCORE - St. Joseph University [44153]
SCORE - St. Louis [41506]
SCORE - St. Paul [41178]
SCORE - Salem, New Hampshire [41979]
SCORE - Salem, Oregon [43931]
SCORE - Salt Lake City [45620]
SCORE - San Antonio [45004]
SCORE - San Diego [36682]
SCORE - San Francisco [36683]
SCORE - San Jose [36684]
SCORE - San Juan Metro [46637]
SCORE - San Leandro [36685]
SCORE - San Luis Obispo [36686]
SCORE - San Mateo [36687]
SCORE - San Rafael [36688]
SCORE - Sandhills [43071]
SCORE - Sandy [45621]
SCORE - Sandy Springs [38671]
SCORE - Santa Ana [36689]
SCORE - Santa Barbara [36690]
SCORE - Santa Clara [36691]
SCORE - Santa Fe and Northern New Mexico [42297]
SCORE - Santa Maria [36692]
SCORE - Santa Monica [36693]
SCORE - Santa Monica Public Library [36694]
SCORE - Saratoga [36695]
SCORE - Saratoga Springs [42486]
SCORE - Savannah [38672]
SCORE - Schaumburg Bank & Trust [39075]
SCORE - Schaumburg Public Library [39076]
SCORE - Schenectady [42487]
SCORE - Scottsbluff [41831]
SCORE - Scottsdale Chamber of Commerce [36296]
SCORE - Scottsdale Civic Center Library [36297]
SCORE - Scottsdale Mustang Library [36298]
SCORE - SE Massachusetts [40540]
SCORE - Seabrook [41980]
SCORE - Seacoast [41981]
SCORE - Seattle [46036]
SCORE - Sebastian [38301]
SCORE - Secaucus [42087]

SCORE - Shelton [38013]
SCORE - Shenandoah Valley [45818]
SCORE - Shirley, Massachusetts [40541]
SCORE - Shirley, New York [42488]
SCORE - Silicon Valley [36696]
SCORE - Silver Spring Library [40359]
SCORE - Silverdale [46031]
SCORE - Simi Valley Chamber of Commerce [36697]
SCORE - Simi Valley Public Library [36698]
SCORE - Simsbury [38014]
SCORE - Simsbury Library [38015]
SCORE - Sioux City [39706]
SCORE - Sioux Falls [44631]
SCORE - Skokie [39077]
SCORE - SLCC Microbusiness Connection Branch [45622]
SCORE - Smyrna [38673]
SCORE - Snellville [38674]
SCORE - Somerset [42088]
SCORE - Somerville FabVille Design Lab [40542]
SCORE - Somerville Public Library [40543]
SCORE - Sonora [36699]
SCORE - South Alabama [36073]
SCORE - South Carolina Lowcountry [44530]
SCORE - South Central Indiana [39506], [39507]
SCORE - South Central Iowa [39707]
SCORE - South Central Minnesota [41179]
SCORE - South Dakota [44632]
SCORE - South East Indiana [39508]
SCORE - South Metro [41180]
SCORE - South Palm Beach [38302]
SCORE - South Sound/Tacoma [46037]
SCORE - South Windsor [38016]
SCORE - Southampton [42489]
SCORE - Southeast Massachusetts [40544]
SCORE - Southeast Minnesota [41181]
SCORE - Southeast Wisconsin [46351]
SCORE - Southeastern Connecticut (SECT) [38017]
SCORE - Southern Arizona [36299]
SCORE - Southern Maryland [40360]
SCORE - Southern New Jersey [42089]
SCORE - Southlake Chamber of Commerce [45005]
SCORE - Southlake Public Library [45006]
SCORE - Southwest Florida [38303]
SCORE - Southwest Louisiana [40142]
SCORE - Southwest Missouri [41507]
SCORE - Space Coast [38304]
SCORE - Spokane [46038]
SCORE - Springfield, Illinois [39078]
SCORE - Springfield, Pennsylvania [44154]
SCORE - Staten Island [42490]
SCORE - Statesboro [38675]
SCORE - Station Island [42491]
SCORE - Steamboat Springs [37808]
SCORE - Sterling Heights [40839]
SCORE - Stevens Point [46352]
SCORE - Stoneham [40545]
SCORE - Streamwood [39079]
SCORE - Stuart [38305]
SCORE - Sturbridge [40546]
SCORE - Sugar Hill [38676]
SCORE - Summit [42090]
SCORE - Sumter [44531]
SCORE - Suncoast/Pinellas [38296]
SCORE - Sunnyvale [36700]
SCORE - Sunrise [38306]
SCORE - Surprise AZ TechCelerator [36300]
SCORE - Susquehanna [44155]
SCORE - Syracuse [42492]
SCORE - Tacoma [46037]
SCORE - Tampa [38307]
SCORE - Tarrytown [42493]
SCORE - Taunton [40540]
SCORE - Taylor [40840]
SCORE - Teaneck [42091]
SCORE - TechTown Detroit [40841]
SCORE - Telford [44156]
SCORE - Tempe [36301]
SCORE - Tempe Public Library [36302]
SCORE - The Woodlands [45007]
SCORE - The Workplace Pacific Gateway [36701]
SCORE - Tip of the Mitt [40842]
SCORE - Titusville [38308]
SCORE - Tomball [45008]
SCORE - Tooele [45623]
SCORE - Topeka [39851]
SCORE - Torrington [38018]
SCORE - Totowa [42092]
SCORE - Traverse City [40843]
SCORE - Treasure Coast [38309]
SCORE - Treasure Valley [38903]
SCORE - Tricounty [44157]
SCORE - Troy, New York [42494]

SCORE - Tulsa [43727]
SCORE - Twin Cities [41174]
SCORE - Ulster [42495]
SCORE - Union [42093]
SCORE - U.S. Virgin Islands [46648]
SCORE - University of Southern California [36702]
SCORE - Upper Shore [40361]
SCORE - Urban Chamber of Commerce [41926]
SCORE - Utica [42496]
SCORE - Vallejo [36703]
SCORE - Valparaiso [39505]
SCORE - Vancouver [46039]
SCORE - Venice [38310]
SCORE - Ventura County [36704]
SCORE - Vernon [38019]
SCORE - Vero Beach Chamber of Commerce [38311]
SCORE - Vienna [45819]
SCORE - Villanova [44158]
SCORE - Virginia Beach [45820]
SCORE - Volusia/Flagler [38312]
SCORE - Waco [45009]
SCORE - Wake Forest [43072]
SCORE - Wallingford [38020]
SCORE - Walnut Creek [36705]
SCORE - Walt Whitman Mall [42497]
SCORE - Warner Robins [38677]
SCORE - Warren, New Jersey [42094]
SCORE - Warren, Rhode Island [44465]
SCORE - Warsaw [39509]
SCORE - Warwick [44466]
SCORE - Washington DC [40362]
SCORE - Washington, DC [38162]
SCORE - Waterbury [38021]
SCORE - Waterford [38022]
SCORE - Waterford Township [40844]
SCORE - Wausau [46353]
SCORE - Wayne [44159]
SCORE - Waynesville [43073]
SCORE - Wellington [38313]
SCORE - Wenatchee [46040]
SCORE - West Chester [44160]
SCORE - West Covina [36706]
SCORE - West Grove [44161]
SCORE - West Hartford [38023]
SCORE - West Hollywood [36707]
SCORE - West Massachusetts [40547]
SCORE - West Shore [44162]
SCORE - West Tisbury [40548]
SCORE - West Virginia [46261]
SCORE - Westborough [40549]
SCORE - Westchester [42498]
SCORE - Western Connecticut [38024]
SCORE - Western Montana [41745]
SCORE - Western North Carolina [43074]
SCORE - Westfield [42095]
SCORE - Westlake Village [36708]
SCORE - Westmoreland County [44163]
SCORE - WeWork Detroit [40845]
SCORE - Wheaton [39080]
SCORE - Wheeling [39081]
SCORE - White Plains [42499]
SCORE - Whitinsville [40550]
SCORE - Whittier [36709]
SCORE - Wichita [39852]
SCORE - Wilkes-Barre [44164]
SCORE - Willamette [43932]
SCORE - Williamsburg [45821]
SCORE - Wilmette [39082]
SCORE - Winchester [44705]
SCORE - Wisconsin Rapids [46354]
SCORE - Wolfeboro [41982]
SCORE - Woodbridge [42096]
SCORE - Woodland Hills [36710]
SCORE - Worcester [40551]
SCORE - Worcester Public Library [40552]
SCORE - Yakima Valley [46041]
SCORE - Yankton [44633]
SCORE - Yonkers [42500]
SCORE - Yonkers Riverfront Library [42501]
SCORE - Youngstown [43392]
Scorecasting: The Hidden Influences Behind How Sports Are Played and Games Are Won [15183], [30026]
Scores Rotisserie & Ribs [14250]
"Scoring Boost Should be Coming for Renters' Credit" in *Providence Business News* (Vol. 29, July 14, 2014, No. 15, pp. 7) [4807], [11077], [13827]
Scotiabank Archives [6726]
"Scotiabank Targets More Baby Boomers" in *Globe & Mail* (March 4, 2006, pp. B5) [6595], [9785], [18322], [19058]
Scott County Chamber of Commerce [44799], [45895]
Scott M. Watson Inc. [31100]
"Scott Rothstein Ponzi Reveals Ethics Issues in Jewelry Biz" in *South Florida Business Journal* (Vol. 33, September 14, 2012, No. 7, pp. 1) [9981], [18684], [23532]

Scott Shor Managing Partner at Edmund's Oast [1950]
Scottdale Area Chamber of Commerce [44295]
Scott's Canadian Dental Directory [10851]
Scott's Canadian Pharmacy Directory [5192]
Scott's Directories: National Manufacturers [10577], [29089]
Scotts Valley Chamber of Commerce (SVCC) [37180]
Scottsbluff/Gering United Chamber of Commerce [41885]
Scottsdale Area Chamber [36359]
Scottsdale Area Chamber of Commerce [36359]
Scottsville-Allen County Chamber of Commerce [40085]
Scottsville Community Chamber of Commerce [45867]
Scout Ventures [42798]
SCP Journal [11348]
"SCPA Members Seek Senate Support for H.R. 872" in *Farm Industry News* (May 26, 2011) [17107], [25528]
The Scranton Enterprise Center (SEC) [44419]
The Scranton Plan News [44296]
Scrap [13741]
Scrap Magazine [13741]
Scrap Processing and Recycling [13741]
Scrap & Stamp Arts [4681]
Scrapbooking for Profit: Cashing in on Retail, Home-Based and Internet Opportunities [4576], [4648], [21770], [26749], [32079], [35482]
Screen Printing Equipment & Supply Startup Checklist [14355]
"Screening for the Best Stock Screens" in *Barron's* (Vol. 90, September 13, 2010, No. 37, pp. 36) [6596], [9786], [24094], [33248]
"Screening-Oriented Recruitment Messages: Antecedents and Relationships with Applicant Pool Quality" in *Human Resource Management* (Vol. 51, May- June 2012, No. 3, pp. 343-360) [5445], [19753], [26653], [27038]
Screenmobile Corporation [16527]
"Screenprinting Marketing Ideas" in *Chron* [14356]
Screven County Chamber of Commerce (SCCC) [38779]
Scrubway Wash And Lube [2114]
"Scrum: The Art of Doing Twice the Work in Half the Time" [28807], [35000]
"SCS Renewables Helps Hook Up Solar Deals" in *Silicon Valley/San Jose Business Journal* (Vol. 30, July 13, 2012, No. 16, pp. 1) [14942], [30806]
The Sculptors Society of Canada (SSC) [1007]
Sculpture Hospitality [1370], [10341], [28020]
SCVCC E-News [37181]
SDDA Annual Session [10883]
SDL Ventures [37483]
Sea Shores Association of Chambers of Commerce [42109]
Seacoast Capital [35457], [40726]
Seacoast SCORE Chapter 185 [41983]
Seafood Festivals [6751]
"Seafood Sustainability — Consumer Preference Study" in *Fresh Seafood* (November 12, 2018) [6752], [23351]
Seagoville Chamber of Commerce (SCC) [45353]
"Seahawks' Win? A Seattle Windfall" in *Puget Sound Business Journal* (Vol. 34, January 10, 2014, No. 39, pp. 3) [1350], [8455], [14013], [15184], [21132]
Seal Beach Chamber of Commerce - California [37182]
Sealmaster [4353]
Sealy Chamber of Commerce [45354]
Sean Finter CEO and Head Coach at Finter Group [14084]
SeaPoint Ventures, LLC [46197]
"The Search for Big Oil" in *Canadian Business* (Vol. 80, April 9, 2007, No. 8, pp. 10) [19059], [24730], [30882]
"Search and Discover New Opportunities" in *DM News* (Vol. 31, December 14, 2009, No. 29, pp. 13) [348], [7703], [9225], [11792], [21969], [30027]
"Search Engine Optimization is Becoming a Must for Businesses, But Unethical Companies Can Hurt Worse than Help" in *Idaho Business Review* (August 3, 2012) [9226], [16464], [23533], [30028]
"Search Engine Optimization Companies Rose From Need and Path of Least Resistance" in *Idaho Business Review* (August 3, 2012) [9227], [16465]
Search Engine Optimization Training [21424]
"Search Engines: Image Conscious" in *Canadian Business* (Vol. 81, February 26, 2008, No. 4, pp. 36) [3520], [3637], [9228], [14823], [16466], [26403], [33899]
"Sears, After Years of Closures, to Open Three Small-Format Stores" in *The Wall Street Journal* (April 4, 2019) [793]
"Sears and H&R Block Offer New Tax Preparation Options and Savings Through Tax Season" in *Benzinga.com* (January 30, 2012) [15412], [31505], [32276], [33900]
"Sears' Lampert Solid in Game of Valuation Chicken" in *Globe & Mail* (February 25, 2006, pp. B2) [6597], [9787], [31506]

"Seasonal Franchises: Strategies to Advance" in *Franchising World* (Vol. 42, August 2010, No. 8, pp. 50) [14014], [24406], [32961], [34878]
"Seattle Art Gallery Upends Curatorial Norms and Centers Indigenous Viewpoints" in *Nonprofit Quarterly* (September 30, 2019) [974]
Seattle Boat Show [10625]
Seattle Metropolitan Chamber of Commerce [46104]
Seattle Southside Chamber of Commerce [46159]
Seattle Sutton's Franchise Corp. [14251]
Seaworthy [2834]
Sebago Lakes Region Chamber of Commerce (SLRCC) [40305]
Sebastian River Area Chamber of Commerce [38498]
Sebastopol Area Chamber of Commerce [37183]
Sebastopol Area Chamber of Commerce and Visitors Center [37183]
"S.E.C. Adopts New Broker Rules That Consumer Advocates Say Are Toothless" in *The New York Times* (June 5, 2019) [9788], [25529]
"SEC Decide if Austin Ventures is VC Firm" in *Austin Business Journal* (Vol. 31, June 17, 2011, No. 15, pp. 1) [9789], [25530], [35382]
"SEC FAQs About Crowdfunding Intermediaries" in *Mondaq Business Briefing* (June 11, 2012) [18685], [25531], [30932]
"SEC, NASAA Tell Small Businesses: Wait To Join the 'Crowd': Crowdfunding Is 'Not Yet Legal Until the Commission Appoints Rules', Says SEC's Kim" in *Investment Advisor* (Vol. 3, August 2012, No. 8, pp. 13) [22971], [25532], [28072], [30900], [35248]
"SEC Report On Rating Agencies Falls Short" in *Barron's* (Vol. 88, July 14, 2008, No. 28, pp. 35) [6598], [9790], [20337], [20497], [21133], [24095], [25533], [34157]
SEC Ventures [37682], [37760]
"Secaucus-Based Freshpet is Barking Up the Right Tree" in *Record* (September 8, 2011) [8045], [12225], [15025]
Second Amendment Foundation (SAF) [7829]
Second Avenue Partners LLC [46198]
"A Second Chance at Road Dollars" in *Orlando Business Journal* (Vol. 26, February 5, 2010, No. 36, pp. 1) [1557], [4224], [25059], [25158]
The Second Cup Ltd. [7591]
"The Second Machine Age: Work, Progress, and Prosperity in a Time of Brilliant Technologies" [21134], [26404]
"The Second Most Fuel-Efficient Tractor of the Decade: John Deere 8320R" in *Farm Industry News* (November 10, 2011) [5705], [5971], [17108], [23352], [29372]
"Second to None" in *Crain's Detroit Business* (Vol. 26, January 18, 2010, No. 3, pp. 9) [18323], [25060], [26654]
Second Source Imaging [10864]
Secondary Materials and Recycled Textiles Association (SMART) [13694]
Secondary Raw Materials [13740]
"The Secret Behind Building Your Own Apps? It's Not As Hard As You Think" in *Mashable* (October 20, 2019) [3638], [21623]
"The Secret to Keeping a School Supplies Store Open in the Amazon Era" in *The New York Times* (September 13, 2018) [15543], [19923], [21977]
The Secret Key to Magnetic Content that Makes Sales [30161]
The Secret Language of Competitive Intelligence: How to See Through and Stay Ahead of Business Disruptions, Distortions, Rumors, and Smoke [19924], [22788]
"The Secret Strategy for Meaningful Sales Meetings" in *Agency Sales Magazine* (Vol. 39, December 2009, No. 11, pp. 40) [17747], [22244], [32614]
"Secrets to Improve Your Small Business Leadership Skills" in *Small Business Trends* (January 17, 2023) [28808]
Secrets of Next-Level Entrepreneurs: 11 Powerful Lessons to Thrive in Business and Lead a Balanced Life [22789]
Secrets of Power Marketing [30029]
"Secrets To Trade Show Success" in *Women Entrepreneur* (September 12, 2008) [15893], [17748], [18324], [24731], [32277], [33249], [35089], [35853]
"Secrets of the World's Top Sales Performers: Book Summary" [32615]
Section for Women in Public Administration (SWPA) [31678]
"Secure Future" in *Small Business Opportunities* (November 2010) [14366], [35510]
Secured Finance Network (SFNet) [28080], [35307]
The Secured Lender [9925]
SecuriJeunes Canada [25687]
"Securing our Cyber Status" in *San Antonio Business Journal* (Vol. 28, May 16, 2014, No. 14, pp. 4) [9229], [14454], [21971], [32035], [32820]

Securities and Exchange Commission - Office of Small Business Policy - Small Business Ombudsman [47359]
Securities Industry Association [9299]
Securities Industry and Financial Markets Association (SIFMA) [9299]
Security Alarm Services Industry in the US - Market Research Report [14487]
Security Equipment Industry Association [14379]
Security Equipment Manufacturers Association [14379]
Security Hardware Distributors Association (SHDA) [10353]
Security Industry Association (SIA) [14379]
Security Management [14489]
Security Nation [14490]
Security Services Industry in the US - Market Research Report [14488]
Security Traders Association (STA) [9300]
"SECU's Tax Preparation Services Net Members More Than $86 Million in Refunds" in *Economics Week* (May 11, 2012) [15413], [17347], [24096], [34367]
Sedalia Area Chamber of Commerce [41629]
Sedalia Area Chamber of Commerce and Convention and Visitors' Bureau [41629]
"Sedentary Shoppers: Point, Click, Buy" in *Barron's* (Vol. 90, September 6, 2010, No. 36, pp. 11) [9791], [18325], [20054], [24097], [32278], [32616], [32962], [34158]
Sedgwick County Zoo Library (SCZ) [5779]
"Sedo Keeps Trucking in Good Times and Bad" in *Crain's Chicago Business* (Vol. 31, April 28, 2008, No. 17, pp. 35) [8760], [16082], [18326], [27712], [31507]
Sedona Chamber of Commerce [36360]
Sedona-Oak Creek Canyon Chamber of Commerce [36360]
Sedro-Woolley Chamber of Commerce [46148]
Seed Capital Partners, LP [45470]
"Seed-Count Labeling" in *Farm Industry News* (October 20, 2010) [17109], [25534]
"Seed Funding: Monsanto Plants Millions in Image Advertising" in *Saint Louis Business Journal* (Vol. 31, July 29, 2011, No. 49, pp. 1) [349], [30030], [35383]
Seed Spot [36402]
Seed-Stage Venture Investing: An Insider's Guide to Start-Ups for Scientists, Engineers, and Investors [22417], [26176], [35249]
SeedStep Angels [43707]
"Seeing the Light" in *American Printer* (Vol. 128, July 1, 2011, No. 7) [3330], [12754], [16206]
"SEEing an Opportunity: Golden's Eyewear Chain Has a National Vision" in *Crain's Detroit Business* (Vol. 24, January 7, 2008, No. 1) [16303], [18327], [22790]
"Seen & Noted: A Home's Identity in Black and White" in *Crain's Chicago Business* (Vol. 31, April 21, 2008, No. 16, pp. 35) [3331], [9230], [13278], [16467], [20498], [34159]
SEEP Network [33488]
Segal Co. [17411]
"Segmenting When It Matters" in *Business Strategy Review* (Vol. 21, Spring 2010, No. 1, pp. 46) [20499], [28809]
Seguin Area Chamber of Commerce (SACC) [45355]
Seguin-Guadalupe County Chamber of Commerce [45355]
SEIU - District 925 [16223]
Seizure: European Journal of Epilepsy [26049]
Selby Venture Partners [37484]
Seldovia Chamber of Commerce [36241]
Select Sandwich Co. [14252]
Select Venture Partners LLC [45992]
SelectBooks Inc. (SB) [43005]
Selected Independent Funeral Homes [7204]
Selecting the Right CPA Firm [16831]
Self-Counsel Press Ltd. [46712]
Self-Employed Tax Solutions: Quick, Simple, Money-Saving, Audit-Proof Tax and Recordkeeping Basics [91], [1772], [15414], [16832], [34879]
"Self-Employment Taxes" in *The Balance Small Business* (June 25, 2019) [32992], [34248], [34880]
"Self-Employment in the United States" in *Montly Labor Review* (Vol. 133, September 2010, No. 9, pp. 17) [4225], [17110], [33250], [34160]
"Self-Employment: What To Know To Be Your Own Boss" in *Occupational Outlook Quarterly* (Vol. 58, Summer 2014, No. 2, pp. 2) [22418], [24556]
Self Guided Tour of Historic Buildings in Deer Lodge [41791]
Self-Made Boss: Advice, Hacks, and Lessons from Small Business Owners [33596]
"Self-Order Kiosks Are Finally Having a Moment in the Fast Food Space" in *Forbes* (July 30, 2019) [10038], [14015]
Self-Publishing for Dummies [1676], [32993]
Self-Service Storage Association [12972]

"The Self Starting Entrepreneurs Handbook" [18867], [22419], [27824], [29563]
Self Storage Association (SSA) [12972]
Self Storage Association Executive Ski Workshop [12990]
Self Storage Association Spring Conference and Tradeshow [12991]
Self-Storage Now! [12989]
"Selfridges Has Already Opened Its Christmas Shop - and There's Still Five Months to Go" in House Beautiful (July 29, 2019) [2924]
"Sell a Movement Within a Smoothie" in Canadian Business (Vol. 87, July 2014, No. 7, pp. 58) [8046], [12431], [18328], [30031], [32617]
"Sellers Face Excess Land Dilemma" in Crain's Cleveland Business (Vol. 28, November 12, 2007, No. 45, pp. 1) [4226], [13279], [13558]
Selling the Invisible: A Field Guide to Modern Marketing [15758], [16009], [18686], [25929], [30032], [32618], [33251]
"Selling a Job When There's Buyer's Remorse" in Contractor (Vol. 56, December 2009, No. 12, pp. 37) [513], [5386], [12657], [14631], [28810]
Selling to Major Accounts: A Strategic Approach (Onsite) [32446]
"Selling Michigan; R&D Pushed as Reason For Chinese To Locate In State" in Crain's Detroit Business (Vol. 24, January 14, 2008) [9792], [11433], [27713], [29373], [32821]
Selling Online: Canada's Bestselling Guide to Becoming a Successful E-Commerce Merchant [1080], [11690], [14455], [21972], [30033], [32279], [32619]
Selling Online for Dummies [11793]
"Selling to Other Businesses: 8 Sales Promotion Methods for a B2B Market" in business.com (April 28, 2020) [19242], [30034]
Selling Power: Success strategies for sales management [32676]
"Selling With Strengths; Talent Trumps Training" in Gallup Management Journal (March 24, 2011) [21624], [32620]
Selling Your Business: Eight Steps [19230]
Sellmeyer Engineering [13058]
Selma District Chamber of Commerce (SDCC) [37184]
SEMA News [1121], [29455]
Semi-Annual Costume Convention [3067], [4557]
"Seminar on Crowdfunding Set for Aug. 1" in Gazette (July 25, 2012) [14519], [25535], [28196], [30933], [35384]
Seminole Chamber of Commerce [43805]
Seminole Community College [38602]
Seminole County/Lake Mary Regional Chamber of Commerce [38499]
Seminole County Regional Chamber of Commerce [38499]
Seminole State College of Florida (SSC) [38602]
Seminole Technology Business Incubation Center (STBIC) [38580]
"Senate Approval Adds Steam to Port of Savannah Project" in Atlanta Business Chronicle (May 30, 2014, pp. 18A) [7047], [25536]
"Senator Grills Collection Agency, Health System Executives" in Collections & Credit Risk (May 31, 2012) [4808], [14456], [18687], [20338], [25537], [25930]
Seneca Chamber of Commerce [39954]
Seneca County Chamber of Commerce [42670]
Seneca Regional Chamber of Commerce and Visitor Services [43569]
Seneca Salamanca Chamber of Commerce [42671]
"Senior-Owned Small Businesses Get a Boost under Kim's Bipartisan Bill" in The Ripon Advance (April 26, 2022) [33073]
Senior Project Management [28416]
"Sense of Discovery" in Business Journal Portland (Vol. 27, November 19, 2010, No. 38, pp. 1) [6599], [9793], [14824], [15283], [18688], [28197], [31508], [33901]
Sensitivity Skills in Working with Others (Onsite) [17612]
Sensors Expo & Conference [24847]
Sentient Ventures [45471]
"Sentiment Split on Financials: Is the Worse Over or Still to Come?" in Barron's (Vol. 88, March 24, 2008, No. 12, pp. M14) [6600], [9794], [20339], [21135], [24098], [28198]
SEO Design Chicago [16151]
The SEO Manifesto: A Practical and Ethical Guide to Internet Marketing and Search Engine Optimization [9231], [16468], [21973], [23534]
SEPA Solar Power International [14961]
Sequel Venture Partners [37929]
Sequim-Dungeness Valley Chamber of Commerce [46149]
Sequoia Capital [37485], [37761]
Seramount [30520]

Seraph Group [38812]
Serendipity Labs [39427]
Serial Number Reference Book for Metalworking Machinery [10435]
"Serious Growth Ahead for Tokyo Joe's" in Denver Business Journal (Vol. 65, April 4, 2014, No. 47, pp. A9) [14016], [19582], [24407]
Serra Ventures [39375]
Service Based Franchising: What Franchisors Want [24408]
The Service Contract Act (Onsite) [35166]
Service Corps of Retired Executives [24591], [28267]
"The Service Imperative" in Business Horizons (Vol. 51, January-February 2008, No. 1, pp. 39) [21625], [27714], [27946], [32036], [32822], [33252]
Service Industry Association (SIA) [33087]
Service Quality Institute (SQI) [20553]
Service-Tech Corp. (STC) [2115]
ServiceMaster of Canada Limited [33326]
Services Cooperative Association (SCA) [45547]
Services de Sante GEM [8285]
"Serving Unfair Customers" in Business Horizons (Vol. 51, January-February 2008, No. 1, pp. 29) [20500]
Servpro Industries, Inc. [4833], [5097], [16243]
"Seton Grows Heart Institute" in Austin Business Journal (Vol. 31, July 15, 2011, No. 19, pp. A1) [18330], [25931]
Seton Hall University College of Arts and Sciences - Center for Public Service [26141]
"Setting Business Goals: The First Step to a Successful Business" in Asana website (Sept. 14, 2021) [19583]
"Setting Out on Your Own? Think Franchises" in Crain's Cleveland Business (Vol. 28, October 8, 2007, No. 40, pp. 20) [24409], [33597], [34161]
Setting Up a Successful Photography Business [12286], [12333]
Setting Up Your Ceramic Studio: Ideas and Plans from Working Artists [4577], [4649], [4703]
Setting Yourself Up for Financial Success with Crystalynn Shelton [24217]
"Seven Annoying People You'll Meet At Your Company Golf Day" in Canadian Business (Vol. 85, August 29, 2012, No. 14, pp. 76) [7527], [17749]
Seven Days in the Art World [975], [3332], [4603]
The Seven Principles of WOM and Buzz Marketing: Crossing the Tipping Point [350], [30035]
"Seven Things Great Employers Do (That Others Don't); Unusual, Innovative, and Proven Tactics To Create Productive and Profitable Working Environments" in Gallup Business Journal (April 15, 2014) [6601], [8456], [14017], [22245], [25932], [28811], [29374], [32280]
"Seven Tips for Continuous Improvement" in American Printer (Vol. 128, July 1, 2011, No. 7) [3333], [12755], [16207], [29375]
Sevierville Chamber of Commerce [44800]
Sevin Rosen Funds (SRF) [45472]
"Sewage from RVs May Be Contaminating Waterways, Seattle Businesses Warn" in King5News (October 24, 2019) [13677], [14632]
Seward Area Chamber of Commerce [36242]
Seward Chamber of Commerce [36243]
"Seward Restaurant Garners Accolades" in Alaska Business Monthly (Vol. 27, October 2011, No. 10, pp. 9) [14018], [15026]
"Sewing Is a Life Skill; Teaching To Sew Is An Art" in Virginia-Pilot (August 31, 2010) [4663], [14659], [21626]
Sexual Harassment and Assault at Work: Understanding the Costs [20577]
Sexual Harassment Policy for Small Businesses [20578]
Seymour Chamber of Commerce [44801]
SF Camerawork Reference Library [12329]
"S.F. Leasing Off to Hottest Start Since 2000" in San Francisco Business Times (Vol. 28, January 17, No. 26, pp. 8) [13559], [13828], [32037]
"S.F. Tourism Soars to Giddy Heights" in San Francisco Business Times (Vol. 28, January 10, 2014, No. 25, pp. 11) [15759], [16010]
SFA Winter Fancy Food Show [2552], [8189], [15054]
SGA Business Systems, Inc. [3667]
SGIA Expo [7599]
Shafter Chamber of Commerce (SCC) [37185]
Shake Shack Inc. [14253]
Shake's Frozen Custard Inc. [8634]
Shakespeare Composite Structures [946]
Shakey's Pizza & Buffet [14254]
Shakopee Chamber of Commerce [41305]
Shakopee Valley Convention and Visitors Bureau [41305]
Shamrock Chamber of Commerce [45356]
Shane's Rib Shack [14255]
Shannon Staffing Inc. [27157], [30223], [31813]
Shape [12446], [16510]

SHAPE America National Convention & Expo [15123]
Share [26050]
Share A Kitchen [39428]
Shared Kitchen Rentals [37631]
"Shared Leadership In Teams: An Investigation of Antecedent Conditions and Performance" in Academy of Management Journal (Vol. 50, No. 5, October 1, 2007, pp. 1217) [22246], [22791], [28812]
SharePoint I (Onsite) [22992]
SharePoint II (Onsite) [22993]
SharePoint III (Onsite) [22994]
"Sharing's Not Just for Start-ups: What Marriott, GE, and Other Traditiional Companies are Learning About the Collaborative Economy" in Harvard Business Review (Vol. 92, September 2014, No. 9, pp. 23) [21136], [21627], [33253]
"Shari's Berries Founder Shuts Last Store" in Sacramento Business Journal (Vol. 28, September 2, 2011, No. 27, pp. 1) [2547], [35854]
Sharkey's Cuts For Kids [2040]
Sharonville Chamber of Commerce [43538]
"Sharp Restarts Toner Manufacturing: Production Moved from Japan to Serve China Market" in Memphis Business Journal (Vol. 34, May 11, 2012, No. 4, pp. 1) [7048], [11668], [21137], [25061], [29376]
"Shattering the Myths About U.S. Trade Policy: Stop Blaming China and India. A More Active Trade Policy Can Lead to a Stronger U.S. Economy" in Harvard Business Review (Vol. 90, March 2012, No. 3, pp. 149) [8761], [19925], [21138], [25538], [27715]
Shattuck Chamber of Commerce [43806]
"A Shave, a Haircut — and a Blood Pressure Check" in U.S. News & World Report (April 15, 2019) [7874], [25933]
Shaw & Associates [20673]
Shaw University - Innovation and Entrepreneurship Center [43251]
Shawano Country Chamber of Commerce [46512]
Shawano County Economic Progress, Inc. (SCEPI) [46573]
Shawnee Chamber of Commerce (SCC) [39955]
She+ Geeks Out, LLC [30430], [30653], [35924]
She Runs It [225], [31844]
"Shear Profit" in Crain's Cleveland Business (Vol. 28, October 29, 2007, No. 43, pp. 3) [657], [17111], [18331], [34881]
"Shear Savvy" in Puget Sound Business Journal (Vol. 35, July 25, 2014, No. 14, pp. 14) [7875]
Sheboygan County Chamber of Commerce [46513]
Sheboygan Falls Chamber Main Street [46514]
"Shedding Light on Innovation" in Rental Product News (Vol. 33, June 2011) [13829], [27947], [29377]
Shedworking: The Alternative Workplace Revolution [4227], [26804], [34162]
Sheerlund Products LLC [2930]
Sheet Metal and Air Conditioning Contractors' National Association (SMACNA) [464]
"Sheet Metal Union Locals Join Forces: Could Help Local Contractors Compete for Bay Area Jobs" in Sacramento Business Journal (Vol. 29, June 29, 2012, No. 18, pp. 1) [10441], [19926], [31509], [35203]
Shefield Gourmet Cup Beverage Station [15713]
Shelburne Museum Research Library [761]
Shelby Area Chamber of Commerce (SACC) [41792]
Shelby County Chamber of Commerce [45357]
Shelby County Chamber of Commerce (SCCC) [39605]
Shelby County Chamber of Commerce & Industry (SCCCI) [39791]
Shelby Report of the Southeast [7805]
Shelby Report of the Southwest [7806]
Shelbyville-Bedford County Chamber of Commerce [44802]
Sheldon Chamber and Development Corp. (SCDC) [39792]
Shell Lake Chamber of Commerce (SLCC) [46515]
"Shell Profits Top $2 Billion as Oil Sands Output Surges" in Globe & Mail (January 26, 2006, pp. B6) [18332], [29378]
"Shell Venture Aims at 'Oil Rocks'" in Globe & Mail (March 22, 2006, pp. B1) [19060], [30883]
"Shellshocked: Dealing With Cyber Insecurity" in Philadelphia Business Journal (Vol. 33, June 13, 2014, No. 18, pp. 4) [3521], [3639], [9232], [14457], [21974]
Shelter Advertising Association [31840]
"Shelters Vie for $500,000 In Adoption Contest" in Pet Product News (Vol. 66, September 2012, No. 9, pp. 19) [696], [7156]
Sheltie Pacesetter [665]
Shelton-Mason County Chamber of Commerce (SMCCC) [46150]
Shelton-Mason County Journal [46151]
Shenandoah Chamber of Commerce [39793]
Shenandoah Chamber and Industry Association (SCIA) [39793]

Shenandoah County Chamber of Commerce [45896]
Shenandoah County Library - Local History and Genealogy Collection [7450]
Shenandoah Valley Small Business Development Center (SVSBDC) [45788]
Shenango Valley Chamber of Commerce [44297]
Shepherd Ventures [37486]
Sherbrooke University - Centre de Recherche sur le Vieillissement (CDRV) [11553]
Sherbrooke University - Gerontology and Geriatrics Research Centre [11553]
Sherbrooke University - Research Centre on Aging [11553]
Sheridan Chamber of Commerce [39589]
Sheridan County Chamber of Commerce [46620]
"Shermag Says Refinishing Not Complete" in Globe & Mail (February 14, 2006, pp. B3) [19061], [19584]
Sherman Oaks Chamber of Commerce [36926]
Sherman Oaks Chamber NEWS [37186]
Sherpa Partners L.L.C. [41338]
Sherpalo Ventures [37487]
"Sherwin-Williams Workers Forgo Travel for Virtual Trade Show" in Crain's Cleveland Business (Vol. 28, October 15, 2007, No. 41, pp. 4) [9233], [15894], [26405], [29379], [35090]
Sherwood Chamber of Commerce (SCC) [36497], [44014]
Sherwood Chamber of Commerce Business and Community Directory [36520]
Shetland Properties L.P. [39429]
Shiawassee Regional Chamber of Commerce (SRCC) [41009]
SHIELD Security Systems [14496]
Shifting Your Company's Culture [28932]
The Shine Factory [1146], [2586]
Shiner Chamber of Commerce [45358]
Shingle Springs/Cameron Park Chamber of Commerce [37187]
Shingle Springs/Cameron Park Chamber of Commerce Member Directory [37188]
"Shining a Light on Entrepreneurial Opportunities" in San Antonio Business Journal (Vol. 28, July 11, 2014, No. 22, pp. 4) [22792], [25062], [28199]
"Ship Shape" in Hawaii Business (Vol. 53, January 2008, No. 7, pp. 46) [30884], [33254]
Shippensburg Area Chamber of Commerce (SACOC) [44298]
Shippensburg University of Pennsylvania - Office of Professional, Continuing and Distance Education [1796]
Shippensburg University Small Business Development Center (SBDC) [44104]
"Shire Seeking New Digs for Headquarters" in Philadelphia Business Journal (Vol. 30, September 2, 2011, No. 29, pp. 1) [5185], [19202], [27716], [32038], [32823], [33410]
Shirley Ryan AbilityLab - Sensory Motor Performance Program (SMPP) [12517]
Shoals Business Incubator (SEI) [36191]
Shoals Chamber of Commerce (SCC) [36151]
Shoals Commercial Culinary Center [36192]
"Shocks and Final Straws: Using Exit-Interview Data to Examine the Unfolding Model's Decision Paths" in Human Resource Management (Vol. 51, January-February 2012, No. 1, pp. 25-46) [17750], [27039]
Shoe Repair Industry in the US - Market Research Report [14664]
Shoe Retailing Today [14690]
Shoe Service Institute of America (SSIA) [14662]
Shoes-n-Feet [14697]
Shoot Commercial Production Directory [6208]
SHOOT Commercial Production and Postproduction Directory [6208]
The SHOOT Directory for Commercial Production and Postproduction [6208]
Shooting Times [856]
Shop Class as Soulcraft [22247], [24732]
"Shop Happy: Harvesting Happiness Announces Grassroots Crowdfunding Site for HH4Heroes" in Marketwired (July 2, 2012) [7157], [11794], [25934], [34368]
Shop 'til You Drop: Starting a Personal Shopping Business [12027]
Shopify for Dummies [11795]
"Shoppers Targets an Upscale Move" in Globe & Mail (January 19, 2007, pp. B4) [19585], [32281]
"ShopSmart: Discounts On Brand-Name Products at Dollar Store" in Entertainment Close-Up (July 17, 2012) [32282], [32621]
Shore Lines [44015]
Shoreline [45897]
Shoreline Chamber of Commerce [38073]
Shoreline Chamber of Commerce (SCC) [46152]

Shoreline Venture Management L.L.C. [37488]
Short Elliott Hendrickson Inc. (SEH) [15246]
Short Story Writers [5324]
"Shorts Season: Is It Time for a Dress Code?" in Legal Zoom (March 21, 2023) [27040]
Shotgun News: The World's Largest Gun Sales Publication [7838]
"Should All Schools Offer Music Programs?" in The New York Times (May 17, 2018) [11184]
"Should the Fed Regulate Wall Street?" in Barron's (Vol. 88, March 24, 2008, No. 12, pp. M15) [6602], [9795], [21139], [24099], [25063], [25539]
"Should Freelancers Establish Themselves as an LLC?" in Small Business Trends (August 9, 2021) [26805], [27192]
"Should I or Shouldn't I?" in Indoor Comfort Marketing (Vol. 70, February 2011, No. 2, pp. 30) [5972], [9796], [23353], [24100], [30036], [34163]
"Should I Stay or Should I Go?" in Entrepreneur (August 2014) [17751], [22793], [35001]
Should I Use a Third-Party Delivery Service or Create My Own? [6918]
"Should Managers Focus on Performance or Engagement? Gallup Examined this Question and Found That the Answer Isn't as 'Either/Or' as Many Companies Might Think" in Gallup Business Journal (August 5, 2014) [22248], [28813]
"Should My Business Get a Toll-Free Number?" in Business News Daily (February 21, 2023) [16590], [34545]
Should Startups Think Differently About Workspace? [31052]
"Should State Invest in Startups?" in Providence Business News (Vol. 28, March 3, 2014, No. 48, pp. 1) [9016], [18689], [24933], [25100], [25540], [26177]
"Should We Be Worried About Computerized Facial Recognition?" in The New Yorker (December 10, 2018) [3817]
Should You Buy a Small Business Franchise? [24410]
"Should You Choose a Lump-Sum Pension Payout? Here's How Entrepreneur Ramona Harper Decided" in Black Enterprise (Vol. 44, June 2014, No. 10, pp. 27) [6603], [9955], [17348], [22420], [24101], [35511]
"Should You Go Into Business With Your Spouse?" in Women Entrepreneur (September 1, 2008) [19062], [19586], [23581], [33434]
"Should Your Small Business Become an S-Corp?" in Brex Blog (Feb. 17, 2021) [32412]
"Should Your Small Business Care About CSR? Here's the Honest Answer" in Digital.com (October 7, 2020) [34369]
Should Your Small Business Invest in AI? [30037], [34164]
Show Low Chamber of Commerce [36361]
"Show and Tell: How Everybody Can Make Extraordinary Presentations" [14520], [15895], [17752], [35091]
"Showalter Has Orioles Rising, But is Business Following?: Buck-ing the Trend?" in Baltimore Business Journal (Vol. 28, August 13, 2010, No. 14, pp. 1) [15100], [15185], [16260]
Shreveport Chamber of Commerce [40190]
SHRM Annual Conference & Exposition [31920], [35132]
SHRM Executive Network [26844], [34964]
SHRM Talent Management Conference and Exposition [27120]
SHSMD Annual Conference [26076]
SHSMD Connections [26076]
SHSMD Connections Conference [26076]
Shutterbug [12315], [12353]
Sibley Chamber of Commerce (SCC) [39794]
Sibley Chamber of Commerce - Main Street [39794]
Side Hustle to Small Business: Amity Gleason's Journey from Attorney to Jewelry Maker [6146]
Side Hustle to Small Business: Building a Strong Foundation for Her New Creative Agency [35907]
Side Hustle to Small Business: Connecting Businesses with the Grants They Need [7175]
Side Hustle to Small Business: Creating Inclusive Spaces for Women to Collaborate [35908]
Side Hustle to Small Business: Creating a Support System as a Solopreneur [16272]
Side Hustle to Small Business: Do Not Wait Around to Jump into Entrepreneurship [22916]
Side Hustle to Small Business: Exploring the Ins and Outs of Freelancing in Today's World [16912]
Side Hustle to Small Business: Family Ties and Enterprise: Navigating Family Business Dynamics [23675]
Side Hustle to Small Business: From Designing Video Games to Getting Funded by Mark Cuban [14867]
Side Hustle to Small Business: Helping Girls Overcome Barriers to Become Entrepreneurs [22917]
Side Hustle to Small Business: How Andy O'Brien Is Redefining Work in a Family Business [23676]

Side Hustle to Small Business: How Bonnie Conrad Went from Furniture Builder to Marketer [30162]
Side Hustle to Small Business: How a Craigslist Ad Changed Sarah Flores' Life [14085]
Side Hustle to Small Business: How D.R. Ray Found Entrepreneurial Success Later in Life [33080]
Side Hustle to Small Business: How Joe Koufman Built a Career as a Business Matchmaker [22918]
Side Hustle to Small Business: How Justus Hillebrand Accidentally Became an Entrepreneur [20144]
Side Hustle to Small Business: How Michele Riechman Is Empowering Women Over 40 [6817]
Side Hustle to Small Business: How Ryan Klee Leads with Purpose through Thought Leadership [28933]
Side Hustle to Small Business: How to Turn Past Experiences into Entrepreneurial Success [6818]
Side Hustle to Small Business: How Your Perspective on Entrepreneurship Can Evolve Over Time [22919]
Side Hustle to Small Business: Improving the Work Environment by Going Solo [34470]
Side Hustle to Small Business: Knowing Your Worth After Transitioning to Self-Employment [16681]
Side Hustle to Small Business: Launching a Business to Make a Lasting Impact on the World [15806]
Side Hustle to Small Business: Launching a New Business in the Midst of a Maternity Leave [35909]
Side Hustle to Small Business: Leveraging Existing Skills to Launch a Business [22920]
Side Hustle to Small Business: Moving from Wall Street to Three-Time Entrepreneur [22921]
Side Hustle to Small Business: Nick Courtright's Shift from Academia to Entrepreneurship [1694]
Side Hustle to Small Business: Overcoming Your Fears and Achieving Your Dreams [16682]
Side Hustle to Small Business: Passion to Profit: Transforming Hobbies into Side Hustles [7597], [16273], [22922]
Side Hustle to Small Business: Pitch Pefect: How Rob Friedman Became the Pitching Ninja [15210]
Side Hustle to Small Business: Succeeding in Business after Leaving a Partnership [31595]
Side Hustle to Small Business: Taking the Stage: Courage, Confidence, and Charisma [21679]
Side Hustle to Small Business: The Challenge of Raising Funds for Your Small Business [35430]
Side Hustle to Small Business: Transitioning form the Startup World to Freelance [34639]
Side Hustle to Small Business: Turning a Pandemic Passion Project into a Full-Time Business [2990]
Side Hustle to Small Business: Using Telecommunications to Help Solve Crimes [20145]
Side Hustles for Dummies [26806]
"Side Income: Is It a Hobby or a Business?" in Money Under 30 (March 12, 2019) [4604], [4664], [31135], [33598], [34882]
SideCar Angels, Inc. [35308], [40727]
Sidney Area Chamber of Commerce and Agriculture (SACCA) [41793]
Sidney Chamber of Commerce [41793]
Siebrand-Wilton Associates Inc. (S-WA) [17412], [23569], [27158], [31619]
Siemer Ventures [37522]
Sierra Angels (SA) [41955]
Sierra Club Canada Foundation National Office (SCC) [5502]
Sierra Commons (SC) [37632]
Sierra County Chamber of Commerce [37189]
Sierra Legal Defence Fund [5483]
Sierra Madre Chamber of Commerce [37190]
Sierra Ventures [37489]
Sierra Vista Area Chamber of Commerce (SVAC) [36362]
Siesta Key Chamber of Commerce (SKCC) [38500]
Sightlines [25689]
SIGIR Forum [3536]
Sigma Partners [37490]
Sigma Prime Ventures [40728]
Sign Association of Canada (SAC) [226]
Sign Biz Inc. (SB) [395], [3357]
"Sign of the Times: Temp-To-Perm Attorneys" in HRMagazine (Vol. 54, January 2009, No. 1, pp. 24) [5446], [6110], [14985], [15646], [18690], [26655], [34165]
Signal Graphics Inc. [14709]
Signal Hill Chamber of Commerce (SHCC) [37191]
"The Signal and the Noise: Why So Many Predictions Fail - but Some Don't" [3522], [3640], [21140]
Signal Peak (SPV) [45695]
"A Signaling Theory of Acquisition Premiums: Evidence From IPO Targets" in Academy of Management Journal (Vol. 55, June 1, 2012, No. 3, pp. 667) [9797], [31510], [35385]
Signarama Inc. [14710]
Signature Alert Security [14497]

Signature Franchising Inc. **[2367]**
SignCraft: The guide to profitable and creative sign production **[14707]**
Significant Earthquake Database **[5761]**
Signs Now **[14711]**
"Signs Point To Improving CRE Market" in Birmingham Business Journal (Vol. 31, May 2, 2014, No. 18, pp. 7) **[10675]**, **[13280]**, **[13560]**, **[13830]**
"Signs of the Times" in Harvard Business Review (Vol. 92, May 2014, No. 5, pp. 36) **[16591]**, **[17753]**
Signs by Tomorrow **[14712]**
SIGSOFT Software Engineering Notes **[3657]**
Siguler Guff & Co. (SG) **[42799]**
Sikeston Area Chamber of Commerce **[41630]**
Silas Capital, LLC **[42800]**
Silicon Alley Venture Partners L.L.C. (SAVP) **[42801]**
The silicon valley organization (SVO) **[37192]**
Silicon Slopes **[18821]**
Silicon Slopes - Brigham City **[18822]**
Silicon Slopes - Cedar City **[18823]**
Silicon Slopes - Central Utah **[18824]**
Silicon Slopes - Farmington **[18825]**
Silicon Slopes - Heber Valley **[18826]**
Silicon Slopes - Logan **[18827]**
Silicon Slopes - Ogden **[18828]**
Silicon Slopes - Park City **[18829]**
Silicon Slopes - Price **[18830]**
Silicon Slopes - St. George **[18831]**
Silicon Slopes - Salt Lake City **[18832]**
Silicon Slopes - Sandy **[18833]**
Silicon Slopes - Vernal **[18834]**
Silicon Valley Business Journal **[37697]**
Silicon Valley Business Travel Association (SVBTA) **[19318]**
Silicon Valley Center for Entrepreneurship (SVCE) **[36589]**
Silicon Valley Central Chamber of Commerce (SVCCC) **[37193]**
Silicon Valley Small Business Development Center at West Valley/Mission College (SBDC) **[36590]**
Silicone Expo **[29463]**
Sill Business Incubator (SBI) **[44420]**
Siloam Springs Chamber of Commerce (SSCC) **[36498]**
Silver City Chamber of Commerce [43114]
Silver City-Grant County Chamber of Commerce **[42338]**
Silver City Small Business Development Center at Western New Mexico University (SBDC) **[42287]**
"Silver Dollars" in Small Business Opportunities (September 2008) **[185]**, **[1034]**, **[11520]**, **[24411]**
Silver Lake Sand Dunes Area Chamber of Commerce **[41010]**
Silver Mine Subs (SMS) **[14256]**
Silver Spring Innovation Center (SSIC) **[40469]**
"Silver Springs Creamery Opens Retail Store" in Bellingham Business Journal (Vol. March 2010, pp. 3) **[7773]**, **[8591]**, **[15027]**, **[32283]**
"Silver Standard Reports First Quarter 2007 Results" in Marketwired (May 14, 2007) **[6604]**, **[9798]**, **[24102]**
Silverdale Chamber of Commerce **[46153]**
"Silverpop Recognised for Email Marketing Innovations by Econsultancy" in Marketing Weekly News (January 23, 2010, pp. 124) **[9234]**, **[21975]**, **[30038]**
Silverton Area Chamber of Commerce (SACC) **[44016]**
Silverton Partners **[45600]**
"The Silvery Moon Moves to Larger Location" in Bellingham Business Journal (Vol. March 2010, pp. 5) **[9982]**, **[18333]**, **[19203]**, **[33411]**
SIMB Annual Meeting and Exhibit **[32925]**
Simi Valley Chamber of Commerce **[37194]**
Simmons College Graduate School of Library and Information Science Library (SLIS) **[1713]**
Simon Fraser University - Canadian Centre for Studies in Publishing [1714]
Simon Fraser University - Canadian Institute for Studies in Publishing (CISP) **[1714]**
Simon Fraser University Faculty of Environment - Centre for Sustainable Development (CSD) **[21281]**
The Simple Checklist You Can Use to Grow Your Business with Donald Miller **[18449]**
"A Simple Old Reg that Needs Dusting Off" in Barron's (Vol. 88, June 30, 2008, No. 26, pp. 35) **[9799]**, **[17112]**, **[18691]**, **[25541]**, **[33255]**
The Simple Path to Wealth: Your Road Map to Financial Independence and a Rich, Free Life **[6045]**, **[6605]**, **[24103]**
Simple Systems: Professional Organizing **[12819]**
Simple Systems: The Business of Organizing **[12820]**
Simplified Events Management: A Text Book to Event Planning, Fundraising and Safety Managment **[6096]**
Simplified Incorporation Kit **[24733]**, **[32413]**
Simplified Technology Co. (STC) **[31015]**, **[31101]**
Simpsonville Area Chamber of Commerce **[44582]**
Simsbury Chamber of Commerce (SCOC) **[38074]**
"Sinai Doctor's Research May Lead to Rival Plavix Drug" in Baltimore Business Journal (Vol. 28, July 16, 2010, No. 10, pp. 1) **[5186]**, **[19927]**, **[25935]**, **[27948]**, **[30807]**
Single Audit Information Service **[115]**
"Single Most Important Problem" in Small Business Economic Trends (February 2008, pp. 18) **[21141]**, **[24734]**, **[34166]**
Sinton Chamber of Commerce (SCC) **[45359]**
SIOR Report **[13323]**, **[13606]**
Sioux Center Chamber of Commerce (SCCC) **[39795]**
Sioux City Chamber of Commerce [39796]
Sioux Falls Area Chamber of Commerce (SFACC) **[44658]**
Sioux Falls Small Business Development Center **[44625]**
Siouxland Chamber of Commerce (SCC) **[39796]**
Sir Speedy Inc. **[4497]**, **[12782]**
Sir Speedy Print Signs Marketing [4497], [12782]
"Siri Creator SRI International Hopes Lola Cashes In, Too" in Silicon Valley/San Jose Business Journal (Vol. 30, July 6, 2012, No. 15, pp. 1) **[3877]**, **[14825]**, **[24104]**
Sisters Area Chamber of Commerce **[44017]**
Sisters in Crime (SinC) **[5299]**
"Sisters Partner to Open Beauty Supply Store" in The Philadelphia Tribune (August 27, 2019) **[1393]**, **[22794]**
Site Design Group Ltd. **[11654]**
Site Selection Magazine **[33426]**
Sitter4Paws **[12279]**
"Sitting, Sitting, Sitting-Snapshots of Homes that Just Won't Sell" in Crain's Chicago Business (Vol. 31, April 21, 2008, No. 16) **[13281]**, **[13561]**
Situational Leadership II Workshop (Onsite) **[28417]**
Siver Insurance Consultants **[27375]**
"Six Arkansas Construction Projects Get LEED Certification" in Arkansas Business (Vol. 29, July 23, 2012, No. 30, pp. 19) **[911]**, **[4228]**, **[5706]**, **[5973]**, **[23354]**, **[25159]**
"Six Brand-Building Strategies for Small Businesses and Startups" in Forbes (February 20, 2019) **[17452]**
"Six Flags Fiesta Texas Could See More Reinvestment" in San Antonio Business Journal (Vol. 28, April 25, 2014, No. 11, pp. 6) **[611]**
"Six Great Stock Funds for the Long Haul" in Barron's (Vol. 89, July 13, 2009, No. 28, pp. L5) **[6606]**, **[9800]**, **[24105]**
"The Six Reasons the Fitness Industry is Booming" in Forbes (September 26, 2018) **[12432]**
"Six Sears Board Members to Resign in April" in Globe & Mail (March 1, 2006, pp. B1) **[28814]**, **[32284]**
"Six Steps To Close the Sale" in Birmingham Business Journal (Vol. 31, April 11, 2014, No. 15, pp. 13) **[32622]**
Six Strategies for Fraud Prevention in Your Business **[19281]**
"Six Things for Employers to Consider When Hiring Individuals With Disabilities" in U.S. Chamber of Commerce (Aug. 25, 2022) **[26656]**, **[30603]**
"Six Ways Employees on LinkedIn Benefit the Boss" in South Florida Business Journal (Vol. 34, April 25, 2014, No. 40) **[26657]**, **[27386]**, **[28815]**
"Six Ways to Make Customer Programs Work; Most Customer Satisfaction Programs Aren't Effective. Two Consultants Explain Why and How Companies Can Fix Them" in Gallup Business Journal (June 17, 2014) **[20127]**, **[20501]**
"Six Ways to Make Your Bridal Business More Profitable - Overnight" in Mid-America Jewelry News (October 1, 2019) **[9983]**
Six Ways a Professional Organizer Can Help Your Small Business **[12846]**
"Size Does Matter" in International Journal of Globalisation and Small Business (Vol. 4, September 21, 2010, No. 1, pp. 61) **[19928]**, **[22249]**, **[27717]**, **[28046]**, **[29380]**, **[31511]**
"Sizing Up Bentley" in Barron's (Vol. 92, September 17, 2012, No. 38, pp. 16) **[11434]**, **[19929]**, **[23355]**, **[29381]**
Sizzler Inc. **[14257]**
SJF Ventures (SJF) **[43228]**
Skagway Chamber of Commerce **[36244]**
Skagway Member Directory **[36245]**
Skamania County Chamber of Commerce **[46154]**
Skaneateles Area Chamber of Commerce **[42672]**
Skaneateles Community Directory **[42673]**
Skeet Shooting Review **[857]**
SketchPad Graphic Design **[4954]**
Ski **[14741]**
Ski Industries America [14735]
Ski Industries Association [14735]
Skiatook Chamber of Commerce **[43807]**
"Skill Seekers" in South Florida Business Journal (Vol. 34, February 7, 2014, No. 29, pp. 15) **[5447]**, **[21628]**, **[26658]**
"A Skimmer's Guide to the Latest Business Books" in Inc. (Volume 32, December 2010, No. 10, pp. 34) **[1677]**, **[16592]**, **[24735]**
Skin Inc.: Professional Skin Care **[1399]**, **[1596]**, **[4531]**
Skokie Chamber of Commerce (SCC) **[39309]**
Skowhegan Area Chamber of Commerce (SACC) **[40306]**
SKU **[45548]**
"Sky Harvest Windpower Corp. - Operational Update" in Investment Weekly News (March 10, 2012, pp. 744) **[5707]**, **[5974]**, **[14943]**, **[21142]**, **[23356]**, **[25064]**, **[27718]**, **[31512]**
Sky Valley Chamber of Commerce **[46155]**
Skyhawks Sports & Supertots Sports Academy **[15214]**
Skyline Chili, Inc. **[14258]**
Skyline Ventures **[37491]**
"Skype Ltd. Acquired GroupMe" in Information Today (Vol. 28, October 2011, No. 9, pp. 12) **[2790]**, **[9801]**, **[19691]**, **[21976]**
"The Skype's the Limit" in Canadian Business (Vol. 80, February 12, 2007, No. 4, pp. 70) **[9802]**, **[18334]**, **[26406]**, **[33256]**
Skypoint Capital Corp. **[46806]**
"The Sky's the Limit" in Retail Merchandiser (Vol. 51, July-August 2011, No. 4, pp. 64) **[2548]**, **[27949]**, **[30808]**, **[32285]**
"Slater Progress Stalled" in Providence Business News (Vol. 28, March 10, 2014, No. 49, pp. 1) **[7158]**, **[25160]**, **[26407]**, **[35386]**
Slater Technology Fund **[44485]**
Slaton Chamber of Commerce **[45360]**
Slayton Area Chamber of Commerce (SACC) **[41306]**
"Sleeman Cuts Again as Cheap Suds Bite" in Globe & Mail (March 3, 2006, pp. B3) **[9803]**, **[19063]**, **[19587]**
Sleep **[26051]**
"Sleep Apnea Pill Nears Human Tests" in Philadelphia Business Journal (Vol. 33, May 9, 2014, No. 13, pp. 8) **[5187]**, **[25936]**, **[32039]**
Sleep Inn **[8515]**
"Sleep It Off In a Silo B&B" in Chicago Tribune (December 14, 2008) **[1422]**, **[17113]**, **[19394]**
"Sleeping with Your Smartphone: How to Break the 24/7 Habit and Change the Way You Work" **[2202]**, **[2791]**, **[6111]**, **[10488]**, **[20128]**, **[22250]**, **[35002]**
Sleepy Eye Area Chamber of Commerce (SEACC) **[41307]**
"A Slice of Danish; Fixing Finance" in The Economist (Vol. 390, January 3, 2009, No. 8612, pp. 55) **[6607]**, **[9804]**, **[11078]**, **[20340]**, **[21143]**, **[24106]**, **[27719]**, **[28200]**
Slidell City Map **[40191]**
Slidell Connection **[40192]**
"Slimmed-Down Supplier TI Automotive Relaunches" in Crain's Detroit Business (Vol. 26, January 11, 2010, No. 2, pp. 14) **[8762]**, **[19064]**, **[19588]**, **[20651]**, **[27720]**, **[29382]**, **[30039]**
"Slimmer Interiors Make Small Cars Seem Big" in Automotive News (Vol. 86, October 31, 2011, No. 6488, pp. 16) **[1109]**, **[11435]**, **[29383]**, **[34167]**
"Sloan's Ice Cream Inks First Franchise Deal In San Diego" in FastCasual.com (September 12, 2014) **[8536]**, **[24300]**
Slovenian Mutual Benefit Association [17258]
"Slow-Down Startups Hot" in Austin Business JournalInc. (Vol. 28, September 12, 2008, No. 26, pp. 1) **[22421]**, **[24557]**, **[24934]**
"Slow Mortgage Market Drags JPMorgan Chase Q1 Earnings Down 18.5 Percent" in Boston Business Journal (Vol. 34, April 11, 2014, No. 10) **[9805]**, **[11079]**
"Slow but Steady into the Future" in Barron's (Vol. 88, July 7, 2008, No. 27, pp. M) **[9806]**, **[14826]**, **[17754]**, **[19930]**, **[26408]**, **[32040]**, **[32824]**, **[33257]**, **[33902]**
"SLU, Des Peres Hospitals Face Unions" in St. Louis Business Journal (Vol. 32, June 1, 2012, No. 41, pp. 1) **[25937]**, **[35204]**
SMA Annual Scientific Assembly conference [10961]
SMACNA's Annual Convention **[538]**
"Small Bank Has Big Lending Plans, New Hire" in Silicon Valley/San Jose Business Journal (Vol. 30, September 21, 2012, No. 26, pp. 1) **[25065]**, **[26659]**, **[28201]**
Small Biz 101: Digital Edge: Meeting New Website Standards for Business Success **[16496]**
Small Biz 101: Hidden Treasures: Unveiling Small Business Resources at Your Public Library **[16683]**
Small Biz 101: How to Keep Clients Coming Back: Insights from Alex Theis **[24218]**
Small Biz 101: Legal Considerations for Small Business Owners **[18738]**
Small Biz 101: Sales Spark: Igniting Success in Your Small Business **[32686]**
Small Biz 101: Strategic Steps to Marketing Success **[30163]**

Master Index

Small Business Sourcebook • 42nd Edition 3335

Small Master Index

Small Biz 101: Unlocking Business Growth and Financial Freedom **[16684]**
"Small Biz Owners Are Tapping Into Health Savings Plans" in Small Business Opportunities (Fall 2007) **[8964]**, **[17349]**, **[25938]**, **[27337]**
Small Brewers Association [1890]
Small Brewers Committee [1890]
"Small Budget, Big Impact" in Small Business Opportunities (Summer 2010) **[21977]**, **[30040]**, **[32623]**
Small Business Accelerator (UBC) **[46691]**
"Small Business Accounting 101: How to Set Up and Manage Your Books" in Shopify Blog (Oct. 1, 2021) **[16833]**
Small Business Administration (SBA) **[40742]**
Small Business Administration District Advisory Councils **[38158]**
Small Business Administration Reference Library **[34232]**
Small Business Advisory Group Inc. **[37683]**
Small Business: An Entrepreneur's Plan **[22795]**, **[24736]**, **[34461]**
Small Business Assistance Center [40500]
Small Business Assistance Corporation (SBAC) **[38813]**
Small Business Association for International Companies (SBAIC) **[24936]**
Small Business Association of Michigan (SBAM) **[40819]**
Small Business Bartering Increased During the Pandemic. Is It Right for You? **[17257]**
The Small Business Bible: Everything You Need to Know to Succeed in Your Small Business **[92]**, **[351]**, **[1773]**, **[16834]**, **[24107]**, **[24737]**, **[30041]**, **[31885]**
"Small Business, Big Mentality" in Plumber Magazine (October 2017) **[12658]**
Small Business, Big Mindset: AI for Writers: Friend or Foe? **[5343]**
Small Business, Big Mindset: Creating a Truly Scalable Offer **[18450]**
Small Business, Big Mindset: How to Create a Visual Brand **[7598]**
Small Business, Big Mindset: Mastering the Art of the Hire **[26725]**
Small Business, Big Mindset: The 4 Critical Steps to Starting a Business **[16685]**
Small Business, Big Mindset: The Must-Do Offer Pre-Launch Process **[34640]**
"Small Business Capital Outlays" in Small Business Economic Trends (April 2008, pp. 16) **[18335]**, **[24108]**
"Small Business Capital Outlays" in Small Business Economic Trends (July 2010, pp. 16) **[24109]**, **[34168]**
Small Business Centre (SBC) **[46852]**, **[46854]**
The Small Business Centre (SBC) **[46853]**
Small-Business Collections Help **[20341]**
"Small Business Compensation" in Small Business Economic Trends (February 2008, pp. 10) **[17350]**, **[24738]**, **[34169]**
"Small Business Contract Discrimination" in Investopedia (Sept. 25, 2021) **[20579]**
Small Business Council of America (SBCA) **[25181]**
Small Business: Creating Value through Entrepreneurship **[16593]**
The Small Business Debt Collection Process **[20342]**
Small Business Development Center (JSU SBDC) **[36053]**
Small Business Development Center (SBDC) **[41969]**
Small Business Development Center **[41970]**
Small Business Development Center Aberdeen, South Dakota **[44626]**
Small Business Development Center Broward County [38237]
Small Business Development Center at Edison Community College **[43366]**
Small Business Development Center at Florida A&M University Perry **[38226]**
Small Business Development Center at Florida A&M University Tallahassee **[38227]**
Small Business Development Center at Florida Atlantic University - Boca Raton **[38228]**
Small Business Development Center at Florida Atlantic University Downtown Campus **[38229]**
Small Business Development Center at Florida Atlantic University - Florida Keys Community College (FAU) **[38230]**
Small Business Development Center at Florida Atlantic University - Treasure Coast **[38231]**
Small Business Development Center at Florida Gulf Coast University Cape Coral **[38232]**
Small Business Development Center at Florida Gulf Coast University Clewiston (SBDCFGCU) **[38233]**
Small Business Development Center at Florida Gulf Coast University Fort Myers **[38234]**
Small Business Development Center at Florida Gulf Coast University Immokalee **[38235]**
Small Business Development Center at Florida Gulf Coast University Port Charlotte **[38236]**
Small Business Development Center Fort Lauderdale **[38237]**
Small Business Development Center Greater Sacramento **[36591]**
Small Business Development Center at Gulf Coast Community College [38238]
Small Business Development Center at Gulf Coast State College **[38238]**
Small Business Development Center of the Heartland at South Florida Community College [38223]
Small Business Development Center at Indian River State College Stuart **[38239]**
Small Business Development Center at Kean University (SBDC at Kean University) **[42043]**
Small Business Development Center at Lake County Economic Development Center **[43367]**
Small Business Development Center at Manatee Community College - Sarasota [38242]
Small Business Development Center at Manatee Community College - Venice [38218]
Small Business Development Center at Maumee Valley Planning Organization **[43368]**
Small Business Development Center Miami-Dade Hialeah Gardens **[38240]**
Small Business Development Center at Northern New Mexico College (NMSBDC) **[42288]**
Small Business Development Center at Palm Beach Community College Boca Raton **[38241]**
Small Business Development Center Seacoast (SBDC) **[41971]**
Small Business Development Center at Shasta College (SBDC) **[36592]**
Small Business Development Center - Southeast Missouri State University [41491]
Small Business Development Center at State College of Florida Manatee Sarasota **[38242]**
Small Business Development Center The College of New Jersey (SBDC) **[42044]**
Small Business Development Center at University of Central Florida Kissimmee **[38243]**
Small Business Development Center at University of Central Florida Orlando **[38244]**
Small Business Development Center at University of Cincinnati **[43369]**
Small Business Development Center at the University of North Alabama (SBDC UNA) **[36054]**
Small Business Development Center at University of North Florida Gainesville **[38245]**
Small Business Development Center at University of North Florida Jacksonville **[38246]**
Small Business Development Center at University of North Florida Ocala/Marion County **[38247]**
Small Business Development Center University of St. Thomas **[41156]**
Small Business Development Center at University of South Florida: Hillsborough County **[38248]**
Small Business Development Center at University of South Florida St. Petersburg (SBDC) **[38249]**
Small Business Development Center at University of South Florida: Tampa **[38250]**
Small Business Development Center at University of West Florida Fort Walton Beach **[38251]**
Small Business Development Center University of West Georgia (UGA SBDC) **[38632]**
Small Business Development Center West Central Minnesota (WC MN SBDC) **[41157]**
Small Business Development Center of West Virginia University at Parkersburg **[46253]**
Small Business Development Center at Western Kentucky University **[40003]**
Small Business Development Centers of Northern California (SBDC) **[36593]**
"Small Business Development Centers and Rural Entrepreneurial Development Strategies: Are We Doing Enough for Rural America?" in Journal of Small Business Strategy (Vol. 31, December 1, 2021, No. 4, 57-63) **[33599]**
Small Business Development Corp. of Orange County [36584]
Small Business Development and International Trade Center **[44939]**
Small Business Development and Management Institute [40236]
Small Business Distribution Strategy **[20652]**
Small Business for Dummies **[93]**, **[16835]**, **[17508]**, **[18336]**, **[22422]**, **[24110]**, **[24558]**, **[28816]**, **[29564]**
Small Business Ecommerce: How to Go Digital in a Big Market **[21978]**
"Small Business Economic Trends: Moderate Improvement but No Clear Direction" in Small Business Economic Trends (March 2008, pp. 3) **[6608]**, **[15544]**, **[21144]**, **[24111]**, **[25542]**, **[26660]**, **[27041]**, **[28009]**, **[34170]**
Small Business Economics: An Entrepreneurship Journal **[16721]**
Small Business Employee Compensation Packages: Choosing What's Right for You **[19754]**
"Small Business Employment in 22 Rich Economies" in Small Business Economic Trends (January 2008, pp. 9) **[26661]**, **[27042]**, **[34171]**
"Small Business Employment" in Small Business Economic Trends (September 2010, pp. 9) **[26662]**, **[27043]**
Small Business Encyclopedia **[24739]**
Small Business and Enterprise Development [33701]
Small Business Entrepreneur: Launching a New Venture and Managing a Business on a Day-to-Day Basis **[22423]**, **[24559]**
Small Business and Entrepreneurship Council (SBEC) **[16531]**
Small Business Ethics Policies **[23535]**
Small Business Expo **[33639]**
Small Business Exporters Association [8680]
Small Business Exporters Association of the United States (SBEA) **[8680]**
Small Business Finance Frequently Asked Questions **[24276]**
Small Business Financing: A Resource Guide **[22947]**, **[24280]**, **[33711]**
"Small Business Financing Options That Bypass Traditional Banks" in Business News Daily (Jan. 3, 2022) **[30934]**
Small Business Fraud and the Trusted Employee **[19282]**
Small Business Goals 101: Your Guide to Setting Business Goals the SMART Way **[19589]**
"Small Business Grants Available for Environmental Upgrades" in Small Business Trends(December 24, 2022) **[23357]**, **[33600]**
"Small Business Grants: Free Money for Your Business" in Nav (Jan. 28, 2022) **[25066]**
"Small Business Grants: Here Are 32 You Can Apply for in 2022" in digital.com (Jan. 28, 2022) **[25067]**
"Small-Business Grants for Minorities: 10 Opportunities" in NerdWallet (Nov. 4, 2021) **[30382]**
"Small-Business Grants: Where to Find Free Money" in NerdWallet (Nov. 3, 2021) **[25068]**
Small Business Grants: Where to Find Funds **[25069]**
"Small-Business Grants for Women: Best Options for Free Funding" in NerdWallet (Oct. 14, 2022) **[35855]**
Small Business Growth: Buidling a Freepreneur Lifestyle **[16686]**
"Small Business Growth Statistics: 50 Facts of Successful Businesses" in SmartBooks (Nov. 20, 2019) **[18337]**
"Small Business Growth Statistics That May Surprise You" in SmartBiz Blog (Oct. 4, 2021) **[18338]**
"Small Business Guide to Alternative Lending" in business.com (Feb. 1, 2022) **[30935]**
The Small Business Guide to Avoiding Workplace Discrimination and Harassment **[20580]**
Small Business Guide to Benefits That Attract and Retain Employees **[17351]**
"The Small Business Guide to Branding" in Foundr (June 16, 2021) **[17453]**
"The Small Business Guide to Sustainable Business Practices" in Cultivating Capital **[23358]**
Small Business Has a Big Fraud Problem **[19283]**
"Small Business Health Insurance Costs: What Can You Expect?" in PeopleKeep (Oct. 17, 2021) **[17352]**
Small Business Hub: A Research Guide for Entrepreneurs **[22948]**, **[33712]**, **[34666]**
Small Business Ideas for Prepared Food Delivery **[6919]**
Small Business Institute Annual Conference **[33640]**
Small Business Institute Journal **[22943]**, **[33705]**
Small Business Internet Marketing - How Do I Know My Target Audience? **[27812]**
Small Business: Internet Resources **[24905]**
"Small Business Inventories" in Small Business Economic Trends (February 2008, pp. 14) **[28010]**, **[34172]**
Small Business Investment Company Directory and Handbook **[16722]**
"Small Business Investment Company Reforms Proposed by SBA to Address Diversity" in Small Business Trends (October 25, 2022) **[30383]**, **[33601]**
Small Business Investor Alliance (SBIA) **[24592]**, **[35309]**
Small Business Investor Alliance Northeast Private Equity Conference **[24230]**
Small Business Legal Advice: 10 Basics for Business Owners **[18692]**
Small Business Legal Issues **[18693]**
Small Business Legislative Council (SBLC) **[25182]**, **[33935]**
"Small Business Lending Rebounds to 3-Year High" in Washington Business Journal (Vol. 31, August 31, 2012, No. 19, pp. 1) **[28202]**

3336 Small Business Sourcebook • 42nd Edition

"Small Business Loan Approval Rates Up with Some Lenders" in Small Business Trends (September 15, 2022) [28203]
"Small Business Loans for Photography Business" in SmartBiz (April 17, 2020) [12348]
Small Business Majority [33489]
Small Business Management in Canada [22796], [28817]
Small Business Management: Launching and Growing New Ventures [24560], [28249]
"Small Business Marketing on a Budget: 5 Low-Cost High-Impact Strategies" in Benchmark One [29531]
Small Business Marketing for Dummies [30042]
"Small Business Marketing Guide: Everything New and Existing Businesses Should Know About Acquiring New Customers" in Business News Daily (August 17, 2020) [34714]
Small Business Marketing Strategies Need Rethinking [17454], [30043]
Small Business Network [40348]
Small Business Optimism Index [16594]
Small Business Organizing [12847]
"Small Business Outlook" in Small Business Economic Trends (September 2010, pp. 4) [18339], [21145]
"Small Business Owners Ask: Am I Paying My Employees the Right Salary?" in AllBusiness (September 12, 2020) [35480]
"A Small Business Owner's Guide to Managing Payroll Taxes" in Biz2Credit (January 23, 2020) [31642]
"Small Business Owners Share Their Best Advice" in Legal Zoom (February 16, 2023) [16595]
"Small Business Post–COVID-19: Motivational Needs through Uncertain Times" in SAGE Journals (Aug. 14, 2020) [22251]
Small Business Programs Office (SBPO) - Jet Propulsion Laboratory [47297]
Small Business Radio Show: What You Must Know to Successfully Run a Family Business [23677]
Small Business Reference Center [16725]
The Small Business Resource Center [36055]
Small Business Resource Center [24904]
"Small Business Resource Guide for Veterans" in Business News Daily (October 22, 2020) [33602]
Small Business Retirement Savings Advisor [6716]
Small Business Revolution: How Owners and Entrepreneurs Can Succeed [22797]
"Small Business Risk Management" in Patriot Software (April 23, 2019) [32391]
Small Business Rundown: Advocacy - From Grassroots to Elections [16687]
Small Business Rundown: Essential Tips to Grow Your Small Business [16688]
"Small Business Sales: 6 Strategies for Prospecting" in Small Business Economic Trends (April 2008, pp. 7) [18340], [32286], [32624], [34173]
The Small Business School Podcast: Choosing the Perfect Business Location [16689]
The Small Business School Podcast: Empowering Women Entrepreneurs with Erin Sisko [35910]
The Small Business School Podcast: Franchising and Tutus with Genevieve Weeks [24460]
The Small Business School Podcast: The Visibility Journey [22923]
The Small Business School Podcast: When to Hire Consultants in Your Business [20146]
Small Business Sentiment Index [16616]
Small Business Service Bureau, Inc. (SBSB) [40500]
Small Business Sessions: Erika Robinson: Small Businesses Have a Superpower that Big Companies Don't Have [16690]
Small Business Sessions: Why Business Owners Should Embrace Diversity and Inclusion [30417]
The Small Business Show: Recruitment, Retention, and Labor Quality [27113]
Small Business Source [16725]
Small Business Sourcebook [18341], [24740]
"Small Business and the Staffing Shortage by Industry" in Forbes (May 27, 2021) [14986], [33603]
The Small Business Start-Up Kit [16727], [22424], [24561], [25177], [34454], [34718]
The Small Business Start-Up Kit for California [24562], [34883]
Small Business Startup Checklist [16691]
Small Business and Startup Stories [39826]
"Small Business Statistics" in Small Business Trends (July 9, 2021) [18342]
"Small Business Statistics: 19 Essential Numbers to Know" in Fundera (Dec. 21, 2021) [18343]
"Small-Business Statistics: By the Numbers" in NerdWallet (May 14, 2021) [18344]
Small Business Survival Committee [16531]
Small Business Survival Guide [94], [16836], [18694], [19765], [20343], [20502], [22425], [23658], [24563], [24741], [25178]

"Small Business Tax Changes for 2020" in Pitney Bowes (2020) [34249]
"Small Business Tax Obligations: Payroll Taxes" in Investopedia (June 25, 2019) [31643], [34250]
Small Business Taxes for Dummies [34884]
Small Business Taxes and Management [28919], [34934]
Small Business Technology Council (SBTC) [33490]
"Small Business Tips: How to Do Market Research" in Guardian Small Business Network (August 13, 2015) [29499]
Small Business Trends, LLC [33706]
Small Business Trends (Nov. 5, 2017); "Cracking the Code on Anti-Discrimination Policies for Your Small Business" in [20563]
Small Business Turnaround [18345], [24742]
"Small Businesses Are Especially Susceptible to Employee Theft. Here's How to Protect Yourself and Your Company" Inc. (March 21, 2019) [22349]
"Small Businesses Dealing with Higher Gas Prices" in Small Business Trends (October 31, 2022) [16596]
"Small Businesses and Disposal of Hazardous Waste" in HG.org Legal Resources [7961]
"Small Businesses Face 6 Challenges in the Weed Market" in Green Entrepreneur (April 1, 2019) [5021]
"Small Businesses Finding It Easier To Get Capital" in Birmingham Business Journal (Vol. 31, July 11, 2014, No. 28, pp. 10) [20344], [21146], [28204]
"Small Businesses Have Surged in Black Communities. Was It the Stimulus?" in The New York Times (May 24,2021) [30384]
"Small Businesses Not Prepared for a Boom" in Small Business Trends(November 13, 2022) [33604]
"Small Businesses Run by Older Founders Most Likely to Survive" in AARP (February 19, 2019) [33074]
"Small Businesses Support Expansive Tax Reforms Needed to Level the Playing Field and Offset the Costs of 'Build Back Better' Plan" in Business2Community (November 3, 2021) [16723], [34948]
"Small Businesses Unsure of Impact of New Tax Law" in Crain's Detroit Business (Vol. 23, October 15, 2007, No. 42, pp. 13) [33258], [34885]
Small Businesses Without Insurance Take Dangerous Risks [27338]
"Small, But Mighty" in Employee Benefit News (Vol. 25, November 1, 2011, No. 14, pp. 32) [8965], [17353], [20129], [21147], [25543], [25939], [27339]
"Small Butcher Shops Are in 'A Renaissance.' How Did They Survive the Supermarket Offensive?" in Miami Herald (July 2, 2018). [2429]
"Small Changes Can Mean Big Energy Savings" in Crain's Cleveland Business (Vol. 28, November 5, 2007, No. 44, pp. 21) [13282], [13562], [23359], [34174]
"Small Dutch Islands Saba, Statia Content With Low-Key Niche" in Travel Weekly (Vol. 69, August 16, 2010, No. 33, pp. 22) [15760], [16011], [19395], [19931], [30044]
Small Enterprise Education and Promotion Network [33488]
"Small Firms Punch Ticket for Growth" in Houston Business Journal (Vol. 40, January 29, 2010, No. 38, pp. 1) [9807], [25544], [27721], [31513], [33259]
Small Giants Community (SGC) [18835], [33491]
"Small Is Bountiful for Intuit" in Barron's (Vol. 90, September 13, 2010, No. 37, pp. 22) [95], [9808], [14827], [16837], [33903]
"Small is the New Big in Autos" in Globe & Mail (February 16, 2006, pp. B3) [11436], [19065], [19590], [29384], [30045]
Small Publishers Association of North America [1611], [4932]
Small Talk [8993]
Small Time Operator: How to Start Your Own Business, Keep Your Books, Pay Your Taxes, and Stay Out of Trouble [18695], [24564], [34886]
Small Unites [16532]
"Small Wind Power Market to Double by 2015 at $634 Million" in Western Farm Press (September 30, 2011) [5708], [5975], [18346], [23360], [25070]
Small, Women, and Minority Owned Business Incubator [40231]
Smaller Business Association of New England [33481]
Smart Business Dealmakers [29045]
"Smart Businesses See Value, and Profit, in Promoting Women" in Crain's Chicago Business (Vol. 30, February 2007, No. 6, pp. 30) [24743], [31695], [31790]
"Smart Locks, Home Surveillance Change Locksmith Trade" in U.S. News & World Report (June 22, 2019) [10000], [10355]
"Smart Recruiting Strategies for Hiring" in Business News Daily (Nov. 18, 2021) [26663]
"Smart Tips for Successfully Navigating the Initial Franchisor-Franchisee Interview" in Entrepreneur (Jan. 23, 2019) [24412]

Smart Ways to Work [29032], [35017]
Smart Women Finish Rich [35856]
"Smart Year-End Tax Moves" in Business Owner (Vol. 35, November-December 2011, No. 6, pp. 8) [96], [15415], [16838], [21148], [34887]
"Smartcuts: How Hackers, Innovators, and Icons Accelerate Success" [22798]
Smarter Faster Payments Conference [24845]
"The Smartest Ways to Shop for Kids Clothes Without Breaking the Bank: A Guide" in SlickDeals.net (July 1, 2019) [2853]
SmartPros Ltd. [21738]
SMARTRISK [25687]
"Smarts Drive Sales" in Pet Product News (Vol. 64, December 2010, No. 12, pp. 1) [12173], [20503], [32287], [32625]
SMARTstart Pasco Business Incubator [38581]
SMC3 Jump Start [16106]
"The Smell of Fear: Is a Bottom Near?" in Barron's (Vol. 88, March 17, 2008, No. 11, pp. M3) [3142], [6609], [8966], [9809], [24112], [25940], [27340]
Smith Center Chamber of Commerce [39956]
Smith County Chamber of Commerce [44803]
Smith, Dawson & Andrews (SDA) [12960]
Smith Mountain Lake Newcomer and Visitor Guide [45898]
Smith Mountain Lake Regional Chamber of Commerce (SMLRCC) [45899]
Smithsonian Institute Office of Equal Employment and Minority Affairs [47371]
Smithsonian Institution - Smithsonian American Art Museum - National Portrait Gallery Library [3381], [12330]
Smithsonian Institution - Smithsonian American Art Museum Photograph Archives [3382]
Smithville Area Chamber of Commerce [41631]
Smithville - DeKalb County Chamber of Commerce [44804]
Smitty's [14259]
Smocking Arts Guild of America (SAGA) [4584]
Smoking and Health Resource Library [10938], [12469]
Smoking and Tobacco Use Data and Statistics [10938], [12469]
Smoothie King [8078], [8635]
SMPS Build Business [24848]
Smugglers Notch Area Vacation Guide [45735]
Smyth County Chamber of Commerce [45900]
Snaggle Foot LLC [12280]
Snap Fitness [12463]
Snap-on Incorporated [7932]
Snap-On Tools of Canada Ltd. [2575]
"Snapchat for Business: Everything You Need to Know" in Business News Daily (March 17, 2023) [16906]
"Snappy Moves Headquarters to Marietta" in Atlanta Business Chronicle (June 27, 2014, pp. 13A) [514], [19204]
Snappy Tomato Pizza Co. [12593]
SNAXPO: Annual Snack Food Association Convention [15053]
"Sneak Preview: Alamo Revamp" in Austin Business JournalInc. (Vol. 28, December 12, 2008, No. 39, pp. 1) [4229], [11126], [13563]
Snelling Staffing L.L.C. [5461]
The Snip-Its Corp. [2041]
Snohomish Chamber of Commerce [46156]
Snoqualmie Valley Chamber of Commerce [46157]
SnoValley Chamber of Commerce (SVCC) [46157]
Snow Hill Area Chamber of Commerce [40417]
Snowflake/Taylor Chamber of Commerce [36363]
Snowmass Tourism [37896]
Snowmass Village Resort Association [37896]
SnowSports Industries America (SIA) [14735]
SNS Investment Co. [14260]
Snyder Chamber of Commerce [45361]
"So What Is Crowdfunding Anyway? New Legislation by Obama and Congress Relaxes Solicitation by Startups" in Accounting Today (August 6, 2012) [25179], [28073], [31145], [35250]
"So You Think You Want to Own a Dance Studio?" in DanceTeacher (September 12, 2017) [4855], [19066]
So! You Want to Own a Bar: An Insider's Guide to Bar Ownership [1351]
"So You Want to Start a Brewery? The Lagunitas Story" [1934], [22799]
"So You Want to Start a Business? So You Want to Start a Business: What's Your First Move?" in Women Entrepreneur (August 5, 2008) [19067], [19591], [33435], [35857]
"So You Want To Be a Food Truck Vendor?" in Philadelphia Business Journal (Vol. 33, August 15, 2014, No. 27, pp. 7) [3829], [6955], [10009], [27825], [27987], [33334]
"So You Want To Hold a Conference: Event Planning Resources" in Searcher (Vol. 20, July-August 2012, No. 6, pp. 12) [14521], [15896]

Soap Master Index

Soap and Detergent Association [2964]
Soap Lake Chamber of Commerce **[46158]**
Sobey School of Business Development Centre [46748]
Soccer Industry Council of America (SICA) **[15081]**
"Social Apps, Business Style: Savvy App Makers Bring Consumer Features to the Enterprise" in Silicon Valley/San Jose Business Journal (Vol. 30, September 28, 2012, No. 27, pp. 1) **[2792]**, **[9235]**, **[14828]**
"A Social Context Model of Envy and Social Undermining" in Academy of Management Journal (Vol. 55, June 1, 2012, No. 3, pp. 643) **[22252]**, **[25941]**
Social Enterprise: Developing Sustainable Businesses **[21149]**, **[34175]**, **[34370]**
Social Entrepreneurship For Dummies **[22800]**, **[34371]**
Social Entrepreneurship: What Everyone Needs to Know **[22801]**, **[34372]**
Social Implications and Challenges of E-Business **[22033]**
Social Media **[34262]**
"Social Media Advertising for Small Businesses" in The WordStream Blog (July 21, 2020) **[31886]**
The Social Media Bible: Tactics, Tools, and Strategies for Business Success **[352]**, **[17755]**, **[19932]**, **[20504]**, **[21979]**, **[22253]**, **[30046]**, **[32626]**, **[33260]**
"Social Media Conference NW 2010" in Bellingham Business Journal (Vol. February 2010, pp. 3) **[15897]**, **[21980]**, **[26409]**, **[35092]**
"Social Media, E-Mail Remain Challenging for Employers" in Workforce Management (Vol. 88, December 14, 2009, No. 13, pp. 4) **[9236]**, **[16469]**, **[17756]**, **[28818]**, **[30047]**
Social Media For Small Business: Marketing Strategies for Business Owners **[30048]**
Social Media Made Simple **[29606]**, **[33530]**, **[35716]**
"Social Media By the Numbers: Social-Media Marketing Is All the Rage" in Inc. (Vol. 33, November 2011, No. 9, pp. 70) **[21981]**, **[30049]**, **[34176]**
Social Media Marketing (Onsite) **[29607]**
"Social Media News: TikTok Supporting Black Business Owners, Snapchat Available on Chrome" in Small Business Trends (August 19, 2022) **[30385]**
Social Media Overview [34262]
"Social Media Privacy Law Impacts Employers" in Providence Business News (Vol. 29, July 21, 2014, No. 16, pp. 14) **[14458]**, **[18696]**
"Social Media & Your Business: Getting Started" in Legal Zoom (March 23, 2023) **[29532]**, **[30050]**
"Social Networking: Growing Pains" in Canadian Business (Vol. 81, July 22, 2008, No. 12-13, pp. 35) **[15028]**, **[17114]**, **[19068]**, **[19592]**, **[23659]**, **[30051]**
"Social Networks in the Workplace: The Risk and Opportunity of Business 2.0" in Strategy & Leadership (Vol. 38, July-August 2010, No. 4, pp. 50-53) **[17757]**, **[21982]**, **[28819]**, **[30052]**, **[30979]**, **[34177]**
"Social Safety, Thanks to New App" in Providence Business News (Vol. 29, July 21, 2014, No. 16, pp. 10) **[14459]**, **[21983]**
"Social Security for Business Owners" in Fisher Investments (September 13, 2018) **[34251]**
Social Venture Partners (SVP) **[5753]**
Social Work with Groups: A Journal of Community and Clinical Practice **[26052]**
Social Work in Health Care: A Quarterly Journal Adopted by the Society for Social Work Leadership in Health Care **[26053]**
"Social Work Professor's Bridal Shop Helps Those Living With Cancer" in The University Record (August 13, 2018) **[1994]**
Social Work in Public Health **[26054]**
"Socially Responsible Business Practices" in Purpose-Mart Blog (June 14, 2021) **[34373]**
Societe pour la nature et les parcs du Canada (CPAWS) **[5503]**
Societe des designers graphiques du Canada [3288]
Société Canadienne des Biologistes de l'Environnement (CSEB) **[5504]**
Société Canadienne du Cancer (CCS) **[25690]**
Societe Canadienne de Cardiologie [25651]
Societe Canadienne D'indexation [2]
Société Canadienne des Directeurs d'Association [1051]
Societe Canadienne de Genie Agroalimentaire et de Bioingenierie (SCGAB) **[16971]**
Société Canadienne des Infirmiè es et Infirmiers en Gastoénterologie et Travailleurs Associés (CSGNA) **[8243]**
Société Canadienne de l'énergie du sol (SCES) **[5505]**
Société Canadienne de Nutrition [11563]
Société Canadienne de Planificateurs Professionnels d'Événements (CanSPEP) **[14505]**
Société Canadienne de Recherches Cliniques (SCRC) **[25691]**
Societe Culinaire Philanthropique (SCP) **[4484]**
Societe d'Habitation du Quebec - Centre de Documentation **[4369]**
Societe de Genealogie de Quebec Library **[7451]**
Societe canadienne pour l'analyse de documents [2]
Societe de Musique des Universites Canadiennes (SMUC) **[11178]**
Societe canadienne de pediatrie [25660]
Societe Planetaire pour l'Assainissement de l'Energie, Inc. [23046]
Society for Accessible Travel and Hospitality (SATH) **[16047]**
Society for Advancement of Management (SAM) **[28268]**, **[34965]**
Society for the Advancement of Women's Health Research [25694]
Society of American Florists (SAF) **[6850]**
Society of Authors' Representatives [10344]
Society for Automation in Business Education [3422], [3546]
Society for Automation in English and the Humanities [3422], [3546]
Society for Automation in Fine Arts [3422], [3546]
Society for Automation in Professional Education [3422], [3546]
Society for Automation in the Social Sciences [3422], [3546]
Society of Automotive Engineers [14540]
Society of Behavioral Medicine Scientific Sessions **[32926]**
Society for Business Ethics (SBE) **[23463]**
Society for Business Ethics Annual Conference **[23568]**
Society of Cable Telecommunications Engineers (SCTE) **[2445]**
Society of Cable Television Engineers [2445]
Society for Calligraphy (SfC) **[2488]**
Society for Calligraphy--Membership Directory **[2481]**
Society of Chartered Property and Casualty Underwriters (CPCU) **[8880]**
Society of Cleaning and Restoration Technicians (SCRT) **[16227]**
Society of Cleaning Technicians [16227]
Society of Clinical and Medical Electrologists [7847]
Society for Clinical and Medical Hair Removal (SCMHR) **[7847]**
Society of Collision Repair Specialists (SCRS) **[14541]**
Society for Corporate Governance **[16224]**
Society for Data Educators [3422], [3546]
Society of Depreciation Professionals (SDP) **[44]**, **[16754]**
Society for Educational Data Systems [3422], [3546]
Society of Educational Programmers and Systems Analysts [3422], [3546]
Society for Environmental Graphic Design [3291]
Society for Experiential Graphic Design (SEGD) **[3291]**
Society of Financial Service Professionals (SFSP) **[8881]**
Society of Financial Service Professionals Quad City Chapter **[38978]**
Society of Glass and Ceramic Decorated Products Conference **[9064]**
Society of Health and Physical Educators (SHAPE) **[12385]**
Society for Hospitality and Foodservice Management (SHFM) **[13891]**
Society for Human Resource Management [27120]
Society of Independent Gasoline Marketers of America (SIGMA) **[14542]**
Society of Independent and Private School Data Education [3422], [3546]
Society of Industrial Engineers [28268], [34965]
Society of Insurance Accountants [8882]
Society of Insurance Financial Management (SIFM) **[8882]**
Society of Insurance Research (SIR) **[9012]**, **[9014]**
Society of International Business Fellows (SIBF) **[27429]**
Society of Logistics Engineers [12973]
Society of Magazine Photographers [11955], [12288]
Society of Magazine Writers [5268]
Society of Manufacturing Engineers (SME) **[10421]**
Society of Mortgage Consultants [10999]
Society for Nonprofit Organizations (SNPO) **[1052]**
Society for Nutrition Education and Behavior Annual Conference **[11591]**
Society of Professional Accountants of Canada (SPAC) **[45]**, **[1741]**, **[15362]**
Society of Professional Audio Recording Services (SPARS) **[13651]**
Society of Professional Audio Recording Studios [13651]
Society of Professional Investigators (SPI) **[12794]**
Society of Professionals in Dispute Resolution, Inc. [10786]
Society Promoting Environmental Conservation (SPEC) **[5506]**, **[13695]**, **[23052]**
Society for the Psychological Study of Social Issues (SPSSI) **[25692]**
Society of Publication Designers (SPD) **[11973]**
Society for Range Management Annual Meeting **[858]**
Society of Real Estate Appraisers [805], [828]
Society for Scholarly Publishing (SSP) **[1629]**
Society of Scribes (SOS) **[2478]**
Society for the Study of Social Problems (SSSP) **[25693]**, **[26142]**
Society of Tool Engineers - American Society of Tool Engineers - American Society of Tool and Manufacturing Engineers [10421]
Society for Women's Health Research (SWHR) **[25694]**
"A Socko Payout Menu: Rural Phone Carrier Plots to Supercharge Its Shares" in Barron's (Vol. 88, June 30, 2008, No. 26, pp. M5) **[2793]**, **[6610]**, **[9810]**, **[19069]**, **[24113]**, **[33261]**, **[34888]**
SoCo Nexus **[39827]**
"Soda Says, a Curated Consumer Electronics Retail Platform, Launches in the US" in TechCrunch (May 29, 2019) **[4405]**, **[11796]**
Soda Springs Chamber of Commerce **[38942]**
"Sodexo Upgrades Healthy Vending Initiative" in Entertainment Close-Up (September 25, 2011) **[8047]**, **[8106]**, **[16261]**
Sodus Chamber of Commerce [42674]
Sodus Town Chamber of Commerce **[42674]**
Sofia Fund **[41339]**
Sofinnova Ventures **[37492]**
Soft Dolls & Animals **[4620]**, **[4682]**
"Soft Skills, Hard Success: Employers Seek Leaders Who Offer More than Just Education and Credentials" in Black Enterprise (Vol. 45, July-August 2014, No. 1, pp. 44) **[26664]**, **[28820]**
SoftTech VC [37515]
"A Software Company's Whimsical Widgets Were an Instant Hit. But Its Core Product Was Getting Overshadowed" in Inc. (January 2008) **[14829]**, **[30053]**, **[33904]**
"Software Developers" in Business Review Albany (Vol. 41, July 18, 2014, No. 17, pp. 9) **[3433]**, **[14830]**, **[33905]**
Software Focus [14855], [32900]
Software and Information Industry Association (SIIA) **[14752]**
Software: Practice and Experience [14855], **[14857]**, **[30989]**, [32900]
Software Process [14855], [32900]
"Software Publishers Industry: What's Next for the Industry?" in Via.news (June 20, 2020) **[14831]**
Software Publishing Industry in the US - Market Research Report **[14851]**
Software QA Solutions **[26472]**
Software Success **[14887]**
Software Testing, Verification and Reliability, [14855], [32900]
"Software's Last Hurrah" in Canadian Business (Vol. 81, December 24, 2007, No. 1, pp. 27) **[9811]**, **[14832]**, **[31514]**, **[33906]**
"A Soggy Harvest" in Business Journal-Portland (Vol. 24, October 5, 2007, No. 32, pp. 1) **[15029]**, **[17115]**
Sohnen-Moe Associates, Inc. (SMA) **[36417]**
Soho Expo **[11592]**
Solana Beach Chamber of Commerce **[37195]**
Solano College Small Business Development Center **[36594]**
"Solar Choices" in Contractor (Vol. 56, October 2009, No. 10, pp. 32) **[515]**, **[5709]**, **[12659]**, **[14944]**
Solar Energy Industries Association (SEIA) **[14901]**
"Solar Gaining Power in Tennessee" in Memphis Business Journal (Vol. 34, June 15, 2012, No. 9, pp. 1) **[14945]**, **[18347]**, **[29385]**
"Solar Hot Water Sales Are Hot, Hot, Hot" in Contractor (Vol. 56, December 2009, No. 12, pp. 22) **[5976]**, **[12660]**, **[14946]**, **[32627]**, **[35953]**
"Solar Integrity" **[14947]**
Solar Lobby [14900]
Solar Power Industry in the US - Market Research Report **[14960]**
Solar Rating and Certification Corporation (SRCC) **[14902]**
Solar Today **[4290]**
"Soldiers as Consumers: Predatory and Unfair Business Practices Harming the Military Community" **[18697]**, **[23536]**, **[25545]**, **[28205]**
Soldotna Chamber of Commerce (SCC) **[36246]**
"Sole Proprietor vs Independent Contractor Explained" in The Balance Small Business (May 6, 2020) **[32994]**, **[34462]**
"Sole Proprietorship Returns, 2008" in SOI Bulletin (Vol. 30, Summer 2010, No. 1, pp. 6) **[34178]**, **[34463]**
"Sole Proprietorship Returns, 2008 Part 2" in SOI Bulletin (Vol. 30, Summer 2010, No. 1, pp. 27) **[17116]**, **[34179]**, **[34464]**
SOLE - The International Society of Logistics **[12973]**
"Solectria Renewables Supplies Solar Stations for Solar Farm in New England" in Professional Close-Up (October 2, 2012) **[14948]**, **[29386]**

3338 Small Business Sourcebook • 42nd Edition

Solid Vision Consulting (SVC) [37684]
Solid Waste Composting Council [13697]
Solo and Small Firm Incubator (UMKC) [41690]
Solo & Small Practice Incubator (SSPI) [39430]
The Solon Business Directory [43570]
Solon Chamber of Commerce [43571]
"Solon Wire to Ramp Up Plant" in *Memphis Business Journal* (Vol. 33, March 23, 2012, No. 50, pp. 1) [29387], [31515]
The Solopreneur Hour: 3 Steps to a Great Online Business with Chris Farrell [11846]
The Solopreneur Hour: A Massive Passive Income Opportunity in Payment Processing [11847]
The Solopreneur Hour: Ant Anstead of Wheeler Dealers/Master Mechanic - The Passion Behind the Work [1191]
The Solopreneur Hour: Charliee Cannon Built a Drone Empire Using Alibaba at Age 22, Then Cashed Out [36038]
The Solopreneur Hour: How to Save a TON on Taxes, with Christina Lael [34939]
The Solopreneur Hour: Lauren Tickner Is Redefining the Rules of How to Be a Young Entrepreneur [36039]
Solstice Capital [40729]
"The Solution Became the Problem" in *Barron's* (Vol. 92, August 25, 2012, No. 35, pp. 45) [3735], [9812], [17758]
"Solutions to Family Business Problems" in *Contractor* (Vol. 56, October 2009, No. 10, pp. 51) [6046], [23660], [34889]
"Solutions for the Frustrating Feline" in *Pet Product News* (Vol. 64, November 2010, No. 11, pp. 46) [697], [12174], [20505]
Solvang Chamber of Commerce (SCC) [37196]
"Some Credit Unions Are Big on Business Loans" in *South Florida Business Journal* (Vol. 35, September 5, 2014, No. 6, pp. 4) [18348], [28206]
"Some Homeowners Caught in Tax-Code Limbo" in *Providence Business News* (Vol. 29, June 23, 2014, No. 12, pp. 9) [11080], [25546], [34890]
"Some Relief Possible Following Painful Week" in *Barron's* (Vol. 88, July 14, 2008, No. 28, pp. M3) [6611], [8763], [9813], [19933], [21150], [24114], [27722], [29388], [31516], [32825]
Somerset County Chamber of Commerce [44299]
Somerset Pulaski County Chamber of Commerce [40086]
Somerville Chamber of Commerce [40626]
"Sometimes You Have to Ignore the Rule Book" in *Canadian Business* (Vol. 83, September 14, 2010, No. 15, pp. 13) [19396], [20506], [27044]
SON Systems International Inc. [31016]
Sonic, America's Drive-In [14261]
Sonic Drive-In Restaurants [14261]
Sonitrol Corp. [14498]
Sonoma Valley Chamber of Commerce [37197]
Sonora Chamber of Commerce (HSCC) [37198]
Sonora Chamber of Commerce (SCOC) [45362]
Son's [8636]
Sons of the American Revolution Genealogy Research Library (SAR Genealogical Research Library) [7452]
Sons of Utah Pioneers [7436]
Sony Ericsson WTA Tour [15669]
Soody Tronson Law Group [37686]
"The Soon To Be $200B Online Food Delivery Is Rapidly Changing the Global Food Industry" in *Forbes* September 9, 2019) [6920], [11797]
Soperton - Treutlen Chamber of Commerce [38780]
Soperton - Treutlen County Chamber of Commerce [38780]
"Sorrell Digs Deep to Snag TNS" in *Advertising Age* (Vol. 79, July 14, 2008, No. 7, pp. 1) [353], [19070], [19593], [30054], [31517]
SOSV Invesments LLC [42221]
Soul Proprietor: 101 Lessons from a Lifestyle Entrepreneur [4650], [22426], [24565]
The Soul of Startups: The Untold Stories of How Founders Affect Culture [34546]
"Souled Out" in *Canadian Business* (Vol. 81, March 3, 2008, No. 3, pp. 35) [21151], [22802], [33032]
"Sound Check" in *Agency Sales Magazine* (Vol. 39, August 2009, No. 8, pp. 14) [17759], [20507], [31791], [32628]
Sound & Communications Magazine [2818]
Sound Healers Association (SHA) [12491]
Sound & Video Contractor [13658]
SoundBoard Venture Fund [42222]
"Sounders Kicking Ball to Fans" in *Puget Sound Business Journal* (Vol. 29, November 28, 2008, No. 32, pp. 1) [15186], [21984]
Soundings [39310]
Soundings Trade Only: Daily News for Marine Industry Professionals [10615]

"A Souped-Up Digital Pen" in *Inc.* (Vol. 33, November 2011, No. 9, pp. 50) [3736], [30980]
The Source Book [25731]
"Sources" in *Canadian Electronics* (Vol. 23, August 2008, No. 5, pp. 12) [4406], [20653], [26410], [28821], [29389]
Sources [43191]
South Baldwin Chamber of Commerce (SBCC) [36152]
South Belt - Ellington Chamber of Commerce (SBECC) [45363]
The South Bend Chocolate Company Inc. [2560]
South Bend Regional Chamber (SBRC) [39606]
South Bend Small Business Development Center [39474]
South Brevard Chamber [38460]
South Bronx Overall Economic Development Corporation (SoBro) [42827]
South Brunswick Islands Chamber of Commerce [43096]
South Carolina Association of Certified Public Accountants (SCACPA) [16755]
South Carolina Association of Realtors (SCR) [13115]
South Carolina Chamber of Commerce (SCCC) [44583]
South Carolina Component Manufacturers Association [3964]
South Carolina Department of Commerce [44515]
South Carolina Department of Mental Health - Earle E. Morris, Jr. Alcohol & Drug Addiction Treatment Center Library [34695]
South Carolina Department of Transportation (SCDOT) [1182], [5119], [10299], [15535]
South Carolina Division of Small and Minority Business Contracting and Certification (SMBCC) [44516]
South Carolina Jobs-Economic Development Authority [44517]
South Carolina Office of Small and Minority Business Assistance [44516]
South Carolina Procurement Technical Assistance Center - The Frank L. Roddey Small Business Development Center - University of South Carolina - Moore School of Business [44596]
South Carolina Small Business Development Centers (SC SBDC) [44510], [44597]
South Carolina Small Business Development Centers Orangeburg Area (SC SBDC) [44511], [44598]
South Carolina State Beekeepers Association (SCBA) [1451]
South Carolina State Development Board [44515]
South Carolina State Library [47469]
South Carolina Wildlife [15209]
South Carolina Young Farmer and Agribusiness Association (SCYFAA) [16972], [44498]
South Carroll Business Association--Directory (Sykesville, Maryland) [40480]
South Central Iowa SCORE [39707]
South Central Iowa Small Business Development Center [39684]
South Central Kansas Economic Development District (SCKEDD) [39977]
South Central Minnesota Small Business Development Center [41158]
South Central Region [47926]
South Coast Angel Network (SCAN) [35310], [45473]
South College [43257]
South College Library [8534], [33721]
South County Chamber of Commerce (SCCC) [44018]
South Cumberland Chamber of Commerce (SCCC) [44805]
South Dade Chamber of Commerce [38501]
South Dakota Agri-Business Association (SDABA) [16973], [44622]
South Dakota Ambulance Association (SDAA) [569]
South Dakota Association of Realtors Convention [774], [35133]
South Dakota Dental Association Annual Session [10883]
South Dakota Department of Health - Director of Administration [47470]
South Dakota Department of Labor and Regulation (LMIC) - Labor Market Information Center [47471]
South Dakota Department of Tribal Government Relations [44667]
South Dakota Enterprise Institute [44671]
The South Dakota Family Business Association [23587]
South Dakota Family Business Initiative [23587]
South Dakota Fertilizer and Agriculture Chemical Association [16973], [44622]
South Dakota Governor's Office of Economic Development (GOED) [44629]
South Dakota Procurement Technical Assistance Center (West River) [44669]
South Dakota Small Business Development Center [44627]
South Dakota State Library - Documents Department [47472]

South Dakota State University Department of Agricultural and Biosystems Engineering - Water Resources Institute (WRI) [16360]
South Dakota State University - Department of Sociology and Rural Studies [47473]
South Dakota State University - Innovation Center [44672]
South Fairfax Small Business Development Center [45789]
South Florida Business Journal [38608]
"South Florida Lodging Industry Poised for Strong Growth in 2014" in *South Florida Business Journal* (Vol. 34, January 3, 2014, No. 24, pp. 3) [8457], [20130], [32041]
South Fork Chamber of Commerce and Visitors Center [37897]
South Fork Visitors Center [37897]
South Fulton Chamber of Commerce (SFCC) [38781]
South Hadley and Granby Chamber of Commerce [40627]
South Haven Area Chamber of Commerce (GSHACC) [41011]
South Hill Chamber of Commerce (SHCC) [45901]
South Hills Chamber of Commerce (SHCC) [44300]
South Houston Chamber of Commerce [45090]
"South Jersey Office Space in Doldrums" in *Philadelphia Business Journal* (Vol. 31, March 16, 2012, No. 5, pp. 1) [11081], [28207]
South Kansas City Chamber of Commerce (SKCCC) [41632]
South Kingstown Chamber of Commerce (SKCC) [44480]
South Kitsap Chamber of Commerce [46141]
South Lake Chamber of Commerce (SLCC) [38502]
"South Lake Tahoe B&B Blocks Out Nevada's Neon" in *Chicago Tribune* (May 18, 2008) [1423], [19397]
"The South Looks Yummy to Tastykakes" in *Philadelphia Business Journal* (Vol. 31, March 30, 2012, No. 7, pp. 1) [1267], [18349], [32629]
"South Loop Site Lands a Buyer" in *Crain's Chicago Business* (Vol. 31, March 24, 2008, No. 12, pp. 1) [4230], [13283], [13564]
South of Market Community Action Network (SOMCAN) [36556]
South Metro Dayton Area Chamber of Commerce [43572]
South Metro Denver Chamber of Commerce [37898]
South Metro Denver Small Business Development Center Aurora [37794]
South Metro Regional Chamber of Commerce (SMRCOC) [43572]
South Middlesex Area Chamber of Commerce [40602]
South Montgomery County Chamber of Commerce [45415]
South Oklahoma City Chamber of Commerce (SOKC) [43808]
South Orange County Economic Coalition (SOCEC) [37199]
South Orange County Regional Chambers of Commerce [37199]
South Padre Island Chamber of Commerce [45364]
"South Park Draws Brewers, Vintners" in *Puget Sound Business Journal* (Vol. 29, August 29, 2008, No. 19, pp. 1) [1935], [7563], [33412]
South Salt Lake Chamber of Commerce (SSL) [45647]
South San Antonio Chamber of Commerce [45365]
South San Francisco Chamber of Commerce (SSF) [37200]
South Seattle College (SSC) [46231]
South Shore Chamber of Commerce (SSCC) [40628]
"South-Side Bicycle Shop Set to Close After Nearly a Century" in *Indianpolis Business Journal* (June 4, 2019) [1528]
South Side Innovation Center (SSIC) [42929]
South Snohomish County Chamber of Commerce [46078], [46203]
South Tampa Chamber of Commerce (STCOC) [38503]
South-tec [29464]
South Texas Business Partnership [45365]
South Tipton County Chamber of Commerce (STC) [44806]
South Valley Economic Development Center (SVEDC) [42355]
South Valley Small Business Development Center [42274]
South West Communities Chamber of Commerce (SWCCOC) [44301]
South-West Texas Small Business Development Center Network [44940]
Southampton Chamber of Commerce [42675]
Southaven [41429]
Southaven Chamber of Commerce [41430]
SouthCoast Chamber [40629]

Southeast Community College Entrepreneurship Center [41896]
Southeast Dallas Chamber of Commerce (SEDCC) [45366]
Southeast Indiana Small Business Development Center (SBDC) [39477]
Southeast Innovation Center for Innovation and Entrepreneurship [41691]
Southeast Kentucky Chamber of Commerce [40087]
Southeast Louisiana Business Center (SLBC) [40232]
Southeast Minnesota Capital Fund (SMCF) [41340]
Southeast Minnesota SCORE Chapter 406 [41182]
Southeast Minnesota Small Business Development Center [41159]
Southeast Missouri SCORE [41508]
Southeast Missouri State University Small Business and Technology Development Center (SMSU SBTDC) [41491]
Southeast Pennsylvania Procurement Technical Assistance Center (SE PTAC) [44373]
Southeast Small Business Development Center [40004]
Southeast Volusia Chamber of Commerce [38504]
Southeastern Association of Fish and Wildlife Agencies (SEAFWA) [6743]
Southeastern Business College [43688]
Southeastern Connecticut SCORE (SECT) [38025]
Southeastern Fisheries Association (SFA) [6776]
Southeastern Franklin County Chamber of Commerce [43573]
Southeastern Louisiana University - Business Research Center (BRC) [40241]
Southeastern Lumber Manufacturers Association (SLMA) [10386]
Southeastern Massachusetts SCORE [40544]
Southeastern Montana Small Business Development Center [41726]
Southeastern Psychological Association Meeting [26077]
Southern Alleghenies Planning and Development Commission (SAP&DC) [44374]
Southern Arizona SCORE [36303]
Southern Berkshire Chamber of Commerce (SBCC) [40630]
Southern Business Services [1784]
Southern California Advertising Agencies Association [31846]
Southern California Association of Governments (SCAG) [47474]
Southern California College of Optometry - M.B. Ketchum Memorial Library [16318]
Southern California Minority Business Development Council [37267]
Southern California Minority Supplier Development Council (SCMSDC) [37267]
Southern California Mobile Food Vendors Association [6962]
Southern Capitol Ventures [43229]
Southern Chester County Chamber of Commerce (SCCCC) [44302]
Southern Colorado Women's Chamber of Commerce (SCWCC) [37899]
Southern Development Council (SDC) [33508]
Southern Early Childhood Association (SECA) [2874]
Southern Exposure - Southeast Produce Council [17180]
Southern Fauquier Business Owners Association (SFBOA) [33492]
Southern Fish Culturists Inc. [6794]
Southern Florida Minority Supplier Development Council [38530]
Southern Furniture Market [8193]
Southern Humboldt Chamber of Commerce (GRCC) [37201]
Southern Illinois University at Carbondale School of Medicine - Center for Rural Health and Social Service Development (CRHSSD) [26143]
Southern Illinois University at Edwardsville - Regional Research and Development Services [47475]
Southern Illinois University Small Business Incubator [39431]
Southern Maid Donuts [1304]
Southern Medical Association Annual Scientific Assembly [10961]
Southern Methodist University - Cox School of Business - Caruth Institute for Entrepreneurship [22956]
Southern Methodist University - Cox School of Business - Center for Research in Real Estate and Land Use Economics [13637]
Southern Methodist University - Cox School of Business Library [24915]
Southern Midcoast Maine Chamber (SMMC) [40307]
Southern Monmouth Area Chamber of Commerce [42149]
Southern Monmouth Chamber of Commerce [42149]
Southern New Hampshire Chamber of Commerce [42013]
Southern New Hampshire University - Shapiro Library [3078]
Southern New Jersey SCORE [42097]
Southern Oak Flooring Industries [3961]
Southern Ocean County Chamber of Commerce [42189]
Southern Ohio Genealogical Society Research Library (SOGS) [7453]
Southern Ohio Procurement Outreach Center [43635]
Southern Ohio Procurement Technical Assistance Center (SOPTAC) - Lawrence Economic Development Corp. [43640]
Southern Oregon Regional Economic Development, Inc. (SOREDI) [43926]
Southern Oregon University Small Business Development Center [43916]
Southern Paint and Wallcovering Dealers Association [9029], [11873]
Southern Piscataquis County Chamber of Commerce [40298]
Southern Plantations Group Inc. (SPG) [17199]
Southern Plywood Manufacturers Association [10376], [10415]
Southern Public Administration Education Foundation (SPAEF) [31679]
Southern Purchasing Institute [31906]
Southern Region Minority Supplier Development Council (SRMSDC) [40202]
Southern Regional Aquaculture Center (SRAC) [6756]
Southern Ulster County Chamber of Commerce Business Directory [42676]
Southern Ulster County Chamber of Commerce Newsletter [42677]
Southern University at Shreveport Small, Women and Minority-Owned Business Incubator (SUSLA) [40233]
Southern University Small, Women and Minority-Owned Business Incubator [40231]
Southern Utah University - Utah Procurement Technical Assistance Center (UPTAC) [45671]
Southern Virginia Product Advancement Center (SVPAC) [45964]
Southern Wayne County Chamber of Commerce [41012]
Southern Wayne County Regional Chamber (SWCRC) [41012]
Southern Wayne Regional Chamber [44303]
Southern West Virginia Community and Technical College [46307]
Southfield Area Chamber of Commerce (SACC) [41013]
Southfield Chamber of Commerce [41013]
Southlake Chamber of Commerce [45367]
Southport-Oak Island Chamber of Commerce [43192]
Southtowns Regional Chamber of Commerce [42678]
Southwest Broward Regional Chamber of Commerce [38464]
Southwest Car Wash Association Convention and Expo [2583]
Southwest Colorado Small Business Development Center Durango [37795]
Southwest Colorado Small Business Development Center Pagosa [37796]
Southwest Council of Agribusiness (SWCA) [16974]
"Southwest Expected to Forego Subsidy Eventually" in *Wichita Business Journal* (Vol. 27, February 3, 2012, No. 5, pp. 1) [19398], [31518]
"Southwest Expected to Up ICT Passenger Counts by Nearly 30 Percent: Taking Off" in *Wichita Business Journal* (Vol. 27, January 20, 2012, No. 3, pp. 1) [19399], [31519]
Southwest Florida Enterprise Center [38582]
Southwest Georgia Business Development Center [38839]
Southwest Health Center - Medical Library [5222], [11546]
Southwest Horticulture Annual Day of Education [17181]
Southwest Indiana Small Business Development Center [39478]
Southwest King County Chamber of Commerce (SWKCC) [46159]
Southwest Louisiana Economic Development Alliance [40234]
Southwest Louisiana Entrepreneurial & Economic Development Center (SEED) [40235]
Southwest Louisiana SCORE [40143]
Southwest Michigan First [41014]
Southwest Michigan Innovation Center [41125]
Southwest Minority Supplier Development Council (SMSDC) [30305]
Southwest Ontario Angel Group (SWO Angels) [46755]
Southwest Region University Transportation Center (SWUTC) [15537]
Southwest Small Business Development Center Minnesota (SBDC) [41160]
Southwest Small Business Development Center - New Mexico [42287]
Southwest Technology Center Business Incubator (SWTC) [43874]
Southwest Valley Chamber of Commerce [36364], [45648]
Southwestern Auglaize County Chamber of Commerce [43574]
Southwestern College (SWC) [37662]
Southwestern Colorado Small Business Development Center [37797]
Southwestern Michigan College-Workforce Education and Business Solutions [41131]
Southwestern Oklahoma State University Small Business Development Center Weatherford [43717]
Southwestern Oregon Community College (SWOCC) [44073]
Southwestern Oregon Community College Business Development Center [33493]
Southwestern Wisconsin SBDC [46320]
Southwestern Wisconsin Small Business Development Center [46320]
Souvenir Wholesale Distributors Association (SWDA) [7473], [7698]
Souvenirs, Gifts & Novelties Magazine--Buyer's Guide Issue [11483]
Souvenirs & Novelties Magazine--Buyer's Guide Issue [11483]
Space Angels (SA) [42802]
Spacial Design [31102]
Spain-United States Chamber of Commerce [27430]
"Spam's Biggest Fan" in *Barron's* (Vol. 92, August 25, 2012, No. 35, pp. 42) [18350], [28822], [29390]
"Spanish Company to Offer Free Wi-Fi In Miami-Dade County" in *South Florida Business Journal* (Vol. 34, April 25, 2014, No. 40) [354], [21985], [23011]
SPARK Business Works [3465]
Spark Capital [40730]
Spark Center SC [44610]
Spark Centre [46834]
Spark Growth (SG) [38583]
Spark Labs [42930]
SPARK Regional Incubator Network (SRIN) [41114]
Sparking Innovation and Creativity (Onsite) [22066]
Sparkle Carpet Cleaning [16244]
Sparkle Wash International [12697]
Sparkworks Media [31814]
Sparta Area Chamber of Commerce [46516]
Sparta-White County Chamber of Commerce [44807]
Spartanburg Community College - The Center for Business & Entrepreneurial Development [44610]
Spartanburg Small Business Development Center [44512]
"Spate of Recent Eagle Ford Deals Shows Big Success of Small Operators" in *San Antonio Business Journal* (Vol. 28, May 30, 2014, No. 16, pp. 8) [16597]
SPC Business Consulting Ltd. [29033]
Speak! Present! Influence! (Onsite) [17613]
"Speaking In Tongues: Rosetta Stone's TOTALE Adds 'Social' To Language Learning" in *Black Enterprise* (Vol. 41, September 2010, No. 2) [15948], [27723], [30604], [33907]
Speaking Skills for Professionals (Onsite) [17614]
Spearfish Area Chamber of Commerce [44659]
Spearfish Area Chamber of Commerce and Convention and Visitors Bureau [44659]
Spearfish Map [44660]
Spearman Chamber of Commerce (SCC) [45368]
"Spec Homes are Back as Builders Gain Confidence" in *Sacramento Business Journal* (Vol. 29, August 31, 2012, No. 27, pp. 1) [4231], [13284]
"Special Events Pro Mary Tribble Reveals Secrets of Winning Bids for Political Convention Business" in *Special Events Magazine* (May 30, 2012) [15898], [25161], [35093]
Special Libraries Association (SLA) [1630], [8832]
Special Libraries Association Information Revolution [1695], [8842]
"Specialize in Cat Nutrition" in *Pet Product News* (Vol. 66, September 2012, No. 9, pp. 80) [8048], [12226]
Specialized Carriers and Rigging Association (SC&RA) [16067]
Specialized Moderator Skills for Qualitative Research Applications (Onsite) [29608]
Specialty Advertising Association [31841]
Specialty Advertising Association of Canada [29575]
Specialty Advertising Association International [31841]
Specialty Advertising Guild International [31841]
Specialty Advertising National Association [31841]
Specialty Coffee Association (SCA) [3174], [7542]
Specialty Coffee Association of America [3174], [7542]
Specialty Equipment Market Association (SEMA) [1094]
Specialty Food Association Inc. [8002], [15003]
Specialty Food Association Winter Fancy Food Show [2552], [8189], [15054]

"Specialty Food Sales Hit Hight of $170.4 Billion in 2020" in Supermarket News (June 10, 2021) **[15030]**
Specialty Food Stores Industry in the US - Market Research Report **[15038]**
Specialty Graphic Imaging Association Convention [7599]
Specialty Tools and Fasteners Distributors Association (STAFDA) **[10422]**
"Spectre of Iran War Spooks Oil Markets" in Globe & Mail (March 28, 2007, pp. B1) **[6612]**, **[9814]**, **[21152]**, **[29391]**
The Spectrem Group Inc. **[10701]**
Spectrum Gaming Group **[7329]**
Spectrum Health Libraries **[1046]**
Speech Coach for Executives **[27159]**
"Speed, Quality and Health: LA Smoothie Truck Combines Robotics with Self-Order Kiosks" in FoodTruckOperator.com (June 22, 2020) **[7011]**
Speed Queen Laundry **[10203]**
Speed Reading with Evelyn Wood Reading Dynamics **[21425]**
"Speed Traps: Every Fast-Growth Company Eventually Runs Into At Least One of These All-Too-Common Obstacles. How You Handle Them Can Make the Difference Between Success and a High-Speed Smashup" in Inc. (Vol. 34, September 2012, No. 7, pp. 53) **[18351]**, **[22803]**
Speedy CPS [12773]
Speedy Transmission Centers **[14596]**
Spencer Area Association of Business and Industry Chamber of Commerce [39797]
Spencer Chamber of Commerce **[39797]**
Spencer Chamber of Commerce [39593]
Spencer County Regional Chamber of Commerce **[39607]**
Spencer-Owen Chamber of Commerce [39593]
Sphere Consulting Group LLC **[147]**
Spherion Staffing, LLC **[15662]**
Spherix Inc. [22028], [35449]
Spin Doctor Laundromat **[10204]**
"Spin Zone: Where Hawaii's Leaders Face Off, Have High-Tech Tax Credits Helped or Hurt Hawaii?" in Hawaii Business (Vol. 53, December 2007, No. 6, pp. 28) **[9815]**, **[21153]**, **[25071]**, **[25547]**, **[26411]**, **[33605]**, **[34891]**
"Spinout Success: New Leadership Steps In At UW's C4C" in Puget Sound Business Journal (Vol. 35, June 27, 2014, No. 10, pp. 11) **[3523]**, **[3641]**, **[9237]**, **[10895]**, **[10972]**, **[14833]**, **[21629]**, **[21986]**, **[25942]**, **[33908]**
Spirit of Math Schools **[21731]**
Spiritual Counterfeits Project [11348]
Splash Magazine **[614]**
"SPOILED! Children's Consignment Boutique Now Collecting Donations To Support Baby2Baby & Help Children In Need" in Benzinga.com (July 30, 2012) **[2854]**, **[3901]**, **[7159]**, **[34374]**, **[35858]**
Spokane Ag Expo **[17182]**
Spokane Angel Alliance (SAA) **[35311]**, **[46199]**
Spokane Area Economic Development Council [46105], [46204]
Spokane Falls Community College (SFCC) **[46232]**
Spokane Intercollegiate Research and Technology Institute [46217]
"Sponsorships, Booths Available for Business Showcase" in Bellingham Business Journal (February 2010, pp. 3) **[15899]**, **[20508]**, **[30055]**, **[31887]**, **[32630]**, **[35094]**
Spooner Area Chamber of Commerce (SACC) **[46517]**
Sport Clips Haircuts **[7897]**
"Sport: The Peformance Business: Special Report" in Business Strategy Review (Vol. 23, Spring 2012, No. 1, pp. 17) **[15187]**
Sportball Systems Inc. **[12464]**
SPORTDiscus **[12470]**
Sporting Arms and Ammunition Manufacturers' Institute (SAAMI) **[7830]**
Sporting Goods Manufacturers Association [15082]
Sporting Goods Retail - US - 2021 **[15112]**
Sporting Goods Stores Industry in the US - Market Research Report **[15113]**
Sports and Fitness Industry Association (SFIA) **[15082]**
Sports Science Laboratory [12519]
Sports Tech and the Value of Startup Communities **[34641]**
SPOTLIGHT **[37202]**
Spotlight **[42190]**
Spotlight on Carthage **[41633]**
"Spotlight On...Jim Alves, SMUD" in Sacramento Business Journal (Vol. 31, March 28, 2014, No. 5) **[21154]**
"Spotlight on Pensions" in Business Horizons (Vol. 51, March-April 2008, No. 2, pp. 105) **[97]**, **[9816]**, **[16839]**, **[17354]**, **[24115]**
"Spouses, Health Coaching Added to Mix" in Pittsburgh Business Times (Vol. 33, June 6, 2014, No. 47, pp. 5) **[8967]**, **[17355]**, **[25943]**, **[27341]**
"Spouses Plan for the Return of the Company Doctor" in Philadelphia Business Journal (Vol. 33, May 2, 2014, No. 12, pp. 4) **[23661]**, **[25944]**
"Spreading Your Wings" in Canadian Business (Vol. 81, March 17, 2008, No. 4, pp. 31) **[6613]**, **[9817]**, **[17356]**, **[22804]**, **[24116]**, **[27213]**, **[33436]**, **[35251]**
Spring Capital Partners L.P. (SCP) **[40434]**
Spring City Chamber of Commerce **[44808]**
"Spring Cleaning: Getting Your Business in Order" in Legal Zoom (March 20, 2023) **[16598]**, **[34892]**
"Spring Cleaning: Refreshing Your Business Plans" in Legal Zoom (February 17, 2023) **[19071]**
Spring Green Area Chamber of Commerce (SGACC) **[46518]**
Spring-Green Lawn Care Corp. **[10271]**
Spring Hill Chamber of Commerce **[44809]**
Spring River Area Chamber of Commerce (SRACC) **[36499]**
Spring Valley Chamber of Commerce **[37203]**
Springboard **[37633]**
Springboro Chamber of Commerce **[43575]**
Springdale Chamber of Commerce (SCC) **[36500]**
Springerville-Eagar Regional Chamber of Commerce **[36365]**
Springfield Area Chamber of Commerce **[44019]**
Springfield Area Chamber of Commerce (SACC) **[41634]**
Springfield Art Museum Library (SAM) **[3383]**, **[12331]**
Springfield Business Development Corp. (SBDC) **[41492]**
Springfield Business Journal (SBJ) **[41708]**
Springfield College - Babson Library **[12472]**
Springfield College;Babson Library [12472]
Springfield Innovation Inc. **[41692]**
Springfield Motorcycle Show **[11115]**
Springfield Regional Chamber of Commerce **[45736]**
Springfield Technical Community College Student Business Incubator **[40763]**
Springhill-Cullen Chamber of Commerce [40193]
Springhill - North Webster Chamber of Commerce **[40193]**
Springtown Area Chamber of Commerce **[45369]**
Springville Area Chamber of Commerce **[42679]**
Springville Chamber of Commerce **[37204]**
"Sprinkler Advocates Beat Builders Again" in Contractor (Vol. 56, November 2009, No. 11, pp. 58) **[12661]**, **[34180]**
Sprout **[41354]**
SproutBox Management Inc. **[39651]**
"Sprouts Farmers Market Reexamines Marketing Strategy to Increase Sales" in Supermarket News (November 5, 2021) **[7774]**, **[8049]**
Spur Capital Partners **[43831]**
"Spying on Your Employees? Better Understand the Law First" in Business News Daily (March 9, 2023) **[22254]**
Square One DSM [39826]
Square One Rental Kitchen & Events **[43319]**
Square Roots **[16980]**
S.R. One Ltd. **[44355]**
SRDS Direct Marketing List Source **[10466]**
SRDS International Media Guides: Newspapers Worldwide **[2993]**
SRIC-BI News **[10683]**
SRM Annual Meeting [858]
SRSU Rio Grande College Small Business Development Center **[44941]**
SSA Convention **[1128]**, **[1137]**, **[1166]**, **[11464]**, **[16108]**
SSA Spring Conference & Trade Show [12991]
SS&C Technologies Inc. **[6712]**, **[9933]**
SSM Partners **[44826]**
SSR [857]
SSSP Annual Meetings **[21699]**
Stable Value Association [9301]
Stable Value Investment Association (SVIA) **[9301]**
"Stadium Developers Seek a Win With the State" in The Business Journal-Serving Metropolitan Kansas City (Vol. 26, August 22, 2008) **[13565]**, **[15188]**, **[19072]**, **[19594]**, **[21155]**, **[34893]**
Staff Association of the Organization of American States [14976]
"Staffing Firms are Picking Up the Pieces, Seeing Signs of Life" in Milwaukee Business Journal (Vol. 27, February 5, 2010, No. 19) **[5448]**, **[6112]**, **[16083]**, **[21156]**, **[33262]**
Stage 1 Ventures, LLC **[40731]**
Stage Equipment and Lighting Inc. **[11132]**
"Staging a Martini-and-GQ Lifestyle" in Crain's Chicago Business (April 21, 2008) **[9048]**, **[13285]**, **[13566]**, **[19934]**, **[34181]**
"A Stakeholder--Human Capital Perspective on the Link Between Social Performance and Executive Compensation" in Business Ethics Quarterly (Vol. 24, January 2014, No. 1, pp. 1) **[17357]**, **[27045]**, **[28823]**, **[34375]**
"Stakes Rising on Business Cyber Security" in Denver Business Journal (Vol. 63, May 18, 2012, No. 52, pp. A1) **[14460]**, **[25548]**
"Staking Claim as Hub for Design" in Providence Business News (Vol. 28, March 17, 2014, No. 50, pp. 1) **[860]**, **[9017]**, **[22427]**, **[35252]**
"'Stalking Horse' Bidder Keeping Plextronics Here" in Pittsburgh Business Times (Vol. 33, March 28, 2014, No. 37, pp. 6) **[5415]**, **[14949]**, **[31520]**, **[32042]**, **[32826]**
Stamford Chamber of Commerce **[38075]**
Stamford Innovation Center (SIC) **[38111]**
"Stamped Out" in The New York Times (September 29, 2017) **[3237]**
Stamping Arts & Crafts [4681]
"Stan Chesley Fighting Kentucky Disbarment" in Business Courier (Vol. 27, September 10, 2010, No. 19, pp. 1) **[18698]**, **[23537]**, **[25549]**
"Stand Out Via Service: How Volunteering Can Boost Your Professional Bottom Line" in Black Enterprise (Vol. 44, June 2014, No. 10, pp. 42) **[27046]**, **[28824]**, **[34376]**
"Stand-Up Guy: From Bear Stearns to Bear Market" in Barron's (Vol. 88, July 7, 2008, No. 27, pp. L11) **[6614]**, **[9818]**, **[24117]**
Standard And Poor's Financial Services LLC. (S&P) **[43006]**
Standard & Poor's Industry Surveys **[380]**, **[434]**, **[800]**, **[1116]**, **[1396]**, **[1687]**, **[1947]**, **[2816]**, **[3159]**, **[3198]**, **[3652]**, **[3748]**, **[4269]**, **[4447]**, **[5195]**, **[6834]**, **[7569]**, **[7796]**, **[7928]**, **[8217]**, **[8473]**, **[8985]**, **[10400]**, **[10470]**, **[10859]**, **[11271]**, **[11456]**, **[11526]**, **[13312]**, **[13736]**, **[14041]**, **[14852]**, **[15800]**, **[16091]**
Standard Rate & Data Service--Direct Mail List Rates & Data [10466]
Standing Tall **[35156]**
Standish Press [40777]
Stanford Business **[24893]**
Stanford Business School Magazine [24893]
Stanford Heart Disease Prevention Program [34703]
Stanford University - Center for Entrepreneurial Studies (CES) **[37663]**
Stanford University Department of Electrical Engineering - Information Systems Laboratory (ISL) **[3799]**
Stanford University - Stanford Prevention Research Center (SPRC) **[34703]**
Stanley-Sawtooth Chamber of Commerce **[38943]**
Stanley Steemer International Inc. **[16245]**
Stanly County Chamber of Commerce (SCCoC) **[43193]**
Stanton Chamber Directory **[37205]**
"Star Power Versus (Somewhat) Green Power" in Globe & Mail (January 18, 2007, pp. B2) **[23361]**, **[24744]**
Star Valley Chamber of Commerce (SVCCOM) **[46621]**
"Starbucks and Alibaba Launch Voice Ordering and Delivery" in Vending Times (October 4, 2019) **[3190]**
"Starbucks' Wheel Strategy" in Puget Sound Business Journal (Vol. 29, October 3, 2008, No. 24, pp. 1) **[7564]**, **[19073]**
Starke-Bradford County Chamber of Commerce [38472]
Starke County Chamber of Commerce **[39608]**
"Start 2022 with a Bang with These Grants" in Small Business News (Dec. 31, 2021) **[30386]**, **[35859]**
Start A Christmas Tree Farm - Business Ideas **[2948]**
Start Business in California, 3E **[22428]**, **[24566]**
"Start or Buy? It's a Tough Question for Eager Entrepreneurs" in Crain's Cleveland Business (Vol. 28, October 8, 2007, No. 40, pp. 24) **[19692]**, **[22805]**, **[33606]**
Start Co. **[44827]**, **[44853]**
"Start an Estate Sale Company in 7 Steps" in EstateSales.org Blog **[6074]**
"Start Filling Your Talent Gap - Now" in Business Strategy Review (Vol. 21, Spring 2010, No. 1, pp. 56) **[22255]**, **[26665]**, **[27047]**, **[28825]**
Start Garden **[41115]**
Start a Profitable Laundromat: Let's Crunch Some Numbers **[10177]**
"Start: Punch Fear in the Face, Escape Average and Do Work that Matters" **[21987]**, **[34182]**
Start and Run a Delicatessen: Small Business Starters Series **[4875]**, **[13875]**, **[18868]**, **[32043]**, **[33413]**
Start, Run, & Grow a Successful Small Business **[18352]**, **[22806]**, **[24567]**
Start and Run a Home-Based Food Business **[2662]**, **[26750]**
Start an RV Rental Business Using Other People RVs with Garr Russell **[13848]**
Start. Scale. Exit. Repeat. What Makes a Startup Successful with Colin Campbell **[34642]**
Start Small, Finish Big **[4876]**, **[13876]**, **[22807]**, **[24301]**
"Start a Translating Business" in Business Know-How (November 20, 2019) **[15949]**
Start U Up **[38115]**
"Start Up Boom in the Pandemic Is Growing Stronger" in New York Times (August 19, 2021) **[30387]**, **[34547]**
Start-Up and Emerging Companies: Planning, Financing, and Operating the Successful Business, with Forms on Disk **[34548]**

Small Business Sourcebook • 42nd Edition 3341

Start-Up Nation [21157], [27724]
"Start-Up! So You Want to Be an Entrepreneur. So You Want to Be Rich" [22429], [26178]
"Start Your Business Off Right with a Business Plan Outline" in Legal Zoom (March 14, 2023) [19074]
Start Your Crafting Business [4651]
Start Your Own Business [22430], [24568]
Start Your Own Event Planning Business [6097], [34549]
Start Your Own Fashion Accessories Business [355], [2997], [3085], [6121], [26751], [30056], [31888]
Start Your Own Freelance Writing Business: The Complete Guide to Starting and Scaling from Scratch [5325], [26807], [30489]
Start Your Own Lawn Care or Landscaping Business: Your Step-by-Step Guide to Success [10069], [24569]
Start Your Own Wedding Consultant Business [1958], [24570]
Starta Accelerator [42931]
Starta Captial [43028]
Starta Ventures [42803]
STARTech Early Ventures [45474]
StartEngine (SE) [37762]
StartFast Venture Accelerator [42932]
"Starting an Adult Day Care Center: What You Need to Know for Success" in Verywell (July 30, 2019) [186]
"Starting an Arbitration & Mediation Service [10801]
Starting a Bed and Breakfast: Bite Sized Interviews with Successful B&B's on Building a Brand That Lasts [1424]
The Starting Block [41116]
The Starting Block Inc. [41116]
Starting a Business After Retirement: 12 Business Ideas for the Over 50s [33075]
Starting a Business All-in-One for Dummies [33607], [34550]
Starting a Business from Home [26835]
"Starting a Business from Home - Legal, Tax, and Financial Concerns" in CPA Journal (July 2017) [26808]
Starting a Business QuickStart Guide [33608]
Starting a Coffee Service Business [3191]
Starting an Etsy Business for Dummies [11798]
Starting a Franchise Restaurant Business [14086], [24461]
"Starting a Grocery Shopping Business in 6 Easy Steps" in Grocery Shopping Business website (April 19, 2019) [12028]
"Starting a Home Business With a Spouse" in Gaebler Ventures Resources for Entrepreneurs [26809]
"Starting a Laundromat Business: Expectations vs. Reality" in Laundrylux [10178]
"Starting an Organizing Business for Little or No Money" in ZenBusiness blog (Dec. 13, 2021) [12815]
Starting a Personal Shopper Business [12029]
Starting & Running Your Own Horse Business [8298], [8968], [16918], [27342], [34894]
"Starting and Scaling a Small Business as a Minority Entrepreneur" in Sahan Journal (Nov. 1, 2021) [30388], [33609]
Starting a Successful Business [16724]
Starting a Successful Business in Canada [22431], [24571]
"Starting a Successful Home Security Company: Step-By-Step Guide" in Home Business (January 30, 2023) [14461], [26810]
"Starting a Sustainable Agriculture Business" in Texas A&M Forest Service [17117]
"Starting Up All Over Again: Alex Bogusky Backs Bootcamp for Advertising Startup" in Denver Business Journal (Vol. 65, February 7, 2014, No. 39, pp. 8) [205], [22432], [26179], [29565]
"Starting Up As A Professional Genealogist" in Professional Family History Blog (November 22, 2018) [7371]
Starting Up On Your Own: How to Succeed as an Independent Consultant or Freelance [2168], [20074]
"Starting Your Genealogy Business" in The Armchair Genealogist Blog [7372]
Starting Your Own Mediation Business [10802]
StartingPoint Ventures [43029]
StartingUp Now (SUN) [33510]
StartingUp Now Facilitator Guide [21630], [22433], [24572]
StartOut [30306]
Startup 405 [43875]
"Startup Activity Among Jobless Execs is the Highest Since 2009, Survey Says" in South Florida Business Journal (Vol. 34, February 21, 2014, No. 31, pp. 3) [24573], [26666], [28250]
The Startup Blueprint: The Young Entrepreneur's Step-by-Step Guide To Starting Your Own Business [22434], [36002]
Startup Boards: A Field Guide to Building and Leading an Effective Board of Directors [34551]

Startup Capital Ventures (SCV) [37763]
Startup Communities: Building an Entrepreneurial Ecosystem in Your City [22435], [24574], [35253]
Startup CXO: A Field Guide to Scaling Up Your Company's Critical Functions and Teams [34552]
Startup Ecology [42933]
Startup Edmonton [46670]
Startup Financial Model (SFM) [45475]
The Startup Garage (TSG) [37685]
Startup Grind [33641], [34662]
StartUp Health Academy [42934]
Startup Leadership Program (SLP) [40772]
Startup Lloydminster [46677]
"Startup Lucena Taking On Wall Street" in Atlanta Business Chronicle (May 23, 2014, pp. 1A) [6615], [9819], [14746], [33737]
Startup Maryland [40470]
"Startup Osteosphere Formed to Develop Laboratory Discovery" in Houston Business Journal (Vol. 40, January 8, 2010, No. 35, pp. 1) [25945], [26412], [32044], [32827], [35387]
The Startup Owner's Manual: The Step-By-Step Guide for Building a Great Company [34553]
Startup San Diego (SSD) [37634]
The Startup Santa [34643]
"The Startup of Something Big" in Philadelphia Business Journal (Vol. 33, July 11, 2014, No. 22, pp. 4) [21300], [31146], [31929], [32707], [33335]
"STARTUP STATISTICS 2023 – The Numbers You Need to Know" in Small Business Trends (December 27, 2022) [34554], [34581]
Startup Tips for Non-Technical Founders [34644]
Startup Tucson [36403]
Startup Virginia (SVA) [45965]
"A Startup's Guide to Business Ethics and Social Responsibility" in Embroker Blog (Aug. 23, 2021) [23538]
Startup52 [42935]
Startupbootcamp FinTech New York (SCP) [42936]
StartupNation Media Group Inc. [33707]
"Startups, It's Time to Think Like Camels -- Not Unicorns" in Harvard Business Review (October 16, 2020) [34555]
Startups for the Rest of Us: Building, Buying, and Selling SaaS Companies [34645]
Startups for the Rest of Us: Building a Recurring, Annual Price Increase into Your SaaS [31668]
Startups for the Rest of Us: Equipping Sales & Support with Critical Product Knowledge as You Grow [24825]
Startups for the Rest of Us: Founder Regrets, DIY vs. Hiring, Defining Your ICP, and More Later Stage Listener Questions [16692]
Startups for the Rest of Us: From Side Hustle to Full-Time & Profitable (with Mike Taber) [34646]
Startups for the Rest of Us: How to Generate Startup Idea (Plus 8 Ideas You Can Steal) [34647]
Startups for the Rest of Us: Make Ever-Increasing and Manageably-Sized Mistakes (A Rob Solo Adventure) [16693]
Startups for the Rest of Us: Mock Features, a Failed Launch, Becoming a Freelancer, and More Listener Questions (A Rob Solo Adventure) [34648]
Startups for the Rest of Us: Why Launching a Second Product Is Usually a Bad Idea [16694]
StartX [37635]
"StartX Med Prescribed for Innovation" in Silicon Valley/San Jose Business Journal (Vol. 30, June 8, 2012, No. 11, pp. 1) [10815], [10898], [22436], [25180], [31930], [32708]
Stat Communications Ltd. [46242]
"State Accuses Eight Companies of Making Sales Calls to People Who Signed up to Stop Them" in WTVA.com (September 4, 2019) [15551], [25550]
State of Alaska Department of Commerce, Community and Economic Development - Division of Community and Regional Affairs (DCRA) - Serve Alaska Commission [47476]
"State Aviation Fuel Tax Proposal Runs Into Turbulence" in Crain's Detroit Business (Vol. 25, June 15, 2009, No. 24, pp. 5) [19400], [34895]
State Bar of Georgia Business Law Section [18479]
State Bar of Michigan Business Law Section (SBM BLS) [18480], [40808]
State Beer Association of Executives of America [35485]
State Beer Wholesalers Secretaries [35485]
State Board Report [116]
"The State of Boomer-Owned Small Business" in Small Business Trends (November 6, 2022) [16599]
"State Center Lease Deal High for Md." in Baltimore Business Journal (Vol. 28, August 6, 2010, No. 13, pp. 1) [4232], [13567], [13831], [31696], [33414]
State Chapter Convention [3394]
State of Connecticut Department of Economic and Community Development - Research and Planning [47477]

State of Delaware Senate Small Business Committee [38146]
"State Democrats Push for Changes to Plant Security Law" in Chemical Week (Vol. 172, July 19, 2010, No. 17, pp. 8) [14462], [18699], [25551], [29392]
"State Fairgrounds Adding Year-Round Attractions" in Crain's Detroit Business (Vol. 24, February 18, 2008, No. 7, pp. 17) [15900], [35095]
"State Fund That Aids New Companies Likely To Wither" in Crain's Detroit Business (Vol. 24, February 25, 2008, No. 8, pp. 16) [28074], [35254]
"The State & Future of CBD in Beauty" in Global Cosmetic Industry (October 12, 2019) [4521]
State of Illinois (OMB) - Office of Management and Budget [47478]
"State Investment Goes Sour" in Business Journal Portland (Vol. 26, December 4, 2009, No. 39, pp. 1) [5710], [5977], [17118], [23362], [25072], [28208]
State of Kentucky - Department for Libraries and Archives [47479]
State Library of Florida Division of Library and Information Services [47480]
State Library of Iowa [47481]
State Library of Kansas [47482]
State Library of North Carolina Division of State Library (SLNC) [47483]
State Library of Ohio [47484]
"The State of Minority Entrepreneurship in America" in Next Avenue (Nov. 9, 2021) [30389]
"State Moves to Improve Child Care" in Providence Business News (Vol. 29, April 7, 2014, No. 1, pp. 1) [2885], [21631], [25073]
State of New Jersey Department of Environmental Protection - Division of Solid and Hazardous Waste [47006]
State of Oregon Office of Economic Analysis - Department of Administrative Services (DAS) [47485]
"State of Play" in Canadian Business (Vol. 79, June 19, 2006, No. 13, pp. 25) [6616], [9820], [18353], [26413]
"State Pressure Keeps Rates Low" in Sacramento Business Journal (Vol. 31, August 8, 2014, No. 24, pp. 4) [25552], [27343]
"State Regulators Reject AEP Ohio's Plans to Build 400MW of Solar Funded by Ratepayers" in Greentech Media (November 21, 2019) [14950], [25553]
"State Reverses Food Truck Order" in Cape Cod Times (May 15, 2012) [3856], [7012], [18700], [25554], [30490]
State of Rhode Island Office of Library and Information Services - Department of Administration [47486]
"State of the States" in Barron's (Vol. 92, August 27, 2012, No. 38, pp. 23) [6617], [17358], [24118]
State and Territorial Air Pollution Program Administrators and Association of Local Air Pollution Control Officials [23040]
State & Territories Small Business Profiles [16600]
State of Texas Office of the Governor - Department of Economic Development and Tourism - Division of Business Development [45423]
State of Texas Office of the Governor Economic Development & Tourism Div. [45578]
"State Unemployment Fraud Rising Sharply" in Sacramento Business Journal (Vol. 28, October 21, 2011, No. 34, pp. 1) [18701], [34183]
"State of the Unions" in Canadian Business (Vol. 81, December 8, 2008, No. 21, pp. 23) [30057], [31521]
State University of New York at Buffalo - Clinical Research Institute on Addictions (CRIA) [34696], [34704]
State University of New York at Buffalo - Music Library [11240]
State University of New York at Buffalo - Research Institute on Addictions [34696], [34704]
State University of New York at Buffalo - Research Institute on Alcoholism [34696], [34704]
State University of New York at Buffalo School of Management - Center for Executive Development [15781]
State University of New York at Cortland Memorial Library [12473]
State University of New York - Fashion Institute of Technology - Gladys Marcus Library [1205], [3079], [3172], [4569], [6153], [7938], [9079]
State University of New York at Fredonia - Fredonia Technology Incubator (FTI) [42937]
"State VC Fund To Get At Least $7.5 Million" in Crain's Detroit Business (Vol. 24, February 25, 2008, No. 8, pp. 14) [25555], [28209], [35388]
State of Vermont Agency of Commerce and Community Development - Tourism and Marketing [47487]
"State Wants to Add Escape Clause to Leases" in Sacramento Business Journal (Vol. 28, October 14, 2011, No. 33, pp. 1) [13286], [13568], [13832], [19935], [25556], [28210]

Stateline Chamber [39311]
Staten Island Chamber of Commerce (SICC) [42680]
States Organization for Boating Access (SOBA) [2830]
Statesboro-Bulloch Chamber of Commerce [38782]
Staunton Chamber of Commerce (SCC) [39312]
Staunton Makerspace [45966]
"Stay In Your Home" in Consumer Reports Money (Vol. 9, May 20, 2012, No. 5, pp. 1) [912], [4233], [11521]
"Staying Engaged: Location, Location" in Black Enterprise (Vol. 38, February 2008, No. 7, pp. 64) [17760], [22808], [28826]
Staying Inspired as a Content Creator with Tieghan Gerard of Half-Baked Harvest [27818]
"Staying Social Complements Retail Goals" in Pet Product News (Vol. 66, September 2012, No. 9, pp. 34) [9238], [12227], [30058], [32288]
Staying Solo: Bigger is Not Better: Staying Solo as a Strategic Choice [34471]
Staying Solo: Grow Your Strategy, Not Your Stress [34472]
Staying Solo: Sorry, Not Sorry: When the Client Is Wrong [33310]
Staying Solo: Strategy Over Scale: How to Break the Time-Money Trap [34473]
Staying Solo: The Capacity Code: Managing Time and Energay as a Solo Business Owner [34474]
Stayton Area Chamber of Commerce [44020]
Stayton - Sublimity Chamber of Commerce (SSCC) [44020]
"Steady Spending In Retail, But Job Losses Are Rising" in Business Week (September 22, 2008, No. 4100, pp. 13) [18354], [21158], [32289]
Steak-Out Charbroiled Delivery [2694], [14262]
Steal These Ideas!: Marketing Secrets That Will Make You a Star [30059], [30662]
Stealthmode Partners [36404]
Steam Systems Maintenance, Safety & Optimization (Onsite) [19459], [21426]
Steamatic Inc. [2116]
Steamboat Springs Chamber Resort Association (SSCRA) [37900]
Stearns, Conrad and Schmidt Engineers Inc. [5780]
Stearns County Historical Society [7464]
Stearns County History Museum [7464]
Stearns History Museum (SHM) [7464]
Stearns, Weaver, Miller, Weissler, Alhadeff and Sitterson P.A. [9952]
Steel Can Recycling Institute [13696]
Steel Recycling Institute (SRI) [13696]
Steel Truss and Component Association [3964]
"Steel Yard Eyes Funding Balance" in Providence Business News (Vol. 29, May 26, 2014, No. 8, pp. 1) [7160], [21632]
"Steelhead Makes High-Tech Tanks" in Denver Business Journal (Vol. 65, March 28, 2014, No. 46, pp. A7) [9821], [26414]
"Steeling for Battle" in Crain's Chicago Business (Vol. 31, April 21, 2008, No. 16, pp. 3) [8969], [17359], [27344], [29393], [35205]
"Steeling Themselves: Price Hikes Testing The Mettle of Scrap Dealers" in Baltimore Business Journal (Vol. 30, July 6, 2012, No. 9, pp. 1) [26667], [29394], [31522]
Steelville Area Chamber of Commerce [41635]
"Steering a Steady Course Through Turbulent Waters" in Providence Business News (Vol. 29, June 2, 2014, No. 9, pp. 22) [13044], [30060], [34377]
"Steering Toward Profitability" in Black Enterprise (Vol. 41, December 2010, No. 5, pp. 72) [1110], [11437], [24413], [29395], [30390]
Steigerwaldt Tree Farms [2957]
Steilacoom Chamber of Commerce [46160]
Steinmann Facility Development Consultants (SFDC) [4339]
Stellaria Community Incubator Kitchen [44068]
Stemtree [16172]
Step-by-Step Guide to Starting an Online T-shirt Printing Business in 2020 [14357]
"Step-by-Step Guide to Starting a Personal Training Business" in NASM (March 24, 2020) [12433]
"A Step Up" in Black Enterprise (Vol. 38, January 2008, No. 6, pp. 53) [28827], [35860]
"Step Up to Help Regionalism Step Forward" in Crain's Cleveland Business (Vol. 28, November 12, 2007, No. 45, pp. 10) [21159], [24745]
Stephen M. Segal Inc. [13623]
Stephenville Chamber of Commerce [45370]
"Stepping Out" in Small Business Opportunities (Get Rich At Home 2010) [14665], [24302]
"Steps to Motivate Your Employees" in business.com (Aug. 18, 2020) [22256]
StepStone Business Partners [39634]
Sterling [148]
Sterling Area Chamber of Commerce [39307]

Sterling Business & Technology Park [44421]
Sterling Chamber of Commerce [39957]
Sterling Heights Regional Chamber of Commerce & Industry [41015]
Sterling-Hoffman (SH) [3668]
Sterling Optical [16314]
Sterling Partners (SP) [39376], [40435]
Sterling Small Business Technology Center [39432]
STERNbusiness [24894]
"Sterotaxis Needs $10 Million in 60 Days" in Saint Louis Business Journal (Vol. 32, October 7, 2011, No. 6, pp. 1) [10852], [28211]
Steve Burns Inc. [149]
Steve Moeller's American Business Vision L.L.C. [30224]
Steve Wilson and Co. [22331]
Steven E. Kramer CpA [150]
Steven Salm Founder & CEO of PLANTA [14087]
Steven Winter Associates Inc. (SWA) [12921]
Stevens, Reed, Curcio and Potholm Media [7180], [12961]
Stevens County Business Resource Center [46004]
Stevens Venture Center (SVC) [42248]
Stevenson Real Estate Group Ltd. [13624]
Stewart County Chamber of Commerce (SCCC) [44810]
Stigma: Whose Business Is It Anyway? [35431]
"Stikemans' Ascent, Its Legacy, and Its Future" in Globe & Mail (January 29, 2007, pp. B2) [18702], [19595], [19936], [31523]
"Still No Arena Financing Plan" in Sacramento Business Journal (Vol. 28, May 27, 2011, No. 13, pp. 1) [4234], [15189], [28212]
"Still Stretching" in Business Courier (Vol. 24, December 28, 2008, No. 37, pp. 1) [7775], [18355], [30391]
"Still Unprepared For Natural Disasters: Blacks More Likely to be Affected and Less Prepared" in Black Enterprise (Vol. 38, January 2008, No. 6, pp. 28) [19075], [30392]
Stillwater Chamber of Commerce (SCC) [43809]
Stillwater Commerce [43810]
Stillwater County Chamber of Commerce [41794]
Stillwater Insurance Group [151], [16886], [24267]
"Stimulating Fare at the SBA" in Barron's (Vol. 89, July 20, 2009, No. 29, pp. 12) [9239], [16470], [34184]
"Stirring Again: Bart Vandaele's New Venture" in Washington Business Journal (Vol. 31, August 24, 2012, No. 18, pp. 1) [14019]
STLGip [37686]
STLVentureWorks-Grand Center [41693]
"STMicroelectronics" in Canadian Electronics (Vol. 23, February 2008, No. 1, pp. 1) [4407], [9822], [26415], [31524]
STN Inc. [3788]
"Stock Car Racing" in Canadian Business (Vol. 81, September 15, 2008, No. 14-15, pp. 29) [6618], [9823], [11438], [18703], [19076], [19596], [23363], [24119], [29396]
"A Stock Worth Trading Down To" in Barron's (Vol. 88, July 14, 2008, No. 28, pp. 36) [7776], [9824], [17119], [29397], [31525]
Stockbridge Chamber of Commerce (SCC) [40631]
"Stockerts Open Repair Business" in Dickinson Press (July 13, 2010) [783], [23662], [33263]
Stockton Area Chamber of Commerce (SACC) [41636]
The Stoller Co. [17413]
Stone Harbor Chamber of Commerce [42191]
Stoneham Chamber of Commerce [40632]
"Stoneham Drilling Trust Announces Cash Distribution for May 2007" in Canadian Corporate News (May 16, 2007) [19597], [33264]
Stonewall Chamber of Commerce (SCC) [45371]
Stonewood Capital Management, Inc. [44446]
Stony Brook Small Business Development Center [42414]
Stony Brook University Business Incubator at Calverton [42938]
Stony Brook University (CEBIP) - Clean Energy Business Incubator Program [42939]
Stony Brook University Incubator at Calverton [42940]
Stony Brook University - School of Marine and Atmospheric Sciences - Living Marine Resources Institute (LIMRI) [6805]
Stony Brook University - Small Business Development Center (SBDC) [42415]
"Stop the Innovation Wars" in Harvard Business Review (Vol. 88, July-August 2010, No. 7-8, pp. 76) [18356], [27950], [28828], [30809]
"Stop Trying to Delight Your Customers" in Harvard Business Review (Vol. 88, July-August 2010, No. 7-8, pp. 116) [20509], [32631]
Storage Council [3475], [12970]
Storage & Warehousing Leasing Industry in the US - Market Research Report [12987]
"StorageByMail Lets Customers Ship Away Their Clutter" in Inc. (Vol. 33, April 2011, No. 3, pp. 92) [7049], [12848]

"Store Front: Invest in Energy-Efficient Equipment for Your Pet Store" in Pet Product News (Vol. 66, September 2012, No. 9, pp. 43) [516], [5416], [5711], [5978], [12228], [23364]
StorePoint Fashion [32358]
Storey's Guide to Keeping Honey Bees [1487]
Stork News [1203]
Storm Lake Chamber of Commerce [39798]
Storm Lake United (SLU) [39798]
Storm Ventures [37493]
Storm Water Management: How to Comply with Federal and State Regulations (Onsite) [25193]
Story City Chamber of Commerce [39799]
Story City Greater Chamber Connection [39799]
"The Story of a Complex Project, Seen From a Bridge" in Business Review Albany (Vol. 41, June 27, 2014, No. 14, pp. 7) [3524], [3737], [29398]
The Story Lab [37636]
"The Story Of Diane Greene" in Barron's (Vol. 88, July 14, 2008, No. 28, pp. 31) [14834], [26416], [26668], [28829], [31526], [33909], [35206]
Stoughton Chamber of Commerce (SCC) [46519]
Stow-Munroe Falls Chamber of Commerce (SMFCC) [43576]
Stow-Munroe Falls Chamber of Commerce Member Business Directory [43577]
Stowe Area Association [45737]
"Stoyan Kenderov on Preparing Your Business for Recession" in Small Business Trends (July 26, 2022) [33910]
Straight North L.L.C. [16152]
Strand Consuilting [33690]
"Strange Brew" in Canadian Business (Vol. 85, June 11, 2012, No. 10, pp. 52) [1352], [1936], [10334], [15031], [30810], [32632]
Strategic Account Management Association (SAMA) [10570], [24283]
Strategic Agility and Resilience: Embracing Change to Drive Growth [28418]
Strategic Air Command Judo Association [10716]
Strategic Business Alliance [7181]
Strategic Business Planning Co. (SBP) [2317]
Strategic Business Services Inc. (SBS) [2318]
Strategic and Competitive Intelligence Professionals (SCIP) [28021]
Strategic Computer Solutions Inc. [13059]
Strategic Decisions Group (SDG) [29054]
Strategic Design Thinking: Innovation in Products, Services, Experiences and Beyond [29399]
Strategic Diversity Retention (Onsite) [28419]
"Strategic Issue Management as Change Catalyst" in Strategy and Leadership (Vol. 39, September-October 2011, No. 5, pp. 20-29) [19077], [25946], [28830]
Strategic Management Society (SMS) [28269]
Strategic Planning: From Vision-to-Action [22067]
Strategic Planning for Organizational Success (Onsite) [19460]
Strategic Press Inc. [41964]
Strategic Sales Negotiations (Onsite) [32447]
Strategic Services on Unemployment and Workers' Compensation and the National Foundation for UC & WC [19731]
The Strategic Speed-Reading Advantage for Executives & Legal Professionals [34976]
"Strategies and Formulas for Pricing Services at Your Small Business" in Patriot (November 5, 2019) [31656]
Strategies for a More Effective Collections Policy [20345]
Strategies for Social Change L.L.C. (SSC) [35458]
Strategies for Success: A Conversation with a Multi-Talented Real Estate Entrepreneur with Timothy Lyons [13608]
Strategies for Successful Product Launches [29550]
Strategize Magazine: Tomorrow's Ideas for Today's Business [24895]
The Strategy Center (TSC) [43876]
Strategy Execution: Getting it Done (Onsite) [29609]
The Strategy Hour: 9 Critically Important Lessons I've Learned from 9 Years in Business [16695]
The Strategy Hour: How to Deal with Stres and Anxiety - And Still Stay Productive [35013]
The Strategy Hour: Incubator Client Strategy Breakdown: Bonnie Hit $30K Months & Took a !0-Day Vacay 5 Months into the Incubator Program [8825]
The Strategy Hour: Making a Difference and a Profit: Inside Talitha Coffee's Mission-Driven Business [34439]
The Strategy Hour: What's Possible: From Solopreneur to Scalable Enterprise with Ryan Deiss [18451]
"Strategy Migration In a Changing Climate" in Harvard Business Review (Vol. 92, May 2014, No. 5, pp. 42) [7161], [24120], [31527], [31792]
Stratford Area Chamber of Commerce [46520]
Straw Hat Pizza [12594]

Streamlined Ventures [37494]
Streator Area Chamber of Commerce and Industry (SACCI) [39313]
"Street Bistro Brings Food Truck Treats to Bangor" in Bangor Daily News (June 26, 2012) [3830], [7013], [14020], [22809], [23582], [30450]
Street Corner Inc. [4454]
"Street Survival to Offer Teen Driver Training" in Savannah Now (October 15, 2019) [5105]
Street Vendors Industry in the US - Market Research Report [7022]
Streetsboro Area Chamber of Commerce (SACC) [43578]
Streetwise Finance and Accounting for Entrepreneurs: Set Budgets, Manage Costs, Keep Your Business Profitable [98], [16840], [17509], [24121]
Streetwise Small Business Book of Lists: Hundreds of Lists to Help You Reduce Costs, Increase Revenues, and Boost Your Profits! [99], [16841], [17510], [18357], [24746], [32633]
Streetwise Small Business Turnaround: Revitalizing Your Struggling or Stagnant Enterprise [18358], [19598]
"Strengthen the Support for Women in Biz" in Crain's Detroit Business (Vol. 30, September 8, 2014, No. 36, pp. 1) [18359], [35861]
Strengthening Your People Skills in the Workplace (Onsite) [17615]
Strengths Based Leadership [22810], [28831]
"Stress-Test Your Strategy: the 7 Questions to Ask" in Harvard Business Review (Vol. 88, November 2010, No. 11, pp. 92) [20510], [22257], [22811], [28832]
"Stressed Out: 7 St. Louis Banks Rated 'At Risks'" in Saint Louis Business Journal (Vol. 32, September 16, 2011, No. 3, pp. 1) [6619], [9825], [24122]
"Stretch Your Last Dollar Or Invest It?" in Business Owner (Vol. 35, November-December 2011, No. 6, pp. 4) [9826], [24123]
"Strict Intersection Types for the Lambda Calculus" in ACM Computing Surveys (Vol. 43, Fall 2011, No. 3, pp. 20) [3434], [3642]
Strictly Slots [7335]
Strive Capital, Inc. [37495]
"Strivers and High Fliers" in Dallas Business Journal (Vol. 37, February 7, 2014, No. 22, pp. 4) [22812], [30393]
"Striving for Self-Verification During Organizational Entry" in Academy of Management Journal (Vol. 55, June 2012, No. 2, pp. 360) [22258], [28833]
"A Strong, Aligned Board of Directors Is Ideal" in South Florida Business Journal (Vol. 35, August 1, 2014, No. 1, pp. 8) [9827], [19078], [19599], [31528]
"Stronger Corn? Take It Off Steroids, Make It All Female" in Farm Industry News (December 5, 2011) [17120], [30811], [32045], [32828]
Strongland Chamber of Commerce [44168]
Strongsville Area Chamber of Commerce [43579]
Strongsville Chamber of Commerce (SCC) [43579]
Strongsville Chamber of Commerce News [43580]
Stroud Chamber of Commerce [43811]
Structural Building Components Association (SBCA) [3964]
Structured Query Language (SQL) I [33814]
Structured Query Language (SQL) II [33815]
"Struggling for Cash Flow? Strategies for Survival" in Business News Daily (Jan. 21, 2022) [19722]
Stuart Matlins Associates [29006]
"StubHub Launches in the UK" in Entertainment Close-Up (March 25, 2012) [11127], [11799], [15190], [18360], [27725]
Stucco Manufacturers Association (SMA) [3965]
"Stuck With Two Mortgages" in Crain's Chicago Business (Vol. 31, April 21, 2008, No. 16) [11082], [13287], [13569], [19937], [20346], [21160], [28213]
Students in Free Enterprise [41673]
"Students' Mounting Interest in Taxidermy" in Sanilac County News (November 24, 2019) [15539], [21633]
Studio 6 [8516]
Studio 6 [8508]
Studio 6 Canada [8517]
Studio City Chamber of Commerce (SCCC) [37206]
"A Study in Diversity: What Women Want: There Are Fundamental Differences Between How Men and Women View Retirement Planning" in Senior Market Advisor (Vol. 13, October 2012, No. 10, pp. 36) [6620], [9828], [24124]
"Study Finds Epigenetic Differences Between Hatchery-Raised and Wild-Born Salmon" in The Scientist (March 1, 2018) [6786]
"Study: Ineffective Customer Communications Can Cost Small Businesses Time, Money and Talent" in Business Wire (Dec. 8, 2021) [17761]
"Study: New Moms Build A Lot of Brand Buzz" in Brandweek (Vol. 49, April 21, 2008, No. 16, pp. 7) [9240], [11998], [15615], [30061], [30812], [32290], [33265]

"Study: Restaurants Should Use Compostable Dinnerware to Reduce Food Waste" in PMQ Pizza Magazine (November 2019) [12535], [13729], [14021]
"Stuff that Works for You: In the Mobikey of Life" in Canadian Business (Vol. 81, June 11, 2008, No. 11, pp. 42) [3643], [14463], [26417], [28834]
Stuft Pizza, Stuft Pizza Bar & Grill, Stuft Pizza Pronto [12595]
"Stung by Recession, Hemmer Regroups with New Strategy" in Business Courier (Vol. 27, June 4, 2010, No. 5, pp. 1) [4235], [19079], [21161], [27048], [30062], [31131]
Stuntmen's Association of Motion Pictures (SAMP) [6223]
Stuntwomen's Association of Motion Pictures (SA) [6170]
Sturgis Area Chamber of Commerce (SACC) [41016]
Sturgis Area Chamber of Commerce & Visitors Bureau [44661]
Sturgis Chamber of Commerce [44662]
Stuttgart Chamber of Commerce [36501]
Style Summit (Onsite) [21427]
"StyleCraft Consolidates HQ, Distribution Facility" in Memphis Business Journal (Vol. 34, June 1, 2012, No. 7, pp. 1) [8212], [20654]
"A Stylish New Labelmaker" in Inc. (Vol. 33, October 2011, No. 8, pp. 48) [11669], [30981]
"Stymiest's RBC Compensation Triggers Shareholder Outrage" in Gl obe & Mail (January 28, 2006, pp. B3) [6621], [9829], [28835]
"Subaru of America Releases September Sales Figures" in Travel & Leisure Close-Up (October 8, 2012) [11439], [18361]
Sublette County Chamber of Commerce (SCCC) [46622]
"Subprime Mess Hits Huntington" in Business First-Columbus (November 26, 2007, pp. A1) [6622], [9830], [11083], [31529]
Subscription Fulfillment Managers Association [29482]
Substance Abuse Librarians and Information Specialists (SALIS) [34673]
"Substantial Deal Expected to Create Jobs, Help Industrial Market" in Tampa Bay Business Journal (Vol. 30, January 8, 2010, No. 3) [6921], [7777], [12982], [18362], [20655]
Suburban Chamber of Commerce [42192]
Suburban Cylinder Express [26832]
Suburban Essex Chamber of Commerce (SECC) [42193]
"Suburban Retailers Go Urban" in Philadelphia Business Journal (Vol. 28, August 17, 2012, No. 27, pp. 1) [4522], [12902], [19205]
Subway [4922], [8121]
:Subway Closings Accerlerate as Cold-Cuts Fail to Draw in Diners" in Bloomberg (March 28, 2019) [4885], [24414]
"Subway Franchise Locations Celebrating National Potato Chip Day with Unique Menu Item" in Small Business Trends (March 9, 2023) [24415]
Subway IP LLC [4922], [8121]
"Subway Launches Expanded Cafes, Drive-Thru Window Locations" in South Florida Business Journal (Vol. 33, August 10, 2012, No. 2, pp. 1) [4886], [7565], [14022], [24416], [33415]
"Succeed With the Right Equipment" in Pet Product News (Vol. 64, November 2010, No. 11, pp. 42) [12076], [29400], [31053], [34185]
"Succeeding at Succession" in Harvard Business Review (Vol. 88, November 2010, No. 11, pp. 29) [28836]
"Success in Business: A Guide for Young Entrepreneurs" in Women in Technology International (Nov. 22, 2021) [36030]
"Success Fees: A Word of Warning" in Canadian Business (Vol. 80, March 12, 2007, No. 6) [18704], [24747]
Success in the Laundry Business [10212]
Success Showcase Publishing [36418]
"Successful First Year for Twin Rivers" in American Printer (Vol. 128, June 1, 2011, No. 6) [3334], [12756], [16208]
Successful Inventory Management (Onsite) [23716], [27992]
Successful Proposal Strategies for Small Businesses: Using Knowledge Management to Win Government, Private-Sector, and International Contracts [24748], [28047]
Successful Sales Skills (Onsite) [32448]
Successfully Managing People [28420], [28421]
Succession Planning: Developing Talent from Within (Onsite) [26867]
Succotash Press [5796]
"Such Crust: Domino's Disses Pizza Hut Dough in Latest Spots" in Advertising Age (Vol. 83, October 1, 2012, No. 35, pp. 3) [356], [12536]
"Sudbury Waits With Future Up in the Air" in Globe & Mail (February 22, 2006, pp. B1) [9831], [31530]

"Sudden Shift Leaves Wells Fargo Vendor Scrambling" in Charlotte Business Journal (Vol. 25, July 9, 2010, No. 16, pp. 1) [12757], [24125], [34186]
Suffern Chamber of Commerce [42681]
Suffield Chamber of Commerce (SCC) [38076]
"Suit: Bank Bypassing Minorities" in Providence Business News (Vol. 29, June 9, 2014, No. 10, pp. 1) [11084], [18705], [20581], [27726]
Suite Spotte [39433]
"Suited for Success" in Retail Merchandiser (Vol. 51, July-August 2011, No. 4, pp. 6) [3143], [19938], [26418], [30982], [32291], [32634]
Suiter Business Builders [2319]
Suiter Financial Systems [2319]
"Suits Keep Flying in Wireless Service Marketing Wars" in Globe & Mail (March 22, 2007, pp. B3) [357], [18706], [33266]
Suki Hana & Chicken Connection [14263]
Sullivan Area Chamber of Commerce [41637]
Sullivan Area Chamber of Commerce [39314]
Sullivan Chamber and Economic Development (SCED) [39314]
Sullivan County Chamber of Commerce (SCCC) [42682]
Sullivan County Chamber of Commerce, Pennsylvania [44304]
Sullivan Spark [39315]
Sulphur Chamber of Commerce [43812]
"Sumitomo Invests in Desert Sunlight Solar Farm, the Largest PV Project Approved for Federal Land" in PR Newswire (October 2, 2012) [14951], [18363], [25557]
Summa Franchise Consulting [2368], [24491]
"Summary. Economic Trends for Small Business" in Small Business Economic Trends (February 2008, pp. 1) [4725], [4750], [4809], [20347], [21162], [28011], [32635], [34187]
"Summer Camp Uses Dance to Teach Students Life Skills" in U.S. News & World Report (July 22, 2019) [4856]
Summer and Casual Furniture Manufacturers Association [8195]
Summer Fancy Food Show [7809]
Summer NAMM [13661]
Summer@Highland [40764]
Summersville Area Chamber of Commerce (SACC) [46288]
Summersville Chamber of Commerce [46288]
The Summit [37901]
Summit Chamber of Commerce [37902]
Summit Collection [42115]
"Summit, Lions Gate are in Talks to Merge Studios" in Wall Street Journal Eastern Edition (November 29, 2011, pp. B2) [6209]
Summit Partners [37496]
Summit Partners L.P. [40732]
Sump Pump Manufacturers Association [14607]
Sump and Sewage Pump Manufacturers Association (SSPMA) [14607]
Sumter Area SBDC [44513]
Sun Books - Sun Publishing [42362]
Sun Valley-Ketchum Chamber of Commerce [38944]
Sun Valley-Ketchum Chamber and Visitors Bureau [38944]
"SunBank Plans Expansion Via Wal-Mart" in Business Journal-Serving Phoenix and the Valley of the Sun (Vol. 10, November 8, 2007) [6623], [18364], [26669], [31531], [32292]
Sunbanque Island Tanning [15271]
Sunbelt Business Brokers [2369]
Sunbelt Business Brokers Ottawa [2164]
Sunbelt Ottawa [2164]
SunBridge Partners [43631]
Sunbrook Academy at Legacy Park [2910]
Sunbury - Big Walnut Area Chamber of Commerce [43581]
Sundance Area Chamber of Commerce (SACC) [46623]
Sunday Business Systems (SBS) [2320]
"The Sunday Newspaper (est. 1891): the Death of Three Postmedia Sunday Papers Leaves Few Remaining" in Canadian Business (Vol. 85, July 16, 2012, No. 11-12, pp. 14) [11999], [25558]
"SunEdison Sells 30MW Spectrum Solar Project To Southern Company and Turner Renewable Energy" in Benzinga.com (September 28, 2012) [4236], [14952], [33033]
Sunland Tujunga Chamber of Commerce [37207]
"SunLink Health Systems Subsidiaries Open Senior Behavioral Care Units in Dahlonega, GA and Fulton, MO" in Mental Health Weekly Digest (July 16, 2012, pp. 326) [11522], [25947]
Sunnyside Chamber of Commerce (SCC) [42683]
Sunnyvale Chamber of Commerce [37208]
SUNO Inc. [40236]
SUNO Small Business Incubator [40236]

"SunRail Route Apartments Coming in 2013" in Orlando Business Journal (Vol. 29, September 14, 2012, No. 13, pp. 1) [4237], [13570]
Sunrise Chamber of Commerce [38420]
Sunrise Ventures, LLC [37764]
Sunriver Area Chamber of Commerce [44021]
Sunset Grill [14264]
Sunshine Pack & Ship [3404]
SUNY Canton College [42972]
SUNY College of Environmental Science and Forestry - Randolph G. Pack Environmental Institute [5789]
SUNY Fredonia Technology Incubator Inc. (FTI) [42941]
Super 8 Motels Inc. [8518]
Super 8 Worldwide Inc. [8518]
Super Suppers [4708]
Super Wash Inc. [2587]
Super Zoo [12103], [12236]
Supercharge Your Sales and Profits with Brian Tracy [32687]
Supercuts [7898]
Supercuts Inc. [7899]
Superfreakonomics [21163]
Superior Area Chamber of Commerce [46521]
The Superior Business Center Inc. (SPC) [46574]
Superior Chamber of Commerce [36366]
Superior Chamber of Commerce [46382]
Superior-Douglas County Area Chamber of Commerce [46382]
Superior Senior Care (SSC) [26095]
Supermaker: Crafting Business on Your Own Terms [4605], [4665], [22813], [33610]
"Supermercado El Rancho Chain Grows Along with Hispanic Population" in Dallas Business Journal (Vol. 35, July 13, 2012, No. 44, pp. 1) [7778], [12983], [18365], [20656], [30394]
"The Superpower Dilemma" in Canadian Business (Vol. 83, August 17, 2010, No. 13-14, pp. 42) [5712], [5979], [8764], [19939], [20055], [23365], [26419], [27727]
"Supersized: Delaware North Ready to Feed 80,000 NFL Fans" in Business First of Buffalo (Vol. 30, January 31, 2014, No. 20, pp. 3) [2680], [6922], [15191]
SuperSuds Laundromats [10205]
SuperSuds Management, LLC [10205]
Supervisors Legal Update [28920]
Supperworks [32069]
"Supplements Mix Nutrition With Convenience" in Pet Product News (Vol. 64, November 2010, No. 11, pp. 44) [698], [11580], [12175], [29401]
Suppliers of Advanced Composite Materials Association [29068]
"Suppliers May Follow Fiat: Local Group Says Italian Firms are Inquiring" in Crain's Detroit Business (Vol. 25, June 15, 2009, No. 24, pp. 1) [1111], [11440], [27728], [29402], [31532], [33416]
"Supply-Chain Collaboration, Image of Industry are OESA Chief's Top Tasks; Q&A Julie Fream, Original Equipment Suppliers Association" in Crain's Detroit Business (Vol. 30, January 6, 2014, No. 1, pp. 4) [1112], [11441], [29403]
"Supply Chain Management: What Small Businesses Need to Know" in Business News Daily (February 21, 2023) [16601]
"The 'Supply Side' of the Auto Industry" in Montly Labor Review (Vol. 133, September 2010, No. 9, pp. 72) [11442], [27951], [29404]
"A Supply-Side Solution for Health Care" in Barron's (Vol. 92, July 23, 2012, No. 30, pp. 30) [25559], [26097], [26670], [28012]
SupplySide East [11593]
Support Services Alliance [33468]
Supporting the Growth of Black Businesses with Karla Causey [30418]
Supporting Multiple Bosses (Onsite) [28422]
Supporting Social Entrepreneurship in Indian Country with Cecelia Pacheco [30419]
Supporting Technology Transfer and Catalyzing Economic Development at the University of New Mexico [42356]
Sure Print & Copy Centers [4498]
Surf City Squeeze [8637]
Surf Incubator [46221]
Surface Creek Valley Chamber of Commerce [37828]
Surface Specialists Systems Inc. [12694]
"Surge in the South" in Canadian Business (Vol. 85, June 11, 2012, No. 10, pp. 48) [18366], [27729], [31533]
"Surgical Center Relocating to St. Joseph Campus" in Business First of Buffalo (Vol. 30, January 24, 2014, No. 19, pp. 3) [19206], [25948]
Surgical Trade Foundation - American Surgical Trade Association [10820], [11500]
"The Surplus Shell Game" in Canadian Business (Vol. 80, March 12, 2007, No. 6, pp. 72) [21164], [25074]

"Surprise Package" in Business Courier (Vol. 27, June 25, 2010, No. 8, pp. 1) [6624], [9832], [17360], [24126], [27049], [28837]
"The Surprising Things You Can Do With CRM" in Small Business Trends (September 13, 2022) [20511]
Surry County Chamber of Commerce (SCCC) [45902]
"Survey: Ag Lenders Less Optimistic" in Idaho Business Review (June 27, 2014) [17121], [28214]
"A Survey of Combinatorial Testing" in ACM Computing Surveys (Vol. 43, Summer 2011, No. 2, pp. 11) [3435], [3644], [14835], [33911]
"A Survey of Comparison-Based System-Level Diagnosis" in ACM Computing Surveys (Vol. 43, Fall 2011, No. 3, pp. 22) [3436], [3645], [14836], [33912]
"Survey: Confident Parts Makers Plan to Expand, Hire" in Crain's Detroit Business (Vol. 30, August 18, 2014, No. 33, pp. 5) [11443], [18367], [29405]
"A Survey of DHT Security Techniques" in ACM Computing Surveys (Vol. 43, Summer 2011, No. 2, pp. 8) [3437], [3525], [3646], [14464]
"Survey: Don't Expect Big Results From Stimulus" in Crain's Detroit Business (Vol. 25, June 1, 2009, No. 22) [4238], [21165], [21634], [25075]
"Survey: Mass. Workers to Get Smaller Raises Than Peers Nationally" in The Boston Business Journal (January 14, 2020) [35481]
"Survey: People Willing to Pay More for Food Delivery" in U.S. News & World Report (July 30, 2019) [10980], [11800]
"Survey Profile" in Small Business Economic Trends (September 2010, pp. 19) [24749], [27050]
Survey Research Center [47537]
"Survey Reveals RV Owners' Internet Needs" in RV News (November 24, 2021) [2523], [13678]
"Survey Reveals Shifting Preferences in Pool Chemicals and Sanitation Systems" in Pool and Spa News (November 20, 2017) [15240], [18368], [19940]
"The Survey Says" in Collections and Credit Risk (Vol. 14, September 1, 2009, No. 8, pp. 16) [4751], [4810], [18369], [20348], [21166]
"Survey Says Commercial Real Estate Headed for Turbulence" in Commercial Property News (March 17, 2008) [8458], [13288], [13571], [13833], [15225], [21167], [22293]
"A Survey of Smart Data Pricing: Past Proposals, Current Plans, and Future Trends" in ACM Computing Surveys (Vol. 46, Summer 2014, No. 2, pp. 15) [2794], [9241], [20056]
Surveyors Historical Society (SHS) [15218]
"Surviving an IRS Audit: Tips for Small Businesses" in Agency Sales Magazine (Vol. 39, July 2009, No. 7, pp. 52) [100], [1774], [15416], [34896]
"Surviving the Storm" in Canadian Business (Vol. 81, July 22, 2008, No. 12-13, pp. 50) [6625], [9833], [21168], [24127], [24750]
Surviving Year One As an Entrepreneur [22924]
Survivor Bootcamp [12465]
"Susan Leger Ferraro Built a $7.2 Million Day Care Business: Now She Wants To Expand-And Cash Out" in Inc. (January 2008, pp. 50-53) [2886], [18370], [35862]
Sushi Shop [15062]
Suspended In Time Inc. [6877], [33327]
Susquehanna Style [44305]
Susquehanna Valley Chamber of Commerce and Visitors Center (SVCC) [44306]
Sussex County Chamber of Commerce [42194]
Sussex County Magazine [42195]
"Sustain Your Focus on DEI" in Associations Now (May 9, 2022) [30605]
"The Sustainability Agenda: Ioannia Ioannou" in Business Strategy Review (Vol. 25, Summer 2014, No. 2, pp. 16) [21635], [34378]
"Sustainability Is Changing How We Do Business...For the Better" in Business.com (May 23, 2019) [34379]
"Sustainability: Is It a Good Choice for Small Companies?" in Inquiries Journal 2010, Vol. 2, No. 10 [23366]
"Sustainability Is Top Priority for GreenTown Chicago" in Contractor (Vol. 56, November 2009, No. 11, pp. 1) [4239], [5387], [5713], [5980], [14953], [23367]
"Sustainable Advantage" in Inc. (Vol. 36, September 2014, No. 7, pp. 86) [5476], [7993], [8087], [10043], [11444], [14896], [23022], [34380]
Sustainable Business Center (SBC) [39434]
"Sustainable Concept of Architectural Conservation" in IEREK (October 22, 2014) [913]
Sustainable Development Technology Canada [20711]
"Sustainable Is Attainable" in Cvent Blog (October 16, 2019) [6098], [23368]
The Sustainable Jobs Fund / SJF Ventures [43230]
"Sustainable Start-Ups Should Consider Corporate Venture Capital First" in The Conversation [34556]

"The Sustainable Supply Chain" in Harvard Business Review (Vol. 88, October 2010, No. 10, pp. 70) [22259], [28013]
"Sustained DEI Efforts Take All Hands on Deck" in Associations Now (May 9, 2022) [30606]
Sutherlin Area Chamber of Commerce [44022]
"Sutter Court Win is Part of Trend" in Sacramento Business Journal (Vol. 31, July 25, 2014, No. 22, pp. 3) [3526], [14465], [18707], [25949]
Sutter Hill Ventures [37497]
Suttons Bay Chamber of Commerce (SBCC) [41017]
Suwannee County Chamber of Commerce [38505]
"Suzlon S88-Powered Wind Farm in Minnesota Secures Long-Term Financing" in PR Newswire (September 21, 2011) [5714], [5981], [23369], [29406]
Suzuki, Myers & Associates Ltd. [15958]
SV Angel (SVA) [37498]
SV Frontier [37499]
SV Health Investors (SV) [40733]
SV Life Sciences [40733]
SW Liquidation, LLC [14265]
Swain County Chamber of Commerce [43194]
Swainsboro/Emanuel County Chamber of Commerce [38783]
Swan/Starts [36405]
Swansea Chamber of Commerce [39248]
Swanson Associates [4340]
Swanton Area Chamber of Commerce (SACC) [43582]
Swanton Chamber of Commerce [45738]
Swap Meet Magazine [3907]
Swartzbaugh-Farber & Associates, Inc. [17414]
Swedish-American Chamber of Commerce Arizona (SACC AZ) [36367]
Swedish-American Chamber of Commerce Chicago [39316]
Swedish-American Chamber of Commerce Colorado (SACC-CO) [37903]
The Swedish-American Chamber of Commerce, Inc.-- Membership Directory [27730]
The Swedish-American Chamber of Commerce of Los Angeles (SACC-LA) [37209]
Swedish American Chamber of Commerce Minnesota (SACCMN) [41308]
Swedish American Chamber of Commerce New England (SACC-NE) [40633]
Swedish-American Chamber of Commerce Ohio [43583]
Swedish-American Chamber of Commerce Philadelphia [44307]
Swedish-American Chamber of Commerce San Diego [37210]
Swedish-American Chamber of Commerce Texas (SACC-TX) [45372]
Swedish-Canadian Chamber of Commerce (SCCC) [20710]
Swedish Canadian Chamber of Commerce - Canadian Swedish Business Association [20710]
"Swedish Candy Shop Adds Frozen Treats" in The New York Times (May 28, 2019) [2549]
"The Swedish Solution" in San Francisco Business Times (Vol. 28, May 2, 2014, No. 41, pp. 4) [20057], [25950]
Sweet Briar College - Martin C. Shallenberger Library [1008]
Sweet Grass County Chamber of Commerce [41795]
Sweet Home Chamber of Commerce [44023]
Sweet Peppers Deli (SPD) [4923], [14266]
"Sweet Tea From McDonald's: A Marketing 50 Case Study" in Advertising Age (Vol. 79, November 17, 2008, No. 43, pp. 4) [14023], [18371], [24417], [30063], [30813], [32636]
"Sweeten Your Bottom Line: How To Bring In Dollars When Times Are Tough" in Small Business Opportunities (November 2007) [17511], [21169], [30064]
Sweets & Snacks Expo [1285], [7818]
SWFL Inc. [38506]
"A Swifter, Better Marketplace" in Barron's (Vol. 89, July 13, 2009, No. 28, pp. M13) [6626], [9834], [24128], [26420]
Swigert & Associates Inc. [24268]
"Swinging For the Fences: The Effects of Ceo Stock Options on Company Risk Taking and Performance" in Academy of Management Journal (Vol. 50, No. 5, October 1, 2007, pp. 1055) [9835], [17361], [27051], [28838]
Swiss Days [39609]
Switch [3669]
Switch: How to Change Things When Change Is Hard [22260], [22814], [28839]
Switzerland of Ohio Chamber of Commerce [40980]
SWLA Business Directory [40194]
"Swope: Breakup Won't Delay East Village" in The Business Journal-Serving Metropolitan Kansas City (Vol. 26, August 22, 2008, No. 50, pp. 1) [4240], [13572], [31534]

SWOT Master Index

"*SWOT Analysis Guide*" in *Small Business Trends (January 20, 2023)* **[18372]**
Swyrich Corp. **[7388]**
SXSW Accelerator [45549]
SXSW Pitch **[45549]**
Sycamore Chamber of Commerce **[39317]**
Sylacauga Chamber of Commerce **[36153]**
Sylvan Learning Center **[16173]**
Sylvania Area Chamber of Commerce (SACC) **[43584]**
"*Sylvie Collection Offers a Feminine Perspective and Voice in Male Dominated Bridal Industry*" in *Benzinga.com (October 29, 2011)* **[1995]**, **[9984]**, **[21988]**, **[30065]**, **[35863]**
"*Symantic Completes Acquisition of VeriSign's Security Business*" in *Internet Wire (August 9, 2010)* **[14466]**, **[19693]**, **[33034]**
"*Symbility Solutions Joins Motion Computing Partner Program*" in *Marketwired (May 14, 2007)* **[8970]**, **[26421]**, **[27345]**, **[30066]**, **[31535]**, **[34465]**
Symmes Maini & McKee Associates (SMMA) **[31103]**
Syndicat Canadien de la Fonction Publique (SCFP) **[35157]**
Synergistic Business Solutions Group L.L.C. (SBSG) **[2321]**, **[24269]**
Synergistic International L.L.C. **[7505]**
SYNERGY Business & Technology Center **[36557]**
Synergy Enterprise Development **[43877]**
Synergy Homecare **[8289]**
Synergy Restaurant Consultants **[14112]**
Syngenta Venutres **[43231]**
Synopsys Inc. **[37500]**
Syntaxis Inc. **[17813]**
"*Synthesis: From Lone Hero to a Culture of Leadership*" in *Harvard Business Review (Vol. 88, November 2010, No. 11, pp. 146)* **[22815]**, **[31536]**
"*Synthetic Drywall Rots Mechanical Product*" in *Contractor (Vol. 56, December 2009, No. 12, pp. 50)* **[5388]**, **[11863]**, **[11881]**
Syosset Woodbury Chamber of Commerce **[42684]**
"*Syracuse Gear Manufacturer Buys Buffalo Company*" in *Business First of Buffalo (Vol. 30, January 24, 2014, No. 19, pp. 3)* **[19694]**, **[29407]**, **[31537]**
Syracuse SCORE **[42502]**
Syracuse Student Sandbox **[42942]**
Syracuse University - Center for Advanced Systems and Engineering (CASE) **[42943]**
Syracuse University - Maxwell School of Citizenship & Public Affairs - Program for the Advancement of Research on Conflict and Collaboration (PARCC) **[10812]**
Syracuse-Wawasee Chamber of Commerce **[39610]**
"*A System for Continuous Organization Renewal*" in *Strategy & Leadership (Vol. 38, July-August 2010, No. 4, pp. 34-41)* **[28840]**
System4 Facility Services **[2117]**
Systems Builders Association [3943]
Systems Service Enterprises Inc. (SSE) **[4955]**
Systems and Strategies for Business Growth **[24826]**
Systems Thinking (Onsite) **[28423]**

T

T. Kondos Associates **[31104]**
"*T-Mobile's Risky Strategy Aims to Get iPhone Owners to Switch*" in *Puget Sound Business Journal (Vol. 33, September 7, 2012, No. 20, pp. 1)* **[2795]**, **[19941]**
T-REX **[41694]**
T. Rowe Price Group, Inc. **[40436]**
TA Associates Management L.P. **[37501]**, **[40734]**
TA Capital **[45476]**
TAA ONE Conference & Expo [775], [35134]
"*Table Games Get a Leg Up*" in *Philadelphia Business Journal (Vol. 28, January 15, 2010, No. 48, pp. 1)* **[7310]**, **[18373]**
Table Rock Lake Chamber of Commerce **[41638]**
Table Rock Lake-Kimberling City Area Chamber of Commerce [41638]
Table Rock Lake Vacation Guide **[41639]**
Table Talk: The Savvy Girl's Alternative to Networking **[17762]**, **[17875]**, **[35003]**, **[35864]**
"*Tabs Says Organic Food Sales Hit Record in 2011. Sales Jump 15-20 Percent*" in *Entertainment Close-Up (February 21, 2012)* **[8050]**, **[17122]**, **[18374]**
"*Tackle Your Taxes Like a Pro*" in *Entrepreneur (November 6, 2018)* **[32995]**
Tackling the Racial Wealth Gap **[30420]**
"*Tackling Tuition Increases Head On*" in *Pittsburgh Business Times (Vol. 34, July 25, 2014, No. 1, pp. 6)* **[21636]**, **[24129]**, **[25076]**
Tackling Wealth Inequities **[30421]**, **[35432]**
Taco Bell Canada [14272]
Taco John's International, Inc. **[14267]**
Taco Maker Inc. **[14268]**
Taco Mayo **[14269]**
Taco Time Canada Inc. **[14270]**
Tacoma Community College Business and Industry Resource Center **[46233]**
Tacoma-Pierce County Business Directory **[46161]**
Tacoma-Pierce County Chamber (TPCC) **[46162]**
TacoTime **[14271]**
Taft Chamber of Commerce [37211]
Taft District Chamber of Commerce **[37211]**
TAG International [10]
Tahlequah Area Chamber of Commerce [43813]
Tahlequah Area Chamber of Commerce and Tourism Council (TACC) **[43813]**
Tahoe Mountain Lab [37562]
Tahoe Technology & Capital Group Inc. (TTCG) **[41956]**
T'ai Chi **[10722]**
"*Tailoring Is the Secret of Well-Dressed Women*" in *The Wall Street Journal (December 11, 2013)* **[15254]**, **[20512]**
TailWaggers Doggy Daycare **[12126]**
Taivara **[43691]**
"*Take Command: Lessons in Leadership: How to Be a First Responder in Business*" **[19942]**, **[22261]**, **[22816]**, **[28841]**
"*Take Control of Your Company's Finances*" in *Green Industry Pro (Vol. 23, March 2011, No. 3, pp. 24)* **[7633]**, **[10114]**, **[10246]**, **[16842]**, **[24130]**
"*Take on an Elephant Without Getting Trampled*" in *Globe & Mail (March 17, 2007, pp. B3)* **[18708]**, **[19600]**
"*Take the 'I' Out of Making Connections*" in *Pittsburgh Business Times (Vol. 33, January 3, 2014, No. 25, pp. 3)* **[17763]**
"*Take It to the Bank*" in *Barron's (Vol. 89, July 13, 2009, No. 28, pp. 20)* **[6627]**, **[9836]**, **[24131]**
"*Take the Money and Run*" in *Entrepreneur (September 2014)* **[7071]**, **[22437]**, **[35255]**
Take Off Pounds Sensibly [16504]
"*Take the Right Approach to Concrete Polishing Rentals*" in *Rental Product News (Vol. 33, June 2011)* **[6832]**, **[13834]**, **[34188]**
"*Take This Job and Love It*" in *Green Industry Pro (Vol. 23, October 2011)* **[7634]**, **[10115]**, **[10247]**, **[20513]**, **[33267]**
Takeda Research Investment INc. [40788]
Takeda Ventures Inc. (TVI) **[40788]**
"*Taking on 911 - and Making a New Tech Biz In the Process*" in *Orlando Business Journal (Vol. 30, January 24, 2014, No. 31, pp. 3)* **[2796]**, **[14467]**, **[21637]**, **[26422]**
Taking Care of Business **[24896]**, **[24897]**
"*Taking Charge of Who's in Charge*" in *Associations Now (May 9, 2022)* **[30607]**
"*Taking Full Advantage: What You Need To Know During Open-Enrollment Season*" in *Black Enterprise (Vol. 38, November 2007, No. 4)* **[8971]**, **[17362]**, **[27346]**
Taking on Greater Responsibility: Step-up Skills for Non-managers (Onsite) **[28424]**
"*Taking the Jump Off the Fiscal Cliff*" in *Barron's (Vol. 92, August 25, 2012, No. 35, pp. 47)* **[21170]**, **[25560]**, **[34897]**
"*Taking a Leap With Mobile Wi-Fi*" in *Austin Business Journal (Vol. 34, July 25, 2014, No. 23, pp. 10)* **[2797]**, **[18375]**, **[26423]**, **[30814]**, **[31538]**
"*Taking Off*" in *Puget Sound Business Journal (Vol. 34, January 31, 2014, No. 42, pp. 4)* **[7162]**, **[14837]**, **[25162]**, **[26424]**
"*Taking the Over-the-Counter Route to U.S.*" in *Barron's (Vol. 88, July 7, 2008, No. 27, pp. 24)* **[6628]**, **[9837]**, **[19207]**, **[21171]**, **[24132]**, **[27731]**, **[31539]**
"*Tale of a Gun*" in *Canadian Business (Vol. 80, February 26, 2007, No. 5, pp. 37)* **[26425]**, **[30815]**
"*Tale of the Tape: IPhone Vs. G1*" in *Advertising Age (Vol. 79, October 27, 2008, No. 40, pp. 6)* **[2798]**, **[9242]**, **[19943]**, **[26426]**
"*A Tale of Two Brothers*" in *Canadian Business (Vol. 80, March 26, 2007, No. 7, pp. 18)* **[22817]**, **[23663]**
"*Tale of Two Tech Facilities*" in *Business Journal Portland (Vol. 30, January 3, 2014, No. 44, pp. 12)* **[26180]**, **[33336]**
The Talent Masters: Why Smart Leaders Put People Before Numbers **[22818]**, **[27052]**, **[28842]**
"*Talent Shows*" in *Canadian Business (Vol. 81, December 24, 2007, No. 1, pp. 14)* **[26671]**, **[27053]**, **[27732]**, **[30067]**, **[30608]**
"*Tales of the City*" in *Canadian Business (Vol. 81, December 8, 2008, No. 21, pp. 37)* **[8765]**, **[27733]**
Talihina Chamber of Commerce **[43814]**
"*Talisman CEO Touts Benefits of Going It Alone*" in *Globe & Mail (March 2, 2006, pp. B1)* **[19080]**, **[19601]**
"*Talk, Inc.: How Trusted Leaders Use Conversation to Power Their Organizations*" in *Canadian Business (Vol. 85, August 13, 2012, No. 13, pp. 59)* **[17764]**, **[22819]**, **[28843]**
"*Talk Like Ted: The 9 Public-Speaking Secrets of the World's Top Minds*" **[14522]**
Talkeetna Chamber of Commerce **[36247]**
"*Talking Tax: The Horse Business*" in *Idaho Business Review (September 3, 2014)* **[8323]**, **[34898]**
Tallahassee Area Chamber of Commerce [38421]
Tallahassee Chamber of Commerce [38421]
Tallahassee SCORE **[38314]**
Tallmadge Chamber of Commerce (TCOC) **[43585]**
Tallwave LLC. **[36406]**
Tallwood Venture Capital **[37502]**
Tama Chamber of Commerce [39800]
Tama/Toledo Area Chamber of Commerce **[39800]**
Tamayo Consulting Inc. **[19149]**, **[21714]**, **[22332]**, **[29034]**
Tamiami Angel Funds **[38540]**
Tampa Bay Beaches Chamber of Commerce **[38507]**
Tampa Bay Business Journal (TBBJ) **[38609]**
Tampa Bay Chamber of Commerce (GTCC) **[38508]**
Tampa Bay Innovation Center (TBIC) **[38584]**
Tampa Bay Kitchen **[38585]**
Tampa Bay Technology Incubator (TBTI) **[38586]**
Tampa Bay WaVE Inc. **[38587]**
Tampa SCORE **[38315]**
Tanana Chiefs Conference (TCC) **[36250]**
Tandem Capital **[37637]**
TandemLaunch **[46900]**
"*Tanning Bed Use Declining Among U.S. Adults*" in *Reuters (June 8, 2017)* **[15264]**
Tanning Salons Industry in the US - Market Research Report **[15265]**
TAO Capital Partners **[37503]**
"*Tao of Downfall: the Failures of High-profile Entrepreneurs in the Chinese Economic Reform*" in *International Journal of Entrepreneurship and Small Business (Vol. 11, August 31, 2010, No. 2, pp. 121)* **[6629]**, **[9838]**, **[21172]**, **[22820]**, **[24133]**, **[25561]**, **[27734]**, **[30609]**
Taos County Chamber of Commerce (TCCC) **[42339]**
"*Tap Into Food Truck Trend to Rev Up Sales, Build Buzz*" in *Nation's Restaurant News (Vol. 45, February 7, 2011, No. 3, pp. 18)* **[7014]**, **[14024]**, **[22821]**, **[30068]**, **[32637]**, **[34189]**
Tapioca Express Inc. **[7592]**
Tappahannock-Essex County Chamber of Commerce **[45903]**
"*Tapping the 'Well' in Wellness*" in *Pet Product News (Vol. 64, November 2010, No. 11, pp. 1)* **[699]**, **[8051]**, **[12176]**, **[20514]**, **[32294]**, **[34190]**
TarboroEdgecombe Chamber of Commerce (TECC) **[43195]**
"*Target Marketing and Market Segmentation*" in *The Balance Small Business (October 27, 2020)* **[34715]**
"*Target Marketing: What Is It?*" in *Bplans* **[34716]**
"*Target to Power New Toys 'R' Us Online Business*" in *Reuters (October 8, 2019)* **[11801]**, **[15793]**, **[21989]**, **[31540]**
Target Technology Center [40327]
"*Targeted Personal Trainer Business Strategies Build Clients, Income, Business and Success*" in *Marketing Weekly News (August 4, 2012)* **[12434]**, **[18376]**, **[30069]**, **[31541]**
"*Targeted Technology Raises More Than $40 Million*" in *San Antonio Business Journal (Vol. 28, September 5, 2014, No. 30, pp. 8)* **[26427]**, **[32046]**, **[32829]**, **[35389]**
"*Targeting New Growth*" in *San Antonio Business Journal (Vol. 28, May 23, 2014, No. 15, pp. 4)* **[18377]**, **[32295]**
Tarleton State University Small Business Development Center **[44942]**
Tarleton State University - Texas Institute for Applied Environmental Research (TIAER) **[23458]**
Tarpon Springs Chamber of Commerce (TSCC) **[38509]**
The Tarrance Group **[12962]**
Tarrant Small Business Development Center **[44943]**
Task Force for Women in Public Administration [31678]
A Taste of Long Island Inc. **[42944]**
Taste of Nature, Inc. [1301]
Taste Profit Marketing, LLC **[8074]**, **[30225]**
"*Tastee-Freez Celebrates 60th Anniversary*" in *Ice Cream Reporter (Vol. 23, July 20, 2010, No. 8, pp. 2)* **[8592]**, **[22822]**, **[27952]**, **[31542]**
"*Tasti D-Lite Has Franchise Agreement for Australia*" in *Ice Cream Reporter (Vol. 23, November 20, 2010, No. 12, pp. 3)* **[8593]**, **[24418]**, **[27735]**, **[31543]**
Tastings-A Wine Experience **[32378]**
Tasty's Made By Hand **[4606]**
TATSoul **[15334]**
"*A Tattoo Artist's Guide to Instagram: How To Promote Your Tattoo Business*" in *PainfulPleasures blog (Nov. 3, 2021)* **[15311]**
Tattoo Artists' Guild **[15283]**
Tattoo Extremeties **[15348]**

3346 Small Business Sourcebook • 42nd Edition

"Tattoo Forms and Waivers Required for Clients" in DaySmart Body Art blog (Aug. 3, 2022) [15312]
"Tattoo School: The Educational Path for Tattoo Artists" in DaySmart Body Art blog (May 11, 2021) [15313]
Tattoo Shop Business Plan Template [15314]
Tattoo Shop Insurance: For Businesses and Individuals [15315]
Tattoo.com [15349]
"Tattooed Bellwethers of Economic Development" in Austin Business Journal (Vol. 34, May 2, 2014, No. 11, pp. A4) [4607], [13289], [13573], [13835], [15316], [21173], [25077]
Tattooing 101 [15285]
Tattooing 101 LLC [15285]
"Tattoos Now Have an Exit Strategy" in The Atlantic (October 29, 2019) [15317]
Taunton Area Chamber of Commerce (TACC) [40634]
Tawas Area Chamber of Commerce [41018]
"Tax Breaks Favor Outsiders, Business Owners Object" in Business Review Albany (Vol. 41, August 22, 2014, No. 22, pp. 7) [25078], [25562], [34899]
"Tax Breaks for Home-Based Businesses Go Unclaimed" in Legal Zoom (March 29, 2023) [26811], [34900]
"Tax and Business Forms You'll Need to Start a Small Business" in Business News Daily (February 21, 2023) [27193], [34557]
Tax Centers of America (TCOA) [15455]
"Tax Credits As Good As Raised Cash for Cyber Firms" in Baltimore Business Journal (Vol. 31, March 28, 2014, No. 48, pp. 16) [14367], [31931], [34719]
"Tax Credits Drive MO Budget Crisis" in St. Louis Business Journal (Vol. 33, September 14, 2012, No. 3, pp. 1) [21174], [34901]
"Tax Credits for Renewables Get Another Shot in Congress" in Greentech Media (November 19, 2019) [14954], [25563]
Tax Executives Institute (TEI) [15363], [15476], [34721]
"Tax-Free Zones Need Shows: Out-of-State Shoppers Are Key To Success" in Crain's Detroit Business (Vol. 24, January 28, 2008, No. 4) [15901], [32296], [34902], [35096]
"Tax Increase Would Leave Heavy Impact" in Memphis Business Journal (Vol. 34, April 27, 2012, No. 2, pp. 1) [34903]
Tax Notes [15438]
Tax Notes Today [15438]
Tax Notes® Today [158], [15460]
"Tax Preparation Made Easier With Carbonite Online Backup" in Investment Weekly News (March 10, 2012, pp. 783) [3527], [14468], [15417], [33268]
Tax Preparation Services Industry in the US - Market Research Report [15430]
Tax Preparations Etc. Inc. [1785], [11942]
Tax Preparer [15462]
Tax Preparer: California Supplement [15463]
The Tax Pros and Cons of S Corp Status for Small Business [32414]
"Tax Relief Available for Livestock Sold Due to Drought" in Southeast Farm Press (October 4, 2012) [17123], [34904]
Tax Savvy for Small Business [15418], [18709], [34905]
"Tax Services Firm Ryan Prepares for Growth" in Dallas Business Journal (Vol. 35, June 29, 2012, No. 42, pp. 1) [15419], [18378], [27736], [31544]
"Tax Tip: Streamlining Sales Tax Collections" in Pet Product News (Vol. 66, September 2012, No. 9, pp. 38) [12229], [15420], [28844], [32297], [34906]
"Tax Tips for Dog Breeders" in AmericanKennelClub.com (March 21, 2016) [658]
Taxi & Limousine Services Industry in the US - Market Research Report [10291], [15526]
"A Taxi Service for the Homeless" in Forest Park Review (April 16, 2019) [15522], [25079]
"Taxis Are Set to Go Hybrid" in Philadelphia Business Journal (Vol. 30, September 16, 2011, No. 31, pp. 1) [5715], [5982], [10289], [15523], [23370], [34191]
The TaxLetter [15439]
Taxpayers' Federation of Illinois (TFI) [15499]
TAXPRO Monthly [15440]
:Taylor Backman on Using All-in-One Solutions to Lower Cost" in Small Business Trends (August 16, 2022) [33611]
Taylor Corporation [41341]
Taylor Society [28268], [34965]
"Taylor Tests Land Grant Program" in Austin Business Journal (Vol. 31, June 3, 2011, No. 13, pp. 1) [4241], [23371], [25080], [26428], [29408], [33417]
Tazewell Area Chamber of Commerce (TACC) [45904]
TB Canada Company [14272]
TCA Annual Convention [16109]
TCBY [8638]
TD Magazine [10005]
Tea Association of the U.S.A. Inc. (TA) [7543]

Tea Council of the United States of America (TC) [7544]
Teach Magazine: Education for Today and Tomorrow [21678]
"Teachable Moments: Worth Every Penny" in Pet Product News (Vol. 64, December 2010, No. 12, pp. 34) [12177], [15902], [20515], [21638], [32298], [32638], [35097]
"Teachers, U.S. Fund Providence Made Moves On BCE Buyout" in Globe & Mail (April 10, 2007, pp. B17) [17363], [31545], [33269]
TEACHING Exceptional Children (TEC) [16146]
"Teaching Sales: Great Sales Professionals are Scarce and Getting Scarcer. Why Aren't Universities Working Harder to Create More?" in (Vol. 90, July-August 2012, No. 7-8, pp. 94) [21639], [31546], [32639]
Teague [3353]
"Teakwood Capital Raises $40M to Buy Tech Companies" in Dallas Business Journal (Vol. 35, March 2, 2012, No. 25, pp. 1) [14838], [19695], [35390]
Team, Funding, and Summary - Back of the Napkin to Business Plan in 11 Slides with Brandon White [16696]
Team Leadership Effectiveness Program 'Team Top Gun' (Onsite) [28425]
Team-Powered Scaling [18452]
"Team Too Big for Regular One-on-Ones? Try These 11 Communication Strategies Instead" in Small Business Trends (December 18, 2022) [22262]
TeamLogic IT [3591]
Teamwork [22297], [29456]
"Teamwork On the Fly: How To Master the New Art of Teaming" in Harvard Business Review (Vol. 90, April 2012, No. 4, pp. 72) [22263], [28845]
Teaneck Chamber of Commerce (TCC) [42196]
Teaneck Economic Development Corp. [42196]
"The Tech 100" in Canadian Business (Vol. 81, July 21, 2008, No. 11, pp. 48) [9839], [18379], [26429], [31793], [32830]
Tech Brewery [41117]
Tech Capital Partners Inc. [46807]
"Tech Coaltion Warns Takeover Spree is Nigh" in Globe & Mail (February 6, 2007, pp. B1) [26430], [32831]
Tech Coast Angels (TCA) [36558]
"Tech Data Launches Unified Communications and Network Security Specialized Business Units" in Wireless News (October 22,2009) [3528], [3772], [14469], [26431]
TECH Fort Worth (TECHFW) [45550]
The Tech Garden (TTG) [42945]
Tech Incubator at Queens College (TIQC) [42946]
"Tech Jobs Rebound from Downturn" in Denver Business Journal (Vol. 65, March 7, 2014, No. 43, pp. A9) [2799], [18380], [21175], [26432], [32832], [34192]
Tech Launch Arizona (TLA) [36407]
Tech Liminal (TL) [37638]
Tech Parks Arizona [36408]
Tech Ranch Austin [45551]
"Tech Startup Challenges (and How to Overcome Them)" in Business News Daily (February 21, 2023) [34558]
Tech Startup School [37639]
"Tech Tools of the Trade" in EstateSales.org Blog [6075]
Tech Wildcatters (TW) [45552]
TechAlliance [46756]
TechArb [41118]
TechBA Arizona [36409]
TechColumbus [43679]
TechConnect [46303]
TechConnect (Onsite) [17616]
TechFire [40471]
TechLaunch, LLC (TL) [42249]
Technation (ITAC) [8833]
TechNexus [39435]
Techni Graphic System, Inc. (pinpointer) [44769]
Technical Conference & Tabletop Exhibition [24230]
Technical Innovation Center (TIC) [40765]
Technical Project Management [28426]
Technical Research & Development Authority Business Innovation Center [38561]
Technical Service Corp. [3867]
Technical Writing: A Comprehensive Hands-On Introduction (Onsite) [17852], [21428]
Technical Writing for Dummies [5326]
"Technically Speaking" in Black Enterprise (Vol. 38, February 2008, No. 7, pp. 64) [26433], [30070], [32640]
TechniScan, LLC [4341]
Technologies du Développement Durable Canada (TDDC) [20711]
Technology Business Incubator (TBI) [38588]
Technology Centre of New Jersey [42250]
"Technology in the Classroom: What the Research Tells Us" in Inside Higher Ed (December 12, 2018) [3551], [21640]
"Technology Companies are Increasing Their Hiring" in Philadelphia Business Journal (Vol. 31, March 16, 2012, No. 5, pp. 1) [358], [26434], [26672]

"Technology: Elder Care Enters the Digital Age: Wireless Companies Devise Ways to Aid Home Health, Let People Stay in Homes" in Atlanta Journal-Constitution (April 29, 2012, pp. D1) [2800], [8265], [25951], [26435]
Technology Entrepreneur Center, Inc. (TEC) [39436]
Technology Ethics for Small Businesses [23539]
Technology Incubator West Houston (TIWH) [45554]
Technology Incubator of West Houston (TIWH) [45553]
Technology Innovation Center (TIC) [41119]
Technology Management Associates Inc. (TMA) [10702]
"Technology-Market Combinations and the Identification of Entrepreneurial Opportunities: an Investigation of the Opportunity-Individual Nexus" in Academy of Management Journal (Vol. 55, August 1, 2012, No. 4, pp. 753) [22823], [26436]
Technology Partners [37504]
Technology Venture Partners (TVP) [41342]
Technology Ventures Corp. (TVC) [42343]
Technology Ventures: From Idea to Enterprise [19081], [22438], [26181]
Technomic Inc. [6947]
TechnoServe Inc. [33494]
TechOperators LLC [38856]
TechPlace [40325]
Tech's Impact on Modern Sales [16913]
TechSci Research [42986]
TechServe Alliance [3423], [3606]
TechSquare Labs [38840]
Techstars [37952]
TechStars Central LLC [37952]
TechStars Chicago [39437]
TechStars LLC [37952]
TechStudios L.L.C. (TS) [45555]
TechTown Detroit [41120]
TechTrends [3558]
Tecterra Inc. [46678]
Tecumseh Chamber of Commerce [43815]
The TED Center [38589]
TED The Electrical Distributor Magazine: Official Publication of the National Association of Electrical Distributors (NAED) [5397]
"TEDx Talk Puts the Pieces Together" in Philadelphia Business Journal (Vol. 33, April 4, 2014, No. 8, pp. 6) [6630], [9840], [22439]
TEEC Angel Fund [37513]
"Teens Could Become Long-Haul Truckers Under New Bill" in The Drive (September 22, 2021) [16084]
Tejara Center [41121]
"Tejas Gadhia on Using Low-Code or No-Code Apps" in Small Business Trends (August 2, 2022) [33913]
Tekamah Chamber of Commerce [41886]
tekMountain [43252]
"Teksapiens, A Leading SEO Company, Offers Free SEO Consulting Services to Dallas Businesses" in Wireless News (March 29, 2012) [2203], [9243], [16471], [20131], [30071], [34381]
Telecommunications Development Fund (TDF) [40437]
Telecommunications Industry Association (TIA) [2703], [16326]
Telephone IP News [4957]
TeleSoft Partners [37505]
Television Broadcasters Association [13021], [13063], [15575]
Television Bureau of Advertising (TVB) [15581], [31845]
Television Bureau of Canada [401]
TelevisionWeek [2472], [13048]
"Teleworkers Confess Biggest At-Home Distractions" in Employee Benefit News (Vol. 25, November 1, 2011, No. 14, pp. 7) [26812], [27054]
Telfair County Chamber of Commerce (TCCC) [38784]
"Tell Me Why" in Business Strategy Review (Vol. 25, Summer 2014, No. 2, pp. 50) [19602], [22824]
Telluride Venture Accelerator [37953]
Telluride Venture Network (TVA) [37953]
Tellus Institute [6017]
Telocator Network of America [1509], [2704]
Telocator, The Personal Communications Industry [1509], [2704]
"TELUS Says No Thanks to Joining BCE Fray" in Globe & Mail (April 24, 2007, pp. B1) [31547], [35391]
Temecula Valley Chamber of Commerce (TVCC) [37212]
Temecula Valley Entrepreneur's Exchange (TVE2) [37640]
"The Temp Economy and the Future of Work" in U.S. News & World Report (August 10, 2018) [5327], [5449], [31136]
"Temp Job, Permanent Fulfillment: How the Desire To Earn a Bit of Extra Cash Opened the Door to a Long-Term Career" in Black Enterprise (Vol. 44, June 2014, No. 10, pp. 41) [14025], [15647], [28846]
Tempe Chamber of Commerce [36368]
"Tempering Urgency Within Your Shop" in Modern Machine Shop (Vol. 84, October 2011, No. 5, pp. 16) [10442], [28847]

Temple City Chamber of Commerce [37213]
Temple Health & Bioscience District (THBD) [45556]
Temple University Libraries - Blitman Resource Center [13066]
Temple University Small Business Development Center (SBDC) [44105], [44375]
Templeton Board of Trade [37214]
Templeton Chamber of Commerce [37214]
TempNet Staffing Association [15639]
"The Ten Commandments of Legal Risk Management" in Business Horizons (Vol. 51, January-February 2008, No. 1, pp. 13) [18710], [23540], [27055], [28848]
The Ten Laws of Enduring Success [6631], [22825]
"Ten Questions to Ask Your Hearing Health Professional" in Healthy Hearing (October 28, 2019) [8135]
"Ten Ways to Save on Business Travel" in Women Entrepreneur (November 21, 2008) [17512], [19401], [24751], [35865]
"Ten of the World's Coolest Bike Shops: 2018 Edition" in CyclingTips (November 7, 2018) [1529]
"Tenant Demands Broaden Medical Office Landscape" in San Antonio Business Journal (Vol. 28, September 12, 2014, No. 31, pp. 8) [25952]
Tenaya Capital [37506]
Tender Loving Care (TLC) [8290]
Tennant Consulting (TC) [37687]
Tennessee Association of Realtors (TAR) [13116]
Tennessee Beekeepers Association (TBA) [1452]
Tennessee Business Travel Association (TBTA) [19319]
Tennessee Chamber of Commerce and Industry [44811]
Tennessee Department of Economic and Community Development - Business Enterprise Resource Office (BERO) [44700], [44819]
Tennessee Department of Economic and Community Development Research Division [47488]
Tennessee Federation of Business and Professional Women [35581]
Tennessee Minority Supplier Development Council (TMSDC) [44820]
Tennessee Procurement Technical Assistance Center - University of Tennessee - Center for Industrial Services of Knoxville (CIS) [44831]
Tennessee Small Business Development Center (TSBDC) [44686]
Tennessee Small Business Development Centers Austin Peay State University (TSBDC) [44687]
Tennessee Small Business Development Centers Chattanooga State Community College [44688]
Tennessee Small Business Development Centers, Chattanooga State Technical Community College [44688]
Tennessee Small Business Development Centers Cleveland State Community College [44689]
Tennessee Small Business Development Centers Dyersburg State Community College [44690]
Tennessee Small Business Development Centers Jackson State Community College (TN TSBDC JSCC) [44691]
Tennessee Small Business Development Centers Knoxville [44692]
Tennessee Small Business Development Centers Memphis [44693]
Tennessee Small Business Development Centers - Middle Tennessee State University (TSBDC) [44694]
Tennessee Small Business Development Centers - Middle Tennessee State University-Columbia [44695]
Tennessee Small Business Development Centers Tennessee State University Brentwood [44696]
Tennessee Small Business Development Centers Tennessee State University Nashville [44697]
Tennessee Small Business Development Centers Tennessee Tech University [44698]
Tennessee Small Business Development Centers Volunteer State Community College [44699]
Tennessee Technological University - Center for Manufacturing Research (CMR) [29480]
Tennessee Technological University - College of Engineering - Center for the Management, Utilization and Protection of Water Resources [16361]
Tennessee Technological University - College of Engineering - Research and Innovation - Center for Energy Systems Research (CESR) [5407]
Tennessee Valley Authority (TVA) [47372]
Tennessee Valley Authority (TVA) - Environmental Research Center - Research Library [17217]
Tennessee Valley Authority (TVA) - Minority Economic and Small Business Development [47373]
Tennis Educational Foundation [15667]
Tennis Foundation of North America [15670]
Tennis Industry Association (TIA) [15670]
Tennis Manufacturers Association [15670]
The Tension for Social Entrepreneurs Between Sales and Product Development wit Graham Hill [34440]
Tera Capital Corp. [46808]

Teralys Capital (TC) [46888]
Terminix Termite & Pest Control [12061]
"Termite Trouble" in Arkansas Business (Vol. 28, March 28, 2011, No. 13, pp. 5) [12036], [23664]
Terpenes and Testing Magazine [5047]
Terra Firma [13324]
Terrascope: A Computer Vision Tale [35433]
Terrazzo Tile and Marble Association of Canada [6821]
Terre de Chez Nous [35158]
Terre Haute Chamber of Commerce (THCC) [39611]
Terrell Chamber of Commerce Convention & Visitors Bureau [45373]
Terrell County Chamber of Commerce [38785]
Territorial Normal School [36410]
"Tesla Eyes Two Sites for New Battery-Pack Plant" in San Antonio Business Journal (Vol. 28, May 16, 2014, No. 14, pp. 8) [11445], [18711], [29409], [33418]
Testing Business Ideas: A Field Guide for Rapid Experimentation [19082]
Tether: Bodyguard of the Grid [35434]
Teton Valley Chamber of Commerce [38945]
Tetra Tech NUS, Inc. Technical Information Center [5781], [6011]
Texarkana Chamber of Commerce [45374]
Texas A&M Forest Service (TFS) [2960]
Texas A&M International University - Texas Center for Border Economic and Enterprise Development (TCBEED) [21282]
Texas A&M University - Bush School of Government and Public Service - Institute for Science, Technology and Public Policy (ISTPP) [26144]
Texas A&M University - Department of Sociology [47489]
Texas A&M University - Dwight Look College of Engineering - Thomas and Joan Read Center [20676]
Texas A&M University - Mays Business School - Center for Retailing Studies [2861]
Texas A&M University - McFerrin Center for Entrepreneurship [45557]
Texas A&M University - Real Estate Center (REC) [13638]
Texas A&M University - Startup Aggieland [45558]
Texas A&M University System - Texas A&M Transportation Institute (TTI) [1566]
Texas A&M University - Texas Forest Service [2960]
Texas A&M University - Texas Real Estate Research Center [13638]
Texas A&M University - Texas Transportation Institute [1566]
Texas Apartment Association Annual Education Conference and Lone Star Expo [775], [35134]
Texas Association of Business Brokers (TABB) [2145], [44903]
Texas Association of Business and Chamber of Commerce (TABCC) [45375]
Texas Association of Mexican-American Chambers of Commerce (TAMACC) [45376]
Texas Association of Realtors (TAR) [13117]
Texas Business and Professional Women's Foundation (TBPWF) [35676]
Texas Business Travel Association (TBTA) [19320]
Texas Center for Policy Studies (TCPS) [5790]
Texas City - La Marque Chamber of Commerce [45377]
Texas City - La Marque Chamber Express [45378]
Texas Comptroller of Public Accounts (TCPA) [45424]
Texas Counseling Association (TCA) [25695]
Texas Department of Economic Development [45578]
Texas Discovery Gardens Horticulture Library [7686]
Texas Economic Development Corporation (TxEDC) [44959]
Texas Geographic Information Office (TNRIS) [47490]
Texas - Houston Small Business Development Center [44944]
Texas Journal of Business Law [18781]
"Texas Lands $1 Billion Investment in Solar and Battery Projects" in Renewable Energy World (November 16, 2021) [14955]
"Texas Legislature Green-Lights Bigger Liquor Chains, but Still Excludes the Biggest Retailer, Walmart" in Dallas News (May 28, 2019) [10335], [25564]
Texas Life-Science Collaboration Center (TLCC) [45559]
Texas Longhorn Breeders Association of America (TLBAA) [16975]
Texas - Northwest Small Business Development Center (NWTSBDC) [33495]
Texas Opportunity & Justice Incubator (TOJI) [45560]
Texas Pharmacy Association Conference and Expo [5207]
Texas Physical Therapy Association Annual Conference [12503]
Texas Press Association Annual Midwinter Conference and Trade Show [17798]
Texas Procurement Technical Assistance Center - El Paso Community College - Contract Opportunities Center [45486]

Texas Procurement Technical Assistance Center - Northwest Texas Regional Network - West Texas A&M University Small Business Development Center [44955], [45492]
Texas Procurement Technical Assistance Center - Pan Handle Regional Planning Commission [45487]
Texas Procurement Technical Assistance Center - San Antonio Procurement Outreach Program [45484]
Texas Procurement Technical Assistance Center (TFC) - Texas Facilities Commission [45488]
Texas Procurement Technical Assistance Center - Texas Tech University [45491]
Texas Procurement Technical Assistance Center - University of Houston Small Business Development Center [45489]
Texas Procurement Technical Assistance Center - University of Texas - Permian Basin Small Business Development Center [45490]
Texas Public Policy Foundation (TPPF) [15500]
Texas Real Estate Business [45587]
Texas Registered Accessibility Specialist Association [3912]
Texas Research Alliance (TRA) [45561]
Texas Research & Technology Foundation (TRTF) [45562]
Texas Restaurant Association Marketplace [14100]
The Texas Restaurant Show [14100]
Texas Southern University - Robert James Terry Library - Business Library [24916]
Texas State Library and Archives Commission (TSLAC) [47491]
"Texas State Seeks Startups" in Austin Business Journal (Vol. 32, April 20, 2012, No. 7, pp. 1) [8797], [21301], [26182]
Texas State University-San Marcos - College of Sciences and Engineering - Edwards Aquifer Research & Data Center (EARDC) [16362]
Texas State University San Marcos Small Business Development Center [44945]
Texas State University - STAR Park [45563]
Texas Tech University - College of Media & Communication - Center for Communications Research (CCR) [15634]
Texas Tech University - Procurement Services [45491]
Texas Tech University - Rawls College of Business - Center for Healthcare Innovation, Education and Research (CHIER) [26145]
Texas Tech University - Rawls College of Business - Institute for Leadership Research (ILR) [26146]
Texas Tech University - Texas Wine Marketing Research Institute (TWMRI) [15073]
Texas Tri-County Chamber of Commerce [45379]
Texas Undergraduate Mathematics Conference [21688]
Texas Venture Association (TxVCA) [35312], [45477]
Texas Water Oriented Data Bank [47490]
Texas Woman's University - Dallas Center Library [12507]
Texas Woman's University - F.W. and Bessie Dye Memorial Library [12507]
TEXO Ventures [45478]
Textile Care Allied Trades Association (TCATA) [5230]
Textured Hair, Crowdfunding and Beauty Tech Innovation [30422]
TGap Ventures LLC [41058]
TGCSA Convention & Expo [7819]
"Thai Ice Cream Cremo Expanding to Middle East" in Ice Cream Reporter (Vol. 23, September 20, 2010, No. 10, pp. 3) [8594], [18381], [27737], [29410]
"Thanks, But No: Small Businesses Shun Payroll Tax Deferral" (September 5, 2020), Associated Press. [31644]
"Thanks for the Feedback: The Science and Art of Receiving Feedback Well" [17765]
"That Empty Feeling" in Crain's Cleveland Business (Vol. 28, October 15, 2007, No. 41, pp. 1) [4242], [13290], [13574], [21176]
"That Was a B2B Ad? How the Pandemic Forced Business Marketers to Pivot Forever" in The Drum (September 22, 2020) [19243], [30072]
"That's About It for Quantitative Easing" in Barron's (Vol. 89, July 20, 2009, No. 29, pp. M11) [6632], [9841], [21177], [24134]
the Art of Eating [15043]
Theatre Historical Society of America (THSA) [11138]
TheCodeFactory [46766]
TheKey [8291]
"Then and Now" in Washington Business Journal (Vol. 32, February 21, 2014, No. 45, pp. 6) [8459], [14026], [15903], [35098]
"Theranos Growing Close to Home in Palo Alto" in Silicon Valley/San Jose Business Journal (Vol. 30, June 29, 2012, No. 14, pp. 1) [10853], [19208]
Therapeutic Recreation Journal [26055]

Master Index
This
Master Index

"*Therealreal's Online Luxury Consignment Shop" in The New Yorker (October 14, 2019)* **[3902]**, **[11802]**
"*There's Always Something Unexpected" in South Florida Business Journal (Vol. 34, June 6, 2014, No. 46, pp. 13)* **[517]**, **[22264]**, **[28849]**
"*There's a Movement Afoot to Allow Legal States to do Business with Each Other" in Green Entrepreneur (October 20, 2020)* **[5022]**
"*There's a New Strategy for Networking in the Digital Age" in Entrepreneur (Jan. 22, 2022)* **[18852]**
"*There's Risk, Reward for Business in Baltimore's Edgier Areas: Taking a Chance" in Baltimore Business Journal (Vol. 28, July 16, 2010, No. 10, pp. 1)* **[14470]**, **[18382]**, **[20516]**, **[22826]**, **[32641]**, **[33419]**
There's Someplace Like Home: Developing an Adult Day Care Center in Your Church **[174]**
Thermal Management Systems Digital Summit [539]
Thermal Management Systems Symposium (TMSS) **[539]**
Thermopolis Chamber of Commerce [46624]
Thermopolis - Hot Springs Chamber of Commerce **[46624]**
"*These 10 Black Bankers Are Reshaping Wall Street" in Bloomberg.com(March 16, 2021)* **[9842]**
"*These Are the Best Cities to Be Your Own Boss" in Entrepreneur (October 11, 2017)* **[32981]**
"*These Are the Women Who Really Mean Business" in Canadian Business (Vol. 87, October 2014, No. 10, pp. 67)* **[4243]**, **[9049]**, **[18383]**, **[22827]**, **[33076]**, **[35866]**
"*These Clothes Use Outlandish Designs to Trick Facial Recognition Software into Thinking You're Not a Human" in Business Insider (October 12, 2019)* **[6140]**, **[34382]**
"*These Custodians are Cleaning Up in More Ways Than One" in New York Post (June 3, 2017)* **[2076]**
"*These States are Where Auto Mechanics are in High Demand" in Small Business Trends(January 25, 2023)* **[1188]**
"*These Trends Have Made Medical Device Manufacturing What It Is Today" in Mass Device (February 16, 2018)* **[10854]**
Theta Sigma Phi [35564]
"*They See It. They Like It. They Want It. They Rent It" in The New York Times (June 8, 2019)* **[13836]**
"*They've Fallen, But Can Senior-Housing Stocks Get Up" in Barron's (Vol. 88, March 10, 2008, No. 10, pp. 43)* **[1035]**, **[6633]**, **[9843]**, **[11523]**, **[13291]**, **[24135]**
THG: Connections **[7386]**
Thibodaux Chamber of Commerce **[40195]**
Thief River Falls Chamber of Commerce **[41309]**
The Thin Book of Naming Elephants: How to Surface Undiscussables for Greater Organizational Success **[18384]**, **[22265]**, **[22828]**
"*Think Again: What Makes a Leader?" in Business Strategy Review (Vol. 21, Autumn 2010, No. 3, pp. 64)* **[22829]**, **[28850]**
Think Big Partners **[41695]**
Think Business: Clean Bathrooms and Competitive Edges with Dave Newell **[14570]**
Think Business: Coding, Coping, and Conquering with Jeremy Nagel **[22925]**
Think Business: Franchise Pitfalls and Prosperity - Giuseppe Grammatico **[24462]**
Think Business: How to Revolutionize Employee Experience and Boost Business Growth with Ryan Englin **[22304]**
Think Business: Learn Loan Essentials for Entrepreneurs from Mark Ritter **[28239]**
Think Business: Mastering the Waves of Entrepreneurship with Rodic Lenhart **[22926]**
Think Business: Revolutionize Your Cash Flow and Achieve Financial Freedom with Rocky Lalvani **[19726]**
Think Business: Turning Loss into Leadership with Business Expert Robert Poole **[22927]**
Think Business with Tyler: Analyzing Proft Margins and Core Metrics in Business - Brian Will **[18453]**
Think Business with Tyler: Building Business Value with Nick McLean **[18454]**
Think Business with Tyler: Business Owners, You're the Problem and Solution - A Talk with Michael Morrison **[16697]**
Think Business with Tyler: Cash Flow Secrets: Uncover the Lifeblood of Small Business with Jason Kruger **[16698]**
Think Business with Tyler: Chelsea Husum Reveals Success Secrets in Male-Dominated Construction World **[35911]**
Think Business with Tyler: From Lawn Mowing to Leading with Entrepreneur Matt Shoup **[32688]**
Think Business with Tyler: Increase Profits with Pricing Strategy Tips from James Wilton **[31669]**
Think Business with Tyler: Leadership and Vision in Business with Bryce Henson **[28934]**
Think Business with Tyler: Mastering Obstacles and Conquering Challenges in Entrepreneurship with Bryan Clayton **[22928]**
Think Business with Tyler: Mind Strategies for Entrepreneurs with Troy Lavinia **[22929]**
Think Business with Tyler: Navigating Rapid Business Growth without Sacrifices - Kim Walsh Phillips **[16699]**
Think Business with Tyler: Overcoming Challenges and Embracing Failure in Entrepreneurship with Kerry-Ann Powell **[22930]**
Think Business with Tyler: Surviving and Thriving after a Career Crisis with Bruce Weinstein **[16700]**
Think Business with Tyler: Sustainable Business Practices with Jonathan Orpin **[24827]**
Think Business with Tyler: Taking Control of Your Business Finances with Financial Coach Alex Engar **[16701]**
Think Business with Tyler: The Real Game-Changers in Business Growth - Carl Gould **[16702]**
Think Business with Tyler: The Role of Mindset and Optimism in Entrepreneural Success wiith Matt Drinkhahn **[22931]**
Think Business with Tyler: Unleashing the True Value of Your Company with Tony Cotrupe **[16703]**
Think Business with Tyler: Why Uniqueness is the Only Survival Strategy for Your Business - Dustin Bogle **[16704]**
Think Business with Tyler: Why Your Business Isn't Meant for Everyone with Glenn Gardone **[16705]**
Think Creative Collective LLC **[2322]**
"*Think Disruptive! How to Manage In a New Era of Innovation" in Strategy & Leadership (Vol. 38, July-August 2010, No. 4, pp. 5-10)* **[2204]**, **[20132]**, **[21178]**, **[27953]**, **[28851]**
"*Think of Start-Ups as Shots On Goal" in (Vol. 90, June 2012, No. 6, pp. 38)* **[21179]**, **[22440]**, **[24575]**
Thinker Ventures **[39377]**
Thinkertots **[21732]**
ThinkFirst Canada [25687]
"*Thinking Aloud" in Business Strategy Review (Vol. 21, Summer 2010, No. 2, pp. 47)* **[28852]**, **[32047]**, **[32833]**
"*Thinking of Expanding Your Food Truck to a Physical Store? Learn the Costs Ahead of Time" in FoodTruckOperator.com (July 27, 2020)* **[7015]**
"*Thinking about Names for Your New Business? These 20 Startup Name Generators Could Help" in Small Business Trends (January 27, 2023)* **[27194]**, **[34559]**
Thinking Outside the Lines for Managers and Supervisors (Onsite) **[28427]**
Thinking Outside the Lines (Onsite) **[28428]**
"*Thinking Strategically About Technology" in Franchising World (Vol. 42, August 2010, No. 8, pp. 9)* **[14839]**, **[24419]**, **[26437]**, **[30983]**, **[33914]**
thinkLA **[31846]**
Thinktiv **[45564]**
thinkTV **[401]**
Thinnes & Dutton P.C. **[713]**
Third Coast Capital Advisors L.L.C. **[39378]**
Third Derivative Institute **[23058]**
"*Third-Party Food Delivery Service License Application Checklist" in NYC Consumer and Worker Protection* **[6923]**
Third Rock Ventures (TRV) **[40735]**
Third Sector New England Inc. (TSNE) **[22940]**
Third Security, LLC **[45927]**
Third Shift Entrepreneur: Keep Your Day Job, Build Your Dream Job **[22830]**, **[34560]**
"*Thirsty Lion Cooks Up Big Expansion Plan" in Business Journal Portland (Vol. 27, November 5, 2010, No. 36, pp. 1)* **[1309]**, **[13877]**, **[18385]**, **[19083]**
"*Thirsty? Now There's a Water Cooler to Suit Every Taste" in Inc. (Vol. 33, October 2011, No. 8, pp. 43)* **[1863]**, **[5716]**, **[5983]**, **[23372]**
"*This Biz Is Booming" in Small Business Opportunities (Winter 2010)* **[8232]**, **[26752]**
"*This Home Necessity Is Disappearing From Store Shelves" in Best Life (May 20, 2021)* **[11864]**
This Is How Much to Pay Yourself If You Run Your Own Business **[19755]**
This Is Small Business: Advice Line with Pete Maldonado of Chomps **[32348]**
This Is Small Business: Business Loans Dos and Don'ts **[28240]**
This Is Small Business: Chevalo and Monique Search for a Product Supplier **[24828]**
This Is Small Business: Danyel Manages a Momentous Merger **[31596]**
This Is Small Business: Detara Finds Funding for Her Business **[24219]**
This Is Small Business: Do You Have What It Takes to Own a Small Business? **[22932]**
This Is Small Business: Entrepreneurial Wisdom: Mastering Marketing, Networking, and Audience Building **[16706]**
This Is Small Business: Growth Secrets for Food Entrepreneurs: Expanding from Farmer's Markets to E-Commerce **[18455]**
This Is Small Business: How to Attract Investors **[35435]**
This Is Small Business: How to Build Your Marketing Strategy **[29551]**
This Is Small Business: How to Buy the Right Business for You **[19702]**
This Is Small Business: How Culture Can Lead to Unique Business Opportunities **[30423]**
This Is Small Business: How to Differentiate Your Product **[24829]**
This Is Small Business: How to Expand to Other Markets **[29552]**
This Is Small Business: How to Find the Right Customer for Your Product **[29553]**
This Is Small Business: How to Foster Workplace Diversity and Inclusion **[34441]**
This Is Small Business: How to Future-Proof Your Business **[28935]**
This Is Small Business: How Good Design Can Help Increase Sales **[17483]**
This Is Small Business: How to Grow a Sustainable Business **[23438]**
This Is Small Business: How to Handle Your Cash Flow **[24220]**
This Is Small Business: How to Hire Your First Employee **[27114]**
This Is Small Business: How to Keep a Seasonal Business Profitable Year-Round **[32970]**
This Is Small Business: How Looking Back Can Lead to Forward-Thinking Business Ideas **[34649]**
This Is Small Business: How to Manufacture Your Own Product **[29458]**
This Is Small Business: How a Patent Can Protect Your Idea **[27973]**
This Is Small Business: How to Prepare for a Business Sale **[33050]**
This Is Small Business: How to Provide Great Customer Service **[20539]**
This Is Small Business: How a Small Business Owner Can Do More for Their Employees **[22305]**
This Is Small Business: How Your Business Can Have an Impact **[34442]**
This Is Small Business: Justin Tackles the Top 3 Steps to Start a Business **[16707]**
This Is Small Business: Leslie Adds a New Product to Her Lineup **[24830]**
This Is Small Business: Making It Work: How to Build a Business with a Small Budget **[17519]**
This Is Small Business: Meghan Parts Ways with Her Business Partner **[31597]**
This Is Small Business: Miguel Connects with His Community to Grow His Brand **[30424]**
This Is Small Business: Next Generation: Balancing Act **[19115]**
This Is Small Business: Next Generation: High $takes **[19116]**
This Is Small Business: Next Generation: The First Eliminations **[19117]**
This Is Small Business: Next Generation: The Practice Pitch (Navigating Nerves and Feedback) **[19118]**
This Is Small Business: Next Generation: Unveiling the Contenders (Part One) **[19119]**
This Is Small Business: Next Generation: Unveiling the Contenders (Part Two) **[19120]**
This Is Small Business: Next Generation: We Win Some, We Lose Some **[19121]**
This Is Small Business: Next Generation: What Comes Next? **[19122]**
This Is Small Business: Pros and Cons of a Business Partnership **[31598]**
This Is Small Business: Renee Aces Achievable Goals **[16708]**
This Is Small Business: Small Business Fun Facts: What to Know Before Starting a Small Business **[16709]**
This Is Small Business: Steps to Accelerate Your Small Business Growth - With Amy Porterfield **[18456]**
This Is Small Business: Strategies for Success as a Woman in Business **[35912]**
This Is Small Business: Top 3 Small Business Mistakes to Avoid **[16710]**
This Is Small Business: Toyin Leverages Small Business Sucess to Drive Community Impact **[34443]**
This Is Small Business: What You Need to Know About Audits **[34940]**
This Is Small Business: Why Public Relations Matter **[31809]**
This Is Small Business: Why You Should Protect Your Intellectual Property **[27974]**
"*This Is When You're Ready to Invest in Real Estate" in U.S. News & World Report (May 31, 2018)* **[13575]**
"*This Is Your Brain on Crafting" in CNN.com (January 5, 2015)* **[4608]**, **[25953]**

Small Business Sourcebook • 42nd Edition **3349**

"This Just In. State House Introduces Film-Industry Stimulus Bills" in Crain's Detroit Business (Vol. 24, March 3, 2008, No. 9) [6210], [25081]
"This Just In: TechTown, Partners Get $1M to Start Tech Exchange" in Crain's Detroit Business (Vol. 25, June 1, 2009, No. 22, pp. 1) [11446], [25082], [28215], [29411], [31548], [34383]
"This Legendary New York Bagel Shop is Finally Going National" in Eat This, Not That (October 10, 2021) [1208], [24420], [42976]
"This Local Lingerie Shop Donated Thousands of Bras to Harvey Victims" in Houstonia (December 25, 2017) [10306]
"This Week: McD's Eyes Ad Plan, Shifts Breakfast Biz" in Crain's Chicago Business (Vol. 30, February 2007, No. 6, pp. 1) [359], [14027], [30073]
This Week in Startups: Angel: Upfront's Mark Suster on the Power of Alignment, Setting Reality, and Raising Capital [34650]
This Week in Startups: Avoiding Accidental Tax Fraud [16860]
This Week in Startups: Benchmark's Sarah Tavel on the State of VC, AI's Impact on Startups & More! [34651]
This Week in Startups: Building a Blood-Testing Startup in 2023 with Vital CEO Vasu Nadella [34652]
This Week in Startups: Developing Drugs to Extend Dog Lifespans with Loyal CEO Celine Halioua [34653]
This Week in Startups: Grammarly CEO Rahul Roy-Chowdhury on the Future of User-Centric Language Tools [34654]
This Week in Startups: Sophia Amoruso on Branding, Raising a Fund, Portfolio Construction & More [34655]
This Week in Startups: Startup Pitch Competition: Jason Invests $25K [34656]
This Week in Startups: State of Early-Stage VC, Finding PMF, Caroline Ellison Testifies & More with Zach Coelius [34657]
This Week in Startups: VenturusAI's Instant MBA & Samantha Wong on Identifying Soon-to-Explode Startup Markets [34658]
"This is What the Hell Livestock Auctioneers are Actually Saying" in Vice (August 23, 2018) [1081]
Thoma Cressey Bravo, Inc. (TCB) [39379]
Thomas Jefferson University - Center for Research in Medical Education and Health Care (CRMEHC) [26147]
Thomas Jefferson University - Paul J. Gutman Library [3080]
Thomas R. Beecher, Jr. Innovation Center (IC) [42947]
Thomas R. Egan Consulting Inc. [31017], [31105]
Thomas Raddall Research Centre Archives [7454]
Thomaston - Upson Chamber of Commerce [38786]
Thomasville Chamber [38787]
Thomasville-Thomas County Chamber of Commerce [38787]
Thompson Falls Chamber of Commerce [41796]
"Thomson Eyes Asia for Expansion" in Globe & Mail (February 10, 2006, pp. B4) [18386], [19084], [19603]
Thomson Reuters Minneapolis-Saint Paul [41367]
Thomvest Ventures (TV) [37765]
"'Those Days In New York Are Over'" in Philadelphia Business Journal (Vol. 33, March 28, 2014, No. 7, pp. 6) [4244], [18712], [35207]
Thousand Oaks - Westlake Village Regional Chamber of Commerce [36917]
Thousand Palms Chamber of Commerce [37215]
"Threat of New Office Space Records Rent Hikes" in Globe & Mail (March 21, 2007, pp. B4) [4245], [13292], [13576]
"ThredUp Is Helping Big Stores Sell Recyled Clothes" in Quartzy (August 21, 2019) [3144], [11803], [21990]
"ThredUP Launches Online Concierge Service to Compete With Children's Consignment" in Benzinga.com (January 25, 2012) [2855], [3903], [11804], [19944]
"The Three Amigos" in Canadian Business (Vol. 81, March 17, 2008, No. 4, pp. 19) [8766], [21180], [27738]
"Three Common Computer Repair Franchise Funding Sources Revealed by SP Home Run Inc." in Investment Weekly News (May 12, 2012) [3571], [28075], [30901]
"Three Emerging Trends in Consumer Digital Mail-Order Health Products" in Mobi Health News (April 15, 2019) [10467]
Three Fork Telephone Book [41797]
Three Forks Chamber of Commerce (TFCC) [41798]
Three House Publishing [41710]
"Three Megatrends to Help Your Business Compete in 2014" in South Florida Business Journal (Vol. 34, January 3, 2014, No. 24, pp. 10) [5717], [17766], [19945], [20517], [23373], [30074], [34193], [34384]
"Three Productivity Solutions" in Contractor (Vol. 57, February 2010, No. 2, pp. 26) [5389], [11882], [12662], [14633], [14840], [33915]

Three Rivers Area Chamber of Commerce [41019]
Three Rivers Chamber of Commerce [37216], [45380]
"Three Signs Your Biz Needs a COO" in Birmingham Business Journal (Vol. 31, April 18, 2014, No. 16, pp. 10) [28853], [32642]
"Three Skills Every 21st Century Manager Needs" in Harvard Business Review (Vol. 90, January-February 2012, No.1-2, pp. 139) [28854]
"Three Steps to Follow when Job Hunting" in Contractor (Vol. 56, September 2009, No. 9, pp. 62) [12663], [26673]
"Three Trails Blazes Tax Credit Deal" in The Business Journal-Serving Metropolitan Kansas City (Vol. 27, November 7, 2008, No. 9) [13577], [21181], [25565], [32299], [34907]
The Three Types of Moving Companies [11151]
"Three Ways Columbia's Stock Can Keep Rising" in Business Journal Portland (Vol. 30, February 21, 2014, No. 51, pp. 8) [3049], [9844], [15101], [27739]
"Three Ways to Improve the Prospect's Experience" in South Florida Business Journal (Vol. 35, September 12, 2014, No. 7, pp. 12) [16472], [30075], [32643]
"Three Ways to Power Up Mobile Marketing" in South Florida Business Journal (Vol. 34, July 18, 2014, No. 52, pp. 12) [21991], [30076], [30491]
Threshold Partners [42223]
Threshold Ventures [37507]
Thrifty Car Sales, Inc. [11467]
Thrifty Rent-A-Car System, LLC [1173]
Thrive-on-Line [2176], [20079]
"Thriving DFW Big Target for Franchisors" in Dallas Business Journal (Vol. 35, March 30, 2012, No. 29, pp. 1) [18387], [21182], [24421], [33420]
"Thriving Small Businesses Boost Real Estate Values" in Business News Daily (February 21, 2023) [13578]
"Throughput Metrics Meet Six Sigma" in Management Accounting Quarterly (Vol. 12, Spring 2011, No. 3, pp. 12) [101], [1775], [15421], [16843]
Thunder Bay Ventures (TBV) [46767]
Thunderbird Global Entrepreneurship Incubator [36411]
Thunderbird International Business Review (TIBR) [27792]
Thurston County Chamber of Commerce [46163]
Thurston County Economic Development Council (TEDC) [46205]
Thurston County Small Business Incubator [46222]
Thurston Economic Development Council [46236]
Tia Clark Founder of Casual Crabbing with Tia [15773]
"TIA Wrestles with Procurement Issues" in Business Journal Serving Greater Tampa Bay (Vol. 30, November 12, 2010, No. 47, pp. 1) [18713], [19402], [25163], [25566]
TIAC Talk [15726], [15977]
Tiburon Peninsula Chamber of Commerce (TPCC) [37217]
TIC Business Consultants Ltd. [3789]
"Tic-Tac-Show: Line Up the Opportunities at Graph Expo" in American Printer (Vol. 128, August 1, 2011, No. 8) [3335], [12758], [14523], [15904], [16209], [35099]
"Ticketmaster Unveils Pink Tickets to Support Breast Cancer Awareness Month" in Travel & Leisure Close-Up (October 8, 2012) [7163], [15192], [25954]
Ticonderoga Area Chamber of Commerce (TACC) [42685]
Ticonderoga Capital Inc. [40737]
Tidings [42014]
TiE Boston [40736]
TiE Orgeon [44069]
TiE Silicon Valley (TiE SV) [37508]
TiE Women [35677]
Tiffin Area Chamber of Commerce [43569]
Tigard Area Chamber of Commerce (TACC) [44024]
TigerLabs [42224]
"Tigers Put to Test: Can Team Win Back Fans, Advertisers?" in Crain's Detroit Business (Vol. 24, October 6, 2008, No. 40, pp. 1) [15102], [15193], [30077]
Tigua Business Center (TBC) [45565]
"Tiki Boats Could Be Start of Untapped Business Opportunity on Detroit River" in Detroit Free Press(August 22, 2019) [15761]
Tilden Your Total Car Care Centers [14597]
Tile Council of America [10734]
Tile Council of North America (TCNA) [10734]
Tile Outlet Always in Stock [4354]
Tile Roofing Institute (TRI) [14324]
Tillamook Area Chamber of Commerce [44025]
Tillamook Bay Community College Small Business Development Center [43917]
Tim Hortons Inc. [7593]
"Tim Tebow Foundation to Hold Pink 'Cleats for a Cure' Auction" in Travel & Leisure Close-Up (October 20, 2011) [1082], [7164], [15194], [21992]
Timber Framing: Journal of the Timber Framers Guild [924], [4291]

"Time For a Change at Canon?" in Barron's (Vol. 92, July 23, 2012, No. 30, pp. 17) [4488], [9845], [11670], [27740], [30984]
"Time to Leave the Party? Re-Evaluating Commodities" in Barron's (Vol. 88, March 24, 2008, No. 12, pp. M16) [6634], [9846], [17124], [21183], [24136]
"Time for a Little Pruning?" in Barron's (Vol. 89, July 6, 2009, No. 27, pp. 13) [6635], [9244], [9847], [18388], [24137]
Time Management (Onsite) [34977]
Time Management Survival Skills (Onsite) [34978]
"Time to Rethink Fishery Management?" in Providence Business News (Vol. 29, April 7, 2014, No. 1, pp. 1) [6753], [6787]
"Time to Tweet: Banks and Fun, Benefits in Social Media" in Philadelphia Business Journal (Vol. 31, February 24, 2012, No. 2, pp. 1) [9245], [20518], [24138], [30078]
"Time Value of Money Rate of Return" in Business Owner (Vol. 35, September-October 2011, No. 5, pp. 8) [24139], [35004]
"Timken Features Solutions at AWEA WINDPOWER 2012" in PR Newswire (June 3, 2012) [5718], [5984], [23374], [35100]
"Timken's Bearings Rolling in China, India" in Crain's Cleveland Business (Vol. 28, October 29, 2007, No. 43, pp. 14) [8767], [18389], [27741], [29412]
Tinley Park Chamber of Commerce (TPCC) [39318]
"Tiny Telecom Big Prize in Bell Aliant Bid Battle" in Globe & Mail (April 4, 2007, pp. B1) [19946], [31549], [33270]
Tioga County Chamber of Commerce (TCCC) [42686]
TIPark Silicon Valley [37641]
Tipping Point Partners (TPP) [42948]
"Tips for Better Email Inbox Management" in Business News Daily (March 13, 2023) [17767]
"Tips for Choosing The Right Location for Your Business" in Business News Daily (February 21, 2023) [34561]
"Tips for Entrepreneurs Pitching to Investors" in Legal Zoom (March 14, 2023) [22831], [34562], [35392]
"Tips From a Turnaround Expert" in Business Owner (Vol. 35, July-August 2011, No. 4, pp. 8) [18390], [22832]
"Tips to Improve Your Direct Mail Results" in Contractor (Vol. 57, January 2010, No. 1, pp. 55) [12664], [30079]
"Tips for Running a Successful Laundry Business" in Hydrofinity blog (October 18, 2018) [5242]
"Tips for Small Business Risk Management" in Business Enterprise Mapping (June 27, 2020) [32392]
Tips for Starting a Laundromat [10164]
Tips for Starting a Successful Family Business [23665]
"Tips and Tools for Great Business Names" in Small Business Trends (December 29, 2022) [34563]
"Tips and Tricks for Seasonal Employment Hiring" in Legal Zoom (February 21, 2023) [26674]
Tipton Chamber of Commerce (TCC) [39612]
Tipton County Chamber of Commerce (TCCC) [39613]
Tire Association of North America [15680]
Tire Business [1131], [11468], [15691]
Tire Business: Your Number One information resource [15685]
"Tire CEOs Focus on Sustainability" in Modern Tire Dealer (November 22, 2019) [15684], [23375]
Tire Industry Association (TIA) [15680]
Tire Retread Information Bureau [15681]
Tire Retread & Repair Information Bureau (TRIB) [15681]
Tire Retreading Institute [15680]
Tire Review [15686]
"Titan to Become New York's Largest Provider of Phone Kiosk Advertising" in Marketing Weekly News (September 11, 2010, pp. 150) [360], [2801], [10039], [30080]
Title, Problem, and Solution - Back of the Napkin to Business Plan in 11 Slides with Brandon White [19123]
The Title Source™ III [1851]
Titusville Area Chamber of Commerce [38510]
Titusville Area Chamber of Commerce (TACC) [44308]
"TiVo, Domino's Team to Offer Pizza Ordering by DVR" in Advertising Age (Vol. 79, November 17, 2008, No. 43, pp. 48) [14028], [18391], [26438], [30081], [31550], [32644], [34194]
Tix Travel and Ticket Agency Inc. [16039]
TL Cramer Associates LLC [152]
TL Ventures, Inc. [44356]
"TLC's 'Jumping the Broom' Red Carpet Wedding Contest" in Benzinga.com (March 30, 2011) [1996]
"TMC Development Closes $1.1 Million Real Estate Purchase for Mansa, LLC Using SBA 504 Real Estate Financing" in Marketwired (September 17, 2009) [4445], [13579], [18392], [25083], [28216], [33612]
TMEA Clinic/Convention [11202], [11287]
TMEA Convention [11202], [11287]

Master Index Tortilla

TMS Journal **[10740]**
TNNA Winter Trade Show **[4631]**
"To Be or Not To Be an S Corporation" in Modern Machine Shop (Vol. 84, September 2011, No. 4, pp. 38) **[10443]**, **[29413]**, **[32415]**, **[34908]**
"To Build for the Future, Reach Beyond the Skies" in Canadian Business (Vol. 83, June 15, 2010, No. 10, pp. 11) **[19403]**, **[22833]**, **[26439]**, **[32834]**
"To Catch Up, Colgate May Ratchet Up Its Ad Spending" in Advertising Age (Vol. 81, December 6, 2010, No. 43, pp. 1) **[361]**, **[1591]**, **[12230]**, **[30082]**
"To-Go Packaging, Streamlined Menus Remain Big in 2022" in Restaurant Business (November 16, 2021) **[2681]**, **[14029]**
"To Keep Freight Rolling, Ill. Has to Grease the Hub" in Crain's Chicago Business (Vol. 31, April 21, 2008, No. 16, pp. 22) **[8768]**, **[19947]**, **[21184]**, **[27742]**, **[33271]**
"To Keep Your Customers, Keep It Simple: They Don't Want a 'Relationship' With You. Just Help Them Make Good Choices" in Harvard Business Review (Vol. 90, May 2012, No. 5, pp. 108) **[20519]**, **[32645]**
"To Live and Thrive in L.A." in Canadian Business (Vol. 81, October 13, 2008, No. 17, pp. 78) **[1353]**, **[14030]**, **[22834]**, **[35867]**
To Niche or Not to Niche: The Pitfalls of Over-Specialization **[34227]**
"To Sell Is Human: The Surprising Truth About Moving Others" **[22835]**, **[32646]**
"To Sell or Not To Sell" in Inc. (December 2007, pp. 80) **[9848]**, **[23666]**, **[33035]**
"To Win With Natural Talent, Go For Additive Effects; Four Human Capital Strategies Combine to Drive Up to 59 Percent More Growth In Revenue Per Employee" in Gallup Business Journal (June 3, 2014) **[27056]**, **[28855]**
Toastmaster **[14527]**
Tobacco Barometer: Cigarettes, Cigars, Smoking Tobacco, Chewing Tobacco and Snuff **[15710]**
Tobacco Merchants Association (TMA) **[15694]**, **[15717]**
Tobacco Plus Expo Trade Show **[15712]**
Tobacconists' Association of America (TAA) **[15695]**
Tobbaco Valley Board of Commerce [41763]
Today's Biggest Security Weakness **[32401]**
"Today's Business Sale Climate" in Business Owner (Vol. 35, September-October 2011, No. 5, pp. 10) **[19696]**, **[21185]**, **[25084]**, **[28217]**, **[33036]**
"Today's Calligraphers Are Inkstagram-Worthy" in Young-Post (April 5, 2017) **[2482]**
Today's Chamber **[42687]**
Today's Facility Manager: The Magazine of Facilities-Interior Planning Team [11646]
Today's Insurance Professional **[8994]**
Today's Laundromat: Coin Laundry Association's Official Guide to Getting Started in the Laundry Business **[10213]**
"Today's Rx: Solo Physician Practice Loses Appeal" in Dallas Business Journal (Vol. 35, July 13, 2012, No. 44, pp. 1) **[25955]**, **[34195]**
Together Inc. **[35141]**
Togo's Eateries, LLC **[4924]**
Toilet Goods Association [1383], [1579], [4507]
The Toilet Paper Entrepreneur: The Tell-It-Like-It-Is Guide to Cleaning Up In Business, Even If You Are At the End of Your Roll **[18869]**, **[20133]**, **[22441]**, **[24576]**, **[28076]**, **[31147]**
Tok Chamber of Commerce **[36248]**
Tokyo Stock Exchange Inc. (TSE) **[43007]**
Toledo Chamber of Commerce [39800]
Toledo Regional Chamber of Commerce (TRCC) **[43586]**, **[43641]**
"Toll Talker: CEO Takes Stock of His Company, the Housing Market" in Philadelphia Business Journal (Vol. 33, May 9, 2014, No. 13, pp. 4) **[4246]**, **[13293]**, **[13580]**, **[21186]**, **[34196]**
Tolland County Chamber of Commerce (TCCC) **[38077]**
Tolloty Technology Incubator **[43680]**
Tom Thomson Art Gallery Archives **[1009]**
Tomahawk Chamber of Commerce **[46522]**
Tombstone Chamber of Commerce (TCC) **[36369]**
Tomiki Aikido of the Americas (TAA) **[10715]**
Tommy's Supplies **[15335]**
Tompkins County Chamber of Commerce **[42688]**
Tompkinsville Area Chamber of Commerce [40088]
Tompkinsville - Monroe County Chamber of Commerce **[40088]**
Toms River - Ocean County Chamber of Commerce [42135]
"TomTom GO910: On the Road Again" in Black Enterprise (Vol. 37, January 2007, No. 6, pp. 52) **[3738]**, **[4408]**, **[19404]**, **[26440]**, **[30816]**
Tonasket Chamber of Commerce **[46164]**
"'Tone-Deaf' Suitor or True Harasser: How to Tell" in HR Specialist (Vol. 8, September 2010, No. 9, pp. 1) **[18714]**, **[20582]**, **[27057]**
"Tony Armand, Shock Doctor CEO" in Business Journal (Vol. 31, March 21, 2014, No. 43, pp. 6) **[10855]**, **[15103]**, **[29414]**, **[31551]**
Tony Roma's Inc. **[14273]**
Too Good to be Threw: The Complete Operations Manual for Resale & Consignment Shops **[3145]**, **[3904]**, **[8213]**
"Too Much Information?" in Black Enterprise (Vol. 37, December 2006, No. 5, pp. 59) **[6636]**, **[20349]**, **[22836]**, **[24140]**, **[28218]**, **[30083]**, **[30395]**, **[31889]**, **[35868]**
"Too Much Precaution About Biotech Corn" in Barron's (Vol. 88, March 17, 2008, No. 11, pp. 54) **[6637]**, **[8769]**, **[9849]**, **[17125]**, **[23376]**, **[24141]**, **[26441]**, **[27743]**
Tooele County Chamber of Commerce **[45649]**
Tooele County Chamber of Commerce and Tourism [45649]
"Tool-o-Rama" in Barron's (Vol. 90, September 6, 2010, No. 36) **[6638]**, **[9850]**, **[21993]**
"Tooling Firm Thinks Being In U.P. Gives It Upper Hand" in Crain's Detroit Business (Vol. 30, October 13, 2014, No. 41, pp. 21) **[10444]**, **[21187]**, **[21641]**
Tooling, Manufacturing and Technologies Association (TMTA) **[10423]**
Tooling & Production: Providing Solutions for Metalworking Manufacturers **[10455]**
"Toolmakers' New Tack: Firms' Goal -- Advance Wind-Turbine Technology" in Crain's Detroit Business (Vol. 25, June 8, 2009,) **[5719]**, **[5985]**, **[23377]**, **[29415]**, **[31552]**
Tools and Techniques of Data Analysis **[29610]**
Tools & Techniques of Data Analysis (Onsite) **[29611]**
The Tools & Techniques of Estate Planning **[6047]**, **[34909]**
Toombs County Chamber of Commerce [38745]
"The Top 4 Tips for Virtual Startups" in Legal Zoom (February 24, 2023) **[11805]**, **[34564]**
"Top 5 Barber Business Trends in 2021" in UpMetrics (November 2, 2021) **[7876]**
The Top 5 Characteristics of Successful Social Entrepreneurs with Cory Ames **[22933]**
"Top 5 Cities to Launch Your Startup Business" in Legal Zoom (March 21, 2023) **[34565]**
"Top 5 Health Insurance Tips for the Self-Employed" in Legal Zoom (March 24, 2023) **[26813]**, **[27347]**, **[32996]**
"Top 5 Lessons From a Kid Entrepreneur (Pay Attention, Public Schools!)" in Entrepreneur (May 13, 2020) **[36031]**
Top 5 Marketing Tips for Your Shop **[14358]**
Top 6 Fraud Risks for Small Businesses **[19284]**
"Top 6 Questions about Compensation from Small Businesses and High Growth Companies" in PayScale (May 1, 2018) **[19756]**
"Top 6 Ways Your Company Could Lose Its Corporate Veil: Is Your Business at Risk?" in Small Business Trends(June 1, 2017) **[27195]**
"Top 7 Free Online Publishing Platforms For New Writers" in Just Publishing Advice (October 13, 2019) **[1678]**
Top 10 Communication Apps for Your Small Business **[17768]**
"The Top 10 Customer Service Blogs for Businesses" in FORA Financial Blog (Oct. 22, 2020) **[20520]**
"Top 10 Hiring Platforms for Small Business" in Entrepreneur (Oct. 19, 2021) **[26675]**
"Top 10 In-demand Profitable Mobile Business Ideas You Can Start in 2022" in StartupTalky **[30492]**
Top 10 Mid-Year Tax Saving Strategies Every Small Business Owner Must Know **[34941]**
"Top 10 Most Popular Online Makeup Stores in the U.S." in US Unlocked **[4523]**, **[11806]**
"The Top 10: Prime Examples of Growth and Prosperity" in South Florida Business Journal (Vol. 34, July 18, 2014, No. 52, pp. 13) **[18393]**, **[21188]**
"Top 10 Retirement Mistakes and How to Avoid Them" in Canadian Business (Vol. 83, July 20, 2010, No. 11-12, pp. 39) **[6639]**, **[9851]**, **[13294]**, **[24142]**, **[25956]**
Top 11 Local SEO Strategies for Professional Organizers **[12849]**
Top 15 Pricing Strategies for Your Small Business **[20058]**
Top 15 Small Business and Startup Accounting Tips **[16844]**
"Top 21 Fundraising Consultants for Nonprofit Success" in Donorsearch (November 14, 2016) **[7165]**
"Top 49ers Alphabetical Listing with Five Years Rank and Revenue" in Alaska Business Monthly (Vol. 27, October 2011, No. 10, pp. 100) **[18394]**, **[24752]**
"Top 50 In Total Revenue" in Canadian Business (Vol. 81, Summer 2008, No. 9, pp. 119) **[6640]**, **[8972]**, **[9852]**, **[18395]**, **[24143]**, **[27348]**
"Top 100 Indy Advisors" in Barron's (Vol. 92, August 25, 2012, No. 38, pp. S2) **[6641]**, **[9853]**, **[24144]**
"Top Architecture Firms" in South Florida Business Journal (Vol. 34, June 13, 2014, No. 47, pp. 13) **[914]**, **[4247]**, **[26442]**
Top-Bar Beekeeping **[1488]**
"Top Body Shop Consolidators Step up Competition with Dealers" in Automotive News (June 18, 2018) **[14558]**
"Top Challenges Female Entrepreneurs Need to Overcome" in Legal Zoom (February 21, 2023) **[35869]**
"Top Commercial Real Estate Developers" in South Florida Business Journal (Vol. 34, July 25, 2014, No. 53, pp. 14) **[13295]**, **[13581]**, **[13837]**
"Top Design Award for Massey Ferguson 7624 Dyna-VT" in Farm Industry News (November 14, 2011) **[17126]**, **[19948]**, **[29416]**
"Top E-Commerce Challenges Facing SMBs" in Business News Daily (Feb. 18, 2022) **[21994]**
"Top Expenses Taking the Biggest Bite out of Your Business" in Legal Zoom (March 27, 2023) **[19085]**, **[19604]**
Top Grocery Trends of 2021 **[7779]**, **[8052]**
"'Top Guns' Take Aim at Industry Issues" in HBS Dealer (November 8, 2021) **[7924]**
"Top Interior Design Firms" in Orlando Business Journal (Vol. 30, April 4, 2014, No. 41, pp. 7) **[9050]**
"Top Law Firms Join Forces" in Business Journal Portland (Vol. 27, December 3, 2010, No. 40, pp. 1) **[6642]**, **[9854]**, **[18715]**, **[24145]**, **[31553]**
Top of the Line Fragrances **[4543]**
"The Top Mistakes of Social Media Marketing" in Agency Sales Magazine (Vol. 39, November 2009, No. 9, pp. 42) **[362]**, **[9246]**, **[16473]**, **[17769]**, **[30084]**
Top Non-Food Franchise Opportunities for 2024 with Jon Ostenson **[24463]**
"The Top Occupational Safety and Health Issues for 2020: An Employer's Guide" in EHS Daily Advisor (December 16, 2019) **[30948]**
Top of Ohio Topics [43429]
"Top Pension Fund Sends a Warning" in Barron's (Vol. 92, July 23, 2012, No. 30, pp. M9) **[6643]**, **[9855]**, **[17364]**, **[24146]**
"Top Reasons to Incorporate Your Business" in Small Business Trends (August 5, 2014) **[27196]**, **[34566]**
"Top Stadium Builders Likely To Vie For Vikings Project" in Business Journal (Vol. 29, May 18, 2012, No. 51, pp. 1) **[915]**, **[4248]**, **[15195]**
"Top Statewide Commercial Real Estate Brokerages" in South Florida Business Journal (Vol. 34, April 4, 2014, No. 37, pp. 14) **[13296]**, **[13582]**, **[13838]**, **[32647]**
Top Tax Savings Ideas: How to Survive in Today's Tough Tax Environment **[15422]**, **[34910]**
"Top Technologies That Will Transform Web Development in 2020" in Medium (August 20, 2020) **[16474]**
"Top Ten Publishing Industry Trends Every Author Needs to Know in 2019" in Written Word Media (January 3, 2019) **[1679]**
"Top Tips for a Killer Facebook Ad Campaign, for Your Gym or Studio' in Glofox blog (April 18, 2017) **[12435]**, **[30085]**
"The Top Trends in Home Care for 2019" in Home Health Care News (January 6, 2019) **[8266]**
Top Value Car & Truck Service Centers **[1130]**
Top of Virginia Regional Chamber (TVRC) **[45905]**
"Top Women In Tech: Whether It's Mobile or Engineering, These Mavens Are Making an Impact on Today's Tech Scene" in Black Enterprise (Vol. 44, February 2014, No. 6, pp. 29) **[26443]**, **[30396]**, **[35870]**
"Top Worst Weeds in Corn" in Farm Industry News (November 29, 2011) **[17127]**, **[32048]**, **[32835]**
Topeka Chamber of Commerce [39897]
Topeka SCORE **[39853]**
Topgolf International, Inc. **[10990]**
"TopGolf Plans Three-Level Entertainment Center in S.A." in San Antonio Business Journal (Vol. 27, January 10, 2014, No. 49, pp. 6) **[7528]**, **[15905]**, **[35101]**
Topics in Clinical Nutrition (TICN) **[11586]**, **[26056]**
Topics in Geriatric Rehabilitation (TGR) **[11530]**
Toppenish Chamber of Commerce **[46165]**
Topper's Pizza **[14274]**
TOPS Club Inc. **[16504]**
Topsail Area Guide **[43196]**
Tornado Business Solutions **[10559]**
"Toro Launches Z Master 7500" in Lawn & Landscape (November 6, 2019) **[10058]**, **[10116]**, **[10248]**
Toronto Business Development Centre (TBDC) **[46835]**
Toronto Fashion Incubator (TFI) **[46836]**
Toronto Reference Library - Arts Centre **[4868]**, **[11241]**
Toronto Rehabilitation Institute **[11547]**
TorQuest Partners **[46809]**
Torrance Area Chamber of Commerce (TACC) **[37218]**
Tortilla Industry Association Convention & Trade Exposition **[1286]**

Small Business Sourcebook • 42nd Edition 3351

"Toss the Gum Before You Speak and Other Tips for Presenting to a Potential Principal" in Agency Sales Magazine (Vol. 39, July 2009, No. 7, pp. 34) **[8669], [31794], [32648]**
Total Business Care, L.L.C. (TBC) **[2323], [24270]**
Total Business Services Inc. (TBSI) **[2324]**
"Total Defense Launches Mobile Security for Business" in Benzinga.com (August 1, 2012) **[2802], [3739], [14471]**
Total Energy Management Professionals [32713]
The Total Money Makeover: A Proven Plan For Financial Fitness **[24147]**
Total Productive Maintenance and 5S **[2058]**
Total Productive Maintenance (TPM) & 5S (Onsite) **[17894], [22068]**
Touching the Future: My Odyssey from Print to Online Publishing **[5427]**
Touching Hearts At Home **[8292]**
"Tough Times for the Irving Clan" in Canadian Business (Vol. 83, August 17, 2010, No. 13-14, pp. 14) **[22837], [28856]**
"Tough Year Ahead for Unions" in Philadelphia Business Journal (Vol. 30, January 13, 2012, No. 48, pp. 1) **[35208]**
"The Toughest Sell: Women Hate to Buy Swimsuits, So Firms Try New Tack" in Inc. (Vol. 36, September 2014, No. 7, pp. 69) **[22442], [26479]**
Tourism and Entrepreneurship: International Perspectives **[15762], [16012]**
Tourism Industry Association of Canada (TIAC) **[15727], [15978]**
Tourism Industry Association of Saskatchewan [46914]
Tourism Saskatchewan **[46914]**
Tourist Attractions and Parks **[3858]**
Touro College - Boro Park Library **[24917]**
Touro College Brighton Beach Library **[24918]**
Touro College Cross River Campus Library **[24919]**
Touro College Forest Hills Library **[24920]**
Touro College Lander College of Liberal Arts & Sciences Midwood Library **[24921]**
Touro College Lander College for Men Library **[24922], [29055]**
Touro College Midtown Library [24919]
Touro College Starrett City Library **[24923]**
Touro College - Sunset Park Library **[24924]**
Tow-Knight Center for Entrepreneurial Journalism **[42949]**
"Toward a Theory of Stakeholder Salience in Family Firms" in Business Ethics Quarterly (Vol. 21, April 2011, No. 2, pp. 235) **[23541], [23667]**
"Tower City Hopes Restrictions on Minors Boost Retail Center" in Crain's Cleveland Business (Vol. 28, November 5, 2007, No. 44) **[32300], [34197]**
Towers Perrin [2423]
Towers Watson Information Center **[2423]**
Towersoudan Chamber of Commerce [41255]
Towing and Recovery Association of America, Inc. (TRAA) **[2576]**
Town of Conconully Chamber of Commerce **[46166]**
The Town Crier **[46289]**
Town of Hunter Chamber of Commerce **[42689]**
Town Map **[40635]**
Town of Parker, CO, Economic Development Department **[37954]**
Towneley Capital Management, Inc. **[9934]**
Towns County Chamber of Commerce **[38788]**
Township of Richland Chamber of Commerce **[44309]**
Towson University Incubator **[40472]**
Toxic Positivity and Leadership in the Impact Space with Satyen Raja **[34444]**
The Toy Association Inc. **[11482], [15784]**
The Toy Book **[11484], [15802]**
Toy Fair **[15809]**
Toy Industry Association, Inc. [11482], [15784]
"Toyota Marks Record Profit Sales" in Globe & Mail (February 7, 2007, pp. B10) **[9856], [11447], [18396], [29417]**
"Toyota Revs Up Plans for Ontario Plant" in Globe & Mail (February 7, 2006, pp. B1) **[26676], [29418]**
"Toyota Tops GM in Global Sales" in Globe & Mail (April 24, 2007, pp. B1) **[18397], [29419]**
Toys & Games--Buyer's Guide Issue (Canada) **[1200]**
Toys & Games: Canada's Toy Industry Magazine **[15803]**
"Toys R Us Is Coming Back But with a Different Approach" in NPR (July 18, 2019) **[15794], [31554]**
"Toys R Us Tries for a Comeback a Year After Going Out of Business" in CNBC (February 11, 2019) **[1198], [15795]**
TPA Conference & Expo [5207]
TPA technologies **[34687]**
TPE Boulder **[40737]**
TPG Growth II Management, LLC **[37766]**
TPI Summer Convention & Field Days **[10132]**
TPI Travel Services **[16040]**
TRAA National Towing E-News **[2578]**
Track Selling System Workshop (Onsite) **[32449]**
"Tracking Your Fleet Can Increase Bottom Line" in Contractor (Vol. 56, November 2009, No. 11, pp. 26) **[518], [5390], [12665], [14316], [14634], [17770], [28857]**
Tracy Area Chamber of Commerce **[41310]**
The Trade Coffee & Coworking **[37642]**
Trade Commission of Norway [27416]
"Trade Craft: Take Pride in Your Trade, Demand Excellence" in Contractor (Vol. 56, October 2009, No. 10, pp. 24) **[519], [5391], [12666], [14635], [21642], [26677]**
Trade Dimensions' Marketing Guidebook [2546], [4444], [7764]
Trade-Off: The Ever-Present Tension Between Quality and Conscience **[20521], [23542], [27954], [30817], [33272]**
"Trade Mission Provides Global Entry Point" in Pittsburgh Business Times (Vol. 33, January 3, 2014, No. 25, pp. 4) **[27744]**
Trade Show Bureau [15817], [29571]
Trade Show Calendar **[11807], [15906]**
Trade Show and Conference Planning Industry in the US - Market Research Report **[15915]**
"Trade Winds" in Canadian Sailings (June 30, 2008) **[8770], [21189], [27745]**
"Trademark and Patent Scams: What to Watch out For" in Legal Zoom (February 17, 2023) **[19285], [27955]**
"A Trader Gets a Better Deal From the IRS Than an Investor" in Barron's (Vol. 88, March 31, 2008, No. 13, pp. 56) **[6644], [7311], [9857], [24148], [34911]**
"Trader Joe's Secret Sauce? An Army of Influencers" in Grocery Dive (November 8, 2019) **[7780], [10676], [11808]**
"Trader Joe's Warehouse May Bring More Business to Daytona" in Orlando Business Journal (Vol. 30, March 14, 2014, No. 38, pp. 8) **[7781], [21190]**
The Traditional Cat Association, Inc. (TCA) **[643]**
Traditional and Non-Traditional Small Business Lending Options **[30936]**
Traditional Siamese Breeders and Fanciers Association [643]
"Traditional vs. Roth IRA" in Black Enterprise (Vol. 37, October 2006, No. 3, pp. 58) **[6645], [24149], [34912]**
Traffic Audit Bureau [219], [31829]
Traffic Audit Bureau for Media Measurement, Inc. [219], [31829]
"Train Now to Get the Competitive Edge" in Contractor (Vol. 56, October 2009, No. 10, pp. 58) **[14636], [19949], [21191], [21643]**
Train the Trainer: Facilitation Skills Workshop Onsite **[26868]**
Training & Development for Dummies **[19605], [22266]**
Training & Development Journal [10005]
Training Difficult Issues in Diversity (Onsite) **[17617], [30523]**
"Training Essential For Growth; It Doesn't Have To Cost Much" in Crain's Detroit Business (Vol. 24, January 21, 2008, No. 3, pp. 14) **[18398], [21644]**
Training for Impact **[26869]**
"Training: an Investment in Performance Improvement" in Franchising World (Vol. 42, September 2010, No. 9, pp. 22) **[24422], [32649]**
Traklight **[36415]**
"Trammell Crow Facility in Houston is a Late Bloomer" in Houston Business Journal (Vol. 40, August 28, 2009, No. 16, pp. 1A) **[6861], [7050], [12984], [13839]**
Trans-Atlantic Business Council (TABC) **[27431]**
TransAccel LLC **[37688]**
Transaction Processing Performance Council (TPC) **[3690]**
TransBIOTech (tbt) **[46905]**
TransComp **[7058]**
"Transcontinental to Exchange Assets with Quad/Graphics" in American Printer (Vol. 128, August 1, 2011, No. 8) **[3336], [9858], [12759], [16210], [31555]**
TransDigest **[7057]**
TransDomo LLC **[44614]**
"Transforming the Business Portfolio: How Multinationals Reinvent Themselves" in Journal of Business Strategy (Vol. 35, May-June 2014, No. 3, pp. 4-17) **[18399], [19086], [27385]**
"Transfusion" in Puget Sound Business Journal (Vol. 33, August 31, 2012, No. 19, pp. 1) **[7166], [26444], [32836], [35393]**
"Transgenerational Trend: New Fans for Fresh Fare" in Barron's (Vol. 92, July 7, 2012, No. 28, pp. 15) **[8053], [17128]**
Transimpex Translations Inc. **[15959]**
"Transitioning From Hobbyist to Entrepreneur: Teen Designer Creates Custom and Handmade Jewelry for the Everyday Diva" in Black Enterprise (Vol. 44, March 2014, No. 7, pp. 14) **[9985], [30397], [35871], [36032]**
Transitioning from Small Business to a Franchisor with Bryan Appell **[24464]**
Translation Services Directory of the American Translators Association [15932]
Translation Services Industry in the US - Market Research Report **[15952]**
Translation for Startups and Small Businesses - Top Tips for Getting the Best from Your Language Services **[15950]**
Translational Research: The Journal of Laboratory and Clinical Medicine **[10933]**
TransLink Capital **[37509]**
Transmedia Capital **[37767]**
Transmission Depot **[14598]**
"Transparency Tops Tate & Lyle's List of Trends" in Food Business News (November 18,2021) **[2682], [7782], [14031]**
"The Transparent Supply Chain" in Harvard Business Review (Vol. 88, October 2010, No. 10, pp. 76) **[3146], [8771], [20522], [26445], [27746], [28014], [34198]**
Transpective Business Consulting Inc. **[10560]**
The Transportation Alliance (TLPA) **[15508]**
Transportation Association of Canada (TAC) **[15509]**
Transportation Research Institute [1565]
Transportation and Warehousing Industry in the US - Market Research Report **[12988], [16092]**
Travel Agencies Industry in the US - Market Research Report **[16021]**
"Travel Agencies Still Make 7 Times More in Commissions Than Fees" in Skift (October 7, 2019) **[16013]**
The Travel Agent's Complete Desk Reference, 5th Edition **[15763], [16014], [26814]**
The Travel Goods Show **[10371]**
Travel Goods Showcase: Products & Trends for Travelers **[10370]**
Travel Guide **[42690]**
The Travel Institute **[15979]**
"Travel Leery" in Crain's Chicago Business (Vol. 31, March 31, 2008, No. 13, pp. 3) **[17513], [19405], [21192], [33273]**
Travel Lines Express Franchise Group **[16041], [26833]**
Travel Media Showcase (TMS) **[15776], [16033]**
"Travel Rewards Take Off" in Inc. (Vol. 33, October 2011, No. 8, pp. 46) **[4726], [4811], [19406], [19950]**
Travel Startups Incubator (TSI) **[38590]**
"Travel Tears" in Crain's Chicago Business (Vol. 31, November 17, 2008, No. 46, pp. 3) **[8460], [14032], [15764], [15907], [16015], [19407], [34913], [35102]**
"Travel Tech: 4 Gadgets for Running Your Business on the Fly" in Entrepreneur (May 2014) **[2803], [19408], [21995], [30985]**
Travel and Tourism Research Association (TTRA) **[16049]**
Travel Tours and Activities: Incl Impact of COVID-19 - US - April 2020 **[16022]**
Travel Weekly: The National Newspaper of the Travel Industry **[16027]**
Travel Weekly's Hotel Search **[15770]**
Travel World News Magazine: The Magazine for Destination Travel Specialists **[16028]**
TravelAge West **[16029]**
"The Traveling Godfather: Beam Global Spirits & Wine Inc." in Canadian Business (Vol. 81, October 13, 2008, No. 17, pp. S10) **[1354], [1937]**
Travelodge Hotels **[8519]**
"Travelodge Intros Program to Streamline Operations, Reduce Waste" in Hotel Business (November 11, 2019) **[8461]**
Travelweek **[15771], [16030]**
Traverse City Area Chamber of Commerce [41020]
Traverse City Regional Educational Media Center - REMC 2 Central **[16179]**
Traverse Connect **[41020]**
Traverse Connect News **[41021]**
TRC Staffing Services Inc. **[5462], [15663]**
Treasure Coast Research Park **[38591]**
Treasure Valley Beekeepers Club (TVBC) **[1453]**
Treasure Valley Community College Small Business Development Center (TVCC SDDC) **[43918]**
Treasury Management Association [23695]
Tree City U.S.A. Bulletin **[7647], [10128]**
Trellis Capital Corp. **[46810]**
Trellis Partners **[45601]**
"A Trend Is His Friend" in Barron's (Vol. 89, July 27, 2009, No. 30, pp. 28) **[6646], [9859], [24150]**
"TrendHR Changes Rockwall Landscape with $25M Office Tower" in Dallas Business Journal (Vol. 35, May 25, 2012, No. 37, pp. 1) **[17365], [20134], [27058]**
"Trends at the 2019 Summer Fancy Food Show" in Food Business News (June 25, 2019) **[15032], [15908]**
Trends® Magazine **[705]**
Trends and Opportunities for Makers and Retail Businesses with Carla Pellicano of Faire **[4629], [32349]**

3352 **Small Business Sourcebook • 42nd Edition**

Trendz Show [2858], [3166], [6147], [10309]
Trendzitions Inc. [2029], [2325], [2393], [10561], [17814], [20225], [29035]
Trenton [41640]
Trenton Area Chamber of Commerce [41641]
TRI-AD Actuaries, Inc. [17415]
Tri-Cities Area Chamber of Commerce [39125]
Tri-Cities Enterprise Center [46223]
Tri-Cities Small Business Development Center (SBDC) [46005]
Tri-City Regional Chamber of Commerce (TCRCC) [46167]
Tri-City West Chamber of Commerce [36364]
Tri-County Area Vo-Tech [43897]
Tri-County Economic Development District (TEDD) [46224]
Tri-County Heritage Society Reference Library [952]
Tri-County Regional Black Chamber of Commerce (TCRBCC) [45381]
Tri-County Regional Chamber of Commerce [44584]
Tri-County SCORE [44165]
Tri County Technology Center (TCTC) [43897]
Tri-Lakes Chamber of Commerce [37904]
Tri-Ology [7648], [12055]
Tri-State Better Business Bureau [39512]
Tri-State CAMP Conference [2530]
Tri-State Chamber of Commerce (TSC) [38078]
"Tri-State to Get New Headquarters" in Business Courier (Vol. 27, October 22, 2010, No. 25, pp. 1) [17129], [19209], [27747]
"Tri-State Lags Peer Cities in Jobs, Human Capital, Study Says" in Business Courier (Vol. 27, September 24, 2010, No. 21, pp. 1) [19606], [26678], [27059]
Tri-State Minority Supplier Development Council Regional Office Kentucky (TSMSDC) [40092]
Tri-Town Chamber of Commerce [40636]
"Triad, Fortune Dump TARP Cut Costs, Boost Lending" in Saint Louis Business Journal (Vol. 32, October 7, 2011, No. 6, pp. 1) [25085], [28219]
Triad Strategies L.L.C. [7182], [12963]
"Trial of Enron Ex-Bosses to Begin Today" in Globe & Mail (January 30, 2006, pp. B1) [18716], [23543], [28858]
Triangle Angel Partners (TAP) [43232]
Triangle Building Supplies and Services Inc. [13858]
Triangle Construction [13858]
Triangle East Chamber of Commerce [43197]
Triangle Peak Partners LP [37510]
Triangles Bulletin [11349]
Tribal Government Institute (TGI) [43846]
Tribeca Angels [42804]
Tribeca Early Stage Partners (TESP) [42804]
"Tribes Roll Dice On Ventures as They Push Outside of Casinos" in Business Journal (Vol. 32, May 30, 2014, No. 1, pp. 8) [7312], [8462]
Tribunal Canadien du Commerce Exterieur [27796]
TriCounty Area Chamber of Commerce (TCACC) [44310]
"Trigate Rebrands Radisson at SMU to Holiday Inn" in Dallas Business Journal (Vol. 35, August 31, 2012, No. 51, pp. 1) [916], [8463]
"The Trillion Dollar R&D Fix: Most Big Companies Should Spend More On R&D. But How Much More?" in Harvard Business Review (Vol. 90, May 2012, No. 5, pp. 76) [32049], [32837]
"Trimming Costs, But Not Looking It" in Crain's Chicago Business (Vol. 31, November 17, 2008, No. 46, pp. 35) [21193], [24753]
Trinity County Chamber of Commerce (TCCC) [37219]
Trinity Peninsula Chamber of Commerce (TPCC) [45382]
Trinity University - Center for Innovation and Entrepreneurship [45566]
Trinity Valley Small Business Development Center (TV-SBDC) [44946]
Trinity Ventures [37511]
Triodyne Inc. (TI) [35987]
"TripIt Itineraries Show Labor Day is the Most Popular Weekend for Wedding Travel" in Benzinga.com (August 26, 2011) [1997]
Triple O's [14275]
TriTech Small Business Development Center [36595]
tritiumDX [42979]
Triton Ventures [45479]
Tronvig Group [42987]
"Tropeano Takes Charge" in Philadelphia Business Journal (Vol. 33, August 22, 2014, No. 28, pp. 11) [8973], [19951], [20059], [27349]
Trophy & Engraving Shops Industry in the US - Market Research Report [5471]
Tropi Tan [15272]
Tropical Fish Hobbyist [842]
Tropical Plant Industry Exhibition [6874]
Tropical Smoothie Cafe, LLC [8639], [14276]
Trott Communications Group, Inc. [2823]

Trotting Horse Museum [8332]
"Trouble Getting Customers to Pay?" in Legal Zoom (March 22, 2023) [16602], [20523]
"The Trouble With $150,000 Wine" in Barron's (Vol. 88, July 7, 2008, No. 27, pp. 33) [15033], [17130], [20657], [24754], [29420], [30086], [32301]
Troubleshooting Mechanical Drive Systems & Rotating Equipment (Onsite) [19461], [21429]
Troubleshooting Mechanical Drive Systems and Rotating Equipment (Onsite) [2059]
Troup Chamber of Commerce [45383]
"Trousseaus of Memories Trail Behind Wedding Gowns" in Oregonian (September 4, 2010) [1998], [3050], [3147]
Trout Unlimited Canada (TUC) [5507]
Troy Area Chamber of Commerce [43587]
Troy Area Chamber of Commerce (TCC) [41642]
Troy Chamber of Commerce [41022]
Troy Chamber of Commerce [39319]
"Troy Complex has New Brand, New Leases" in Crain's Detroit Business (Vol. 24, April 14, 2008, No. 15, pp. 32) [12903], [13297], [13583], [30087]
Troy/Maryville/St. Jacob/Marine Area Chamber of Commerce [39319]
Troy on the Move [41643]
"Troy Patent Law Firm Launches Rent-Free Tech Incubator" in Crain's Detroit Business (Vol. 25, June 8, 2009, No. 23, pp. 4) [18717], [22443], [24577], [26183], [27826], [31932], [32709]
Troy University Small Business Development Center (SBDC) [36056]
Truck-Frame and Axle Repair Association (TARA) [14543]
Truck Parts & Service [14568]
Truck Rental Industry in the US - Market Research Report [1163]
Truck Renting and Leasing Association (TRALA) [1155]
Truckee Donner Chamber of Commerce [37220]
"Trucker Jobs Are Plentiful and Safe . . . but for How Long?" in American Trucker (November 15, 2019) [16085], [32050]
Trucker's Connection [16101]
Trucking Employers [16068]
Trucking Management, Inc. (TMI) [16068]
Truckload [16109]
Truckload Carriers Association (TCA) [16069]
True Food Kitchen [14277]
True North EDI [30431], [30654]
"True Value Ranks No. 1 in National Customer Service Poll" in Hardware Retailing (November 1, 2019) [7925], [20524]
True Ventures [37512]
TrueArtists [15284]
Truepilot L.L.C. [43233]
"Truffles & Trifles' Marci Arthur Plans YouTube Channel, Cookbook" in Orlando Business Journal (Vol. 30, May 2, 2014, No. 45, pp. 3) [794], [1680], [4471], [22267], [23012], [30937], [35872]
TruFund Financial Services, Inc. [20714], [20715], [20716]
Truly Nolen [12062]
Truman State University Small Business Technology & Development Center [41493]
Truman State University's Small Business Development Center [41493]
Trumbull County Carnegie Law Library [15477]
Trussville Area Chamber of Commerce (TACC) [36154]
"Trust Buyouts Not My Fault, Flaherty Says" in Globe & Mail (April 3, 2007, pp. B1) [6647], [9860], [31556]
"The Trust Edge: How Top Leaders Gain Faster Results, Deeper Relationships" [22838], [28859]
"Trust Management of Services in Cloud Environments: Obstacles and Solutions" in ACM Computing Surveys (Vol. 46, Spring 2014, No. 1, pp. 12) [9247], [14472], [32051], [32838]
"Trust Tax Under Fire as Drain on Revenue" in Globe & Mail (April 9, 2007, pp. B1) [21194], [31557], [34914]
"Trusted Choice: Mobile App" in Best's Review (Vol. 113, September 2012, No. 5, pp. 14) [2804], [8974], [9248], [27350]
Trusted Media Brands Inc. (TMB) [12017]
"The Truth about Ecommerce You Might Not Realize" in Small Business Trends(February 1, 2023) [11809]
"Try a Little Social Media" in American Printer (Vol. 128, June 1, 2011, No. 6) [3337], [12760], [16211], [21996], [30088]
TRY US National Minority Business Directory [30370]
"Trying Out a Forgotten (and Free) Service: Personal Shoppers" in The New York Times (November 11, 2016) [12030]
"TSA PreCheck: What It Is, How to Apply, and Benefits" in Fit Small Business (November 1, 2019) [19409]
"Tsingtao's Chairman On Jump-Starting a Sluggish Company" in Harvard Business Review (Vol. 90, April 2012, No. 4, pp. 41) [1938], [18400], [19607], [20525], [22268]

Tsingyuan Ventures [37363]
TSL [9925]
TSS Photography [12323], [12359]
TSVC [37513]
TTV Capital [38857]
TU Incubator [40766]
Tualatin Business and Community Guide [44026]
Tualatin Chamber of Commerce (TCC) [44027]
Tuality Health Information Resource Center [12474]
Tuality Healthcare Health Sciences Library [12474]
Tubac Chamber of Commerce [36370]
Tubby's Sub Shops Inc. [4925], [14278]
Tubular Brass Institute [12611]
Tuck-WBENC Executive Porgram (Tuck I) [35717]
Tuck-WBENC Strategic Growth Program (Tuck II) [35718]
Tucson Metro Chamber [36371]
Tucson Pima Public Library Grants and Nonprofit Information Collection [7189]
Tucumcari-Quay County Chamber of Commerce (TQCCC) [42340]
Tuesday [15772]
"Tuesday Morning's Corporate Clearance Rack" in Dallas Business Journal (Vol. 37, February 28, 2014, No. 25, pp. 4) [8180], [24151], [26679], [28860], [32302]
Tuffy Tire & Auto Service Centers [14599]
Tufts University - Hirsh Health Sciences Library (HHSL) [11618]
"Tufts Wins Grant for K-2 Coding Education" in TuftsNow (October 21, 2019) [3647], [21645]
Tugboat Group [36524]
Tugboat Ventures [36524]
Tulia Chamber of Commerce [45384]
Tullahoma Area Chamber of Commerce (TACC) [44812]
Tulsa Better Business Bureau [43729]
Tulsa Community College (TCC) [43898]
Tulsa Metro Chamber of Commerce [43816]
Tulsa Regional Chamber [43816]
Tulsa Technology Center Procurement Technical Assistance Center [43847]
Tumbles [2911], [12466]
Tumml [37643]
Tumwater Area Chamber of Commerce (TACC) [46168]
Tunex Complete Car Care [14600]
Tunex, Inc. [14600]
Tunica County Chamber of Commerce [41431]
Tunnel Business Magazine: Covering the North American Tunneling Market [4358]
Tuolumne County Chamber of Commerce [37221]
Tupelo/Lee County Regional Business Incubator [41456]
Tupper Lake Chamber of Commerce (TLCC) [42691]
Turbo Leadership Systems Ltd. (TLS) [2370], [10567], [22333]
"Turbulent Times and Golden Opportunities" in Business Strategy Review (Vol. 21, Spring 2010, No. 1, pp. 34) [15765], [16016], [19410], [21195]
Turf and Ornamental Communicators Association (TOCA) [10083]
Turfgrass Producers International - Summer Convention and Field Day [10132]
Turlock Chamber of Commerce [37222]
"Turn the Great Resignation into a Great Employee Retention Strategy" in Minority Business Entrepreneur (Vol. 39, Fall, 2022, No. 4, pp. 16-17) [22269]
"A Turn in the South" in The Economist (Vol. 390, January 3, 2009, No. 8612, pp. 34) [12000], [18401], [21196], [24755]
"Turn Your Genealogy Hobby Into a Side Business" in Business.com (May 1, 2019) [7373]
Turnaround Management Association (TMA) [10479]
Turner Center for Entrepreneurship [39438]
Turner Consulting Group Inc. (TCG) [622]
Turner County Chamber of Commerce [38685]
Turning Artistic Passion into Profit with Jonah Allen [12317]
"Turning Drivers Into Geeks; Auto Dealers Debate Need for Technology Specialists to Bring Buyers Up to Speed" in Crain's Detroit Business (Vol. 30, January 6, 2014, No. 1, pp. 3) [11448], [26446], [29421]
"Turning Uncertainty Into Opportunity: Creating A Home-Based Business" in Forbes (Apr 27, 2020) [26815]
Turnkey Inc. [12237]
Turnstone Capital [38103]
Tuscarawas County Chamber of Commerce (TCCC) [43588]
Tuscola Chamber of Commerce (TCC) [39320]
Tustin Chamber of Commerce (TCC) [37223]
Tutor Doctor [16174]
Tutoring America (TA) [16125]
The Tutoring Center Franchise Corp. [16175]
Tutoring Club L.L.C. (TC) [16176]
TVM Capital Life Science Venture Capital [46912]
"TW Trade Shows to Offer Seminars On Niche Selling, Social Media" in Travel Weekly (Vol. 69, October 4, 2010, No. 40, pp. 9) [15766], [16017], [19411], [21997], [26816]

Twain Harte Area Chamber of Commerce [37224]
Tweed-Weber Inc. (TWD) [29036]
"Tweet Me, Friend Me, Make Me Buy" in (Vol. 90, July-August 2012, No. 7-8, pp. 88) [9249], [30089], [32650]
Twelve-Minute Risk Management: Strategies and Tools Business Owners Need Right Now to Successfully Navigate Today's Business World [33613]
"Twelve Things I Never Knew About Clothes Until I Became a Personal Shopping for Barneys" in Bloomberg (November 14, 2018) [12031]
Twin Cities Chamber of Commerce [46066]
Twin Cities North Chamber of Commerce (TCNCC) [41311]
Twin Cities Quorum [41312]
Twin Cities Small Business Development Center [41161]
Twin City Chamber of Commerce (TC) [43589]
Twin County Chamber of Commerce [45906]
Twin Falls Area Chamber of Commerce [38946]
Twinsburg Chamber of Commerce (TCC) [43590]
TwinWest Chamber of Commerce [41313]
Twisp Chamber of Commerce [46169]
Twist Sport Conditioning Centers [12467]
"Twitter Hack: Made in Japan? User Says Attack Showed Security Flaw" in Houston Chronicle (September 24, 2010, pp. 3) [14473], [21998], [27748]
Two Brown Girls [30655]
"Two Field Service Management Solutions" in Contractor (Vol. 56, November 2009, No. 11, pp. 37) [520], [9250], [14841], [33916]
Two Harbors Area Chamber of Commerce [41253]
"Two Local Bakers Winners of TV's 'Cupcake Wars'" in Toledo Blade (July 6, 2011) [1268]
"Two Local Firms Make Inc. List: Minority Business" in Indianapolis Business Journal (Vol. 31, August 30, 2010, No. 26, pp. 13A) [3740], [18402], [26447], [30398], [31132]
"Two Major Credit Reporting Agencies Have Been Lying to Consumers" in The Atlantic (January 4, 2017) [4812], [23544]
Two Men and A Truck International Inc. [11160]
Two Men and a Truck Canada [11161]
"Two New Apartment Complexes on Tap for West Orange County" in Orlando Business Journal (Vol. 29, September 7, 2012, No. 12, pp. 1) [4249], [13584]
Two Rivers Angel Network [41343]
"Two Small Broker-Dealers Are Down — and Out" in Investment News (October 10, 2019) [9861]
"TWU Offers Course in Project Management" in Bellingham Business Journal (Vol. February 2010, pp. 4) [21646], [28861]
Ty Crandall - Small Business Credit [16711]
Tyler Area Business Incubator (TABI) [45567]
Tyler Area Chamber of Commerce (TACC) [45385]
Tyler Chamber News [45386]
Tyler Convention and Visitors Bureau [45385]
Tyler County Chamber of Commerce [45387]
Tyler Small Business Development Center [44947]
Type Directors Club (TDC) [16181]
"Types of Franchises" in Small Business Trends (February 22, 2023) [24423]
Typography and Font Management (Onsite) [33816]
Tyrone Area Chamber of Commerce [44311]
Tysons Regional Chamber of Commerce (TRCC) [45907]

U

U District Partnership (UDP) [46170]
U-M Tech Transfer [41094]
U-Save Auto Rental of America, Inc. [13859]
U-Save Car & Truck Rental [13859]
"U-Swirl Added to SBA's Franchise Registry" in Ice Cream Reporter (Vol. 23, September 20, 2010, No. 10, pp. 1) [8595], [24424], [25086], [25164], [28220]
"U-Swirl To Open in Salt Lake City Metro Market" in Ice Cream Reporter (Vol. 23, November 20, 2010, No. 12, pp. 4) [8596], [18403], [24425], [31558]
U-Wash Doggie [12127]
"UA, BP Test Unmanned Aircraft" in Alaska Business Monthly (Vol. 27, October 2011, No. 10, pp. 8) [21647], [32052], [32839]
UAMR Confidential Bulletin [10582]
UAMS BioVentures [36512]
"UB Program Offers Free Tax Preparation" in Buffalo News (January 29, 2012) [15423], [21648], [24152], [34385]
UB STOR [42950]
UB Technology Incubator [42951]
Uber Eats [6942]
"Uber, Lyft and the Hard Economics of Taxi Cab Medallions" in The Washington Post (May 24, 2019) [15524]
"Uber Make JFK Airport Helocopter Taxis Available to All Users" in KFGO (October 3, 2019) [431]

UberEATS [6942]
UBuildIt [4355]
"Ubuntu!: An Aspiring Story About an African Tradition of Teamwork and Collaboration [22270], [22839], [28862]
UC Law Business Journal (HBLJ) [18782]
UC Merced Small Business Development Center Regional Network [36596]
"UEDs Would Light Up Street with News, Ads" in Philadelphia Business Journal (Vol. 33, April 11, 2014, No. 9, pp. 8) [363], [14705], [25567]
UF Innovate [38592]
"UFC: Money and the Mayhem" in Canadian Business (Vol. 83, September 14, 2010, No. 15, pp. 52) [15196], [18404]
UG Franchise Operations L.L.C. [12468]
"UIC Medical Ethicist Faces Life-and-Death Decisions Daily" in Crain's Chicago Business (Vol. 34, October 24, 2011, No. 42, pp. 31) [10856], [23545], [25957], [26448]
Ulster County Chamber of Commerce (UCCC) [42692]
Ulster County Regional Chamber of Commerce [42693]
"The Ultimate 5 Step Fitness Studio Branding Framework" in Glofox blog (February 6, 2019) [12436]
"The Ultimate Digital Marketing Guide for Small Business" in Just Creative Blog (March 3, 2020) [27813]
"The Ultimate Guide to Active Selling" in The Produce News (October 9, 2019) [6862]
"The Ultimate Guide to B2B Marketing in 2020" in HubSpot (December 16, 2019) [19244], [30090]
"Ultimate Guide to Business Franchising" in Business News Daily (Dec. 17, 2021) [24426]
"The Ultimate Guide to Business Travel" in Fora Financial (January 24, 2020) [19412]
"The Ultimate Guide to Employee Benefits for Small Businesses" in The Blueprint (July 30, 2020) [17366]
The Ultimate Guide to Franchise Consultants, Franchise Brokers, and Franchise Coaches [24427]
"Ultimate Guide to Google AdWords: How to Access 100 Million People in 10 Minutes" [364], [16475], [21999], [23013], [30091]
"The Ultimate Guide to Green Practices for Your Small Business" in Small Business Trends (April 27, 2017) [23378]
"The Ultimate Guide to Growing Your Plumbing Business" in Blue Corona Blog (October 17, 2018) [12667]
The Ultimate Guide to Growing Your Tattoo Business [15318]
Ultimate Guide: Plumbing [12668]
"The Ultimate Guide to Push Notifications for Fitness Businesses" in Glofox blog (July 29, 2019) [12437], [30092]
The Ultimate Guide for Seasonal Businesses [32963]
The Ultimate Guide to Small Business Customer Service [20526]
The Ultimate Guide to Starting a Credit Repair Business [4731], [20240]
"The Ultimate Guide to Starting a Web Design Business - From Finding Your First Clients to Making a Name for Yourself" in CodeiinWP (July 6, 2020) [16476]
Ultimate Payroll [11945]
"The Ultimate Sales Letter: Attract New Customers. Boost Your Sales" [17771], [17876], [32651]
The Ultimate Social Media Marketing Guide for Pro Organizers [12850]
The Ultimate Supervisor's Workshop (Onsite) [28429]
Ultimate Tattoo Supply [15336]
"The Ultimate Tutoring Marketing Plan: 7 Steps to Boost Your Student Roster" in PostcardMania blog (July 15, 2021) [16141]
"The Ultimate Vending Machine" in Benzinga.com (August 15, 2011) [1209], [1269], [16262]
The Ultimate Win-Win? Partnerships + Collaborations with Erika Rodriguez [30164]
"Ultra Low Sulfur Diesel: The Promise and the Reality" in Indoor Comfort Marketing (Vol. 70, July 2011, No. 7, pp. 22) [521], [5720], [5986], [23379], [30093], [34199]
Ulu Ventures [37514]
"UM-Dearborn to Launch Program for Entrepreneurs" in Crain's Detroit Business (Vol. 24, April 14, 2008, No. 15, pp. 7) [21302], [22444], [30818], [33437], [35256]
UMass Donahue Institute (UMDI) [47492]
Umatilla Chamber of Commerce [38511], [44028]
UMKC Innovation Center [41696]
Umpqua Business Center (UBC) [44070]
Umpqua Community College (UCC) [44074]
UMW EagleWorks Business Incubation Center [45967]
UNB [46736]
"The Unbanking of America" [2838], [16845], [24153]
"Unbound ID Raises $2 Million" in Austin Business JournalInc. (Vol. 28, December 12, 2008, No. 39, pp. 1) [14474], [14842], [33917], [35394]
"Unbreakable: Computer Software" in Canadian Business (Vol. 79, October 9, 2006, No. 20, pp. 111) [14843], [26449], [30819]

UNC BizHub Collaborative [37955]
Uncle Louie G Inc. [8079]
Unclog the Workflow: The Perks of Answering Services for Plumbing Businesses [12669]
"Uncontained Enthusiasm: Container Store Readies for post IPO Growth" in Dallas Business Journal (Vol. 37, January 10, 2014, No. 18, pp. 4) [8181], [12851]
"Unconventional Success: The Story of Naomi Ariel Catering and Event Planning" in The Southern (October 13, 2019) [2683]
Uncork Capital [37515]
Uncovered: The Business of True Crime [11848]
Uncovering Fraud in Core Business Functions (Onsite) [28430]
Uncoverings [746], [4683]
"Under Armour Hopes to Stomp on Nike with Basketball Shoe" in Baltimore Business Journal (Vol. 28, October 22, 2010, No. 24, pp. 1) [14686], [19608], [19952], [20060], [30820]
"Under Armour Wants to Equip Athletes, Too" in Boston Business Journal (Vol. 29, July 8, 2011, No. 9, pp. 1) [3148], [15104], [15197], [27956], [30094], [30821]
"Under Armour's Founder On Learning to Leverage Celebrity Endorsements" in Harvard Business Review (Vol. 90, May 2012, No. 5, pp. 45) [365], [3051], [3149], [15105], [15198], [18405], [20061], [30095]
"Under Fire, Sabia Triggers Battle for BCE" in Globe & Mail (April 14, 2007, pp. B1) [18718], [19609], [31559]
"Under Pressure" in Canadian Business (Vol. 81, July 21, 2008, No. 11, pp. 18) [24756], [26680], [28863]
Underhood Service [1136], [14569]
Understand Your Competitors [19953]
"Understanding Clients Her Key To Shaping Message" in Providence Business News (Vol. 29, July 7, 2014, No. 14, pp. 10) [6648], [30096]
"Understanding Food Truck Insurance Options, Costs" in FoodTruckOperator.com (November 23, 2020) [7016]
"Understanding Geeks: A Field Guide To Your Tech Staff" in Inc. (December 2007, pp. 62-63) [26450], [30986]
"Understanding Payroll Tax Payment and Filing Requirements" in Wolders Kluwer website [31645]
"Understanding Pet Sitting Certifications" in TimeToPet Blog (Feb. 25, 2022) [12262]
Understanding & Troubleshooting Hydraulics (Onsite) [19462], [21430]
Understanding and Troubleshooting Hydraulics (Onsite) [2060]
Understanding Workers Compensation: A Guide for Safety and Health Professionals [17367]
"Unemployment Rates" in The Economist (Vol. 390, January 3, 2009, No. 8612, pp. 75) [21197], [24757], [26681], [27749]
"Unemployment Tax Surge Could Hit Businesses Hard" in Orlando Business Journal (Vol. 26, January 1, 2010, No. 31, pp. 1) [24154], [34915]
"Uneven But Imaginative, Union Sushi & Barbecue Bar Works" in Crain's Chicago Business (Vol. 34, September 12, 2011, No. 37, pp. 30) [1355], [14033]
"Unexpected Guest: Caterpillar-Bucyrus Deal Came Out of Nowhere" in Business Journal-Milwaukee (Vol. 28, November 19, 2010, No. 7, pp. A1) [19697], [29422]
"Unfair Distraction of Employees" in Business Owner (Vol. 35, March-April 2011, No. 2, pp. 8) [4813], [18719], [20350], [27060]
"An Unfair Knock on Nokia" in Barron's (Vol. 88, March 10, 2008, No. 10, pp. 36) [6649], [9862], [18406], [24155], [28015], [28864], [29423]
"Unfilled Hotels Go All Out for Business Meetings" in Crain's Detroit Business (Vol. 25, June 8, 2009, No. 23, pp. 9) [8464], [19954], [20062], [30097]
Unicoi County Chamber of Commerce [44813]
The Unicorn's Shadow: Combating the Dangerous Myths that Hold Back Startups, Founders, and Investors [22840], [34567]
UNIFIED [20597]
Unified Symposium [17183]
Unified Wine & Grape Symposium [17183]
Unified Wine Symposium [17183]
Unifor [35159]
Uniglobe Travel International L.P. [16042]
UNIGLOBE Travel (USA) LLC [16043]
"Unilever Acquiring Danish Operations of Diplom-Is Ice Cream" in Ice Cream Reporter (Vol. 23, August 20, 2010, No. 9, pp. 1) [8597], [9863], [31560]
"Unilever Acquiring EVGA's Ice Cream Brands in Greece" in Ice Cream Reporter (Vol. 23, October 20, 2010, No. 11, pp. 1) [8598], [9864], [20658], [27750], [29424], [31561]
Unilever HPC NA Research Library [4549]
"Unilever to Sustainably Source All Paper and Board Packaging" in Ice Cream Reporter (Vol. 23, July 20, 2010, No. 8, pp. 1) [5721], [5987], [8599], [13730], [23380]

"Unilever's CMO Finally Gets Down To Business" in Advertising Age (Vol. 79, July 7, 2008, No. 26, pp. 11) **[19087]**, **[19610]**, **[28865]**, **[29425]**, **[30098]**
Uninterruptable Power Supply Systems for First Responders **[5361]**
Uninterruptable Power Supply (UPS) Maintenance and Readiness (Onsite) **[19463]**, **[21431]**
Union Area Chamber of Commerce [41644]
Union of Canadian Transportation Employees (UCTE) **[35160]**
Union Chamber of Commerce **[41644]**
Union City Chamber of Commerce **[37225]**
Union County Chamber of Commerce **[43198]**, **[44029]**
Union County Chamber of Commerce (UCCC) **[43591]**, **[44585]**
Union County Chamber of Commerce and Development Board [44585]
Union County Economic Development Corp. (UCEDC) **[42229]**
Union Grove Chamber of Commerce [46424]
"Union, Heal Thyself" in Canadian Business (Vol. 81, July 21, 2008, No. 11, pp. 9) **[18720]**, **[19088]**, **[25087]**, **[25568]**, **[29426]**, **[35209]**
Union Kitchen **[38182]**
"Union Pacific Railroad Receives Minority Business Exchange Award of Excellence" in News Bites US (July 7, 2012) **[7051]**, **[30399]**, **[35873]**
Union Parish Chamber of Commerce (UPCC) **[40196]**
Union des Producteurs Agricoles (UPA) **[35161]**
Union River Center for Innovation **[40326]**
Union Springs/Bullock County Chamber of Commerce **[36155]**
Union Township Chamber of Commerce **[42197]**
"Unions Pony Up $1 Million for McBride Stimulus" in Saint Louis Business Journal (Vol. 31, July 29, 2011, No. 49, pp. 1) **[11085]**, **[25088]**, **[35210]**
Unique Business Services Inc. (UBS) **[16887]**
Unique Employee Benefits: Perks Small Businesses Can Consider **[17368]**
"Unique Ways Small Businesses Can Increase Cash Flow" in business.com (Jan. 5, 2022) **[19723]**
Uniquely Longview **[45388]**
UNITE [1848]
Unite Here **[8353]**
United American Healthcare Corporation (UAHC) **[8278]**
United Bus Owners of America [15510]
United Business Education Association [21316]
United Cannabis Business Association (UCBA) **[4981]**
United Capital Mortgage Assistance, L.L.C. (UCMA) **[13344]**
United Chamber of Commerce [40637]
United Check Cashing **[2841]**
United Drive-in Theatre Owners Association, Inc. (UDITOA) **[11121]**
United Fresh Convention **[7820]**, **[14101]**
United Fresh Fruit and Vegetable Association [16976]
United Fresh Produce Association (UFPA) **[16976]**
United Insurance Consultants Inc. (UIC) **[27376]**
United Inventors Association of the United States of America (UIA) **[27831]**
United Kennel Club (UKC) **[644]**
United Methodist Association of Health and Welfare Ministries (UMA) **[25696]**
United Motorcoach Association (UMA) **[15510]**
United Nations Association of Southern Arizona (UNASA) **[5782]**
United Nations Association of Tucson [5782]
United Nations Commission on the Status of Women (CSW) **[35678]**
United Nations Security Council Reform **[25569]**
"United Natural Foods Establishes Charitable Foundation to Support Healthy, Sustainable and Organic Food Systems" in United Natural Foods, Inc. (May 14, 2012) **[7167]**, **[8054]**, **[15034]**, **[20659]**
United Professional Horsemen's Association (UPHA) **[8312]**
United Regional Chamber of Commerce **[40637]**
United Shipping Solutions **[7060]**
United Shoe Retailers Association (USRA) **[14670]**
United Ski Industries Association [14735]
"United State Organic Food Market Retains Robust Growth amid the Pandemic: Projected to Grow at a CAGR of 8.7% during 2021-2027" in GlobeNewswire (Jan. 25, 2022) **[8055]**
U.S. Agency for International Development - Freedom of Information Act Request - Bureau for Management/ Information and Records Div. (IRD) **[46921]**
U.S. Agency for International Development Library (USAID) **[46922]**
U.S. Agency for International Development - Office of Inspector General (OIG) **[46923]**
U.S. Agency for International Development (MRC) - Office of Small and Disadvantaged Business Utilization - Minority Resource Center **[46924]**
United States Air Force Judo Association [10716]
U.S. Army Corps of Engineers - Engineer Research and Development Center Research Library (ERDC) **[1562]**
U.S. Army Engineer Research and Development Center - Geotechnical and Structures Laboratory (GSL) - Airfields, Pavements, and Mobility Information Analysis Center **[1563]**
United States Association of Independent Gymnastic Clubs (USAIGC) **[12386]**
United States Association for Small Business and Entrepreneurship (USASBE) **[24593]**
U.S. Austrian Chamber of Commerce **[27432]**
U.S. Bancorp Piper Jaffray Private Capital **[41344]**
United States Banker [11101]
U.S. Banker: Charting the Future of Financial Services [11101]
U.S. Banker Online [11101]
U.S. Black Chambers, Inc. (USBC) **[30307]**
United States Bowling Congress (USBC) **[1875]**
U.S. Bureau of Alcohol, Tobacco, Firearms and Explosives Reference Library (ATF) **[15718]**
U.S. Bureau of Alcohol, Tobacco and Firearms - National Laboratory Center Library (NLC) **[7844]**, **[15719]**
"U.S. Buyer Rescues KCP From Trust Tax Burden" in Globe & Mail (April 3, 2007, pp. B1) **[31562]**, **[34916]**
U.S. Cannabis Conference and Expo **[5063]**
U.S. Census Bureau - Atlanta Regional Office **[46942]**
U.S. Census Bureau - Chicago Regional Office **[46943]**
U.S. Census Bureau - Denver Regional Office **[46944]**
U.S. Census Bureau - Florida Department of Economic Opportunity - Labor Market Statistics - State Census Data Center **[47754]**
U.S. Census Bureau - Los Angeles Regional Office **[46945]**
U.S. Census Bureau - New York City Regional Office **[46946]**
United States Census Bureau New York Regional Office **[46947]**
U.S. Census Bureau - Philadelphia Regional Office **[46948]**
United States Census Bureau - State Data Center of Mississippi **[47493]**
U.S. Chapter, International Real Estate Federation [13089]
U.S. Children's Clothing Market Report 2021 **[2856]**, **[32337]**
U.S.-China Business Council (USCBC) **[8681]**
United States Civil Service Commission [47344]
"U.S. Combined Life and Health Writers--Industry's Reported Admitted Assets of $5.7 Trillion" in Best's Review (Vol. 113, September 2012, No. 5, pp. 33) **[8975]**, **[25958]**, **[27351]**
United States Combined Training Association [8315]
United States Competitive Aerobics Federation (USCAF) **[12387]**
"U.S. Competitiveness and the Chinese Challenge" in Harvard Business Review (Vol. 90, March 2012, No. 3, pp. 40) **[19955]**, **[27751]**, **[28048]**, **[30822]**, **[32053]**
U.S. Composting Council (USCC) **[13697]**
United States Council for International Business (USCIB) **[8682]**, **[27433]**
United States Council of the International Chamber of Commerce - United States Associates of the International Chamber of Commerce - USA-BIAC [8682], [27433]
"U.S. Court Reopens Solar-Tariff Loophole That Trump Killed" in Bloomberg (November 16, 2021) **[14956]**
United States Cutting Tool Institute (USCTI) **[10424]**
U.S. Department of Agriculture (USDA) - Administrative Services Div. - Farmers Home Administration - Office of Small and Disadvantaged Business Utilization **[47374]**
U.S. Department of Agriculture - Administrative Services Division - Food and Nutrition Service - Office of Small and Disadvantaged Business Utilization Coordinator **[47375]**
U.S. Department of Agriculture (APD) - Agricultural Research Service - Administrative and Financial Management - Acquisition and Property Div. **[47376]**
U.S. Department of Agriculture (USDA) - Contracts and Procurement Branch - Office of the Inspector General - Office of Small and Disadvantaged Business Utilization Coordinator **[47377]**
U.S. Department of Agriculture - Cooperative State Research, Education, and Extension Service - Small Business Innovation Research Program [47385]
U.S. Department of Agriculture - Departmental Management - Office of Small and Disadvantaged Business Utilization (USDA) **[47378]**
U.S. Department of Agriculture (USDA) - Departmental Management - Office of Small and Disadvantaged Business Utilization Coordinator **[47379]**
U.S. Department of Agriculture - Food Safety and Inspection Service - Office of Administrative Services - Procurement Management Branch **[47380]**
U.S. Department of Agriculture - Management Services Branch - Extension Service - Office of Small and Disadvantaged Business Utilization Coordinator **[47381]**
U.S. Department of Agriculture (USDA) - Management Services Div. - Animal and Plant Health Inspection Service - Office of Small and Disadvantaged Business Utilization Coordinator **[47382]**
U.S. Department of Agriculture - Management Services Div. - Farm Service Agency - Office of Small and Disadvantaged Business Utilization Coordinator **[47383]**
U.S. Department of Agriculture (USDA) - Management Services Div. - Natural Resources Conservation Service - Office of Small and Disadvantaged Business Utilization **[47384]**
U.S. Department of Agriculture (SBIR) - National Institute of Food and Agriculture - Small Business Innovation Research Program (SBIR) **[47385]**
U.S. Department of Agriculture (USDA) - Office of Communications **[47386]**
U.S. Department of Agriculture (OPPM) - Office of Procurement and Property Management **[47387]**
U.S. Department of Agriculture - Rural Development Div. - Electric Program **[47388]**
U.S. Department of Commerce **[46949]**
U.S. Department of Commerce - Alaska Department of Commerce, Community and Economic Development - Alaska State Community Service Commission [47476]
U.S. Department of Commerce - Arizona Department of Economic Security **[47494]**
U.S. Department of Commerce - Bureau of the Census **[46950]**
U.S. Department of Commerce - Bureau of Economic Analysis (BEA) **[47495]**
U.S. Department of Commerce - Capital Region Council of Governments (CRCOG) **[47496]**
U.S. Department of Commerce - Center for Geographic Information and Analysis - Office of State Planning **[47497]**
U.S. Department of Commerce - Colorado State University Libraries - Morgan Library **[47498]**
U.S. Department of Commerce (EAD) - Department of Administration and Information - Economic Analysis Div. **[47499]**
U.S. Department of Commerce - Department of Employment Security - LMEA **[47500]**
U.S. Department of Commerce - Economic Development Administration (EDA) **[47501]**
U.S. Department of Commerce - Geographic Resources Center - University of Missouri-Columbia (GRC) **[47502]**
U.S. Department of Commerce - Georgia Department of Community Affairs - Office of Planning and Quality Growth **[47503]**
U.S. Department of Commerce - Guam Department of Commerce **[47504]**
U.S. Department of Commerce - Headwaters Regional Development Commission (HRDC) **[47505]**
U.S. Department of Commerce - Illinois Department of Commerce and Economic Opportunity - Springfield Office **[47506]**
U.S. Department of Commerce - Indiana Department of Workforce Development - Research and Analysis **[47507]**
U.S. Department of Commerce (IBRC) - Indiana University - Indiana Business Research Center **[47508]**
U.S. Department of Commerce - International Trade Administration - U.S. Commercial Service - Central-Southern New Jersey U.S. Export Assistance Center **[47132]**
U.S. Department of Commerce - International Trade Administration - U.S. Commercial Service - Export Assistance Center **[47133]**
U.S. Department of Commerce (USEAC) - International Trade Administration - U.S. Commercial Service - Export Assistance Center **[47134]**
U.S. Department of Commerce - International Trade Administration - U.S. Commercial Service - Export Assistance Center **[47135]**
U.S. Department of Commerce (EAC) - International Trade Administration - U.S. Commercial Service - Export Assistance Center **[47136]**
U.S. Department of Commerce - International Trade Administration - U.S. Commercial Service - Export Assistance Center **[47137]**
U.S. Department of Commerce (EAC) - International Trade Administration - U.S. Commercial Service - Export Assistance Center **[47138]**
U.S. Department of Commerce - International Trade Administration - U.S. Commercial Service - Export Assistance Center **[47139]**
U.S. Department of Commerce (EAC) - International Trade Administration - U.S. Commercial Service - Export Assistance Center **[47140]**

Small Business Sourcebook • 42nd Edition 3355

U.S. Department of Commerce - International Trade Administration - U.S. Commercial Service - Export Assistance Center [47141]
U.S. Department of Commerce - International Trade Administration - U.S. Commercial Service - Export Assistance Center [47142]
U.S. Department of Commerce - International Trade Administration - U.S. Commercial Service - Export Assistance Center [47143]
U.S. Department of Commerce - International Trade Administration - U.S. Commercial Service - Export Assistance Center [47144]
U.S. Department of Commerce (EAC) - International Trade Administration - U.S. Commercial Service - Export Assistance Center [47145]
U.S. Department of Commerce (USEAC) - International Trade Administration - U.S. Commercial Service - Export Assistance Center [47146]
U.S. Department of Commerce - International Trade Administration - U.S. Commercial Service - Export Assistance Center [47147]
U.S. Department of Commerce - International Trade Administration - U.S. Commercial Service - Export Assistance Center [47148]
U.S. Department of Commerce - International Trade Administration - U.S. Commercial Service - Export Assistance Center [47149]
U.S. Department of Commerce - International Trade Administration - U.S. Commercial Service - Export Assistance Center [47150]
U.S. Department of Commerce - International Trade Administration - U.S. Commercial Service - Export Assistance Center [47151]
U.S. Department of Commerce (EAC) - International Trade Administration - U.S. Commercial Service - Export Assistance Center [47152]
U.S. Department of Commerce - International Trade Administration - U.S. Commercial Service - Export Assistance Center [47153]
U.S. Department of Commerce - International Trade Administration - U.S. Commercial Service - Export Assistance Center [47154]
U.S. Department of Commerce - International Trade Administration - U.S. Commercial Service - Export Assistance Center [47155]
U.S. Department of Commerce (EAC) - International Trade Administration - U.S. Commercial Service - Export Assistance Center [47156]
U.S. Department of Commerce - International Trade Administration - U.S. Commercial Service - Export Assistance Center [47157]
U.S. Department of Commerce (EAC) - International Trade Administration - U.S. Commercial Service - Export Assistance Center [47158]
U.S. Department of Commerce - International Trade Administration - U.S. Commercial Service - Export Assistance Center [47159]
U.S. Department of Commerce - International Trade Administration - U.S. Commercial Service - Export Assistance Center [47160]
U.S. Department of Commerce - International Trade Administration - U.S. Commercial Service - Export Assistance Center [47161]
U.S. Department of Commerce (EAC) - International Trade Administration - U.S. Commercial Service - Export Assistance Center [47162]
U.S. Department of Commerce (EAC) - International Trade Administration - U.S. Commercial Service - Export Assistance Center [47163]
U.S. Department of Commerce - International Trade Administration - U.S. Commercial Service - Export Assistance Center [47164]
U.S. Department of Commerce (EAC) - International Trade Administration - U.S. Commercial Service - Export Assistance Center [47165]
U.S. Department of Commerce (EAC) - International Trade Administration - U.S. Commercial Service - Export Assistance Center [47166]
U.S. Department of Commerce - International Trade Administration - U.S. Commercial Service - Export Assistance Center [47167]
U.S. Department of Commerce (EAC) - International Trade Administration - U.S. Commercial Service - Export Assistance Center [47168]
U.S. Department of Commerce - International Trade Administration - U.S. Commercial Service - Export Assistance Center [47169]
U.S. Department of Commerce - International Trade Administration - U.S. Commercial Service - Export Assistance Center [47170]
U.S. Department of Commerce (EAC) - International Trade Administration - U.S. Commercial Service - Export Assistance Center [47171]
U.S. Department of Commerce (USEAC) - International Trade Administration - U.S. Commercial Service - Export Assistance Center [47172]
U.S. Department of Commerce - International Trade Administration - U.S. Commercial Service - Export Assistance Center [47173]
U.S. Department of Commerce - International Trade Administration - U.S. Commercial Service - Export Assistance Center [47174]
U.S. Department of Commerce - International Trade Administration - U.S. Commercial Service - Export Assistance Center [47175]
U.S. Department of Commerce - International Trade Administration - U.S. Commercial Service - Export Assistance Center [47176]
U.S. Department of Commerce - International Trade Administration - U.S. Commercial Service - Export Assistance Center [47177]
U.S. Department of Commerce (EAC) - International Trade Administration - U.S. Commercial Service - Export Assistance Center [47178]
U.S. Department of Commerce - International Trade Administration - U.S. Commercial Service - Export Assistance Center [47179]
U.S. Department of Commerce - International Trade Administration - U.S. Commercial Service - Export Assistance Center [47180]
U.S. Department of Commerce (USEAC) - International Trade Administration - U.S. Commercial Service - Export Assistance Center [47181]
U.S. Department of Commerce - International Trade Administration - U.S. Commercial Service - Export Assistance Center [47182]
U.S. Department of Commerce (EAC) - International Trade Administration - U.S. Commercial Service - Export Assistance Center [47183]
U.S. Department of Commerce (USEAC) - International Trade Administration - U.S. Commercial Service - Export Assistance Center [47184]
U.S. Department of Commerce (EAC) - International Trade Administration - U.S. Commercial Service - Export Assistance Center [47185]
U.S. Department of Commerce - International Trade Administration - U.S. Commercial Service - Export Assistance Center [47186]
U.S. Department of Commerce - International Trade Administration - U.S. Commercial Service - Export Assistance Center [47187]
U.S. Department of Commerce - International Trade Administration - U.S. Commercial Service - Export Assistance Center [47188]
U.S. Department of Commerce - International Trade Administration - U.S. Commercial Service - Export Assistance Center [47189]
U.S. Department of Commerce (EAC) - International Trade Administration - U.S. Commercial Service - Export Assistance Center [47190]
U.S. Department of Commerce (EAC) - International Trade Administration - U.S. Commercial Service - Export Assistance Center [47191]
U.S. Department of Commerce - International Trade Administration - U.S. Commercial Service - Export Assistance Center [47192]
U.S. Department of Commerce - International Trade Administration - U.S. Commercial Service - Export Assistance Center [47193]
U.S. Department of Commerce - International Trade Administration - U.S. Commercial Service - Export Assistance Center [47194]
U.S. Department of Commerce - International Trade Administration - U.S. Commercial Service - Export Assistance Center [47195]
U.S. Department of Commerce - International Trade Administration - U.S. Commercial Service - Export Assistance Center [47196]
U.S. Department of Commerce - International Trade Administration - U.S. Commercial Service - Export Assistance Center [47197]
U.S. Department of Commerce (EAC) - International Trade Administration - U.S. Commercial Service - Export Assistance Center [47198]
U.S. Department of Commerce - International Trade Administration - U.S. Commercial Service - Export Assistance Center [47199]
U.S. Department of Commerce - International Trade Administration - U.S. Commercial Service - Export Assistance Center [47200]
U.S. Department of Commerce - International Trade Administration - U.S. Commercial Service - Export Assistance Center [47201]
U.S. Department of Commerce - International Trade Administration - U.S. Commercial Service - Export Assistance Center [47202]
U.S. Department of Commerce - International Trade Administration - U.S. Commercial Service - Export Assistance Center [47203]
U.S. Department of Commerce - International Trade Administration - U.S. Commercial Service - Export Assistance Center [47204]
U.S. Department of Commerce - International Trade Administration - U.S. Commercial Service - Export Assistance Center (EAC) [47205]
U.S. Department of Commerce - International Trade Administration - U.S. Commercial Service - Export Assistance Center [47206]
U.S. Department of Commerce (EAC) - International Trade Administration - U.S. Commercial Service - Export Assistance Center [47207]
U.S. Department of Commerce - International Trade Administration - U.S. Commercial Service - Export Assistance Center [47208]
U.S. Department of Commerce - International Trade Administration - U.S. Commercial Service - Orlando U.S. Export Assistance Center [47209]
U.S. Department of Commerce - International Trade Administration - U.S. Commercial Service - U.S. Export Assistance Center [47210]
U.S. Department of Commerce - International Trade Administration - U.S. Commercial Service - U.S. Export Assistance Center [47211]
U.S. Department of Commerce - International Trade Administration - U.S. Commercial Service - U.S. Export Assistance Center [47212]
U.S. Department of Commerce - International Trade Administration - U.S. Commercial Service - U.S. Export Assistance Center [47213]
U.S. Department of Commerce - International Trade Administration - U.S. Commercial Service - U.S. Export Assistance Center [47214]
U.S. Department of Commerce - International Trade Administration - U.S. Commercial Service - U.S. Export Assistance Center [47215]
U.S. Department of Commerce - International Trade Administration - U.S. Commercial Service - U.S. Export Assistance Center [47216]
U.S. Department of Commerce - International Trade Administration - U.S. Commercial Service - U.S. Export Assistance Center (USEAC) [47217]
U.S. Department of Commerce - International Trade Administration - U.S. Commercial Service - U.S. Export Assistance Center [47218]
U.S. Department of Commerce - International Trade Administration - U.S. Commercial Service - U.S. Export Assistance Center [47219]
U.S. Department of Commerce - International Trade Administration - U.S. Commercial Service - U.S. Export Assistance Center (USEAC) [47220]
U.S. Department of Commerce - International Trade Administration - U.S. Commercial Service - U.S. Export Assistance Center [47221]
U.S. Department of Commerce - International Trade Administration - U.S. Commercial Service - U.S. Export Assistance Center [47222]
U.S. Department of Commerce - International Trade Administration - U.S. Commercial Service - U.S. Export Assistance Center [47223]
U.S. Department of Commerce - International Trade Administration - U.S. Commercial Service - U.S. Export Assistance Center [47224]
U.S. Department of Commerce - International Trade Administration - U.S. Commercial Service - U.S. Export Assistance Center [47225]
U.S. Department of Commerce - International Trade Administration - U.S. Commercial Service - U.S. Export Assistance Center [47226]
U.S. Department of Commerce - International Trade Administration - U.S. Commercial Service - U.S. Export Assistance Center [47227]
U.S. Department of Commerce - International Trade Administration - U.S. Commercial Service - U.S. Export Assistance Center [47228]
U.S. Department of Commerce - International Trade Administration - U.S. Commercial Service - U.S. Export Assistance Center [47229]
U.S. Department of Commerce - International Trade Administration - U.S. Commercial Service - U.S. Export Assistance Center [47230]
U.S. Department of Commerce - International Trade Administration - U.S. Commercial Service - U.S. Export Assistance Center [47231]
U.S. Department of Commerce - International Trade Administration - U.S. Commercial Service - U.S. Export Assistance Center [47232]
U.S. Department of Commerce - International Trade Administration - U.S. Commercial Service - U.S. Export Assistance Center [47233]

U.S. Department of Commerce - International Trade Administration - U.S. Commercial Service - U.S. Export Assistance Center [47234]
U.S. Department of Commerce - International Trade Administration - U.S. Commercial Service - U.S. Export Assistance Center [47235]
U.S. Department of Commerce - International Trade Administration - U.S. Commercial Service - U.S. Export Assistance Center [47236]
U.S. Department of Commerce - International Trade Administration - U.S. Commercial Service - U.S. Export Assistance Center [47237]
U.S. Department of Commerce - International Trade Administration - U.S. Commercial Service - U.S. Export Assistance Center [47238]
U.S. Department of Commerce - International Trade Administration - U.S. Commercial Service - U.S. Export Assistance Center [47239]
U.S. Department of Commerce - International Trade Administration - U.S. Commercial Service - U.S. Export Assistance Center (USEAC) [47240]
U.S. Department of Commerce - International Trade Administration - U.S. Commercial Service - U.S. Export Assistance Center [47241]
U.S. Department of Commerce - International Trade Administration - U.S. Commercial Service - U.S. Export Assistance Center [47242]
U.S. Department of Commerce - International Trade Administration - U.S. Commercial Service - U.S. Export Assistance Center [47243]
U.S. Department of Commerce - International Trade Administration - U.S. Commercial Service - U.S. Export Assistance Center (USEAC) [47244]
U.S. Department of Commerce - International Trade Administration - U.S. Commercial Service - U.S. Export Assistance Center [47245]
U.S. Department of Commerce - International Trade Administration - U.S. Commercial Service - U.S. Export Assistance Center [47246]
U.S. Department of Commerce - International Trade Administration - U.S. Commercial Service - U.S. Export Assistance Center [47247]
U.S. Department of Commerce - International Trade Administration - U.S. Commercial Service - U.S. Export Assistance Center [47248]
U.S. Department of Commerce - International Trade Administration - U.S. Commercial Service - U.S. Export Assistance Center [47249]
U.S. Department of Commerce - International Trade Administration - U.S. Commercial Service - U.S. Export Assistance Center [47250]
U.S. Department of Commerce - International Trade Administration - U.S. Commercial Service - U.S. Export Assistance Center [47251]
U.S. Department of Commerce - International Trade Administration - U.S. Commercial Service - U.S. Export Assistance Center [47252]
U.S. Department of Commerce - International Trade Administration - U.S. Commercial Service - U.S. Export Assistance Center [47253]
U.S. Department of Commerce - International Trade Administration - U.S. Commercial Service - U.S. Export Assistance Center [47254]
U.S. Department of Commerce - International Trade Administration - U.S. Commercial Service - U.S. Export Assistance Center [47255]
U.S. Department of Commerce - International Trade Administration - U.S. Commercial Service - U.S. Export Assistance Center [47256]
U.S. Department of Commerce - International Trade Administration - U.S. Commercial Service - U.S. Export Assistance Center [47257]
U.S. Department of Commerce - International Trade Administration - U.S. Commercial Service - U.S. Export Assistance Center [47258]
U.S. Department of Commerce - International Trade Administration - U.S. Commercial Service - U.S. Export Assistance Center [47259]
U.S. Department of Commerce - International Trade Administration - U.S. Commercial Service - U.S. Export Assistance Center [47260]
U.S. Department of Commerce - International Trade Administration - U.S. Commercial Service - U.S. Export Assistance Center [47261]
U.S. Department of Commerce - International Trade Administration - U.S. Commercial Service - U.S. Export Assistance Center [47262]
U.S. Department of Commerce - International Trade Administration - U.S. Commercial Service - U.S. Export Assistance Center [47263]
U.S. Department of Commerce - International Trade Administration - U.S. Commercial Service - U.S. Export Assistance Center [47264]
U.S. Department of Commerce - International Trade Administration - U.S. Commercial Service - U.S. Export Assistance Center [47265]
U.S. Department of Commerce - International Trade Administration - U.S. Commercial Service - U.S. Export Assistance Center [47266]
U.S. Department of Commerce - International Trade Administration - U.S. Commercial Service - U.S. Export Assistance Center [47267]
U.S. Department of Commerce - International Trade Administration - U.S. Commercial Service - U.S. Export Assistance Center [47268]
U.S. Department of Commerce - International Trade Administration - U.S. Commercial Service - U.S. Export Assistance Center [47269]
U.S. Department of Commerce (USEAC) - International Trade Administration - U.S. Commercial Service - U.S. Export Assistance Center [47270]
U.S. Department of Commerce - International Trade Administration - U.S. Commercial Service - U.S. Export Assistance Center [47271]
U.S. Department of Commerce - L. William Seidman Research Institute - W.P. Carey School of Business [47509]
U.S. Department of Commerce - Maine Department of Labor - Center for Workforce Research and Information [47425]
U.S. Department of Commerce - Maryland Department of Planning [47510]
U.S. Department of Commerce - Metropolitan Council Research - Metropolitan Council Data Center [47511]
U.S. Department of Commerce - Michigan Department of Technology, Management, & Budget - Center for Shared Solutions and Technology Partnerships - Michigan Information Center [47512]
U.S. Department of Commerce - Minority Business Development Agency (MBDA) [30308], [47278]
U.S. Department of Commerce - Minority Business Development Agency Business Center [38532]
U.S. Department of Commerce - Minority Business Development Agency District Office - Miami (Florida) Business Center [47279]
U.S. Department of Commerce - Minority Business Development Agency - Philadelphia Regional Enterprise Center [47280]
U.S. Department of Commerce - Minority Business Development Agency - San Francisco Regional Office [47281]
U.S. Department of Commerce - Mississippi Department of Economic and Community Development - Industry Resource Bureau - Mississippi Development Authority [41378], [47513]
U.S. Department of Commerce (MDA) - Mississippi Development Authority [41378], [47513]
U.S. Department of Commerce - National Oceanic and Atmospheric Administration - Library and Information Services Division Central Library [6799]
U.S. Department of Commerce - Nebraska Governor's Policy Research and Energy Office [47514]
U.S. Department of Commerce - Nebraska Policy Research Office [47515]
U.S. Department of Commerce - The Nelson A. Rockefeller Institute of Government [47516]
U.S. Department of Commerce - Office of Business Liaison [47517]
U.S. Department of Commerce - Office of Real Property Programs (ORPP) [47518]
U.S. Department of Commerce - Office of Real Property Tax Services - Department of Taxation and Finance [47519]
U.S. Department of Commerce - Office of Small and Disadvantaged Business Utilization (OSDBU) [47520]
U.S. Department of Commerce - Pennsylvania State Library [47521]
U.S. Department of Commerce - Puget Sound Regional Council [47522]
U.S. Department of Commerce - Research Library [18466]
U.S. Department of Commerce - Rhode Island Department of Elementary and Secondary Education (RIDE) [47523]
U.S. Department of Commerce - U.S. Census Bureau - State Data Center Program - Texas Demographic Center (TXSDC) [47524]
U.S. Department of Commerce - U.S. Patent and Trademark Office - Office of the Chief Communications Officer [47347]
U.S. Department of Commerce - U.S. Patent and Trademark Office - Office of the Commissioner for Patents [47348]
U.S. Department of Commerce - U.S. Patent and Trademark Office - Office of Enrollment and Discipline (OED) [47349]
U.S. Department of Commerce - United States Patent and Trademark Office - Office of Initial Patent Examination (OIPE) [47350]
U.S. Department of Commerce - United States Patent and Trademark Office - Office of Patent Cooperation Treaty (PCT) [47351]
U.S. Department of Commerce - United States Patent and Trademark Office - Office of Patent Publication [47352]
U.S. Department of Commerce - U.S. Patent and Trademark Office - Office of Petitions [47353]
U.S. Department of Commerce - U.S. Patent and Trademark Office - Office of Policy and International Affairs [47354]
U.S. Department of Commerce - United States Patent and Trademark Office - Office of Procurement [47355]
U.S. Department of Commerce - United States Patent and Trademark Office - Office of Public Affairs [47356]
U.S. Department of Commerce - U.S. Patent and Trademark Office - Patent Trial and Appeal Board (PTAB) [47357]
U.S. Department of Commerce - University of North Carolina - Howard W. Odum Institute for Research in Social Science [47525]
U.S. Department of Commerce - Urban Information Center - University of Missouri--St. Louis [47526]
U.S. Department of Commerce - Utah Governor's Office of Economic Development [47527]
U.S. Department of Commerce - Utah Governor's Office of Planning and Budget [47569]
U.S. Department of Commerce - Virgin Islands Department of Economic Development [47528]
U.S. Department of Commerce - Virgin Islands Economic Development Authority (VIEDA) [47529]
U.S. Department of Commerce (VEC) - Virginia Employment Commission [47530]
U.S. Department of Commerce - West Virginia Development Office - Research and Strategic Planning Group [47531]
U.S. Department of Commerce - West Virginia State Library Commission - Reference Library [47532]
U.S. Department of Commerce;Utah Governor's Office of Economic Development [47527]
U.S. Department of Defense (DOD) - Defense Contract Management Agency (DCMA) [47581]
U.S. Department of Defense - Defense Contract Management Agency (DCMA) [47582]
U.S. Department of Defense - Defense Contract Management Agency (DCMA) [47583]
U.S. Department of Defense - Defense Contract Management Agency (DCMA) [47584]
U.S. Department of Defense - Defense Contract Management Agency (DCMA) [47585]
U.S. Department of Defense - Defense Contract Management Agency APO East Hartford [47586]
U.S. Department of Defense - Defense Contract Management Agency Baltimore [47587]
U.S. Department of Defense - Defense Contract Management Agency Garden City [47588]
U.S. Department of Defense - Defense Contract Management Agency Orlando [47589]
U.S. Department of Defense - Defense Contract Management Agency St. Louis [47590]
U.S. Department of Defense - Defense Contract Management Agency San Diego [47591]
U.S. Department of Defense - Defense Contract Management Agency Syracuse (DCMA) [47592]
U.S. Department of Defense - Defense Contract Management Area Operations [47593]
U.S. Department of Defense - Defense Contract Management Area Operations [47594]
U.S. Department of Defense (DOD) - Defense Information Systems Agency (DISA) [47595]
U.S. Department of Defense - Defense Information Systems Agency - Office of Small Business Programs (OSBP) [47596]
U.S. Department of Defense - Defense Logistics Agency - Defense Supply Center (DSCC) [47597]
U.S. Department of Defense - Defense Logistics Agency - Defense Supply Center Philadelphia (DSCP) [44376], [47598]
U.S. Department of Defense - Defense Threat Reduction Agency - Office of Small and Disadvantaged Business Utilization [47599]
U.S. Department of Defense (DOD) - Office of Small Business Programs (OSBP) [47601]
U.S. Department of Defense - Office of Small Business Programs [47600]
U.S. Department of Defense;Defense Logistics Agency;Defense Supply Center Philadelphia [44376], [47598]
U.S. Department of Education - Office of the Deputy Secretary - Office of Small and Disadvantaged Business Utilization (OSDBU) [47602], [47605]

U.S. Department of Energy (USE) [14969]
U.S. Department of Energy (US DOE) - Albuquerque Operations Office (AOO) [47607]
U.S. Department of Energy - Amarillo Field Office [47608]
U.S. Department of Energy (BPA) - Bonneville Power Administration [47609]
U.S. Department of Energy - Chicago Operations Office [47610]
U.S. Department of Energy - Denver Regional Office [47611]
U.S. Department of Energy, Headquarters (DOE) - Office of Small and Disadvantaged Business Utilization [47612]
U.S. Department of Energy - Los Alamos National Laboratory - Computer, Computational, and Statistical Sciences Division (CCS) [3570]
U.S. Department of Energy - National Energy Technology Laboratory (NETL) [47613]
U.S. Department of Energy - National Nuclear Security Administration - Los Alamos Field Office [47614]
U.S. Department of Energy - National Renewable Energy Laboratory (NREL) [14972]
U.S. Department of Energy - Nevada Operations Office [47615]
U.S. Department of Energy (US DOE) - Oak Ridge Operations Office (ORO) [47616]
U.S. Department of Energy - Office of Energy Efficiency and Renewable Energy - Golden Field Office (GFO) [47617]
U.S. Department of Energy - Office of Energy Efficiency & Renewable Energy - Incubator Program [34481]
U.S. Department of Energy - Office of Kansas City Natural Security Campus (KCNSC) [47618]
U.S. Department of Energy - Office of Science - Argonne Site Office (ASO) [47619]
U.S. Department of Energy - Office of Science - Brookhaven Site Office (BHSO) [47620]
U.S. Department of Energy (DOE) - Office of Science - Fermi Site Office (FSO) [47621]
U.S. Department of Energy - Office of Science - Princeton Site Office (PSO) [47622]
U.S. Department of Energy - Pinellas Area Office [47623]
U.S. Department of Energy - Pittsburgh Energy Technology Center [47624]
U.S. Department of Energy - Pittsburgh Naval Reactors (PNR) [47625]
U.S. Department of Energy - Princeton Plasma Physics Laboratory (PPPL) [47626]
U.S. Department of Energy - Richland Operations Office - Office of Organizational Effectiveness and Communications [47627]
U.S. Department of Energy (SNL) - Sandia National Laboratories [47628]
U.S. Department of Energy - Schenectady Naval Reactors Office [47629]
U.S. Department of Energy - Southeastern Power Administration (SEPA) [47630]
U.S. Department of Energy - Waste Isolation Pilot Plant - Carlsbad Field Office (CBFO) [47631]
U.S. Department of Energy - Western Area Power Administration (WAPA) [47632]
U.S. Department of Energy;Pittsburgh Naval Reactors [47625]
U.S. Department of Health and Human Services (HHS) - Division of Grants and Contracts - Small Business Specialist [47636]
U.S. Department of Health and Human Services (HHS) - Health Resources and Services Administration - Office of Equal Opportunity, Civil Rights and Diversity Management [47637]
U.S. Department of Health and Human Services - National Institutes of Health - National Institute of Mental Health - Division of AIDS Research - Small Business Innovation Research Program (NIH) [40349]
U.S. Department of Health and Human Services - National Institutes of Health - National Institute of Mental Health - Division of AIDS Research - Small Business Technology Transfer Program [40350]
U.S. Department of Health and Human Services - Office of Equal Employment Opportunity (HHS) [47638]
U.S. Department of Health & Human Services - Office of Grants and Acquisition Policy and Accountability - Division of Acquisitions Management [47639]
U.S. Department of Health and Human Services (OSDBU) - Office of Small and Disadvantaged Business Utilization (OSDBU) [47640]
U.S. Department of Health and Human Services - Program Support Center - Small and Disadvantaged Business Utilization Specialist - Division of Acquisition (DA) [47641]
U.S. Department of Health and Human Services - Region 1 [47642]

U.S. Department of Health and Human Services - Region 2 [47643]
U.S. Department of Health and Human Services - Region 3 [47644]
U.S. Department of Health and Human Services - Region 4 [47645]
U.S. Department of Health and Human Services - Region 5 [47646]
U.S. Department of Health and Human Services - Region 6 [47647]
U.S. Department of Health and Human Services - Region 7 [47648]
U.S. Department of Health and Human Services - Region 8 [47649]
U.S. Department of Health and Human Services - Region 9 [47650]
U.S. Department of Health and Human Services - Region 10 [47651]
U.S. Department of Homeland Security Customs and Border Protection [47044], [47779]
U.S. Department of Homeland Security (FEMA) - Federal Emergency Management Agency [47045]
U.S. Department of Homeland Security - Federal Emergency Management Agency - Office of Procurement [47046]
U.S. Department of Homeland Security - Federal Emergency Management Agency Office of Procurement Operations [47046]
U.S. Department of Homeland Security - Federal Emergency Management Agency, Region 1 - Boston Regional Office [47047]
U.S. Department of Homeland Security - Federal Emergency Management Agency Region 2 - New York Regional Office [47048]
U.S. Department of Homeland Security - Federal Emergency Management Agency, Region 3 (FEMA) - Philadelphia Regional Office (R3) [47049]
U.S. Department of Homeland Security - Federal Emergency Management Agency, Region 4 - Atlanta Regional Office [47050]
U.S. Department of Homeland Security - Federal Emergency Management Agency, Region 5 - Chicago Regional Office [47051]
U.S. Department of Homeland Security - Federal Emergency Management Agency, Region 6 - Denton Regional Office [47052]
U.S. Department of Homeland Security - Federal Emergency Management Agency, Region 7 - Kansas City Regional Office [47053]
U.S. Department of Homeland Security - Federal Emergency Management Agency, Region 8 - Denver Regional Office [47054]
U.S. Department of Homeland Security - Federal Emergency Management Agency, Region 9 - Oakland Regional Office [47055]
U.S. Department of Homeland Security - Federal Emergency Management Agency, Region 10 - Bothell Regional Office [47056]
U.S. Department of Homeland Security - Federal Law Enforcement Training Center (FLETC) [47780]
U.S. Department of Homeland Security - Federal Law Enforcement Training Center Artesia [47057]
U.S. Department of Homeland Security - Federal Law Enforcement Training Center Charleston [47058]
U.S. Department of Homeland Security - Federal Law Enforcement Training Center Cheltenham [47059]
U.S. Department of Homeland Security - Federal Law Enforcement Training Center Glynco (FLETC) [47060], [47781]
U.S. Department of Homeland Security - Federal Law Enforcement Training Center - Washington Operations [47061]
U.S. Department of Homeland Security Office of Procurement Operations [47062]
U.S. Department of Homeland Security - Office of Small and Disadvantaged Business Utilization (OSDBU) [47063]
U.S. Department of Homeland Security - Transportation Security Administration - Small and Disadvantaged Business Office [47064]
U.S. Department of Homeland Security (DHS) - U.S. Coast Guard - Aviation Logistics Center [47065]
U.S. Department of Homeland Security - U.S. Coast Guard Office of Contract Operations [47066]
U.S. Department of Homeland Security - U.S. Coast Guard Office of Procurement Management [47067]
U.S. Department of Homeland Security - U.S. Coast Guard - Surface Forces Logistics Command - Atlantic (SFLC) [47068]
U.S. Department of Homeland Security - U.S. Coast Guard - Surface Forces Logistics Command - Pacific (SFLC) [47069]
U.S. Department of Homeland Security - U.S. Secret Service - Procurement Div. [47070], [47782]

U.S. Department of Housing and Urban Development - Deputy Assistant Secretary for Economic Development - Grants Management Div. [47655]
U.S. Department of Housing and Urban Development Library (HUD) [4370]
U.S. Department of Housing and Urban Development - Office of the Chief Procurement Officer (OCPO) [47656]
U.S. Department of Housing and Urban Development - Office of Departmental Operations and Coordination (ODOC) [47657]
U.S. Department of Housing and Urban Development - Office of Security and Emergency Planning [47658]
U.S. Department of Housing and Urban Development (HUD) - Office of Small and Disadvantaged Business Utilization (OSDBU) [47659]
U.S. Department of Housing and Urban Development - Region 1 [47660]
U.S. Department of Housing and Urban Development - Region 2 [47661]
U.S. Department of Housing and Urban Development - Region 3 [47662]
U.S. Department of Housing and Urban Development - Region 4 [47663]
U.S. Department of Housing and Urban Development - Region 5 [47664]
U.S. Department of Housing and Urban Development - Region 6 [47665]
U.S. Department of Housing and Urban Development - Region 7 [47666]
U.S. Department of Housing and Urban Development - Region 8 (HUD) [47667]
U.S. Department of Housing and Urban Development - Region 9 (HUD) [47668]
U.S. Department of Housing and Urban Development - Region 10 [47669]
U.S. Department of the Interior - Bureau of Indian Affairs - Eastern Regional Office [47685]
U.S. Department of the Interior - Bureau of Indian Affairs - Juneau Office [47686]
U.S. Department of the Interior - Bureau of Indian Affairs - Navajo Regional Office [47687]
U.S. Department of the Interior - Bureau of Land Management - Alaska State Office [47688]
U.S. Department of the Interior - Bureau of Land Management - Amarillo Field Office [47633]
U.S. Department of the Interior - Bureau of Land Management - Arizona State Office [47689]
U.S. Department of the Interior - Bureau of Land Management - Business Utilization and Development Specialist - Branch of Procurement Management [47690]
U.S. Department of the Interior - Bureau of Land Management - California State Office [47691]
U.S. Department of the Interior - Bureau of Land Management - Colorado State Office [47692]
U.S. Department of the Interior (BLM) - Bureau of Land Management - Eastern States Office [47693]
U.S. Department of the Interior - Bureau of Land Management - Idaho State Office [47694]
U.S. Department of the Interior - Bureau of Land Management - Montana State Office [47695]
U.S. Department of the Interior - Bureau of Land Management - Nevada State Office [47696]
U.S. Department of the Interior (NMSO) - Bureau of Land Management - New Mexico State Office [47697]
U.S. Department of the Interior (BLM) - Bureau of Land Management - Oregon State Office [47698]
U.S. Department of the Interior - Bureau of Land Management - Utah State Office [47699]
U.S. Department of the Interior - Bureau of Land Management - Wyoming State Office [47700]
U.S. Department of the Interior - Bureau of Reclamation - Business Utilization and Development Specialist - Acquisition and Assistance Management Services [47707]
U.S. Department of the Interior (GPR) - Bureau of Reclamation - Business Utilization and Development Specialist - Great Plains Region [47701]
U.S. Department of the Interior - Bureau of Reclamation - Business Utilization and Development Specialist - Lower Colorado Region [47702]
U.S. Department of the Interior - Bureau of Reclamation - Business Utilization and Development Specialist - Mid-Pacific Region [47703]
U.S. Department of the Interior (PNR) - Bureau of Reclamation - Business Utilization and Development Specialist - Pacific Northwest Region [47704]
U.S. Department of the Interior - Bureau of Reclamation - Business Utilization and Development Specialist - Phoenix Area Office [47705]
U.S. Department of the Interior - Bureau of Reclamation - Business Utilization and Development Specialist - Upper Colorado Region [47706]

U.S. Department of the Interior - Bureau of Reclamation - Management Services Office - Acquisition and Assistance Management Div. (AAMD) **[47707]**
U.S. Department of the Interior - National Park Service - Alaska Region **[47708]**
U.S. Department of the Interior - National Park Service - Intermountain Region **[47709]**
U.S. Department of the Interior - National Park Service - Midwest Region **[47710]**
U.S. Department of the Interior - National Park Service - National Capitol Regional Office **[47711]**
U.S. Department of the Interior (US DIO-NPS) - National Park Service - Northeast Region **[47712]**
U.S. Department of the Interior - National Park Service - Pacific West Region **[47713]**
U.S. Department of the Interior - National Park Service - Southeast Region **[47714]**
U.S. Department of the Interior - Office of Small and Disadvantaged Business Utilization **[47715]**
U.S. Department of the Interior - Office of the Solicitor **[47716]**
U.S. Department of the Interior - Office of Surface Mining Reclamation and Enforcement (OSMRE) - Mid-Continent Regional Office (MCR) **[47717]**
U.S. Department of the Interior - Office of Surface Mining Reclamation and Enforcement - Western Regional Office **[47718]**
U.S. Department of Justice - Federal Bureau of Investigation - Seattle Div. **[47739]**
The United States Department of Justice - Federal Bureau of Prisons - National Contracts and Policy Section **[47740]**
U.S. Department of Justice - Justice Management Div. - Procurement Services Staff (PSS) **[47741]**
U.S. Department of Justice - Office of Small and Disadvantaged Business Utilization **[47742]**
U.S. Department of Labor - Bureau of Labor Statistics (BLS) **[47755]**
United States Department of Labor - Occupational Safety and Health Administration (OSHA) **[47339]**
U.S. Department of Labor Occupational Safety and Health Administration Office of Communications (OOC) **[47340]**
U.S. Department of Labor - Occupational Safety and Health Administration - Office of Small Business Assistance - Directorate of Cooperative and State Programs (DCSP) **[47341]**
U.S. Department of Labor-Occupational Safety & Health Administration-Region III Library **[35988]**
U.S. Department of Labor - Occupational Safety and Health Administration - Region VIII Library **[35989]**
U.S. Department of Labor - Occupational Safety & Health Administration - Region X Library **[35990]**
U.S. Department of Labor - Office of Small and Disadvantaged Business Utilization (OSDBU) **[47756]**
U.S. Dept. of Labor - OSHA Billings Area Office Library **[35991]**
U.S. Department of Labor - OSHA Technical Data Center (TDC) **[35992]**
U.S. Department of Labor - United States Patent and Trademark Office - Office of Enrollment and Discipline (OED) **[47358]**
U.S. Department of the Navy - Office of the Secretary of the Navy - Office of Small Business Programs (OSBP) **[47603]**
U.S. Department of the Navy - Space and Naval Warfare Systems **[47822]**
U.S.D.A. Agricultural Research Service (USDA ARS) - Western Regional Research Center (WRRC) **[11619]**
U.S.D.A. Economic Research Service Reference Center (USDA ERS) **[17218]**
U.S.D.A. Forest Service (FPL Library) - Forest Products Laboratory Library **[10414]**
U.S.D.A. National Agricultural Library (NAL) - Food and Nutrition Information Center (FNIC) **[8084], [11620]**
U.S.D.A. National Agricultural Library - Rural Information Center (RIC) **[21260], [33722]**
U.S. Department of State - Bureau of Diplomatic Security (DSS) - Office of Foreign Missions (OFM) **[47757]**
U.S. Department of State Office of Civil Rights (S/OCR) **[47758]**
U.S. Department of State Office of the Inspector General (OIG) **[47759]**
U.S. Department of State - Office of Small and Disadvantaged Business Utilization (OSDBU) **[47760]**
U.S. Department of Transportation - Federal Aviation Administration - Small Business Innovative Research (SBIR) **[47761]**
U.S. Department of Transportation (USDOT) - Federal Aviation Administration - Small Business Utilization Office **[47762]**
U.S. Department of Transportation - Federal Highway Administration - Central Federal Lands Highway Div. **[47763]**

U.S. Department of Transportation - Federal Highway Administration - Eastern Federal Lands Highway Div. - Small and Disadvantaged Business Utilization Liaison **[47764]**
U.S. Department of Transportation - Federal Highway Administration - Office Federal Lands Highway (FLH) **[47765]**
U.S. Department of Transportation (WFLHD) - Federal Highway Administration - Office of Federal Lands Highway - Western Federal Lands Highway Div. **[47766]**
U.S. Department of Transportation - Federal Highway Administration - Office of Small Disadvantaged Business Utilization - Procurement Assistance Division - Small Business Specialist **[47767]**
U.S. Department of Transportation - John A. Volpe National Transportation Center - Office of Management Services - Contracts and Small Business Programs Branch **[47768]**
U.S. Department of Transportation - John A. Volpe National Transportation Systems Center - Research and Innovative Technology Administration - Contracts and Small Business Branch **[47769]**
U.S. Department of Transportation - Maritime Administration - Virtual Office of Acquisition **[47770]**
U.S. Department of Transportation - Office of Research and Technology **[47771]**
U.S. Department of Transportation - Office of Small and Disadvantaged Business Utilization (OSDBU) **[47772]**
U.S. Department of Transportation - Office of Small and Disadvantaged Business Utilization - Procurement Assistance Div. **[47773]**
U.S. Department of Transportation - Pipeline and Hazardous Materials Safety Administration **[47774]**
U.S. Department of Transportation - St. Lawrence Seaway Development Corporation - Office of the Associate Administrator **[47775]**
U.S. Department of Transportation - Small Business Specialist - Federal Transit Administration **[47776]**
U.S. Department of Transportation - Small Business Specialist - Office of Acquisition **[47777]**
U.S. Department of Transportation (FRA) - Small Business Specialist - Office of Small Disadvantaged Business Utilization - Procurement Assistance Division - Federal Railroad Administration **[47778]**
U.S. Department of the Treasury - Acquisition Management **[47783]**
U.S. Department of the Treasury - Acquisition and Procurement Office [47806]
U.S. Department of the Treasury - Alcohol and Tobacco Tax and Trade Bureau **[47784]**
U.S. Department of the Treasury - Bureau of Engraving & Printing - Office of Acquisitions **[47785]**
U.S. Department of the Treasury - Bureau of Engraving and Printing Washington **[47786]**
U.S. Department of the Treasury - Bureau of the Public Debt **[47787]**
U.S. Department of the Treasury - Chicago Financial Center **[47788]**
U.S. Department of the Treasury - Federal Law Enforcement Training Center (FLETC) **[47789]**
U.S. Department of the Treasury - Federal Law Enforcement Training Center (FLETC) **[47790]**
U.S. Department of the Treasury (FLETC) - Federal Law Enforcement Training Center **[47791]**
U.S. Department of the Treasury - Financial Management Service **[47792]**
U.S. Department of the Treasury Internal Revenue Service - Detroit Computing Center **[47793]**
U.S. Department of the Treasury Internal Revenue Service (ECCMTB) - Enterprise Computing Center - Martinsburg **[47794]**
U.S. Department of the Treasury - Internal Revenue Service - Mid-States Area **[47795]**
U.S. Department of the Treasury (MSR) - Internal Revenue Service - Mid-States Region **[47796]**
U.S. Department of the Treasury - Internal Revenue Service Northeast Area **[47797]**
U.S. Department of the Treasury - Internal Revenue Service Salisbury **[47798]**
U.S. Department of the Treasury - Kansas City Financial Center (NPCE) **[47799]**
U.S. Department of the Treasury - Library **[170], [15478]**
U.S. Department of the Treasury - Office of the Comptroller of the Currency - Central District - Chicago Field Office **[47800]**
U.S. Department of the Treasury - Office of the Comptroller of the Currency - Northeastern District - Washington D.C. Field Office **[47801]**
U.S. Department of the Treasury - Office of the Comptroller of the Currency - Southern District - Atlanta Field Office **[47802]**
U.S. Department of the Treasury - Office of the Comptroller of the Currency - Southern District - Dallas Field Office **[47803]**

U.S. Department of the Treasury - Office of the Comptroller of the Currency - Western District **[47804]**
U.S. Department of the Treasury - Office of the Comptroller of the Currency - Western District - Santa Ana Field Office **[47805]**
U.S. Department of the Treasury - Office of the Procurement Executive (OPE) **[47806]**
U.S. Department of the Treasury - Office of Thrift Supervision **[47807]**
U.S. Department of the Treasury - Philadelphia Financial Center **[47808]**
U.S. Department of the Treasury - Small Business and Community Development Programs - Office of Small and Disadvantaged Business Utilization **[47809]**
U.S. Department of the Treasury - U.S. Mint **[47810]**
U.S. Department of the Treasury;Kansas City Financial Center [47799]
U.S. Department of Veterans Affairs (VA) - Office of Small and Disadvantaged Business Utilization - Minorities in Franchising **[46925]**
United States Disc Jockey Association (USDJA) **[4961]**
United States Dressage Federation (USDF) **[8313]**
U.S. Drug Enforcement Administration Library **[34697]**
U.S. Drug Enforcement Administration - Office of Acquisition and Relocation Management **[47743]**
U.S. Drug Stores Market Report 2021 **[5196]**
U.S. Environmental Protection Agency (AWBERC Library) - Andrew W. Breidenbach Environmental Research Center Library **[12067]**
U.S. Environmental Protection Agency Headquarters and Chemical Libraries **[5783], [6012]**
U.S. Environmental Protection Agency Headquarters Library **[5784], [6013], [7985]**
U.S. Environmental Protection Agency (EPA) - National Enforcement Investigations Center Environmental Forensics Library **[12068]**
U.S. Environmental Protection Agency - Region 10 (EPA) [47007]
U.S. Environmental Protection Agency State Superfund Office [47014]
U.S. Environmental Protection Agency State Superfund Office - Department of Environmental Management - Land Div. [47008]
U.S. Environmental Protection Agency State Superfund Office - Department for Environmental Protection - Division of Waste Management (DWM) [47009]
U.S. Environmental Protection Agency State Superfund Office - Department of Toxic Substances Control (DTSC) [47010]
U.S. Environmental Protection Agency State Superfund Office - Division of Environmental Protection - Department of Conservation and Natural Resources (DCNR) [47011]
U.S. Environmental Protection Agency State Superfund Office - Environmental Improvement Division - Hazardous Waste Bureau (HWB) [47012]
U.S. Environmental Protection Agency State Superfund Office (OLQ) - Indiana Department of Environmental Management - Office of Environmental Response - Office of Land Quality [47013]
U.S. Equal Employment Opportunity Commission (EEOC) **[20598]**
United States Equestrian Federation (USEF) **[8314]**
United States Equestrian Team [8314]
United States Eventing Association (USEA) **[8315]**
U.S. Executive Office of the President - Office of Management and Budget - Office of E-Government and Information Technology **[47104]**
U.S. Federal Aviation Administration - Mike Monroney Aeronautical Center Library (MMAC) **[448]**
U.S. Federal Communications Commission (FCC) **[2825], [4958]**
U.S. Federal Prisons Industries/UNICOR - Procurement Branch **[47744]**
U.S. Fish and Wildlife Service - Alaska Region **[47719]**
U.S. Fish and Wildlife Service - Budget and Administration Div. - Region 5 - Northeast Regional Office **[47720]**
U.S. Fish and Wildlife Service (CGS) - Business Utilization and Development Specialist - Division of Contracting and General Services **[47721]**
U.S. Fish and Wildlife Service - Contracting & General Services Chief - Alaska Region **[47722]**
U.S. Fish and Wildlife Service - Contracting & General Services Chief - Region 4 **[47723]**
U.S. Fish and Wildlife Service - Contracting & General Services Officer - Region 2 **[47724]**
U.S. Fish and Wildlife Service - Contracting Officer - Region 6 [47725]
U.S. Fish and Wildlife Service - Contracting & Procurement Officer - Region 3 **[47726]**
U.S. Fish and Wildlife Service - Division of Contracting and General Services **[47727]**

Small Business Sourcebook • 42nd Edition   **3359**

U.S. Fish and Wildlife Service - Midwest Region (https://www.fws.gov/midwest/) **[47728]**
U.S. Fish and Wildlife Service - Mountain Prairie Region **[47729]**
U.S. Fish and Wildlife Service - Northeast Region **[47730]**
U.S. Fish and Wildlife Service - Pacific Region **[47731]**
U.S. Fish and Wildlife Service - Policy, Management and Budget - Great Lakes, Big Rivers Region **[47732]**
U.S. Fish and Wildlife Service - Procurement Assistant - Region 1 **[47733]**
U.S. Fish and Wildlife Service - Southeast Region **[47734]**
U.S. Fish and Wildlife Service - Southwest Region **[47735]**
U.S. Food & Drug Administration Biosciences Library (FDA) - Center for Food Safety and Applied Nutrition Branch Library (CFSAN) **[4550]**, **[11621]**
U.S. Food & Drug Administration - Center for Devices & Radiological Health Library HFZ-46 **[10966]**
U.S. Food and Drug Administration - Division of Contracts and Grants Management - Office of Management (OM) **[47652]**
U.S. Food and Drug Administration - Office of Acquisitions and Grants Services - Office of Regional Operations **[47653]**
U.S. General Services Administration - Great Lakes Region - Business Service Center **[47105]**
U.S. General Services Administration - Greater Southwest Region - Business Service Center **[47106]**
U.S. General Services Administration (GSA) - The Heartland Region - Business Service Center **[47107]**
U.S. General Services Administration - Mid-Atlantic Region - Office of Business and Public Affairs **[47108]**
U.S. General Services Administration - National Capital Region - Business Services Center **[47109]**
U.S. General Services Administration - New England Region - Business Service Center **[47110]**
U.S. General Services Administration (GSA) - Northwest/Arctic Region - Business Service Center **[47111]**
U.S. General Services Administration-Office of Global Supply-Logistics Operations Center **[47112]**
U.S. General Services Administration - Office of Management and Budget - Office of E-Government and Information Technology [47104]
U.S. General Services Administration - Office of Small Business Utilization (OSBU) **[47113]**
U.S. General Services Administration - Rocky Mountain Region - Business Service Center **[47114]**
U.S. General Services Administration - Southeast Sunbelt Region - Business Service Center **[47115]**
U.S. Geological Survey - Business Utilization and Development Specialist **[47736]**
U.S. Geological Survey - Central Region **[47737]**
United States Golf Association (USGA) **[7514]**, **[7539]**, **[10985]**
United States Harness Writers' Association (USHWA) **[5300]**
United States Hispanic Chamber of Commerce (USHCC) **[30309]**
"U.S. House Approves Concrete Masonry Products Promotion Act" in Masonry Magazine (November 15, 2016) **[10738]**
"U.S. Import Prices Fall 0.5% in October Amid Steep Drop in Fuel Prices" in Nasdaq (November 15, 2019) **[8772]**
U.S. International Development Finance Corporation (DFC) **[38147]**
U.S. and International Directory of Hotel, Restaurant, and Tourism Management Schools [15743]
U.S. International Trade Commission (USITC) - Office of Economics **[47274]**
U.S. International Trade Commission - Office of Industries **[47275]**
U.S. International Trade Commission - Office of Unfair Import Investigations **[47276]**
United States Judo Association (USJA) **[10716]**
United States K-12 Tutoring Market Research Report 2022 **[16144]**
U.S. Key Elements of Ecommerce Market Report 2021 **[11837]**, **[29503]**, **[32338]**
United States Lawn Tennis Association [15673]
U.S. Machine Tool Directory [10425]
U.S. Marshals Service - Procurement Policy and Oversight Team **[47745]**
United States-Mexico Chamber of Commerce (USMCOC) **[27434]**
U.S. Missile Defense Agency (MDA) **[47604]**
United States National Amateur Athletic Union Taekwondo Committee [10717]
U.S. National Highway Traffic Safety Administration - Technical Information Services (TIS) **[407]**, **[5120]**
U.S. National Park Service - Blue Ridge Parkway Archives **[4371]**, **[10149]**

U.S. Nuclear Regulatory Commission (USNRC) - Office of Small and Disadvantaged Business Utilization/Civil Rights **[47811]**
U.S. Nuclear Regulatory Commission Region 1 (U.S. NRC Region I) **[47812]**
U.S. Nuclear Regulatory Commission Region 2 (U.S. NRC Region II) **[47813]**
U.S. Nuclear Regulatory Commission Region 3 (U.S. NRC Region III) **[47814]**
U.S. Nuclear Regulatory Commission Region 4 (U.S. NRC Region IV) **[47815]**
U.S. Office of Personnel Management (USOPM) **[47344]**
United States Office of Personnel Management [47344]
U.S. Office of Personnel Management (OSDBU) - Office of Small and Disadvantaged Business Utilization - Contracting Group **[47345]**
"U.S. Office Supply Revenue to Rise 8% in 2021" in Progressive Grocer (August 30, 2021) **[11671]**
United States Online Gambling Market to Reach US 7.61 Billion by 2028 **[7313]**
U.S. Pan Asian American Chamber of Commerce (USPAACC) **[27435]**
United States Pan Asian Chamber of Commerce [27435]
U.S. Patio and Backyard Living Market Report 2021 **[8218]**
United States Pony Clubs, Inc. (USPC) **[8316]**
U.S. Postal Inspection Postal Service (USPIS) - Dangerous Mail Investigations Program **[47816]**
U.S. Postal Service (ITD) - Administrative Operations - Information Technology Div. **[47817]**
U.S. Postal Service - Environmental and MRO Category Management Center **[47818]**
U.S. Postal Service - Intelligent Mail and Address Quality **[47819]**
U.S. Postal Service - Investigations and Security - Dangerous Mail Investigations and Homeland Security [47816]
U.S. Postal Service-Memphis Purchasing Service Center (USPS) **[47820]**
U.S. Postal Service (USPIS) - United States Postal Inspection Service **[47821]**
U.S. Poultry & Egg Association **[16977]**
"U.S. Primaries: An Amazing Race" in Canadian Business (Vol. 81, February 12, 2008, No. 3, pp. 25) **[8773]**, **[19089]**, **[21198]**, **[25570]**, **[27752]**
United States Professional Lawn Tennis Association [15671]
United States Professional Tennis Association (USPTA) **[15671]**
United States Professional Tennis Association Convention **[15124]**, **[15678]**
United States Professional Tennis Registry [15668]
U.S. Public Health Service - Administrative Services Center - Small and Disadvantaged Business Utilization Specialist - Division of Acquisitions Management [47639]
United States Racquet Stringers Association (USRSA) [15672]
United States Racquetball Association **[12389]**, [15675]
"U.S. Recession Officially Over: Is Recovery Ever Going to Arrive?" in Montana Business Quarterly (Vol. 49, Spring 2011, No. 1, pp. 6) **[21199]**, **[34200]**
"U.S. Retailer Eyes 'Tween' Market" in Globe & Mail (January 30, 2007, pp. B1) **[18407]**, **[19611]**, **[30099]**, **[32303]**
U.S.-Russia Business Council (USRBC) **[27436]**
United States Seamless **[2658]**
U.S. Securities and Exchange Commission-Atlanta Regional Office **[47360]**
U.S. Securities and Exchange Commission-Boston Regional Office **[47361]**
U.S. Securities and Exchange Commission-Chicago Regional Office (CRO) **[47362]**
U.S. Securities and Exchange Commission-Denver Regional Office **[47363]**
U.S. Securities and Exchange Commission-Fort Worth Regional Office **[47364]**
U.S. Securities and Exchange Commission-Los Angeles Regional Office **[47365]**
U.S. Securities and Exchange Commission-Miami Regional Office **[47366]**
U.S. Securities and Exchange Commission-New York Regional Office **[47367]**
U.S. Securities and Exchange Commission-Philadelphia Regional Office **[47368]**
U.S. Securities and Exchange Commission - Salt Lake Regional Office **[47369]**
U.S. Securities and Exchange Commission - San Francisco Regional Office **[47370]**
United States Ski Writers Association [5295], [11971]
U.S. Small Business Administration (SBA) **[38192]**, **[47823]**
U.S. Small Business Administration - Alabama District Office **[47824]**

U.S. Small Business Administration - Alaska District Office **[47825]**
U.S. Small Business Administration - Albuquerque District Office **[47826]**
U.S. Small Business Administration - Arizona District Office **[47827]**
U.S. Small Business Administration - Arkansas District Office **[47828]**
U.S. Small Business Administration - Baltimore District Office **[47829]**
U.S. Small Business Administration - Boise District Office **[47830]**
U.S. Small Business Administration (SBA) - Buffalo District Office **[47831]**
U.S. Small Business Administration - Buffalo District Office - Rochester Branch Office **[47832]**
U.S. Small Business Administration - Business Information Center **[47833]**
U.S. Small Business Administration - Business Information Center **[47834]**
U.S. Small Business Administration (SBA) - Business Information Center **[47835]**
U.S. Small Business Administration - Business Information Center **[47836]**
U.S. Small Business Administration - Business Information Center **[47837]**
U.S. Small Business Administration - Cedar Rapids Branch Office **[47838]**
U.S. Small Business Administration - Charleston Branch Office **[47839]**
U.S. Small Business Administration - Chicago District Office [47868]
U.S. Small Business Administration (SBA) - Cleveland District Office **[47840]**
U.S. Small Business Administration - Cleveland U.S. Export Assistance Center **[47841]**
U.S. Small Business Administration - Colorado District Office (CDO) **[47842]**
U.S. Small Business Administration - Columbus District Office **[47843]**
U.S. Small Business Administration (SBA) - Connecticut District Office **[47844]**
U.S. Small Business Administration - Corpus Christi Branch Office **[47845]**
U.S. Small Business Administration - Dallas District Office **[47846]**
U.S. Small Business Administration (SBA) - Dallas/Fort Worth District Office (DFWDO) **[47847]**
U.S. Small Business Administration - Delaware District Office **[47848]**
U.S. Small Business Administration - Denver U.S. Export Assistance Center (USEACs) **[47849]**
U.S. Small Business Administration Des Moines District Office **[47850]**
U.S. Small Business Administration - Detroit District Office **[47851]**
U.S. Small Business Administration (SBA) - Disaster Assistance Customer Service Center **[47852]**
U.S. Small Business Administration - Disaster Assistance Processing & Disbursement Center **[47853]**
U.S. Small Business Administration - Disaster Office Customer Service Center (CSC) **[47854]**
U.S. Small Business Administration - Disaster Offices - Disaster Field Operations Center - East (FOCE) **[47855]**
U.S. Small Business Administration - Disaster Offices - Disaster Field Operations Center - West **[47856]**
U.S. Small Business Administration - El Paso District Office **[47857]**
U.S. Small Business Administration - Elmira Branch Office **[47858]**
U.S. Small Business Administration - Fargo District Office **[47859]**
U.S. Small Business Administration (SBA) - Fresno District Office **[47860]**
U.S. Small Business Administration - Georgia District Office **[47861]**
U.S. Small Business Administration - Gulfport Branch Office **[47862]**
U.S. Small Business Administration - Hartford District Office **[47863]**
U.S. Small Business Administration (SBA) - Hawaii District Office **[47864]**
U.S. Small Business Administration Headquarters Office - Office of International Trade **[47865]**
U.S. Small Business Administration - Helena District Office **[47866]**
U.S. Small Business Administration - Houston District Office **[47867]**
U.S. Small Business Administration - Illinois District Office **[47868]**
U.S. Small Business Administration - Indiana District Office **[47869]**

U.S. Small Business Administration - Indianapolis District Office [47870]
U.S. Small Business Administration - Jackson District Office [47871]
U.S. Small Business Administration (SBA) - Kansas City District Office [47872]
U.S. Small Business Administration (SBA) - Kentucky District Office [47873]
U.S. Small Business Administration - The Klamath Tribes - Business Information Center [47874]
U.S. Small Business Administration (SBA) - Las Vegas District Office [47875]
U.S. Small Business Administration - Little Rock District Office [47876]
U.S. Small Business Administration - Loans & Grants - Small Business Loans - Office of Loan Programs [47877]
U.S. Small Business Administration - Los Angeles District Office [47878]
U.S. Small Business Administration (LRGVDO) - Lower Rio Grande Valley District Office [47879]
U.S. Small Business Administration - Lubbock District Office [47880]
U.S. Small Business Administration (MDO) - Madison District Office [47881]
U.S. Small Business Administration (MDO) - Maine District Office [47882]
U.S. Small Business Administration - Massachusetts District Office [47883]
U.S. Small Business Administration - Melville Branch Office [47884]
U.S. Small Business Administration - Miami U.S. Export Assistance Center [47885]
U.S. Small Business Administration - Michigan District Office [47886]
U.S. Small Business Administration (SBA) - Minneapolis District Office [47887]
U.S. Small Business Administration - Minnesota District Office [47888]
U.S. Small Business Administration (MDO) - Montana District Office [47889]
U.S. Small Business Administration - Montpelier District Office [47890]
U.S. Small Business Administration (NDO) - Nebraska District Office [47891]
U.S. Small Business Administration - Nevada District Office [47892]
U.S. Small Business Administration - New Hampshire District Office [47893]
U.S. Small Business Administration (SBA) - New Jersey District Office [47894]
U.S. Small Business Administration - New York District Office [47895]
U.S. Small Business Administration - New York U.S. Export Assistance Center [47896]
U.S. Small Business Administration (SBA) - Newark District Office [47897]
U.S. Small Business Administration (NCDO) - North Carolina District Office [47898]
U.S. Small Business Administration - North Texas Export Assistance Center [47899]
U.S. Small Business Administration - North Texas U.S. Export Assistance Center [47900]
U.S. Small Business Administration (SBA) - Office of 8(a) Business Development [47901]
U.S. Small Business Administration - Office of Advocacy [47902]
U.S. Small Business Administration - Office of Communications and Public Liaison [47903]
U.S. Small Business Administration - Office of Entrepreneurial Development (OED) [47904]
U.S. Small Business Administration - Office of Financial Assistance - Office of Loan Programs [47877]
U.S. Small Business Administration - Office of Government Contracting [38175]
U.S. Small Business Administration - Office of Government Contracting, Area III - Procurement Center Representative - Alabama [36167]
U.S. Small Business Administration - Office of Government Contracting & Business Development [38175]
U.S. Small Business Administration - Office of the Inspector General [47905]
U.S. Small Business Administration (SBA) - Office of International Trade [47906]
U.S. Small Business Administration - Office of Minority Enterprise Development - Division of 8(a) Program Certification and Eligibility [47907]
U.S. Small Business Administration - Office of the National Ombudsman [47908]
U.S. Small Business Administration - Office of Native American Affairs [47909]
U.S. Small Business Administration (SBA) - Office of Small Business Development Centers (SBDC) [47910]

U.S. Small Business Administration (SBA) - Office of Women's Business Ownership (OWBO) [47911]
U.S. Small Business Administration - Office of Women's Business Ownership Entrepreneurial Development [47911]
U.S. Small Business Administration - Oklahoma City District Office [47912]
U.S. Small Business Administration - Omaha District Office [47913]
U.S. Small Business Administration - Philadelphia District Office [47914]
U.S. Small Business Administration - Philadelphia U.S. Export Assistance Center [47915]
U.S. Small Business Administration (SBA) - Phoenix District Office [47916]
U.S. Small Business Administration (SBA) - Pittsburgh District Office [47917]
U.S. Small Business Administration - Portland District Office [47918]
U.S. Small Business Administration - Puerto Rico and U.S. Virgin Islands District Office [47919]
U.S. Small Business Administration Region I (SBA Region I) [47920]
U.S. Small Business Administration Region II [47921]
U.S. Small Business Administration Region III [47922]
U.S. Small Business Administration Region IV [47923]
U.S. Small Business Administration - Region IX Office [47924]
U.S. Small Business Administration Region V [47925]
U.S. Small Business Administration Region VI [47926]
U.S. Small Business Administration Region VII (SBA Region VII) [47927]
U.S. Small Business Administration Region VIII (SBA Region VIII) [47928]
U.S. Small Business Administration Region X [47929]
U.S. Small Business Administration - Rhode Island District Office [47930]
U.S. Small Business Administration - Richmond District Office [47931]
U.S. Small Business Administration - Sacramento Branch Office [47932]
U.S. Small Business Administration - Sacramento District Office [47933]
U.S. Small Business Administration - St. Croix Post of Duty [47934]
U.S. Small Business Administration - St. Louis District Office [47935]
U.S. Small Business Administration - Salt Lake City District Office [47936]
U.S. Small Business Administration (SADO) - San Antonio District Office [47937]
U.S. Small Business Administration - San Diego District Office [47938]
U.S. Small Business Administration (SFDO) - San Francisco District Office [47939]
U.S. Small Business Administration (SADO) - Santa Ana District Office [47940]
U.S. Small Business Administration - SBA/Greater El Paso Chamber of Commerce - Business Information Center [47941]
U.S. Small Business Administration - Seattle District Office [47942]
U.S. Small Business Administration (SFDO) - Sioux Falls District Office [47943]
U.S. Small Business Administration - South Carolina District Office (SCDO) [47944]
U.S. Small Business Administration - South Dakota District Office [47945]
U.S. Small Business Administration (SFDO) - South Florida District Office [47946]
U.S. Small Business Administration - Spokane Branch Office [47947]
U.S. Small Business Administration - Springfield Branch Office [47948]
U.S. Small Business Administration - Springfield Branch Office [47949]
U.S. Small Business Administration - Syracuse District Office [47950]
U.S. Small Business Administration - Tennessee District Office [47951]
U.S. Small Business Administration (US SBA) - U.S. Export Assistance Center (USEACs) [47952]
U.S. Small Business Administration (SBA) - U.S. Export Assistance Center [47953]
U.S. Small Business Administration - U.S. Export Assistance Center (USEACS) [47954]
U.S. Small Business Administration - U.S. Export Assistance Center (USEACS) [47955]
U.S. Small Business Administration - U.S. Export Assistance Center (USEAC) [47956]
U.S. Small Business Administration - U.S. Export Assistance Center (USEACs) [47957]
U.S. Small Business Administration - U.S. Export Assistance Center [47958]

U.S. Small Business Administration - U.S. Export Assistance Center [47959]
U.S. Small Business Administration - U.S. Export Assistance Center (USEACs) [47960]
U.S. Small Business Administration - U.S. Export Assistance Center [47961]
U.S. Small Business Administration - Vermont District Office [47962]
U.S. Small Business Administration (SBA) - West Virginia District Office (WVDO) [47963]
U.S. Small Business Administration - Wichita District Office [47964]
U.S. Small Business Administration - Wilkes-Barre Branch Office [47965]
U.S. Small Business Administration - Wilmington Branch Office [47966]
U.S. Small Business Administration (WDO) - Wisconsin District Office [47967]
U.S. Small Business Administration (US SBA) - Wyoming District Office (WDO) [47968]
U.S. Social Security Administration - Office of Acquisitions and Grants - Small and Disadvantaged Business Utilization Specialist [47654]
U.S. Sourcebook of R & D Spenders [32054]
"U.S. to Spend $10 Billion to Boost Small Businesses" in *The Wall Street Journal (Jan. 8, 2022)* [30400]
United States Squash Racquets Association [15674]
U.S. Surveyors Association (USSA) [15219]
U.S. Taekwondo (USTU) [10717]
United States Tax Court [171], [15479]
United States Tennis Association (USTA) [15673]
U.S. The Arts and Crafts Consumer Market Report 2021 [1018], [4610], [4667]
U.S. The Future of Live Events Market Report 2021 [6099], [11895]
United States Tour Operators Association (USTOA) [15728], [15980]
U.S. Trade and Development Agency (USTDA) [45756]
U.S. Travel Association [15779], [15981], [16048], [19423]
U.S. Trout Farmers Association (USTFA) [6777]
U.S. Venetian Blind Association [1571], [9031]
U.S. Venture Partners (USVP) [37516]
United States Veteran Business Alliance (USVBA) [33496]
United States Veterinary Medical Association [678]
U.S. Virgin Islands SCORE [46649]
United States Water Fitness Association (USWFA) [12388]
U.S. Weekly Statistics [6722], [9942], [11104]
U.S.A. Directory of Machine Tools, Manufacturing Machinery and Related Products [10425]
U.S.A. Equestrian Association [8314]
U.S.A. Karate Federation (USAKF) [10718]
United Steelworkers of America - Canadian Branch (USWA) [35162]
United Way of Dane County [200], [11548]
"United Way Offers Free Tax Assistance for Local Low-Income Families" in *The Blade (January 6, 2012)* [15424], [31563], [34386]
United Way of Rhode Island (UWRI) [47533]
UnitedAg [16978]
"United's Next Hurdle: Costly Repairs" in *Crain's Chicago Business (Vol. 31, April 14, 2008, No. 15, pp. 1)* [25571], [33274], [35954]
Univalor (UV) [46901]
Universal City North Hollywood Chamber of Commerce (UCNH) [37226]
Universal Payroll Company [11943]
Universidad de Puerto Rico Recinto de Río Piedras Sistema de Bibliotecas Colección de las Artes [3384]
Université de Calgary - Institut Canadien du Droit des Ressources [5508]
Université de Montréal - Bibliothèque de Kinésiologie [12475]
Universities Space Research Association (USRA) [32717]
University of Akron (UA) [43689]
University of Akron College of Business Administration - Fisher Institute for Professional Selling [32703]
University of Akron - College of Business Administration - Fisher Institute of Professional Selling - Sales Education Learning Library [32702]
University of Alabama - Alabama International Trade Center [36064]
University of Alabama at Birmingham School of Public Health - Lister Hill Center for Health Policy (LHC) [26148]
University of Alabama - Capstone International Center (CIC) [10710], [36200]
University of Alabama - Culverhouse College of Commerce and Business Administration - Center for Business and Economic Research (CBER) [47534]

University Master Index

University of Alabama - Culverhouse College of Commerce and Business Administration - Center for Business and Economic Research - Alabama State Data Center (ASDC) **[36201]**
University of Alabama in Huntsville - Northeast Alabama Regional Small Business Development Center (NEAR SBDC) **[36057]**
University of Alabama in Huntsville Small Business Development Center (UAH) **[36058]**
University of Alabama - Small Business Development Center (SBDC) **[36060]**
University of Alabama Small Business Development Center **[36059]**
University of Alaska Anchorage (UAA) **[47535]**
University of Alaska Anchorage - Matanuska-Susitna College **[36253]**
University at Albany, State University of New York - Institute for Informatics, Logics, and Security Studies (ILS) **[3686]**
University of Alberta - Botanic Garden **[7687]**, **[10150]**
University of Alberta - Devonian Botanic Garden [7687], [10150]
University of Alberta - Faculty of Arts - Department of Economics - Institute for Public Economics (IPE) **[21283]**
University of Arizona - Arizona Center on Aging (ACOA) **[11554]**
University of Arizona - Center for Creative Photography Archives **[12363]**
University of Arizona Center for Innovation (AzCI) **[36412]**
University of Arizona - Eller College of Management - Economic and Business Research Center (EBRC) **[47536]**
University of Arizona - Karsten Turfgrass Research Facility (KTRF) **[10275]**
University of Arizona - Native American Research and Training Center (NARTC) **[26149]**
University of Arkansas - GENESIS Technology Incubator **[36517]**
University of Arkansas at Little Rock - Arkansas Economic Development Institute (AEDI) **[33731]**
University of Arkansas at Little Rock - College of Business Administration - Institute for Economic Advancement - Census State Data Center (CSDC) **[46951]**
University of Arkansas at Little Rock - Institute for Economic Advancement [33731]
University of Arkansas - Sam M. Walton College of Business - Center for Business and Economic Research (CBER) **[36521]**
University of Baltimore (MSB) - Merrick School of Business **[40476]**
University of British Columbia - Botanical Garden **[12605]**
University of British Columbia Faculty of Land and Food Systems - Wine Research Centre (WRC) **[15074]**
University of British Columbia - Fisheries Centre (FC) **[6806]**
University of British Columbia Music, Art and Architecture Library **[3081]**
University of British Columbia (UBC) - Sauder School of Business - Centre for Operations Excellence (COE) **[29061]**
University of British Columbia - Sauder School of Business - W. Maurice Young Centre Entrepreneurship and Venture Capital Research **[22957]**
University at Buffalo Technology Incubator **[42952]**
University of Calgary - Canadian Institute of Resources Law **[5508]**
University of Calgary Canadian Institute of Resources Law [5508]
University of Calgary - Department of Psychology - Vision and Aging Laboratory (VAL) **[16321]**
University of Calgary Faculty of Kinesiology - Human Performance Laboratory (HPL) **[12518]**
University of Calgary Laboratory for Human Performance Studies [12518]
University of California, Berkeley - Berkeley Roundtable on International Economy (BRIE) **[26478]**
University of California, Berkeley - California Institute for Energy and Environment (CIEE) **[550]**
University of California, Berkeley - Center for Labor Research and Education **[26150]**
University of California, Berkeley - Fisher Center for Real Estate and Urban Economics (FCREUE) **[782]**
University of California, Berkeley - Giannini Foundation of Agricultural Economics Reference/Reading Room **[17219]**
University of California, Berkeley - Institute of Governmental Studies (IGS) **[31731]**
University of California, Berkeley - Institute of Governmental Studies Library [31731]
University of California, Berkeley - Magnes Collection of Jewish Art and Life - Western Jewish History Center (WJHC) **[7455]**
University of California, Berkeley - Marian Koshland Bioscience, Natural Resources & Public Health Library **[11622]**
University of California, Berkeley - School of Public Health - Labor Occupational Health Program Library **[35993]**
University of California, Berkeley - UC DATA **[47537]**
University of California Botanical Garden at Berkeley - Myrtle R. Wolf Botanical & Horticultural Library **[7688]**
University of California, Davis - Agricultural and Resource Economics Library **[17220]**
University of California, Davis - Air Quality Group **[565]**
University of California, Davis - Archives and Special Collections **[1506]**, **[1956]**, **[15072]**
University of California, Davis - Information Center for the Environment (ICE) **[23459]**
University of California, Davis - School of Veterinary Medicine - Center for Companion Animal Health (CCAH) **[723]**
University of California, Davis - School of Veterinary Medicine - Veterinary Genetics Laboratory (VGL) **[671]**
University of California, Davis - Serology Laboratory [671]
University of California, Los Angeles - Anderson School of Management - Harold and Pauline Price Center for Entrepreneurial Studies **[23019]**
University of California, Los Angeles (UCLA) - David Geffen School of Medicine - Jules Stein Eye Institute (JSEI) **[16322]**
University of California, Los Angeles - Grunwald Center for the Graphic Arts **[3389]**
University of California, Los Angeles - Music Library **[11242]**
University of California, Los Angeles - UCLA Film and Television Archive - Research and Study Center **[15631]**
University of California, San Francisco - Center for AIDS Prevention Studies (CAPS) **[10943]**
University of California, San Francisco - Philip R. Lee Institute for Health Policy Studies (PRL-IHPS) **[26151]**
University of California, San Francisco - San Francisco Injury Center (SFIC) **[574]**
University Center for Instructional Media and Technology [21755]
University of Central Florida Business Incubation Program (UCFBIP) **[38593]**
University of Central Florida - Florida Solar Energy Center (FSEC) **[14973]**
University of Central Florida - Rosen College of Hospitality Management - Dick Pope Sr. Institute for Tourism Studies (DPI) **[15782]**
University of Central Missouri Small Business and Technology Development Center (SBDC) **[41497]**
University of Chicago - Booth School of Business - Center for Research in Security Prices (CRSP) **[6738]**
The University of Chicago - Polsky Center for Entrepreneurship and Innovation **[39439]**
University of Cincinnati College Conservatory of Music - Albino Gorno Memorial Music Library **[4869]**, **[11243]**
University of Cincinnati Institute for Policy Research (UCIPR) **[47538]**
University of Cincinnati (UC) - Robert A. Deshon and Karl J. Schlachter Library for Design, Architecture, Art, and Planning **[3082]**
University City Science Center (UCSC) **[44422]**
University of Colorado at Boulder - Center for Advanced Manufacturing and Packaging of Microwave, Optical and Digital Electronics (CAMPMODE) **[3408]**
University of Colorado at Boulder Department of Economics - Carl McGuire Center for International Studies **[21284]**
University of Colorado at Boulder - Environmental Program **[6018]**
University of Colorado at Boulder - Leeds School of Business - Business Research Division (BRD) **[15783]**, **[47539]**
University of Colorado at Boulder - Natural Hazards Center **[4826]**
University of Colorado - Boulder - William M. White Business Library **[33723]**
University of Colorado at Denver School of Medicine - Division of Health Care Policy and Research (HCPR) **[26152]**
University of Connecticut - Connecticut Center for Economic Analysis (CCEA) **[21285]**
University of Connecticut - Institute for Teaching and Learning (ITL) **[21755]**
University of Connecticut - School of Medicine - Department of Public Health Sciences - Center for International Community Health Studies (CICHS) **[26153]**
University of Connecticut Technology Incubation Program (UCONN TIP) **[38112]**
University CoWork **[33691]**
University of Dayton - Center for Business and Economic Research [43698]
University of Dayton School of Business Administration - Business Research Group (BRG) **[43698]**
University of Delaware (UD) **[47606]**
University of Delaware - College of Health Sciences - Department of Kinesiology and Applied Physiology - Human Performance Laboratory **[12519]**
University of Delaware Department of Chemical Engineering - Center for Molecular and Engineering Thermodynamics (CMET) **[32940]**
University of Delaware - Institute for Public Administration (IPA) **[31732]**
University of Delaware School of Public Policy & Administration **[47540]**
University of Denver - Penrose Library Special Collections and Archives **[4485]**
University Film and Video Association (UFVA) **[6171]**
University of Florida - College of Health and Human Performance - Department of Applied Physiology and Kinesiology - Center for Exercise Science (CES) **[12520]**
University of Florida - Database Systems Research Center (DSR) **[3543]**
University of Florida - Hinkley Center for Solid and Hazardous Waste Management (FCSHWM) **[7987]**
University of Florida - Institute of Food and Agricultural Sciences (IFAS) **[17237]**
University of Florida - Institute of Food and Agricultural Sciences - Center for Nutritional Sciences **[11627]**
University of Florida - Institute of Food and Agricultural Sciences - Entomology and Nematology Department - Florida Medical Entomology Laboratory (FMEL) **[12073]**
University of Florida - Institute of Food and Agricultural Sciences - Florida Medical Entomology Laboratory [12073]
University of Florida - M. E. Rinker, Sr. School of Construction Management - Powell Center for Construction and Environment **[23460]**
University of Florida - Sid Martin Biotechnology Incubator **[38594]**
University of Florida - Sid Martin Biotechnology Institute **[38595]**
University of Florida - Warrington College of Business Administration - Bergstrom Center for Real Estate Studies **[13639]**
University of Georgia - Carl Vinson Institute of Government **[31733]**
University of Georgia - Center for Remote Sensing and Mapping Science [3687]
University of Georgia Department of Geography - Center for Geospatial Research (CGR) **[3687]**
University of Georgia - Innovation Gateway **[38841]**
University of Georgia - Institute for Behavioral Research - Center for Family Research (CFR) **[2918]**
University of Georgia Libraries - Map & Government Information Library (MAGIL) **[47541]**
University of Georgia - Small Business Development Center - Albany Office **[38633]**
University of Georgia - Small Business Development Center - Atlanta Office [25173], [38631]
University of Georgia - Small Business Development Center - Augusta Office **[38634]**
University of Georgia - Small Business Development Center - Brunswick Office (UGA SBDC) **[38635]**
University of Georgia Small Business Development Center at Clayton State University (SBDC) **[38636]**
University of Georgia - Small Business Development Center - Columbus Office (SBDC) **[38637]**
University of Georgia - Small Business Development Center - DeKalb Office **[38638]**
University of Georgia - Small Business Development Center - Gainesville Office **[38639]**
University of Georgia Small Business Development Center at Georgia Southern University [38629], [38644]
University of Georgia Small Business Development Center at Georgia State University [25173], [38631]
University of Georgia - Small Business Development Center - Gwinnett Office **[38640]**
University of Georgia - Small Business Development Center - Kennesaw Office [38641]
University of Georgia Small Business Development Center at Kennesaw State University (UGA SBDC) **[38641]**
University of Georgia - Small Business Development Center - Macon Office **[38642]**
University of Georgia - Small Business Development Center - Morrow Office [38636]
University of Georgia - Small Business Development Center - Rome/Dalton Area [38643]
University of Georgia - Small Business Development Center - Rome Office (UGA SBDC) **[38643]**

3362 Small Business Sourcebook • 42nd Edition

Master Index University

University of Georgia - Small Business Development Center - Savannah Office (UGA SBDC) **[38644]**
University of Georgia - Small Business Development Center - Southern Coastal [38644]
University of Georgia - Small Business Development Center - Southern Coastal Office [38629]
University of Georgia - Small Business Development Center - State Office **[38628]**
University of Georgia Small Business Development Center at University of West Georgia [38646]
University of Georgia - Small Business Development Center - Valdosta Office [38645]
University of Georgia Small Business Development Center at Valdosta State University **[38645]**
University of Georgia - State Botanical Garden of Georgia **[6880]**, **[7689]**, **[10151]**
University of Georgia - Terry College of Business - Center for Insurance Education and Research **[9015]**
University of Guam - Robert F. Kennedy Memorial Library Instructional Media Division **[3385]**
University of Guelph - Arboretum **[10155]**
University of Guelph - Guelph Turfgrass Institute (GTI) **[10276]**
University of Hartford College of Engineering, Technology and Architecture - Engineering Applications Center - Acoustics Laboratory **[11317]**
University of Hartford - Construction Institute **[4377]**
University of Hartford Entrepreneurial Center - Women's Business Center (EC) **[38085]**
University of Hartford - William H. Mortensen Library - Anne Bunce Cheney Art Collection **[4645]**, **[4700]**
University of Hawaii - John A. Burns School of Medicine Health Sciences Library **[11623]**
University of Hawaii at Manoa - Water Resources Research Center (WRRC) **[16352]**
University of Hawaii at West O'ahu - Center for Labor Education and Research - CLEAR Labor Law Library **[18798]**
University of Houston Coastal Plains Small Business Development Center (UH/CP SBDC) **[44948]**
University of Houston College of Liberal Arts and Social Sciences - African American Studies Program (AAS) **[30660]**
University of Houston Fort Bend Small Business Development Center **[44949]**
University of Houston - Small Business Development Center (UHSBDC) **[44950]**
University of Houston Small Business Development Center Network **[44951]**
University of Houston Victoria Small Business Development Center **[44952]**
University of Idaho - Aquaculture Research Institute (ARI) **[6807]**
University of Idaho - Center for Business Development and Entrepreneurship (CBDE) **[38963]**
University of Idaho Office of Economic Development (ORED) **[38900]**
University of Idaho Research Park (UIRP) **[33516]**
University of Illinois at Chicago - Center for Urban Economic Development (CUED) **[30445]**, **[35932]**
University of Illinois at Chicago - Chicago Area Geographic Information Study (CAGIS) **[47542]**
University of Illinois at Chicago Department of Computer Science - Electronic Visualization Laboratory (EVL) **[14894]**
University of Illinois at Urbana-Champaign - College of Business - Bureau of Economic and Business Research **[18469]**
University of Illinois at Urbana, Champaign College of Business - Office of Real Estate Research **[13640]**
University of Illinois at Urbana-Champaign College of Fine and Applied Arts - Illinois School of Architecture - Building Research Council (BRC) **[4378]**
University of Illinois at Urbana-Champaign - Communications Library **[12964]**
University of Illinois at Urbana, Champaign Coordinated Science Laboratory (CRHPC) - Reliable and High Performance Computing Research Group **[3800]**
University of Illinois at Urbana-Champaign - Isaac Funk Family Library of Agricultural, Consumer and Environmental Sciences **[17221]**
University of Iowa - Center for Health Effects of Environmental Contamination (CHEEC) **[7988]**
University of Iowa - Henry B. Tippie College of Business - McGladrey Institute of Accounting Education and Research **[1797]**
University of Iowa - Public Policy Center - Iowa Social Science Research Center (ISRC) **[47543]**
University of Iowa Research Park - Business Incubation Program **[39828]**
University of Iowa (SBDC) - Small Business Development Center **[39685]**
University of Iowa Small Business Development Center **[39686]**
University of Iowa Technology Innovation Center **[39829]**
University of Kansas - Institute for Policy and Social Research - Center for Research on Global Change (CRGC) **[47544]**
University of Kentucky - Business & Economics Information Center **[172]**, **[10571]**, **[16900]**, **[21261]**, **[24284]**, **[30234]**
University of Kentucky - College of Agriculture, Food and Environment - Department of Animal and Food Sciences - Horse Unit **[8339]**
University of Kentucky College of Engineering - Kentucky Transportation Center (KTC) **[1183]**, **[5121]**, **[10300]**, **[15536]**
University of Kentucky College of Engineering - Kentucky Transportation Research Program [1183], [5121], [10300], [15536]
University of Kentucky College of Engineering - Local Technical Assistance Program [1183], [5121], [10300], [15536]
University of Kentucky College of Medicine - Center on Drug and Alcohol Research (CDAR) **[34705]**
University of Kentucky (UK) - Gluck Equine Research Center - John A. Morris Memorial Library **[8335]**
University of Kentucky Office of Commercialization and Development - Advanced Science and Technology Commercialization Center (ASTeCC) **[40109]**
University of Louisiana at Lafayette - Louisiana Small Business Development Center (LSBDC) **[40132]**
University of Louisiana at Monroe (ULM) - Small Business Development Center (SBDC) **[40133]**
University of Louisville (LMC) - Labor-Management Center **[35222]**
University of Louisville School of Urban and Public Affairs (USI) - Urban Studies Institute **[47545]**
University of Louisville Urban Studies Institute (USI) **[47546]**
University of Maine at Machias (UMM) **[40328]**
University of Manitoba - Manitoba Centre for Nursing and Health Research (MCNHR) **[26154]**
University of Manitoba - W.R. McQuade Laboratory **[10752]**
University of Mary Washington - College of Arts and Sciences - Department of Historic Preservation - Center for Historic Preservation (CHP) **[959]**
University of Mary Washington Small Business Development Center Fredericksburg Office **[45790]**
University of Mary Washington Small Business Development Center Warsaw Office **[45791]**
University of Maryland at Baltimore School of Pharmacy - Center on Drugs and Public Policy (CDPP) **[5223]**
University of Maryland Bio Park (UMB) **[40473]**
University of Maryland College of Agriculture and Natural Resources - Northeastern Regional Aquaculture Center (NRAC) **[6757]**
University of Maryland at College Park - A. James Clark School of Engineering - Institute for Systems Research (ISR) **[3801]**
University of Maryland at College Park - Center on Aging **[26155]**
University of Maryland at College Park - Center for Global Business Education (CGBE) **[27799]**
University of Maryland at College Park - College of Agriculture and Natural Resources - Department of Animal and Avian Sciences (CAF) - Crane Aquaculture Facility **[6808]**
University of Maryland at College Park Department of Economics - Center for International Economics **[21286]**
University of Maryland at College Park - Institute for Advanced Computer Studies (UMIACS) **[3802]**
University of Maryland at College Park - Institute for Governmental Service and Research (IGSR) **[31734]**
University of Maryland at College Park - International Communications and Negotiations Simulations (ICONS) **[27800]**
University of Maryland at College Park - Maryland Technology Enterprise Institute (Mtech) **[40474]**
University of Maryland at College Park - Robert H. Smith School of Business - Dingman Center for Entrepreneurship **[32422]**
University of Maryland (DCS) - Department of Computer Science **[47547]**
University of Maryland Libraries - Hornbake Library **[13067]**
University of Massachusetts at Amherst - Water Resources Research Center (WRRC) **[16363]**
University of Massachusetts Boston - Gerontology Institute **[11555]**
University of Massachusetts at Lowell - Lydon Library **[29056]**
University of Memphis - College of Arts and Sciences - Department of Biological Sciences - Ecological Research Center (ERC) **[6809]**
University of Michigan - College of Engineering - Department of Industrial and Operations Engineering - Center for Ergonomics **[35996]**
University of Michigan - Human Performance and Safety Engineering Laboratory [35996]
University of Michigan - Kresge Hearing Research Institute (KHRI) **[8142]**
University of Michigan - Stephen M. Ross School of Business - Office of Tax Policy Research (OTPR) **[15501]**
University of Michigan - The Venture Center **[41122]**
University of Minnesota - Charles Babbage Institute for Computing, Information, and Culture **[2126]**, **[3540]**
University of Minnesota - Charles Babbage Institute for the History of Information Technology [2126], [3540]
University of Minnesota - Children's Literature Research Collections (CLRC) **[3279]**
University of Minnesota, Crookston Library **[8336]**
University of Minnesota Duluth Center for Economic Development - Small Business Development Center (SBDC) **[41355]**
University of Minnesota, Duluth College of Liberal Arts - Center for Community and Regional Research (CCRR) **[31735]**
University of Minnesota - Eric Sevareid Journalism Library **[3386]**
University of Minnesota Libraries Business Information **[3541]**
University of Minnesota - Minnesota Landscape Arboretum **[7690]**
University of Minnesota, St. Paul - Magrath Library **[17222]**
University of Minnesota School of Public Health - Health Policy & Management Division (HPM) **[26156]**
University of Minnesota - The Venture Center **[41356]**
University of Mississippi - Mississippi Small Business Development Center (MSBDC) **[34238]**, **[41374]**
University of Mississippi School of Applied Sciences - Institute of Child Nutrition (ICN) **[11571]**
University of Mississippi Small Business Development Center (UMSBDC) **[41375]**
University of Missouri - Columbia - Business Research and Information Development Group (BRIDG) **[33692]**
University of Missouri - Columbia - Center for Small Business and Entrepreneurism [33692]
University of Missouri - Columbia - Frank Lee Martin Memorial Journalism Library **[12965]**
University of Missouri-Kansas City Center for Economic Information (UMKC CEI) **[47548]**
University of Missouri Kansas City Small Business and Technology Development Center (UMKC SBTDC) **[41494]**
University of Missouri, Kansas City (UMKC) - Small Business and Technology Development Center (SBTDC) **[41656]**
University of Missouri - Missouri Procurement Technical Assistance Center - Howell County Extension Center **[41668]**
University of Missouri, St. Louis College of Business Administration - Center for Business and Industrial Studies (CBIS) **[30862]**
University of Missouri St. Louis SBDC South County **[33497]**
University of Montana Bureau of Business and Economic Research (UM BBER) **[47549]**
University of Montana (UM) - Montana Business Connections **[41735]**
University of Montana School of Business Administration **[47550]**
University of Nebraska at Kearney - Nebraska Business Development Center (NBDC) **[28242]**
University of Nebraska - Lincoln - Center for Entrepreneurship **[33732]**
University of Nebraska at Lincoln Center for Entrepreneurship (UNLC4E) **[41900]**
University of Nebraska-Lincoln - C.Y. Thompson Library [11624]
University of Nebraska-Lincoln - Dinsdale Family Learning Commons **[11624]**
University of Nebraska at Omaha - Center for Public Affairs Research - Nebraska State Data Center (NSDC) **[47551]**
University of Nebraska, Omaha College of Business Administration - Nebraska Business Development Center (NBDC) **[19153]**
University of Nebraska-Omaha College of Information Science & Technology - Center for Management of Information Technology (CMIT) **[12702]**
University of Nebraska at Omaha (UNO) - Nebraska Business Development Center (NBDC) **[41897]**
University of Nevada, Las Vegas Architecture Studies Library **[953]**, **[4372]**, **[9080]**, **[10152]**
University of Nevada, Las Vegas - Lee Business School - Center for Business and Economic Research (CBER) **[41965]**

Small Business Sourcebook • 42nd Edition 3363

University of Nevada, Las Vegas - Lied Institute for Real Estate Studies [13641]
University of Nevada, Las Vegas Music Library (UNLV) [11244], [11304]
University of Nevada, Las Vegas Special Collections Gaming Studies Collection [7339]
University of Nevada - Reno - Mathewson-IGT Knowledge Center [24925]
University of New Brunswick - New Brunswick Cooperative Fish and Wildlife Research Unit (NBCFWRU) [5791]
University of New Brunswick (UNB TG) - Transportation Group [16113]
University of New Hampshire - New Hampshire Sea Grant College Program [6810]
University of New Hampshire (UNH) - New Hampshire Small Business Development Center (NHSBDC) [34239]
University of New Hampshire - Office of Biometrics [47552]
University of New Hampshire - Peter T. Paul College of Business and Economics - Center for Venture Research (CVR) [35313]
University of New Mexico - Bureau of Business & Economic Research - Data Bank (UNM BBER) [47553]
University of New Mexico - Bureau of Business and Economic Research - Data Bank [47553]
University of New Mexico (UNM) - Bureau of Business and Economic Research - New Mexico State Data Center/Business and Industrial Data Center Program (SDC/BIDC) [47554]
University of New Mexico - Earth Data Analysis Center (EDAC) [47298]
University of New Mexico-Gallup Small Business Development Center [42289]
University of New Mexico - Technology Application Center [47298]
University of New Orleans - Institute for Economic Development & Real Estate Research Library [13356]
University of North Carolina at Chapel Hill - Cecil G. Sheps Center for Health Services Research [17422]
University of North Carolina at Chapel Hill - Highway Safety Research Center (HSRC) [5123]
University of North Carolina at Chapel Hill - Kenan-Flagler Business School - Frank Hawkins Kenan Institute of Private Enterprise [22336], [43050]
The University of North Carolina at Charlotte - Charlotte Research Institute (CRI) [43253]
University of North Carolina at Charlotte - Urban Institute [33733]
University of North Carolina at Greensboro - Martha Blakeney Hodges Special Collections & University Archives - Cello Music Collections (CMC) [11245]
University of North Carolina at Greensboro - Martha Blakeney Hodges Special Collections & University Archives - History of Physical Education and Dance Collection [12476]
University of North Carolina at Greensboro - Special Collections & Rare Books, Jackson Library - Dance Collection [4870]
University of North Carolina School of the Arts - Semans Library [1010], [4871], [6221], [11246], [11305]
University of North Carolina School of the Arts;Semans Library [1010], [4871], [6221], [11246], [11305]
University of North Dakota - Center for Innovation (CFI) [30863], [43278], [43321], [43326]
University of North Dakota Center for Innovation (UND) [43320]
University of North Dakota Center for Innovation Foundation (UND) [43322]
University of North Dakota Department of Geography and Geographic Information Science [47555]
University of North Dakota-Workforce Development [43324]
University of North Florida - College of Arts and Sciences - Department of Sociology, Anthropology, and Social Work - Center for Community Initiatives (CCI) [31736]
University of North Florida - Training and Services Institute (UNF) - Institute of Police Technology and Management (IPTM) [14895]
University of North Texas - Center for Economic Development and Research [21287]
University of Northampton - Park Campus Library [24926]
University of Northern Colorado - James A. Michener Library [47556]
University of Northern Iowa College of Social and Behavioral Sciences - Center for Social and Behavioral Research (CSBR) [47557]
University of Northern Iowa - Iowa Waste Reduction Center (IWRC) [7989]
University of Northern Iowa Small Business Development Center [39687]

University of Notre Dame - Mendoza College of Business - Eugene D. Fanning Center for Business Communication [17888]
University of Nottingham - Business Library [24927]
University of Oklahoma Center for Business and Economic Development [43723]
University of Oklahoma - College of Allied Health Clinics - John W. Keys Speech and Hearing Center [8143]
University of Oklahoma - Michael F. Price College of Business - Center for Economic & Management Research (CEMR) [47558]
University of Oklahoma - Price College of Business - Division of Finance - Center for Financial Studies (CFS) [24285]
University of Oregon Library - Document Center [47559]
University of Ottawa - Startup Garage [46841]
University of Paisley - Ayr Campus Library [24928]
University of Pennsylvania - Leonard Davis Institute of Health Economics (LDI) [26157]
University of Pennsylvania - Morris Arboretum [7691], [10156]
University of Pennsylvania - Samuel Zell and Robert Lurie Real Estate Center at Wharton [13642]
University of Pennsylvania - Wharton Real Estate Center [13642]
University of Pennsylvania - The Wharton School Finance Department - Rodney L. White Center for Financial Research [6739]
University of Pennsylvania;Morris Arboretum [7691], [10156]
University of Pittsburgh Small Business Development Center [44106]
"University Place Building Gets an Anchor Tenant: Groundbreaking 2.0" in Philadelphia Business Journal (Vol. 30, September 23, 2011, No. 32, pp. 1) [4250], [13298], [13585], [13840], [31697]
University of Puerto Rico - Library System - Arts Collection [3384]
University of Redlands - Armacost Library Special Collections [11247]
University of Rhode Island - Research Center in Business and Economics (RCBE) [1798]
University of Scranton Small Business Development Center (SBDC) [44107]
University of South Alabama Small Business Development Center (USA SBDC) [36061]
University of South Carolina Career Center Library [2628]
University of South Carolina at Columbia - South Carolina Real Estate Center (SCCRE) [13643]
University of South Carolina - Darla Moore School of Business - Division of Research [21288]
University of South Carolina - Darla Moore School of Business - Elliott White Springs Business Library [18467], [19642]
University of South Carolina Small Business Development Center (SC SBDC) [44514]
University of South Dakota - Christian P. Lommen Health Sciences Library [12508]
University of South Dakota College of Arts & Sciences - Government Research Bureau (GRB) [31737]
University of South Florida College of Medicine - Suncoast Gerontology Center - The Eastern Star Library on Alzheimer's Disease [11549]
University of South Florida-Florida Procurement Technical Assistance Center-Tampa Office [38548]
University of South Florida - Louis de la Parte Florida Mental Health Institute College of Behavioral and Community Sciences - Center for HIV Education and Research [26158]
University of South Florida, Saint Petersburg - Nelson Poynter Memorial Library and Special Collections [23573]
University of South Florida - Small Business Development Center (SBDC) [23020]
University of Southern California - Cinematic Arts Library [11137]
University of Southern California - Marshall School of Business - Center for Effective Organizations [22337]
University of Southern California School of Engineering - Information Sciences Institute (ISI) [3688]
University of Southern Maine (USM) - Lewiston-Auburn College Library (LAC) [29057]
University of Southern Maine - Maine State Data Center - Center for Business and Economic Research (MCBER) [47560]
University Technology Park at Illinois Institute of Technology (UTP) [39440]
University of Tennessee Center for Industrial Services Chattanooga (UT CIS) [44832]
University of Tennessee Center for Industrial Services Jackson (UT) [44833]
University of Tennessee Center for Industrial Services - Procurement Technical Assistance Center (PTAC) [44834]

University of Tennessee Center for Industrial Services;Procurement Technical Assistance Center [44834]
University of Tennessee Chattanooga Center for Industrial Services (PTAC) - Procurement Technical Assistance Center [44835]
University of Tennessee at Chattanooga College of Engineering and Computer Science - SimCenter-Center of Excellence in Applied Computational Science and Engineering (CEACSE) [3810]
University of Tennessee - College of Business Administration - Boyd Center for Business and Economic Research [47561]
University of Tennessee (PTAC) - Institute for Public Service - Center for Industrial Services - Procurement Technical Assistance Center [44836]
University of Texas at Arlington - Center for Information Technologies Management (CITM) [3811]
University of Texas at Arlington College of Engineering - Human Performance Institute (HPI) [12521]
University of Texas at Arlington - Construction Research Center (CRC) [4379]
University of Texas at Austin - Center for American Architecture and Design (CAAD) [960]
University of Texas at Austin - Center for Transportation Research (CTR) [1567]
University of Texas at Austin - College of Pharmacy's Drug Dynamics Institute (DDI) - Drug Dynamics Institute [45568]
University of Texas at Austin - Council for Advanced Transportation Studies [1567]
University of Texas at Austin - IC2 Institute - Bureau of Business Research (BBR) [21289]
University of Texas at Austin - Office of Technology Commercialization (OTC) [45569]
University of Texas at Brownsville (UTB) - Entrepreneurship and Commercialization Center (ECC) [45570]
University of Texas at Dallas - Center for Translation Studies [15961], [15962]
"University of Texas Deans Serious about Biz" in Austin Business Journal (Vol. 31, May 20, 2011, No. 11, pp. 1) [21649], [24578], [31564]
University of Texas Health Science Center - Biotechnology Commercializatinon Center (BCC) [45571]
University of Texas Pan American Small Business Development Center [44954]
University of Texas of the Permian Basin Small Business Development Center (SBDC) [44953]
University of Texas Rio Grande Valley Small Business Development Center (UTRGV-SBDC) [44954]
The University of Texas at San Antonio College of Business - Center for Innovation, Technology and Entrepreneurship (CITE) [45572]
University of Texas Southwestern Medical Center at Dallas - Center for Human Nutrition [11628]
University of Texas—Houston Health Science Center - Hermann Eye Center [16320]
The University of Toledo - LaunchPad Incubation Program (LPI) [43681]
The University of Toledo (UT) - Minority Business Development Center (MBDC) [43682]
University of Toronto - Institute for the History and Philosophy of Science and Technology (IHPST) [32941]
University of Toronto - Institute for Policy Analysis [15502]
University of Toronto - Institute for Quantitative Analysis of Social and Economic Policy [15502]
University of Toronto - Joseph L. Rotman School of Management - Institute for International Business [15502]
University of Toronto - Ontario Institute for Studies in Education - International Centre for Educational Change (ICEC) [21756]
University of Tulsa - Mary K. Chapman Center for Communicative Disorders [8144]
University of Utah - Center for Public Policy and Administration [31738]
University of Utah - College of Health - Department of Exercise and Sport Science - Human Performance Research Laboratory [12522]
University of Utah - Kem C. Gardner Policy Institute (CPPA) [31738]
University of Utah - Rocky Mountain Center for Occupational and Environmental Health (RMCOEH) [35997]
University Venture Fund (UVF) [45667]
University of Vermont - Center for Rural Studies (CRS) [47562]
University of Vermont - College of Medicine - Department of Orthopaedics and Rehabilitation (MMRC) - McClure Musculoskeletal Research Center [12523]
University of the Virgin Islands - Eastern Caribbean Center (ECC) [47563]

University of Virginia (UVA) - Darden School of Business - i.Lab Incubator [45968]
University of Virginia - Darden School of Business - Olsson Center for Applied Ethics [34449]
University of Virginia - Weldon Cooper Center for Public Service [47564]
University of Washington Botanic Gardens - Elisabeth C. Miller Horticulture Library [7692]
University of Washington Botanic Gardens - Elisabeth C. Miller Library [7692]
University of Washington - Center for Social Science Computation and Research (CSSCR) [47565]
University of Washington - CoMotion [46225]
University of Washington Department of Psychology - Addictive Behaviors Research Center (ABRC) [34706]
University of Waterloo School of Accounting and Finance - Centre for Accounting Research and Education (CARE) [11950]
University of West Alabama Small Business Development Center (UWA SBDC) [36062]
University of West Florida - Fort Walton Beach Office Procurement Technical Assistance Center [38549]
University of West Florida - Small Business Development Center (SBDC) [38252]
University of West Georgia (UWG) - Richards College of Business [38845]
University of West Georgia - Richards College of Business - Small Business Development Center (UWG SBDC) [38646]
University of West Georgia - Small Business Development Center - Carrollton Office [38646]
University of the West of Scotland - Ayr Campus Library [24928]
University of Windsor (EPIC) - Entrepreneurship Practice and Innovation Centre [46837]
University of Wisconsin - Green Bay - Archives and Area Research Center (ARC) [7465]
University of Wisconsin--Madison - Center for Health System Research and Analysis (CHSRA) [26159]
University of Wisconsin, Madison College of Agricultural and Life Sciences - Hancock Agricultural Research Station (HARS) [2961]
University of Wisconsin - Madison (APL) - Department of Community and Environmental Sociology - Applied Population Laboratory [47566]
University of Wisconsin-Madison-Land Tenure Center Collection (LTC) [17223]
University of Wisconsin-Madison - MGE Innovation Center [46575]
University of Wisconsin--Madison - Ruth Ketterer Harris Library - Helen Louise Allen Textile Collection [4570]
University of Wisconsin - Madison Small Business Development Center [46321]
University of Wisconsin--Madison - Solar Energy Laboratory (SEL) [14974]
University of Wisconsin, Madison - Steenbock Memorial Library [17224]
University of Wisconsin--Madison - University Research Park (URP) [46576]
University of Wisconsin - Milwaukee Small Business Development Center (SBDC) [46322]
University of Wisconsin - Parkside - Archives and Area Research Center [7466]
University of Wisconsin - River Falls Small Business Development Center [46323]
University of Wisconsin - Stevens Point Small Business Development Center [46324]
University of Wisconsin-Stevens Point - Small Business Development Center (SBDC) [46544]
University of Wisconsin - Stout (UW-STOUT) - Robert S. Swanson Library and Learning Center [15780]
University of Wisconsin - Superior - Northern Center for Community and Economic Development (NCCED) [21290]
University of Wisconsin - Whitewater - Wisconsin Innovation Service Center (WISC) [27985]
University of Wyoming - Wyoming State Veterinary Laboratory (WSVL) [724]
University of Wyoming - Wyoming Survey and Analysis Center (WYSAC) [47567]
"Univest Charter Switch Signals Banking Trend" in Philadelphia Business Journal (Vol. 30, September 2, 2011, No. 29, pp. 1) [21200], [24156], [25572], [34201]
Univiersity of Connecticut (CCEI) - Connecticut Center for Entrepreneurship and Innovation [38113]
"Unleashing the Power of Marketing" in Harvard Business Review (Vol. 88, October 2010, No. 10, pp. 90) [366], [30100], [30823], [32652]
"Unlicensed Utah Collection Agency Settles with State Finance Department" in Idaho Business Review, Boise (July 15, 2010) [4814], [18721], [20351], [25573], [27957]

Unlimited Future Inc. (UFI) [46304]
Unlocking Capital Opportunities [35436]
"Unpleasant Surprise - When a Stock Distribution is Taxed as Dividend Income" in Barron's (Vol. 88, March 24, 2008, No. 12, pp. 60) [6650], [9865], [14687], [18722], [24157]
Unraveling ESG: Understanding Enviornmental, Social, and Governance Factors in Business - Part 1 [25613]
Unraveling ESG: Understanding Enviornmental, Social, and Governance Factors in Business - Part 2 [25614]
"Unretirement: How Baby Boomers are Changing the Way We Think About Work, Community, and the Good Life" [21201], [22841], [34202], [34387]
"Unused Coupons Still Pay Off" in Harvard Business Review (Vol. 90, May 2012, No. 5, pp. 32) [367], [20063], [30101], [32304], [32653]
"Unveiling the Secrets Behind Hispanic Business' 100 Fastest-Growing Companies" in Hispanic Business (Vol. 30, July-August 2008, No. 7-8, pp. 22) [18408], [22842], [24758], [28866], [30401], [32055], [33614]
"Up to $2 Million in Grants Available for Dairy Businesses, Child Care Centers, and More" in Small Business Trends(February 26, 2023) [33615], [47978]
"Up Close With: Learfield Sports CEO Greg Brown" in San Antonio Business Journal (Vol. 28, February 28, 2014, No. 3, pp. 7) [15199], [30102]
"Up In the Air" in The Business Journal-Serving Greater Tampa Bay (Vol. 28, July 18, 2008, No. 30, pp. 1) [612], [15767], [16018], [19413], [21202], [31565], [34917]
"Up On The Farm" in Canadian Business (Vol. 81, March 31, 2008, No. 5, pp. 23) [8774], [17131], [21203], [25574], [27753]
Up and Running: Opening a Chiropractic Office [24579], [25638]
"Up To Code? Website Eases Compliance Burden for Entrepreneurs" in Black Enterprise (Vol. 38, March 1, 2008, No. 8, pp. 48) [9251], [16477], [18723], [22000], [22843], [25575]
The Update [46523]
UPdate [41023]
"Updated LGMA Website Provides Food Safety News, Resources" in Western Farm Press (October 14, 2014) [16478], [17132]
Upfront Ventures [37517]
"Upgrade Old Vending Machines and Offer Your Customers More Options" in Vending Connection (November 1, 2021) [16263]
"Upgrade Your Pricing Strategy to Match Consumer Behavior" in Harvard Business Review (May 28, 2020) [29533], [31657]
Upholstered Furniture Action Council (UFAC) [8201]
UpHonest Capital [37518]
Upland Chamber of Commerce (UCC) [37227]
"UPMC Aims to Profit From Billing Angst" in Pittsburgh Business Times (Vol. 33, Jun3 27, 2014, No. 50, pp. 8) [10896], [25959], [33275]
"UPMC Develops Own Billing Solutions" in Pittsburgh Business Times (Vol. 33, January 17, 2014, No. 27, pp. 6) [102], [16846], [22001], [25960], [33276]
Upper Bucks Chamber of Commerce (UBCC) [44312]
Upper Coastal Plain Business Development Center [43254]
Upper Shore SCORE [40361]
Upper Tampa Bay Regional Chamber of Commerce [38512]
Upper Valley Bi-State Regional Chamber of Commerce (UVB-SRCC) [45739]
Upper Valley Business Alliance (UVBA) [42015]
Upper WestShore Chamber of Commerce [41775]
The UPS Store Canada [3405], [12783]
The UPS Store Inc. [2410], [3406]
UPS Strategic Enterprise Fund [38814]
"Upscale Consignment Shop Opens In Brandon" in Tampa Tribune (January 25, 2012) [2998], [3086], [3882], [31134], [35512]
Upshur County Development Authority - Innovation Center [46305]
"The Upside of Fear and Loathing" in Barron's (Vol. 88, March 24, 2008, No. 12, pp. 11) [6651], [9866], [21204], [24158], [24759]
Upside Group Franchise Consulting Corp. [2371], [24492], [33056]
The Upside Within Reach: A New Way to Create a Prosperous Business [33616]
Upstage Ventures LLC [42805]
UpStart Center for Entrepreneurship [40327]
UpStart Inc. [37956]
Upstate Capital Association of New York [42388]
Upstate Carolina Angel Network (UCAN) [44593]
"Upsurge" in Puget Sound Business Journal (Vol. 33, July 13, 2012, No. 12, pp. 1) [10445], [18409], [27754], [29427]

"Uptick in Clicks: Nordstrom's Online Sales Surging" in Puget Sound Business Journal (Vol. 29, August 22, 2008, No. 18, pp. 1) [3150], [11810], [18410], [22002], [32305]
Uptown Chamber of Commerce [38513], [39321]
"Uptown Goes Local To Fill Final Entertainment District Vacancy" in Birmingham Business Journal (Vol. 31, May 9, 2014, No. 19, pp. 8) [2430], [15035], [32306]
Uptown Kitchen [39652]
Uptown San Diego Examiner: Business News [37698]
Uptown Shelby Association Inc. (USA) [947]
UpWest Labs [37644]
"Uranerz Acquires Additional Uranium Property Adjoining Nichols Ranch" in Marketwired (May 14, 2007) [30885], [31566], [32964]
"Uranium Energy Corp Provides an Update on Its Goliad Operations" in Canadian Corporate News (May 16, 2007) [7962], [23381], [30886]
Urban Affairs Institute [34234]
"Urban Beekeeping Raises Southern California Concerns" in The Sacramento Bee (October 13, 2019) [1489]
Urban Future Lab (UFL) [42953]
Urban Greater DC [47568]
Urban Kitchen [14279]
Urban Land Magazine [33427]
Urban League of Greater Atlanta (ULGATL) [38801]
Urban League of Greater New Orleans Women's Business Resource Center [40203]
"Urban League Training Program Finds Jobs for Cincinnati's 'Hard to Serve'" in Business Courier (Vol. 27, July 2, 2010, No. 9, pp. 1) [21650], [26682], [27061], [34388]
"Urban Organics Launches Aquaponic Farm in Old Hamm's Brewery" in Business Journal (Vol. 31, April 11, 2014, No. 46, pp. 4) [1939], [6759], [7994], [16919]
Urban Ventures [44488]
URBAN-X [42954]
Urbana-Champaign Angel Network (UCAN) [39380]
Urbana - Champaign County Chamber of Commerce [43441]
Urbandale Chamber of Commerce [39801]
Urbantech NYC [42955]
Urgent Communications: Technical Information for Paging, Trunking and Private Wireless Networks [2819], [30493]
"URI Centre Seen as Bridge From Campus to Employment" in Providence Business News (Vol. 29, June 30, 2014, No. 13, pp. 4) [3529], [21651], [27062]
US Alcoholic Beverages Online Market Report 2021 [1360], [6930], [10339], [11838]
US Aquatics Inc. [4342]
US Cannabeauty: CBD and Hemp in BPC Market Report 2021 [4526], [5033]
US Cannabidiol (CBD) Market (by Types, Distribution Channels & Products): Insights & Forecast with Potential Impact of COVID-19 (2020-2024) [5034]
US Casino Magazine [7336]
US Convenience Stores Market Report 2020 [4448]
US Digital Advertising Market Report 2021 [381], [11839], [16911]
"US Firm The Bakery Companies Gets Fresh Investment" in Just-Food (October 9, 2019) [1270]
US Footwear Online Retailing Market Report 2021 [11840], [14689], [32339]
US Gen Z Beauty Consumer Market Report 2021 [1377], [1397], [4527]
US Grocery Retailing Industry Report 2021 [7797], [8062]
US Hispanics: Online Shopping Behaviors Market Report 2021 [29504], [32340]
"US Hygiene Adds Bed Bug Fix to Its Line of Highly Effective Cleaning and Pest Control Products" in Benzinga.com (October 29, 2011) [12047], [30824]
US Lawn and Garden Products Market Report 2020 [10252]
US Market Access Center (USMAC) [37645]
US Movie Theaters Industry Report 2020 [11129]
US Online Apparel Retailing (Men's and Women's) Market Report 2021 [11841], [32341]
US Retail and eCommerce & the Impact of COVID-19 - One Year Later 2021 [21246], [29505], [32342]
US Shopping Small Business Market Report 2021 [32343], [33623]
US Squash [15674]
US Teen and Tween Beauty and Personal Care Market Report 2020 [4528]
US The Natural/Organic Food Shopper Market Report 2020 [7798], [8063]
US Tobacco Trade Barometer: Exports [15711]
US Traditional Toys and Games Market Report 2020 [15801]

US Watches and Jewelry Market Report 2021 **[9988]**
USA Cycling **[1515]**
USA Engage **[20712]**
USA Equestrian [8314]
USA Hockey Magazine **[14724]**
USA Racquetball (USAR) **[12389]**, **[15675]**
USA Toy Library Association (USA-TLA) **[2875]**, **[15785]**
"USDA Invests $270 Million to Assist Meat, Poultry Producers" in Meat+Poultry (November 24, 2021) **[2431]**, **[7783]**
"Use Benefits Checklist to Smooth New-Hire Onboarding" in HR Specialist (Vol. 8, September 2010, No. 9, pp. 4) **[17369]**, **[26683]**, **[27063]**
"Use Perceived Value to Determine Your Food Truck Menu Prices" in Mobile-Cuisine.com (October 16, 2017) **[7017]**, **[19612]**, **[31658]**
"Use Social Media to Enhance Brand, Business" in Contractor (Vol. 56, December 2009, No. 12, pp. 14) **[368]**, **[9252]**, **[12670]**, **[14637]**, **[17772]**, **[30103]**, **[32654]**
"Use These Unique Resources to Start a Moving Business" in A Touch of Business (June 23, 2020) **[11152]**
Used Car Dealer **[11462]**
Used Machinery Buyer's Guide **[10446]**
Used Truck Association (UTA) **[11365]**
Used Truck Sales Network [11365]
"USF Plans $30M Sports Complex" in Tampa Bay Business Journal (Vol. 29, October 23, 2009, No. 44, pp. 1) **[917]**, **[4251]**, **[15200]**
"USHCC Applauds 10 Best U.S. Corporations for Veteran-Owned Businesses for 2012" in Economics Week (April 20, 2012, pp. 153) **[30402]**, **[30610]**, **[32977]**, **[34389]**
USI Kitchen Rental **[46226]**
"Using an LLC for Estate Planning" in Investopedia (July 29, 2020) **[6048]**
Using Mediation for Resolving Disputes **[10803]**
Using Other People's Money to Get Rich: Secrets, Techniques, and Strategies Investors Use Every Day Using OPM to Make Millions **[9867]**, **[24159]**
"Using Quality as a Competitive Differentiator in the Cannabis Industry" in Cannabis Business Executive (February 3, 2020) **[5023]**
"Using the SBA to Help Your Business Grow" in Legal Zoom (February 10, 2023) **[16603]**
Using Technology and Data to Build Marketing for Your Laundromat **[10179]**
"Using Technology as a Learning Tool, Not Just the Cool New Thing" in Educause **[3552]**, **[21652]**
"USM Focuses on Turning Science Into New Companies, Cash" in Boston Business Journal (Vol. 29, July 1, 2011, No. 8, pp. 1) **[21653]**, **[24580]**, **[32056]**, **[32840]**
USPTA Florida Division Convention [15124], [15678]
USPTA Pacific Northwest Division Convention [15124], [15678]
USPTA San Diego Division Convention [15124], [15678]
USPTA Southwest Division Convention [15124], [15678]
USU Incubator Kitchen **[45684]**
Utah Association of Certified Public Accountants (UACPA) **[16756]**
Utah Association of Realtors (UAR) **[13118]**
Utah Business and Professional Women **[35679]**
Utah Business Travel Association (UBTA) **[19321]**
"Utah Collection Agency Settles File-Sharing Charges" inPaymentsSource (June 11, 2012) **[4815]**, **[14475]**, **[20352]**, **[25576]**
Utah Community and Culture Department - Office of Indian Affairs [45656]
Utah Department of Heritage and Arts - Division of Indian Affairs **[45656]**
Utah Foundation **[15503]**
Utah Governor's Office of Planning & Budget **[47569]**
Utah Governor's Office of Economic Development (PTAC) - Procurement Technical Assistance Center **[45672]**
Utah Governor's Office of Economic Development;Procurement Technical Assistance Center [45672]
"Utah Liquor Stores to Pour Cases of Beer Down the Drain" in U.S. News & World Report (October 24, 2019) **[10336]**, **[25577]**
Utah Procurement Technical Assistance Center [45675]
Utah Procurement Technical Assistance Center (UPTAC) - Bear River Association of Governments **[45673]**
Utah Procurement Technical Assistance Center - Dixie Business Alliance **[45674]**
Utah Small Business Development Center (USBDC) **[45613]**
Utah State University - Central Utah Veterinary Diagnostic Laboratory (UVDL) **[725]**
Utah Valley Business Quarterly **[45688]**
Utah Valley BusinessQ [45688]
Utah Valley Chamber of Commerce **[45650]**
Utah Valley State College [45685]
Utah Valley University (UVU) - Business Resource Center **[45685]**
Utah's APEX Accelerator (PTAC) **[45675]**
"uTest Discusses the Evolution of Crowdsourcing Models at CrowdConf 2010" in Marketwired (October 1, 2010) **[14844]**, **[30825]**, **[33918]**
Utica Area Chamber of Commerce [42605]
Utica SCORE **[42503]**
"UTM Appliances Protect Small Businesses/Hotspots/ Branch Offices" in Product News Network (March 7, 2012) **[14476]**, **[26451]**, **[30987]**
"UTSA Entrepreneur Program Receives Federal Designation" in San Antonio Business Journal (Vol. 28, June 6, 2014, No. 17, pp. 7) **[21654]**, **[22844]**, **[25089]**, **[26452]**, **[32841]**
Uvalde Area Chamber of Commerce (UACC) **[45389]**
Uvalde Chamber of Commerce [45389]
"UW Wary of WSU's Wish for Spokane Medical School" in Puget Sound Business Journal (Vol. 35, May 9, 2014, No. 3, pp. 9) **[21655]**, **[25165]**, **[25961]**
UWC: Strategic Services on Unemployment and Workers' Compensation (UWC) **[19731]**

V

"VA Exceeds Government-Wide Goal for Veteran-Owned Business Procurement" in Benzinga.com (July 3, 2012) **[25090]**, **[25166]**, **[28221]**
"VA Seeking Bidders for Fort Howard" in Baltimore Business Journal (Vol. 28, June 25, 2010, No. 7, pp. 1) **[4252]**, **[11524]**, **[25962]**, **[31698]**
"Vacation, All I Ever Wanted" in Entrepreneur (August 2014) **[17370]**, **[22271]**
Vacation Guide **[41314]**
Vacation Rental Management Association (VRMA) **[12869]**
Vacation Rental Managers Association [12869]
"Vacation, What Vacation?" in Black Enterprise (Vol. 41, August 2010, No. 1, pp. 36) **[19414]**, **[34203]**
Vacaville Chamber of Commerce (VCC) **[37228]**
"Vaccine 'Battle' Halts Child Care Business Operations" in Nashville Business Journal (July 29, 2021) **[11327]**
Vaccine and Infectious Disease Organization [687]
Vaccine and Infectious Disease Organization - International Vaccine Centre **[687]**
Vacuum Cleaner Manufacturers Association [785]
VAIS Annual Professional Conference **[11465]**
Valar Ventures **[42806]**
Valdosta-Lowndes County Chamber of Commerce (VLCCC) **[38789]**
Valdosta State University College of Business Administration - Center for Business and Economic Research (CBER) **[38854]**
Valdosta State University - Harley Langdale, Jr. College of Business Administration - Small Business Development Center [38645]
Vale Chamber of Commerce **[44030]**
"Valener Announces that Gaz Metro has Achieved a Key Step in Acquiring CVPS" in CNW Group (September 30, 2011) **[5722]**, **[5988]**, **[6652]**, **[9868]**, **[23382]**, **[31567]**
"Valenti: Roots of Financial Crisis Go Back to 1998" in Crain's Detroit Business (Vol. 24, October 6, 2008, No. 40, pp. 25) **[6653]**, **[9869]**, **[11086]**, **[13299]**, **[20353]**, **[21205]**, **[24160]**, **[24760]**, **[25091]**, **[25578]**, **[26453]**, **[28222]**, **[34204]**
Valentine Chamber of Commerce **[41887]**
Valhalla Angels [46663]
Valhalla Private Capital Inc. **[46663]**
Vallecito Lake Chamber of Commerce **[37905]**
Vallejo Chamber of Commerce (VCC) **[37229]**
Valley Business [46523]
Valley Calligraphy Guild Newsletter **[2485]**
Valley Center Chamber of Commerce (VCCC) **[37230]**
Valley City Area Chamber of Commerce **[43305]**
Valley Economic Development Centers (VEDC) **[37646]**
Valley Focus **[40638]**
Valley Seminar [821]
Valley West Chamber of Commerce [45631]
Valparaiso Magazine **[39614]**
"Valuable Lessons" in Minority Business Entrepreneur (Vol. 39, Fall, 2022, No. 4, pp. 28-31) **[28867]**
"Valuation: Confusing and Misunderstood" in Business Owner (Vol. 35, July-August 2011, No. 4, pp. 10) **[22845]**, **[24761]**
"Valuation of Intangible Assets in Franchise Companies and Multinational Groups: A Current Issue" in Franchise Law Journal (Vol. 27, No. 3, Winter 2008) **[18724]**, **[24428]**, **[28049]**
Valuations Businesses Securities and Real Estate **[24898]**
"The Value of Conversations With Employees; Talk Isn't Cheap" in Gallup Management Journal (June 30, 2011) **[17773]**, **[22272]**, **[28868]**
Value Creation Group Inc. **[24271]**, **[24850]**, **[31620]**
The Value Equation: A Business Guide to Wealth Creation for Entrepreneurs, Leaders & Investors **[22846]**
Value Line DataFile **[6723]**, **[9943]**
Value Line Estimates and Projections Datafile [6723], [9943]
Value Line's Fundamental DataFile **[6724]**, **[9944]**
Value Place [8520]
The Value of Product Teams **[30845]**
"The Value of Social Media Advertising Strategies on Tourist Behavior: A Game-Changer for Small Rural Businesses" in Journal of Small Business Strategy (Vol. 31, December 1, 2021, No. 4, 64-75) **[16907]**
Values and Brand Messaging with Ashlee Sang **[17484]**
Values-Centered Entrepreneurs and Their Companies **[22847]**, **[23383]**, **[23546]**, **[34390]**
Values and Opportunities in Social Entrepreneurship **[22848]**, **[32057]**, **[32842]**, **[34205]**, **[34391]**, **[35395]**
Valuing Early Stage and Venture Backed Companies **[24581]**, **[35396]**
Valve Manufacturers Association [29082]
Valve Manufacturers Association of America (VMA) **[29082]**
Valvoline Instant Oil Change (VIOC) **[13010]**, **[14601]**
Van Alstyne Chamber of Commerce **[45390]**
Van Area Chamber of Commerce (VACC) **[45391]**
Van Buren Area Chamber of Commerce **[36502]**
Van Buren-Big Spring Area Chamber of Commerce [36502]
Van Buren Chamber of Commerce (VBCC) **[36503]**
Van Wert Area County Chamber of Commerce (VWCCC) **[43592]**
"Vancouver, B.C. Shines - at Seattle's Expense?" in Puget Sound Business Journal (Vol. 35, May 9, 2014, No. 3, pp. 6) **[19956]**, **[33421]**
Vancouver Business Journal **[46239]**
"Vandal-Resistant Mortise Locks" in Building Design and Construction (Vol. 49, September 1, 2008, No. 12, pp. 78) **[10356]**, **[14477]**
Vandalia Chamber of Commerce [39187]
Vanderbilt University - Vanderbilt Institute for Public Policy Studies (VIPPS) **[26160]**
VanderCook College of Music - Harry Ruppel Memorial Library **[11248]**
Vanedge Capital Partners Ltd. **[46717]**
Vanguard Cleaning Systems, Inc. (VCS) **[2118]**
Vanguard Communications Corp. **[20554]**
Vanouver Island Technology Park (VITP) **[46709]**
VANTEC Angel Network **[46699]**
"Vape, Smoke Shops on Edge as Santa Maria Mulls Ban of Flavored Tobacco Products" in Santa Maria Times (November 17, 2019) **[15704]**, **[25579]**
"Vaping: From 'Safer Than Cigarettes' to Public Health Crisis" in U.S. News & World Report (September 30, 2019) **[15705]**
Variable Frequency Drives (Onsite) **[5362]**, **[19464]**, **[21432]**
"Variations in R&D Investments of Family and Nonfamily Firms: Behavioral Agency and Myopic Loss Aversion Perspectives" in Academy of Management Journal (Vol. 55, August 1, 2012, No. 4, pp. 976) **[23668]**, **[32058]**
Varsity Tutors LLC **[16153]**
"VASCO DIGIPASS GO3 in Combination With IDENTIKEY Enhances the Security of Business Intelligence Solution Developed by CDS for General Motors Brazil" in News Bites US (March 29, 2012) **[3773]**, **[14478]**, **[27755]**, **[29428]**
Vashon Island Marijuana Entrepreneurs Alliance (VIMEA) **[45998]**
Vayner/RSE **[42807]**
"VC-Heavy, Revenue-Light Sensicore Sold to GE Division" in Crain's Detroit Business (Vol. 24, April 14, 2008, No. 15, pp. 28) **[30826]**, **[31568]**, **[33277]**, **[35397]**
"VC Money Down In State, Number of Deals Up" in Crain's Detroit Business (Vol. 24, January 28, 2008, No. 4, pp. 18) **[28223]**, **[35398]**
"VC Round Will Pay for 'Sham' Surgery Trial" in Business Journal (Vol. 31, April 11, 2014, No. 46, pp. 6) **[25963]**, **[32059]**, **[35399]**
"The VC Shakeout" in Harvard Business Review (Vol. 88, July-August 2010, No. 7-8, pp. 21) **[18411]**, **[33037]**, **[35400]**
VCapital Management **[39381]**
Veenstra & Kimm Inc. **[15247]**
Vegan Journal **[8111]**
Vegas Tech Fund [41957]
Vegetarian Journal [8111]
Vegetarian Journal's Foodservice Update **[8112]**
"The Vegetarians Who Turned Into Butchers" in The New York Times (August 6, 2019) **[2432]**

3366 Small Business Sourcebook • 42nd Edition

"Vehicle Towing and Recovery - Expert Article" in Robson Forensic (July 9, 2013) **[2577]**
Vehicle Tracking Solutions **[3791]**
Velocity **[46838]**
"Velvet Ice Cream" in Ice Cream Reporter (Vol. 21, July 20, 2008, No. 8, pp. 7) **[8600]**, **[20064]**
Venable L.L.P. **[6064]**
Venango Area Chamber of Commerce (VACC) **[44313]**
Vencon Management Inc. (VMI) **[31621]**, **[42808]**
Vending Machine Operators Industry in the US - Market Research Report **[16265]**
Venezuelan American Association of the United States (VAAUS) **[27437]**
Venice Area Chamber of Commerce (VACC) **[38514]**
Venice Area Chamber of Commerce **[37231]**
Venice Area Chamber of Commerce and Visitors Bureau **[37231]**
Venice Chamber of Commerce **[37231]**
"Venmo Reaches Small Business Milestone" in Small Business Trends (August 22, 2022) **[16604]**
Venrock **[37519]**, **[42809]**
Venstrat LLC **[42261]**
Vente et Gestion **[24906]**
Ventura Chamber of Commerce **[37232]**
Ventura Ventures Technology Center (V2TC) **[37647]**
Venture Acceleration Program (VAP) **[46710]**
Venture Accelerator Partners **[46855]**
Venture Access Inc. **[40343]**
Venture Capital Association of Alberta (VCAA) **[46655]**
Venture Capital Fund of America Inc. (VCFA) **[42810]**
The Venture Capital Fund of New England (VFCNE) **[40738]**
Venture Capital Journal [19700], **[35407]**
Venture Capital and Private Equity **[19700]**, **[35407]**
The Venture Centre **[46759]**
Venture Coaches (VC) **[20238]**
Venture Development Center (VDC) **[40767]**
"Venture Gap" in Canadian Business (Vol. 81, February 26, 2008, No. 4, pp. 82) **[8775]**, **[9870]**, **[21206]**, **[33617]**, **[34918]**, **[35401]**
Venture Hive **[38596]**
Venture Investors L.L.C. **[46553]**
Venture Marketing Associates L.L.C. **[2372]**, **[24493]**, **[33693]**
Venture Niagara Community Futures Development Corporation **[46811]**
"Venture: Nonprofit Aims to Spur New Companies" in South Florida Business Journal (Vol. 34, April 18, 2014, No. 39, pp. 8) **[7168]**, **[31569]**, **[32060]**, **[32843]**, **[35402]**
Venture Out Business Center (VOBC) **[39653]**
Venture Planning Associates, Inc. (VPA) **[35459]**
Venture51 [37387]
VentureArchetypes (VA) **[37689]**
VentureCrushFG **[42956]**
VentureLab Incubator **[45969]**
VentureNet Iowa **[39691]**
VentureOut **[42957]**
Ventures **[40739]**, **[46200]**
Ventures West Capital Ltd. **[46700]**
VentureScope, LLC **[45970]**
VentureSouth **[44594]**
VentureTech Alliance LLC **[37520]**
"Venturing Into New Territory: Career Experiences of Corporate Venture Capital Managers and Practice Variation" in Academy of Management Journal (Vol. 55, June 1, 2012, No. 3, pp. 563) **[16530]**, **[26454]**, **[35403]**
Vera Foundation [22358]
Vera Institute of Justice **[22358]**
Verbit & Co. **[24272]**, **[27160]**, **[29037]**, **[31018]**
Verge Economic Development (EDA) **[46679]**
Verge Fund **[42367]**
Veriti Consulting LLC **[7330]**
Verizon Business Group **[3790]**
"Verizon Loses Wireless Phone Customers" in The Wall Street Journal (April 23, 2019) **[2805]**
"Verizon Small Business Opens New Round of Digital Ready Grants" Small Business Trends (March 14, 2023) **[43618]**
"Verizon, Union Dispute is a Vestige of the Past" in Philadelphia Business Journal (Vol. 30, August 26, 2011, No. 28, pp. 1) **[2806]**, **[35211]**
"Verizon's Big Gamble Comes Down to the Wire" in Globe & Mail (February 3, 2007, pp. B1) **[9253]**, **[26455]**, **[30104]**
Verlo Mattress Store **[8227]**
Vermilion Advantage (VA) **[39322]**
Vermilion Chamber of Commerce **[40197]**
Vermilion Chamber of Commerce (VCC) **[43593]**
Vermillion Area Chamber of Commerce **[44663]**
Vermont Association of Realtors (VAR) **[13119]**
Vermont Beekeepers Association (VBA) **[1454]**

Vermont Business Association for Social Responsibility **[34258]**
Vermont Business Magazine (VBM) **[45754]**
Vermont Business Magazine **[45753]**
Vermont Business Roundtable (VBR) **[45698]**
Vermont Businesses for Social Responsibility (VBSR) **[34258]**
Vermont Cannabis and Hemp Convention **[5048]**
Vermont Center for Emerging Technologies (VCET) **[45748]**
Vermont Chamber of Commerce **[45740]**
Vermont Department of Environmental Conservation (DEC) **[47014]**
Vermont Department of Libraries **[47570]**
Vermont Food Venture Center (VFVC) **[45749]**
Vermont Slauson Economic Development Corporation (VSEDC) **[37648]**
Vermont Small Business Development Center Addison County Economic Development Corporation **[45699]**
Vermont Small Business Development Center Bennington County **[45700]**
Vermont Small Business Development Center Caledonia/Essex/Orleans Counties **[45701]**
Vermont Small Business Development Center Grand Isle County **[45702]**
Vermont Small Business Development Center Lamoille County (VTSBDC) **[45703]**
Vermont Small Business Development Center Lead Office (VtSBDC) **[45704]**, **[45710]**, **[45750]**
Vermont Small Business Development Center Orange/Windsor Counties **[45705]**
Vermont Small Business Development Center Southern Windsor County **[45706]**
Vermont Small Business Development Center Washington County **[45707]**
Vermont Small Business Development Center Windham/Southern Windsor Counties **[45708]**
Vernal Area Chamber of Commerce (VACC) **[45651]**
Vernal Directory **[45652]**
Vernal Small Business Development Center **[45614]**
Vernon Chamber of Commerce **[37233]**, **[45392]**
Vernon Chamber of Commerce (VCC) **[42198]**
Vernon Economic Development Corporation (VEDA) **[46316]**
Vero Beach Christian Business Association--Directory **[38610]**
Verona Area Chamber of Commerce (VACC) **[46524]**
Versailles Area Chamber of Commerce (VACC) **[41645]**
Versant Ventures **[37521]**
Versar, Inc. **[23448]**
Version One Ventures LLC **[46701]**
Vertex Consultants Inc. **[10703]**
Vertex Ventures **[37768]**
Vertical Aviation Conference & Trade Show [439]
The Vertical Group (TVG) **[42225]**
Vertical Integration and Sustainability in the Hospitality Industry with Levar Jackson **[23439]**
Vertical Systems Analysis Inc. (VSA) **[948]**
Verticon [439]
VertueLab **[44071]**
Veryon **[449]**
Vestavia Hills Chamber of Commerce (VHCC) **[36156]**
Vet-Tech **[37649]**
Veteran Business Association **[33498]**
Veteran Business Owners Association (VBOA) **[33499]**
Veteran Business Owners Initiative [33499]
Veteran Entrepreneur Alliance (VEA) **[33500]**
Veteran Entrepreneurial Training & Resource Network (VETRN) **[33501]**
"Veteran-Owned Business 3E Services Gains Recognition in 2011 and Welcomes 2012 With New Offerings" in Marketwired (January 10, 2012) **[4409]**, **[5392]**, **[18412]**, **[29429]**
"Veteran-Owned Business Energizes Employees To Give Back" in Investment Weekly News (June 23, 2012, pp. 768) **[26684]**, **[34392]**
"Veteran-owned Business: EPG Security Group" in Business Journal (Vol. 31, May 16, 2014, No. 51, pp. 10) **[14479]**, **[22849]**
"Veteran-Owned Firm Enlists Street" in Traders (Vol. 25, May 1, 2012, No. 337) **[25167]**, **[34393]**
Veterans Business Outreach Center (VBOC) **[38257]**
Veterans and Military Business Owners Association (VAMBOA) **[24594]**
"Veterans Train to Use Military Skills In Civilian Workforce" in South Florida Business Journal (Vol. 34, April 18, 2014, No. 39, pp. 10) **[7169]**, **[21656]**, **[26685]**, **[34394]**
Veterinary Clinics of North America: Equine Practice **[706]**
Veterinary Clinics of North America: Large Animal Practice [706]
Veterinary Hospital Managers Association (VHMA) **[688]**

Veterinary Infectious Disease Organization [687]
VetFran **[24312]**
VFDA Winter Conference [7222]
VHCA-VCAL Convention & Trade Show [26078], [35135]
VHooters of America LLC. **[6943]**, **[14280]**
Via Media Publishing Co. **[42363]**
Vickers Weekly Insider [24278]
Vickers Weekly Insider Report **[9926]**, **[24278]**
Vicksburg-Warren County Chamber of Commerce (VWCCC) **[41432]**
Victoria Chamber of Commerce **[45393]**
Victorville Chamber of Commerce (VCC) **[37234]**
"Victory Healthcare Moves Into Dallas-Fort Worth Market" in Dallas Business Journal (Vol. 35, May 18, 2012, No. 36, pp. 1) **[12495]**, **[25964]**
Victory Lane Quick Oil Change **[13011]**
"Victory Not Resting On Its Laurels" in Philadelphia Business Journal (Vol. 33, April 11, 2014, No. 9, pp. 6) **[1940]**, **[18413]**
Victory Studios **[15626]**
Vidalia Chamber of Commerce [40163]
Vidalia-Lyons/Toombs County Chamber of Commerce [38745]
Video Marketing Made Easy **[29554]**
Video Software Dealers Association [14748]
"Video Surveillance Enters Digital Era, Makes Giant Strides" in Arkansas Business (Vol. 26, September 28, 2009, No. 39, pp. 1) **[14480]**
VIDEO: Why Does Cold Brew Taste Different? **[7566]**
Vietnamese American Chamber of Commerce (VACOC) **[37235]**
"The View from the Field: Six Leaders Offer Their Perspectives On Sales Success" in (Vol. 90, July-August 2012, No. 7-8, pp. 101) **[20527]**, **[21657]**, **[25580]**, **[30611]**, **[32655]**
"The View From the Front Row" in Philadelphia Business Journal (Vol. 32, January 31, 2014, No. 51, pp. 6) **[369]**, **[10677]**, **[15201]**, **[30105]**
Views **[15953]**
Villa Enterprises [12596], [14281]
Villa Park Chamber of Commerce **[39323]**
Villa Restaurant Group Inc. (VRG) **[12596]**, **[14281]**
Village Capital **[38196]**
"Village at Waugh Chapel $275M Expansion Begins" in Baltimore Business Journal (Vol. 28, August 27, 2010, No. 16, pp. 1) **[7784]**, **[13586]**, **[26686]**, **[27064]**, **[32307]**
Villanova University - Falvey Memorial Library Special Collections **[762]**, **[1853]**
Vince Emery Productions **[37704]**
Vincennes Area Chamber of Commerce [39566]
Vincennes University (VU) **[1876]**
Vine Street Ventures **[43700]**
Vinita Area Chamber of Commerce (VACC) **[43817]**
"Vino Volo Debuts at the Airmall at Boston Logan" in Travel & Leisure Close-Up (October 8, 2012) **[14034]**, **[15036]**, **[19415]**
Vintage Stock **[32379]**
Vinton Area Chamber of Commerce (VACC) **[45908]**
Vinton County Chamber of Commerce **[43594]**
Virgin Islands Small Business Development Center (VI SBDC) **[46645]**
The Virgin Islands Small Business Development Center St. Croix **[46646]**
The Virgin Islands Small Business Development Center St. Thomas/St. John **[46647]**
"Virgin Mobile has Big Plans for Year Two" in Globe & Mail (March 6, 2006, pp. B5) **[18414]**, **[19090]**, **[19613]**, **[26456]**, **[33278]**
"The Virgin Way" **[22273]**, **[22850]**
Virginia Asphalt Association (VAA) **[1549]**
Virginia Association of Chamber of Commerce Executives (VACCE) **[45909]**
Virginia Association of Realtors (VAR) **[13120]**
Virginia Barbeque (VA BBQ) **[14282]**
Virginia Business (VB) **[45983]**
Virginia Business **[45982]**
Virginia Business Innovation Association (VBIA) **[45765]**
Virginia Business Travel Association (VBTA) **[19322]**, **[45766]**
Virginia Capital Partners L.L.C. **[45928]**
Virginia Chamber of Commerce (VCC) **[45910]**
Virginia Chamber of Commerce [41256]
Virginia Commonwealth University - Center for Public Policy **[31739]**
Virginia Commonwealth University School of Allied Health Professions - Virginia Center on Aging - Information Resources Center **[201]**, **[8297]**, **[11550]**, **[33081]**
Virginia Commonwealth University - Virginia Biotechnology Research Park **[45971]**
Virginia Community Capital **[45990]**
Virginia Department of Agriculture and Consumer Services - Office of International Marketing **[45794]**

Virginia Department of Business Assistance - Small Business Development Div. [45795]
Virginia Department of Business Assistance - Small Business Financing Authority [45796]
Virginia Department of General Services - Division of Purchases and Supply - Procurement Assistance [45933]
Virginia Department of Small Business and Supplier Diversity (SBSD) [45795]
Virginia Department of Small Business and Supplier Diversity - Virginia Small Business Financing Authority (VSBFA) [45796]
Virginia Economic Development Partnership (VEDP) [45797]
Virginia Funeral Directors Association Conference [7222]
Virginia Health Care Association Annual Convention and Trade Show [26078], [35135]
Virginia Highlands SBDC [45792]
Virginia Highlands Small Business Development Center [45792]
Virginia Highlands Small Business Incubator (VHSBI) [45972]
Virginia Innovation Partnership Corporation (VIPC) [45987]
Virginia Institute of Marine Science (VIMS) - William J. Hargis, Jr. Library [1236]
Virginia Law and Business Review [18857]
Virginia Mason Research Center [26105]
Virginia Minority Supplier Development Council [45915]
Virginia Mountain Iron Gilbert Area Chamber of Commerce [41256]
Virginia Peninsula Chamber of Commerce (VPCC) [45911]
Virginia Polytechnic Institute and State University - Center for High Performance Manufacturing (CHPM) [30864]
Virginia Polytechnic Institute and State University - Virginia-Maryland Regional College of Veterinary Medicine - Marion DuPont Scott Equine [726]
Virginia Procurement Technical Assistance Center (CPDC) - Crater Planning District Commission [45934]
Virginia Procurement Technical Assistance Center of George Mason University (PTAC) [45935]
Virginia Procurement Technical Assistance Center - Southwest Virginia Community College [45936]
Virginia Senate Committee on Commerce and Labor [45978]
Virginia Small Business Development Center (VASBDC) [33502]
Virginia Small Business Development Center Southwest Virginia Community College [45793]
Virginia Society of Tax & Accounting Professionals (VSTAP) [16757]
Virginia State Beekeepers Association (VSBA) [1455]
Virginia State Chamber of Commerce [45910]
Virginia Tech University Art & Architecture Library [4373]
Virtual Assistants [3878]
"Virtually Secure" in *Rough Notes* (Vol. 155, February 2012, No. 2, pp. 46) [8976], [9254], [14481], [27352]
"Virtue and Vice" in *Entrepreneur* (September 2014) [6654], [9871], [20583], [22274], [24161], [34395]
"Virtus.com Wins 'Best of Industry' WebAward for Excellence in Financial Services" in *Investment Weekly News* (October 24, 2009, pp. 227) [6655], [9255], [9872], [16479], [24162], [30106]
"VISA: Canadians Spend $97 Million on Mom This Mother's Day" in *Canadian Corporate News* (May 16, 2007) [6863], [7481], [18415]
"Visa Wants Creators to Get Paid Faster" in *Small Business Trends* (November 8, 2022) [11938]
Visalia Chamber of Commerce (VCC) [37236]
"Vision for Camden in Better Focus" in *Philadelphia Business Journal* (Vol. 30, September 30, 2011, No. 33, pp. 1) [4253], [13300], [13587], [18416], [21658], [31699]
The Vision Council [16295]
Vision Council of America [16295]
Vision Council Lab Division [16296]
Vision Industry Council of America [16295]
Vision Interface [3421], [3604]
"Vision Statement: Do You Really Know Who Your Best Salespeople Are?" in *Harvard Business Review* (Vol. 88, December 2010, No. 12, pp. 34) [3052]
"Vision Statement: How This First Lady Moves Markets" in *Harvard Business Review* (Vol. 88, November 2010, No. 11, pp. 38) [3052], [3151]
"Vision Statement: Mapping the Social Internet" in *Harvard Business Review* (Vol. 88, July-August 2010, No. 7-8, pp. 32) [9256], [22003], [27756]
"Vision Statement: Tired of PowerPoint? Try This Instead" in *Harvard Business Review* (Vol. 88, September 2010, No. 9, pp. 30) [14524], [17774], [30988]
"Vision Statement: Why Mumbai at 1 PM is the Center of the Business World" in *Harvard Business Review* (Vol. 88, October 2010, No. 10, pp. 38) [17775], [17877], [27757], [35005]

Vision: The Journal of Business Perspective [24899]
"Vision vs. Mission Statement: What's the Difference?" in *MasterClass* (Dec. 3, 2021) [19614]
Visionaire [3061]
Visions International Presentations [46681]
VisionTech Angels [39633]
VisionTech Partners, LLC [39634]
Visit Camp Verde Arizona [36372]
Visiting Angels [8293]
Visitor's Guide [37237], [38516], [40308]
Visitors Guide [37238], [37906], [38139], [38515], [41024], [42016], [43199], [46290]
Visitors' Guide [46525]
Visitor's Guide and Business Directory [44031]
Visitors and Residents Guide [43181]
Vista Chamber of Commerce [37239]
"Vistaprint Survey Indicates that Online Marketing Taking Hold Among Small Businesses" in *Marketwired* (December 10, 2009) [9257], [17776], [17878], [22004], [30107], [34206]
Visual Artists and Galleries Association (VAGA) [965]
Visual Design I (Onsite) [21433]
Visual Design II (Onsite) [21434]
Visual Design III (Onsite) [21435]
Visual Design IV (Onsite) [21436]
"Vitabath: Sweet Smell of Success" in *Retail Merchandiser* (Vol. 51, September-October 2011, No. 5, pp. 82) [1592], [20660], [30827]
Vital Audio [34659]
Vital Business Solutions (VBS) [27161]
Vital Records Handbook [7367]
Vitalize Van Nuys Inc. [37646]
Vitalize Venture Group [39382]
VitalizeVC [39383]
"Viva Brazil" in *Business Strategy Review* (Vol. 21, Autumn 2010, No. 3, pp. 24) [21207], [27758]
Viva Fresh Expo [7821]
Vivo Capital (VC) [37769]
VIXIO Regulatory Intelligence [7270]
VMS Inc. [3354]
VMware Ultimate Bootcamp [33817]
Vocal Point [44314]
Vocap Partners (VP) [38815]
Vocational Instructional Materials Laboratory [9993]
Vocational Rehabilitation Association of Canada (VRA) [12492]
Vocelli Pizza [12597]
The Voice [39324], [43306], [43595], [44315]
Voice for Animals, Inc. (VOICE) [670], [718], [8085], [8128]
Voice for Business [40418]
"Voice: Rebuilding Trust" in *Business Strategy Review* (Vol. 21, Summer 2010, No. 2, pp. 79-80) [6656], [8670], [9873], [12948], [23547], [31795]
The Voice of the Valley [44316]
"Voices Boomer's Blueprint: How CPAs and Auditors Will Remain Relevant" in *AccountingToday* (October 2, 2019) [103]
"Voices: Breaking the Corruption Habit" in *Business Strategy Review* (Vol. 21, Autumn 2010, No. 3, pp. 67) [18725], [21208], [23548], [32061], [32844]
"Voices From the Front Lines: Four Leaders on the Cross-Border Challenges They've Faced" in *Harvard Business Review* (Vol. 92, September 2014, No. 9, pp. 77) [27065], [27759], [30612]
"Voices: More Important than Results" in *Business Strategy Review* (Vol. 21, Summer 2010, No. 2, pp. 81) [22275], [28869]
"Voices: The Strategic Innovation Cube" in *Business Strategy Review* (Vol. 23, Spring 2012, No. 1, pp. 84) [27958], [28870]
Volition Capital [40783]
Volkswagen American Dealers Association [11357]
Volta Voices [8136]
Volume Footwear Retailers of America [14667]
Volume Footwear Retailers Association [14667]
Voluntary Protection Programs Participants' Association (VPPPA) [35934]
Volunteers of America of Pennsylvania - Working Order Incubator [44423]
"Volunteers Needed" in *Canadian Business* (Vol. 81, October 27, 2008, No. 18, pp. 60) [5723], [5989], [23384], [25581], [34207]
"Volvo: Logistics Agreement to Reduce Environmental Impact" in *Ecology, Environment & Conservation Business* (July 19, 2014, pp. 28) [7052], [11449], [23385], [29430], [31570]
Voodoo Ventures, LLC [40207]
"Vote Count Chocula in 2014" in *Canadian Business* (Vol. 27, July 2014, No. 7, pp. 28) [370], [20528], [30108]
Vote Hemp (VH) [4982]
Vows: The Bridal and Wedding Business Journal [2007]

Voyager Capital (VC) [46201]
Voyageur Magazine: Northeast Wisconsin's Historical Review [7387]
"VPA to Pay $9.5 Million to Settle Whistle-Blower Lawsuits" in *Crain's Detroit Business* (Vol. 26, January 11, 2010, No. 2, pp. 13) [8267], [8977], [18726], [25092], [25965], [27353]
VRTRADER.com [9935]
VT KnowledgeWorks [45973]
VTF Capital [41957]

W

W Meda Ventures [46701]
W. Michael Hoffman Center for Business Ethics (HCBE) [34450]
W.A. Rankin Memorial Library [7456]
"Wabtec Delivering Strategic Plan for Long-term Growth" in *Pittsburgh Business Times* (Vol. 33, July 11, 2014, No. 52, pp. 10) [9874], [18417], [19615], [27760], [30828]
Wachusett Area Chamber of Commerce [40639]
"Waco Pawn Shop Owners Say Reality Isn't Much Like 'Pawn Stars' TV Show" in *Waco Tribune-Herald* (August 15, 2010) [11921]
Waconia Chamber of Commerce [41315]
Waddington Chamber of Commerce [42694]
Wadley-Donovan GrowthTech L.L.C. (WDGT) [19217]
Wadsworth Chamber of Commerce (WACC) [43596]
Wag! [12254]
Wag Labs Inc. [12254]
Wage and Hour Law Compliance (Onsite) [35167]
"Wagering Opportunities" in *Memphis Business Journal* (No. 35, April 4, 2014, No. 52, pp. 8) [7314], [8465]
Wahoo Chamber of Commerce [41888]
Wahoo Chamber of Commerce and Economic Development [41888]
Wahpeton Area Chamber of Commerce and CVB [43307]
Wahpeton Breckenridge Area Chamber of Commerce and Visitors Center [43307]
Waiting for the Perfect Time Might Be Delaying Your Dreams [22934]
"Waiting for the Sunset on Taxes" in *Memphis Business Journal* (Vol. 34, September 28, 2012, No. 24, pp. 1) [15425], [25582], [34919]
Wakarusa Chamber of Commerce [39615]
Wake Forest Area Chamber of Commerce [43200]
Wake Forest Journal of Business & Intellectual Property Law [18783]
"Wakefern's ShopRite Tests Online Meal Planning Service" in *Supermarket News* (November 4, 2019) [7785], [11811]
Wakefield Chamber of Commerce [41025]
Wakulla County Chamber of Commerce (WCCC) [38517]
"Wal-Mart China Woes Add Up" in *Wall Street Journal Eastern Edition* (October 17, 2011, pp. B3) [25583], [27066], [27761], [28871], [32308]
"'Wal-Mart Effect' Feeds Grocer Price Wars" in *Globe & Mail* (March 15, 2007, pp. B14) [7786], [18418], [20065], [32309]
"Wal-Mart Is Testing Mobile Checkout: App Would Let Shoppers Scan Items, Pay at Kiosks; Giant Saves $12 Million a Year for Every Second It Can Cut" in *Wall Street Journal. Europe* (September 4, 2012, pp. A19) [10040], [32310]
"Wal-Mart Offering In-Store Tax Return Preparation Services" in *Tax Notes* (Vol. 134, January 16, 2012, No. 3, pp. 301) [15426], [32311], [34396]
"Wal-Mart Proposed for Timmerman Plaza" in *Business Journal-Milwaukee* (Vol. 28, December 31, 2010, No. 14, pp. A1) [4254], [18419], [32312]
"Wal-Mart Sharpens Focus on Roxbury" in *Boston Business Journal* (Vol. 31, July 8, 2011, No. 24, pp. 1) [26687], [30403], [32313], [33422], [34397]
Walcott Chamber of Commerce (WCC) [39802]
Walden Venture Capital (WVC) [37770]
Waldport Chamber of Commerce [44032]
"Walgreens Turns to Robots to Fill Prescriptions, as Pharmacists Take on More Responsibilities" in *CNBC.com* (March 30, 2022) [5188], [25966]
Walhalla Area Chamber of Commerce [43308]
"Walk-In Retail Clinics Enjoying Robust Health" in *Memphis Business Journal* (Vol. 34, April 27, 2012, No. 2, pp. 1) [25967], [32314]
"Walk-Ins Being Accepted for Free Tax-Preparation Service" in *Akron Beacon Journal* (January 26, 2012) [15427], [34398]
The Walk The Talk Co. [2326], [20226], [31924]
Walker Art Center - Library & Archives [3387], [12332]
Walker Art Center - Staff Reference Library [3387], [12332]
Walker County Chamber of Commerce [38790]

"Walker Seeks More Business Participation" in Business Journal-Milwaukee (Vol. 28, December 10, 2010, No. 10, pp. A1) **[19091]**, **[19616]**, **[21209]**, **[24762]**, **[25093]**, **[25584]**, **[26688]**, **[27067]**, **[31700]**
Walkerton Area Chamber of Commerce (WACC) **[39616]**
Walkerton Chamber of Commerce [39616]
"Wall Street Is No Friend to Radical Innovation" in Harvard Business Review (Vol. 88, July-August 2010, No. 7-8, pp. 28) **[6657]**, **[9875]**, **[27959]**, **[30829]**, **[33279]**
Wall Street Services, Inc. **[35460]**
Wall Street Share L.L.C. **[42958]**
Walla Walla Area Chamber of Commerce **[46171]**
Walla Walla Valley Chamber of Commerce (WWVCC) **[46171]**
Wallcovering Installers Association (WIA) **[11875]**
Wallcovering Manufacturers Association [11855], [11876]
Wallcoverings Association (WA) **[11855]**, **[11876]**
Walled Lake Chamber of Commerce [40953]
Waller Area Chamber of Commerce (WACC) **[45394]**
Wallowa County Chamber of Commerce **[44033]**
Walls & Ceilings **[10741]**
"The Walmart Foundation and Leading Nonprofits Launch the MyFreeTaxes Program, Offering Eligible Taxpayers Free Tax Preparation in 2012" in Economics Week (February 10, 2012, pp. 274) **[7170]**, **[15428]**, **[34399]**
"Walmart's New-Store Roll-Out Proving to be Development Magnet" in San Antonio Business Journal (Vol. 27, January 24, 2014, No. 51, pp. 4) **[18420]**, **[32315]**
Walnut Chamber of Commerce (WCC) **[39325]**
Walnut Creek Chamber of Commerce **[37240]**
Walnut Creek Chamber Membership Directory **[37241]**
"Walnut Hill Sheds Its Past, Name" in Philadelphia Business Journal (Vol. 33, April 4, 2014, No. 8, pp. 8) **[918]**, **[4255]**, **[12904]**, **[13301]**, **[13588]**, **[13841]**
Walnut Ventures **[35314]**, **[40740]**
Walpole Chamber of Commerce (WCC) **[40640]**
Walt Disney World Global Business Technology Strategy Library **[3472]**, **[3596]**, **[3683]**, **[3758]**, **[27165]**
Walt Disney World - Information Services Technical Resource Center [3472], [3596], [3683], [3758], [27165]
Walter Sedovic Architects [949]
Walterboro-Colleton Chamber of Commerce (WCCC) **[44586]**
Walthall County Chamber of Commerce **[41433]**
Waltham Chamber of Commerce **[40641]**
Waltham West Suburban Chamber of Commerce [40641]
Walton Area Chamber of Commerce **[38518]**
Walton County Chamber of Commerce (WCCC) **[38791]**
Wamego Chamber of Commerce **[39958]**
WAMVentures Group L.L.C. **[42959]**
"Wannabe Buyers Take Their Own Sweet Time" in Crain's Chicago Business (Vol. 31, April 21, 2008, No. 16, pp. 50) **[13302]**, **[13589]**, **[21210]**
"Want Free Publicity for your Business? Try These 11 Tactics" in Forbes **[31890]**
"Want Leverage? Multi-Unit Franchisees Deliver Substantial Savings" in Franchising World (Vol. 42, October 2010, No. 10, pp. 39) **[24429]**, **[31571]**, **[32316]**
Want More Engagement? Start Here. **[30165]**
"Want to Open A Bakery? Keep These Expert Tips in Mind" in Entrepreneur (September 8, 2016) **[1271]**
"Want to Start Your Own Food Truck? Read This First" in Eater (November 21, 2019) **[3857]**, **[6956]**, **[14035]**
"Want to Target Generation Z? You Need a Snapchat Marketing Strategy" in Forbes (October 23, 2020) **[29534]**
"Want To Increase Hospital Revenues? Engage Your Physicians. When Doctors Are Frustrated, Patient Care and Hospital Revenues Suffer. Here's How to Boost Physicians' Engagement -- and the Bottom Line" in Gallup Business Journal (June 5, 2014) **[22276]**, **[25968]**
"Want to Work for Amazon? You May Get the Chance Soon" in Pharmacy Times (May 17, 2017) **[5189]**, **[11812]**
"Wanted: African American Professional for Hire" in Black Enterprise (Vol. 37, November 2006, No. 4, pp. 93) **[6113]**, **[26689]**, **[27068]**, **[28872]**, **[30613]**
Wapakoneta Area Chamber of Commerce (WACC) **[43597]**
"War Veteran Hit Payoff with Repair Business" in Tulsa World (July 28, 2010) **[795]**, **[33280]**
Warburg Pincus L.L.C. **[42811]**
Wardrobe Crisis: How We Went from Sunday Best to Fast Fashion **[3053]**, **[23386]**
Ward's Business Directory of Mexican and Canadian Companies [24900]
Ward's Business Directory of Private and Public Companies in Mexico and Canada **[24900]**
Ward's Business Directory of U.S. Private and Public Companies **[24763]**, **[27795]**

Warehaus Business Center **[41123]**
Warehouse Distributors Association [12971]
Warehousing Education and Research Council (WERC) **[12974]**, **[12996]**
Warfield's Business Record [40479]
Warner Robins Area Chamber of Commerce [38777]
WarnerMedia Investments **[42812]**
"Warning Lights Flashing for Air Canada: Carty's Back" in Globe & Mail (February 22, 2006, pp. B1) **[19957]**, **[30109]**, **[33281]**
"A Warning Sign From Global Companies" in Harvard Business Review (Vol. 90, March 2012, No. 3, pp. 74) **[21211]**, **[27762]**
"Warning: You Need to Reinvest in Job Training" in U.S. News & World Report (October 19, 2018) **[10001]**
Warp 9, Inc. [3658]
Warren County Chamber of Business and Industry (WCCBI) **[44317]**
Warren County Chamber of Commerce **[38792]**
Warren County Community College Library Special Collections **[33724]**
Warren County Genealogical Society (WCGS) **[7457]**
Warren County Regional Chamber of Commerce **[43201]**
Warren-Forest Counties Economic Opportunity Council (WFEOC) **[44424]**
Warren Hills County Regional Chamber of Commerce [43201]
Warrensburg Chamber of Commerce **[42695]**
Warrenton Area Chamber of Commerce **[41646]**
Warrick County Chamber of Commerce **[39617]**
Warsaw Area Chamber of Commerce **[41647]**
Warsaw Area Chamber of Commerce [43202]
Warsaw Chamber of Commerce (WCC) **[43202]**
Warsaw - Kosciusko County Chamber of Commerce [39567]
Warsaw-Richmond County Chamber of Commerce (WRC) **[45912]**
Warwick Valley Chamber of Commerce (WVCC) **[42696]**
Wasabi Ventures LLC (WVP) **[37771]**
Wasatch Venture Corp. / EPIC Ventures **[45668]**
Waseca Area Chamber of Commerce (WACC) **[41316]**
Wash Broker Ltd. **[10199]**
Washburn Area Chamber of Commerce (WACC) **[46526]**
Washington Area Chamber of Commerce **[41648]**
Washington - Beaufort County Chamber of Commerce (WBCCC) **[43203]**
Washington Business Journal **[38184]**
Washington Calligraphers Guild (WCG) **[2479]**
Washington Chamber of Commerce (WCC) **[39326]**
Washington County Business Directory **[40419]**
Washington County Chamber of Commerce **[38793]**, **[41889]**, **[45395]**, **[45913]**
Washington County Chamber of Commerce (WCCC) **[38519]**
Washington County Chamber of Commerce (WCCOC) **[44318]**
Washington County Historical & Genealogical Society Library (WCHGS) **[7458]**
Washington County Magazine **[45396]**
Washington, D.C. Small Business Development Center at Howard University (DC SBDC) **[38159]**
Washington DC Women's Business Center (DCWBC) **[38170]**
Washington Department of Commerce - International Trade & Economic Development Division **[46020]**
Washington Economic Development Finance Authority (WEDFA) **[46202]**
Washington Feed Association - Pacific Northwest Pea Growers and Dealers - Pacific Northwest Grain Dealers [16966]
"Washington Hospitality Businesses Eligible for $100 Million Grant Program" in Small Business Trends (March 13, 2023) **[8466]**
Washington Minority Business Enterprise Center **[46181]**
Washington Policy Center (WPC) **[21291]**, **[25631]**
"Washington Post Licenses Its Arc Software to BP" in Techradar.pro (September 26, 2019) **[14845]**
Washington Press Club [5349], [15629]
Washington Procurement Technical Assistance Center - Columbia River Economic Development Council (CREDC) **[46206]**
Washington Procurement Technical Assistance Center - Economic Development Alliance of Skagit County (EDASC) **[46207]**
Washington Procurement Technical Assistance Center - Grays Harbor Economic Development Council **[46208]**
Washington Procurement Technical Assistance Center - William Factory Small Business Incubator **[46209]**, **[46227]**
Washington Research Council (WRC) **[15504]**
Washington Research Project [2868]
Washington SBDC Lacey **[46006]**
Washington SBDC Moses Lake **[46007]**

Washington SBDC Mount Vernon **[46008]**
Washington SBDC Omak **[46009]**
Washington SBDC Port Angeles **[46010]**
Washington SBDC Pullman **[46011]**
Washington SBDC Seattle **[46012]**
Washington SBDC Spokane **[46013]**
Washington SBDC Tacoma **[46014]**
Washington SBDC Vancouver **[46015]**
Washington SBDC Wenatchee **[46016]**
Washington SBDC Yakima **[46017]**
Washington Small Business Development Center (WSBDC) **[46018]**
Washington Small Business Development Center Lacey [46006]
Washington Small Business Development Center Moses Lake [46007]
Washington Small Business Development Center Mount Vernon [46008]
Washington Small Business Development Center Omak [46009]
Washington Small Business Development Center Port Angeles [46010]
Washington Small Business Development Center Pullman [46011]
Washington Small Business Development Center Seattle [46012]
Washington Small Business Development Center Spokane [46013]
Washington Small Business Development Center Tacoma [46014]
Washington Small Business Development Center Vancouver [46015]
Washington Small Business Development Center Wenatchee [46016]
Washington Small Business Development Center Yakima [46017]
Washington State Department of Commerce - Business Development Div. **[46021]**
Washington State Department of Natural Resources Public Land Survey Office Library (PLSO) **[15234]**
Washington State Department of Revenue (DOR) **[46022]**
Washington State Library (WSL) **[47571]**
Washington State Office of Financial Management - Forecasting Div. **[47572]**
Washington State Office of Minority and Women's Business Enterprises (M/WBE) **[46182]**
Washington State University Research Technology Park (WSU) **[46228]**
Washington State University - School of Economics Sciences **[47573]**
Washington Tariff & Trade Letter **[27783]**
Washington-Wilkes Chamber of Commerce **[38794]**
Washoe County Law Library **[7340]**
Waste Collection Services Industry in the US - Market Research Report **[7969]**, **[23415]**
Waste Equipment Manufacturers Institute [7941]
"Waste Management Exec First 'Undercover Boss' in Series Kicking Off on Super Bowl Sunday" in Houston Business Journal (Vol. 40, January 22, 2010, No. 37, pp. A1) **[7963]**, **[13731]**
Waste Management Symposia **[23446]**
Waste Treatment & Disposal Services Industry in the US - Market Research Report **[7970]**, **[23416]**
Waste360 Business Leadership Forum **[13747]**, **[23447]**
"Watch Hill Gaining Traction as Luxury Destination" in Providence Business News (Vol. 28, March 24, 2014, No. 51, pp. 1) **[8467]**, **[15768]**, **[16019]**
Watch It! Inc. **[11486]**, **[32380]**
"Watch Out, Uber Eaters: Online Food Delivery Can Lead to Overspending and Isolation" in Tennessean (June 25, 2019) **[6924]**, **[11813]**
"Watchdogs for Health Care" in Money (Vol. 41, October 2012, No. 9, pp. 63) **[25585]**, **[25969]**
"Watchful Eye: Entrepreneur Protects Clients and His Bottom Line" in Black Enterprise (Vol. 38, March 1, 2008, No. 8, pp. 46) **[14482]**, **[17514]**, **[18421]**, **[22851]**, **[24163]**
Water Center [16361]
Water Conditioning Association International [16331]
Water Conditioning Foundation [16331]
Water Conditioning & Purification--Buyers Guide Issue **[16335]**
"Water Conservation Helps GC's Building Attain LEED Gold Status" in Contractor (Vol. 56, September 2009, No. 9, pp. 5) **[4256]**, **[5724]**, **[5990]**, **[12671]**, **[14957]**, **[23387]**
Water Depot (WD) **[1867]**
Water Desalination Report **[16339]**
"Water Efficiency Bills Move Through Congress" in Contractor (Vol. 56, July 2009, No. 7, pp. 20) **[522]**, **[12672]**, **[14638]**, **[23388]**, **[25586]**, **[34920]**
Water Policy Report **[5745]**, **[16340]**, **[23419]**, **[25612]**

Water Quality Association (WQA) [16331]
Water Quality Research Journal of Canada [23053]
Water Quality Technology Conference and Exposition (WQTC) [16346]
"Water-Recycling Trend Could Ease Demand for Injection Wells" in *San Antonio Business Journal* (Vol. 28, June 13, 2014, No. 18, pp. 6) [5725], [7964]
Water Ski Industry Association [15083]
Water Sports Industry Association (WSIA) [15083]
Water Technology [16341]
Water Treatment for Boilers, Chillers & Cooling Towers (Onsite) [19465], [21437]
"Water Treatment Player Zenon Goes to GE" in *Globe & Mail* (March 15, 2006, pp. B1) [31572], [33282]
"Water Woes Force Big Brewers to Tighten the Tap" in *Idaho Business Review* (June 11, 2014) [1941], [5726], [23389]
"Waterdog Herb Farm Sees Sunny Times Ahead" in *SF Weekly* (October 17, 2019) [5024], [8157]
Waterfield Center for Business and Governmental Research [31727]
Waterford Area Chamber of Commerce (WACC) [41026]
The Waterfront Center (TWC) [17239]
Waterfront Press [17239]
Waterloo Chamber of Commerce [39327]
Waterloo Chamber of Commerce [39749]
"Waterloo Gardens Files for Bankruptcy" in *Philadelphia Business Journal* (Vol. 28, July 20, 2012, No. 23, pp. 1) [7635], [19210], [28016]
Watertown Area Chamber of Commerce [46527]
Watertown Area Chamber of Commerce (WACC) [44664]
Watertown Small Business Development Center [42416]
Waterville Area Chamber of Commerce (WACC) [43598]
Watford City Area Chamber of Commerce [43309]
Watkins College of Art, Design, & Film Library [1011], [6222], [9081]
Watkins Glen Area Chamber of Commerce (WGACC) [42697]
Watonga Chamber of Commerce [43818]
Watseka Area Chamber of Commerce (WACC) [39328]
"Watson May Study New Field" in *Business Review Albany* (Vol. 41, July 18, 2014, No. 17, pp. 10) [3530], [26457], [30830]
Watsonville Area Chamber of Commerce [37077]
Wauconda Area Chamber of Commerce (WCC) [39329]
Waukegan Chamber of Commerce [39218]
Waukesha Area Chamber of Commerce [46528]
Waukesha County Business Alliance [46528]
Waukesha County Chamber of Commerce [46528]
"Waukesha Firm Hit for $8.9M for Junk Faxes" in *Business Journal Milwaukee* (Vol. 29, August 3, 2012, No. 45, pp. 1) [8978], [18727], [20354], [25970], [33283]
Waukon Chamber of Commerce [39803]
Waunakee Area Chamber of Commerce [46530]
Waunakee Area Chamber of Commerce News [46529]
Waunakee/Westport Chamber of Commerce [46530]
Waupaca Area Association of Commerce [46531]
Waupaca Area Chamber of Commerce (WACC) [46531]
Waupun Area Chamber of Commerce (WACC) [46532]
Wausau Region Chamber of Commerce (WRCC) [46533]
Wausau SCORE [46355]
Wauseon Chamber of Commerce (WCC) [43599]
Wauseon Commerce Club [43599]
Waushara Area Chamber of Commerce (WACC) [46534]
The Wave [43600]
"Wave of Resale, Consignment Shops Pop Up In Springs" in *Gazette* (March 19, 2012) [3152], [3905], [5991], [13732], [15106], [23390], [34208]
Wavemaker Partners [37522]
WaveMAX Laundry [10206]
Waverly Area Development Group [39804]
Waverly Chamber of Commerce [39804]
Waverly Chamber - Main Street [39804]
Waxahachie Chamber of Commerce (WCC) [45397]
"A Way Forward for Small Businesses" in *Harvard Business Review* (April 13, 2020) [21212], [33619]
"Way More Than Mowing" in *Green Industry Pro* (Vol. 23, September 2011) [7636], [10117], [10249], [19958], [33284]
"The Way of the Seal: Think Like an Elite Warrior to Lead and Succeed" [22852]
"Wayfair Unveils New Mobile App Features" in *Home Accents Today* (November 13, 2019) [8182], [9051], [11814]
Wayne Brown Institute [45669]
Wayne Chamber of Commerce (WCC) [41027]
Wayne County Area Chamber of Commerce (WCACC) [39618]
Wayne County Chamber of Commerce [38795], [43204], [44814]
"Wayne, Oakland Counties Create Own 'Medical Corridor'" in *Crain's Detroit Business* (Vol. 24, October 6, 2008, No. 40, pp. 8) [4257], [25971], [26690], [31573], [33620]

Wayne State College - Nebraska Business Development Center (NBDC) [30235]
Wayne State University [41132]
Wayne State University - Center for Urban Studies (CUS) - Michigan Metropolitan Information Center (MIMIC) [47574]
Waynesville Area Chamber of Commerce [43601]
Waynesville-St. Robert Area Chamber of Commerce [41649]
"Ways AI is Changing HR Departments" in *Business News Daily* (March 21, 2023) [27069]
The Ways Discrimination Negatively Affects Businesses [20584]
"Ways for a Small Business to Show Social Responsibility" in *Chron* [34400]
WBENC Allyship Program [30313], [33531], [35719]
WBENC Business Lab [35720]
WBENC Collegiate Accelerator [35918]
WBENC Energy Executive Program [21438], [35721]
WBENC Industry Spotlight [6239], [25700], [29088], [35722]
WBENC Lift Financial Center of Excellence [22467], [23717], [35723]
WBENC Women & Pride [22468], [30314]
WBusiness Books [37705]
WCC Community Guide [39330]
WCMA Cheese Industry Conference [7808]
WDA: The RV Aftermarket Association [12971]
We Are All Human (WAAH) [30521]
"We Asked 10 Brewers: What's the Most Underrated Brewery?" in *Vinepair* (September 26, 2019) [1942]
"We Do: Copreneurs Simultaneously Build Happy Marriages and Thriving Enterprises" in *Black Enterprise* (Vol. 38, February 1, 2008) [23669], [30404]
"We Have Surpassed Our Early Goals...Everything Else Is a Bonus" in *Business Journal* (Vol. 32, June 6, 2014, No. 2, pp. 13) [1943], [19617], [20661]
"We Must Put an End to 'Male, Pale, and Stale' Corporate Boards" in *Black Enterprise* (Vol. 45, July-August 2014, No. 1, pp. 10) [20585], [30405]
We Scream for Ice Cream: An Industry Guide [8642]
W.E. Upjohn Institute for Employment Research [5466]
"Wealth Advisory Firms Are Merging, but What's In It for Clients?" in *The New York Times* (September 13, 2019) [6049], [6658], [24164]
"Wealth and Jobs: the Broken Link" in *Harvard Business Review* (Vol. 88, November 2010, No. 11, pp. 44) [22853], [25587], [26691], [27070], [30831]
Wealth Management Real Estate [13325], [13607]
Wealth Management and Trust Conference [6706], [24231], [35136]
The Wealth and Retirement Management Advisor Forum [6707]
Wealthsimple Investments Inc [9302]
"Weather Jitters Boost Coffee" in *Barron's* (Vol. 92, July 23, 2012, No. 30, pp. M12) [6659], [9876], [17133]
Weatherford Area Chamber of Commerce (WACC) [43819]
Weatherford Chamber of Commerce (WCC) [45398]
Weatherford Chamber of Commerce [43819]
"Weathering the Economic Storm" in *Playthings* (Vol. 107, January 1, 2009, No. 1, pp. 10) [15796], [19092], [21213], [28017]
The Weathersby Guild, Inc. [7252]
"Web-Based Marketing Excites, Challenges Small Business Use" in *Colorado Springs Business Journal* (January 20, 2010) [371], [9258], [20662], [22005], [30110], [32657], [34209]
"Web-Based Solutions Streamline Operations" in *Contractor* (Vol. 56, December 2009, No. 12, pp. 28) [523], [9259], [12673], [16480], [28873]
"Web Design and Development Companies" in *Business Review Albany* (Vol. 41, August 15, 2014, No. 21, pp. 6) [16481]
"Web Design Trends 2020: 5 Popular UI Styles" in *Digital Agency Network* (September 30, 2020) [16482]
"Web Exclusive: What happens after disaster strikes?" in *Hotel Business* (October 21, 2021) [4827], [8468]
Web Graphics with Adobe Photoshop (Onsite) [33818]
Web Marketing: Design. Navigation. Analytics. Understanding the Big Picture (Onsite) [29612]
"Web Move Puts Rack Ahead of Pack" in *Puget Sound Business Journal* (Vol. 35, May 16, 2014, No. 4, pp. 8) [11815], [32317], [32658]
"Web to Print" in *American Printer* (Vol. 128, August 1, 2011, No. 8) [3338], [12761], [16212], [16483], [22006]
"Web Site Focuses on Helping People Find Jobs, Internships with Area Businesses" in *Crain's Detroit Business* (Vol. 26, Jan. 4, 2010) [9260], [16484], [26692], [28874]
"Web Tax Holiday About to End" in *Silicon Valley/San Jose Business Journal* (Vol. 30, September 7, 2012, No. 24, pp. 1) [1839], [11816], [32318]

"Web Translation Made Simple" in *Inc.* (Vol. 33, October 2011, No. 8, pp. 44) [15951], [16485], [22007], [33285], [33919]
Webb City Area Chamber of Commerce [41650]
Webb Investment Network (WIN) [37523]
Webby Dance Co. [4863]
Weber Business Services L.L.C. [29038]
Webinars with a WOW Factor: Creating Memorable Meeting Across the Globe (Onsite) [17618], [22995]
Website Optimization (Onsite) [33819]
Website Relief [160], [15464]
"Website promotion from scratch, where to start" in *Geekers Magazine* (September 20, 2021) [29557]
"Website Triples Traffic in Three Weeks Using Press Releases" in *PR Newswire* (January 5, 2010) [9261], [16486], [30111]
Webster Area Chamber of Commerce [46535]
Webster Chamber of Commerce [42698]
Webster Groves-Shrewsbury Area Chamber of Commerce [41651]
Webster Groves-Shrewsbury-Rock Hill Area Chamber of Commerce (WGSRH) [41651]
Wedbush Capital Partners [37524]
"Wedding Bells on a Budget: Cash Saving Tips for the Big Day" in *Benzinga.com* (June 11, 2011) [1999]
"Wedding DJ Cost Guide" in *WeddingWire* [4963]
Wedding and Event Videographers Association International (WEVA) [1962], [6172]
Wedding International Professionals Association (WIPA) [6084]
Wedding Photographers of America [1963], [12337]
Wedding Photographers International [1963], [12337]
Wedding and Portrait Photographers International (WPPI) [1963], [12337]
Wedding and Portrait Photographers International Competition [12354]
"Wedding Present Shopping - What to Get the Couple Who Have Everything" in *Benzinga.com* (April 19, 2011) [2000], [32319]
Wedding Services Industry in the US -Market Research Report [6079]
"WeddingChannel.com Reviews Tops More than 200,000 Wedding Reviews" in *Benzinga.com* (June 23, 2011) [2001]
Wednesday in Washington [10865]
Weed Chamber of Commerce (WCC) [37242]
Weed Man USA [10272]
"Week on the Web" in *Crain's Detroit Business* (Vol. 25, June 22, 2009, No. 25, pp. 19) [8979], [25972], [27354]
"A Week of the Worst Kind of Selling" in *Barron's* (Vol. 88, June 30, 2008, No. 26, pp. M3) [6660], [9877], [24165], [29431], [31574]
The Weekly Business View [36157]
Weekly Enews [39959]
Weekly Facts [41317]
Weekly Update [40420]
"The Weeks Ahead" in *Crain's New York Business* (Vol. 24, January 7, 2008, No. 1, pp. 26) [14525], [15909], [21214], [22854], [34921], [35103], [35874]
"Wegmans Adding 1,600-Plus Jobs Here Over the Next Year" in *Boston Business Journal* (Vol. 34, February 14, 2014, No. 2, pp. 3) [7787], [18422], [19618], [23670], [26693]
"Wegmans, Fairway Lead Off Impossible Burger's East Coast Launch" in *Supermarket News* (September 25, 2019) [8056]
"Wegmans Uses Database for Recall" in *Supermarket News* (Vol. 56, September 22, 2008, No. 38) [3531], [7788], [8776], [12231], [14483], [27763], [33920]
Weichert Real Estate Affiliates Inc. [13345]
"Weigh in: 9 ways your store can better support BIPOC-owned brands" in *Natural Foods Merchandiser* (September 14, 2021) [30442], [32381]
Weight Loss Services Industry in the US - Market Research Report [16509]
"Weightplan.com Launches 'Gymcodes' the Virtual Personal Trainer - Scan QR Codes on Gym Equipment for on the Spot Exercise Tuition" in *America's Intelligence Wire* (June 11, 2012) [2807], [12438]
WeIGNITE [35724]
Weill-Lenya Research Center (WLRC) [11249], [11306]
Weimar Area Chamber of Commerce [45399]
Weimar Chamber of Commerce [45399]
Weirton Area Chamber of Commerce (WCC) [46291]
Weiser Chamber of Commerce [38947]
Weiss, Peck & Greer Venture Partners [37424]
Welcome to Austin [41318]
"Welcome to Babesland" in *Women In Business* (Vol. 62, June 2010, No. 2, pp. 33) [11267], [13656], [15910], [35104], [35875]
Welcoming Center for New Pennsylvanians [44425]
The WELDER [10456]

Welfare Research, Inc. (WRI) [26161]
"A Well-Crafted Employee Handbook Can Make Work Run More Smoothly" in Idaho Business Review (September 17, 2014) [14484], [17371], [18728], [19757], [21659], [22277], [25973], [27071], [28875]
"Well-Heeled Startup Plots Course for a Run at Garmin" in Business Journal Portland (Vol. 27, November 12, 2010, No. 37, pp. 1) [3054], [6141], [14666], [29065], [30112], [30832], [32320], [35404]
"Well-Timed Entrance" in Barron's (Vol. 92, July 23, 2012, No. 30, pp. 24) [6661], [9878], [11087], [21215], [24166]
Wellesley Chamber of Commerce [40642]
Wellfleet Chamber of Commerce [40643]
Wellington Chamber of Commerce [38520]
Wells Area Chamber of Commerce [41319]
Wells Chamber of Commerce [40309], [41951]
Wells County Chamber of Commerce [39619]
"Wells Fargo and NeighborWorks America Offer Down Payment Assistance: Low- to Middle-Income Consumers Get the Help They Need" in Black Enterprise (Vol. 44, June 2014, No. 10, pp. 34) [11088], [34401]
"Wells' Is Title Sponsor for Volleyball Championship" in Ice Cream Reporter (Vol. 22, August 20, 2008, No. 9, pp. 4) [8601], [15202]
Wellsboro Area Chamber of Commerce (WACC) [44319]
Wellsburg Chamber of Commerce [46292]
Wellsville Area Chamber of Commerce (WCC) [42699]
Wellsville Chamber of Commerce [39960]
Welsh, Carson, Anderson and Stowe (WCAS) [42813]
Wenatchee Valley Chamber of Commerce (WVCC) [46172]
Wenatchee Valley Chamber of Commerce Business Directory and Relocation Guide [46173]
Wendell Chamber of Commerce (WCC) [43205]
Wendy's Restaurants of Canada Inc. [14283]
"Wenmat Sells Last Fitness Clubs" in Sacramento Business Journal (Vol. 31, June 6, 2014, No. 15, pp. 6) [12439], [19698], [33038]
"Wenzel Downhole Tools Ltd. Announces First Quarter Results for 2007" in Marketwired (May 14, 2007) [6662], [9879], [24167], [29432]
WERC DX Annual Conference [12992]
"We're Drowning In Fine Print" in Canadian Business (Vol. 87, July 2014, No. 7, pp. 30) [18729], [25588]
"'We're Full," Car Dealers Say as Auto Sales Slow after a Long Boom" in The New York Times (July 23, 2019) [11450], [21216]
"We're Ignoring the Only Industry We Can't Do Without" in Entrepreneur (Apr 11, 2019) [17134], [26458]
We're Rolling Pretzel Co. [15063]
Wes Watkins Technology Center Business Incubator (WWTC) [43878]
Weslaco Area Chamber of Commerce [45400]
Wesley-Kind Associates Inc. [12995], [20674]
WESST [42341]
WESST Enterprise Center (WEC) [42357]
West Allis/West Milwaukee Chamber of Commerce [46536]
West Baton Rouge Chamber of Commerce (WBRCC) [40198]
West Bend Area Chamber of Commerce Inc. (WBACC) [46537]
West Bend Chamber of Commerce [39805]
West Bloomfield Chamber of Commerce [40930]
West Bloomfield Community Directory [40885]
West Branch Area Chamber of Commerce (WBACC) [41028]
West Central Indiana Small Business Development Center [39479]
West Central Small Business Development Center (SDBC) [37798]
West Central Small Business Development Center Chaffee and Lake County [37799]
West Chamber of Commerce Serving Jefferson County [37907]
West Chambers County Chamber of Commerce (WCCC) [45401]
West Coast Commercial Credit [2373]
West Columbia Chamber of Commerce (WCCC) [45402]
West Des Moines Chamber of Commerce (WDMCC) [39806]
West Fargo Chamber of Commerce [41229]
West Hants Historical Society - Genealogies Collections [7459]
West Hartford Chamber of Commerce (WHCC) [38079]
West Haven Chamber of Commerce (WHCC) [38080]
West I-10 Chamber of Commerce [45403]
West Jordan Business and Professional Directory [45654]
West Jordan Chamber of Commerce (WJCC) [45653]
West Jordan Chamber of Commerce--Business Directory [45654]

West Kauai Business and Professional Association [33503]
West Los Angeles Chamber of Commerce [37243]
West Marin Chamber of Commerce [37244]
West Metro Branch of the Greater Columbia Chamber of Commerce [44548]
West Metro Chamber of Commerce [44548]
West Metro Chamber Serving Jefferson County [37907]
West Michigan APEX Accelerator (MAFPTAC) [41070]
West Michigan Science & Technology Initiative [41124]
West Milford Chamber of Commerce (WMCC) [42199]
West Monroe-West Ouachita Chamber of Commerce [40199]
West Orange Chamber of Commerce (WOCC) [38521]
West Orange County Chamber of Commerce [38521]
"West Palm Beach Bed and Breakfast is a Labor of Love" in Palm Beach Post (April 7, 2012) [1425], [23671]
West Pasco Chamber of Commerce (WPCC) [38522]
West Piedmont Business Development Center [45974]
West Plains Chamber of Commerce (WPCC) [46174]
West Point Chamber of Commerce (WPCC) [41890]
West Sacramento Chamber of Commerce [37245]
"West Sacramento Food Shipper Changes Hands" in Sacramento Business Journal (Vol. 31, May 30, 2014, No. 3) [6925], [20663], [31575]
West St. Louis County Chamber of Commerce (WSLCCC) [41652]
West Seattle Chamber of Commerce (WSCC) [46175]
West Seneca Chamber of Commerce [42700]
West Shore Chamber of Commerce [43602], [44320]
West Side Charlies [1544]
West Suburban Angels (WSA) [35315], [39384]
West Suburban Chamber of Commerce [39331]
West Suburban Chamber of Commerce and Industry (WSCCI) [39331]
West Texas A&M University Small Business Development Center [44955], [45492]
West Union Chamber of Commerce (WUCC) [39807]
West Valley-Taylorsville-Kearns Area Chamber of Commerce [45631]
West Virginia Chamber of Commerce [46293]
West Virginia Commercial L.L.C. [13625]
West Virginia Development Office - Business and Industrial Development Division (BID) [46257]
West Virginia Northern Community College (WVNCC) [46308]
West Virginia Northern Community College Small Business Development Center (WV SBDC) [46254]
West Virginia-Ohio Valley Chapter National Electrical Contractors Association (WV OV NECA) [46249]
West Virginia Procurement Technical Assistance Center (PTAC) [46299]
West Virginia Small Business Development Center (WV SBDC) [46255]
West Virginia University College of Business and Economics - Bureau of Business and Economic Research (BBER) [21262], [47575]
West Virginia University Health Sciences Center (OHSR) - Office of Health Services Research [47576]
West Virginia University - Office of Health Services Research (OHSR) [47577]
West Virginia Wood Technology Center (WWWTC) [46306]
West Volusia Regional Chamber of Commerce [38523]
West Yellowstone Chamber of Commerce (WYCC) [41799]
West Yuma County Chamber of Commerce [37908]
WestCap Partners Inc. [24273]
Westchester Angels [35316], [42814]
Westchester Chamber of Commerce [39332]
Westchester County Chamber of Commerce [42530]
Westchester SCORE [42504]
Westchester Small Business Development Center [42413]
Western Apicultural Society (WAS) [1456]
Western Arborists Inc. [10134], [10263]
Western Association of Chamber Executives (WACE) [37246]
Western Association of Food Chains Annual Convention [7822], [14102]
Western Building Material Association (WBMA) [10387]
Western Business Services Ltd. (WBS) [2327], [29039]
Western Canada Conservation and Reclamation Association [23023]
Western Canada Wilderness Committee [5509]
Western Candy Conference [2553]
Western Chester County Chamber of Commerce (WCCCC) [44321]
Western Connecticut State University (WCSU) - Ruth A. Haas Library [11250]
Western Costume Company [4571]
Western Dairyland Business Centers (WDBC) [46577]

Western Douglas County Chamber of Commerce (WDCCC) [41891]
Western DuPage Chamber of Commerce (WDCC) [39333]
Western Fairs Association (WFA) [3835]
Western Floor Covering Association [6827]
Western Floors [6836], [16231]
Western Food Service & Hospitality Expo Los Angeles [8115], [35137]
Western Foodservice & Hospitality Expo [8115], [35137]
Western Home Furnishings Association [8194]
Western Illinois Area Agency on Aging (WIAAA) - Greta J. Brook Elderly Living and Learning Facility [202], [11551]
Western Iowa Tech Small Business Development Center (SBDC) [39688]
Western Kentucky University - Small Business Accelerator (SBA) [40110]
Western Maryland Regional Library (WMRL) [763], [14605], [17225]
Western Michigan University - Center for the Study of Ethics in Society [23576]
Western Michigan University - College of Engineering and Applied Sciences - Department of Industrial and Manufacturing Engineering - Human Performance Institute (HPI) [11657]
Western Michigan University - Haworth College of Business [41071]
Western Michigan University - Paper and Imaging [14363]
Western Monmouth Chamber of Commerce [42164]
Western Nebraska Community College Business Linkubator (WNCC) [41898]
Western New York Venture Association (WNYVA) [42389]
Western Real Estate Business: Connecting Real Estate in the West [13349]
Western Red Cedar Lumber Association (WRCLA) [10388]
Western Regional Aquaculture Center (WRAC) [6811]
Western Research Institute (WRI) [1568]
Western Retail Lumbermen's Association [10387]
Western Rockingham Chamber of Commerce (WRCC) [43206]
Western Shoe Retailers Association [14670]
Western Sizzlin Corp. [14284]
"Western & Southern to Trim Rich Retirement Plan" in Business Courier (Vol. 27, October 15, 2010, No. 24, pp. 1) [6663], [8980], [9880], [17372], [24168], [27355]
Western States Advertising Agencies Association [31846]
Western States Investment Group (WSIG) [37525]
Western Technology Center - Burns Flat Campus [43899]
Western Technology Investment (WTI) [37526]
Western Universities Technology Innovation Fund [46702]
Western Vehicle Leasing Association [1152]
Western View [44322]
Western Washington University (OSR) - Office of Institutional Effectiveness [47578]
Western Washington University - Office of Survey Research [47578]
Western Washington University Small Business Development Center (WWU SBDC) [46019]
Western White Mountains Chamber of Commerce [42017]
Western Wholesale Druggists [5138]
Western Wholesale Pet Supply Association [835], [12183]
Western Winter Sports Representatives Association (WWSRA) [14736]
Western Wood Moulding Producers - Wood Moulding and Millwork Producers - Wood Moulding and Millwork Producers Association [2631]
Western Wood Products Association (WWPA) [10389]
Western World Pet Supply Association [835], [12183]
Westerville Area Chamber of Commerce [43603]
WestEx - Colorado Foodservice & Restaurant Conference [8116], [8494], [14103], [35138]
Westfield Area Chamber of Commerce [42137]
Westfield Chamber of Commerce (WCC) [46538]
WestGate Technology Hub [39654]
"WestJet Gears Up for Domestic Dogfight" in Globe & Mail (May 1, 2007, pp. B6) [19959], [33286]
Westlake Village Chamber of Commerce [36917]
Westland Chamber of Commerce [41029]
Westlife Consultants and Advisors [24274], [29040], [30226], [31898], [32698]
The Westly Group [37527]
Westminster Chamber of Commerce [37247], [37909]
Westminster Choir College - Rider University - Talbott Library [11251]

Westmont Master Index

Westmont Chamber of Commerce and Tourism Bureau (WCCTB) **[39334]**
Westmoreland Chamber of Commerce **[44323]**
Weston A. Price Memorial Foundation [8083], [11617]
Westport-Grayland Chamber of Commerce **[46176]**
Westport-Weston Chamber of Commerce (WWCC) **[38081]**
Westridge Chamber of Commerce (WRCC) **[39335]**
Westwood Capital LLC **[42815]**
WEtech Alliance **[46839]**
Wethersfield Chamber of Commerce **[38082]**
WeTHRIVE **[35725]**
Wetzel's Pretzels **[14285]**, **[15064]**
WEVE Acceleration **[42960]**
weVENTURE **[38597]**
Wewoka Chamber of Commerce **[43820]**
"WeWork Closing About 40 Locations in the US" in Small Business Trends(November 16, 2022) **[32997]**
Weyauwega Area Chamber of Commerce **[46539]**
"Weyerhaeuser's REIT Decision Shouldn't Scare Investors Away" in Barron's (Vol. 88, June 30, 2008, No. 26, pp. 18) **[6664]**, **[9881]**, **[13590]**, **[19093]**, **[19619]**, **[24169]**, **[28876]**, **[34922]**
W.G. Grinders **[4926]**
A Whack on the Side of the Head: How You Can Be More Creative **[20135]**, **[22855]**, **[28877]**
Wharton Alumni Angels **[44357]**
Wharton Chamber of Commerce (WCC) **[45404]**
"What 126 Studies Say About Education Technology" in MIT News (February 26, 2019) **[3553]**, **[21660]**
"What Are the Costs Involved with a Hair Transplant?" in Medical News Today (November 26, 2017) **[7849]**
"What Are Employee Compensation Packages?" in business.com (Feb. 3, 2022) **[19758]**
What Are Estimated Taxes and How Do I Pay Them? **[34942]**
"What Are Payroll Taxes?" in Business News Daily (Nov. 10, 2021) **[31646]**
"What Are the Real Costs of Running a Barber Shop?" in Appointfix (February 17, 2020) **[7877]**
"What Are You Doing Differently?" in Agency Sales Magazine (Vol. 39, December 2009, No. 11, pp. 3) **[19094]**, **[19620]**, **[32659]**
"What Big Companies Can Teach Small Business Owners About Sustainability" in Entrepreneur (October 27, 2017) **[34402]**
"What Business Expenses Do You Need to Track?" in Business News Daily (February 21, 2023) **[34923]**
"What Business Schools Can Learn From the Medical Profession" in Harvard Business Review (Vol. 90, January-February 2012, No.1-2, pp. 38) **[21661]**, **[25974]**
"What is C2C?" in Business News Daily (February 21, 2023) **[16605]**
"What Can Michael Brown Do For Biz?" in Washington Business Journal (Vol. 31, June 15, 2012, No. 8, pp. 1) **[21217]**, **[25589]**, **[32321]**
"What Can You Implement into Your Business to Make It More Attractive to Buyers?" in Minority Business Entrepreneur (Vol. 39, Fall, 2022, No. 4, pp. 34-35) **[19231]**
"What Choice Did I Have?" in Entrepreneur (Vol. 37, October 2009, No. 10, pp. 88) **[8981]**, **[17373]**, **[25975]**, **[27356]**
"What Comes After That Job Is Cut?" in Business Review Albany (Vol. 41, August 15, 2014, No. 21, pp. 4) **[6665]**, **[28878]**, **[34210]**
"What Companies Are Required to Meet OSHA Regulations?" in Chron (July 7, 2020) **[30949]**
What Contracts Do You Need for Your Business? **[18739]**
"What is a CRM System and What Can It Do for Small Businesses?" in Small Business Trends (August 30, 2022) **[20529]**
"What is a DBA (Doing Business As) and How to Register One" in Business News Daily (February 8, 2023) **[27197]**, **[34568]**
"What is the Difference Between a Mentor and Coach?" in Small Business Trends (June 7, 2016) **[34569]**
"What Direction Is Your Company Moving In?" in South Florida Business Journal (Vol. 35, August 29, 2014, No. 5, pp. 8) **[19095]**, **[19621]**, **[28243]**
What to Do About Marketing Overwhelm **[30166]**
"What to Do with Business Waste" in ERC Blog **[7965]**
"What Do Developers Want?" in Real Estate Review (Vol. 41, Summer 2012, No. 2, pp. 77) **[13591]**
"What to Do in an Economic Upswing Before It's too Late" in Agency Sales Magazine (Vol. 39, November 2009, No. 10, pp. 36) **[21218]**, **[30113]**
"What Do I Need to Start a Lunchtime Delivery Food Service?" in Chron (April 11, 2019) **[6887]**
"What to Do If You Suspect Employee Theft at Your Business" in Insureon Small Business Blog **[22350]**, **[32393]**
"What to Do in Retirement: 9 Awesome Business Ideas for Seniors" in Senior Outlook Today (May 3, 2020) **[33077]**
"What to Do When Your Business Model No Longer Work" in Legal Zoom (February 21, 2023) **[19096]**
"What Do Your ISO Procedures Say?" in Modern Machine Shop (Vol. 84, September 2011, No. 4, pp. 34) **[10447]**, **[25590]**, **[29433]**
"What Does It Costs to Open a Coffee Shop?" in The New York Times (October 17, 2019) **[3192]**, **[34211]**
"What Does the Secretary of State Do?" in Legal Zoom (March 15, 2023) **[16606]**
"What is the Easiest Business to Start?" in Small Business Trends (April 26, 2022) **[34570]**
"What Employees Worldwide Have in Common" in Gallup Management Journal (September 22, 2011) **[22278]**, **[27072]**, **[30614]**
"What Equipment Do You Need to Open a Dry Cleaners?" in Careertrend.com (December 27, 2018) **[5243]**
"What to Expect from a Home Inspection" in The New York Times (March 23, 2018) **[2077]**
"What Franchises Need From an Accountant" in Entrepreneur (May 5, 2020) **[16847]**, **[24430]**
"What is the Future of Disk Drives, Death or Rebirth?" in ACM Computing Surveys (Vol. 43, Fall 2011, No. 3, pp. 23) **[3438]**, **[3532]**, **[3648]**, **[3741]**, **[34212]**
"What the Future Holds for Consumers" in Black Enterprise (Vol. 41, August 2010, No. 1, pp. 47) **[4816]**, **[14485]**, **[20355]**, **[22008]**, **[25591]**, **[32322]**, **[34213]**
"What Goes into a Good Cabinet?" in Woodshop News (September 1, 2021) **[2640]**
"What Happens in Vegas Could Happen in Baltimore, Too" in Boston Business Journal (Vol. 29, June 17, 2011, No. 6, pp. 1) **[4258]**, **[7315]**, **[13592]**, **[25592]**
"What Has Sergey Wrought?" in Barron's (Vol. 89, July 13, 2009, No. 28, pp. 8) **[6666]**, **[9882]**, **[14846]**, **[21219]**, **[22351]**, **[24170]**
"What I Learned Starting a Small Fitness Business" in Salon business strategy (September 18, 2019) **[12440]**
"What Is A Profit And Loss Statement?" in Business News Daily (March 6, 2023) **[19097]**
"What Is Agribusiness?" in The Balance Small Business (Dec. 18, 2020) **[17135]**
"What Is an Annual Report?" in Legal Zoom (March 15, 2023) **[27198]**
"What Is the Average Income for Genealogists?" in Chron (June 16, 2020) **[7374]**
"What Is B2B, and How Does It Differ From B2C and DTC?" in Business News Daily (February 21, 2023) **[16607]**
"What Is B2B?" in Business News Daily (June 23, 2020) **[19245]**, **[30114]**
"What Is the Best Way to Promote My New Company?" in Legal Zoom (March 9, 2023) **[372]**, **[16908]**, **[30115]**
What Is Brand Equity and What Does it Mean for Small Businesses? **[17455]**
"What Is a Business Casual Policy?" in Business News Daily (March 9, 2023) **[27073]**
"What Is a Business Consultant?" in Business News Daily (February 21, 2023) **[20136]**
"What Is a Business Incubator and How Does It Work?" in Draper University Blog (May 22, 2020) **[8798]**, **[8817]**
"What Is Business Networking?" in The Balance Small Business (Jan. 17, 2021) **[18853]**
"What Is a C Corporation?" in Business News Daily (February 21, 2023) **[27199]**, **[34571]**
"What Is Cash Flow? Cash Flow Guide for Small Businesses" in Wave Blog (March 4, 2019) **[19724]**
"What Is Commercial Photography? Great Tips to Get Started" in Expert Photography **[12310]**
"What Is Corporate Social Responsibility?" in Business News Daily (June 26, 2020) **[23391]**, **[34403]**
"What Is the Cost to Start a Massage Business?" in Chron (April 9, 2019) **[10774]**
"What Is Creative Commons? 5 Frequently Asked Questions" in Legal Zoom (March 27, 2023) **[27960]**
"What Is a Credit Card Issuer?" in The Balance (July 30, 2018) **[4727]**, **[4817]**
"What Is Crowdfunding?" in Business News Daily (February 28, 2023) **[7171]**, **[34572]**
"What Is Defensive Driving?" in SafeMotorist.com **[5106]**
"What Is DEI and How Can It Benefit Your Small Business?" in America's Small Business Development Center blog (April 4, 2022) **[30615]**
"What Is Desktop Publishing?" in Lifewire (May 22, 2019) **[4942]**
"What Is the Difference Between an App and a Mobile Website?" in Business News Daily (March 8, 2023) **[16608]**
What Is the Difference Between a Small Business and a Franchise? **[24431]**
"What Is the Difference between S Corp and C Corp?" in Legal Zoom (February 15, 2023) **[27200]**
"What Is an EIN and Does Your Business Need One?" in Legal Zoom (March 15, 2023) **[34924]**
What Is a Franchise Consultant and What Do They Do? **[24432]**
"What Is a Franchise Consultant??" in The Entrepreneur's Source **[24433]**
"What Is a Geothermal Heat Pump" in Indoor Comfort Marketing (Vol. 70, August 2011, No. 8, pp. 14) **[524]**, **[5727]**, **[5992]**, **[23392]**, **[34214]**
"What Is In Your Company Library?" in Modern Machine Shop (Vol. 84, October 2011, No. 5, pp. 60) **[10448]**, **[29434]**, **[31054]**
"What Is an LLC?" in Business News Daily (February 21, 2022) **[27201]**
"What Is Negative Cash Flow & How to Manage It?" in FreshBooks Hub **[16848]**
"What Is Payroll Tax and How Much Does it Cost?" in Xero **[31647]**
"What Is a Picker Sale? Estate Sales vs. Picker Sales" in EstateSales.org Blog **[6076]**
"What Is the Profit Potential with a New Cleaning Business?" on The Maid Coach (November 8, 2019) **[2980]**, **[19098]**
"What Is Publicity?" in The Balance Small Business (September 17, 2020) **[31891]**
"What Is Risk Management for Small Business?" in Insureon **[32394]**
What Is an S Corp and Should I Become One in 2023? **[32416]**
What Is an SBA Loan? **[28241]**
What Is Strategic Planning? **[19124]**
"What Is a Vision Statement and How to Write One (+Examples and Template)" in Small Business Trends (February 13, 2023) **[33621]**, **[34573]**
"What Is a Vision Statement?" in Business News Daily (Dec. 21, 2021) **[19622]**
"What It Takes to Be an Effective Leader" in Black Enterprise (Vol. 41, December 2010, No. 5, pp. 62) **[28879]**, **[30616]**
"What It Takes to Run a Personal Training Business" in Entrepreneur (November 1, 2016) **[12441]**
"What It Takes To Be a $200,000-a-Year Nanny" in CNN (June 13, 2019) **[11328]**
"What Keeps Global Leaders Up at Night" in Harvard Business Review (Vol. 90, April 2012, No. 4, pp. 32) **[21220]**, **[23393]**, **[25593]**, **[26459]**, **[27764]**, **[34404]**
"What Kind of Business Methods Can You Patent?" in Legal Zoom (March 13, 2023) **[27961]**
"What Kind of Golfer Are You?" in Baltimore Business Journal (Vol. 29, May 4, 2012, No. 53, pp. 1) **[7529]**, **[22856]**, **[28880]**
"What Kind of Leader Are You?" in Inc. (Vol. 36, September 2014, No. 7, pp. 76) **[19623]**, **[22857]**, **[28881]**
What to Know Before Buying a Gas Station Franchise **[14559]**, **[24434]**
What Leading Businesses Do Differently to Increase Diversity and Inclusion **[30617]**
"What Makes a Great Tweet" in Harvard Business Review (Vol. 90, May 2012, No. 5, pp. 36) **[23014]**, **[30116]**, **[31796]**, **[31892]**
What Makes People Tick: How to Understand Yourself and Others **[28882]**, **[35212]**
"What Managers Can Do to Keep Women in Engineering" in Harvard Business Review (June 12, 2018) **[35876]**
"What Marketers Misunderstand about Online Reviews: Managers Must Analyze What's Really Driving Buying Decisions - and Adjust Their Strategies Accordingly" in Harvard Business Review (Vol. 92, January-February 2014, No. 1-2, pp. 23) **[4410]**, **[14036]**, **[20530]**, **[22009]**, **[30117]**, **[33287]**
"What Meal and Break Laws Does Your Business Need to Know?" in Business News Daily (March 17, 2023) **[27074]**
"What No One Told Me about Running an Organizing Business" in A Personal Organizer blog **[12852]**
"What Noncitizens Need to Know about Filing an LLC" in Legal Zoom (March 15, 2023) **[27202]**
"What Not to Do When Starting a Home-Based Business" in Home Business (March 22, 2023) **[26817]**, **[34574]**
"What Online Brokers Are Doing To Keep Their Customers' Accounts Safe" in Barron's (Vol. 88, March 10, 2008, No. 10, pp. 37) **[6667]**, **[9262]**, **[9883]**, **[19286]**, **[22010]**, **[24171]**, **[26460]**
"What OSHA Regulations Apply to Small Business?" in allBusiness **[30950]**
"What the Popeyes Chicken Sandwich Feeding Frenzy Means for Rivals" in Barron's (September 10, 2019) **[4887]**, **[24435]**

3372 Small Business Sourcebook • 42nd Edition

Master Index Which

"What Professional Organizers Really Do, and How They Can Help You" in The New York Times (January 16, 2019) **[12853]**
"What Really Happens at the Dry Cleaner?" in The Spruce (May 4, 2019) **[5244]**
"What Should Franchises Look for in a Law Firm?" Entrepreneur (Dec. 10, 2019) **[24436]**
"What Should You Look For in a Business Bank Account" in Business News Daily (February 21, 2023) **[16849]**, **[34925]**
"What Should Your Insurance Agent Do for You?" in U.S. News & World Report (May 24, 2018) **[8982]**, **[27357]**
"What is an SKU and How Your Small Business Can Use One" in Small Business Trends(March 3, 2023) **[32323]**
"What Slump? Davis Likely to Fill Borders Gap Quickly" in Sacramento Business Journal (Vol. 28, July 29, 2011, No. 22, pp. 1) **[1840]**, **[32324]**
"What Small Business Owners Should Know About Wrongful Termination Lawsuits" in Entrepreneur (Feb. 4, 2020) **[20586]**
"What Small Businesses Need to Know about Holiday Pay" in Legal Zoom (February 17, 2023) **[27075]**
"What Small Businesses Should Know About Application Modernization" in BizTech (June 17, 2021) **[3674]**
"What Solo Owners of Corporations Need to Know about Annual Meetings" in Small Business Trends (November 12, 2019) **[27203]**
"What Supplies Do I Need to Start My Massage Business?" in Chron **[10775]**
"What the T-Mobile Takeover of Sprint Means for Your Wireless Bill" in The Wall Street Journal (August 1, 2019) **[2808]**
What Type of License Does a Food Delivery Service Need? **[6926]**
"What We Know - And What We Don't - About Apple TV" in Barron's (Vol. 92, August 25, 2012, No. 38, pp. 27) **[2470]**, **[15616]**, **[26461]**
"What Will the Interior Design Profession Look Like 10 Years in the Future?" in Architectural Digest (April 2. 2019) **[9052]**
What Works: A Comprehensive Framework to Change the Way We Approach Goal Setting **[22858]**
What Works: Success in Stressful Times **[18423]**, **[22859]**, **[24764]**, **[27765]**
What Year-End Tax Strategies Are Available to Business Owners? **[34943]**
What You Must Know about Highly Seasonal Businesses **[32965]**
"What You Need to Build Your Startup" in Minority Business Entrepreneur (Vol. 39, Fall, 2022, No. 4, pp. 12-13) **[34575]**
"What You Need to Know Before Opening a Tattoo Shop Franchise" in Black Hat Tattoo blog **[15319]**
"What You Need to Know about the Federal Overtime Rules" in Business News Daily (March 17, 2023) **[26694]**, **[27076]**, **[31648]**
"What You Need to Know about Hiring Independent Contractors" in Legal Zoom (March 22, 2023) **[5328]**, **[26695]**, **[26818]**, **[27077]**, **[32998]**
"What You Should Know About Home Appraisals" in Investopedia (June 25, 2019) **[817]**
"What You Should Know about Zoning Laws" in Legal Zoom (March 15, 2023) **[16609]**, **[26819]**
"What Your Employees Need to Know; They Probably Don't Know How They're Performing" in Gallup Management Journal (April 13, 2011) **[22279]**, **[28883]**
"What Your Logo Design Says about Your Business and Why It Matters" in Legal Zoom (February 15, 2023) **[17456]**
"What Your Workplace Wellness Programs are Missing; Companies Can Benefit From Taking a Holistic Approach To Their Employees. Here's How" in Gallup Business Journal (July 7, 2014) **[22280]**, **[25976]**
What's the Best Entity Type for a Family Business? **[23672]**
"What's the Difference Between a Tax ID Number and a Corporate Number?" in Business News Daily (February 21, 2023) **[27204]**, **[34926]**
Whata Lotta Pizza **[12598]**, **[14286]**
"Whatever Happened to TGIF? How Much Of the Recession Is Priced into Stocks?" in Barron's (Vol. 88, March 10, 2008, No. 10, pp. M3) **[6668]**, **[9884]**, **[21221]**, **[24172]**
"What's Ahead for Fannie and Fred?" in Barron's (Vol. 90, August 30, 2010, No. 35, pp. 26) **[11089]**, **[13303]**, **[13593]**, **[25094]**, **[25594]**
"What's Amazon Doing in the Pet Consumables Market?" in veterinarynews.dvm360.com (October 2, 2018) **[11817]**, **[12232]**
"What's Behind the Rise of G-Beauty" in The New York Times (April 10, 2019) **[1593]**, **[4524]**
"What's Good Faith Got to Do With Contracts?" in Contractor (Vol. 56, November 2009, No. 11, pp. 41) **[4259]**, **[18730]**
What's Happening in Frederick **[43821]**
"What's Holding Down Small Business?" in Business Owner (Vol. 35, November-December 2011, No. 6, pp. 3) **[18424]**, **[21222]**, **[34215]**
"What's In a Relationship? The Case of Commercial Lending" in Business Horizons (Vol. 51, March-April 2008, No. 2, pp. 93) **[6669]**, **[28224]**, **[31576]**
"What's In That Diaper?" in Inc. (November 2007, pp. 126) **[1199]**, **[23394]**
"What's In Your Toolbox" in Women In Business (Vol. 61, August-September 2009, No. 4, pp. 7) **[9263]**, **[16487]**, **[17777]**, **[30118]**, **[31893]**
"What's More Important: Stag or Flation?" in Barron's (Vol. 88, July 14, 2008, No. 28, pp. M8) **[6670]**, **[9885]**, **[21223]**, **[24173]**, **[25595]**
"What's More Important: Talent or Engagement? A Study With Retailer ANN INC. Seeks To Find the Essential Ingredients To High-Performing Managers and Employees" in Gallup Business Journal (April 22, 2014) **[3153]**, **[22281]**, **[26696]**, **[28884]**, **[32325]**
"What's Needed Are More Seats at the Table" in Crain's Chicago Business (November 12, 2021) **[30406]**
What's New in Benefits & Compensation **[17385]**
What's New with ChatGPT and Scaling into Product Market Fit **[26473]**
"What's That Business? Part of Savers Thrift Store Proceeds Go To Charity" in Duluth News-Tribune (February 27, 2012) **[3906]**, **[7172]**, **[34405]**
"What's the Ticket to a Higher-Paying Corporate Position?" in Orlando Business Journal (Vol. 29, September 14, 2012, No. 13, pp. 1) **[19759]**, **[28885]**
"What's Working Now: In Providing Jobs for North Carolinians" in Business North Carolina (Vol. 28, February 2008, No. 2, pp. 16) **[15706]**, **[21662]**, **[26462]**, **[26697]**, **[27078]**, **[29435]**
"What's Your Language Strategy? It Should Bind Your Company's Global Talent Management and Vision" in Harvard Business Review (Vol. 92, September 2014, No. 9, pp. 70) **[17778]**, **[19960]**, **[30618]**
"What's Your Social Media Strategy?" in Black Enterprise (Vol. 41, November 2010, No. 4, pp. 75) **[17779]**, **[22011]**, **[30119]**
Wheat Flour Institute [16962]
Wheaton Business Innovation Center **[40475]**
Wheaton Chamber of Commerce **[39336]**
WHEDco [42961]
Wheel Fun Rentals (WFR) **[13860]**
"Wheel Genius" in Entrepreneur (June 2014) **[10816]**, **[11354]**, **[25977]**, **[29066]**, **[30666]**
Wheeler & Associates Inc. **[27162]**
Wheeler County Chamber of Commerce **[38796]**
Wheeling Area Chamber of Commerce **[46294]**
Wheeling-Prospect Heights Area Chamber of Commerce and Industry (WPHACCI) **[39337]**
"When Anything (And Everything) Goes" in Globe & Mail (January 20, 2007, pp. B4) **[13304]**, **[13594]**, **[31577]**
"When Are Sales Representatives Also Franchisees?" in Franchise Law Journal (Vol. 27, Winter 2008, No. 3, pp. 151) **[18731]**, **[24437]**, **[32660]**
"When is the Best Time to Trademark Your Company Name?" in Small Business Trends (June 26, 2014) **[34576]**
"When Do I Need to Register My Business In Another State?" in Small Business Trends (March 8, 2021) **[34577]**
"When Emotional Reasoning Trumps IQ" in Harvard Business Review (Vol. 88, September 2010, No. 9, pp. 27) **[22282]**, **[28886]**
When Family Businesses are Best: The Parallel Planning Process for Family Harmony and Business Success **[17780]**, **[18425]**, **[19099]**, **[23673]**
When the Headline Is You: An Insider's Guide to Handling the Media **[8671]**, **[12949]**, **[31797]**, **[31894]**
"When and How to Innovate Your Business Model" in Strategy & Leadership (Vol. 38, July-August 2010, No. 4, pp. 17-26) **[27962]**, **[28887]**
When Inclusive Language Leaves Us at a Loss for Words **[30619]**
"When Incubators Go Wrong" in Inc. **[8818]**
"When Is On-the-Job Training the Right Solution?" in Training Industry (May 2, 2019) **[10002]**
"When Key Employees Clash: How Should a Business Owner Handle a Conflict Between Two Senior Managers?" in Harvard Business Review (Vol. 90, June 2012, No. 6, pp. 135) **[22283]**, **[28888]**
"When to Move from Independent Living to Assisted Living" in U.S.News & World Report (August 9, 2019) **[1036]**
"When the Nanny Leaves" in The New York Times (August 21, 2017) **[11329]**
"When One Business Model Isn't Enough: LAN Airlines Flourishes By Running Three Distinctly Different Operations at the Same Time" in Harvard Business Review (Vol. 90, January-February 2012, No.1-2, pp. 132) **[432]**, **[7053]**, **[19416]**
"When Profit Is Not the Incentive" in Business North Carolina (Vol. 28, February 2008, No. 2, pp. 42) **[21224]**, **[24765]**, **[34406]**
"When R&D Spending Is Not Enough: The Critical Role of Culture When You Really Want to Innovate" in Human Resource Management (Vol. 49, July-August 2010, No. 4, pp. 767-792) **[22284]**, **[24174]**, **[27079]**, **[27963]**, **[29436]**
"When to Roll Over" in Black Enterprise (Vol. 37, November 2006, No. 4, pp. 50) **[6671]**, **[9886]**, **[24175]**
When to Take Business Personally and When to Let Go with Kathleen Shannon **[24831]**
"When To Drop an Unprofitable Customer: A Supplier Contemplates Cutting Off One Of Its Biggest Accounts" in Harvard Business Review (Vol. 90, April 2012, No. 4, pp. 137) **[20066]**, **[20664]**
"When To Make Private News Public: Should a Job Candidate Reveal That She's Pregnant?" in Harvard Business Review (Vol. 90, March 2012, No. 3, pp. 161) **[26698]**, **[27080]**
"When, Why and How to Sell Your Small Business" in SCORE.org (April 4, 2019) **[19232]**
"When the Windshield Helps Drive the Car, a Repair Isn't So Simple" in The New York Times (February 7, 2019) **[2572]**, **[7496]**
"When You Need to Find outside Help for Your Business" in Legal Zoom (March 21, 2023) **[16610]**, **[34578]**
"When You Need Strong Millennials in Your Workplace" in Agency Sales Magazine (Vol. 39, November 2009, No. 10, pp. 22) **[23549]**, **[26699]**, **[28889]**
"Where Are All the Builders?" in U.S. News & World Report (June 15, 2018) **[4260]**, **[21225]**
"Where Are They Now?" in Canadian Business (Vol. 79, October 9, 2006, No. 20, pp. 71) **[22860]**, **[24766]**, **[28890]**
"Where Can a Small Business Owner Get Education and Training" in Financing Solutions (June 21, 2021) **[21663]**
"Where Do Women Stand? Leaders Don't Skirt the Issue" in Birmingham Business Journal (Vol. 31, April 4, 2014, No. 14, pp. 4) **[28891]**, **[35877]**
Where Does the Tidiness Craze Leave Self-Storage Stocks? **[12985]**
"Where a Dozen Bagels Will Cost You 45 Bucks" in Philadelphia Business Journal (Vol. 28, July 6, 2012, No. 21, pp. 1) **[15911]**, **[35105]**
"Where to Find Bridesmaid Dresses for Less" in The New York Times (July 4, 2018) **[2002]**
"Where to Find Business Loans for Senior Citizens" in Fast Capital 360 (Dec. 2, 2021) **[33078]**
"Where to Find Businesses for Sale" in Small Business Trends (Apr 13, 2021) **[19699]**
"Where to Find a Small Business for Sale" in JustBusiness (October 22, 2020) **[19233]**
"Where to Get Free Legal Advice for Your Business: 5 Options for Businesses on a Budget" in Fundera Blog (May 7, 2021) **[18732]**
"Where Good Ideas Come From: The Natural History of Innovation" in Business Owner (Vol. 35, July-August 2011, No. 4, pp. 6) **[27964]**, **[30833]**
"Where the Money Is" in Conde Nast Portfolio (Vol. 2, June 2008, No. 6, pp. 113) **[6672]**, **[9887]**, **[24176]**, **[25978]**, **[29437]**, **[32845]**
"Where New Economy Initiative Grants Have Gone" in Crain's Detroit Business (Vol. 25, June 1, 2009, No. 22, pp. M014) **[21664]**, **[27965]**, **[30938]**, **[34407]**
"Where Pet Nutrition Meets Love" in Pet Product News (Vol. 66, September 2012, No. 9, pp. S14) **[12233]**, **[16508]**, **[19961]**, **[29438]**
"Where Should I Take a Used Car for Inspection?" in Autolist (December 18. 2018) **[2573]**
"Where Small Biz Gets a 'Yes' More Often" in Denver Business Journal (Vol. 65, February 28, 2014, No. 42, pp. A10) **[24177]**, **[28225]**, **[34216]**
"Where to Stash Your Cash" in Barron's (Vol. 88, March 17, 2008, No. 11, pp. 41) **[6673]**, **[9888]**, **[11090]**, **[20356]**, **[24178]**, **[28226]**
"Where Women Business Owners Turn for Encouragement and Inspiration" in Legal Zoom (March 14, 2023) **[35878]**
"Whether You Are Opening Up Now or Later, You Must Understand the Business of Planning for Your Massage Practice" in Massage Magazine (June 18, 2020) **[10776]**
The Whetstone Project Business Accelerator [41110]
"Which Accelerator Program Is Right for Your Company?" in Inc. **[8799]**, **[8819]**
"Which Direction are Herbicides Heading?" in Farm Industry News (October 11, 2011) **[17136]**, **[34217]**
"Which Franchise Is Right For You? Follow These Steps" in Entrepreneur (Jan. 15, 2019) **[24438]**
"Which Iron Cage? Endo- and Exo-Isomorphism In Corporate Venture Capital Programs" in Academy of Management Journal (Vol. 55, April 1, 2012, No. 2, pp. 477) **[35405]**

Small Business Sourcebook • 42nd Edition 3373

Which Master Index

"Which LLC Taxes Must Your Business File?" in Business News Daily (February 28, 2023) **[27205]**, **[34927]**
Which Wich Superior Sandwiches **[4927]**
"While Tech Threatens Jobs, Janitorial Industry Continues to Flourish" in Services (November 21, 2021) **[2981]**
"Whirlpool Virtual Showroom Opens for Business on Pinterest" in AdWeek (October 28, 2021) **[796]**
"Whistling in the Dark" in Canadian Business (Vol. 79, September 25, 2006, No. 19, pp. 17) **[25095]**, **[32846]**
"Whistling Past the Graveyard? Higher Quality Stocks Beckon to Investors?" in Barron's (Vol. 88, March 17, 2008, No. 11, pp. 15) **[6674]**, **[9889]**, **[24179]**, **[25096]**, **[25596]**
White Bear Area Chamber of Commerce **[41320]**
White Bear Lake Area Chamber of Commerce [41320]
White Center Chamber of Commerce (WCCC) **[46177]**
White Cloud Area Chamber of Commerce [40999]
White County Chamber of Commerce **[38797]**
"The White Flint Plan: Planning a Transit Oriented District in Suburbia" in Real Estate Review (Vol. 41, Summer 2012, No. 2, pp. 53) **[13595]**
White Glove Placement, Inc. **[5463]**
White Hall Chamber of Commerce (WH) **[36504]**
White House Area Chamber of Commerce (WCC) **[44815]**
White, Hutchinson, Leisure & Learning Group (WHLLG) **[13331]**
White Lake Area Chamber of Commerce **[41030]**
White Mountain Publications **[46864]**
White Pine Chamber of Commerce **[41952]**
White Pine County Chamber of Commerce [41952]
White River Junction Chamber of Commerce [45739]
White River Valley Chamber of Commerce **[45741]**
White Rock Publishing **[46906]**
White Settlement Area Chamber of Commerce (WSACC) **[45405]**
White Spot Restaurants **[14287]**
"A Whiteboard that Peels and Sticks" in Inc. (Volume 32, December 2010, No. 10, pp. 58) **[27966]**, **[30120]**, **[30834]**, **[31055]**
Whitecap Venture Partners **[46877]**
Whitefish Area Chamber of Commerce [41800]
Whitefish Chamber of Commerce **[41800]**
Whitehall Area Chamber of Commerce **[46540]**
Whitehall Ohio Chamber of Commerce **[43604]**
Whitehouse Area Chamber of Commerce **[45406]**
Whitesboro Area Chamber of Commerce (WCC) **[45407]**
Whitewater Area Chamber of Commerce **[46541]**
Whitewater University Technology Park **[46578]**
Whiting - Robertsdale Chamber of Commerce **[39620]**
Whitley County Chamber of Commerce & Visitors Center **[39621]**
Whittier Area Chamber of Commerce (WACC) **[37248]**
"Who Hangs Out Where?" in Harvard Business Review (Vol. 90, July-August 2012, No. 7-8, pp. 34) **[9264]**, **[17781]**, **[32062]**, **[32847]**
"Who Is Eligible for Maternity and Paternity Leave?" in Legal Zoom (February 15, 2023) **[27081]**
"Who Writes the Best Tax Code?" in Barron's (Vol. 92, February 20, 2012, No. 8, pp. 30) **[15429]**
The Whole Child Learning Company **[21733]**
"Whole Foods: A Big Boost for Midtown" in Sacramento Business Journal (Vol. 31, August 1, 2014, No. 23, pp. 3) **[7789]**, **[8057]**
Whole Foods: Informing and Educating Natural Products Retailers on Dietary Supplements, Herbs, HBC, Homeopathy, Foods **[8065]**
"Whole Foods' Local Foragers Fill Store Shelves" in Supermarket News (October 22, 2019) **[8058]**
Wholesale Beer Association Executives of America [35485]
Wholesale Commission Florists of America [6851]
Wholesale Florist and Florist Supplier Association (WF&FSA) **[6851]**
Wholesale Florist & Florist Supplier Association--Membership Directory **[6864]**
Wholesale Florists and Florist Suppliers of America [6851]
Wholesale Grocer & Foodservice Distributor Leads **[2684]**, **[7790]**, **[14038]**
Wholesale, Hiring + Taking Your Business Temperature with Katie Hunt **[35498]**
Wholesale Nursery Growers of America - American Association of Nurserymen - American Association of Nurserymen, Florists and Seedsmen [7604], [10045]
Who's Got Your Back **[22861]**, **[24767]**
Who's Who in Finance and Business **[29046]**
Who's Who in Finance and Industry [29046]
Who's Who in Floor Covering Distribution [6831]
Who's Who Membership Directory [4517]
Who's Who--Personal Care Products Council Membership Directory [4517]
Who's Who of RV Dealers [13676]
Who's Who--The CTFA Membership Directory [4517]
"Why "Competition" Is Great for Small Businesses" in Business 2 Community (Aug. 19, 2019) **[19962]**
"Why Alabama's Aerospace Is Still Sitting Pretty After 777X" in Birmingham Business Journal (Vol. 31, January 10, 2014, No. 2, pp. 3) **[26463]**, **[33423]**
Why All Businesses Should Embrace Sustainability **[23395]**, **[34408]**
Why Are Small Businesses So Important for the Economy? **[21226]**
"Why Asset Allocation Is Important: Don't Only Focus On Your Client's Finances, Start With Their Goals" in Retirement Advisor (Vol. 13, October 2012, No. 10, pp. 20) **[6675]**, **[9890]**, **[24180]**
Why Blockchain, Cryptocurrency and NFTs are Important for You to Understand with Joel Comm **[24221]**
"Why Bossy Is Better for Rookie Managers" in Harvard Business Review (Vol. 90, May 2012, No. 5, pp. 30) **[28892]**
"Why Brand Image Is Important for a Small Business?" in appypie (August 5, 2020) **[17457]**
Why Building Software Is Getting Easier **[26474]**
"Why Business Budget Planning Is So Important" in The Balance Small Business (March 9, 2021) **[17515]**
"Why Business Ethics Needs Rhetoric: an Aristotelian Perspective" in Business Ethics Quarterly (Vol. 24, January 2014, No. 1, pp. 119) **[23550]**
"Why Business Focus Is a Crucial Entrepreneurial Talent; Successful Entrepreneurs are Profit-Oriented and Judge the Value of Decisions and Relationships By Their Effect On Business" in Gallup Business Journal (June 10, 2014) **[20531]**, **[22862]**
"Why Change?" in Canadian Business (Vol. 80, October 8, 2007, No. 20, pp. 9) **[8777]**, **[21227]**, **[25597]**, **[27766]**, **[29439]**, **[33288]**
Why Competition Is Good for Business **[19963]**
"Why Competition Is a Good Thing" in Bplans **[19964]**
"Why Creating Organizational Change Is So Hard; Resistance To Change Is Entrenched In Most Companies. Here's How To Overcome Obstacles and Create Change That Lasts" in Gallup Business Journal (May 22, 2014) **[22285]**, **[28893]**
Why CSR Is Essential in 2022 **[34409]**
"Why Customer Engagement Matters So Much Now; Wary Consumers Will Give More Money to the Businesses they Feel Emotionally Connected To -- While Ignoring Others" in Gallup Business Journal (July 22, 2014) **[20532]**, **[21228]**, **[32661]**, **[33289]**
"Why CVS May Not Get Burned By Its Tobacco Decision (Part 2); Looking at CVS' Decision To Discontinue Selling Tobacco Products In Purely Dollar Terms Misses the Bigger Picture" in Gallup Business Journal (March 20, 2014) **[5190]**, **[15707]**, **[19100]**, **[19624]**, **[32662]**
"Why Digital Marketing Is Important for Small Business" by Digital Marketing Institute (Nov. 3, 2021) **[17458]**, **[30121]**
Why Diversity, Equity and Inclusion Are a Business Priority **[30620]**
"Why Do I Owe Taxes from My Business despite Receiving No Money?" in Legal Zoom (March 14, 2023) **[34928]**
"Why Do Small Businesses Need a Substance Abuse Policy?" in Chron **[34682]**
"Why Do Stores Put Christmas Decorations Out So Early?" in CheatSheet (October 24, 2018) **[2925]**, **[32966]**
Why Do You Need a Trademark or Copyright for Your Business? **[18740]**
"Why Does Firm Reputation In Human Resource Policies Influence College Students? The Mechanisms Underlying Job Pursuit Intentions" in Human Resource Management (Vol. 51, January-February 2012, No. 1, pp. 121-142) **[8672]**, **[19760]**, **[21665]**, **[22286]**, **[26700]**, **[27082]**, **[31798]**
"Why Entrepreneurs Matter More Than Innovators" in Gallup Management Journal (November 22, 2011) **[22863]**, **[26701]**, **[27967]**, **[30835]**
"Why Entrepreneurs Will Save the World" in Women In Business (Vol. 61, December 2009, No. 6, pp. 12) **[21229]**, **[24768]**
"Why the Ethanol King Loves Driving his SUV" in Globe & Mail (January 29, 2007, pp. B17) **[23396]**, **[29440]**
"Why Every Business Owner Needs a Trust" in Legal Zoom (March 24, 2023) **[16611]**, **[24181]**
Why Every Small Business Should Engage in E-Commerce? **[22012]**
"Why Franchise Consulting Franchises Are Taking Off In 2022" in International Franchise Association blog **[20237]**
"Why the Future of Streetwear is Female" in The Wall Street Journal (August 21, 2019) **[3055]**
"Why the Gap is Stalking Lululemon" in Canadian Business (Vol. 85, August 22, 2012, No. 14, pp. 7) **[3056]**, **[3154]**, **[12442]**, **[15107]**, **[18426]**, **[19965]**, **[32326]**
Why GM Matters: Inside the Race to Transform an American Icon **[11451]**, **[29441]**
Why Good Graphic Design Will Make Your Small Business Better **[3339]**
"Why Good Jobs Are Good for Retailers: Some Companies Are Investing In Their Workers and Reaping Healthy Profits" in Harvard Business Review (Vol. 90, January-February 2012, No.1-2, pp. 124) **[20067]**, **[22287]**, **[32327]**
"Why Great Managers Are So Rare; Companies Fail To Choose the Candidate With the Right Talent For the Job 82 Percent of the Time, Gallup Finds" in Gallup Business Journal (March 25, 2014) **[26702]**, **[28894]**
"Why Hair Salons and Day Spas Fail" in Entrepreneur (September 9, 2014) **[7878]**
"Why High Confidence Is Crucial for Entrepreneurs; It Helps Them Start Businesses, Persist In the Face of Ambiguity and Failure, and Remain Poised In Meeting Challenges" in Gallup Business Journal (July 17, 2014) **[22445]**
"Why His Merit Raise Is Bigger Than Hers" in Harvard Business Review (Vol. 90, April 2012, No. 4, pp. 26) **[17374]**, **[20587]**, **[27083]**
"Why the Hospital Pager Withstood the Test of Time" in Health Tech (June 21, 2019) **[1510]**
"Why HR Practices Are Not Evidence-Based" in Academy of Management Journal (Vol. 50, No. 5, October 1, 2007, pp. 1033) **[27084]**, **[28050]**, **[28895]**
"Why I Stopped Firing Everyone and Started Being a Better Boss" in Inc. (Vol. 34, September 2012, No. 7, pp. 86) **[21666]**, **[22288]**, **[26703]**, **[28896]**, **[35879]**
"Why 'I'm Sorry' Doesn't Always Translate" in (Vol. 90, June 2012, No. 6, pp. 26) **[17782]**, **[27767]**, **[30621]**
"Why Intel Should Dump Its Flash-Memory Business" in Barron's (Vol. 88, March 10, 2008, No. 10, pp. 35) **[6676]**, **[9891]**, **[19101]**, **[19625]**, **[24182]**, **[26464]**, **[29442]**, **[31578]**
"Why Investing in Women-Led Startups Is the Smart Move" in Entrepreneur (March 8, 2018) **[35880]**
"Why Is Accounting Important for the Start Up of a Business?" in Chron **[16850]**
"Why Is Accounting Important?" in FreshBooks Article Hub **[16851]**
"Why Is It So Hard To Find Good People? The Problem Might Be You" in Inc. (Vol. 33, November 2011, No. 9, pp. 100) **[22864]**, **[26704]**, **[27085]**
"Why Is Social Responsibility Important in Marketing?" in Investopedia (Dec. 9, 2021) **[30122]**, **[34410]**
"Why It Is Essential to Put Strategy Before Tactics" in Duct Tape Marketing podcast **[29535]**
"Why Japan Is So Interested In Alabama" in Birmingham Business Journal (Vol. 31, August 1, 2014, No. 31, pp. 11) **[25598]**, **[27768]**, **[33424]**, **[34929]**
"Why Join a Food Truck Association" in mobile-cuisine.com **[7018]**
"Why Landscape Businesses Fail...and How to Keep Yours From Being One of Them" in Irrigation & Green Industry (September 6, 2018) **[10118]**
Why a Laundromat Is the Best Recession-Proof Business **[10180]**
"Why Life Science Needs Its Own Silicon Valley: Human Genomics Won't Reach Its Full Potential Until It Has a Sizable Industry Cluster" in Harvard Business Review (Vol. 90, July-August 2012, No. 7-8, pp. 25) **[3533]**, **[3649]**, **[26465]**, **[27968]**, **[30836]**, **[31579]**, **[32063]**, **[32848]**
"Why LinkedIn is the Social Network that Will Never Die" in Advertising Age (Vol. 81, December 6, 2010, No. 43, pp. 2) **[17783]**, **[19966]**, **[22013]**, **[24769]**
"Why Loyalty Programs Alienate Great Customers" in Harvard Business Review (Vol. 90, July-August 2012, No. 7-8, pp. 38) **[17375]**, **[19417]**, **[20533]**
"Why Make Diversity So Hard to Achieve?" in (Vol. 90, June 2012, No. 6, pp. 40) **[27086]**, **[30622]**
"Why Marketing Slogans Matter" in Canadian Business (Vol. 85, June 11, 2012, No. 10, pp. 18) **[8673]**, **[12950]**, **[30123]**, **[31799]**
"Why Men Still Get More Promotions Than Women" in Harvard Business Review (Vol. 88, September 2010, No. 9, pp. 80) **[27087]**, **[28897]**, **[35881]**
"Why Messaging Is the Future of Market Research" in Entrepreneur (July 2, 2019) **[10678]**, **[11818]**
"Why Millennials Are Reviving This Once-Tacky Home Accessory" in Refinery29 (October 4, 2018) **[14713]**
Why Most Entrepreneurs Struggle to Get the Growth, Profit and Freedom They Want with Clate Mask **[18457]**
"Why Motivating People Doesn't Work...and What Does: The New Science of Leading, Energizing, and Engaging" **[22289]**, **[27088]**, **[28898]**, **[32064]**, **[32849]**
Why Multifamily - All the Reasons to be All in Now with Arleen Garza **[13609]**
"Why My Company Prioritizes Hiring Employees with Disabilities" in U.S. Chamber of Commerce (Sept. 14, 2022) **[26705]**, **[30623]**

3374 Small Business Sourcebook • 42nd Edition

Master Index Winchester-Clark

"*Why Nestle Should Sell Alcon*" in *Barron's (Vol. 88, March 17, 2008, No. 11, pp. M12)* **[17137]**, **[19967]**, **[29443]**, **[31580]**
Why Networking Is Important for Small Business **[18854]**
"*Why Noncompete Agreements Are Falling out of Favor*" in *Legal Zoom (February 13, 2023)* **[27089]**
"*Why Oil Fell, and How It May Rise*" in *Globe & Mail (January 18, 2007, pp. B2)* **[24770]**, **[32967]**
"*Why Optimism Over Europe Won't Last*" in *Barron's (Vol. 92, August 25, 2012, No. 38, pp. M6)* **[9892]**, **[20357]**, **[21230]**, **[25599]**, **[27769]**
Why Outsourcing Your Accounting Could Be the Right Solution for Your Small Business **[16852]**
"*Why People Believe Things That Aren't True inside Your Company*" in *Small Business Trends (October 3, 2022)* **[22290]**, **[28899]**
"*Why Press Releases Are More Important Than Ever*" in *Legal Zoom (March 22, 2023)* **[30124]**
"*Why Recruiters Need to Expand Their Reach*" in *Onrec.com (October 21, 2019)* **[6114]**
"*Why Restaurateur Mike Hoque Took a Chance on Downtown*" in *Dallas Business Journal (Vol. 35, July 6, 2012, No. 43, pp. 1)* **[14037]**
"*Why the Rout in Financials Isn't Over*" in *Barron's (Vol. 88, June 30, 2008, No. 26, pp. 23)* **[6677]**, **[9893]**, **[18427]**, **[24183]**
Why Running a Seasonal Business Is Different Than Any Other Kind of Business **[32968]**
"*Why Screen Printers Should Add DTG to Their Shops*" in *Advertising Specialty Institute (April 16, 2019)* **[14359]**
"*Why Seattle Children's Appealed*" in *Puget Sound Business Journal (Vol. 35, May 30, 2014, No. 6, pp. 6)* **[25600]**, **[25979]**, **[27358]**
Why Should Small Business Owners Think About Ethics? **[23551]**
"*Why Slacking Off Is Great For Business*" in *Canadian Business (Vol. 85, August 13, 2012, No. 13, pp. 60)* **[7530]**, **[28900]**, **[35006]**
Why Small Businesses Still Need to Network in the Local Community **[18428]**
"*Why Small Businesses Struggling to Hire New Employees Should Embrace Gig Workers*" in *Entrepreneur (Sept. 8, 2021)* **[26706]**
"*Why Some Get Shafted By Google Pricing*" in *Advertising Age (Vol. 79, July 14, 2008, No. 7, pp. 3)* **[373]**, **[22014]**
"*Why Some Prices Are More Right Than Others*" in *Entrepreneur (September 15, 2016)* **[31659]**
Why Start a Mobile Coffee Business? **[3193]**
Why Startups Get Stuck & the Pitfalls of Raising Money **[34660]**
"*Why Successful Entrepreneurs Are Effective Delegators; Shifting from a Do-It-Yourself Executive Style to a More Hands-Off Approach is Essential When They're Growing a Business*" in *Gallup Business Journal (August 26, 2014)* **[19626]**, **[22865]**, **[28901]**
"*Why Sustainable Business Practices Are Better for Business and for the Planet*" in *Intuit: Official Blog (Nov. 3, 2021)* **[23397]**
"*Why Taking a Vacation Is Your Patriotic Duty*" in *South Florida Business Journal (Vol. 34, June 27, 2014, No. 49, pp. 14)* **[17376]**, **[21231]**
"*Why These 3 Advisors Paid to Say 'No' Are Your Best Allies When Buying a Franchise*" in *Entrepreneur (Feb. 13, 2019)* **[24439]**
"*Why This Investing Expert Is Bullish On the Energy Sector: William Heard Expects the Changing Landscape to Lead to Greater Opportunities*" in *Black Enterprise (Vol. 45, July-August 2014, No. 1, pp. 25)* **[6678]**, **[9894]**, **[24184]**
"*Why To Embrace Positive Leadership*" in *Birmingham Business Journal (Vol. 31, February 7, 2014, No. 6, pp. 14)* **[22291]**, **[28902]**
"*Why Top Young Managers Are In a Nonstop Job Hunt*" in *Harvard Business Review (Vol. 90, July-August 2012, No. 7-8, pp. 28)* **[21667]**, **[27090]**, **[28903]**, **[34218]**
"*Why U.S. Competitiveness Matters to All of Us: The World Wants America to Regain Its Vibrancy. Let's Stop Assigning Blame and Instead Focus on Solutions*" in *Harvard Business Review (Vol. 90, March 2012, No. 3, pp. 49)* **[19968]**, **[21232]**, **[27770]**
"*Why We'll Never Escape Facebook*" in *Canadian Business (Vol. 83, June 15, 2010, No. 10, pp. 28)* **[18429]**, **[22015]**
"*Why WestJet's Culture Guru Chooses to Fly Under the Radar*" in *Globe & Mail (January 22, 2007, pp. B1)* **[6679]**, **[9895]**
Why Women Need to Put Themselves Forward for Leadership **[35913]**
"*Why Work with a Franchise Consultant?*" in *FranchiseWire (May 3, 2021)* **[24440]**
"*Why You Aren't Buying Venezuelan Chocolate* " in *Harvard Business Review (Vol. 88, December 2010, No. 12, pp. 25)* **[8778]**, **[27771]**, **[30125]**
Why You Can't Afford Not to Hire with Kira La Forgia **[27115]**
"*Why You Don't Get Published: An Editor's View*" in *Accounting and Finance (Vol. 52, June 2012, No. 2, pp. 343)* **[1681]**, **[4943]**, **[5329]**, **[11476]**
"*Why You Need a New-Media 'Ringmaster'*" in *Harvard Business Review (Vol. 88, December 2010, No. 12, pp. 78)* **[374]**, **[10679]**, **[22016]**, **[30126]**, **[32663]**
"*Why You Need to Opt for Custom Web Design?*" in *DigitalAgencyNetwork (November 13, 2019)* **[16488]**
"*Why You Should Become an Environmentally Friendly Company*" in *Hiscox Blog* **[23398]**
Why You Should Start a Dog Breeding Business **[659]**
Why You Shouldn't Be an S Corporation in 2024 **[32417]**
"*Why Your Business Credit Score Matters*" in *Legal Zoom (March 9, 2023)* **[20358]**, **[24185]**
"*Why Your Company Must Be Mission-Driven; A Clear Mission Inspires Employee Engagement, Fosters Customer Engagement, and Helps Boost Company Performance -- Among Other Benefits*" in *Gallup Business Journal (March 6, 2014)* **[20534]**, **[22292]**, **[28904]**
"*Why Your Employees Aren't Working the Way They Used To*" in *Small Business Trends(March 6, 2023)* **[16612]**
"*Why Your First Suitor Isn't Always the Best*" in *Business Journal Portland (Vol. 30, January 24, 2014, No. 47, pp. 10)* **[1083]**, **[33039]**
Why Your Screen Printing Shop Needs a Well-Crafted Business Plan **[14360]**
"*Wi-Fi Finds Its Way Despite Nixed Plan for Free System*" in *Crain's Cleveland Business (Vol. 28, November 12, 2007, No. 45, pp. 3)* **[9265]**, **[17784]**, **[17879]**, **[25168]**, **[26466]**
WI Harper Group **[37528]**
Wichita Business Journal (WBJ) **[39983]**
Wichita Falls Board of Commerce and Industry **[45408]**
Wichita Genealogical Society (WGS) **[7460]**
Wichita Regional Chamber of Commerce (WRCC) **[39961]**
Wichita SCORE Chapter **[39854]**
Wichita State University - Center for Economic Development and Business Research (CEDBR) **[47579]**
Wichita State University Center for Entrepreneurship **[39981]**
Wichita State University College of Applied Studies Technology Center **[39847]**
Wichita State University College of Education Technology Center [39847]
Wichita Technology Corp. (WTC) **[39978]**
Wickenburg Chamber of Commerce **[36373]**
Widener University Procurement Technical Assistance Center (PTAC) **[44377]**
Widener University Small Business Development Center **[44108]**
Wider Wake **[43030]**
"*Wielding a Big Ax*" in *Barron's (Vol. 89, July 13, 2009, No. 28, pp. 26)* **[5191]**, **[6680]**, **[9896]**, **[24186]**
Wienerschnitzel **[8640]**, **[14288]**
Wikinomics: How Mass Collaboration Changes Everything **[9266]**, **[22017]**, **[24771]**, **[31581]**
Wilburton Chamber of Commerce **[43822]**
Wilco Angel Network [45480]
Wilco Funding Portal **[45480]**
Wild Bird Centers of America Inc. **[12244]**
Wild Birds Unlimited Inc. (WBU) **[12245]**
Wildcat Venture Partners (WVP) **[37529]**
Wilderness Committee (WC) **[5509]**
"*Wilderness Leadership - On the Job: Five Principles From Outdoor Exploration That Will Make You a Better Manager*" in *Harvard Business Review (Vol. 90, April 2012, No. 4, pp. 127)* **[22866]**, **[28905]**
Wilfrid Laurier University - LaunchPad **[46840]**
Wilkes Chamber of Commerce **[43207]**
Wilkes University Small Business Development Center **[44109]**
Wilkinsburg Chamber of Commerce (WCC) **[44324]**
"*Will Bush Cuts Survive? Tax Thriller in D.C.*" in *Barron's (Vol. 90, August 30, 2010, No. 35, pp. 17)* **[25601]**, **[34930]**
Will County Center for Economic Development (CED) **[39338]**
Will County Chamber of Commerce [39338]
"*Will Focus on Maryland Businesses Continue?*" in *Baltimore Business Journal (Vol. 28, November 5, 2010, No. 26, pp. 1)* **[18733]**, **[19969]**, **[24772]**, **[25097]**, **[25602]**
"*Will Home Buyers Pay for Green Features?*" in *Contractor (Vol. 56, October 2009, No. 10, pp. 70)* **[4261]**, **[5728]**, **[13305]**, **[23399]**, **[34219]**
"*Will mCommerce Make Black Friday Green?*" in *Retail Merchandiser (Vol. 51, September-October 2011, No. 5, pp. 8)* **[2809]**, **[3742]**, **[22018]**, **[32328]**, **[32664]**, **[32969]**
"*Will Mobile's Massive Growth Ever Equal Real Revenue?*" in *Advertising Age (Vol. 83, October 1, 2012, No. 35, pp. 18)* **[375]**, **[2810]**, **[9267]**, **[30127]**
"*Will Training Help Your Company's Sales Team?*" in *South Florida Business Journal (Vol. 34, May 16, 2014, No. 43, pp. 17)* **[32665]**
Willamette Management Associates Library **[6732]**, **[15480]**
Willamette SCORE **[43933]**
Willapa Harbor Chamber of Commerce **[46178]**
Willard Area Chamber of Commerce **[41653]**
Willcox Chamber of Commerce and Agriculture (WCCA) **[36374]**
William Blades L.L.C. **[30227]**, **[32699]**
William Blair Capital Partners **[39385]**
William Paterson University Small Business Development Center **[42045]**
Williams College - Center for Development Economics (CDE) **[21292]**
Williams College Center for Environmental Studies - Matt Cole Memorial Library **[5785]**, **[6014]**
Williams College - Chapin Library of Rare Books **[3388]**
Williams Fresh Cafe Inc. **[3209]**
Williams-Grand Canyon Chamber of Commerce (WGCCC) **[36375]**
Williamsburg Area Chamber of Commerce [45869]
Williamsburg Chamber of Commerce **[39808]**
Williamsburg County Chamber of Commerce [44587]
Williamsburg HomeTown Chamber of Commerce **[44587]**
Williamson County Chamber of Commerce (WCCC) **[44816]**
Williamson County Magazine **[44817]**
Williamson Inc [44816]
Williamsport-Lycoming Chamber of Commerce (WLCC) **[44325]**
Williamston Area Chamber of Commerce **[41031]**
Williamstown Board of Trade [40644]
Williamstown Chamber of Commerce **[40644]**
Williston Area Chamber of Commerce **[38524]**
Williston Area Chamber of Commerce (WACC) **[43310]**
Williston Park Chamber of Commerce [42546]
Willits Chamber of Commerce (WCC) **[37249]**
Willmar Lakes Area Chamber of Commerce (WLACC) **[41321]**
Willoughby Area Chamber of Commerce [43605]
Willoughby Western Lake County Chamber of Commerce (WWLC) **[43605]**
Willow Creek Chamber of Commerce **[37250]**
Willowbrook/Burr Ridge Chamber of Commerce and Industry **[39339]**
Willowridge Partners Inc. **[42816]**
Willows Chamber of Commerce **[37251]**
Wills Point Chamber of Commerce **[45409]**
Willy Dogs **[3864]**
Wilmette Chamber of Commerce [39340]
Wilmette/Kenilworth Chamber of Commerce **[39340]**
Wilmington Board of Trade [38134]
Wilmington Chamber of Commerce **[37252]**, **[39341]**, **[40645]**
Wilmington-Clinton County Chamber of Commerce (WCCCC) **[43606]**
Wilmington Minority Business Enterprise Office (SMBEO) **[38140]**
Wilson Art Index [3358], [11656]
Wilson Business Periodicals Index [2994], [24902]
Wilson Chamber of Commerce (WCC) **[43208]**
Wilson Community College Small Business Center (WCCSBC) **[43258]**
Wilson Humanities Full Text [4637]
Wilson Library Literature & Information Science Full Text [8844], [14996]
Wilsonville Chamber of Commerce (WACC) **[44034]**
Wilsonville Community and Business Directory **[44035]**
Wilton Chamber of Commerce **[38083]**, **[39809]**
WIM Fox Valley (WIM) **[28270]**
Wimberley Chamber of Commerce and Visitor's Center [45410]
Wimberley Valley Chamber of Commerce **[45410]**
Wimpy's Diner Inc. **[14289]**
Win Government Contracts for Your Small Business **[25169]**
WIN Home Inspection **[2042]**
"*WIN Home Inspection Garners Recognition as 2012 Military Friendly Franchise by G.I. Jobs Magazine*" in *Entertainment Close-Up (May 21, 2012)* **[2009]**, **[24303]**, **[34254]**
Win-Win Negotiations Training **[28431]**
Winchester Chamber of Commerce **[40646]**
Winchester-Clark County Chamber of Commerce (WCCC) **[40089]**

Small Business Sourcebook • 42nd Edition 3375

"Wind Farm Is Planned for Yolo Farmland" in Sacramento Business Journal (Vol. 29, September 21, 2012, No. 30, pp. 1) **[5729]**, **[5993]**, **[17138]**, **[21233]**, **[23400]**
"Wind Gets Knocked Out of Energy Farm Plan" in Buffalo News (September 28, 2011) **[5730]**, **[5994]**, **[23401]**
Wind Point Partners **[39386]**
Windham Region Chamber of Commerce [38036]
Windom Area Chamber of Commerce and Visitors Bureau (WACCVB) **[41322]**
Window Covering Manufacturers Association (WCMA) **[1571]**, **[9031]**
Window and Door Manufacturers Association (WDMA) **[2632]**
Window Gang [12698]
Window Gang Inc. **[12698]**
Window Genie (WG) **[2119]**, **[12699]**
"WindPower Solutions Announces Its Best In Class 'Next Gen' 85kw Wind Turbine" in Marketwired (June 6, 2012) **[5731]**, **[5995]**, **[23402]**
Windsor Area Chamber of Commerce **[41654]**
Windsor/Bertie County Chamber of Commerce **[43209]**
Windsor Chamber of Commerce (WCC) **[37253]**, **[37910]**, **[38084]**
Windsor County Area Chamber of Commerce [43209]
Windsor Locks Chamber of Commerce [38031]
Windspeed Ventures **[40789]**
Windward Ventures **[37530]**
Wine Business Monthly: The Industry's Leading Publication for Wineries and Growers **[15068]**
Wine Lovers Agency **[15065]**
Wine & Spirits Magazine **[15044]**
Wine and Spirits Shippers Association (WSSA) **[16070]**
Wine and Spirits Wholesalers of America (WSWA) **[10313]**
Wines & Vines **[15045]**
Winfield Chamber of Commerce (WCC) **[39962]**
Winfred L. and Elizabeth C. Post Foundation - Post Art Library **[764]**
Winfred L. and Elizabeth C. Post Foundation - Post Memorial Art Reference Library [764]
"Wing and a Prayer" in Canadian Business (Vol. 81, November 10, 2008, No. 19, pp. 70) **[21234]**, **[29444]**
Wingate Partners L.L.P. **[45481]**
Winger's Grill & Bar **[14290]**
Wingers Restaurant & Alehouse [14290]
Wings to Go **[14291]**
Wingstop Inc. **[14292]**
Wingstop Restaurants Inc. [14292]
Winklevoss Capital Management, LLC **[42817]**
Winnemucca Nevada Small Business Development Center **[41919]**
Winner Area Chamber of Commerce (WACC) **[44665]**
Winner Chamber of Commerce [44665]
"Winners Dream: A Journey from Corner Store to Corner Office" **[14847]**, **[19761]**, **[19970]**, **[22293]**, **[22867]**, **[32666]**, **[33921]**
"Winners & Losers" in Canadian Business (Vol. 85, July 16, 2012, No. 11-12, pp. 22) **[7054]**, **[9897]**, **[17378]**, **[22294]**, **[26467]**, **[32065]**, **[32850]**
"Winners and Losers" in Crain's Detroit Business (Vol. 25, June 22, 2009, No. 25, pp. 18) **[17377]**, **[21235]**, **[28906]**
Winning with Honest Feedback **[17795]**
"Winning With Women" in Marketing to Women (Vol. 22, August 2009, No. 8, pp. 6) **[4411]**, **[30128]**
Winnsboro Area Chamber of Commerce **[45411]**
Winnsboro-Franklin Chamber of Commerce [40200]
Winnsboro-Franklin Parish Chamber of Commerce (WFPCC) **[40200]**
Winona Area Chamber of Commerce (WACC) **[41323]**
Winslow Chamber of Commerce **[36376]**
Winston County Business and Industry Incubator (WCBI) **[41457]**
Winston-Dillard Area Chamber of Commerce **[44036]**
Winston-Salem Chamber of Commerce (WSCOC) **[43210]**
Winter Academic Conference **[21700]**
"Winter of Discontent" in Philadelphia Business Journal (Vol. 33, March 14, 2014, No. 5, pp. 4) **[21236]**
Winter Fancy Food Show [2552], [7809], [8189], [15054]
Winter Harbor Chamber of Commerce [40304]
Winter Harbor/Couldsboro/Schoodic Peninsula Chamber of Commerce [40304]
Winter Haven **[38525]**
"Winter Puts Golf Industry Off Course" in Baltimore Business Journal (Vol. 31, April 4, 2014, No. 49, pp. 17) **[7531]**, **[15203]**
Winter Park Angels [38618]
Winter Park Chamber of Commerce (WPCC) **[38526]**
Winter Park-Fraser Valley Chamber of Commerce **[37911]**
Winters Chamber of Commerce **[37254]**

Winterset Area Chamber of Commerce [39766]
Winthrop Chamber of Commerce **[40647]**, **[46179]**
Winthrop Lakes Region Chamber of Commerce (WLRCC) **[40310]**
Winthrop University - Small Business Development Center Library **[24929]**
Wireless **[2821]**
Wireless Cellular I WiMAX **[2820]**
Wireless Infrastructure Association (WIA) **[1509]**, **[2704]**
Wireless Satellite and Broadcasting **[14347]**
"Who's On Top in the Telecom Turf Fight" in Dallas Business Journal (Vol. 37, April 25, 2014, No. 33, pp. 4) **[2811]**, **[19971]**, **[20068]**, **[20535]**
Wisconsin Agri-Business Association (WABA) **[16979]**, **[46317]**
Wisconsin Association of Accountants (WAA) **[16758]**
Wisconsin Association for Financial Professionals (WIAFP) **[23700]**
Wisconsin Association of Life Underwriters [27222]
Wisconsin Association of Mortgage Brokers **[11006]**
Wisconsin Association for Public Procurement (WAPP) **[31907]**
Wisconsin Black Chamber of Commerce, Inc. **[46542]**
Wisconsin Business Incubation Association [33509], **[46318]**
Wisconsin Business Innovator's Support Association (WBIA) **[33509]**, **[46318]**
Wisconsin Business Travel Association **[19323]**
Wisconsin Department of Administration - Division of Enterprise Operations - Minority Business Enterprise Program (MBE) **[46545]**
Wisconsin Department of Agriculture, Trade and Consumer Protection - Bureau of Consumer Protection **[46335]**
Wisconsin Department of Natural Resources - Managing Waste and Materials **[47015]**
Wisconsin Economic Development Corp. (WEDC) **[46336]**
Wisconsin Economic Devlopment Corporation - Business Development **[46337]**, **[46546]**
Wisconsin Investment Partners (WIP) **[35317]**, **[46554]**
Wisconsin Manufacturers & Commerce (WMC) **[46543]**
Wisconsin Medical Directory **[25980]**
Wisconsin Minority Business Opportunity Center [46545]
Wisconsin Procurement Institute (WPI) - Regional PTAC **[46556]**
Wisconsin Procurement Technical Assistance Centers **[46556]**
Wisconsin Retail Lumber Association [10385]
Wisconsin Small Business Development Center - Lead Office **[46325]**
Wisconsin Small Business Development Center at University of Wisconsin - Eau Claire **[46326]**
Wisconsin Small Business Development Center at University of Wisconsin - Green Bay **[46327]**
Wisconsin Small Business Development Center at University of the Wisconsin - La Crosse **[46328]**
Wisconsin Small Business Development Center at University of Wisconsin - Oshkosh **[46329]**
Wisconsin Small Business Development Center at University of Wisconsin - Parkside **[46330]**
Wisconsin Small Business Development Center at University of Wisconsin - Superior **[46331]**
Wisconsin Small Business Development Center at University of Wisconsin - Whitewater **[46332]**
Wisconsin Treasury Management Association [23700]
Wisconsin Veterinary Medical Association Annual Convention **[711]**
Wisconsin Womens Business Initiative Corp. (WWBIC) **[35698]**, **[35699]**, **[35700]**
Wisdom From Rich Dad, Poor Dad **[9898]**, **[24187]**
Wise County Chamber of Commerce **[45412]**
Wisonsin Innovation Kitchen (WINK) **[46579]**
"With 54 Million to Go, This Airbag Recall is Never Going to End" in The Wall Street Journal (June 26, 2017) **[403]**
"With Algoma Steel Gone, Is Stelco Next?" in Globe & Mail (April 16, 2007, pp. B1) **[29445]**, **[31582]**
"With Building Plans in Flux, County Could Sell Key Site" in Crain's Cleveland Business (Vol. 28, October 8, 2007, No. 40, pp. 1) **[4262]**, **[13306]**, **[13596]**
"With Car-Leasing Prices on the Rise, Here's What to Know Before You Sign on the Dotted Line" in CNBC (April 17, 2019) **[1160]**
"With Funeral Home Rules Due for an Update, There's a Push for Online Prices" in The New York Times (March 29, 2019) **[7215]**, **[11819]**
"With the Indian Market, You Take Good With the Bad" in Globe & Mail (March 23, 2007, pp. B11) **[9899]**, **[21237]**
"With Measure 2 Defeated, Voters Still Looking for Property Tax Relief" in Dickinson Press (September 8, 2012) **[34931]**

"With Mine Approval, Crystallex's Value as Target Seen on Rise" in Globe & Mail (March 28, 2006, pp. B3) **[6681]**, **[9900]**, **[25603]**
"With Traffic Jam in Super Bowl, Can Any Auto Brand Really Win?" in Advertising Age (Vol. 81, December 6, 2010, No. 43, pp. 1) **[376]**, **[11452]**, **[15204]**, **[30129]**
"With Whom Do You Trade? Defensive Innovation and the Skill-Bias" in Canadian Journal of Electronics (Vol. 43, November 2010) **[8779]**, **[27772]**, **[27969]**, **[28051]**, **[30837]**
WITI Summit [35730]
"The Witte Museum to Undergo Major Makeover This Fall" in San Antonio Business Journal (Vol. 28, July 25, 2014, No. 24, pp. 7) **[919]**, **[4263]**
"Wix Has a New Editor for Creating Web Pages" in Small Business Trends (August 23, 2022) **[16489]**
W.J. Whatley Inc. **[950]**
WKU Small Business Accelerator [40110]
W.L. Lyons Brown III Innovation Laboratory [45968]
WMed Innovation Center **[41125]**
Wolf Point Small Business Development Center **[41727]**
"Wolferman's Bakery Introduces New Brand Positioning" in Snack Food & Wholesale Bakery Magazine (October 3, 2019) **[1272]**, **[11820]**
Wolfforth Area Chamber of Commerce and Agriculture **[45413]**
Wolfpack Investor Network (WIN) **[43234]**
Wolverine Venture Fund (WVF) **[41145]**
"Woman-Owned Firm 3D Strategic Management to Operate New Location of Orlando Business Center" in Orlando Business Journal (November 10, 2021) **[30407]**, **[35882]**
"A Woman's Advantage" in Black Enterprise (Vol. 38, December 2007, No. 5, pp. 86) **[19972]**, **[21668]**, **[27091]**, **[28907]**
Woman's Benefit Association [17268]
Woman's Life Insurance Society **[17268]**
Women in 3D Printing: From Bones to Bridges and Everything in Between **[12762]**
Women 2.0 [3669]
"Women as 21st Century Leaders" in Women In Business (Vol. 63, Summer 2011, No. 2, pp. 26) **[21669]**, **[22868]**, **[28908]**, **[33290]**, **[35883]**
Women in Advertising and Marketing [35564]
Women Amplified: How to Navigate Age in a Multigenerational Workplace **[27116]**
Women Amplified: Improv Your Work: Unlocking Creativity and Collaboration **[22306]**
Women Amplified: Juggling Team Engagement & Balance **[22307]**
Women Amplified: The Art & Science of Effective Communication **[17796]**
"Women Are Crushing the Gender Pay Gap" in Legal Zoom (March 16, 2023) **[16613]**, **[35884]**
Women in Aviation Conference **[426]**
Women in Business **[45655]**
"Women in Business Networking Begins in North Fulton" in Atlanta Business Chronicle (July 25, 2014, pp. 2B) **[35885]**
Women Business Owners (WBO) **[35680]**
Women Business Owners Connection (WBOC) **[35681]**
Women Business Owners Network (WBON) **[35682]**
Women Business Owners Network of Vermont [35682]
"Women Business Owners: Where We Stand Now" in SCORE Association Blog (Oct. 12, 2021) **[35886]**
Women in Business and the Workforce **[22949]**, **[35929]**
Women in Cable [2446]
Women in Cable Telecommunications (WICT) **[2446]**
Women Chefs and Restaurateurs (WCR) **[13892]**
"Women Clicking to Earn Virtual Dollars" in Sales and Marketing Management (November 11, 2009) **[9268]**, **[11821]**, **[16490]**, **[18430]**, **[22019]**, **[30130]**, **[32667]**, **[34220]**
Women of Color Program **[22469]**, **[30315]**, **[35726]**
Women in Communications [35564]
Women Construction Owners and Executives U.S.A. (WCOE USA) **[3966]**
Women Count: A Guide to Changing the World **[34411]**, **[35887]**
Women in Development of Greater Boston (WID) **[35683]**
Women in Development New York (WIDNY) **[35684]**
Women Empowered for Entrepreneurial Excellence (WEEE) **[44426]**
Women in the Enterprise of Science and Technology (WEST) **[35685]**
Women Entrepreneurs of Saskatchewan Inc. (WESK) **[46918]**
Women Entrepreneurs in The Global Marketplace **[22869]**, **[28227]**, **[30408]**, **[35888]**
Women & Environments International (WEI) **[5510]**, **[23054]**, **[34259]**
Women in Financial Development [35684]

Women Grocers of America (WGA) [7717]
Women and Health: A Multi Disciplinary Journal of Women's Health Issues [26057]
"Women and Higher Education" in *Montly Labor Review* (Vol. 133, September 2010, No. 9, pp. 70) [21670], [35889]
Women Impacting Public Policy (WIPP) [35686]
Women in Leadership [28359]
Women On Wheels International Ride-In [11116]
Women Owned in Retail [32087], [35727]
"Women-Owned Small Business Resources" in *SBDC Net* (Nov. 16, 2021) [35890]
"Women of Power Summit" in *Black Enterprise* (Vol. 38, February 2008, No. 7, pp. 163) [15912], [30409], [35106], [35891]
"Women Prefer Cookbooks Over Word-Of-Mouth for Recipe Suggestions" in *Marketing to Women* (Vol. 23, November 2010, No. 11, pp. 6) [1682], [30131]
Women & Pride [35728]
Women in Technology [35729]
Women in Technology Summit [35730]
"Women Up: Kathleen Ligocki of Harvest Power Inc." in *Boston Business Journal* (Vol. 34, April 11, 2014, No. 10) [5732], [5996], [7966], [17139], [23403], [35892]
Women Writing the West (WWW) [5301]
Womenpalante [25697]
Women's Business Alliance (WBA) [36159]
Women's Business Border Center (WBBC) [45425]
Women's Business Center (WBC) [42708]
Women's Business Center of Fayetteville (WBCFAY) [43216]
Women's Business Center Inc. [36159]
Women's Business Center of Kentucky (WBC) [40007]
Women's Business Center of South Alabama [36067]
Women's Business Council Gulf Coast [35690]
Women's Business Council Southwest (WBCS) [45426]
Women's Business Development Center (WBDC) [35687]
Women's Business Development Center - Minnesota (WBDCMN) [41328]
Women's Business Enterprise Alliance (WBEA) [35688]
Women's Business Enterprise Council Pennsylvania - Delaware - South New Jersey [35689]
Women's Business Enterprise Council South (WBEC) [35690]
Women's Business Enterprise Council West [35691]
Women's Business Enterprise National Council (WBENC) [35692]
Women's Business Exchange (WBE) [35693]
Women's Business Network, Inc. (WBN) [35694]
Women's Business Network of Pennsylvania [35694]
Women's Capital Connection (WCC) [39968]
Women's Chamber of Commerce of Texas [45414]
Women's Chamber of Commerce of Texas in Austin (WCCT) [45414]
Women's Clothing Stores Industry in the US - Market Research Report [3060], [3160]
The Women's Conference [21439]
Women's Council of Realtors (WCR) [13121]
Women's Council of Realtors of the National Association of Realtors [13121]
Women's Enterprise Centre of Manitoba (WECM) [46726]
Women's Enterprise National Council [35918]
Women's Entrepreneurial Network (WEN) [43618]
Women's Entrepreneurial Opportunity Project, Inc. (WEOP) [35695]
Women's Health Boutique (WHB) [1598], [4544], [7850]
Women's Health Concerns Sourcebook [25981]
Women's Healthy Environments Network (WHEN) [5511], [23055], [34260]
Women's Housing & Development Corp. Kitchen Incubator [42961]
"Women's Initiative for Self Employment Honors Home Instead Senior Care Owner as 2012 Woman Entrepreneur of the Year" in *Marketwired* (September 11, 2012) [8268], [22870], [35893]
Women's International Professional Tennis Council [15669]
Women's Jewelry Association (WJA) [9970]
Women's National Book Association (WNBA) [1631], [1809]
Women's Professional Golf Association [7511]
Women's Regional Publications of America (WRPA) [29576], [35696]
Women's Rural Entrepreneurial Network (WREN) [42018]
Women's Sailing Foundation [2828]
Women's Small Business Accelerator [43683]
Women's Tennis Council [15669]
Women's VC Fund II [44049]
Women's Venture Fund (WVF) [42709]
"Wondering Where Publishing is Headed? Ask Its Future Leaders" in *Publishers Weekly* (January 4, 2019) [1683]

Wood Dale Chamber of Commerce [39342]
Wood Design & Building [4292]
Wood Digest: Productivity Solutions for Manufacturers of Furniture, Cabinets, Millworks and Speciality Wood Products [2645]
"Wood Increasingly Used in School Construction" in *Arkansas Business* (Vol. 29, July 23, 2012, No. 30, pp. 11) [4264], [5733], [5997], [10398], [23404], [25604]
Wood and Synthetic Flooring Institute [6824]
Wood Truss Council of America [3964]
Woodall's Camping Guide for Great Lakes States [2524]
Woodall's Camping Guide for New York & New England [2519]
Woodall's Great Lakes Campground Guide [2524]
Woodall's Great Lakes Regional Campground Guide [2524]
Woodbridge Metro Chamber of Commerce [42200]
Woodburn Area Chamber of Commerce (WACC) [44037]
Woodburn Chamber News [44038]
Woodbury Area Chamber of Commerce (WACC) [41324]
Woodbury University Library [3083], [9082], [27797], [29058]
Woodcraft Franchise L.L.C. [7933]
Woodford County Chamber of Commerce [40090]
The Woodhouse Day Spa [1405]
The Woodhouse Spas Corp. (WH) [1405]
Woodland Area Chamber of Commerce (WCC) [37255]
Woodland Chamber [37255]
Woodland Chamber of Commerce [37255]
Woodland Kitchen and Business Incubator [46580]
Woodland Park Chamber of Commerce [37862]
Woodland Small Business Development Center [36597]
The Woodlands Area Chamber of Commerce [45415]
"Woodlands Tech Company Grapples With a Rapidly Changing Market" in *Houston Business Journal* (Vol. 44, January 10, 2014, No. 36, pp. 6) [26468]
Woodridge Area Chamber of Commerce [39123]
Woodshop News: The News Magazine for Professional Woodworkers [2646], [4621]
Woodsmith [4622]
Woodson County Chamber of Commerce [39963]
WoodSpring Suites [8520]
Woodstock Area Chamber of Commerce [45742]
Woodstock Chamber of Commerce [42701]
Woodstock Chamber of Commerce and Arts (WCOCA) [42701]
Woodstock Chamber of Commerce and Industry (WCCI) [39343]
Woodward Chamber of Commerce (WCC) [43823]
Woody's Bar-B-Q [14293]
"Woof Gang Bakery & Grooming Claws Through Recession" in *Orlando Business Journal* (Vol. 29, July 6, 2012, No. 3, pp. 1) [1273], [12099], [21238], [32668]
Woofie's [12128]
Wool Gathering [4623]
Wooster Area Chamber of Commerce (WACC) [43607]
Worcester Area Chamber of Commerce [40648]
Worcester Business Development Corp. (WBDC) [40501]
Worcester Business Journal [40776]
Worcester County Horticultural Society Library [7693]
Worcester Regional Chamber of Commerce (WRCC) [40648]
Worcester SCORE [40553]
Word Engines Press Inc. [46682]
"A Word With Connie Runia of Collection Bureau" in *Idaho Business Review* (September 8, 2014) [4818], [20359], [25605]
"WordPress May NOT Be Right for This Type of Business" in *Small Business Trends* (January 10, 2023) [11822], [16614]
"Words at Work" in *Information Today* (Vol. 26, February 2009, No. 2, pp. 25) [2812], [9269], [17785], [17880], [20588], [34221]
"WordStream Announces a Pair of Firsts for SEO & PPC Keyword Research Tools" in *Marketwired* (November 10, 2009) [9270], [16491], [22020], [30132]
Work-Bench Co-op L.L.C. [42962]
Work at Home Moms [26757]
"Work Less, Earn More" in *Canadian Business* (Vol. 80, March 12, 2007, No. 6, pp. 30) [21671], [24773]
"Work/Life Balance" in *Dallas Business Journal* (Vol. 37, June 20, 2014, No. 41, pp. 4) [17379], [22295], [26707], [27359], [34222]
WORK Petaluma [37650]
"Work for Play: Careers in Video Game Development" in *Occupational Outlook Quarterly* (Vol. 55, Fall 2011, No. 3, pp. 2) [586], [2607], [3743], [15797]
Work & Stress [35957]
The Work Truck Show [16110]
Work Truck Week [16110]
Workers' Compensation [25194]
Workforce Needs in Veterinary Medicine [660], [700]

Workforce Small Business Development Center - Summersville [46256]
Working with Affiliates at Scale [30167]
"Working From Home: A Guide to Setting Up You Own Work From Home Income: On Your Own Terms with Real Companies" [26753]
Working: How a Professional Pen Expert Makes a Living [23017]
Working Together: Why Great Partnerships Succeed [24774], [31583]
Working for Yourself: Law & Taxes for Independent Contractors, Freelancers & Consultants [18734], [20137], [22871], [26820], [34932]
Workmen's Benefit Fund of the U.S.A. (WBF) [17269]
Workplace Bullying Institute (WBI) [29062]
Workplace Bullying and Trauma Institute [29062]
The Workplace Center [34698]
Workplace Dimensions Inc. [27163]
"Workplace Harassment: How to Recognize and Report It" in *Business News Daily* (Dec. 21. 2021) [20589]
"Workplaces: The Human Element" in *Canadian Business* (Vol. 80, April 23, 2007, No. 9, pp. 78) [9901], [27092]
WorkSafeNB - Communications Department [35994]
The Workshop for Personnel/HR Assistants (Onsite) [26870]
Worland-Ten Sleep Chamber of Commerce [46625]
World Airlines Clubs Association (WACA) [425]
World Amateur Golf Council [7510]
World Aquatic Coalition, Inc. [12371]
World of Asphalt [4303]
World of Asphalt Show & Conference [4303]
World Bowling Writers [5284]
World Business Forum [33642]
World Coin News [3250]
World Confederation of Productivity Science (WCPS) [28271]
"World Cup Kicks G-Form Into High Gear for Protection" in *Providence Business News* (Vol. 29, August 4, 2014, No. 18, pp. 4) [15108]
The World Directory of Custom Bullet Makers [7837]
World Federation of Direct Selling Associations (WFDSA) [32436]
World Floor Covering Association (WFCA) [6827]
World Food Logistics Organization [12968]
"The World Is Your Oyster" in *Canadian Business* (Vol. 80, October 22, 2007, No. 21, pp. 140) [21672], [27773], [28909]
World Jurist Association (WJA) [34240]
World Martial Arts Association (WMAA) [10719]
World Massage Festival [10780]
World Media Association [11965]
World Millwork Alliance (WMA) [2633]
"A World of Opportunity: Foreign Markets Offer Diversity to Keen Investors" in *Canadian Business* (Vol. 81, Summer 2008, No. 9) [6682], [9902], [18431], [21239], [24188], [27774]
World Organization for Early Childhood Education - Canada [2876]
World Organization of Webmasters (WOW) [9088]
World Peace Through Law Center [34240]
World Pet Association (WPA) [835], [12183]
World Pinball Directory [587]
"The World is Their Classroom" in *Crain's Chicago Business* (Vol. 31, March 24, 2008, No. 12, pp. 24) [21673], [27775]
World Trade Association/International Department, San Francisco Chamber of Commerce [37153]
World Trade Centers Association (WTCA) [8683]
World Trade Centre Montreal [20691]
World Trade Centre Vancouver (WTC-V) [20713]
"World Watch: Where Michigan Does Business" in *Crain's Detroit Business* (Vol. 30, October 13, 2014, No. 41, pp. 22) [8780], [27776], [31584]
World of Water International Ltd. [1868]
World Waterpark Association (WWA) [599]
World Wide Pet Industry Association [835], [12183]
World Wide Pet Supply Association [835], [12183]
World of Wood Convention [10410]
World Workplace [24778]
WorldatWork, the Total Rewards Association [19732]
"World's Best CEOs" in *Barron's* (Vol. 88, March 24, 2008, No. 12, pp. 33) [6683], [9903], [22872], [24189], [28910]
Worldview Technology Partners Inc. [37531]
Worldwide Express [3407]
"Worldwide Food Services (EREI) Tests Mini Dollar Store Program" in *Marketwired* (August 6, 2009) [7482], [20665], [32329]
WorldWide Tattoo Supply [15337]
Worldwide Wireless [2824], [33328]
Worm Digest: Worms Deepening Our Connection to Food and Soil [5746]

Worry **Master Index**

"Worry No. 1 at Auto Show: Recession" in Crain's Detroit Business (Vol. 24, January 21, 2008, No. 3, pp. 1) **[11453], [15913], [21240], [29446], [35107]**
"The Worst Lies Ahead for Wall Street: More Losses Certain; More Expensive Capital to Be Needed" in Crain's New York Business (Vol. 24, January 20, 2008, No. 3, pp. 1) **[6684], [9904], [11091], [13597], [20360], [21241], [24190], [28228]**
"Worth His Salt" in Hawaii Business (Vol. 53, January 2008, No. 7, pp. 45) **[19102], [19627], [22873], [24441], [28911], [35213]**
Worthington Area Chamber of Commerce **[41325]**
Worthwhile Referral Sources (WRS) **[37706]**
WOW Cafe & Wingery **[14294]**
"WQA Develops Certification Program" in Contractor (Vol. 57, January 2010, No. 1, pp. 56) **[12674], [16336], [25606]**
"WQA's Leadership Conference Tackles Industry Issues" in Contractor (Vol. 56, October 2009, No. 10, pp. 3) **[15914], [16337], [23405], [25607], [34223], [35108]**
Wrangell Chamber of Commerce (WCC) **[36249]**
Wray Chamber of Commerce **[37912]**
WRC Chamber of Commerce [45912]
WRF Capital **[46244]**
WRI Solutions [26161]
Wright City Area Chamber of Commerce **[41655]**
Wrightsville - Johnson County Chamber of Commerce **[38798]**
Wrightwood Chamber of Commerce **[37256]**
"Wrigley's Newest Taste: Wolfberry" in Crain's Chicago Business (Vol. 31, March 31, 2008, No. 13, pp. 1) **[18432], [27777], [30133]**
Write It Well (WIW) **[17885]**
Write Wise Communications L.L.C. **[17815]**
The Writer Magazine: The Pioneer (Oldest) Magazine for Writers **[5341]**
"Writing Annual Reports for Your Business" in Legal Zoom (March 15, 2023) **[27206]**
Writing Children's Books for Dummies **[5330]**
Writing Effective EEO Investigative Reports **[18499]**
Writing and Presenting Actionable Marketing Research Reports (Onsite) **[29613]**
Writing a Romance Novel for Dummies **[5331]**
Writing Sci-Fi, Fantasy, & Horror for Dummies **[5332]**
Writing Statements of Work: The Heart of Any Contract (Onsite) **[17619]**
Writing That Works **[17881]**
Writing for the Web **[17853]**
WSI Internet **[9281]**
WSWA Annual Convention & Exposition **[1952]**
WT Enterprise Center (WTEC) **[45573]**
WTA Tout [15669]
WTC Vancouver [20713]
WUTIF Capital Inc. **[46702]**
WVC Annual Conference (WVC) **[712]**
Wyandot Chamber of Commerce **[43608]**
Wyckoff Chamber of Commerce **[42201]**
Wylie Chamber of Commerce **[45416]**
"Wyndham Program Targeting Women Hotel Owners Signs 30 Franchisees in First Year" in Bizwomen (March 24, 2023) **[8469], [24442]**
Wynne Chamber of Commerce [36451]
Wynnewood Chamber of Commerce **[43824]**
Wyoming Business Council (WBC) **[46593]**
Wyoming County Chamber of Commerce (WCCC) **[42702]**
Wyoming Department of Administration and Information - Procurement Section **[46626]**
Wyoming Department of Environmental Quality - Water Quality Div. (WQD) **[47016]**
Wyoming Entrepreneur **[33504]**
Wyoming Kentwood Area Chamber of Commerce (WKACC) **[41032]**
Wyoming Small Business Development Center - Lead Office (WSBDC) **[46590]**
Wyoming Small Business Development Center - Region 2 **[46591]**
Wyoming Small Business Development Center - Region 4 **[46592]**
Wyoming Technology Business Center [46627]
Wytheville-Wythe-Bland Chamber of Commerce (WWBCC) **[45914]**

X

"Xbox 360 Excels As a Media Hub" in Hispanic Business (October 2009, pp. 40) **[3744], [15798], [34224]**
xElle Ventures **[43235]**
Xenia Area Chamber of Commerce (XACC) **[43609]**
Xenia Community Profile Book **[43610]**
Xerox Business Research Group **[2394], [30228]**
Xerox Corporation - Wilsonville Library **[3684]**
"Xerox Diverts Waste from Landfills" in Canadian Electronics (Vol. 23, February 2008, No. 1, pp. 1) **[4489], [13733], [23406], [29447]**
Xfund (XF) **[37532]**
XG Ventures **[37533]**
XLerateHealth (XLH) **[40111]**
Xlibris L.L.C. **[39667]**
XLR8HI **[35318], [38884]**
XML Development I (Onsite) **[33820]**
XML Development II (Onsite) **[33821]**
XML Development III (Onsite) **[33822]**
XML Web Services (Onsite) **[17620], [33823]**
XRC Labs [32086]
XRC Ventures **[32086]**
XSeed Capital **[37534]**
"Xstrata and CAW Get Tentative Deal" in Globe & Mail (February 2, 2007, pp. B3) **[11454], [29448], [35214]**
"Xstrata's Takeover Bid Comes Up Short in Shareholders' Eyes" in Globe & Mail (March 27, 2007, pp. B16) **[6685], [9905], [31585]**
"Xtium Has Its Head in the Clouds" in Philadelphia Business Journal (Vol. 30, September 23, 2011, No. 32, pp. 1) **[3650], [3745], [3774], [9271], [22021], [33291], [35406]**
"Xymogen Poised for Huge Growth, Hiring" in Orlando Business Journal (Vol. 29, September 14, 2012, No. 13, pp. 1) **[26708]**

Y

Y Combinator Management, LLC **[37651]**
Yachats Area Chamber of Commerce (YACC) **[44039]**
Yachting: The Best of Today's Boats & Gear **[10616]**
Yadkin County Chamber of Commerce **[43211]**
Yadkin Valley Chamber of Commerce **[43212]**
"The Yahoo Family Tree" in Conde Nast Portfolio (Vol. 2, June 2008, No. 6, pp. 34) **[9272], [16492], [22022], [26469], [31586]**
Yakima County Development Associations - Washington Procurement Technical Assistance Center **[46210]**
Yakima County Development Associations;Washington Procurement Technical Assistance Center [46210]
Yakima Valley SCORE **[46042]**
Yale University - Center for Business and the Environment (CBEY) **[16726]**
Yale University Drama Collection **[4572]**
Yale University - Robert B. Haas Family Arts Library Special Collections **[1735], [2489], [16220]**
Yaletown Partners **[46703]**
"Yammer Gets Serious" in Inc. (Volume 32, December 2010, No. 10, pp. 58) **[14848], [17786], [22023], [33292], [33922]**
Yancey County/Burnsville Chamber of Commerce **[43213]**
Yankee Dental Congress **[26079]**
Yankton SBDC **[44628]**
"Yao Ming Courts China's Wine Boom" in Wall Street Journal Eastern Edition (November 28, 2011, pp. B4) **[15037], [27778], [34225]**
Yard & Garden [10250]
The Yarmouth Chamber **[40311]**
Yarmouth Chamber of Commerce **[40312]**
"Yates Helps Turn Log Home Green" in Contractor (Vol. 56, November 2009, No. 11, pp. 1) **[525], [4265], [23407]**
"Yates Turns Log Home Green - Part Three" in Contractor (Vol. 57, January 2010, No. 1, pp. 5) **[526], [5734], [5998], [14958], [23408]**
Yaya's Flame Broiled Chicken **[14295]**
Ybor City Chamber of Commerce **[38527]**
"Year In Review: Houston-Area IPOs Included Nation's Largest" in Houston Business Journal (Vol. 44, January 3, 2014, No. 35, pp. 5) **[9906], [31587]**
Yeast **[32913]**
Yellow Springs Chamber of Commerce **[43611]**
Yellowstone Capital Partners LLC (YCP) **[45602]**
Yellville Area Chamber of Commerce **[36505]**
Yelm Area Chamber of Commerce (YACC) **[46180]**
"Yes They Can! Program Boosts Number of Women Construction Workers" in The Wall Street Journal (February 12, 2019) **[2641]**
"Yes, You're Paying About 15% More to Move This Year. Here's Why." in Forbes (August 3, 2021) **[11153], [16086]**
Yeung's Lotus Express Franchise Corp. **[14296]**
"Yield Vanishes, Inflation Lurks" in Barron's (Vol. 92, September 17, 2012, No. 38, pp. M12) **[9907], [21242], [25608]**
YJLaurent Consulting **[30656]**
Yoakum Area Chamber of Commerce (YACC) **[45417]**
Yoakum Chamber of Commerce [45417]
The Yoga Expo **[12449]**
Yogen Fruz (YF) **[8641]**
Yogi Bear's Jellystone Park Camp-Resorts **[2532], [8521]**
"Yogun Fruz Adds First Location in Southern New York State" in Ice Cream Reporter (Vol. 23, September 20, 2010, No. 10, pp. 2) **[8059], [8107], [8602], [18433], [24443]**
"Yogurtini" in Ice Cream Reporter (Vol. 23, September 20, 2010, No. 10, pp. 7) **[8603], [18434]**
Yonkers Chamber of Commerce **[42703]**
Yorba Linda Chamber of Commerce (YLCC) **[37257]**
York Angel Investors (YAI) **[46867]**
York County Chamber of Commerce [44326]
York County Economic Alliance (YCEA) **[44326]**
York County Economic Development Corporation [44326]
York County Regional Chamber of Commerce (YCRC) **[44588]**
York Small Business Enterprise Centre (YSBEC) **[46768]**
York Technical College - Anne Springs Close Library **[31022]**
York University - Centre for Research on Work and Society (CRWS) **[10807], [35218]**
"York Wallcoverings Seals Deal with Lemieux" in Home Accents Today (November 12, 2019) **[8183], [9053]**
YorKitchen **[44427]**
Yorktown Chamber of Commerce (YCC) **[42704]**
Yorkville Area Chamber of Commerce (YACC) **[39344]**
"You Better Shop Around: Four Steps to Getting the Best Deal on a Home Loan" in Black Enterprise (Vol. 40, July 2010, No. 12, pp. 78) **[11092], [13307], [28229]**
"You Call It Craft, I Call It Art" in The New York Times (August 23, 2019) **[4609], [11823]**
You Can Do It Too: The 20 Essential Things Every Budding Entrepreneur Should Know **[22446], [24582]**
"You Can Take It With You, and Museums Hope You Will" and The New York Times (March 12, 2018) **[7483]**
"You Don't Have to Go to New York City for an Excellent Bagel" in Houstonia (January 28, 2019) **[1210]**
"You Have to Lead From Everywhere" in Harvard Business Review (Vol. 88, November 2010, No. 11, pp. 76) **[28912], [31800], [31895]**
You Need THIS Mindset (Attention Small Biz Owners!) with Julie Sellers **[28936]**
"You Shouldn't Start a Massage Practice Without These 3 Items" in Massage Magazine (October 2, 2017) **[10777]**
"You Won't Believe How Much the Greeting Card Industry Is Worth" in Southern Living (May 9, 2018) **[7704]**
"You Won't Go Broke Filling Up On The Stock" in Barron's (Vol. 88, July 14, 2008, No. 28, pp. 38) **[6686], [9908], [13308], [13598], [18435], [24191], [25609], [27779], [33293]**
"You're Being Sued: A Guide to Handling a Business Lawsuit" in Business News Daily (February 21, 2023) **[10219]**
"You'll Golf Better If You Think Tiger Has Used Your Clubs" in Harvard Business Review (Vol. 90, July-August 2012, No. 7-8, pp. 32) **[7532], [32066], [32851]**
"Young Adults, Childless May Help Fuel Post-Recession Rebound" in Pet Product News (Vol. 64, November 2010, No. 11, pp. 4) **[12178], [21243], [30134], [32330], [32669]**
Young & Associates Inc. (YA) **[10704], [33694]**
Young Business Leaders of Birmingham (YBL) **[36047]**
Young Children: The Journal of the National Association for the Education of Young Children **[2890]**
Young Entrepreneur Council (YEC) **[36006]**
"Young Entrepreneur Gets Some Recognition and Some Help for College" in Philadelphia Inquirer (August 30, 2010) **[1084], [11824], [21674], [36033]**
Young Entrepreneur Society (YES) **[36007]**
"Young Entrepreneur's Business Plan? An Ice Cream Boat? Really Floats: Maine at Work" in Portland Press Herald (August 9, 2010) **[8537], [19103], [36034]**
Young Entrepreneurs' Organization [33456], [36003], [45949]
"Young Executives Share Leadership Lessons" in Pittsburgh Business Times (Vol. 33, April 25, 2014, No. 41, pp. 4) **[28913]**
"Young Latino Business Owners Getting Helping Hand Amid Hispanic Heritage Month" in Business 2 Community (October 6, 2021) **[22944], [30443]**
Young Men's Business Association [39293]
"Young Millionaires" in Entrepreneur (Vol. 35, October 2007, No. 10, pp. 76) **[19104], [22874], [36035]**
"Young Money" **[6687], [9909], [21675], [23552]**
"Young People Speak Out On Credit Union Board Involvement" in Credit Union Times (Vol. 21, July 14, 2010, No. 27, pp. 20) **[6688], [9910], [24192]**
Young Presidents' Organization (YPO) **[36008]**
Young Rembrandts - The Power Of Drawing **[21734]**
Young Women Social Entrepreneurs (YWSE) **[35697]**
"Younger, Permenter Build New Real Estate Firm in Dallas" in Dallas Business Journal (Vol. 35, May 18, 2012, No. 36, pp. 1) **[13075], [13759], [31588]**
Youngstown Business Incubator (YBI) **[43684]**
Youngstown SCORE **[43393]**
Youngstown/Warren Regional Chamber of Commerce **[43612]**

3378 **Small Business Sourcebook • 42nd Edition**

"Youngstown's Business Incubator Looks to the Future" in U.S. News & World Report (February 20, 2019) **[8820]**
Yountville Chamber of Commerce (YCC) **[37258]**
Your Business **[40649]**
Your Business Values in Action **[24832]**
"Your Car Repair Handbook" in Consumer Reports (September 9, 2021) **[404]**, **[1113]**, **[1189]**, **[2574]**
"Your Career: Is It Time for a Change?" in Rental Product News (Vol. 33, October 2011) **[13842]**, **[33923]**
"Your Cold Calling?" in Inc. (December 2007, pp. 34) **[13679]**, **[33040]**
Your Complete Guide to a Successful & Secure Retirement **[6050]**, **[6689]**, **[24193]**
"Your Employees Are Probably Stealing From You. Here Are Five Ways To Put An End To It." in Forbes (Dec. 28, 2018) **[22352]**
"Your Exposure to Bear Steams" in Barron's (Vol. 88, March 17, 2008, No. 11, pp. 45) **[6690]**, **[9911]**, **[11093]**, **[20361]**, **[21244]**, **[24194]**, **[28230]**
"Your First 100 Days on Your New Job" in Women In Business (Vol. 63, Spring 2011, No. 1, pp. 28) **[17787]**, **[22296]**, **[26709]**, **[27093]**, **[28914]**
"Your First Commercial Lease: How to Prepare and What to Expect" in Business News Daily (February 21, 2023) **[13309]**, **[16615]**
Your First Year in Real Estate: Making the Transition from Total Novice to Successful Professional **[13310]**, **[13599]**, **[19973]**, **[22024]**, **[30135]**
"Your Guide to An Estate Sale Business Plan and Requirements" in EstateSales.org Blog **[6077]**
Your Guide to Arranging Bank & Debt Financing for Your Own Business in Canada **[6691]**, **[24195]**, **[28231]**
Your Guide to Canadian Export Financing: Successful Techniques for Financing Your Exports from Canada **[8781]**, **[24196]**, **[28232]**
"Your Guide to Credit Counseling Services" in Forbes Advisor (August 3, 2021) **[4728]**, **[4752]**, **[4819]**, **[20362]**
Your Guide to Experiential Marketing - 10 Insider Tips and Tricks for a Successful Brand Roadshow with Ray Sheehan **[30168]**
"Your Guide to Getting a Business License" in Business News Daily (February 21, 2023) **[27970]**, **[34579]**
Your Guide to Preparing a Plan to Raise Money for Your Own Business **[19105]**, **[24197]**, **[28233]**
"Your Guide to Starting an Affiliate Business Sitting in Your Home" in Home Business (June 21, 2022) **[30136]**
"Your Merchandising and Promotions Exchange: Web Coupon Users Shop More" in Pet Product News (Vol. 66, September 2012, No. 9, pp. 101) **[7791]**, **[32670]**
Your Million-Dollar Idea: From Concept to Marketplace **[22447]**, **[24583]**, **[30667]**, **[33085]**
"Your Scarcest Resource: Time Is Money, But Few Organizations Treat It That Way" in Harvard Business Review (Vol. 92, May 2014, No. 5, pp. 74) **[35007]**

"Your Ultimate Business Startup Checklist" in Small Business Trends (January 11, 2023) **[34580]**
"Your Web Brand Counts" in Black Enterprise (Vol. 44, June 2014, No. 10, pp. 46) **[9273]**, **[16493]**, **[26710]**, **[28915]**
Your Writing Partner **[20555]**
You're Never Too Old to Get Rich If You Follow These Seven Tips for Starting a Business **[33079]**
"You're a What? Wind Turbine Service Technician" in Occupational Outlook Quarterly (Vol. 54, Fall 2010, No. 3, pp. 34) **[5735]**, **[5999]**, **[23409]**, **[33294]**
Youth Media Alliance (YMA) **[15632]**
"YouTube Handles are Here – What it Means for Your Business" in Small Business Trends (October 19, 2022) **[30137]**, **[33622]**
Ypsilanti Area Chamber of Commerce **[40852]**, **[41077]**
Yreka Chamber of Commerce (YCC) **[37259]**
YSCHAMBER **[43613]**
Yuba Community College District Small Business Development Center **[36598]**
Yuba-Sutter Chamber of Commerce **[37260]**
Yucaipa Valley Chamber of Commerce (YVCC) **[37261]**
"Yudelson Challenges San Antonio Groups" in Contractor (Vol. 56, October 2009, No. 10, pp. 6) **[4266]**, **[5393]**, **[5736]**, **[6000]**, **[14959]**, **[23410]**
Yukon Chamber of Commerce **[43825]**
Yukon Conservation Society (YCS) **[5512]**, **[13698]**, **[23056]**
Yukon Department of Economic Development **[46920]**
Yuma County Chamber of Commerce (YCCC) **[36377]**
YWCA Anchorage **[36251]**
YWCA Resource Center Library **[2629]**

Z

Z-Coil Pain Relief Footwear **[14698]**
Z Pizza **[12599]**
Z80 Labs **[42963]**
Zachary Chamber of Commerce (ZCC) **[40201]**
Zachry Construction Corporation (ZCC) **[4374]**
"Zacks Industry Outlook Highlights: Starbucks, Nike, Big Lots, Deckers Outdoor and Family Dollar Stores" in PR Newswire (August 8, 2012) **[3155]**, **[3194]**, **[7567]**, **[15109]**, **[32331]**
"Zacks Industry Outlook Highlights: Target, Cabela's and Family Dollar Stores" in Marketing Weekly News (April 28, 2012, pp. 351) **[15110]**, **[28018]**, **[32332]**, **[32671]**
Zaetric Business Solutions L.L.C. **[2395]**
Zahn Innovation Center **[37652]**
Zahn Innovation Platform Launchpad **[37652]**
"Zalondo Commits to Carbon Neutrality" in Fashion-United (October 30, 2019) **[6142]**, **[23411]**
Zanesville-Muskingum County Chamber of Commerce **[43614]**

"Zara Eludes the Pain in Spain: Clothing Giant Inditex Sees Its First-Quarter Profits Rise By 30 Percent" in Canadian Business (Vol. 85, September 17, 2012, No. 14, pp. 67) **[3057]**, **[3156]**, **[6692]**, **[9912]**, **[18436]**, **[19628]**, **[32333]**, **[32672]**
Zarco Einhorn Salkowski and Brito P.A. **[18762]**
Zbikowski Business Initiatives L.L.C. (ZBI) **[29041]**
Zebulon Chamber of Commerce **[43214]**
Zeeland Chamber of Commerce **[40976]**
Zelkova Ventures **[42818]**
"Zell Takes a Gamble on Tribune" in Globe & Mail (April 3, 2007, pp. B1) **[6693]**, **[9913]**, **[19106]**, **[19629]**
Zen-Do Kai Martial Arts International (ZDK) **[10720]**
Zentek Computer Consulting **[31019]**
Zephyrhills Chamber of Commerce **[38528]**
The Zero Burnout Social Entrepreneur Launch with Paul Zelizer **[34661]**
"The Zero Marginal Cost Society: The Internet of Things, the Collaborative Commons, and the Eclipse of Capitalism" **[20069]**, **[21245]**, **[22025]**, **[22875]**, **[23015]**, **[33295]**
"Zero to One: Notes on Startups, or How to Build the Future" **[19766]**, **[22448]**, **[24584]**
Zero Waste Grocery Guide **[6001]**, **[7792]**, **[23412]**
Zero's Subs **[4928]**
ZeroTo510 **[44859]**
Ziebart International Corporation **[1147]**, **[2568]**, **[14602]**
Ziglar Inc. **[20556]**
"Zions Offers Step-by-Step Small Business Guidance" in Idaho Business Review (September 1, 2014) **[21676]**, **[22876]**, **[24198]**, **[28234]**, **[30138]**, **[32673]**
Zips Dry Cleaners **[5262]**
Zoo Biology **[32914]**
"Zoo Entertainment Inc. Aims for the Sky" in Business Courier (Vol. 27, September 24, 2010, No. 21, pp. 1) **[588]**, **[18437]**, **[32674]**
Zoom Express Laundry **[10207]**
Zoomin Groomin **[12129]**
Zotero for Genealogy: Harnessing the Power of Your Research **[7375]**, **[11825]**, **[14849]**
ZOUP! **[14297]**
Z's Cafe Kitchen Incubator and Commissary **[45574]**
ZS Engineering P.C. (ZSE) **[2328]**, **[20227]**
"Zuckerberg Says Ecommerce Trends After Pandemic Led to Mass Layoffs" in Small Business Trends(November 17, 2022) **[11826]**
Zuckerman Consulting Group Inc. **[10562]**
"Zucker's HBC Shakeup Imminent" in Globe & Mail (February 20, 2006, pp. B3) **[9914]**, **[19107]**, **[19630]**, **[31589]**
Zyng Asian Grill **[14298]**
Zynik Capital Corp. **[46687]**, **[46715]**, **[46718]**

www.ingramcontent.com/pod-product-compliance
Lightning Source LLC
Jackson TN
JSHW060748100425
82367JS00003B/63